1 CHRYSLER/DODGE/PLYMOUTH 1

ACCLAIM • DAYTONA • DYNASTY • FIFTH AVENUE • IMPERIAL • LE BARON • LE BARON LANDAU NEON • NEW YORKER • SHADOW • SPIRIT • SUNDANCE

SPECIFICATIONS

ENGINE IDENTIFICATION

Year	Model	Engine Displacement Liters (cc)	Engine Series (ID/VIN)	Fuel System	No. of Cylinders	Engine Type
1993	Daytona	2.2 (2213)	A	Turbo III	4	DOHC
	Daytona	2.5 (2507)	B, K	MPI	4	SOHC
	LeBaron	2.5 (2507)	B, K	MPI	4	SOHC
	Daytona	3.0 (2966)	3	MPI	6	SOHC
	LeBaron	3.0 (2966)	3	MPI	6	SOHC
	Shadow	2.2 (2213)	D	EFI	4	SOHC
	Sundance	2.2 (2213)	D	EFI	4	SOHC
	Shadow	2.5 (2507)	B, K	MPI	4	SOHC
	Sundance	2.5 (2507)	B, K	MPI	4	SOHC
	Shadow	3.0 (2966)	3	MPI	6	SOHC
	Sundance	3.0 (2966)	3	MPI	6	SOHC
	Spirit	2.5 (2507)	B, K	MPI	4	SOHC
	Acclaim	2.5 (2507)	B, K	MPI	4	SOHC
	Spirit	2.5 (2507)	V	FF	4	SOHC
	Acclaim	2.5 (2507)	V	FF	4	SOHC
	Spirit	3.0 (2966)	3	MPI	6	SOHC
	Acclaim	3.0 (2966)	3	MPI	6	SOHC
	LeBaron Landau	3.0 (2966)	3	MPI	6	SOHC
	Dynasty	3.0 (2966)	3	MPI	6	SOHC
	New Yorker	3.0 (2966)	3	MPI	6	SOHC
	Fifth Avenue	3.0 (2966)	3	MPI	6	SOHC
	Imperial	3.0 (2966)	3	MPI	6	SOHC
	Dynasty	3.3 (3294)	R	MPI	6	SOHC
	New Yorker	3.3 (3294)	R	MPI	6	SOHC
	Fifth Avenue	3.3 (3294)	R	MPI	6	SOHC
	Imperial	3.3 (3294)	R	MPI	6	SOHC
	Dynasty	3.8 (3786)	L	MPI	6	SOHC
	New Yorker	3.8 (3786)	L	MPI	6	SOHC
	Fifth Avenue	3.8 (3786)	L	MPI	6	SOHC
	Imperial	3.8 (3786)	L	MPI	6	SOHC
1994	LeBaron	2.5 (2507)	K	TBI	4	SOHC
	LeBaron	3.0 (2966)	3	MFI	6	SOHC
	Shadow	2.2 (2213)	D	TBI	4	SOHC
	Sundance	2.2 (2213)	D	TBI	4	SOHC
	Shadow	2.5 (2507)	K	TBI	4	SOHC
	Sundance	2.5 (2507)	K	TBI	4	SOHC
	Shadow	3.0 (2966)	3	TBI	6	SOHC
	Sundance	3.0 (2966)	3	TBI	6	SOHC
	Spirit	2.5 (2507)	K	TBI	4	SOHC
	Acclaim	2.5 (2507)	K	TBI	4	SOHC
	Spirit	2.5 (2507)	V	FF	4	SOHC

ENGINE IDENTIFICATION

Year	Model	Engine Displacement Liters (cc)	Engine Series (ID/VIN)	Fuel System	No. of Cylinders	Engine Type
1994	Acclaim	2.5 (2507)	V	FF	4	SOHC
	Spirit	3.0 (2966)	3	MFI	6	SOHC
	Acclaim	3.0 (2966)	3	MFI	6	SOHC
	LeBaron Landau	3.0 (2966)	3	MFI	6	SOHC
1995	Neon	2.0 (2000)	C	SFI	4	SOHC
	Neon	2.0 (2000)	Y	SFI	4	DOHC
	LeBaron	2.5 (2507)	K	TBI	4	SOHC
	LeBaron	3.0 (2966)	3	MFI	6	SOHC
	Spirit	2.5 (2507)	K	TBI	4	SOHC
	Acclaim	2.5 (2507)	K	TBI	4	SOHC
	Spirit	2.5 (2507)	V	FF	4	SOHC
	Acclaim	2.5 (2507)	V	FF	4	SOHC
	Spirit	3.0 (2966)	3	MFI	6	SOHC
	Acclaim	3.0 (2966)	3	MFI	6	SOHC

SOHC–Single Overhead Cam
DOHC–Dual Overhead Cam
EFI–Electronic Fuel Injection
MFI–Multi-port Fuel Injection
MPI–Multi-port Fuel Injection
SFI–Sequential Fuel Injection
TBI–Single Point Injection
FF–Flex Fuel

REFRIGERANT CAPACITIES

Year	Model	Refrigerant (oz.)	Oil (fl. oz.)	Refrigerant Type
1993	All	32	7.25	Fixed Displacement 10PA17, TR105, SD709P
	All	32	8.7	Variable Displacement 6C17
1994	All Except Neon	26	7.25	Fixed Displacement 10PA17
1995	All Except Neon	26	7.25	Fixed Displacement 10PA17
	Neon	29	4.75	Fixed Displacement 10PA17–R134A

AIR CONDITIONING BELT TENSION

Year	Model	Engine Liters (cc)	Belt Type	Specifications New (lbs.)	Specifications Used (lbs.)
1993	All	2.2 (2213)	V	135②	80②
	All	2.2 (2213) Turbo III	Serpentine	①	①
	All	2.5 (2507)	V	135②	80②
	All	3.0 (2966)	V	135②	80②

AIR CONDITIONING BELT TENSION

Year	Model	Engine Liters (cc)	Belt Type	Specifications New (lbs.)	Specifications Used (lbs.)
1993	All	3.3 (3294)	Serpentine	①	①
	All	3.8 (3786)	Serpentine	①	①
1994	All	2.2 (2213)	V	135②	80②
	All	2.5 (2507)	V	135②	80②
	All	3.0 (2966)	V	125②	80②
	All	3.3 (3294)	V	150②	120②
1995	All	2.0 (2000)	V	135②	100②
	All	2.2 (2213)	V	125②	80②
	All	2.5 (2507)	V	125②	80②
	All	3.0 (2966)	V	125②	80②
	All	3.3 (3294)	V	150②	120②

① Equipped with automatic dynamic tensioner.

② Specifications given in pounds are measured with appropriate belt gauge at midpoint of longest belt run.

SYSTEM DESCRIPTION

General Information

Conventional System

The components used in vehicles with heater only are very similar to those in vehicles equipped with air conditioning. Heater-only vehicles do not have the evaporator and recirculating air door used in the A/C-heater housing of air conditioned vehicles. Additionally, vehicles with Automatic Temperature Control (ATC) share many basic air conditioning components with vehicles equipped with a conventional system, for the most part, only the control system is different. All vehicles are equipped with a common A/C-heater housing fitted with different internal components, depending on its application.

The air flow system pulls outside air through the cowl opening at the base of the windshield and into the plenum chamber above the A/C-heater housing. On air conditioned vehicles, the air passes through the evaporator, then is either directed through or around the heater core by adjusting the blend air door with the **TEMP** control on the control panel. The air flow can be directed from the panel, panel and floor (bi-level), or floor and defrost outlets. The velocity of the flow can be controlled with the blower speed switch on the control panel.

On air conditioned vehicles, the intake of outside air can be shut off by moving the **TEMP** control knob to the **RECIRC** position, which closes the recirculation door and recirculates air already inside the passenger compartment. Depressing the **DEFROST** or A/C button will engage the compressor and remove heat and humidity from the air before it is directed through or around the heater core. Forced ventilation is directed from the instrument panel and/or floor outlets when the selector on the control panel is on the panel or bi-level position. The temperature of the forced vent air can be regulated with the **TEMP** control knob.

The side window demisters receive air from the A/C-heater housing and direct the flow to the front windows. The outlets are located either on the top outer corners of the instrument panel or on the doors themselves. The side demisters operate when the A/C control mode selector is in the **FLOOR, DEFROST** or **BI-LEVEL** setting.

Automatic Temperature Control (ATC) System

The totally electronic ATC system allows the driver to regulate the passenger compartment environment. A built-in computer regulates the desired temperature, air flow direction and blower speed. The operator may also select an AUTO mode feature, where the computer selects the variables.

The system goes into a maximum cool recirculated air lock-in mode when:

- A temperature setting of 65°F (18°C) is selected
- The compressor is turned on (snowflake illuminated)
- The system is not in the DEFROST mode
- The TEMP button is held in for 10 seconds.

In the lock-in mode, the temperature will not be regulated until the system is turned off or the temperature setting is raised.

The system operates through the power module which receives pulse width modulated logic signals from the computer control. The power module then varies voltage signals to the blower to vary speeds according to settings or need. An ambient temperature sensor on the A/C housing provides an ambient temperature signal to the computer control to regulate low blower, temperature offsets and mode control. Three door actuators provide air flow control and an in-car temperature sensor sends the computer signals according to changes in the interior temperature. A water temperature sensor on the heater core plate picks up engine coolant temperature signals. A sun sensor on the dash board senses intense sun positions and helps modulate mode door positions.

Service Valve Location

The discharge service port is located on the discharge line between the compressor and condenser. On some systems, the suction service port is located on the compressor itself. If this valve is not on the compressor, it will be located on the suction line between the compressor and the expansion valve.

System Discharging

R-12 refrigerant used on all 1993 models is a chloroflourocarbon which, when mishandled, can contribute to the depletion of the ozone layer in the upper atmosphere. Ozone filters out harmful radiation from the sun. In order to protect the ozone layer, an approved R-12 Recovery/Recycling machine that meets SAE standard J1991 should be employed when discharging the system. Follow the operating instructions provided with the approved equipment exactly to properly discharge the system.

All 1994–95 vehicles use a new type of refrigerant called R–134a. It is non–toxic, non–flammable, clear color–less liquified gas. This refrigerant is not compatible with R–12 refrigerant in an air conditioning system. Even small amounts of R–12 in a R–134a system will cause compressor failure, lubricant sludging or poor A/C performance. Never add R–12 to a system designed to use R–134a. System failure will occur.

System Evacuating

If the air conditioning system has been opened to the atmosphere, it should be air and moisture free before being recharged with refrigerant. Moisture and air mixed with refrigerant will raise the compressor head pressure, possibly damage the system's components and will reduce the performance of the system. Moisture will boil at normal room temperature when exposed to a vacuum. To evacuate, or rid the system of air and moisture:

1. Leak test the system and repair any leaks found.
2. Connect an approved charging station, Recovery/Recycling machine or manifold gauge set and vacuum pump to the discharge and suction ports. The red hose is normally connected to the discharge (high pressure) line, and the blue hose is connected to the suction (low pressure) line.
3. Open the discharge and suction ports and start the vacuum pump. If the pump is not able to pull at least 26 in. Hg, there is a leak that must be repaired before evacuation can occur.
4. Once the system has reached at least 26 in. Hg, allow the system to evacuate for at least 10 minutes. The longer the system is evacuated, the more contaminants will be removed.
5. Close all valves and turn the pump off. If the system loses more than 2 in. Hg after 15 minutes, there is a leak that should be repaired.

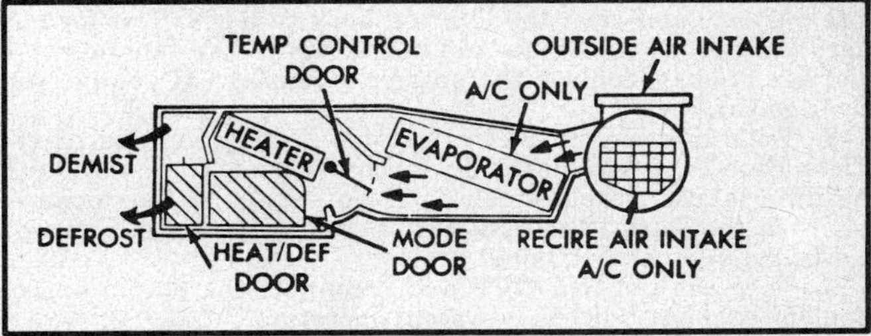

Air conditioner/heater housing components

System Charging

1. Connect an approved charging station, Recovery/Recycling machine or manifold gauge set to the discharge and suction ports. The red hose is normally connected to the discharge (high pressure) line, and the blue hose is connected to the suction (low pressure) line.
2. Follow the instructions provided with the equipment and charge the system with the specified amount of refrigerant.
3. Perform a leak test.

SYSTEM COMPONENTS

Radiator

REMOVAL AND INSTALLATION

1. Disconnect the negative battery cable.
2. Properly drain and recover the coolant.
3. Remove the radiator hoses and coolant reserve tank hose from the radiator.
4. If equipped, remove the automatic transmission cooling hoses.
5. Detach the electric cooling fan shroud. On New Yorker, Dynasty and Imperial models, retaining clips for the fan shroud are located on the top half of the shroud only. On all other models, clips are at the top and bottom of the shroud.
6. Carefully lift the fan and fan support assembly up and out of the vehicle.
7. Remove the upper mounting screws. Disconnect the engine heater wire, if equipped.
8. On A/C equipped models, remove the condenser attaching screws at the top front of the radiator. Now lift the radiator out of the vehicle.

To install:

9. Lower the radiator into position. Install the mounting screws for condenser and radiator.
10. Position and reattach the cooling fan assembly as removed.
11. Connect the automatic transaxle cooler lines, if equipped.
12. Connect the radiator hoses and coolant reserve tank hose.
13. Fill the system with coolant.
14. Connect the negative battery cable, run the vehicle until the thermostat opens, fill the radiator completely and check the automatic transaxle fluid level, if equipped.
15. Once the vehicle has cooled, recheck the coolant level.

COOLING SYSTEM BLEEDING

The system is designed to automatically bleed itself. Should air get trapped in the system, when the engine is next brought to full operating temperature, the air will be forced past the radiator cap and into the coolant recovery tank.

Cooling Fan

TESTING

1. Remove the fan motor wire connector and connect a 12-volt battery source directly to the motor. Be sure positive and negative connections are correct. Fan should run smoothly, without unnecessary noise. If not, replace the fan motor.
2. Run the engine to normal operating temperature.
3. Check all connectors in the fan motor circuit to ensure solid, clean connections.
4. Plug a diagnostic scan tool into the diagnostic connector behind the battery. Check for stored codes 88, 12, 35 or 55.

5. If a code is detected, turn ignition switch to **RUN** position and test for battery voltage (single pin connector) at the fan relay. If voltage is okay, go to Step **6**. If voltage was not okay, go to Step **7**.
6. Turn ignition to **OFF**. Disconnect the 60-pin connector (near the battery) and turn the ignition back to **RUN**. Check for battery voltage at cavity "31" of the connector. If okay and female terminal is not damaged, replace the engine controller. If voltage was zero, repair open or short in the fan motor circuit.
7. Turn ignition **OFF**. Disconnect the 60-pin connector (near the battery) and turn the ignition back to **RUN**. Test for battery voltage at the single pin connector of the fan relay. If voltage is okay, replace the engine controller. If voltage was 0–1, go the Step **7**.
8. With ignition in **RUN**, test for battery voltage at the Dark Blue/Pink wire in the 3-way connector of the fan relay. If reading is okay, replace relay. If no voltage, repair open or short in the Dark Blue/Pink wire between the engine controller board and the fan relay.
9. Turn the ignition **OFF** and reconnect the 60-pin engine controller connector. Test system operation.

REMOVAL AND INSTALLATION

1. Disconnect the negative battery cable.
2. Unplug the connector.
3. Remove the shroud clips and fan assembly mounting screws.
4. Remove the fan assembly from the vehicle.
5. The installation is the reverse of the removal procedure.
6. Connect the negative battery cable and check the fan for proper operation.

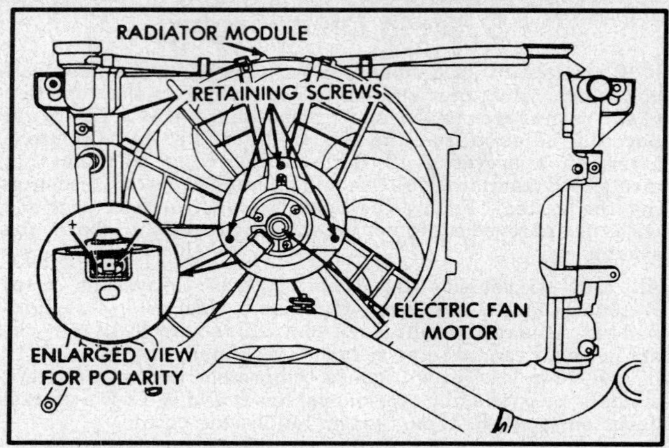

Testing electrical fan motor

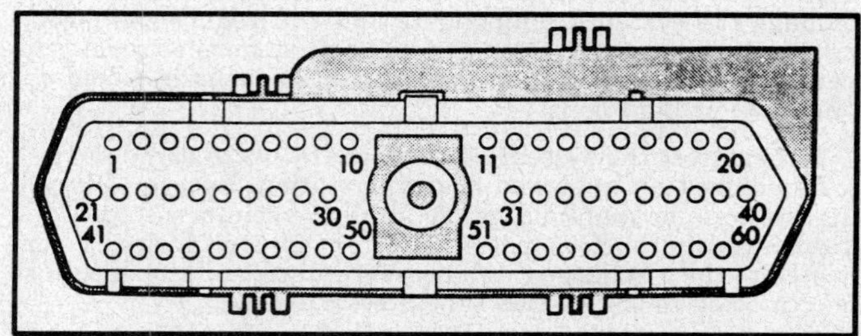

Showing location of cavity "31" in engine controller connector

Condenser

REMOVAL AND INSTALLATION

1. Disconnect the negative battery cable.
2. Properly discharge the air conditioning system.
3. Remove the refrigerant lines attaching nut and separate the lines from the condenser sealing plate. Discard the gasket.
4. Cover the exposed ends of the lines to minimize contamination.
5. Remove the coolant overflow tank, the electric cooling fan(s) and the radiator assembly, if required. On some mountings, the radiator may be detached and moved slightly rearward to provide clearance for condenser removal.
6. Remove the bolts that attach the condenser to the radiator support.
7. Lift the condenser and remove from the vehicle.

To install:

8. Position the condenser and install the bolts.
9. Coat the new gasket with wax-free refrigerant oil and install. Connect the lines, using new O-rings, to the condenser sealing plate and tighten the nut.
10. Install the radiator, if removed, the overflow tank and the electric fans. Fill the system with coolant, if drained.
11. Evacuate and recharge the air conditioning system. Add 1 oz. of refrigerant oil during the recharge. Check for leaks.

Compressor

REMOVAL AND INSTALLATION

1. Disconnect the negative battery cable.
2. Properly discharge the air conditioning system.
3. Remove the compressor drive belt. Disconnect the compressor lead.
4. Remove the refrigerant lines from the compressor and discard the gaskets or O-rings as equipped. Cover the exposed ends of the lines to minimize contamination.
5. Remove the compressor mounting nuts and bolts.
6. Lift the compressor off of its mounting studs and remove from the engine compartment.

To install:

7. Install the compressor and tighten all mounting nuts and bolts.
8. Coat the new gaskets or O-rings with wax-free refrigerant oil and install. Connect the refrigerant lines to the compressor and tighten the bolts.
9. Install the drive belt and adjust to specification. Connect the electrical lead.
10. Evacuate and recharge the air conditioning system. Check for leaks.

Receiver/Drier

REMOVAL AND INSTALLATION

1. Disconnect the negative battery cable.
2. Properly discharge the air conditioning system.
3. Remove the nuts that fasten the refrigerant lines to sides of the receiver/drier assembly.

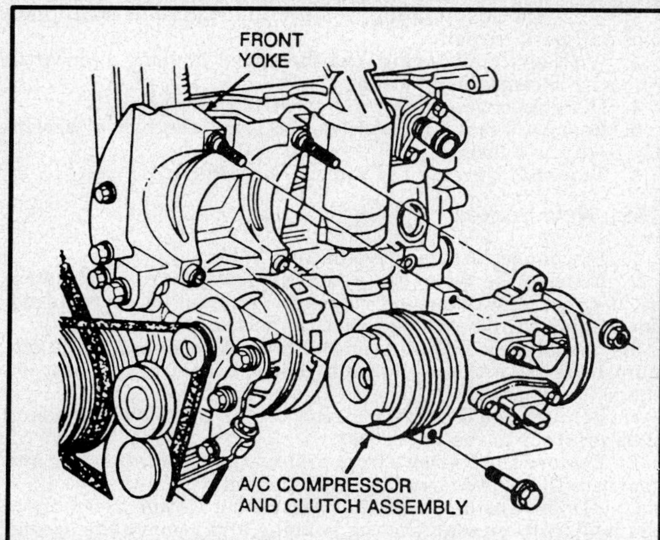

Typical air conditioning compressor mounting—2.2L and 2.5L engines

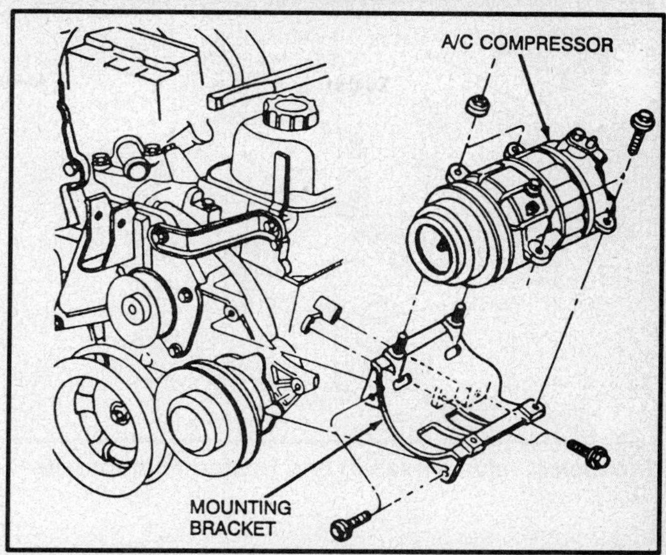

Air conditioning compressor mounting—3.3L and 3.8L engines

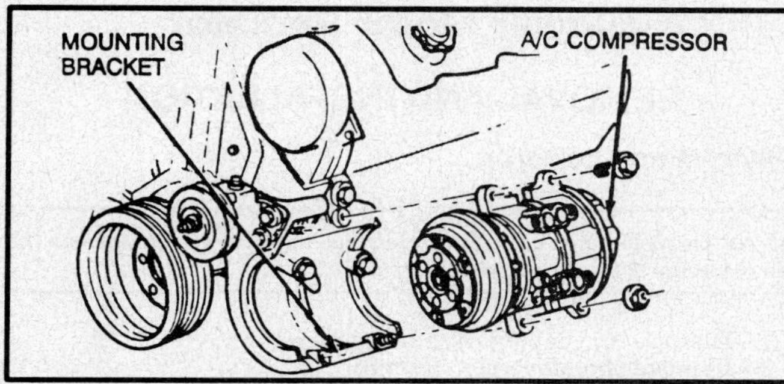

Air conditioning compressor mounting—3.0L engine

4. Remove the refrigerant lines from the receiver/drier and discard the gaskets. Cover the exposed ends of the lines to minimize contamination.
5. Remove the mounting strap bolts and remove the receiver/drier from the engine compartment.

To install:

6. Transfer the mounting strap to the new receiver/drier.
7. Coat the new gaskets with wax-free refrigerant oil and install. Connect the refrigerant lines to the receiver/drier and tighten the nuts.
8. Evacuate and recharge the air conditioning system. Add 1 oz. of refrigerant oil during the recharge. Check for leaks.

Expansion Valve (H-Valve)

TESTING

1. With the ambient temperature between 70-85°F, connect a manifold gauge set or charging station to the air conditioning system. Verify adequate refrigerant level in the sight glass.
2. If the vehicle is not equipped with ATC, remove the right side kick panel. Locate and switch the connections of the recirculating door actuator vacuum lines (dark green and light green).
3. Detach the a fin-sensing cycling clutch switch, jump the outer wires in the connector. Disconnect and plug the vacuum line at the water valve, if equipped.
4. Disconnect the low pressure cut off switch connector and jump the wires inside the boot.
5. Close all doors, windows and vents to the passenger compartment.
6. If equipped with ATC, set the automatic temperature control to **A/C, 85°F, FLOOR** and high blower speed.
7. If not equipped with ATC, set controls to **A/C**, full heat, **FLOOR** and high blower speed.
8. Start the engine and hold the idle speed at 1000 rpm. After the engine has reached normal operating temperature, allow the passenger compartment to heat up to create the need for maximum refrigerant flow into the evaporator.
9. The discharge (high pressure) gauge should read 140–240 psi and suction (low pressure) gauge should read 20–30 psi, providing the refrigerant charge is sufficient.
10. If neither high or low side pressure is correct, replace the expansion valve.
11. If the suction side is within specifications, freeze the expansion valve control head using a very cold substance (liquid CO2 or dry ice) for 30 seconds (do not spray with R-12):
    - If equipped with a silver H-valve used with fixed displacement compressor, the suction side pressure should drop to 15 in. Hg. If not, replace the expansion valve.
    - If equipped with a black H-valve used with variable displacement compressor, the discharge pressure should drop about 15%. If not, replace the expansion valve.
12. Allow the expansion valve to thaw. As it thaws, the pressures should stabilize to the values in Step 9. If not, replace the expansion valve.
13. Once the test is complete, put the vacuum lines back in their original locations, and perform and overall performance test.

REMOVAL AND INSTALLATION

1. Disconnect the negative battery cable.
2. Properly discharge the air conditioning system.
3. Disconnect the low pressure cutoff switch.
4. Remove the attaching bolt at the center of the refrigerant plumbing sealing plate.

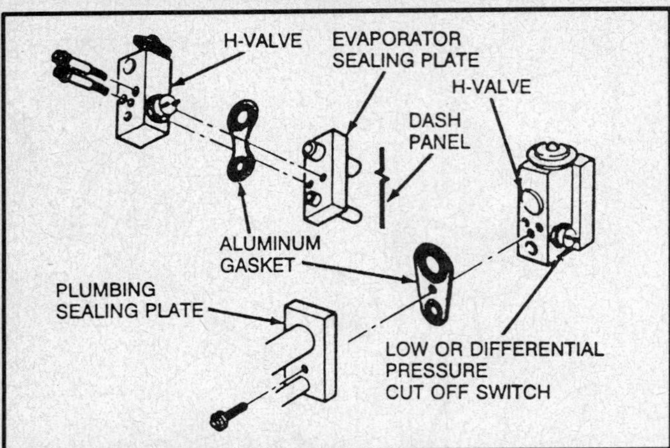

Expansion valve (H-valve) and related components

5. Carefully pull the refrigerant line assembly away from the expansion valve, avoid scratching sealing surface of valve with evaporator pilot tubes. Cover the exposed ends of the lines to minimize contamination.
6. Remove the 2 Torx® screws that mount the expansion valve to the evaporator sealing plate.
7. Remove the valve and discard the gaskets.

To install:

8. Transfer the low pressure cutoff switch to the new valve, if necessary.
9. Install a new aluminum gasket on the evaporator sealing plate.
10. Carefully install the expansion valve to the evaporator sealing plate and torque the Torx® screws to 100 inch lbs.
11. Install a new aluminum gasket on the refrigerant line sealing plate. Hold the sealing plate and line assembly to the expansion valve, install the bolt and tighten to 200 inch lbs.
12. Connect the low pressure cutoff switch connector.
13. Evacuate and recharge the air conditioning system. Check for leaks.

Blower Motor

REMOVAL AND INSTALLATION

Except Neon and New Yorker

1. Disconnect the negative battery cable.
2. Remove the glove box assembly, lower right side instrument panel trim cover and right cowl trim panel, as required. Disconnect the blower lead wire connector.
3. If the vehicle is equipped with air conditioning, disconnect the 2 vacuum lines from the recirculating door actuator and position the actuator aside.
4. Remove the 2 screws at the top of the blower housing that secure it to the unit cover.
5. Remove the 5 screws from around the blower housing and separate the blower housing from the unit.
6. Remove the 3 screws that secure the blower assembly to the heater or air conditioning housing and remove the assembly from the unit. Remove the fan from the blower motor.
7. The installation is the reverse of the removal procedure.
8. Connect the negative battery cable and check the blower motor for proper operation.

Neon

1. Disconnect the negative battery cable.
2. With Air Conditioning, remove the right side scuff plate and pull back carpet
3. With air conditioning, cut the wheel housing silencer in line with blower motor wiring.
4. Disconnect the blower motor wiring connector.
5. Remove 3 retaining screws and lower the blower assembly from the housing.
6. To install, reverse the removal procedure.

1993 New Yorker

1. Disconnect the negative battery cable.
2. Remove the glove box assembly, lower right side instrument panel trim cover and right cowl trim panel, as required. Disconnect the blower lead wire connector.
3. If equipped with air conditioning, disconnect the 2 vacuum lines from the recirculating door actuator and position the actuator aside.
4. Remove the 2 screws at the top of the blower housing that secure it to the unit cover.
5. Remove the 5 screws from around the blower housing and separate the blower housing from the unit.
6. Remove the 3 screws that secure the blower assembly to the heater or air conditioning housing and remove the assembly from the unit. Remove the fan from the blower motor.
7. The installation is the reverse of the removal procedure.
8. Connect the negative battery cable and check the blower motor for proper operation.

Blower Motor Resistor

REMOVAL AND INSTALLATION

Daytona and LeBaron

CAUTION

Do not touch the blower resistor coils directly and do not operate the blower motor with the resistor removed.

1. Disconnect the negative battery cable.
2. Remove the glove box assembly.
3. Remove the security and lamp outage modules, if equipped.
4. Locate the resistor block above and to the front of the glove box opening on the dash panel and disconnect the electrical connector.
5. Remove the 2 attaching screws and pull the resistor straight from the panel to avoid damaging the coils.
6. Make sure there is no contact between any of the coils before installing.
7. The installation is the reverse of the removal procedure.
8. Connect the negative battery cable and check the blower system for proper operation.

Except Daytona and LeBaron

1. Disconnect the negative battery cable.
2. On Sundance, Shadow, Spirit, Acclaim and LeBaron Landau, raise the hood and remove the wiper arms, then remove the cowl plenum grille (5 screws). On Neon remove wipers only.
3. Remove the 4 air intake shield attaching screws and remove the shield.
4. On 1993 Dynasty, Fifth Avenue, Imperial and New Yorker, remove the resistor block cover, then on all models, disconnect the wire harness from the resistor, located behind the windshield washer reservoir.
5. Remove the attaching screws and pull the resistor straight from the panel.
6. Make sure there is no contact between any of the coils before installing.
7. The installation is the reverse of the removal procedure.

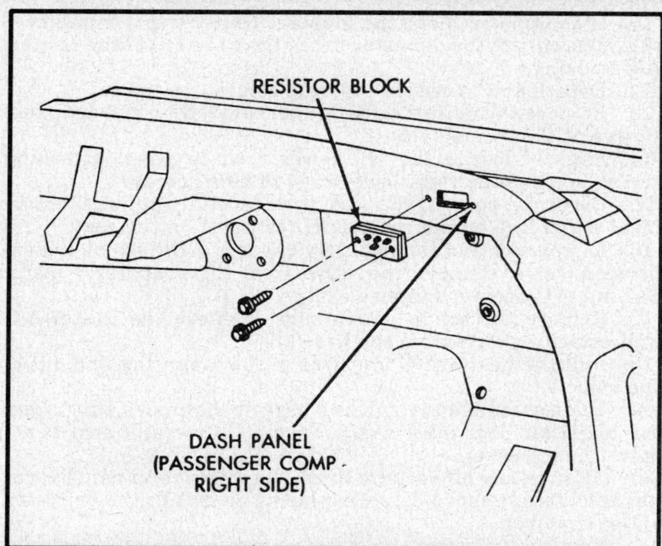

Blower resistor location—Daytona and LeBaron

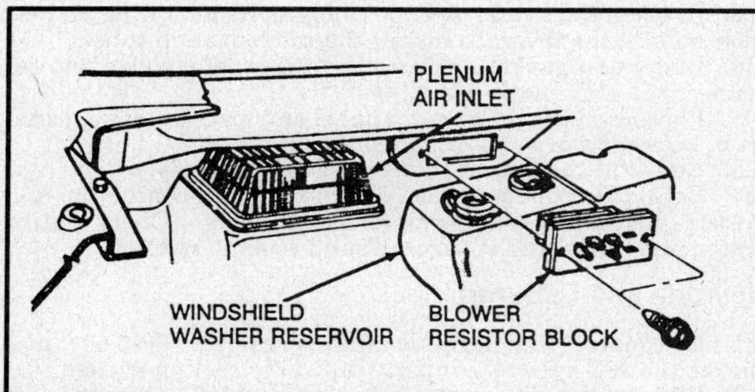

Blower resistor location—except Daytona and LeBaron

8. Connect the negative battery cable and check the blower system for proper operation.

Heater Core and Evaporator Assembly

REMOVAL AND INSTALLATION

1993 Dynasty, Fifth Avenue, New Yorker and Imperial

1. Disconnect the negative battery cable. Properly discharge the air conditioning system. Drain the cooling system.
2. Detach the heater hoses from the heater core tubes. Plug the hose ends and the core tubes to prevent spillage of coolant.
3. Remove the condensation tube.
4. Disconnect the vacuum lines.
5. Remove the glove box, right side upper and lower underpanel silencers, the steering column cover and left under-panel silencer.
6. Remove the right instrument panel reinforcement. Take out the ashtray. Remove the center and defroster distribution ducts.
7. Disconnect the relay module, blower motor connector and demister hoses from the heater-A/C unit.
8. If not equipped with ATC, disconnect the temperature control cable flag from the bottom of the unit. Free the cable from the clip and move it out of the way.
9. Disconnect the vacuum harness at the connection at the housing. If equipped with ATC, disconnect the instrument panel wiring from the rear of the climate control unit.
10. Disconnect the 25-pin connector bracket and fuse box from the right side of the panel.
11. Remove the 4 retaining nuts from the firewall side.
12. Disconnect the hanger strap from the package and rotate it aside.
13. Remove the entire housing assembly from the dash panel and rotate it to clear the instrument panel.
14. To disassemble the unit, remove the 1 retaining nut front the blend-air door pivot shaft and take off the crank arm.
15. Disconnect the defrost and mode vacuum actuator lines. Take out 3 screws from the defrost outlet chamber and 2 screws from the air inlet plenum.
16. Remove 11 cover attaching screws and take off the cover.
17. Remove the retaining screw from the heater core or evaporator and remove the unit from the housing assembly.

To install:

18. Assemble the housing, making sure all vacuum tubing is properly routed.
19. Position the assembly on the mounting studs, reattach the hanger strap screw and secure the unit with nuts on firewall side.
20. Reinstall the 25-pin connector and fuse box on right side. Connect the instrument panel wiring to the rear of the ATC unit or reattach the temperature control cable, as removed.
21. Attach demister hoses, blower motor connector and relay module.
22. Reinstall the instrument panel trim pieces, air ducts, and reinforcements as removed.
23. Install the glove box and right side kick and sill panels.
24. Connect the vacuum lines, the condensation tube, and reattach the heater hoses.
25. Using the proper equipment, evacuate and recharge the air conditioning system. If the evaporator was replaced, add 2 oz. of refrigerant oil during the recharge.
26. Fill the cooling system.
27. Connect the negative battery cable and check the entire climate control system for proper operation and leakage.

Shadow and Sundance

1. Disconnect the negative battery cable. Properly discharge the air conditioning system. Drain the cooling system.
2. Disconnect the heater hoses at the heater core tubes. Plug the hose ends and the core tubes to prevent spillage of coolant. Remove the condensation tube and disconnect the vacuum lines.
3. Remove the steering column cover and the ash tray.
4. Remove the right A-pillar trim.
5. Remove the right cowl side trim.
6. Remove the glove box assembly and the right side instrument panel reinforcement.
7. Remove the following:
   - Right instrument panel lower mounting screw.
   - Center bezel.
   - Floor console.
   - Panel support brace from steering column to right side of panel.
   - Support bracket below glove box opening.
   - Ashtray and radio.
   - Instrument panel top cover.
   - Right side panel to windshield edge attaching 3 screws.
8. Remove the center distribution and defroster adaptor ducts.
9. Disconnect the relay module.
10. Remove the instrument panel to heater-A/C housing bracket, then remove the lower air distribution duct.

11. Disconnect the blower motor wiring and the demister hoses from the top of the housing.
12. If not equipped with ATC, disconnect the temperature control cable flag from under the heater-A/C housing and unclip the cable from the heater duct. Detach the vacuum lines from the housing.
13. If equipped with ATC, disconnect the panel wiring harness from the rear of the ATC control panel.
14. Fold carpeting back on the right side of the housing.
15. Remove 4 housing retaining nuts from the engine side of the firewall.
16. Remove the housing strap lower screw and rotate the strap out of the way. Then, move the heater-A/C assembly rearward off the mounting studs.
17. Disconnect the demister hoses from the top of the package. Now slide the assembly out while pulling the instrument panel rearward.
18. To disassemble the housing assembly, remove 1 nut from the blend air door pivot shaft. Take off the crank arm to remove the top cover.
19. After taking off vacuum lines, the defrost and panel vacuum actuators, remove 3 upward facing screws at the defroster outlet chamber.
20. Remove 2 heater-A/C cover screws at the air inlet plenum, then remove 11 cover screws to lift off the cover.

To install:

21. Assemble the package, making sure all vacuum tubing is properly routed.
22. Connect the vacuum harness and demister hoses. Install the nuts to the firewall and connect the hanger strap inside the passenger compartment.
23. Fold the carpeting back into position.
24. Connect the wiring to the ATC unit, if equipped.
25. If not with ATC, reattach the cable to the housing, as removed.
26. Attach the blower motor wiring. Install the floor, center distribution and defroster adaptor ducts. Be sure the strap is secured to the housing with the lower screw.
27. Install the relay module, then install the remaining instrument panel trim pieces and components as removed in Steps **3–7** above.
28. Connect the heater hoses.
29. Using the proper equipment, evacuate and recharge the air conditioning system. If the evaporator was replaced, add 2 oz. of refrigerant oil during the recharge.
30. Fill the cooling system.
31. Connect the negative battery cable and check the entire climate control system for proper operation and leakage.

Acclaim, Spirit and LeBaron Landau

1. Disconnect the negative battery cable. Properly discharge the air conditioning system. Properly drain the cooling system.
2. Remove the glove box, disconnect 2 vacuum lines from the recirc air door actuator, and disconnect the blower lead wire.
3. Remove 2 screws at the top of the blower housing and 5 screws from around the edge of the blower housing. Separate the blower motor from the unit. Remove 3 screws holding blower wheel to the heater-A/C housing.
4. Remove the relay panel above the glove box. Disconnect A/C vacuum line connector and radio noise capacitor connectors.
5. Remove panel trim from left windshield pillar and left lower side cowl.
6. Detach hood release handle. Remove the steering column covers.
7. Disconnect the parking brake release mechanism rod (access through the fuse panel opening).
8. Remove the silencer and reinforcement from left side of the panel and the center panel bezel around the radio.
9. Remove the front floor console. Detach and remove the radio and climate control panel assemblies. Remove the cigar lighter.
10. If equipped remove the message center/trip computer.
11. Disconnect the demister tubes from the top of the heater-A/C housing.
12. Detach and lower the steering column.
13. Remove the defrost outlet panel cover, then extract panel screws at the windshield.
14. Slightly loosen the left lower cowl to panel attaching screw. Remove the right lower cowl to panel screw.
15. Cover the passenger's seat, then carefully pull the instrument panel free on the right side, resting it on the seat.
16. Disconnect and immediately cap the A/C lines at the expansion valve. Remove the valve from the evaporator plate. Seal all A/C openings immediately.
17. Remove the condensation tube. Remove the heater-A/C unit attaching nuts from the firewall.
18. Pull the heater-A/C unit free of the mounting and out of the vehicle.
19. To disassemble the housing assembly, remove 1 nut from the blend air door pivot shaft. Take off the crank arm to remove the top cover.
20. After taking off vacuum lines, the defrost and panel vacuum actuators, remove 3 upward facing screws at the defroster outlet chamber.
21. Remove 2 heater-A/C cover screws at the air inlet plenum, then remove 11 cover screws to lift off the cover.

To install:

22. Reassemble the unit, noting vacuum line routing.
23. Position the heater-A/C assembly to its mounting and attach nuts at the firewall. Install the condensation tube.
24. Using new gaskets, reinstall the expansion valve and reconnect the A/C lines.
25. Reposition the instrument panel and install screws, panel trim, bezels, covers and components as removed.
26. Reinstall the blower motor assembly and glove box.
27. Refill the cooling system. Evacuate and recharge the A/C system. Reconnect the negative battery cable. Check entire system operation and refrigerant and coolant levels.

Daytona and LeBaron

1. Disconnect the negative battery cable. Properly discharge the A/C system. Properly drain the cooling system.
2. Remove the expansion valve, capping all openings immediately.
3. Disconnect the heater hoses from the firewall, plugging hose and tube openings to prevent coolant spillage. Remove the evaporator condensation tube.
4. Disconnect the vacuum lines from the supply nipple. Remove the heater-A/C unit attaching nuts at the dash panel.
5. Remove the passenger front seat, the right kick panel and sill plate, the body computer (at lower right door pillar), the glove box, and the right reinforcement brace and bracket assembly.
6. If equipped, remove the carpet panels from both sides of the console. Remove the radio capacitor, lamp outage module and security alarm module.
7. Carefully cut the plastic only of the instrument panel along the indented line in the padded cover to the right of the glove box opening (on some models, this area is marked for cutting). Remove the reinforcement, with piece of panel riveted to it.
8. Remove right and left under-panel silencers.
9. Detach demister hoses from top of heater-A/C unit, disconnect radio antenna cable, blower motor connector, and the blend air door cable (detach and position out of the way).
10. Pull back carpet away from heater-A/C unit.
11. Remove the lower steering column cover and reinforcement, the support bracket at the left of the radio, then remove the distribution duct and defroster adapter from the left side of the panel.
12. Detach the hangar strap and remove the heater-A/C unit.
13. To disassemble the housing assembly, remove 1 nut from the blend air door pivot shaft. Take off the crank arm to remove the top cover.

14. After taking off vacuum lines, the defrost and panel vacuum actuators, remove 3 upward facing screws at the defroster outlet chamber.
15. Remove 2 heater-A/C cover screws at the air inlet plenum, then remove 11 cover screws to lift off the cover.

To install:

16. Reassemble the unit, noting vacuum line routing.
17. Position assembly to its mounting and attach the hanger strap.
18. Reinstall the ducts, brackets, reinforcements, covers and trim as removed in Step **11**. Replace the carpet.
19. Reattach the cables, blower connector and demister hoses to the unit.
20. Install remaining panel trim pieces, braces, components, glove box, and front seat as removed in Steps **5–8**. Note edge of panel plastic as cut to be sure no jagged edges remain or show.
21. Reattach the vacuum lines to the supply nipple, then reattach the heater hoses.
22. Using new gaskets reinstall the expansion valve and A/C lines to the evaporator tubes.
23. Refill the cooling system. Evacuate and recharge the A/C system. Connect the battery cable. Check entire system operation, including cooling and refrigerant levels.

Neon

1. Disconnect the negative battery cable. Properly discharge the A/C system.
2. Remove the instrument panel from the vehicle.
3. Drain the cooling system and remove the heater hoses at the dash panel. Place plugs in the heater core outlets to prevent coolant spillage during unit housing removal.
4. Recover the refrigerant from the A/C system (if equipped).
5. Remove the suction line at the expansion valve. Place a piece of tape over the open refrigerant line to prevent moisture and/or dirt from entering the line.
6. Remove the expansion valve from the evaporator fitting to prevent moisture and/or dirt from entering the evaporator.
7. Remove the rubber drain tube extension from the condensation drain tube.
8. Remove 3 retaining nuts located in the engine compartment, on the dash panel.
9. Remove the right side retaining screw.
10. Remove the remaining nut located on the dash panel stud.
11. Disconnect the blue five way connector from the plenum. The module wiring harness must be removed with the module.
12. Remove the assembly from the vehicle.
13. Remove the clips and screws that hold the unit to the housing.
14. Remove the 4 retaining screws from the inlet air duct on the module. Then remove the air inlet and recirc. door assembly from the module.
15. Disconnect the sensing switch from its harness.
16. Remove the upper to lower case retaining clips and screws. Separate the case halves and remove the evaporator.
17. To install reverse the removal procedure.

Refrigerant Lines

REMOVAL AND INSTALLATION

1. Disconnect the negative battery cable.
2. Properly discharge the air conditioning system.
3. Remove the nuts or bolts that attach the refrigerant line sealing plates to the adjoining components.
4. Remove the lines and discard the gaskets.
5. To install reverse the removal procedure.

Manual Control cable

ADJUSTMENT

Except Neon, all control cables are self-adjusting. If the cable is not functioning properly, check for kinks and lubricate dry moving parts. The cable cannot be disassembled; replace if faulty.

REMOVAL AND INSTALLATION

1. Disconnect the negative battery cable.
2. Remove the necessary bezel(s) in order to gain access to the control head.
3. Remove the screws that fasten the control head to the instrument panel.
4. Pull the unit out and disconnect the temperature control cable by pushing the flag in and pulling the end from its seat.
5. The temperature control cable end is located at the bottom of the A/C-heater housing. Disconnect the cable end by pushing the flag in and pulling the end from its seat.
6. Except Neon, disconnect the self-adjusting clip from the blend air or mode door crank.
7. Take note of the cable's routing and remove the from the vehicle.

To install:

8. Install the cable by routing it in exactly the same position as it was prior to removal.
9. Connect the self-adjusting clip, except Neon, to the door crank and click the flag into the seat.
10. Connect the upper end of the cable to the control head.
11. Place the temperature lever on the COOL side of its travel. Allowing the self-adjusting clip to slide on the cable, rotate the blend air door counterclockwise by hand until it stops.
12. Cycle the lever back and forth a few times to make sure the cable moves freely.
13. For the Neon turn the control knob completely counter–clockwise, pull on black casing of cable and snap cable hold down clip into position.
14. Connect the negative battery cable and check the entire climate control system for proper operation.

Electronic Control Head

REMOVAL AND INSTALLATION

1. Disconnect the negative battery cable.
2. Remove the necessary bezel(s) in order to gain access to the control head.
3. Remove the screws that fasten the control head to the instrument panel.

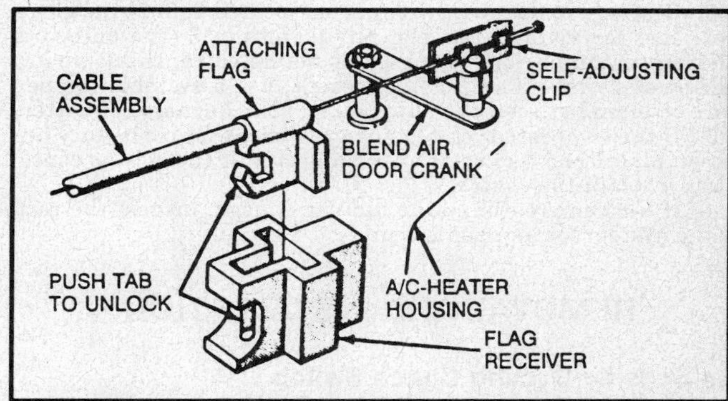

Typical conventional cable attachment flag and door crank—non-ATC

4. Pull the unit out and unplug the wire harness.

5. Remove the control head from the instrument panel.
6. The installation is the reverse of the removal procedure.
7. Connect the negative battery cable and check the entire climate control system for proper operation.

SENSORS AND SWITCHES

Compressor Clutch Coil Cycling Switches

NOTE: Vehicles equipped with a variable displacement compressor do not have clutch cycling switches. The compressor is designed to change displacement to match the vehicle's air conditioning demand without cycling. The variable displacement compressor can be identified by the location of the high pressure line mounted to the end of the compressor case.

OPERATION

Fin Sensing Cycling Clutch Switch

The Fin Sensing Cycling Clutch Switch (FCCS) is used on systems with fixed displacement compressors and is located in the A/C-heater housing near the blower motor and is inserted into the evaporator fins. The FCCS prevents evaporator freeze-up by cycling the compressor clutch coil off when the evaporator temperature drops below freezing point. The coil will be cycled back on when the temperature rises above the freeze point. The FCCS uses a thermistor probe in a capillary tube inserted between the evaporator fins. The switch is a sealed unit that should be replaced if found to be defective.

TESTING

Fin Sensing Cycling Clutch Switch (FCCS)

The compressor clutch coil should cycle 2–3 times per minute at ambient temperatures of 68–90°F (20–32°C). At temperatures above 90°F (32°C), the coil may not cycle at all.

1. Test the switch in an area with ambient temperature of at 70–90°F (21–32°C).
2. Disconnect the switch connector, located behind the glove box. Test for voltage between pin 1 and pin 3 (the outboard pins on the connector). If voltage is not detected, check wiring circuit of switch. If voltage is present, use a suitable jumper wire to jump between the outer pins of the harness connector.
3. If the compressor clutch engages, check for continuity between pins 1 and 3 of the FCCS connector. If there is no continuity, replace the switch.
4. If the compressor clutch did not engage, inspect the rest of the system for an open circuit.

REMOVAL AND INSTALLATION

Fin Sensing Cycling Clutch Switch

1. Disconnect the negative battery cable. Remove the blower motor housing/cover. The blower motor does not have to be removed.

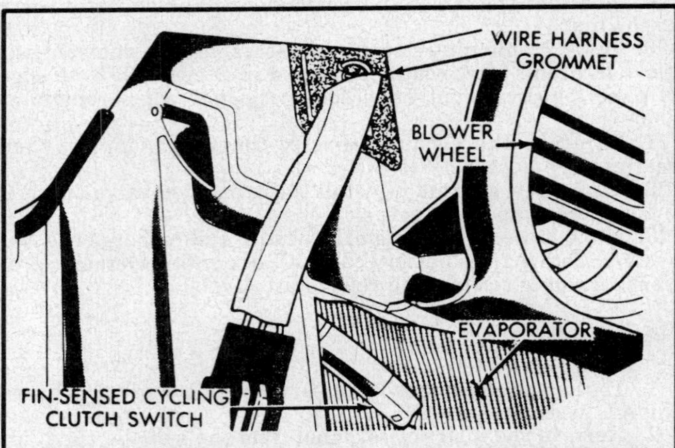

Location of components for fin sensing cycling clutch switch removal

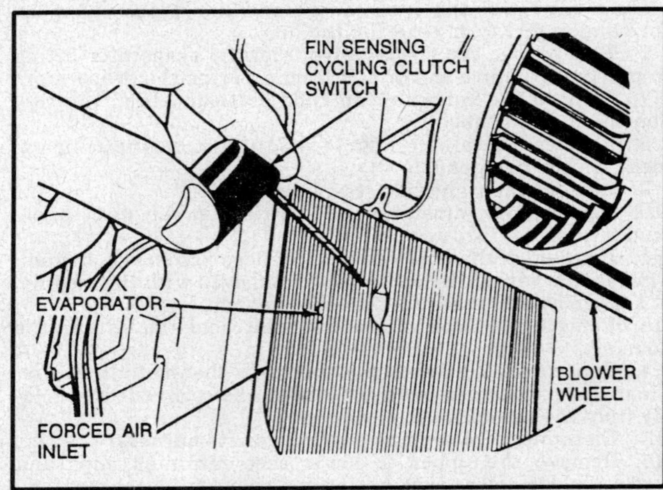

Fin-sensing cycling clutch switch

2. Disconnect the 3-pin connector from the clutch cycling switch sensor harness. Push the wire grommet through the housing and feed the connector through the opening and into the housing.
3. Working through the air inlet opening, pull the switch carefully from the evaporator core (probe is inserted about 3 inches into the coil).
4. The installation is the reverse of the removal procedure, but install the probe about 3 or 4 fins to either side of the original location.
5. Connect the negative battery cable and check the entire climate control system for proper operation.

Cut Off Switches

OPERATION

Low Pressure Cut Off and Differential Pressure Cut Off Switches

The low pressure cut off switch monitors the refrigerant gas pressure on the suction side of the system and is only used with fixed displacement compressors. The differential pressure cut off switch monitors the liquid refrigerant pressure on the liquid side of the system and is only used with variable displacement compressors. The switches operate similarly in that they turn off voltage to the compressor clutch coil when the monitored pressure drops to levels that could damage the compressor. The switches are sealed units that must be replaced if faulty.

High Pressure Cut Off Switch

The high pressure cut off switch used in vehicles equipped with a variable displacement compressor and is located on or near the high pressure relief valve. The function of the switch is to disengage the compressor clutch by monitoring the discharge pressure when levels reach dangerously high levels. This switch is on the same circuit as the differential pressure cut off switch and the ambient sensor.

Thermal Limiter Switch

The thermal limiter switch is used only on models with 2.2L Turbo III engine (TR105 fixed displacement compressor) and is located on the side of the compressor case. It measures compressor surface temperature and is used as a safety device to cut battery voltage to the compressor clutch coil if the case temperature exceeds safe levels. Once the compressor has cooled to its normal temperature, the switch closes and allows voltage to energize the clutch coil. It is not used to cycle the clutch coil.

Ambient Temperature Switch

The ambient switch is used in vehicles equipped with a variable displacement compressor and is located behind the grille and in front of condenser. The ambient sensor prevents the compressor clutch from engaging when the ambient temperature is below 50°F (10°C). The ambient switch is a sealed unit and should be replaced if defective.

Condenser Fan Control Switch

The condenser fan control switch is used in vehicles with a variable displacement compressor and is located on the discharge line at the compressor. The fan control switch turns the radiator/condenser fan on and off by monitoring the compressor discharge pressure. The radiator top tank sensor can override this switch and cycle the fan any time the engine temperature gets too high.

TESTING

Low Pressure Cut Off and Differential Pressure Cut Off Switches

1. Start the engine and allow to idle. Turn the air conditioner ON.
2. Disconnect the switch connector and use a jumper wire to jump between terminals inside the connector boot.
3. If the compressor clutch does not engage, inspect the system for a faulty fuse, faulty clutch cycling switch, or an open circuit.
4. If the clutch engages, connect an air conditioning manifold gauge to the system.
5. Read the low pressure gauge. The low pressure cut off switch should complete the circuit at pressures of at least 14 psi. The differential pressure switch will complete the circuit at pressure of at least 41 psi. Check the system for leaks if the pressures are too low.
6. If the pressures are nominal and the system works when the terminals are jumped, the cut off switch is faulty and should be replaced.

High Pressure Cut Off Switch

1. Start the engine and allow to idle. Turn the air conditioner ON.
2. Connect an air conditioning manifold gauge to the system. The system should operate at high gauge pressure below 430 psi.

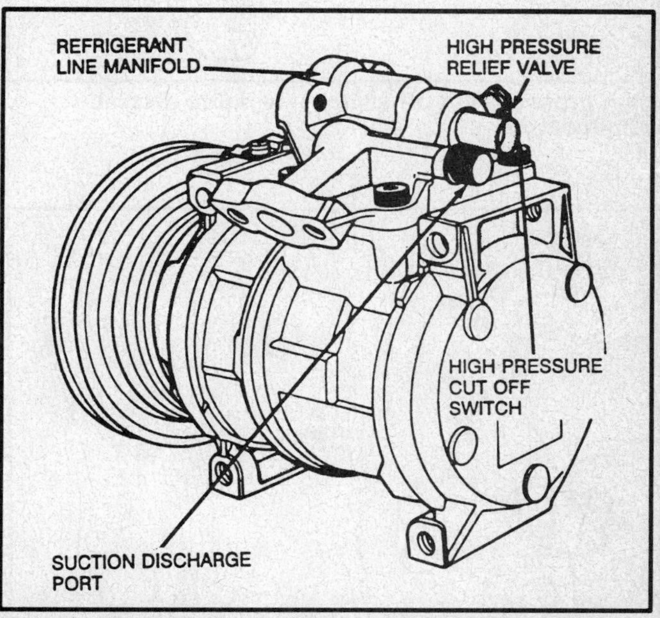

High pressure cut off switch—fixed displacement compressor model 10PA17

3. Without allowing the engine to overheat, block the flow of air to the condenser with a cover. When the high pressure reaches 450 psi, the clutch should disengage.
4. Remove the cover. When the gauge reading falls below 265 psi, the clutch should cycle back on.
5. Replace the switch if it does not operate properly.

Thermal Limiter Switch

1. Disconnect the connector from the thermal limiter switch.
2. Check for continuity between the 2 leads. If no continuity is detected, replace the switch.
3. The switch should open when the temperature reaches 255°F (125°C). If this occurs, check the system for causes of overheating.
4. The switch should close when the temperature comes down to 230°F (110°C).

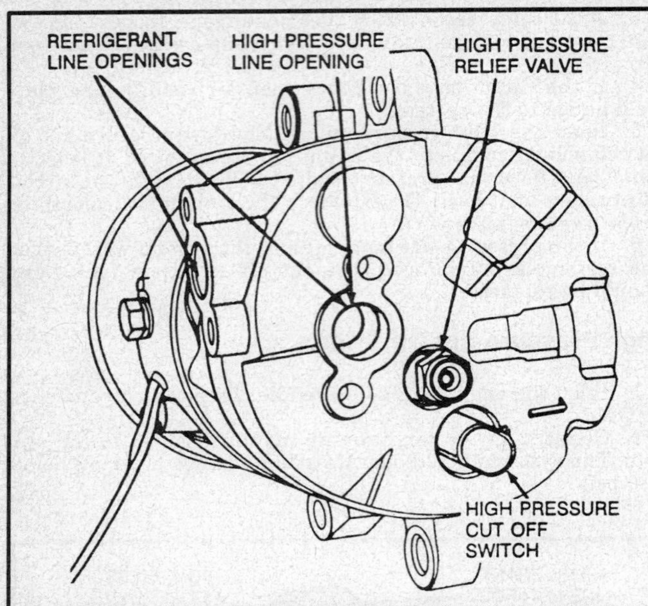

High pressure cut off switch—variable displacement compressor

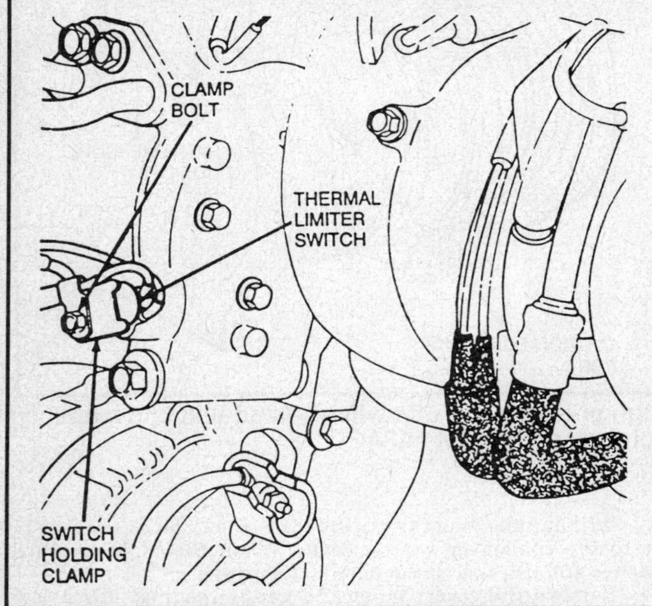

Thermal limiter switch—2.2L Turbo III engine

Ambient Temperature Switch

1. Disconnect the ambient switch connector.
2. Check the continuity across the switch terminals. At ambient temperatures above 50°F (10°C), the circuit should be complete.
3. Chill the switch with ice to below 50°F (10°C) and recheck for continuity. The switch should be open at below the specified temperature.
4. Replace the switch if it is found to be defective.

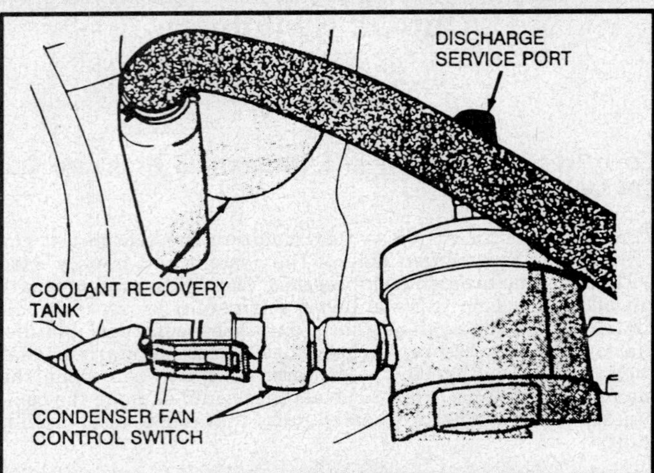

Condenser fan control switch—variable displacement compressor

Condenser Fan Control Switch

1. Disconnect the fan control switch connector.
2. Connect an air conditioning manifold gauge to the system.
3. Jump across the terminals in the wire connector with a jumper wire.
4. Connect an ohmmeter to the switch terminals.
5. Start the engine and allow to idle at 1300 rpm. The radiator fan should run constantly.
6. Turn the air conditioner to **ON** and the blower to **HI**.
7. If the high pressure reads below 160 psi, the switch should be open (no continuity).
8. Without allowing the engine to overheat, block the flow of air to the condenser with a cover. When the high pressure reaches 230 psi, the switch should close (continuity).
9. Remove the cover from the condenser. When the pressure drops to below 160 psi, the switch should open again.
10. Replace the switch if it is defective.

REMOVAL AND INSTALLATION

Low Pressure Cut Off and Differential Pressure Cut Off Switches

1. Disconnect the negative battery cable.
2. Properly discharge the air conditioning system.
3. Unplug the boot connector from the switch.
4. Using an oil pressure sending unit socket, remove the switch from the H-valve.

To install:

5. Seal the threads of the new switch with teflon tape.
6. Install the switch to the H-valve and connect the boot connector.
7. Evacuate and recharge the system. Check for leaks.
8. Check the switch for proper operation.

High Pressure Cut Off Switch

1. Disconnect the negative battery cable.
2. Properly discharge the air conditioning system.
3. Disconnect the connector from the switch.
4. Remove the snap ring that retains the switch in the compressor.
5. Pull the switch straight from the compressor and discard the O-ring.

To install:

6. Replace the O-ring and lubricate with refrigerant oil before installing.
7. Install the switch to the compressor and secure with a new snap ring.

8. Evacuate and recharge the system. Check for leaks.
9. Check the switch for proper operation.

Thermal Limiter Switch

1. Disconnect the negative battery cable. System does not have to be discharged.
2. Disconnect the connector from the switch.
3. Remove the bolt retaining the hold-down clamp and switch at the side of the compressor.
4. Using a small prying tool, remove the switch from the compressor.
5. Thoroughly clean the old silicone sealer from the case.

To install:

6. Apply silicone sealer evenly to the copper surface of the switch. Do not touch sealer with your hand.
7. Install the switch to the compressor case and connect the connector.
8. Check the switch for proper operation.

Ambient Temperature Switch

1. Disconnect the negative battery cable.
2. Remove the 1 attaching screw. Remove the ambient sensor and bracket assembly.
3. To install, reverse the procedure.

Condenser Fan Control Switch

NOTE: System discharging is not necessary to remove the condenser fan control switch; only a small amount of freon will escape as the switch is being rotated. Take the proper precautions.

1. Disconnect the negative battery cable.
2. Disconnect the connector from the switch.
3. Loosen and quickly rotate the switch counterclockwise.
4. Remove the switch from the high pressure line.
5. The installation is the reverse of the removal procedure.
6. Check the switch for proper operation.

Automatic Temperature Control (ATC) System Components

OPERATION

Computer Controller

The ATC computer controller, which is actually the control head in the instrument panel, manages all of the system's electronic functions. It electronically operates the power module and various door actuators. It also retains the operator's selected settings when the vehicle is not running and measures return inputs from the sensors. After measuring all input information, the computer will complete the output circuits to provide logic signals for automatic system regulation.

Power Module

This module receives signals from the computer controller (control head). It then supplies varied voltage to the blower motor ground circuit for different blower speeds.

Ambient Temperature Sensor

The ambient temperature sensor is located on the A/C-heater housing above the glove box. It is a thermistor that will react to the environmental ambient temperature. The computer controller uses the information provided by the ambient sensor to regulate the low blower speed, temperature offsets and mode control.

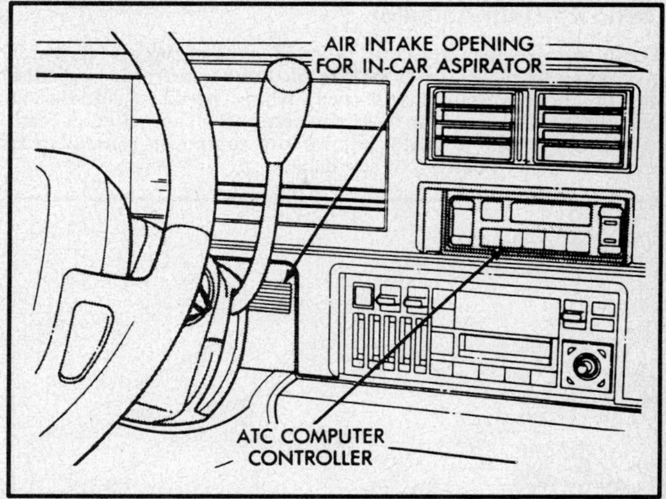

Location of ATC computer controller and in-car aspirator—1993 models

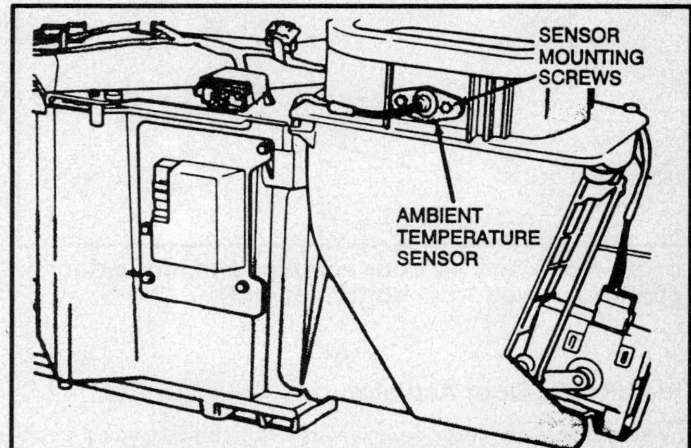

ATC system ambient temperature sensor location—1993 models

In-Car Temperature Sensor/Aspirator Assembly

On 1993 models a small fan in the aspirator draws air through an intake on the instrument panel near the steering column. On 1994–95 models it is located behind the name plate on the right side of the instrument panel. The air flows over the temperature sensor's thermistor, which detects temperature variations. The computer controller then makes adjustments to maintain a constant passenger compartment temperature.

Water Temperature Sensor

The water temperature sensor is located on the heater core mounting plate. Its function is to detect the engine coolant temperature. The computer controller uses this information to determine the cold engine lockout time.

Sun Sensor

The sun sensor is mounted on the top of the driver's side of the instrument panel and is a light-sensitive photo diode. The sun sensor responds to sun light intensity and not temperature. It is used to aid in determining proper mode door position.

Blend Air Door Actuator

The blend air door actuator is an electric servo motor which mechanically positions the A/C unit temperature door. Actuation of the servo motor will occur when the drive signals are supplied to the actuator from the computer controller. A feedback strip in the actuator allows the computer controller to know the exact position of the door at all times.

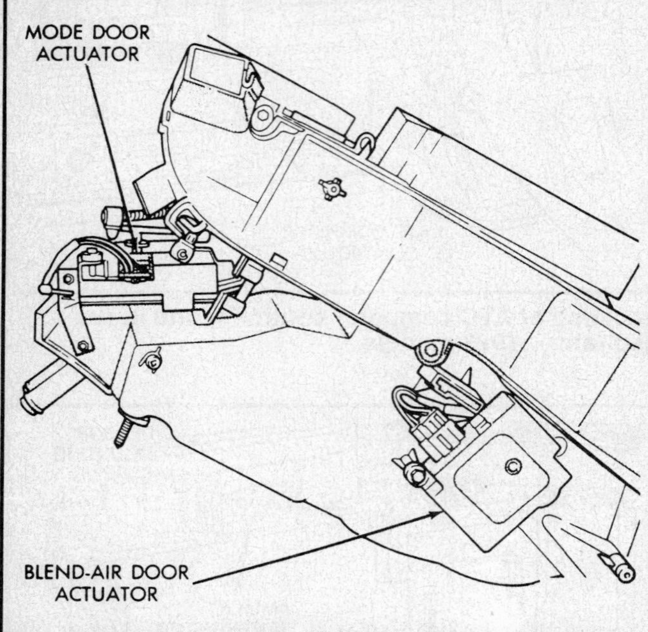

Location of blend air door actuator and mode door actuator (viewed from bottom of unit)

Fresh/Recirc Door Actuator

The actuator is an electric servo motor which positions the A/C unit door in the open or closed position by way of linkages. Actuation of the servo motor will occur when the drive signals are supplied to the actuator from the computer controller. This actuator does not have a feedback strip in the actuator, so the computer controller does not know the exact position of the door.

Mode Door Actuator

This actuator is an electric servo motor which positions the A/C unit panel/bi-level door and the floor/defrost door by way of linkages. Actuation of the servo motor will occur when the drive signals are supplied to the actuator from the computer controller. A feedback strip in the actuator allows the computer controller to know the exact position of the door at all times.

REMOVAL AND INSTALLATION

Computer Controller

1. Disconnect the negative battery cable.
2. Remove the necessary bezel(s) in order to gain access to the control head.
3. Remove the screws that fasten the control head to the instrument panel.
4. Pull the unit out and unplug the wire harness.
5. Remove the control head from the instrument panel.
6. The installation is the reverse of the removal procedure.
7. Connect the negative battery cable and check the entire climate control system for proper operation.

Power Module

1. Disconnect the negative battery cable.
2. Remove the glove box and ash tray assembly.
3. Remove the 4 mounting screws.
4. Disconnect the electrical connector.
5. Remove the module from the A/C-heater housing and remove from the vehicle.
6. The installation is the reverse of the removal procedure.
7. Connect the negative battery cable and check the entire climate control system for proper operation.

Ambient Temperature Sensor

1. Disconnect the negative battery cable.
2. Remove the glove box and ash tray assembly, on 1993 models.
3. Remove 2 attaching screws on the sensor receptacle.

NOTE: When removing the sensor from the A/C-heater housing, pull it straight out slowly or the sensor may hang up on the plastic housing. This may cause the sensor to disengage from the receptacle and possibly fall in to the housing.

4. Unplug the sensor from the receptacle.
5. The installation is the reverse of the removal procedure.
6. Connect the negative battery cable and check the entire climate control system for proper operation.

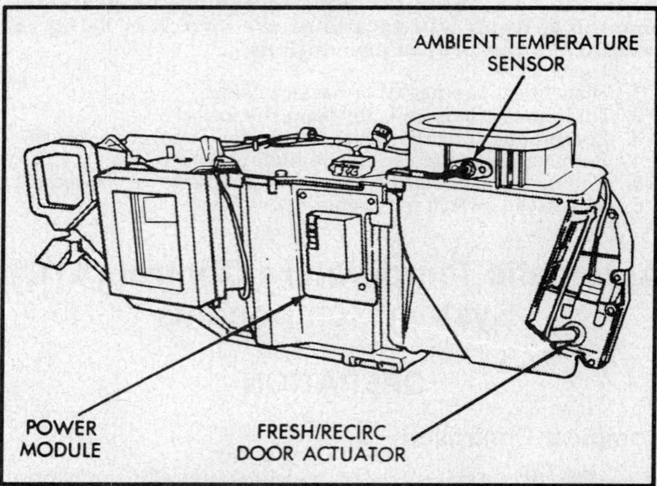

Location of power module, ambient temperature sensor and fresh/recirc door actuator

In-Car Temperature Sensor/Aspirator Assembly

For the 1993 models the in-car temperature sensor and aspirator assembly is located in the instrument panel to the right of the steering column. They are wired together and must be replaced as an assembly.

1. Disconnect the negative battery cable.
2. Remove the instrument cluster bezels, pull off the trip reset knob and remove the cluster lens.
3. If equipped with transmission range indicator, remove the guide tube from behind the fuse block and detach the cable eyelet from the column actuating arm. Remove the lock bar on the column insert by squeezing assembly. Remove rear window defogger bezel and radio bezel. Remove upper steering column cover.
4. On all models, remove 4 cluster attaching screws. As cluster is pulled out, reach behind and disconnect wiring. Remove the instrument cluster.

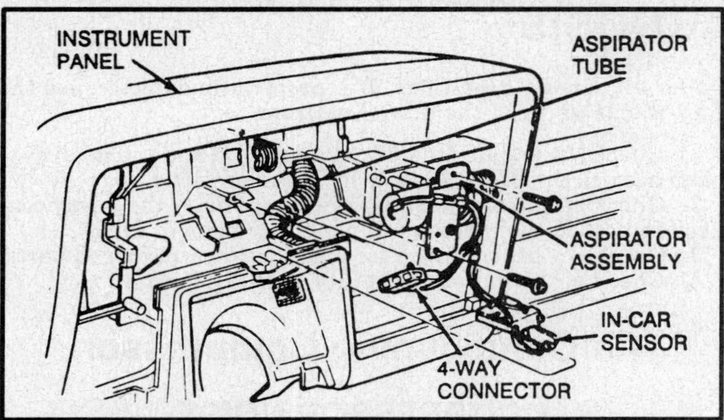

ATC system in-car temperature sensor/aspirator assembly—Dynasty, New Yorker and Imperial

5. Unsnap the sensor from the instrument panel.
6. Remove the 2 aspirator mounting screws.
7. Disconnect the aspirator intake hose from the instrument panel.
8. Remove the assembly with the wiring from the vehicle.
9. The installation is the reverse of the removal procedure.
10. Connect the negative battery cable and check the entire climate control system for proper operation.

Water Temperature Sensor

1. Disconnect the negative battery cable.
2. Remove the A/C-heater housing.
3. Remove the sensor mounting screw.
4. Disconnect the pigtail connector and remove the sensor from the vehicle.
5. The installation is the reverse of the removal procedure.
6. Connect the negative battery cable and check the entire climate control system for proper operation.

Sun Sensor

1. Disconnect the negative battery cable.
2. Using a suitable small prying tool and a clean rag to prevent damage to the top of the instrument panel, pry the sensor from the panel.
3. Pull up and disconnect the connector.
4. The installation is the reverse of the removal procedure. Make sure the sensor is securely snapped in place.
5. Connect the negative battery cable and check the entire climate control system for proper operation.

Blend Air Door Actuator

NOTE: Removing an electronic actuator with power applied can damage the unit. The actuators do not have built-in mechanical stops and if the actuator rotates while disconnected from the assembly, it will become un-calibrated.

1. Disconnect the negative battery cable.
2. Remove the under panel silencers.
3. Remove the carpeted cover over the air bag module.
4. Remove the floor air distribution duct.
5. Remove the actuator attaching screws.
6. Lower the actuator from the housing and disengage from the blend air door shaft.
7. Detach the electrical connector and remove the actuator.

To install:

8. Align the blend air door shaft with the slot in the actuator. Make sure the shaft is properly engaged to prevent damage when tightening the screws.
9. Install and tighten the attaching screws.
10. Connect the connector.
11. Install the actuator attaching screws.
12. Install the floor air duct.
13. Install the carpeted cover over the air bag module and the under panel silencers.
14. Connect the negative battery cable.

Fresh/Recirc Door Actuator

NOTE: Removing an electronic actuator with power applied can damage the unit. The actuators do not have built-in mechanical stops and if the actuator rotates while disconnected from the assembly, it will become un-calibrated.

1. Disconnect the negative battery cable.
2. Remove the glove box and ash tray assembly.
3. Remove the under panel silencer pad.
4. Remove the carpeted cover over the air bag module.
5. Remove the right front kick panel.
6. Remove the metal instrument panel brace.
7. Remove the screws that attach the actuator mounting bracket to the A/C-heater housing.
8. Remove the screws that attach the actuator to the bracket. Make sure the innermost screw does not fall into the case.
9. Disconnect the electrical connector from the actuator.
10. Tilt the actuator to release it from the actuating linkage and remove from the vehicle.

To install:

11. Attach the actuator and bracket assembly to the linkage and install to the housing. Connect the connector to the actuator.
12. Install the attaching screws.
13. Install the metal brace and kick panel.
14. Install the carpeted cover over the air bag module and the under panel silencer pad.
15. Install the glove box and ash tray assembly.
16. Connect the negative battery cable.

Mode Door Actuator

NOTE: Removing an electronic actuator with power applied can damage the unit. The actuators do not have built-in mechanical stops and if the actuator rotates while disconnected from the assembly, it will become un-calibrated.

1. Disconnect the negative battery cable.
2. Remove the under panel silencer.
3. Disconnect the electrical connector from the actuator.
4. Pinch and remove the lower plastic clip from the actuator arm.
5. Remove the 3 actuator bracket mounting screws.
6. Rotate the actuator to gain access to the upper plastic clip. Pinch and remove the clip.
7. Remove the actuator to mounting bracket screws.
8. Remove the actuator from the mounting bracket and remove from the vehicle.

To install:

9. Install the actuator and mounting bracket assembly.
10. Attach the upper and lower plastic clips.
11. Connect the connector to the actuator.
12. Install the attaching screws.
13. Install the under panel silencer.
14. Connect the negative battery cable.

SYSTEM DIAGNOSIS

Air Conditioning Performance

OVERALL PERFORMANCE TEST

Air temperature in the testing area must be at least 70°F (21°C) to ensure the accuracy of this test.

1. Connect a manifold gauge set to the system.
2. Set the controls to **A/C RECIRC, PANEL** or **MAX A/C**, temperature control level on full **COOL** and the blower on high.
3. Start the engine and adjust the idle speed to 1000 rpm with the compressor clutch engaged.
4. Allow the engine come to normal operating temperature and keep doors and windows closed.
5. Insert a thermometer in the left center A/C outlet and operate the engine for 5 minutes. The A/C clutch may cycle depending on the ambient conditions.
6. With the clutch engaged, compare the discharge air temperature to the performance chart.
7. Disconnect and plug the gray vacuum line going to the heater water control valve. Observe the valve arm for movement as the line is disconnected. If there is no movement, check the valve for sticking.
8. Operate the A/C for 2 additional minutes and observe the discharge air temperature again. If the discharge air temperature increased by more than 5°F, check the blend air door for proper operation. If not, compare the temperature, suction and discharge pressures to the chart. Reconnect the gray vacuum line.
9. If the values do not meet specifications, check system components for proper operation.

Vacuum Actuating System

INSPECTION

Check the system for proper operation. Air should come from the appropriate vents when the corresponding mode is selected under all driving conditions. If a problem is detected use the flow-charts to check the flow of vacuum.

1. Check the engine for sufficient vacuum and the main supplier hose at the brake booster for leaks or kinks.
2. Check all interior vacuum lines, especially the 7-way connection behind the instrument panel for leaks or kinks.
3. Check the control head for leaky ports or damaged parts.
4. Check all actuators for ability to hold vacuum.

Air Conditioning Compressor

COMPRESSOR NOISE

Noises that develop during air conditioning operation can be misleading. A noise that sounds like serious compressor damage may only be a loose belt, mounting bolt or clutch assembly. Improper belt tension can also emit a noise that can be mistaken for more serious problems. Check and adjust all possible causes of the noise before replacing the compressor.

COMPRESSOR CLUTCH INOPERATIVE

The air conditioning compressor clutch electrical circuit is controlled by the engine controller (SMEC or SBEC) located in the engine compartment. If the compressor clutch does not engage, check the basics and continue on to the diagnostic charts if the basics check out.

1. Verify refrigerant charge and charge as required.
2. Check for battery voltage at the clutch coil connection. If voltage is detected, check the coil.
3. If battery voltage is not detected at the coil, check for voltage at the low pressure or differential cut off switch. If voltage is not detected there either, check fuses etc. If the fuses are good, use the DRBII or digital volt-ohmmeter in conjunction with the charts to determine the location of the problem.

NOTE: Do not use a 12 volt test light to probe wires or damage to relevant on-board computers may result.

AIR CONDITIONING SYSTEM PRESSURES

Ambient Temperature °F(°C)	Air Temperature at Center Panel Vent °F(°C)	Compressor Discharge Pressure PSI (kPa)	Evaporator Suction Pressure PSI (kPa)
70 (21)	35–46 (2–8)	140–210 (965–1448)	10–35 (69–241)
80 (27)	39–50 (4–10)	180–235 (1240–1620)	16–38 (110–262)
90 (32)	44–55 (7–13)	210–270 (1448–1860)	20–42 (138–290)
100 (38)	50–62 (10–17)	240–310 (1655–2137)	25–48 (172–331)
110 (43)	56–70 (13–21)	280–350 (1930–2413)	30–55 (2)7–379)

CLUTCH COIL TESTING

1. Verify the battery is fully charged.
2. Connect a 0–10 scale ammeter in series with the clutch coil terminal. Use a volt meter with clips to measure the voltage across the battery and clutch coil.
3. Turn the A/C on and switch the blower to LOW speed. Start the engine and run at normal idle.
4. The A/C clutch should engage immediately and the clutch voltage should be within 2 volts of battery voltage. If the clutch does not engage, test the fusible link.
5. The clutch coil is considered good if the current draw is 2.0–3.7 amperes at 12 volts at the clutch coil. If the voltage is more than 12.5 volts, add loads by turning on accessories until the voltage drops below 12.5 volts.
6. If the coil current reads 0, the coil is open and should be replaced.

7. If the ammeter reading is 4 or more amps, then the coil is shorted and should be replaced.
8. If the coil voltage is not within 2 volts of battery voltage, test the clutch coil feed circuit for excessive voltage drop.

Automatic Temperature Control (ATC) System

NON-COMPUTER AIDED DIAGNOSTICS

The system should go to maximum cooling or heating if the panel temperature setting is changed 4 degrees or more. Check coolant level, refrigerant charge, drive belt tension, radiator air flow, radiator fan operation and in-car temperature sensor/aspirator air suction (by holding tissue in front of aspirator grille near steering column-tissue should stick to grille).

COMPUTER AIDED SELF-DIAGNOSTICS

The system's computer is equipped with a self-diagnostic capabilities. Should the computer detect a failure within the system, the temperature indication on the display would be replaced by the failure code number when in the diagnostics mode.

The diagnostic test will display 2 types of trouble codes: 01—22 have been detected during the diagnostic test and codes 23—36 have been detected during normal ATC operation. These last codes would be stored in the computer and are retrieved during the diagnostic test.

First, check the basics:

- Fuses, fusible links, cartridge fuses and relays
- Coolant level
- Heater core water valve operation
- Refrigerant charge and compressor operation
- Tension of compressor drive belt
- Tightness of vacuum line connections
- Radiator air flow and coolant flow through thermostat
- Radiator fan operation
- In-car sensor air intake is clear and air is drawn in

Initial Test Procedure for 1993 Models

1. Start the engine and allow to come to normal operating temperature.
2. Simultaneously depress the **AUTO**, **FLOOR** and **DEFROST** buttons. The display should be flashing on and off.
3. During the test, check for the following symptoms:
   - Any or all display symbols and indicators do not illuminate.
   - The blower does not operate at its highest speed.
   - Outlet temperature does not get hot and/or cycle cold.
   - Flow of air does not start at the defrost outlets and/or cycle to the panel outlets.

If none of these symptoms are present and no codes are shown, the system will return to normal operation. If any of the symptoms are present, continue.

Symptom A

If any or all display symbols and indicators do not illuminate:

1. After self-diagnostics are complete, select the function that will display the malfunction.
2. If the system operates properly and the display does not, replace the control panel computer.

Symptom B

If the blower motor does not operate and no failure code is displayed:

CAUTION

Keep hands and arms clear of both the blower motor and power vacuum module heat sink to avoid personal injury. Also, do not run the system for longer than 10 minutes with the module removed from the unit.

1. Check the connections at the power module and blower motor. Check both ends of the fuse for 12 volts. If fuse is good, check the green wire at the blower connector for 12 volts to ground.
2. Turn ignition to **ON**, with the blower motor connected, check for 12 volts to body ground on the black/tan wire of the blower 2-pin connector.
3. Check for 12 volts at the black and tan wire in the power module connector and check the black wire at the power module connector for ground. If correct, replace the power module. If not, find the open or shorted wire and repair.

Symptom C

If the outlet temperature does not get hot and/or cycle cold:

1. Make sure the blend air door is properly attached to the actuator.
2. If cold air is not discharged from the outlets, check overall air conditioning system performance.
3. If hot air is not discharged from the outlets, check the heating and engine cooling system.

Symptom D

If the flow of air does not start at the defrost outlets and/or cycle to the panel outlets:

1. Check the linkages from the mode door actuators for binding.
2. Check for proper door travel in the housing. The computer will do 1 of 2 things:
   - It will return control settings to those selected before the diagnostic test was run, meaning no codes are stored in the system, it will resume normal operation.
   - If there are any failure codes present, the blower will stop and each code can be displayed; after each failure code appears, record the code and push the **PANEL** button to display the next code.

On 1994–95 Models

To place the system into it's diagnostic mode, press and hold the floor, mix and defrost buttons (at the same time). The ATC head display will begin to blink. When the control head display begins to blink release the floor, mix and defrost buttons. Once the control head enters diagnostic mode, the display on the control head will continue to blink. This occurs until it completes its tests and calibrations. Then it will display any diagnostic trouble codes that are present in the body controller. If there are no diagnostic trouble codes the system will return it its normal operation as indicated by temperature display.

Trouble Codes

Trouble Code 1—Output Failure With All Outputs Low

1. Remove pin No. 2 from the 21-way control head connector and retest the system. If Code 1 does not appear, the control is good.
2. Disconnect the 21-way connector from the control head. Measure the resistance between pins No. 2 and 12 of the control head connector. The specification is 2600–2800 ohms. If within specification, the power module is good. The source of the voltage at pin No. 2 is in the wiring; repair and retest the system. If not within specification, replace the power module. Retest; if the code still exists, continue.

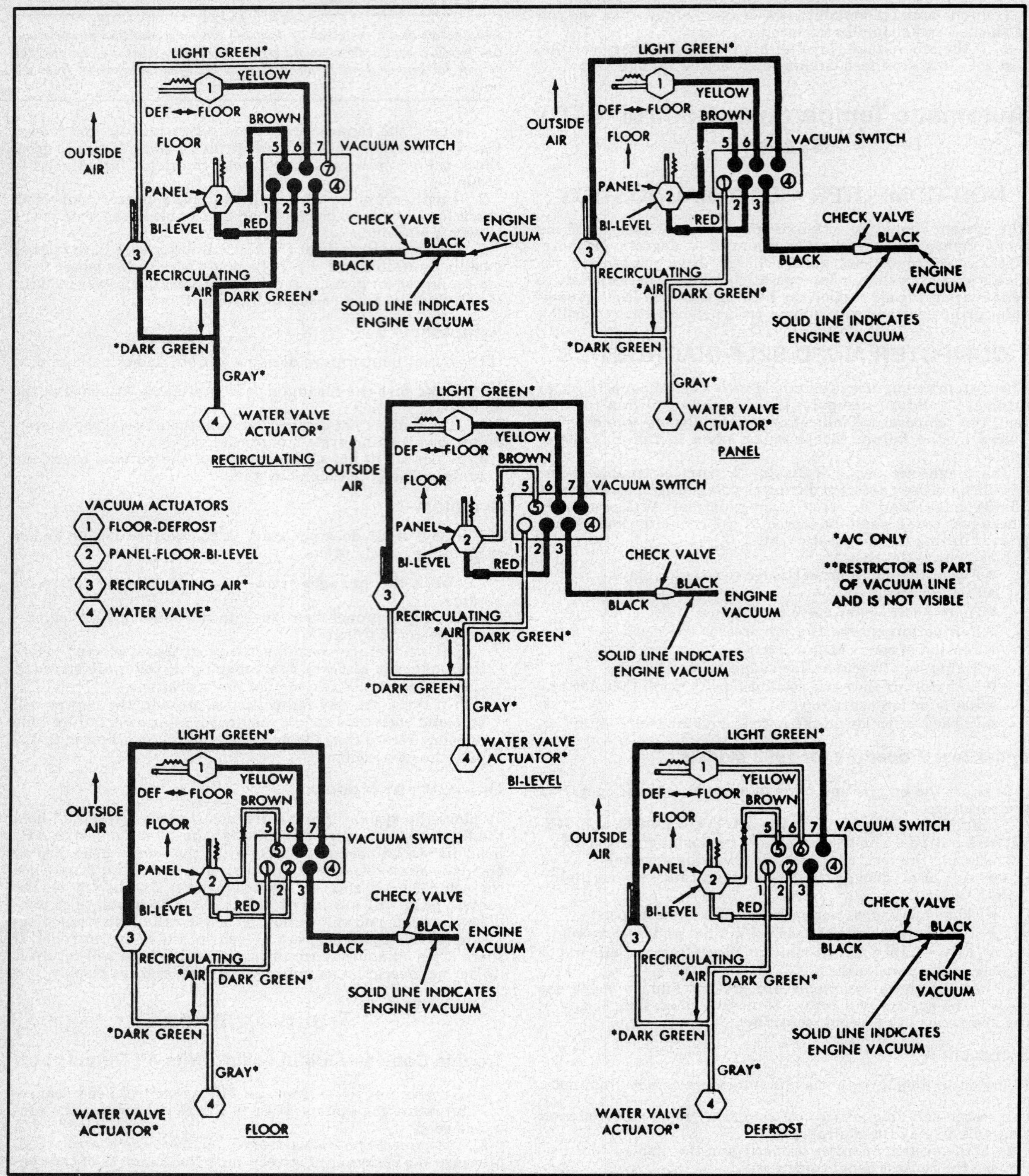

Heating and air conditioning system vacuum control circuits—1993 Models

A/C SYSTEM DIAGNOSIS–FIXED DISPLACEMENT COMPRESSOR—1993 MODELS

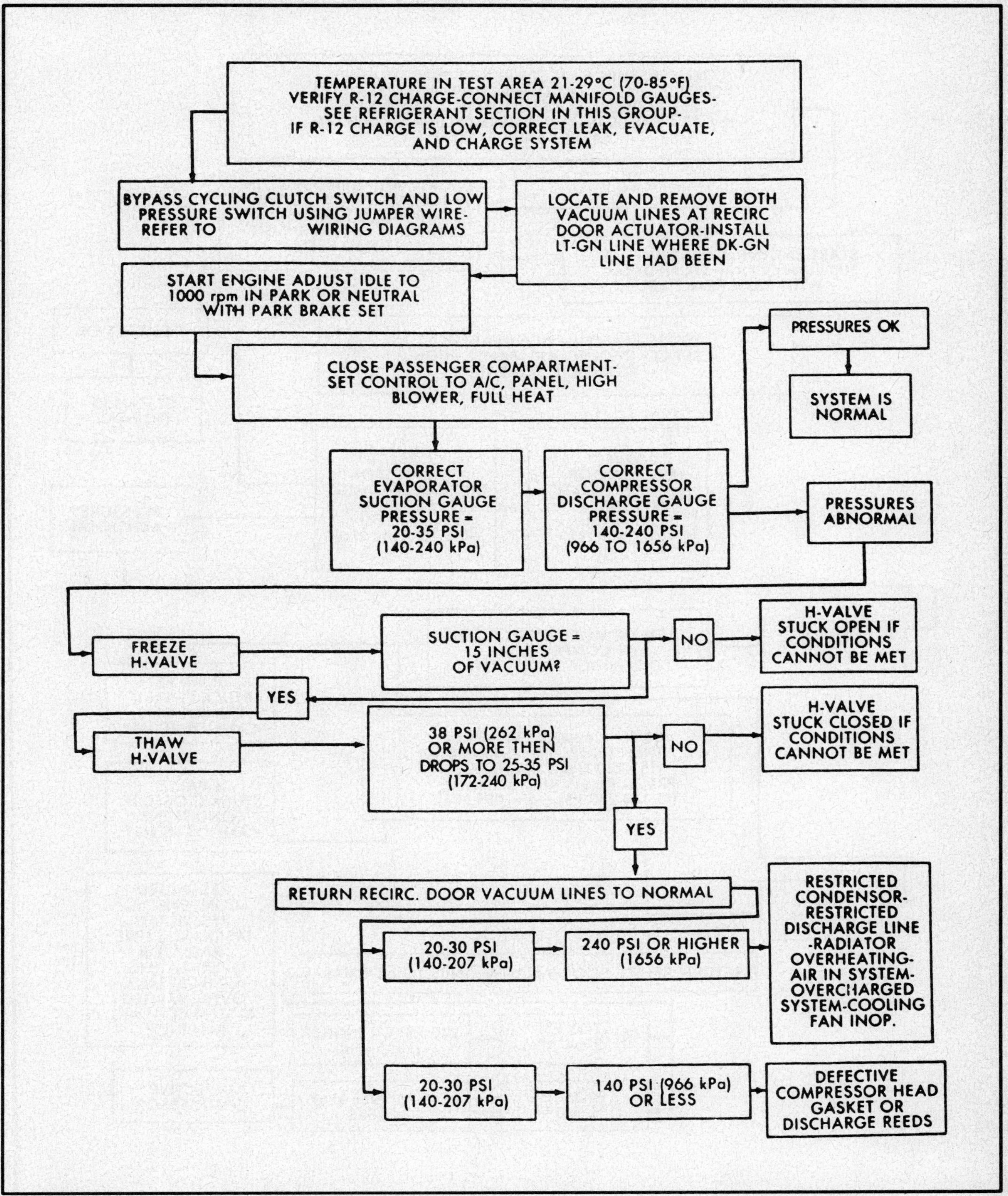

TEMPERATURE IN TEST AREA 21-29°C (70-85°F)
VERIFY R-12 CHARGE-CONNECT MANIFOLD GAUGES-
SEE REFRIGERANT SECTION IN THIS GROUP-
IF R-12 CHARGE IS LOW, CORRECT LEAK, EVACUATE, AND CHARGE SYSTEM
BYPASS CYCLING CLUTCH SWITCH AND LOW PRESSURE SWITCH USING JUMPER WIRE-REFER TO WIRING DIAGRAMS
LOCATE AND REMOVE BOTH VACUUM LINES AT RECIRC DOOR ACTUATOR-INSTALL LT-GN LINE WHERE DK-GN LINE HAD BEEN
START ENGINE ADJUST IDLE TO 1000 rpm IN PARK OR NEUTRAL WITH PARK BRAKE SET
CLOSE PASSENGER COMPARTMENT-SET CONTROL TO A/C, PANEL, HIGH BLOWER, FULL HEAT
CORRECT EVAPORATOR SUCTION GAUGE PRESSURE = 20-35 PSI (140-240 kPa)
CORRECT COMPRESSOR DISCHARGE GAUGE PRESSURE = 140-240 PSI (966 TO 1656 kPa)
PRESSURES OK
SYSTEM IS NORMAL
PRESSURES ABNORMAL
FREEZE H-VALVE
SUCTION GAUGE = 15 INCHES OF VACUUM?
NO
H-VALVE STUCK OPEN IF CONDITIONS CANNOT BE MET
YES
THAW H-VALVE
38 PSI (262 kPa) OR MORE THEN DROPS TO 25-35 PSI (172-240 kPa)
NO
H-VALVE STUCK CLOSED IF CONDITIONS CANNOT BE MET
YES
RETURN RECIRC. DOOR VACUUM LINES TO NORMAL
20-30 PSI (140-207 kPa)
240 PSI OR HIGHER (1656 kPa)
RESTRICTED CONDENSOR-RESTRICTED DISCHARGE LINE -RADIATOR OVERHEATING-AIR IN SYSTEM-OVERCHARGED SYSTEM-COOLING FAN INOP.
20-30 PSI (140-207 kPa)
140 PSI (966 kPa) OR LESS
DEFECTIVE COMPRESSOR HEAD GASKET OR DISCHARGE REEDS

A/C SYSTEM DIAGNOSIS—VARIABLE DISPLACEMENT COMPRESSOR

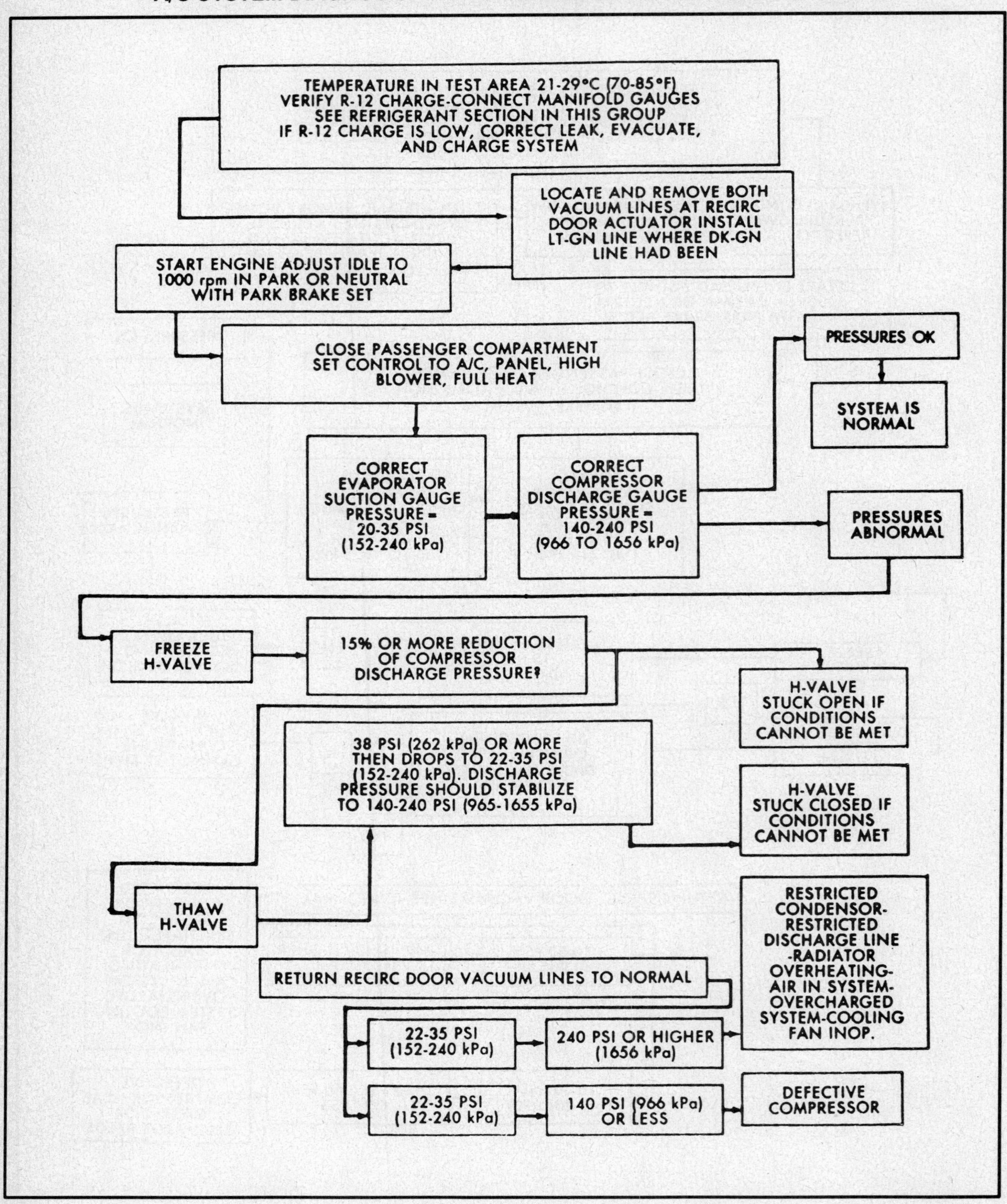
TEMPERATURE IN TEST AREA 21-29°C (70-85°F)
VERIFY R-12 CHARGE-CONNECT MANIFOLD GAUGES
SEE REFRIGERANT SECTION IN THIS GROUP
IF R-12 CHARGE IS LOW, CORRECT LEAK, EVACUATE, AND CHARGE SYSTEM
LOCATE AND REMOVE BOTH VACUUM LINES AT RECIRC DOOR ACTUATOR INSTALL LT-GN LINE WHERE DK-GN LINE HAD BEEN
START ENGINE ADJUST IDLE TO 1000 rpm IN PARK OR NEUTRAL WITH PARK BRAKE SET
CLOSE PASSENGER COMPARTMENT SET CONTROL TO A/C, PANEL, HIGH BLOWER, FULL HEAT
PRESSURES OK
SYSTEM IS NORMAL
CORRECT EVAPORATOR SUCTION GAUGE PRESSURE = 20-35 PSI (152-240 kPa)
CORRECT COMPRESSOR DISCHARGE GAUGE PRESSURE = 140-240 PSI (966 TO 1656 kPa)
PRESSURES ABNORMAL
FREEZE H-VALVE
15% OR MORE REDUCTION OF COMPRESSOR DISCHARGE PRESSURE?
H-VALVE STUCK OPEN IF CONDITIONS CANNOT BE MET
38 PSI (262 kPa) OR MORE THEN DROPS TO 22-35 PSI (152-240 kPa). DISCHARGE PRESSURE SHOULD STABILIZE TO 140-240 PSI (965-1655 kPa)
H-VALVE STUCK CLOSED IF CONDITIONS CANNOT BE MET
THAW H-VALVE
RESTRICTED CONDENSOR-RESTRICTED DISCHARGE LINE -RADIATOR OVERHEATING-AIR IN SYSTEM-OVERCHARGED SYSTEM-COOLING FAN INOP.
RETURN RECIRC DOOR VACUUM LINES TO NORMAL
22-35 PSI (152-240 kPa)
240 PSI OR HIGHER (1656 kPa)
22-35 PSI (152-240 kPa)
140 PSI (966 kPa) OR LESS
DEFECTIVE COMPRESSOR

A/C SYSTEM DIAGNOSIS–FIXED DISPLACEMENT COMPRESSOR—1994–95 MODELS

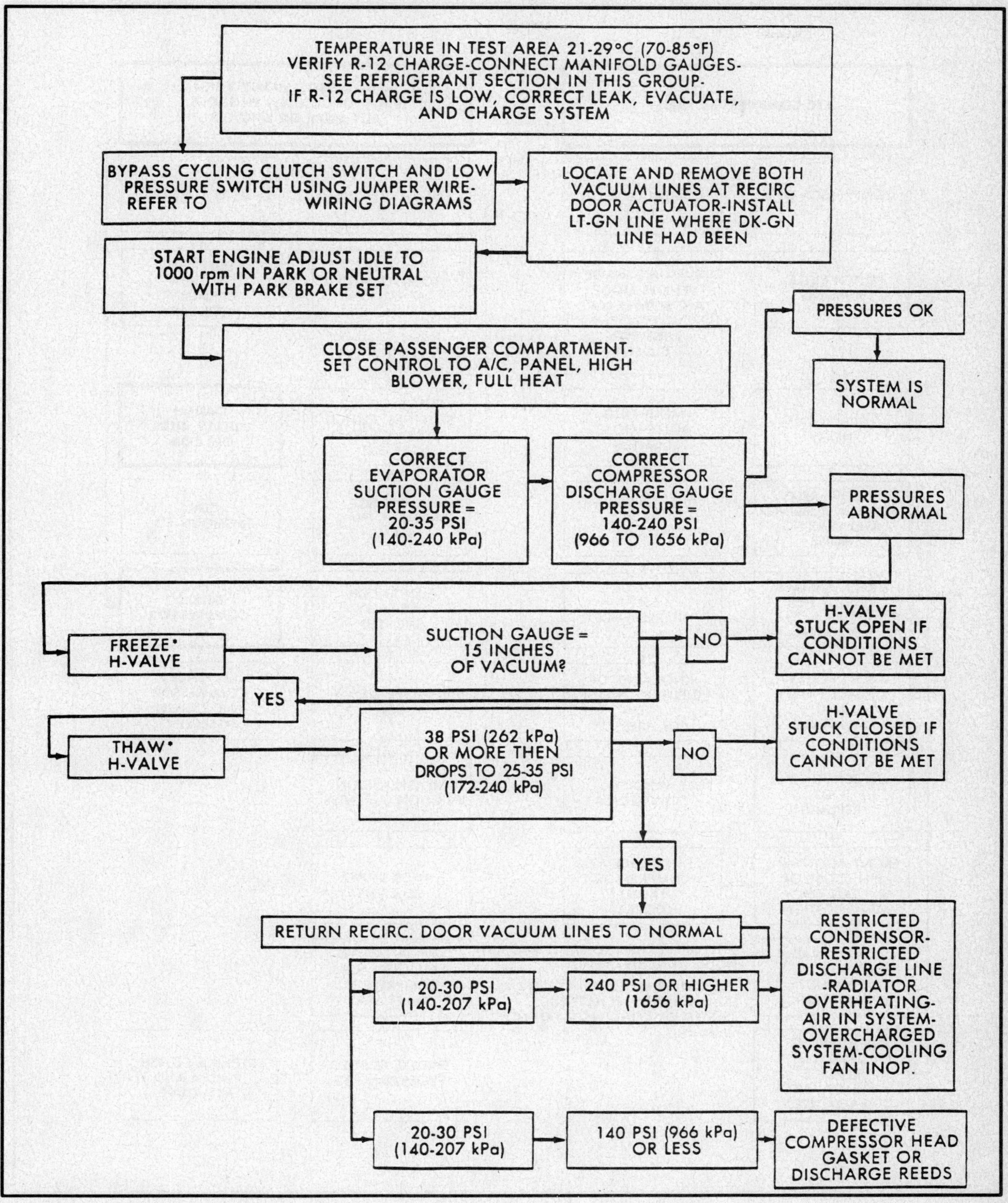
TEMPERATURE IN TEST AREA 21-29°C (70-85°F)
VERIFY R-12 CHARGE-CONNECT MANIFOLD GAUGES-
SEE REFRIGERANT SECTION IN THIS GROUP-
IF R-12 CHARGE IS LOW, CORRECT LEAK, EVACUATE, AND CHARGE SYSTEM
BYPASS CYCLING CLUTCH SWITCH AND LOW PRESSURE SWITCH USING JUMPER WIRE-REFER TO WIRING DIAGRAMS
LOCATE AND REMOVE BOTH VACUUM LINES AT RECIRC DOOR ACTUATOR-INSTALL LT-GN LINE WHERE DK-GN LINE HAD BEEN
START ENGINE ADJUST IDLE TO 1000 rpm IN PARK OR NEUTRAL WITH PARK BRAKE SET
CLOSE PASSENGER COMPARTMENT-SET CONTROL TO A/C, PANEL, HIGH BLOWER, FULL HEAT
PRESSURES OK
SYSTEM IS NORMAL
CORRECT EVAPORATOR SUCTION GAUGE PRESSURE = 20-35 PSI (140-240 kPa)
CORRECT COMPRESSOR DISCHARGE GAUGE PRESSURE = 140-240 PSI (966 TO 1656 kPa)
PRESSURES ABNORMAL
FREEZE* H-VALVE
SUCTION GAUGE = 15 INCHES OF VACUUM?
NO
H-VALVE STUCK OPEN IF CONDITIONS CANNOT BE MET
YES
THAW* H-VALVE
38 PSI (262 kPa) OR MORE THEN DROPS TO 25-35 PSI (172-240 kPa)
NO
H-VALVE STUCK CLOSED IF CONDITIONS CANNOT BE MET
YES
RETURN RECIRC. DOOR VACUUM LINES TO NORMAL
20-30 PSI (140-207 kPa)
240 PSI OR HIGHER (1656 kPa)
RESTRICTED CONDENSOR-RESTRICTED DISCHARGE LINE -RADIATOR OVERHEATING-AIR IN SYSTEM-OVERCHARGED SYSTEM-COOLING FAN INOP.
20-30 PSI (140-207 kPa)
140 PSI (966 kPa) OR LESS
DEFECTIVE COMPRESSOR HEAD GASKET OR DISCHARGE REEDS

COMPRESSOR AND CLUTCH DIAGNOSIS

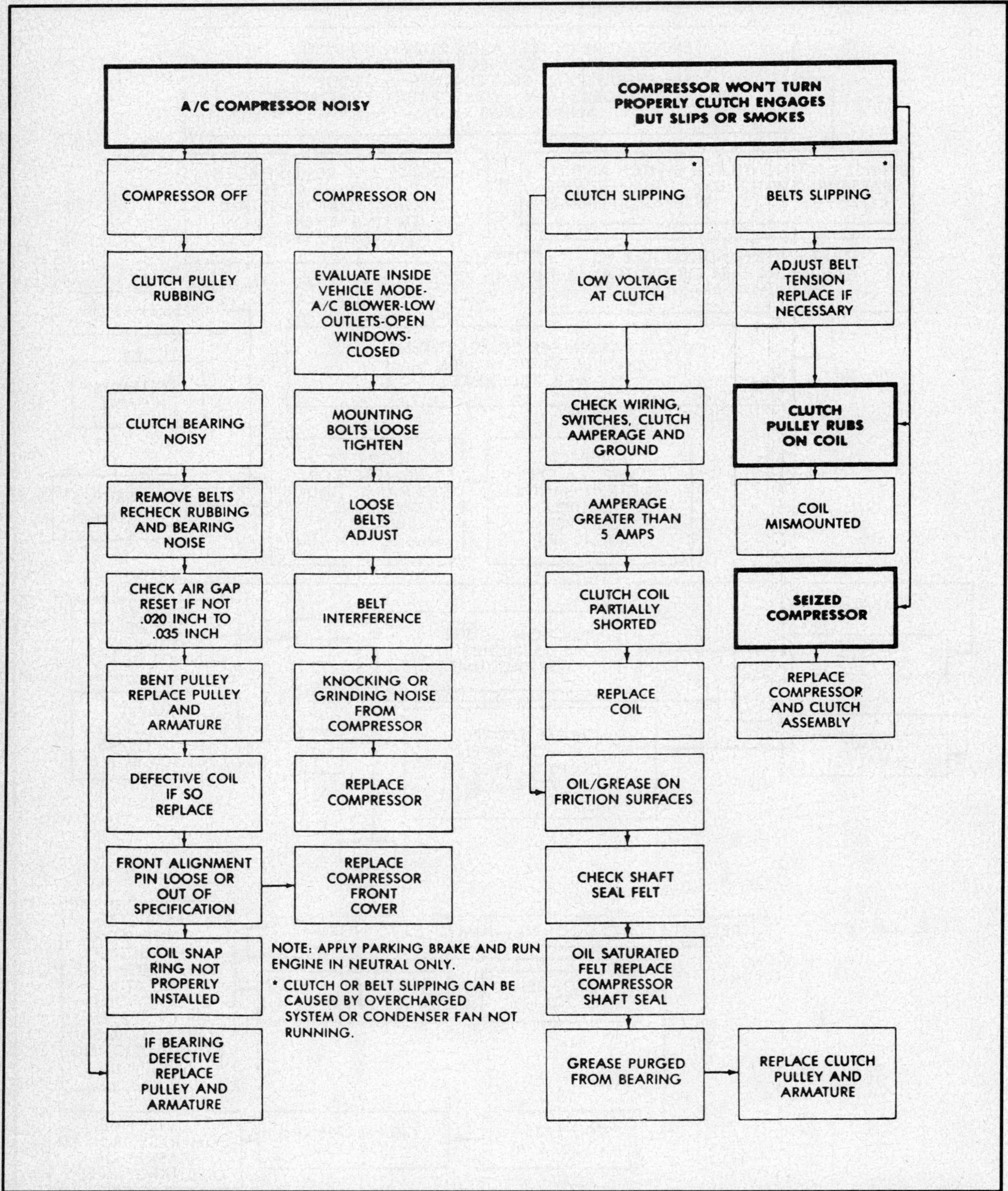
A/C COMPRESSOR NOISY
COMPRESSOR OFF
COMPRESSOR ON
CLUTCH PULLEY RUBBING
EVALUATE INSIDE VEHICLE MODE-A/C BLOWER-LOW OUTLETS-OPEN WINDOWS-CLOSED
CLUTCH BEARING NOISY
MOUNTING BOLTS LOOSE TIGHTEN
REMOVE BELTS RECHECK RUBBING AND BEARING NOISE
LOOSE BELTS ADJUST
CHECK AIR GAP RESET IF NOT .020 INCH TO .035 INCH
BELT INTERFERENCE
BENT PULLEY REPLACE PULLEY AND ARMATURE
KNOCKING OR GRINDING NOISE FROM COMPRESSOR
DEFECTIVE COIL IF SO REPLACE
REPLACE COMPRESSOR
FRONT ALIGNMENT PIN LOOSE OR OUT OF SPECIFICATION
REPLACE COMPRESSOR FRONT COVER
COIL SNAP RING NOT PROPERLY INSTALLED
IF BEARING DEFECTIVE REPLACE PULLEY AND ARMATURE
NOTE: APPLY PARKING BRAKE AND RUN ENGINE IN NEUTRAL ONLY.
* CLUTCH OR BELT SLIPPING CAN BE CAUSED BY OVERCHARGED SYSTEM OR CONDENSER FAN NOT RUNNING.
COMPRESSOR WON'T TURN PROPERLY CLUTCH ENGAGES BUT SLIPS OR SMOKES
CLUTCH SLIPPING *
BELTS SLIPPING *
LOW VOLTAGE AT CLUTCH
ADJUST BELT TENSION REPLACE IF NECESSARY
CHECK WIRING, SWITCHES, CLUTCH AMPERAGE AND GROUND
CLUTCH PULLEY RUBS ON COIL
AMPERAGE GREATER THAN 5 AMPS
COIL MISMOUNTED
CLUTCH COIL PARTIALLY SHORTED
SEIZED COMPRESSOR
REPLACE COIL
REPLACE COMPRESSOR AND CLUTCH ASSEMBLY
OIL/GREASE ON FRICTION SURFACES
CHECK SHAFT SEAL FELT
OIL SATURATED FELT REPLACE COMPRESSOR SHAFT SEAL
GREASE PURGED FROM BEARING
REPLACE CLUTCH PULLEY AND ARMATURE

3. Remove pin No. 5 from the control head connector and retest the system. If Code 1 does not appear, the control is good. Locate and repair the source of the voltage on pin No. 5. Retest; if the code still exists, continue.
4. Remove pin No. 6 from the control head connector and retest the system. If Code 1 does not appear, control is good. Locate and repair the source of the voltage on pin No. 6. Retest; if the code still exists, continue.

Failure Code 2—Blend Air Door Actuator Drive Signal Not High

NOTE: If both failure Codes 2 and 3 occur simultaneously, perform both check procedures. Normally, there is only 1 actual failure.

1. Remove pin No. 6 from the 21-way control head connector and retest the system. Note that removing this pin may generate additional codes which may be disregarded at this time. If Code 2 still exists, replace the control head. If not, the problem is a shorted blend door actuator motor or short to ground in the circuit involving pin No. 6.
2. Remove the 21-way control head connector and check pin No. 6 for continuity to chassis ground. If there is continuity, repair the wiring and retest. If not, continue.
3. Check the resistance across pins No. 4 and 6 of the 21-way connector for a shorted actuator motor. The specification is 20–50 ohms. If out of specification, replace the actuator and retest.

Failure Code 3—Mode Door Actuator Signal Not High

NOTE: If both failure Codes 3 and 2 occur simultaneously, perform both check procedures. Normally, there is only 1 actual failure.

1. Remove pin No. 5 from the 21-way control head connector and retest the system. Note that removing this pin may generate additional codes which may be disregarded at this time. If Code 3 still exists, replace the control head. If not, the problem is a shorted mode door actuator motor or short to ground in the circuit involving pin No. 5.
2. Remove the 21-way control head connector and check pin No. 5 for continuity to chassis ground. If there is continuity, repair the wiring and retest. If not, continue.
3. Check the resistance across pins No. 4 and 5 of the 21-way connector for a shorted actuator motor. The specification is 20–50 ohms. If out of specification, replace the actuator and retest.

Failure Code 4—Actuator Drive Common Signal Not High

NOTE: If both failure Codes 4 and 5 occur simultaneously, perform both check procedures. Normally, there is only 1 actual failure.

1. Remove pin No. 4 from the 21-way control head connector and retest the system. Note that removing this pin may generate additional Codes which may be disregarded at this time. If Code 4 still exists, replace the control head. If not, the problem is a shorted actuator motor or short to ground in the circuit involving pin No. 4.
2. Remove pin No. 15 from the control head connector and retest the system. If Code 1 does not appear, the control is good. Locate and repair the source of the voltage on pin No. 15 and retest.
3. Remove the 21-way control head connector and check pin No. 4 for continuity to chassis ground. If there is continuity, repair the wiring and retest. If not, continue.
4. Check the resistance across pins No. 4 and 5; 4 and 6; and 4 and 15 of the 21-way connector for a shorted actuator motor. The specification is 20–50 ohms. If out of specification, replace the appropriate actuator and retest.

Failure Code 5—Fresh/Recirc Actuator Drive Signal Not High

NOTE: If both failure Codes 5 and 4 occur simultaneously, perform both check procedures. Normally, there is only 1 actual failure.

1. Remove pin No. 15 from the 21-way control head connector and retest the system. Note that removing this pin may generate additional codes which may be disregarded at this time. If Code 5 still exists, replace the control head. If not, the problem is a shorted actuator motor or short to ground in the circuit involving pin No. 15.
2. Remove the 21-way control head connector and check pin No. 15 for continuity to chassis ground. If there is continuity, repair the wiring and retest. If not, continue.
3. Check the resistance across pins No. 4 and 15 of the 21-way connector for a shorted actuator motor. The specification is 20–50 ohms. If out of specification, replace the actuator motor and retest.

Failure Code 6—Compressor Drive Signal Not High

1. Disconnect the low pressure cut off switch and retest diagnostics.
2. If Code 6 disappears, check the wiring between the low pressure cut out switch and the engine controller. If all wiring is satisfactory, replace the engine controller.
3. If Code 6 still exists, disconnect the 21-way connector from the control head and check pin No. 13 for continuity to chassis ground. If continuity exists, repair the wire from the low pressure cut off switch. If there is no continuity, replace the control head and retest.

Failure Code 7—Blower Drive Signal Not High

1. Turn the ignition **ON** and check for ignition voltage at pin No. 1 of the power module. If ignition is present at the power module, proceed to Step 3. If not, continue.
2. Check for power module ignition feed at pin No. 12 of the control head connector. If there is no voltage, replace the control head. If voltage is present, repair the open wire between the 2 pins checked.
3. Turn the ignition **OFF** and disconnect the control head 21-way connector. Measure the resistance between pins No. 2 and 12. The specification is 2600–2800 ohms. If within specification, replace the control head. If not, continue.
4. Disconnect the 4-way connector from the power module. Check for continuity between pin No. 2 of the control head connector and pin No. 2 of the power module connector. If the circuit is complete, replace the power module and retest. If the circuit is open, repair the wire and retest.

Failure Code 8—A/D Convertor Internal Failure

Failure Code 8 will be displayed when the internal reference voltage of the A/D convertor is not correct, a condition which is not serviceable. In this case, the control head must be replaced.

Failure Code 9—Sun Sensor

1. Disconnect the control head 21-way connector and check pin No. 19 for continuity to ground. If continuity is present, repair the shorted wire. If not, continue.
2. Remove pin No. 19 from the connector, plug it back in and perform diagnostics again. If Code 9 is still present, replace the control head. If not, replace the sun sensor.

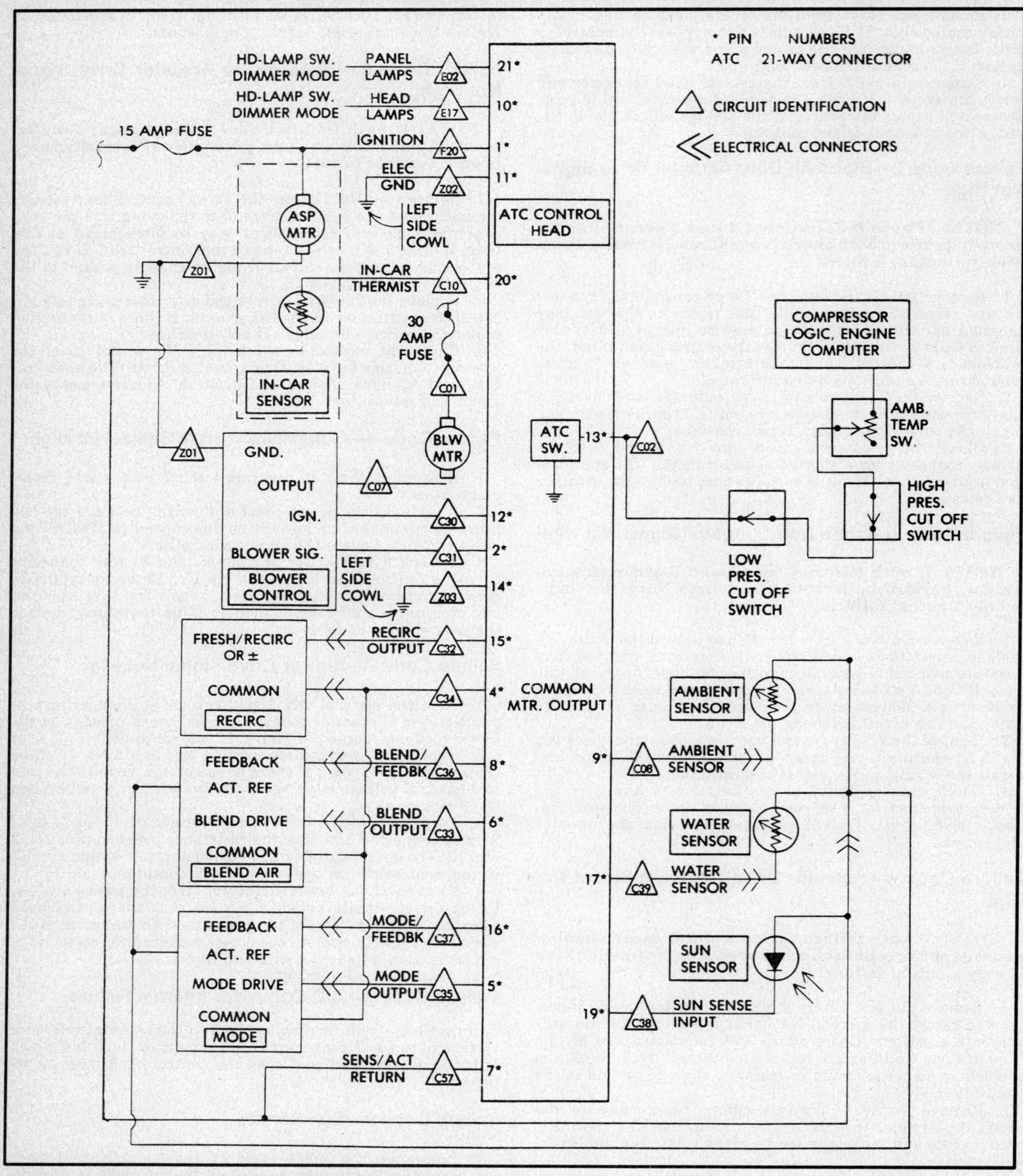

Automatic Temperature Control (ATC) schematic

Failure Code 10—Water Temperature Sensor Failure

1. Disconnect the control head 21-way connector. Measure the resistance between pins No. 7 and 17. The value should change according to the water temperature/resistance relationships below:
   20°F—136,050 ohms
   40°F—77,250 ohms
   60°F—45,700 ohms
   80°F—27,900 ohms
   100°F—17,550 ohms
   150°F—6,150 ohms
   200°F—2,500 ohms
2. Replace the water temperature sensor if the resistance does not approximately match the figures.
3. If the values agree, check pin No. 17 for continuity to ground. If continuity is present, repair the short to ground and retest.

Failure Code 11—Ambient Temperature Sensor

1. Disconnect the control head 21-way connector. Measure the resistance between pins No. 7 and 9. The value should change according to the ambient temperature/resistance relationships below:
   20°F—52,500 ohms
   40°F—38,000 ohms
   60°F—12,670 ohms
   80°F—9,310 ohms
   100°F—5,730 ohms
   120°F—3,550 ohms
2. Replace the ambient temperature sensor if the resistance does not approximately match the figures.
3. If the values agree, check pin No. 9 for continuity to ground. If continuity is present, repair the short to ground and retest.

Failure Code 12—In-Car Temperature Sensor/Aspirator

1. Disconnect the control head 21-way connector. Measure the resistance between pins No. 7 and 20. The value should change according to the ambient temperature/resistance relationships shown above for Failure Code 11.
2. Replace the assembly if the resistance does not approximately match the figures.
3. If the values agree, check pin No. 20 for continuity to ground. If continuity is present, repair the short to ground and retest.

Failure Code 13—Blend Door Failed to Drive to Heat Position

1. Check the door and linkage for binding or other mechanical problems.
2. Disconnect the control head 21-way connector and the blend air door actuator 5-way connector. Check for continuity between pin No. 6 of the 21-way connector and pin No. 5 of the 5-way connector. If the circuit is open, repair the wire and retest. If the circuit is complete, continue.
3. Plug the 5-way connector back in and check the resistance between pins No. 4 and 6 of the 21-way connector. A resistance of 20–50 ohms should be detected. If not, replace the actuator. If the resistance is within specification, replace the ATC control head.

Failure Code 14—Blend Door Failed to Drive to Cold Position

1. Check the door and linkage for binding or other mechanical problems.
2. Disconnect the control head 21-way connector. Turn the ignition **ON** and check for ignition voltage between pin No. 8 and chassis ground. If voltage is present, repair the circuit for a short to ignition voltage. If not, continue.
3. Turn ignition **OFF** and disconnect the 5-way connector from the blend air door actuator. Check for continuity between pin No. 8 of the 21-way connector and pin No. 1 of the 5-way connector. If the circuit is open, repair the wire and retest. If the circuit is complete, continue.
4. Plug the connector back into the blend air door actuator and check for continuity between pins No. 7 and 8 of the 21–way connector. If continuity is present, replace the ATC control head. If not, replace the blend air door actuator.

Failure Code 15—Blend Door Feedback Shorted to Ground

1. Disconnect the connectors from the control head and the blend air actuator.
2. Check pin No. 8 of the 21-way connector for continuity to ground. If continuity is present, repair the short to ground. If not, continue.
3. Plug the connector back into the actuator and measure the resistance across pins No. 7 and 8 of the control head connector. If the resistance is less than 10 ohms, replace the actuator. If not, replace the control head.

Failure Code 16—Mode Door Moved During Blend Air Door Test

1. Disconnect the connectors from the control head and all actuators.
2. Check for continuity between pin No. 4 of the control head connector and pin No. 4 of each actuator connector. Repair any open circuit found. If continuity is found in all circuits, continue.
3. Plug the connectors back into the actuators and check for resistance between pins No. 4 and 6 (blend air actuator) and pins No. 4 and 5 (mode actuator). The resistance should be 20–50 ohms. Replace the actuator corresponding to the failed resistance check. If both were within specification, replace the ATC control head.

Failure Code 17—Mode Door Failed to Drive to Defrost

1. Disconnect the control head 21-way connector and the blend air door actuator 5-way connectors. Check for continuity between pin No. 5 of the 21-way connector and pin No. 5 of the 5-way connector. If the circuit is open, repair the wire and retest. If not, continue.
2. Plug the 5-way connector back in and check for resistance between pins No. 4 and 5 of the 21-way connector. The resistance should be 20–50 ohms. If not within specification, replace the actuator. If both were within specification, replace the ATC control head.

Failure Code 18—Mode Door Failed to Drive to Panel

1. Check the door and linkage for binding or other mechanical problems.
2. Disconnect the control head 21-way connector. Turn the ignition **ON** and check for ignition voltage between pin No. 16 and chassis ground. If voltage is present, repair the circuit for a short to ignition voltage. If not, continue.
3. Turn the ignition **OFF** and disconnect the 5-way connector from the mode door actuator. Check for continuity between pin No. 16 of the 21-way connector and pin No. 1 of the 5-way connector. If the circuit is open, repair the wire and retest. If the circuit is complete, continue.
4. Plug the connector back into the mode door actuator and check for continuity between pins No. 7 and 16 of the 21 way connector. If continuity is present, replace the ATC control head. If not, replace the mode door actuator.

Failure Code 19—Mode Door Feedback Shorted to Ground

1. Disconnect the connectors from the control head and the mode door actuator.
2. Check pin No. 16 of the 21-way connector for continuity to ground. If continuity is present, repair the short to ground. If not, continue.
3. Plug the 5-pin connector back into the actuator and measure the resistance across pins No. 7 and 16 of the 21-pin connector. If the resistance is less than 10 ohms, replace the actuator. If not, replace the control head.

Failure Code 20—Blend Door Moved During Mode Door Test

1. Disconnect the connectors from the control head and all actuators.
2. Check for continuity between pin No. 4 of the control head connector and pin No. 4 of each actuator connector. Repair any open circuit found. If continuity is found in all circuits, continue.
3. Plug the connectors back into the actuators and check for resistance between pins No. 4 and 6 (blend air actuator) and pins No. 4 and 5 (mode actuator). The resistance should be 20–50 ohms. Replace the actuator corresponding to the failed resistance check. If both were within specification, replace the ATC control head.

Failure Code 21—ROM Check Sum Error

During diagnostics, the computer control head will verify its own internal program. If it finds any faulty part, it will set a Code 21, a condition which is not serviceable. In this case, the control head must be replaced.

Failure Code 22—Computer Error

If incorrect data is detected within the computer control head, it will set a Code 22, a condition which is not serviceable. In this case, the control head must be replaced.

Failure Code 23–36

Codes 23–36 set during normal ATC operation. The failure code will be set only after the system has been in operation for 15 minutes. The control head will compensate for the feedback failure immediately upon power up, thus the failure code will not be set until the time limit has been met.

- For Code 23—Blend Door Feedback, follow the repair procedure for Codes 14 and 15 when repairing.
- For Code 24—Mode Door Feedback, follow the repair procedure for Codes 18 and 19 when repairing.
- For Code 25—Ambient Temperature Sensor, follow the repair procedure for Code 11 when repairing.
- For Code 26—In-Car Temperature Sensor/Aspirator, follow the repair procedure for Code 12 when repairing.
- For Code 27—Sun Sensor, follow the repair procedure for Code 12 when repairing.
- For Code 28—Water Temperature Sensor, follow the repair procedure for Code 10 when repairing.
- For Code 31–Recirculation Door Stall Failure
- For Code 32–Blend Door Stall Failure
- For Code 33–Mode Door Stall Failure
- For Code 34–Engine Temperature Message Not Received
- For Code 35–Evaporator Sensor Failure
- For Code 36–Head Communication Failure

All codes will stored within the ATC control head and must be erased after the failure has been repaired. Intermittent Codes 23–28 will be stored for 60 ignition ON/OFF cycles.

ERASING FAILURE CODES

1. Run the diagnostic test.
2. Depress the **PANEL** button to access all failure codes. When the display starts flashing alternating zeros, any of the following 3 options can be performed:
    - Do nothing. In 5 seconds the system will return to normal ATC operation and all codes will remain in memory.
    - Depress any button (except the **AC** button) within 5 seconds and stop the test, in which case the system will return to normal ATC operation and all codes will remain in memory.
    - Depress the **AC** button within 5 seconds and proceed to the erasing procedure (Step 3). Depressing the **AC** button will not erase any codes, but it will access the next part of the procedure.
3. After the **AC** button has been depressed, the display should begin flashing the letter **E** for ERASE. Now 2 options exist:
    - Do nothing. In 5 seconds all failure Codes 23–28 will be erased from memory.
    - Depress any button within 5 seconds and the codes will not be erased.
4. The ATC system should automatically return to normal operation after the above steps have been completed.

21–PIN CONNECTOR REFERENCE CHART (ATC)

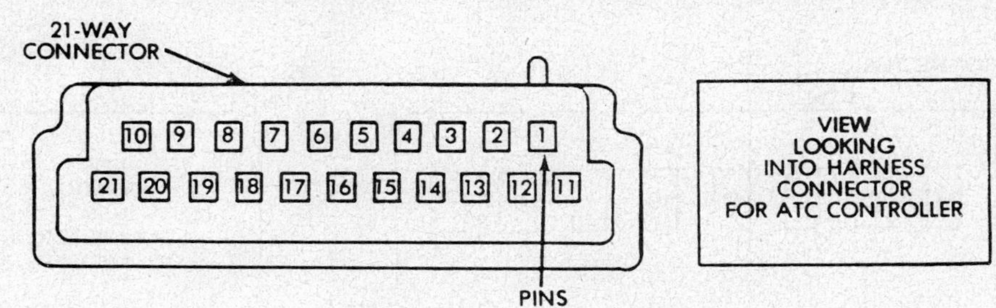

PIN/ CAVITY NUMBER	CIRCUIT DESIGNATION/ WIRE COLOR		DESCRIPTION
1	F20	18WT	IGNITION FEED
2	C31	20LB	BLOWER SIGNAL FROM CONTROLLER
3	OPEN		OPEN
4	C34	20RD/LG	+/− TO BLEND, MODE, RECIRC
5	C35	20OR/DG	+/− TO MODE
6	C33	20LB/RD	+/− TO BLEND AIR
7	C57	20DB/GY	SENSOR/ACT GRND. TO CONTROLLER
8	C36	20GY/OR	BLEND AIR FEEDBACK
9	C08	20DG/RD	AMBIENT SENSOR SIGNAL TO CONTROLLER
10	E17	18BK/YL	DIMMER SIGNAL
11	Z02	18BK/LG	ELEC. GROUND
12	C30	18VT	BLOWER-IGNITION FROM CONTROLLER
13	C02	18DB/YL	CLUTCH CYCLE SIGNAL
14	Z03	20BK/OR	PANEL LAMP GROUND
15	C32	20YL/PK	+/− TO RECIRC
16	C37	20DG/WT	MODE FEEDBACK SIGNAL
17	C39	20LB/VT	WATER TEMP SIGNAL
18	OPEN		OPEN
19	C38	20BK/DG	SUN SENSOR SIGNAL
20	C10	20RD/TN	IN-CAR SENSOR SIGNAL
21	E02	18OR	PANEL LAMPS

A/C HARNESS 14–PIN CONNECTOR REFERENCE CHART

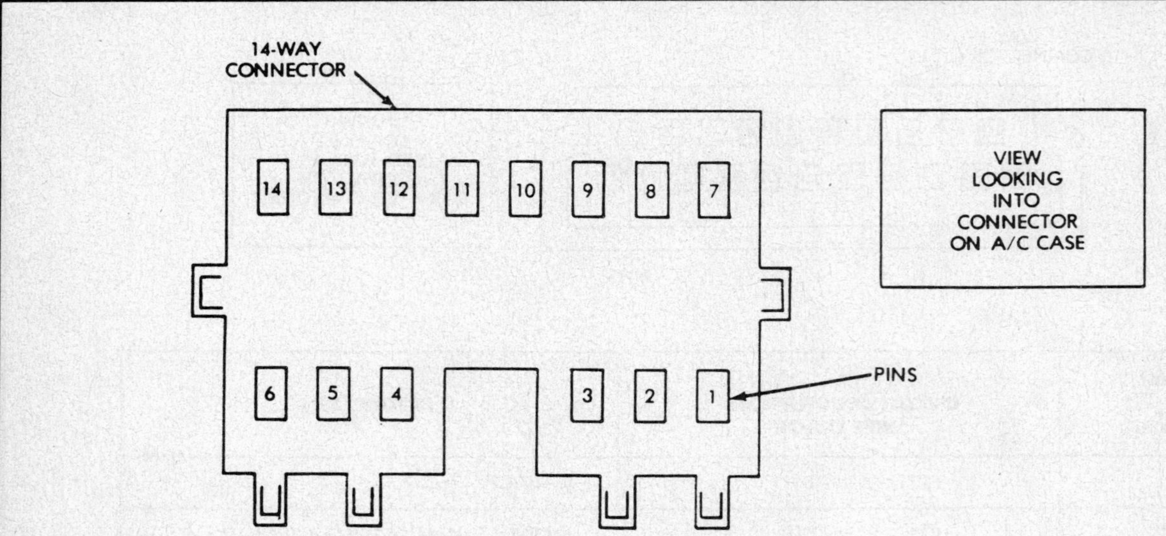

PIN/ CAVITY NUMBER	CIRCUIT DESIGNATION/ WIRE COLOR		DESCRIPTION
1	OPEN		OPEN
2	C34	20RD/LG	+/– TO BLEND AIR, MODE RECIRC ACT.
3	C35	20OR/DG	+/– MODE ACT.
4	C33	20LB/RD	+/– BLEND AIR ACT.
5	C37	20DG/WT	MODE ACT. FEEDBACK TO CONTROL
6	C32	20YL/PK	+/– RECIRC ACT.
7	OPEN		OPEN
8	OPEN		OPEN
9	C08	20DG/RD	AMBIENT SENSOR, I/P TO CONTROLLER
10	C39	20LB/VT	WATER SENSOR CONTROL
11	C57	20DG/GY	SENSOR/ACT COMM. GROUND TO CONTROLLER
12	C36	20GY/OR	BLEND AIR ACT. FEEDBACK TO CONTROLLER
13	OPEN		OPEN
14	OPEN		OPEN

4–PIN CONNECTOR REFERENCE CHART

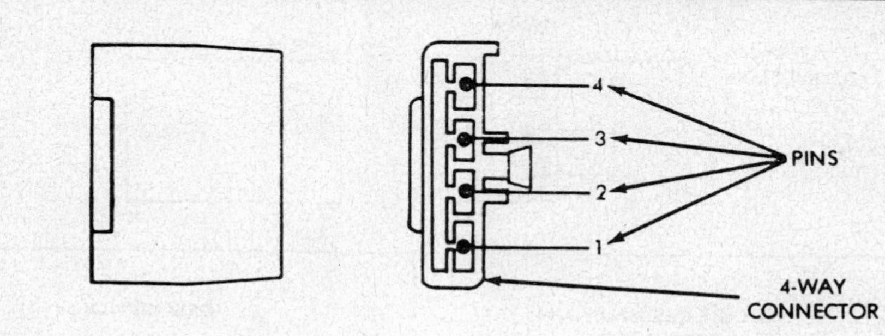

PIN/ CAVITY NUMBER	CIRCUIT DESIGNATION/ WIRE COLOR	DESCRIPTION
1	C30 18VT	IGNITION FROM CONTROLLER
2	C31 20LB	BLOWER SIGNAL FROM CONTROLLER
3	Z01 10BK	GROUND
4	C07 12BK/TN	BLOWER MOTOR GROUND SIGNAL

2–PIN SUN SENSOR CONNECTOR REFERENCE CHART

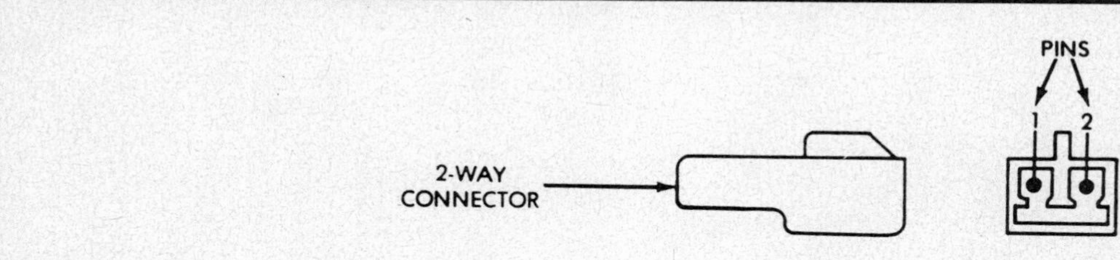

PIN/ CAVITY NUMBER	CIRCUIT DESIGNATION/ WIRE COLOR	DESCRIPTION
1	C57 20DB/GY	SENSOR ACT. GND. TO CONT.
2	C38 20BK/DG	SUN SENSOR SIGNAL

6–PIN IN–CAR & SUN SENSOR CONNECTOR REFERENCE CHART

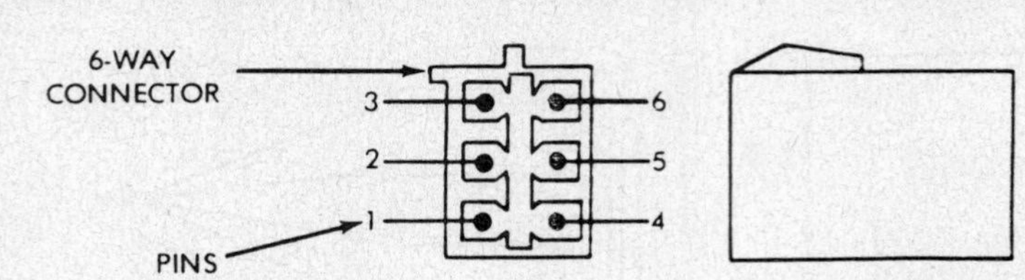

PIN/ CAVITY NUMBER	CIRCUIT DESIGNATION/ WIRE COLOR		DESCRIPTION
1	C10	22RD/TN	IN CAR SENSOR TO CONTROLLER
2	F20	18WT	IGNITION
3	Z01	20BK	GROUND
4	C57	20DB/GY	SENSOR/ACT COMMON GROUND TO CONTROLLER
5	OPEN		OPEN
6	C38	20TN	SUN SENSOR SIGNAL +

WIRING SCHEMATICS

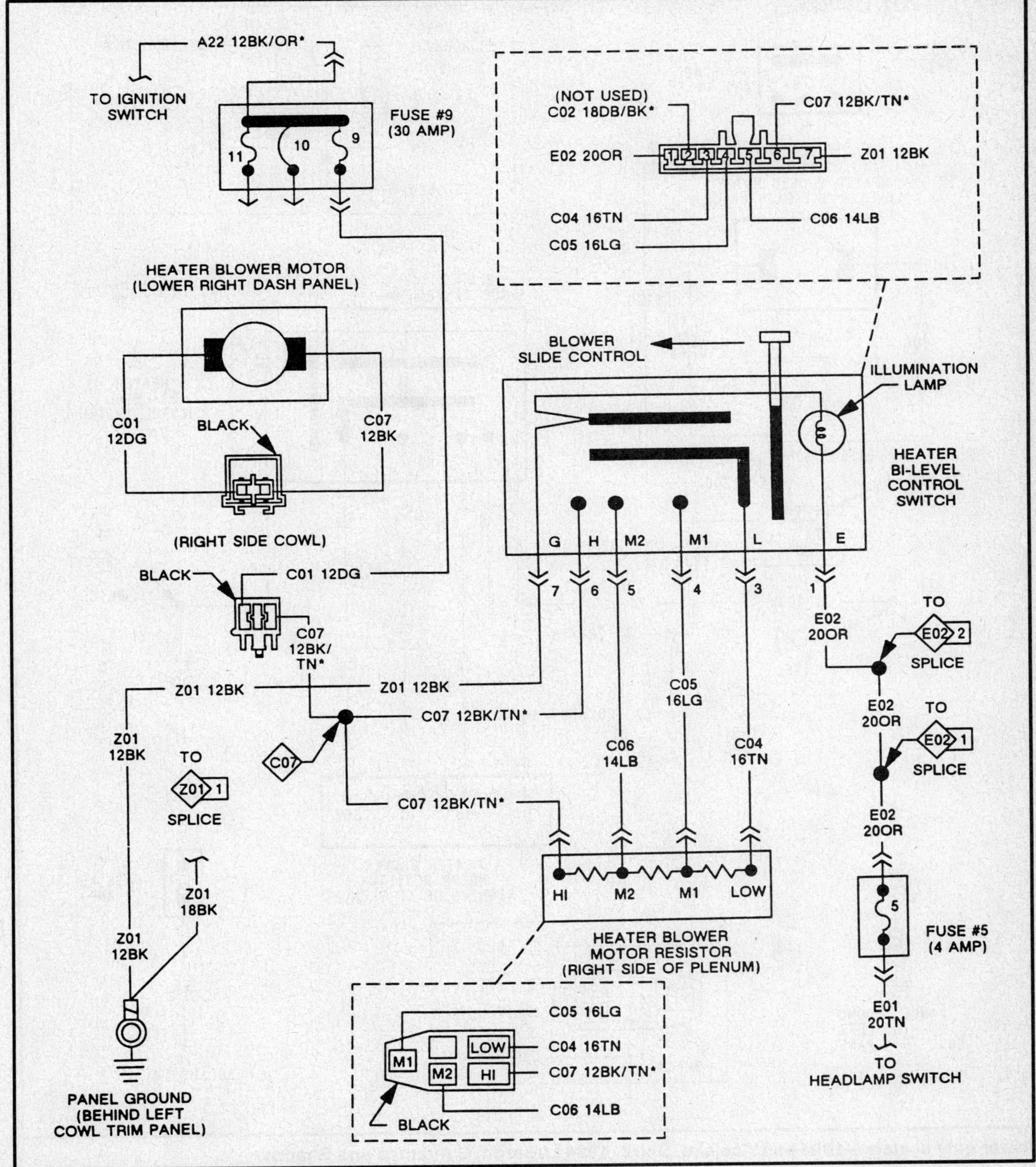

Heater only system wiring schematic—Acclaim, Spirit and LeBaron Landau

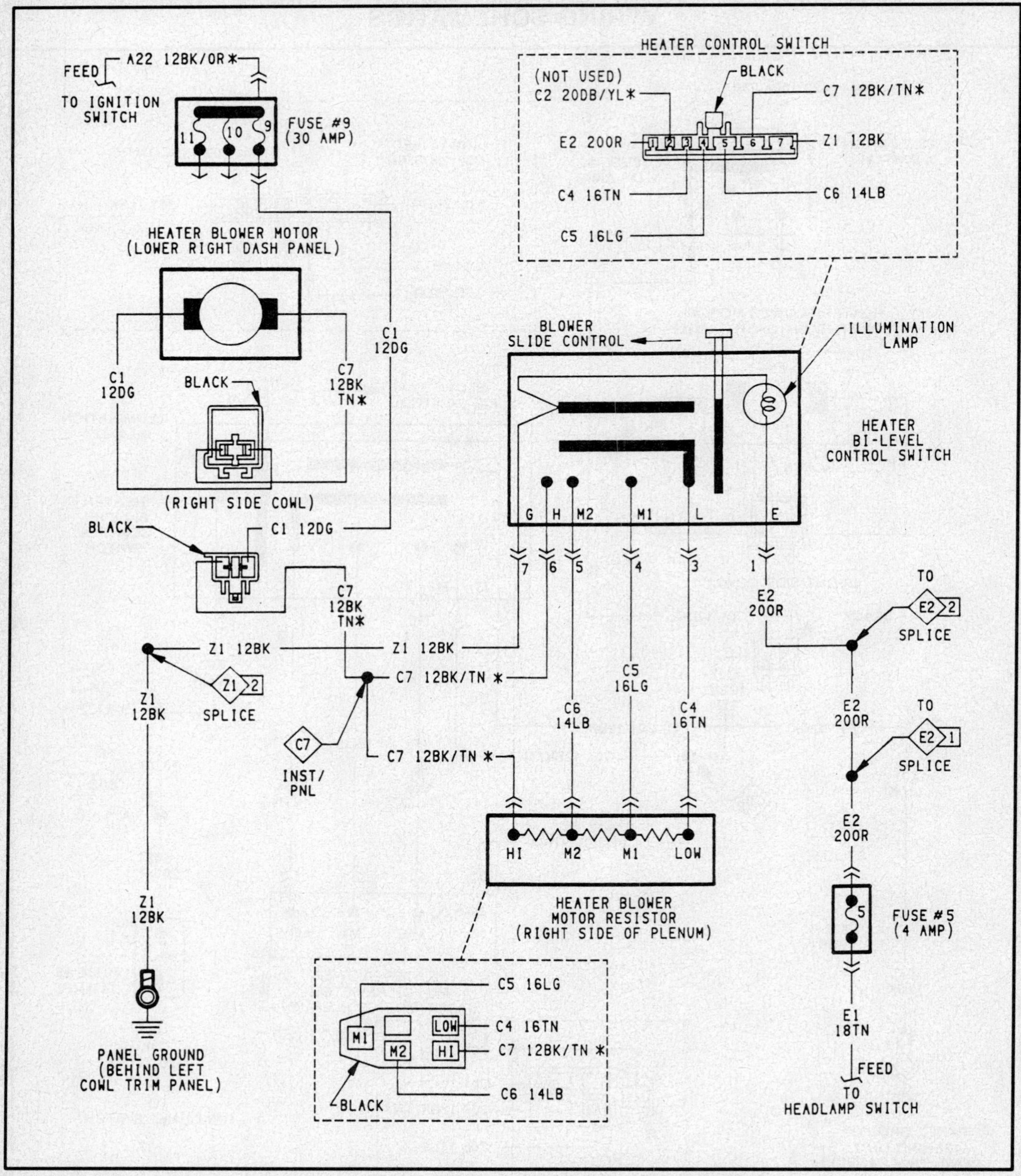

Heater only system—1994–95 Acclaim, Spirit, 1994 LeBaron, Sundance and Shadow

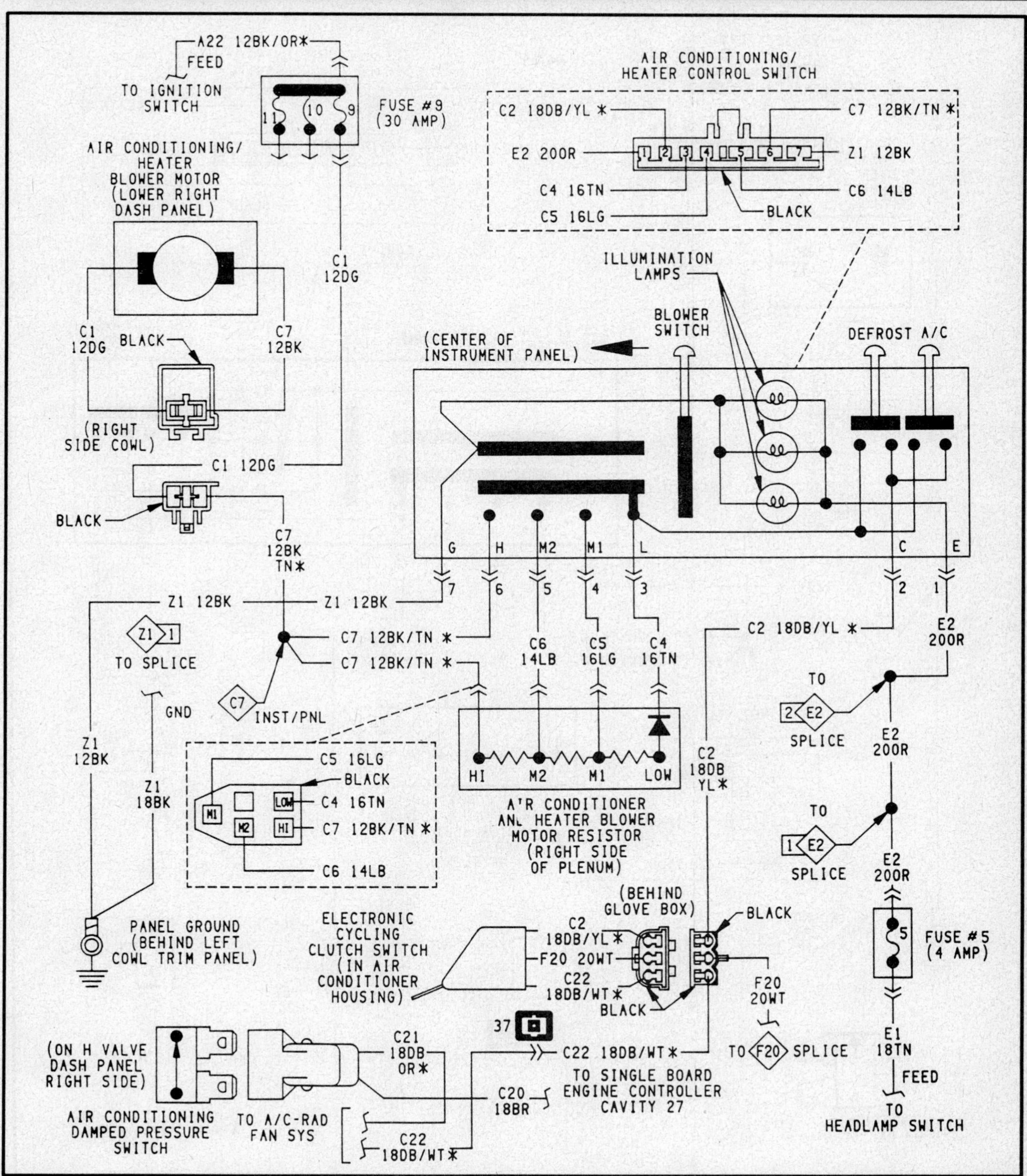

Heater–A/C system passenger compartment wiring schematic—1993 Acclaim, Spirit and LeBaron Landau with 2.5L engine

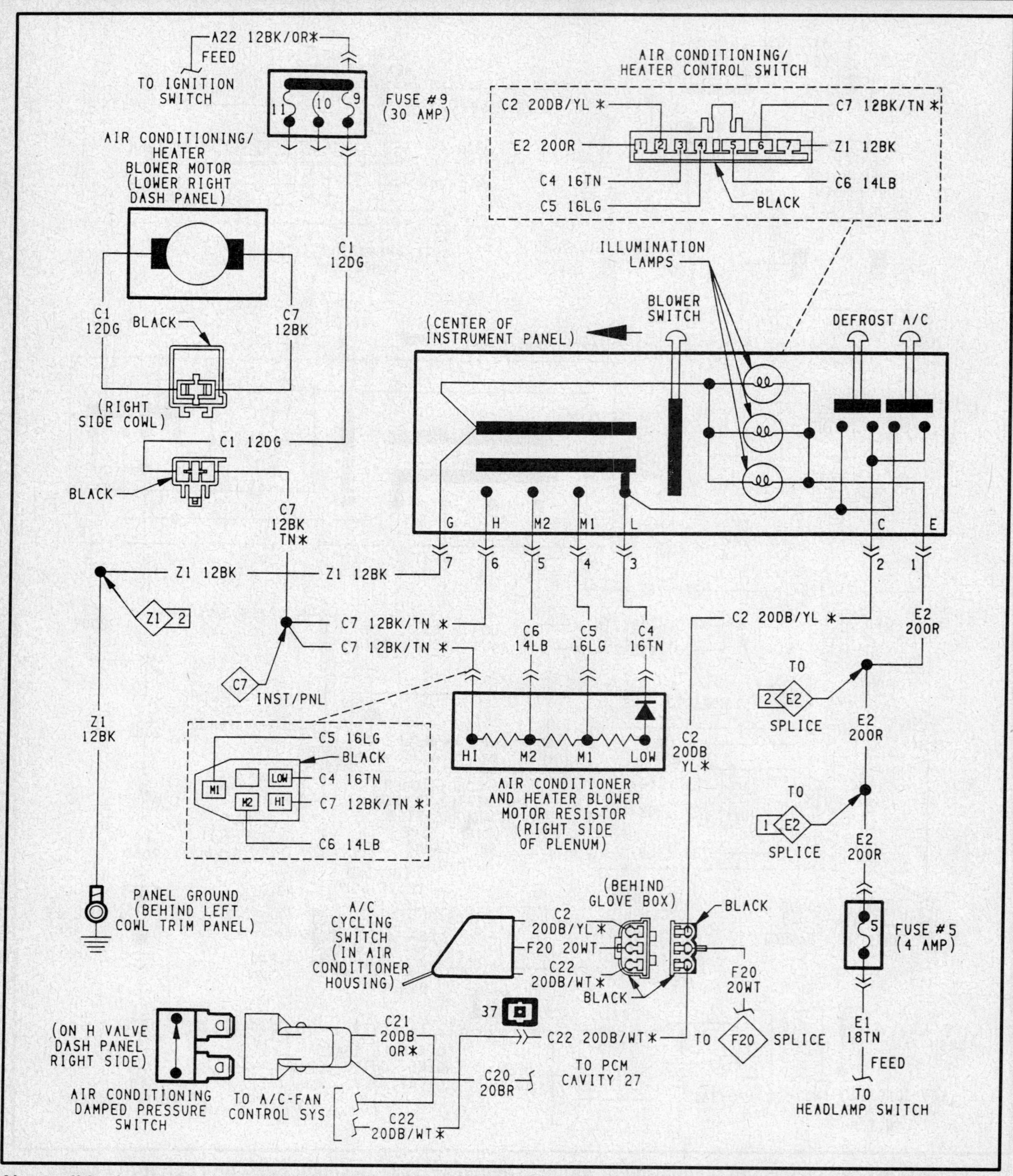

Air conditioning system—1994–95 Acclaim, Spirit, 1994 LeBaron, Sundance and Shadow with 2.5L engine

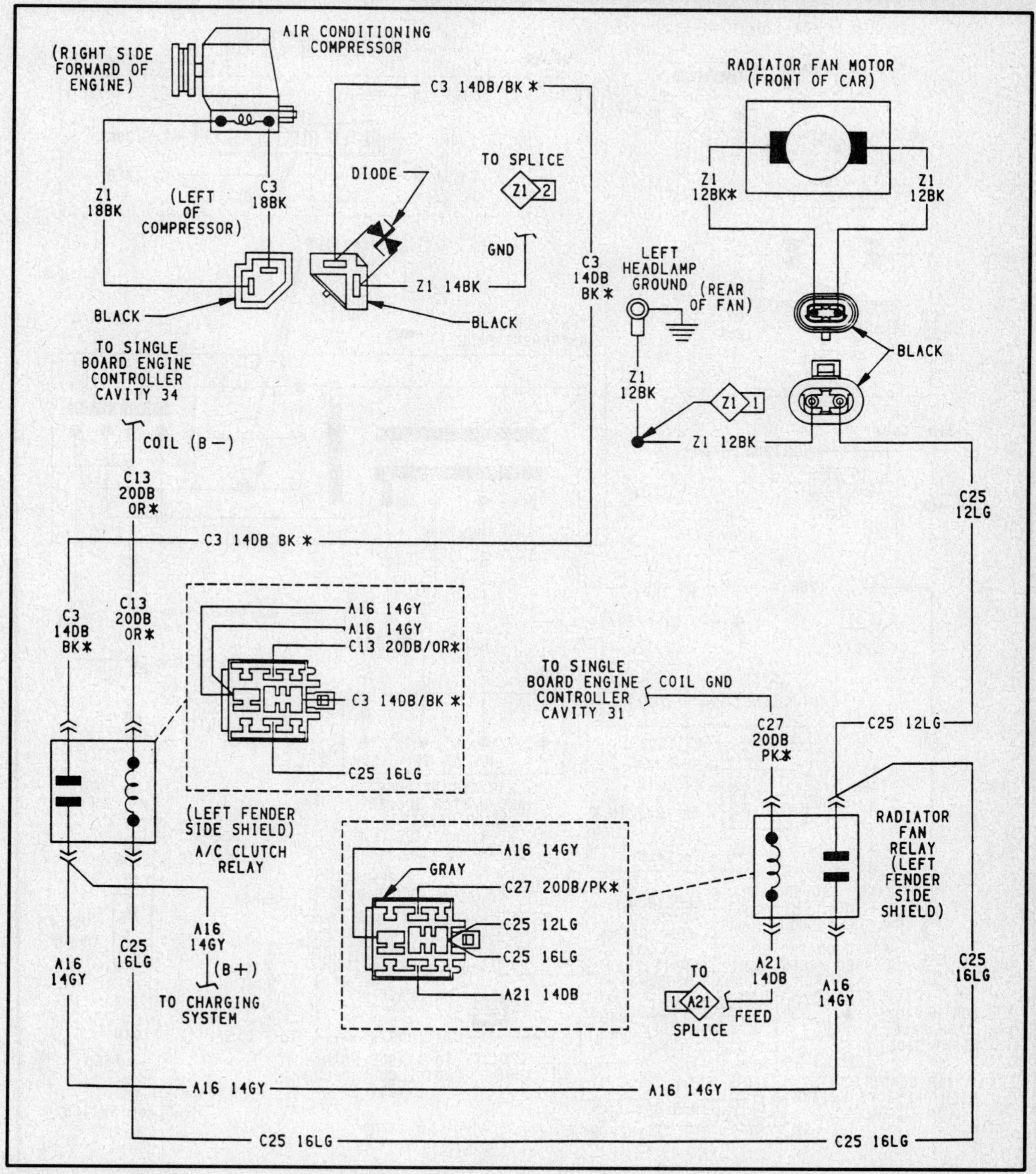

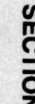

Heater–A/C system engine compartment wiring schematic—1993 Acclaim, Spirit and LeBaron Landau with 3.0L engine

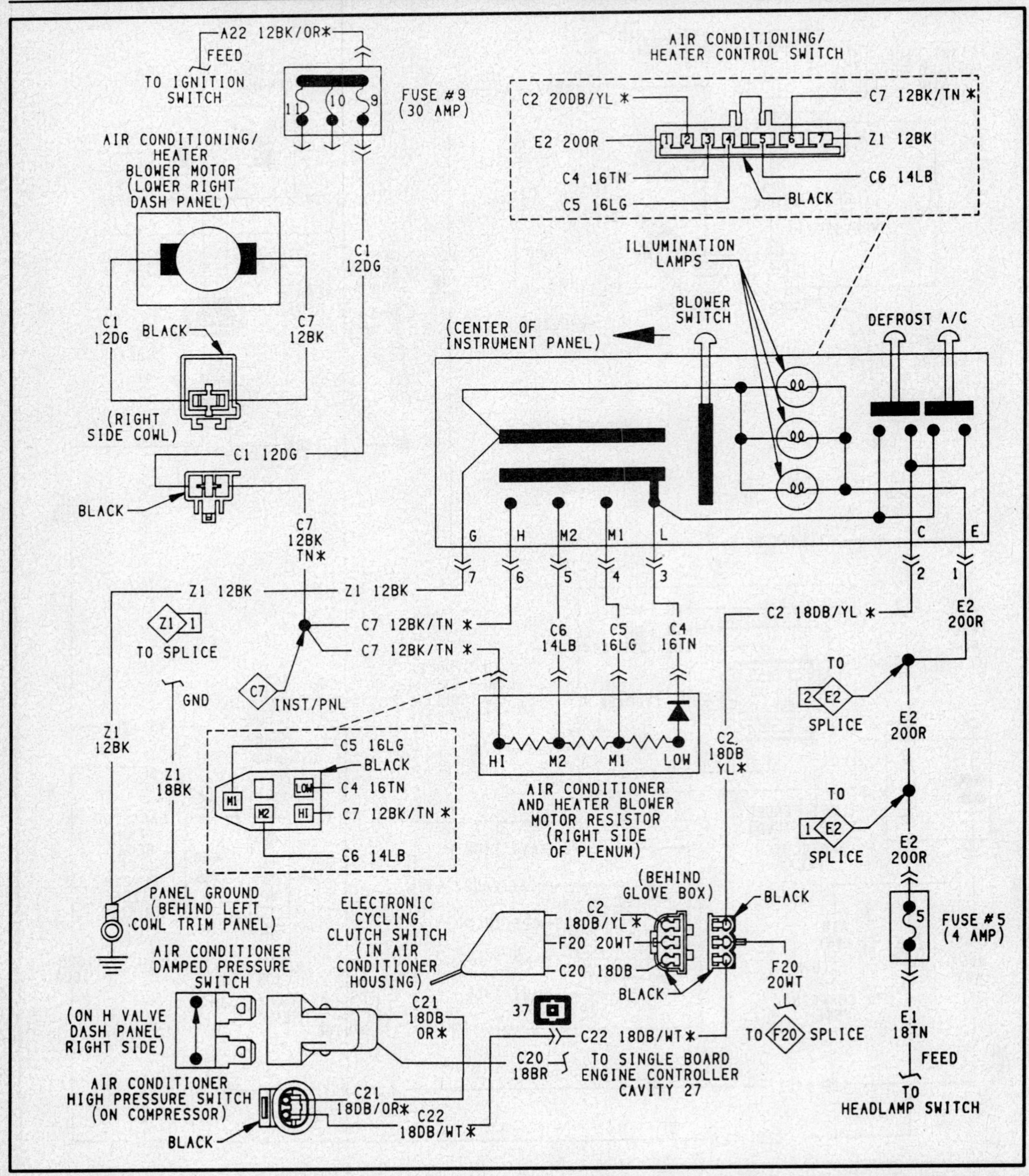

Heater–A/C system engine compartment wiring schematic—1993 Acclaim, Spirit and LeBaron Landau with 3.0L engine, Cont'd

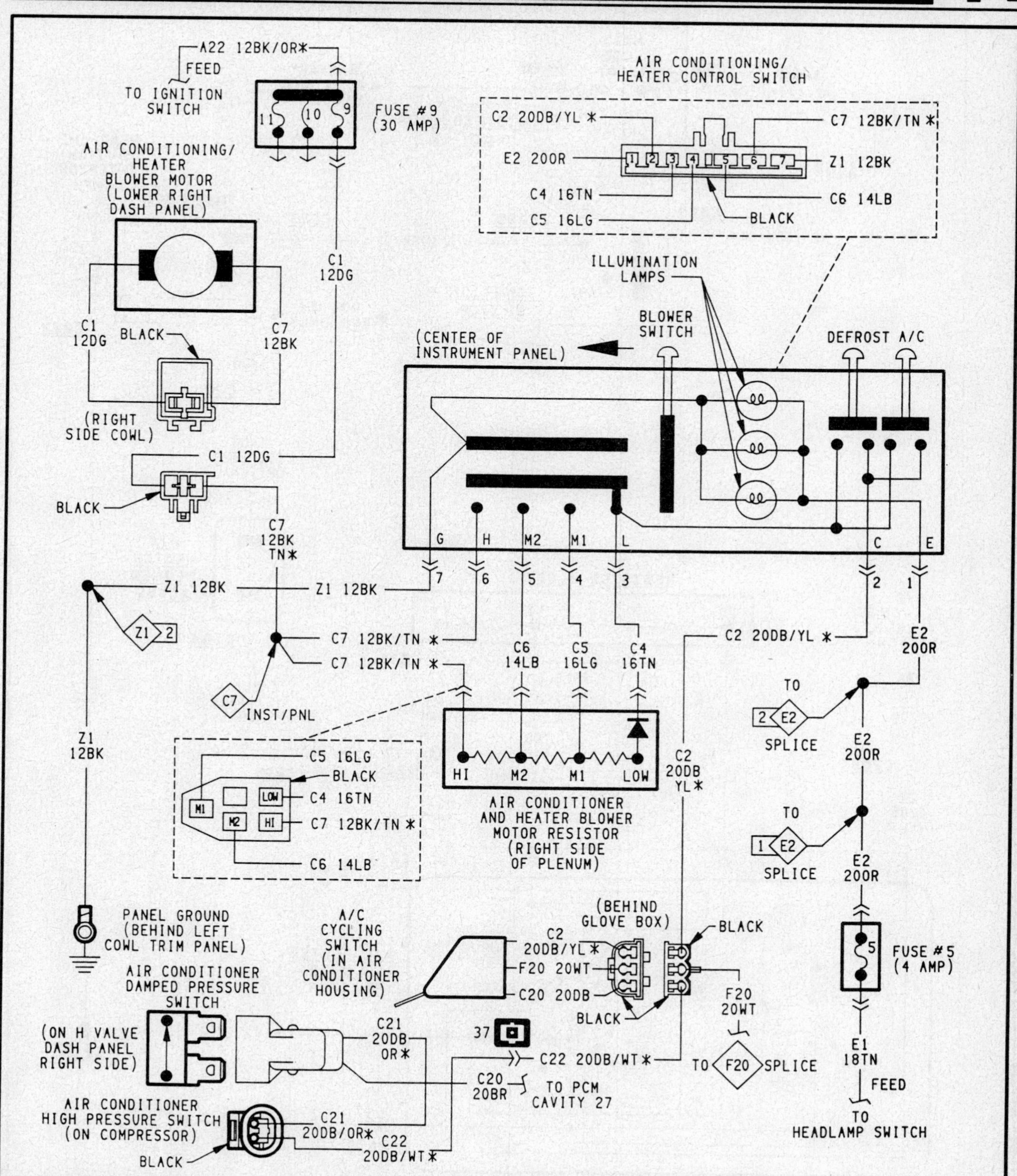

Air conditioning system—1994–95 Acclaim, Spirit, 1994 LeBaron, Sundance and Shadow with 3.0L engine

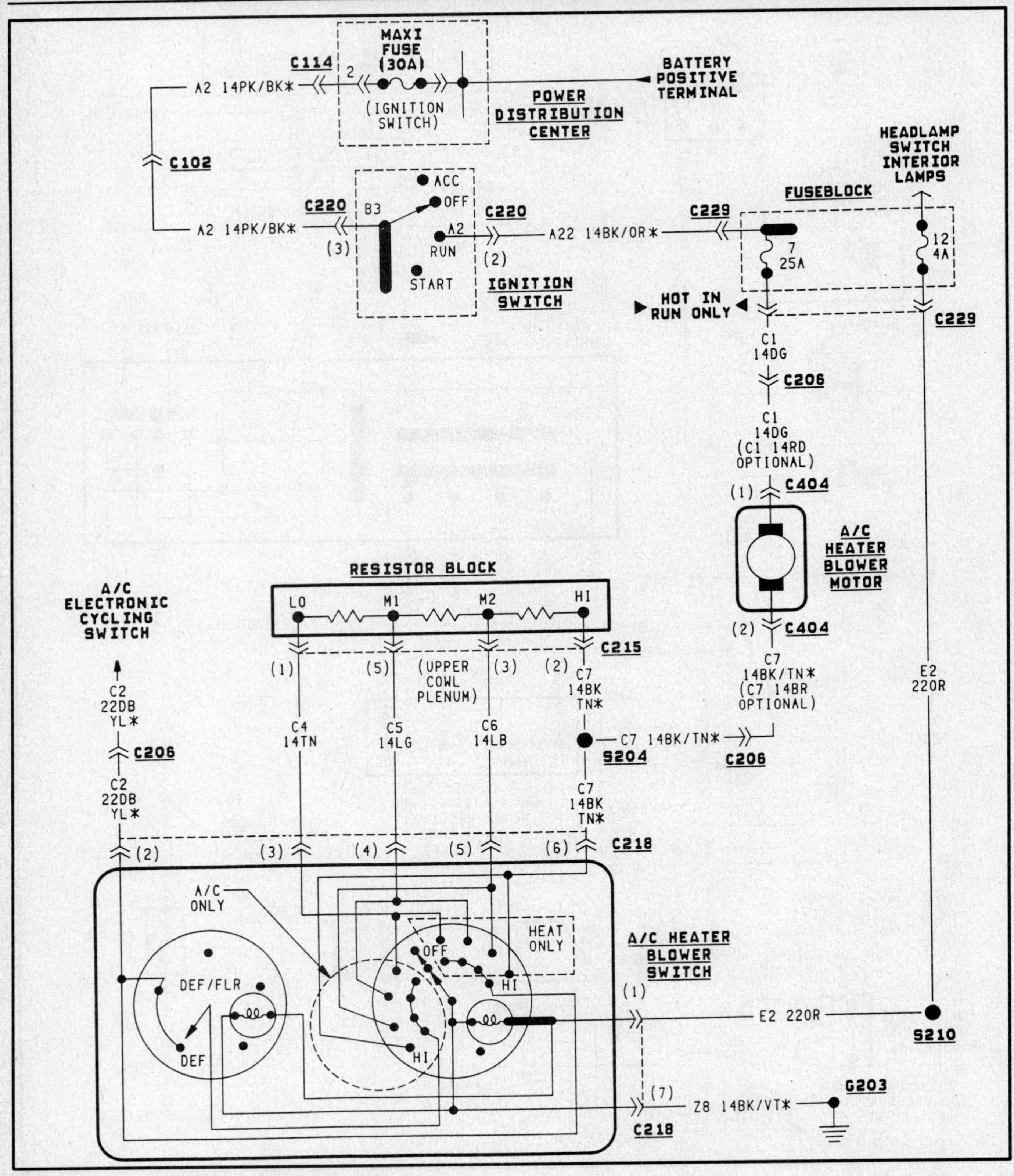

Heater-A/C system wiring schematic—Neon

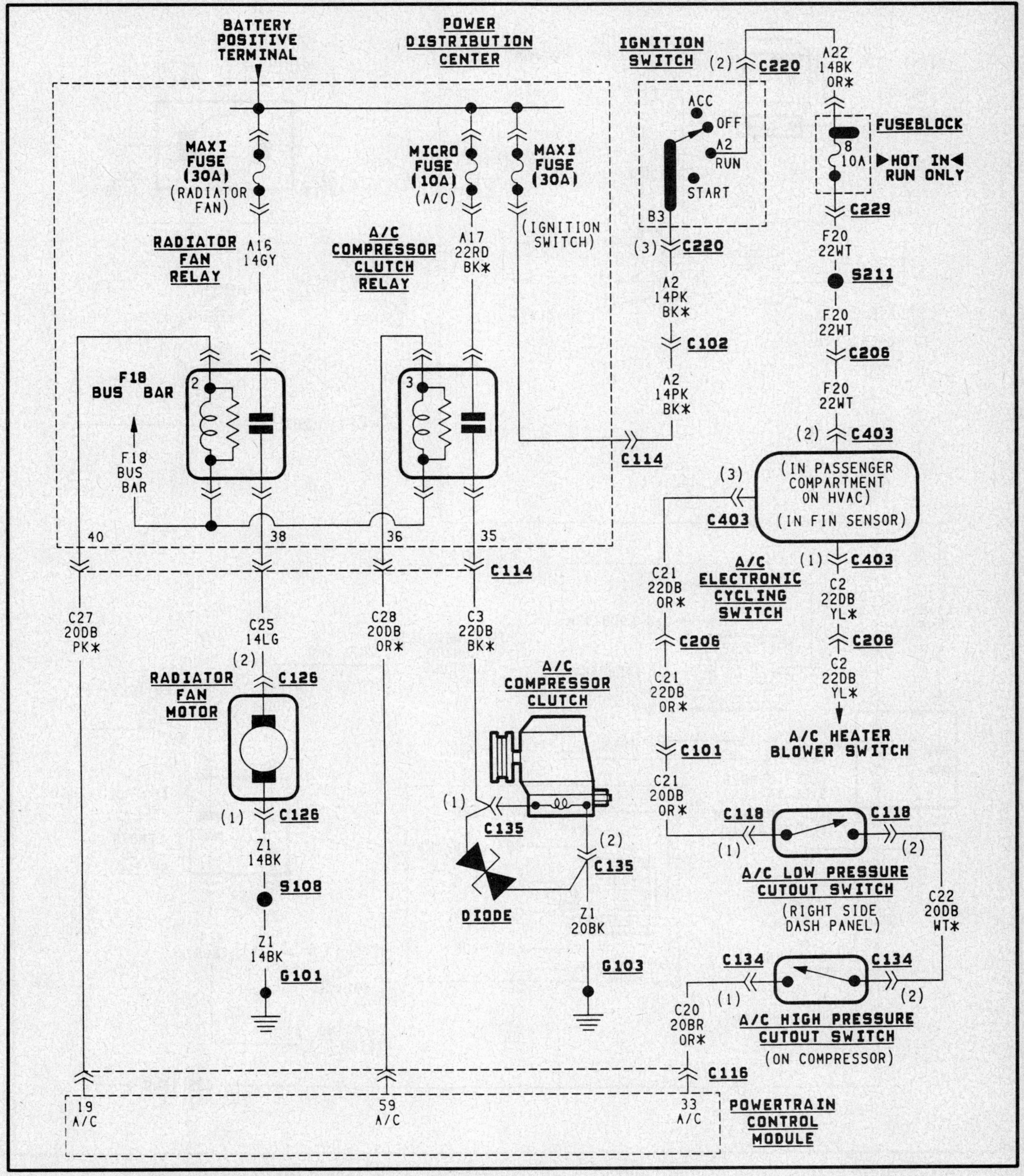

Heater-A/C system wiring schematic—Neon, Cont'd

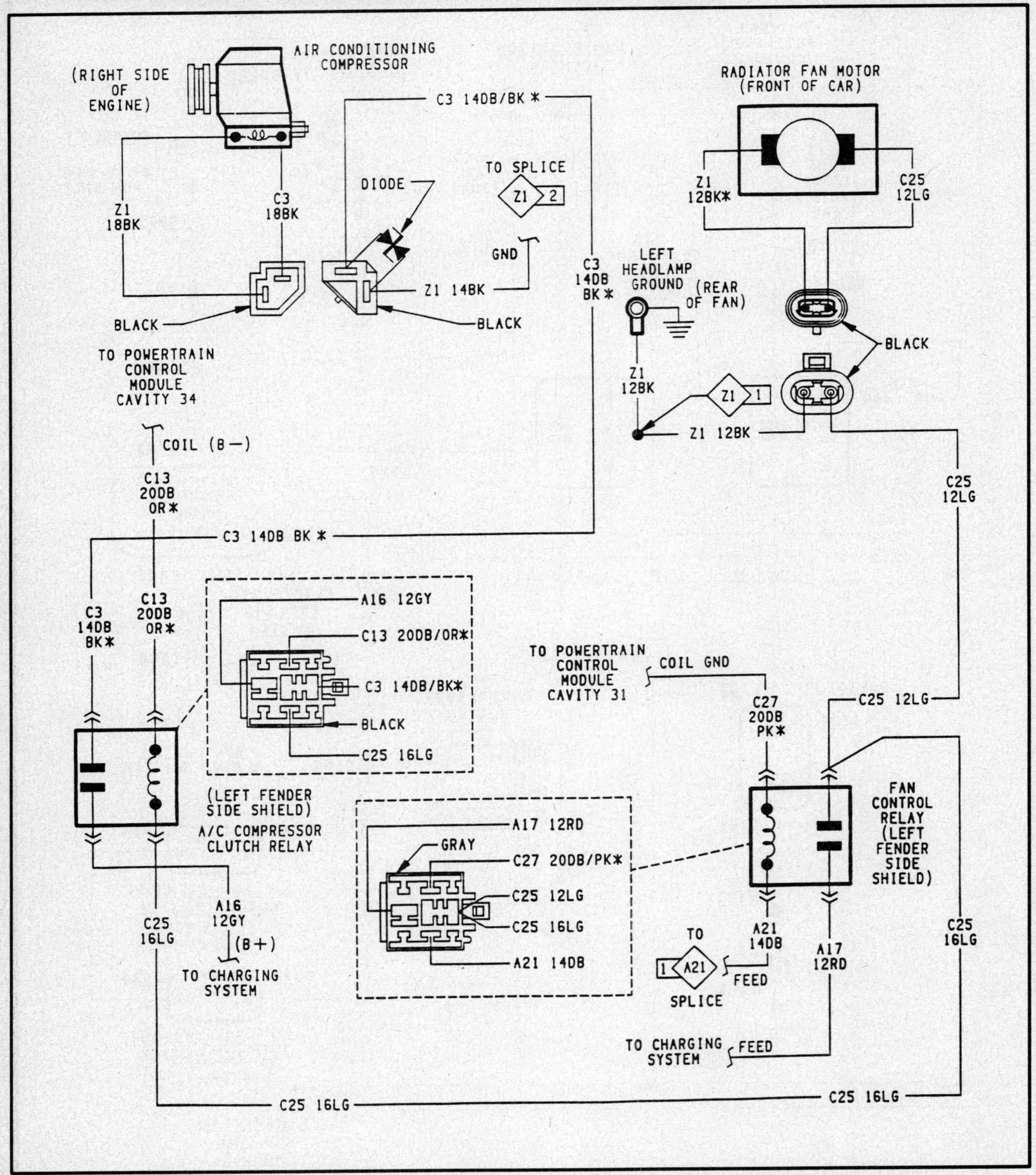

Heater-A/C system engine compartment wiring schematic—1994–95 Acclaim, Spirit, 1994 Lebaron, Sundance and Shadow with 3.0L engine

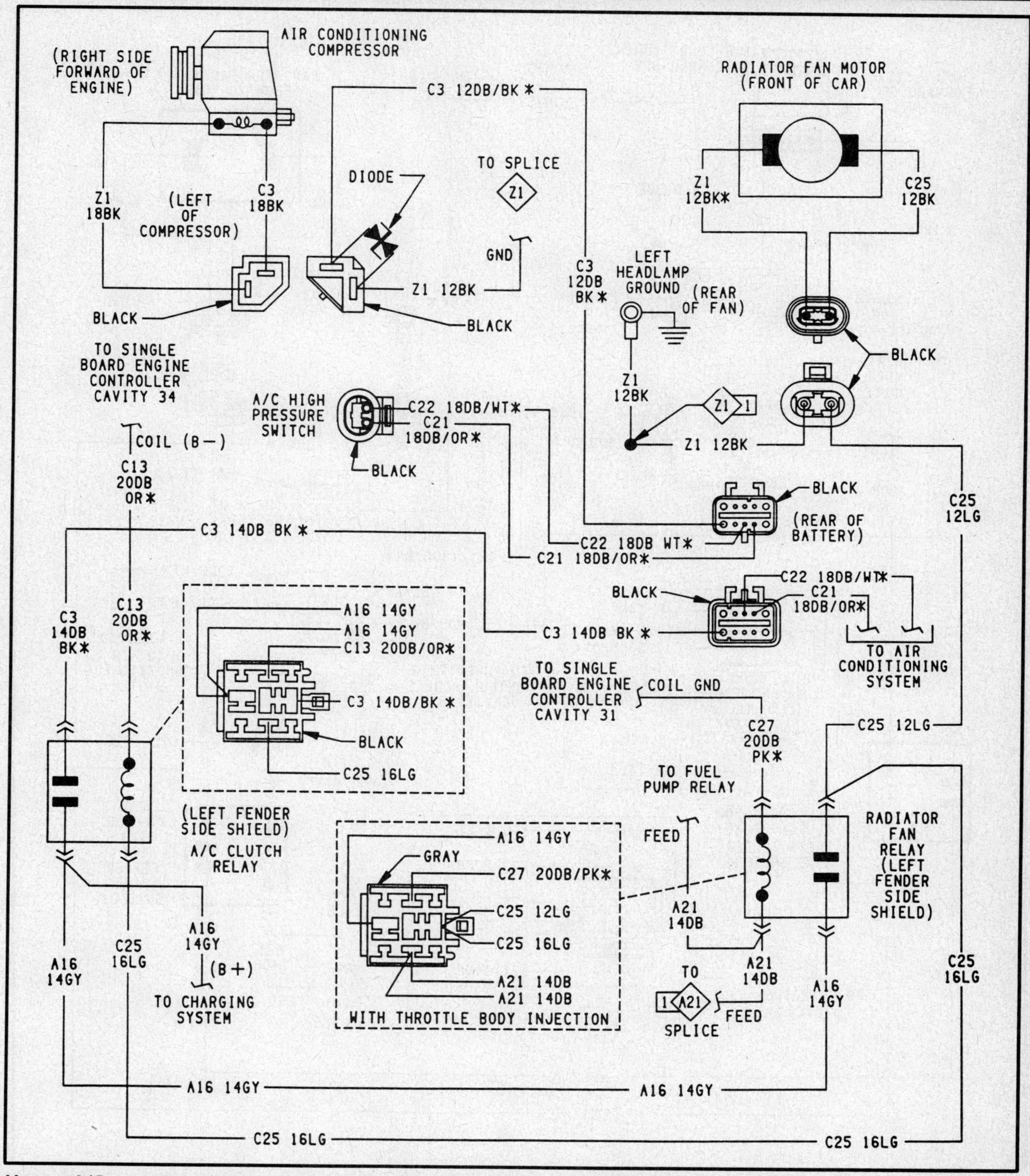

Heater-A/C system engine compartment wiring schematic—1993 Acclaim, Spirit and LeBaron Landau with 2.5L engine

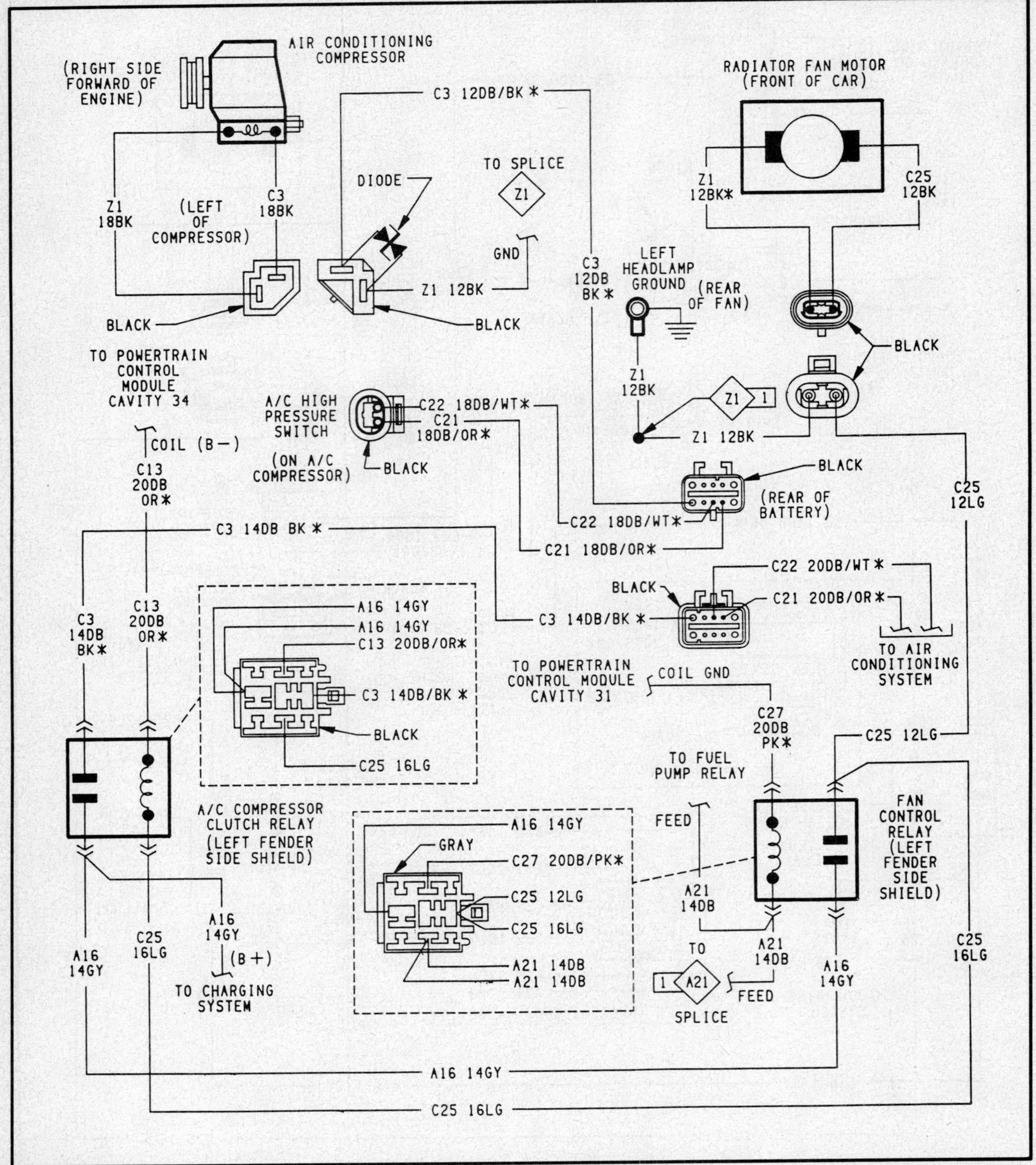

Heater-A/C system engine compartment wiring schematic—1994 LeBaron, Sundance, Shadow, 1994–95 Acclaim and Spirit with 2.5L engine

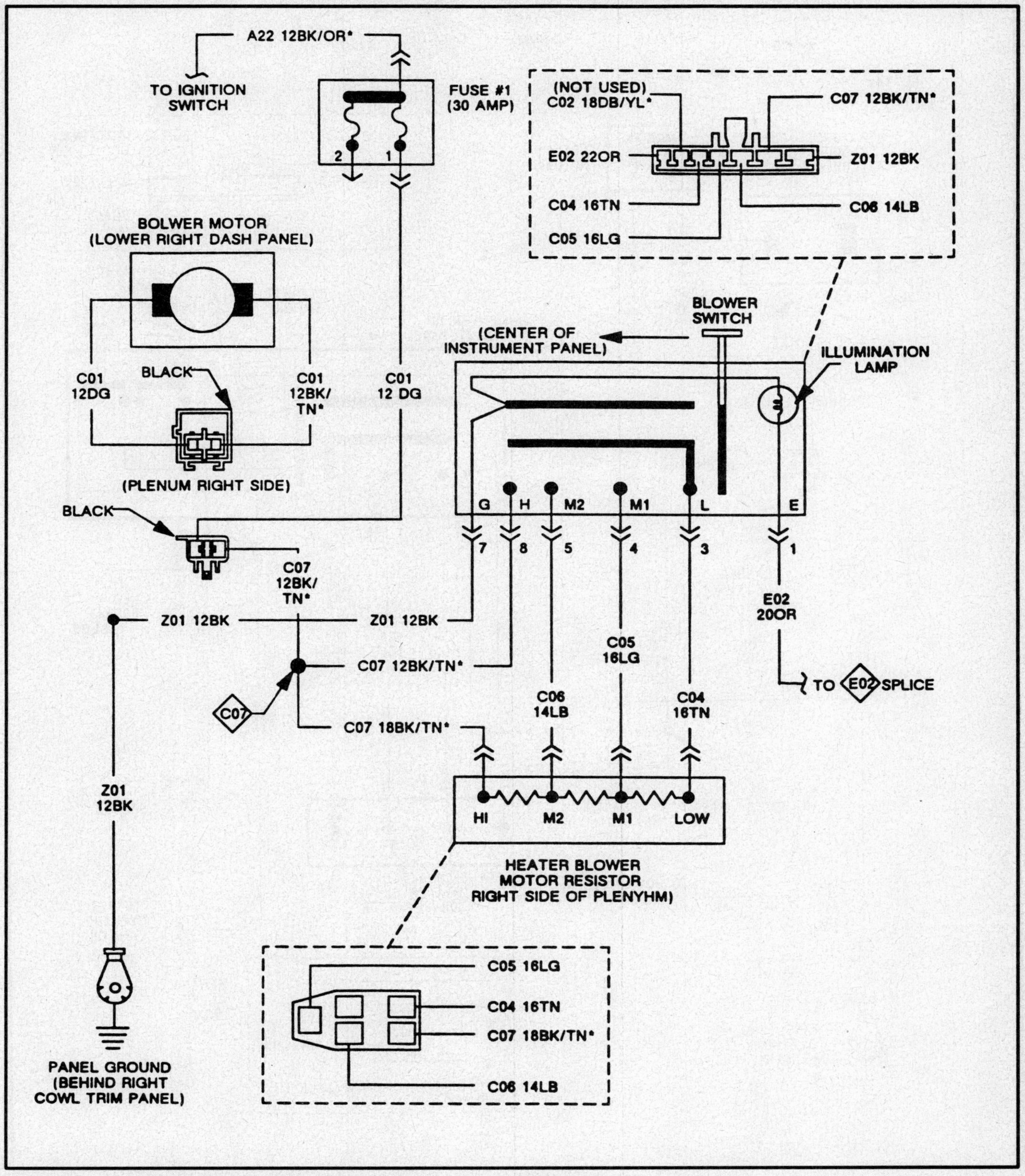

Heater only system wiring schematic—1993 Daytona and LeBaron

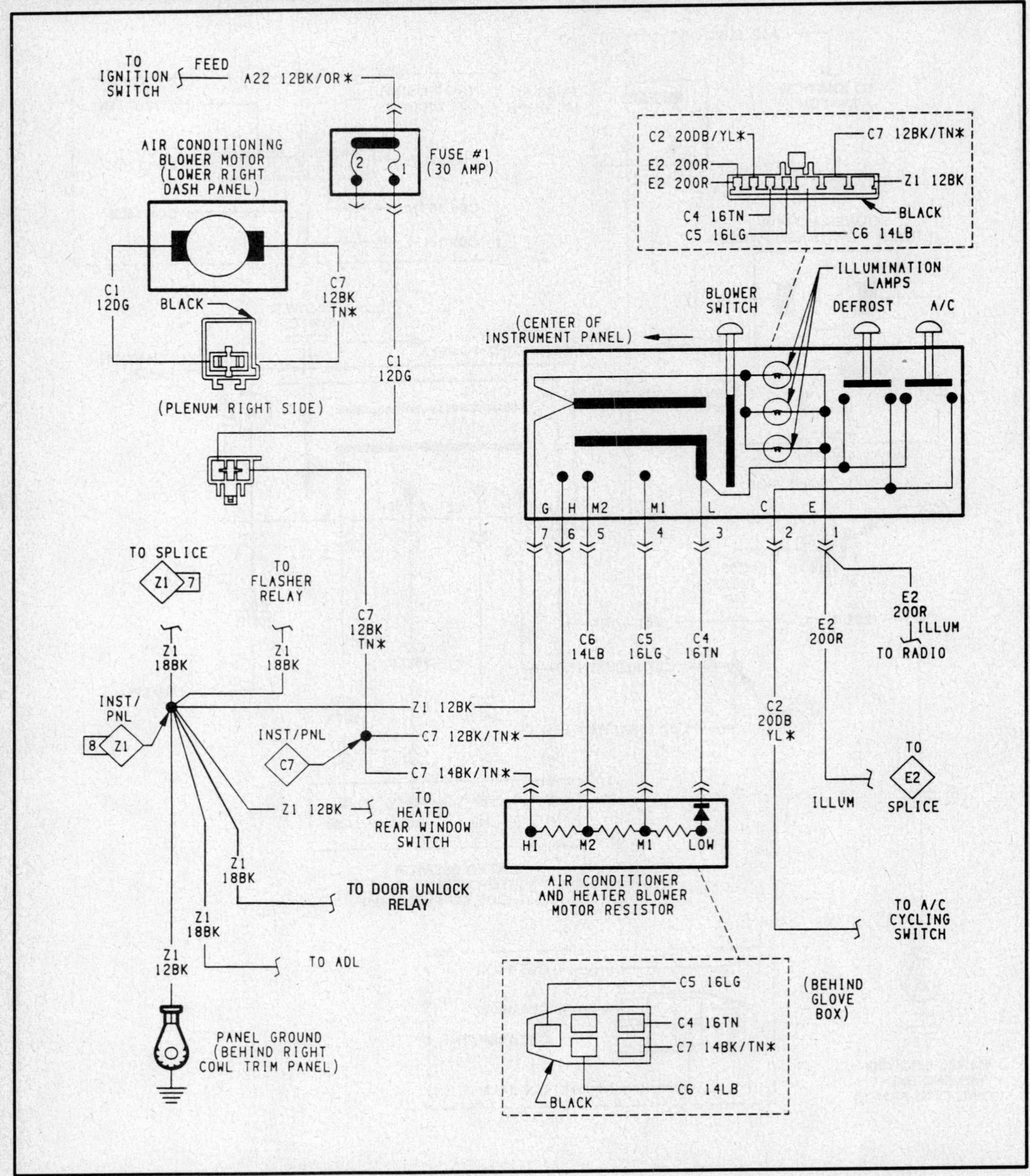

Heater–A/C system wiring schematic—1995 LeBaron

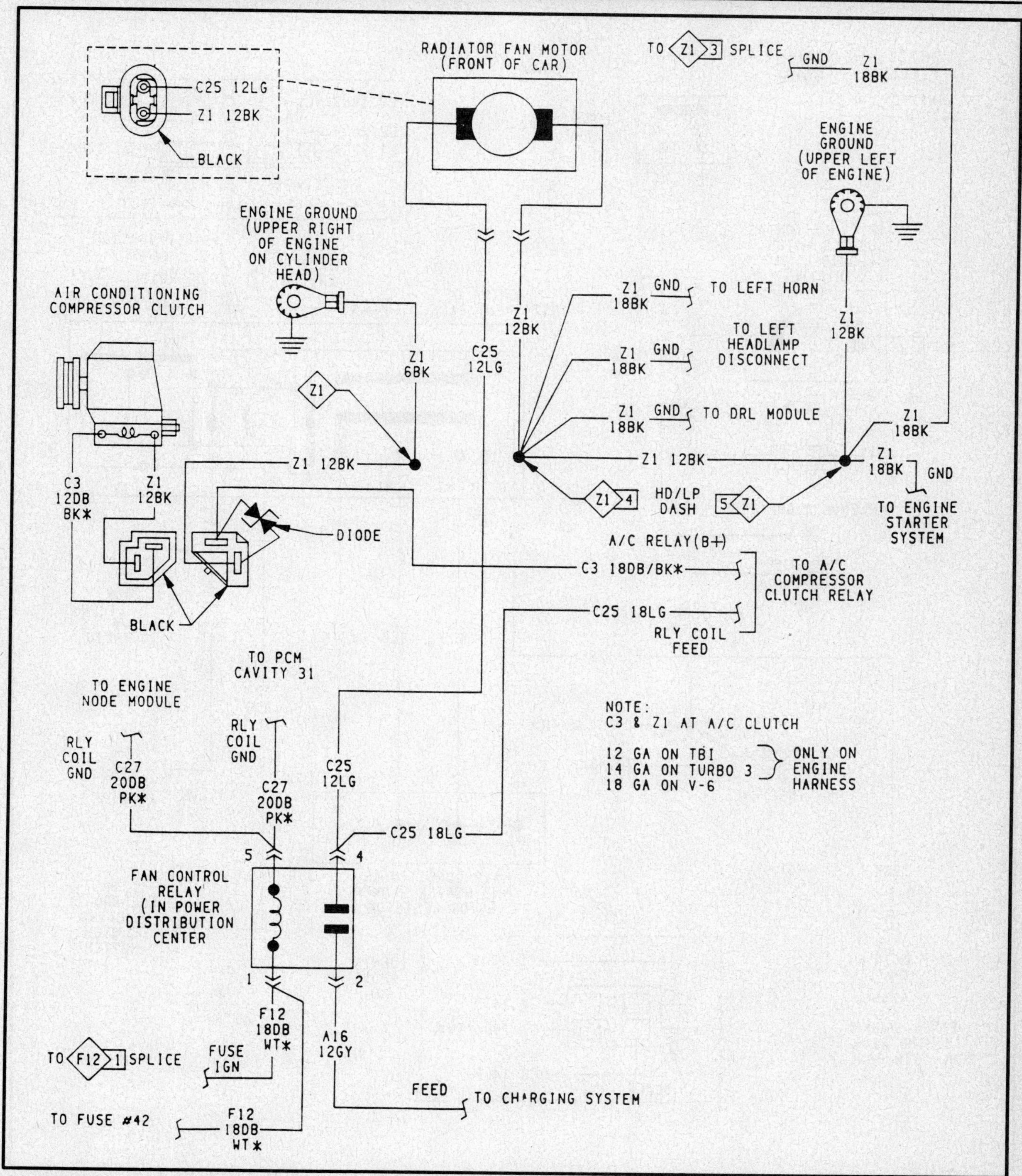

Heater-A/C system engine compartment wiring schematic—1993 Daytona and LeBaron

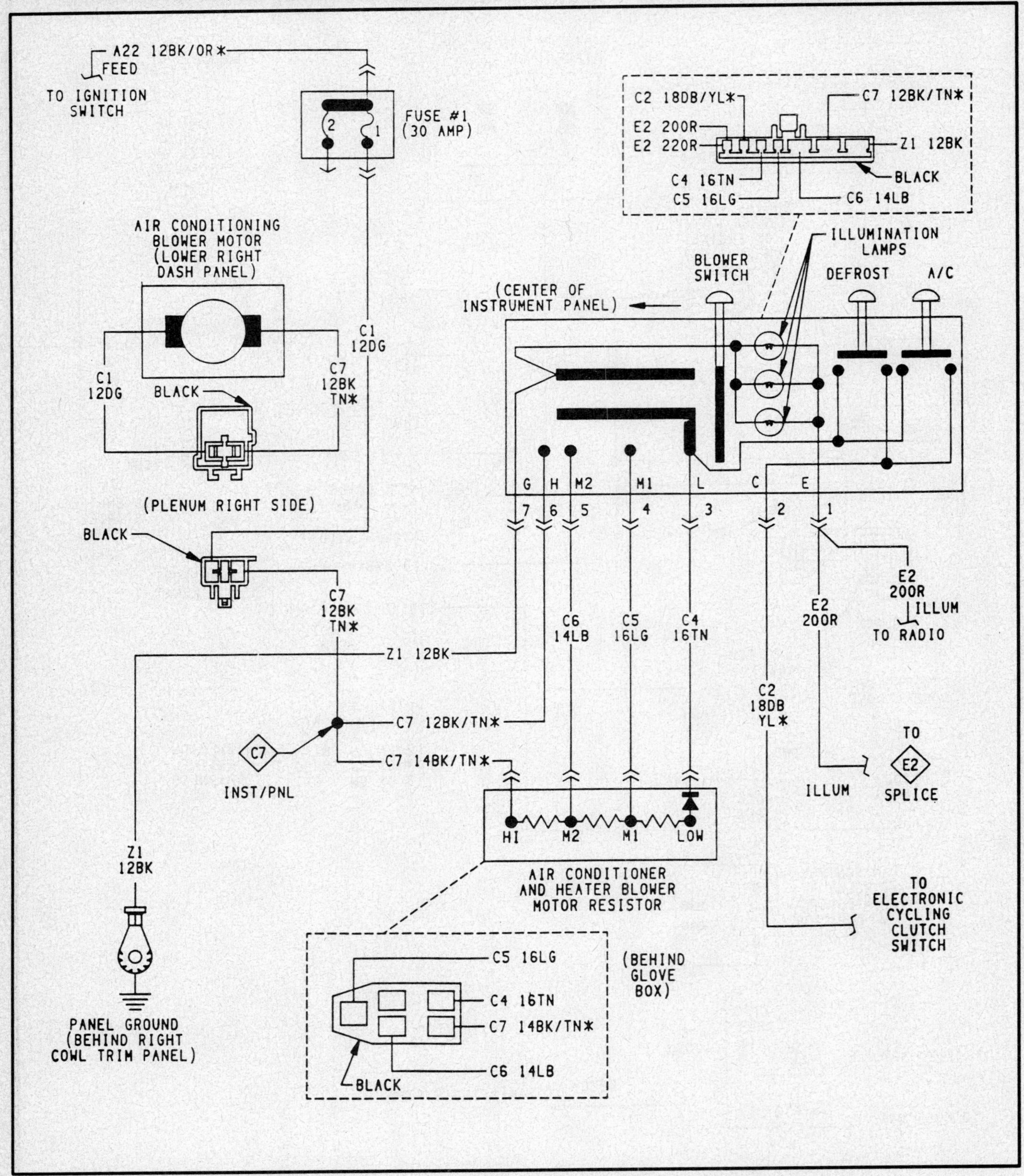

Heater-A/C system firewall components wiring schematic—1993 Daytona and LeBaron

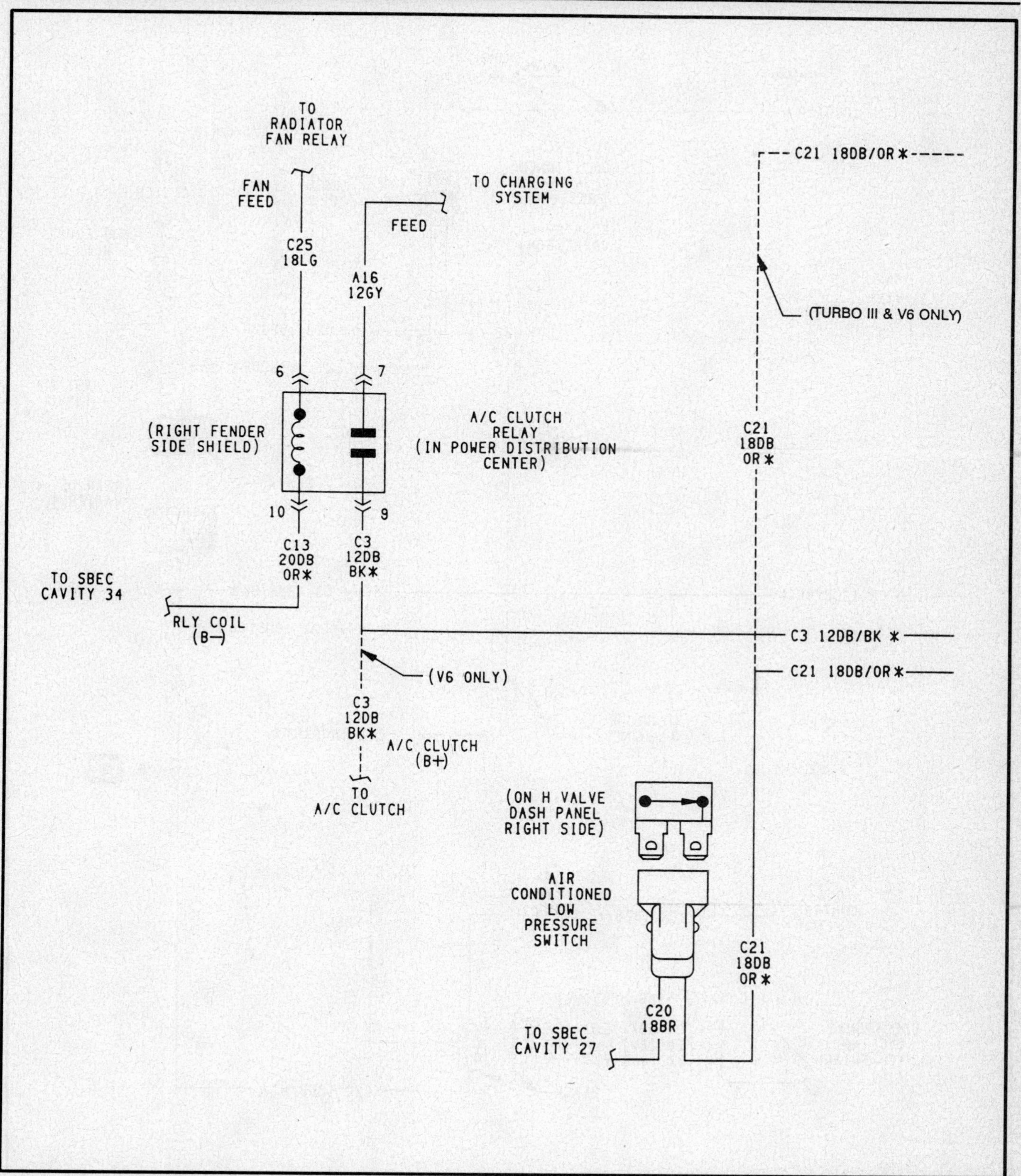

Heater-A/C system passenger compartment wiring schematic—1993 Daytona and LeBaron

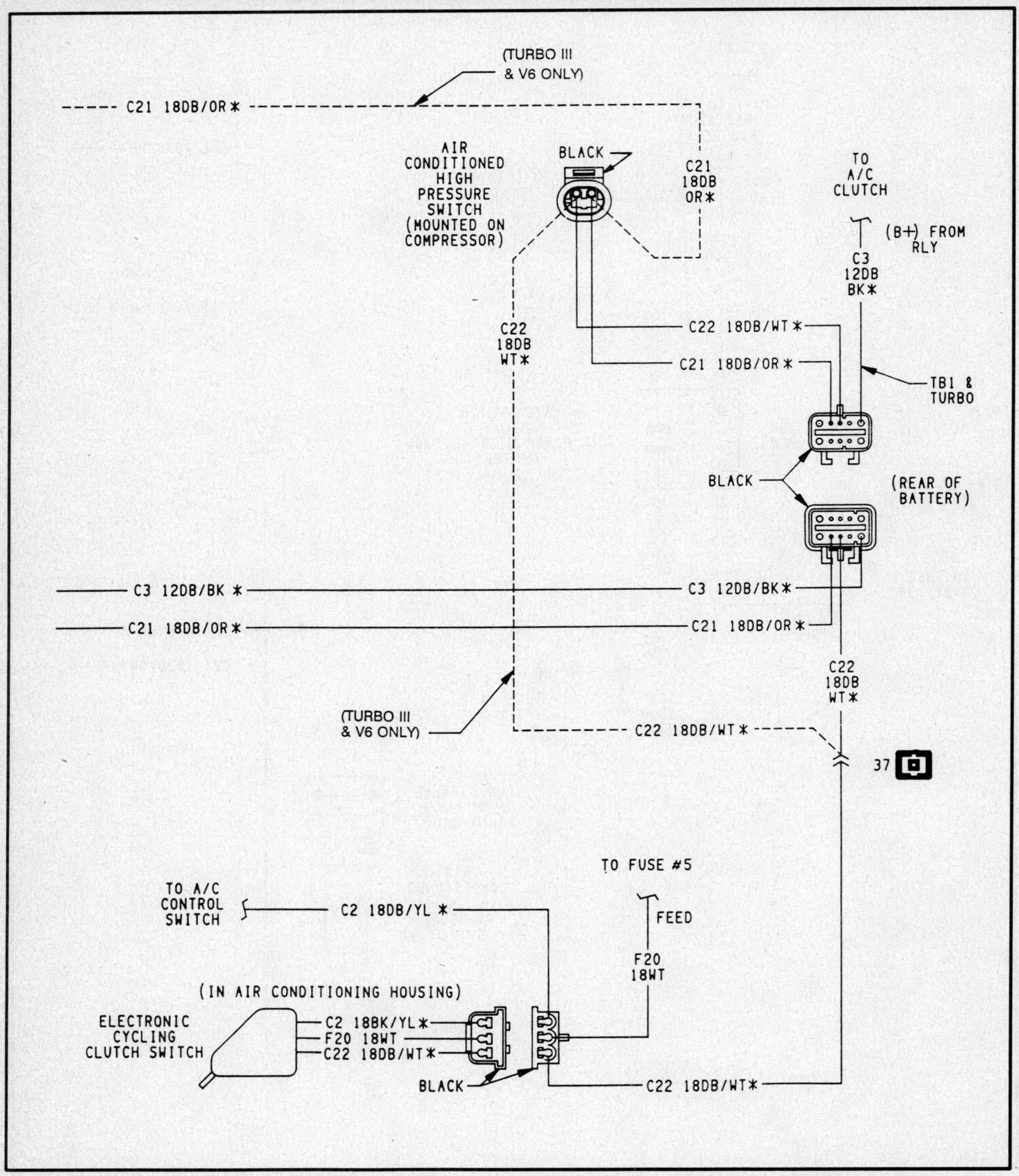

Heater-A/C system cycling clutch switch circuit wiring schematic—1993 Daytona and LeBaron

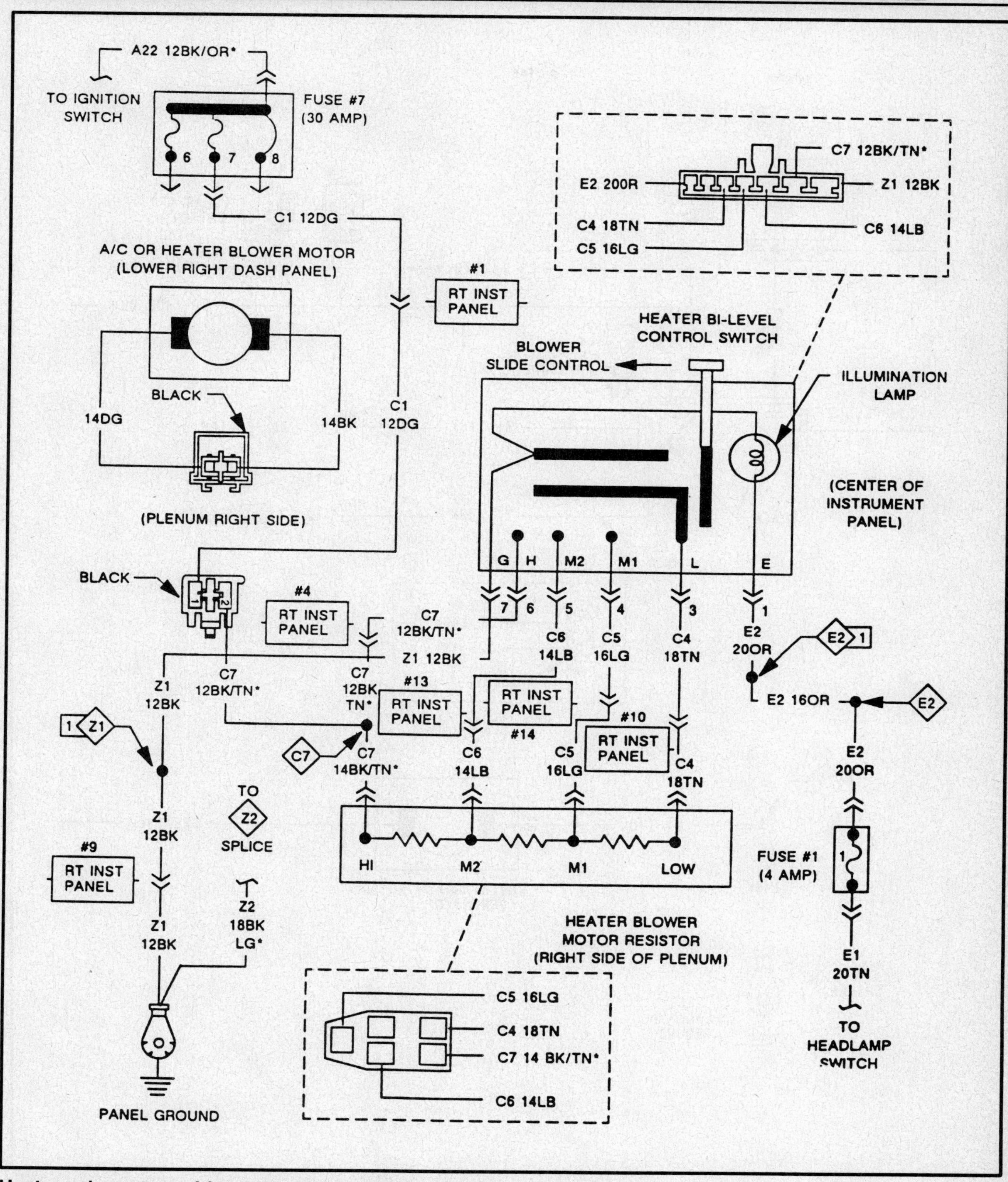

Heater only system wiring schematic—1993 Shadow and Sundance

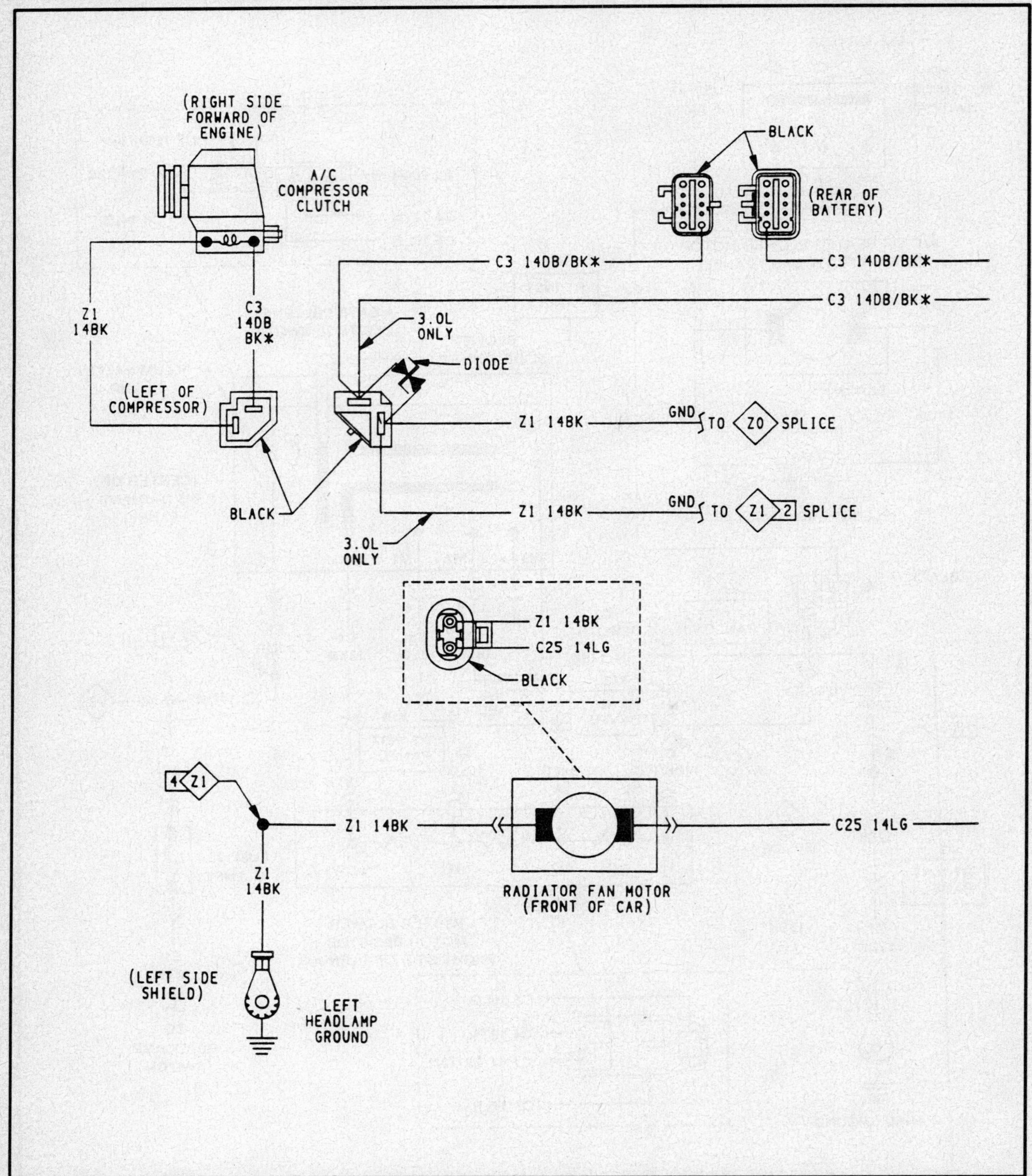

Heater-A/C system engine compartment wiring schematic—1993 Shadow and Sundance

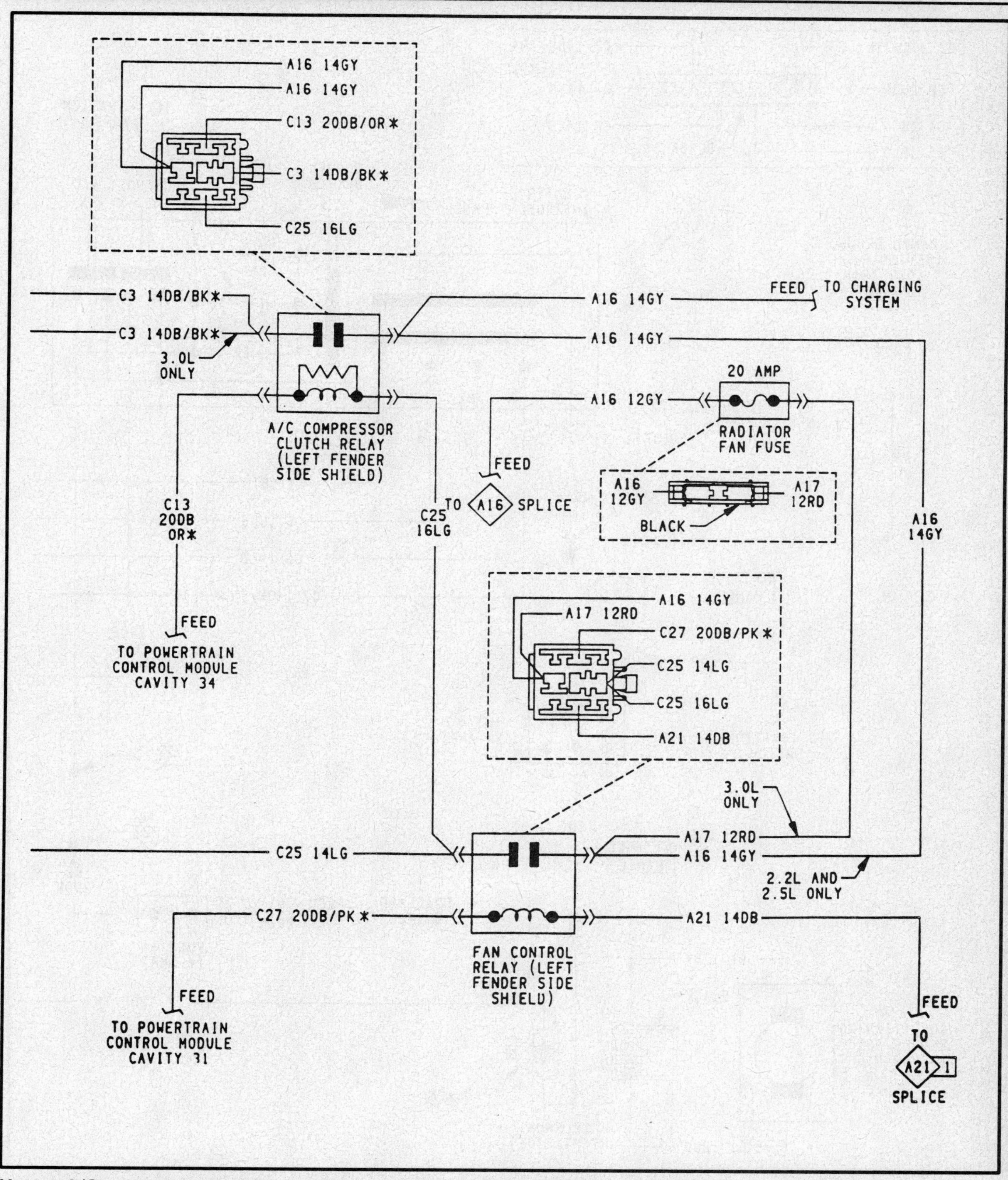

Heater-A/C system engine compartment wiring schematic—1993 Shadow and Sundance, Cont'd

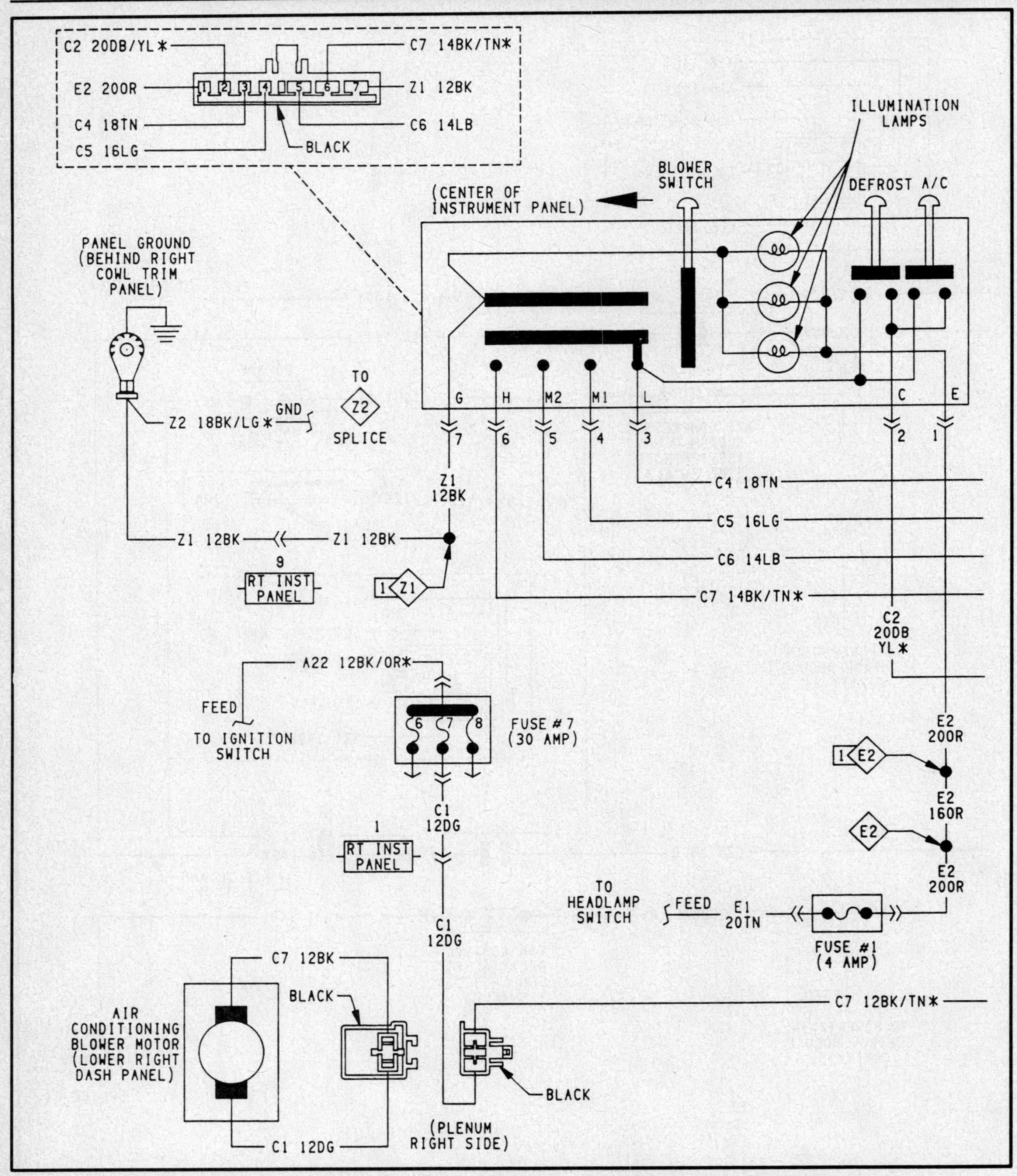

Heater-A/C system passenger compartment wiring schematic—1993 Shadow and Sundance

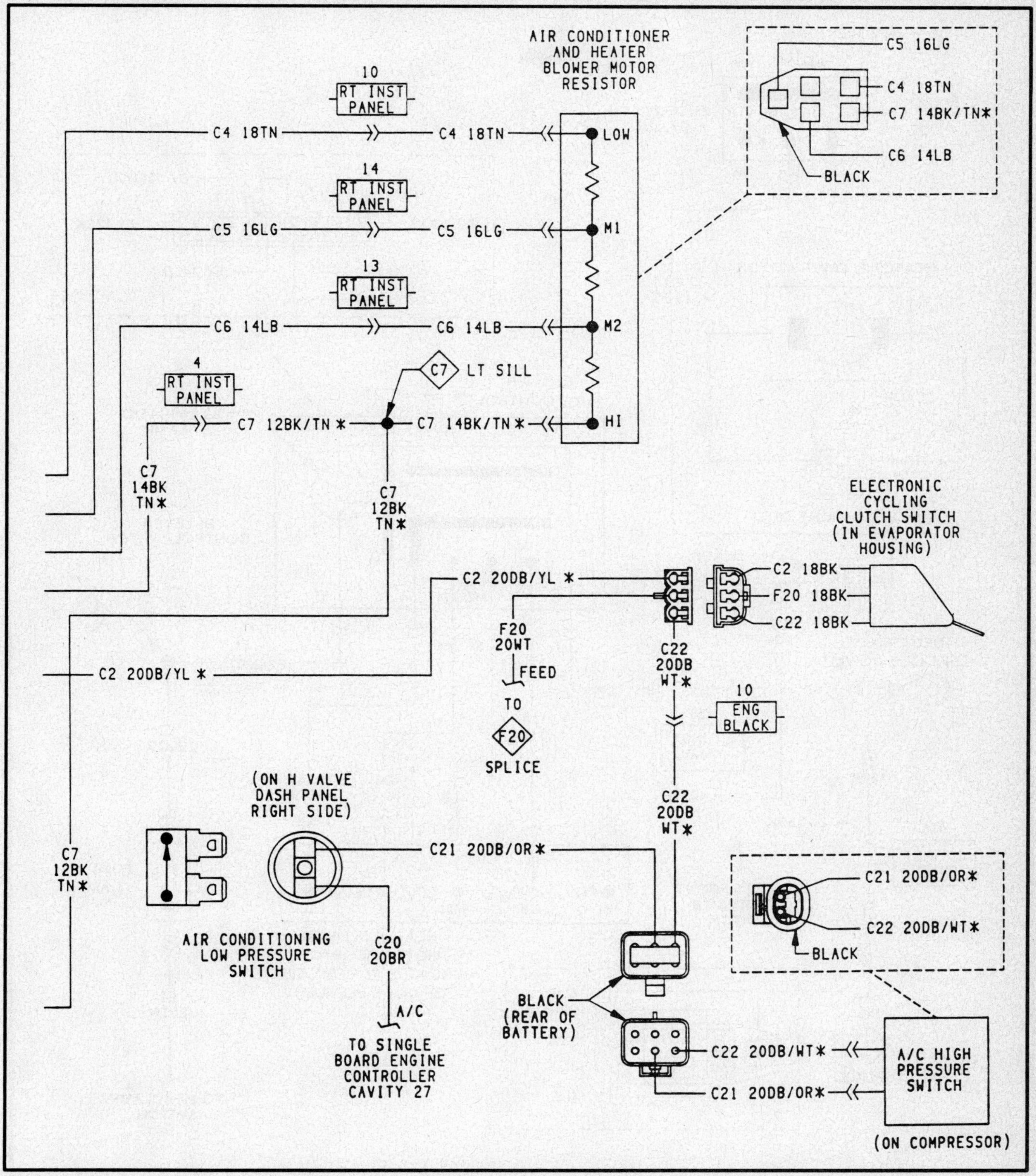

Heater-A/C system clutch cycling switch, low pressure switch and blower resistor circuits—1993 Shadow and Sundance

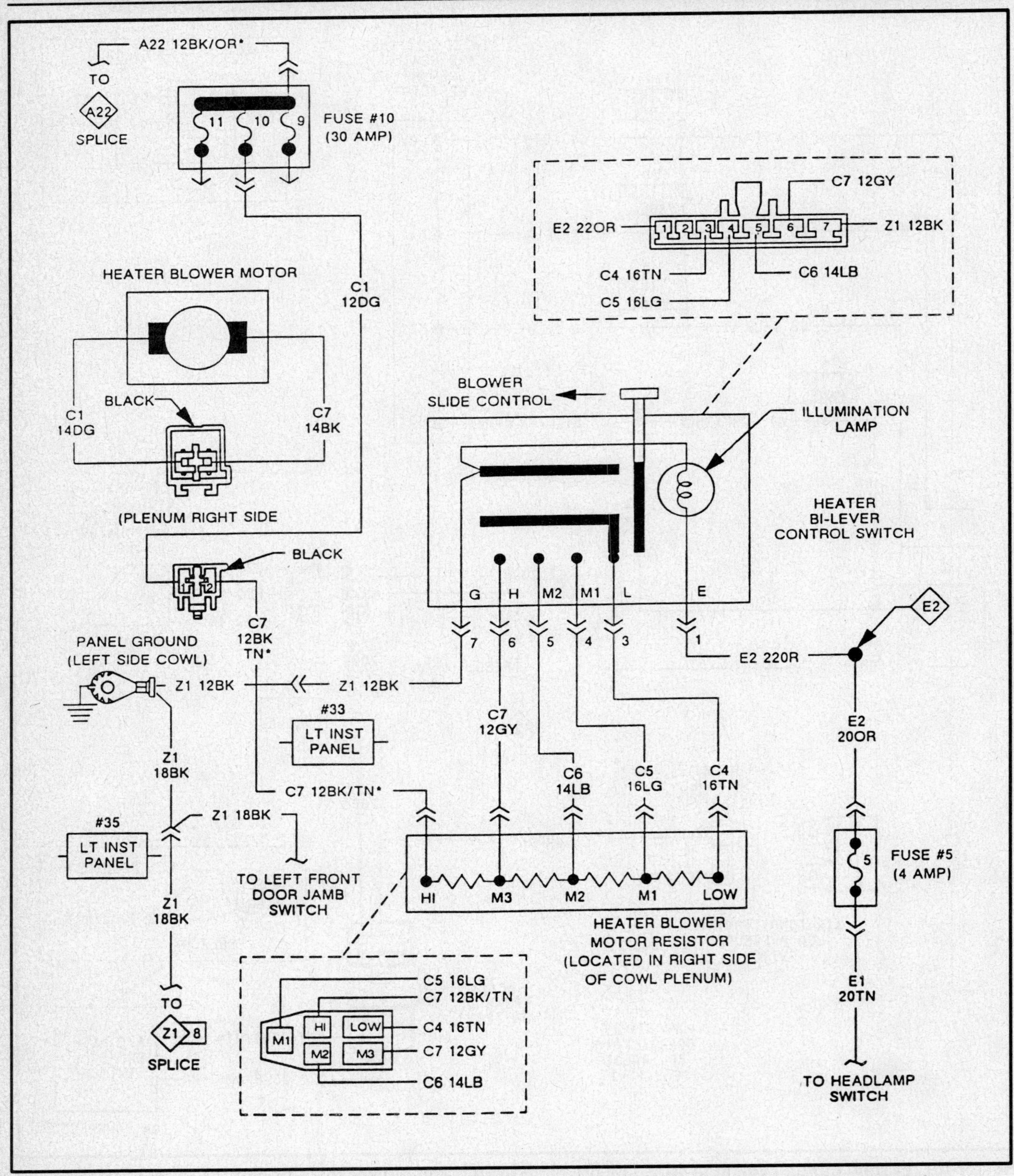

Heater only system wiring schematic—1993 Dynasty, Fifth Avenue, Imperial and New Yorker with 2.5L engine

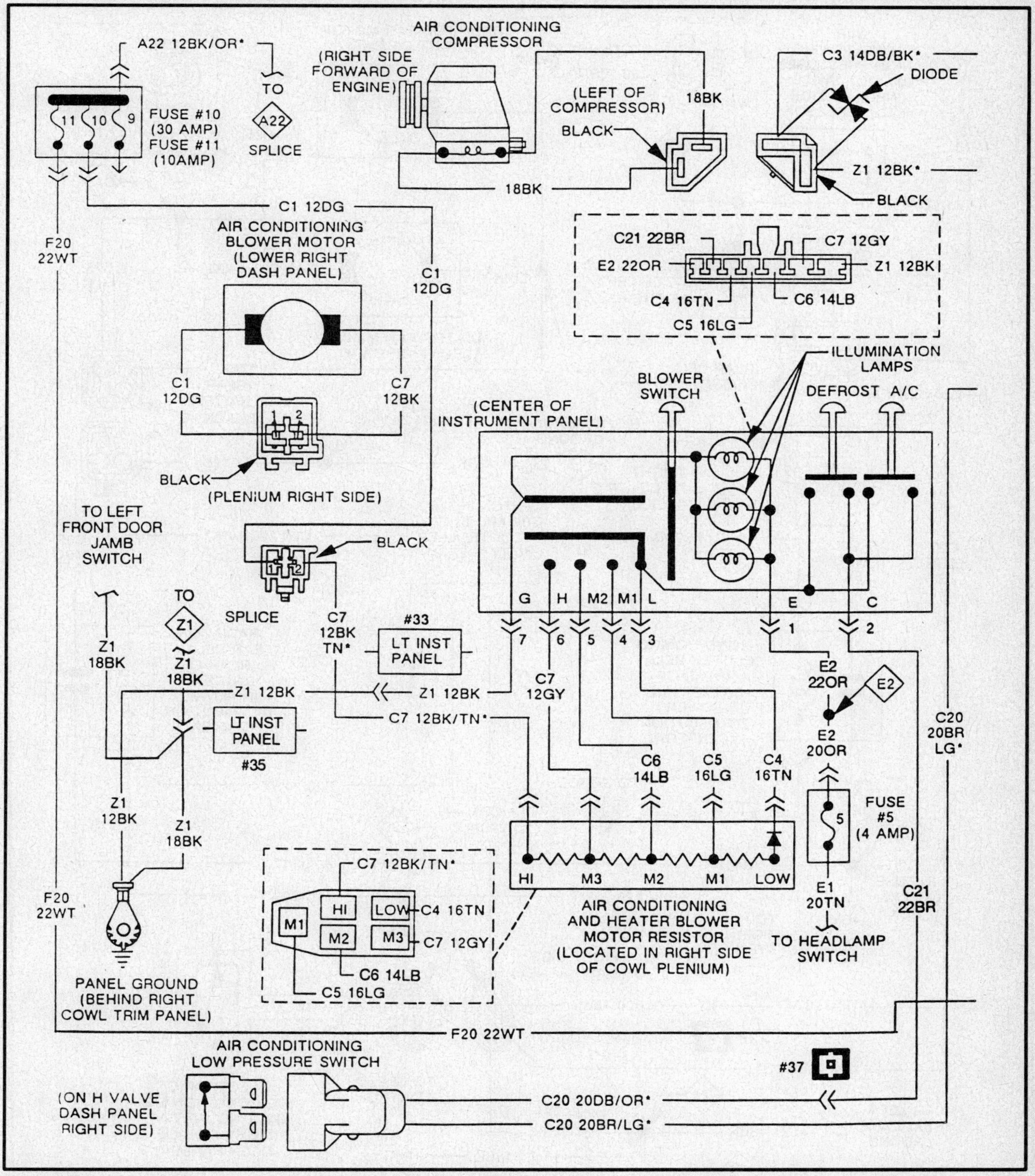

Heater-A/C system wiring schematic—1993 Dynasty, Fifth Avenue, Imperial and New Yorker with 2.5L engine

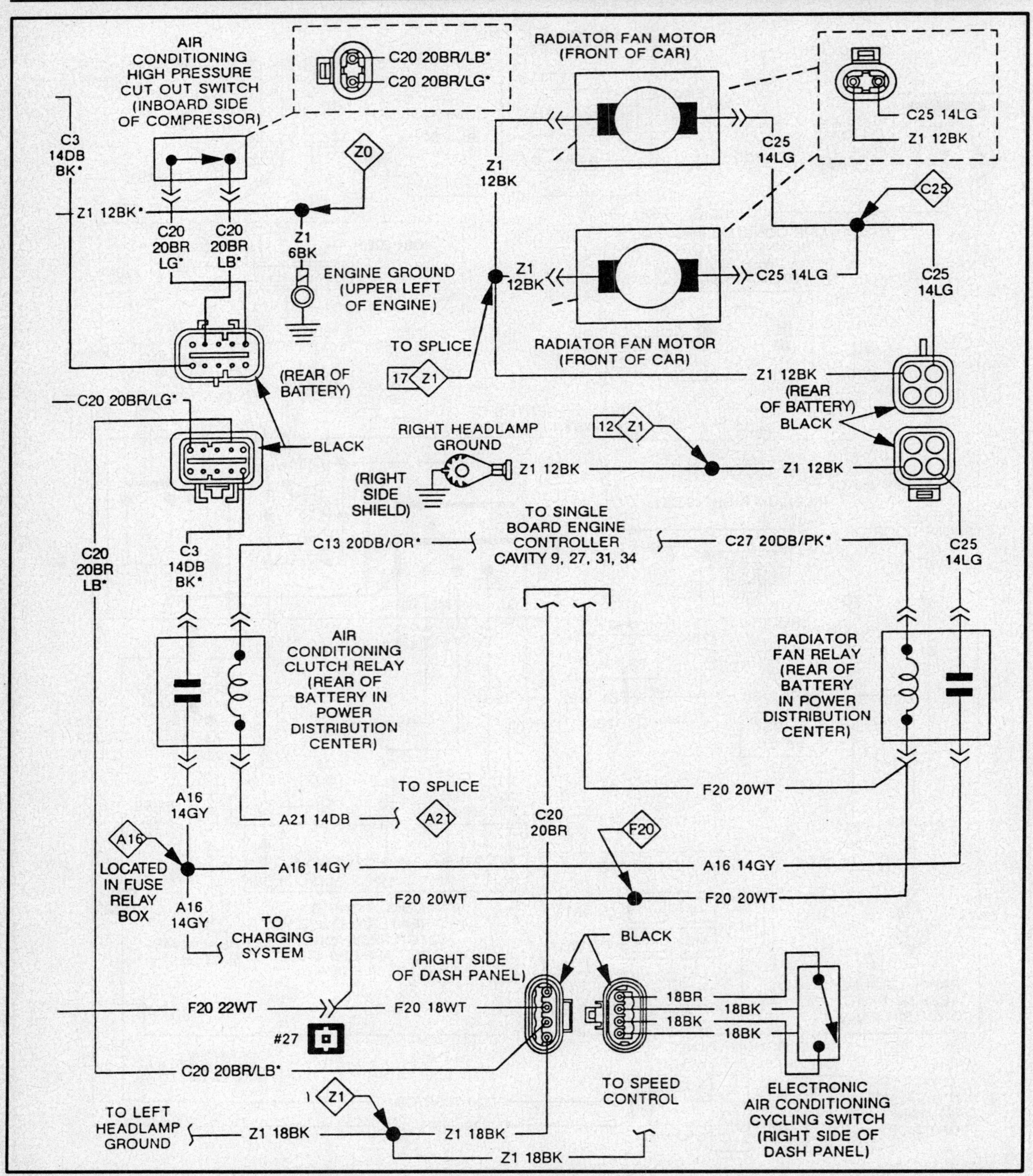

Heater-A/C system wiring schematic—1993 Dynasty, Fifth Avenue, Imperial and New Yorker with 2.5L engine, Cont'd

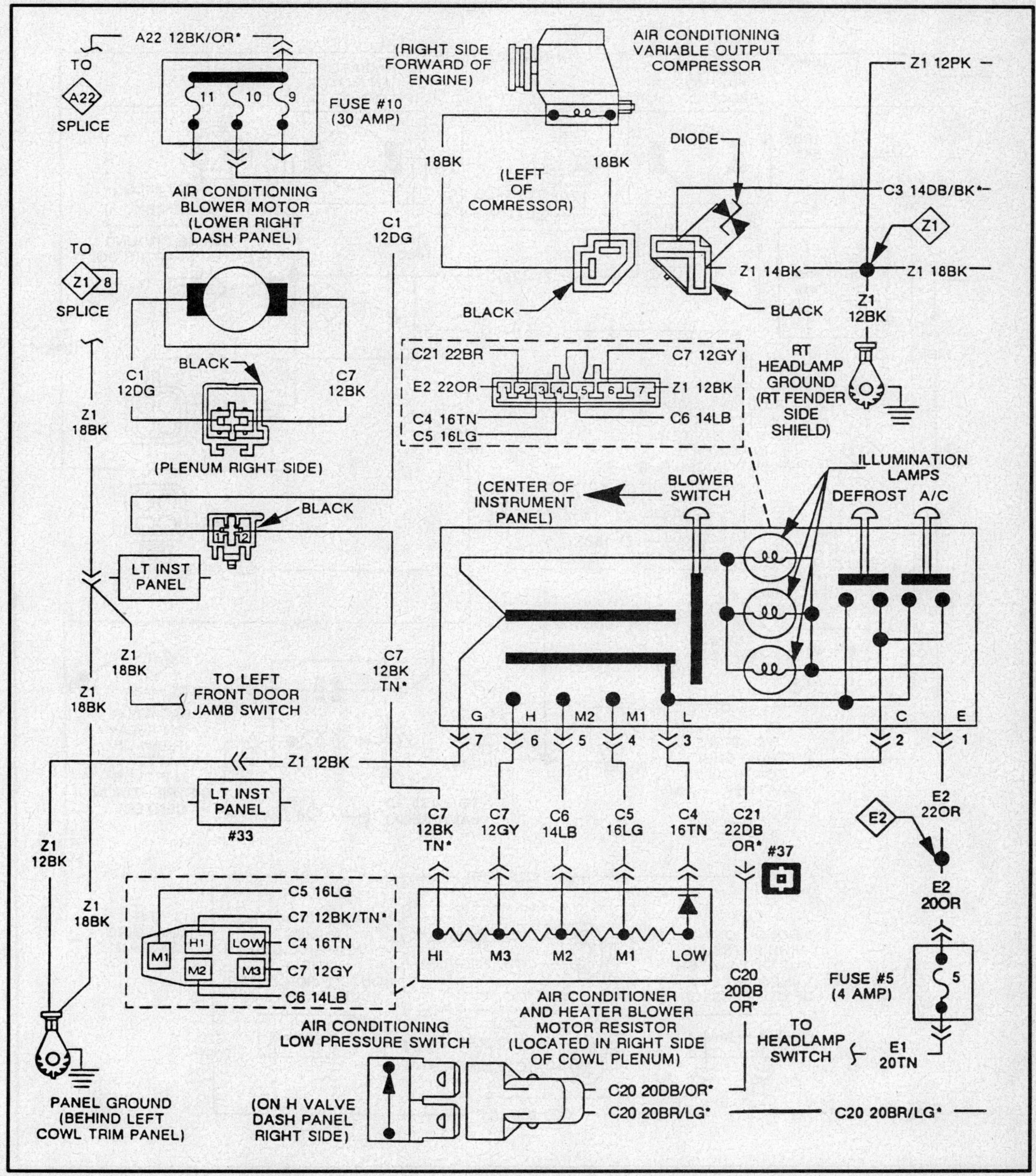

Heater-A/C system wiring schematic—1993 Dynasty, Fifth Avenue, Imperial and New Yorker with 3.0L, 3.3L, 3.8L engine

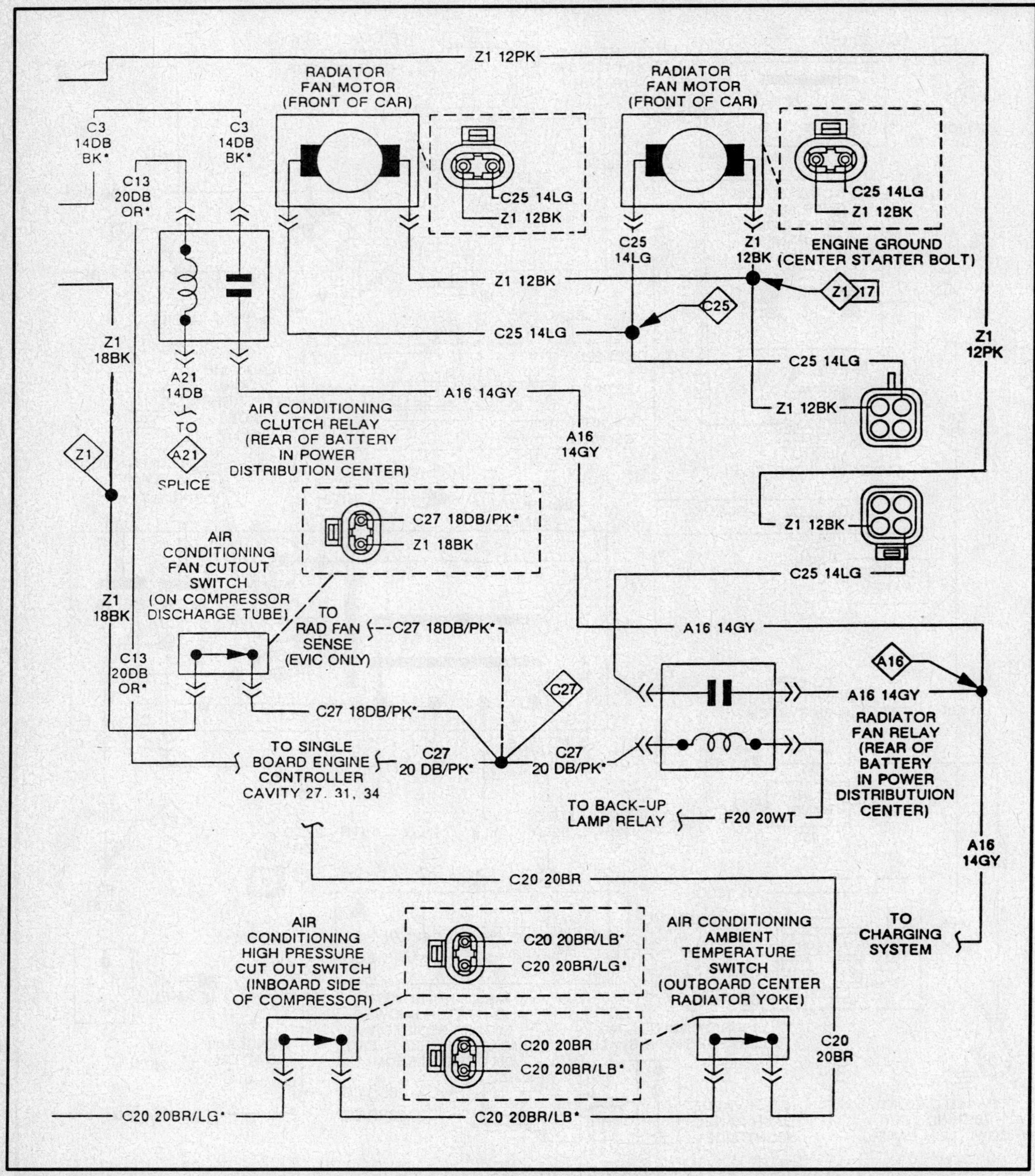

Heater-A/C system wiring schematic—1993 Dynasty, Fifth Avenue, Imperial and New Yorker with 3.0L, 3.3L, 3.8L engine, Cont'd

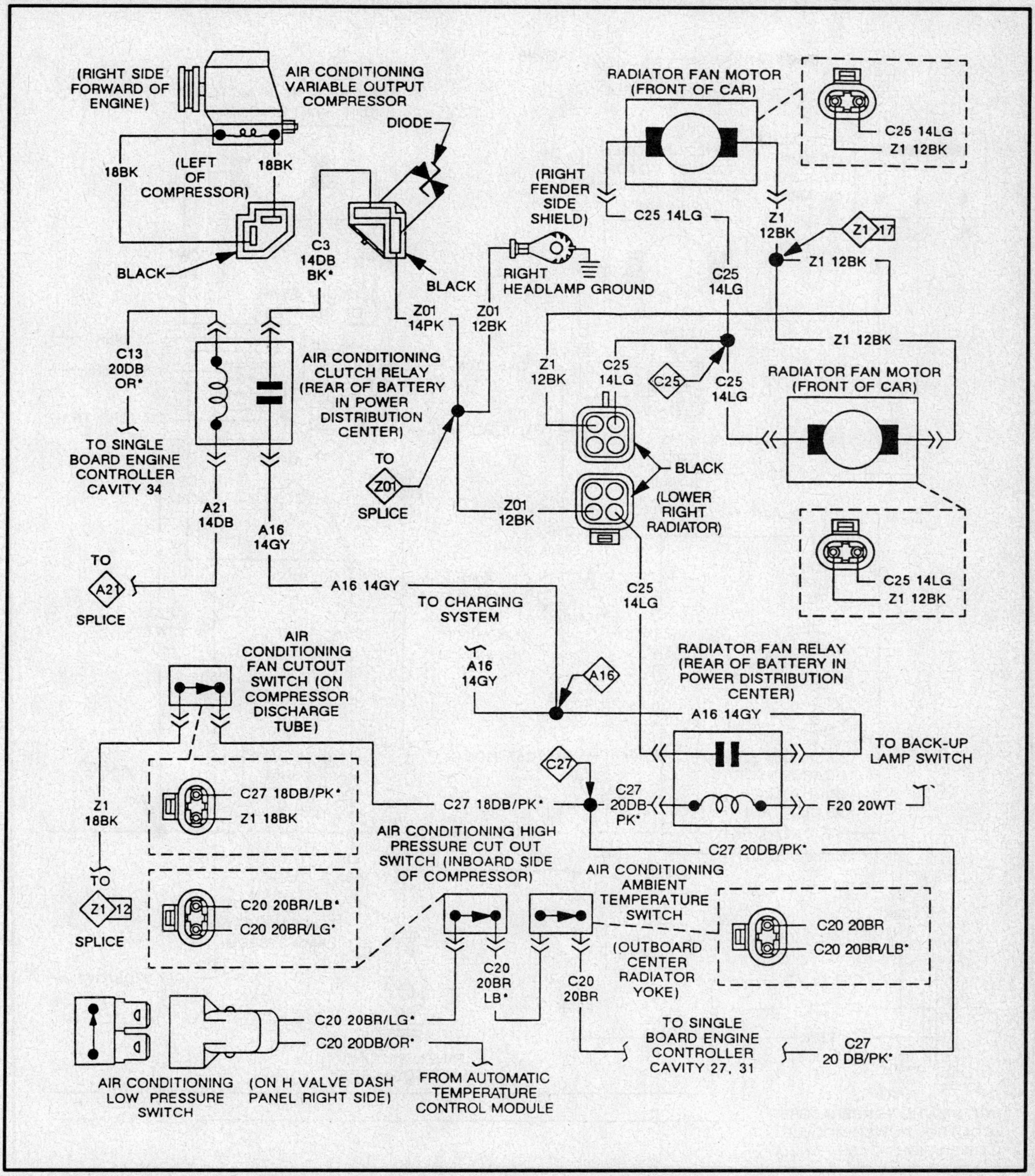

Automatic Temperature Control (ATC) system wiring schematic—1993 Dynasty, Fifth Avenue, Imperial and New Yorker

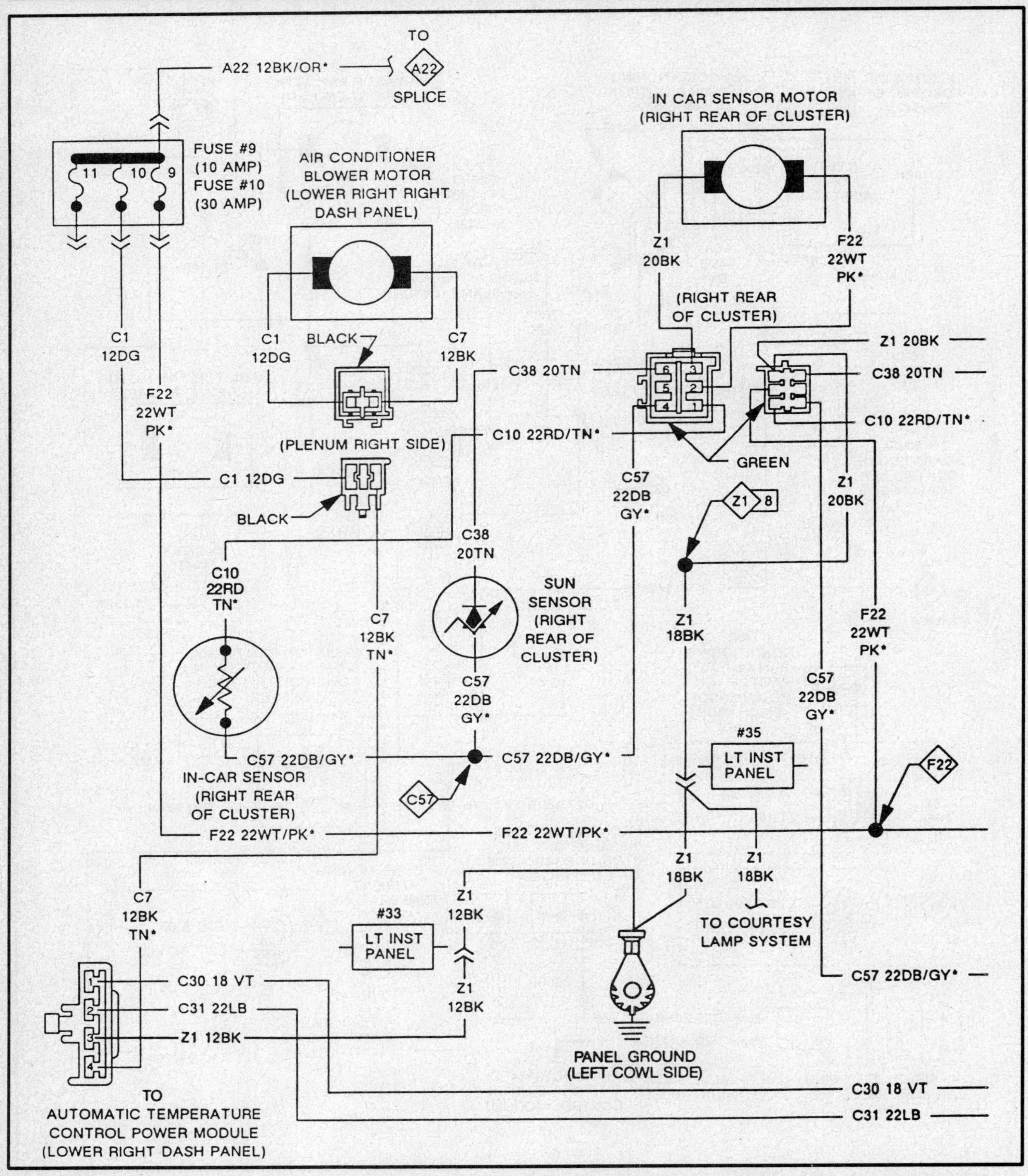

Automatic Temperature Control (ATC) system wiring schematic—1993 Dynasty, Fifth Avenue, Imperial and New Yorker, Cont'd

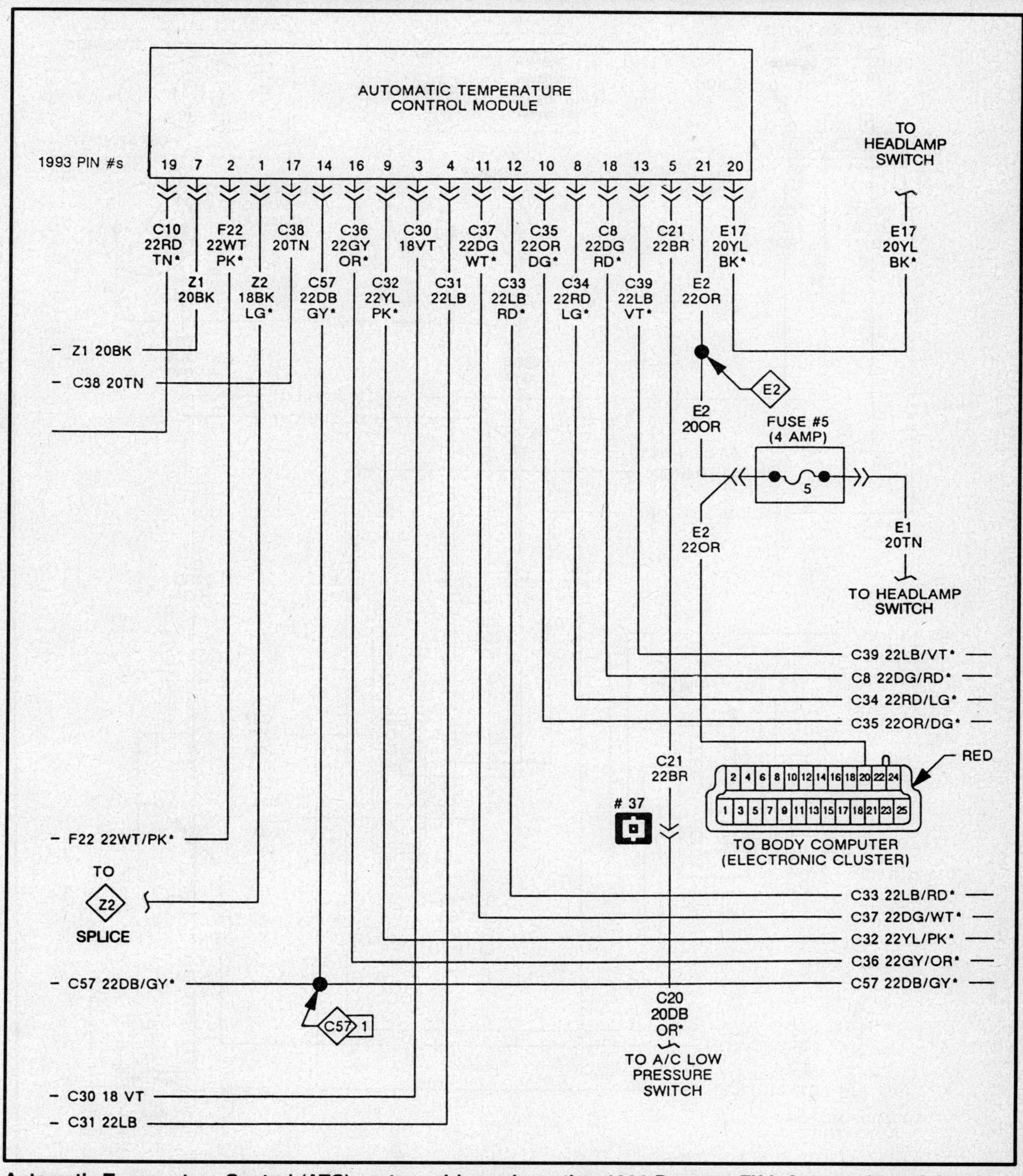

Automatic Temperature Control (ATC) system wiring schematic—1993 Dynasty, Fifth Avenue, Imperial and New Yorker, Cont'd

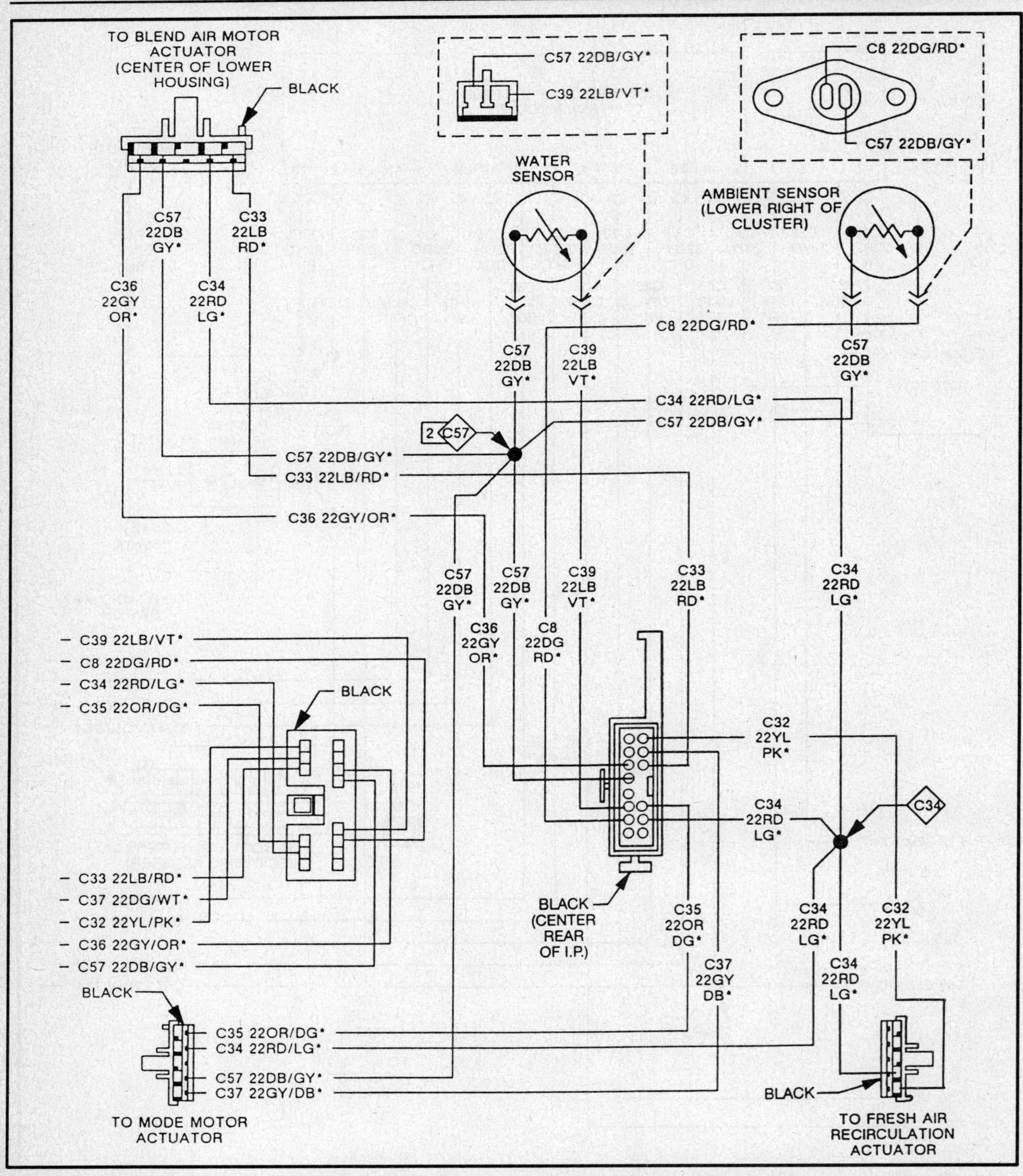

Automatic Temperature Control (ATC) system wiring schematic—1993 Dynasty, Fifth Avenue, Imperial and New Yorker, Cont'd

2 CHRYSLER/DODGE/PLYMOUTH/EAGLE 2

AVENGER • CIRRUS • CONCORDE • INTREPID • LASER • LHS • NEW YORKER • SEBRING • STEALTH • STRATUS • SUMMIT • SUMMIT WAGON • TALON • VISION

SPECIFICATIONS

ENGINE IDENTIFICATION

Year	Model	Engine Displacement Liters (cc)	Engine Series (ID/VIN)	Fuel System	No. of Cylinders	Engine Type
1993	Concorde	3.3 (3294)	EGB (T)	MFI	6	OHV
	Intrepid	3.3 (3294)	EGB (T)	MFI	6	OHV
	Vision	3.3 (3294)	EGB (T)	MFI	6	OHV
	Concorde	3.5 (3518)	EGE (F)	MFI	6	DOHC
	Intrepid	3.5 (3518)	EGE (F)	MFI	6	DOHC
	Vision	3.5 (3518)	EGE (F)	MFI	6	DOHC
	Laser	1.8 (1754)	4G37 (B)	MFI	4	SOHC
	Talon	1.8 (1754)	4G37 (B)	MFI	4	SOHC
	Laser	2.0 (2000)	4G63 (E)	MFI	4	DOHC
	Talon	2.0 (2000)	4G63 (E)	MFI	4	DOHC
	Laser	2.0 (2000)	4G63 (F)	MFI	4	DOHC
	Talon–Turbo	2.0 (2000)	4G63 (F)	MFI	4	DOHC
	Stealth	3.0 (2972)	6G72 (H)	MFI	6	SOHC
	Stealth	3.0 (2972)	6G72 (J)	MFI	6	DOHC
	Stealth–Turbo	3.0 (2972)	6G72 (K)	MFI	6	DOHC
	Summit	1.5 (1468)	4G15 (A)	MFI	4	SOHC
	Summit	1.8 (1834)	4G93 (C)	MFI	4	SOHC
	Summit Wagon	1.8 (1834)	4G93 (C)	MFI	4	SOHC
	Summit Wagon	2.4 (2350)	4G64 (G)	MFI	4	SOHC
1994	Concorde	3.3 (3294)	EGB (T)	MFI	6	OHV
	Concorde	3.5 (3523)	EGE (F)	MFI	6	DOHC
	Intrepid	3.3 (3294)	EGB (T)	MFI	6	OHV
	Intrepid	3.5 (3523)	EGE (F)	MFI	6	DOHC
	Laser	1.8 (1754)	4G37 (B)	MFI	4	SOHC
	Laser	2.0 (2000)	4G63 (E)	MFI	4	DOHC
	LHS	3.5 (3523)	F	MFI	6	DOHC
	New Yorker	3.5 (3523)	F	MFI	6	DOHC
	Stealth	3.0 (2972)	6G72 (H)	MFI	6	SOHC
	Stealth–Non–Turbo	3.0 (2972)	6G72 (J)	MFI	6	DOHC
	Stealth–Turbo	3.0 (2972)	6G72 (K)	MFI	6	DOHC
	Summit	1.5 (1468)	4G15 (A)	MFI	4	SOHC
	Summit	1.8 (1834)	4G93 (C)	MFI	4	SOHC
	Summit Wagon	1.8 (1834)	4G93 (C)	MFI	4	SOHC
	Summit Wagon	2.4 (2350)	4G64 (G)	MFI	4	SOHC
	Talon	1.8 (1754)	4G37 (B)	MFI	4	SOHC
	Talon–Non–Turbo	2.0 (2000)	4G63 (E)	MFI	4	DOHC
	Talon–Turbo	2.0 (2000)	4G63 (F)	MFI	4	DOHC
	Vision	3.3 (3294)	EGB (T)	MFI	6	OHV
	Vision	3.5 (3523)	EGE (F)	MFI	6	DOHC
1995	Avenger	2.0 (2000)	420A	MFI	4	DOHC

ENGINE IDENTIFICATION

Year	Model	Engine Displacement Liters (cc)	Engine Series (ID/VIN)	Fuel System	No. of Cylinders	Engine Type
1995	Avenger	2.5 (2497)	6G73	MFI	6	SOHC
	Cirrus	2.5 (2491)	H	MFI	6	SOHC
	Concorde	3.3 (3294)	EGB (T)	MFI	6	OHV
	Concorde	3.5 (3518)	EGE (F)	MFI	6	DOHC
	Intrepid	3.3 (3294)	EGB (T)	MFI	6	OHV
	Intrepid	3.5 (3523)	EGE (F)	MFI	6	DOHC
	LHS	3.5 (3523)	F	MFI	6	DOHC
	New Yorker	3.5 (3523)	F	MFI	6	DOHC
	Sebring	2.0 (2000)	420A	MFI	4	DOHC
	Sebring	2.5 (2497)	6G73	MFI	6	SOHC
	Stealth	3.0 (2972)	6G72 (H)	MFI	6	SOHC
	Stealth–Non–Turbo	3.0 (2972)	6G72 (J)	MFI	6	DOHC
	Stealth–Turbo	3.0 (2972)	6G72 (K)	MFI	6	DOHC
	Stratus	2.0 (1999)	C	MFI	4	OHV,SOHC
	Stratus	2.4 (2425)	X	MFI	4	OHV,DOHC
	Stratus	2.5 (2491)	H	MFI	6	SOHC
	Summit	1.5 (1468)	4G15 (A)	MFI	4	SOHC
	Summit	1.8 (1834)	4G93 (C)	MFI	4	SOHC
	Summit Wagon	1.8 (1834)	4G93 (C)	MFI	4	SOHC
	Summit Wagon	2.4 (2350)	4G64 (G)	MFI	4	SOHC
	Talon	1.8 (1754)	4G37 (B)	MFI	4	SOHC
	Talon–Non–Turbo	2.0 (2000)	4G63 (E)	MFI	4	DOHC
	Talon–Turbo	2.0 (2000)	4G63 (F)	MFI	4	DOHC
	Vision	3.3 (3294)	EGB (T)	MFI	6	OHV
	Vision	3.5 (3523)	EGE (F)	MFI	6	DOHC

MFI–Multi-Port Fuel Injection
SOHC–Single Overhead Cam
DOHC–Dual Overhead Cam
OHV–Overhead Valves

REFRIGERANT CAPACITIES

Year	Model	Refrigerant (oz.)	Oil (fl. oz.)	Compressor Type
1993	Concorde	28①	4.75①	10PA17–R134a
	Intrepid	28①	4.75①	10PA17–R134a
	Vision	28①	4.75①	10PA17–R134a
	Laser	33	2.7	10PA17
	Talon	33	2.7	10PA17
	Stealth	29	5.4	FX–105VS
	Summit	26–30	4.4	FX–105VS or VL
	Summit Wagon	30	2.7	10PA15
1994	Concorde	28①	4.75①	10PA17–R134a
	Intrepid	28①	4.75①	10PA17–R134a
	Laser	33	2.7	10PA17
	LHS	28①	4.75①	10PA17–R134a

REFRIGERANT CAPACITIES

Year	Model	Refrigerant (oz.)	Oil (fl. oz.)	Compressor Type
1994	New Yorker	28①	4.75①	10PA17–R134a
	Stealth	28①	9.8①	MSC105
	Summit	26–30①	4.4–5.1①	
	Summit Wagon (1.8L)	26.8	4.1	10A17C
	Summit Wagon (2.4L)	26.8	2.7	10A17C
	Talon	33	2.7	10PA17
	Vision	28①	4.75①	10PA17–R134a
1995	Avenger	23	(SOHC) 5.7	(SOHC) MSC105CVS
	Avenger	23	(DOHC) 3.4	(DOHC) 10PA17C
	Cirrus	28①	4.75	TRS–90
	Concorde	28①	4.75①	10PA17–R134a
	Intrepid	28①	4.75①	10PA17–R134a
	LHS	28①	4.75①	10PA17–R134a
	New Yorker	28①	4.75①	10PA17–R134a
	Sebring	23	(SOHC) 5.7	(SOHC) MSC105CVS
	Sebring	23	(DOHC) 3.4	(DOHC) 10PA17C
	Stealth	28①	9.8①	MSC105
	Stratus	28①	4.75	TRS–90
	Summit	26–30①	4.4–5.1①	NA
	Summit Wagon (1.8L)	26.8①	4.1①	10PA17C
	Summit Wagon (2.4L)	26.8①	2.7①	10PA17C
	Talon	33	2.7	10PA17
	Vision	28①	4.75①	10PA17–R134a

NA–Not available
① Uses R–134a refrigerant and corresponding oil. Do not mix any R–12 refrigerant, oil, service equipment of components.

AIR CONDITIONING BELT TENSION

Year	Model	Engine Liters (cc)	Belt Type	Specifications New (lbs.)	Specifications Used (lbs.)
1993	Concorde	3.3 (3294)	Poly–V	②	②
	Concorde	3.5 (3523)	Poly–V	②	②
	Intrepid	3.3 (3294)	Poly–V	②	②
	Intrepid	3.5 (3523)	Poly–V	②	②
	Vision	3.3 (3294)	Poly–V	②	②
	Vision	3.5 (3523)	Poly–V	②	②
	Laser	1.8 (1754)	Poly–V	0.16–0.20①	0.22–0.24①
	Talon	1.8 (1754)	Poly–V	0.16–0.20①	0.22–0.24①
	Laser	2.0 (2000)	Poly–V	0.18–0.20①	0.22–0.24①
	Talon	2.0 (2000)	Poly–V	0.18–0.20①	0.22–0.24①
	Stealth	3.0 (2967)③	Poly–V	0.26–0.28①	0.28–0.33①
	Stealth	3.0 (2967)④	Poly–V	0.14–0.16①	0.16–0.20①
	Summit	1.5 (1468)	Poly–V	0.20–0.24①	0.24–0.28①
	Summit	1.8 (1834)	Poly–V	0.20–0.24①	0.24–0.28①
	Summit Wagon	1.8 (1834)	Poly–V	0.22–0.24①	0.27–0.30①

AIR CONDITIONING BELT TENSION

Year	Model	Engine Liters (cc)	Belt Type	Specifications New (lbs.)	Specifications Used (lbs.)
1993	Summit Wagon	2.4 (2350)	Poly–V	0.15①	0.17①
1994	Concorde	3.3 (3294)	Poly–V	②	②
	Concorde	3.5 (3518)	Poly–V	②	②
	Intrepid	3.3 (3294)	Poly–V	②	②
	Intrepid	3.5 (3518)	Poly–V	②	②
	Laser	1.8 (1754)	Poly–V	0.16–0.20①	0.22–0.24①
	Laser	2.0 (2000)	Poly–V	0.18–0.20①	0.22–0.24①
	LHS	3.5 (3523)	Poly–V	②	②
	New Yorker	3.5 (3523)	Poly–V	②	②
	Stealth	3.0 (2972)③	Poly–V	0.26–0.28①	0.28–0.34①
	Stealth	3.0 (2972)④	Poly–V	0.14–0.16①	0.16–0.20①
	Summit	1.5 (1486)	Poly–V	0.20–0.24①	0.24–0.28①
	Summit	1.8 (1834)	Poly–V	0.22–0.24①	0.27–0.30①
	Summit Wagon	1.8 (1834)	Poly–V	0.22–0.24①	0.27–0.30①
	Summit Wagon	2.4 (2350)	Poly–V	0.17–0.19①	0.21–0.24①
	Talon	1.8 (1754)	Poly–V	0.16–0.20①	0.22–0.24①
	Talon–Turbo	2.0 (2000)	Poly–V	0.18–0.20①	0.22–0.24①
	Vision	3.3(3294)	Poly–V	②	②
	Vision	3.5 (3518)	Poly–V	②	②
1995	Avenger	2.0 (2000)	Poly–V	0.32–0.35①	0.39–0.43①
	Avenger	2.5 (2497)	Poly–V	0.28–0.32①	0.32–0.35①
	Cirrus	2.5 (2491)	Poly–V	150	80
	Concorde	3.3 (3294)	Poly–V	②	②
	Concorde	3.5 (3518)	Poly–V	②	②
	Intrepid	3.3 (3294)	Poly–V	②	②
	Intrepid	3.5 (3518)	Poly–V	②	②
	LHS	3.5 (3523)	Poly–V	②	②
	New Yorker	3.5 (3523)	Poly–V	②	②
	Sebring	2.0 (2000)	Poly–V	0.32–0.35①	0.39–0.43①
	Sebring	2.5 (2497)	Poly–V	0.28–0.32①	0.32–0.35①
	Stealth	3.0 (2972)③	Poly–V	0.26–0.28①	0.28–0.34①
	Stealth	3.0 (2972)④	Poly–V	0.14–0.16①	0.16–0.20①
	Stratus	2.0 (1999)	Poly–V	150	80
	Stratus	2.4 (2425)	Poly–V	150	80
	Stratus	2.5 (2491)	Poly–V	150	80
	Summit	1.5 (1486)	Poly–V	0.20–0.24①	0.24–0.28①
	Summit	1.8 (1834)	Poly–V	0.22–0.24①	0.27–0.30①
	Summit Wagon	1.8 (1834)	Poly–V	0.22–0.24①	0.27–0.30①
	Summit Wagon	2.4 (2350)	Poly–V	0.14–0.15①	0.17–0.18①
	Talon	1.8 (1754)	Poly–V	0.16–0.20①	0.22–0.24①
	Talon–Turbo	2.0 (2000)	Poly–V	0.18–0.20①	0.22–0.24①
	Vision	3.3 (3294)	Poly–V	②	②
	Vision	3.5 (3518)	Poly–V	②	②

① Except where noted, specification is inches of deflection at center of longest run of belt with standard deflection gauge.

② Equipped with automatic tensioner.

③ SOHC–Single Overhead Cam

④ DOHC–Dual Overhead Cam

SYSTEM DESCRIPTION

General Information

Laser, Talon and Summit

The heater unit is located in the center of the vehicle with the blower housing and blend-air system. In the blend-air system, hot air and cool air are controlled by blend-air damper to make a fine adjustment of the temperature. The heater system is also designed as a bi-level heater in which a separator directs warm air to the windshield or to the floor and cool air through the panel outlet.

The temperature inside the car is controlled by means of the temperature control lever, the position of which determines the opening of the blend-air damper and the resulting mixing ratio of cool and hot air is used to control the outlet temperature.

The air conditioning compressor coil will be energized when all of the following conditions are met:

1. The air conditioner switch is depressed in either the **ECONO** or **A/C** position.
2. The blower motor switch is not in the **OFF** position.
3. The evaporator outlet air temperature sensor is reading at least 39°F (4°C).
4. The evaporator inlet air temperature sensor is reading at least 39°F (4°C).
5. On Summit, the compressor discharge side refrigerant temperature must be less than 293°F (145°C).

Stealth

MANUAL HEATER-A/C SYSTEM

Stealth uses a manually operated heater and air conditioning system which uses a 3-way air flow, blend air system. Its component operations are controlled and protected by radiator and condenser fan relays, an engine coolant temperature switch, blower relays, a dual pressure switch, an air inlet sensor, evaporator fin thermo sensor, and an air conditioner control unit. Circuit inputs are also received from the belt lock controller (DOHC only), the rpm sensor (DOHC only) and the MPI control unit.

AUTOMATIC A/C SYSTEM

Optionally, Stealth is equipped with a full automatic A/C system. In addition to the standard components used on the manual system, a compartment temperature sensor, outside (ambient) air temperature sensor, photo (sunlight) sensor, air mix damper potentiometer and an outlet selector (mode) damper potentiometer are used to maintain driver-selected temperature settings.

Summit Wagon

The manual heater and air conditioning system is controlled by a triple pressure switch to monitor pressures and cut off compressor operation at extreme high or low pressures. An A/C compressor relay is used to engage the compressor when the A/C switch on the panel is depressed and coolant temperature is adequate for system operation. An automatic compressor control unit receives input signals from the air inlet sensor and air thermo sensor, plus the signal from the control panel, to activate the compressor via the belt lock controller (1.8L engine).

Concorde, Intrepid, LHS, New Yorker and Vision

MANUAL HEATER OR A/C SYSTEM

All systems are equipped with a common unit housing assembly with the heater, evaporator (except heater only) and blower. The compressor will engage if the **DEFROST**, **MIX** or **A/C** button is depressed. Side window demisters are also used to keep the windows clear. Air doors are operated by electrical motor actuators (recirculation door, mode door and temperature door).

AUTOMATIC A/C SYSTEM

The automatic system uses a digital display on the instrument panel for setting temperatures and push buttons for setting mode operations. A series of sensors provide inputs to the ATC control module to regulate heating or cooling operations. An ambient sensor near the radiator senses exterior temperature. An in-car sensor measures interior temperature. A sun sensor measures the amount of direct sunlight in BTUs as a signal to the ATC control module.

Avenger and Sebring

The heater system uses a two-way flow full-air-mix system including an independent face air blowing function and a cool air bypass function. The air conditioning system is manually controlled. Its components are controlled and protected by radiator and condenser fan relays, an engine coolant temperature switch, blower relays, a dual pressure switch, air inlet and fin thermo sensors, an automatic compressor-ECM, and a powertrain control module.

Cirrus and Stratus

Air conditioning is standard equipment on Cirrus and Stratus and all vehicles are equipped with a common A/C-heater unit housing assembly. The system pulls outside (ambient) air through the cowl opening at the base of the windshield. Then it goes into the plenum chamber above the A/C-heater unit housing and air passes through the evaporator. At this point the air flow can be directed either through or around the heater core. This is done by adjusting the blend–air door with the **TEMP** control on the control head. After the air passes the blend-air door, the air flow can then be directed from the **PANEL**, **BI-LEVEL** (panel and floor), and **FLOOR-DEFROST** outlets. Air flow velocity can be adjusted with the blower speed selector switch on the control head.

Ambient air intake can be shut off by closing the recirculating air door. This will recirculate the air that is already inside the vehicle. This is done by rotating the knob on the control head. Rotating the control knob to the **DEFROST/FLOOR** or **DEFROST** setting on the control head will engage the compressor. This will send refrigerant through the evaporator, and remove heat and humidity from the air before it goes through the heater core. The compressor can also be engaged by depressing the **A/C** button on the control head (with the fan **ON**).

NOTE: These models use non-CFC refrigerant R-134a in the A/C system. This refrigerant, its corresponding oil and components cannot be intermixed with R-12 in any amounts. Therefore, do not use the same service equipment (recycling/recharging stations, manifold gauge sets, leak detectors, etc.) or components interchangeably. Check equipment manufacturers specifications before using any test equipment on an R-134a system.

Service Valve Location

Summit, Laser and Talon

The suction (low pressure) port is located on the compressor itself. The discharge (high pressure) port is located on the discharge line at the left front corner of the engine compartment.

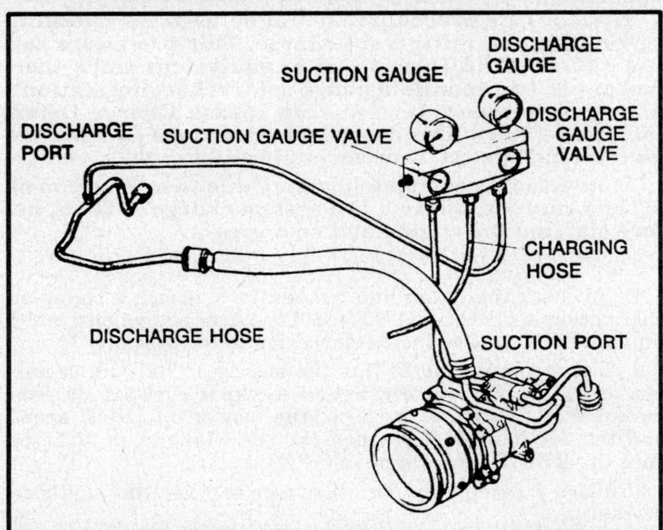

Service valve locations—Summit, Laser and Talon similar

Stealth

The high pressure service port is located on the high pressure line near the compressor. The low pressure service port is located on the accumulator, under the cycling pressure switch.

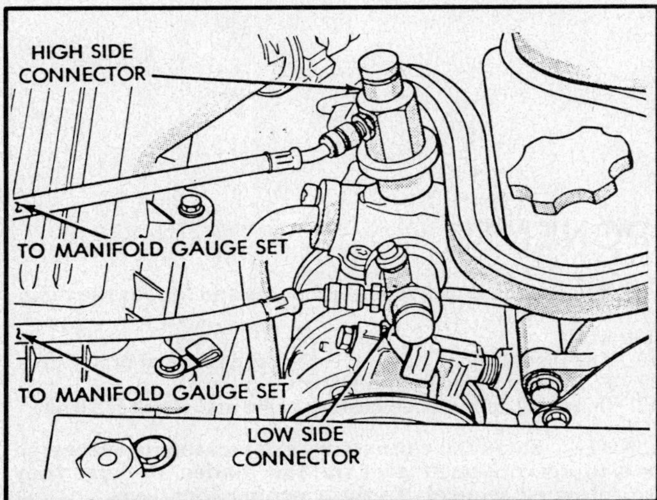

Service valve locations and manifold gauge hook-up—Concorde, Intrepid, LHS, New Yorker and Vision

Summit Wagon

The high pressure (discharge) service valve is located on the high pressure line near the receiver/drier. The low pressure (suction) service valve is located on the compressor.

Concorde, Intrepid, LHS, New Yorker and Vision

Both the high and low side service valves are located on the compressor. This system uses R-134a refrigerant and corresponding oil. Different service valves are used on this system to prevent hook-up of R-12 service equipment.

Avenger and Sebring

The low pressure (suction) service valve is located in the refrigerant line suction hose.

Cirrus and Stratus

Both of the service ports to charge the air conditioning system are located on the hoses. New design of service ports is used to ensure that the system is not accidentally filled with the wrong refrigerant (R-12).

System Discharging

R-12 Systems

The R-12 refrigerant is a chloroflourocarbon which, when mishandled, can contribute to the depletion of the ozone layer in the upper atmosphere. Ozone filters out harmful radiation from the sun. In order to protect the ozone layer, an approved R-12 recovery/recycling machine that meets SAE standard J1991 should be employed when discharging the system. Follow the operating instructions provided with the approved equipment exactly to properly discharge the system.

NOTE: To access the low pressure service port on the Stealth, disconnect the cycling pressure switch connector and unscrew the switch from the port.

R-134a Systems

The R-134a refrigerant is a non-chloroflourocarbon with different chemical characteristics than R-12. Although it is designed to be less hazardous to the ozone layer of the atmosphere, it should still be discharged only into a recycling type machine and not vented to the atmosphere. Follow equipment manufacturer's instructions for this system. Use only dedicated equipment for R-134a systems.

CAUTION

Avoid breathing R-134a vapors, as it can cause irritation. Never pressure test or leak test R-134a service equipment with compressed air. Some mixtures of air and R-134a have been shown to be combustible, especially at higher pressures. Such a mixture may result in fire or explosion. Use appropriate cautions.

System Evacuating

If the air conditioning system has been opened to the atmosphere, it should be air and moisture free before being recharged with refrigerant. Moisture and air mixed with refrigerant will raise the compressor head pressure, possibly damage the system's components and will reduce the performance of the system. Moisture will boil at normal room temperature when exposed to a vacuum. To evacuate, or rid the system of air and moisture:

1. Leak test the system and repair any leaks found.
2. Connect an approved charging station, recovery/recycling machine or manifold gauge set and vacuum pump to the discharge and suction ports. The red hose is normally connected to the discharge (high pressure) line, and the blue hose is connected to the suction (low pressure) line.
3. Open the discharge and suction ports and start the vacuum pump. If the pump is not able to pull at least 26 in. Hg of vacuum on R-12 system or 28 in. Hg on R-134a systems, there is a leak that must be repaired before evacuation can occur.
4. Once the system has reached at least 26-28 in. Hg of vacuum, allow the system to evacuate for at least 15 minutes. The longer the system is evacuated, the more contaminants will be removed.
5. Close all valves and turn the pump OFF. If the system loses more than 2 in. Hg of vacuum after 10 minutes, there is a leak that should be repaired.

System Charging

R-12 Systems

1. Connect an approved charging station, recovery/recycling machine or manifold gauge set to the discharge and suction ports. The red hose is normally connected to the discharge (high pressure) line, and the blue hose is connected to the suction (low pressure) line.
2. Follow the instructions provided with the equipment and charge the system with the specified amount of refrigerant.
3. Perform a leak test.

R-134a Systems

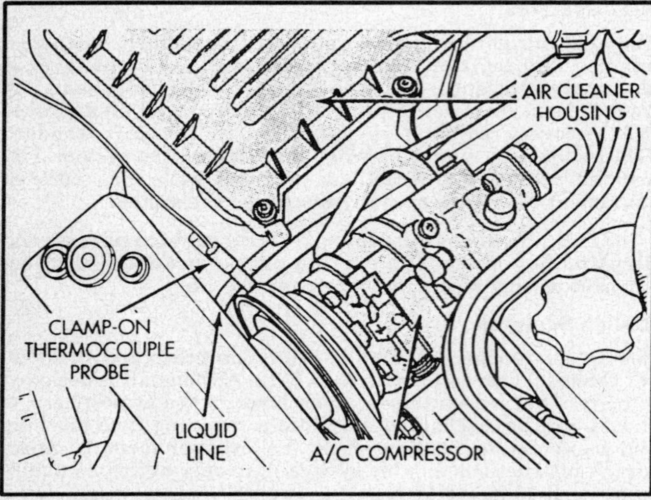

Thermocouple attachment point for system checking—Concorde, Intrepid and Vision

NOTE: This procedure should be used for checking or refilling the refrigerant charge. This procedure can use either a DRB II scan tool or equivalent and a thermocouple, or a manifold gauge set (recharging station), a special thermocouple, and an R-134a Charge Determination Chart. The described procedure is with the manifold gauge set, thermocouple and graph.

If system was completely empty due to evacuation or system rupture, put in a full system charge of 28 oz. before starting the engine and compressor.

1. To check the liquid line temperature, attach a clamp-on thermocouple PSE 66-324-0014, 80PK-1A, or equivalent, to the liquid line as close to the condenser outlet as possible.
2. Put the vehicle in **P**. Run the engine at 700 rpm at normal operating temperature. Set air intake to **FRESH** air, temperature at COLDEST position, the blower on **HIGH** speed and the **A/C** button **ON**. Open the car windows. If ATC, be sure the **RECIRC** operation is **OFF**.
3. Place a cover over the condenser to raise the high side pressure.
4. Observe the discharge pressure and the liquid line temperature. Refer to the R-134a Charge Determination Chart to determine the current operating status.
5. Adjust (add or reclaim) the system charge in 2 oz. increments until proper system charge is determined.
6. Remove the condenser cover and detach equipment and thermocouple.

SYSTEM COMPONENTS

Radiator

REMOVAL AND INSTALLATION

Laser, Talon, Stealth, Summit and Summit Wagon, Avenger and Sebring

1. Disconnect the negative battery cable.
2. Drain the cooling system.

NOTE: Turbocharged engines may have air intake ducting which interferes with access to the radiator and fan components. Remove this as necessary before proceeding.

3. Disconnect the overflow tube. If necessary, remove the overflow tank.
4. Disconnect upper and lower radiator hoses.
5. Disconnect the electrical connectors for the water level switch, cooling fan and air conditioning condenser fan, as equipped.
6. Disconnect thermo sensor wires.
7. Disconnect and plug automatic transmission cooler lines, if equipped.
8. On Stealth, remove the cooling fan assemblies before taking out the radiator.
9. Remove the upper radiator mounts and lift out the radiator/fan assembly.

To install:

10. The installation is the reverse of the removal procedures.
11. Fill the radiator with coolant.
12. Connect the negative battery cable and check for leaks.

NOTE: Some fan connectors are located in a recessed area to keep them free of the fan blades. Be sure they are returned securely to their proper locations.

Concorde, Intrepid, LHS, New Yorker, and Vision

1. Disconnect the negative battery cable.
2. Properly drain the cooling system.
3. For LHS and New Yorker, remove the sight shield and the right and left head lamp modules.
4. For LHS and New Yorker, properly discharge the A/C system.
5. Remove the upper radiator crossmember.
6. Remove the hose clamps and hoses from the radiator.
7. Disconnect the automatic transmission hoses from the cooler and plug off.
8. Disconnect the fan wiring connector from the RFI module.
9. Remove the upper radiator mounting screws.
10. Disconnect the engine block heater wire if equipped.

CHARGE DETERMINATION GRAPH—R-134a SYSTEMS

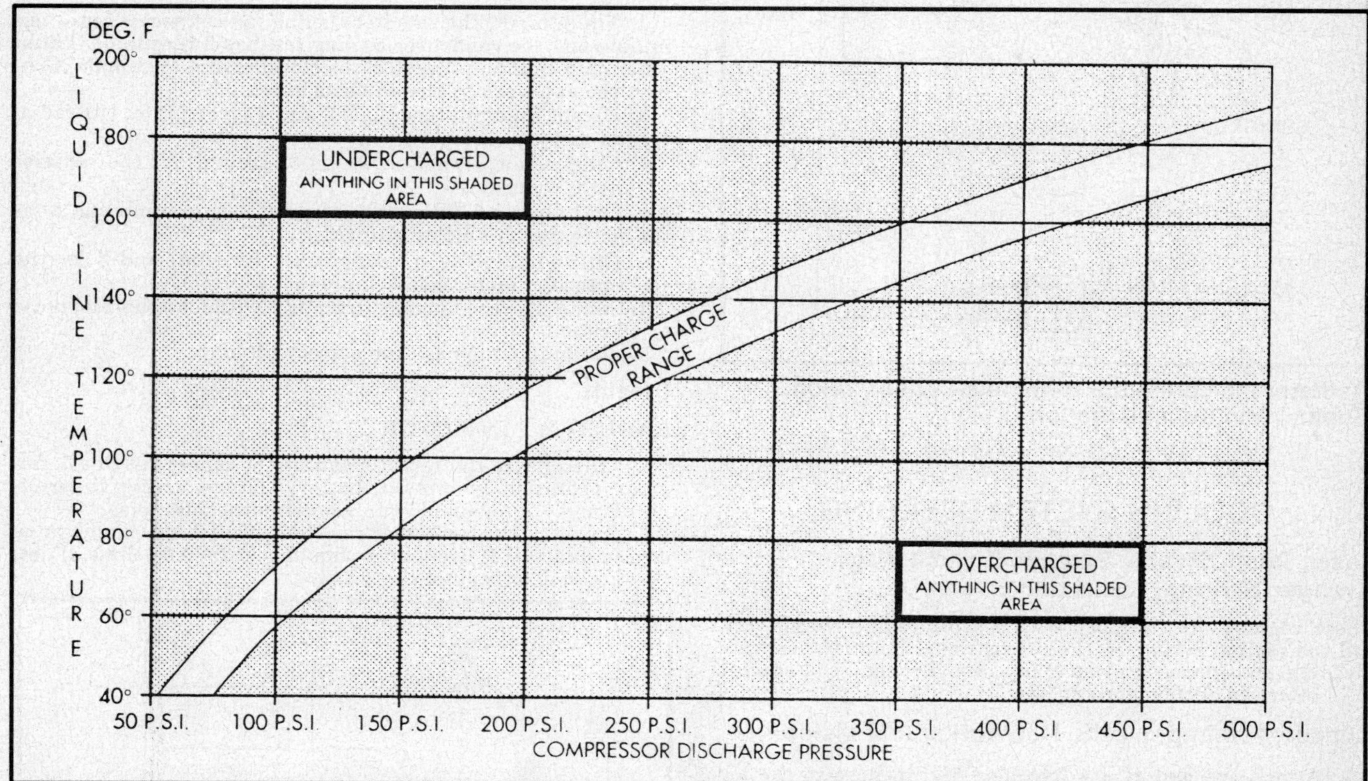

11. Remove the air conditioning condenser attaching screws located at the front of the radiator. Lean the condenser forward against the bumper. Avoid bending the condenser inlet tube. On LHS and New Yorker, the condenser cannot be separated from the radiator in the vehicle. The entire module must be removed.
12. Remove the radiator from the engine compartment. Use care not to damage radiator cooling fins or water tubes during removal.
13. Installation is the reverse of the removal procedure.

Cirrus and Stratus

1. Disconnect the negative battery cable.
2. Remove the air inlet resonator.
3. Drain the cooling system.
4. Remove the upper radiator crossmember.
5. Remove the hose clamps and hoses from the radiator.
6. Disconnect the engine block heater wire, if equipped.
7. Disconnect the automatic transmission hoses from the cooler and plug off.
8. Disconnect the fan wiring connector.
9. Remove the air conditioning condenser attaching screws located at the front of the radiator. It is not necessary to discharge the air conditioning system to remove the radiator.
10. Lift the radiator free from the engine compartment. Use care not to damage the radiator cooling fins or water tubes during removal.

To install:

11. The installation is the reverse of the removal procedures.
12. Fill the radiator with coolant and check for leaks.

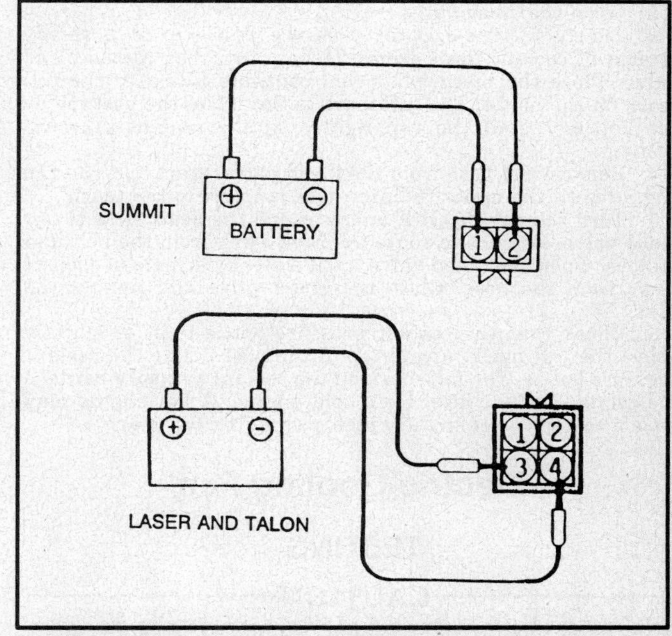

Condenser fan connector terminals—Laser, Talon and Summit

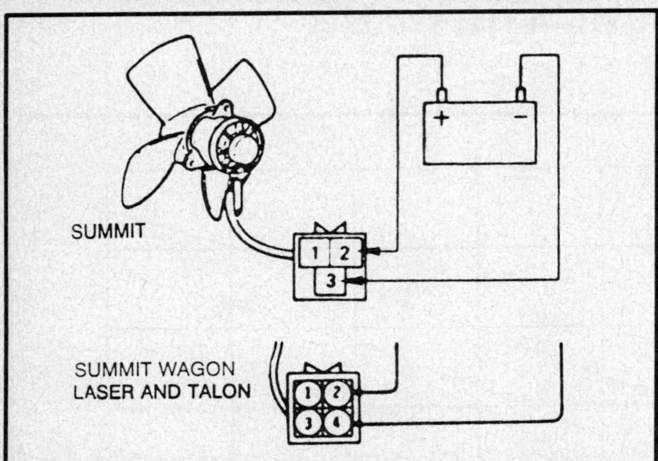

Radiator fan connector terminals—Laser, Talon, Summit and Summit Wagon

COOLING SYSTEM BLEEDING

Laser, Talon, Stealth, Summit, Summit Wagon, Avenger, Sebring, Cirrus and Stratus

These vehicles are equipped with a self-bleeding thermostat. Fill the cooling system in the conventional manner; separate bleeding procedures are not necessary. Recheck the coolant level after the vehicle and cooled.

Concorde, Intrepid, LHS, New Yorker and Vision

1. Attach one end of a 4 foot long 1/4 in. hose to the air bleed on the thermostat housing. Carefully route the hose away from the drive belt and pulleys. Place the other end of the hose in a clean container. The purpose of this hose is to keep coolant away from the belt and pulleys.
2. Open the bleed valve.
3. Slowly fill the coolant pressure bottle until a steady stream of coolant flows from the hose attached to the bleed valve. Close the bleed valve and continue filling to the full mark on the bottle. The full mark is the top of the post inside the bottle. Install the cap tightly on the coolant pressure bottle.
4. Remove the hose from the bleed valve, start and run the engine until the upper radiator hose is warm to the touch.
5. Turn the engine **OFF** and reattach the drain hose to the bleed valve. Be sure to route the hose away from the belt and pulleys. Open the bleed valve until a steady stream of coolant flows from the hose. Close the bleed valve and remove the hose.
6. Check that the coolant pressure bottle is at or slightly above the full mark, at the top of the post inside the coolant pressure bottle. The full mark on the coolant pressure bottle is the correct coolant level for a cold engine. A hot engine may have a coolant level slightly higher than the full mark.

Electric Cooling Fan

TESTING

CAUTION

Make sure the key is in the OFF position when checking the electric cooling fan. If not, the fan could turn ON at any time, causing serious personal injury.

Laser, Talon, Summit and Summit Wagon

1. Disconnect the negative battery cable.
2. Disconnect the electrical plug from the fan motor harness.
3. On Summit, the radiator cooling fan connector has 3 terminals and the condenser cooling fan has 2 terminals. Laser, Talon and Summit Wagon connectors have 4 terminals. Connect the appropriate terminals as shown:
   - Except Summit, terminals **2** and **4** (ground) for the radiator fan motor connector
   - On Summit, terminals **2** and **3** (ground) for the radiator fan motor connector.
   - On Laser and Talon only, terminals **1** (ground) and **2** for the condenser fan motor connector
   - On Summit Wagon, terminals **1** (ground) and **3** for the condenser fan motor connector.
4. Make sure the fan runs smoothly, without abnormal noise or vibration.
5. Reconnect the negative battery cable.

Stealth

RADIATOR FAN MOTOR

1. Disconnect the radiator fan motor connector. Check fan motor operation by applying battery voltage directly to terminals **2** and **4**. Fan should run smoothly without noise.
2. To check the fan motor resistor, connect an ohmmeter to terminals **1** and **3**. Resistance should be 0.29–0.35 ohms. If not, check wiring or replace the resistor.

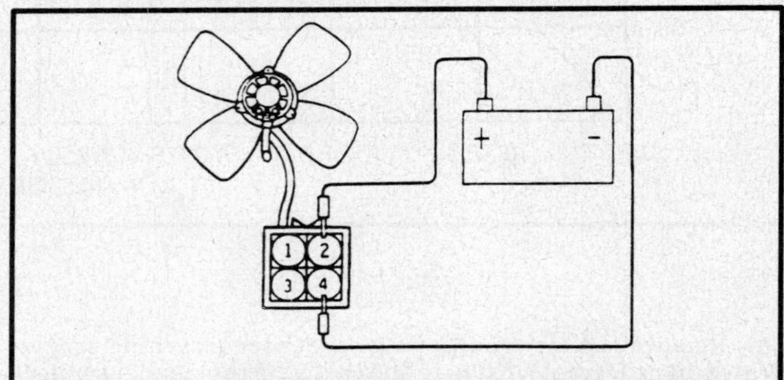

Radiator fan connector terminals—Stealth

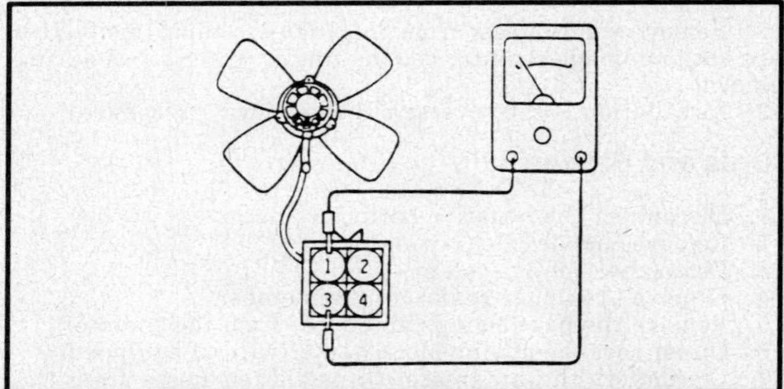

Radiator fan resistor check—Stealth

CONDENSER FAN MOTOR

1. Disconnect the condenser fan motor dual connectors. Apply battery voltage to terminals **3** and **4** (ground). Condenser fan motor should turn without noise or vibration.
2. Now, apply battery voltage to terminals **1** and **2** (ground). Again, condenser fan motor should turn without noise or vibration.

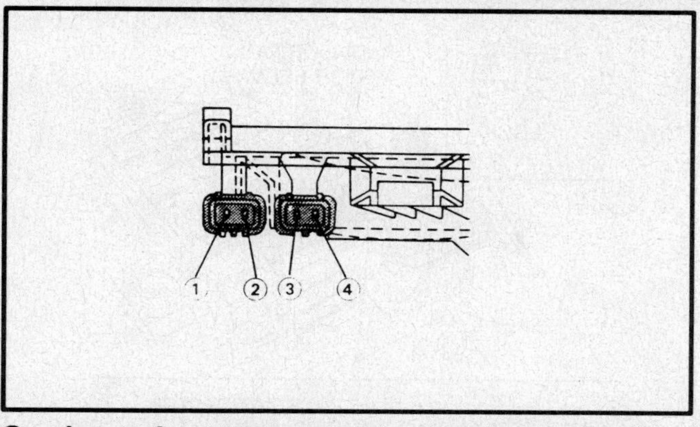

Condenser fan motor connector terminals—Stealth

COOLING FAN TEMPERATURE SWITCH

1. Turn ignition switch to **RUN**. Connect a jumper wire between coolant temperature switch terminals **A** and **B**. The cooling fan should operate.
2. If the cooling fan operates, replace the cooling fan temperature switch.
3. Remove switch and immerse the sensor end in an oil bath. As oil is heated, and with ohmmeter attached to terminals, switch should be OFF when temperature is at or below normal operating temperature:
   - On Laser, Talon, and Stealth, about 234°F (112°C).
   - On Summit and Summit Wagon, about 171°F (77°C).
4. If the cooling fan does not operate, check the cooling fan relay.

COOLING FAN RELAY

1. Remove the radiator fan motor relay and connect direct voltage and an ohmmeter.
2. Compare results to "RADIATOR FAN MOTOR RELAY CONTINUITY CHART."

Avenger and Sebring

RADIATOR FAN MOTOR

1. Disconnect the radiator fan motor connector.
2. For DOHC engine with manual transmission, apply battery voltage between terminals **1** and **2** (ground). Fan should run smoothly without noise.
3. For DOHC engine with automatic transmission or SOHC engine, apply battery voltage between terminals **1** and **2** (ground) or **3** and **4** (ground). The fan should run smoothly without noise.

CONDENSER FAN MOTOR

1. Disconnect the condenser fan motor connector.
2. Apply battery voltage between terminals **1** and **4** (ground). The fan should run smoothly without noise.
3. In this same condition, apply battery voltage between terminal **3** and **2** (ground). Check that the condenser fan motor operates faster at this time.

Cirrus and Stratus

RADIATOR FAN MOTOR

1. Disconnect the radiator fan motor connector.
2. Apply battery voltage to terminals **2** and **3** (ground). The low speed radiator fan motor should run smoothly without noise.
3. Apply battery voltage to terminals **1** and **3** (ground). The high speed radiator fan motor should run smoothly without noise.

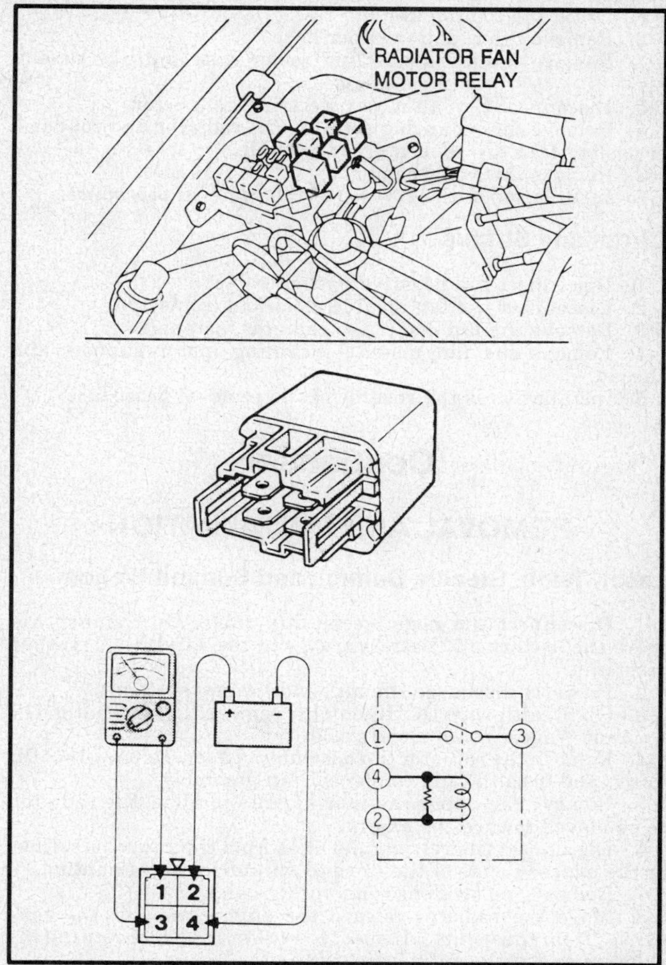

Checking radiator fan motor relay—Laser and Talon

REMOVAL AND INSTALLATION

Laser, Talon, Stealth, Summit and Summit Wagon

1. Disconnect the negative battery cable. Properly drain the cooling system if removing the upper radiator hose.
2. Unplug the fan motor connector. Remove the upper radiator hose if necessary.
3. Remove the mounting screws. The radiator and condenser cooling fans are separately removable.
4. Remove the fan assembly.

To install:

5. The installation is the reverse of the removal procedure.
6. Check the coolant level and refill as required.
7. Connect the negative battery cable and check the fan for proper operation.

Concorde, Intrepid, LHS, New Yorker and Vision

1. Disconnect the negative battery cable.
2. Disconnect the electric lead to the RFI module.
3. Remove the fan module to radiator fasteners and retaining clips.
4. Remove the fan module assembly from the radiator.
5. Installation is the reverse of the removal procedure.

Avenger and Sebring

1. Disconnect the negative battery cable.

2. Drain the cooling system.
3. Remove the radiator upper hose.
4. Remove the transaxle fluid cooler hose and pipe assembly.
5. Disconnect the fan motor electrical connector.
6. Remove the mounting screws. The radiator and condenser cooling fans are separately removable.
7. Remove the fan assembly.
8. Installation is the reverse of the removal procedure.

Cirrus and Stratus

1. Disconnect the negative battery cable.
2. Disconnect the fan module electrical connector.
3. Remove the fan module to radiator fasteners.
4. Remove the fan module including motor support and shroud.
5. Installation is the reverse of the removal procedure.

Condenser

REMOVAL AND INSTALLATION

Laser, Talon, Stealth, Summit and Summit Wagon

1. Disconnect the negative battery cable. On Summit, remove the battery and battery tray, and the windshield washer reservoir.
2. Properly discharge the air conditioning system.
3. On Stealth with DOHC engine, remove the alternator. On Summit Wagon, remove the grille.
4. Remove the radiator fan assembly (Laser, Talon with 2.0L Turbo and Stealth) and condenser fan assembly.
5. Remove the upper radiator mounts to allow the radiator to be moved toward the engine.
6. Disconnect the refrigerant lines from the condenser. Cover the exposed ends of the lines to minimize contamination.
7. Remove the condenser mounting bolts.
8. Move the radiator toward the engine and lift the condenser from the vehicle. Inspect the lower rubber mounting insulators and replace if necessary.

To install:

9. Lower the condenser into position and align the dowels with the lower mounting insulators. Install the bolts.
10. Using new O-rings, connect the refrigerant lines.
11. Install the radiator mounts and cooling fans.
12. Install the grille, alternator, windshield washer reservoir, battery tray and battery, if removed.
13. Evacuate and recharge the air conditioning system. Add 2 oz. of refrigerant oil during the recharge.
14. Connect the negative battery cable and check the entire climate control system for proper operation. Check the system for leaks.

Concorde, Intrepid and Vision

1. Disconnect the negative battery cable. Properly discharge the air conditioning system, using R-134a equipment.
2. Disconnect and plug the refrigerant lines from the condenser.
3. Remove the condenser mounting bolts. Unscrew the nut at the receiver/drier bracket. Spread the bracket and remove the receiver/drier.
4. Lift the condenser out of the vehicle.
5. Installation is the reverse of the removal procedure. Add 1.0 oz. of R-134a refrigerant extra during recharge.

LHS and New Yorker

1. Disconnect the negative battery cable.
2. Remove the sight shield and the right and left headlamp modules.

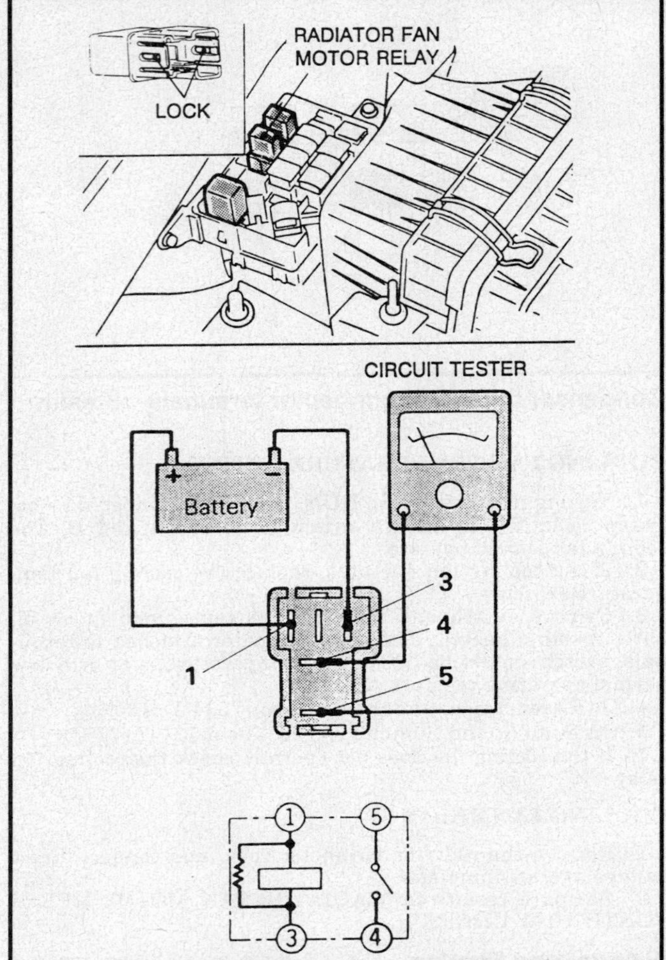

Checking radiator fan motor relay—Summit

3. Drain the engine cooling system.
4. Remove the refrigerant from the A/C system using a recovery machine.
5. Disconnect and cap the A/C lines at the condenser.
6. Remove the upper radiator crossmember.
7. Remove the hose clamps and hoses from the radiator.
8. Disconnect the automatic transaxle cooler line hoses from the cooler. Temporarily plug the cooler lines after removal.
9. Disconnect the fan wiring connector from the RFI module.
10. Remove the upper radiator mounting screws to the body. Access to the mounting screws can be obtained through the hole in the headlamp module bracket.
11. Lift entire cooling module (radiator and condenser) from the vehicle.
12. Installation is the reverse of the removal procedure.

Avenger and Sebring

1. Disconnect the negative battery cable.
2. Properly discharge the air conditioning system.
3. Remove the radiator fan motor assembly.
4. Remove the condenser fan motor and shroud assembly.
5. Remove the upper insulator installation bolts.
6. Disconnect and plug the refrigerant lines from the condenser.
7. Move the radiator to the engine side and lift the condenser from the vehicle.
8. Installation is the reverse of the removal procedure.

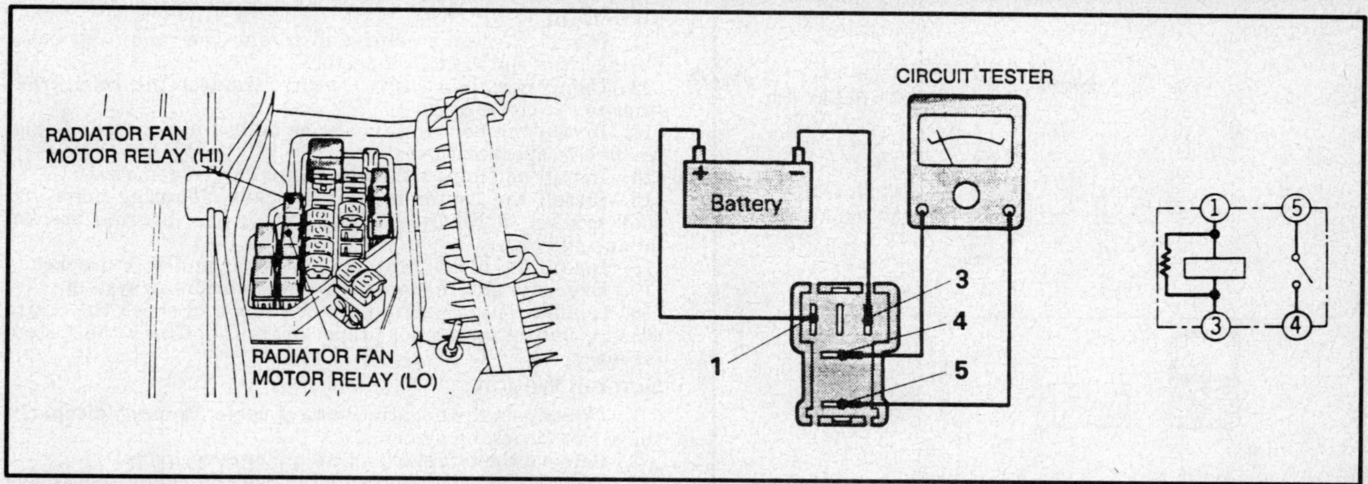

Checking radiator fan motor relay—Summit Wagon

RADIATOR FAN MOTOR RELAY CONTINUITY CHART

Laser and Talon		
When current is flowing	Between terminals 2 and 4	Continuity
When current is not flowing	Between terminals 1 and 3	No continuity
When current is not flowing	Between terminals 2 and 4	No continuity
Summit and Summit Wagon		
When current is flowing	Between terminals 4 and 5	Continuity
When current is not flowing	Between terminals 1 and 3	No continuity
When current is not flowing	Between terminals 4 and 5	No continuity
Stealth		
When current is flowing	Between terminals 1 and 3	Continuity
When current is not flowing	Between terminals 1 and 3	No continuity
When current is not flowing	Between terminals 2 and 4	No continuity

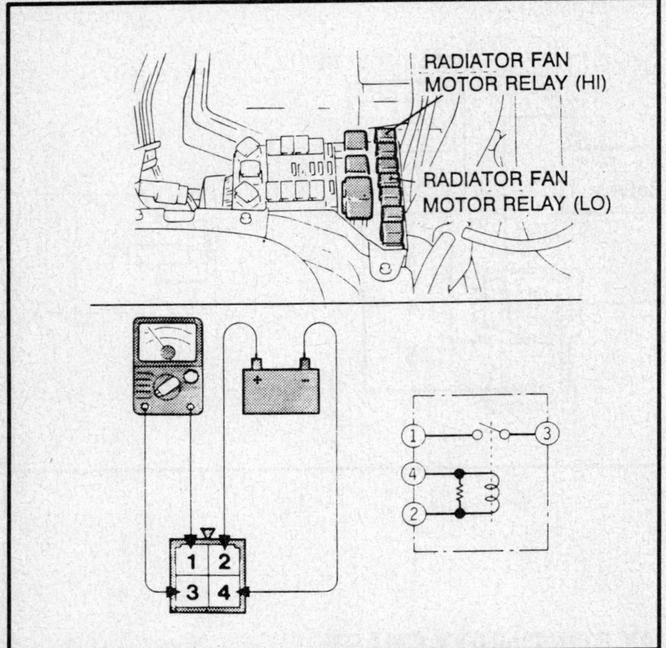

Condenser radiator fan motor relay—Stealth

Cirrus and Stratus

1. Disconnect the negative battery cable.
2. Properly discharge the air conditioning system.
3. Disconnect and cap the refrigerant lines at the condenser.
4. Remove the grille retainers.
5. Remove the upper radiator support crossmember.
6. Remove the condenser lines. Use special tool kit 7193 for quick disconnect couplers.
7. Remove the radiator fan module mounts.
8. Remove the condenser line support bracket.
9. Remove the condenser mounting bolts.
10. Lift the condenser from the vehicle.
11. Installation is the reverse of the removal procedure.

Compressor

REMOVAL AND INSTALLATION

Laser, Talon, Summit, Stealth, Concorde, Intrepid, Vision, Avenger, Sebring, LHS and New Yorker

1. Disconnect the negative battery cable.
2. Properly discharge the air conditioning system.
3. On some applications, removal of the distributor cap and wires may be required for clearance.
4. On Laser and Talon with turbocharged engine, remove the VSV bracket on the cowl top.
5. On Talon with AWD, remove the center bearing bracket mounting bolts.
6. If the alternator is in front of the compressor belt, remove it.
7. If equipped, remove the tensioner pulley assembly.
8. Remove the compressor drive belt. Disconnect the clutch coil connector.
9. Disconnect the refrigerant lines from the compressor and discard the O-rings. Cover the exposed ends of the lines to minimize contamination.
10. Remove the compressor mounting bolts and the compressor.

To install:

11. Install the compressor and torque the mounting bolts. Connect the clutch coil connector.
12. Using new lubricated O-rings, connect the refrigerant lines to the compressor.
13. Install the belt and tensioner pulley, if removed. Adjust the belt to specifications.
14. Install and adjust the alternator belt, if removed.
15. Install the center bearing bracket mounting bolts and VSV bracket, if removed. Torque the center bearing bracket mounting bolts.
16. Install the distributor cap and wires and VSV bracket.
17. Evacuate and recharge the air conditioning system.
18. Connect the negative battery cable and check the entire climate control system for proper operation. Check the system for leaks.

Summit Wagon

1. Disconnect the negative battery cable. Properly discharge the air conditioning system.
2. Remove the left side engine under cover panel.
3. Loosen the tensioner and remove the compressor drive belt.
4. Disconnect and plug the refrigerant lines from the compressor.
5. Remove the electrical connections from the compressor.
6. Remove the mounting bolts and take out the compressor.
7. Installation is the reverse of the removal procedure. Adjust the compressor oil level.

Cirrus and Stratus

1. Disconnect the negative battery cable.
2. Loosen and remove the drive belt.
3. Disconnect the compressor clutch wire lead.
4. Properly discharge the air conditioning system.
5. Remove the refrigerant lines from the compressor.
6. Remove the compressor mounting bolts and the compressor.
7. Installation is the reverse of the removal procedure.

Receiver/Drier

REMOVAL AND INSTALLATION

The receiver/drier is located at the left side of the engine compartment on Cirrus, Stratus, Stealth, Summit and Summit Wagon, and forward of the condenser on the Laser, Talon, Concorde, Intrepid, Vision, Avenger, Sebring, LHS and New Yorker.

1. Disconnect the negative battery cable.
2. Properly discharge the air conditioning system.
3. Disconnect the electrical connector from the switch on the receiver/drier, if equipped.
4. Disconnect the refrigerant lines from the receiver/drier assembly. Discard the O-rings. Cover the exposed ends of the lines to minimize contamination.
5. On Concorde, Intrepid and Vision, remove the condenser bolt and the receiver/drier nut.
6. Open or remove the mounting strap and the receiver/drier from its bracket.

To install:

7. The installation is the reverse of the removal procedures. Use new lubricated O-rings when assembling.
8. Evacuate and recharge the air conditioning system. Add 1 oz. of refrigerant oil during the recharge.
9. Connect the negative battery cable and check the entire climate control system for proper operation. Check the system for leaks.

Expansion Valve

REMOVAL AND INSTALLATION

Laser, Talon, Stealth, Summit, Summit Wagon, Avenger and Sebring

1. Disconnect the negative battery cable.

2. Properly discharge the air conditioning system.
3. Remove the evaporator housing and separate the upper and lower cases.
4. Remove the expansion valve from the evaporator lines.
5. The installation is the reverse of the removal procedures. Use new lubricated O-rings when assembling.
6. Evacuate and recharge the air conditioning system.
7. Connect the negative battery cable and check the entire climate control system for proper operation. Check the system for leaks.

Concorde, Intrepid, LHS, New Yorker and Vision

1. Properly discharge the air conditioning system, using a recovery machine.
2. Remove the engine air inlet tube and the air distribution duct for 3.5L engines.
3. Disconnect the refrigerant lines from the expansion valve. Plug the lines to prevent contamination.
4. Remove 2 retaining bolts and remove the valve and gasket.
5. Installation is the reverse of the removal procedure, using a new gasket. Evacuate, recharge and leak test the system.

Cirrus and Stratus

The expansion valve is located on the engine side of the dash panel, near the right shock tower.

1. Disconnect the negative battery cable.
2. Properly discharge the air conditioning system.
3. Disconnect the clips from the expansion valve lines.
4. Using special tool kit 7193, disconnect the quick connectors on the expansion valve.
5. Remove the lines at the expansion valve.
6. Remove 2 retaining bolts from the expansion valve.
7. Remove the expansion valve and gasket.
8. Installation is the reverse of the removal procedure. Use a new gasket when replacing the expansion valve.

Blower Motor

REMOVAL AND INSTALLATION

Summit

1. Disconnect the negative battery cable. Remove the under cover below the glove box.
2. Remove the glove box, right speaker cover and the glove box cross support.

NOTE: At this point the blower motor only may be removed after the resistor is removed and the blower motor screws are removed. Otherwise, the rest of this procedure will remove the complete blower housing assembly.

3. If heater only, remove duct between heater housing and blower housing. If air conditioning, remove nut attaching blower housing to the evaporator housing.
4. Detach the air door cable. Remove the right kick panel.
5. Remove the engine control module. Remove the bracket below the ECM. Remove the blower assembly.
6. Installation is the reverse of the removal procedure. Adjust the fresh/recirc air door cable.

Laser and Talon

1. Disconnect battery negative cable.
2. Remove the right side duct, if equipped.
3. Remove the molded hose from the blower assembly.
4. Remove the blower motor assembly.
5. Remove the packing seal.
6. Remove the fan retaining nut and fan in order to renew the motor.

To install:

7. Check that the blower motor shaft is not bent and that the packing is in good condition. Clean all parts of dust, etc.
8. Assemble the motor and fan. Install the blower motor then connect the motor terminals to battery voltage. Check that the blower motor operates smoothly. Then, reverse the polarity and check that the blower motor operates smoothly in the reverse direction.
9. Install the molded hose and duct, if removed.
10. Connect the negative battery cable and check the entire climate control system for proper operation.

Summit Wagon

1. Disconnect the negative battery cable.
2. Remove the lap heater duct.
3. Remove the glove box assembly.
4. Remove the blower resistor, the right speaker cover and the glove box frame.
5. Remove the electrical connection, the retaining screws and lower the blower motor out of its housing.
6. Installation is the reverse of the removal procedure.

Stealth

1. Disconnect the negative battery cable. Remove the glove box assembly.
2. Remove the under cover below the glove box and the horizontal frame piece.
3. Remove the evaporator to blower housing nut, if equipped with A/C.
4. Detach the fresh/recirc door cable from the blower housing.
5. Remove the side frame.
6. Remove the electrical connection, the retaining nuts and remove the blower assembly, or remove the blower motor screws and take out only the blower motor.
7. Installation is the reverse of the removal procedure. Adjust the fresh/recirc door cable.

Concorde, Intrepid, LHS, New Yorker, Vision, Cirrus and Stratus

1. Disconnect the negative battery cable. Remove the lower right under panel silencer duct. Remove the electric connector from the resistor block.
2. Remove the blower motor housing cover.
3. Remove the blower motor retaining screws and lower the blower motor out of the housing.
4. Installation is the reverse of the removal procedure.

Avenger and Sebring

1. Disconnect the negative battery cable.
2. Remove the blower motor housing cover.
3. Remove the electrical connectors.
4. Remove the automatic compressor ECU (vehicles with air conditioning).
5. Remove the retaining screws and lower the blower motor out of its housing.
6. Installation is the reverse of the removal procedure.

Blower Motor Resistor

REMOVAL AND INSTALLATION

Laser, Talon, Stealth, Summit and Summit Wagon

1. Disconnect the negative battery cable.
2. Remove the glove box assembly. The resistor is mounted on the left side of the glove box opening.
3. Disconnect the wire harness from the resistor.

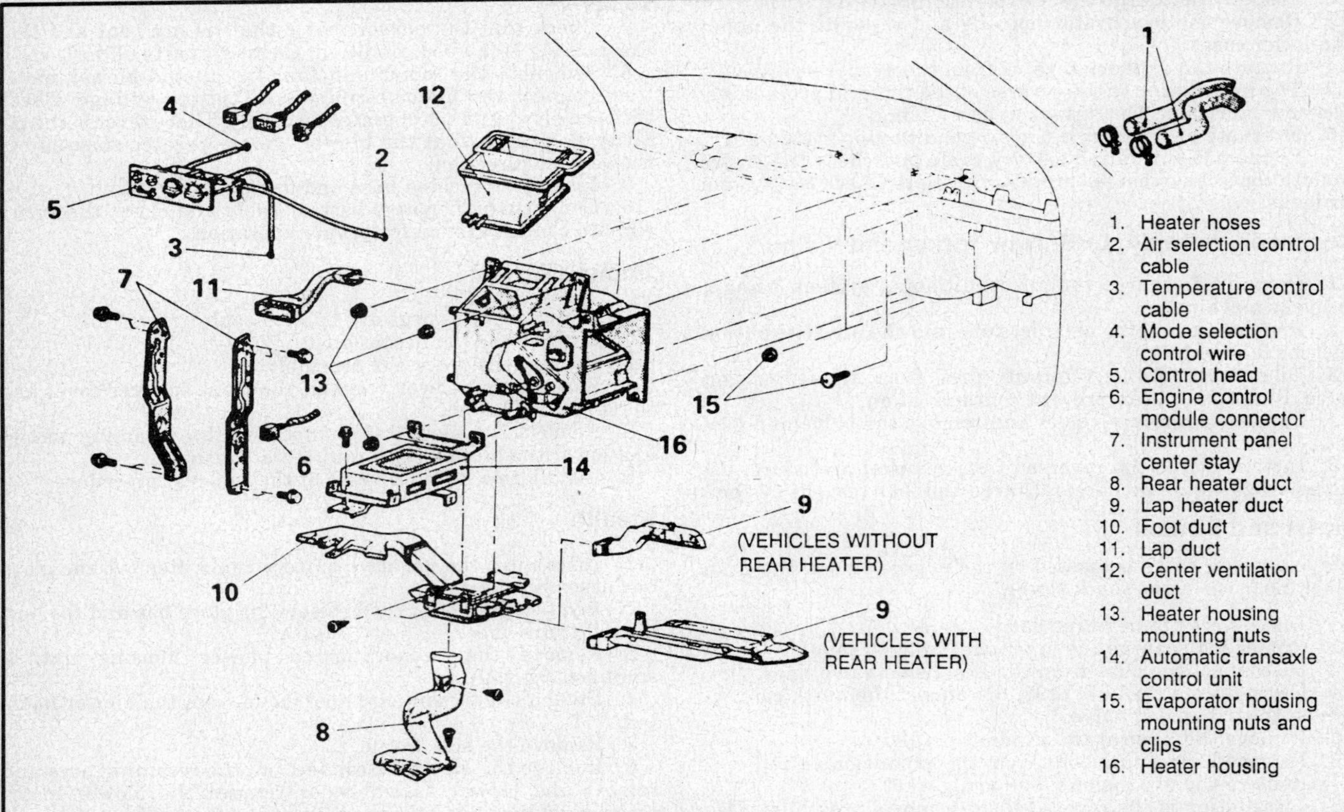

Heater core housing and related parts—Summit

4. Remove the mounting screws and the resistor.

NOTE: On Stealth with DOHC engine, the belt lock controller, mounted on the under cover, is in the same circuit with the resistor and may need testing or replacement at this time.

5. The installation is the reverse of the removal procedure.
6. Connect the negative battery cable and check the entire climate control system for proper operation.

Concorde, Intrepid, LHS, New Yorker, Vision, Cirrus and Stratus

1. Disconnect the negative battery cable. Remove the right under panel silencer duct.
2. Disconnect the blower motor resistor electrical connector.
3. Remove the resistor from the blower motor housing.
4. Installation is the reverse of the removal procedure.

Avenger and Sebring

1. Disconnect the negative battery cable.
2. Remove the glove box stoppers and lower the glove box assembly to gain access to the blower motor resistor.
3. Disconnect the blower motor resistor electrical connector.
4. Remove the mounting screws and the resistor.
5. Installation is the reverse of the removal procedure.

Heater Core and Evaporator

REMOVAL AND INSTALLATION

Summit

HEATER CORE

1. Disconnect the negative battery cable. Properly drain the cooling system.
2. Remove the instrument panel as follows:
   - Remove the floor console.
   - Remove the knee panel below the steering column.
   - Remove the sunglass pocket, steering column cover and instrument cluster bezel.
   - Remove the instrument cluster, disconnecting speedometer cable and electrical connections when cluster is pulled out.
   - Remove the remote control mirror switch, rheostat or plug.
   - Remove the coin box or rear wiper switch.
   - The air outlet panel from the left side and the ashtray from the center panel.
   - Detach the air bypass cable from the lever on the heater unit. Remove the center panel bezel and air outlet assembly.
   - Remove the radio and cup holder.
   - Remove the under cover beneath the glove box, then remove the glove box and the right speaker cover (corner panel).
   - Remove the climate control panel, disconnecting electrical connectors and cables.
   - Remove both panel speakers, then take out the left and right defroster grilles.

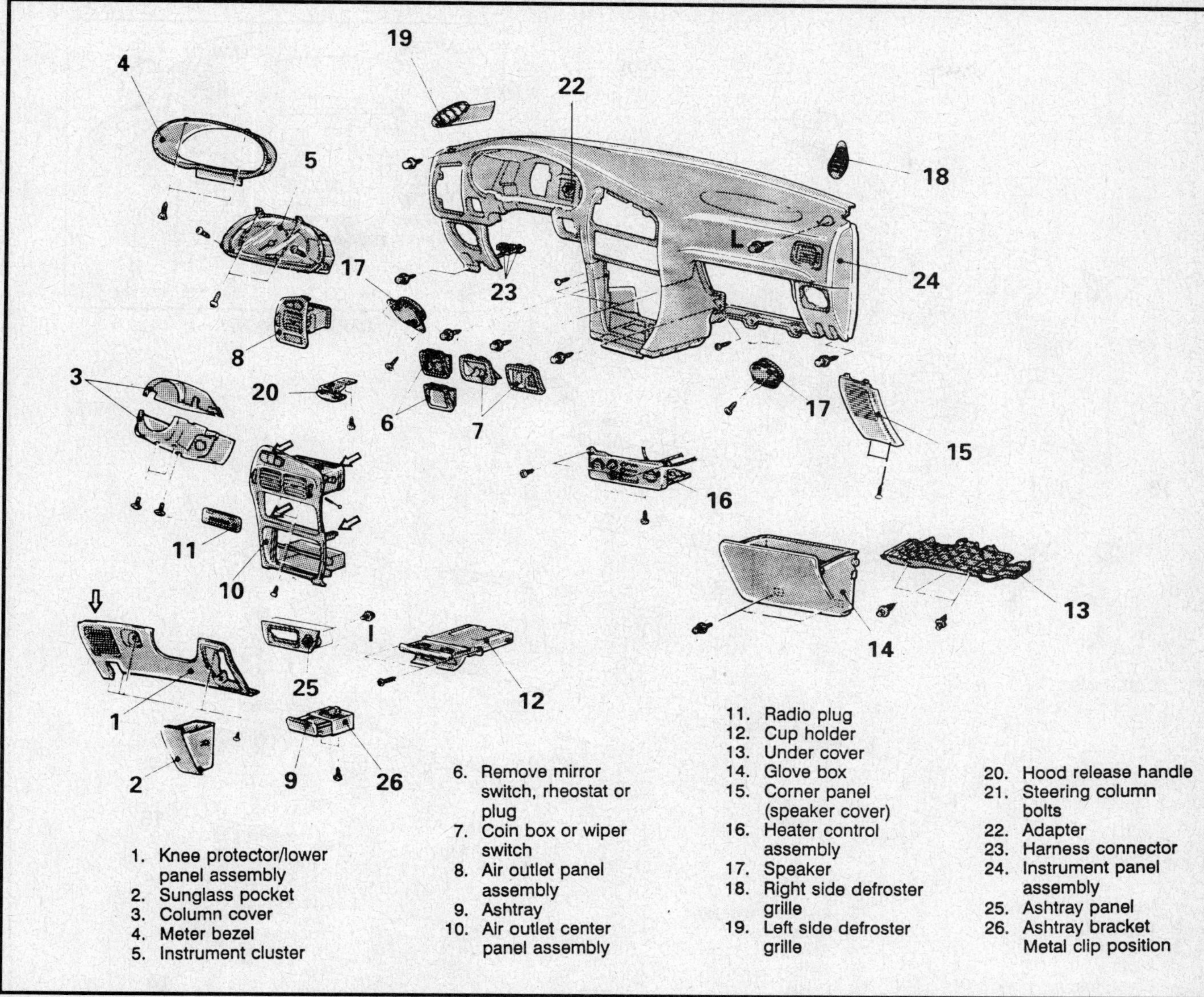

Instrument panel exploded view for removal—Summit

- Remove the hood release handle. Remove the steering column bolts and lower the column.
- Remove the speedometer cable adapter after removing its locking pin and pulling the cable slightly rearward.
- Remove the wiring harness connector at the left side.
- Remove the instrument panel assembly.

3. Remove and plug the heater hoses from the firewall.
4. Remove the joint air duct between the heater and blower assemblies (heater only).
5. Remove the foot duct, the center reinforcement and center ventilation duct.
6. Remove the evaporator installation nut (A/C models).
7. Remove the heater unit, then remove the heater core.

To install:

8. Position the heater unit in place and attach with the nuts.
9. Reinstall the evaporator nut (if A/C). Install the center vent duct, foot duct and center reinforcement. If heater only, install the air duct to the blower assembly.
10. Install heater hoses at the firewall.
11. Install the instrument panel by reversing the removal steps.
12. Refill the cooling system. Connect the battery cable and check the heater system operation.

EVAPORATOR

1. Disconnect the negative battery cable.
2. Properly discharge the air conditioning system.
3. Disconnect the refrigerant lines from the evaporator. Cover the exposed ends of the lines to minimize contamination.
4. Remove the condensation drain hose.
5. Remove the glove box assembly and lap heater duct work.
6. Remove the cowl side trim and speaker cover.
7. Remove the glove box bezel and frame.
8. Disconnect the electrical connector at the top of the evaporator housing.
9. Remove the mounting bolts and nuts and the housing.
10. Disassemble the housing and remove the expansion valve and evaporator.

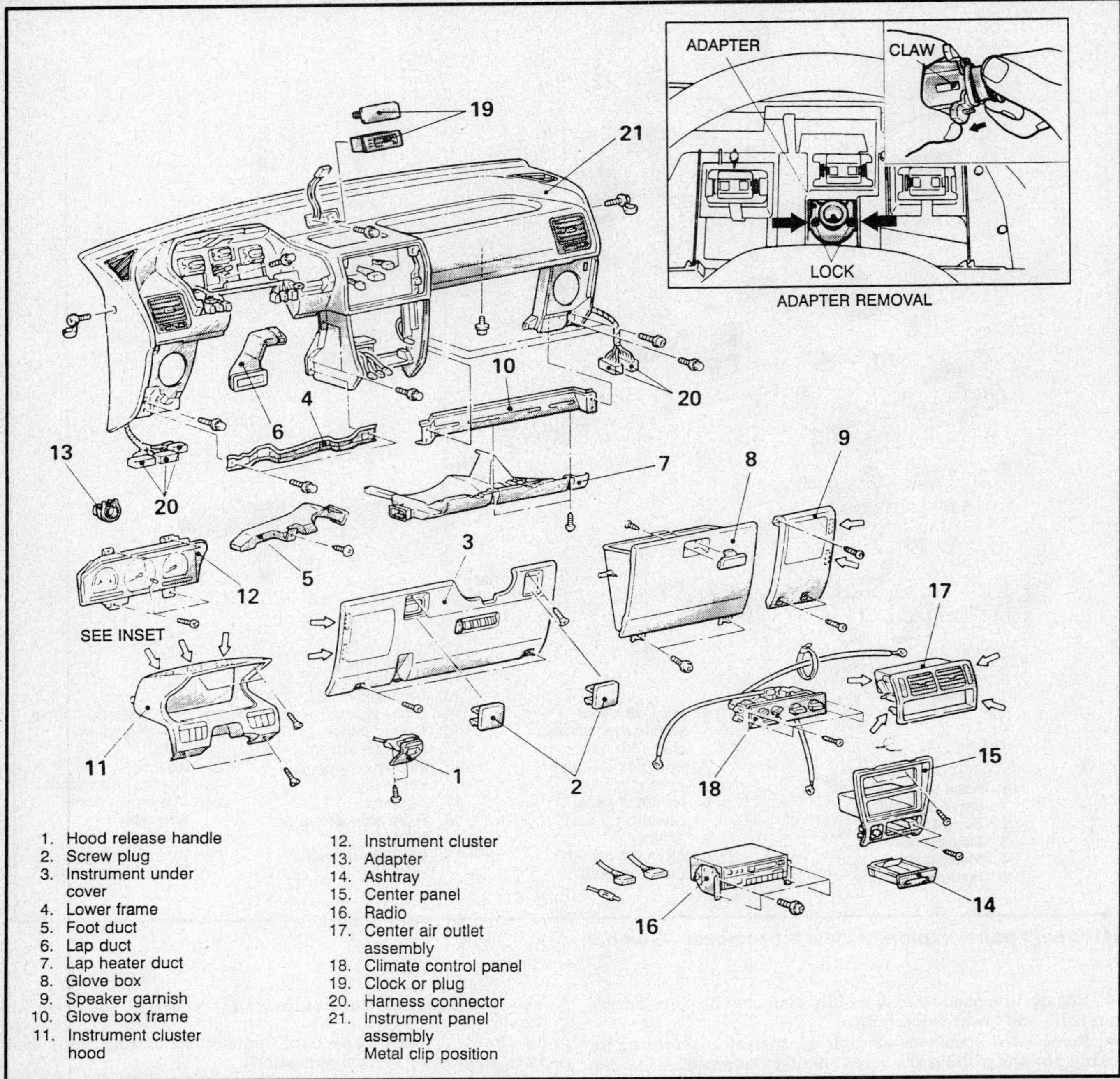

Instrument panel exploded view for removal—Summit Wagon

To install:

11. Assemble the housing, evaporator and expansion valve, making sure the gaskets are in good condition.
12. Install the housing to the vehicle and connect the connector.
13. Install the glove box frame and bezel.
14. Install the speaker cover and side cowl trim.
15. Install the lap heater ductwork and glove box assembly.
16. Install the condensation drain hose.
17. Using new lubricated O-rings, connect the refrigerant lines to the evaporator.
18. Evacuate and recharge the air conditioning system. If the evaporator was replaced, add 2 oz. of refrigerant oil during the recharge.
19. Connect the negative battery cable and check the entire climate control system for proper operation. Check the system for leaks.

Summit Wagon

HEATER UNIT

1. Disconnect the negative battery cable. Properly drain the cooling system.

2. Remove the instrument panel as follows:
- Remove the floor console.
- Remove the hood release handle.
- Remove the panel cover below the steering column.
- Remove the horizontal lower frame in the cover opening.
- Remove the floor air duct, the lap duct and the heater lap duct.
- Remove the glove box, speaker cover and glove box frame.
- Remove the instrument cluster cover, the instrument cluster (remove the speedometer cable adapter lock).
- Remove the ashtray, center panel bezel, then the radio assembly.
- Remove the center air outlet by inserting a small pry bar through the outlet grille and detaching the clip in each upper corner.
- Remove the heater-A/C control panel.
- Remove the clock or clock plug from top center of the instrument panel.
- Detach the harness triple connector at the left side and the harness double connector at the right side.
- Remove the instrument panel.

3. Disconnect and plug the heater hoses at the firewall.
4. Remove the joint duct between the heater unit and blower assembly if heater only; otherwise, remove the plate sub-assembly and the evaporator installation nut.
5. Remove the center reinforcement and the ABS control unit.
6. Remove the rear heater duct, foot duct and center vent duct.
7. Remove the automatic transmission control unit from the front of the heater unit.
8. Remove the heater unit assembly. The heater core can now be removed.

To install:

9. Position the heater unit in place and attach with the retaining nut and bolt.
10. Install the automatic transmission control unit to the heater housing.
11. Install the center, foot and rear air ducts.
12. Install the ABS control unit, center reinforcements and install the evaporator nut and plate sub-assembly or heater joint air duct as removed.
13. Attach the heater hoses at the firewall.
14. Install the instrument panel and components in reverse of the removal procedure.
15. Refill the cooling system. Connect the battery cable. Check heater system operation.

EVAPORATOR

1. Disconnect the negative battery cable. Properly discharge the air conditioning system.
2. Disconnect and plug the refrigeration lines at the firewall connection. Discard the O-rings. Remove the drain hose.
3. Remove the lap heater duct beneath the glove box, then remove the glove box, speaker cover and glove box frame.
4. Remove the push clips and retaining nuts from the evaporator housing. Detach electrical connections and remove the evaporator.
5. The evaporator core can be removed on the bench.
6. To install, reverse the removal procedure. Evacuate, recharge and leak test the system.

Laser and Talon

NOTE: The evaporator housing can be removed by itself, without removing the console, instrument panel or heater core. The heater core, though, cannot be removed without removing the evaporator.

1. Disconnect the negative battery cable.
2. Drain the cooling system and properly discharge the air conditioning system and disconnect the refrigerant lines from the evaporator, if equipped. Cover the exposed ends of the lines to minimize contamination.
3. Remove the floor console by first removing the plugs, then the screws retaining the side covers and the small cover piece in front of the shifter. Remove the shifter knob, manual transmission, and the cup holder. Remove both small pieces of upholstery to gain access to retainer screws. Disconnect both electrical connectors at the front of the console. Remove the shoulder harness guide plates and the console assembly.
4. Remove the instrument panel assembly by performing the following:
- Locate the rectangular plugs in the knee protector on either side of the steering column. Pry these plugs out, remove the screws. Remove the screws from the hood lock release lever and the knee protector.
- Remove the upper and lower column covers.
- Remove the narrow panel covering the instrument cluster cover screws the cover.
- Remove the radio panel and the radio.
- Remove the center air outlet assembly by reaching through the grille and pushing the side clips out with a small flat-tipped tool while carefully prying the outlet free.
- Pull the heater control knobs off and remove the heater control panel assembly.
- Open the glove box, remove the plugs from the sides and the glove box assembly.
- Remove the instrument gauge cluster and the speedometer adapter by disconnecting the speedometer cable from the transaxle, pulling the cable sightly towards the vehicle interior, then giving a slight twist on the adapter to release it.
- Remove the left and right speaker covers from the top of the instrument panel.
- Remove the center plate below the heater controls.
- Remove the heater control assembly installation screws.
- Remove the lower air ducts.
- Drop the steering column by removing the bolts.
- Remove the instrument panel mounting screws, bolts and the instrument panel assembly.

5. Remove both stamped steel reinforcement pieces.
6. Remove the lower ductwork from the heater box.
7. Remove the upper center duct.
8. Vehicles without air conditioning will have a square duct in place of the evaporator. Remove this duct if present. If the vehicle is equipped with air conditioning, remove the evaporator assembly:
   - Remove the wiring harness connectors and the electronic control unit.
   - Remove the drain hose and lift out the evaporator unit.
   - If servicing the assembly, disassemble the housing and remove the expansion valve and evaporator.
9. With the evaporator removed, remove the heater unit. To prevent bolts from falling inside the blower assembly, set the inside/outside air-selection damper to the position that permits outside air introduction.
10. Remove the cover plate around the heater tubes and remove the core fastener clips. Pull the heater core from the heater box, being careful not to damage the fins or tank ends.

To install:

11. Install the heater core to the heater box. Install the clips and cover.
12. Install the heater box and connect the duct work.
13. Assemble the housing, evaporator and expansion valve, making sure the gaskets are in good condition. Install the evaporator housing.
14. Using new lubricated O-rings, connect the refrigerant lines to the evaporator.
15. Install the electronic transmission ELC box. Connect all wires and control cables.

16. Install the instrument panel assembly and the console by reversing their removal procedures.
17. Evacuate and recharge the air conditioning system. If the evaporator was replaced, add 2 oz. of refrigerant oil during the recharge.
18. Connect the negative battery cable and check the entire climate control system for proper operation. Check the system for leaks.

Stealth

HEATER UNIT

1. Disconnect the negative battery cable. Properly drain the cooling system.
2. Remove the center floor console. Remove the instrument panel by removing the following parts:
   - Hood lock release handle.
   - Lighting rheostat.
   - Switch bezel to the right of the steering column.
   - Knee protector panel below the steering column.
   - Steering column covers.
   - Glove box assembly.
   - Center air outlet assembly.
   - Heater-A/C panel screws only.
   - Instrument cluster and bezel.
   - Speedometer cable adapter (mechanical speedometer).
   - Left and right speakers and covers.
   - Wiring harness connectors left, center and right.
   - Steering column mounting bolts (lower the column).
   - Instrument panel assembly.
3. Disconnect and plug the heater hoses at the firewall.
4. Remove the center reinforcement assembly and the right under cover.
5. Remove the foot distribution duct and outlet and the lap cooler duct.
6. Remove the evaporator mounting nut (A/C vehicles) or detach the heater to blower joint duct (heater only).
7. Remove the upper center duct.
8. Remove the heater unit (4 nuts). Remove the plate at the heater core tubes and take out the heater core.

To install:

9. Install the heater unit (4 nuts), then the upper center duct and attach the evaporator or joint duct, as removed.
10. Install remaining air ducts as removed.
11. Install the center reinforcement assembly and the right under cover.
12. Attach the heater hoses.
13. Install the instrument panel in reverse of the removal steps.
14. Install the floor console.
15. Refill the cooling system. Connect the battery cable and check system operation.

EVAPORATOR

1. Remove the battery. Properly discharge the air conditioning system with recovery equipment.
2. Detach the air conditioning lines from the evaporator core tubes. Immediately cap the lines. Discard the O-rings.
3. Remove the drain hose.
4. Remove the glove box assembly and the under cover and lower frame.
5. Remove the A/C control unit from the front of the evaporator housing.
6. Detach the electrical connectors at the housing, remove the mounting bolt and nut and remove the evaporator housing from the vehicle.
7. To install, reverse the removal procedure. Use new O-rings when attaching the refrigerant lines. Evacuate, recharge and leak test the system.

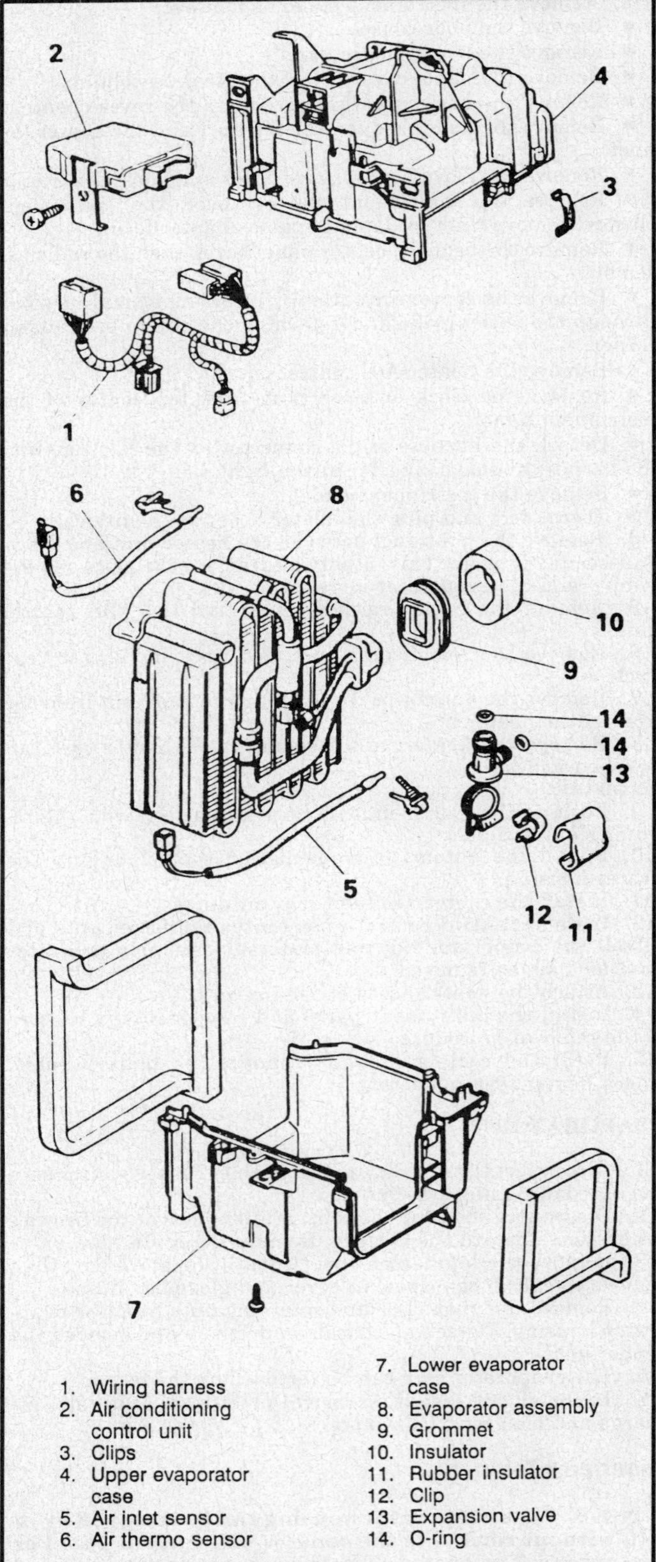

Exploded view of the evaporator and related parts—Laser and Talon, Summit similar

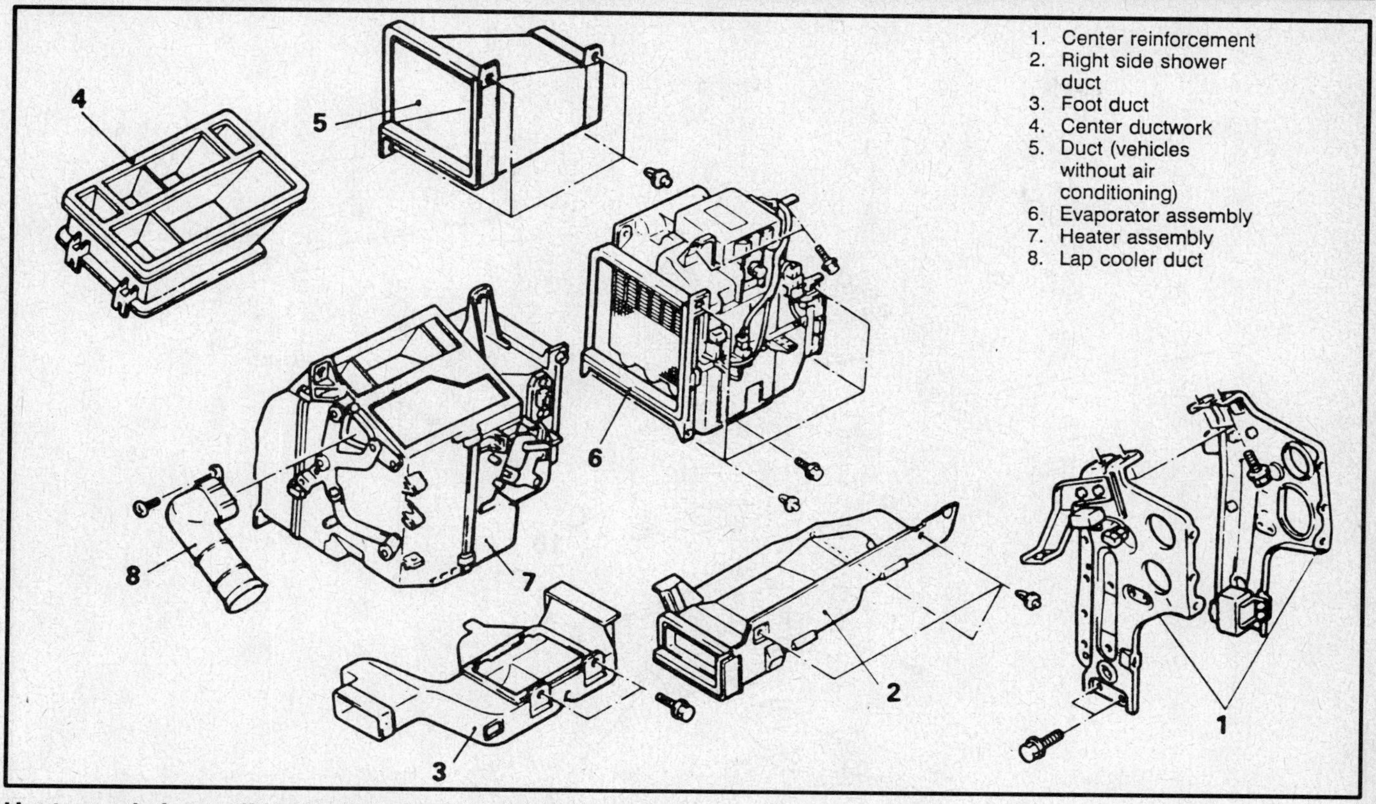

1. Center reinforcement
2. Right side shower duct
3. Foot duct
4. Center ductwork
5. Duct (vehicles without air conditioning)
6. Evaporator assembly
7. Heater assembly
8. Lap cooler duct

Heater and air conditioning housings—Laser and Talon

Concorde, Intrepid, LHS, New Yorker and Vision

NOTE: The heater-A/C assembly must be removed in order to remove the heater core or the evaporator core.

1. Disconnect the negative battery cable. Properly discharge the air conditioning system into an approved R-134a recovery machine.
2. Remove the air cleaner hose and air duct from the engine. Properly drain the cooling system. Detach and plug the heater hoses from the firewall.
3. Using special tool 7193 (or equivalent) disconnect the quick-fit connectors for the refrigerant lines at the expansion valve. Cap all openings immediately.
4. Remove 3 nuts from the studs in the engine compartment.
5. Careful pry off the right and left end caps from the instrument panel.
6. Remove the right and left interior door post kick panel. Remove the right side bezel from the instrument panel.
7. Remove the radio center bezel (6 clips). Remove the radio assembly and the climate control panel (protect from scratching the face plates).
8. Remove the center horizontal panel bezel (4 clips). Remove the center floor console, if equipped.
9. If equipped with a passenger's air bag, press in on the sides of the glove box and lower it down. Remove 4 air bag mounting screws, then close the glove box.
10. Remove the lower bolster screws, lower the bolster and disconnect the trunk release and glove box light wiring. Remove the bolster.
11. Remove the instrument panel top cover (clips at both ends). Remove the right and left "A" pillar trim covers.
12. Remove 5 bolts holding the instrument panel in place (bolts are at the base of the windshield).

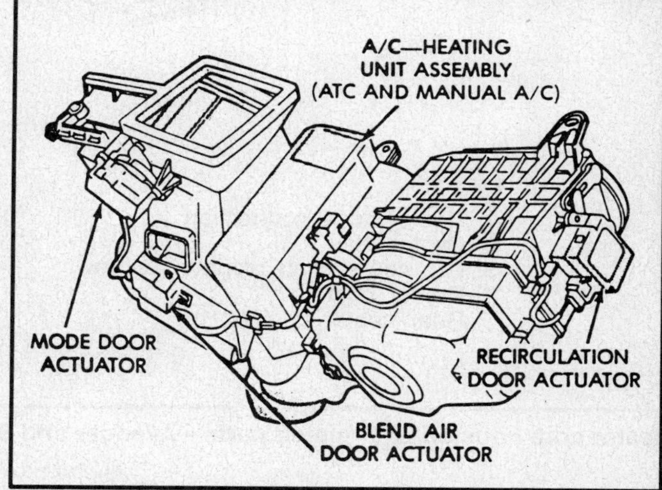

Heater and air conditioner housing assembly—Concorde, Intrepid, LHS, New Yorker and Vision

13. Disconnect the DRB II scan tool connector from the brace. Remove the instrument panel ground strap at lower left of center console.
14. Remove left knee panel support bracket, remove the under column duct and left floor duct, then detach the 60-way wiring connector. Disconnect all related connectors.
15. Detach the fuse panel connectors and the brake light switch.
16. Remove the steering column covers, the column bolts and lower the column to the floor.

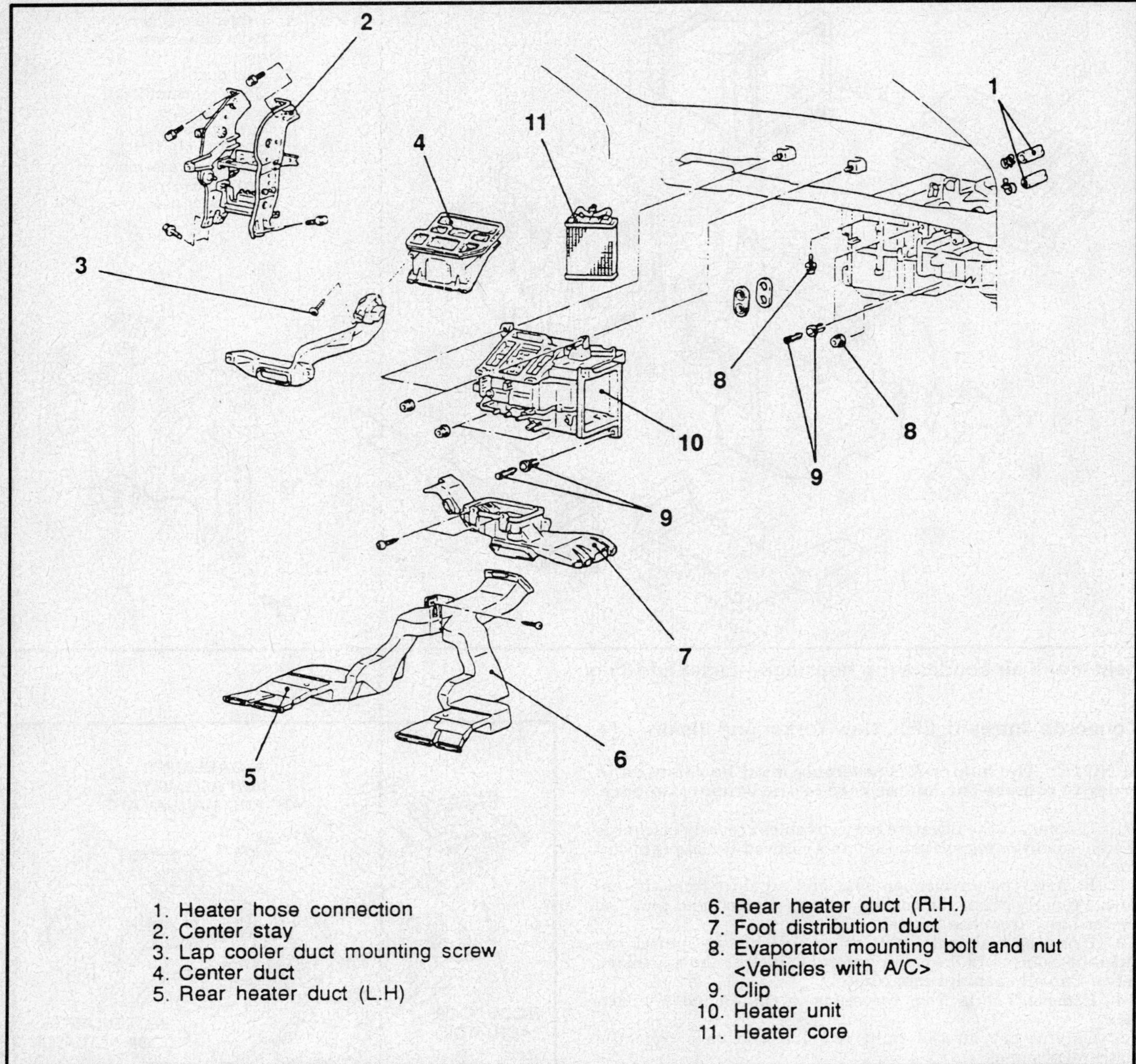

Heater core housing and related parts—Avenger and Sebring

17. Remove the steering column wiring. Remove the air bag connectors.
18. Remove the right floor air duct.
19. Detach the 10-way connector, blower module connector and blower motor connector.
20. Remove the body control module. Detach the right wiring harness connector and the antenna connector.
21. Remove the right and left upper instrument panel screws in the door jam.
22. Remove the upper instrument panel with all harnesses and gauges attached (requires assistant for removal).
23. Remove rear heater air duct. Remove the air bag module (handle carefully and protect on the bench).
24. Remove 3 bolts holding heater housing in place. Carefully roll the heater housing out of the vehicle. Remove the drain tube.
25. After the heater housing is removed, remove the recirc door actuator, door and housing.
26. Remove the upper heater-evaporator housing screws and remove the upper half of the housing. Lift the evaporator out of the housing.
27. Installation is the reverse of the removal procedure. Use a new gasket for the expansion valve if replaced. Transfer the evaporator sensor, positioning it in the same location in the new evaporator core. Install the housing drain tube from beneath the vehicle.

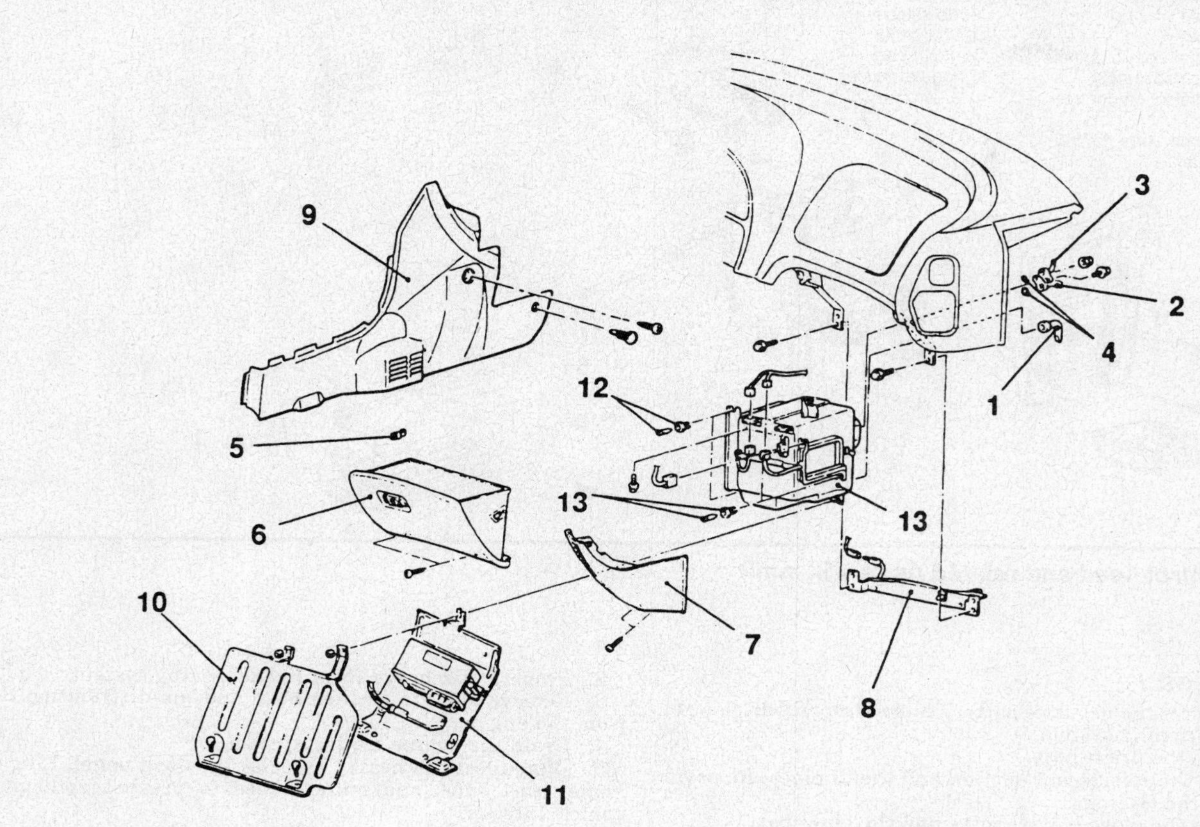

1. Drain hose
2. Suction pipe connection
3. Liquid pipe connection
4. O-ring
5. Stopper
6. Glove box
7. Corner panel
8. Glove box under frame
9. Console side cover <RH>
10. Control unit cover
11. ABS-ECU bracket
12. Clip
13. Evaporator

Evaporator core housing and related parts—Avenger and Sebring

28. Add 2 oz. of R-134a refrigerant oil if evaporator was replaced. Evacuate, recharge and leak test the system. Check entire system operation.

Avenger and Sebring

HEATER UNIT

1. Disconnect the negative battery cable. Properly drain the cooling system.
2. Remove the attaching clip and nuts and remove the heater unit.
3. Remove the heater core from the heater unit.
4. Remove the instrument panel.
5. Disconnect and plug the heater hoses.
6. Remove the center stay assembly.
7. Remove the lap cooler duct mounting screw and the center duct.
8. Remove the rear heater ducts.
9. Remove the foot distribution duct.
10. Remove the evaporator mounting bolt and nut (if vehicle is equipped with air conditioning).
11. Installation is the reverse of the removal procedure.

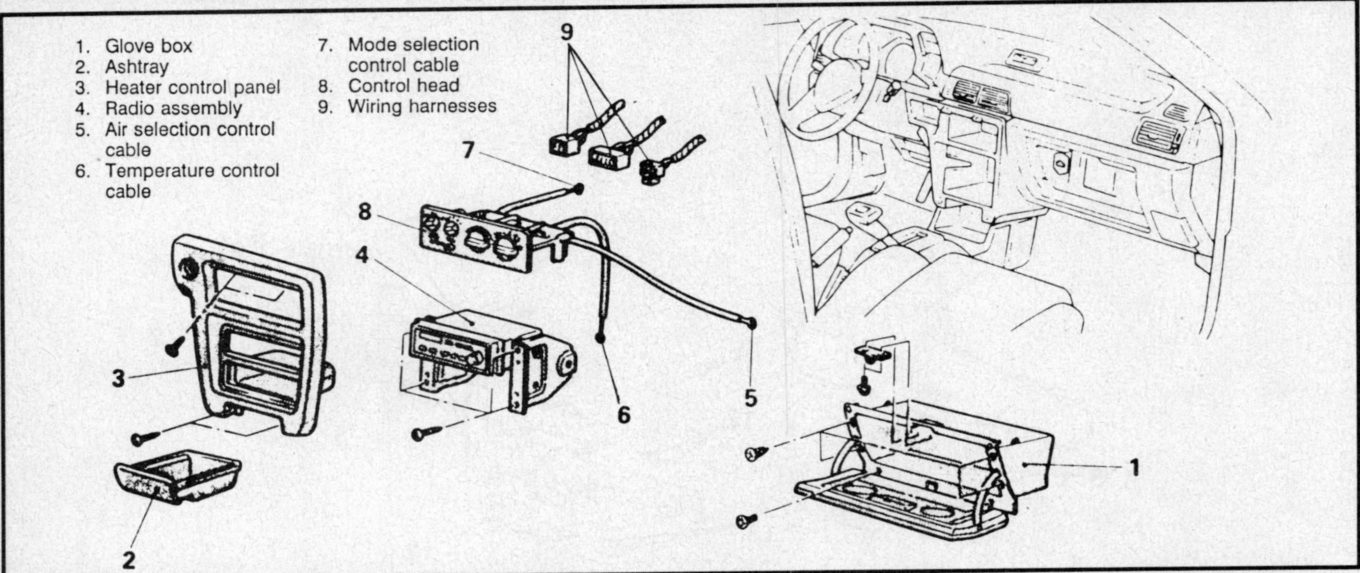

Manual control head and related parts—Summit

EVAPORATOR

1. Disconnect the negative battery cable. Properly discharge the air conditioning system.
2. Remove the drain hose.
3. Detach the refrigerant suction and liquid pipes. Remove and discard the O–rings.
4. Remove the glove box stoppers and the glove box.
5. Remove the corner panel.
6. Remove the attaching screws and remove the glove box under frame.
7. Remove the right hand console side cover.
8. Remove the control unit cover.
9. Remove the ABS–ECU bracket.
10. Remove the attaching clips and connectors and remove the evaporator unit from the vehicle.
11. Installation is the reverse of the removal procedure.

Cirrus and Stratus

HEATER CORE

1. Disconnect the negative battery cable.
2. Remove the radio/control module bezel.
3. Remove the right instrument panel trim.
4. Remove 2 screws at lower right side support beam.
5. Remove the bolt for instrument panel support at A-pillar.
6. Remove the left instrument panel side trim.
7. Remove the upper instrument panel bezel.
8. Remove the lower knee bolster.
9. Remove console screws at the instrument panel.
10. Remove the gearshift knob.
11. Remove the shifter bezel.
12. Remove console screws at rear and remove the rear half of console.
13. Remove front console screws and remove the front half of console.
14. Remove the right side instrument panel support strut.
15. Properly drain the cooling system.
16. Remove the heater hoses at the cowl.
17. Remove the heater core cover screws and the cover.
18. Remove the heater core.
19. Installation is the reverse of the removal procedure.

EVAPORATOR

1. Disconnect the negative battery cable.
2. Properly discharge the air conditioning system.
3. Remove the air cleaner hose and air distribution duct from the engine.
4. Drain the engine cooling system.
5. Disconnect the heater hoses at the dash panel. Plug the heater core inlet and outlet tubes to prevent spillage on vehicle interior.
6. Remove both refrigerant lines from the expansion valve. Cap the expansion valve openings and the refrigerant hose openings.
7. Remove the trim bezel around the A/C control module.
8. Remove the cluster hood bezel retaining screws in the trim bezel opening.
9. Pry up the cluster hood bezel a few inches to expose the cubby bin/cigar lighter bezel screws.
10. Remove the cubby bin/cigar lighter bezel and wiring.
11. Remove the control module retaining screws.
12. Drop the A/C control module into the cubby bin/cigar lighter bezel opening; then, disconnect the wiring on the rear of the control module.
13. Release the cable clips from the top of the control module and retain the clips for re-installation. Disconnect the temperature control and recirculation control cables.
14. Remove the control module.
15. Remove the upper instrument panel bezel.
16. Remove the right and left instrument panel end caps.
17. Remove the left lower knee bolster. Disconnect the mode door motor wiring.
18. Remove the right and left interior door post kick panel.
19. Remove the front and rear halves of the floor console.
20. Remove the radio.
21. Remove the right side lower silencer/duct.
22. Remove the glove box assembly.
23. Remove the right side vertical support strut brace.
24. Remove the left side vertical support strut brace.
25. Remove the center lower distribution housing.
26. Remove the bolts securing the heater-A/C housing to the metal instrument panel frame.
27. Remove the upper instrument panel cowl trim cover.
28. Disconnect the steering column from the instrument panel. Lower the steering column.
29. Remove the instrument panel bolts at the cowl fence.
30. Remove the bolts at the lower A-posts.

31. Remove the instrument panel frame and wiring.
32. Remove the bolts securing the heater-A/C housing to the cowl and remove the housing from the vehicle.
33. Remove the recirculation door inlet cover.
34. Remove the evaporator temperature probe.
35. Remove the clips retaining the evaporator housing to the heater/distribution housing.
36. Separate the evaporator housing from the heater/distribution housing.
37. Remove the seal around the evaporator tube inlet.
38. Remove the evaporator housing upper cover.
39. Lift the evaporator out of the lower housing.
40. Remove the styro foam seal from around the evaporator.
41. Transfer the evaporator sensor. Place the evaporator sensor in the same location as on the previous evaporator.
42. Installation is the reverse of the removal procedure. Verify that the cables are properly adjusted and the control module is seated properly.

Refrigerant Lines

REMOVAL AND INSTALLATION

Laser, Talon, Stealth, Summit, Summit Wagon, Avenger and Sebring

1. Disconnect the negative battery cable.
2. Properly discharge the air conditioning system.
3. Remove the nuts or bolts that attach the refrigerant lines sealing plates to the adjoining components. If the line is not equipped with a sealing plate, separate the flare connection.
4. Remove the line and discard the O-rings.

To install:

5. Coat the new O-rings refrigerant oil and install. Connect the refrigerant lines to the adjoining components and tighten the nuts, bolts or flare connections.
6. Evacuate and recharge the air conditioning system.
7. Connect the negative battery cable and check the entire climate control system for proper operation. Check the system for leaks.

Concorde, Intrepid, LHS, New Yorker, Vision, Cirrus and Stratus

NOTE: Cap all line and component openings immediately on disconnect in order to minimize contamination.

1. Disconnect the negative battery cable. Properly discharge the air conditioning system using an approved R-134a recovery machine.
2. Remove the quick connect clips at each location of line to be removed.
3. Disconnect the quick connectors on the expansion valve, if required. Use tool 7193 or equivalent.

NOTE: Liquid line at receiver/drier may require removal of upper radiator crossmember. Discharge line removal at compressor requires 6 mm hex wrench.

4. Installation is the reverse of the removal procedure.

Manual Control Head

REMOVAL AND INSTALLATION

Summit

1. Disconnect the negative battery cable.
2. Remove the knee pad panel beneath the steering column. Detach the mode selection cable from the heater unit, then remove the center panel assembly screws and remove the panel.
3. Remove the foot duct.
4. Remove the glove box.
5. Detach the fresh/recirc cable, temperature control cable, and mode selection cable from their respective air doors.
6. Remove the control head assembly. Remove the clock or plug from the bottom of the assembly.
7. Installation is the reverse of the removal procedure. Adjust the cables as required.

Laser and Talon

1. Disconnect the negative battery cable.
2. Remove the glove box assembly.
3. Remove the dial control knobs from the control head.
4. Remove the center air outlet by disengaging the tabs with a flat blade tool and carefully prying out.
5. Remove the instrument cluster bezel and radio bezel.
6. Remove the knee protector and lower the hood lock release handle.
7. Remove the left side lower duct work.
8. Disconnect the air, temperature and mode selection control cables from the heater housing.
9. Remove the mounting screws and the control head from the instrument panel.

To install:

10. Feed the control cable through the instrument panel, connect the connectors, install the control head assembly and secure with the screws.
11. Move the mode selection lever to the **DEFROST** position. Move the mode selection damper lever fully inward and connect the cable to the lever. Install the clip.
12. Move the temperature control lever to its HOTTEST position. Move the blend air damper lever FULLY DOWNWARD and connect the cable to the lever. Install the clip.
13. Move the air selection control lever to the **RECIRC** position. Move the air selection damper fully inward and connect the cable to the lever. Install the clip.
14. Connect the negative battery cable and check the entire climate control system for proper operation.
15. If everything is satisfactory, install the remaining interior pieces.

Stealth

1. Remove the negative battery cable.
2. Remove the center floor console.
3. Remove the glove box assembly.
4. Detach the fresh/recirc cable from the air door lever.
5. Remove the hood lock handle, the rheostat, rear wiper switch and the knee pad panel beneath the steering column.
6. Remove the left air distribution duct behind the panel opening.
7. Detach the mode cable and temperature cable from their door levers.
8. Remove the center assembly with the air outlet (clips accessible through the air outlet grille).
9. Remove the control panel assembly.
10. Installation is the reverse of the removal procedure. Adjust cables as required.

Summit Wagon

1. Disconnect the negative battery cable. Remove the lap heater duct beneath the glove box.
2. Remove the glove box assembly.
3. Remove the hood release handle and the knee panel under the steering column.

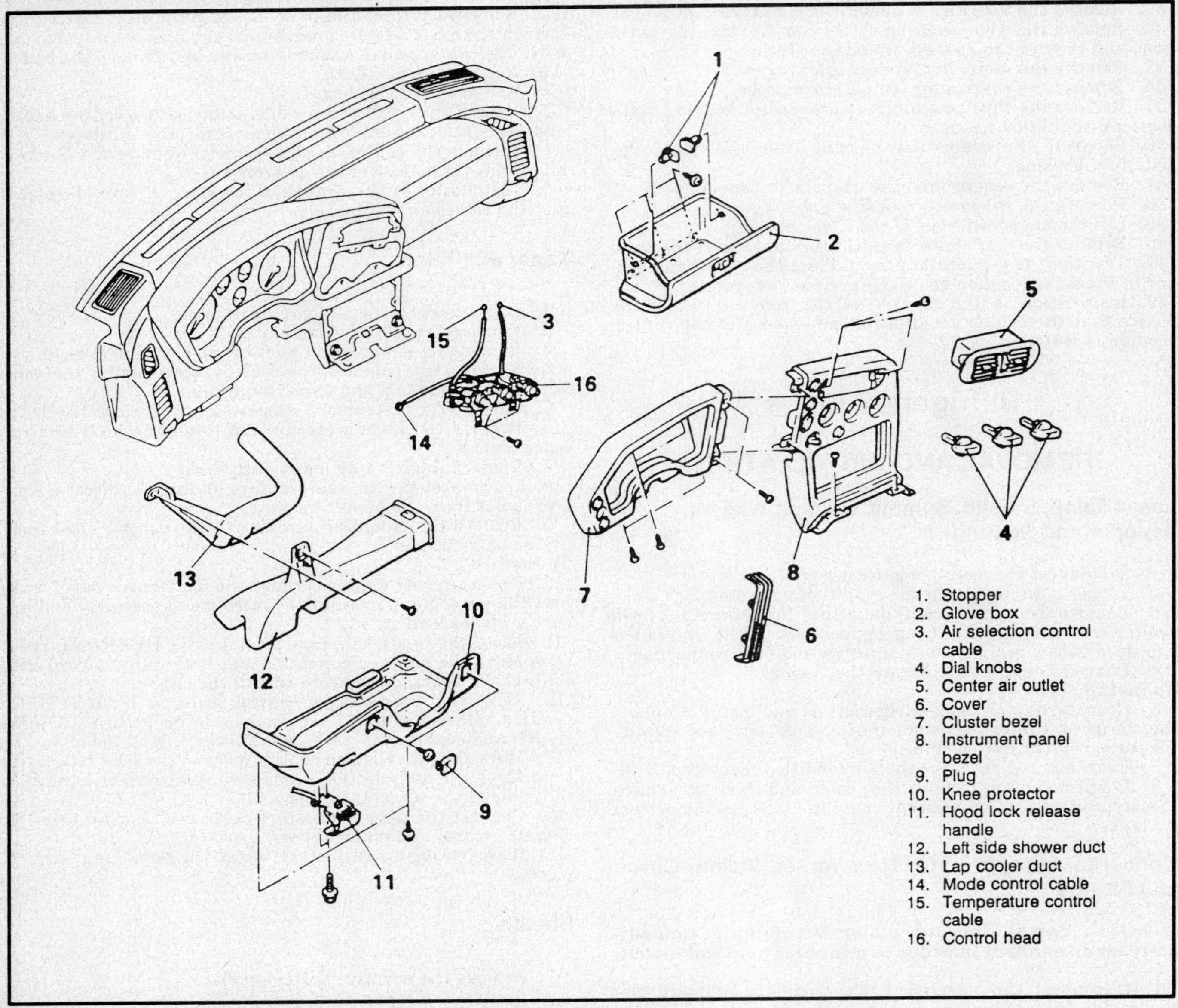

Manual control head and related parts—Laser and Talon

4. Remove the left side lap air duct.
5. Remove the ashtray, the center panel bezel and the radio assembly.
6. Remove the clip on the lower section of the center air outlet. Then, insert a small prybar into the outlet grille and disconnect the top spring clips. Remove the air outlet assembly.
7. Detach the cables at the air doors. Remove the control panel assembly, detaching electrical connectors.
8. Installation is the reverse of the removal procedure. Adjust cables as required.

Concorde, Intrepid, LHS, New Yorker and Vision

NOTE: These models use electrically operated door actuators; therefore, no cable connections are involved.

1. Disconnect the negative battery cable.
2. Remove the control panel bezel.
3. Remove the control panel screws, pull the panel out and detach the 2 connectors from the rear of the panel.
4. Install in reverse of the removal procedure.

Avenger and Sebring

1. Disconnect the negative battery cable.
2. Remove the center panel clips and panel.
3. Remove the floor console.
4. Remove the radio and tape player.
5. Remove the stoppers and lower the glove box.
6. Press the lever pin and disconnect the air outlet changeover damper cable. Disconnect remaining cables and connectors, as required.
7. Remove the heater control assembly mounting screws.
8. Remove the heater control assembly boss from the center reinforcement.
9. Installation is the reverse of the removal procedure. Adjust the cables as required.

Cirrus and Stratus

1. Disconnect the negative battery cable.
2. Remove the trim bezel from around the heater-A/C control module.
3. Remove the cluster hood bezel retaining screws in the trim bezel opening.
4. Pry up the cluster hood bezel a few inches to expose the cubby bin/cigar lighter bezel screws.
5. Remove the cubby bin/cigar lighter bezel and wiring.
6. Remove the control module retaining screws.
7. Drop the control module into the cubby bin/cigar lighter bezel opening; then, disconnect the wiring on the rear of the control module.
8. Release the cable clips from the top of the control module and retain the clips for re-installation.
9. Disconnect the temperature control and recirculation control cables.
10. Remove the control module.
11. Installation is the reverse of the removal procedure. Verify that the cables are properly adjusted and the control module is seated properly.

Manual Control Cables

ADJUSTMENT

Summit

1. Disconnect the negative battery cable. Remove the glove box, if necessary.
2. Move the mode selection panel knob to **DEF**. Set the mode door lever (cable connection end) to the **DEF** position (push away from the cable). Pull the outer cable cover away from the lever until the slack is gone, then clip it in place.
3. Set the temperature control knob to **MAX HOT**. Move the temperature (air mix) door lever to the **MAX HOT** position (cable attaching end pushed away from the cable). Pull the cable outer cover away from the lever until the slack is gone, then clip it in place.
4. Set the fresh/recirc selector lever to the **RECIRC** position. Move the door lever toward the cable so it is at the **RECIRC** location, attach the cable. Pull the outer cable housing to remove all slack, then clip cable in place.

Laser and Talon

1. Disconnect the negative battery cable. Remove the glove box, if necessary.
2. Move the mode selection lever to the **DEFROST** position. Move the mode selection damper lever FULLY INWARD and connect the cable to the lever. Adjust as required.
3. Move the temperature control lever to its HOTEST position. Move the blend air damper lever FULLY DOWNWARD and connect the cable to the lever. Adjust as required.
4. Move the air selection control lever to the **RECIRC** position. Move the air selection damper FULLY INWARD and connect the cable to the lever. Adjust as required.

Summit Wagon

1. Set the fresh/recirc control knob to the **RECIRC** position. Pull the top end of the air door lever toward the cable to set the lever against its stopper. Install the cable and pull the cable housing away from the lever to remove all slack. Clamp it in place.
2. Set the mode control knob to **DEF**. Move the air outlet door lever so the cable attachment end moves away from the cable clip. Attach the cable on the lever, then in the clip.
3. Move the temperature knob to **MAX HOT**. Move the temperature door lever until the cable attaching end is upward toward the cable clip until it stops. Attach the cable and install it firmly in the clip.

Stealth

1. Move the temperature lever to **HOT**. With the blend air door lever pressed completely down (away from the cable), connect the cable and secure it in the retaining clip.
2. Move the mode selector lever to **DEF**. Press the damper lever inward (toward the cable clip). Connect the cable end to the lever and snap the cable into its retaining clip.
3. Set the fresh/recirc air selection lever to **RECIRC**. Press the air selection damper lever so the cable attachment is as far toward the cable clip as possible. Attach the cable to the lever and snap it into its retaining clip.

Cirrus and Stratus

1. Attach the cable to the lever arm of the control module.
2. Turn the control knob fully counterclockwise.
3. Pull the cable jacket away from the cable end until taut.
4. Clip the cable jacket to the control module.
5. The control knob should travel a full 180 degrees if the cable is properly adjusted.

Electronic Control Panel

REMOVAL AND INSTALLATION

Stealth, Concorde, Intrepid and Vision

1. Disconnect the negative battery cable.
2. On Stealth, remove the center air outlet assembly above the control panel. On Concorde, Intrepid and Vision, remove the control panel bezel.
3. Remove the electronic control panel, detaching the electrical connectors as the panel is pulled out.
4. On Stealth, remove the A/C control unit from the bottom of the control panel.
5. Installation is the reverse of the removal procedure.

SENSORS AND SWITCHES

Air Door Actuators

REMOVAL AND INSTALLATION

Concorde, Intrepid, LHS, New Yorker and Vision

RECIRC DOOR ACTUATOR

Located on the right side of the heater housing, this actuator positions the recirc door open or closed. The actuator is not adjustable and must be replaced if faulty.

1. Disconnect the negative battery cable.
2. Remove the floor console or instrument panel center lower cover.
3. Remove the lower instrument panel assembly.
4. Remove the body control module at the right side of the instrument panel.
5. Mark the position of the actuator shaft to the door arm for installation in the same position (motor is keyed to this position). Remove the actuator screws and pull the actuator straight off the door shaft. Disconnect the electrical connection.

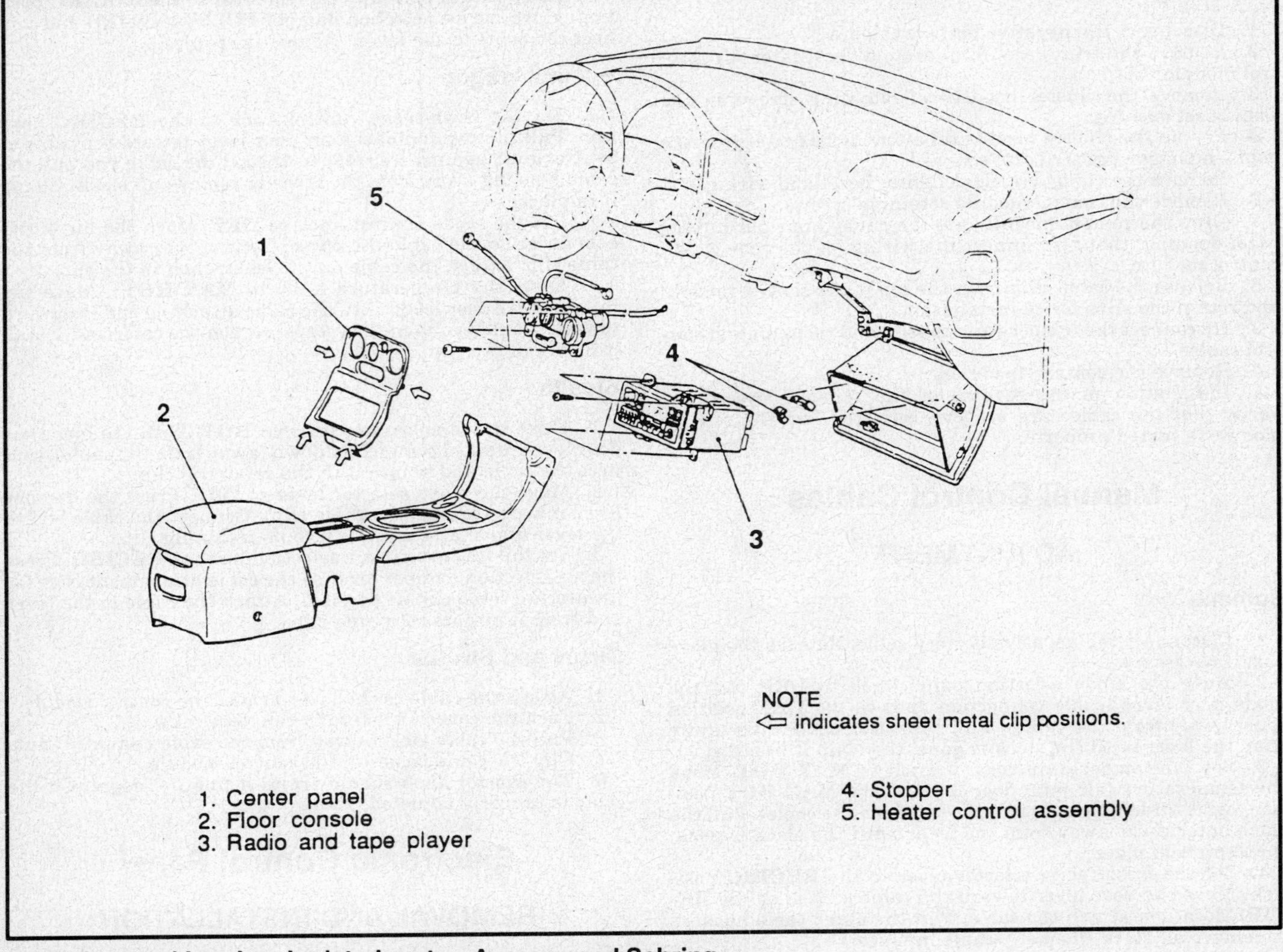

Manual control head and related parts—Avenger and Sebring

6. Installation is the reverse of the removal procedure.

MODE DOOR ACTUATOR

1. Disconnect the negative battery cable. Remove the left and right under panel silencers and ducts.
2. Remove the floor console.
3. Remove the center floor heat adapter duct.
4. Remove the rear heat duct forward adapter.
5. Loosen the center support bracket and pry rearward to access the actuator.
6. Remove the actuator screws. Pull actuator straight down, noting shaft position for reinstallation in this same position (motor is keyed to this position). Disconnect the electrical connection.
7. Installation is the reverse of the removal procedure.

TEMPERATURE (BLEND AIR) DOOR ACTUATOR

1. Disconnect the negative battery cable. Remove the left and right under panel silencers and ducts.
2. Remove 2 screws from the actuator (accessible on the right side of the center stack). Remove 1 screw from the actuator on the left side.
3. Pull the actuator straight down and detach electrical connections. Note shaft position for reinstallation in this same position (motor is keyed to this position).
4. Installation is the reverse of the removal procedure.

Cirrus and Stratus

MODE DOOR ACTUATOR

1. Disconnect the negative battery cable.
2. Remove the left under panel silencer/duct.
3. Remove the electrical connection on the actuator.
4. Remove the actuator retaining screws; then pull the actuator straight down. Upon removal, note the shaft position of the actuator (the shaft on this motor is keyed. When installing a new actuator, its shaft must be positioned in the same location.
5. Installation is the reverse of the removal procedure.

Blower Motor Relays

TESTING

1. If the relay is suspect, disconnect the relay and plug the connector into a known good relay.
2. If the system works properly with the replacement relay, the relay was faulty.
3. If not, check the rest of the system.

Power Relays

OPERATION

Laser, Talon, Summit, Stealth, Avenger and Sebring

The vehicles use relays to control the compressor clutch coil, heater, condenser fan and speed of the condenser fan.

On Summit, the compressor coil, condenser fan and condenser fan speed relays are in a small relay block located in the left front of the engine compartment next to the power steering fluid reservoir. The heater relay is located in an interior relay block under the left side of the instrument panel.

On Laser and Talon, the compressor coil, condenser fan and condenser fan speed relays are in a small relay block located in the left rear corner of the engine compartment. The heater relay is located on top of the interior junction block under the left side of the instrument panel.

On Summit Wagon, the condenser fan high and low relays and the A/C compressor relay are on the relay block in the engine compartment. The heater relay is on a junction block behind the front left speaker.

On Stealth, the condenser fan motor relays and A/C compressor relay are on the relay box on the left of the engine compartment. The blower motor relay is on the junction box. The blower high relay is on the blower case.

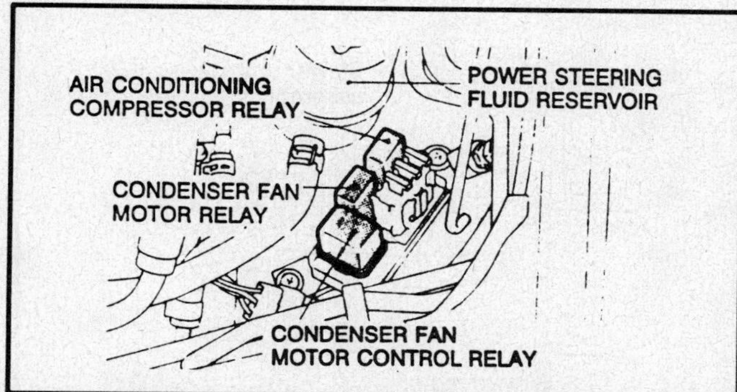

Underhood relay identification—Summit

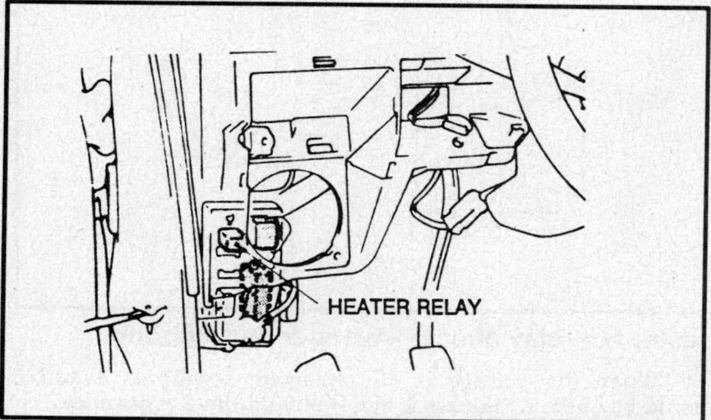

Heater relay location—Summit

On Avenger and Sebring, the condenser fan motor relays and the A/C compressor relay are on the relay box in the engine compartment. The blower motor relay is on the junction box under the instrument panel. The blower high relay is on the blower unit assembly.

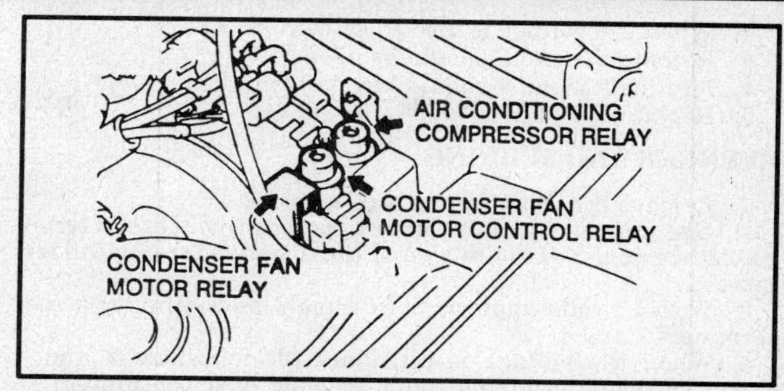

Underhood relay identification—Laser and Talon

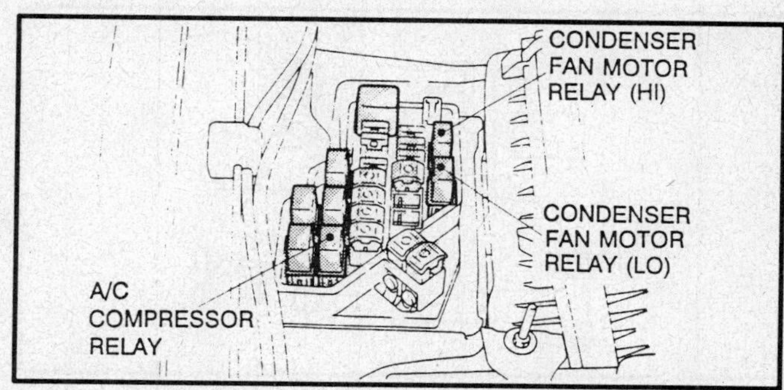

Underhood relay identification—Summit Wagon

Passenger compartment relay identification—Summit Wagon

Cirrus, Stratus, Concorde, Intrepid, LHS, New Yorker and Vision

These vehicles use relays to control the compressor clutch, blower motor and radiator fan system. The relays are located in the Power Distribution Center (PDC). The radiator fan system uses two relays; one relay is used for **LOW** speed fan operation and the other is for **HIGH** speed operation. The Powertrain Control Module (PCM) controls the operation of the relays depending on engine coolant temperature or A/C operation.

TESTING

Heater Fan Relays

1. Remove the relay.
2. Use jumper wires to connect the positive battery terminal to terminal **2** of the relay and the negative terminal to terminal **4**.
3. With 12 volts applied, there should be continuity across terminals **1** and **3**.

4. When the voltage is disconnected:
- Terminals **1** and **3** should be open.
- Terminals **2** and **4** should have continuity.

5. Replace the relay if faulty.

AVENGER AND SEBRING

1. Remove the relay from the relay block.
2. Use jumper wires to connect the positive battery terminal to terminal **3** of the relay and the negative terminal to terminal **1**.
3. With 12 volts applied, there should be continuity across terminals **2** and **4**.
4. When the voltage is disconnected, terminals **2** and **4** should be open; terminals **1** and **3** should have continuity.
5. Replace the relay if faulty.

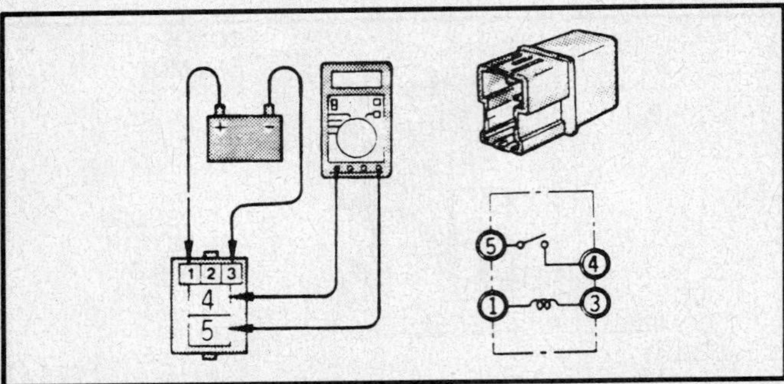

A/C compressor relay and condenser high/low fan relay checking—Summit Wagon

Condenser Fan Control Relay

SUMMIT

1. Remove the relay from the relay block.
2. Use jumper wires to connect the positive battery terminal to terminal **2** of the relay and the negative terminal to terminal **5**.
3. With 12 volts applied:
- Terminals **1** and **3** should be open.
- Terminals **3** and **6** should have continuity.

4. When the voltage is disconnected:
- Terminals **1** and **3** should have continuity.
- Terminals **3** and **6** should be open.
- Terminals **2** and **5** should have continuity.

5. Replace the relay if faulty.

LASER AND TALON

1. Remove the relay.
2. Use jumper wires to connect the positive battery terminal to terminal **3** of the relay and the negative terminal to terminal **5**.
3. With 12 volts applied, there should be continuity across terminals **1** and **2**.
4. When the voltage is disconnected:
- Terminals **1** and **4** should have continuity.
- Terminals **3** and **5** should have continuity.
- Terminals **1** and **2** should be open.

5. Replace the relay if faulty.

AVENGER AND SEBRING

1. Remove the relay from the relay block.
2. Use jumper wires to connect the positive battery terminal to terminal **1** of the relay and the negative terminal to terminal **3**.
3. With 12 volts applied, there should be continuity across terminals **4** and **5**.

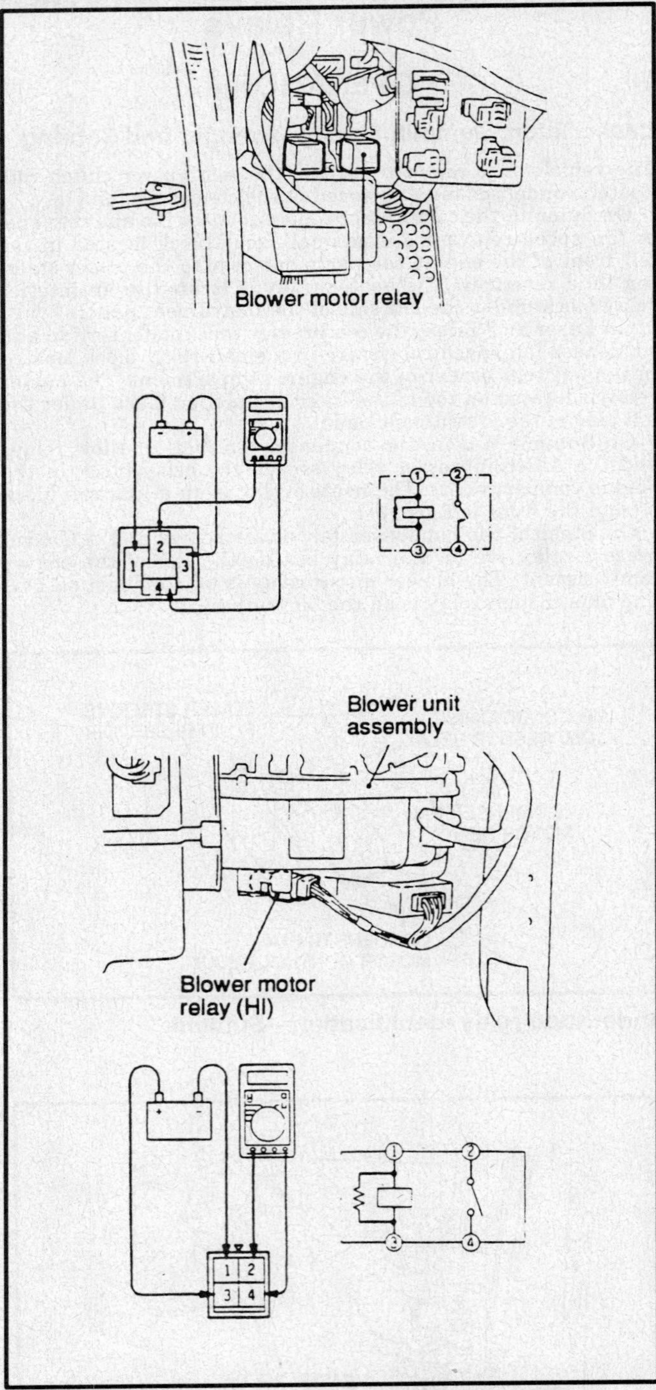

Heater fan relay check—Avenger and Sebring

4. When the voltage is disconnected, terminals **4** and **5** should be open; terminals **1** and **3** should have continuity.
5. Replace the relay if faulty.

Dual or Triple Pressure Switch

OPERATION

The Laser, Talon, Stealth, Avenger and Sebring use a dual pressure switch, which is a combination of a low pressure cut off switch and high pressure cut off switch. Summit with 1.5L engine uses a dual pressure switch, while the 1.8L models use a triple pressure switch. Summit Wagon also uses a triple pressure switch.

The functions of these switches will prevent the operation of the compressor in the event of either high or low refrigerant charge, preventing damage to the system. The switch is located on the receiver/drier on Stealth, Summit, Summit Wagon, Avenger and Sebring and near the sight glass on the refrigerant line on Laser and Talon.

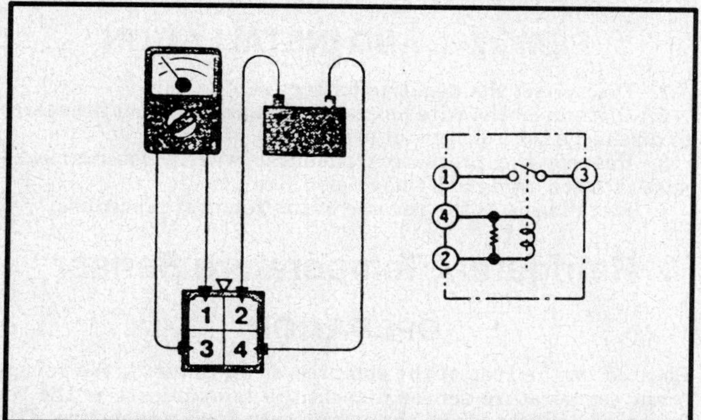

Heater fan relay check—Summit, Laser, Talon and Summit Wagon

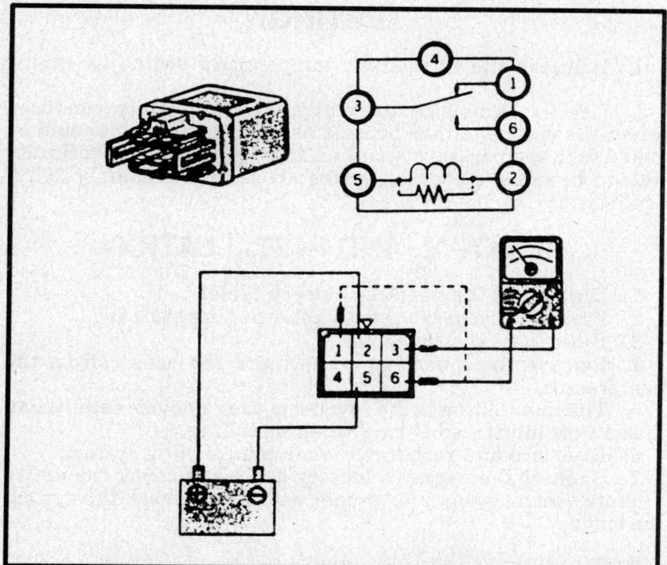

Condenser fan control relay check—Summit

The dual pressure switch is designed to cut off voltage to the compressor coil when the pressure either drops below 28 psi or rises above 455 psi.

TESTING

1. Check for continuity through the switch, using a jumper wire at the switch harness and an ohmmeter on the switch terminals.
2. If the switch is open, check for insufficient refrigerant charge or excessive pressures.
3. If neither of the above conditions exist and the switch is open, replace the switch.

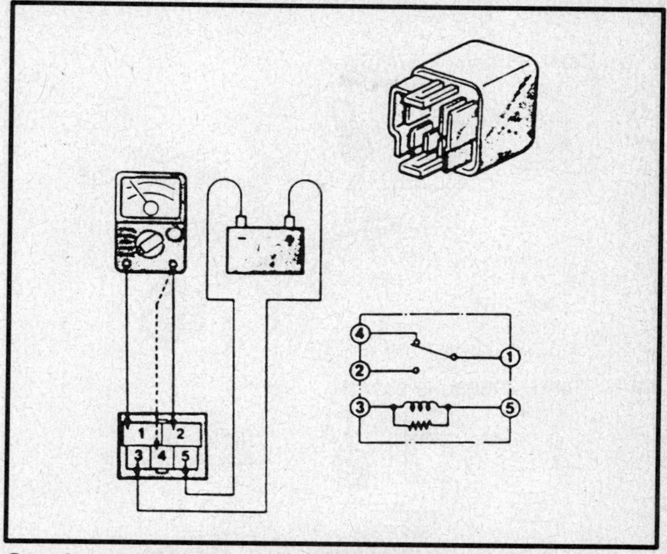

Condenser fan control relay check—Laser and Talon

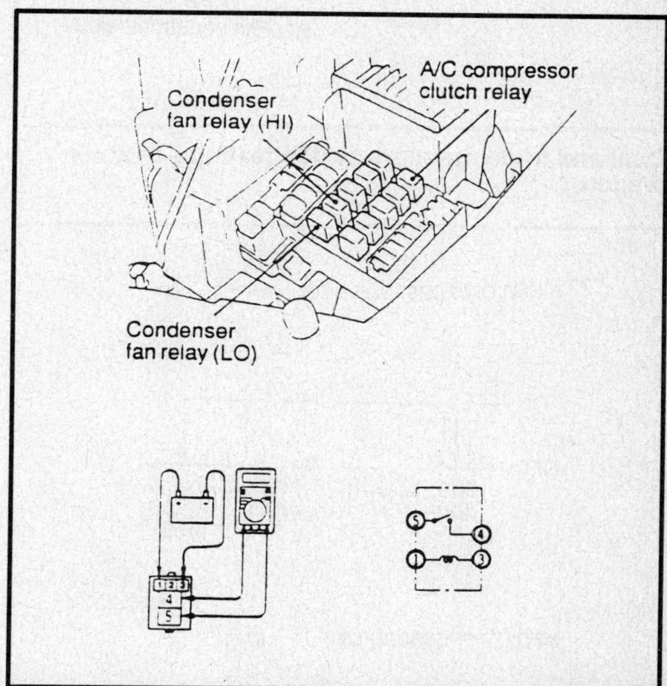

Condenser fan control relay check—Avenger and Sebring

REMOVAL AND INSTALLATION

1. Disconnect the negative battery cable.
2. Properly discharge the air conditioning system.
3. Remove the switch from the refrigerant line or receiver/drier.
4. The installation is the reverse of the removal installation.
5. Evacuate and recharge the air conditioning system.
6. Connect the negative battery cable and check the entire climate control system for proper operation. Check the system for leaks.

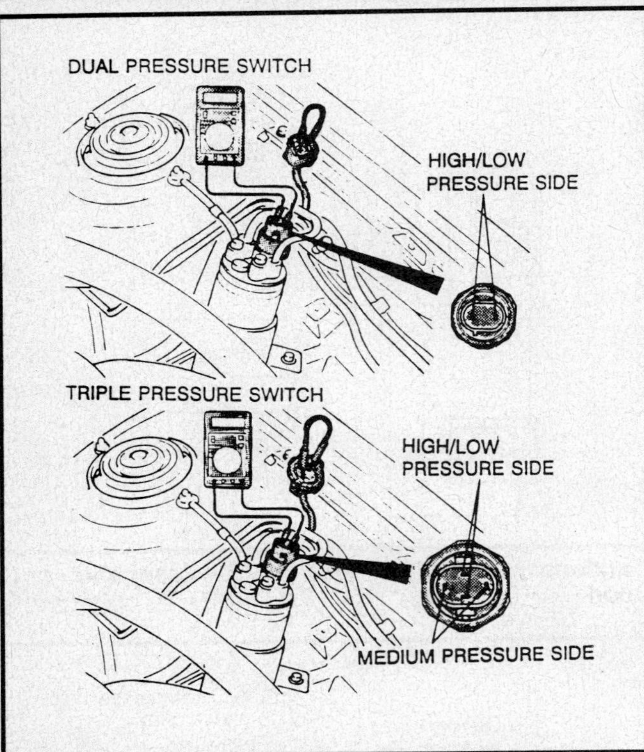

Dual and triple pressure switch testing—Summit Wagon

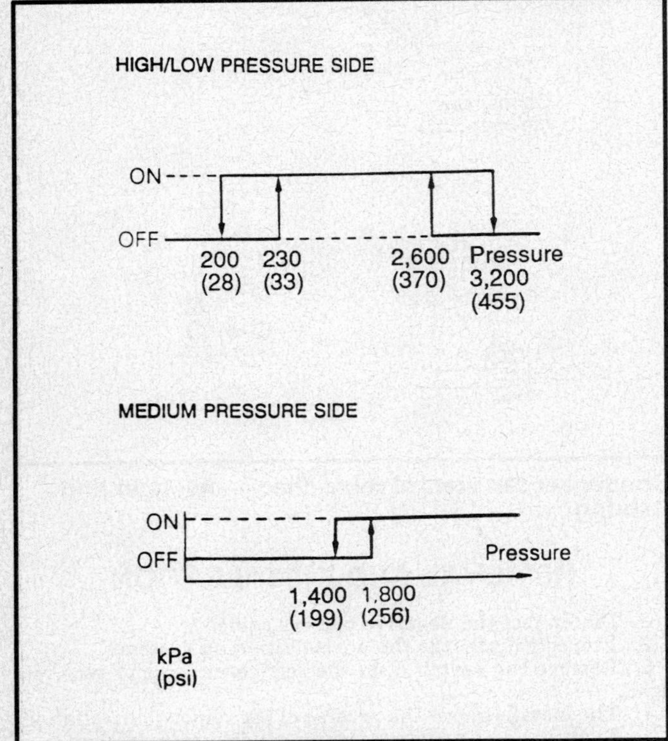

Dual and triple pressure switch operating parameters—1994–95 Summit Wagon

A/C Pressure Transducer

OPERATION

The Cirrus, Stratus, Concorde, Intrepid, LHS, New Yorker and Vision use an A/C pressure transducer to support the condenser/radiator fans and compressor functions. The A/C pressure transducer is screwed onto a valve on the discharge line near the condenser. The pressure transducer functions as the refrigerant system pressure sensor.

REMOVAL AND INSTALLATION

1. Disconnect the negative battery cable.
2. Disconnect the wire harness connector. It is not necessary to discharge the refrigerant system.
3. Remove the pressure transducer with a counterclock–wise rotation using a 3/4 open–end wrench.
4. Installation is the reverse of the removal procedure.

Refrigerant Temperature Sensor

OPERATION

Located on the rear of the compressor on Summit, the refrigerant temperature sensor detects the temperature of the refrigerant delivered from the compressor during operation. The switch is designed to cut off the compressor when the temperature of the refrigerant exceeds 293°F (145°C), preventing overheating.

TESTING

1. Immerse the refrigerant temperature switch in engine oil.
2. Use an ohmmeter to confirm the continuity condition when the engine oil has become heated. Continuity should be noted with temperature less than 293°F (145°C). No continuity should be noted at temperatures above approximately 293°F (145°C).

REMOVAL AND INSTALLATION

1. Disconnect the negative battery cable.
2. Properly discharge the air conditioning system.
3. Disconnect the connector.
4. Remove the mounting screws and the sensor from the compressor.
5. The installation is the reverse of the removal installation. Use a new lubricated O-ring when installing.
6. Evacuate and recharge the air conditioning system.
7. Connect the negative battery cable and check the entire climate control system for proper operation. Check the system for leaks.

Air Thermo and Air Inlet Sensors

OPERATION

These sensors function as cycling switches on Avenger, Sebring, Laser, Talon, Stealth, Summit and Summit Wagon. The air thermo sensor only is used on Summit. Both sensors are located inside the evaporator housing; the air inlet sensor is normally on the right side of the housing and the air thermo sensor is normally on the left side.

The air thermo sensor detects the temperature of the air in the passenger compartment and the air inlet sensor detects the temperature of the air coming into the cooling unit. The information is input to the auto compressor control unit and the information is processed, causing the compressor clutch to cycle.

Cirrus and Stratus use an A/C evaporator temperature sensor located in the heater-A/C housing. This sensor function's as an air inlet sensor and provides the Body Control Module (BCM) with the evaporator temperature to prevent the evaporator from freezing. Information on evaporator temperature is sent to the Powertrain Control Module (PCM). The PCM uses this information to control operation of the A/C compressor clutch.

TESTING

1. Disconnect the sensor connector near the evaporator case.
2. Measure the resistance across the wires of the sensor that is suspect.
3. The resistance specifications for the air thermo sensor at different temperatures for Laser, Talon and Summit are:
   32°F (0°C)—11.4 kilo ohms
   50°F (10°C)—7.32 kilo–ohms
   68°F (20°C)—4.86 kilo–ohms
   86°F (30°C)—3.31 kilo–ohms
   104°F (40°C)—2.32 kilo–ohms
4. The resistance specifications for the air inlet sensor at different temperatures for the Laser, Talon and Summit are:
   32°F (0°C)—3.31 kilo–ohms
   50°F (10°C)—2.00 kilo–ohms
   68°F (20°C)—1.25 kilo–ohms
   86°F (30°C)—0.81 kilo–ohms
   104°F (40°C)—0.53 kilo–ohms
5. The resistance specifications for both the air inlet and air thermo sensors for the Stealth and Summit Wagon are:
   32°F (0°C)—4.8 kilo–ohms
   50°F (10°C)—3.0 kilo–ohms
   68°F (20°C)—1.8 kilo–ohms
   68°F (30°C)—1.5 kilo–ohms
6. Replace the sensor if not within 10 percent of specifications.

REMOVAL AND INSTALLATION

1. Disconnect the negative battery cable.
2. Properly discharge the air conditioning system.
3. Remove the evaporator housing and the covers.
4. Unclip the sensor wires from the housing and remove the sensor(s).
5. The installation is the reverse of the removal procedure.
6. Evacuate and recharge the air conditioning system.
7. Connect the negative battery cable and check the entire climate control system for proper operation. Check the system for leaks.

A/C Control Unit/Automatic Compressor Control Unit

OPERATION

On the Avenger, Sebring, Laser, Talon, Stealth, Summit and Summit Wagon, an electronic control unit is used to process information received from various sensors and switches to control the air conditioning compressor. The unit is located behind the glove box on top of the evaporator housing or on the blower unit. The function of the control unit is to send current to the dual or triple pressure switch when the following conditions are met:

1. The air conditioning switch is in either the **ECONO** or **A/C** mode.
2. The refrigerant temperature sensor, if equipped, is reading 293°F (145°C) or less.
3. The air thermo and air inlet sensors are both reading at least 39°F (4°C).

TESTING

1. Disconnect the control unit connector.
2. Turn the ignition switch **ON**.
3. Turn the air conditioning switch **ON**.

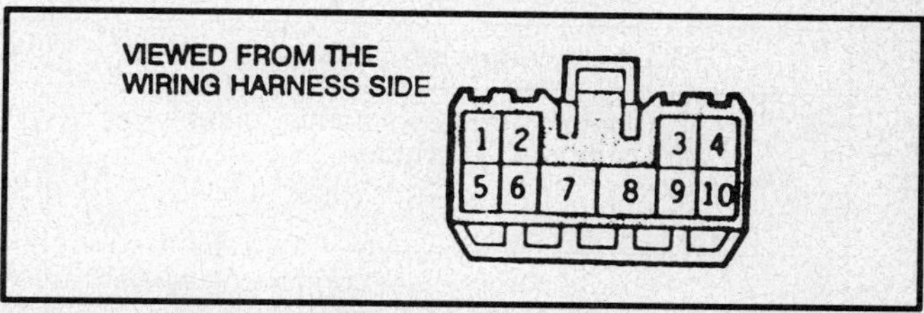

Air conditioning control unit connector terminals—Laser, Talon and Summit Wagon

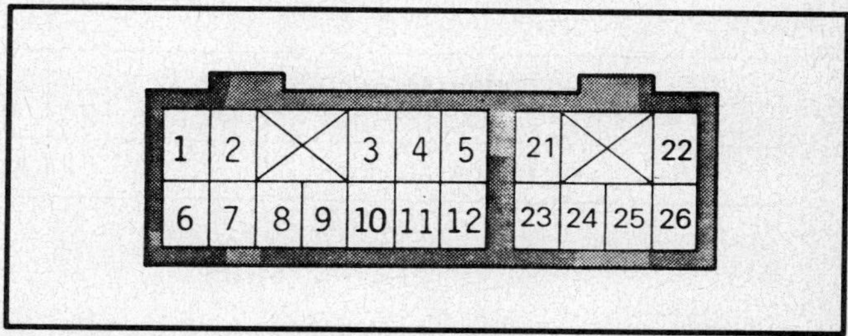

Air conditioning control unit connector terminals—Summit and Stealth

4. Turn the temperature control lever too its COOLEST position.
5. Turn the blower switch to its HIGHEST position.
6. Follow the chart and probe the various terminals of the control unit connector under the specified conditions. This will rule out all possible faulty components in the system.
7. If all checks are satisfactory, replace the control unit. If not, check the faulty system or component.

REMOVAL AND INSTALLATION

1. Disconnect the negative battery cable.
2. Remove the glove box and locate the control module.
3. Disconnect the connector to the module and remove the mounting screws.
4. Remove the module from the evaporator housing.
5. The installation is the reverse of the removal installation.
6. Connect the negative battery cable and check the entire climate control system for proper operation.

Temperature Sensors

OPERATION

Stealth

Stealth automatic air conditioner uses a photo sensor on the dashboard to measure sunlight and temperature, a water temperature sensor behind the glove box to measure engine coolant temperature and an outside air temperature sensor, located by the glove box, to measure exterior air temperature.

AUTO COMPRESSOR CONTROL UNIT DIAGNOSTICS—SUMMIT

Terminal No.	Name of Signal	Condition	Terminal voltage
1	Auto compressor control unit power supply	Ignition switch ON	Battery positive voltage
8	Auto compressor control unit earth	At all times	0V
7	Auto compressor control unit power supply (DRY mode)	When the ignition switch and the blower switch are ON, and the air conditioning switch has been turned to the second level	Battery positive voltage
2	Auto compressor control unit power supply (ECONO mode)	When the ignition switch and the blower switch are ON, and the air conditioning switch has been turned to the first level	Battery positive voltage
6	Air conditioning compressor clutch relay	When the compressor ON conditions are satisfied	Battery positive voltage
22	Air thermo sensor power supply	The ignition switch, blower switch and air conditioning switch are all ON	Approx. 3V
26	Air thermo sensor	At all times	0V

AIR CONDITIONING CONTROL UNIT DIAGNOSTICS—LASER AND TALON

Terminal	Measurement item	Tester connection	Conditions		Specified value
1	Resistance	1–6	—		1,500±150 Ω at 25°C (77°F)
2	Voltage	2–3 2–8	Air conditioner switch	ON	System voltage
				OFF	0 V
3	Continuity	3-Ground	—		Continuity
4	Continuity	4-Ground	—		Continuity
5	Resistance	5–7	—		1,500±150 Ω at 25°C (77°F)
8	Continuity	8-Ground	—		Continuity
9	Voltage	9–3 9–8	Thermo sensor	OFF 78°C (172°F)	System voltage
				ON 85°C (185°F)	0 V
10	Voltage	10–3 10–8	ECONO switch	ON	System voltage
				OFF	0 V

If the connector on the wire harness side is correct, replace the air conditioner control unit.

AIR CONDITIONING CONTROL UNIT DIAGNOSTICS—STEALTH

Terminal	Signal	Conditions	voltage
8, 9	Auto compressor control unit ground	At all times	0V
1	Auto compressor control unit power supply	When ignition switch is ON	positive voltage
6	Air conditioning compressor relay	When all conditions for switch-ON of the compressor are satisfied	Battery positive voltage
7	Air conditioning switch: A/C	When air conditioning switch pressed in to second step	Battery positive voltage
2	Air conditioning switch: ECONO	When air conditioning switch pressed in to first step	Battery positive voltage
21	Fin-thermo sensor ⊕	Ignition switch, blower switch and air conditioning switch: ON	Approx. 2.5V
22	Air-inlet sensor ⊕	Ignition switch, blower switch and air conditioning switch: ON	Approx. 1V
23	Fin-thermo sensor ⊖	Ignition switch, blower switch and air conditioning switch: ON Ambient temperature: 4°C (39°F)	0V
26	Air-inlet sensor ⊖	Ignition switch, blower switch and air conditioning switch: ON Ambient temperature: 4°C (39°F)	0V

AUTO COMPRESSOR CONTROL UNIT DIAGNOSTICS—SUMMIT WAGON

Terminal	Name of Signal	Condition	Terminal voltage
7	Auto compressor control unit earth	At all time	0V
3	Auto compressor control unit power supply (A/C mode)	When the ignition switch and the blower switch are ON, and the air conditioner switch has been turned to the second level	System voltage
5	Auto compressor control unit power supply (ECONO mode)	When the ignition switch and the blower switch are ON, and the air conditioner switch has been turned to the first level	System voltage
1	Air conditioner compressor relay	When the compressor ON conditions are satisfied	System voltage
8	Air thermo sensor power supply	The ignition switch, blower switch and air conditioner switch are all ON	5V
10	Air thermo sensor	Sensor temperature is 25°C (77°F) [1.5 kΩ]	2.2V
4	Air inlet sensor power source	The ignition switch, blower switch and air conditioner switch are all ON	4.8V
9	Air inlet sensor	Sensor temperature is 25°C (77°F) [1.5 kΩ]	3.3V

AUTO COMPRESSOR CONTROL UNIT DIAGNOSTICS—AVENGER AND SEBRING (SOHC)

Terminal No.	Name of Signal	Condition	Terminal voltage
1	Automatic compressor ECU power supply	The ignition switch is ON.	Battery positive voltage
2	Automatic compressor ECU power supply (ECONO mode)	When the ignition switch and the blower switch are ON, and the A/C switch has been turned to the first level.	Battery positive voltage
6	A/C compressor clutch relay	When the compressor ON conditions are satisfied.	Battery positive voltage
7	Automatic compressor ECU power supply (DRY mode)	When the ignition switch and the blower switch are ON, and the A/C switch has been turned to the second level.	Battery positive voltage
8,9	Automatic compressor ECU ground	At all time	0V
21	Air inlet sensor	Sensor temperature is 25°C [1.5 kΩ].	Approx. 3V
22	Fin thermo sensor	Sensor temperature is 25°C [1.5 kΩ].	Approx. 3V
23	Air inlet sensor power supply	The ignition switch, blower switch and A/C switch are all ON.	5V
26	Fin thermo sensor power supply	The ignition switch, blower switch and A/C switch are all ON.	5V

Air conditioning control unit connector terminals—Avenger and Sebring (SOHC)

Concorde, Intrepid, LHS, New Yorker and Vision

These models, equipped with automatic air conditioning, use an in-car temperature sensor, located behind the nameplate on the right side of the instrument panel, to use aspirated air samples of the interior temperature. An ambient temperature sensor is located on the inside of the left front bumper beam to provide signal to the ATC of exterior temperature. A sun sensor on the instrument panel top cover acts as a diode to determine sun intensity and help set mode door position

REMOVAL AND INSTALLATION

Photo/Sun Sensor

STEALTH

1. Disconnect the negative battery cable.
2. Remove the glove box out case.
3. Detach the photo sensor connector.
4. Remove the photo sensor from the instrument panel.
5. Installation is the reverse of the removal procedure.

CONCORDE, INTREPID, LHS, NEW YORKER AND VISION

1. Disconnect the negative battery cable.
2. Remove the top instrument panel cover.
3. Lift out the sensor and disconnect the wiring.
4. Installation is the reverse of the removal procedure.

Outside/Ambient Air Sensor

STEALTH

1. Disconnect the negative battery cable.
2. Remove the glove box stopper and glove box assembly.
3. Remove the outside air temperature sensor.
4. Installation is the reverse of the removal procedure.

CONCORDE, INTREPID, LHS, NEW YORKER AND VISION

1. Disconnect the negative battery cable.
2. Remove the sensor mounting screw.
3. Disconnect the sensor wire and remove the sensor.
4. Installation is the reverse of the removal procedure.

Water Temperature Sensor

STEALTH

1. Disconnect the negative battery cable.
2. Remove the glove box stopper and glove box assembly.
3. Remove the plate from the sensor.

AUTO COMPRESSOR CONTROL UNIT DIAGNOSTICS—AVENGER AND SEBRING (DOHC)

Terminal No.	Name of Signal	Condition	Terminal voltage
1	A/C compressor clutch relay	When the compressor ON conditions are satisfied.	Battery positive voltage
2	Automatic compressor ECU ground	At all time	0V
4	Automatic compressor ECU power supply (ECONO mode)	When the ignition switch and the blower switch are ON, and the A/C switch has been turned to the first level.	Battery positive voltage
5	Automatic compressor ECU power supply	The ignition switch is ON.	Battery positive voltage
6	Air inlet sensor	Sensor temperature is 25°C [1.5 kΩ].	Approx. 3V
7	Fin thermo sensor	Sensor temperature is 25°C [1.5 kΩ].	Approx. 3V
12	Fin thermo sensor power supply	The ignition switch, blower switch and A/C switch are all ON.	5V
13	Automatic compressor ECU power supply (DRY mode)	When the ignition switch and the blower switch are ON, and the A/C switch has been turned to the second level.	Battery positive voltage
14	Air inlet sensor power supply	The ignition switch, blower switch and A/C switch are all ON.	5V

1	2	3		4	5	6
7	8	9	10 11	12	13	14

Air conditioning control unit connector terminals—Avenger and Sebring (DOHC)

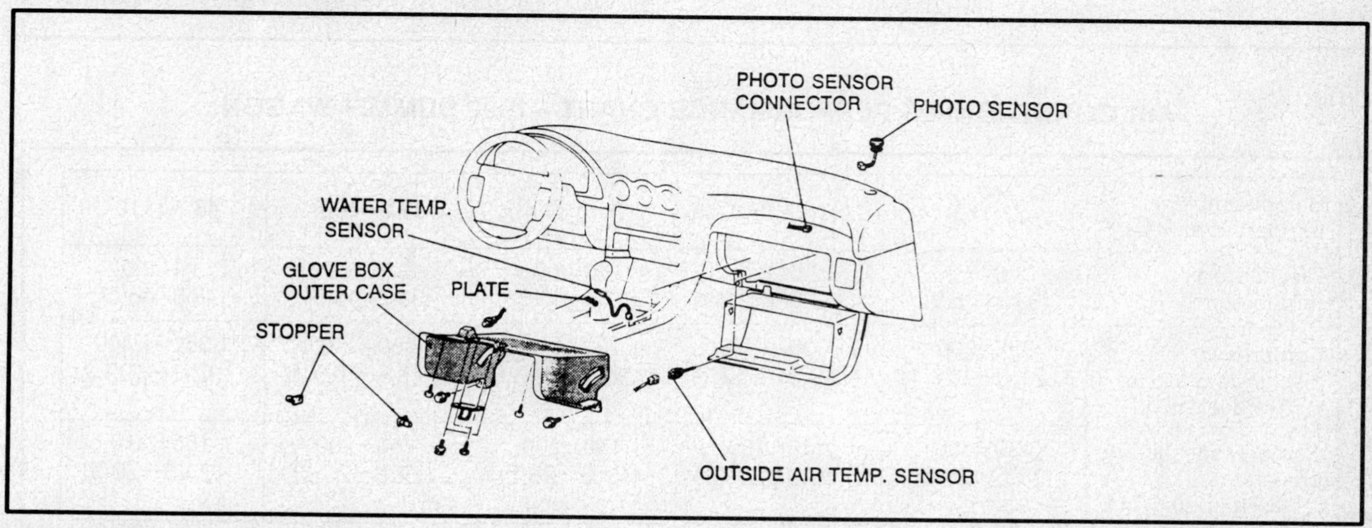

ATC sensor locations—Stealth

4. Disconnect the sensor and remove it.
5. Installation is the reverse of the removal procedure.

In-Car Temperature Sensor

CONCORDE, INTREPID, LHS, NEW YORKER AND VISION

1. Disconnect the negative battery cable.
2. Remove the right side instrument panel trim cap (gently pry off).
3. Remove the right horizontal front trim (1 screw).
4. Remove the sensor retaining screws, pull the sensor out and disconnect the wiring.
5. Installation is the reverse of the removal procedure.

SYSTEM DIAGNOSIS

Air Conditioning Performance

PERFORMANCE TEST

Air temperature in the testing area must be at least 70°F (21°C) to ensure the accuracy of this test.

1. Connect a manifold gauge set to the system.
2. Set the controls to **RECIRC** or **MAX**, the mode lever to the **PANEL** position, temperature control level to the COOLEST position and the blower on its HIGHEST position.
3. Start the engine and adjust the idle speed to 1000 rpm with the compressor clutch engaged.
4. Allow the engine come to normal operating temperature and keep doors and windows closed.
5. Insert a thermometer in the left center panel outlet and operate the engine for 10 minutes. The clutch may cycle depending on the ambient conditions.
6. With the clutch engaged, compare the discharge air temperature to the performance chart.
7. If the values do not meet specifications, check system components for proper operation.

Air Conditioning Compressor

COMPRESSOR NOISE

Noises that develop during air conditioning operation can be misleading. A noise that sounds like serious compressor damage may only be a loose belt, mounting bolt or clutch assembly. Improper belt tension can also emit a noise that can be mistaken for more serious problems. Check and adjust all possible causes of the noise, including oil level, before replacing the compressor.

AIR CONDITIONING PERFORMANCE CHART—LASER, TALON AND SUMMIT

Ambient Temperature °F (°C)	Air Temperature at Center Panel Vent °F (°C)	Compressor Discharge Pressure PSI (kPa)	Compressor Suction Pressure PSI (kPa)
70 (21)	35–45 (2–8)	130–188 (896–1295)	10–21 (69–145)
80 (27)	35–45 (2–8)	145–210 (1000–1447)	13–25 (90–172)
90 (32)	35–45 (2–8)	165–245 (1140–1688)	15–30 (103–207)
100 (38)	37–50 (3–10)	190–270 (1336–1860)	20–33 (138–227)
110 (43)	39–55 (4–13)	200–300 (1406–2109)	20–35 (138–241)

AIR CONDITIONING PERFORMANCE CHART—1993 SUMMIT WAGON

Garage ambient temperature °C (°F)	21 (70)	26.7 (80)	32.2 (90)	37.8 (100)	43.3 (110)
Discharge air temperature °C (°F)	2.5–7.5 (36.5–45.5)	2.5–8.0 (36.5–46.5)	3.0–8.0 (37.4–46.5)	3.5–8.0 (38.3–46.5)	3.5–8.0 (38.3–46.5)
Compressor discharge pressure kPa (psi)	850–900 (121.0–128.1)	1,000–1,070 (142.3–152.3)	1,100–1,150 (156.5–163.6)	1,250–1,320 (177.9–187.8)	1,350–1,400 (192.1–199.2)
Compressor suction pressure kPa (psi)	130–190 (18.5–27.0)	140–190 (19.9–27.0)	140–200 (19.9–28.5)	160–200 (22.8–28.5)	165–210 (23.5–29.9)

AIR CONDITIONING PERFORMANCE CHART—STEALTH

Garage ambient temperature °C (°F)	21 (70)	26.7 (80)	32.2 (90)	37.8 (100)	43.3 (110)
Discharge air temperature °C (°F)	0.0 – 3.0 (32.0 – 37.4)	1.0 – 4.0 (33.8 – 39.2)	1.0 – 4.0 (33.8 – 39.2)	1.0 – 4.0 (33.8 – 39.2)	2.0 – 5.0 (35.6 – 41.0)
Compressor discharge pressure kPa (psi)	690 – 740 (98.1 – 105.3)	780 – 830 (110.9 – 118.1)	870 – 920 (123.7 – 130.9)	1,080 – 1,130 (153.6 – 160.7)	1,210 – 1,260 (172.1 – 179.2)
Compressor suction pressure kPa (psi)	130 – 190 (18.5 – 27.5)	130 – 190 (18.5 – 27.5)	130 – 190 (18.5 – 27.5)	130 – 190 (18.5 – 27.5)	130 – 190 (18.5 – 27.5)

AIR CONDITIONING PERFORMANCE CHART—1994–95 SUMMIT WAGON

Garage ambient temperature °C (°F)	20 (68)	25 (77)	35 (95)	45 (113)
Discharge air temperature °C (°F)	10.8 (51.4)	16.8 (62.2)	23.5 (74.3)	24.3 (95.7)
Compressor discharge pressure kPa (psi)	1,030 (149)	1,128 (164)	1,393 (202)	1,736 (252)
Compressor suction pressure kPa (psi)	178 (26)	184 (27)	196 (28)	210 (30)

AIR CONDITIONING PERFORMANCE CHART—AVENGER AND SEBRING (SOHC)

Garage ambient temperature °C (°F)	20 (68)	25 (77)	35 (95)	40 (104)
Discharge air temperature °C (°F)	2.5–5.0 (37–41)	3.0–6.0 (37–43)	3.5–7.5 (38–46)	4.0–8.0 (39–46)
Compressor high pressure kPa (psi)	892 (129.4)	892 (129.4)	1,422 (206.3)	1,824 (264.6)
Compressor low pressure kPa (psi)	186 (27.0)	186 (27.0)	206 (29.9)	275 (39.9)

AIR CONDITIONING PERFORMANCE CHART—AVENGER AND SEBRING (DOHC)

Garage ambient temperature °C (°F)	20 (68)	25 (77)	35 (95)	40 (104)
Discharge air temperature °C (°F)	2.0–7.0 (36–45)	3.0–7.0 (37–45)	6.0 (43)	12 (54)
Compressor high pressure kPa (psi)	1,089–1,304 (158.0–189.2)	1,422–1,579 (206.3–229.1)	1,863 (270.3)	2,167 (314.4)
Compressor low pressure kPa (psi)	177–304 (25.7–44.1)	206–226 (29.9–32.8)	265 (38.4)	343 (49.8)

AIR CONDITIONING PERFORMANCE CHART—CONCORDE, INTREPID, LHS, NEW YORKER AND VISION

Ambient Temperature	21°C (70°F)	26.5°C (80°F)	37.5°C (90°F)	37.5°C (100°F)	43°C (110°F)
Maximum Allowable Air Temperature at Center Left Panel Outlet	7°C (45°F)	9°C (49°F)	12°C (54°F)	13°C (56°F)	15°C (59°F)
Compressor Discharge Pressure	772–1448 kPa (112–210 PSI)	903–1475 kPa (131–214 PSI)	1241–1482 kPa (180–215 PSI)	1400–1986 kPa (203–288 PSI)	1600–2282 kPa (232–331 PSI)
Compressor Suction Pressure	69–255 kPa (10–37 PSI)	117–262 kPa (17–38 PSI)	145–324 kPa (21–47 PSI)	193–352 kPa (28–51 PSI)	207–365 kPa (30–53 PSI)

COMPRESSOR CLUTCH INOPERATIVE

1. Verify refrigerant charge, and charge as required.
2. Check for 12 volts at the clutch coil connection. If voltage is detected, check the coil.
3. If no voltage is detected at the coil, check the fuse or fusible link. If the fuse is not blown, check for voltage at the clutch relay. If voltage is not detected there, continue working backwards through the system's switches, etc. until an open circuit is detected.
4. Inspect all suspect parts and replace as required.
5. When the repair is complete, perform a complete system performance test.

CLUTCH COIL TESTING

Laser, Talon, Stealth, Summit, Summit Wagon, Avenger and Sebring

1. Disconnect the negative battery cable.
2. Disconnect the compressor clutch connector.
3. Apply 12 volts to the wire leading to the clutch coil. If the clutch is operating properly, an audible click will occur when the clutch is magnetically pulled into the coil. If no click is heard, inspect the coil.
4. Check the resistance across the coil lead wire and ground. The specification is 3.4–3.8 ohms at approximately 70°F (20°C).
5. Replace the clutch coil if not within specification.

Cirrus and Stratus

1. Verify battery state of charge. Test indicator in the battery should be green.
2. Connect an ammeter (0–10 ampere scale) in series with the clutch coil terminal. Use a voltmeter (0–20 volt scale) with clip leads measuring voltage across the battery and A/C clutch.
3. With the A/C control in the A/C mode and blower at **LOW** speed, start the engine and run at normal idle.
4. The A/C clutch should engage immediately and the clutch voltage should be within 2 volts of the battery voltage. If the A/C clutch does not engage, test the fusible link.
5. The A/C clutch coil is acceptable if the current draw is 2.0–4.15 amperes at 11.5–12.5 volts at the clutch coil.

- This is with the work area temperature at 70°F (21°C).
- If the voltage is more than 12.5 volts, add electrical loads by turning **ON** electrical accessories until the voltage reads below 12.5 volts.
- If coil current reads zero, the coil is open and should be replaced.
- If the ammeter reading is 5 amperes or more, the coil is shorted and should be replaced.
- If the coil voltage is not within 2 volts of the battery voltage, test the clutch coil feed circuit for excessive voltage drop.

Manual Air Conditioning System

Concorde, Intrepid, LHS, New Yorker and Vision

Non-ATC systems have built in self-diagnostics. Trouble codes are read through the rear window defogger switch LED light.

1. Start the engine and allow it to run throughout the test (vehicle must be stationary).
2. Set the left knob (blower control) to any speed setting. Set the center temperature knob to full **COOL** position. Set the right knob (mode) to **DEFROST** position. The A/C button can be **ON** or **OFF**.
3. Press the rear window defogger switch and hold it for 3–5 seconds. The rear window defogger light will begin to flash, indicating the system in now in self-diagnostics, and the actuators are being calibrated and checked (this takes about 30 seconds).

NOTE: The self-diagnostic mode can be exited at any time by turning the blower switch OFF or pushing the A/C switch or rear window defogger switch one time. This mode can also be exited by changing the temperature or mode selector knob settings.

4. If the actuator calibration was successful, the rear defogger light will go out. If so, skip to Step **6**. If the light stays ON (indicating a calibration problem or a problem in the control head), go to Step **5**.
5. To determine where the problem is, perform the following:
   - Move the mode knob to **MIX** position. If the defogger light stays ON, it indicates an internal control head prob-

lem, and the control head requires replacement. If the light goes OFF, the control head is okay.

- Move the mode knob to **FLOOR** position. If the defogger light stays ON, the blend door actuator wiring or the blend (temp) door has a problem which must be repaired or replaced. If the light goes OFF when the mode knob is moved, the blend door circuit is okay.
- Move the mode knob to **BI-LEVEL**. If the light stays ON, the mode actuator or circuit has a problem that must be repaired or replaced. If the light went OFF, this circuit, the mode door and actuator are okay.

6. To check the mode actuator knob function, perform the following:

- If not already performed, run calibration procedure (steps **1** through **3**).
- Place the mode knob in **MIX**. The rear defogger light should flash twice then pause. It should continue this 2-flash sequence. If so, the **MIX** mode is okay.
- Place the mode knob in **FLOOR**. The rear window defogger switch light should flash 3 times then pause and then repeat the 3-flash sequence. If so, the **FLOOR** mode is okay.
- Place the mode knob in **BI-LEVEL**. The defogger switch light should flash 4 times, then pause and then repeat the 4flash sequence. If so, the **BI-LEVEL** mode is okay.
- Place the mode knob in **PANEL**. The defogger switch light should flash 5 times, then pause and then repeat the 5-flash sequence. If so, the **PANEL** mode is okay.
- Place the mode knob in **RECIRC** position. The defogger switch light should flash 6 times, pause, then repeat the 6-flash sequence. If so, the **RECIRC** mode is okay.
- Place the mode knob in **RECIRC BI-LEVEL** position. The defogger switch light should flash 7 times, pause, then repeat the 7-flash sequence. If so, the **RECIRC BI-LEVEL** mode is okay.

7. To check the temperature control knob function, perform the following:

- Place the mode knob in **DEFROST**. Slowly turn the temperature knob to the right while watch the rear window defogger switch light. As the knob is turned the switch will start to flash and the flashing will speed up as the knob is turned further to the right. At full **HEAT** position, the light will go out.
- Mode the mode knob between **PANEL** and **RECIRC PANEL** positions and watch the recirculation door for movement. If the door moves correctly, the recirc door, actuator and circuits are okay.

8. This completes the self-diagnostic sequence. Exist the diagnostic mode by turning OFF the blower or pushing the **A/C** switch or rear window defogger switch once.

Full Automatic Temperature Control System

ON-BOARD DIAGNOSTICS

Stealth

GENERAL TROUBLESHOOTING

1. Check that the air ducts and actuator rods are in place.
2. Check that connectors are tight and clean and that the fuses are okay.
3. Using an analog voltmeter, check the diagnostic output. If a failure code is output, check the failing system and repair as necessary.

Self-diagnostics hook-up and terminal locations—Stealth

4. If the outputs are normal, check for terminal voltage or continuity with a circuit tester as shown in the appropriate charts.
5. Use the "Troubleshooting Quick Reference Chart" to find the item number to check. When checking components, be sure to detach the connectors first.

SELF-DIAGNOSIS CHECKING

Self-diagnosis checking is performed when there has been an automatic cancellation, without cancel switch operation. The following method can be used to check the diagnosis. Note that the diagnosis check connector is located under the driver's side instrument panel.

NOTE: An appropriate scan tool can also be used to read the trouble codes.

1. Connect an analog voltmeter across the self-diagnostic output terminal **7** and the ground terminal **12** of the diagnosis connector.
2. Turn the ignition to **ON**.
3. Watch the voltmeter pointer deflection and read the self-diagnosis pattern (long and short pointer movements which must be counted as they occur).
4. Refer to the appropriate chart, find the faulty item and make repairs.
5. Erase the failure code by the following procedure:
   - Turn the ignition switch to **OFF**.
   - Disconnect the negative battery cable and leave it OFF for 10 seconds or more, then reconnect the cable.
   - Turn the ignition switch to **ON** and read the self-diagnostics output code to be sure the correct code is being output.

Concorde, Intrepid, LHS, New Yorker and Vision

SELF-DIAGNOSTICS

1. The ATC control head can only be placed into the diagnostic mode while the engine is running, and the vehicle is not moving. Place the temperature control to **75°**.
2. Press and hold the **FLOOR, MIX** and **DEFROST** buttons at the same time. The ATC control head will begin to blink. When it does, release the buttons. The control head is now in the diagnostic mode and will continue to blink until it completes its calibrations and tests.
3. Once the blinking has stopped the panel will display any trouble codes stored in the Body Control Module (BCM) relating to ATC operations.

NOTE: If no trouble codes are stored, the control head will return to normal operating temperature display.

4. Write down the trouble code as it is shown. If there is more than one code stored, each will be shown in sequence. Scroll through the multiple codes (if shown) by pressing the **PANEL** button.

NOTE: Fault code "26" can be created if the in-car sensor is disconnected while the system is operating; this results in the control head display disappearing. To correct, erase fault code "26" from the BCM.

ERASING DIAGNOSTIC TROUBLE CODES

Disconnect the negative battery cable for 10 minutes to erase the BCM trouble code memory.

SELF DIAGNOSTIC TROUBLE CODE CHART—CONCORDE, INTREPID, LHS, NEW YORKER AND VISION

CODE	DESCRIPTION
23	ATC Blend Door Feedback Failure
24	ATC Mode Door Feedback Failure
25	Ambient Sensor
26	ATC In-Car Sensor
27	Sun Sensor Failure
31	ATC Recirculation Door Stall Failrue
32	ATC Blend Door Stall Failure
33	ATC Mode Door Stall Failure
34	Engine Temperature Message not Received
35	Evaporator Sensor Failure
36	ATC Head Communication Failure

AIR CONDITIONING TROUBLESHOOTING CHART—AVENGER AND SEBRING

Trouble symptom	Problem cause	Remedy
When the ignition switch is "ON", the A/C does not operate.	A/C compressor clutch relay is defective.	Replace A/C compressor clutch relay.
	Magnetic clutch is defective.	Replace the armature plate, rotor or clutch coil.
	Refrigerant leak or overfilling of refrigerant	Refill the refrigerant, repair the leak or take out some of the refrigerant.
	Dual pressure switch is defective.	Replace the dual pressure switch.
	A/C switch is defective.	Replace the A/C switch.
	Blower switch is defective.	Replace the blower switch.
	Air inlet sensor is defective.	Replace the sensor.
	Fin thermo sensor is defective.	
	Refrigerant temperature switch is defective. <SOHC>	Replace the refrigerant temperature switch.
	Automatic compressor ECU is defective.	Replace the automatic compressor ECU.
	Revolution pick up sensor is defective. <DOHC>	Replace the revolution pick up sensor.
When the A/C is operating, temperature inside the passenger compartment doesn't decrease (no cool air).	Refrigerant leak	Refill the refrigerant and repair the leak.
	Dual pressure switch is defective.	Replace the dual pressure switch.
	Air inlet sensor is defective.	Replace the sensor.
	Fin thermo sensor is defective.	
	Refrigerant temperature switch is defective. <SOHC>	Replace the refrigerant temperature switch.
	Automatic compressor ECU is defective.	Replace the automatic compressor ECU.
Blower-motor/fan inoperative	Blower relay is defective.	Replace the blower relay.
	Blower fan and motor is defective.	Replace the blower fan and motor.
	Resistor (for blower motor) is defective.	Replace the resistor.
	Blower switch is defective.	Replace the blower switch.

AIR CONDITIONING TROUBLESHOOTING CHART—AVENGER AND SEBRING, CONT'D

Trouble symptom	Problem cause	Remedy
Blower fan and motor keeps running	Short circuit of the harness between the blower fan and motor and the blower switch	Repair the harness.
	Blower switch is defective.	Replace the blower switch.
	Blower relay is defective.	Replace the blower relay.
When the A/C is operating, condenser fan does not operate.	Condenser fan motor is defective.	Replace the condenser fan motor.
	Condenser fan relay (LO) is defective.	Replace the condenser fan relay (LO).
	Condenser fan relay (HI) is defective.	Replace the condenser fan relay (HI).
	Resistor (for condenser fan relay LO side) is defective.	Replace the resistor.

AIR CONDITIONING TROUBLESHOOTING CHART—SUMMIT

No.	Trouble symptom	Problem cause	Remedy
1	Air conditioning does not operate when the ignition switch is in the ON position.	Air conditioning compressor clutch relay is defective	Replace air conditioning compressor clutch relay
		Magnetic clutch is defective	Replace the magnetic clutch
		Refrigerant leak or overfilling of refrigerant	Refill the refrigerant, repair the leak or take out some of the refrigerant
		Dual pressure switch or triple pressure switch is defective	Replace the dual pressure switch or triple pressure switch
		Air conditioning switch is defective	Replace the air conditioning switch
		Blower switch is defective	Replace the blower switch
		Air thermo sensor is defective	Replace the sensor
		Auto compressor control unit is defective	Replace the auto compressor control unit
		Refrigerant temperature switch is defective	Replace the refrigerant temperature switch
2	Interior temperature does not lower (No cold air coming out).	Refrigerant leak	Refill the refrigerant and repair the leak
		Dual pressure switch or triple pressure switch is defective	Replace the dual pressure switch or triple pressure switch
		Air thermo sensor is defective	Replace the sensor
		Refrigerant temperature switch is defective	Replace the refrigerant temperature switch
		Auto compressor control unit is defective	Replace the auto compressor control unit
3	Blower motor does not rotate.	Blower motor relay is defective	Replace the blower motor relay
		Blower motor is defective	Replace the blower motor
		Blower switch is defective	Replace the blower switch
		Resistor (for blower motor) is defective	Replace the resistor
4	Blower motor does not stop rotating.	Short circuit of the harness between the blower motor and the blower switch	Repair the harness
		Blower switch is defective	Replace the blower switch
		Blower motor relay is defective	Replace the blower motor relay
5	Condenser fan does not operate when the air conditioning is activated.	Condenser fan motor relay is defective	Replace the condenser fan motor relay
		Fan motor control relay is defective <1.8L Engine>	Replace the fan motor control relay
		Condenser fan motor is defective	Replace the condenser fan motor
		Dual pressure switch or triple pressure switch is defective	Replace the dual pressure switch or triple pressure switch
		Resistor is defective <1.8L Engine>	Replace the resistor

AIR CONDITIONING TROUBLESHOOTING CHART—SUMMIT WAGON

No.	Trouble symptom	Problem cause	Remedy
1	When the ignition switch is "ON", the air conditioning does not operate.	Air conditioning compressor clutch relay is defective	Replace air conditioning clutch compressor relay
		Magnetic clutch is defective	Replace the magnetic clutch
		Refrigerant leak or overfilling of refrigerant	Replenish the refrigerant, repair the leak or take out some of the refrigerant
		Triple pressure switch is defective	Replace the triple pressure switch
		Air conditioning switch is defective	Replace the air conditioning switch
		Blower switch is defective	Replace the blower switch
		Air thermo sensor is defective	Replace the sensor
		Automatic compressor control unit is defective	Replace the automatic compressor control unit
		Belt lock controller is defective <1.8L Engine>	Replace the belt lock controller
		Revolution pick-up sensor is defective <1.8L Engine>	Replace the revolution pick-up sensor
2	When the air conditioning is operating, temperature inside the passenger compartment doesn't decrease (No cool air)	Refrigerant leak	Replenish the refrigerant and repair the leak
		Triple pressure switch is defective	Replace the triple pressure switch
		Air thermo sensor is defective	Replace the sensor
		Automatic compressor control unit is defective	Replace the automatic compressor control unit
3	Blower motor is inoperative	Heater relay is defective	Replace the heater relay
		Blower motor is defective	Replace the blower motor
		Blower switch is defective	Replace the blower switch
		Resistor (for blower motor) is defective	Replace the resistor
4	Blower motor keeps running	Heater relay is defective	Replace heater relay
		Short circuit of the harness between the blower motor and the blower switch	Repair the harness
		Blower switch is defective	Replace the blower switch
5	When the air conditioning is operating, condenser fan does not operate.	Condenser fan motor relay is defective	Replace the condenser fan motor relay
		Condenser fan motor is defective	Replace the condenser fan motor
		Triple pressure switch is defective	Replace the triple pressure switch
		Resistor (for condenser fan motor relay LO side) is defective	Replace the resistor

DIAGNOSTIC DISPLAY PATTERNS AND CODES—STEALTH

No.	Display pattern (output codes) (use with voltmeter)	Cause	Fail safe
1	ON OFF Continuous	Normal	–
2		Open-circuited room-temperature sensor	Condition in which 25°C (77°F) is detected
3		Short-circuited room-temperature sensor	
4		Open-circuited outside-air sensor	Condition in which 20°C (68°F) is detected
5		Short-circuited outside-air sensor	
6		Open-circuited air thermo sensor	Condition in which −2°C (−35.6°F) is detected
7		Short-circuited air thermo sensor	
8		Short-circuited and open-circuited air mix damper potentiometer	MAX. HOT (or MAX. COOL when it is at MAX. COOL)
9		Short-circuited and open-circuited mode selector damper potentiometer	DEF. (or FACE when it is at FACE)
10		Defective air mix damper motor	–
11		Defective mode selector damper motor	–

NOTE: (1) If two or more abnormal conditions occur at the same time, the code numbers are alternately displayed, in order, repeatedly.
(2) The nature of the malfunction is entered and stored in the memory from the time the malfunction occurs until the ignition switch is next turned to OFF.

AUTOMATIC A/C TROUBLESHOOTING QUICK REFERENCE CHART—STEALTH

No.	Inspection item / Symptom	Fuse	Harness (incl. connectors)	Compressor relay	Magnetic clutch	Sensors	A/C engine coolant temperature switch	Pressure switch	Air-conditioning control panel	Refrigerant amount	Receiver	Expansion valve	Compressor	Thermostat	Belt lock controller	Air conditioning control unit	MFI control unit	On-board diagnostic outputs	Blend air damper motor and potentiometer	Heater link	Heater relay	Power transistor	Blower motor	Blower motor relay	Air selection damper motor	Mode selection damper motor/potentiometer	Condenser fan relay	Resistor	Condenser fan motor
1	Air conditioning does not operate when the ignition switch in the ON position.	1	2	3	4		6	7	9	8				5	10	11	12												
2	Interior temperature does not raise even the air conditioning is operating (No warm air coming out).		5		2				6							7		1	3	4									
3	Interior temperature does not lower even the air conditioning is operating (No cold air coming out).	1	4	5	13	11	12		14	6	7	8	9	10		15		2	3										
4	Blower motor does not rotate.	1	4						6							7					2	3	5						
5	Blower motor does not stop rotating.		3						4							5						2		1					
6	Air selection damper does not operate.		2						3							4									1				
7	Mode selection damper does not operate.		3						4							5		1								2			
8	Condenser fan does not operate when the air conditioning is activated.	1																									2	3	4
9	Air-conditioning graphic display does not function correctly.	1	2						3							4													
10	Air conditioning control panel blinks.					2			3				1		4	5	6												
11	Set temperature returns to 25°C (122°F) when the ignition switch is turned ON and OFF.	1	2						3																				

NOTE
(1) ○ indicates the component requiring inspection. (Numbers in ○ are the priority order.)
(2) Use an analog voltmeter to check the control unit.

AUTOMATIC A/C SYSTEM DIAGNOSIS CHART—STEALTH

No.	Symptom	Probable cause	Remedy
1	Air conditioning does not operate when the ignition switch in the ON position.	Open-circuited power circuit harness	Correct harness.
		Defective control panel	Replace control panel.
		Defective air conditioning control unit	Check on-board diagnostic output.
		Defective compressor relay in relay box	Replace.
		Defective magnet clutch	Replace.
		Defective thermostat	Replace.
		Defective A/C engine coolant temperature switch for air conditioning cut off	Replace.
		Defective dual pressure switch	Replace.
		Refrigerant leak	Charge refrigerant, correct leak.
		Excessive refrigerant	Discharge refrigerant.
		Defective belt lock controller <DOHC>	Replace belt lock controller.
		Defective MFI control unit	Replace MFI control unit
2	Interior temperature does not raise (No warm air coming out).	Defective interior temperature sensor input circuit	Check on-board diagnostic output. Replace defective parts.
		Defective blend air damper potentiometer input circuit	
		Defective blend air damper drive motor	Replace blend air damper drive motor.
		Incorrect engagement of blend air damper drive motor lever and blend air damper	Engage correctly.
		Sticking blend air damper	Correct blend air damper.
		Open-circuited harness between blend air damper drive motor and air conditioning control unit	Correct harness.
		Defective control panel	Replace control panel.
		Defective air conditioning control unit	Replace air conditioning control unit.
3	Interior temperature does not lower (No cold air coming out).	Defective interior temperature sensor input circuit	Check on-board diagnostic output. Replace defective parts.
		Defective air inlet sensor input circuit	
		Defective air thermo sensor input circuit	
		Defective blend air damper potentiometer input circuit	

AUTOMATIC A/C SYSTEM DIAGNOSIS CHART—STEALTH, CONT'D

No.	Symptom	Probable cause	Remedy
3	Interior temperature does not lower (No cold air coming out).	Defective blend air damper drive motor	Replace blend air damper drive motor.
		Incorrect engagement of blend air damper drive motor lever and blend air mix damper	Engage correctly.
		Sticking blend air damper	Correct blend air damper.
		Open-circuited harness between blend air damper drive motor and air conditioning control unit	Correct harness.
		Open-circuited harness between photo sensor and air conditioning control unit	Correct harness.
		Defective air-conditioning compressor relay in the relay box	Replace.
		Defective thermostat	Replace thermostat
		Defective revolution pick up sensor <DOHC>	Replace revolution pick up sensor
		Refrigerant leak	Charge refrigerant, correct leak.
		Excessive refrigerant	Discharge refrigerant.
		Clogged receiver	Replace receiver.
		Clogged expansion valve	Replace expansion valve.
		Defective compressor	Replace compressor.
		Defective air inlet sensor	Replace air inlet sensor.
		Defective magnetic clutch	Replace.
		Defective belt lock controller	Replace belt lock controller.
		Defective control panel	Replace control panel.
		Defective air conditioning control unit	Replace air conditioning control unit.
4	Blower motor does not rotate.	Defective blower motor	Replace blower motor.
		Blown thermal fuse inside air conditioning power transistor	Replace air conditioning power transistor.
		Defective blower motor relay	Replace blower motor relay.
		Open-circuited harness between fuse and blower motor relay	Correct harness.

AUTOMATIC A/C SYSTEM DIAGNOSIS CHART—STEALTH, CONT'D

No.	Symptom	Probable cause	Remedy
4	Blower motor does not rotate.	Open-circuited harness between blower motor relay and blower motor	Correct harness.
		Open-circuited harness between air conditioning power transistor and air conditioning control unit	Correct harness.
		Defective control panel	Replace control panel.
		Defective air conditioning control unit	Replace air conditioning control unit.
5	Blower motor does not stop rotating.	Defective blower motor HI relay	Replace power relay.
		Short-circuited harness between blower motor relay and air conditioning power transistor air conditioning control unit	Correct harness.
		Defective control panel	Replace control panel.
		Defective air conditioning control unit	Replace air conditioning control unit.
		Defective air conditioning control unit	Replace air conditioning control unit
		Defective air conditioning power transistor	Replace air conditioning power transistor
6	Air selection damper does not operate.	Defective air selection drive motor	Replace air selection drive motor.
		Incorrect engagement of air selection drive motor damper	Engage correctly.
		Malfunctioning air selection damper	Correct air selection damper.
		Open-circuited harness between air selection motor and air conditioning control unit	Correct harness.
		Defective control panel	Replace control panel
		Defective control panel	Replace control panel.
		Defective air conditioning control unit	Replace air conditioning control unit.

AUTOMATIC A/C SYSTEM DIAGNOSIS CHART—STEALTH, CONT'D

7	Mode selection damper does not operate.	Defective mode selection damper potentiometer input circuit	Check on-board diagnostic output. Replace defective parts.
		Defective mode selection drive motor	Replace mode selection drive motor.
		Incorrect engagement of mode selection drive motor and mode selection damper	Engage correctly.
		Malfunctioning DEF., FACE, and FOOT damper	Correct DEF., FACE, and FOOT damper.
		Open-circuited harness between mode selection motor and control unit	Correct harness.
		Defective control panel	Replace control panel.
		Defective air conditining control unit	Replace air conditioning control unit.
8	Condenser fan does not operate when the air conditioning is activated.	Defective condenser fan motor relay	Replace power relay.
		Defective condenser fan motor	Replace condenser fan motor.
9	Air-conditioning graphic display does not function correctly	Open-circuited harness between control panel and air conditioning control unit	Correct harness.
		Defective control panel	Replace control panel.
		Defective air conditioning control unit	Replace air conditioning control unit.
10	Air conditioning control panel blinks. <DOHC>	Wet compressor drive belt	Dry.
		Insufficient compressor drive belt tension	Check and adjust.
		Defective compressor drive belt	Replace.
		Defective compressor	Check and replace.
		Defective revolution pick-up sensor	Check and replace.
		Defective air conditioning switch	Replace air conditioning control panel
		Defective belt lock controller	Replace belt lock controller
		Defective air conditioning control unit	Replace air conditioning control unit
		Defective MFI contorl unit	Replace MFI control unit
11	Set temperature returns to 25°C (112°F) when the ignition switch is turned ON and OFF.	Open-circuited power circuit harness	Correct harness.
		Defective air conditioning control unit	Replace air conditioning control unit.

1. CHECKING A/C CONTROL UNIT POWER SOURCE CIRCUIT—1993 STEALTH

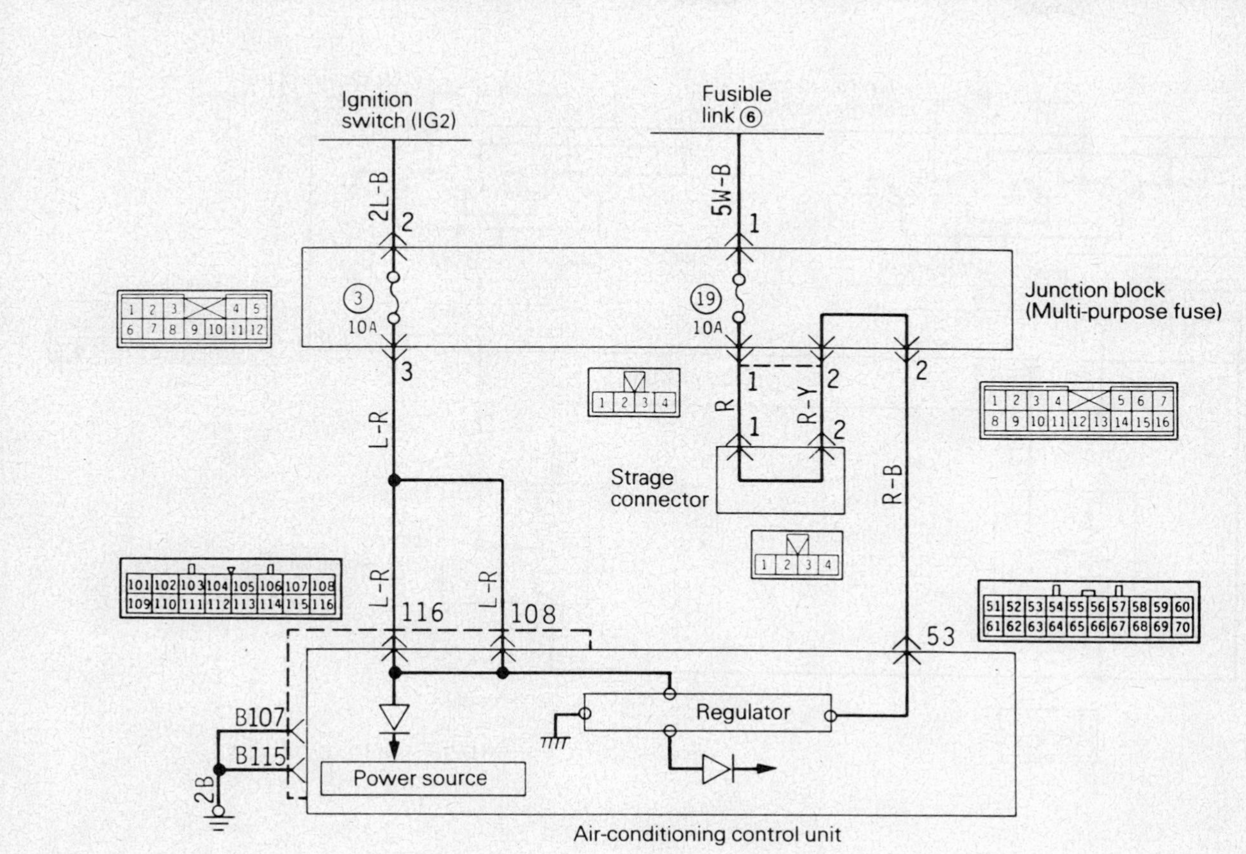

Troubleshooting Hints

- Air conditioning control unit terminal voltage

Terminal No.	Signal name	Condition	Terminal voltage
53	Backup power source	Normally	Battery positive voltage
108, 116	Air conditioning control unit power source	Ignition switch ON	Battery positive voltage
107, 115	Air conditioning control unit ground	Normally	0 V

2. CHECKING OF POTENTIOMETER CIRCUIT—1993 STEALTH

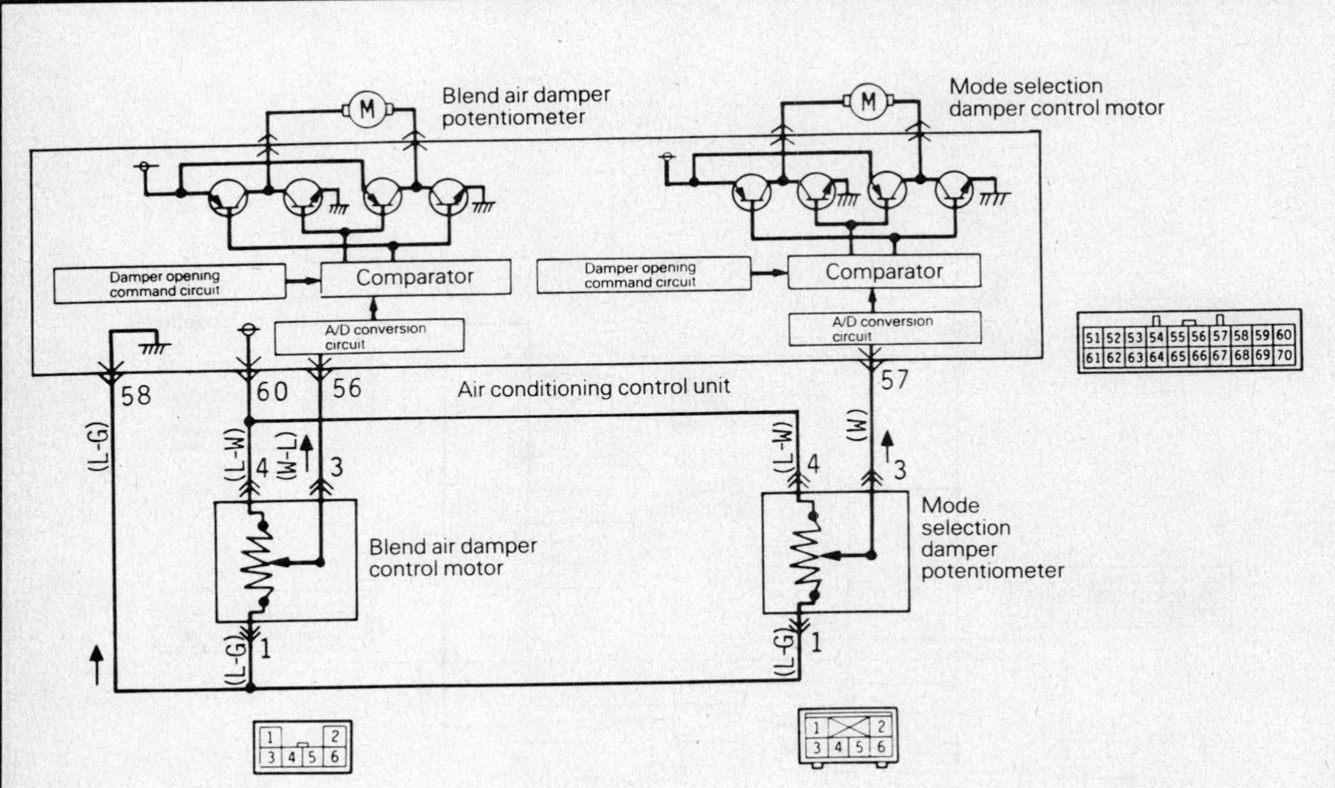

Troubleshooting Hints

- Diagnosis
  No. 31 (Fix blend air damper at MAX. HOT position, or at MAX. COOL position when it is at MAX COOL position.)
  No. 32 (Fix mode selection damper at FACE position, or at FACE position when it is at FACE position.)
- Air conditioning control unit terminal voltages

Terminal No.	Signal name	Condition	Terminal voltage
56	Blend air damper potentiometer (input)	Blend air damper at MAX. COOL position	0.1 – 0.3 V
		Blend air damper at MAX. HOT position	4.7 – 5.0 V
57	Mode selection damper potentiometer (input)	Mode selection damper at FACE position	0.1 – 0.3 V
		Mode selection damper at DEF. position	4.7 – 5.0 V
58	Blend air damper and mode selection damper potentiometer ⊖	Normally	0 V
60	Sensor power source	Normally	4.8 – 5.2 V

3. CHECKING IN–CAR TEMP. SENSOR, AMBIENT TEMP. SENSOR AND AIR THERMO SENSOR CIRCUITS—1993 STEALTH

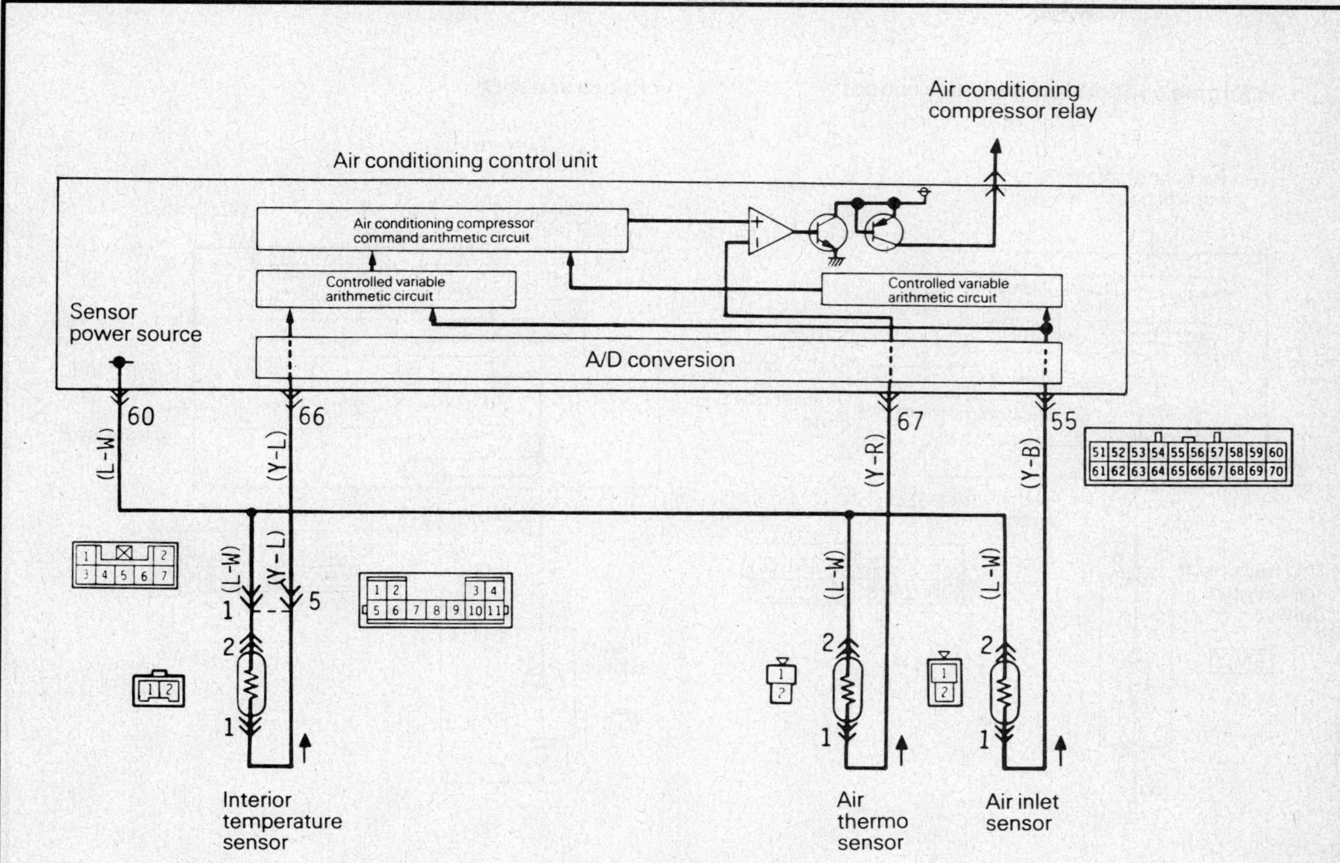

Troubleshooting Hints

- Diagnosis
  No. 11, 12 [Fix interior temperature sensor input signal at 25°C (77°F).]
  No. 13, 14 [Fix air inlet sensor input signal at 15°C (59°F).]
  No. 21, 22 [Fix air thermo sensor input signal at −2°C (−35.6°F).]
- Air conditioning control unit terminal voltages

Terminal No.	Signal name	Condition	Terminal voltage
55	Air inlet sensor	Temperature at sensor 25°C (77°F) (4 kΩ)	2.2 – 2.8 V
60	Sensor power source	Normally	4.8 – 5.2 V
66	Interior temperature sensor	Temperature at sensor 25°C (77°F) (4 kΩ)	2.3 – 2.9 V
67	Air thermo sensor	Temperature at sensor 25°C (77°F) (4 kΩ) when air conditioning is OFF	2.3 – 2.9 V

4. CHECKING WATER TEMP. SENSOR AND PHOTO SENSOR CIRCUITS—1993 STEALTH

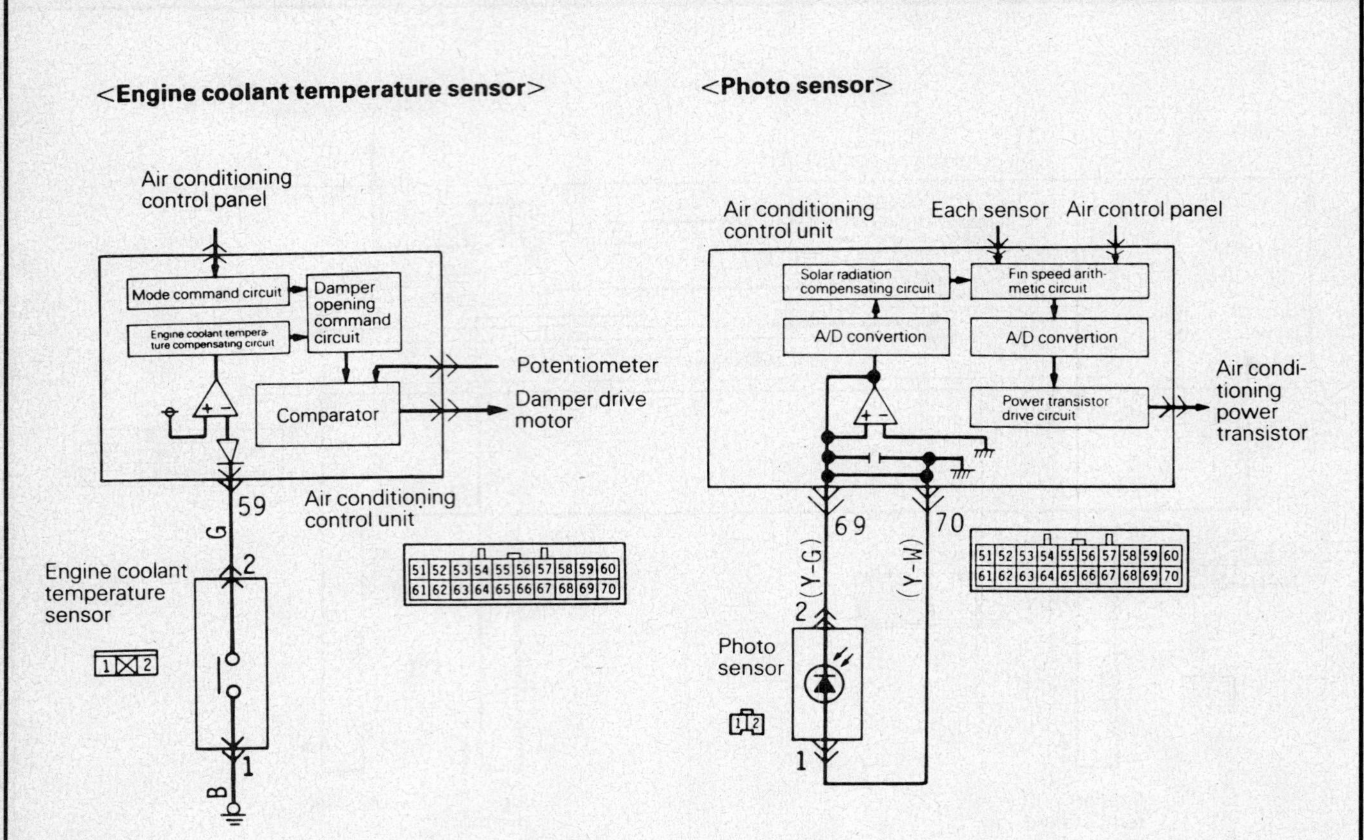

Troubleshooting Hints

- Air conditioning control unit terminal voltages

Terminal No.	Signal name	Condition	Terminal voltage
69	Photo sensor ⊖	Illuminance 100,000 lux or more	–0.1 to –0.2 V
		Illuminance less than 0 lux	0 V
70	Photo sensor ⊕	Normally	0 V
59	Engine coolant temperature sensor ⊕	Switch OFF [Engine coolant temperature less than 50°C (122°F)]	Battery positive voltage
		Switch ON [Engine coolant temperature 50°C (122°F) or higher]	0 V

5. CHECKING BELT LOCK CONTROLLER CIRCUIT—1993 STEALTH

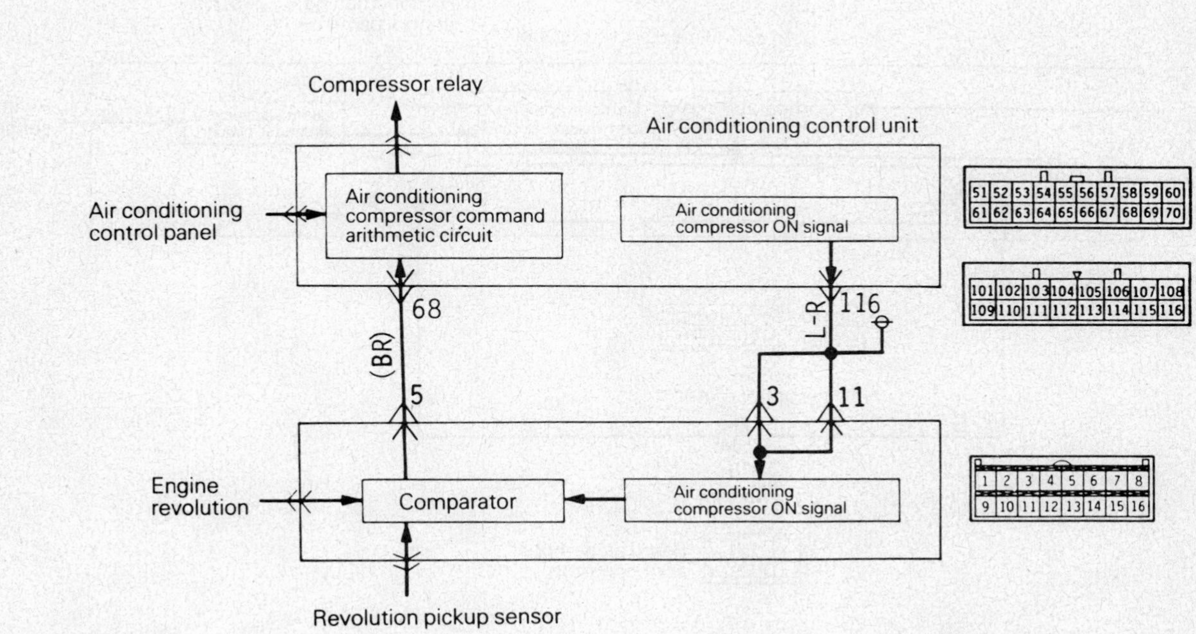

Troubleshooting Hints

- Air conditioning control unit terminal voltages

Terminal No.	Signal name	Condition	Terminal voltage
116	Air conditioning output	Compressor ON	10 V to battery positive voltage

6. CHECKING AIR MIX, OUTLET, AND FRESH/RECIRC DAMPER DRIVE CIRCUITS—1993 STEALTH

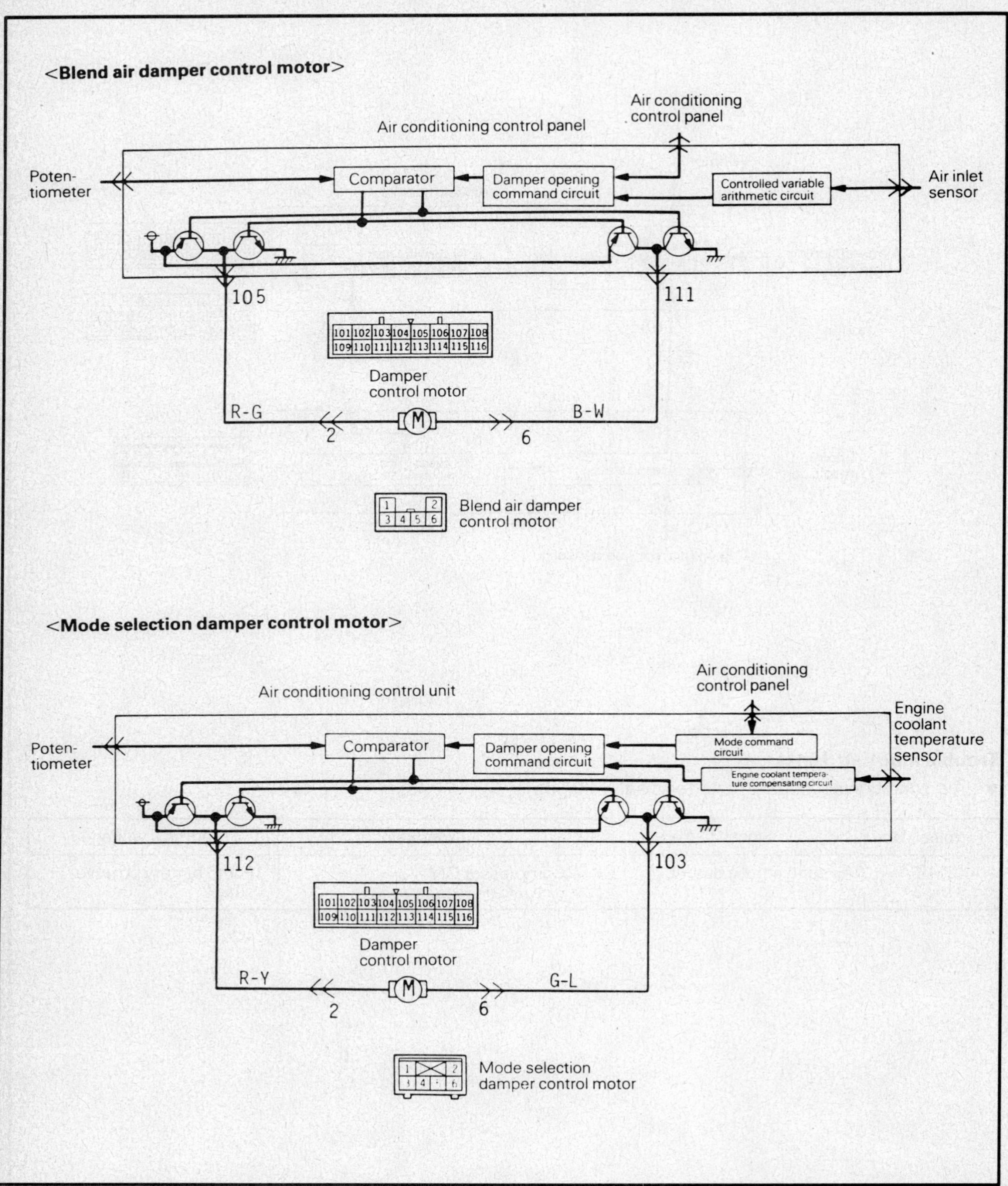

6. CHECKING AIR MIX, OUTLET, AND FRESH/RECIRC DAMPER DRIVE CIRCUITS—1993 STEALTH CONT'D

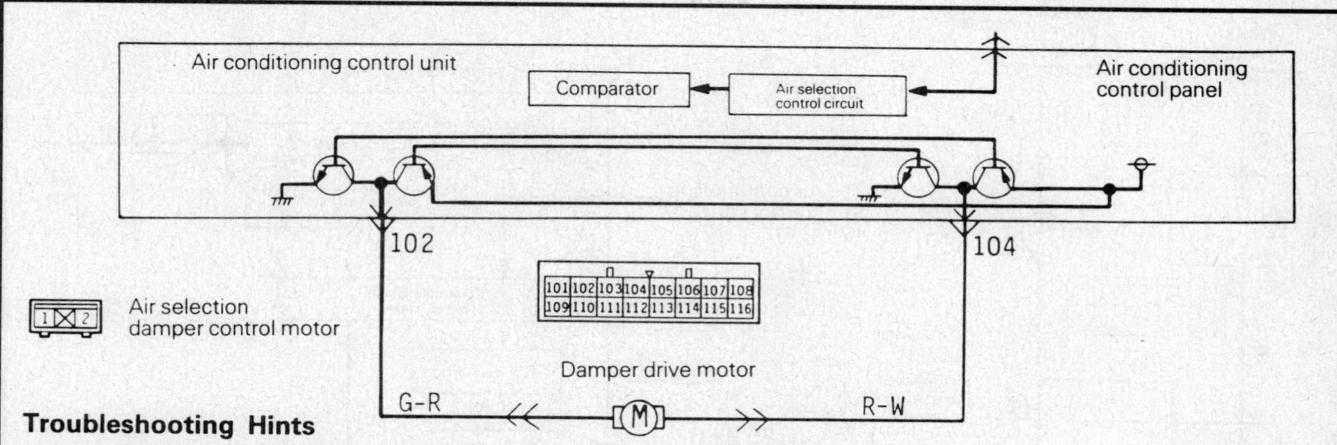

Troubleshooting Hints

- Air conditioning control unit terminal voltages

Terminal No.	Signal name	Condition	Terminal voltage
102	Air selection damper control motor ⊖	Inside-air switch ON (Output turns OFF 40 seconds after the damper moved to inside air position.)	0.5 V
		Outside-air switch ON (Output turns OFF 40 seconds after the damper moved to outside air position.)	10 V
103	Mode selection damper control motor ⊖	FACE switch ON (Output turns OFF 40 seconds after the damper moved to FACE position.)	0.5 V
		DEF. switch ON (Output turns OFF 40 seconds after the damper moved to DEF. position.)	10 V
104	Air selection damper control motor ⊕	Inside-air switch ON (Output turns OFF 40 seconds after inside air has been activated.)	10 V
		Outside-air switch ON (Output turns OFF 40 seconds after outside air has been activated.)	0.5 V
105	Blend air damper control motor ⊕	Temperature is set at 17°C (62.6°F). (Output turns OFF 40 seconds after the damper moved to MAX. COOL position.)	0.5 V
		Temperature is set at 32.5°C (90.5°F). (Output turns OFF 40 seconds after the damper moved to MAX. HOT position.)	10 V
111	Blend air damper control motor ⊖	Temperature is set at 17°C (62.6°F). (Output turns OFF 40 seconds after the damper moved to MAX. COOL position.)	10 V
		Temperature is set at 32.5°C (90.5°F). (Output turns OFF 40 seconds after the damper moved to MAX. HOT position.)	0.5 V
112	Mode selection damper control motor ⊕	FACE switch ON (Output turns OFF 40 seconds after the damper moved to FACE position.)	10 V
		DEF. switch ON (Output turns OFF 40 seconds after the damper moved to DEF. position.)	0.5 V

7. CHECKING POWER TRANSISTOR AND BLOWER MOTOR RELAY CIRCUITS—1993 STEALTH

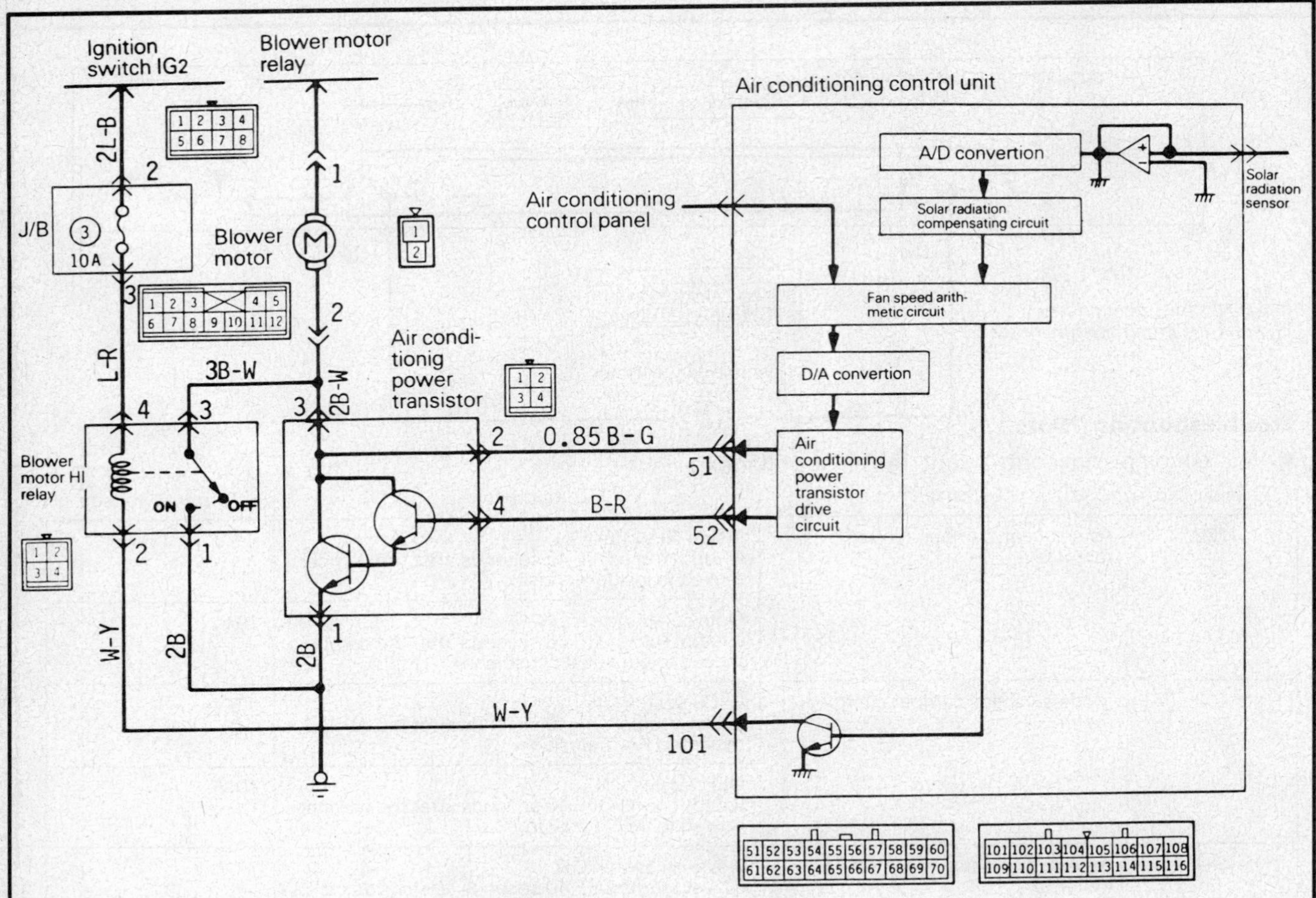

Troubleshooting Hints

- Air conditioning control unit terminal voltages

Terminal No.	Signal name	Condition	Terminal voltage
51	Air conditioning power transistor collector	Switch is turned OFF.	Battery positive voltage
		Switch is placed in LO.	Approx. 7 V
		Switch is placed in HI.	0 V
52	Air conditioning power transistor base	Blower switch is turned OFF.	0 V
		Blower switch is placed in LO.	Approx. 1.3 V
		Blower switch is placed in HI.	Approx. 1.2 V
101	Blower motor HI relay	Fan switch HI is ON.	1.5 V or less
		Fan switch in ME, LO, or OFF.	Battery positive voltage

AIR CONDITIONING CONTROL UNIT CIRCUIT—1994–95 STEALTH

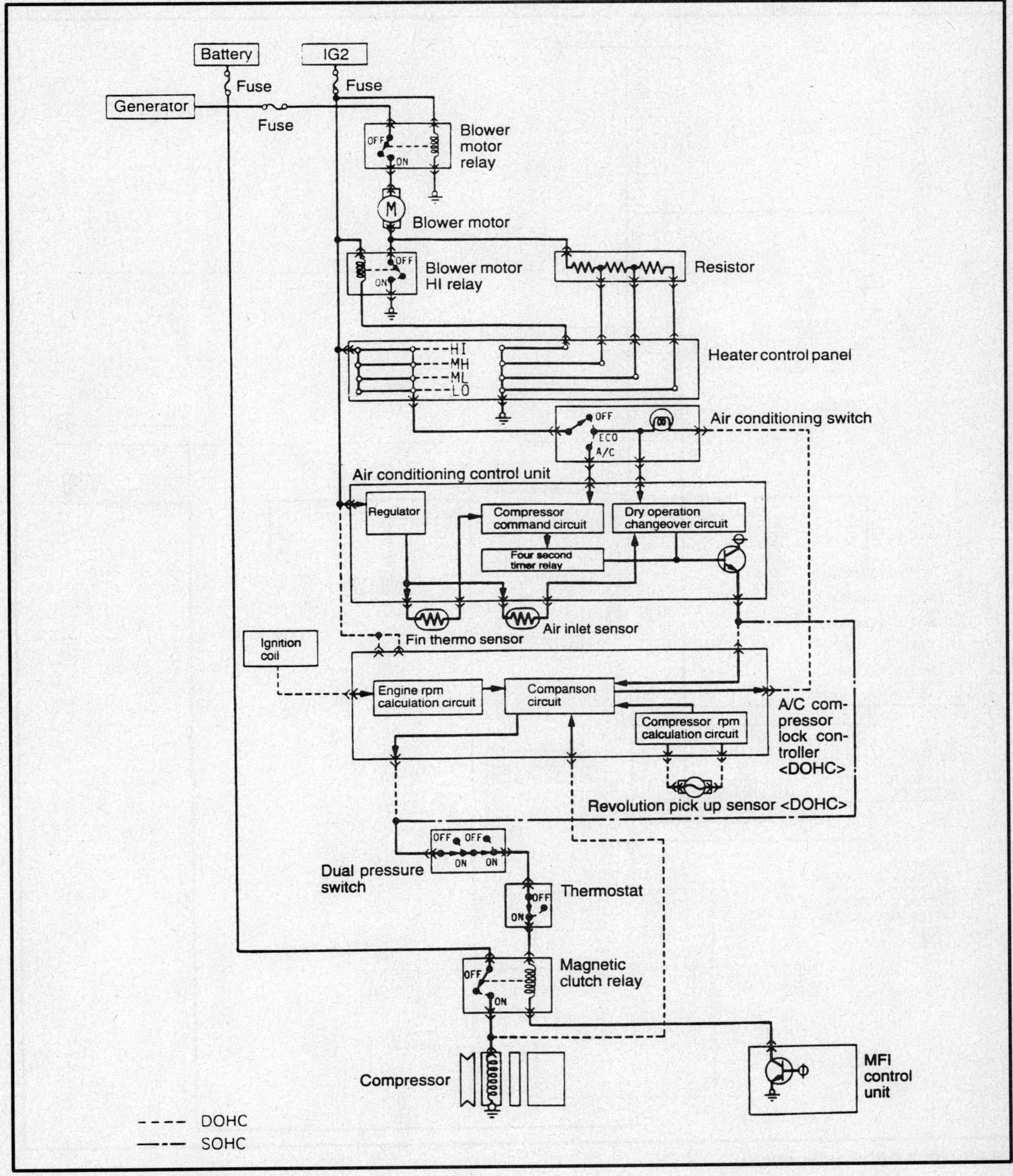

WIRING SCHEMATICS

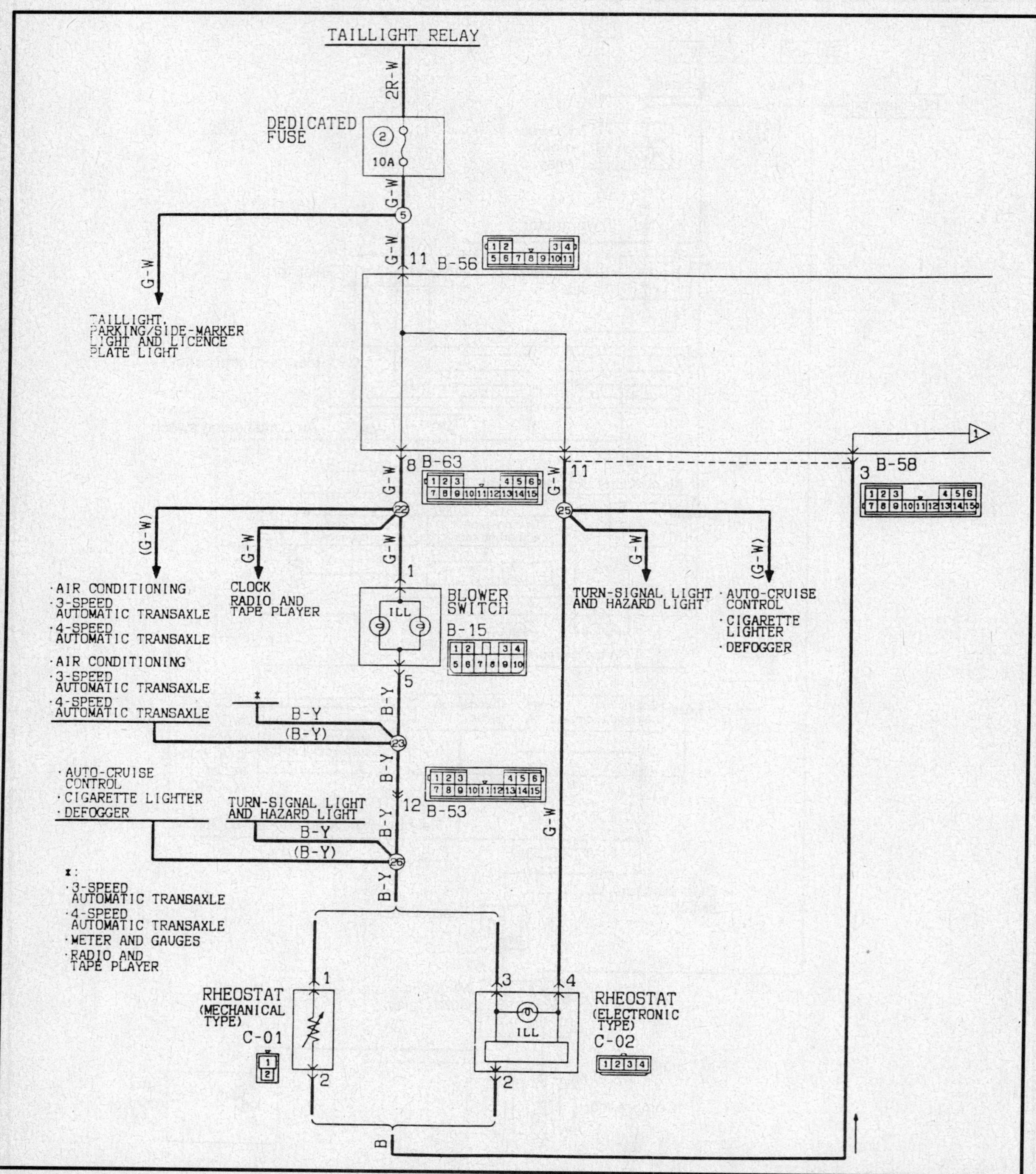

1993 Summit with heater only

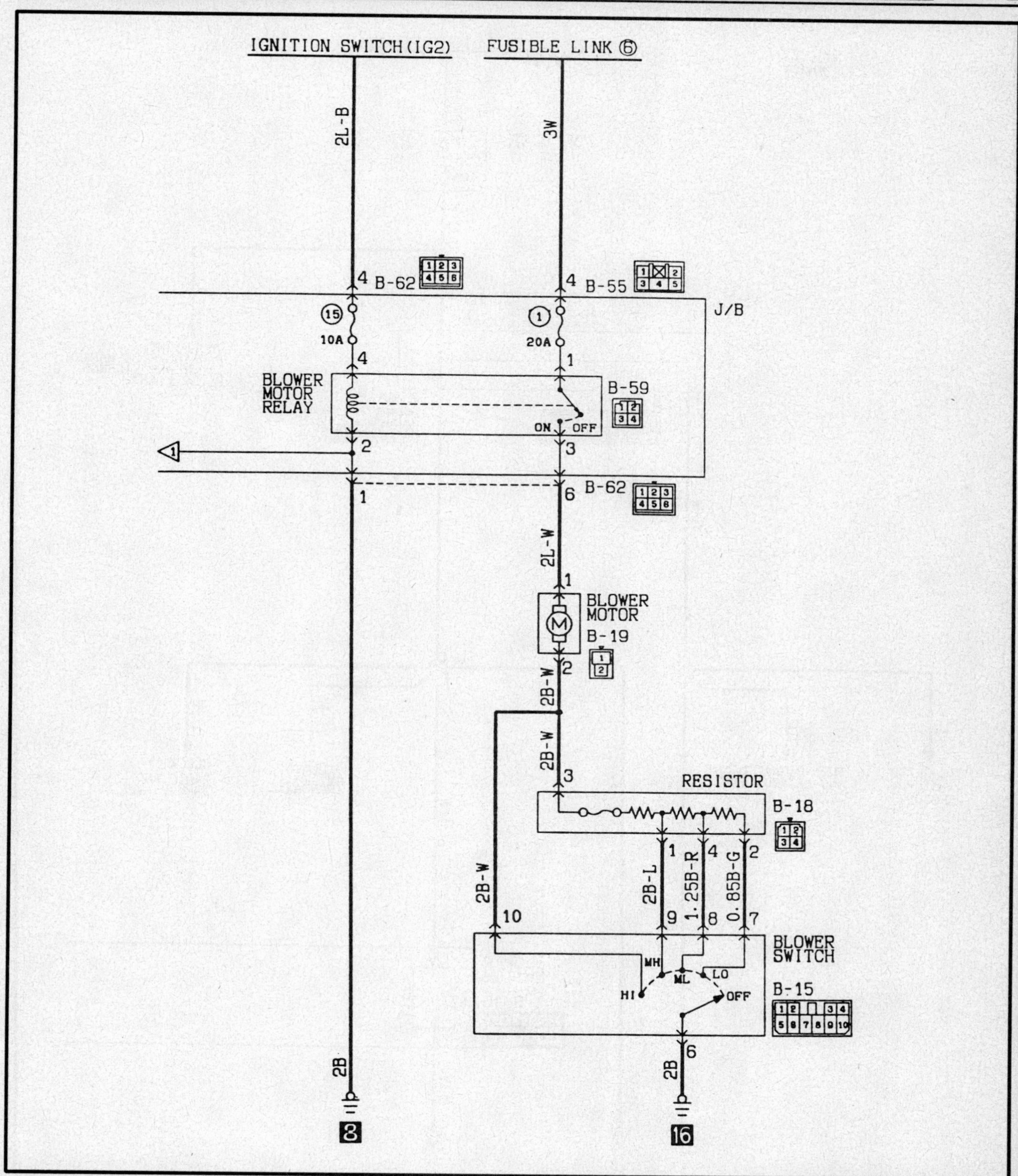

1993 Summit with heater only, Cont'd

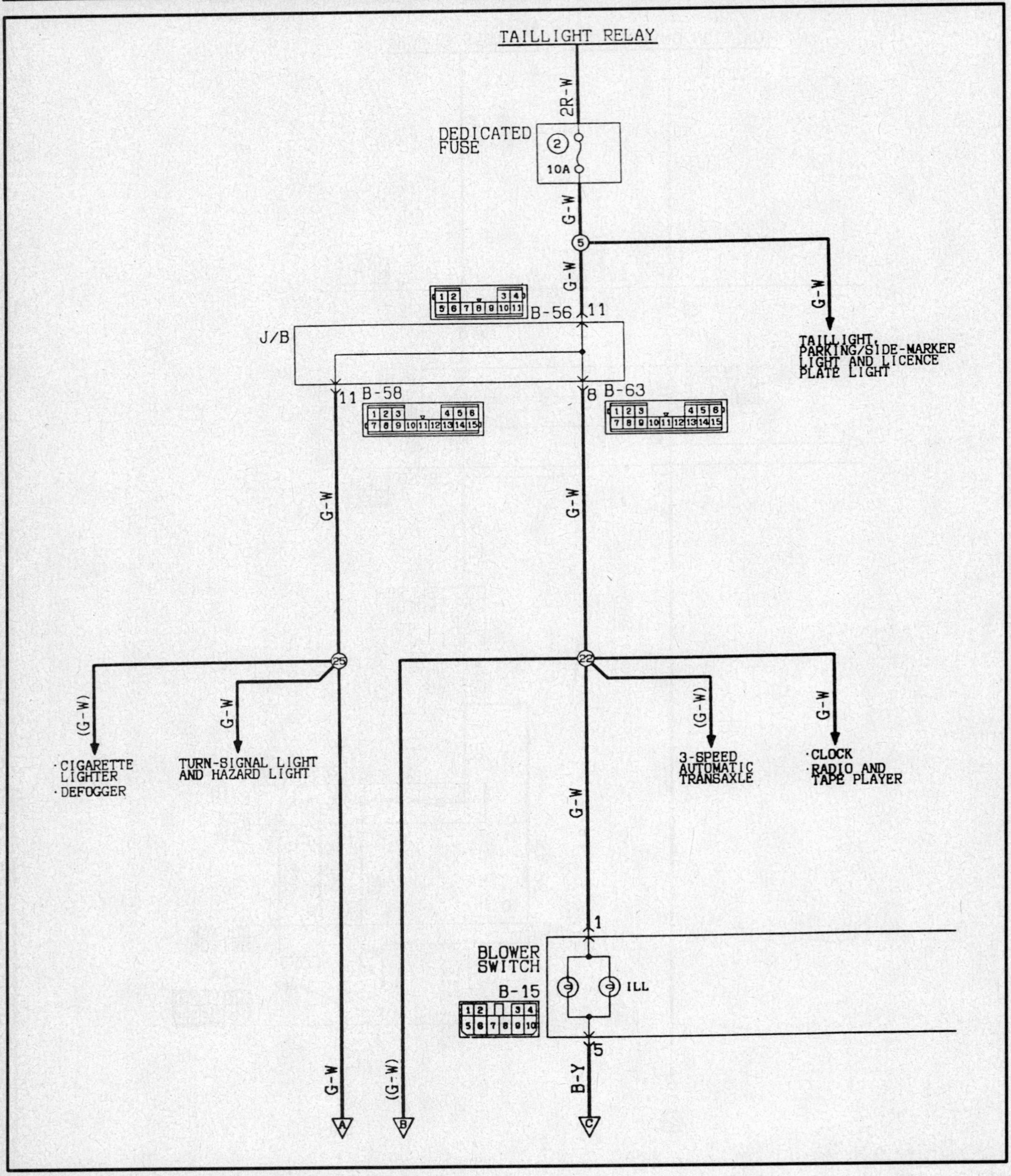

1993 Summit with air conditioning—1.5L engine

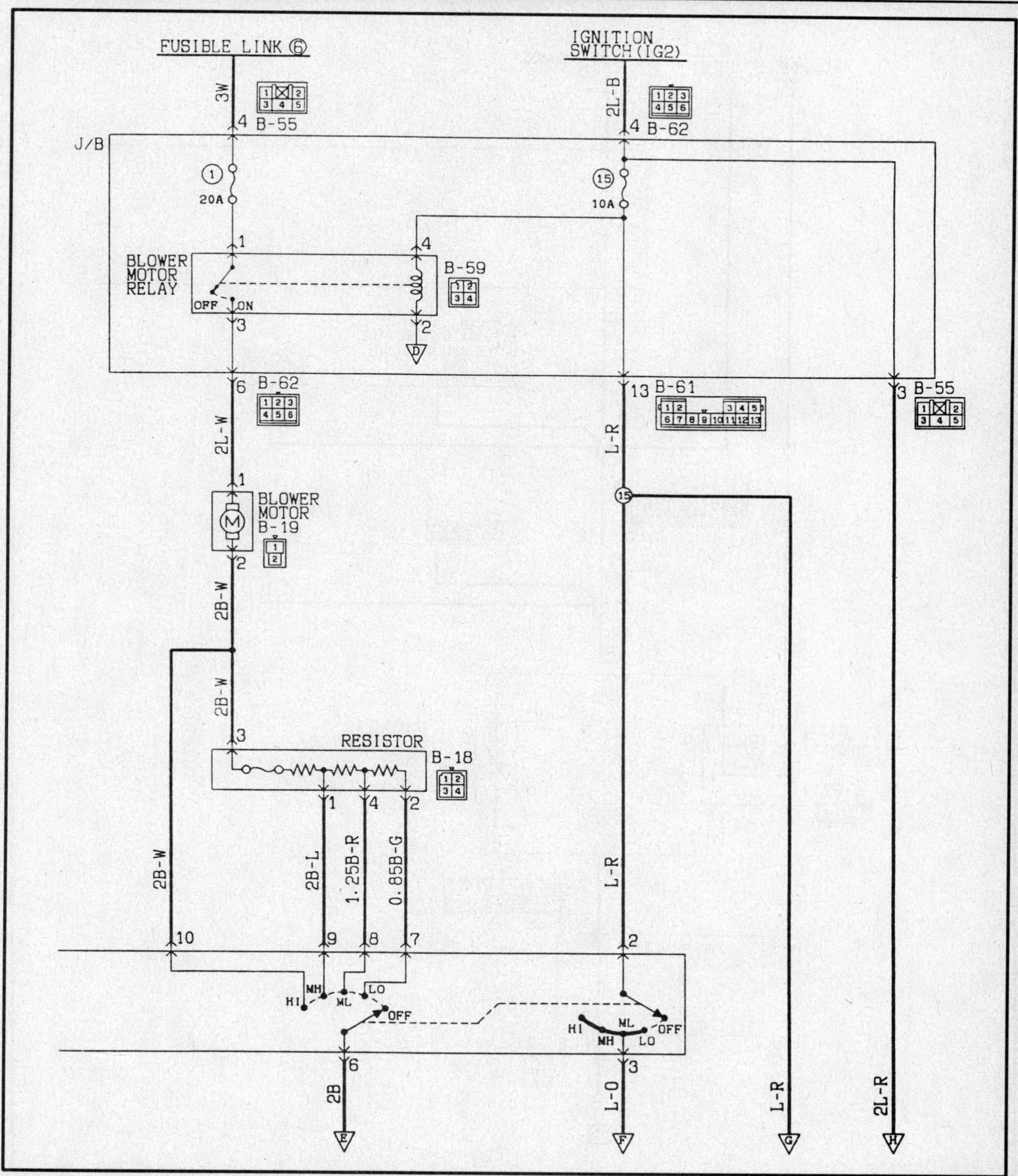

1993 Summit with air conditioning—1.5L engine, Cont'd

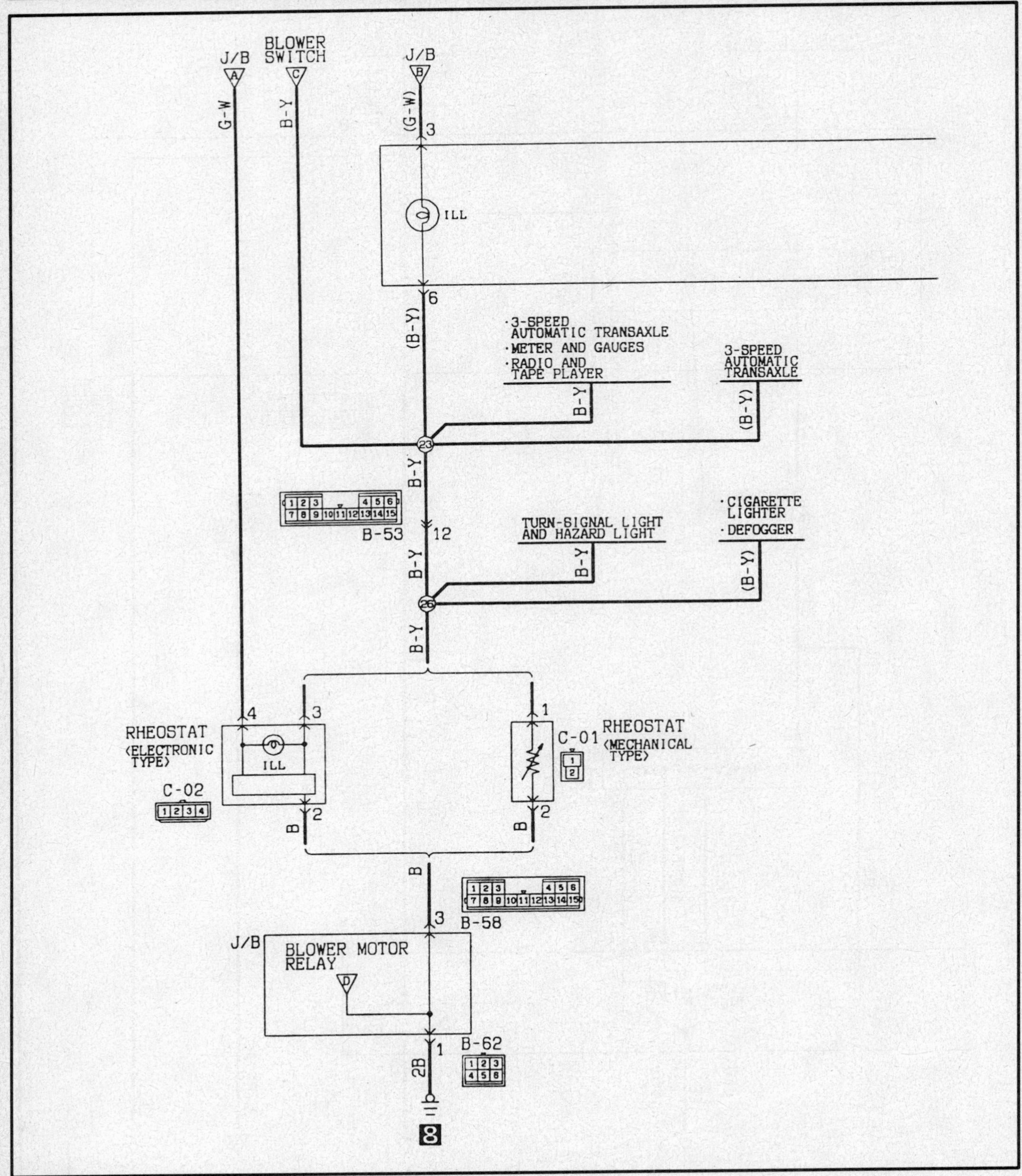

1993 Summit with air conditioning—1.5L engine, Cont'd

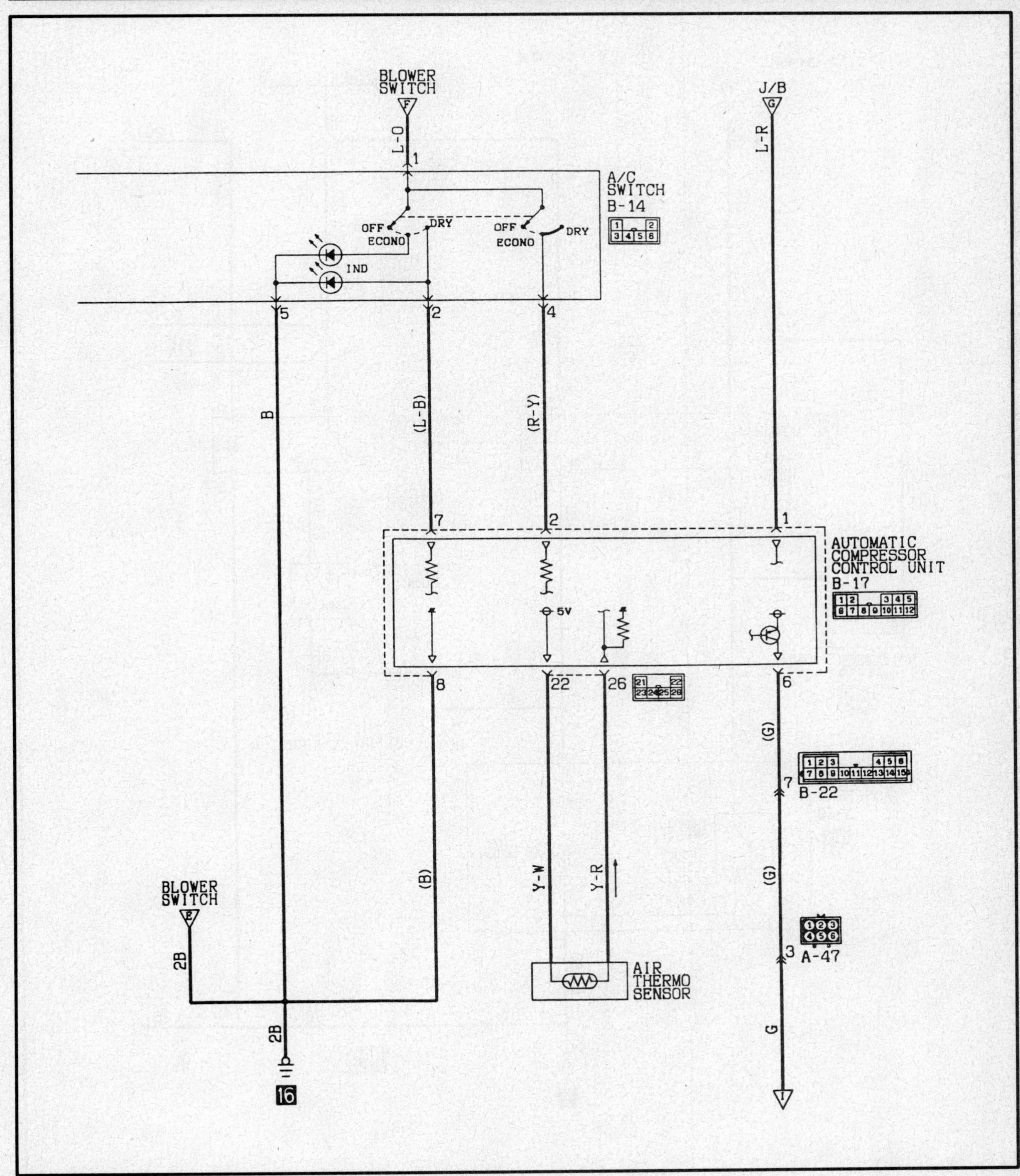

1993 Summit with air conditioning—1.5L engine, Cont'd

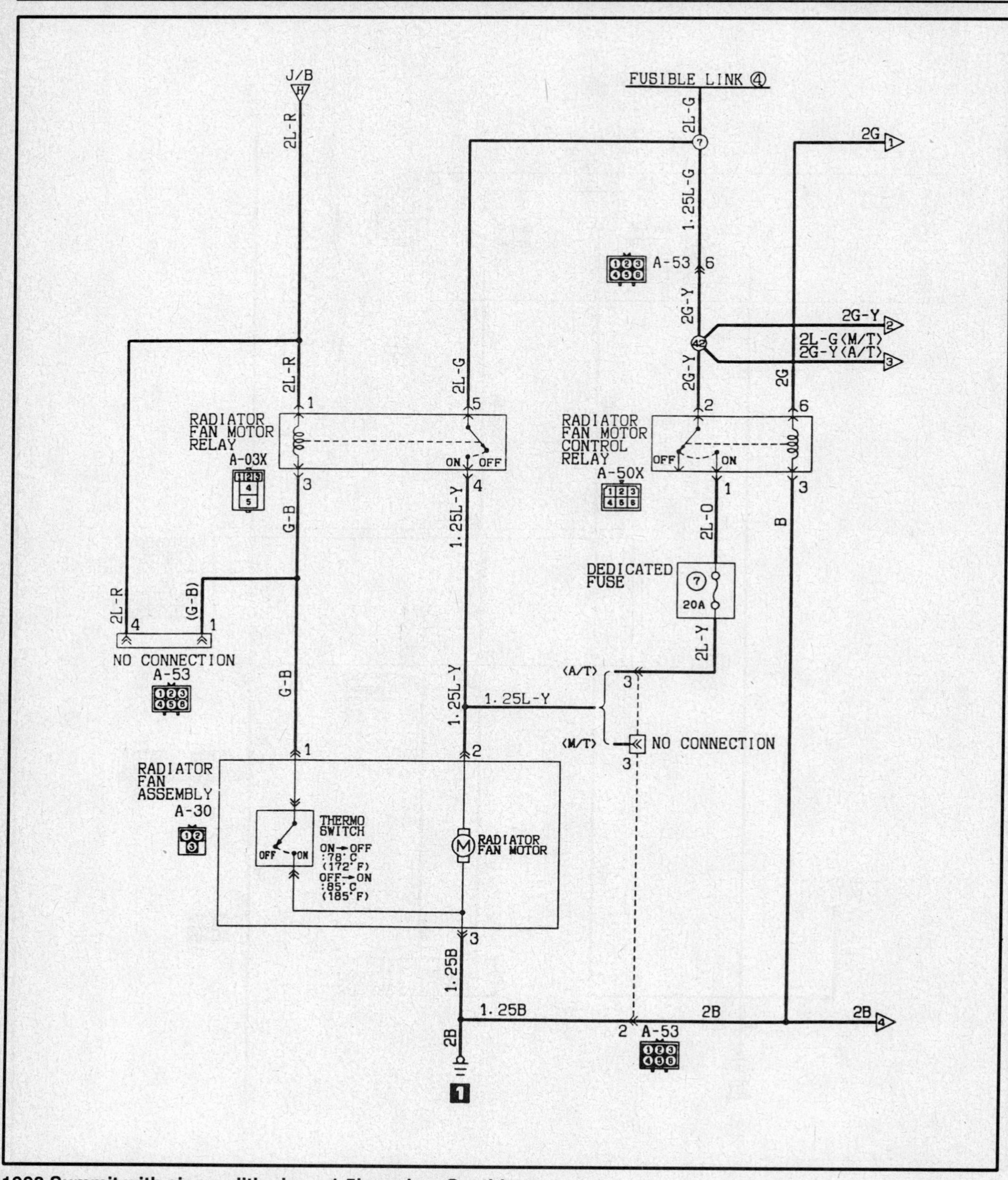

1993 Summit with air conditioning—1.5L engine, Cont'd

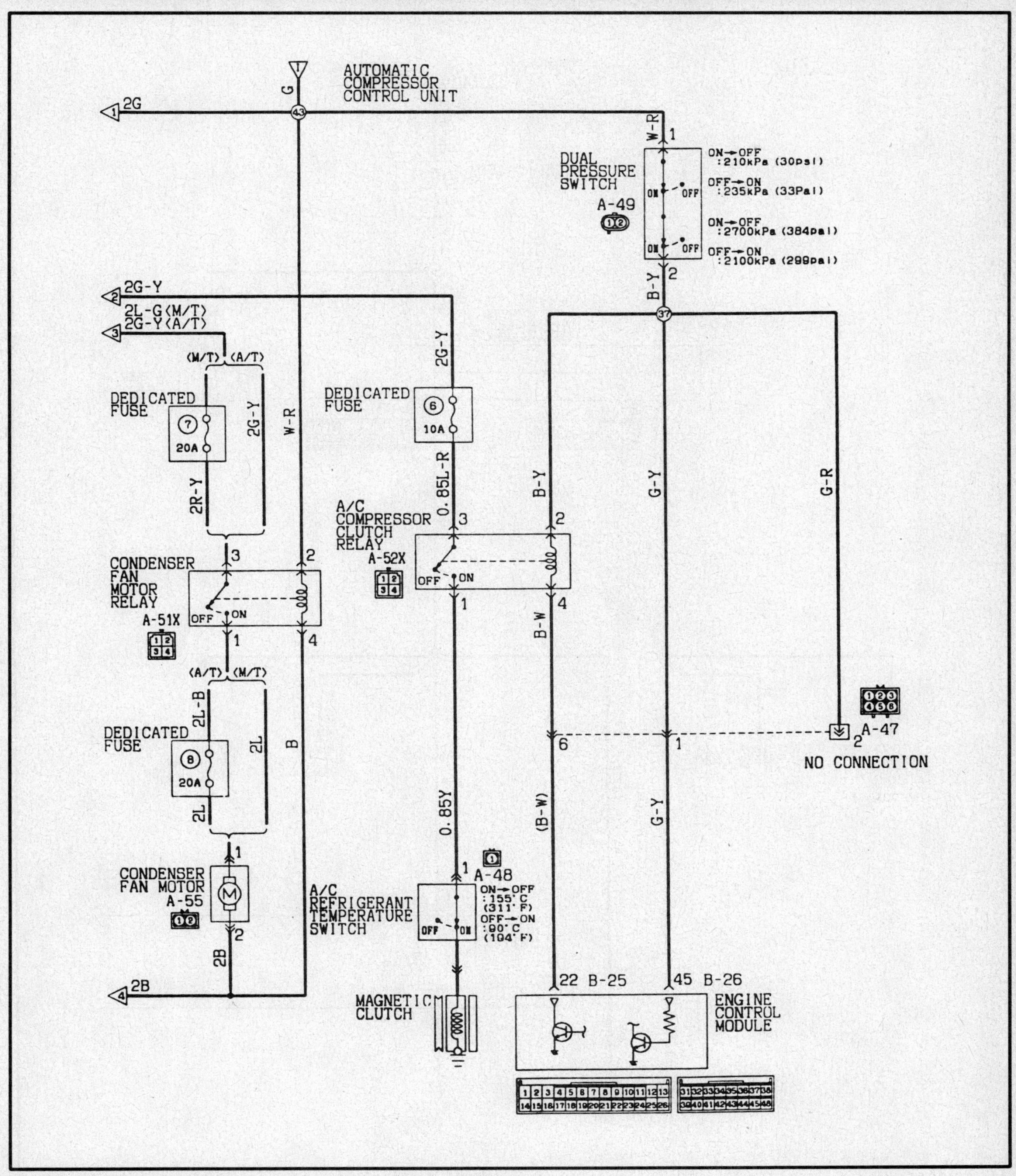

1993 Summit with air conditioning—1.5L engine, Cont'd

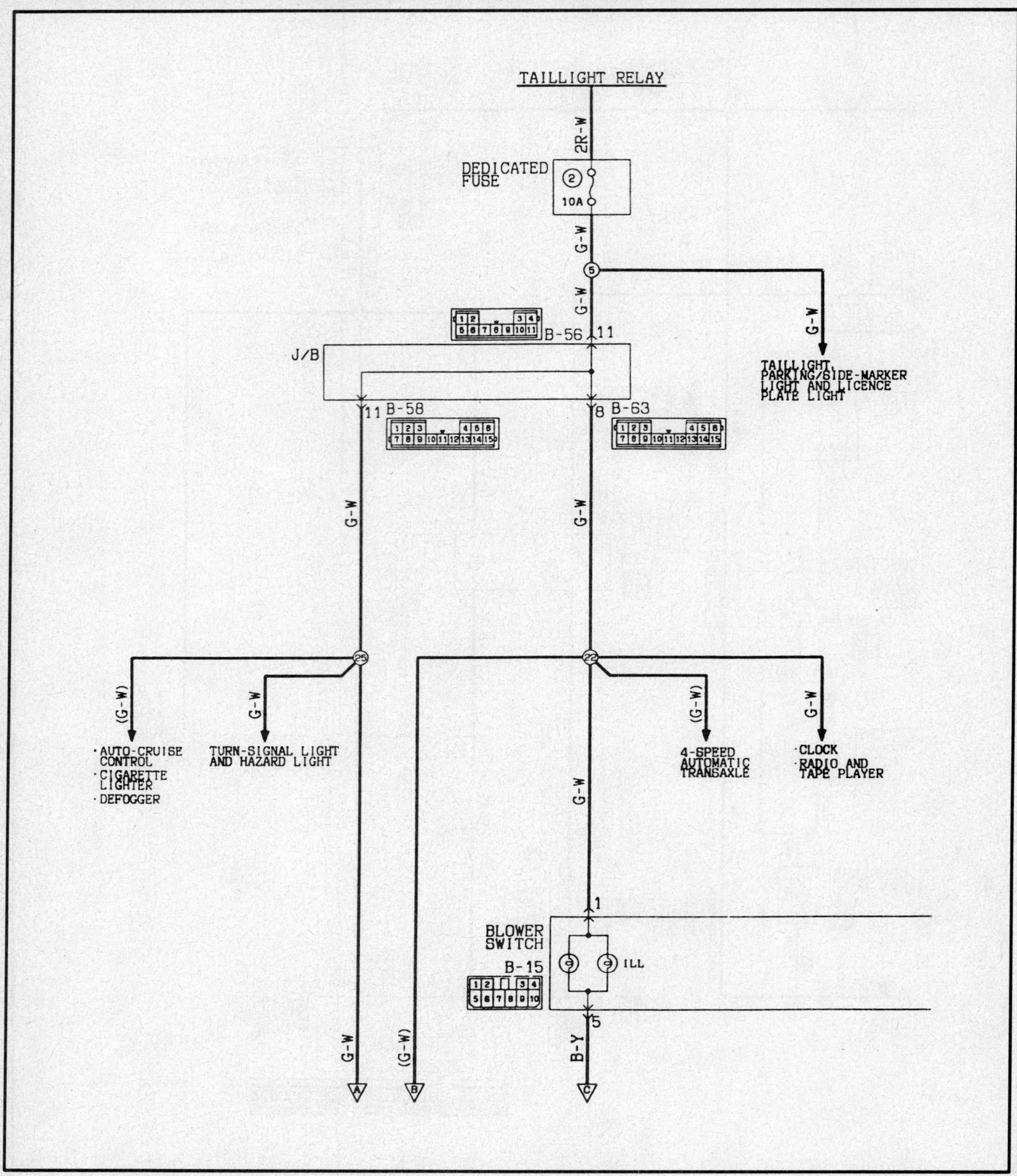

1993 Summit with air conditioning—1.8L engine

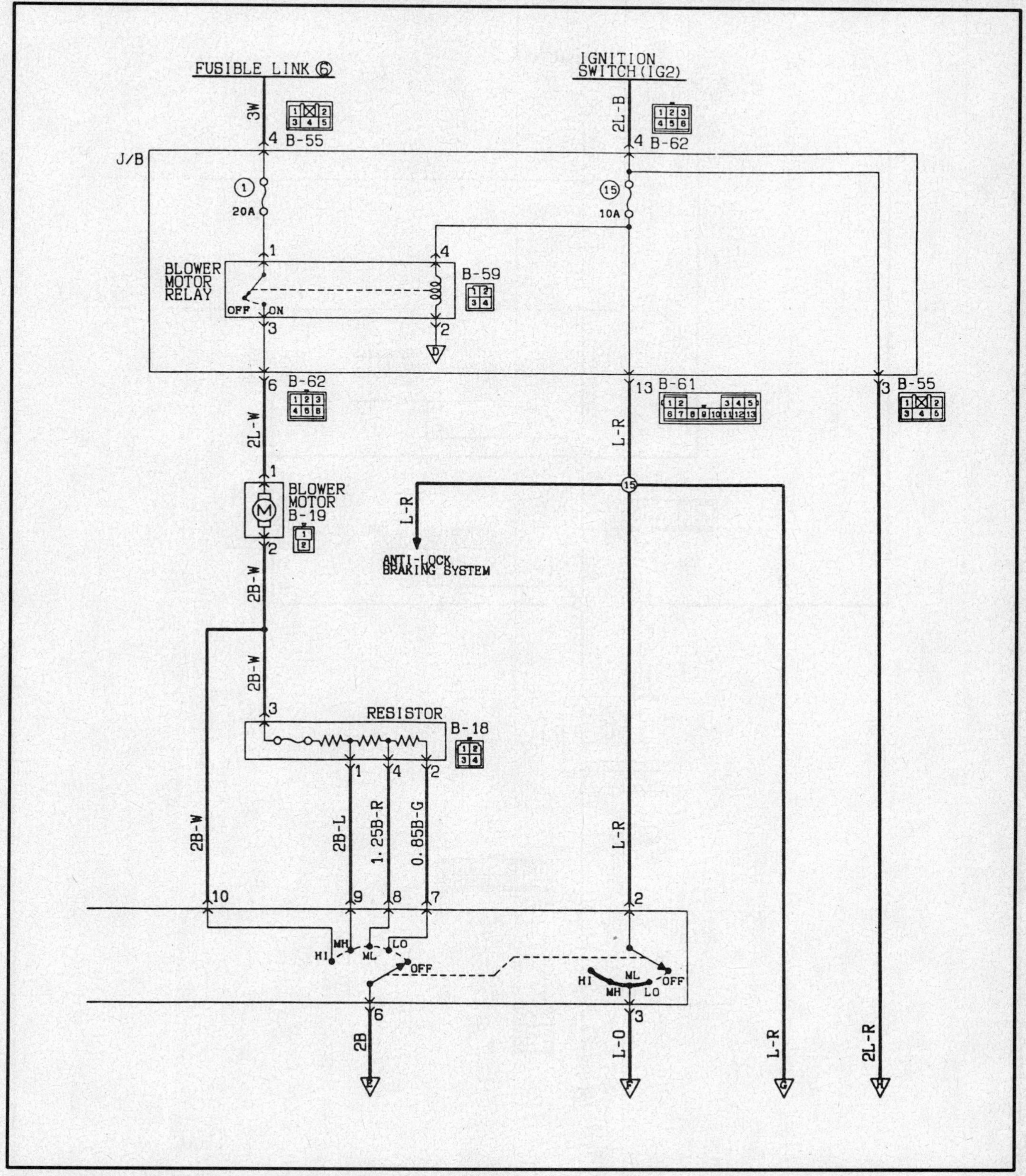

1993 Summit with air conditioning—1.8L engine, Cont'd

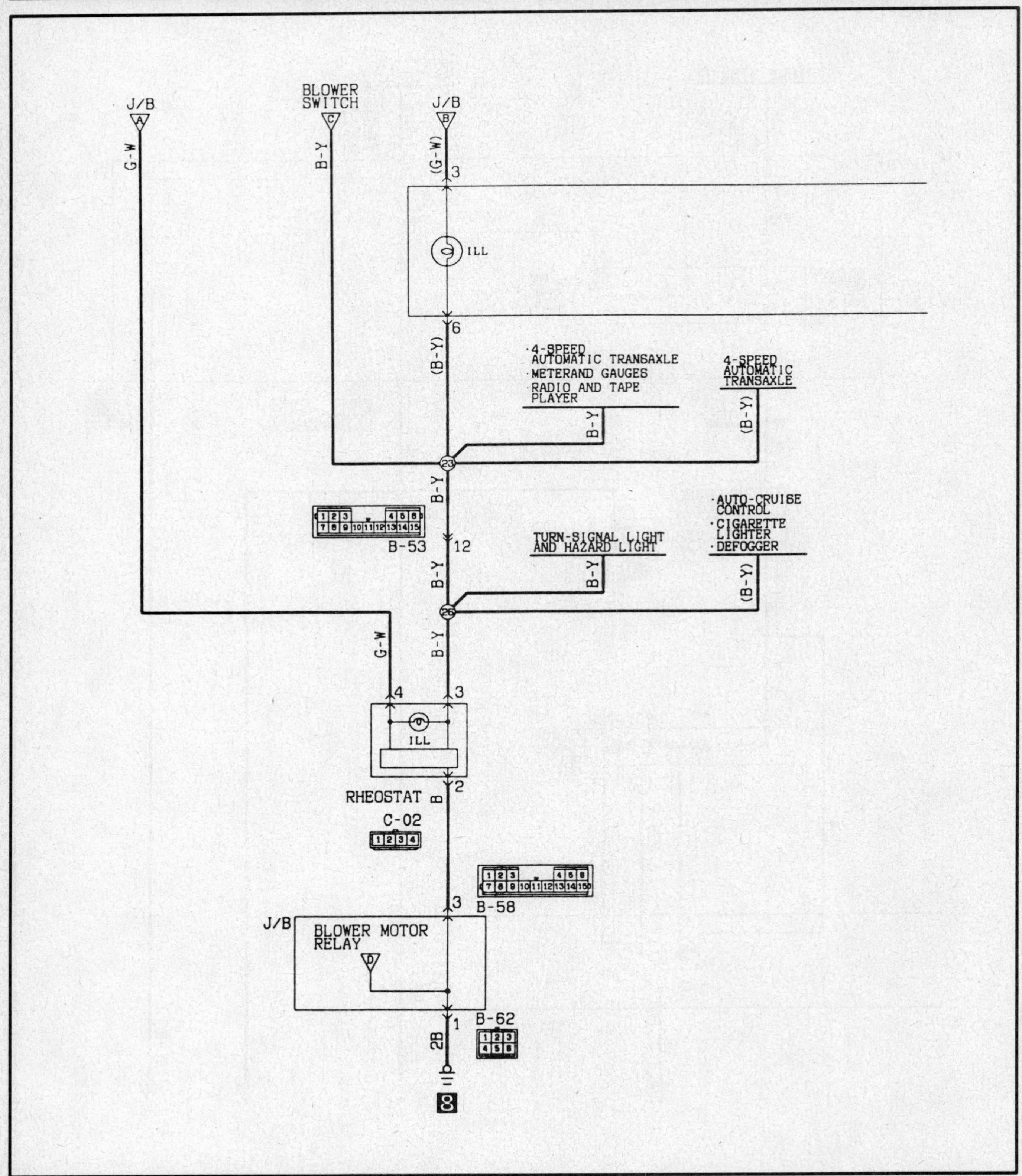

1993 Summit with air conditioning—1.8L engine, Cont'd

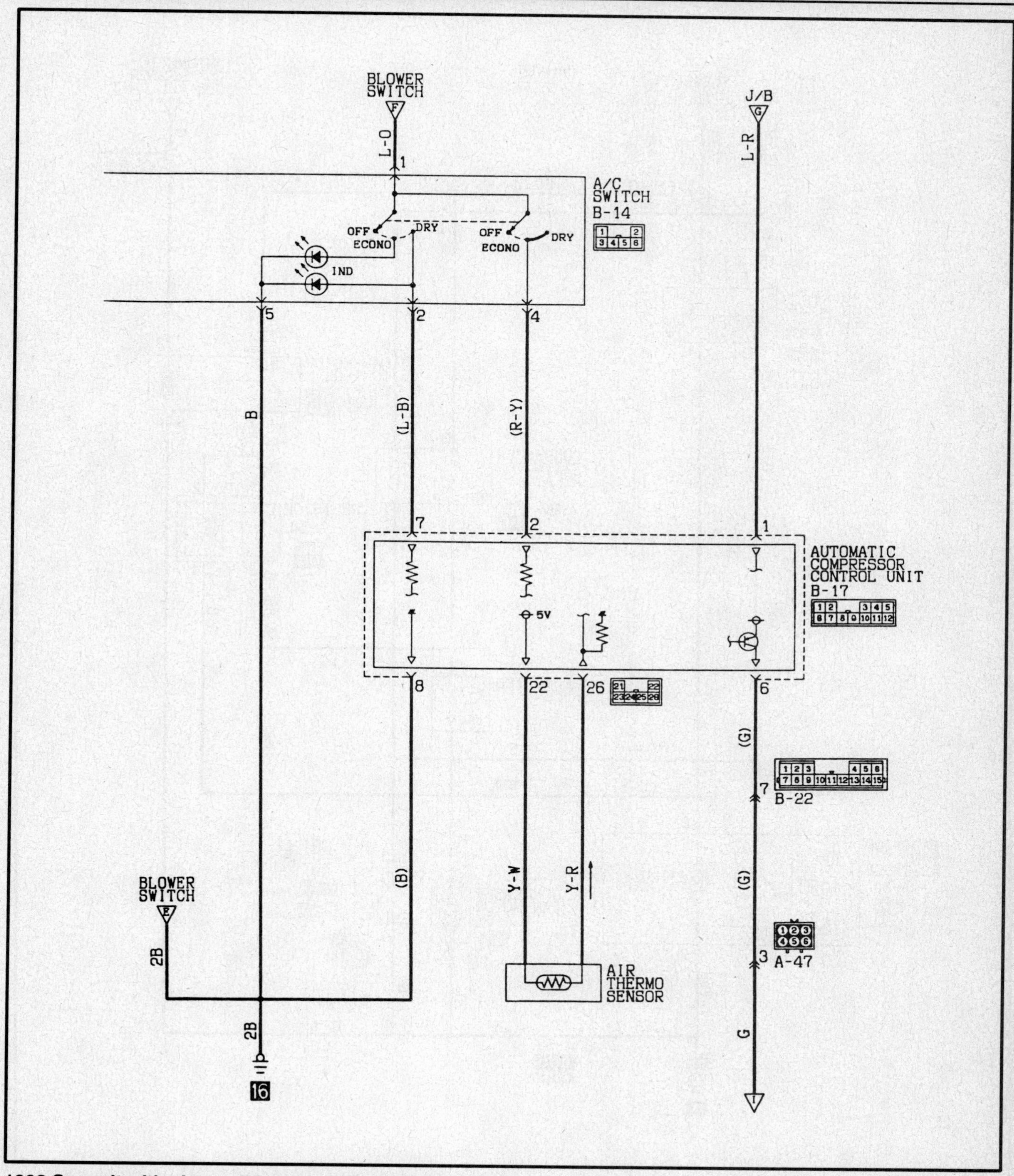

1993 Summit with air conditioning—1.8L engine, Cont'd

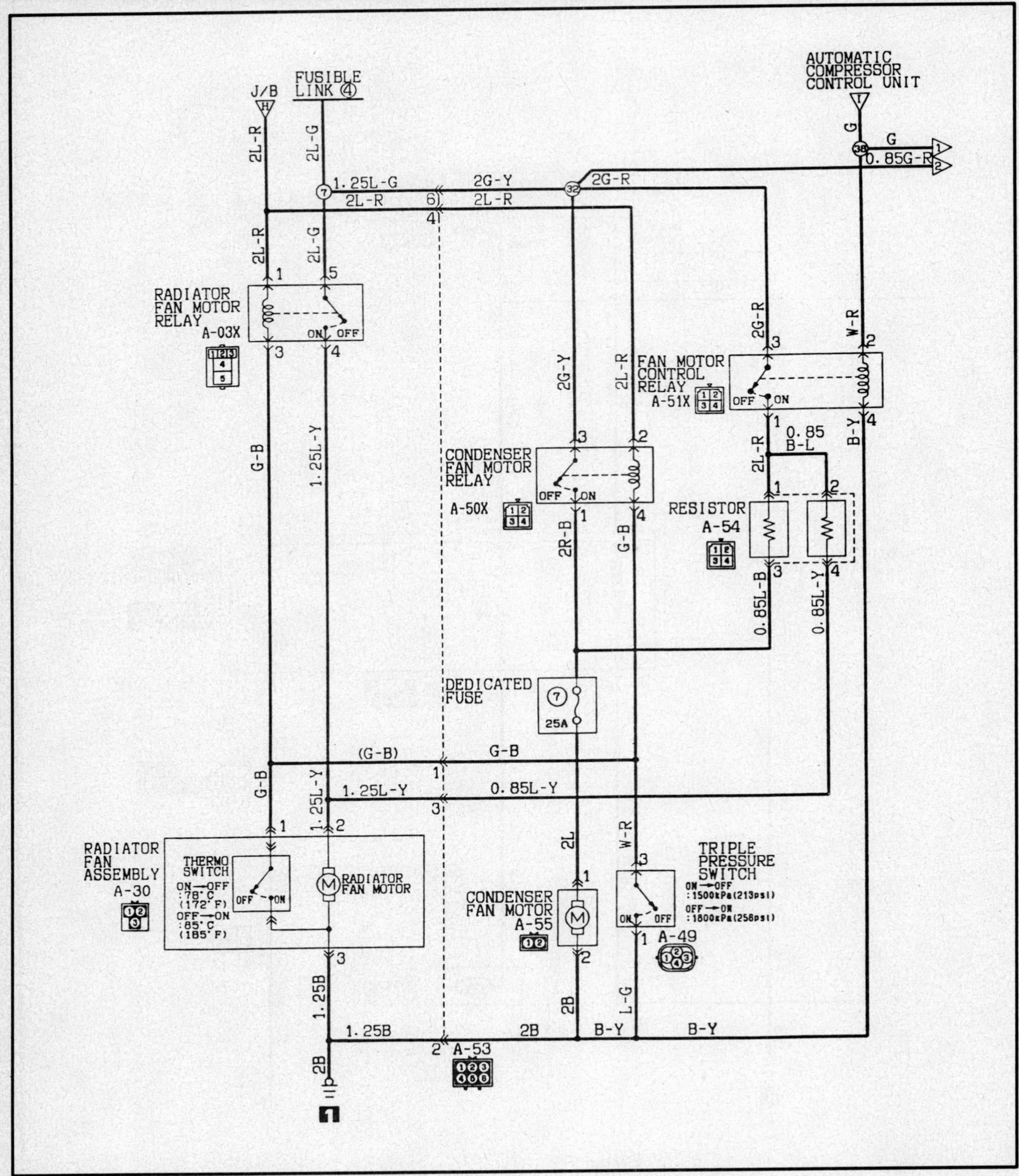

1993 Summit with air conditioning—1.8L engine, Cont'd

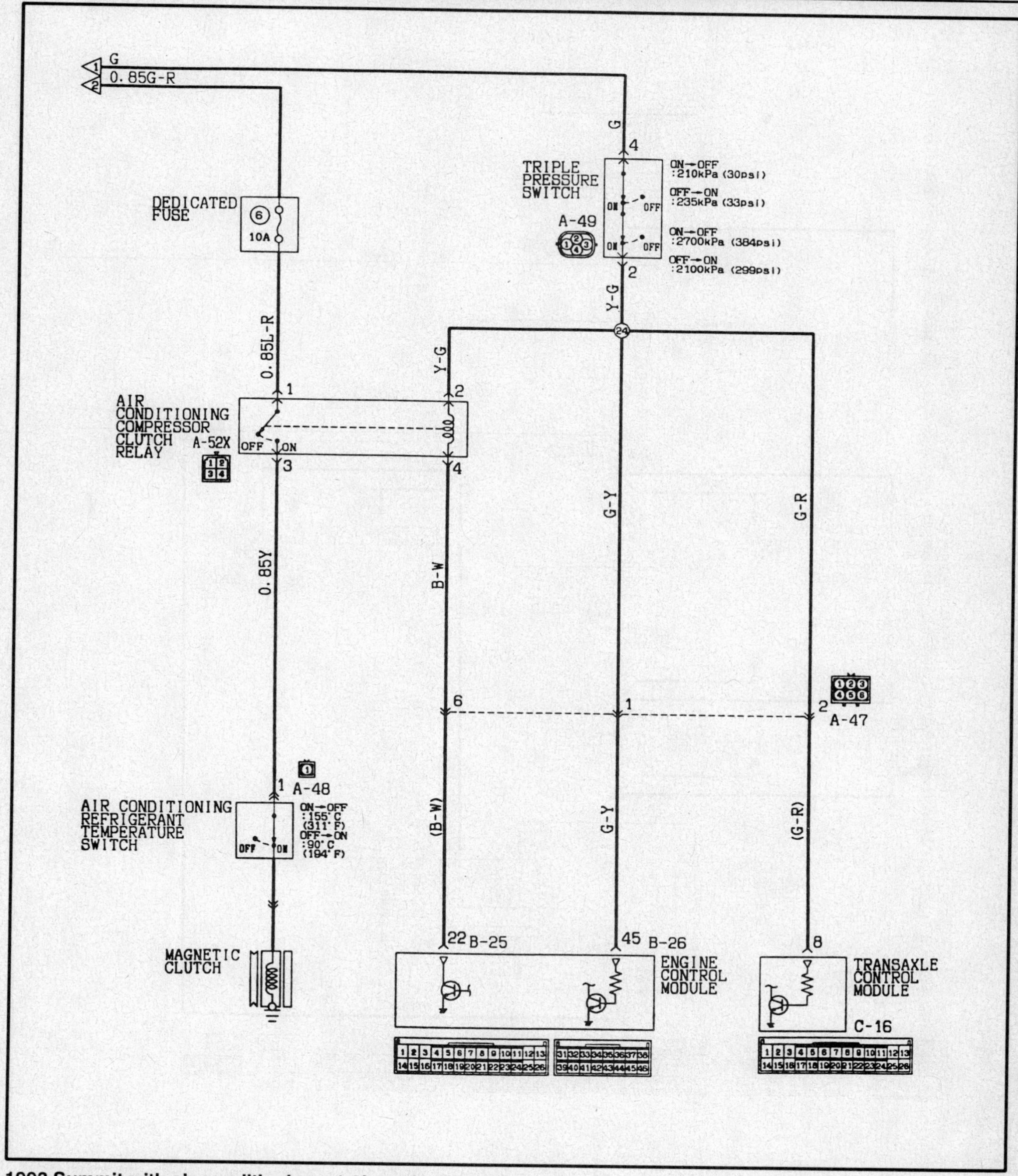

1993 Summit with air conditioning—1.8L engine, Cont'd

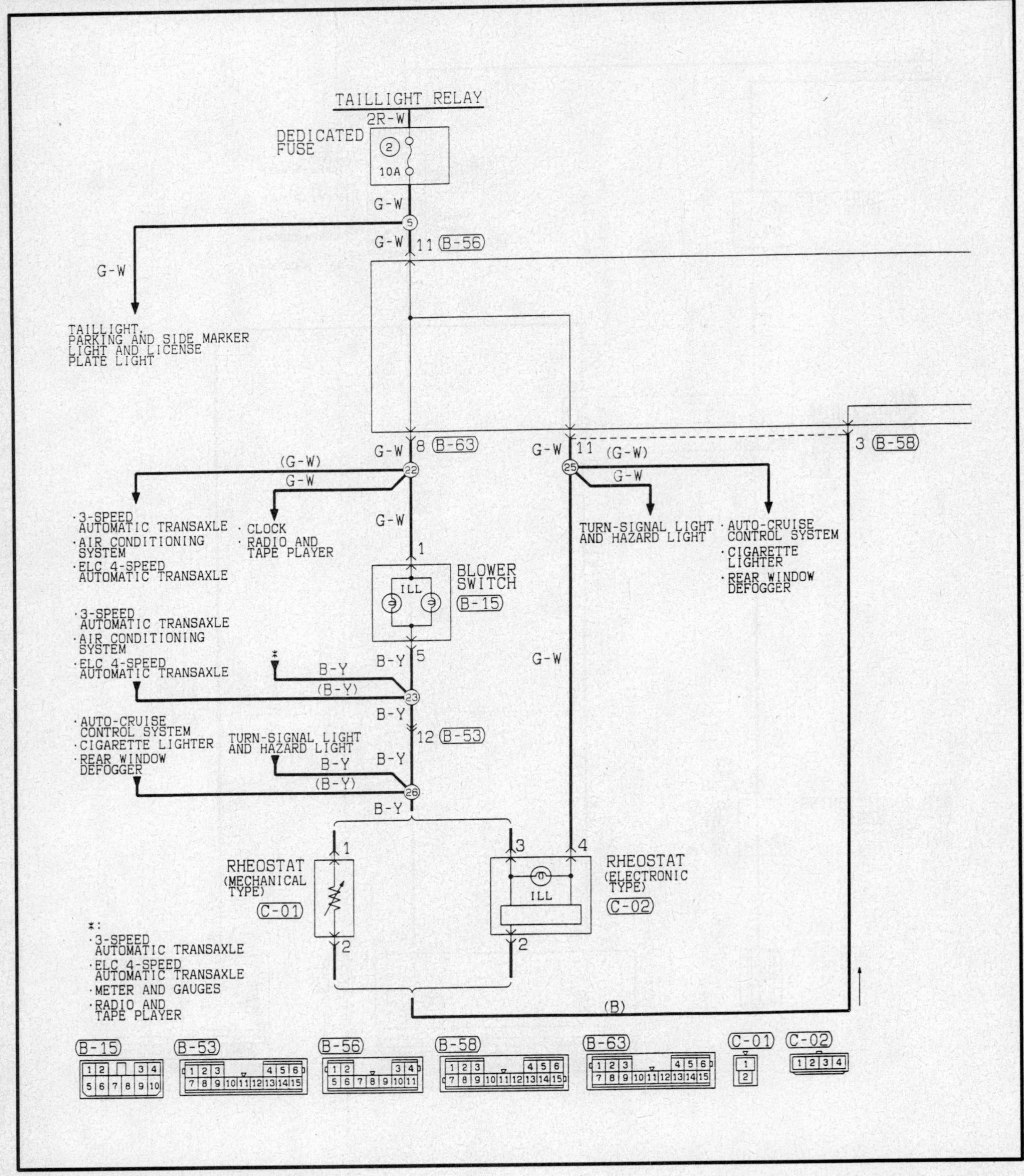

1994–95 Summit with heater only

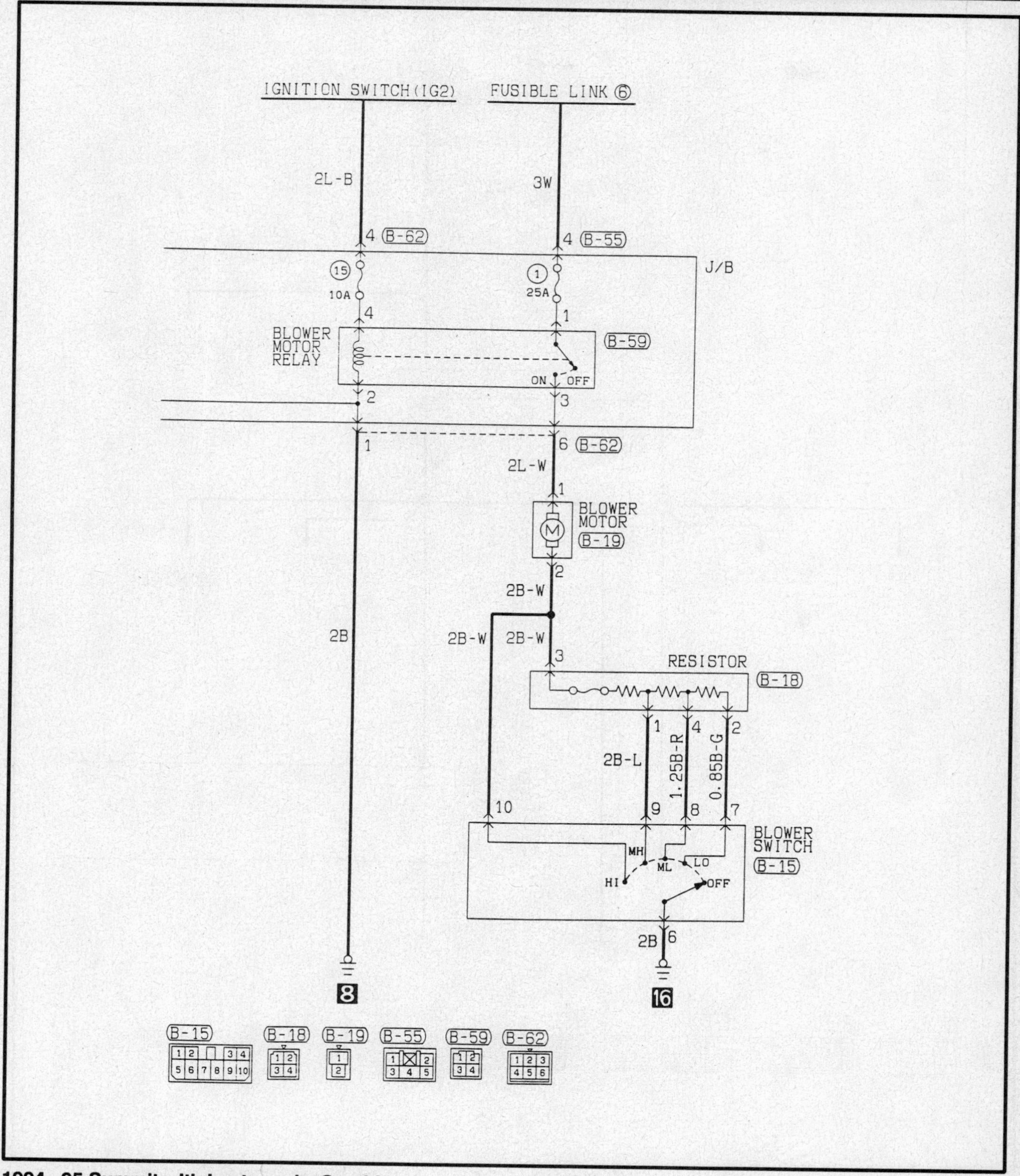

1994–95 Summit with heater only, Cont'd

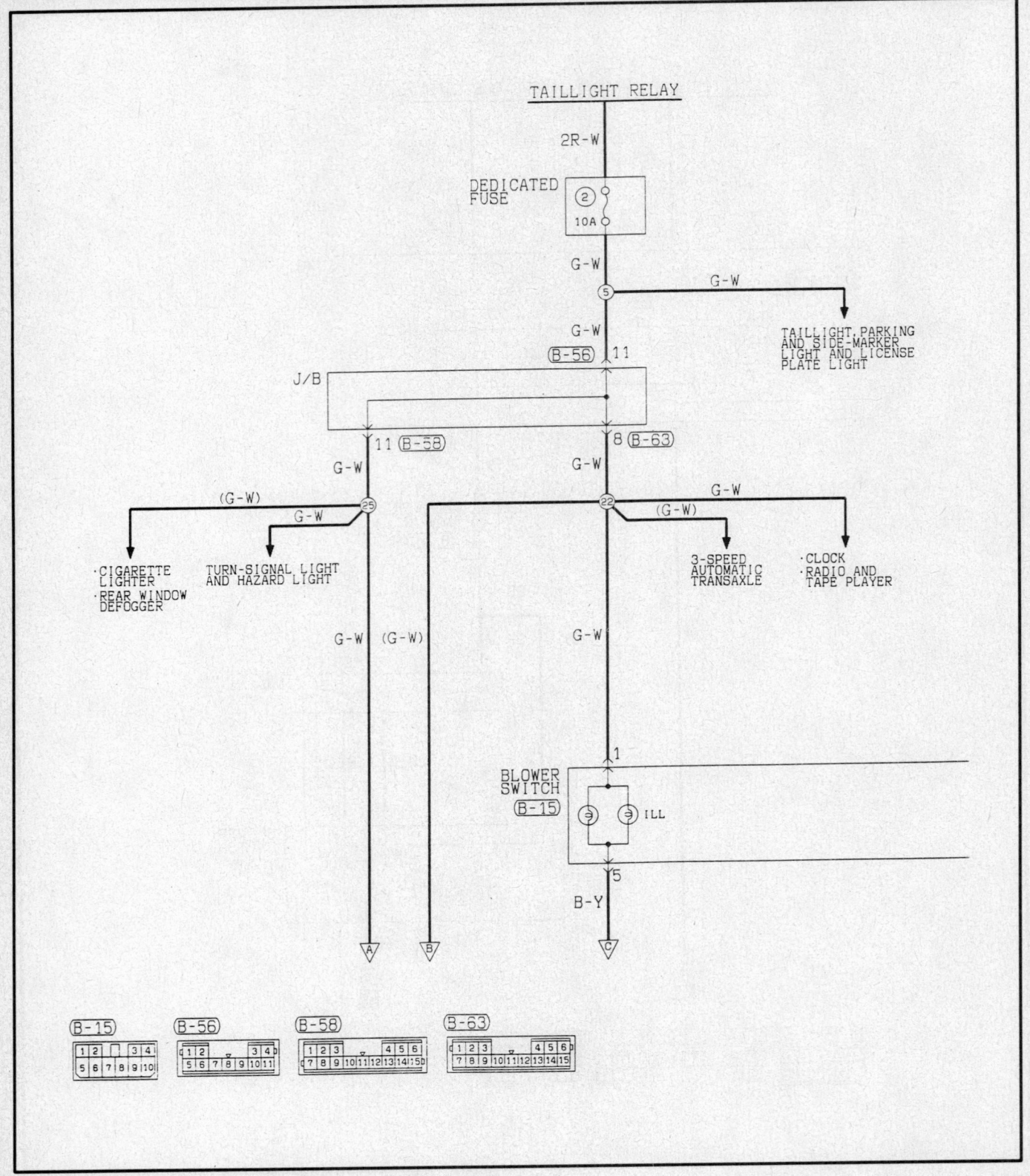

1994–95 Summit with air conditioning—1.5L engine

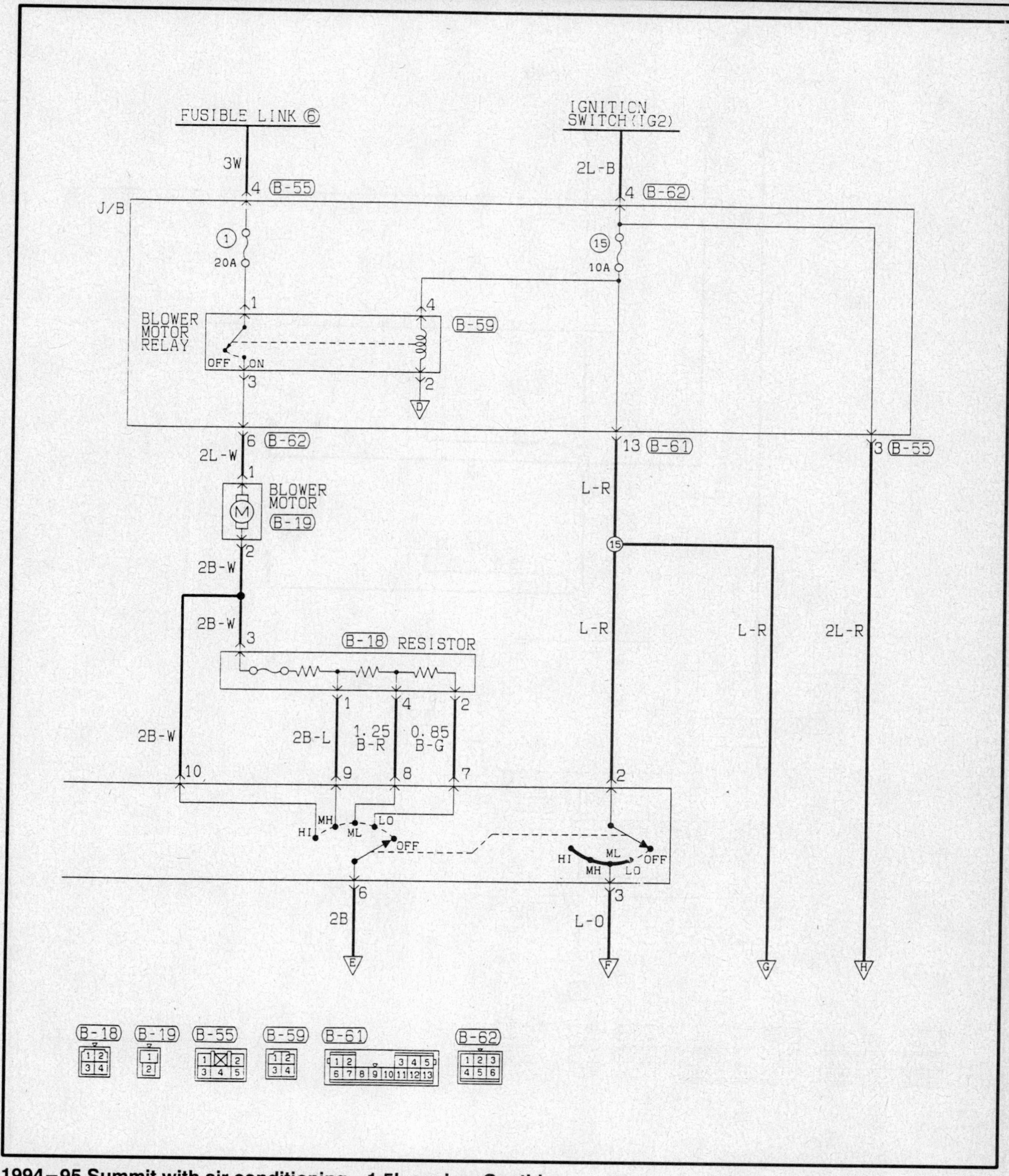

1994–95 Summit with air conditioning—1.5L engine, Cont'd

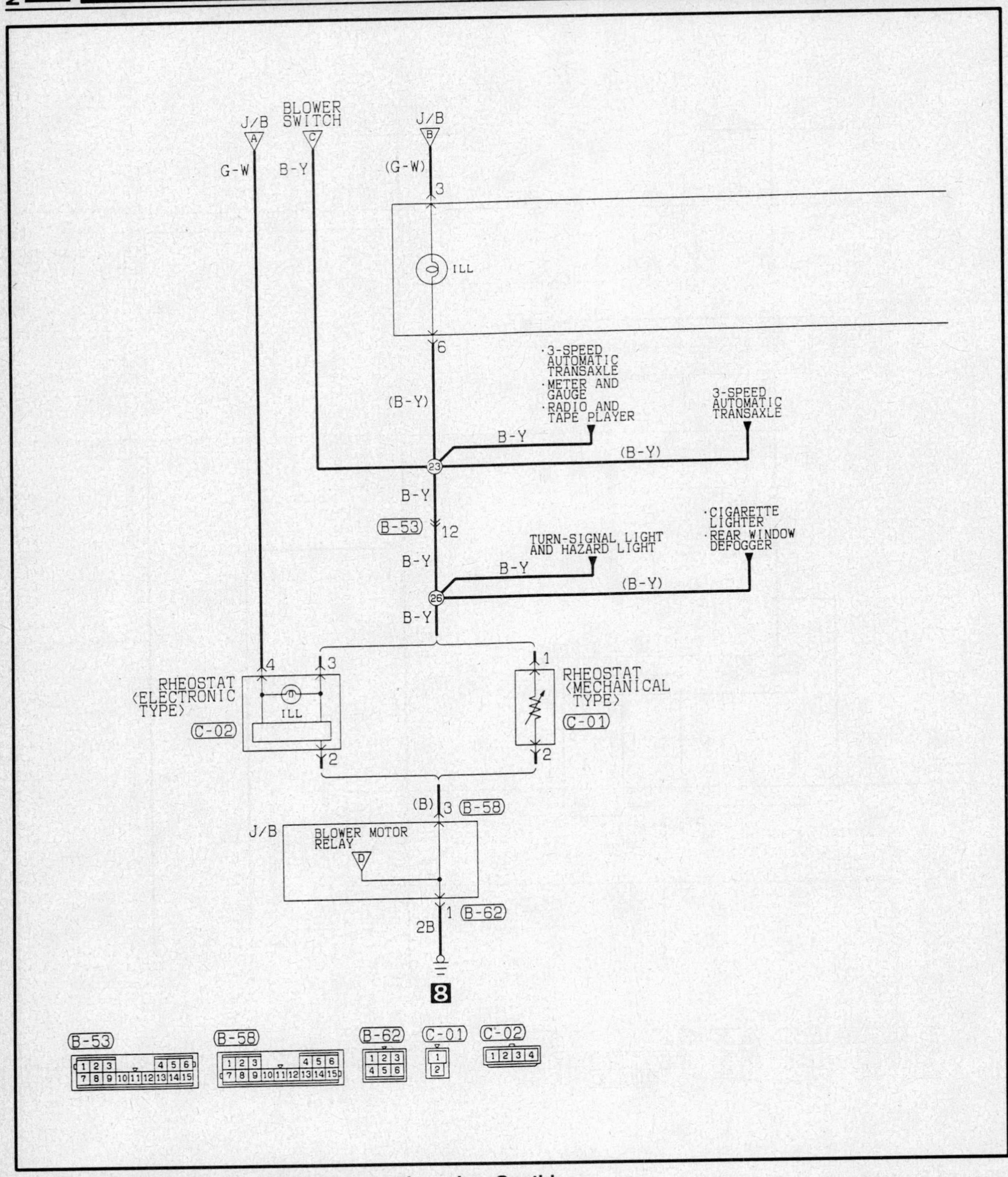

1994–95 Summit with air conditioning—1.5L engine, Cont'd

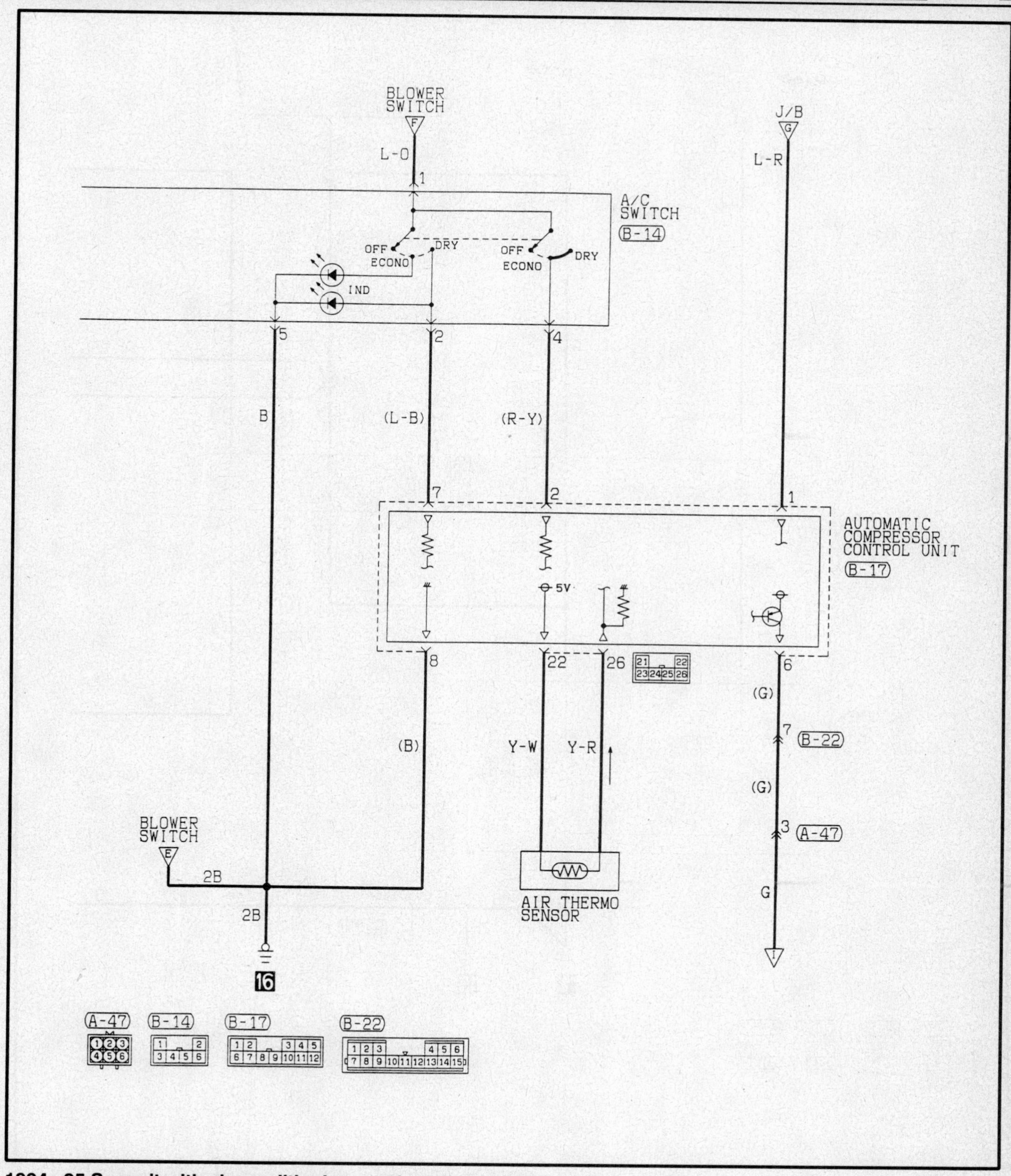

1994–95 Summit with air conditioning—1.5L engine, Cont'd

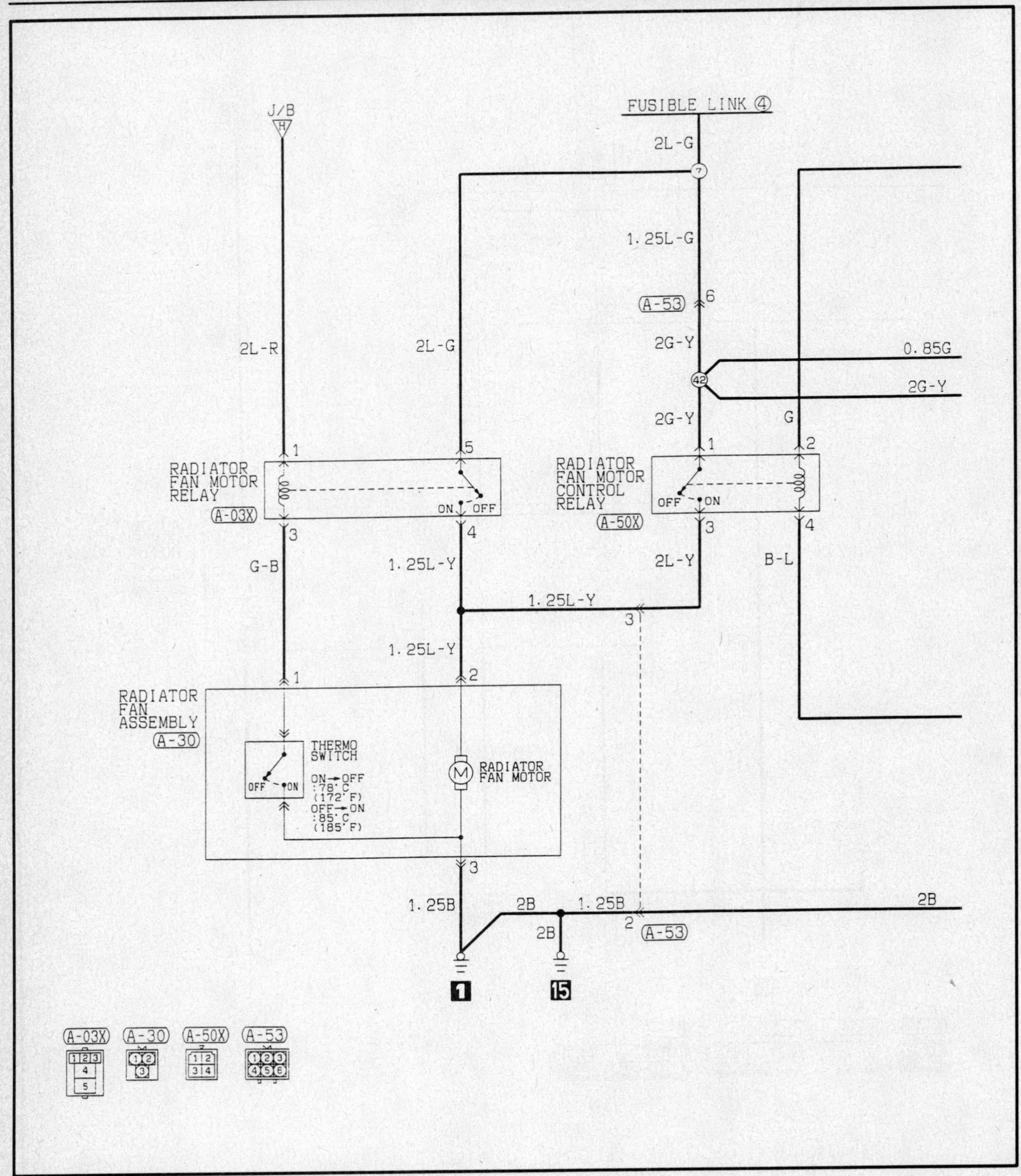

1994–95 Summit with air conditioning—1.5L engine, Cont'd

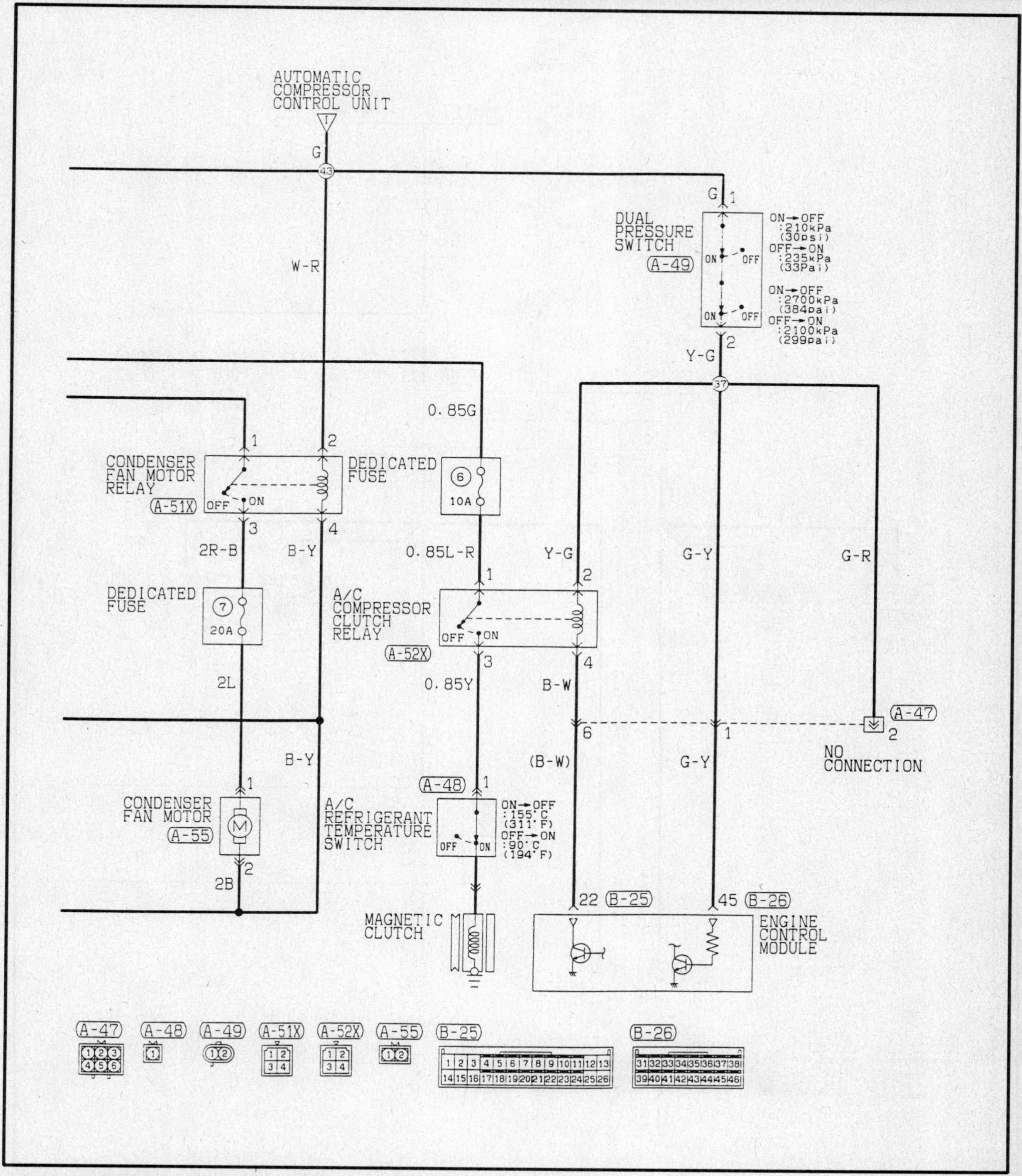

1994–95 Summit with air conditioning—1.5L engine, Cont'd

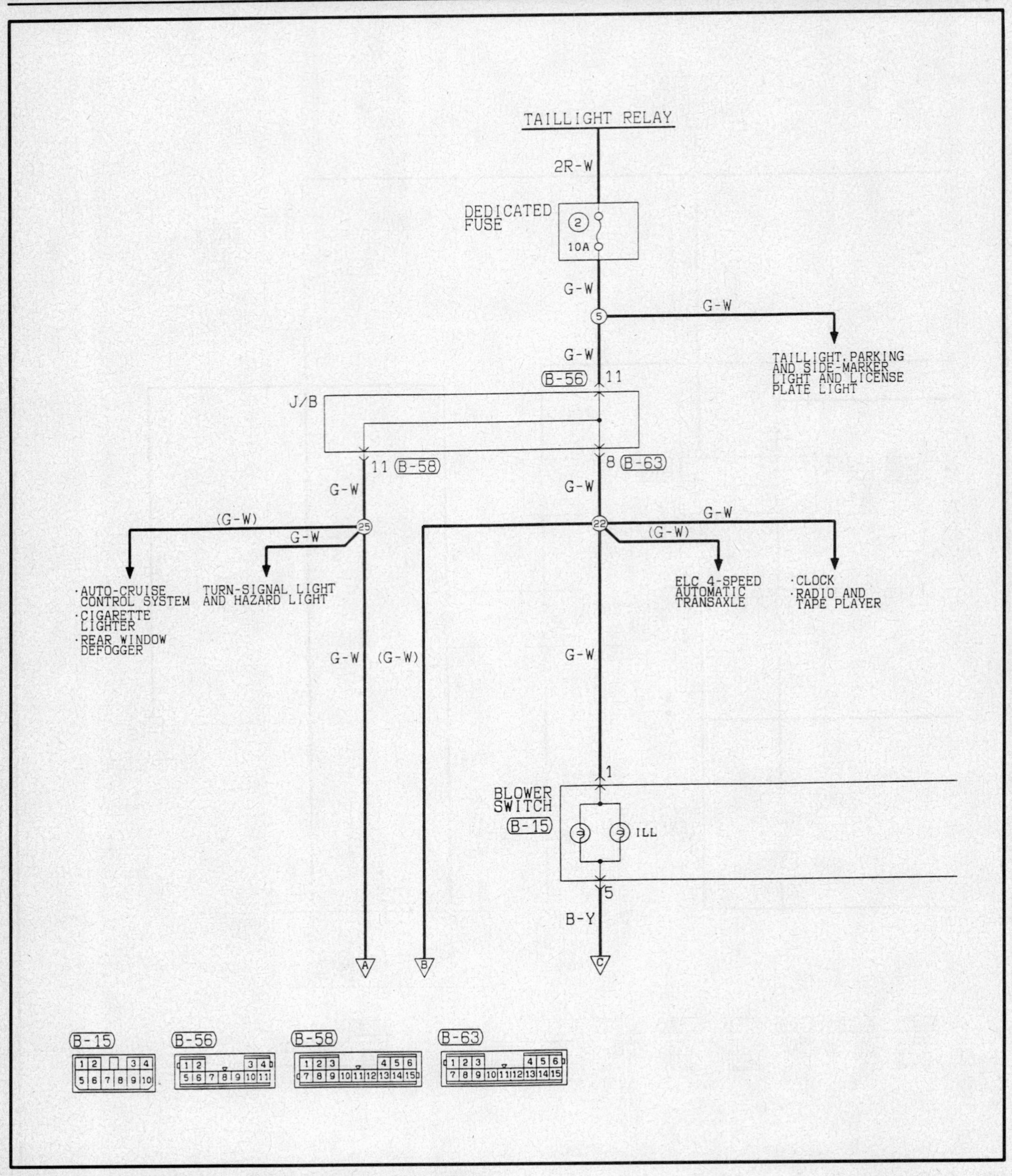

1994–95 Summit with air conditioning—1.8L engine

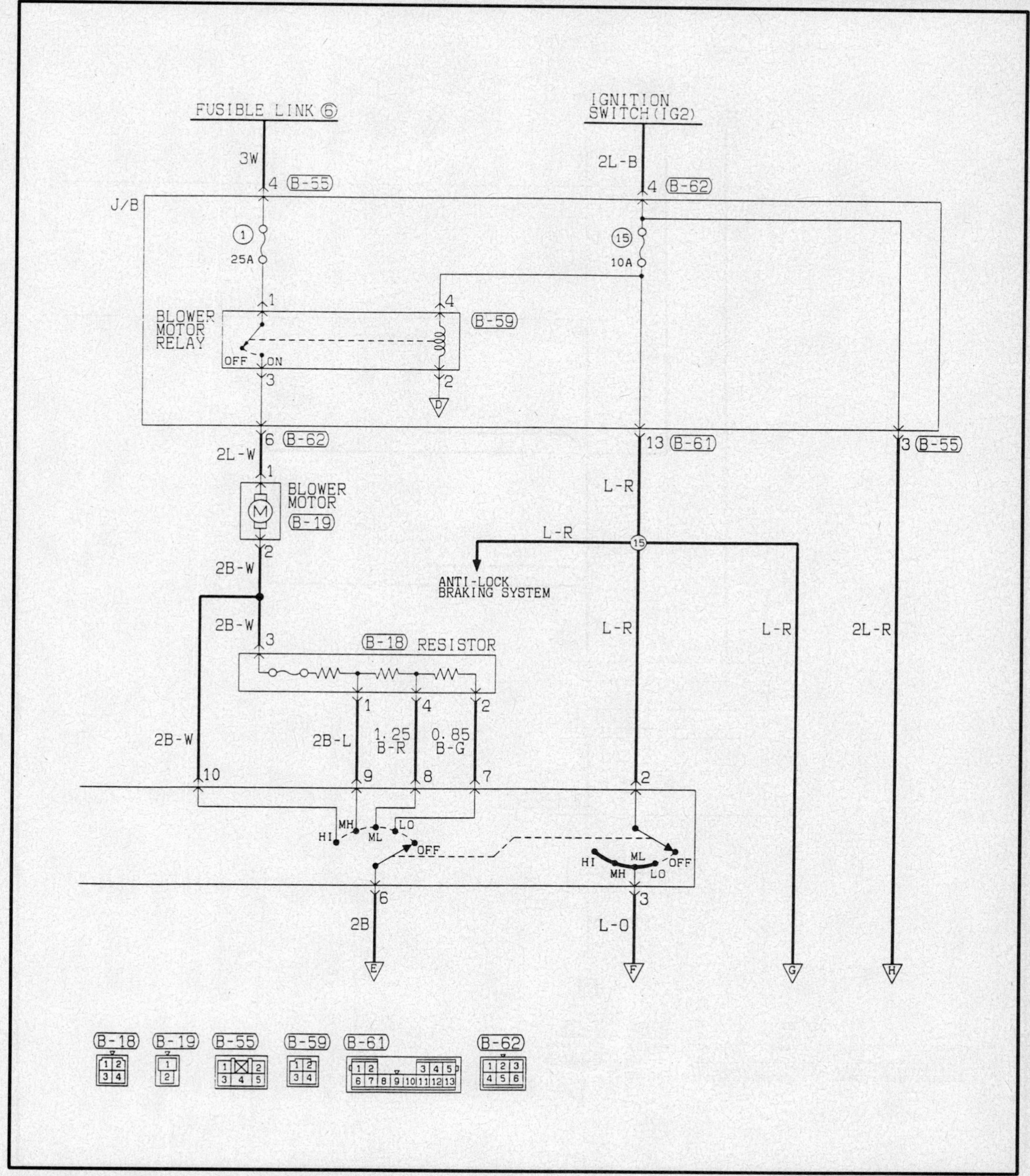

1994–95 Summit with air conditioning—1.8L engine, Cont'd

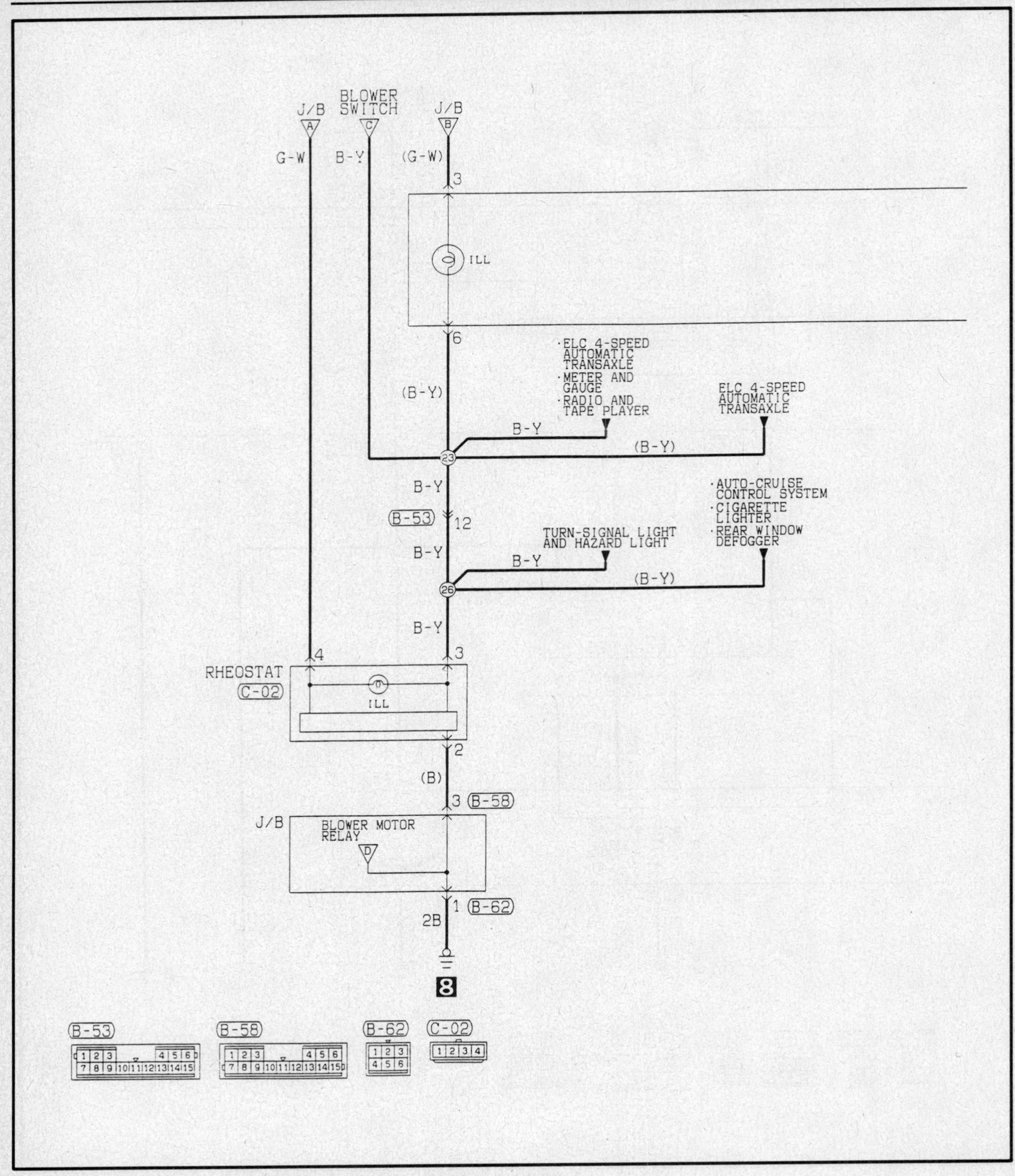

1994–95 Summit with air conditioning—1.8L engine, Cont'd

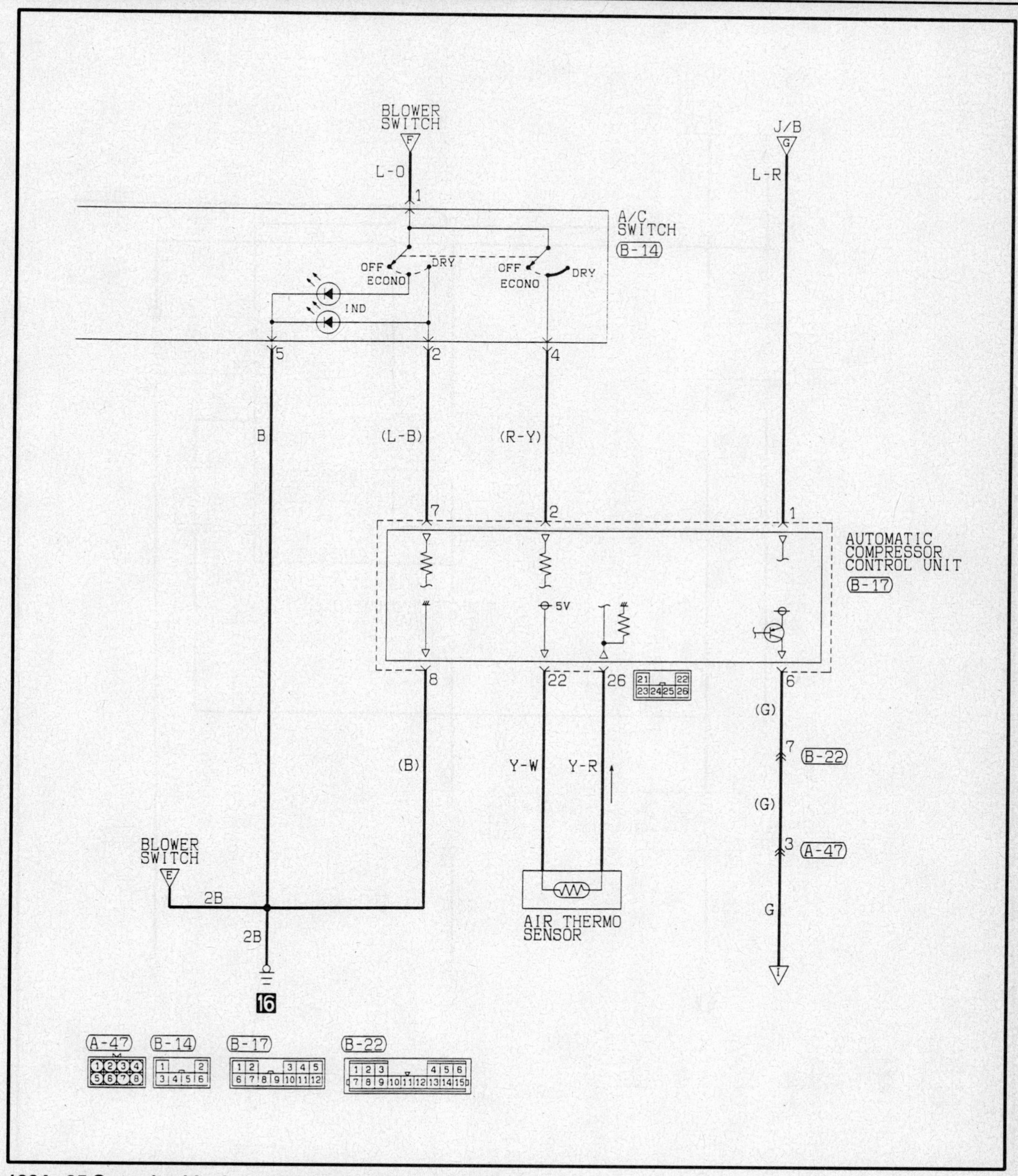

1994–95 Summit with air conditioning—1.8L engine, Cont'd

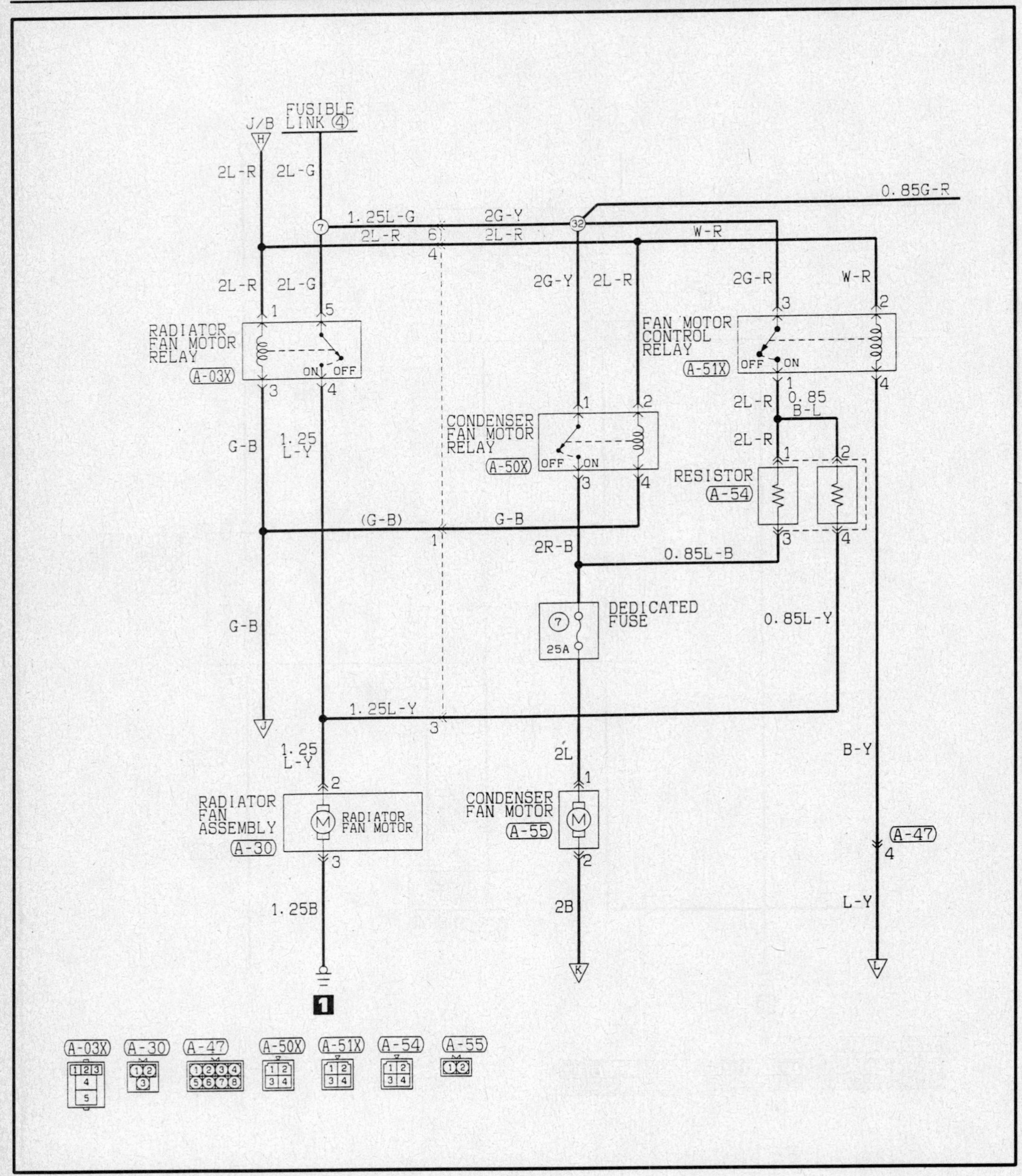

1994–95 Summit with air conditioning—1.8L engine, Cont'd

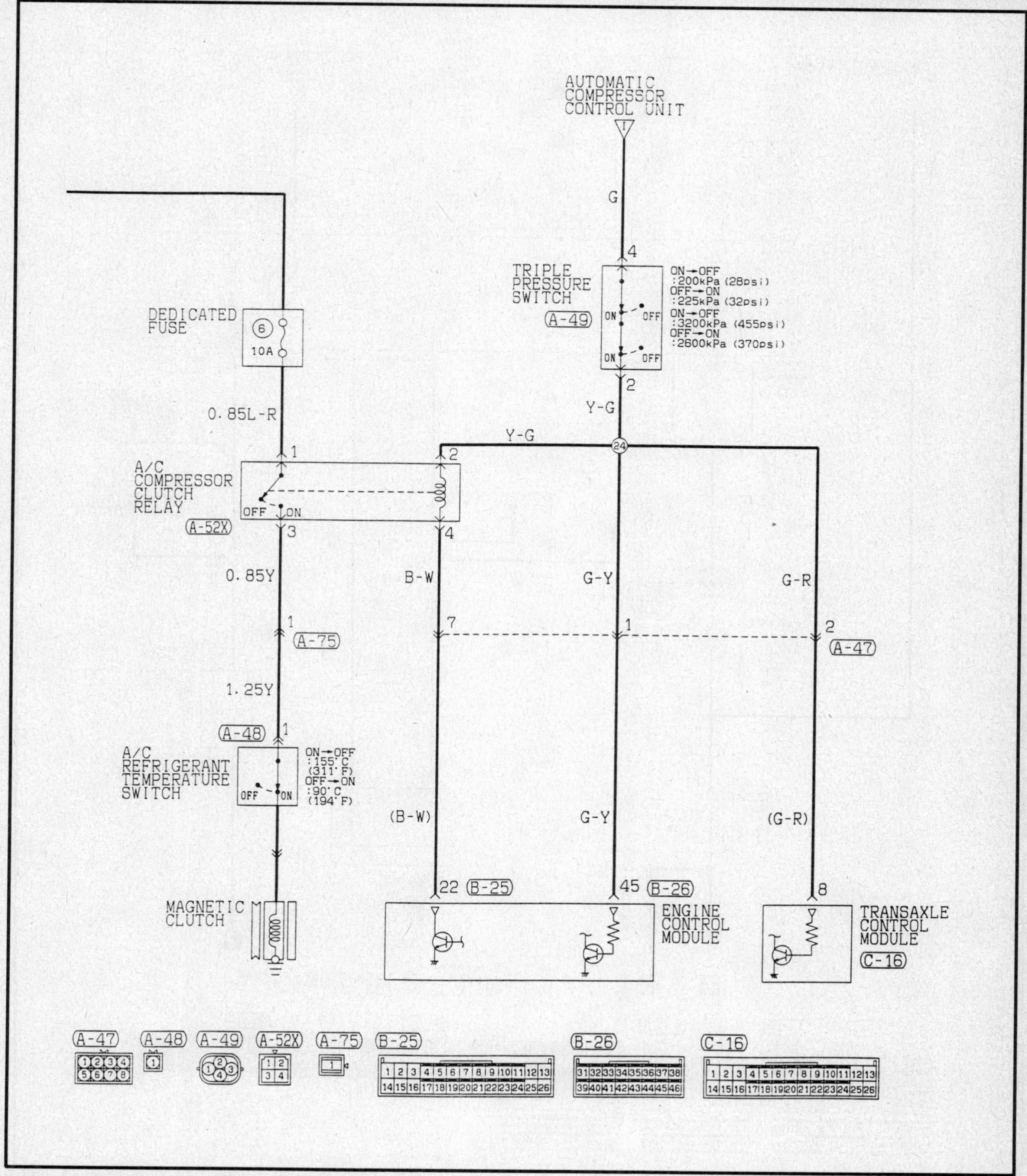

1994–95 Summit with air conditioning—1.8L engine, Cont'd

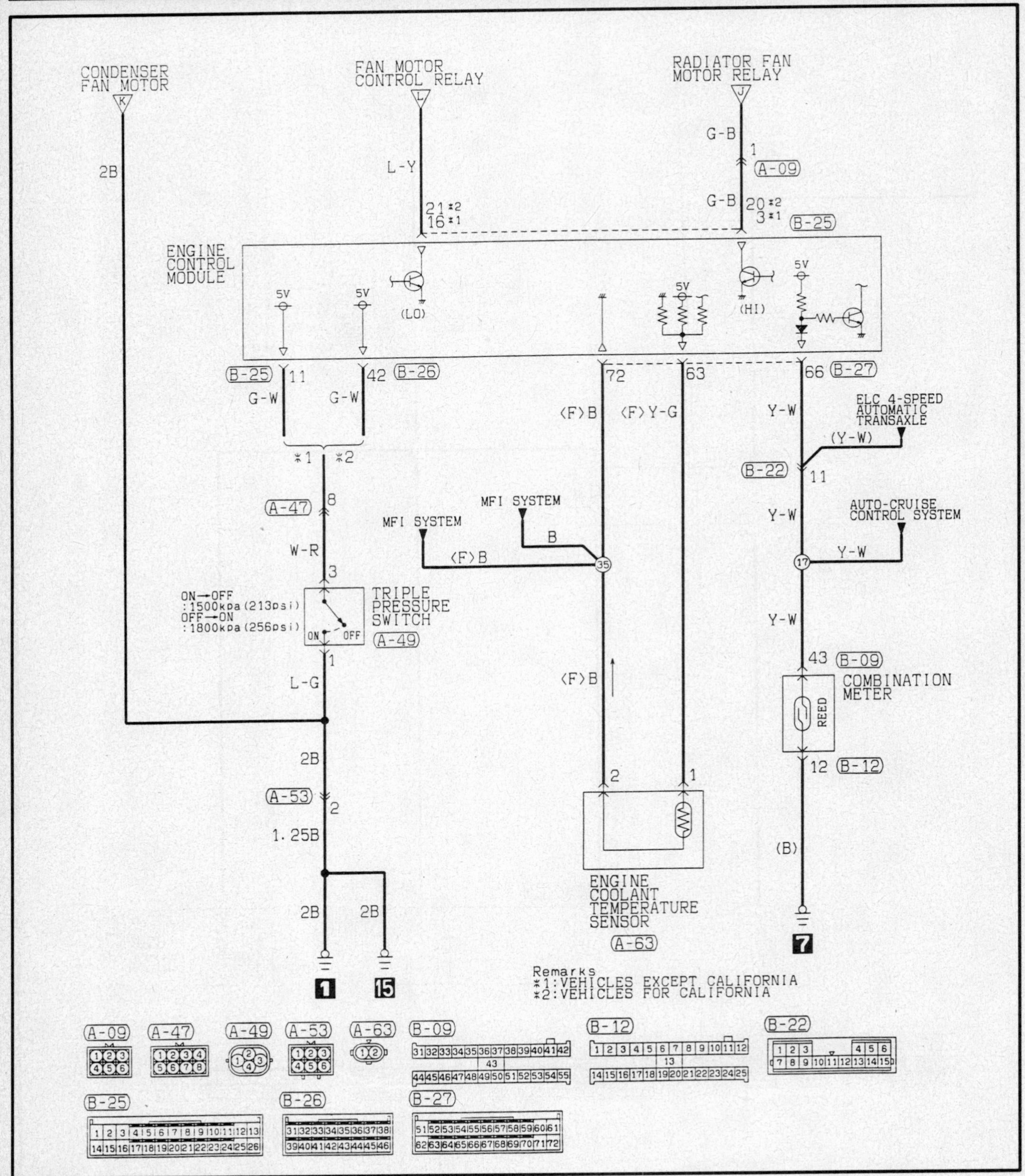

1994–95 Summit with air conditioning—1.8L engine, Cont'd

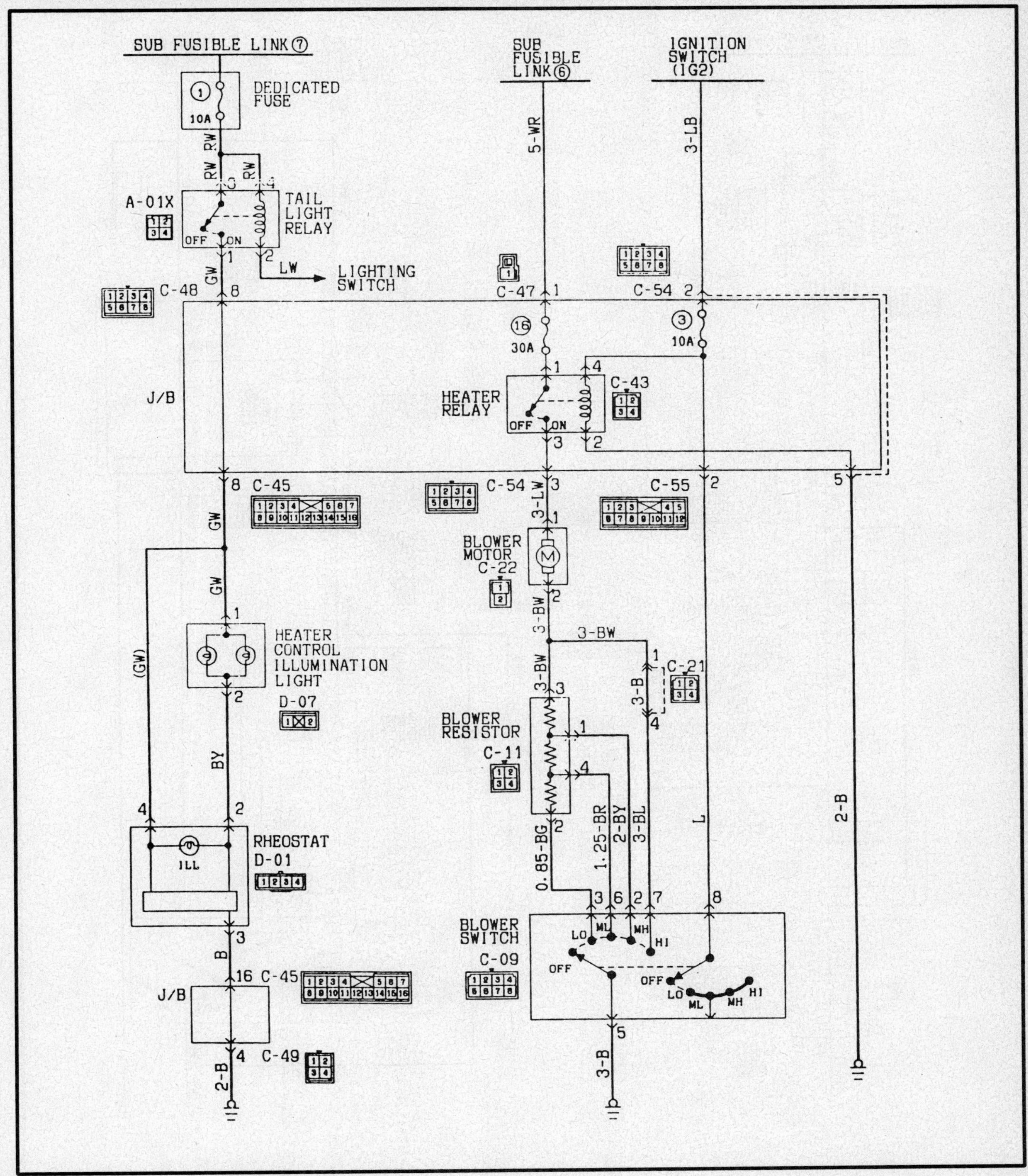

1993 Laser and Talon with heater only

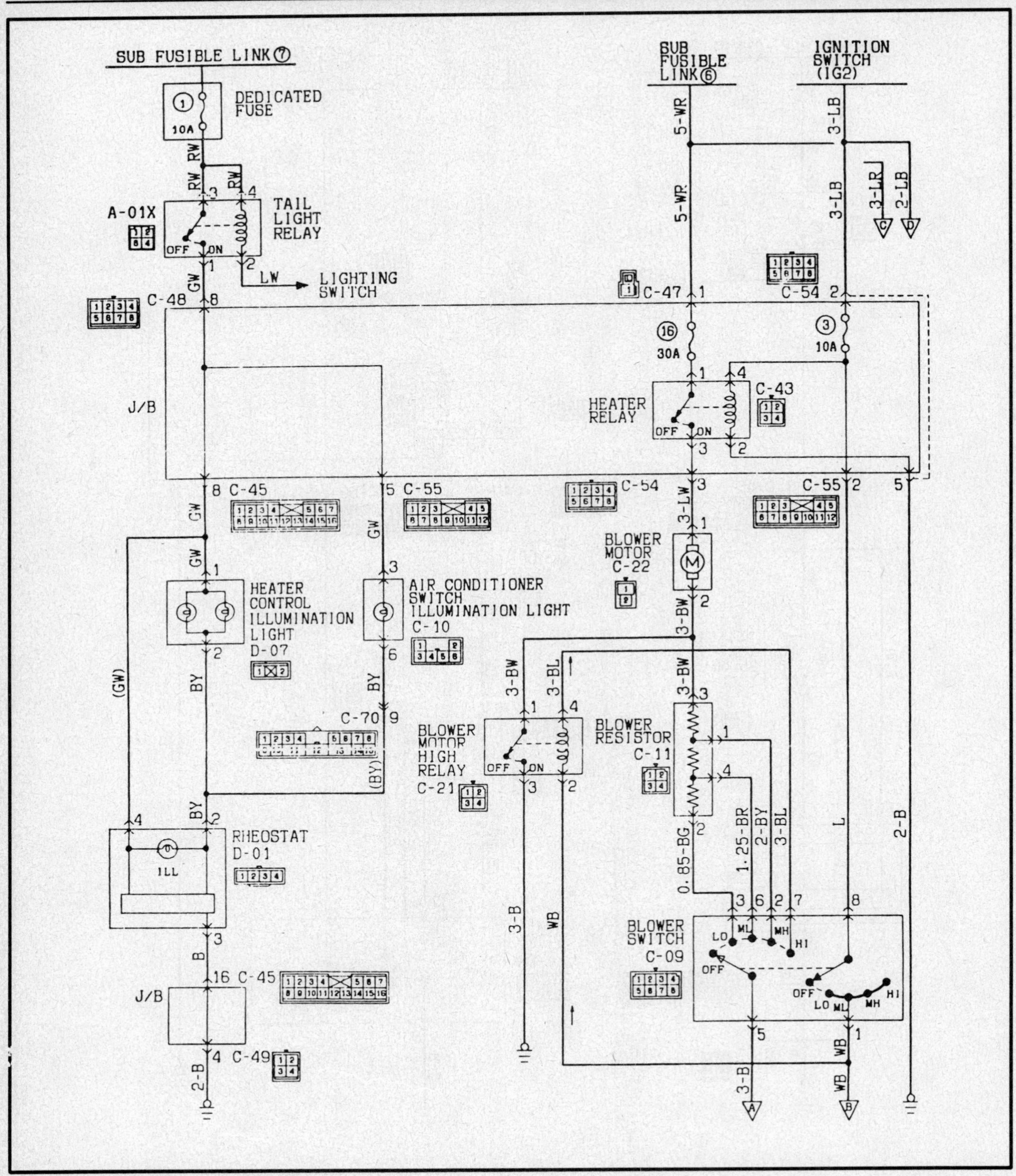

1993 Laser and Talon with air conditioning

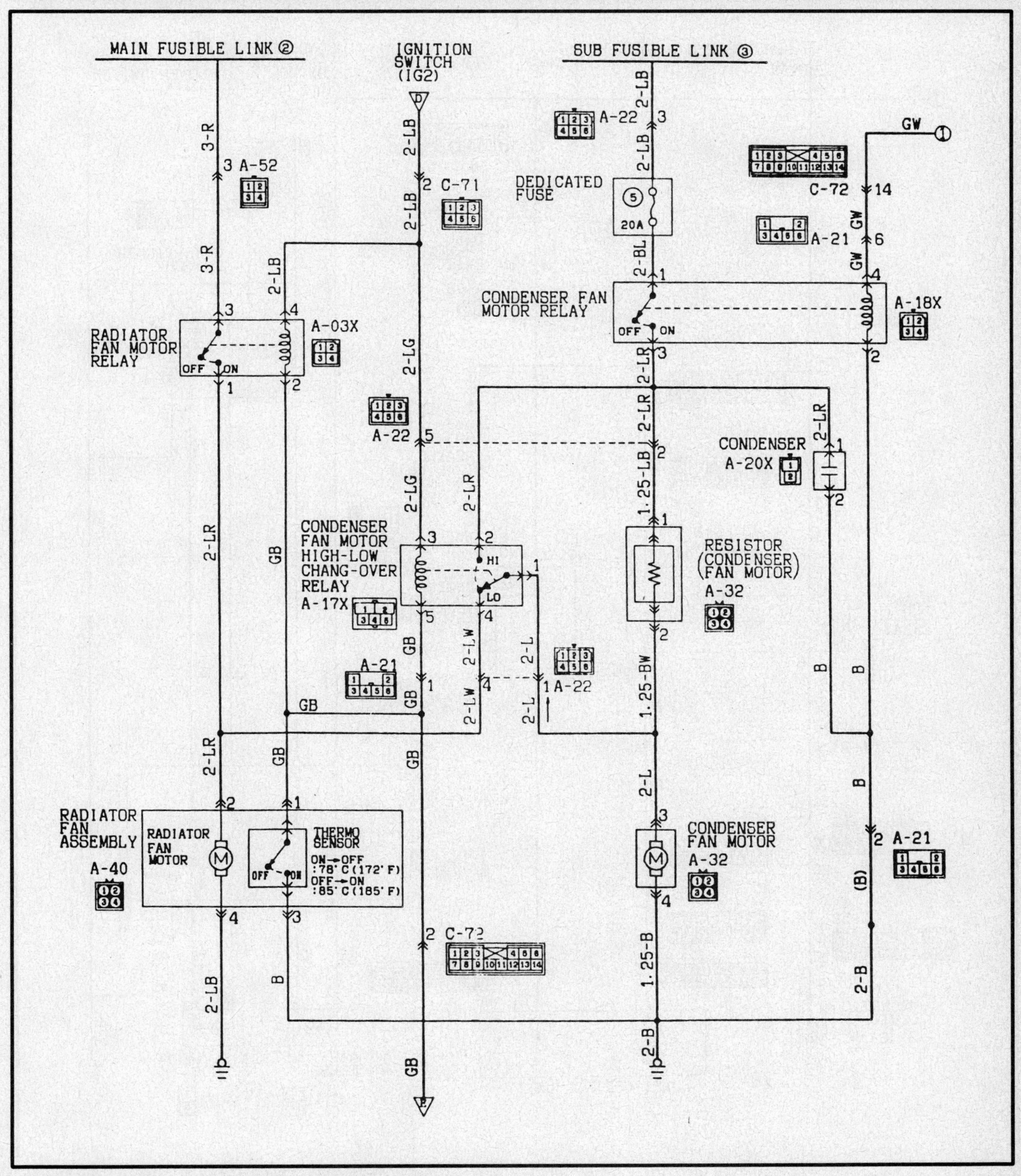

1993 Laser and Talon with air conditioning, Cont'd

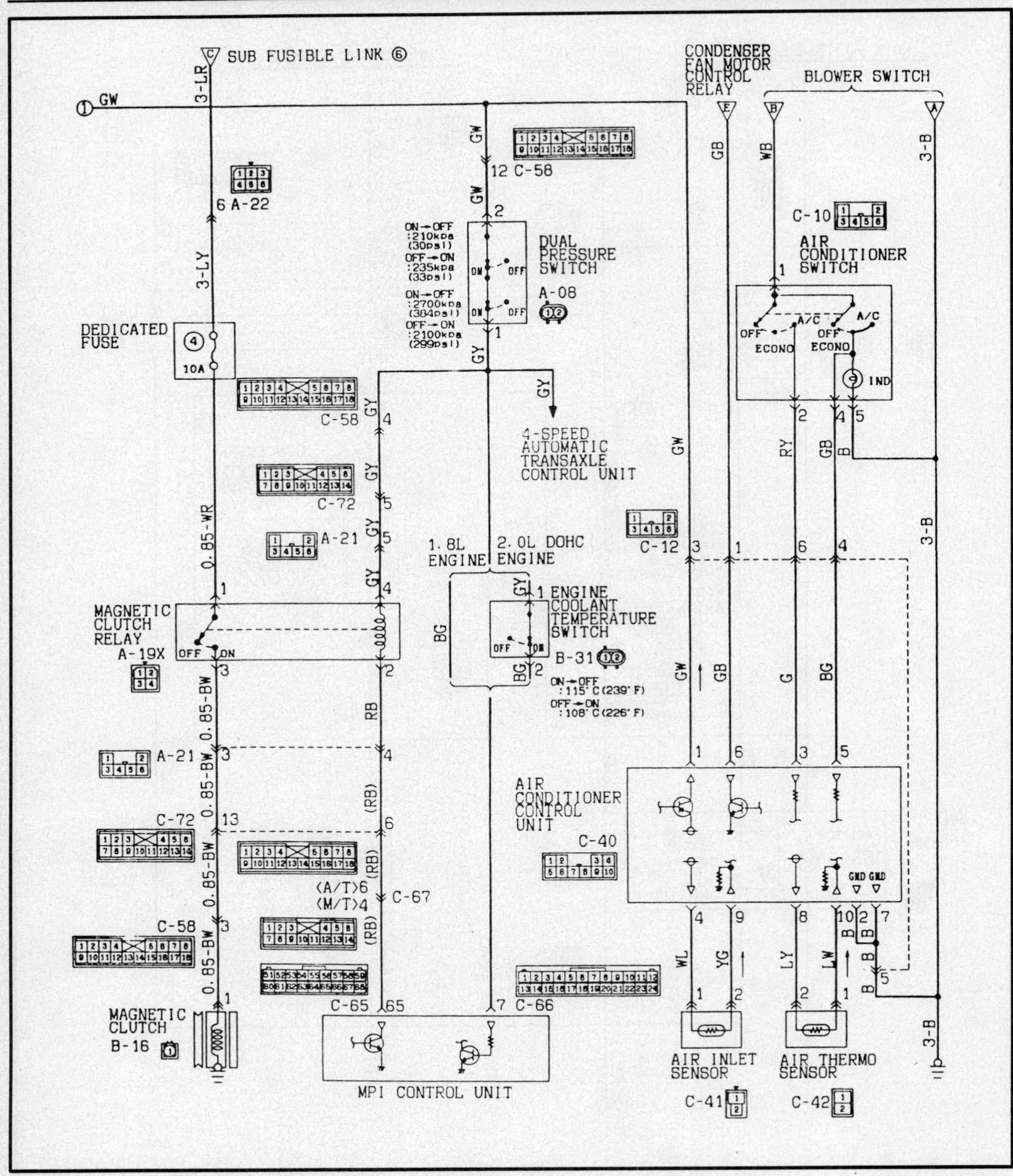

1993 Laser and Talon with air conditioning, Cont'd

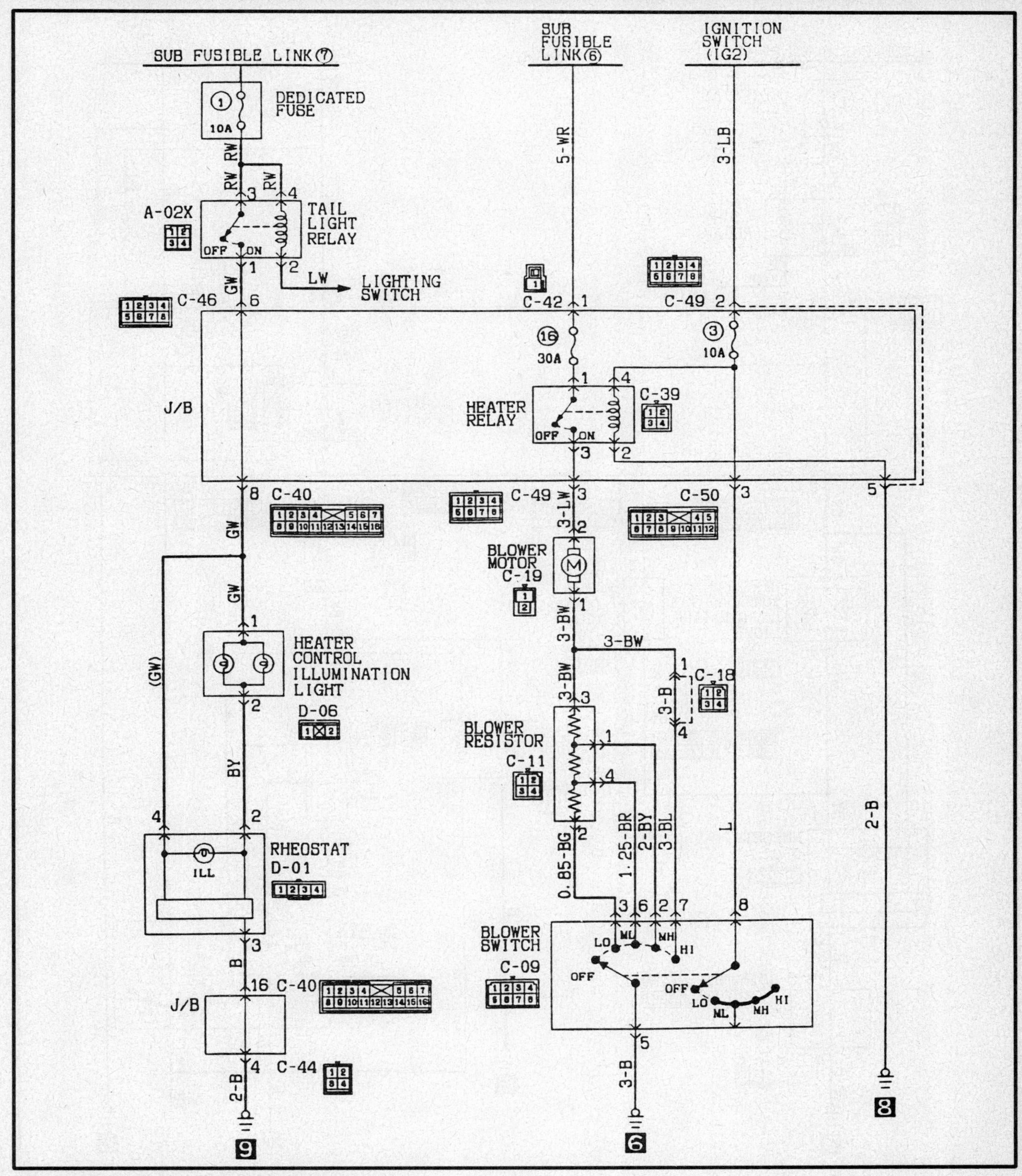

1994 Laser and Talon with heater only

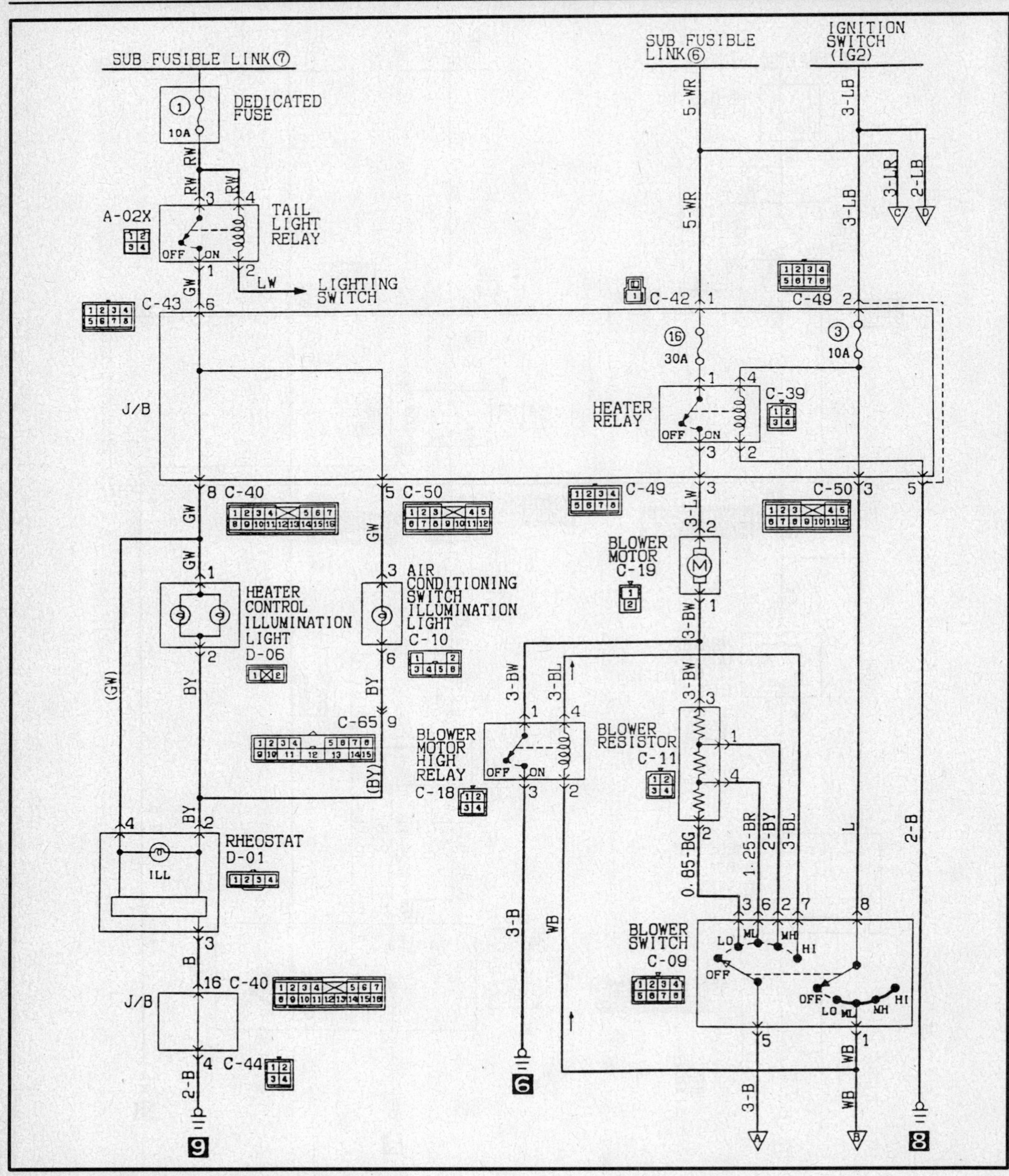

1994 Laser and Talon with air conditioning

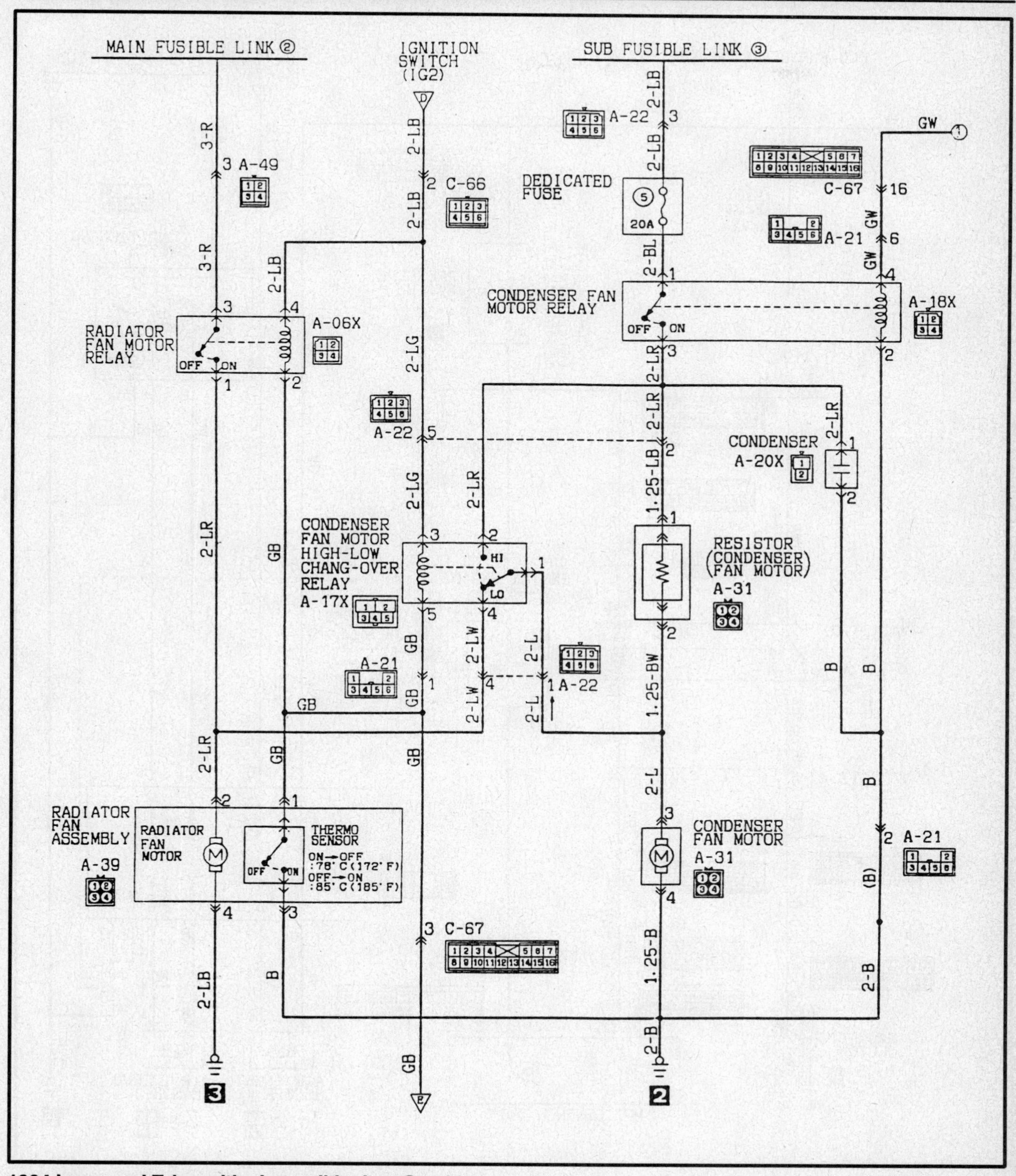

1994 Laser and Talon with air conditioning, Cont'd

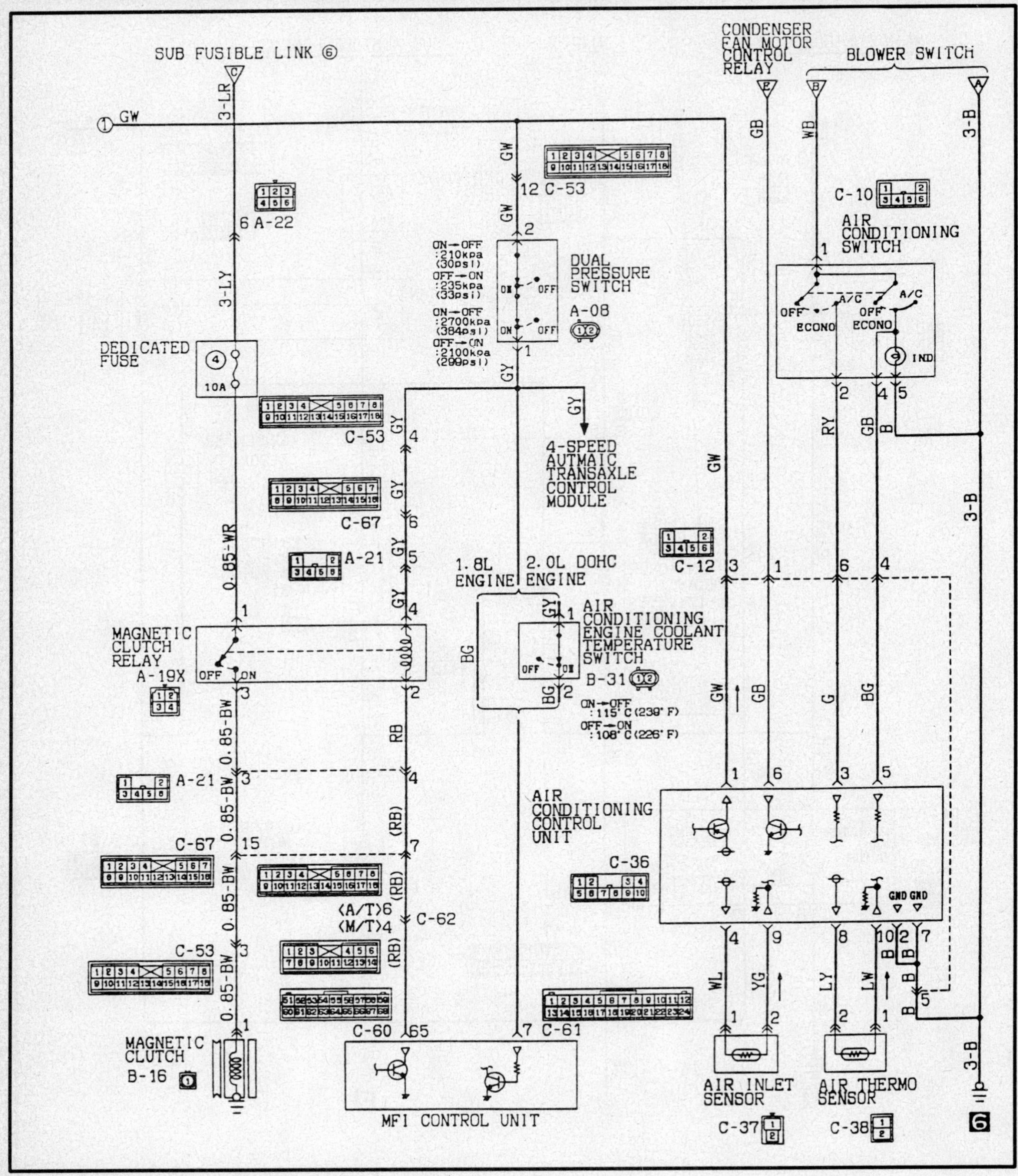

1994 Laser and Talon with air conditioning, Cont'd

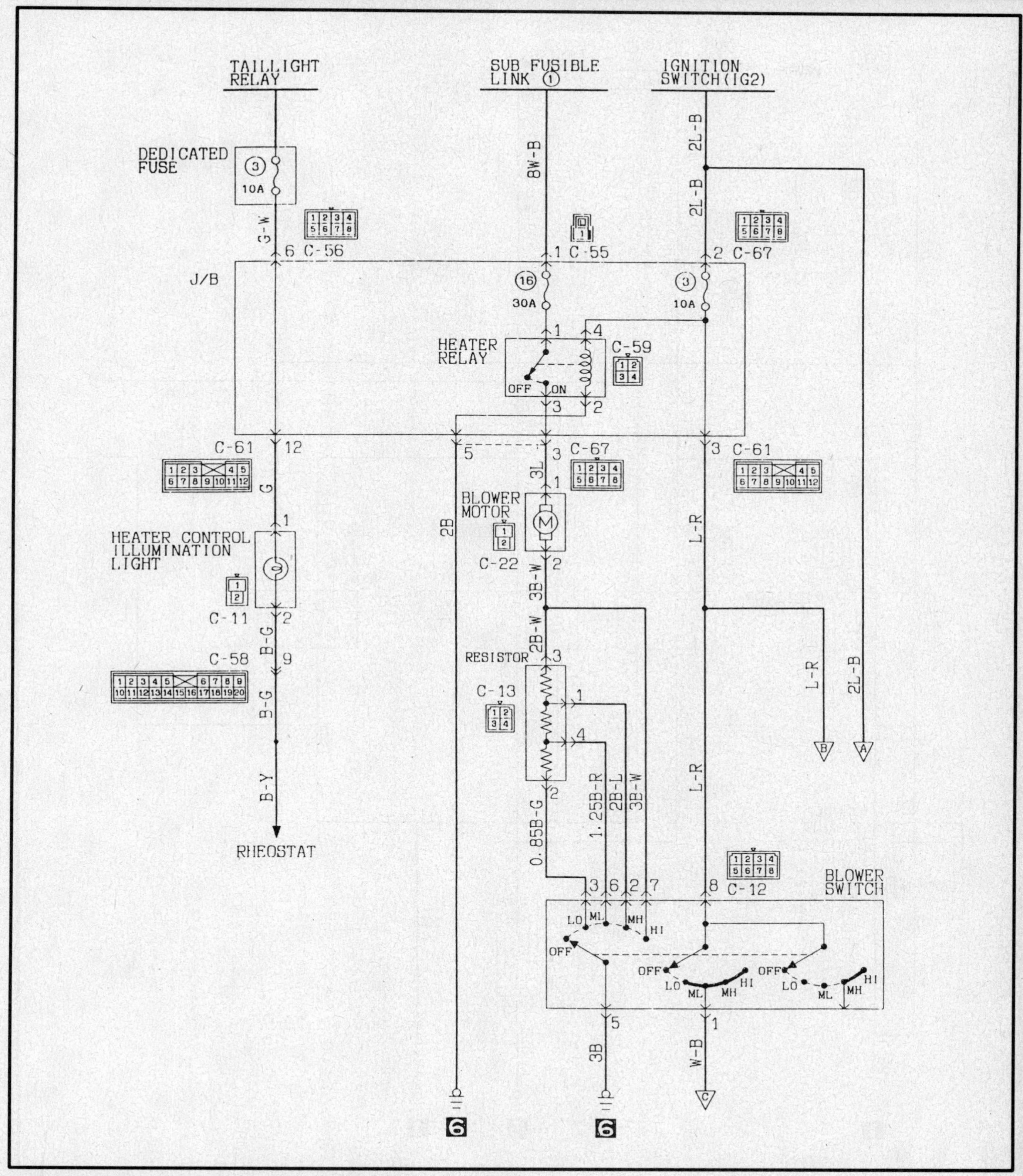

1993 Summit Wagon with air conditioning—1.8L engine

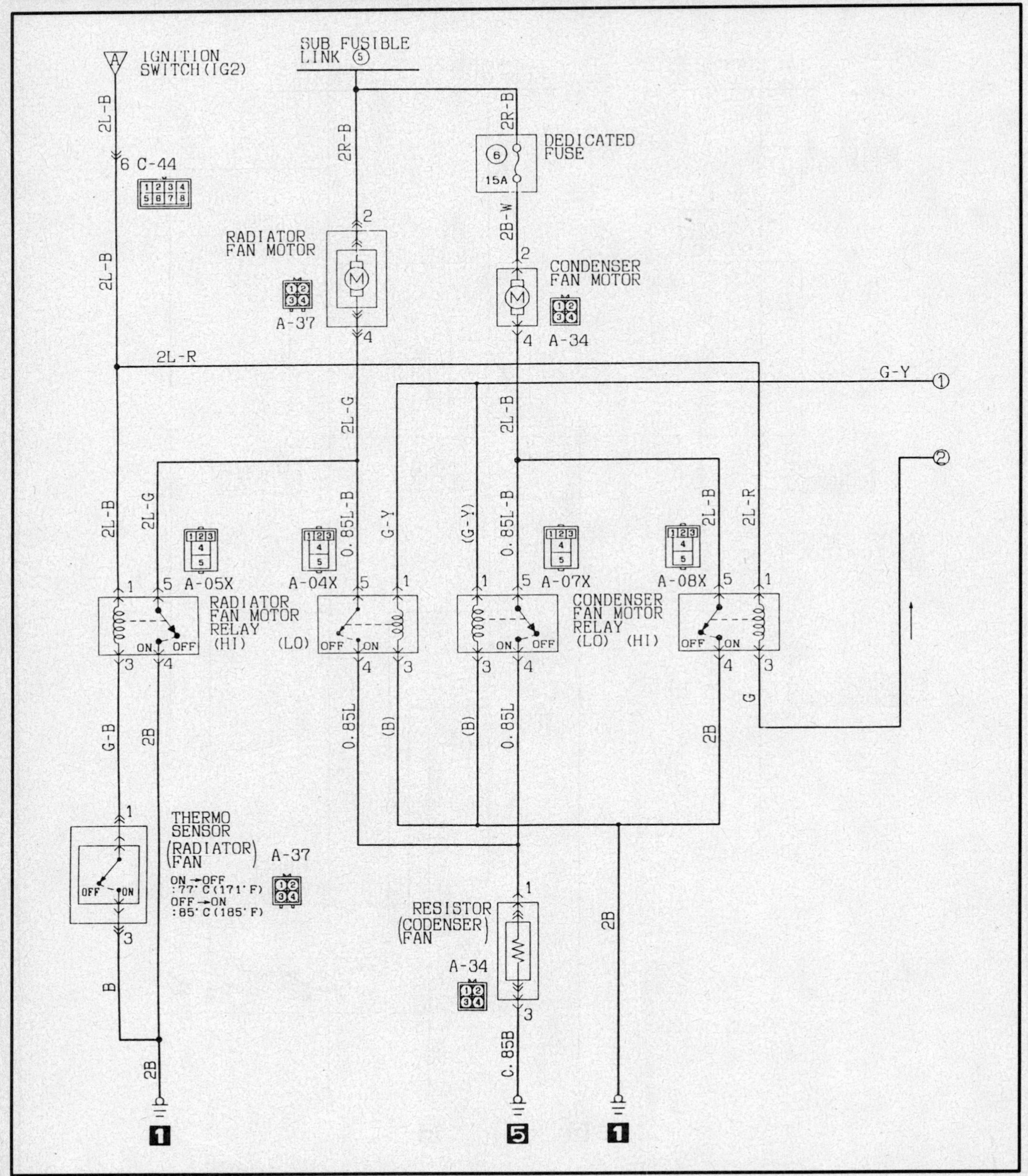

1993 Summit Wagon with air conditioning—1.8L engine, Cont'd

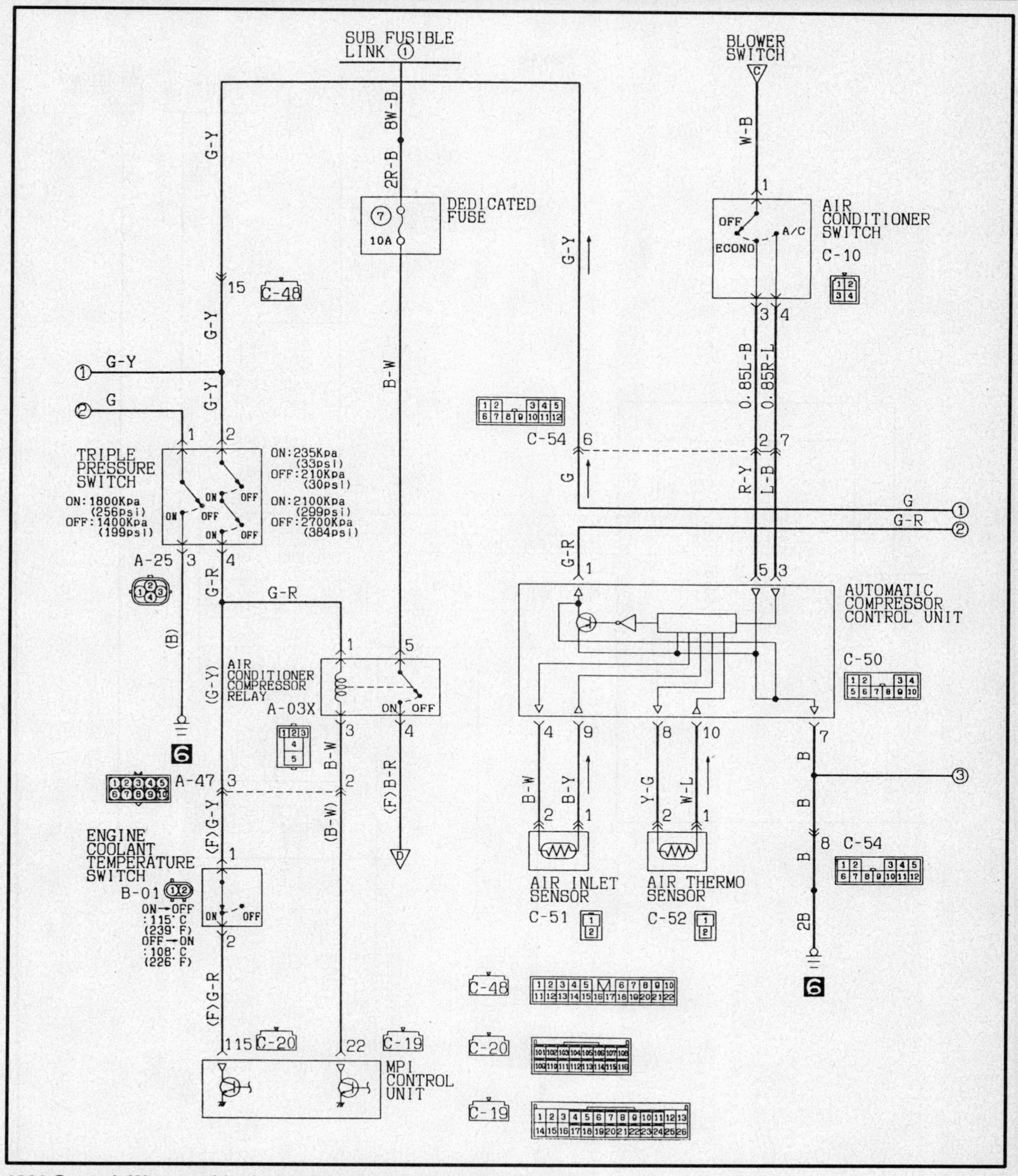

1993 Summit Wagon with air conditioning—1.8L engine, Cont'd

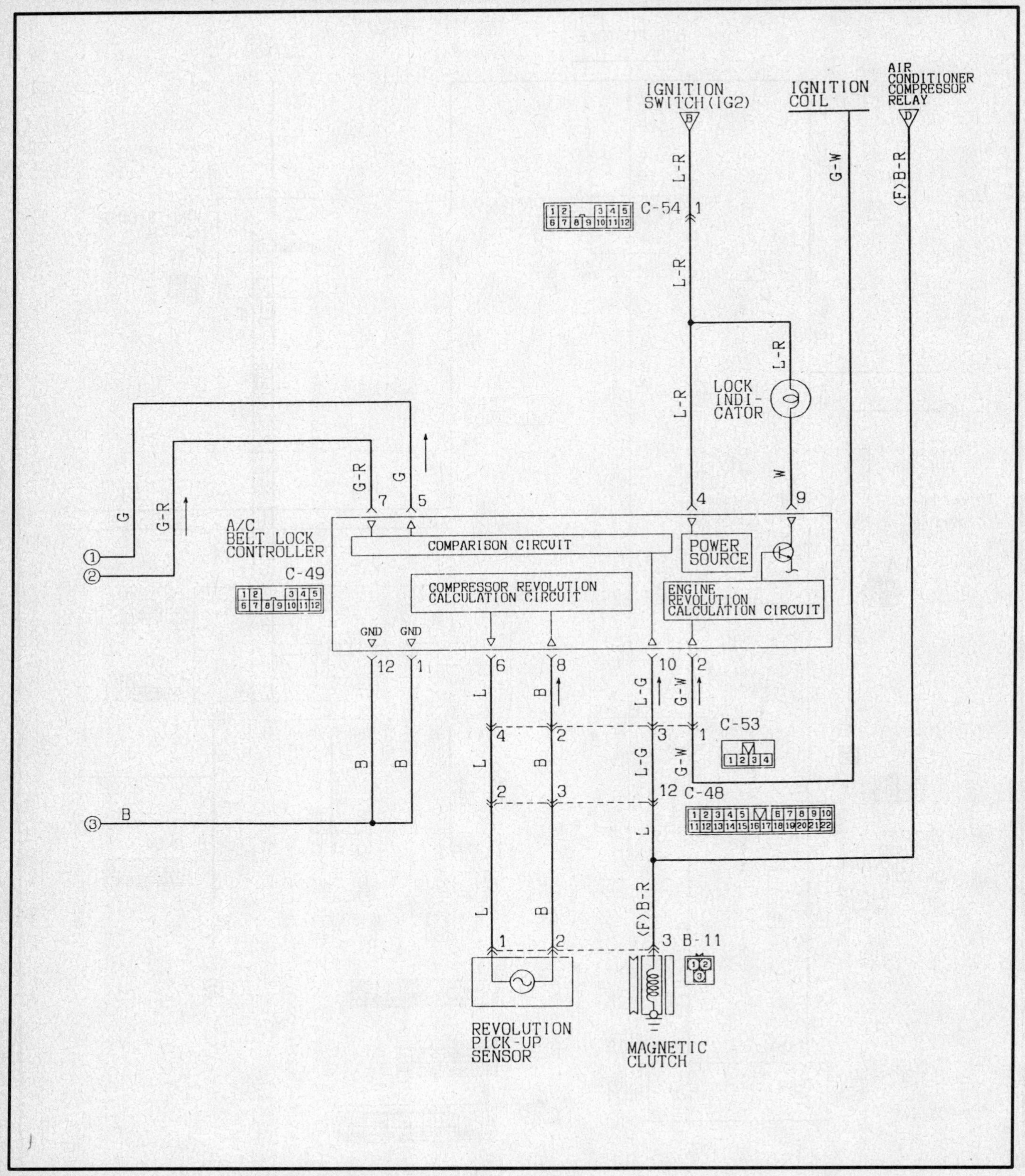

1993 Summit Wagon with air conditioning—1.8L engine, Cont'd

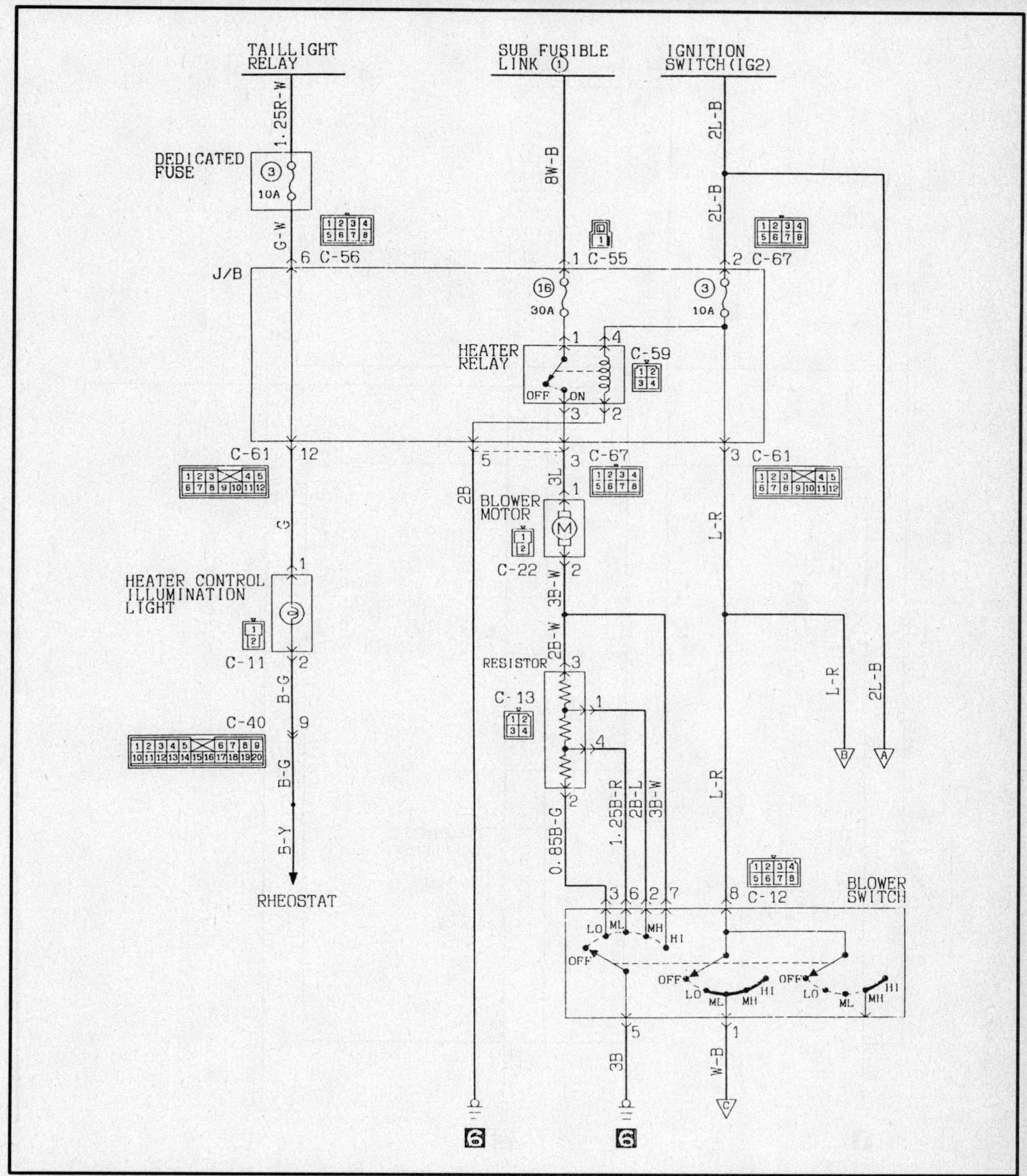

1993 Summit Wagon with air conditioning—2.4L engine

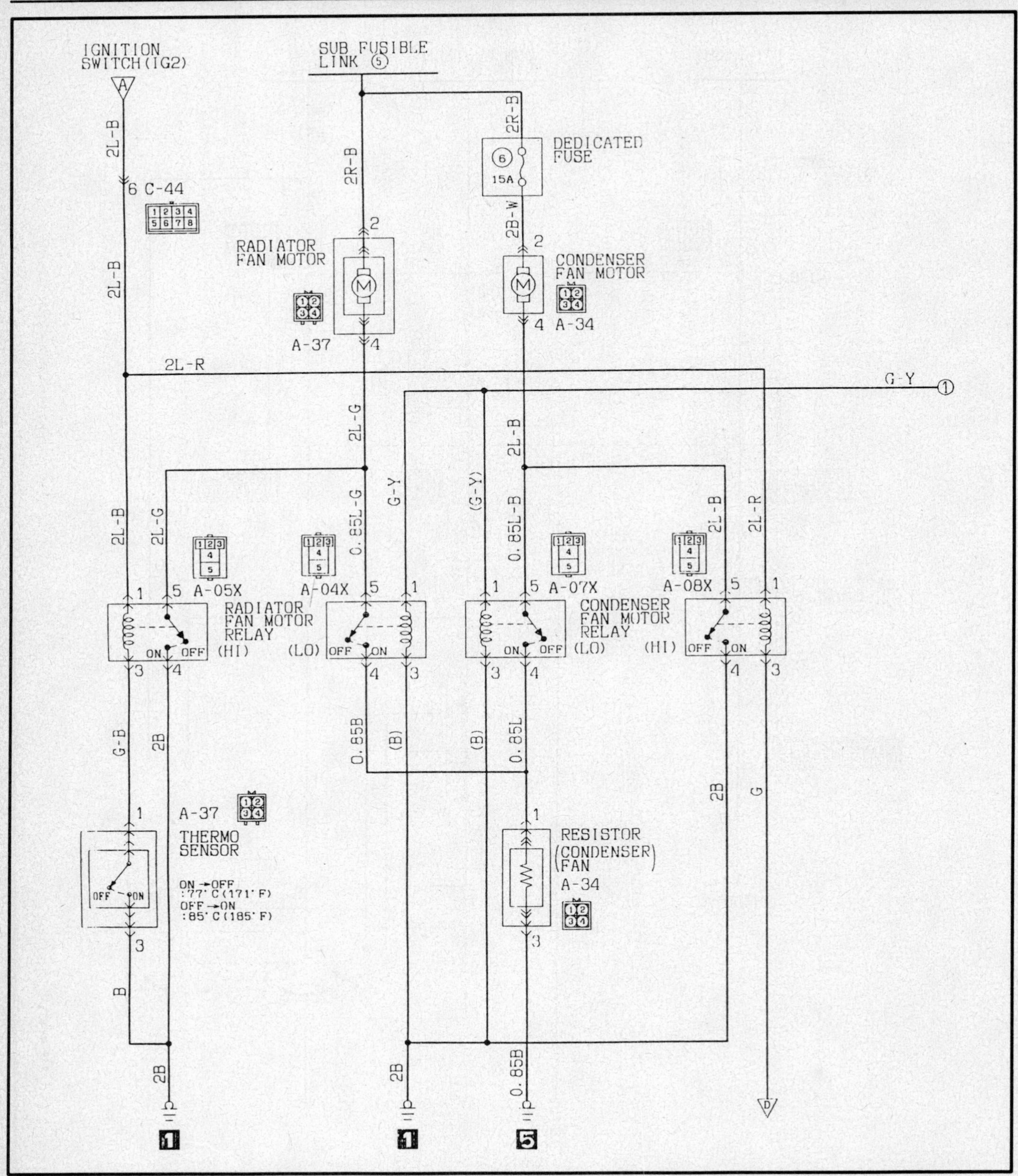

1993 Summit Wagon with air conditioning—2.4L engine, Cont'd

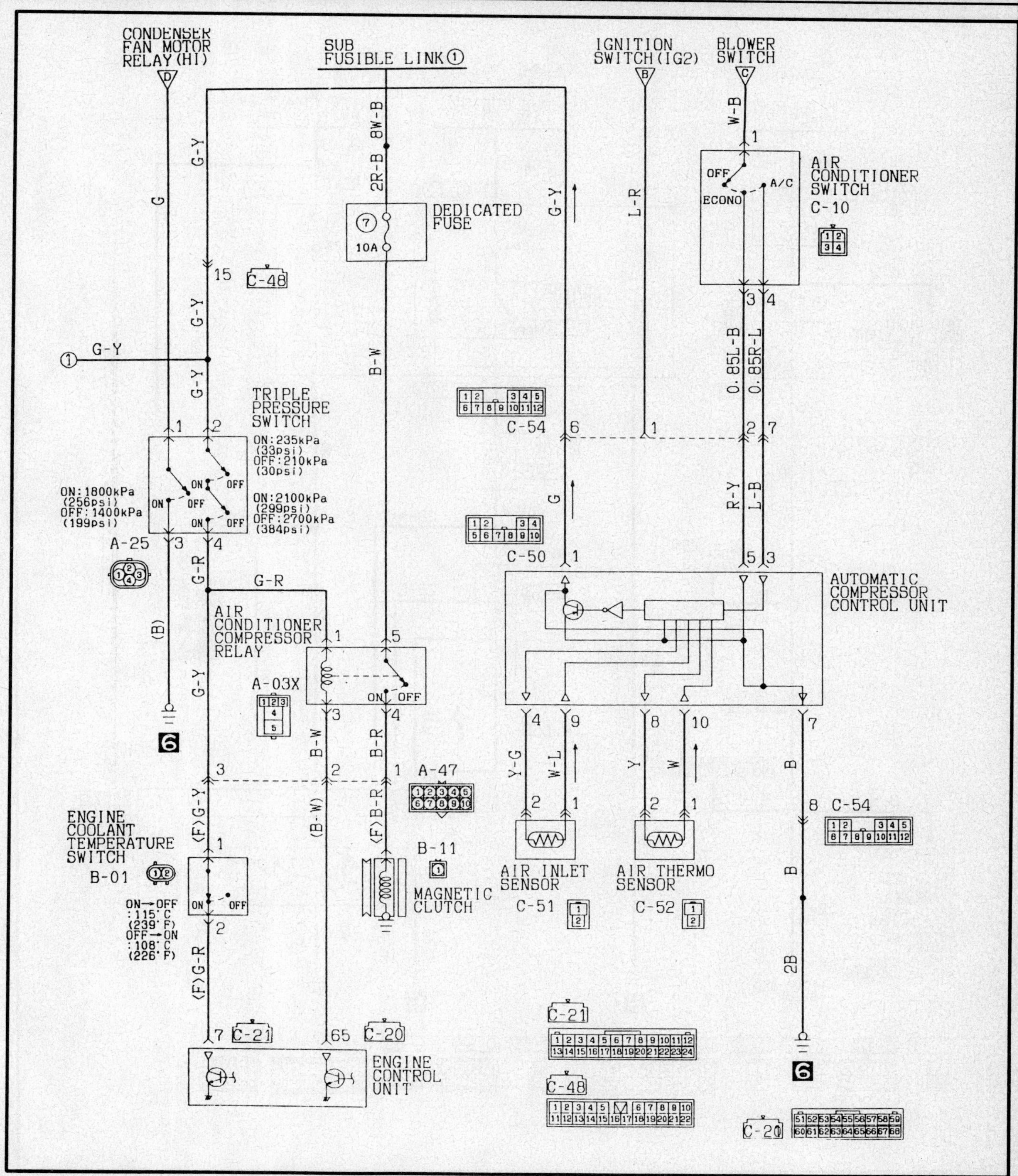

1993 Summit Wagon with air conditioning—2.4L engine, Cont'd

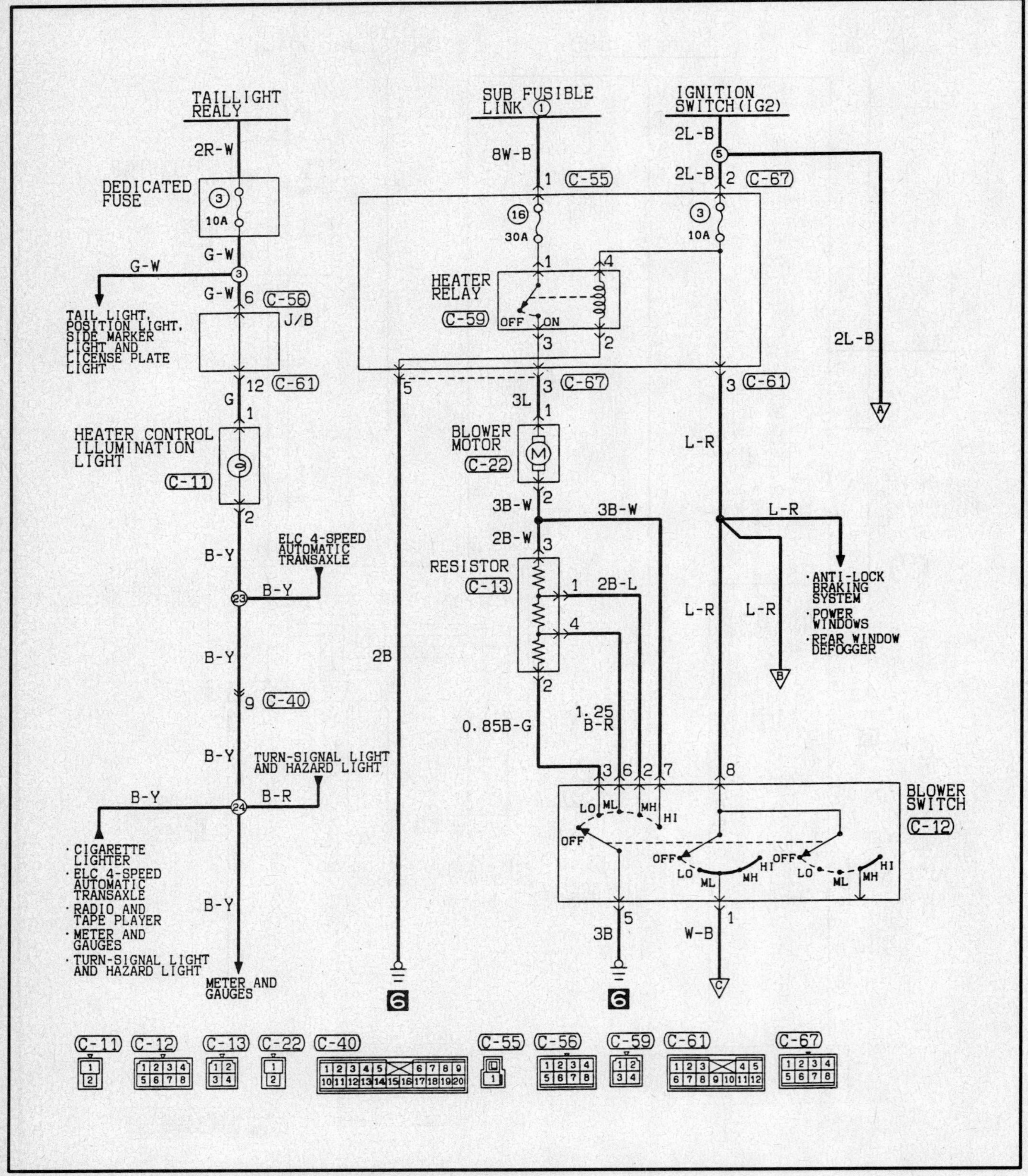

1994–95 Summit Wagon with air conditioning—1.8L engine

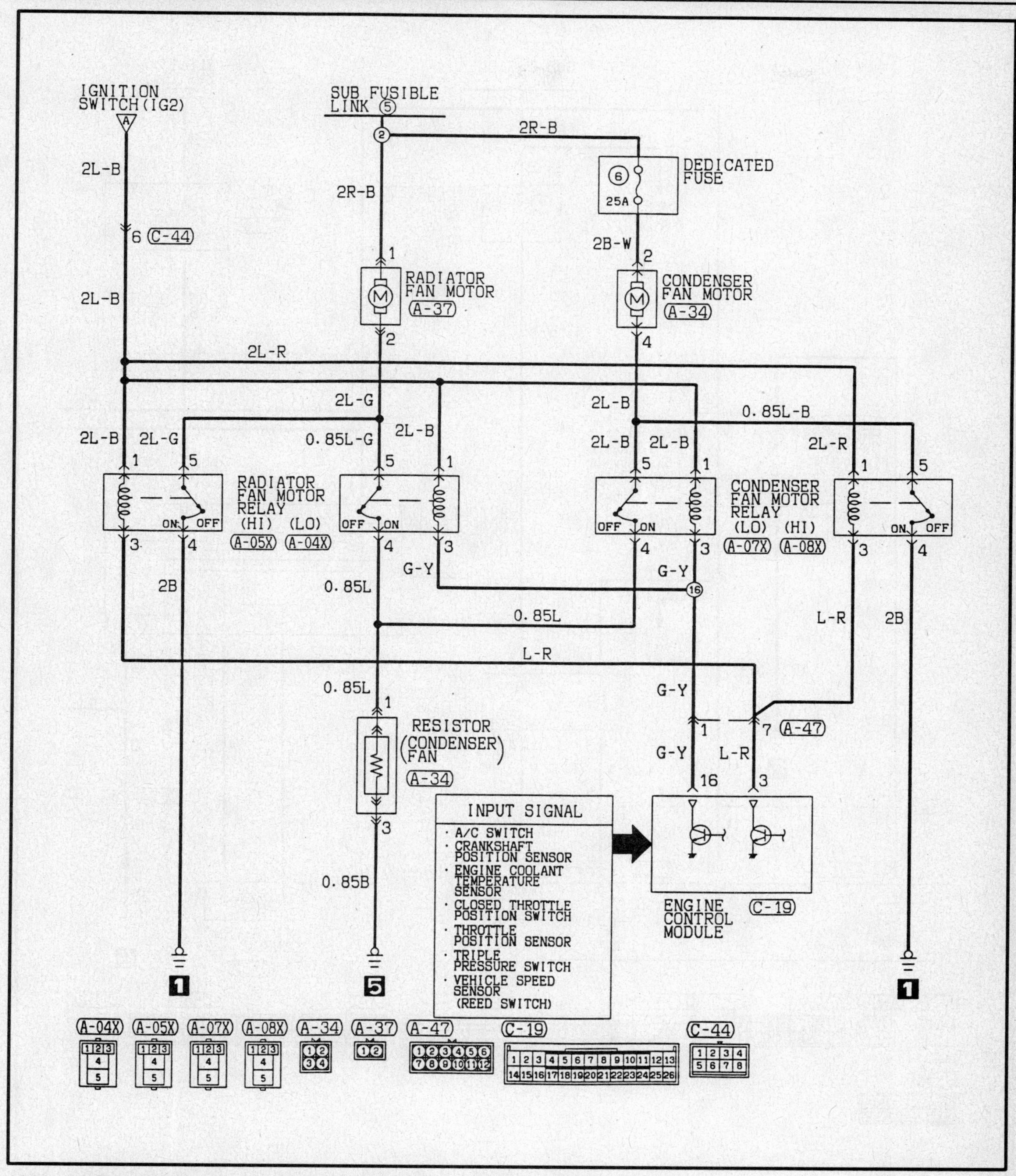

1994–95 Summit Wagon with air conditioning—1.8L engine, Cont'd

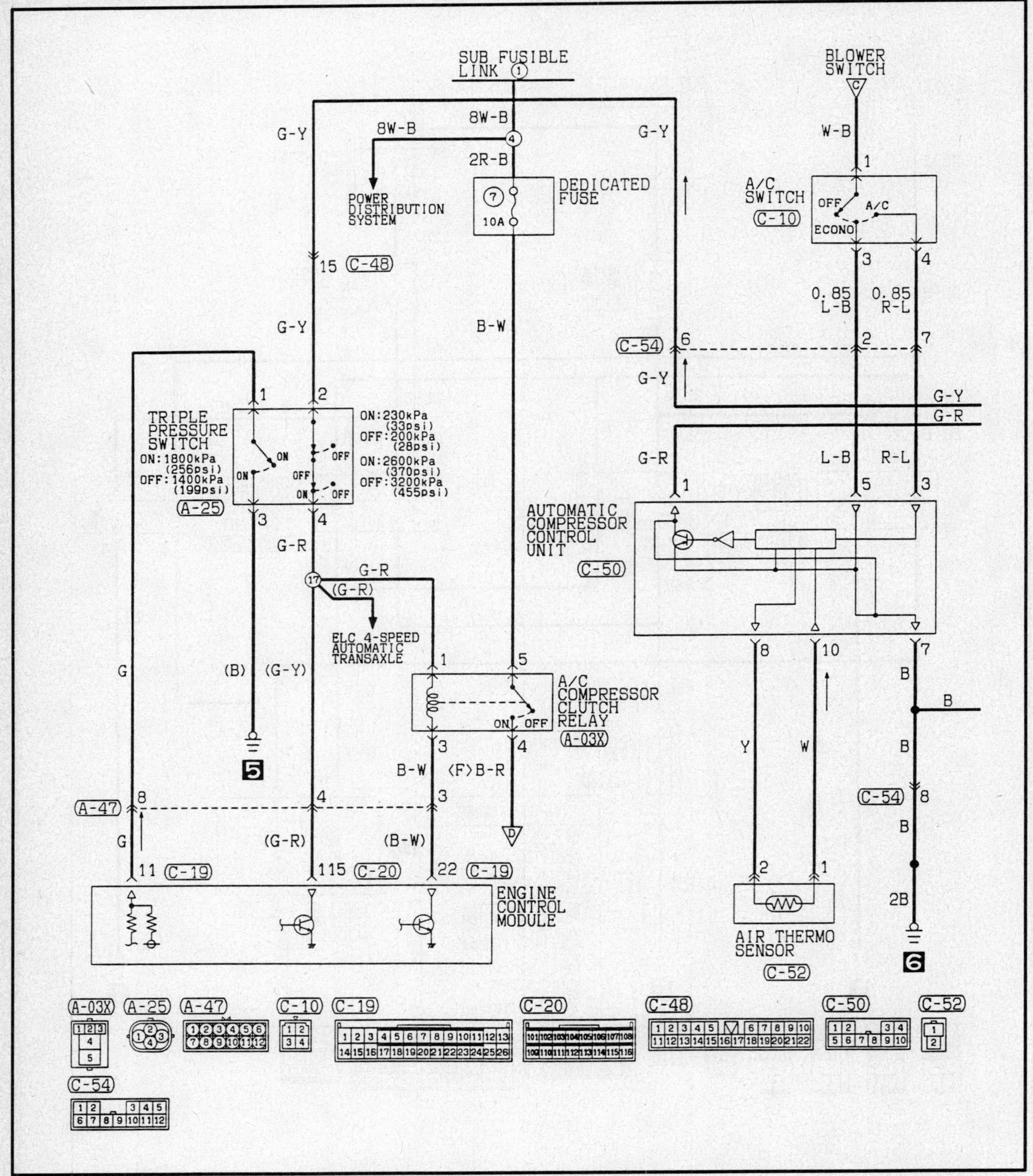

1994–95 Summit Wagon with air conditioning—1.8L engine, Cont'd

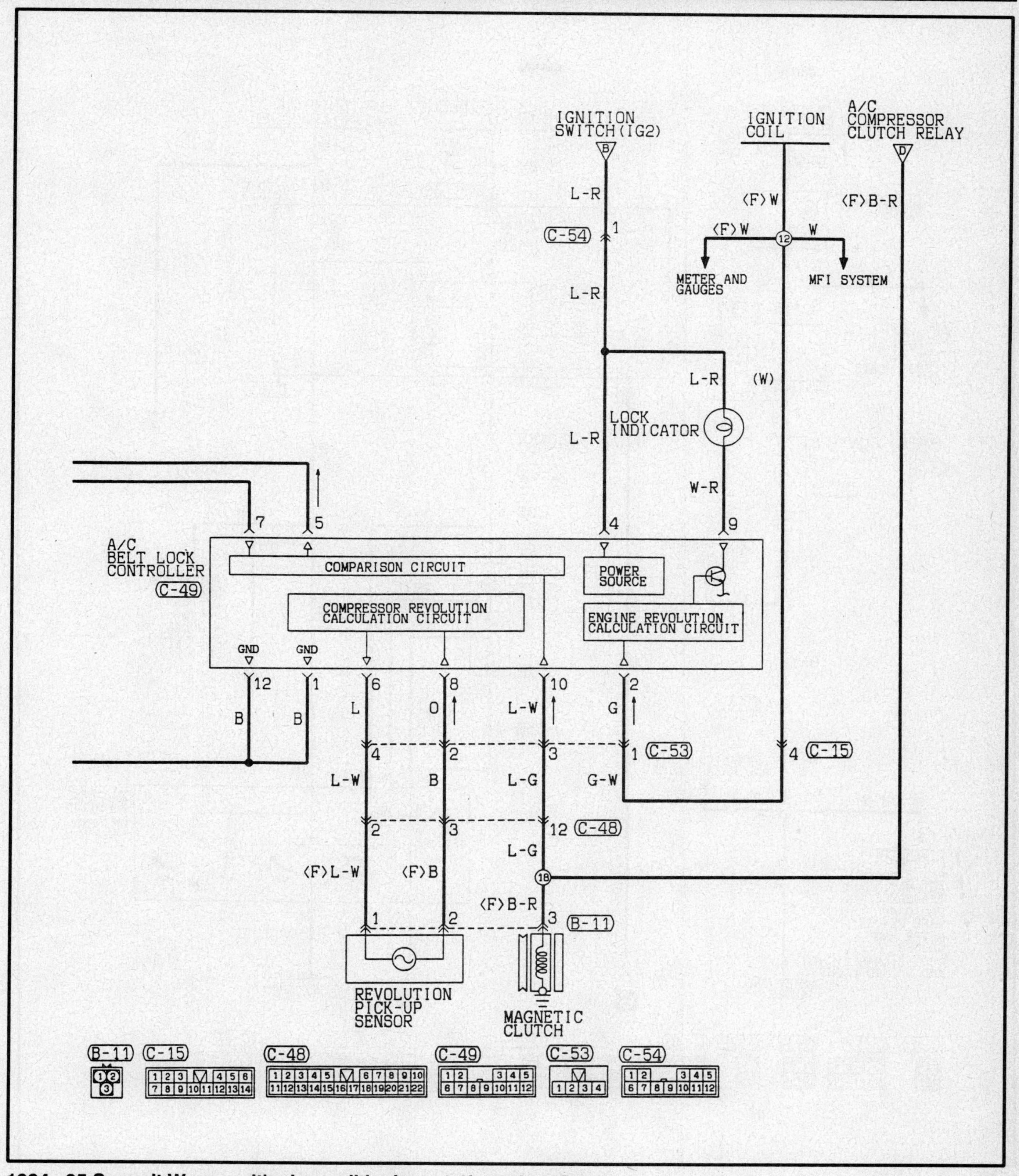

1994–95 Summit Wagon with air conditioning—1.8L engine, Cont'd

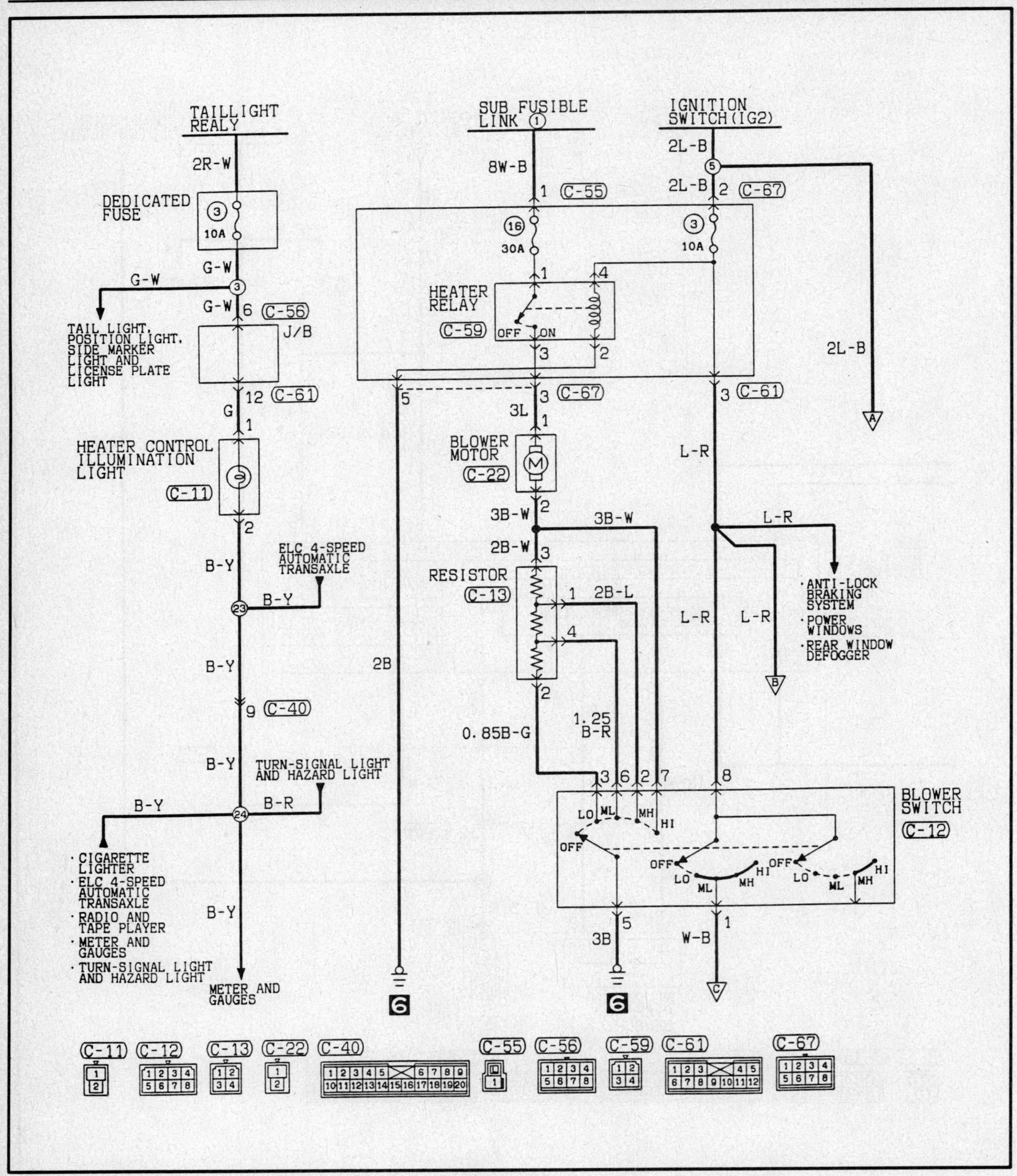

1994–95 Summit Wagon with air conditioning—2.4L engine

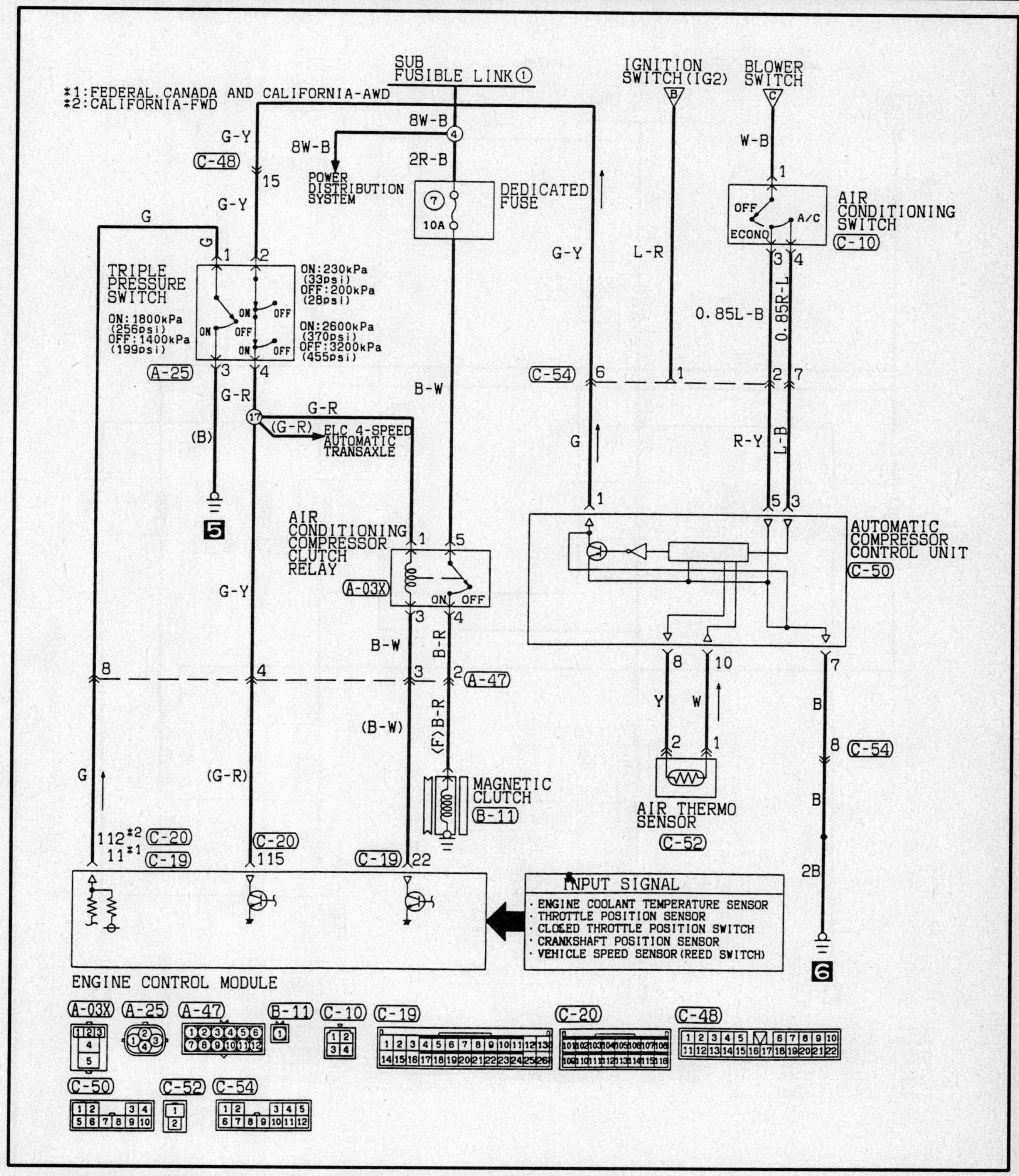

1994–95 Summit Wagon with air conditioning—2.4L engine Cont'd

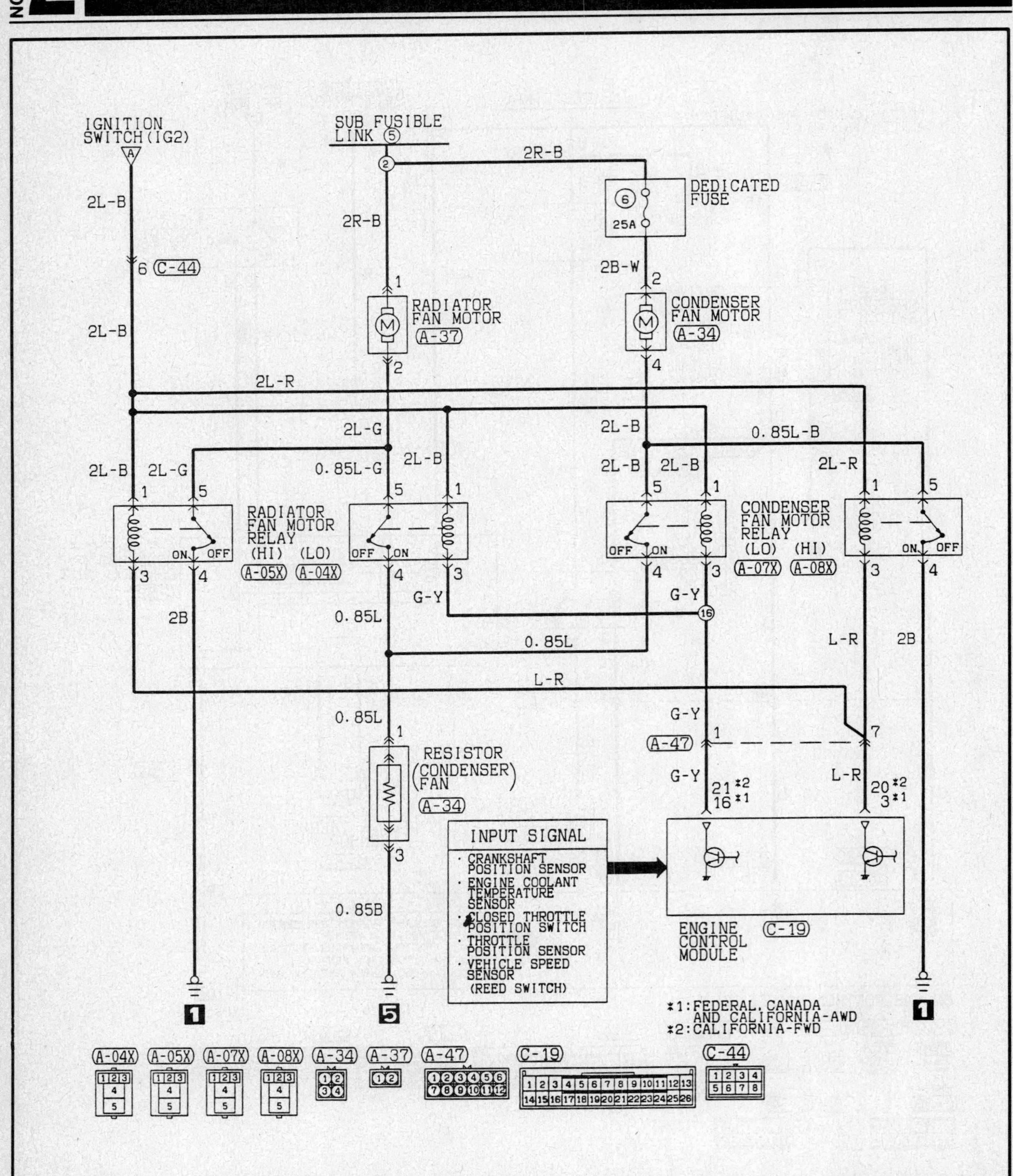

1994–95 Summit Wagon with air conditioning—2.4L engine Cont'd

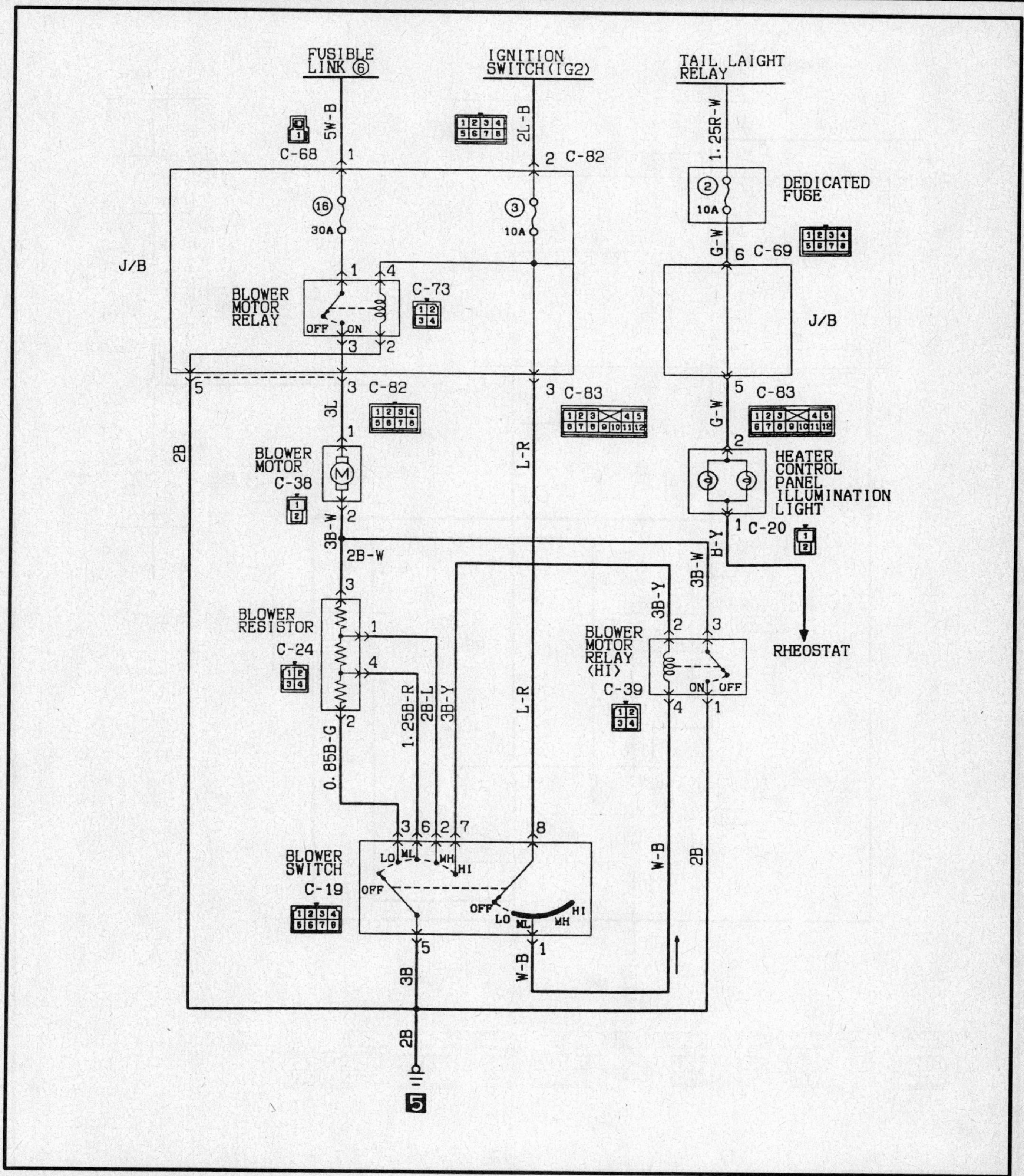

1993–94 Stealth with heater only

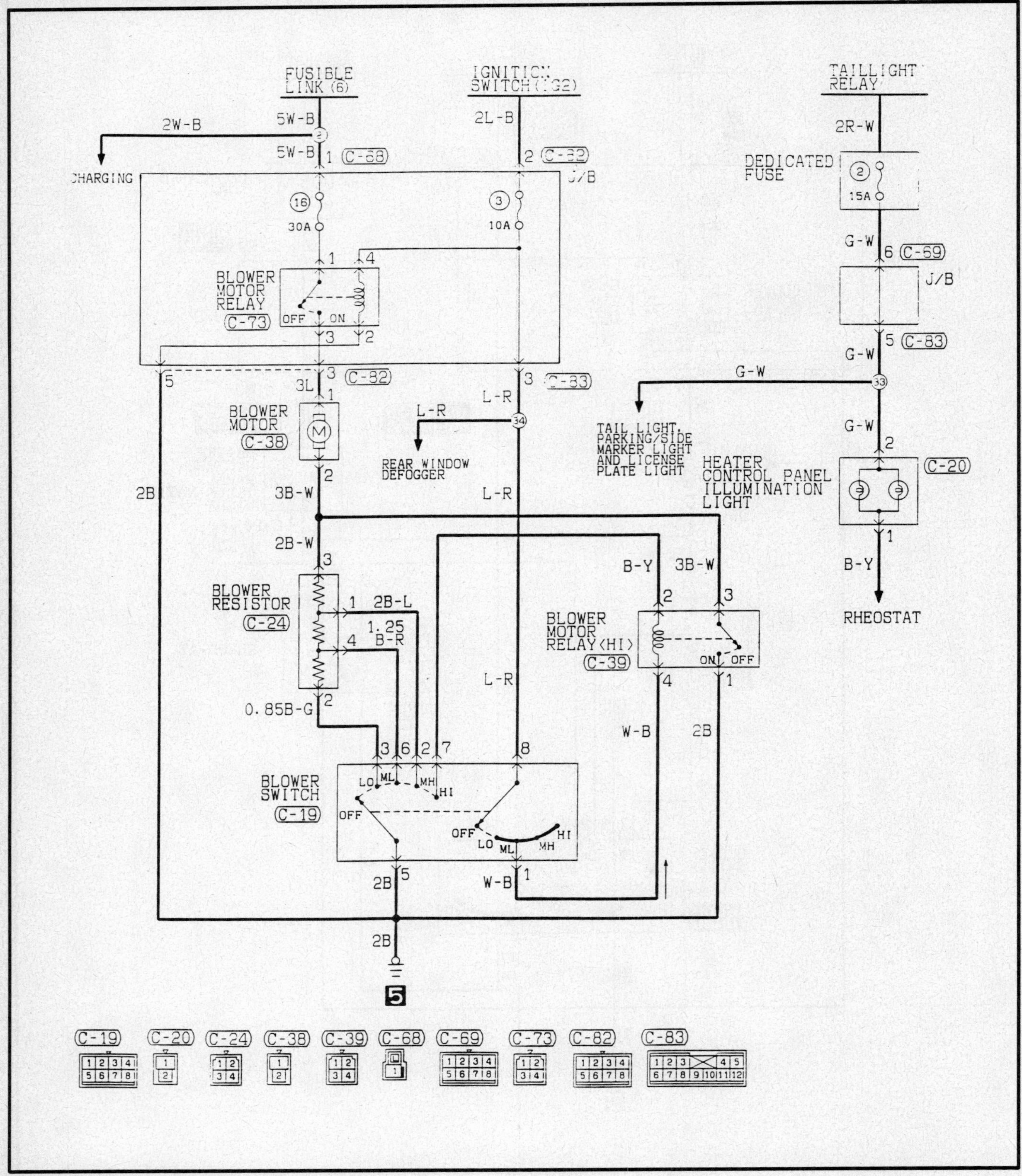

1995 Stealth with heater only

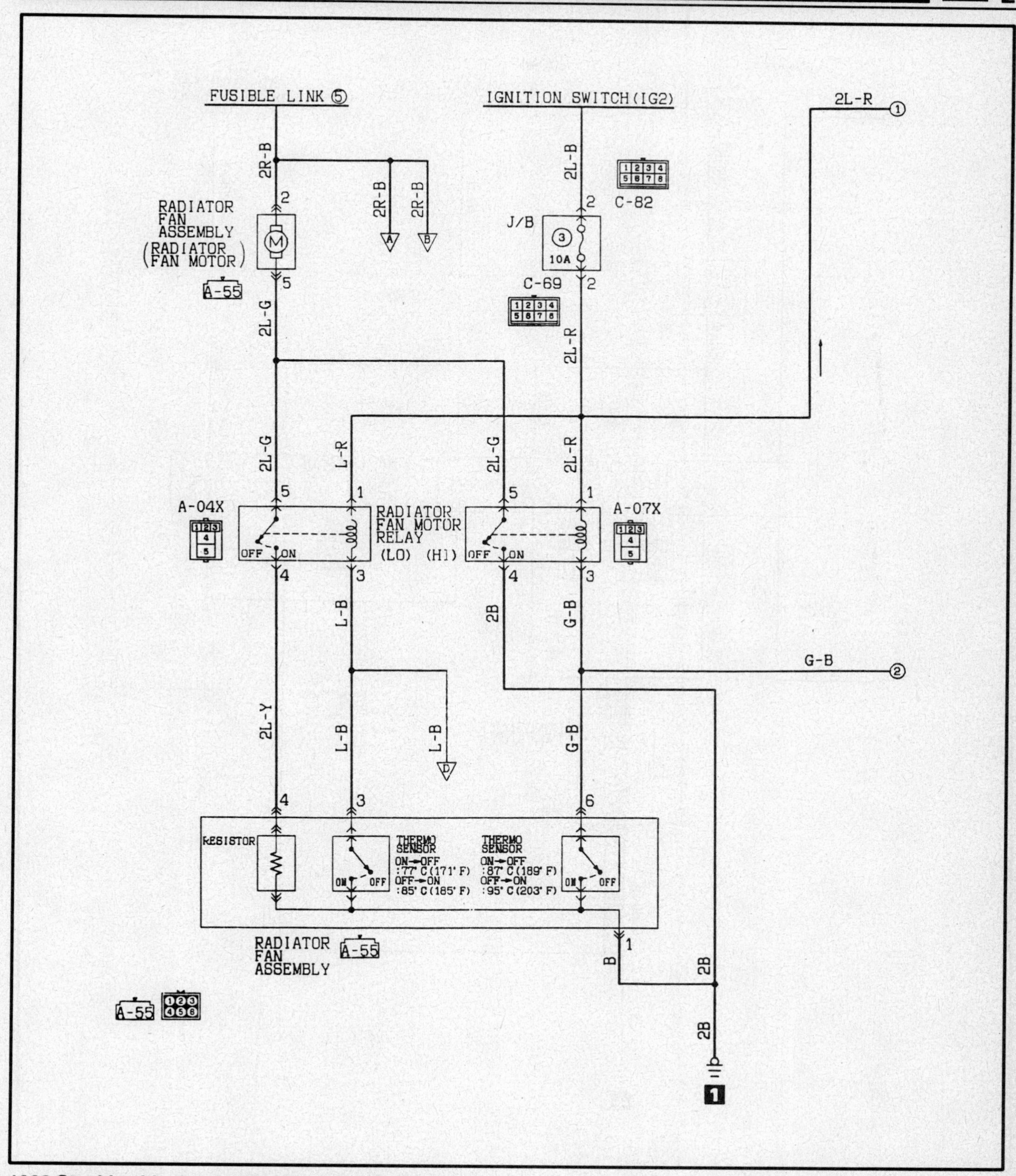

1993 Stealth with air conditioning—SOHC engine

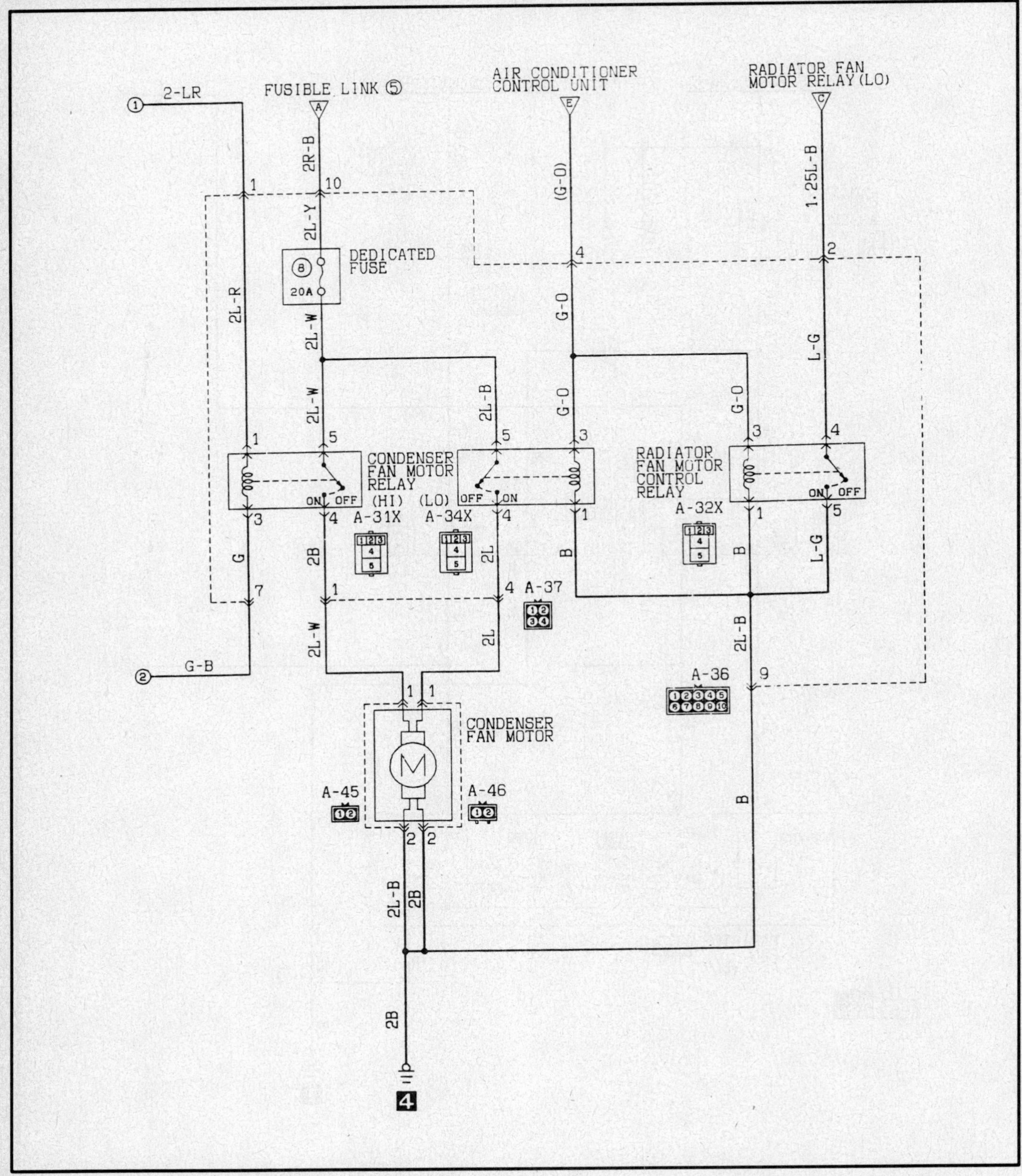

1993 Stealth with air conditioning—SOHC engine, Cont'd

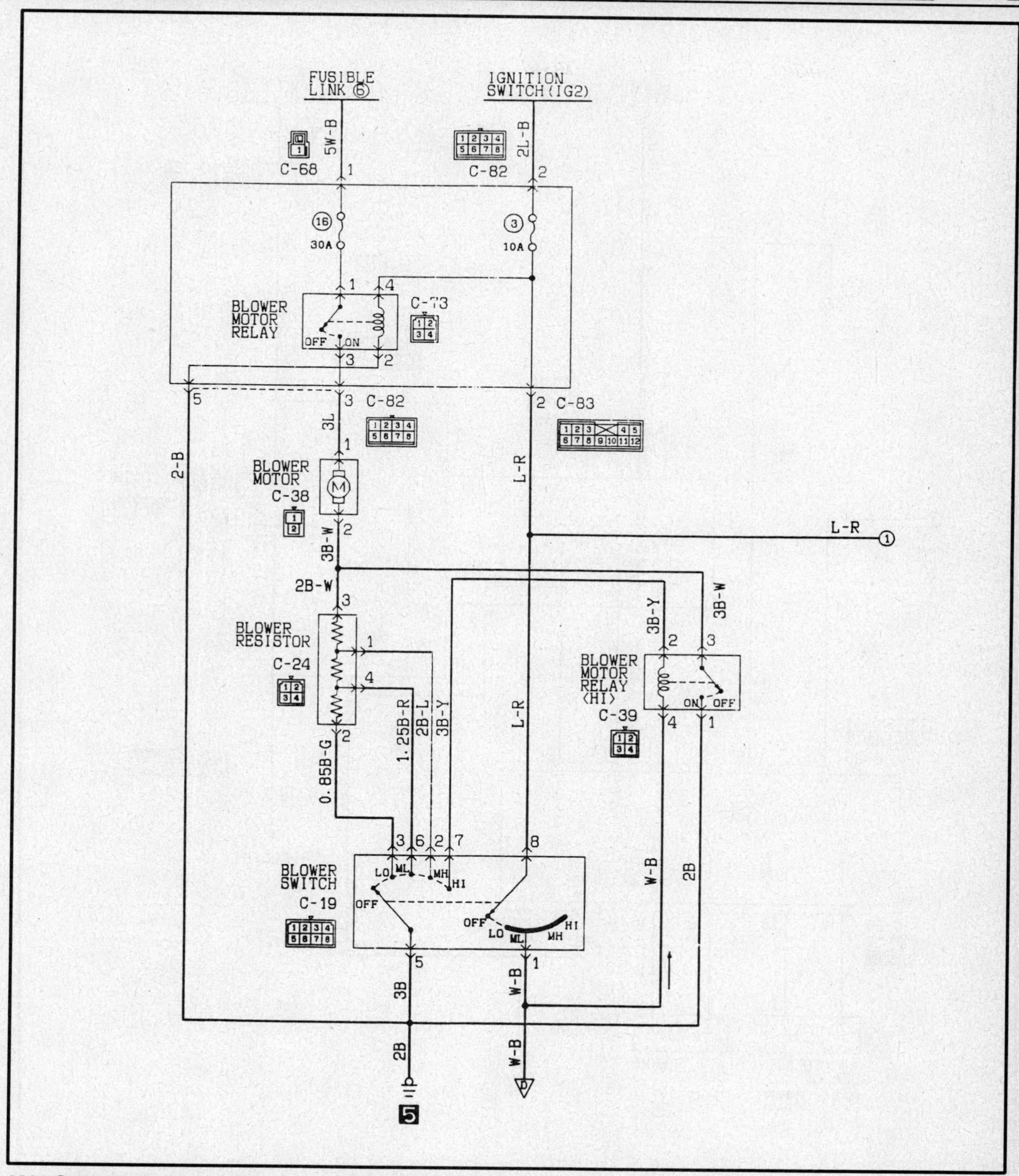

1993 Stealth with air conditioning—SOHC engine, Cont'd

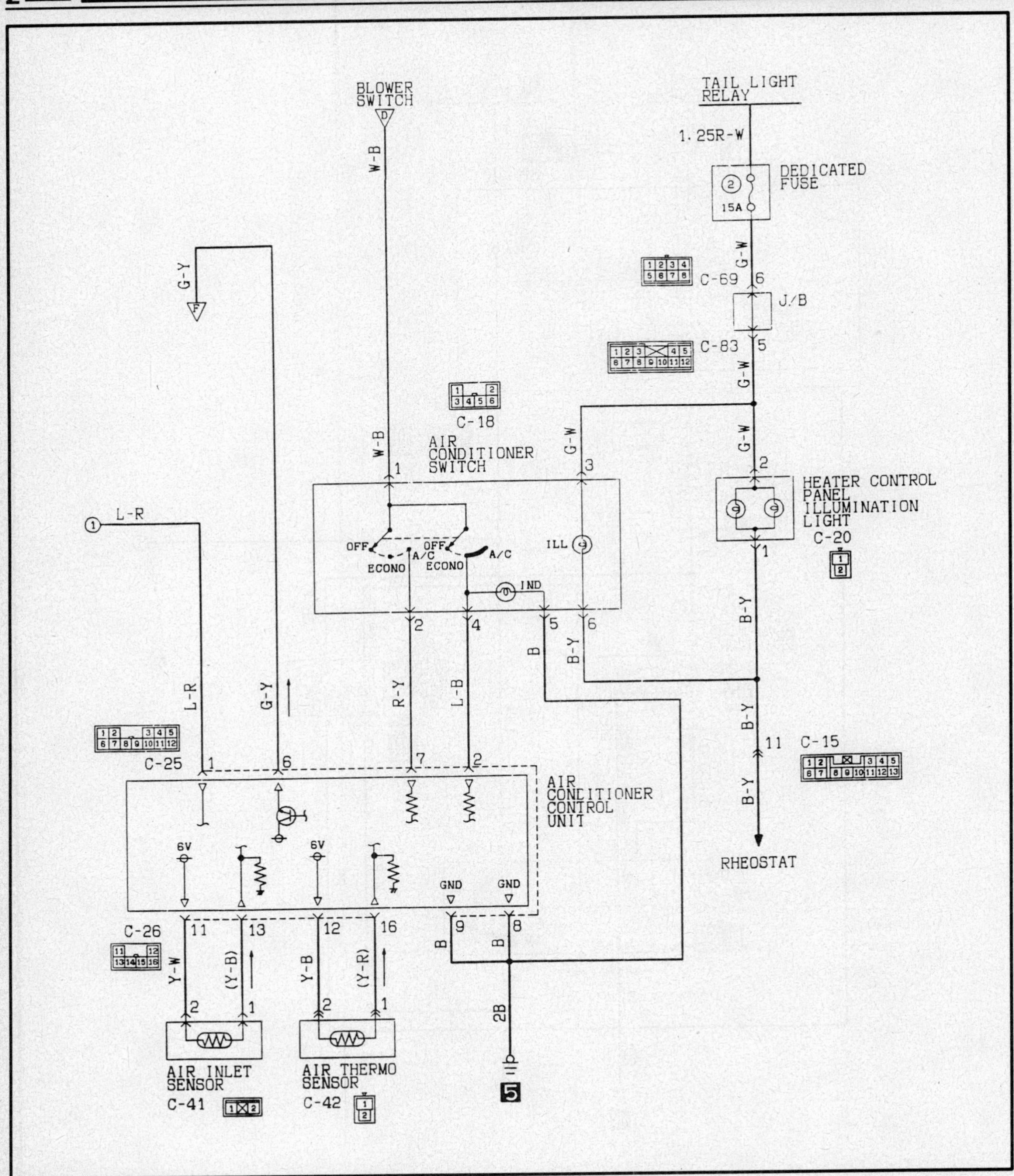

1993 Stealth with air conditioning—SOHC engine, Cont'd

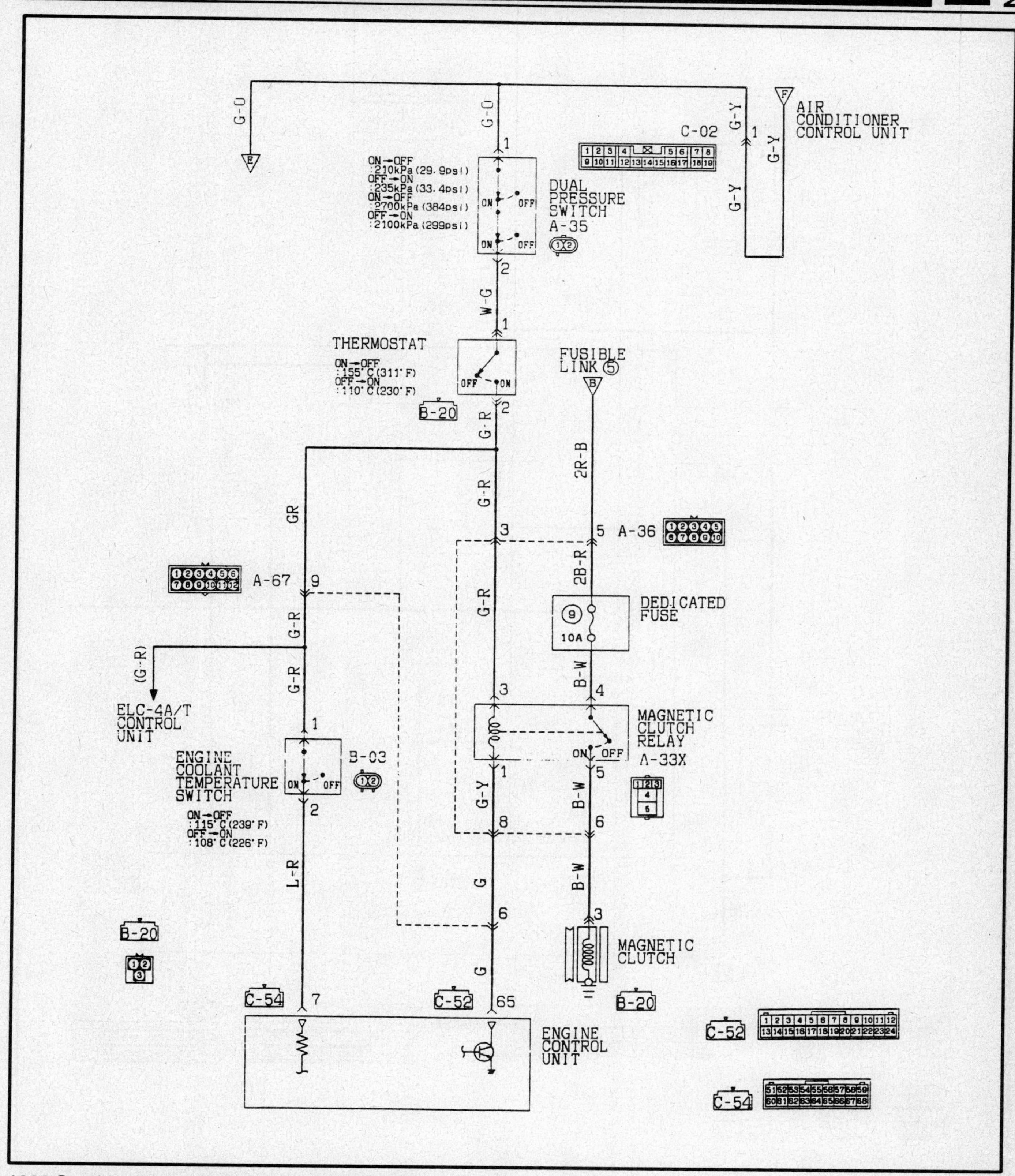

1993 Stealth with air conditioning—SOHC engine, Cont'd

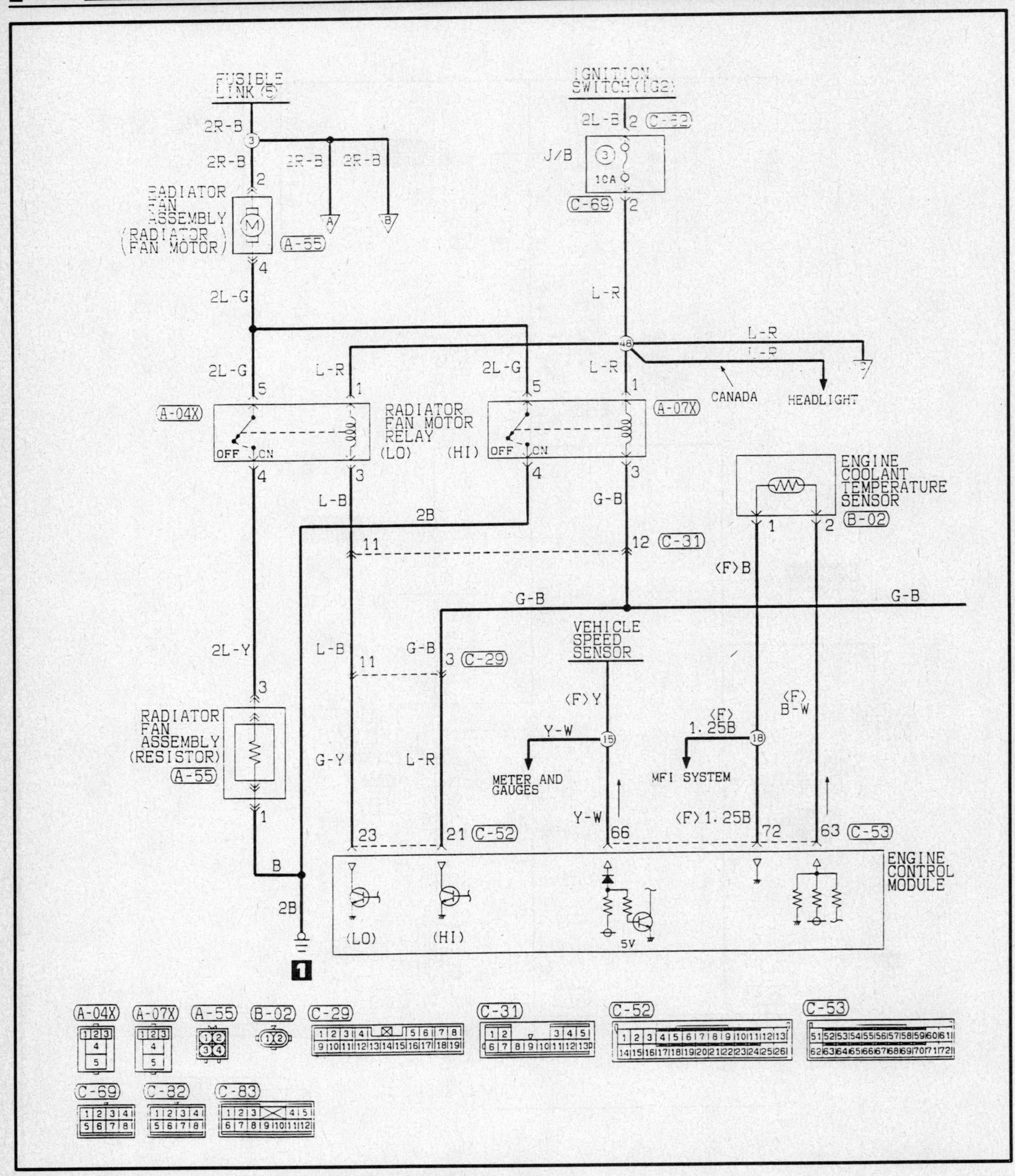

1994–95 Stealth with manual air conditioning—SOHC engine

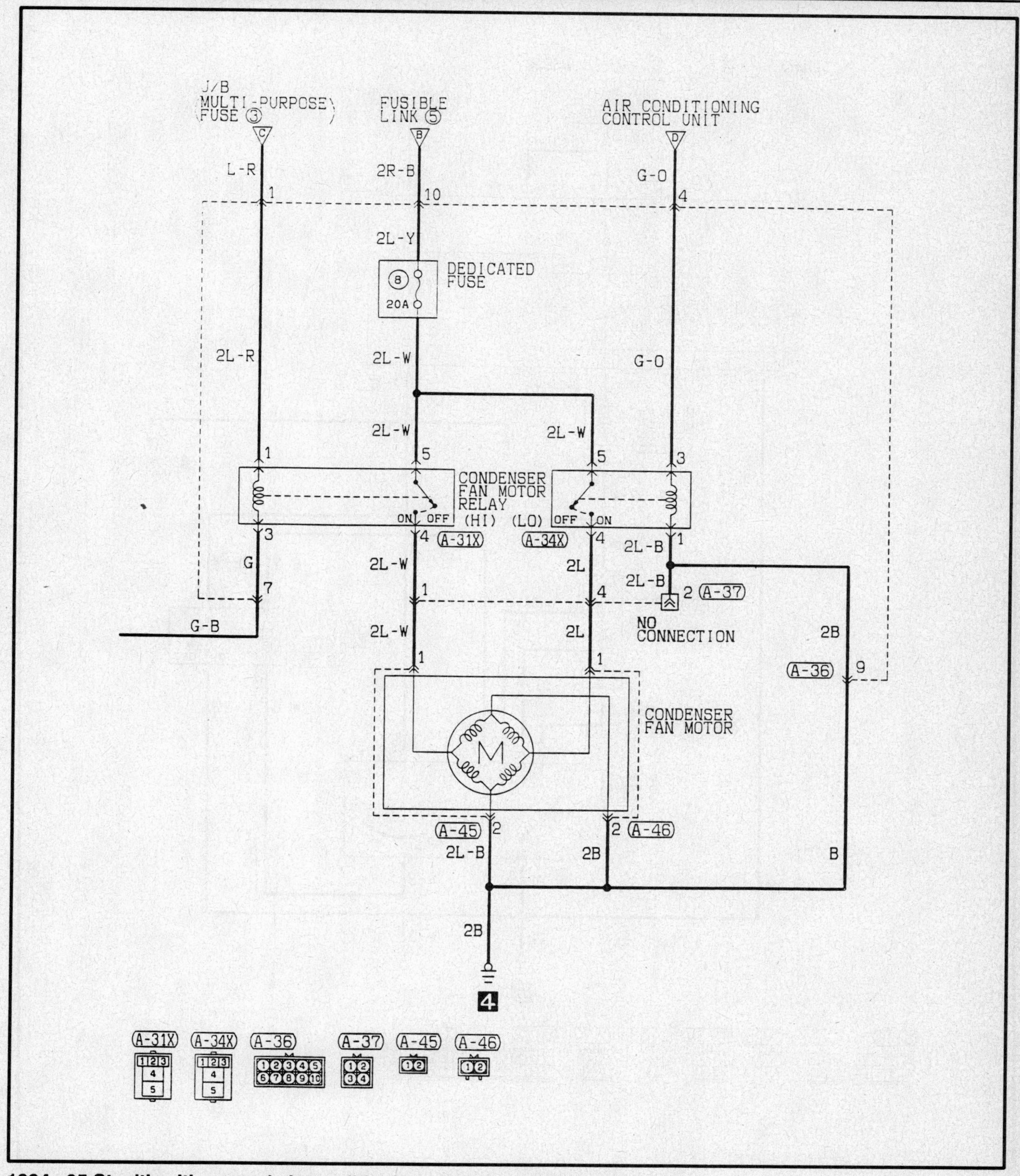

1994–95 Stealth with manual air conditioning—SOHC engine, Cont'd

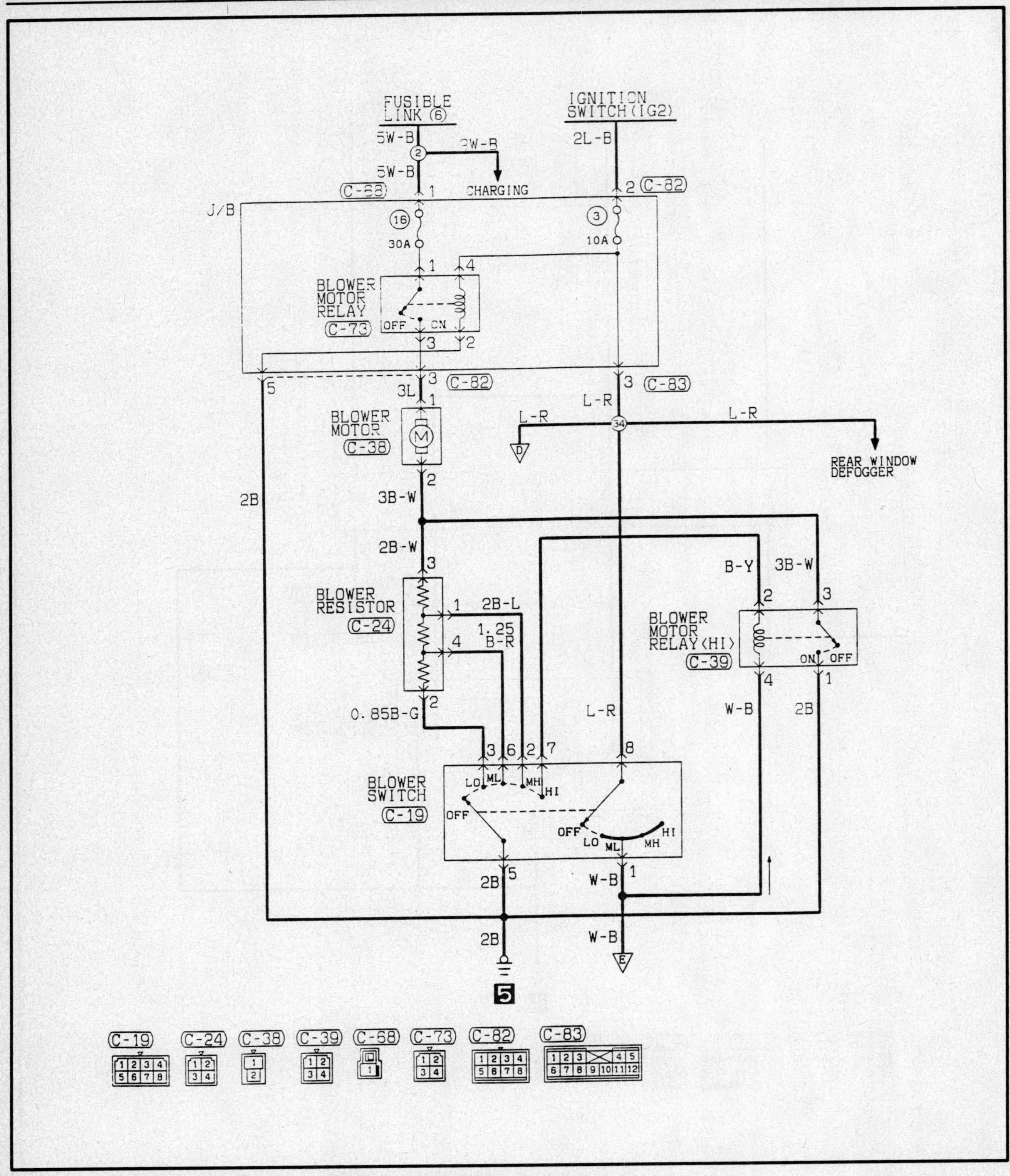

1994–95 Stealth with manual air conditioning—SOHC engine, Cont'd

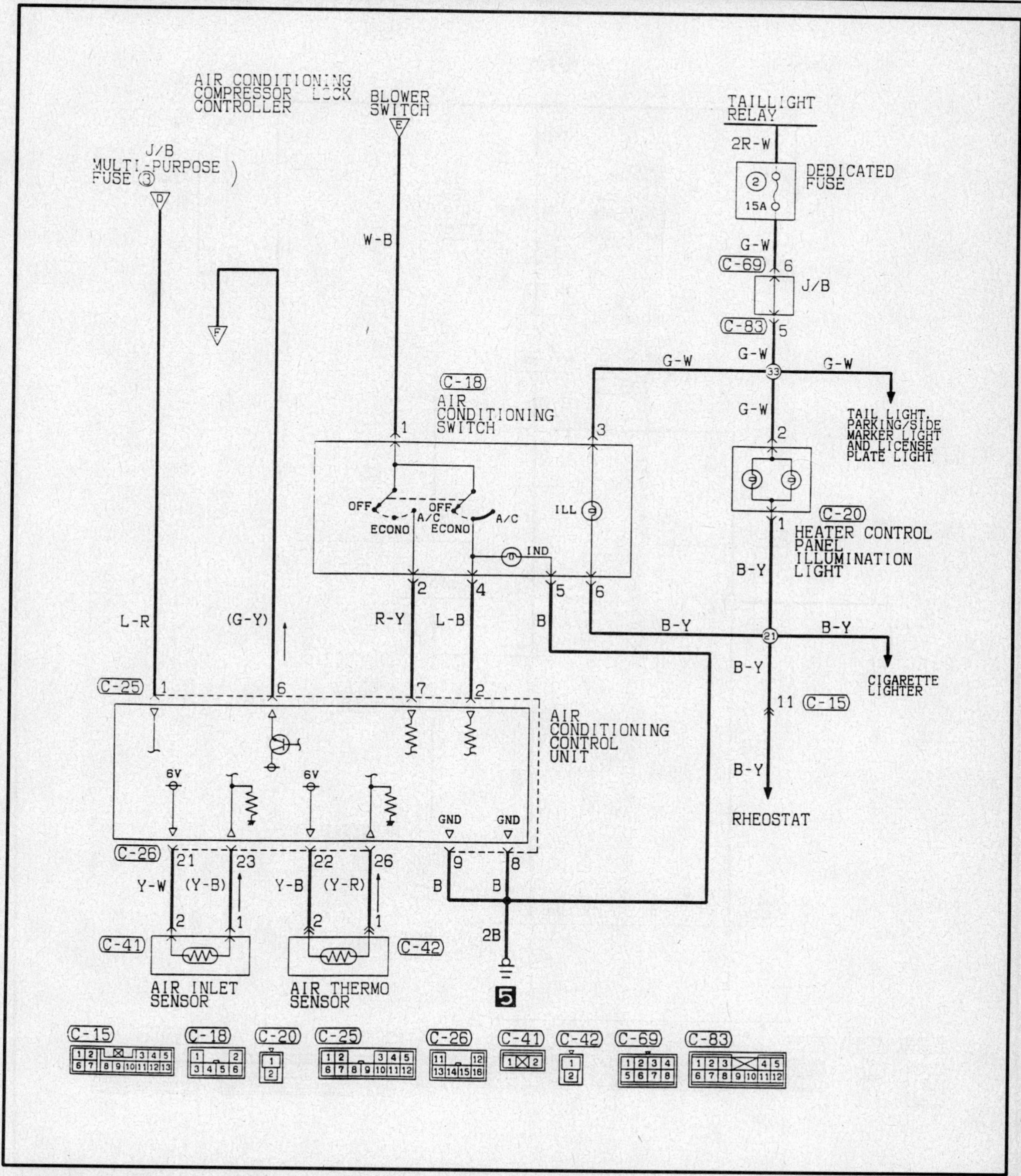

1994–95 Stealth with manual air conditioning—SOHC engine, Cont'd

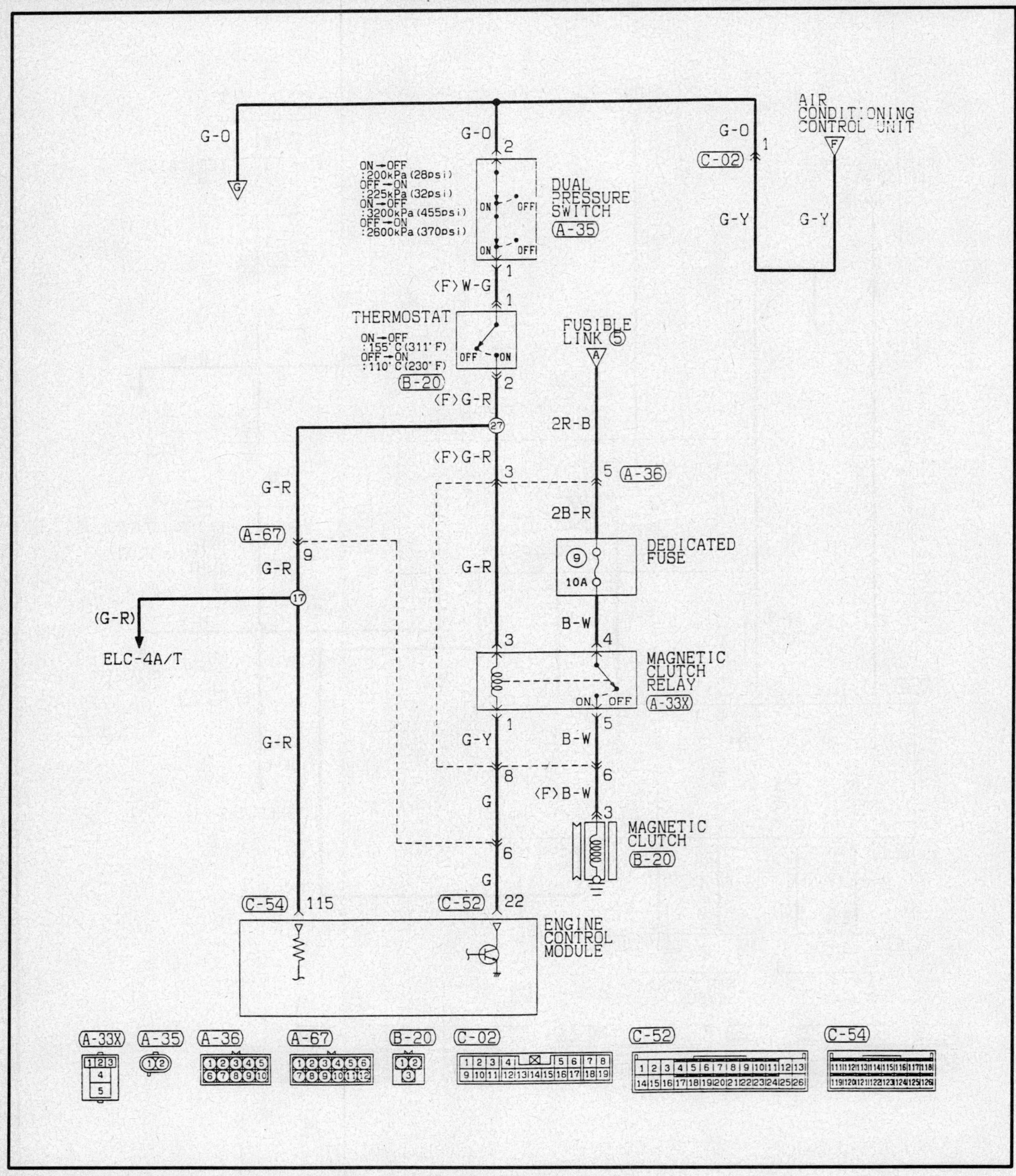

1994–95 Stealth with manual air conditioning—SOHC engine, Cont'd

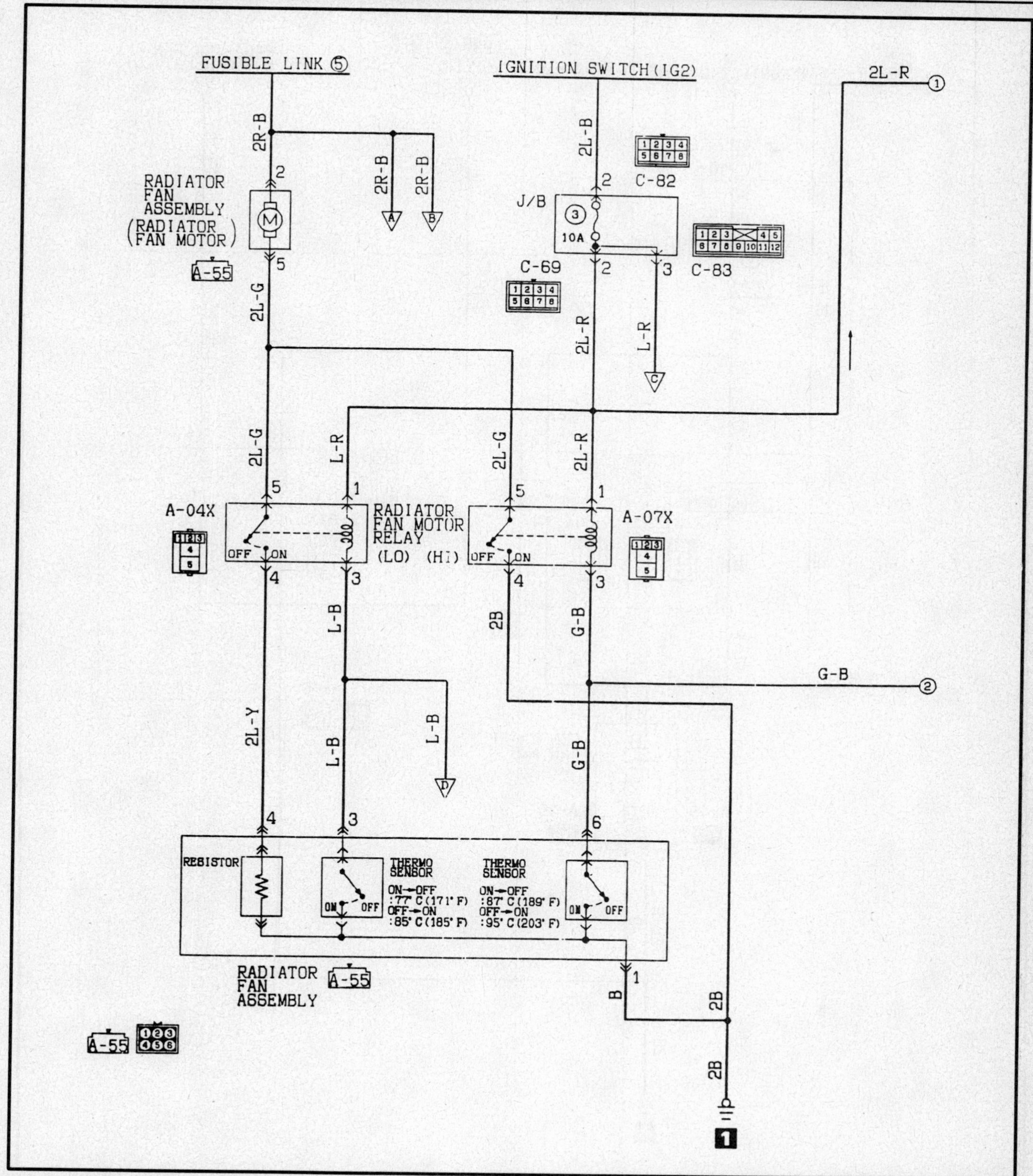

1993 Stealth with air conditioning—DOHC engine

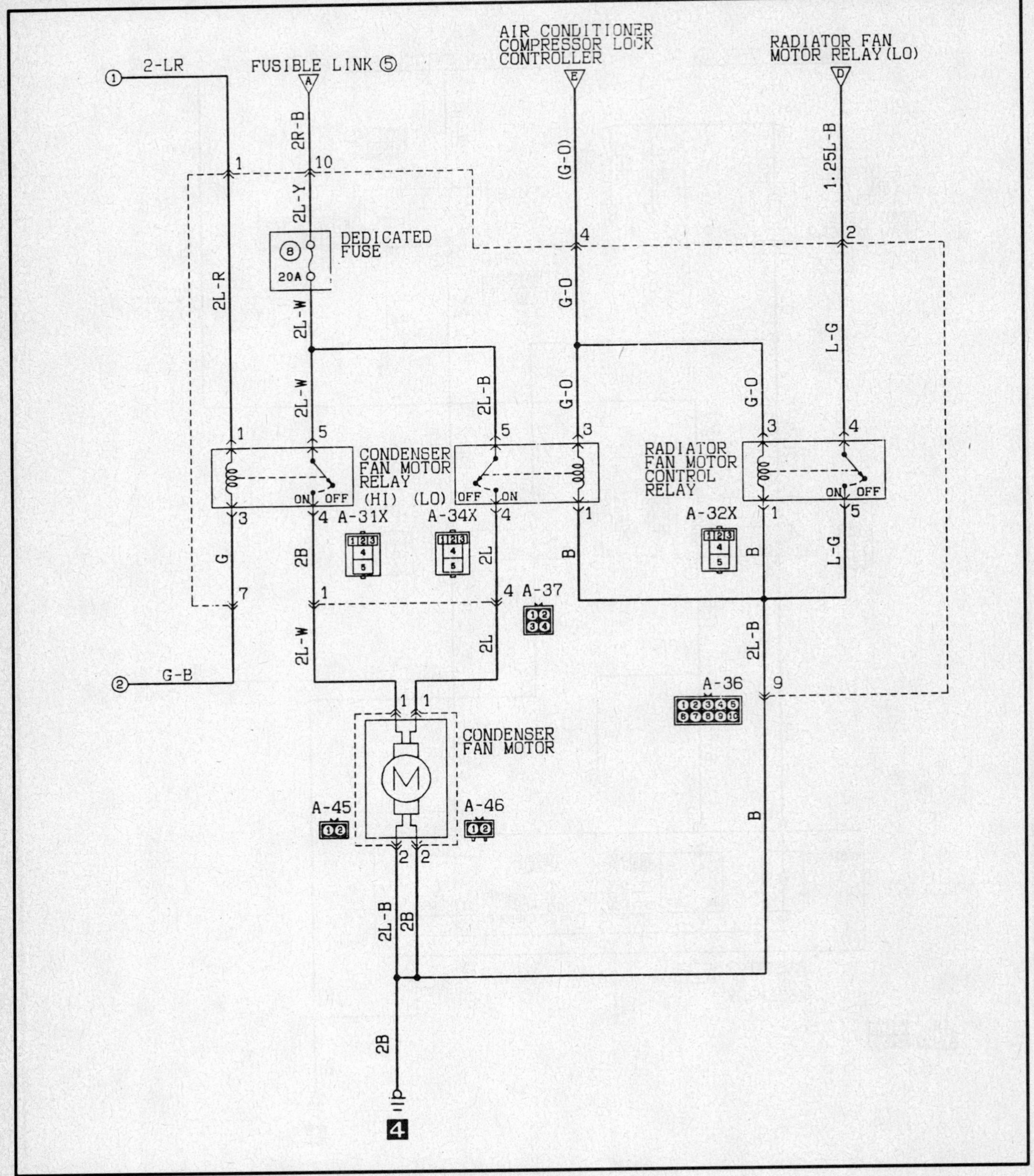

1993 Stealth with air conditioning—DOHC engine, Cont'd

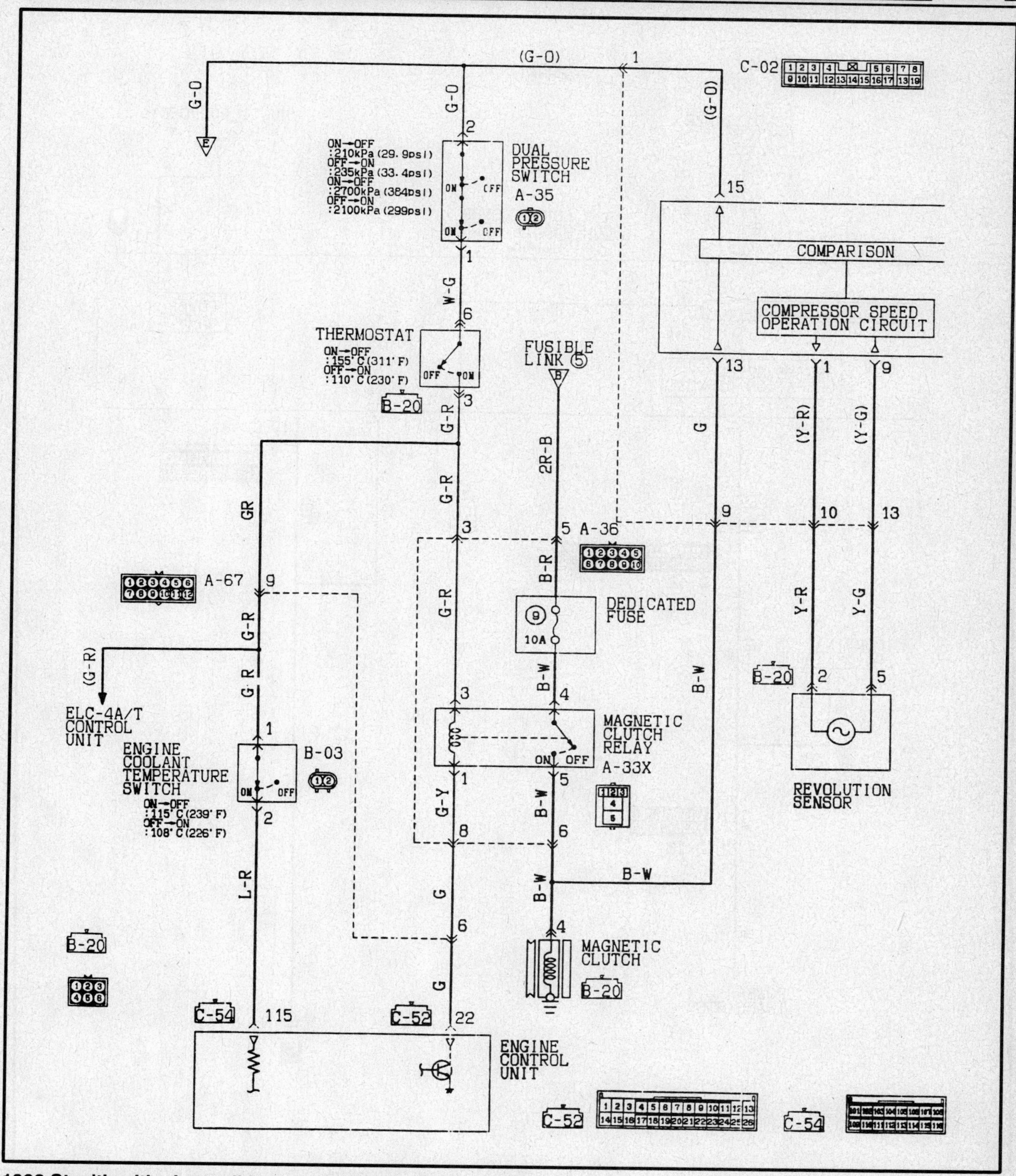

1993 Stealth with air conditioning—DOHC engine, Cont'd

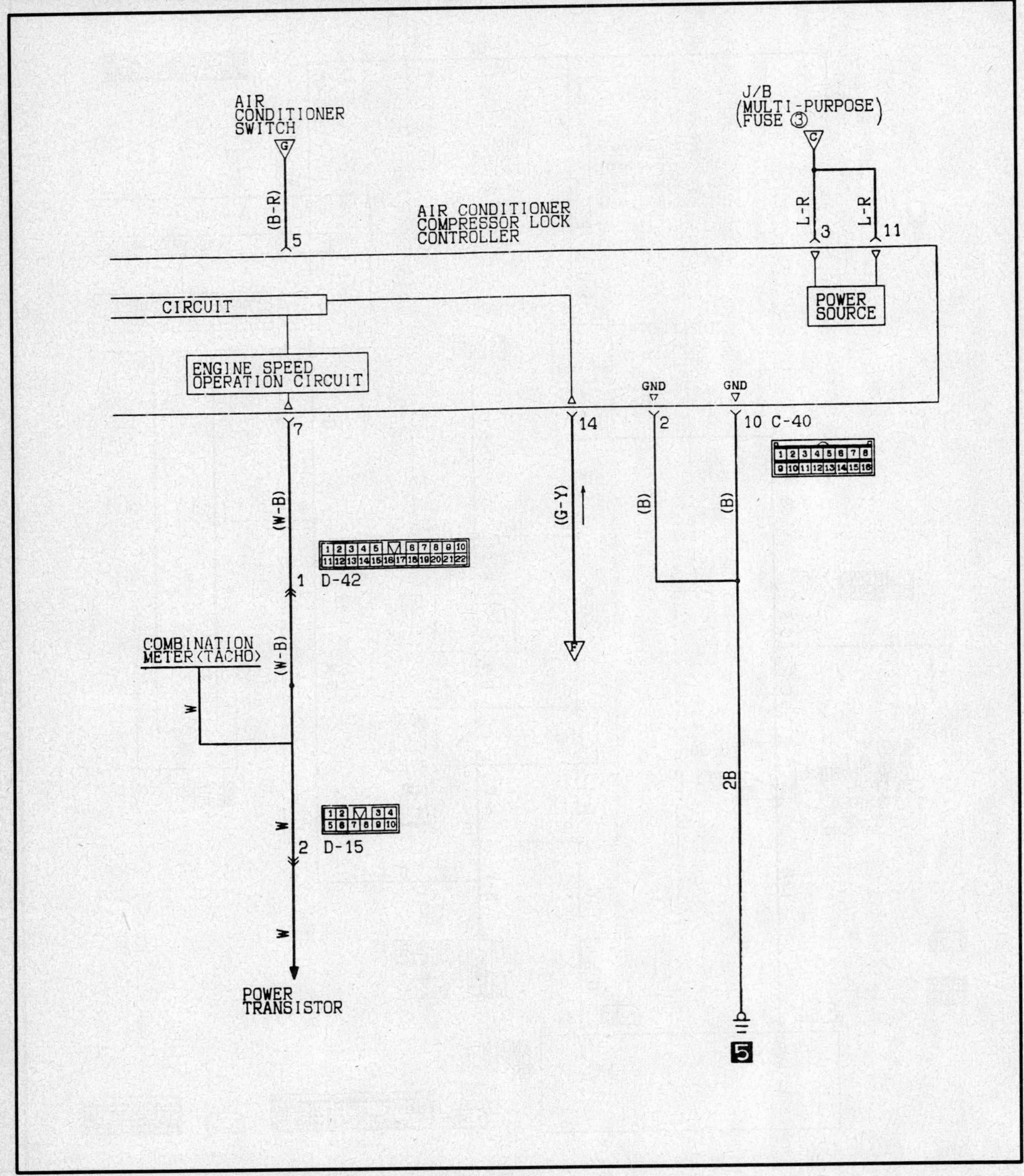

1993 Stealth with air conditioning—DOHC engine, Cont'd

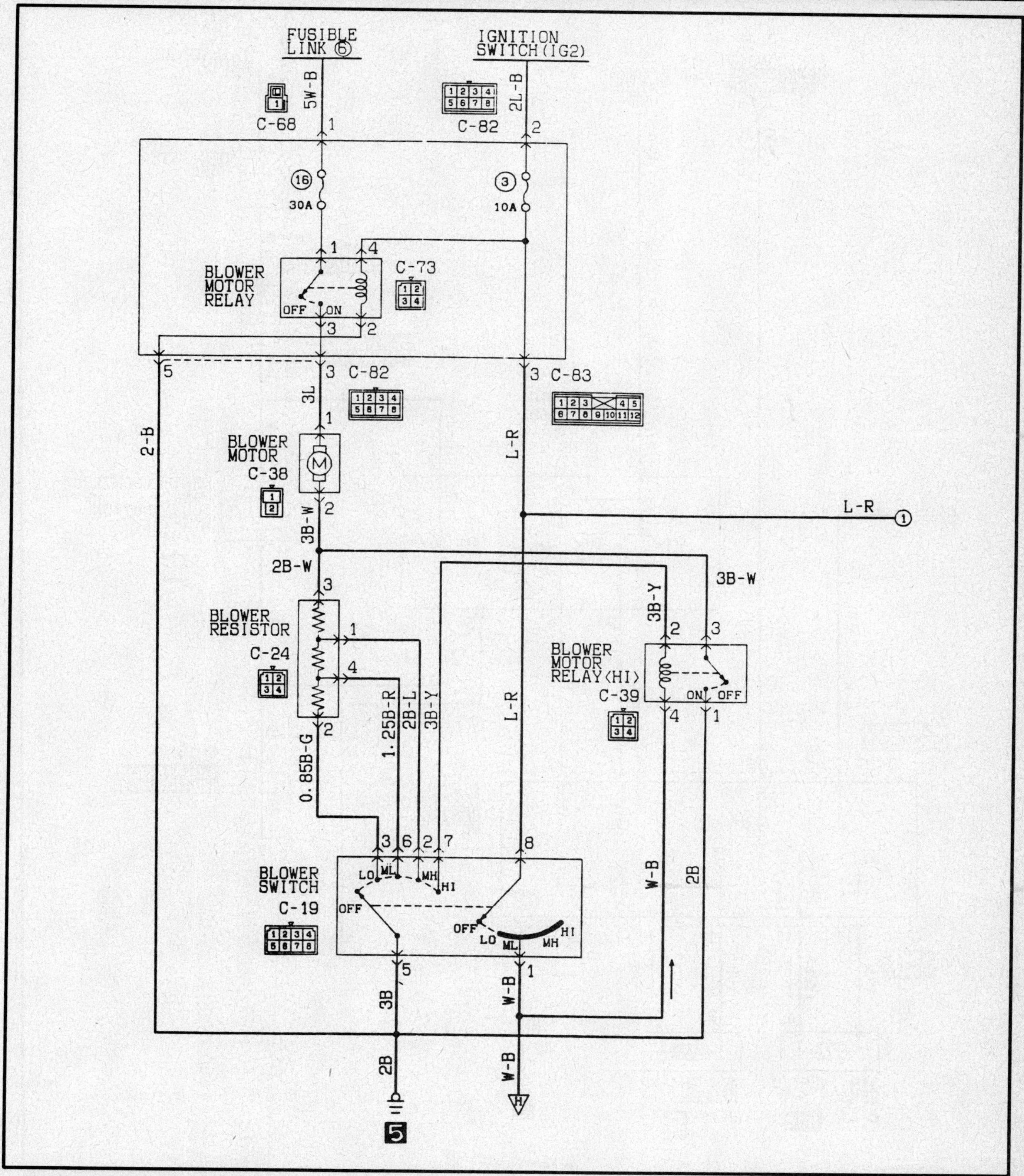

1993 Stealth with air conditioning—DOHC engine, Cont'd

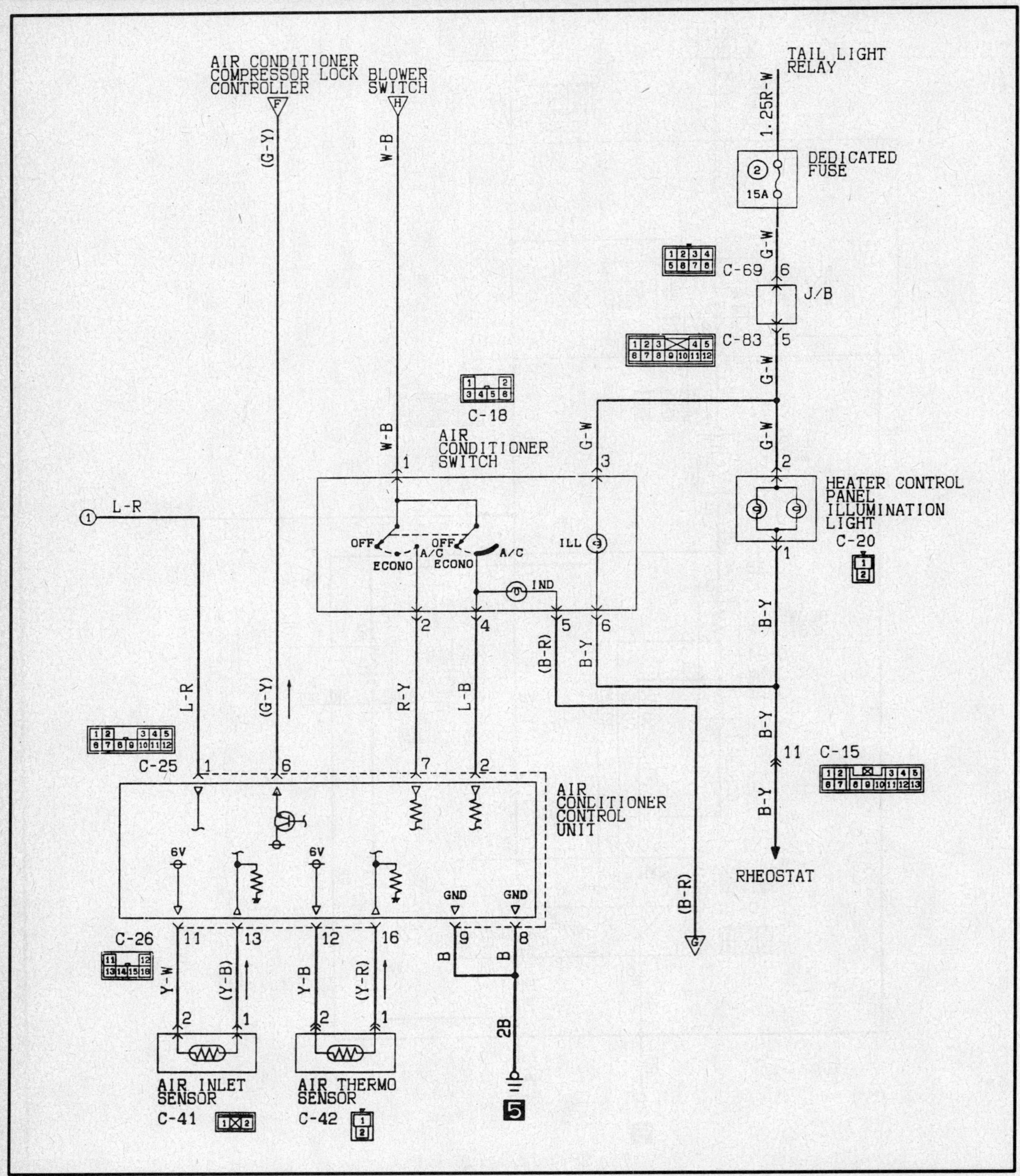

1993 Stealth with air conditioning—DOHC engine, Cont'd

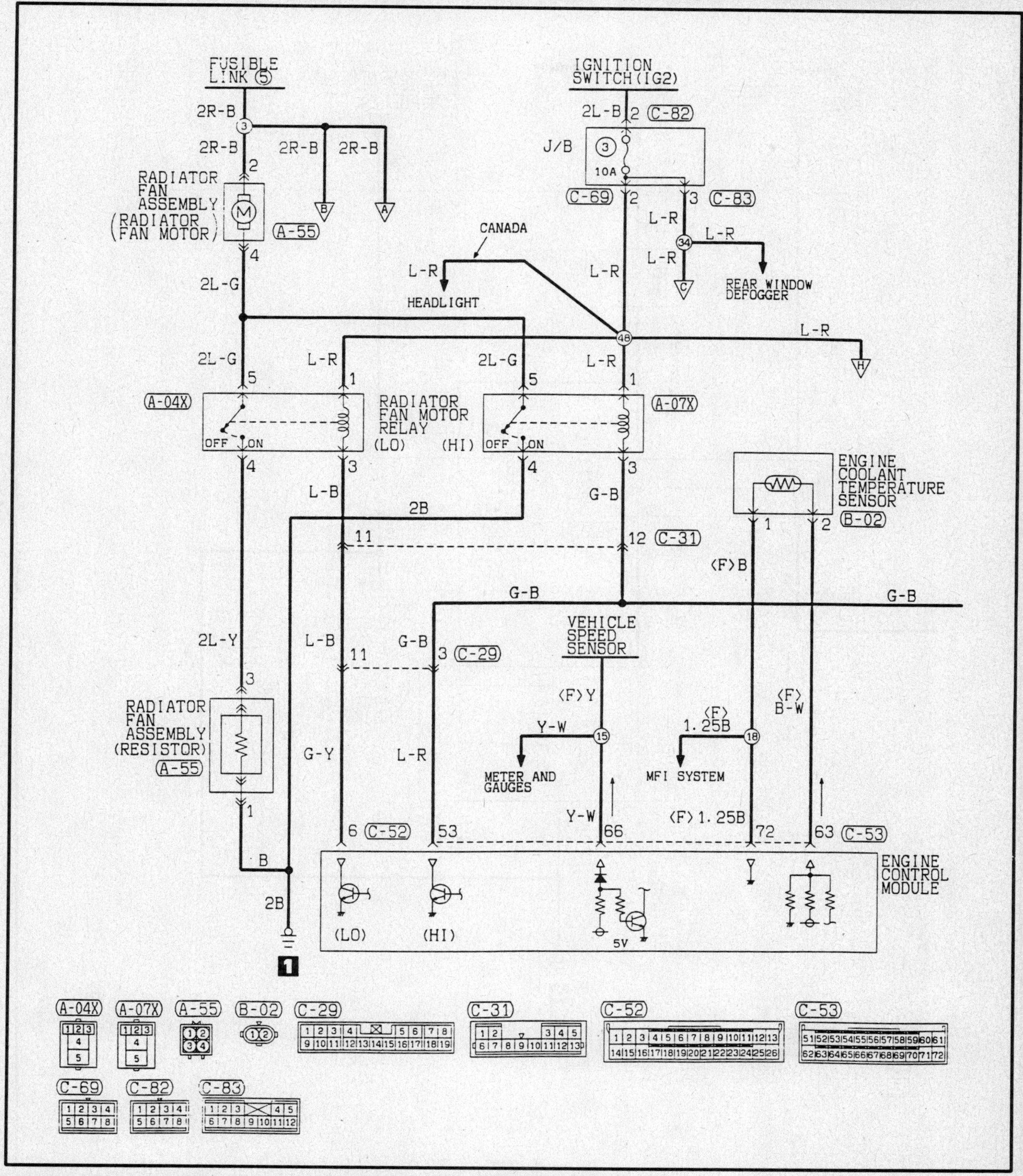

1994–95 Stealth with manual air conditioning—DOHC non-turbo engine

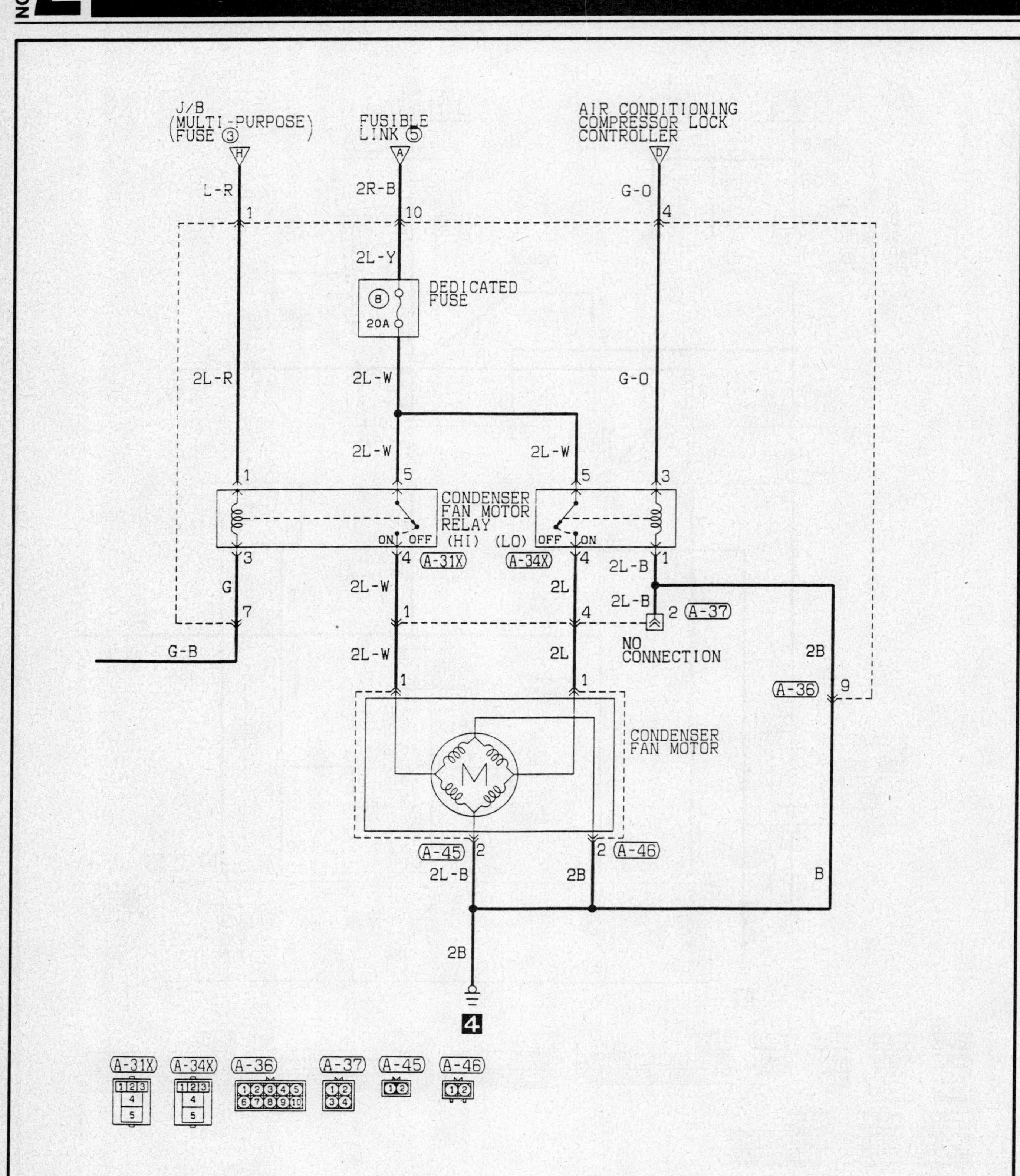

1994–95 Stealth with manual air conditioning—DOHC non-turbo engine, Cont'd

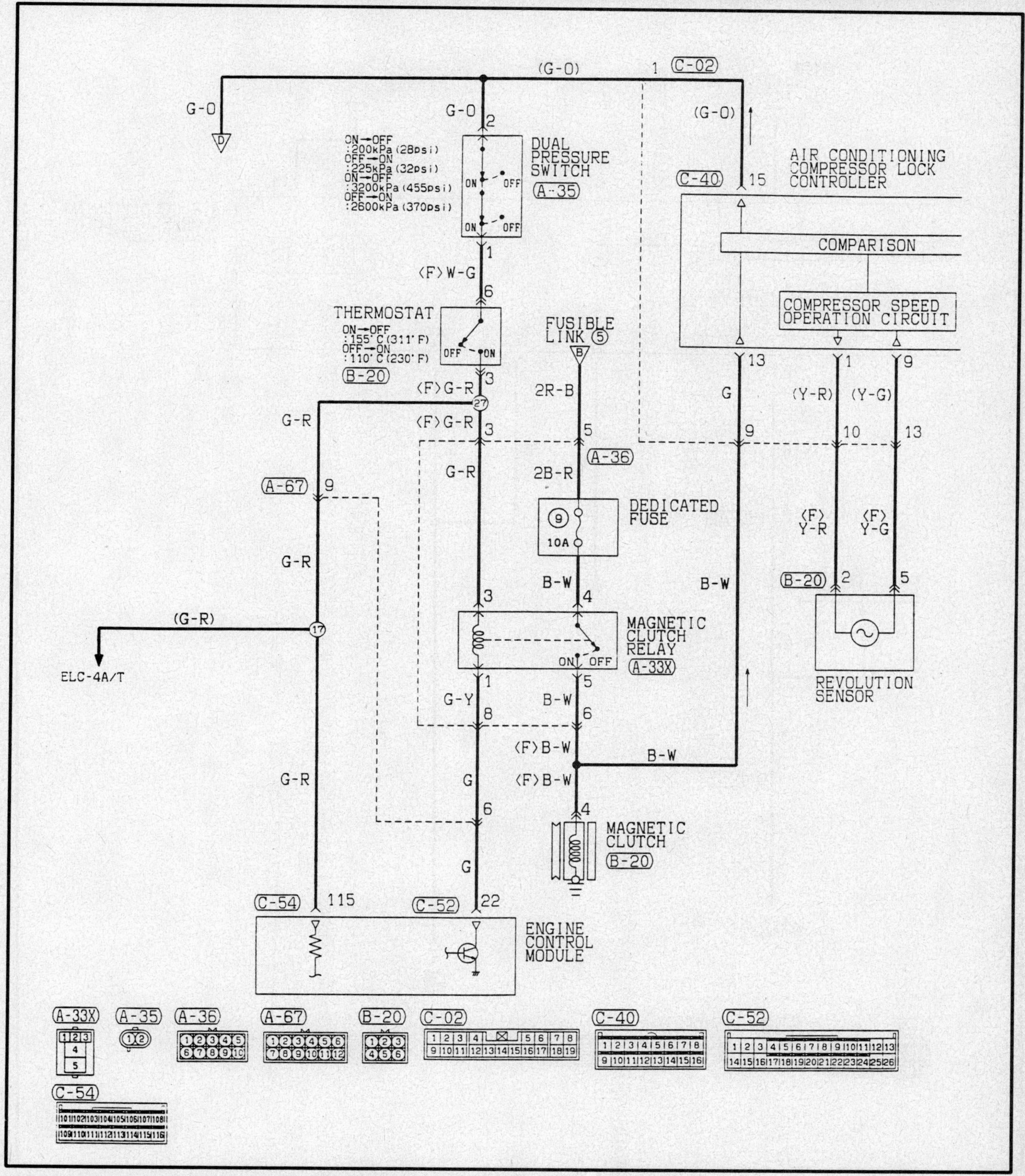

1994–95 Stealth with manual air conditioning—DOHC non-turbo engine, Cont'd

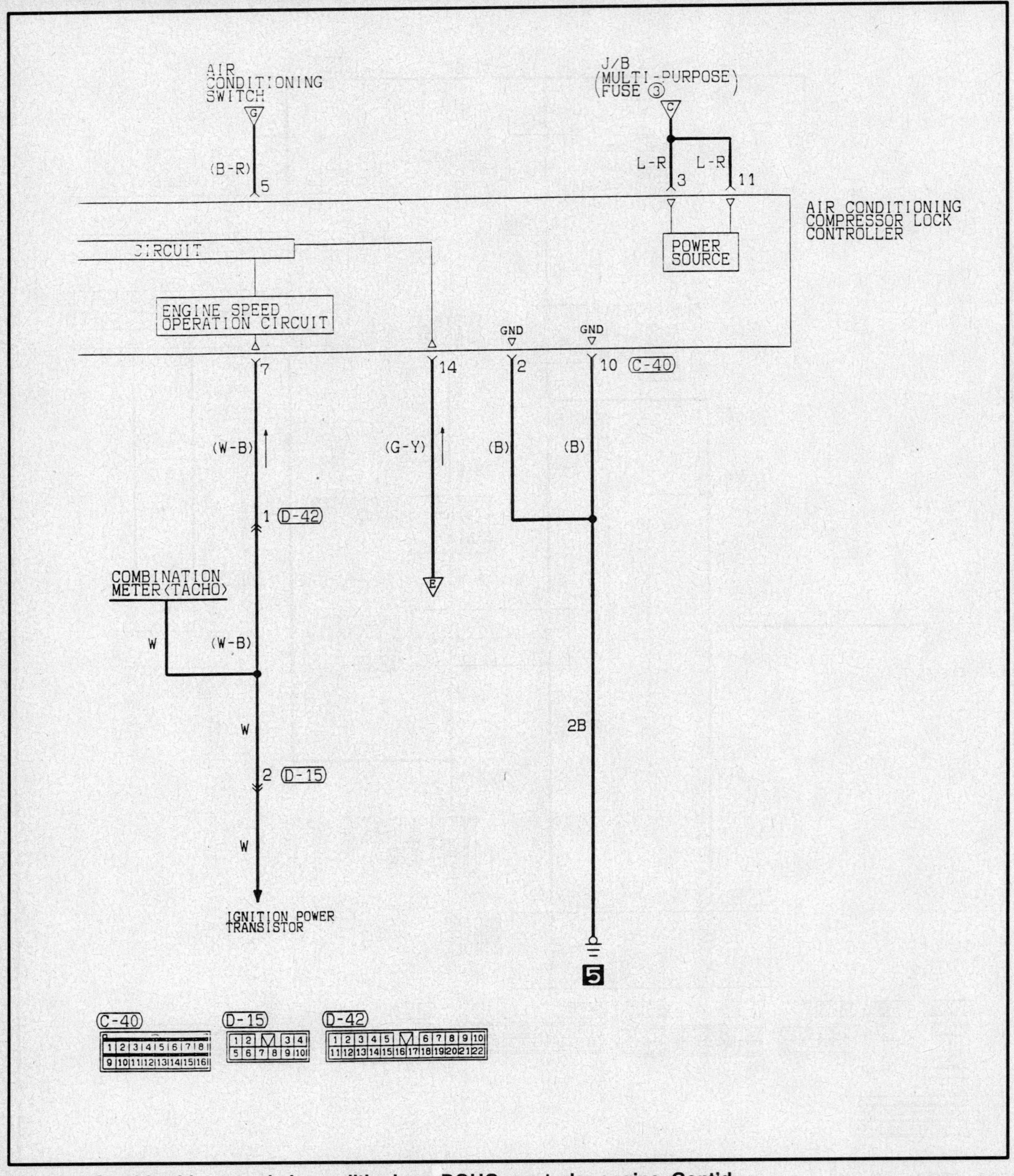

1994–95 Stealth with manual air conditioning—DOHC non-turbo engine, Cont'd

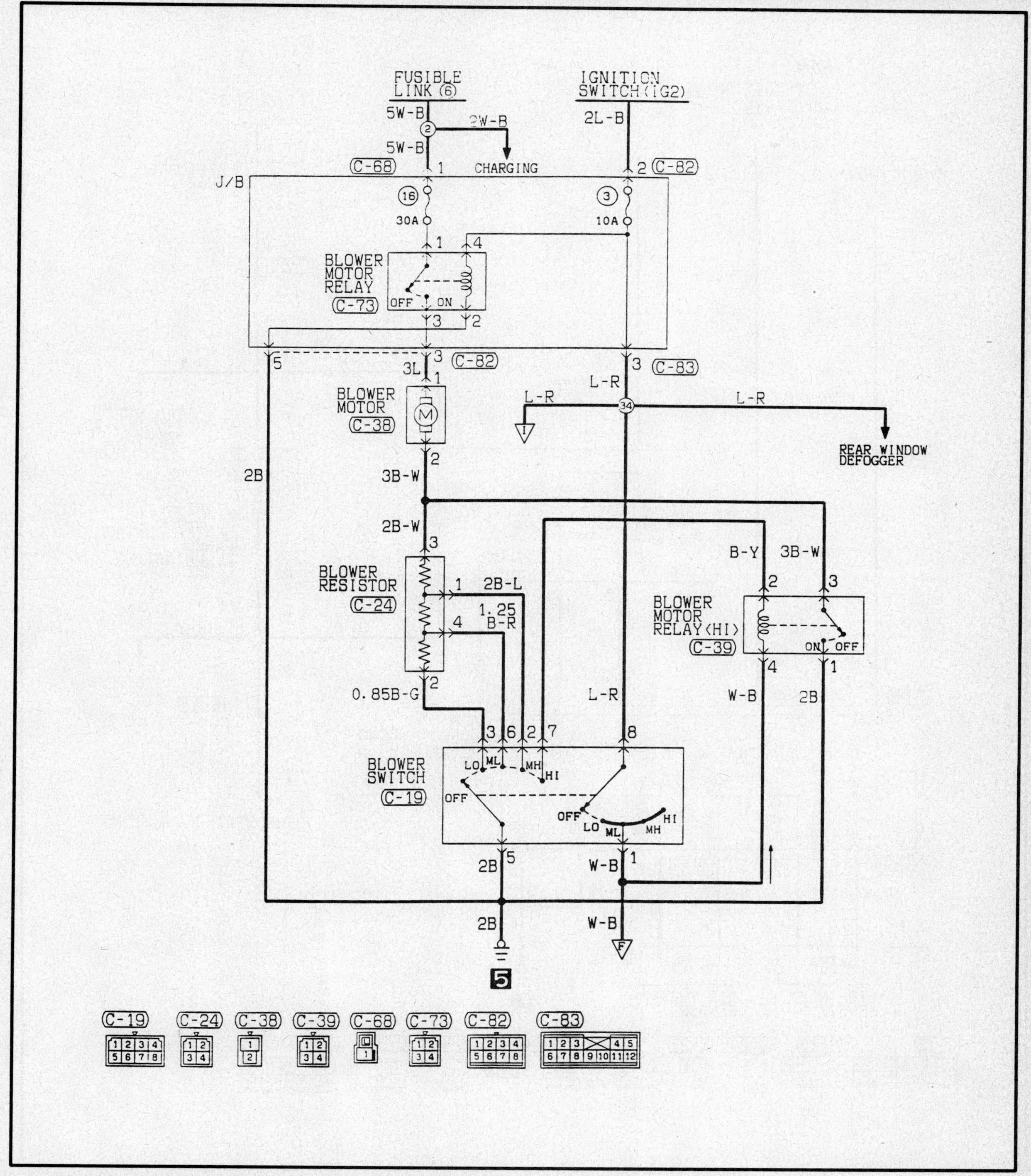

1994–95 Stealth with manual air conditioning—DOHC non-turbo engine, Cont'd

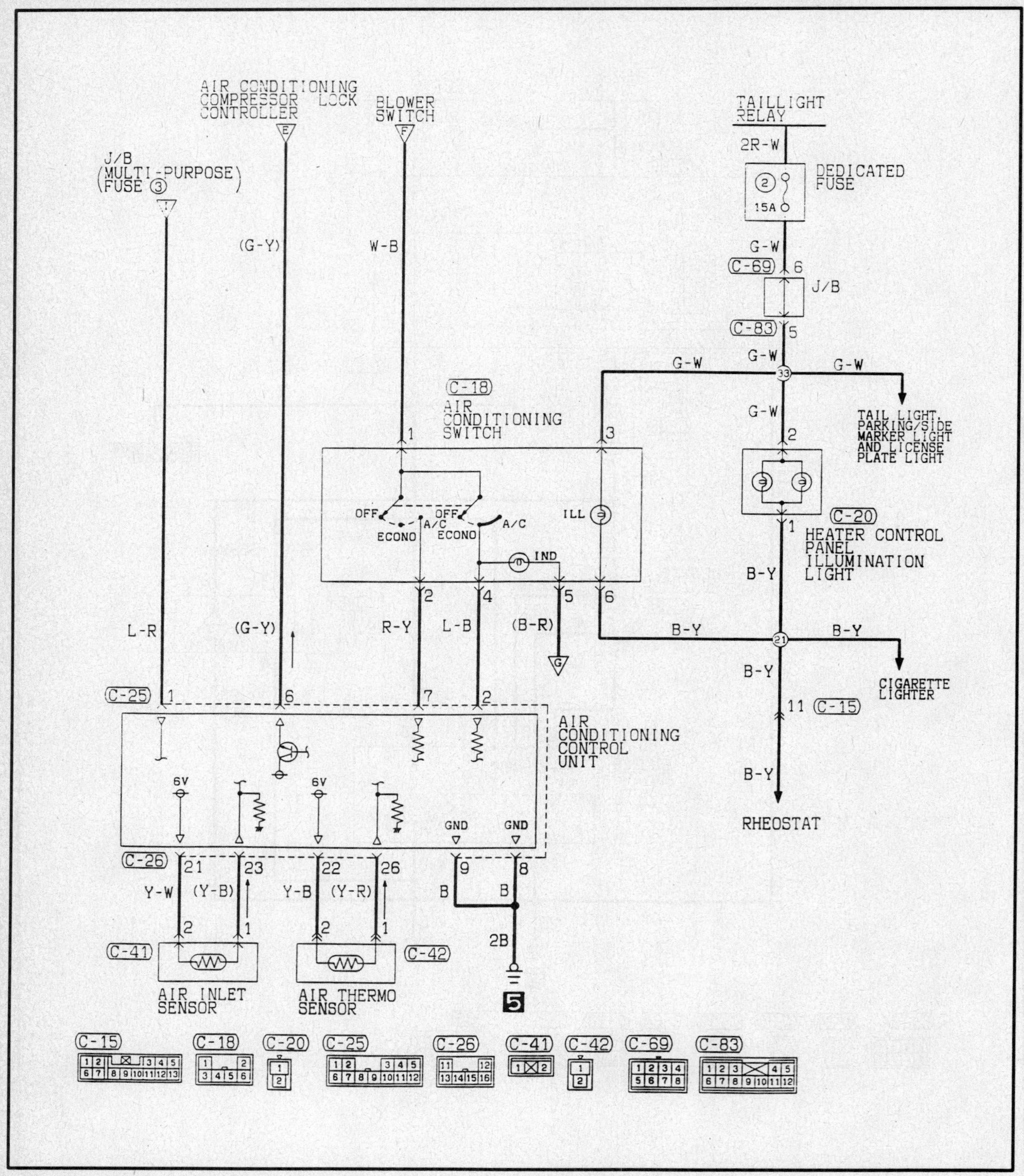

1994–95 Stealth with manual air conditioning—DOHC non-turbo engine, Cont'd

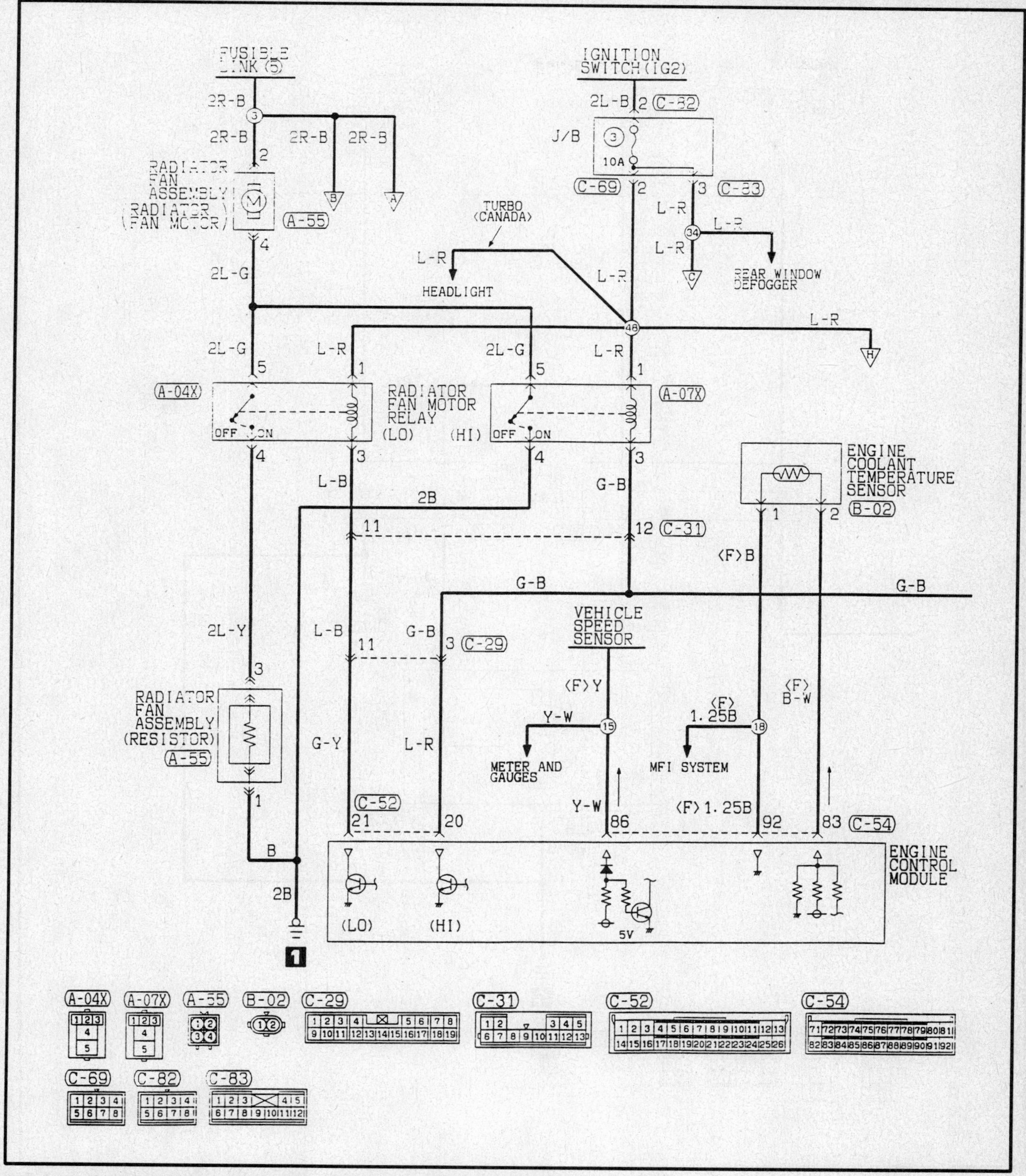

1994–95 Stealth with manual air conditioning—DOHC turbo engine

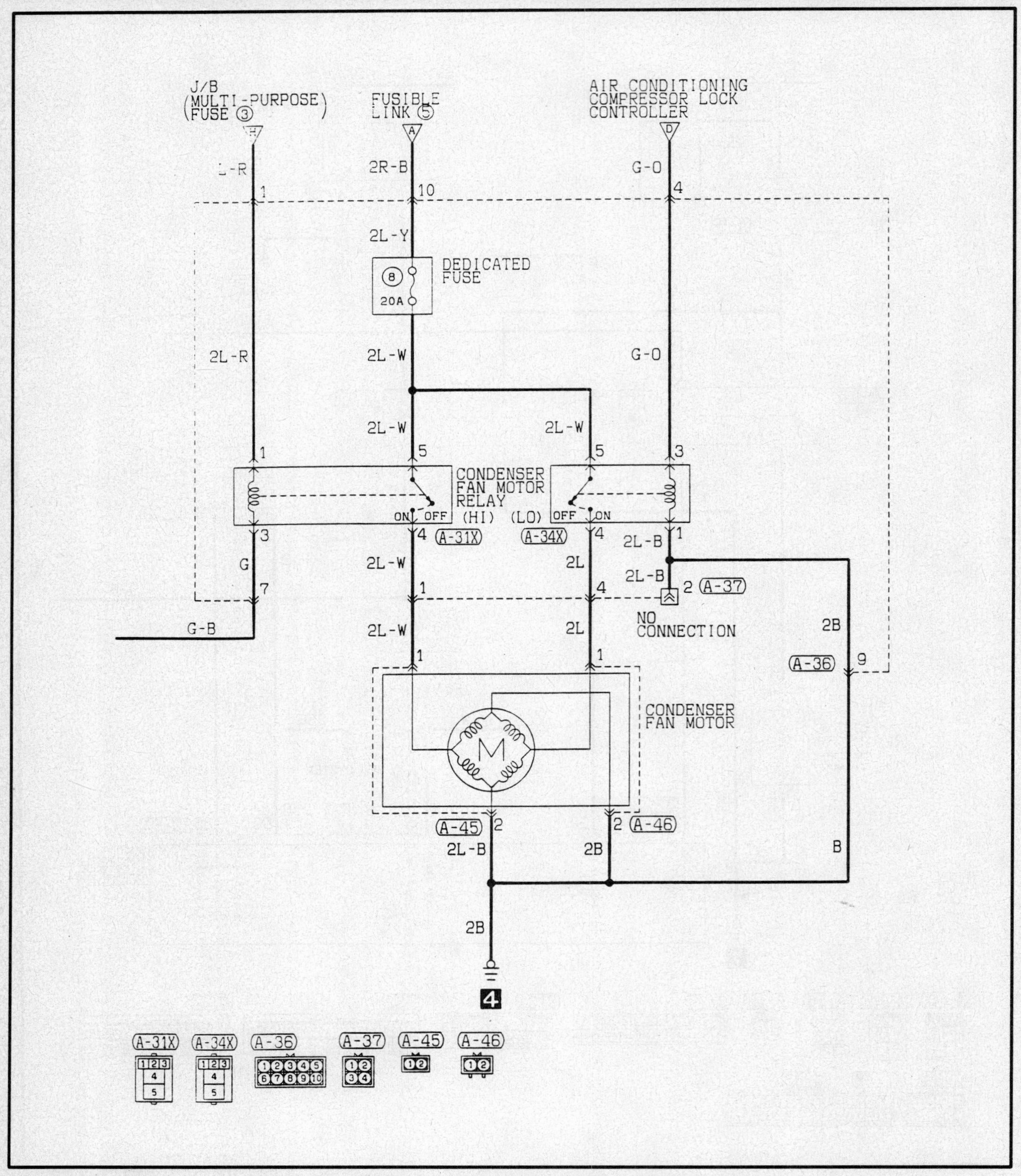

1994–95 Stealth with manual air conditioning—DOHC turbo engine, Cont'd

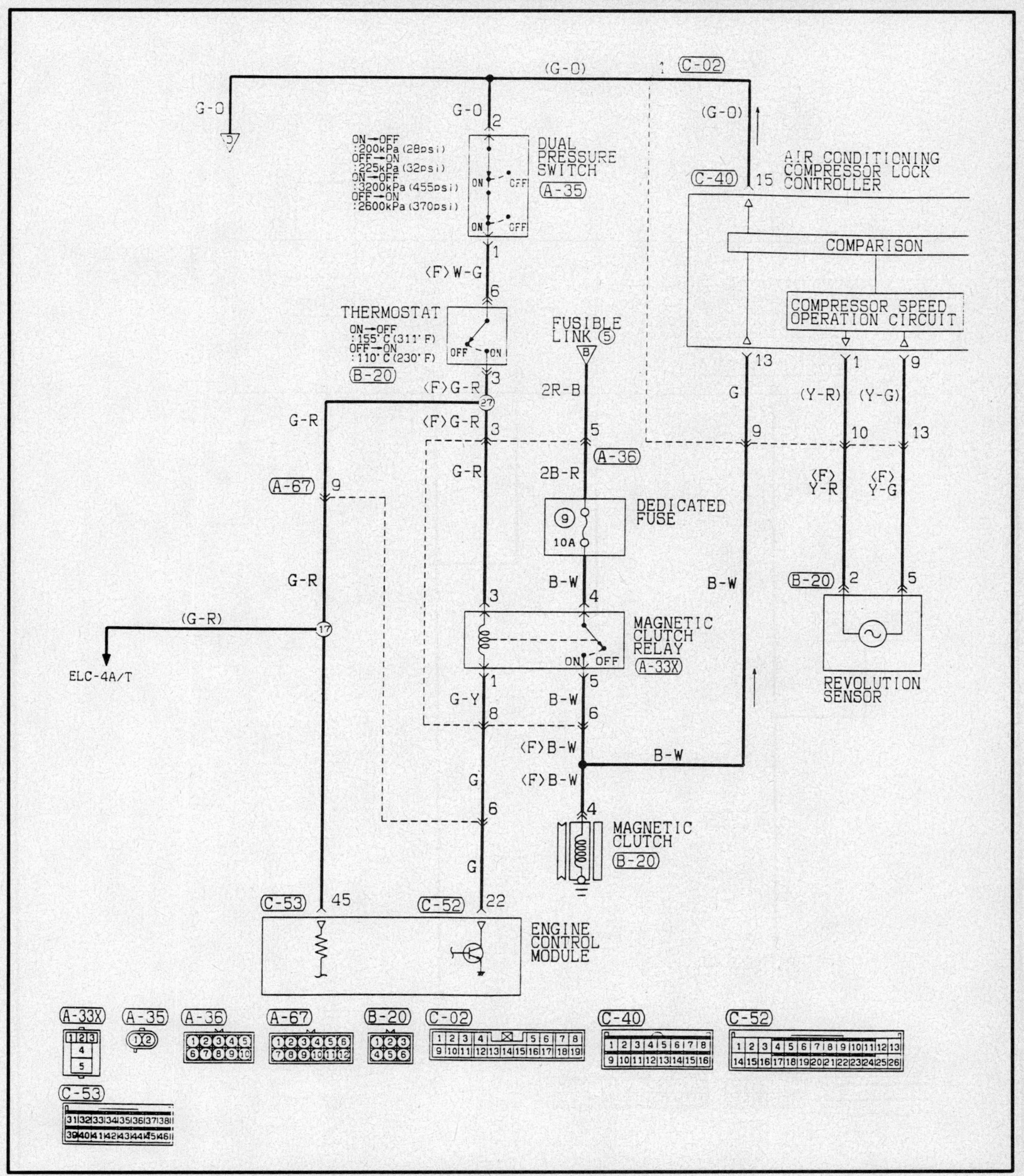

1994–95 Stealth with manual air conditioning—DOHC turbo engine, Cont'd

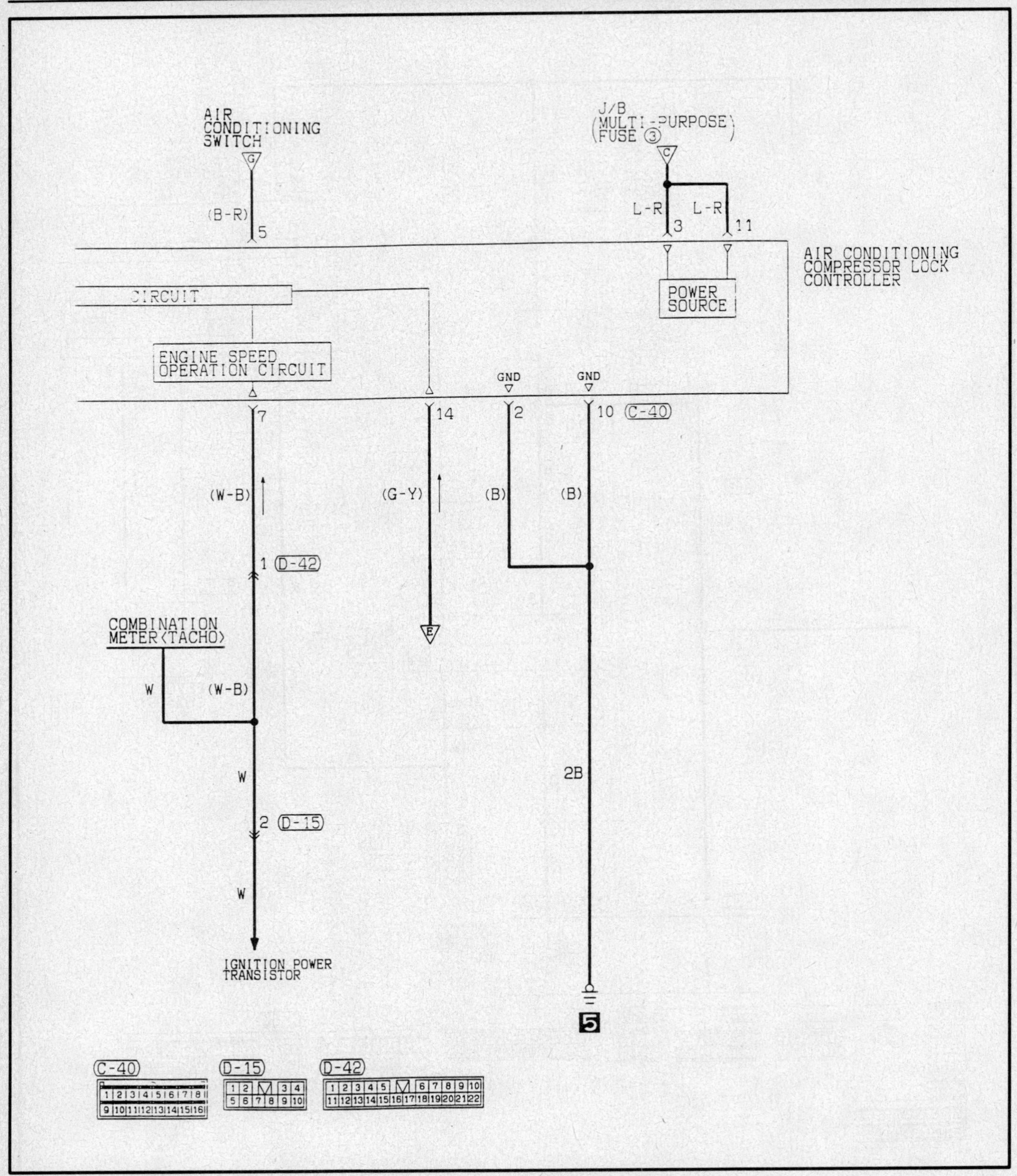

1994–95 Stealth with manual air conditioning—DOHC turbo engine, Cont'd

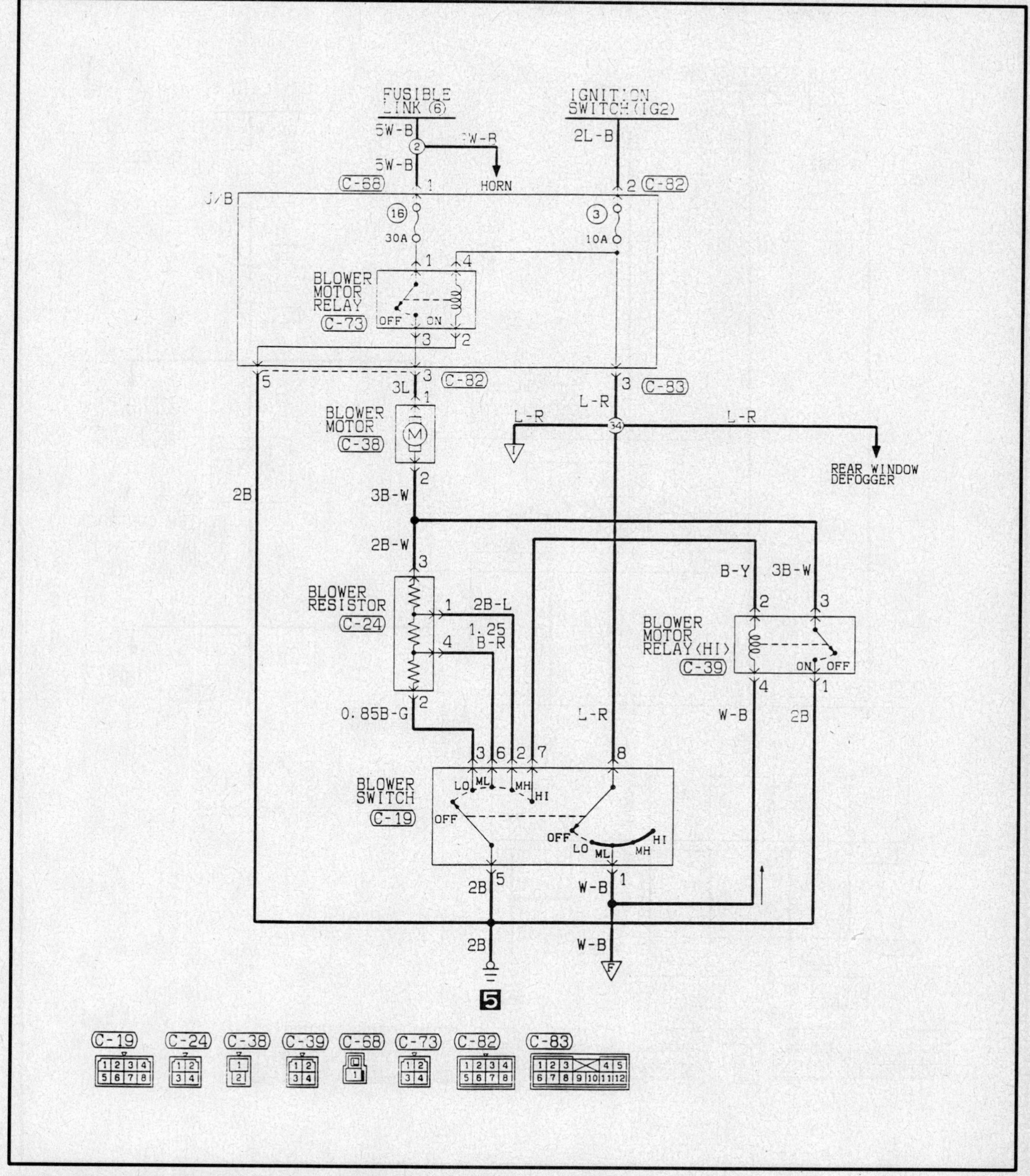

1994–95 Stealth with manual air conditioning—DOHC turbo engine, Cont'd

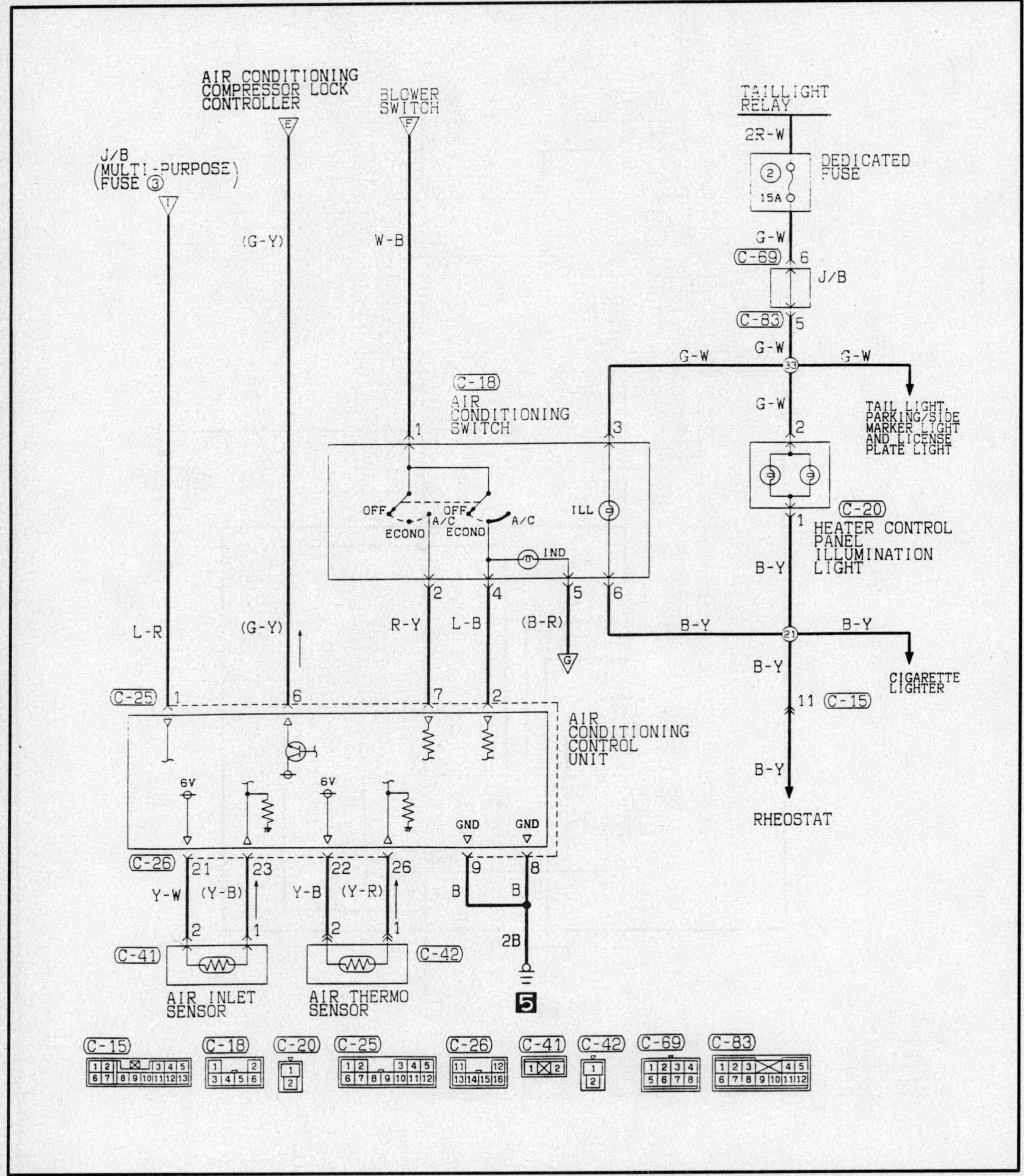

1994–95 Stealth with manual air conditioning—DOHC turbo engine, Cont'd

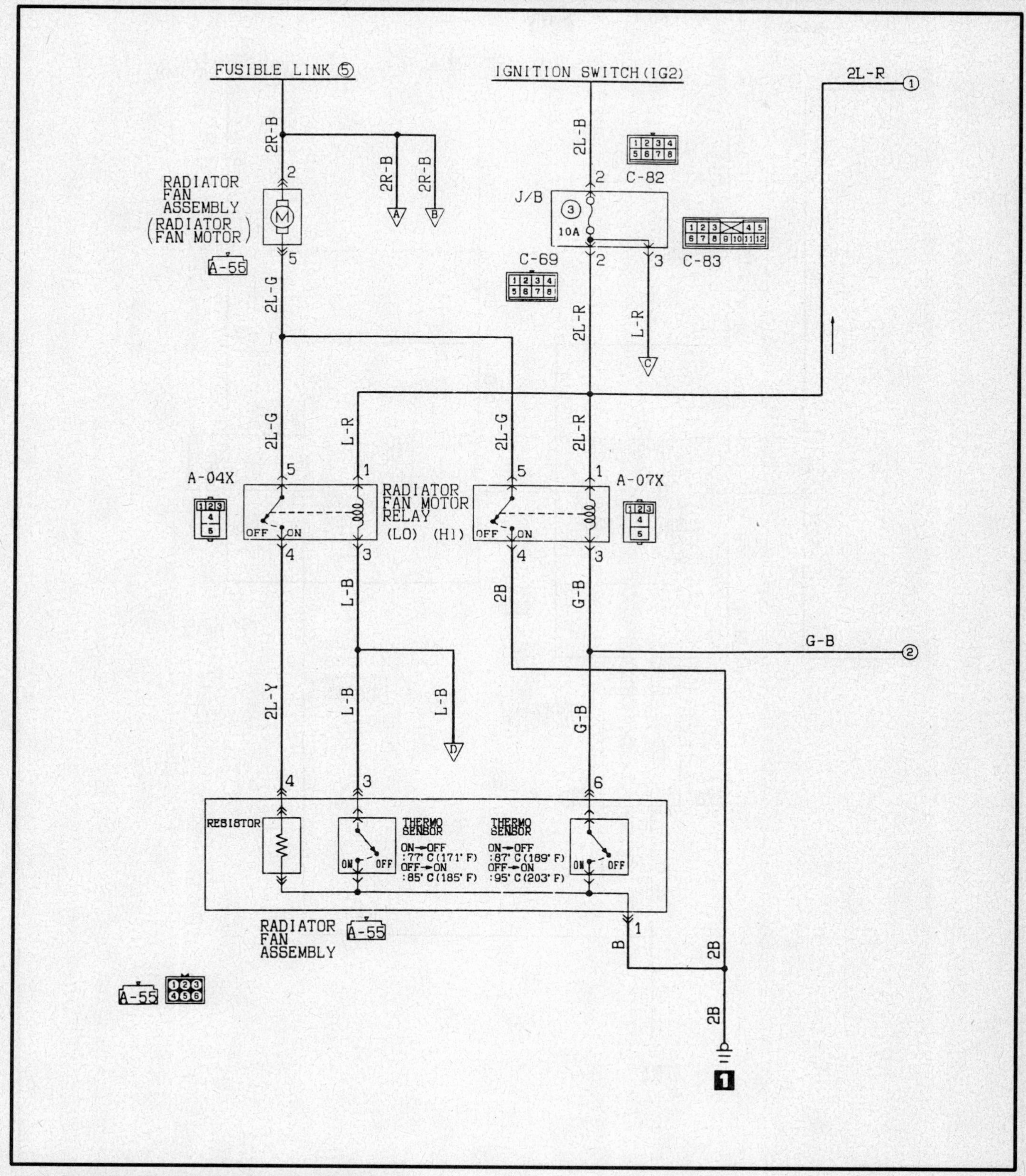

1993 Stealth with automatic air conditioning

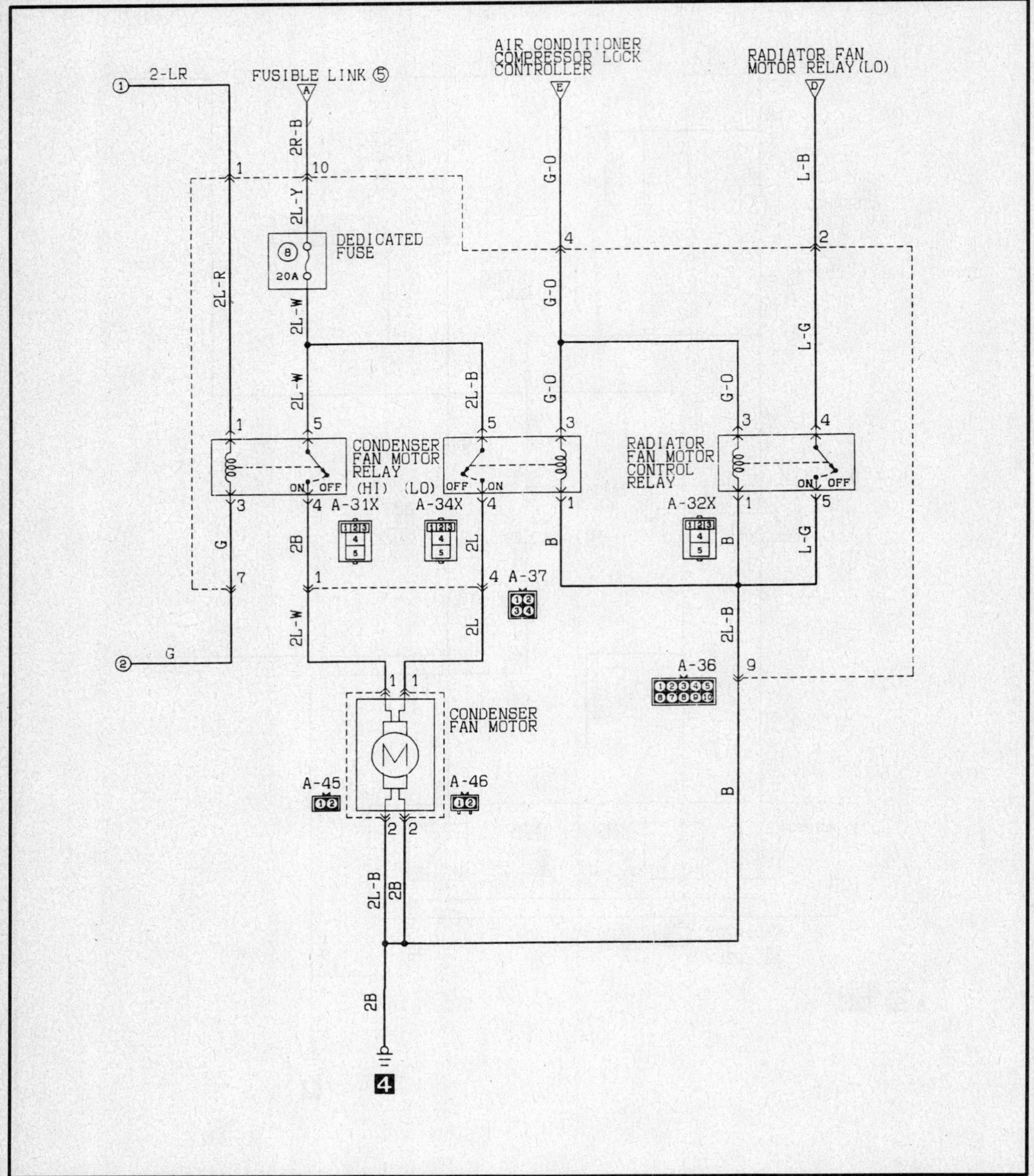

1993 Stealth with automatic air conditioning, Cont'd

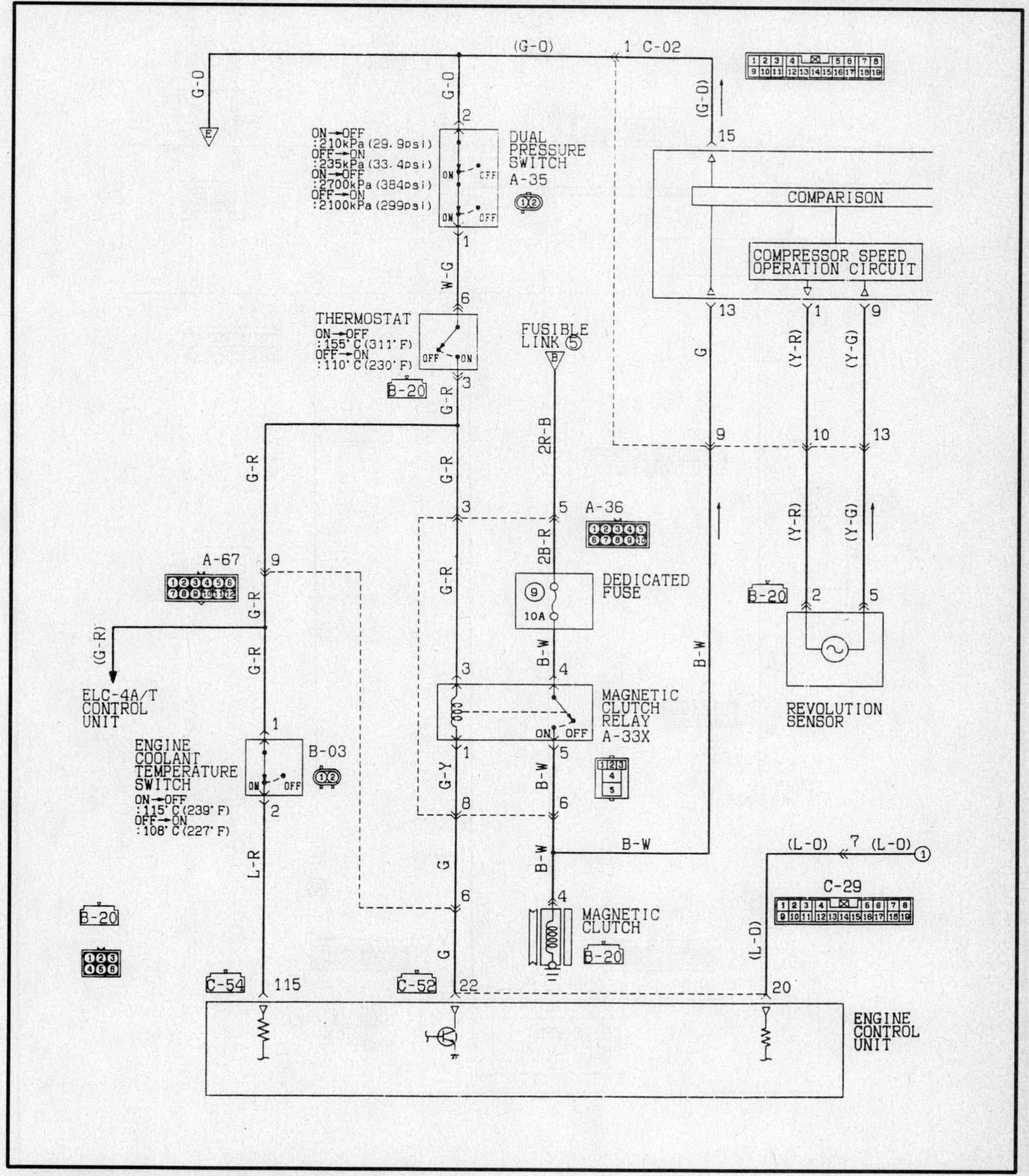

1993 Stealth with automatic air conditioning, Cont'd

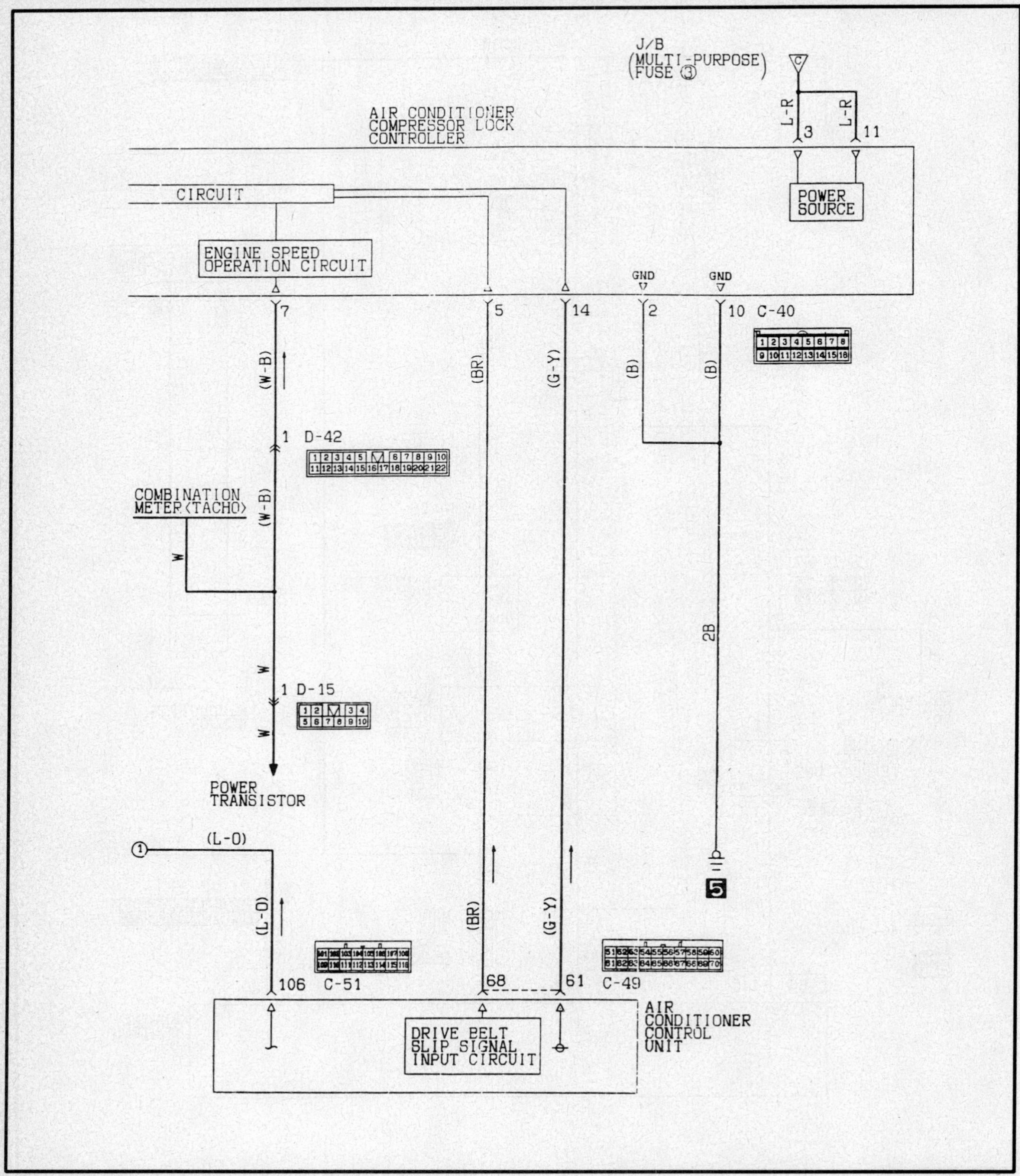

1993 Stealth with automatic air conditioning, Cont'd

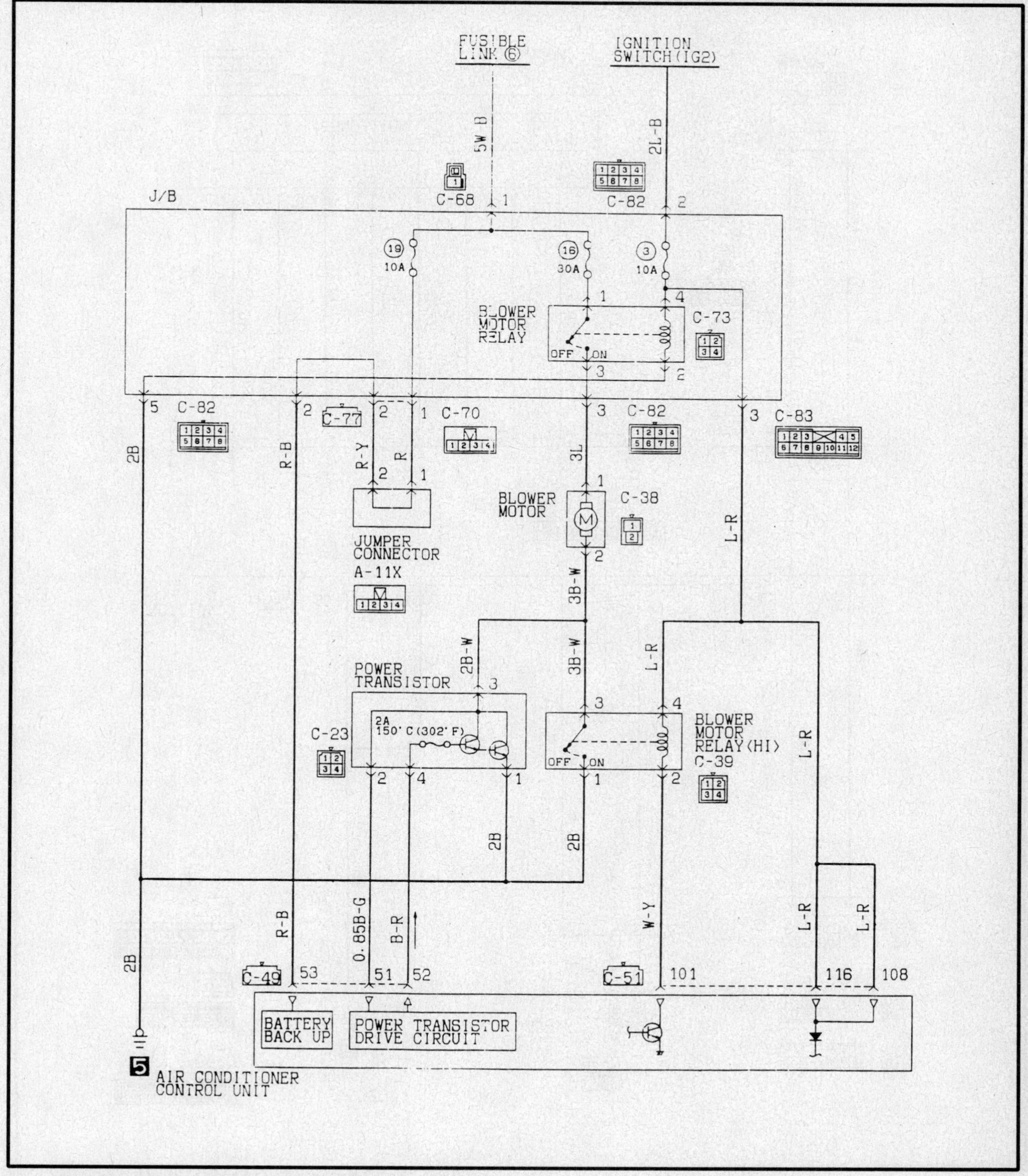

1993 Stealth with automatic air conditioning, Cont'd

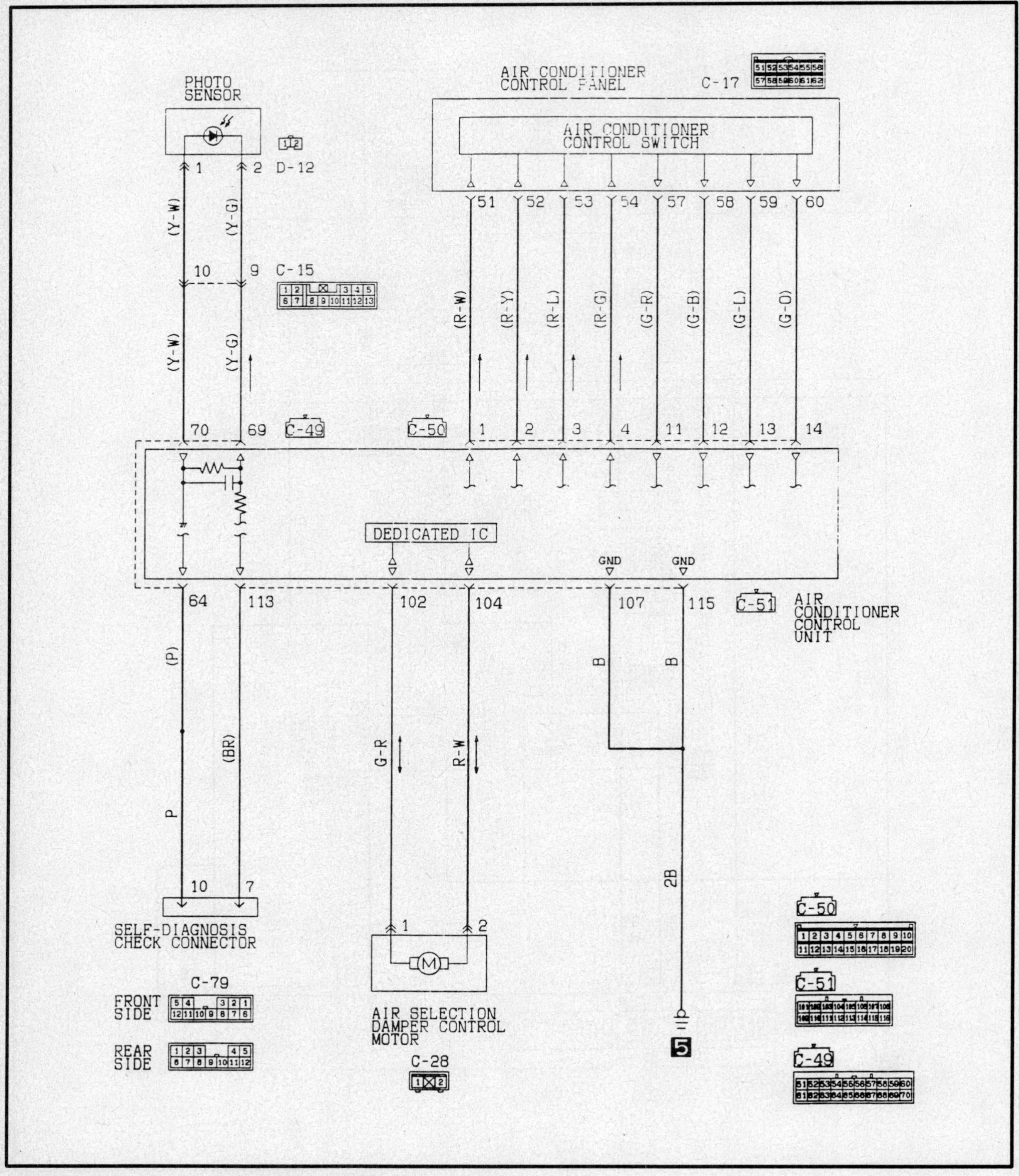

1993 Stealth with automatic air conditioning, Cont'd

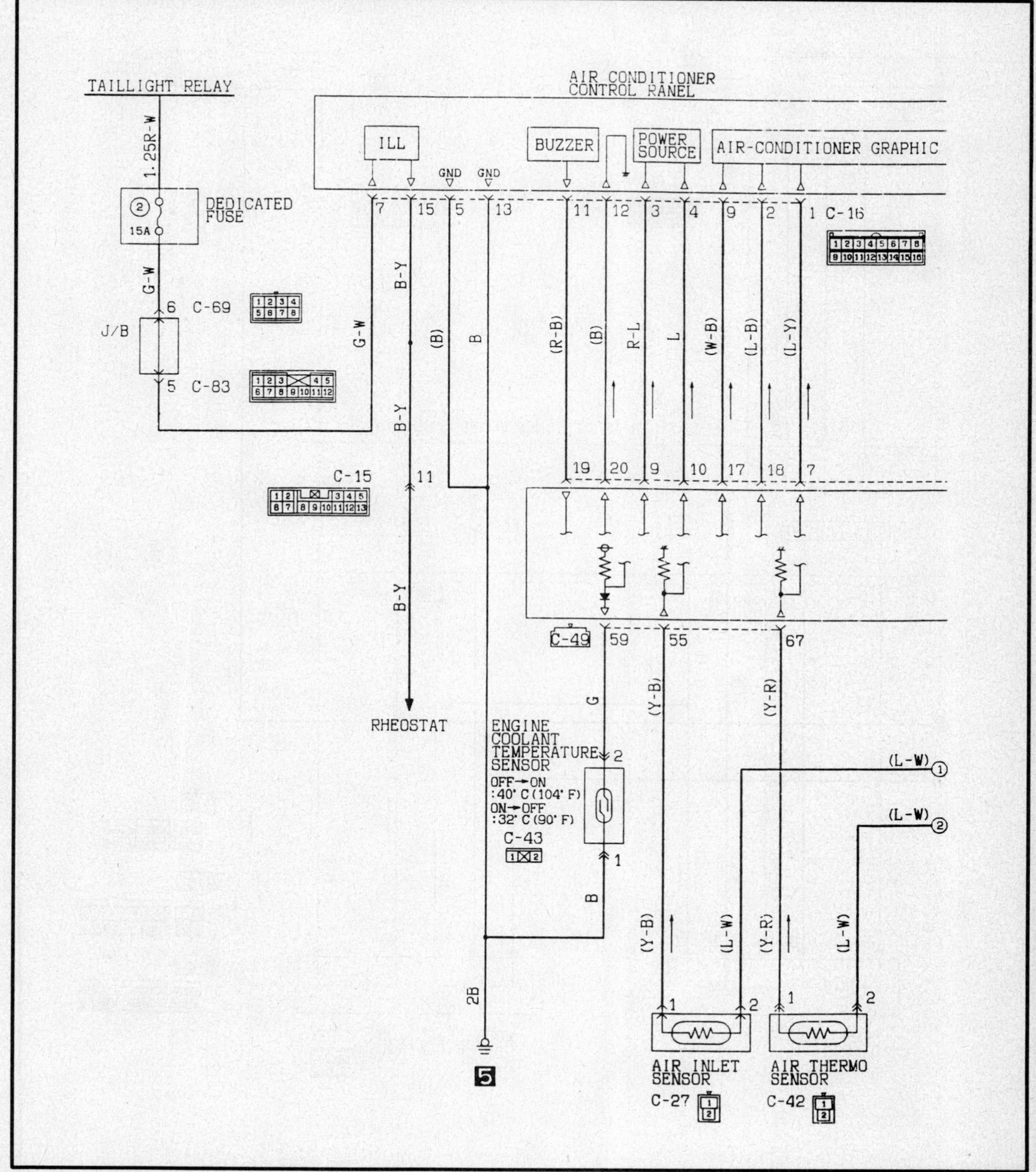

1993 Stealth with automatic air conditioning, Cont'd

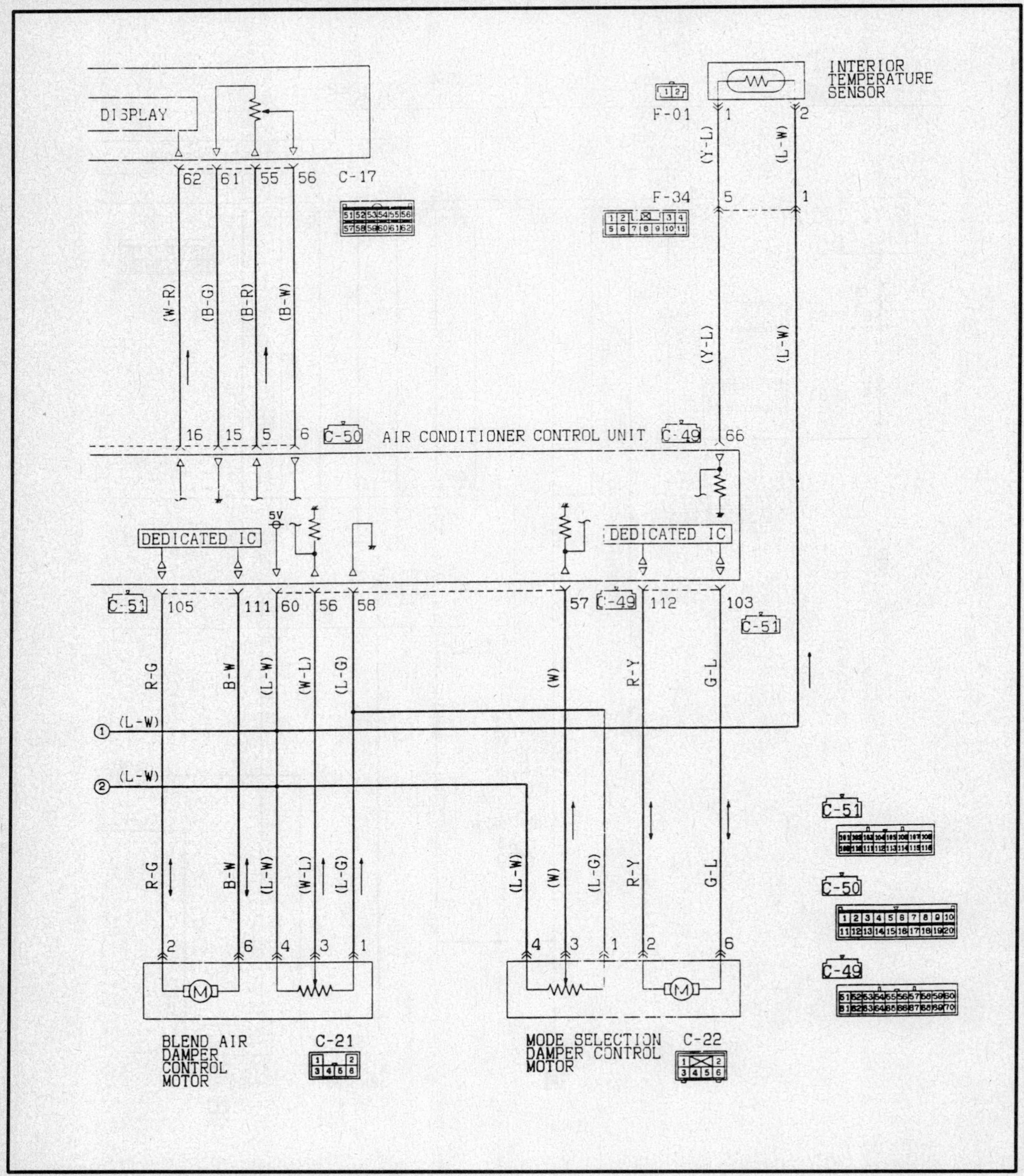

1993 Stealth with automatic air conditioning, Cont'd

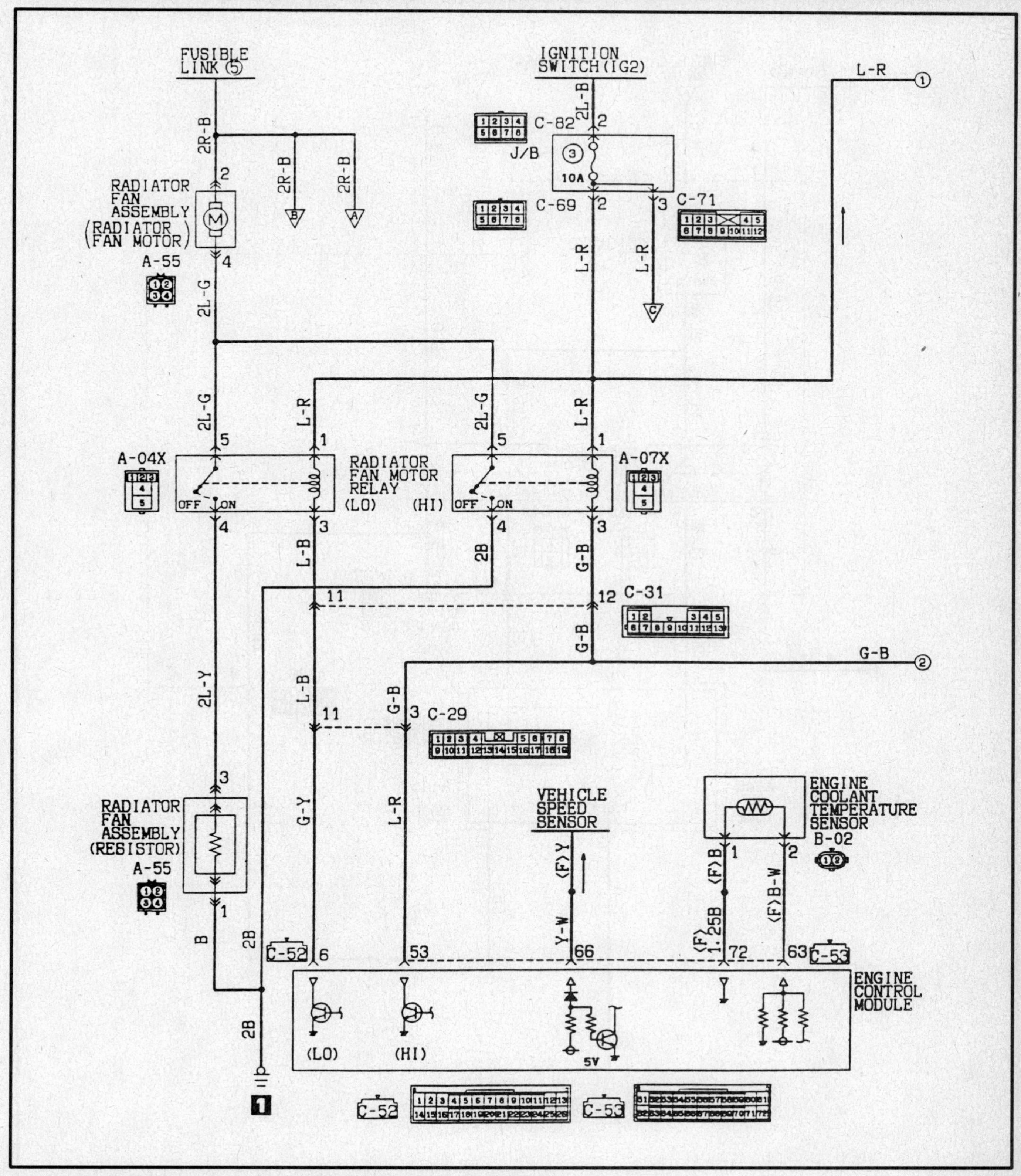

1994 Stealth with full auto air conditioning—DOHC non-turbo engine

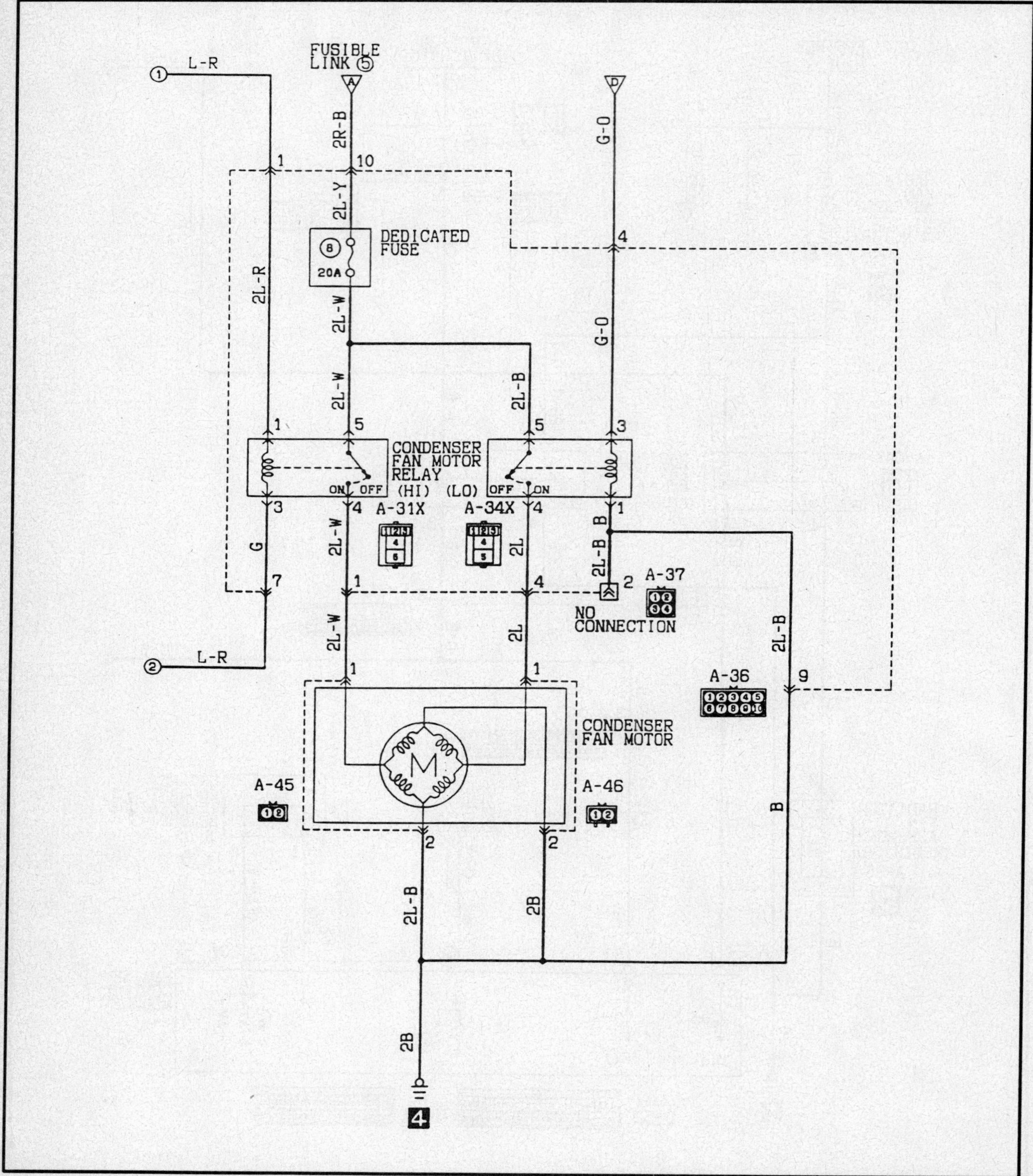

1994 Stealth with full auto air conditioning—DOHC non-turbo engine, Cont'd

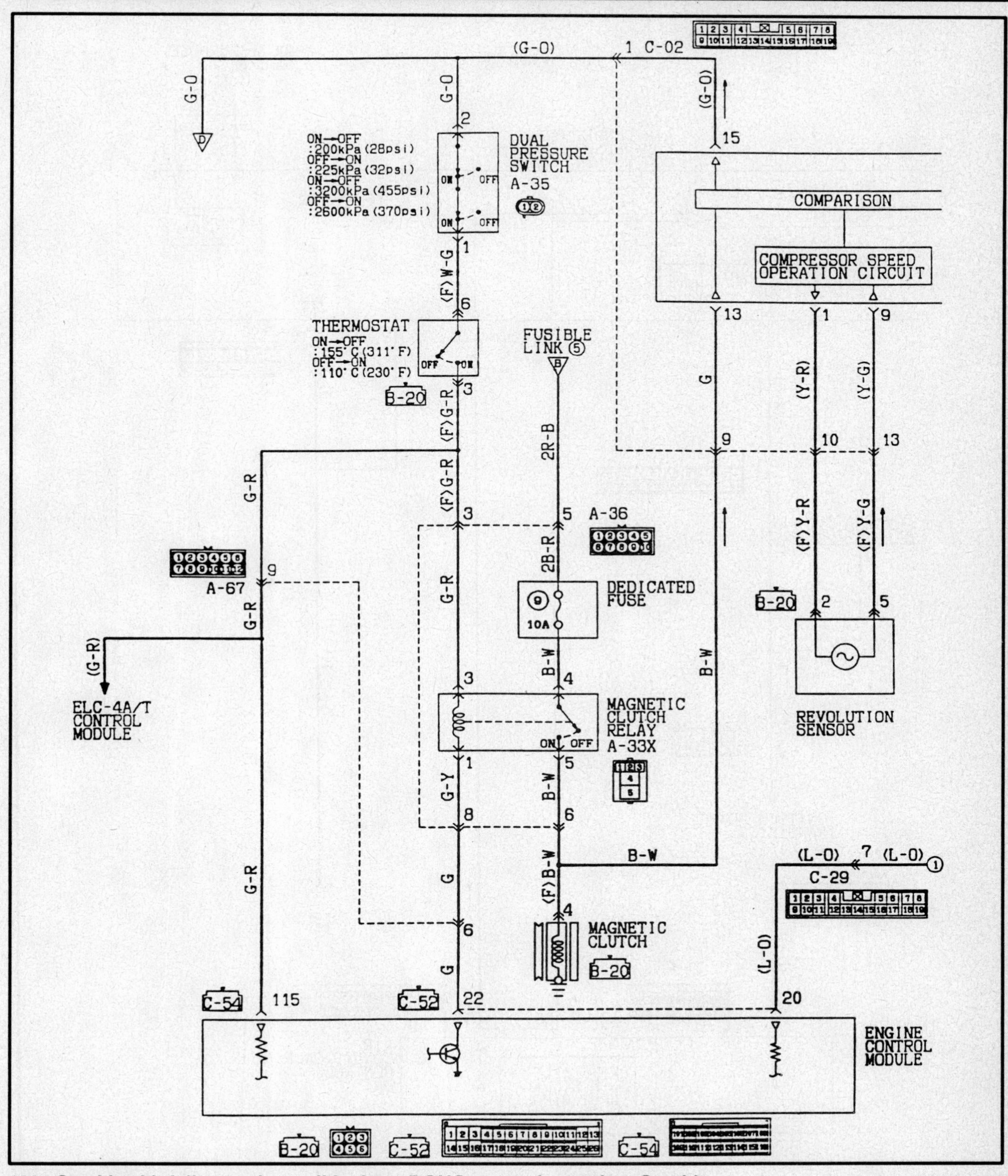

1994 Stealth with full auto air conditioning—DOHC non-turbo engine, Cont'd

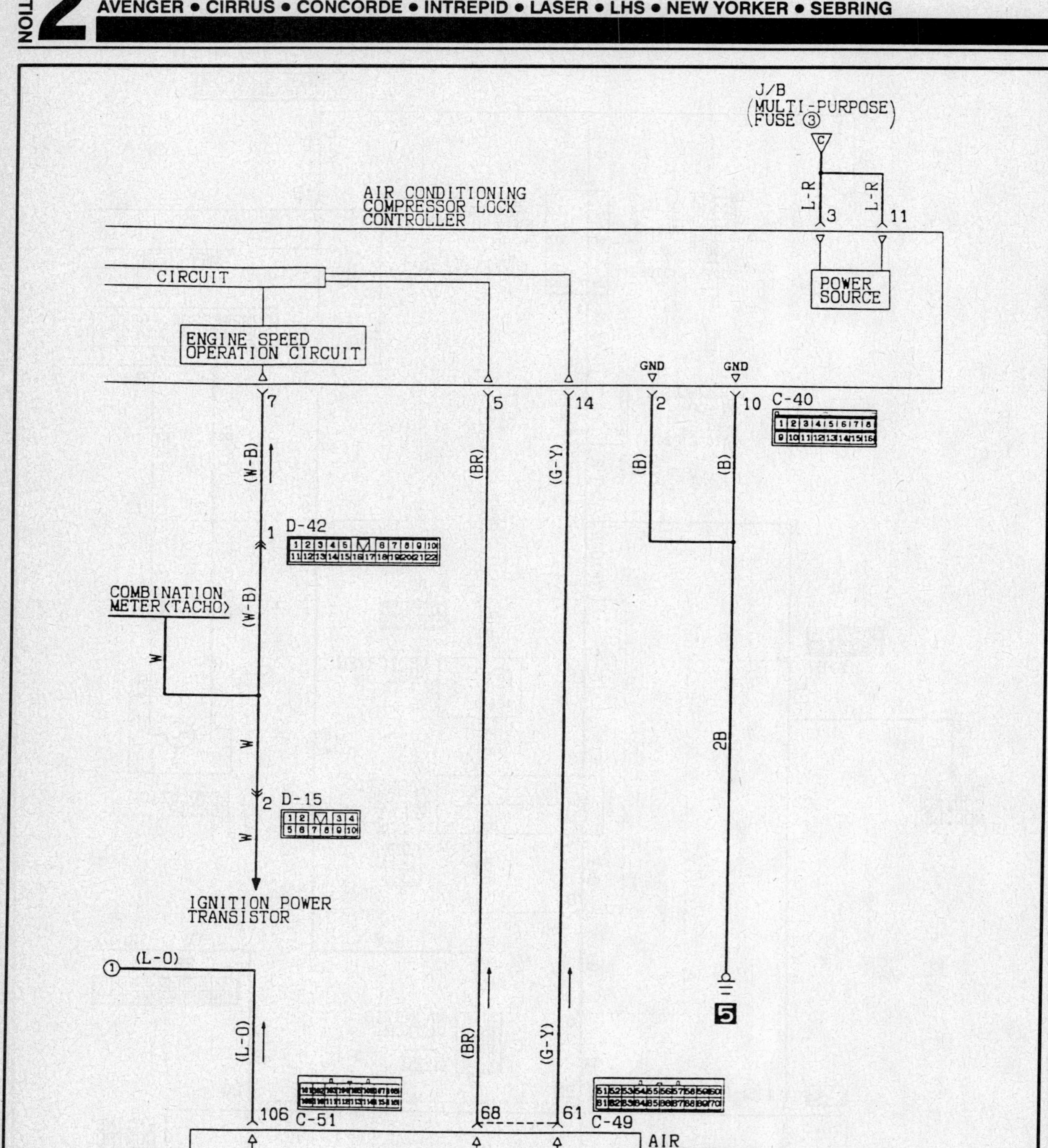

1994 Stealth with full auto air conditioning—DOHC non-turbo engine, Cont'd

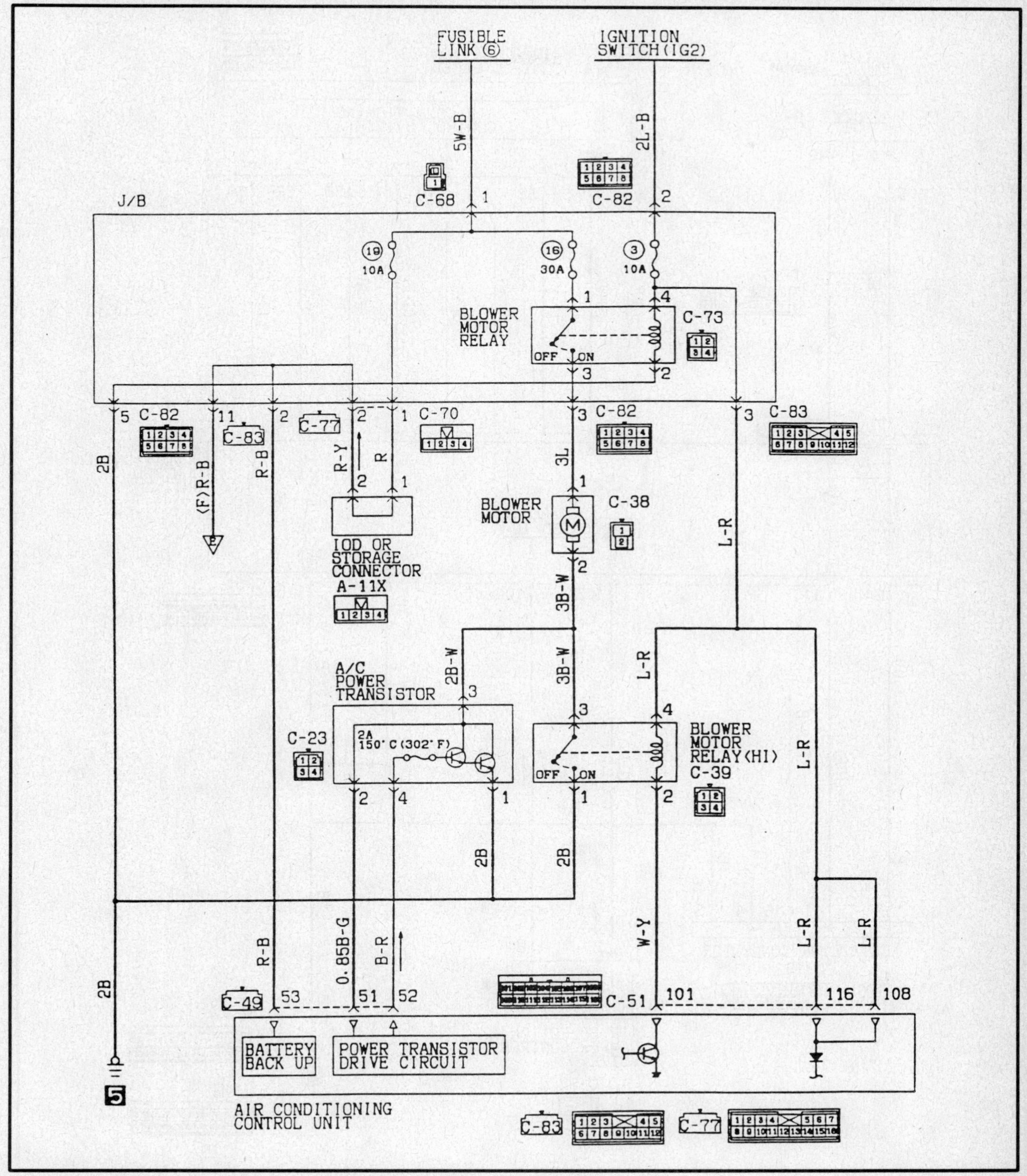

1994 Stealth with full auto air conditioning—DOHC non-turbo engine, Cont'd

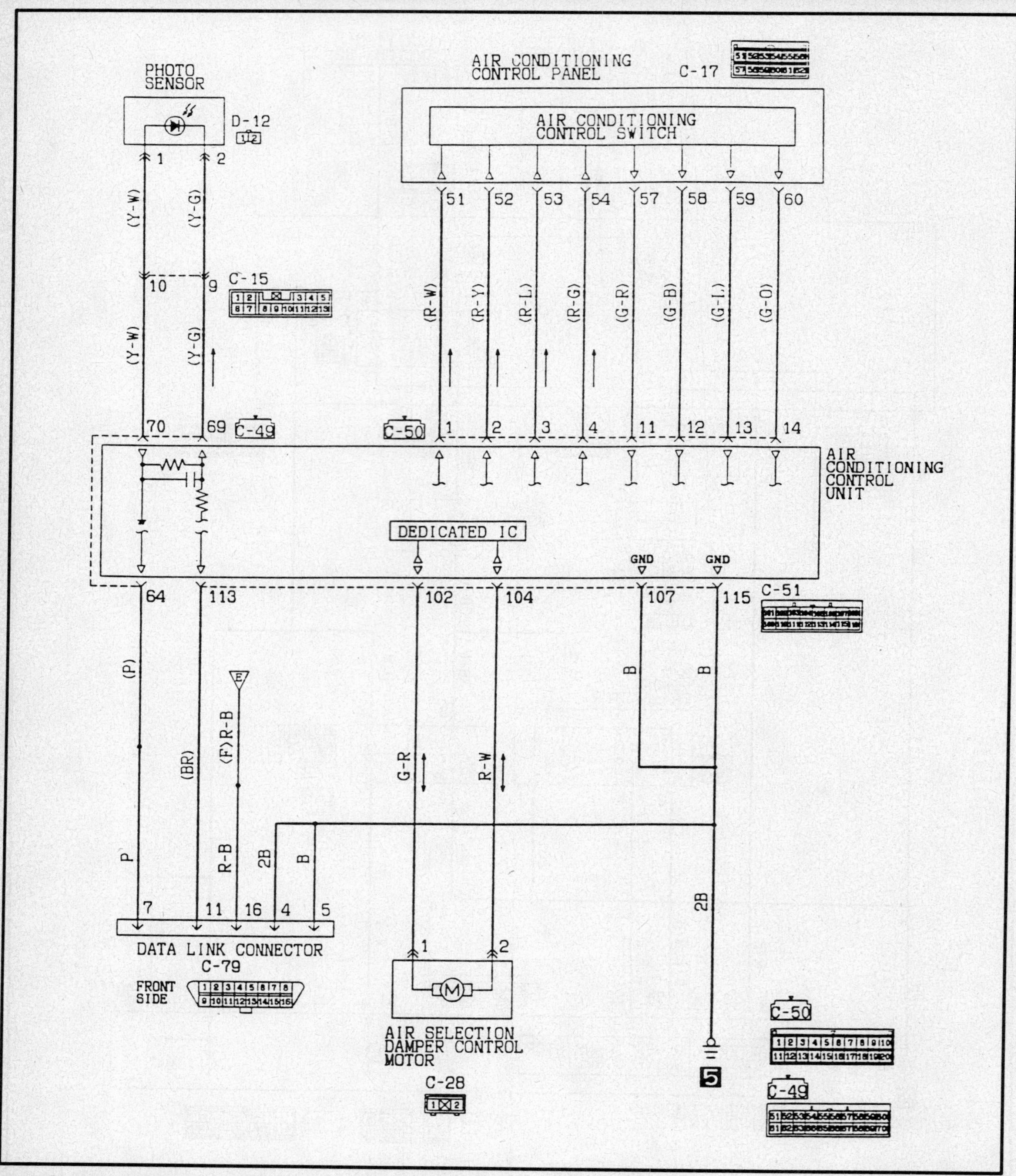

1994 Stealth with full auto air conditioning—DOHC non-turbo engine, Cont'd

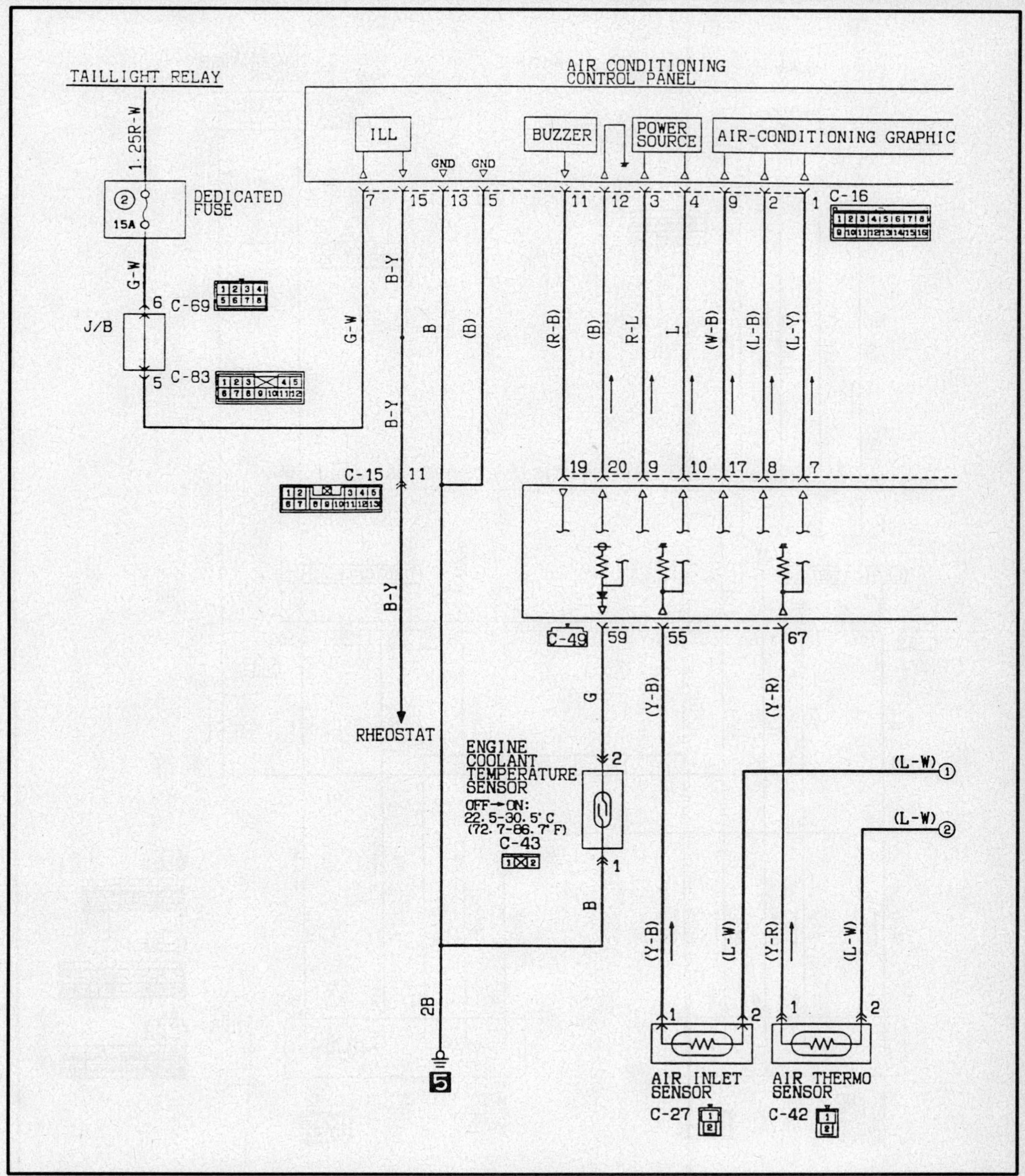

1994 Stealth with full auto air conditioning—DOHC non-turbo engine, Cont'd

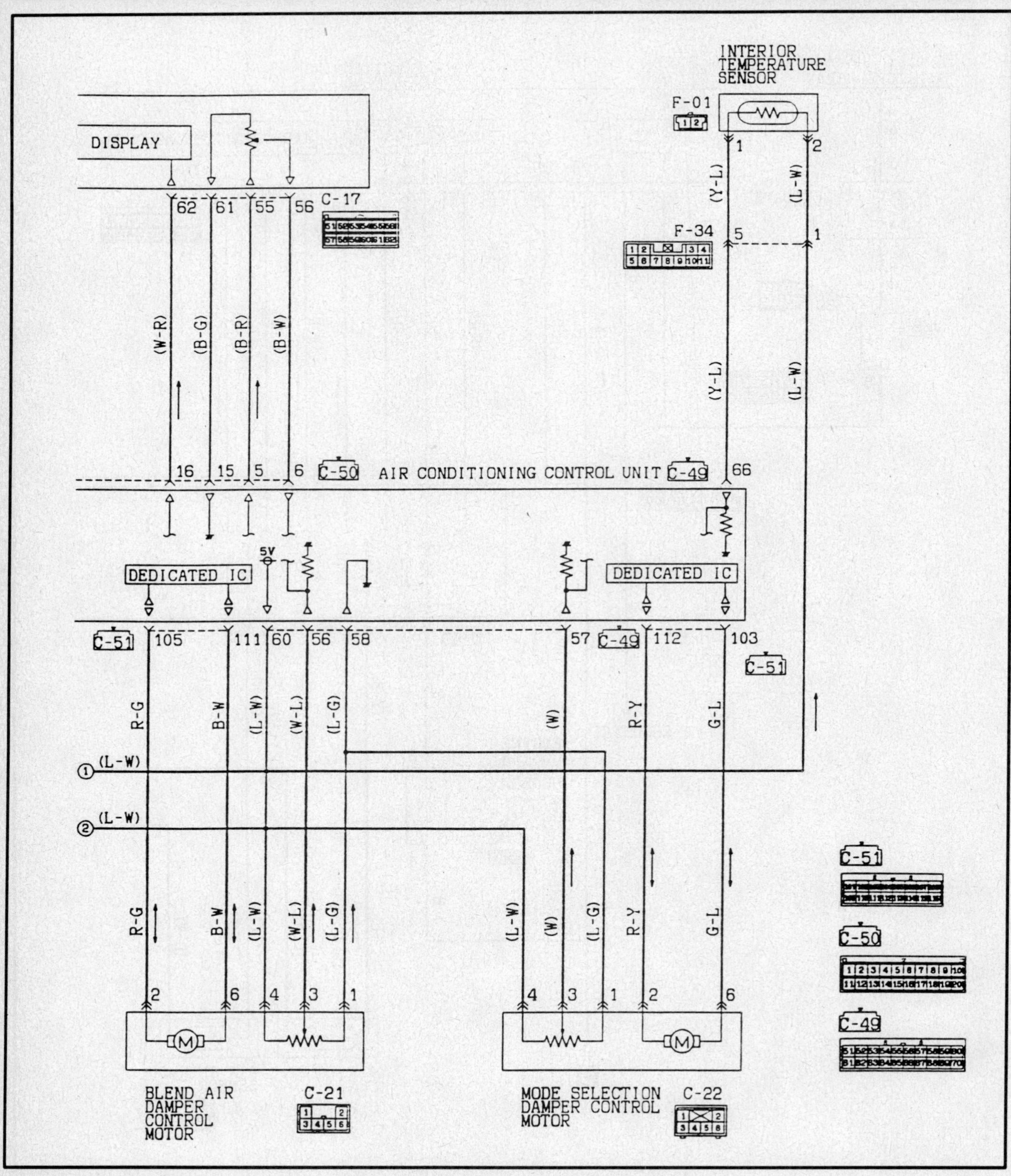

1994 Stealth with full auto air conditioning—DOHC non-turbo engine, Cont'd

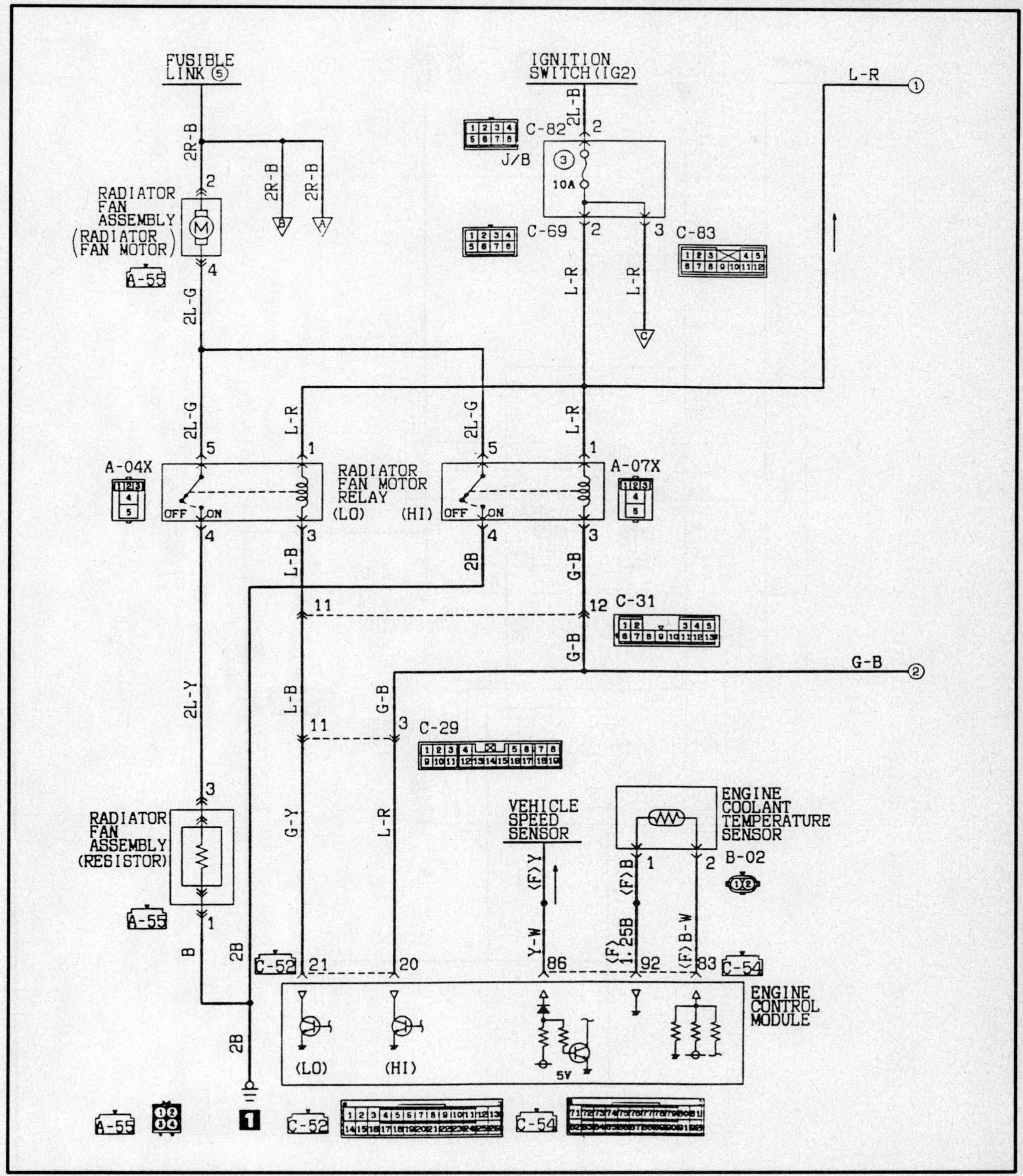

1994 Stealth with full auto air conditioning—DOHC turbo engine

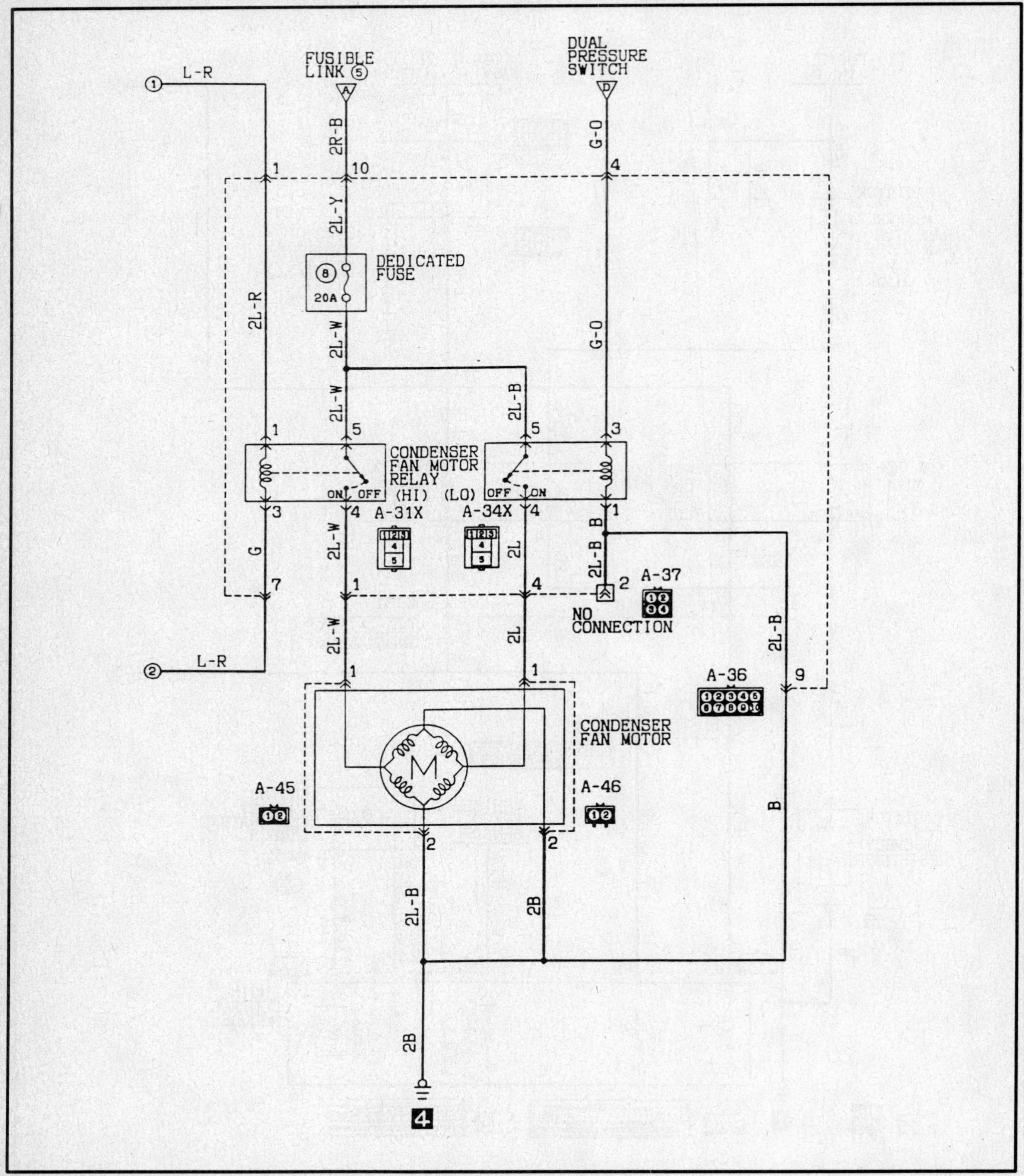

1994 Stealth with full auto air conditioning—DOHC turbo engine, Cont'd

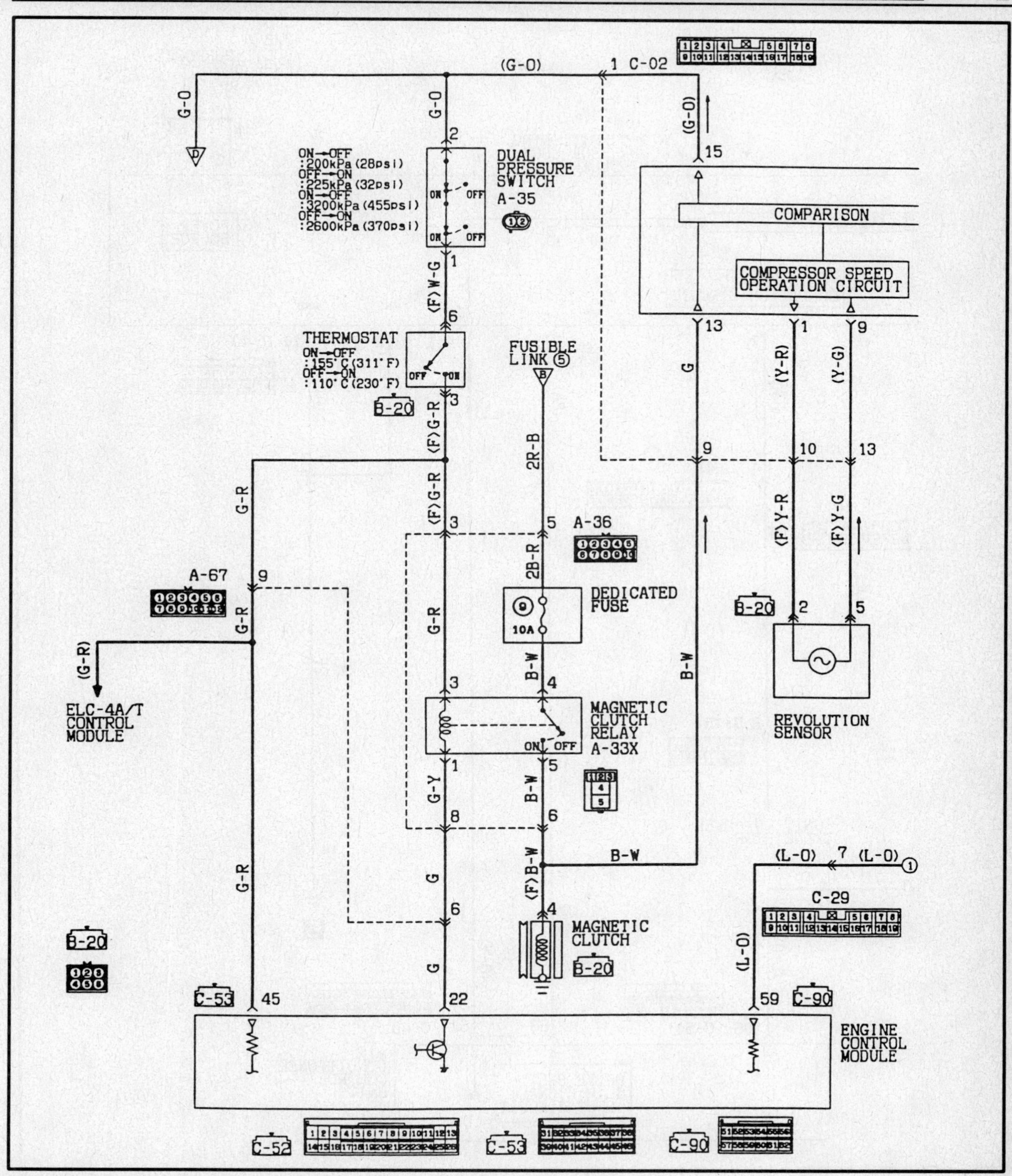

1994 Stealth with full auto air conditioning—DOHC turbo engine, Cont'd

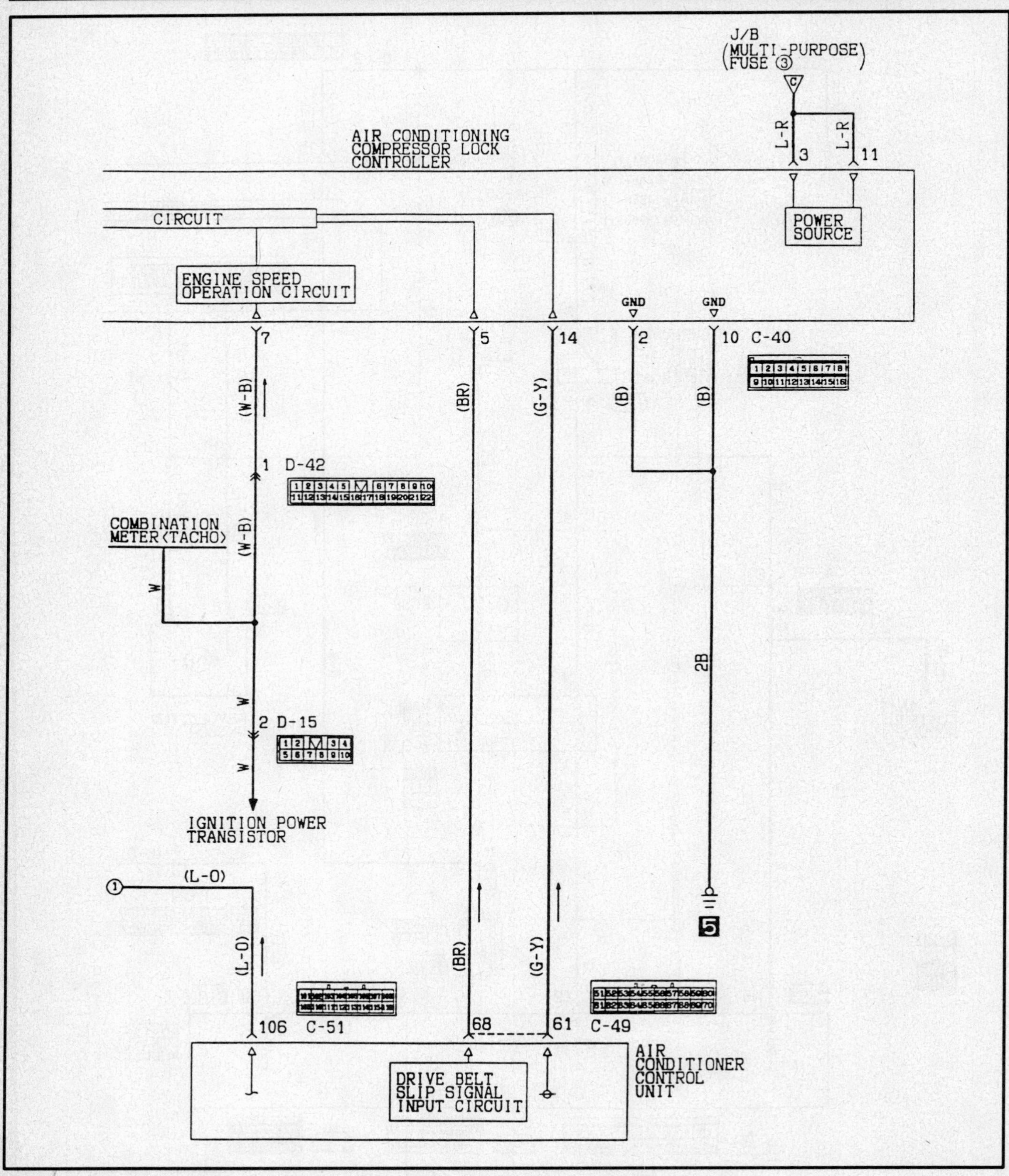

1994 Stealth with full auto air conditioning—DOHC turbo engine, Cont'd

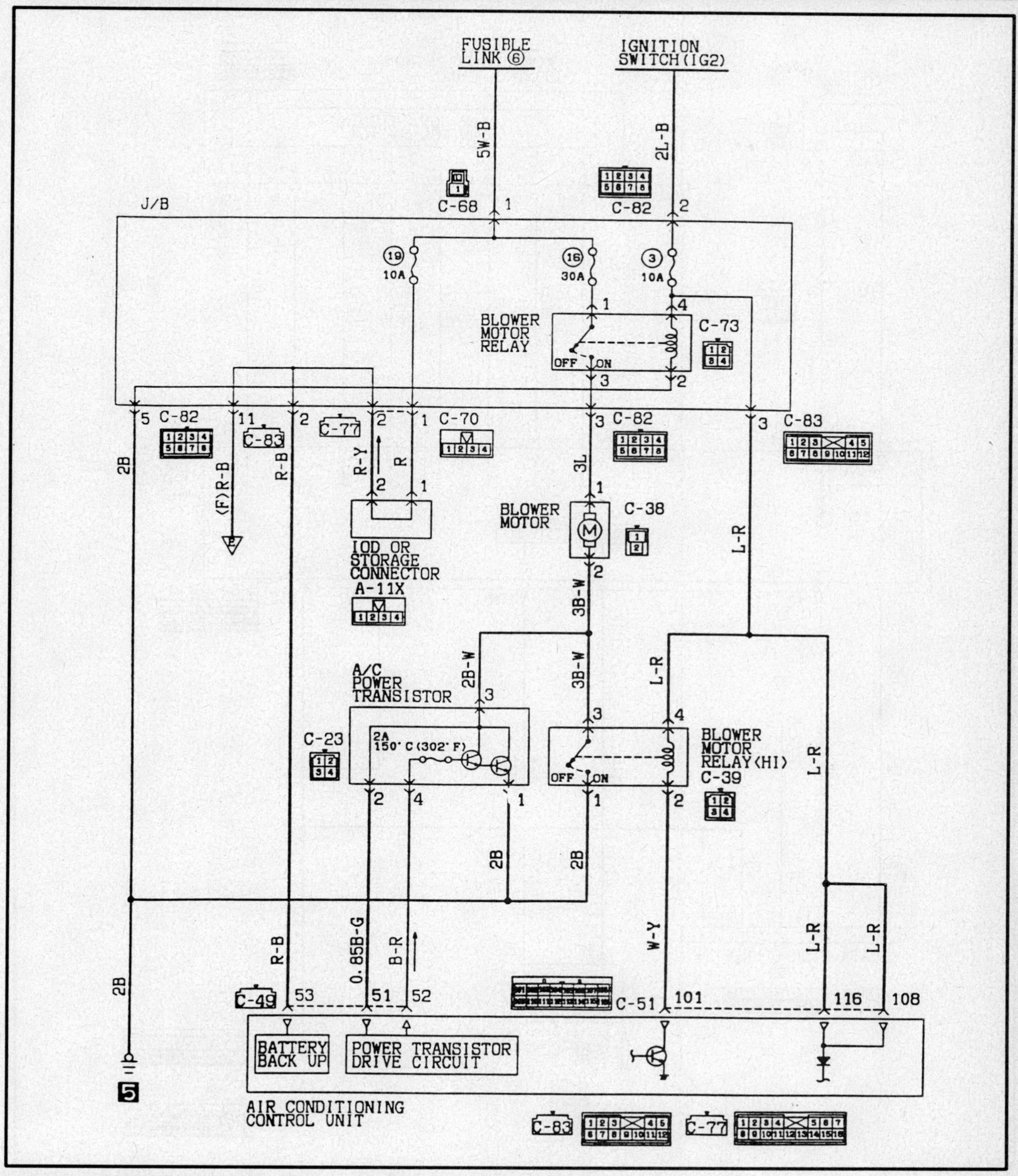

1994 Stealth with full auto air conditioning—DOHC turbo engine, Cont'd

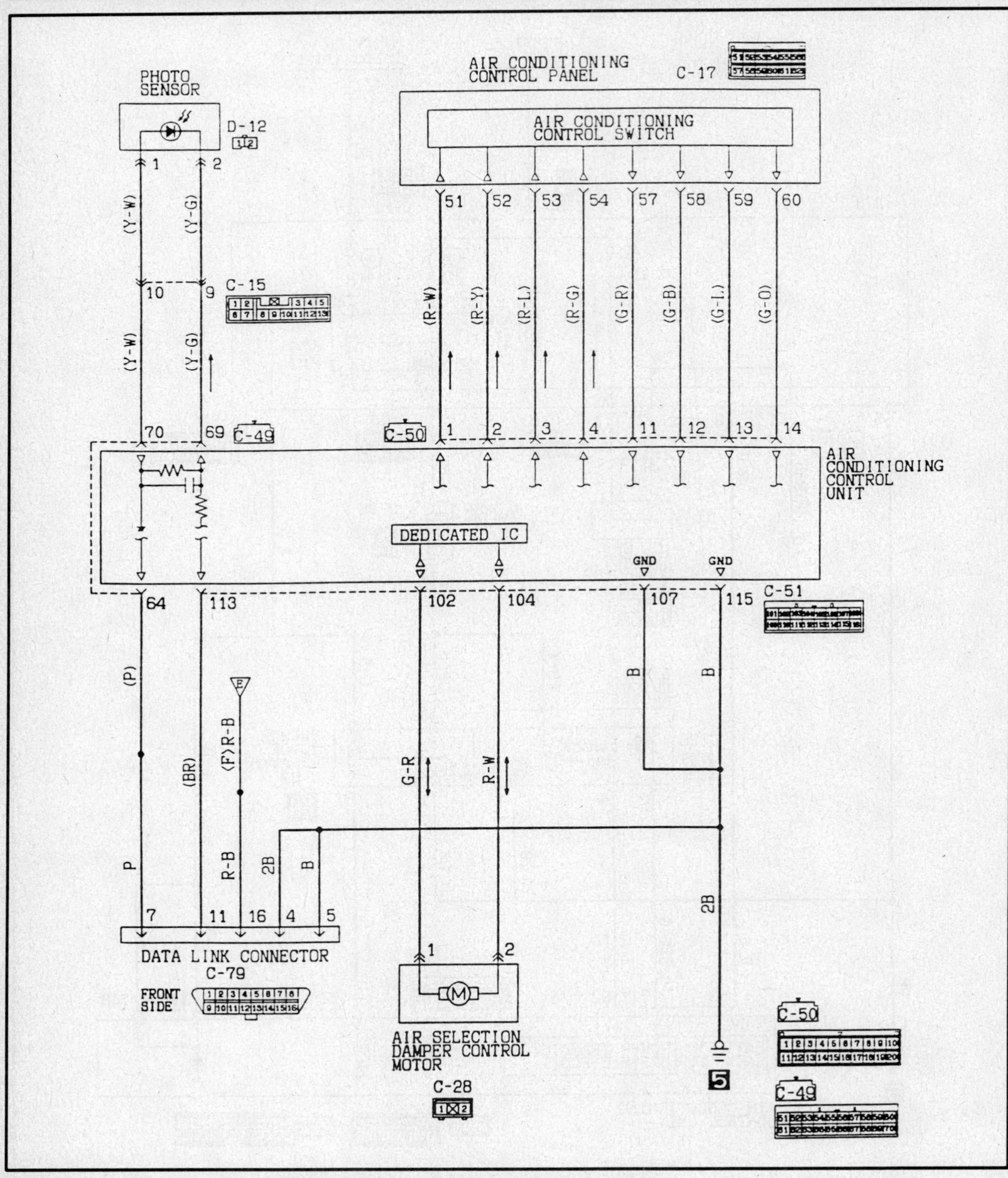

1994 Stealth with full auto air conditioning—DOHC turbo engine, Cont'd

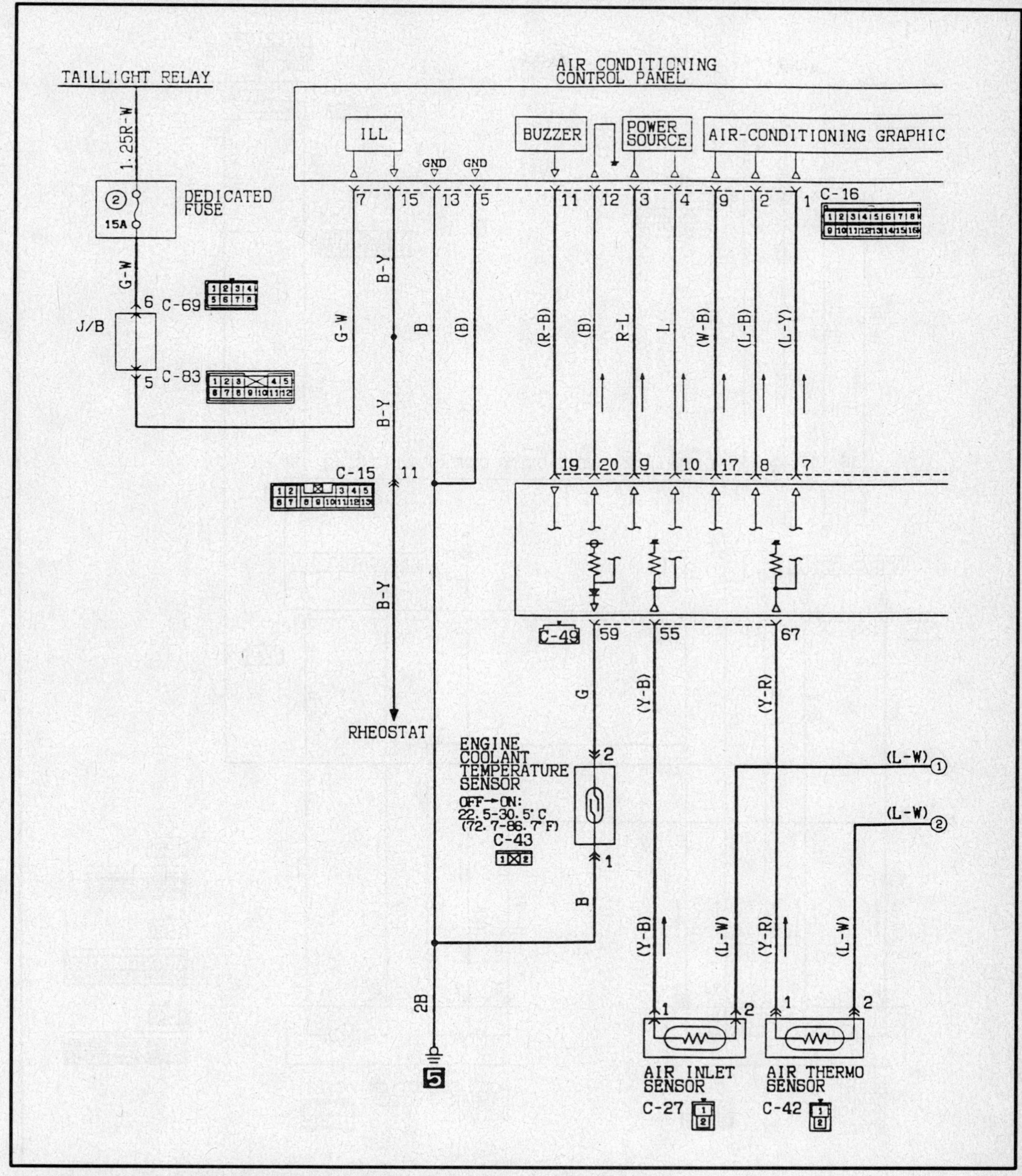

1994 Stealth with full auto air conditioning—DOHC turbo engine, Cont'd

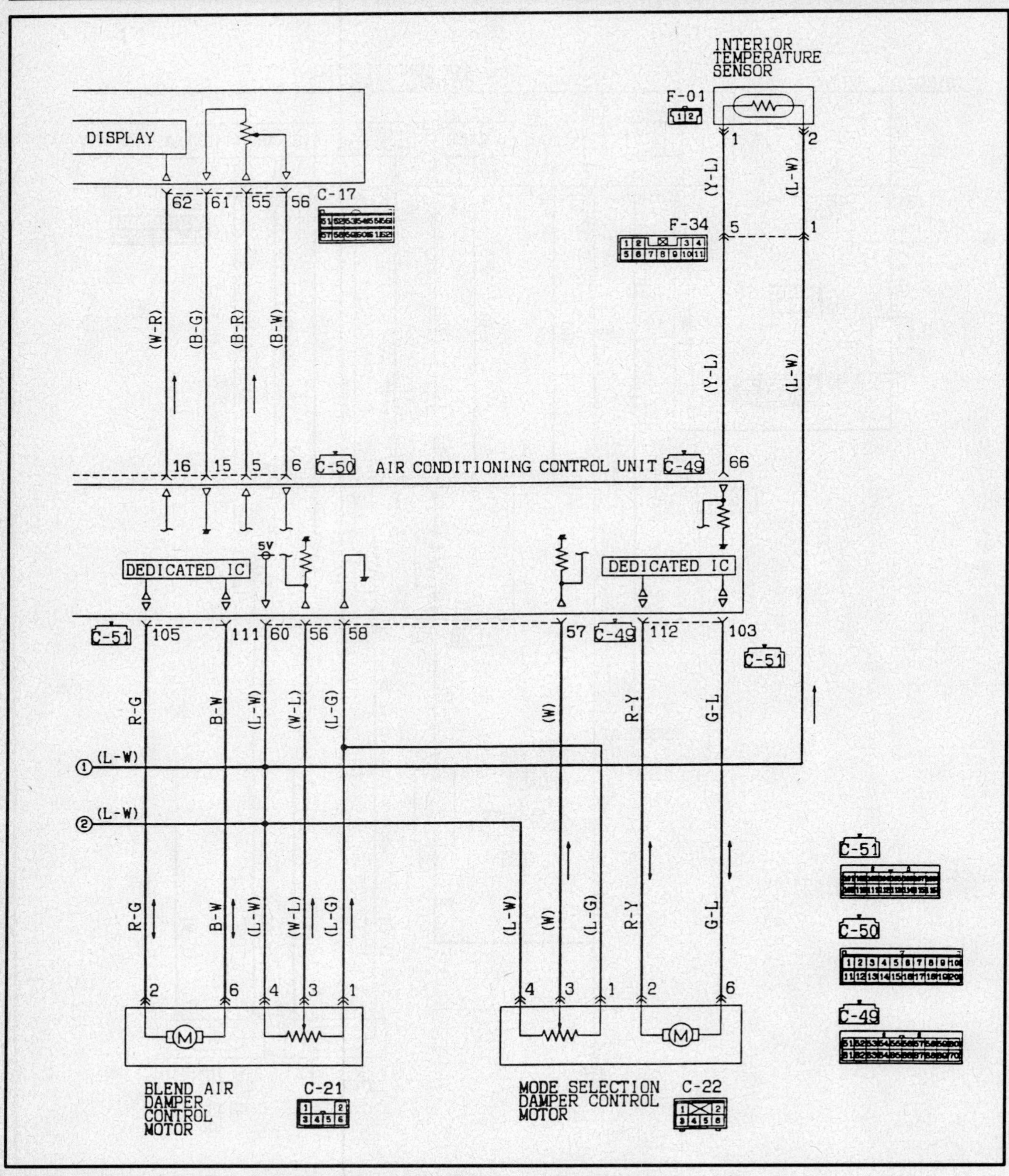

1994 Stealth with full auto air conditioning—DOHC turbo engine, Cont'd

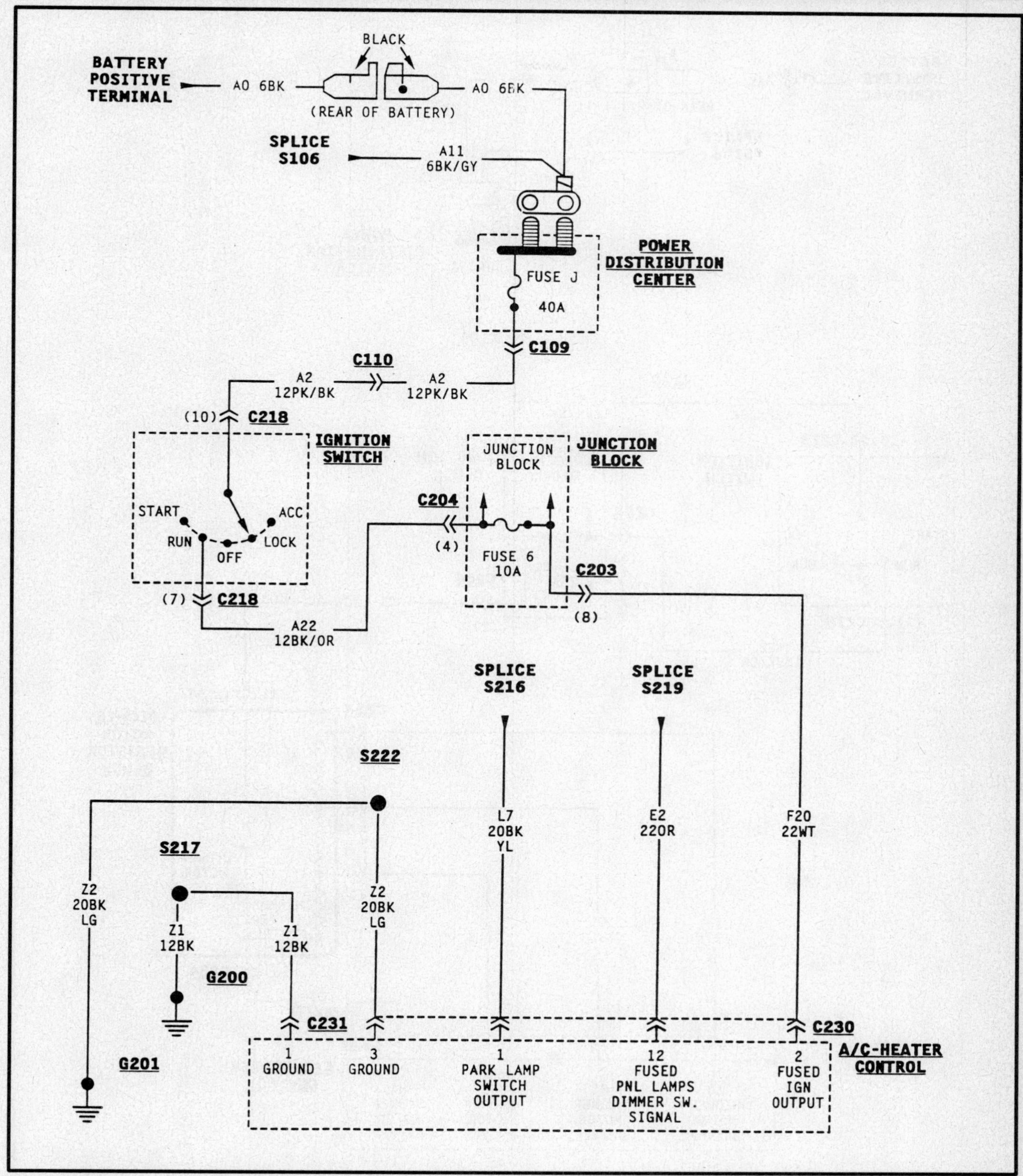

Concorde, Intrepid, LHS, New Yorker and Vision with air conditioning/heater without ATC

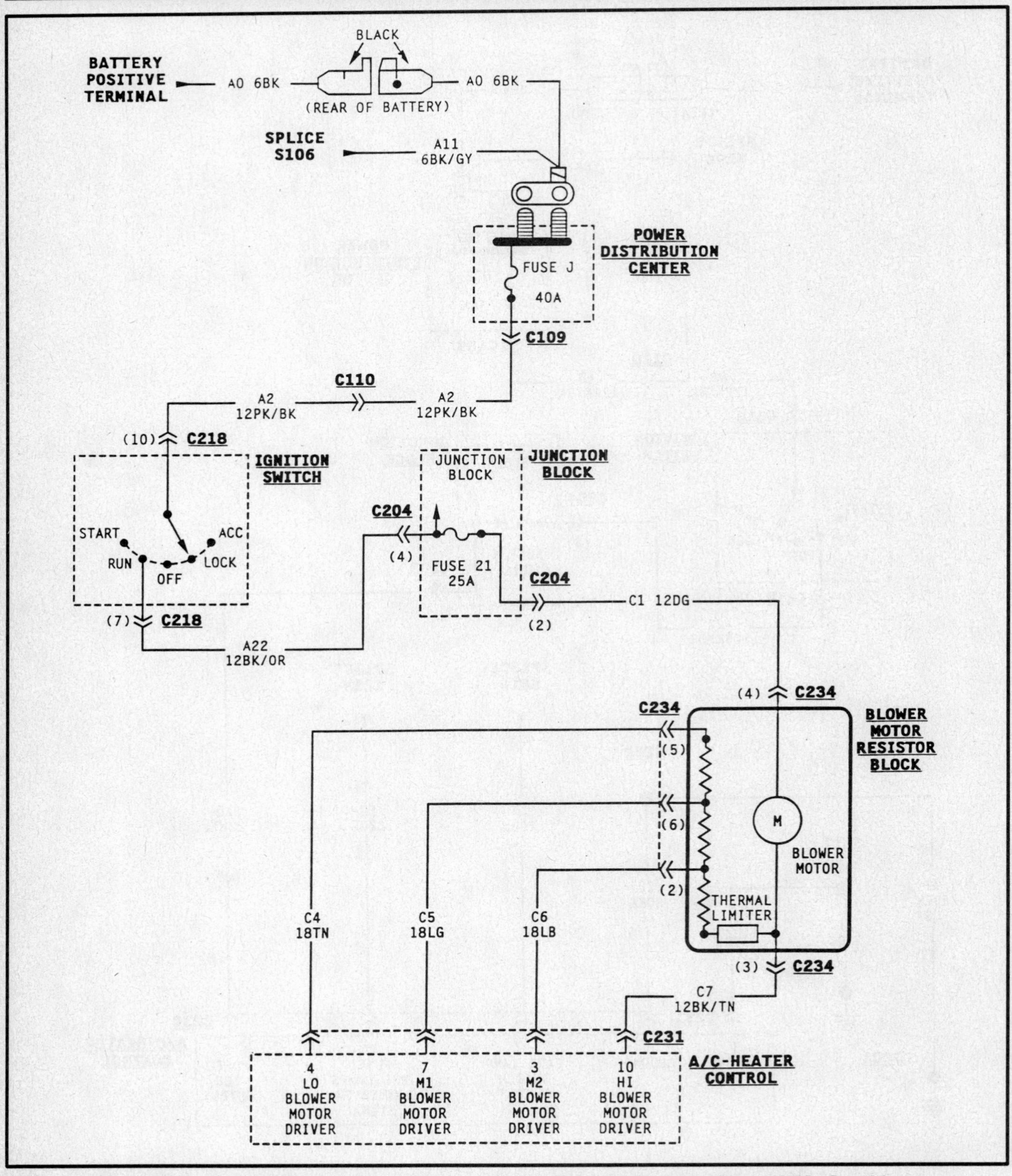

Concorde, Intrepid, LHS, New Yorker and Vision with air conditioning/heater without ATC, Cont'd

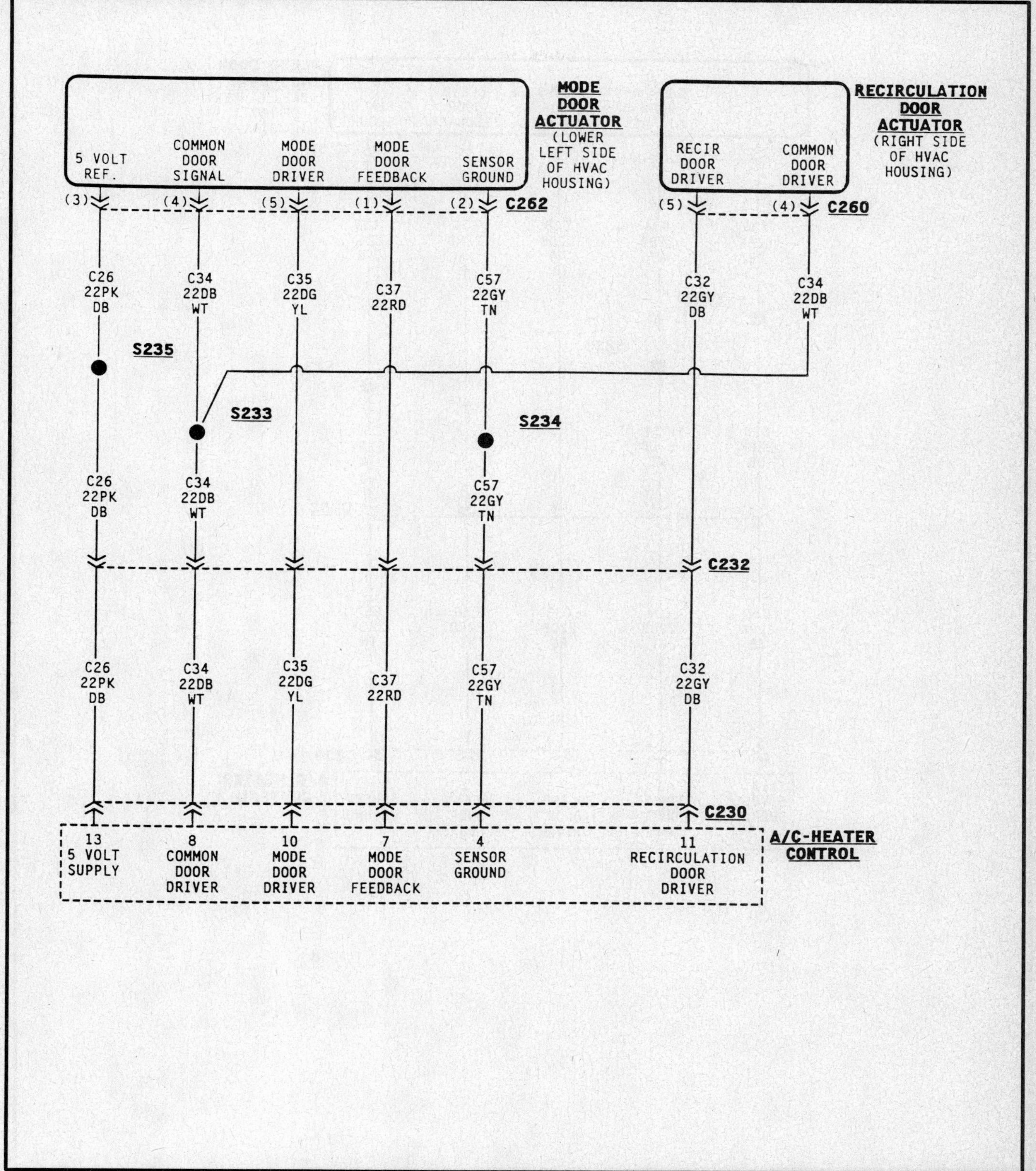

Concorde, Intrepid, LHS, New Yorker and Vision with air conditioning/heater without ATC, Cont'd

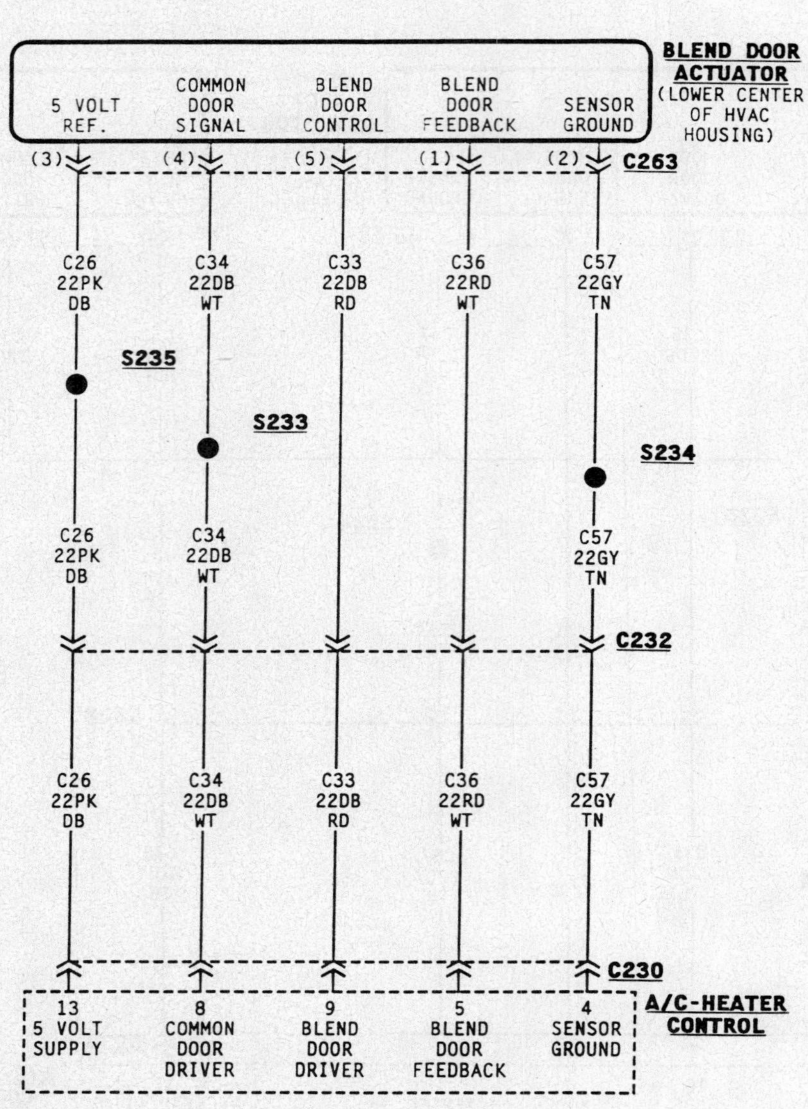

Concorde, Intrepid, LHS, New Yorker and Vision with air conditioning/heater without ATC, Cont'd

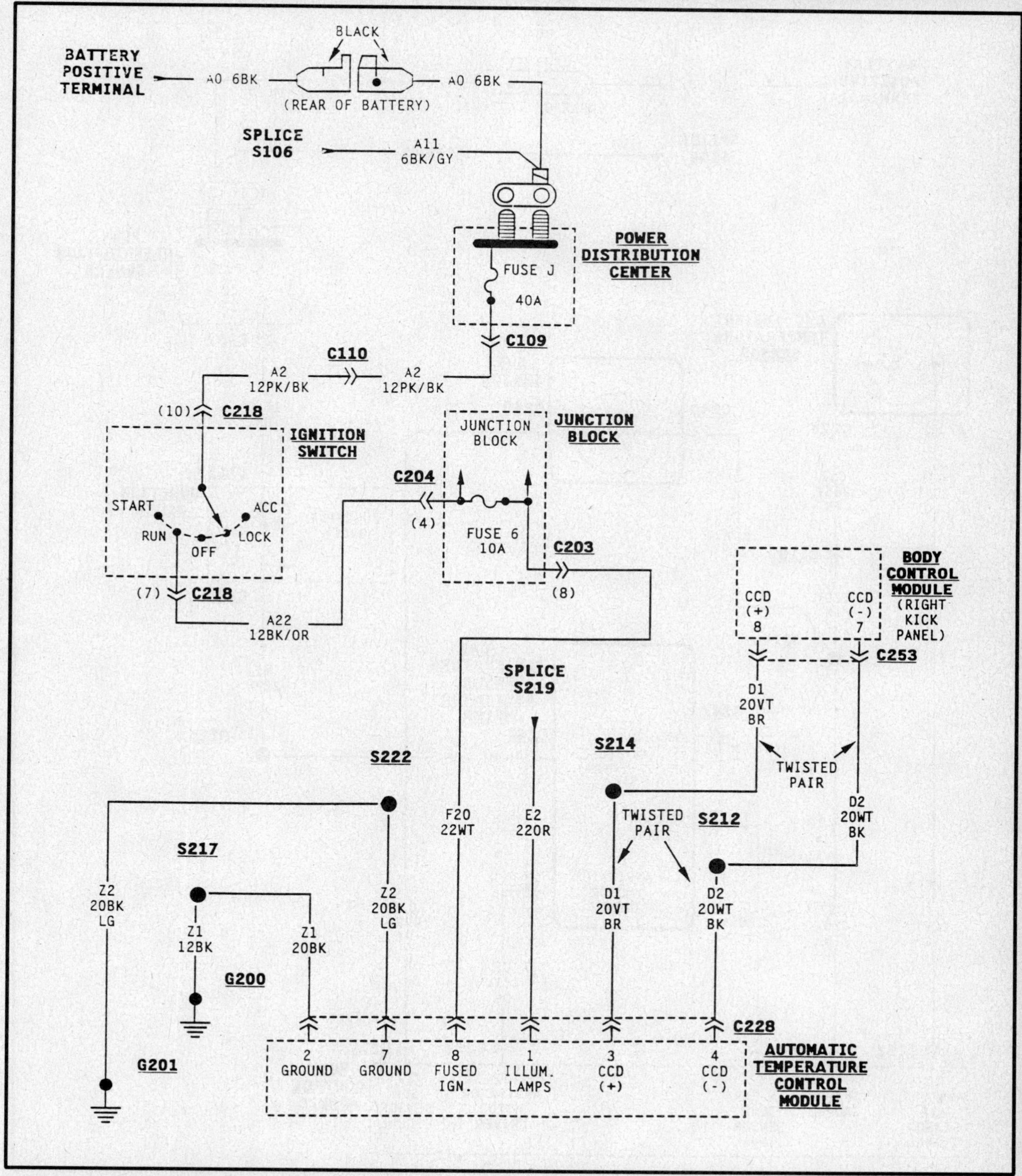

Concorde, Intrepid, LHS, New Yorker and Vision with air conditioning/heater with ATC only

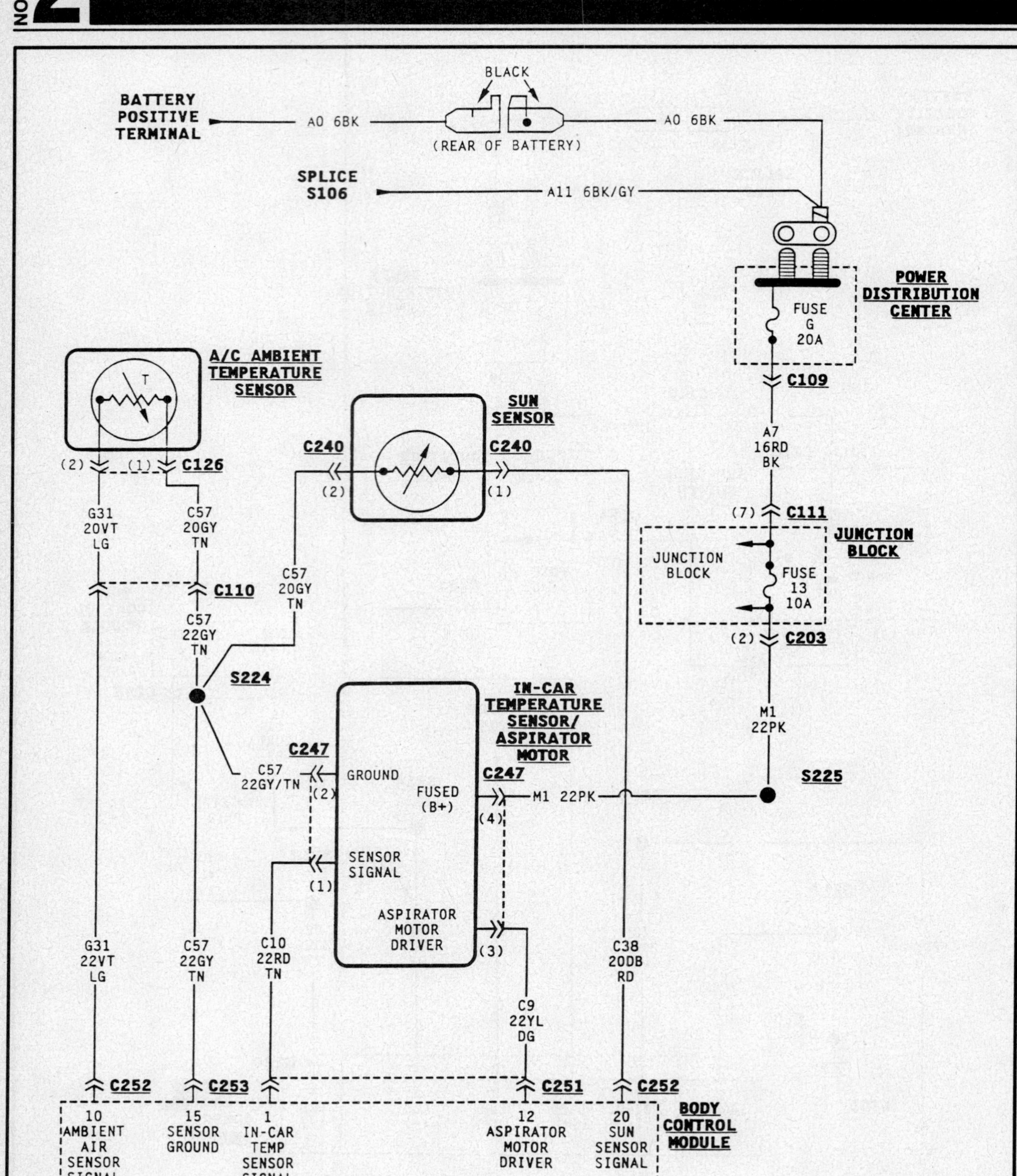

Concorde, Intrepid, LHS, New Yorker and Vision with air conditioning/heater with ATC only, Cont'd

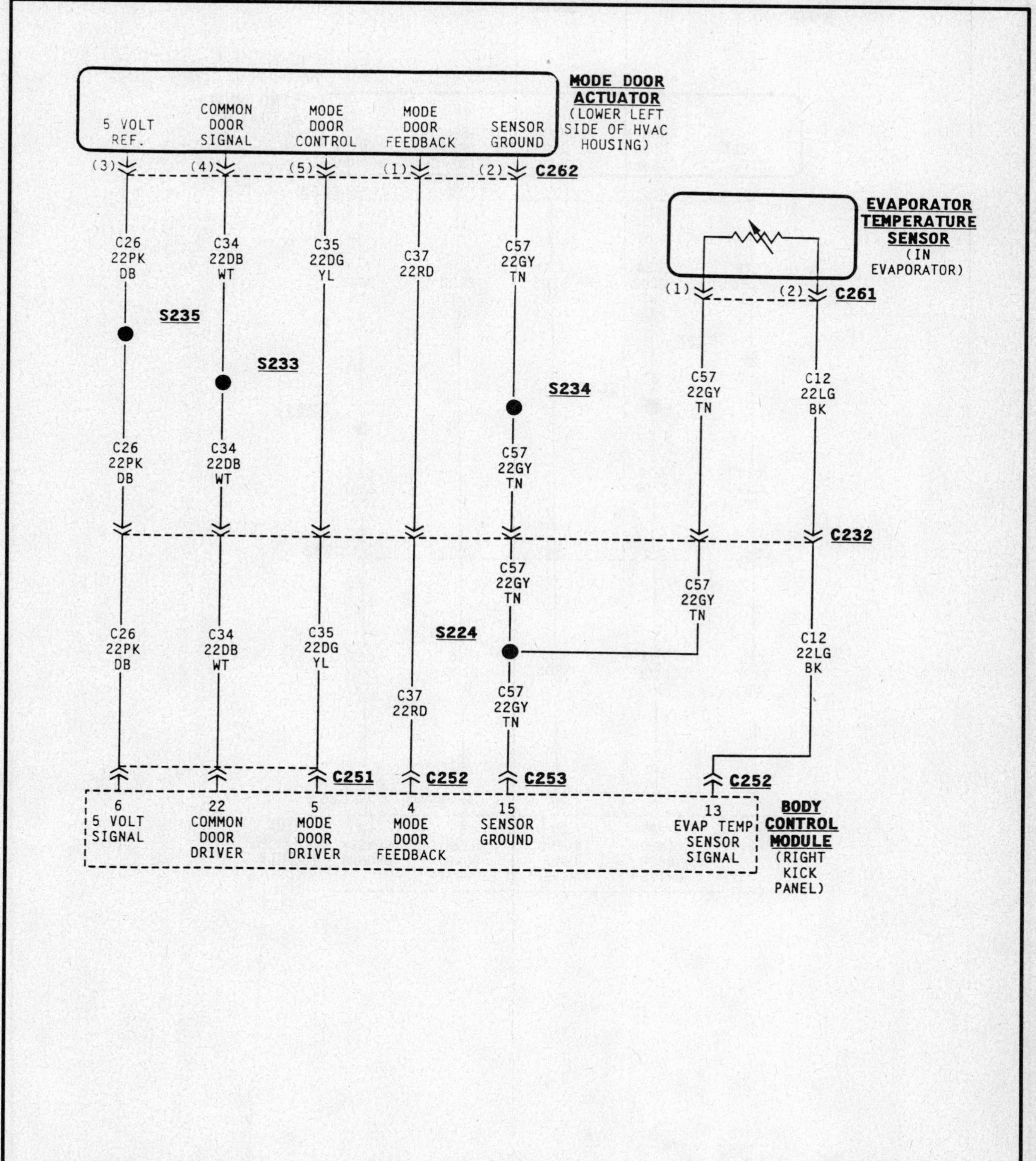

Concorde, Intrepid, LHS, New Yorker and Vision with air conditioning/heater with ATC only, Cont'd

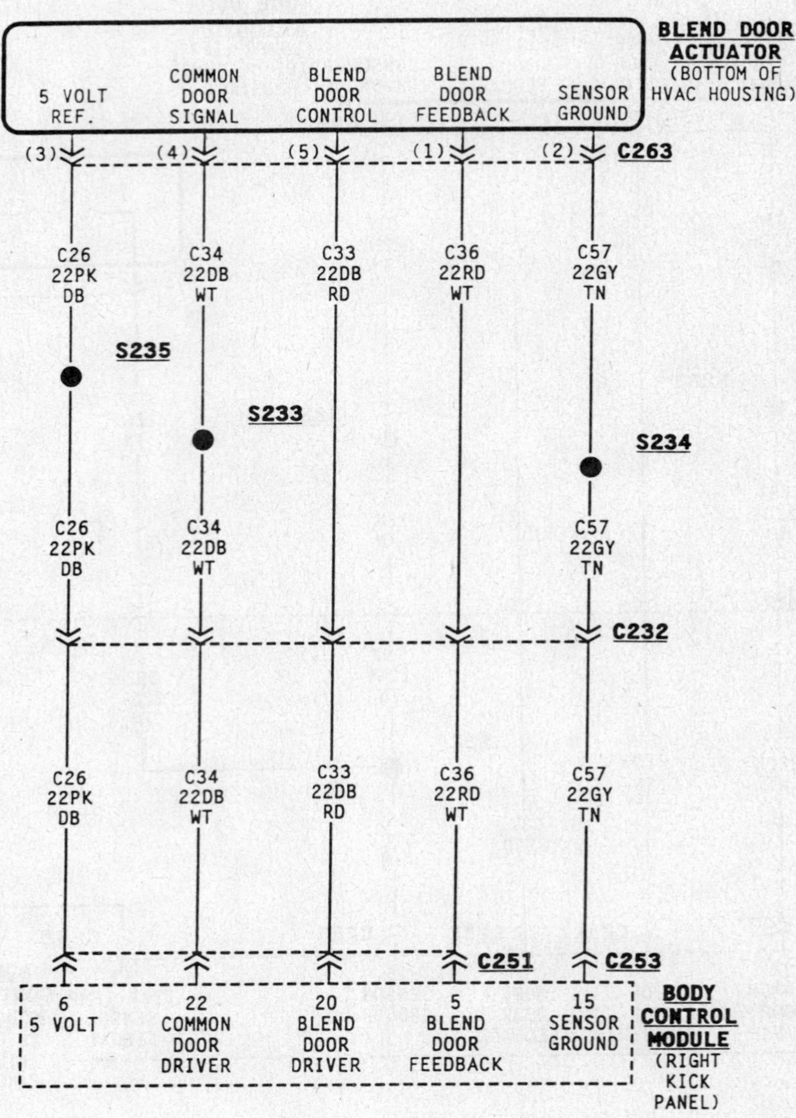

Concorde, Intrepid, LHS, New Yorker and Vision with air conditioning/heater with ATC only, Cont'd

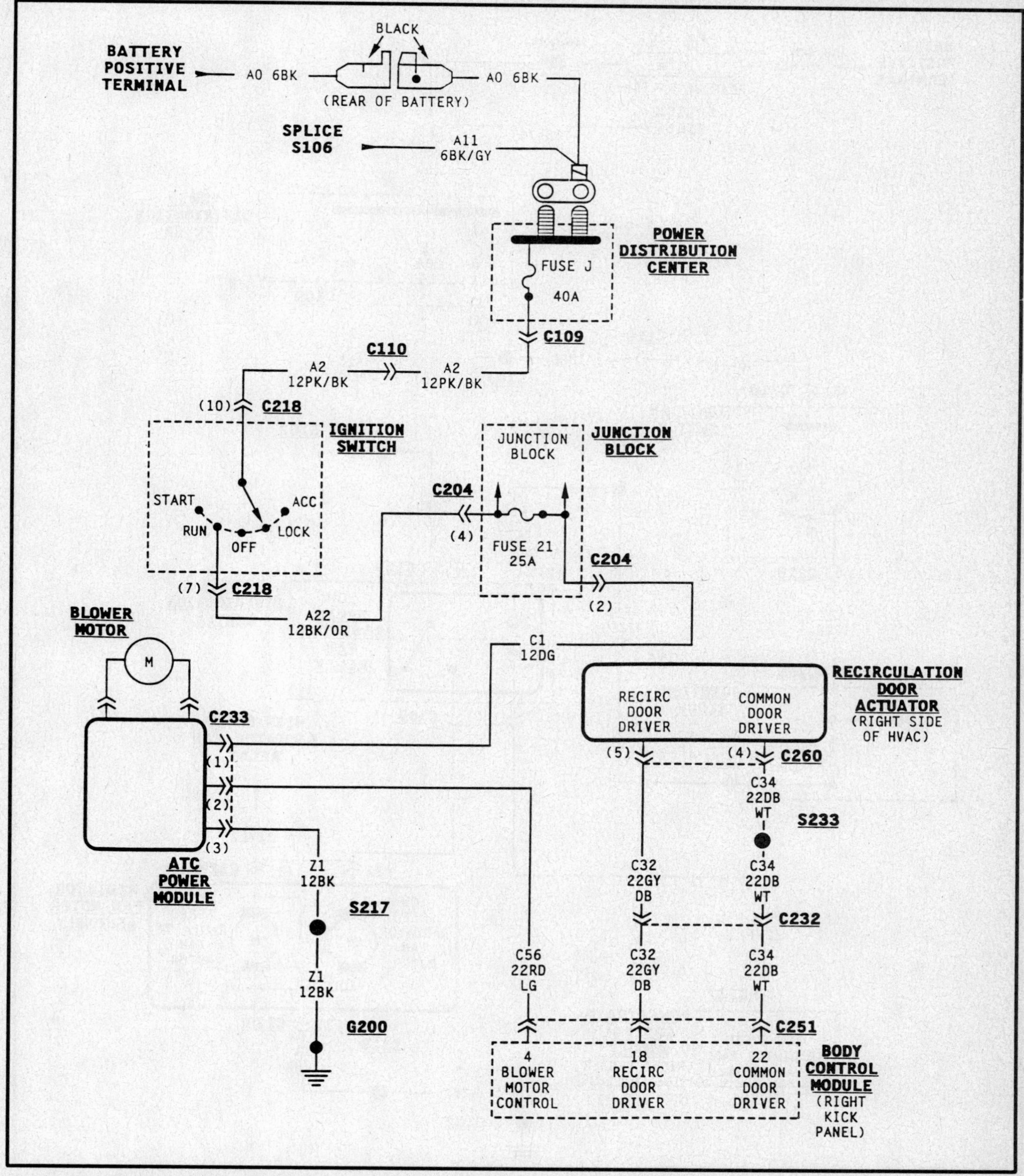

Concorde, Intrepid, LHS, New Yorker and Vision with air conditioning/heater with ATC only, Cont'd

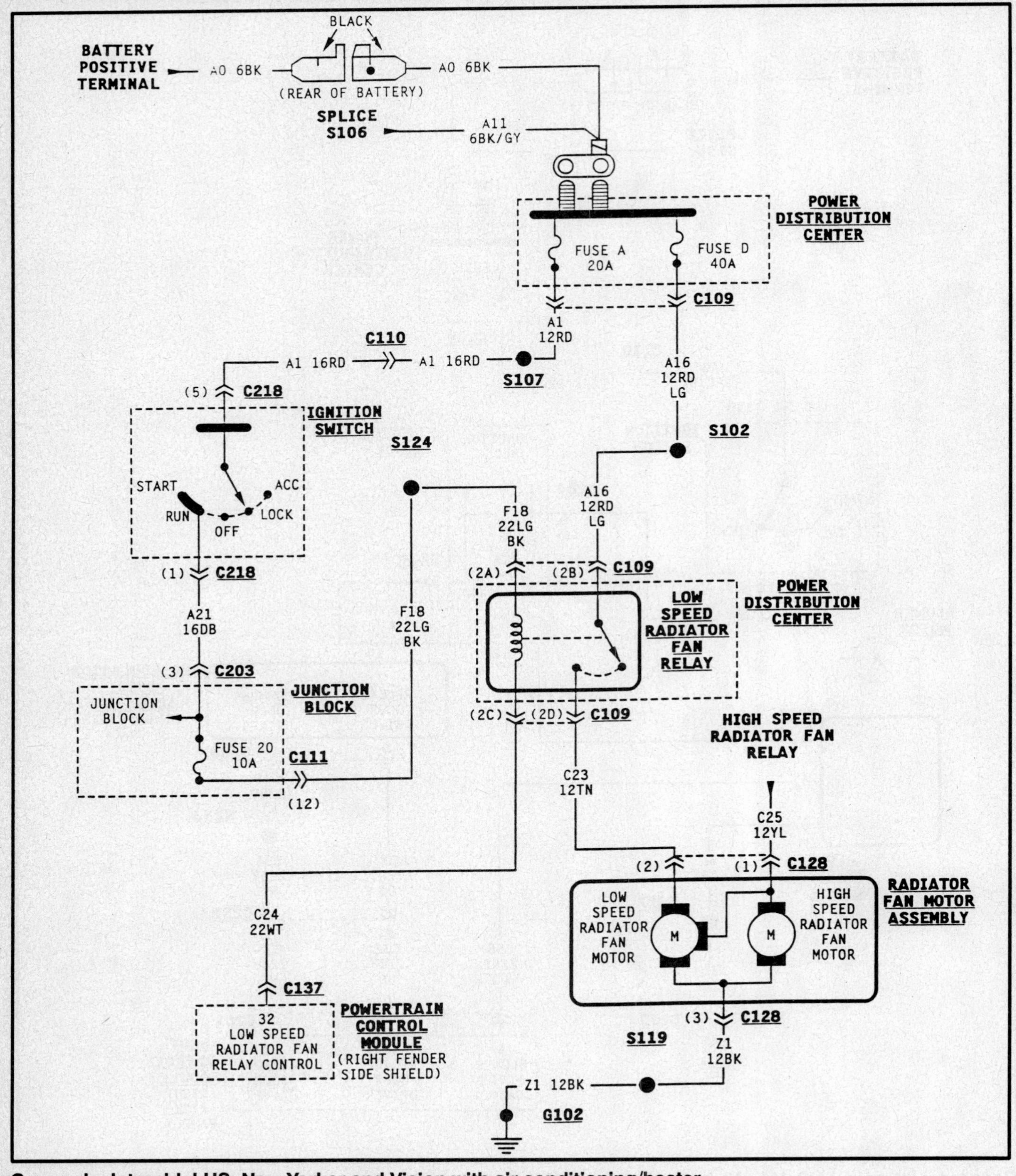
BLACK
BATTERY POSITIVE TERMINAL
A0 6BK
A0 6BK
(REAR OF BATTERY)
SPLICE S106
A11 6BK/GY
POWER DISTRIBUTION CENTER
FUSE A 20A
FUSE D 40A
C109
A1 12RD
C110
A1 16RD
A1 16RD
S107
A16 12RD LG
(5) C218
IGNITION SWITCH
S102
S124
START
ACC
RUN
LOCK
OFF
F18 22LG BK
A16 12RD LG
(1) C218
(2A)
(2B) C109
A21 16DB
F18 22LG BK
POWER DISTRIBUTION CENTER
LOW SPEED RADIATOR FAN RELAY
(3) C203
JUNCTION BLOCK
JUNCTION BLOCK
FUSE 20 10A
C111
(12)
(2C)
(2D) C109
HIGH SPEED RADIATOR FAN RELAY
C23 12TN
C25 12YL
(2)
(1) C128
C24 22WT
LOW SPEED RADIATOR FAN MOTOR
M
M
HIGH SPEED RADIATOR FAN MOTOR
RADIATOR FAN MOTOR ASSEMBLY
C137
32 LOW SPEED RADIATOR FAN RELAY CONTROL
POWERTRAIN CONTROL MODULE (RIGHT FENDER SIDE SHIELD)
(3) C128
S119
Z1 12BK
Z1 12BK
G102

Concorde, Intrepid, LHS, New Yorker and Vision with air conditioning/heater

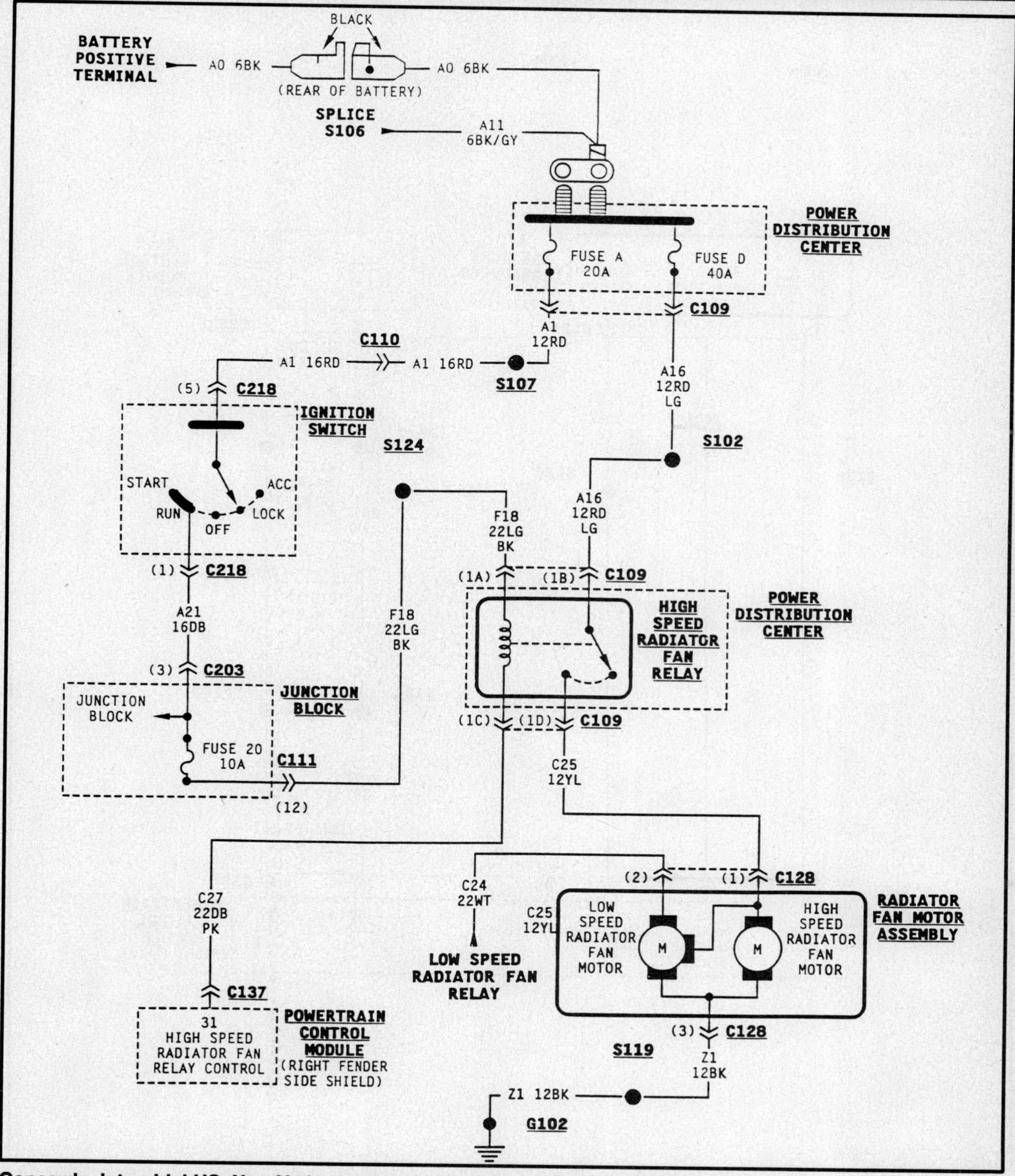

Concorde, Intrepid, LHS, New Yorker and Vision with air conditioning/heater, Cont'd

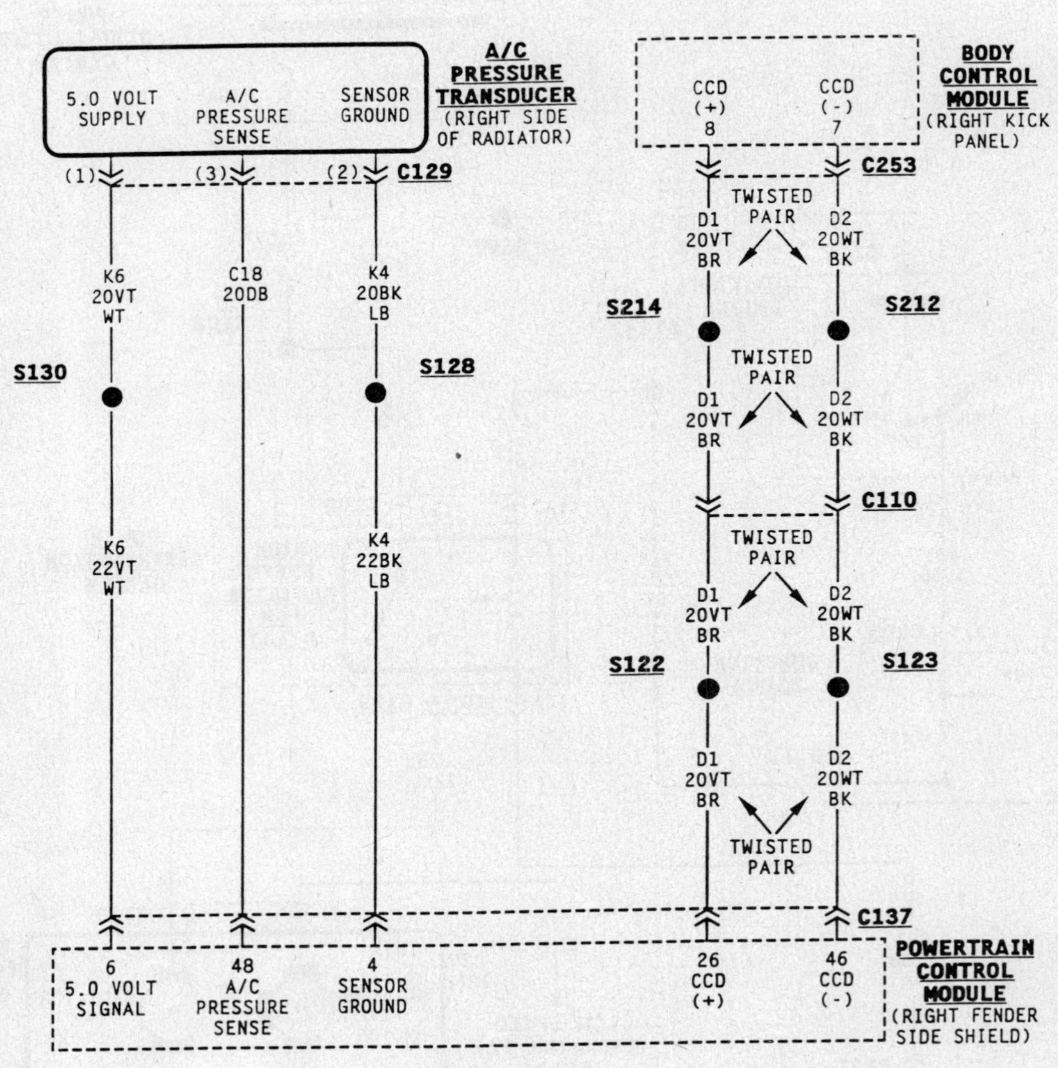

Concorde, Intrepid, LHS, New Yorker and Vision with air conditioning/heater, Cont'd

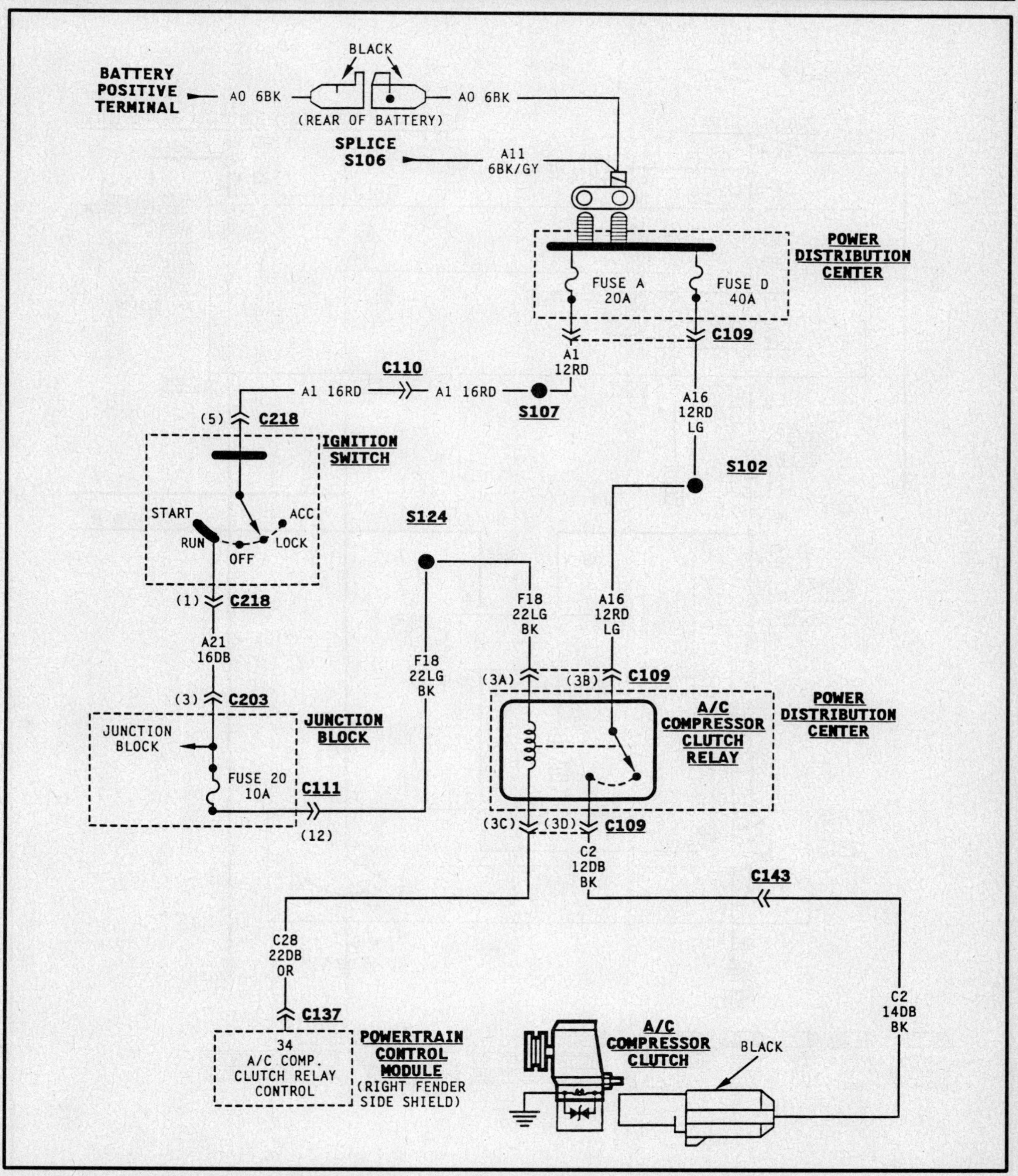

Concorde, Intrepid, LHS, New Yorker and Vision with air conditioning/heater, Cont'd

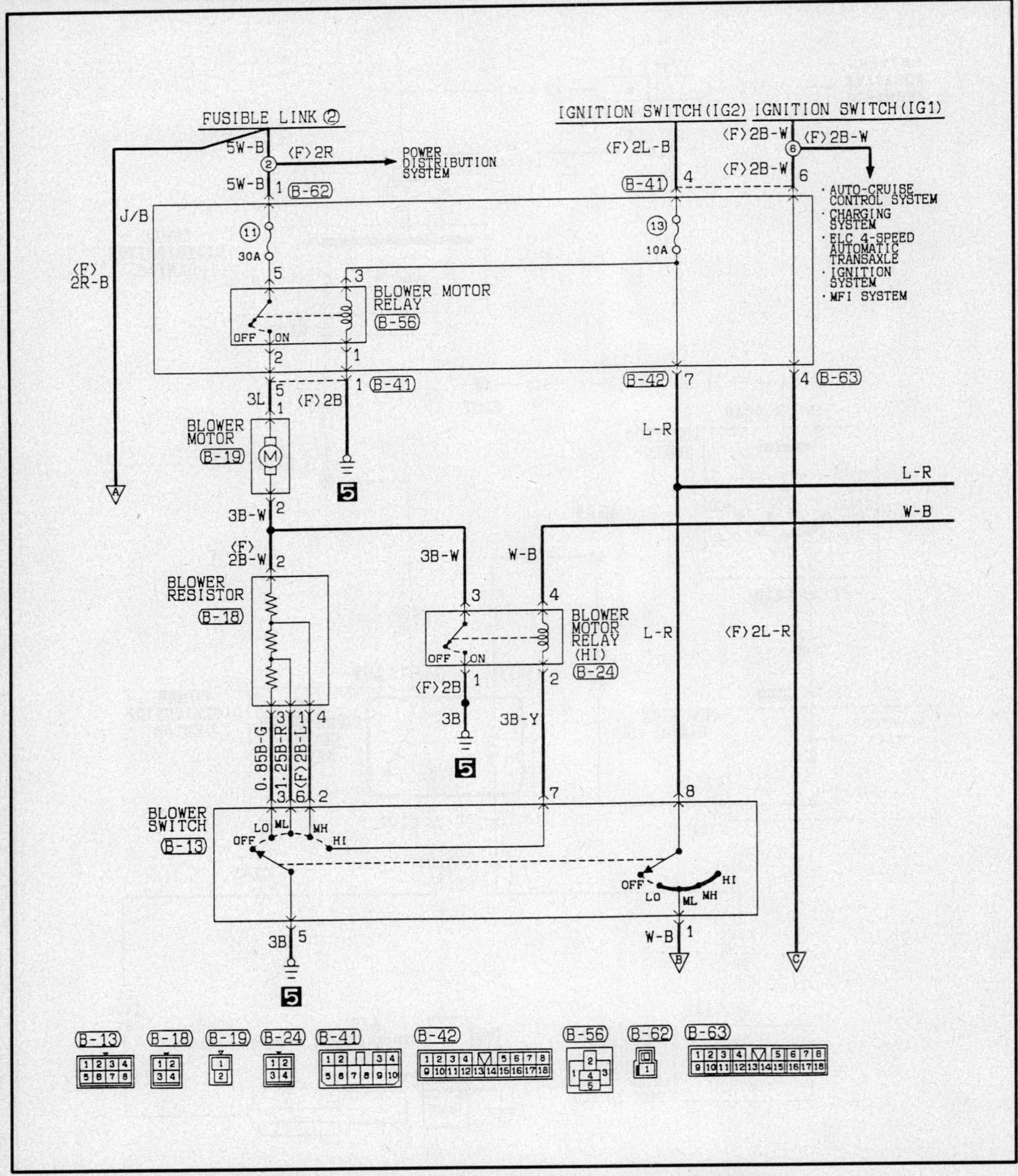

Avenger and Sebring with air conditioning—DOHC engine with manual transmission

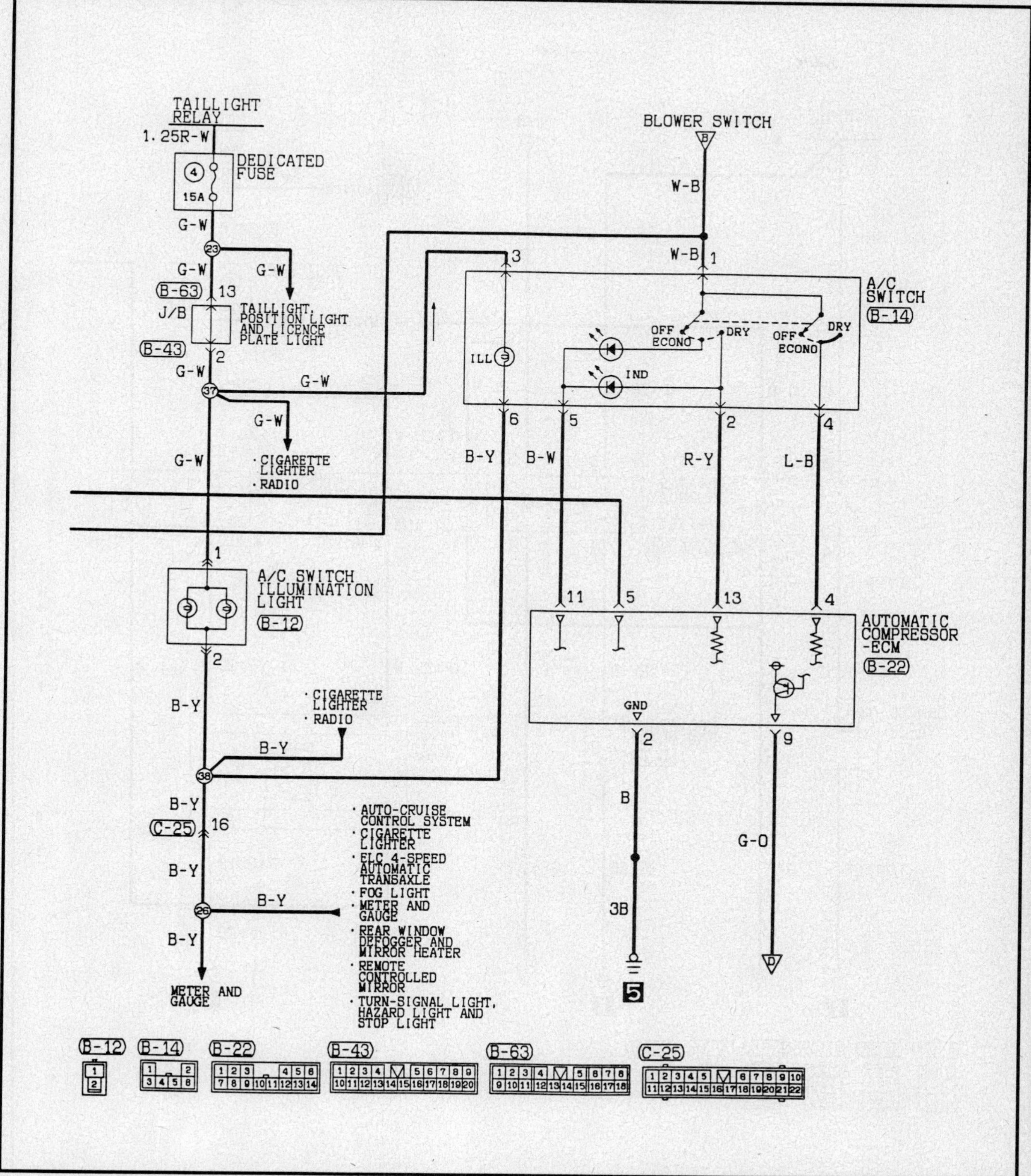

Avenger and Sebring with air conditioning—DOHC engine with manual transmission, Cont'd

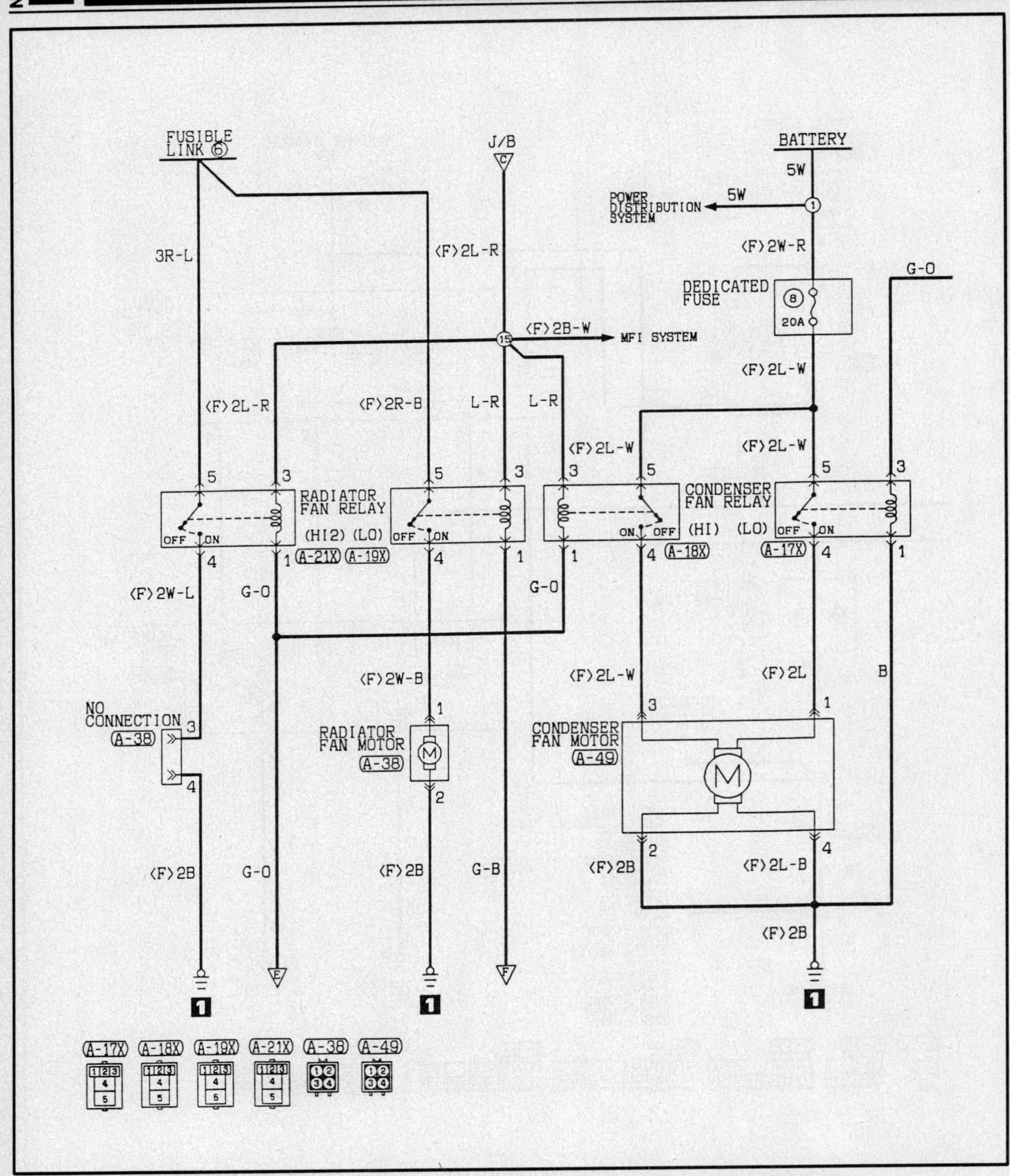

Avenger and Sebring with air conditioning—DOHC engine with manual transmission, Cont'd

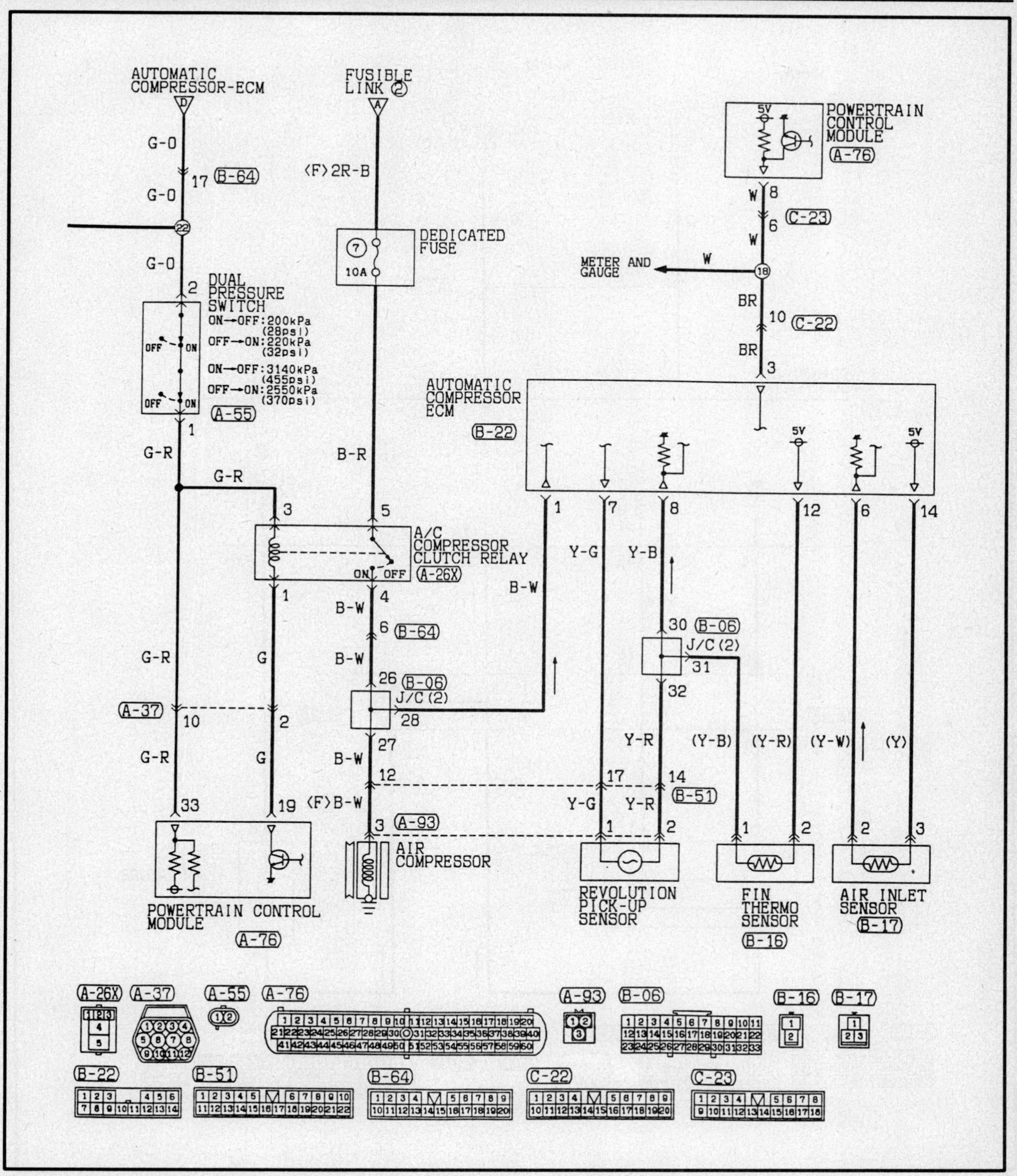

Avenger and Sebring with air conditioning—DOHC engine with manual transmission, Cont'd

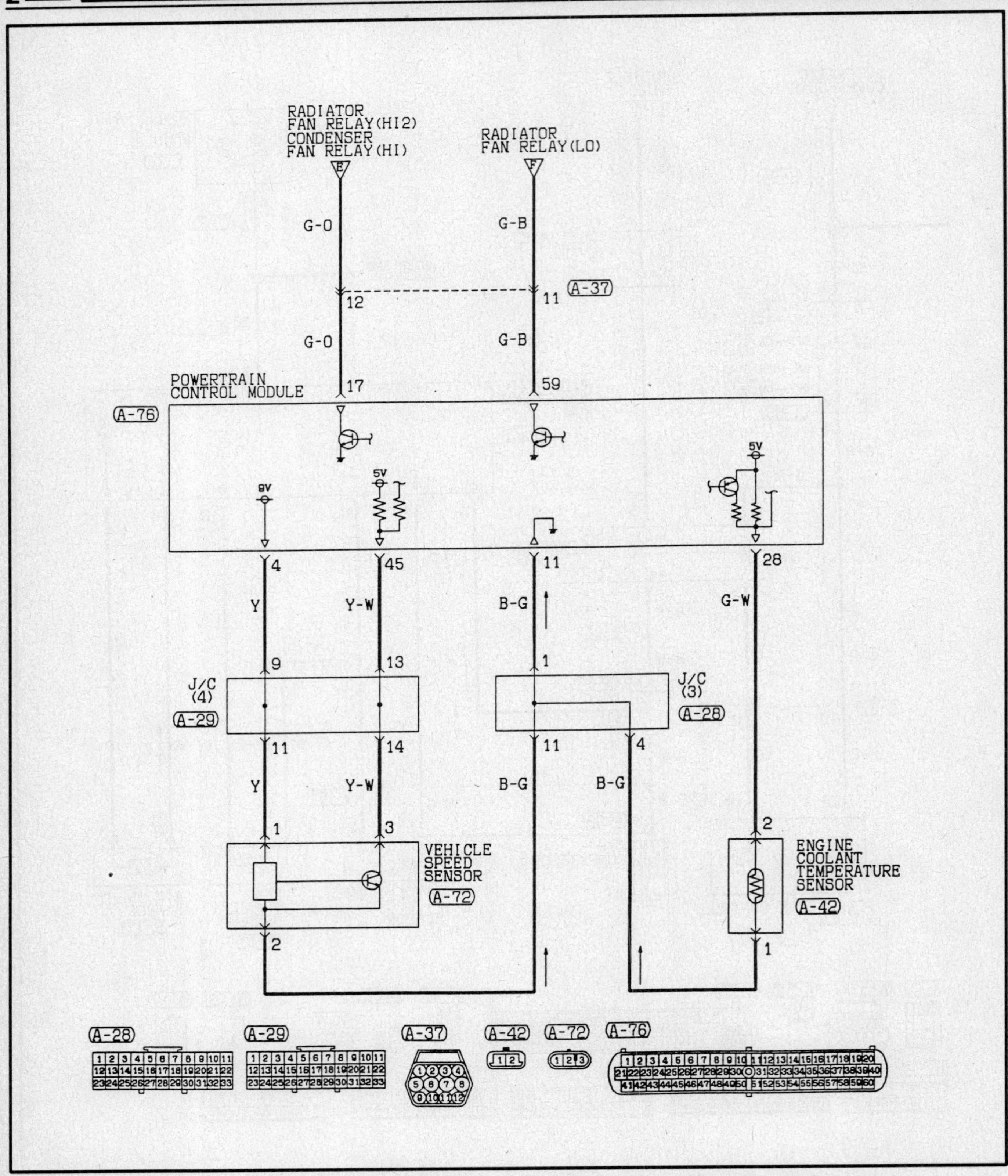

Avenger and Sebring with air conditioning—DOHC engine with manual transmission, Cont'd

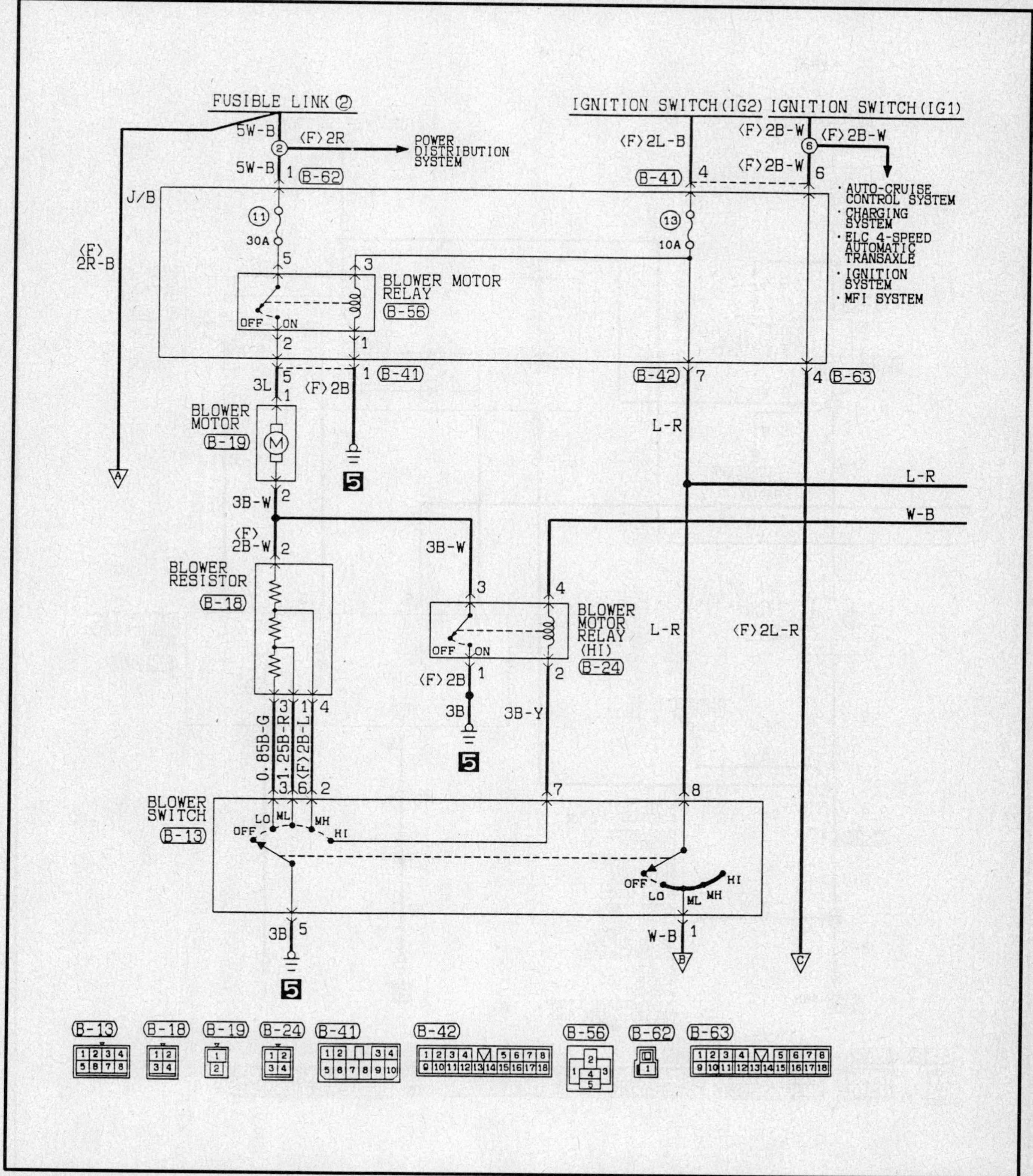

Avenger and Sebring with air conditioning—DOHC engine with automatic transmission

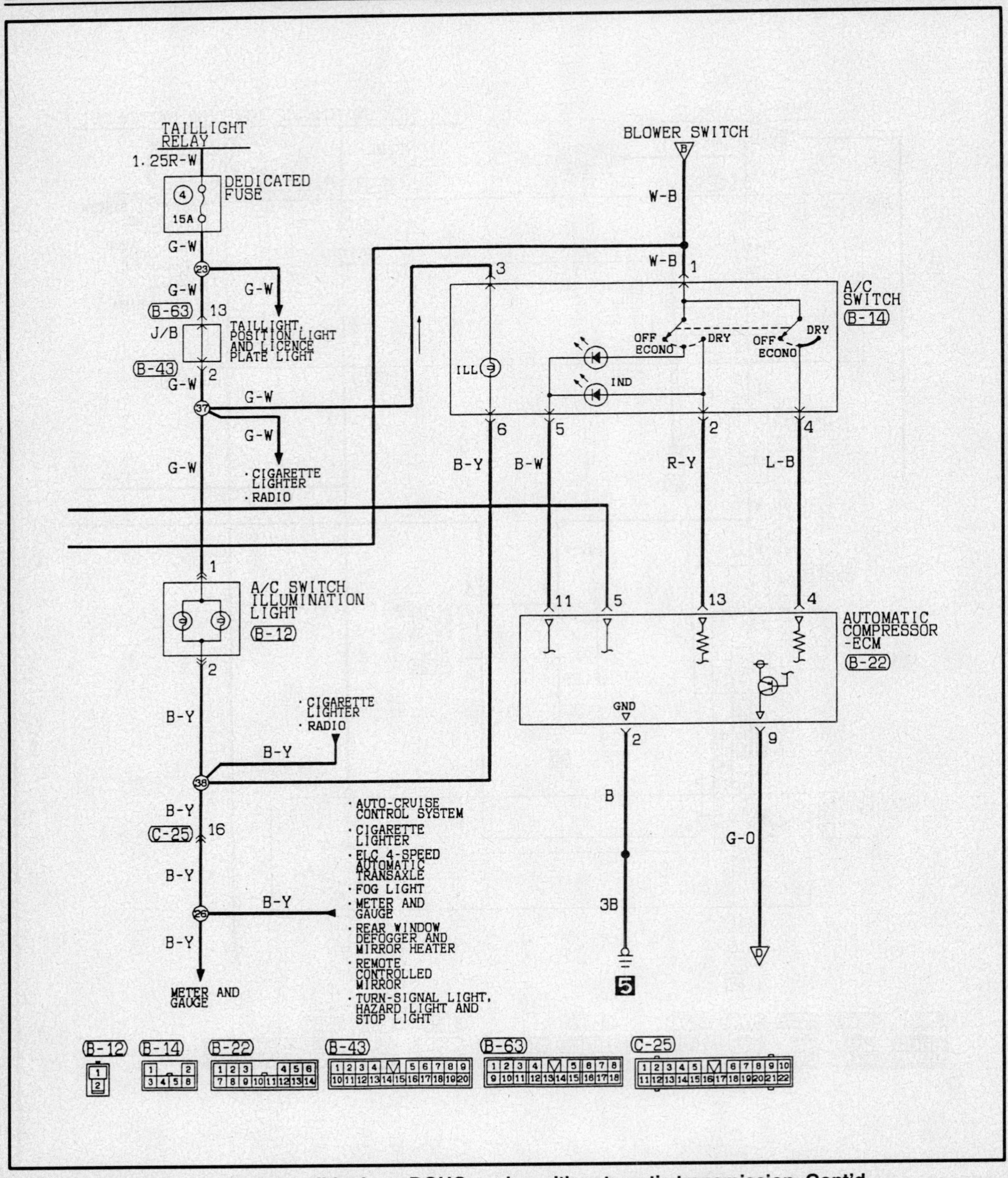

Avenger and Sebring with air conditioning—DOHC engine with automatic transmission, Cont'd

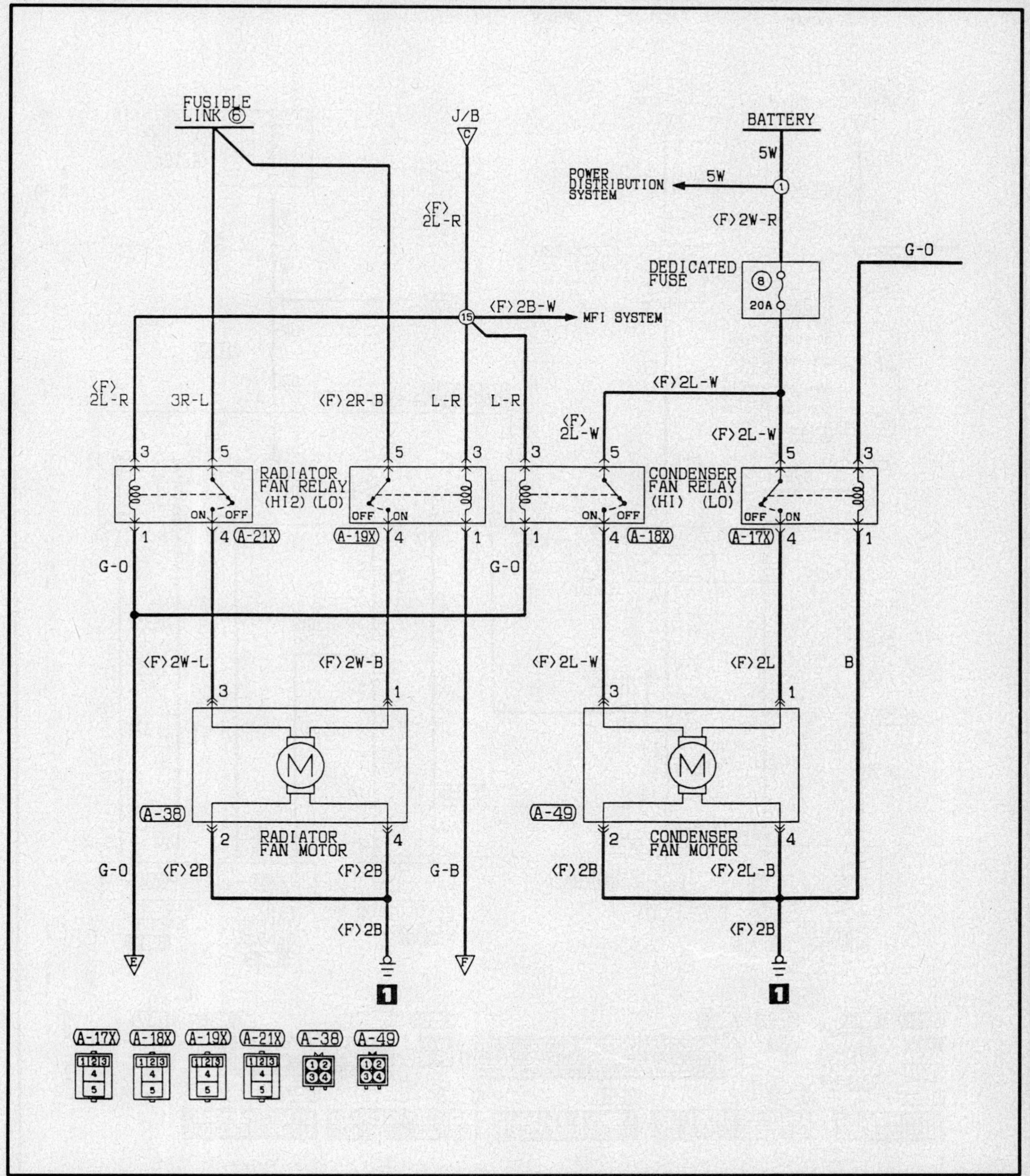

Avenger and Sebring with air conditioning—DOHC engine with automatic transmission, Cont'd

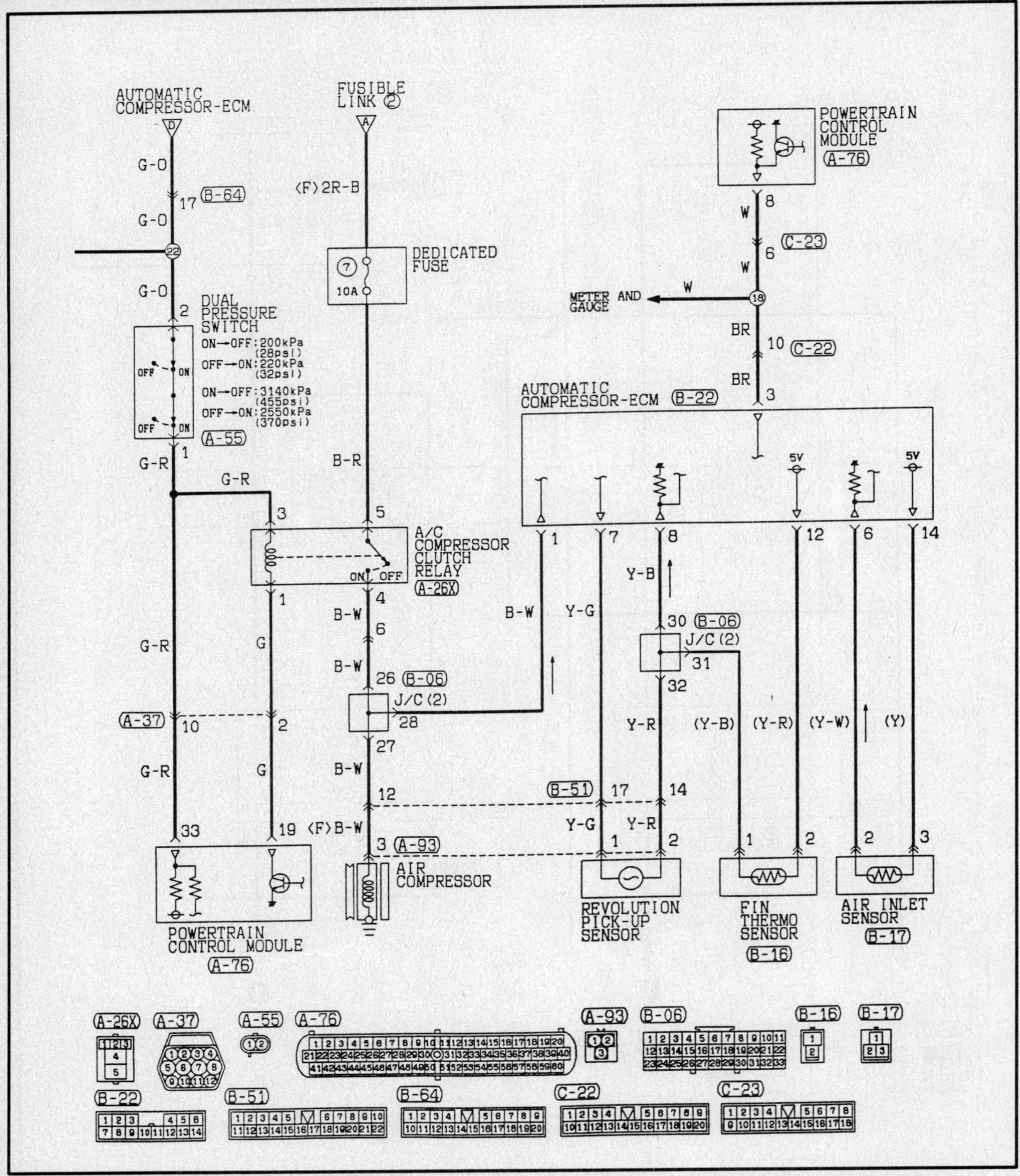

Avenger and Sebring with air conditioning—DOHC engine with automatic transmission, Cont'd

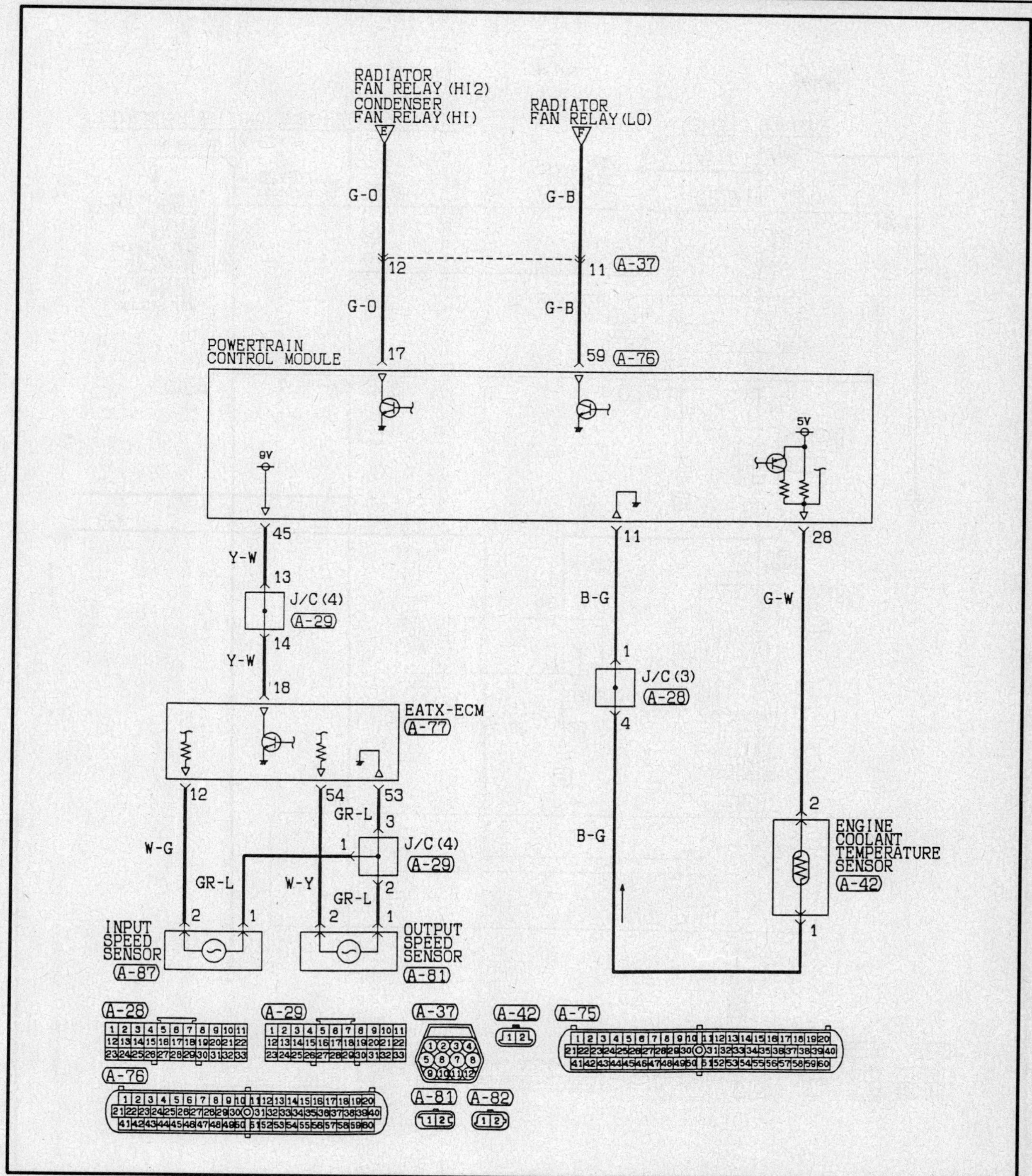

Avenger and Sebring with air conditioning—DOHC engine with automatic transmission, Cont'd

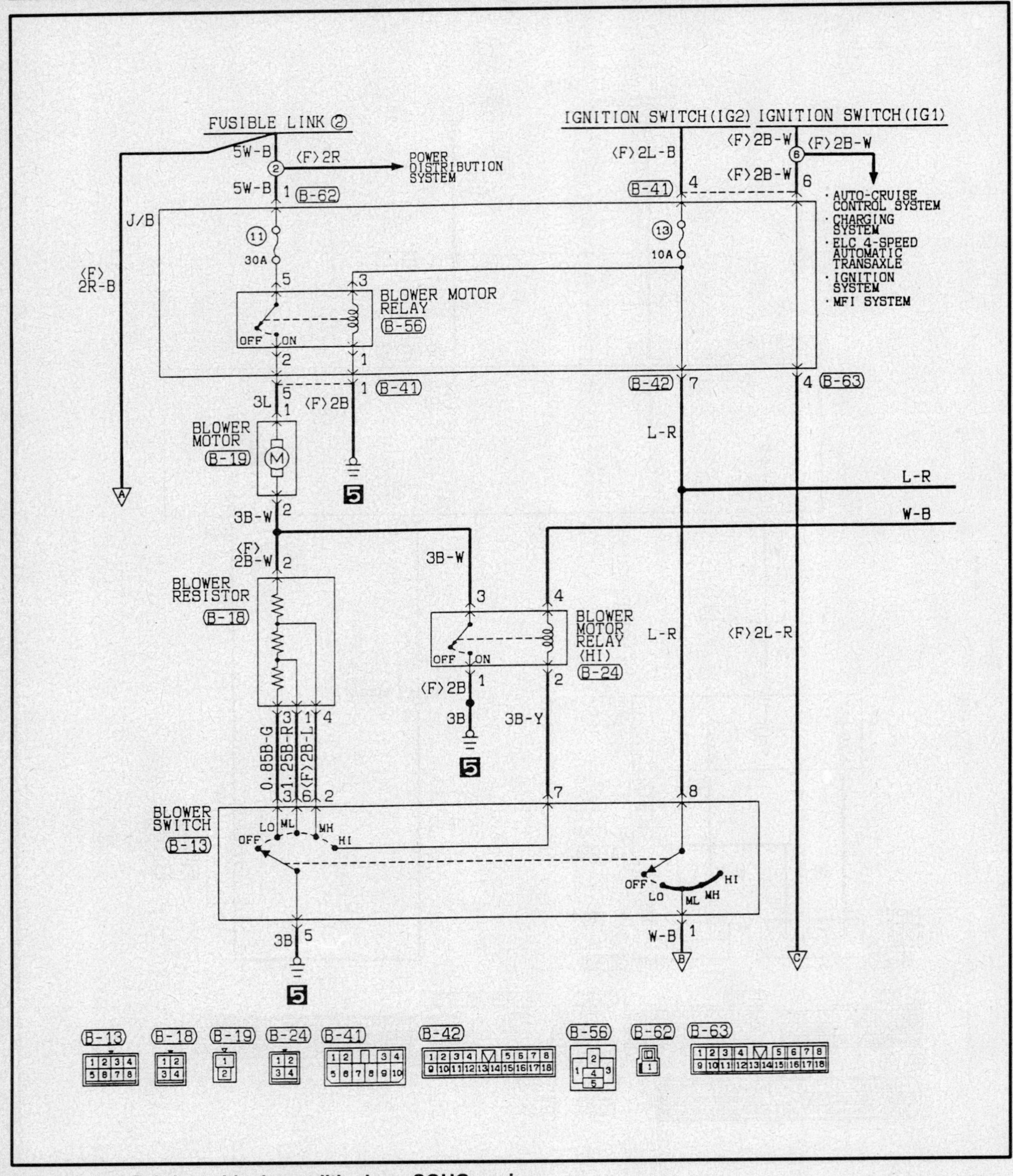

Avenger and Sebring with air conditioning—SOHC engine

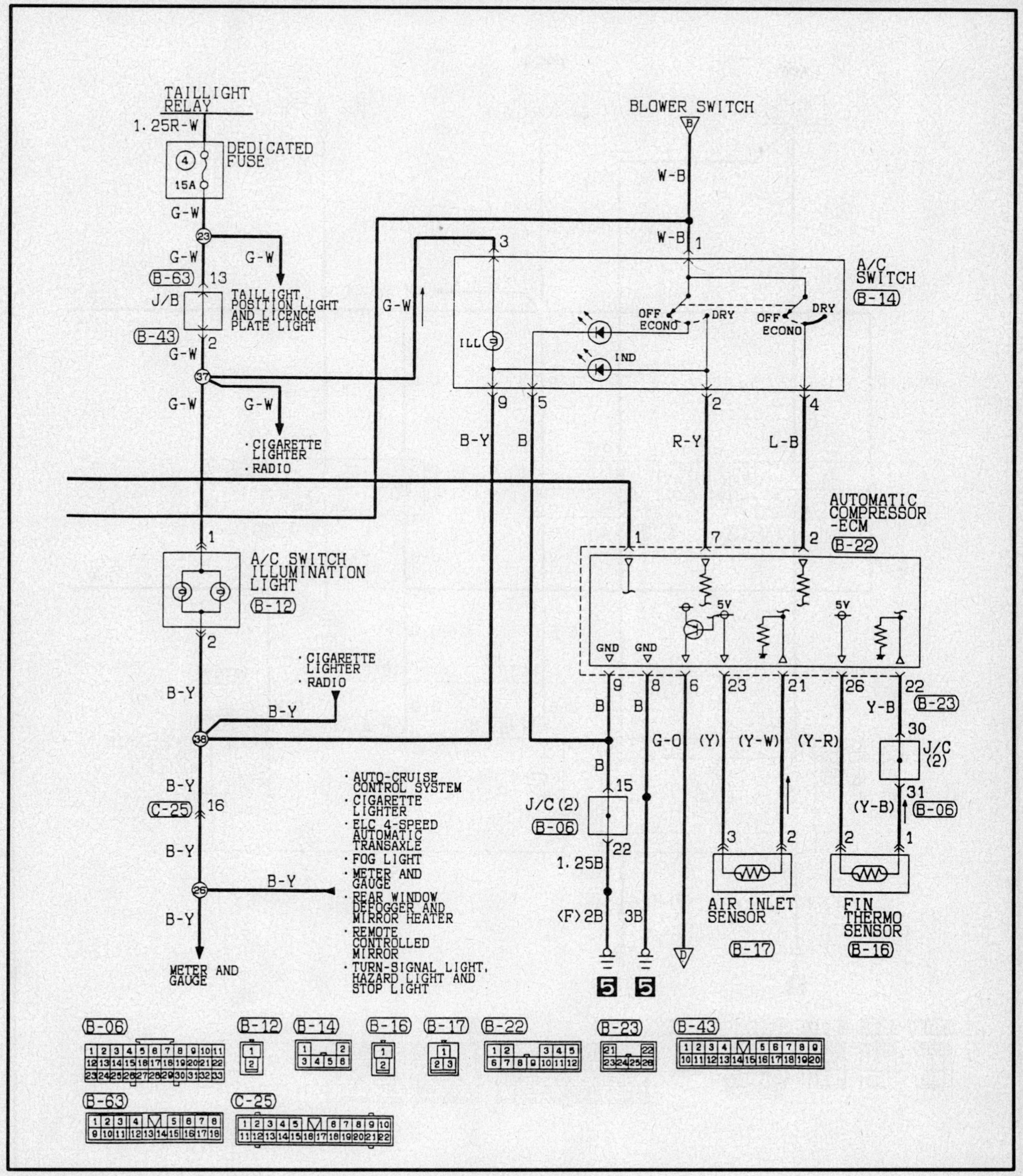

Avenger and Sebring with air conditioning—SOHC engine, Cont'd

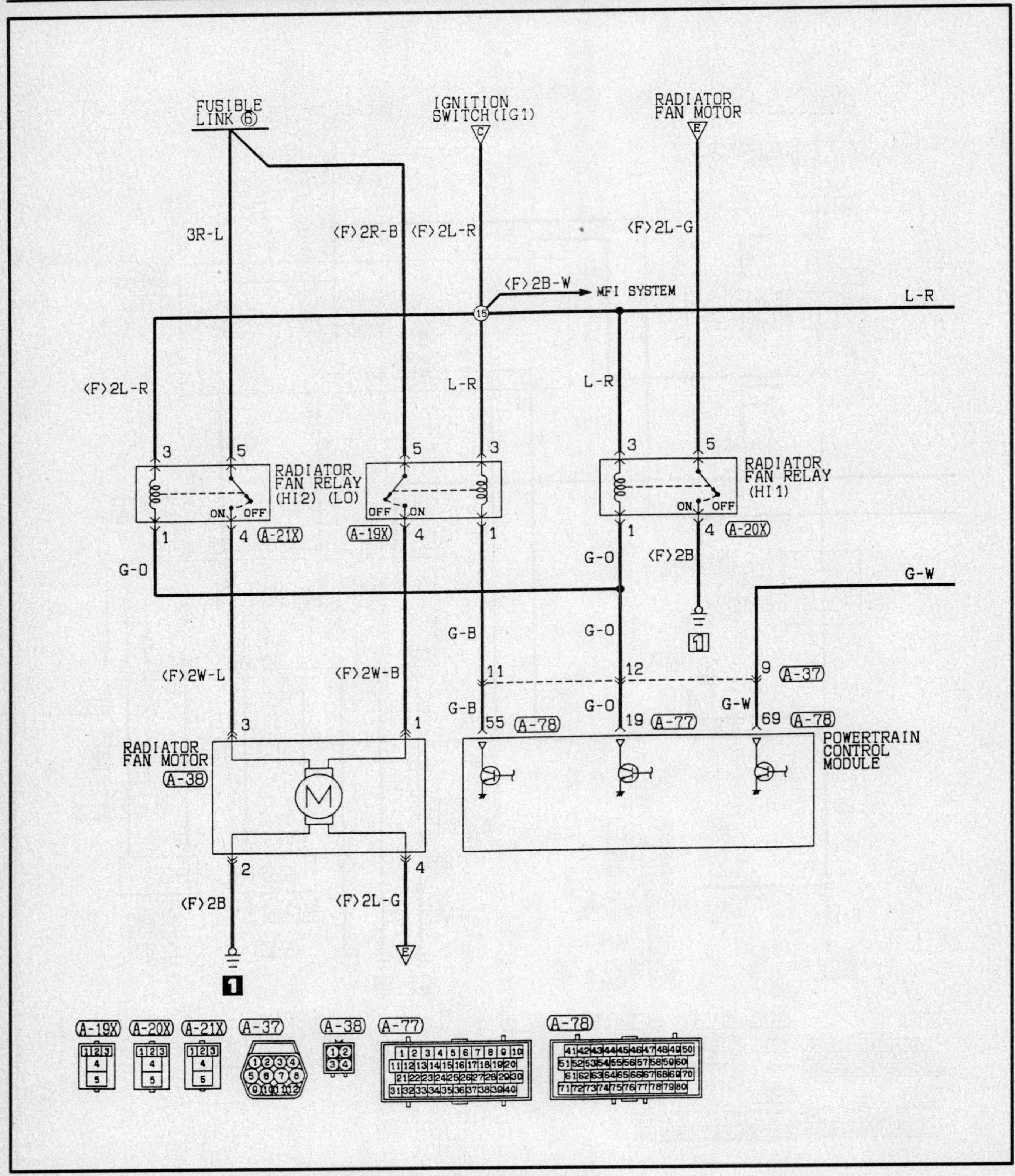

Avenger and Sebring with air conditioning—SOHC engine, Cont'd

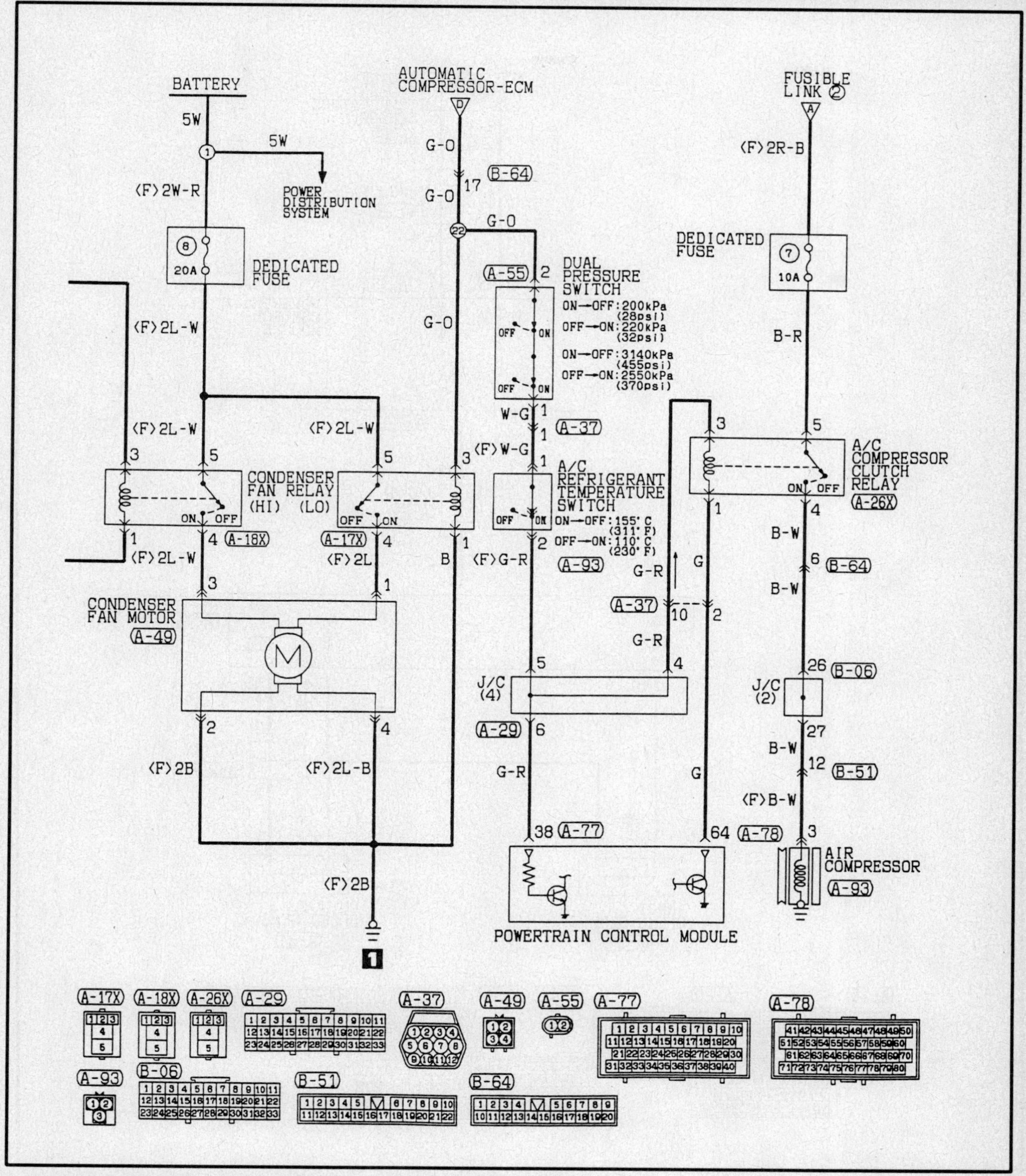

Avenger and Sebring with air conditioning—SOHC engine, Cont'd

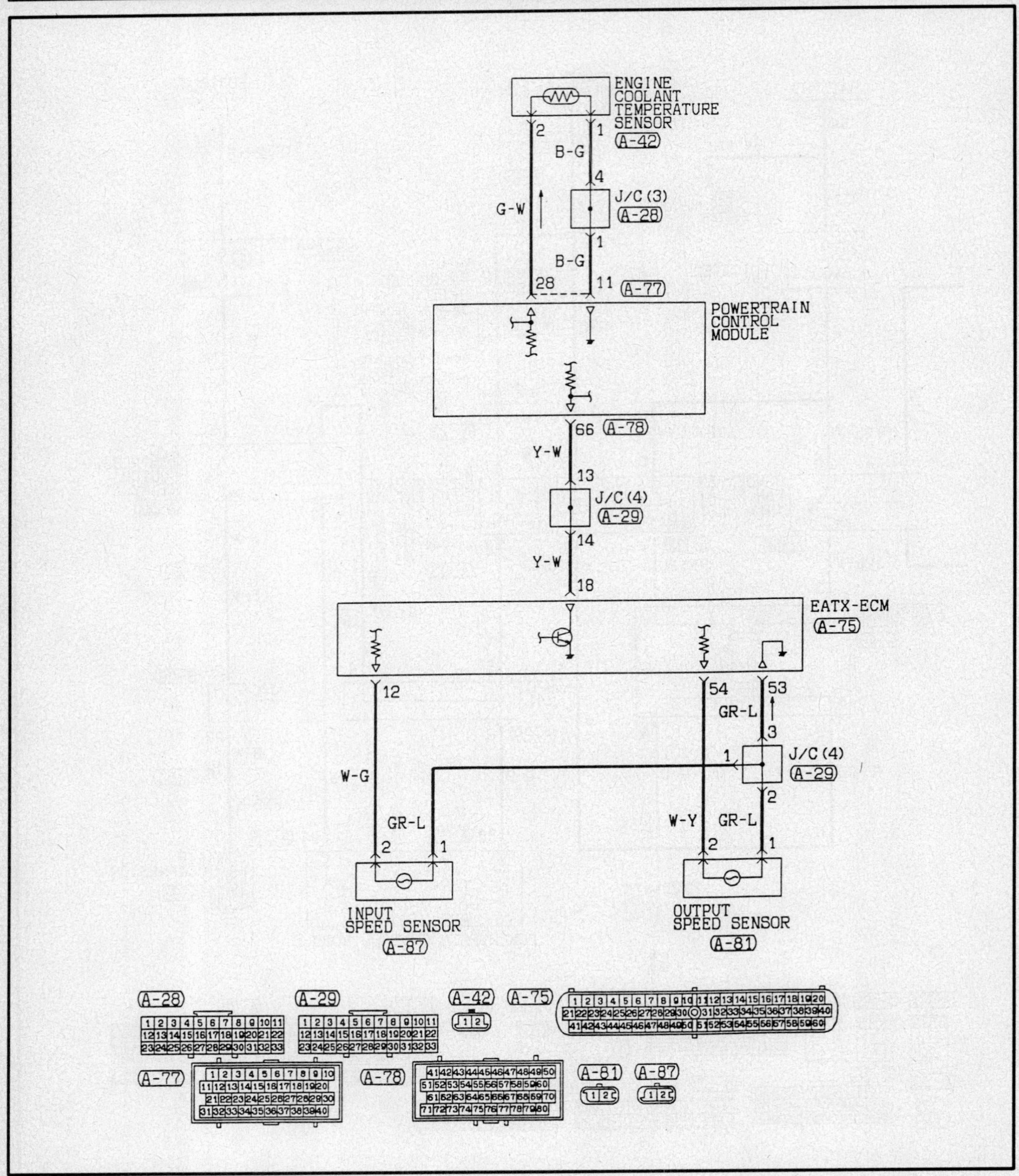

Avenger and Sebring with air conditioning—SOHC engine, Cont'd

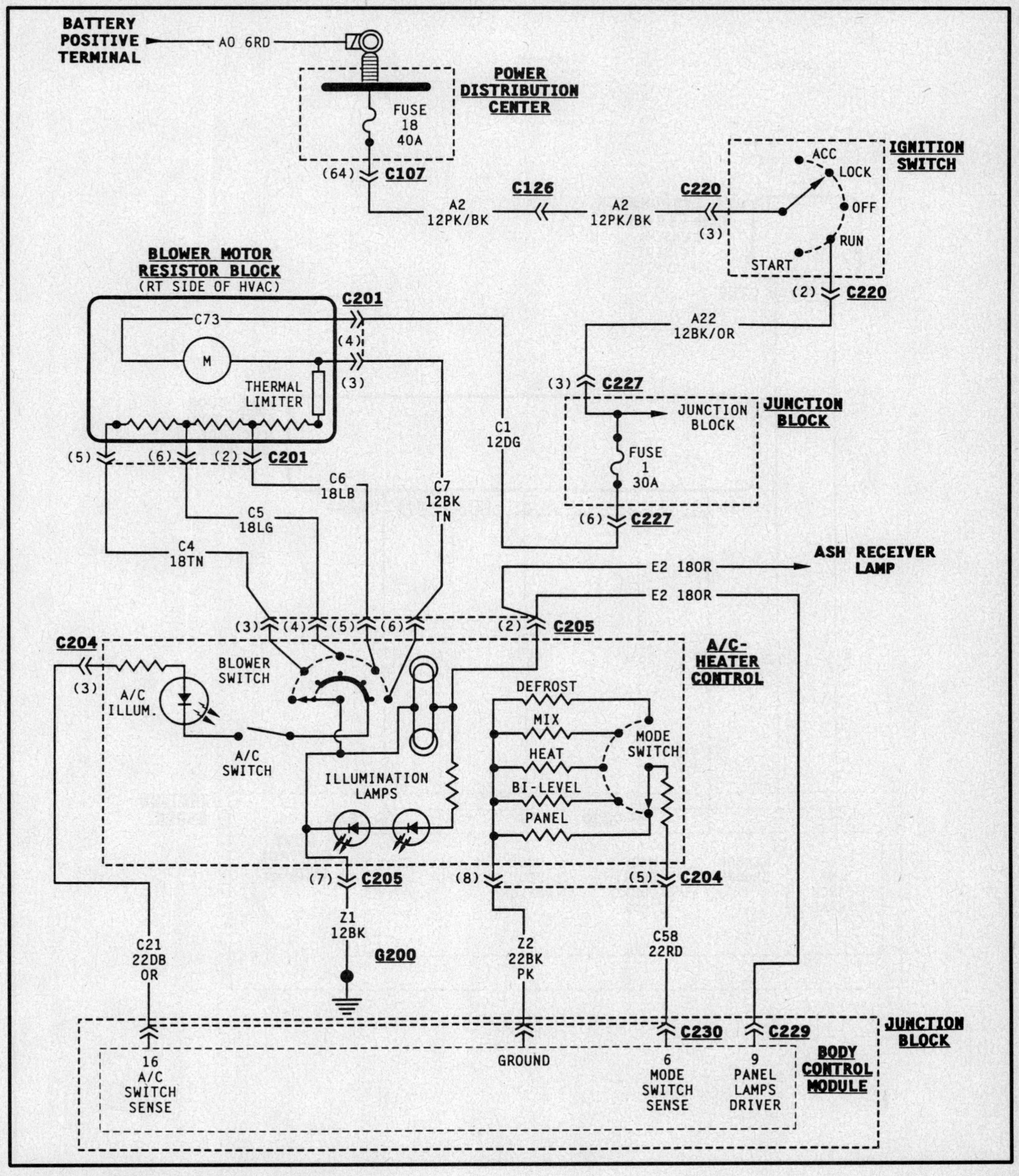

Cirrus and Stratus with air conditioning

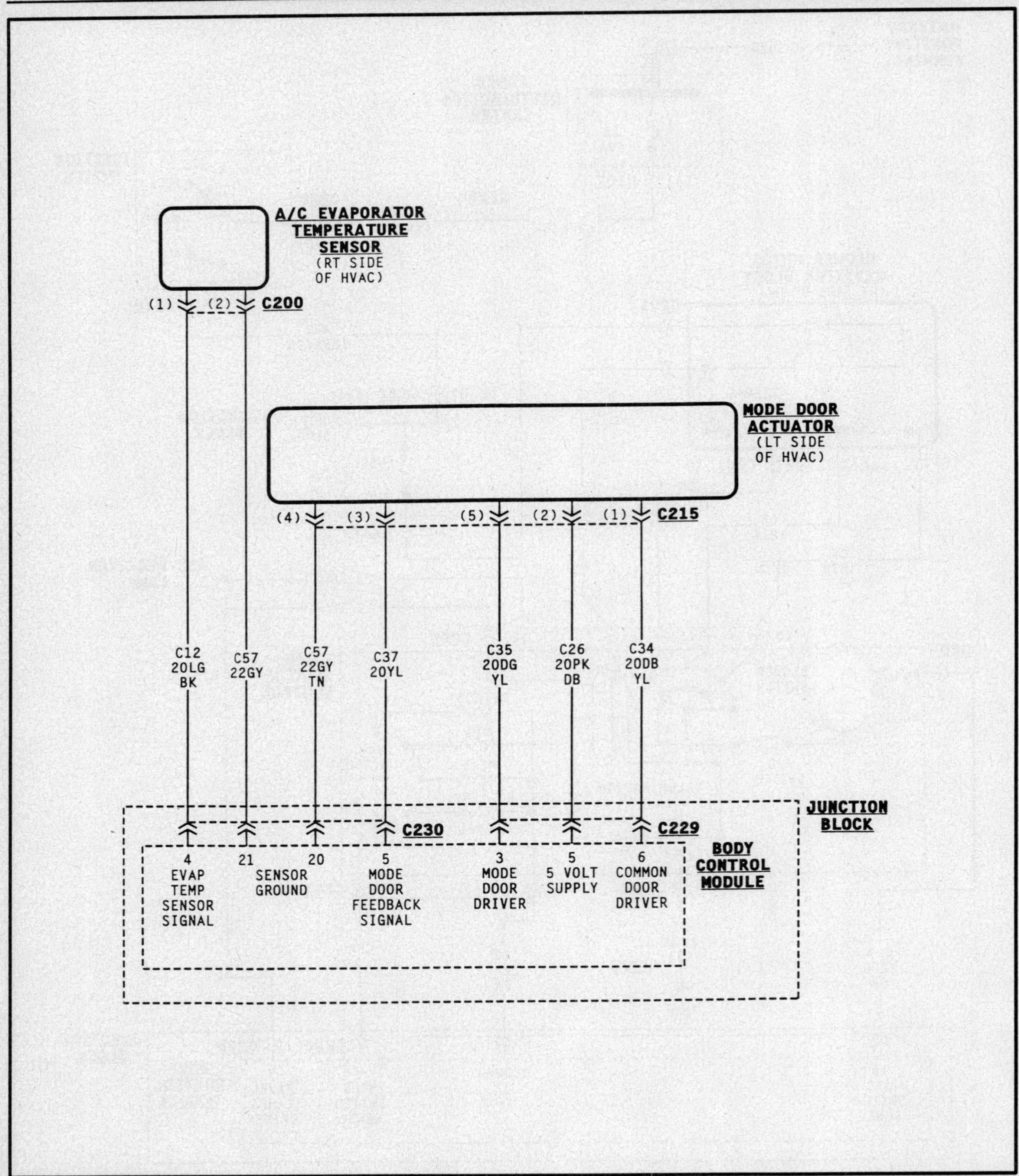

Cirrus and Stratus with air conditioning, Cont'd

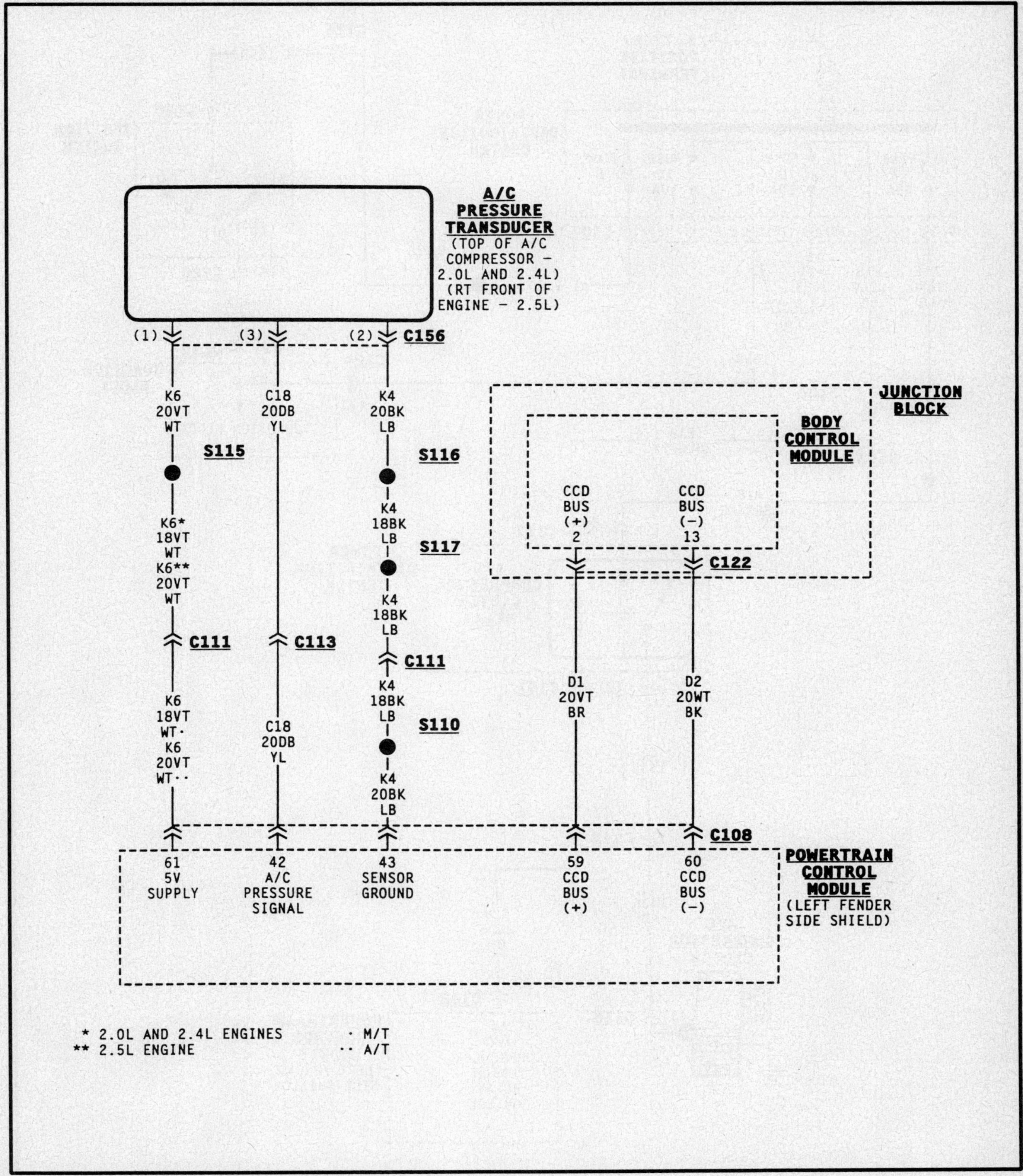

Cirrus and Stratus with air conditioning, Cont'd

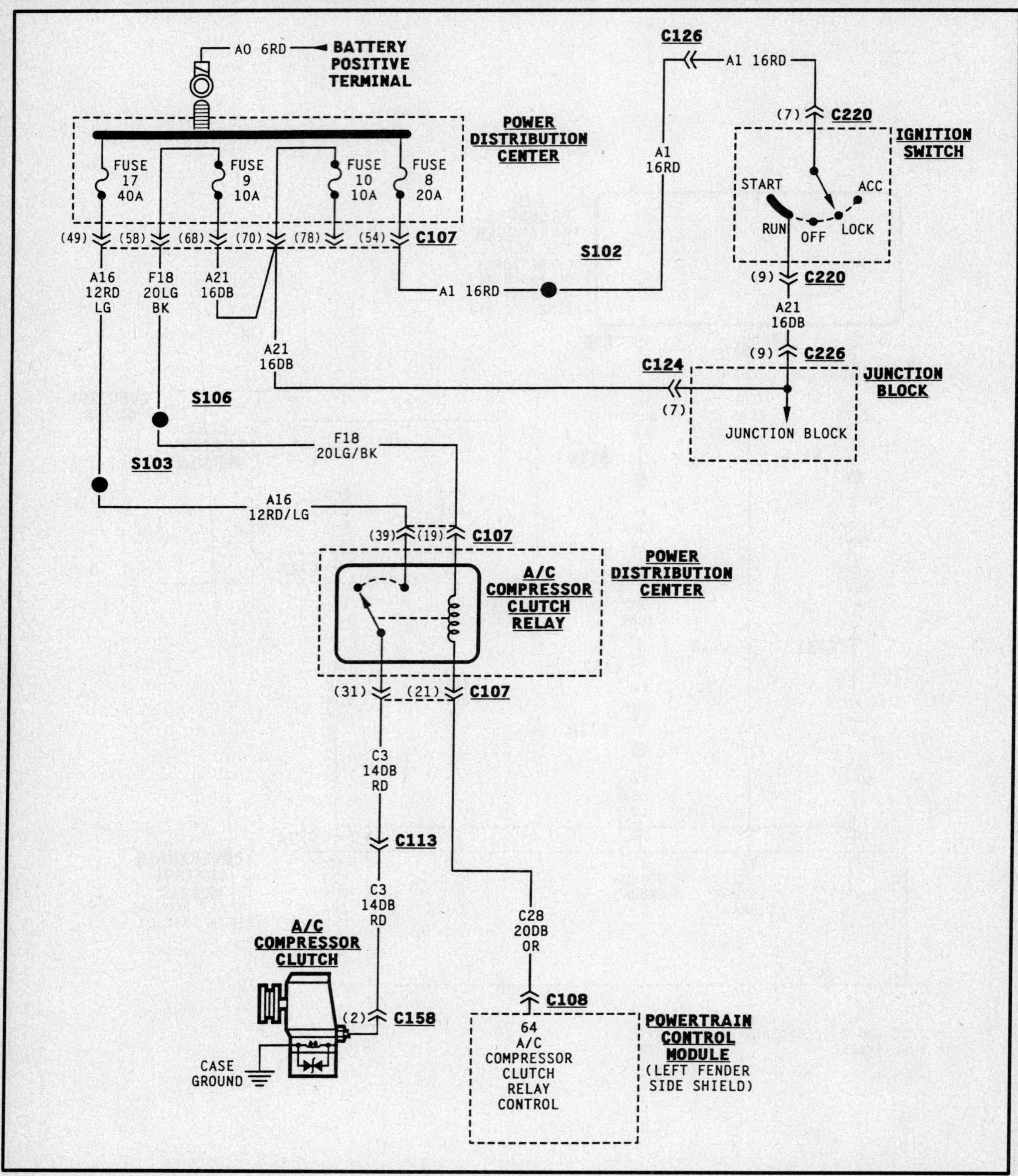

Cirrus and Stratus with air conditioning, Cont'd

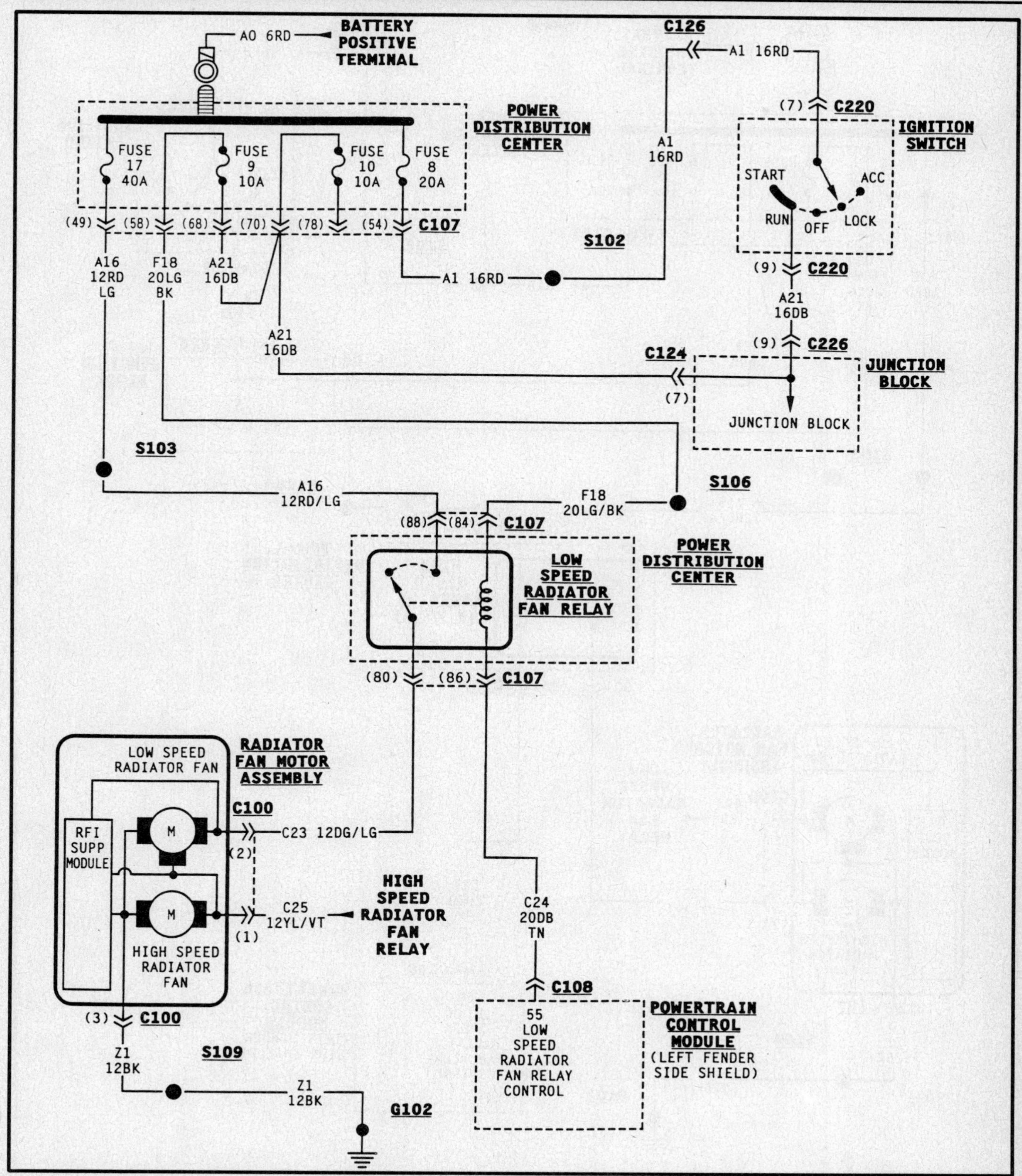

Cirrus and Stratus with air conditioning, Cont'd

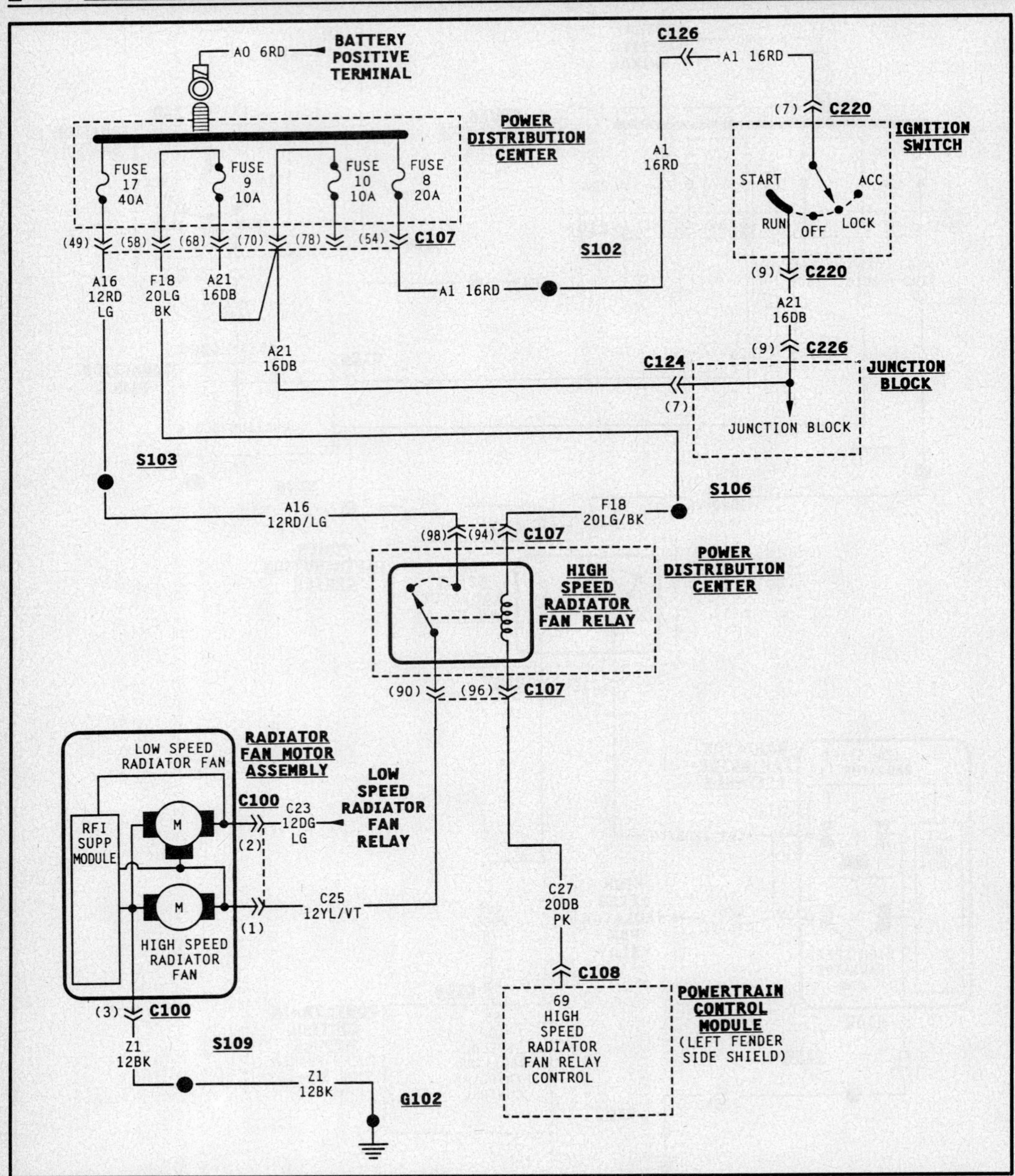

Cirrus and Stratus with air conditioning, Cont'd

3 CHRYSLER CORPORATION 3

CARAVAN • DAKOTA • PICK-UP • RAMCHARGER • TOWN & COUNTRY • VAN • VOYAGER

SPECIFICATIONS

ENGINE IDENTIFICATION

Year	Model	Engine Displacement Liters (cc)	Engine Series (ID/VIN)	Fuel System	No. of Cylinders	Engine Type
1993	Caravan	2.5 (2507)	K	TBI	4	OHC
	Voyager	2.5 (2507)	K	TBI	4	OHC
	Caravan	3.0 (2966)	3	MPI	6	OHC
	Voyager	3.0 (2966)	3	MPI	6	OHC
	Caravan	3.3 (3294)	R	MPI	6	OHC
	Voyager	3.3 (3294)	R	MPI	6	OHC
	Town & Country	3.3 (3294)	R	MPI	6	OHC
	Dakota	2.5 (2507)	K	TBI	4	OHC
	Dakota	3.9 (3824)	X	MPI	6	OHC
	Dakota	5.2 (5088)	Y	MPI	8	OHV
	Pick-Up	3.9 (3824)	X	MPI	6	OHV
	Ramcharger	3.9 (3824)	X	MPI	6	OHV
	Pick-Up	5.2 (5088)	Y	MPI	8	OHV
	Ramcharger	5.2 (5088)	Y	MPI	8	OHV
	Pick-Up	5.9 (5760)	Z	MPI	8	OHV
	Ramcharger	5.9 (5760)	Z	MPI	8	OHV
	Pick-Up	5.9 (5760)	5	MPI	8	OHV (HDC)
	Ramcharger	5.9 (5760)	5	MPI	8	OHV (HDC)
	Pick-Up	5.9 (5760)	8	MPI	8	OHV
	Ramcharger	5.9 (5760)	8	MPI	8	OHV
	Van	3.9 (3824)	X	MPI	6	OHV
	Van	5.2 (5088)	Y	MPI	8	OHV
	Van	5.9 (5760)	Z	MPI	8	OHV
1994	Caravan	2.5 (2507)	K	TBI	4	OHC
	Voyager	2.5 (2507)	K	TBI	4	OHC
	Caravan	3.0 (2966)	3	MFI	6	OHC
	Voyager	3.0 (2966)	3	MFI	6	OHC
	Caravan	3.3 (3294)	R	MFI	6	OHC
	Voyager	3.3 (3294)	R	MFI	6	OHC
	Town & Country	3.3 (3294)	R	MFI	6	OHC
	Dakota	2.5 (2507)	K	TBI	4	OHC
	Dakota	3.9 (3824)	X	MFI	6	OHC
	Dakota	5.2 (5088)	Y	MFI	8	OHV
	Pick-Up	3.9 (3824)	X	TBI	6	OHV
	Pick-Up	5.2 (5088)	Y	MFI	8	OHV
	Pick-Up	5.9 (5760)	Z	MFI	8	OHV
	Pick-Up	5.9 (5760)	5	MFI	8	OHV (HDC)
	Pick-Up	8.0 (7994)	W	MFI	10	OHV (HDC)

ENGINE IDENTIFICATION

Year	Model	Engine Displacement Liters (cc)	Engine Series (ID/VIN)	Fuel System	No. of Cylinders	Engine Type
1994	Pick-Up	5.9 (5760)	C	MFI	6	OHV ①
	Van	3.9 (3824)	X	MPI	6	OHV
	Van	5.2 (5088)	Y	MPI	8	OHV
	Van	5.2 (5088)	T	CNG	8	OHV
	Van	5.9 (5760)	A	MPI	8	OHV
1995	Caravan	2.5 (2507)	K	TBI	4	OHC
	Voyager	2.5 (2507)	K	TBI	4	OHC
	Caravan	3.0 (2966)	3	MPI	6	OHC
	Voyager	3.0 (2966)	3	MPI	6	OHC
	Caravan	3.3 (3294)	R	MPI	6	OHC
	Voyager	3.3 (3294)	R	MPI	6	OHC
	Town & Country	3.3 (3294)	R	MPI	6	OHC
	Dakota	2.5 (2507)	G	TBI	4	OHC
	Dakota	3.9 (3824)	X	MPI	6	OHC
	Dakota	5.2 (5088)	Y	MPI	8	OHV
	Pick-Up	3.9 (3824)	X	MPI	6	OHV
	Pick-Up	5.2 (5088)	Y	MPI	8	OHV
	Pick-Up	5.9 (5760)	Z	MPI	8	OHV (LDC)
	Pick-Up	5.9 (5760)	5	MBI	8	OHV (HDC)
	Pick-Up	8.0 (7994)	W	MBI	8	OHV (HDC)
	Pick-Up	5.9 (5760)	C	MPI	6	OHV ①
	Van	3.9 (3824)	X	MPI	6	OHV
	Van	5.2 (5088)	Y	MPI	8	OHV
	Van	5.2 (5088)	T	CNG	8	OHV
	Van	5.9 (5760)	Z	TBI	8	OHV

OHC–Overhead Cam
OHV–Overhead Valves
TBI–Throttle Body Injection
MPI–Multi-Point Injection
CNG–Compressed Natural Gas
LDC–Light Duty Cycle
HDC–Heavy Duty Cycle
① Turbo Diesel

REFRIGERANT CAPACITIES

Year	Model	Refrigerant (oz.)	Oil (fl. oz.)	Compressor Type
1993	Caravan	36 ② ③	7.4 ③	Fixed Displacement
	Voyager	36 ② ③	7.4 ③	Fixed Displacement
	Town & Country	36 ② ③	7.4 ③	Fixed Displacement
	Dakota	44	4.6	Fixed Displacement

REFRIGERANT CAPACITIES

Year	Model	Refrigerant (oz.)	Oil (fl. oz.)	Compressor Type
1993	Pick-Up	44	4.6	Fixed Displacement
	Ramcharger	44	4.6	Fixed Displacement
	Van	45 ①	7.25	Fixed Displacement
1994	Caravan	36 ② ③	7.25	Fixed Displacement
	Voyager	36 ② ③	7.25	Fixed Displacement
	Caravan	36 ② ③	8.7	Fixed Displacement
	Voyager	36 ② ③	8.7	Fixed Displacement
	Town & Country	36 ② ③	8.7	Fixed Displacement
	Dakota	40	7.25	Fixed Displacement
	Pick-Up	44	7.25	Fixed Displacement
	Van	45 ①	7.25	Fixed Displacement
1995	Caravan	36 ② ③		Fixed Displacement
	Voyager	36 ② ③		Fixed Displacement
	Caravan	36 ② ③	8.7	Fixed Displacement
	Voyager	36 ② ③	8.7	Fixed Displacement
	Town & Country	36 ② ③	8.7	Fixed Displacement
	Dakota	40	7.25	Fixed Displacement
	Pick-Up	44	7.25	Fixed Displacement
	Van	45 ①	7.25	Fixed Displacement

① With auxiliary rear system, capacity is 65 oz.
② With auxiliary rear system, capacity is 50 oz.
③ System uses R-134a refrigerant and special compressor oil only

AIR CONDITIONING BELT TENSION

Year	Model	Engine Liters	Belt Type	Specifications New (lbs.)	Specifications Used (lbs.)
1993	Caravan	2.5 & 3.0	V	125	80
	Voyager	2.5 & 3.0	V	125	80
	Caravan	3.3	Serpentine	①	①
	Voyager	3.3	Serpentine	①	①
	Town & Country	3.3	Serpentine	①	①
	Dakota	2.5	V	160	80
	Dakota	3.9 & 5.2	Serpentine	①	①
	Pick-Up	All	Serpentine	①	①
	Ramcharger	All	Serpentine	①	①
	Van	All	Serpentine	①	①
1994	Caravan	2.5 & 3.0	V	125	80
	Voyager	2.5 & 3.0	V	125	80
	Caravan	3.3	Serpentine	①	①
	Voyager	3.3	Serpentine	①	①

AIR CONDITIONING BELT TENSION

Year	Model	Engine Liters	Belt Type	Specifications New (lbs.)	Specifications Used (lbs.)
1994	Town & Country	3.3	Serpentine	①	①
	Dakota	2.5	V	160	80
	Dakota	3.9	Serpentine	①	①
	Dakota	5.2	Serpentine	①	①
	Pick-Up	exc. Diesel	Serpentine	①	①
	Pick-Up	Diesel	Serpentine	①	①
	Van	All	Serpentine	①	①
1995	Caravan	2.5 & 3.0	V	125	80
	Voyager	2.5 & 3.0	V	125	80
	Caravan	3.3	Serpentine	①	①
	Voyager	3.3	Serpentine	①	①
	Town & Country	3.3	Serpentine	①	①
	Dakota	2.5	V	160	80
	Dakota	3.9 & 5.2	Serpentine	①	①
	Pick-Up	5.9 gas	V	120	75
	Pick-Up	All other	Serpentine	①	①
	Van	5.9	Serpentine	①	①
	Van	3.9 & 5.2	Serpentine	①	①

① Automatic dynamic tensioner

SYSTEM DESCRIPTION

General Information

The air flow system pulls outside air through the cowl opening at the base of the windshield and into the plenum chamber above the heater/air conditioning housing. On air conditioned vehicles, the air passes through the evaporator, then is either directed through or around the heater core by adjusting the blend air door with the **TEMP** control on the control panel. The air flow can be directed from the panel, panel and floor (bi-level) or floor and defrost outlets. The volume of the flow is adjusted with the blower speed switch on the control panel.

On air conditioned vehicles, the intake of outside air can be shut off by moving the **TEMP** control knob to the **RECIRC** position or depressing the **MAX A/C** button, which closes the recirculation door and recirculates existing air inside the passenger compartment. Depressing the **DEFROST** or **A/C** button may engage the compressor and remove heat and humidity from the air before it is directed through or around the heater core. Forced ventilation is directed from the instrument panel and/or floor outlets when the selector on the control panel is on the panel or bi-level position. The temperature of the forced vent air can be regulated with the **TEMP** control knob.

On Caravan, Voyager, Town & Country and Dakota, the side window demisters receive air from the heater/air conditioning housing and direct the flow to the front windows. The outlets are located on the top outer corners of the instrument panel. The side demisters operate when the mode control selector is in the **FLOOR** or **DEFROST** setting.

WARNING: The 1993 Caravan, Voyager and Town & Country models use non-choloroflourocarbon refrigerant R-134a. It cannot be mixed, in any amount, with R-12. Never add R-12 to a system using R-134a or system failure will occur. Systems with R-134a also required a different type refrigerant oil to be used. Be sure to follow special handling and servicing information for R-134a in this article.

Service Valve Location

Except 1993 Caravan, Voyager and Town & Country

The discharge (high pressure) service port is a 1/4 in. fitting and is located either on the discharge line near the compressor or the high pressure liquid line near the condenser. The suction (low pressure) service port is a 3/8 in. fitting and is located either on the compressor or on the suction line between the expansion valve and the compressor.

1993 Caravan, Voyager and Town & Country

As this system is charged with R-134a refrigerant, special service valves are fitted to the system to ensure a standard R-12 service fitting cannot be hooked to the system. Both service ports are located on the high and low side hoses.

System Discharging

R-12 refrigerant is a chloroflourocarbon which, when mishandled, can contribute to the depletion of the ozone layer in the upper atmosphere. Ozone filters out harmful radiation from the sun. In order to protect the ozone layer, an approved R-12 Recovery/Recycling machine that meets SAE standard J1991 should be employed when discharging the system. Follow the operating instructions provided with the approved equipment exactly to properly discharge the system.

R-134a in a non-toxic, non-flammable, clear liquified gas which requires special handling procedures. Use and follow approved A/C recycling equipment instructions.

System Evacuating

If the air conditioning system has been opened to the atmosphere, it should be air and moisture free before being recharged with refrigerant. Moisture and air mixed with refrigerant will raise the compressor head pressure, possibly damage the system's components and will reduce the performance of the system. Moisture will boil at normal room temperature when exposed to a vacuum. To evacuate or rid the system of air and moisture:

1. Leak test the system and repair any leaks found.

CAUTION

R-134a service equipment or vehicle A/C system should not be pressure tested or leak tested with compressed air. Compressed air and R-134a mixture can be combustible under certain conditions and can result in injury or damage.

NOTE: A leak detector designed for R-12 type systems will not detect leaks in R-134a systems.

Special effort must be used to keep all R-134a system components capped to prevent moisture from getting into the system and mixing with the oil. It is very difficult to remove moisture adequately, and compressor problems may develop. If system is open for an extended time (due to leak, disconnected or broken part) it is recommended the system oil be drained and replaced to eliminate contamination problems.

2. Connect an approved charging station, recovery/recycling machine or manifold gauge set and vacuum pump to the discharge and suction ports. The red hose is normally connected to the discharge (high pressure) line and the blue hose is connected to the suction (low pressure) line.
3. Open the discharge and suction ports and start the vacuum pump. If the pump is not able to pull at least 26 in. Hg vacuum, there is a leak that must be repaired before evacuation can occur.
4. Once the system has reached at least 26 in. Hg vacuum, allow the system to evacuate for at least 15 minutes. The longer the system is evacuated, the more contaminants will be removed.
5. Close all valves and turn the pump off. If the system loses more than 2 in. Hg vacuum after 15 minutes, there is a leak that should be repaired.

System Charging

1. Connect an approved charging station, recovery/recycling machine or manifold gauge set to the discharge and suction ports. The red hose is normally connected to the discharge (high pressure) line and the blue hose is connected to the suction (low pressure) line.
2. Follow the instructions provided with the equipment and charge the system with the specified amount of refrigerant.
3. Perform a leak test, noting special leak testing information if system has R-134a refrigerant.

SYSTEM COMPONENTS

Radiator

REMOVAL AND INSTALLATION

Caravan, Voyager, Town & Country, and Dakota

1. Disconnect the negative battery cable.
2. Drain the coolant.
3. Remove the upper and lower hoses, if accessible, and coolant reserve tank hose from the radiator.
4. Remove the automatic transmission cooling hoses, if equipped.
5. If equipped with an electric cooling fan, remove the fan assembly by disconnecting the wiring, removing the upper shroud screws, then lifting the shroud and fan out.
6. If equipped with a belt-driven fan, remove the shroud from the radiator and position it over the fan and away from the radiator.
7. If not previously removed, raise the vehicle and remove the lower radiator hose.
8. On 1993 Caravan and Voyager, remove the front grille by removing the retaining screws and light assemblies, then remove the grille. Remove the condenser-to-radiator fasteners and move condenser away from the radiator.
9. Remove the upper radiator mounting brackets and/or screws. Disconnect the engine block heater wire, if equipped. Carefully lift the radiator from the engine compartment.

To install:

10. Lower the radiator into position. Install the mounting brackets or screws.
11. Attach the block heater wire, if removed.
12. Raise the vehicle and connect the automatic transaxle cooler lines, if equipped, and the lower radiator hose. Be sure to attach the hose to the retaining clip to keep it away from the fan. Lower the vehicle.
13. Reattach the condenser to the radiator and install the lights and grille on 1993 Caravan and Voyager.
14. Install the cooling fan or shroud, as removed.
15. Connect the upper hose and coolant reserve tank hose.
16. Fill the system with coolant and bleed, if necessary.
17. Connect the negative battery cable, run the vehicle until the thermostat opens, fill the radiator completely and check the automatic transaxle fluid level, if equipped.
18. Once the vehicle has cooled, recheck the coolant level.

Dakota—3.9L and 5.2L Engine

1. Disconnect the negative battery cable from battery.
2. Properly drain the cooling system.
3. Remove the throttle cable at fan shroud.
4. Unsnap the coolant reserve/overflow tank from the fan shroud (T-shaped slots). Lift straight up.

5. Remove the fan shroud retaining hardware (two clips at top-two bolts at bottom).
6. Position the fan shroud towards engine. Fan shroud does not have to be removed from vehicle.
7. Disconnect the transmission cooler lines at radiator. (if equipped)
8. Remove the upper and lower radiator hose clamps and hoses at radiator.
9. Remove the two upper radiator-to-radiator support bolts. The radiator has two alignment pins to align lower part of radiator to lower radiator support.
10. Lift the radiator up and out of engine compartment. Do not allow cooling fins of radiators to contact any other vehicle component. Radiator fin damage could result.

To install:

11. Lower the radiator into engine compartment. Position alignment pins into alignment holes in radiator lower support.
12. Install the two upper radiator bolts.
13. Install the transmission cooler lines (if equipped).
14. Install both the radiator hoses and hose clamps.
15. Install the fan shroud to radiator (two clips at top-two bolts at bottom).
16. Install the coolant reserve/overflow tank. Snaps into position.
17. Connect the throttle cable to fan shroud. Snaps in.
18. Connect the negative battery cable to battery.
19. Fill the cooling system.
20. Start and warm the engine. Check for leaks.

Van

1. Disconnect the negative battery cable.
2. Properly drain the cooling system. Remove the upper radiator hose(s) from the radiator and remove the coolant overflow tube, if equipped.
3. Unscrew the fan shroud mounting bolts and move rearward for clearance. Remove the radiator upper mounting bolts.
4. If equipped with A/C, remove grille (headlight bezels, parking lamp connectors, and upper and lower mounting screws) to access condenser to radiator mounting bolts.
5. Raise the vehicle. Disconnect the automatic transmission cooling lines, if equipped. Cap all openings.
6. Remove the lower radiator hose.
7. Keep the radiator supported while removing the two lower mounting bolts. Carefully lower the radiator out of the vehicle.

To install:

8. Be sure shroud is positioned to give clearance for radiator, then carefully raise it into position and secure the lower mounting bolts.
9. Connect the lower radiator hose and the transmission cooling lines.
10. Lower the vehicle. Install the upper radiator mounting bolts and, if removed, install the condenser mounting bolts and replace the grille.
11. Position the fan shroud into place and install the retaining nuts.
12. Connect the upper radiator hose and the overflow tube. Fill the cooling system and check operation.

1993 Pick-Up and Ramcharger

1. Disconnect the negative battery cable.
2. Properly drain the cooling system.
3. Disconnect the throttle cable from the radiator shroud.

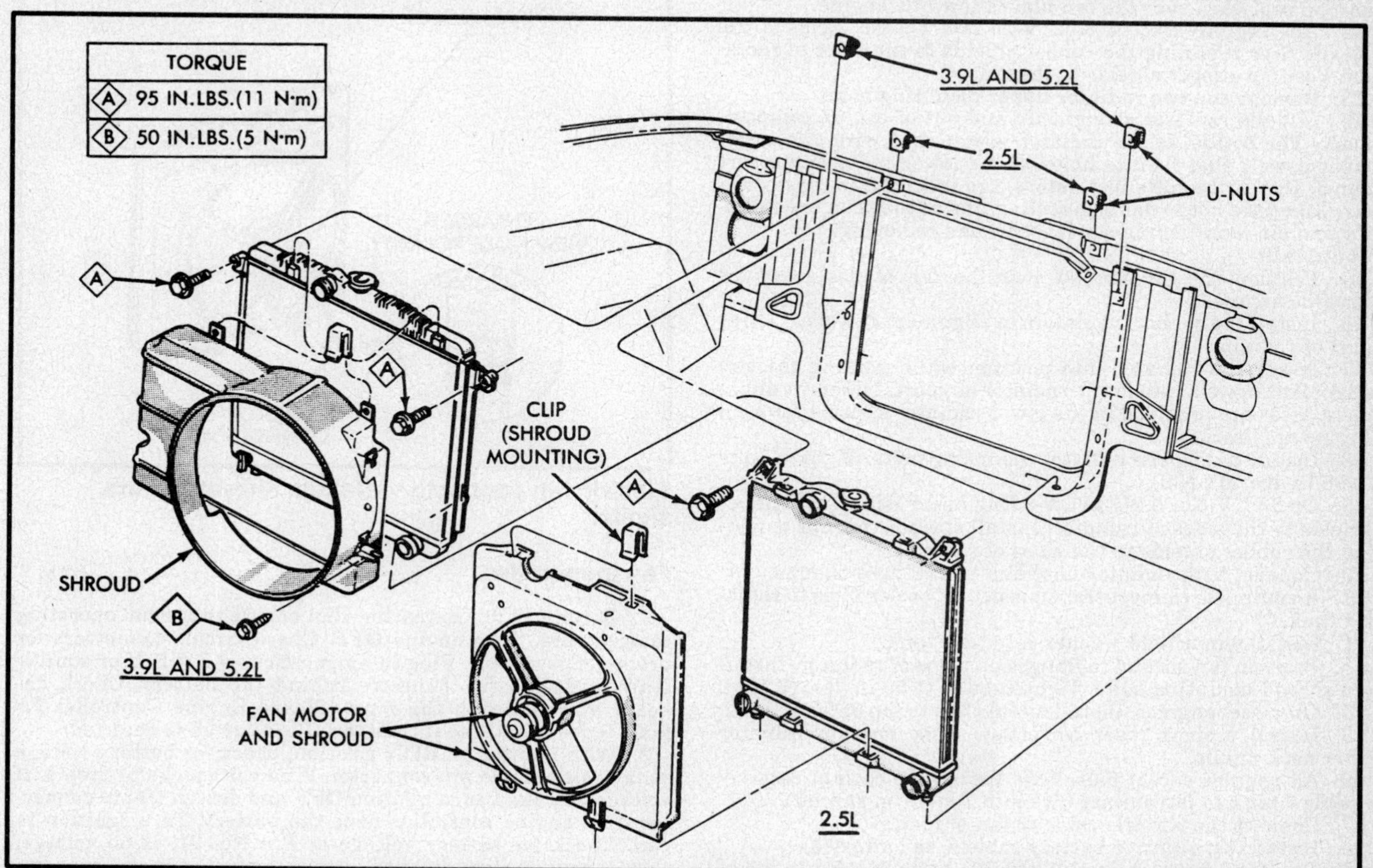

Typical radiator and fan shroud removal/installation

4. Remove the upper and lower radiator hoses and the coolant overflow tube, if equipped.
5. Detach fan shroud and move it rearward for clearance. Remove the mounting bolts and carefully lift the radiator up and out of the vehicle.
6. Installation is the reverse of removal procedure. Fill cooling system and check for proper operation.

Pick-Up

1. Disconnect the negative battery cable from battery.
2. On diesel engine, disconnect both negative battery cables at both batteries. Remove the nuts retaining the positive cable to the top of radiator. Position positive battery cable to rear of vehicle.
3. Drain the cooling system.
4. Disconnect the throttle cable from clip at top of radiator fan shroud.
5. Remove the hose clamps and hoses from radiator.
6. Remove the coolant reserve/overflow tank hose from radiator filler neck nipple.
7. All engines except 8.0L V-10. Remove the coolant reserve/overflow tank from the fan shroud (pull straight up). The tank slips into T-slots on the fan shroud.
8. Disconnect the electrical connectors at windshield washer reservoir tank and remove tank.
9. If equipped with an automatic transmission (all engines except diesel), disconnect oil cooler lines (hoses) at radiator tank. A special tool must be used to disconnect the lines.
10. On diesel engines, remove the two metal clips retaining the upper part of fan shroud to the top of radiator.
11. Remove the four fan shroud mounting bolts. Position shroud rearward over the fan blades towards engine.
12. All Engines Except 8.0L V-10 and Diesel. Remove the plastic clips retaining the rubber shields to the sides of radiator. Position rubber shields to the side.
13. Remove the two radiator upper mounting bolts.
14. Lift the radiator straight up and out of engine compartment. The bottom of the radiator is equipped with two alignment dowels that fit into holes in the lower radiator support panel. Rubber biscuits (insulators) are installed to these dowels. Take care not to damage cooling fins or tubes on the radiator and air conditioning condenser when removing.

To install:

15. Position the fan shroud over the fan blades rearward towards engine.
16. Install the rubber insulators to alignment dowels at lower part of radiator.
17. Lower the radiator into position while guiding the two alignment dowels into lower radiator support. Different alignment holes are provided in the lower radiator support for each engine application.
18. Install two upper radiator mounting bolts. Tighten bolts to 95 in. lbs. (11 Nm).
19. On 3.9L V-6 or 5.2L/5.9L V-8 Engines. Position the rubber shields to the sides of radiator. Install the plastic clips retaining the rubber shields to the sides of radiator.
20. Connect both radiator hose and install hose clamps.
21. If equipped, connect transmission oil cooler lines to radiator tank.
22. Install windshield washer reservoir tank.
23. Position fan shroud to flanges on sides of radiator. Install fan shroud mounting bolts. Tighten bolts to 50 in. lbs. (6 Nm).
24. On diesel engines, install metal clips to top of fan shroud.
25. Install coolant reserve/overflow tank hose to radiator filler neck nipple.
26. All engines except 8.0L V-10. Install the coolant reserve/overflow tank to fan shroud (fits into T-slots on shroud).
27. Connect the throttle cable to fan shroud.
28. Install the negative battery cable(s) to battery(s).
29. On diesel engines, install positive battery cable to top of radiator. Tighten radiator-to-battery cable mounting nuts.
30. Position the heater controls to **FULL HEAT** position.
31. Fill the cooling system with coolant.
32. Operate the engine until it reaches normal temperature. Check cooling system and automatic transmission (if equipped) fluid levels.

COOLING SYSTEM BLEEDING

The system is self-bleeding and requires no special procedure as radiator cap is equipped with pressure release valve which relieves air from the system.

Electric Cooling Fan

Caravan, Voyager, and Dakota—2.5L Engine

CAUTION

Make sure the key is in the OFF position when checking the electric cooling fan. If not, the fan could turn ON at any time, causing serious personal injury.

TESTING

General Test

To check general operation, unplug the fan connector, connect the fan to a good battery (be sure to note positive and negative connections to ensure proper polarity). The fan should run smoothly. If not, the fan is defective and should be replaced. Check wiring and motor for any signs of heat damage. If so, voltage may be too high.

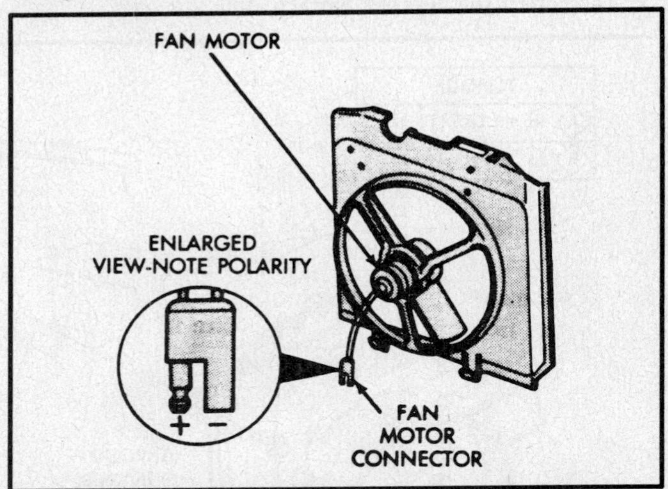

Electric fan connector—Dakota shown; others similar

Fan Inoperative

1. Reconnect fan connector. Run engine to normal operating temperature. Turn engine **OFF**. Check circuit connectors for proper engagement. Plug in diagnostic tool (DRB-II or equivalent) to diagnostic connector behind the battery. Check onboard diagnostics in the Single Board Engine Controller for fault codes. Continue if codes 88, 12, 35 or 55 is detected.
2. With ignition in **RUN** position, check for battery voltage at fan relay single pin connector. If no voltage, go to Step 4. If voltage was okay, turn ignition **OFF** and detach 60-pin connector from engine controller near the battery. Turn ignition to run. Check for battery voltage at Pin No. **31**. If no voltage, repair open or short in wire from this pin to the radiator fan relay. If battery voltage was present, replace the engine controller.

3. With ignition in **RUN** position, test for battery voltage at the blue wire in the 3-pin fan relay connector. If voltage is okay, replace fan relay. If no voltage, repair open or short in the circuit.

4. Turn ignition **OFF** and reconnect the 60-pin connector to the engine controller. Test fan system operation.

REMOVAL AND INSTALLATION

1. Disconnect the negative battery cable.
2. Unplug the connector.
3. Remove the mounting screws.

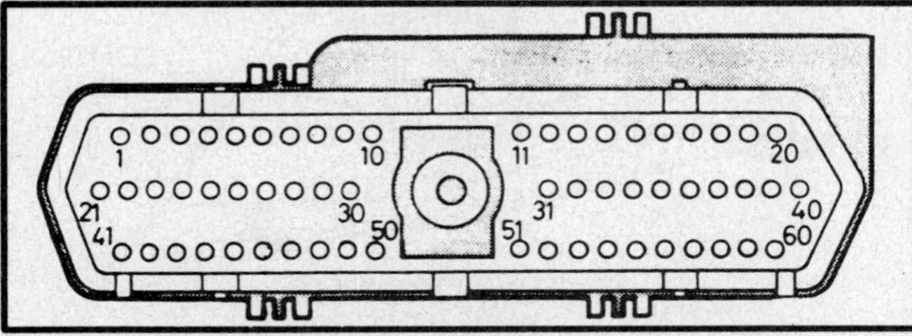

60-pin engine controller connector showing pin No. 31—2.5L, 3.0L and 3.3L engines

4. Remove the fan assembly from the vehicle.
5. The installation is the reverse of the removal procedure.
6. Connect the negative battery cable and check the fan for proper operation.

Condenser

REMOVAL AND INSTALLATION

Caravan, Voyager, Town & Country and Dakota

1. Disconnect the negative battery cable.
2. Properly discharge the air conditioning system.
3. Remove the headlight bezels in order to gain access to the grille. Remove the headlight/sidelight assemblies as required. Remove the grille assembly. A hidden screw fastens the grille to the center vertical support.
4. On Dakota and 1993 Caravan and Voyager, remove the center brace. Remove the auxiliary transmission cooler, if equipped. Remove the core support plastic panel (1993 Caravan, Voyager and Town & Country).
5. Remove the refrigerant lines attaching nut and separate the lines from the condenser sealing plate. Discard the gasket.
6. Immediately cover all line and condenser openings to minimize contamination.
7. Remove the bolts that attach the condenser to the radiator support.
8. Remove the condenser from the vehicle.

To install:

9. Position the condenser and install the bolts.
10. Coat the new gasket with wax-free refrigerant oil and install. Connect the lines to the condenser sealing plate and tighten the nut.
11. Install the support pieces and grille assembly as removed.
12. Evacuate and recharge the air conditioning system. Add 1 oz. of refrigerant oil during the recharge.
13. Connect the negative battery cable and check the entire climate control system for proper operation and leaks.

Pick-Up, Ramcharger and Van

1. Disconnect the negative battery cable.
2. Properly discharge the air conditioning system.
3. Properly drain cooling system. Remove the radiator.
4. On Van, it may be necessary to remove the grille to access the condenser mounting bolts.
5. Remove the refrigerant lines attaching nut and separate the lines from the condenser sealing plate. Discard the gasket.
6. Cover the exposed ends of the lines to minimize contamination.
7. Remove the bolts that attach the condenser to the radiator support.
8. Lift the condenser and remove from the vehicle.

To install:

9. Position the condenser and install the bolts.
10. Coat the new gasket with wax-free refrigerant oil and install. Connect the lines to the condenser sealing plate and tighten the nut.
11. Install the radiator and fill with coolant.
12. Evacuate and recharge the air conditioning system. Add 1 oz. of refrigerant oil during the recharge.
13. Connect the negative battery cable and check the entire climate control system for proper operation and leaks.

Compressor

REMOVAL AND INSTALLATION

NOTE: NOTE: Thoroughly clean area around the suction and discharge service ports before disconnecting lines at these points.

1. Disconnect the negative battery cable.
2. Properly discharge the air conditioning system.
3. Remove the compressor drive belt(s). Disconnect the compressor lead.
4. Remove the refrigerant lines from the compressor and discard the gaskets and/or O-rings. Cap all openings to minimize contamination.
5. Remove the compressor mounting nuts and bolts.
6. Lift the compressor off of its mounting studs and remove from the engine compartment.
7. Drain and measure the compressor oil for proper refill during installation.

To install:

8. Install the compressor and tighten all mounting nuts and bolts.
9. Coat the new gaskets or O-rings with wax-free refrigerant oil and install. Connect the refrigerant lines to the compressor and tighten the bolts.
10. Install the drive belt(s) and adjust to specification. Connect the electrical lead.
11. Evacuate and recharge the air conditioning system.
12. Connect the negative battery cable and check the entire climate control system for proper operation and leaks.

Receiver/Drier

REMOVAL AND INSTALLATION

1. Disconnect the negative battery cable.
2. Properly discharge the air conditioning system.
3. On Caravan, Voyager and Town & Country, remove the vehicle jack.
4. Remove the nuts that fasten the refrigerant lines to sides of the receiver/drier assembly.
5. Remove the refrigerant lines from the receiver/drier and discard the gaskets. Cover the exposed ends of the lines to minimize contamination.
6. Remove the mounting strap bolts and remove the receiver/drier from the engine compartment.

To install:

7. Transfer the mounting strap to the new receiver/drier.
8. Coat the new gaskets with wax-free refrigerant oil and install. Connect the refrigerant lines to the receiver/drier and tighten the nuts. Replace the jack, if removed.

9. Evacuate and recharge the air conditioning system. Add 1 oz. of refrigerant oil during the recharge. Check for leaks.

Expansion Valve

TESTING

1. Connect a manifold gauge set or charging station to the air conditioning system. Verify adequate refrigerant level.
2. Disconnect and plug the vacuum hose at the water control valve.
3. On Dakota, find and remove the vacuum lines at the recirculating air door actuator and install the light green vacuum line where the dark green line had been.
4. Disconnect the low pressure or differential pressure cut off switch connector and jump the wires inside the boot.
5. Close all doors, windows and vents to the passenger compartment.
6. Set controls to **A/C**, full heat (to electrically by-pass the evaporator fin sensor) and high blower.
7. Start the engine and hold the idle speed at 1000 rpm (On Dual Unit Vans 800 RPM). After the engine has reached normal operating temperature, allow the passenger compartment to heat up to create the need for maximum refrigerant flow into the evaporator.
8. The discharge (high pressure) gauge should read 140-240 psi and suction (low pressure) gauge should read 20-30 psi, providing the refrigerant charge is sufficient.

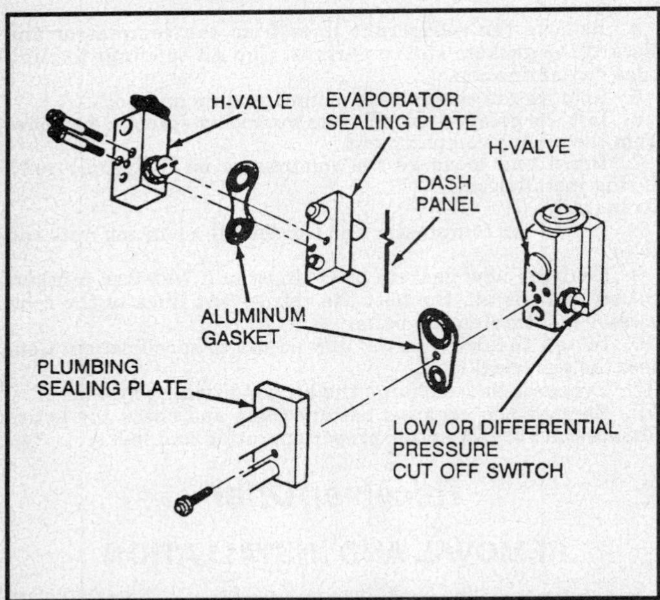

Exploded view of the expansion valve (H-valve)

9. If the suction side is within specifications, freeze the expansion valve control head using a very cold substance (liquid CO_2 or dry ice; do not use R-12 to spray the H-valve.) for 30 seconds:
   - If equipped with a silver H-valve used with fixed displacement compressor, the suction side pressure should drop to 15 in. Hg vacuum. If not, the expansion valve is stuck open and should be replaced.
   - If equipped with a black H-valve used with variable displacement compressor, the discharge pressure should drop about 15 percent. If not, the expansion valve is stuck open and should be replaced.

10. Allow the expansion valve to thaw. As it thaws, the pressures should stabilize to the values in Step 8. If not, replace the expansion valve.
11. Once the test is complete, put the vacuum line and connector back in the original locations, and perform the overall performance test.

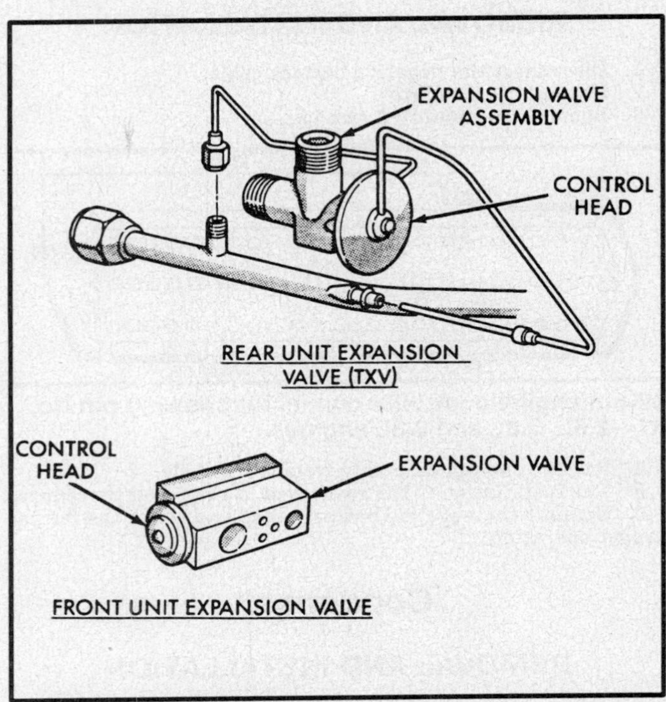

Dual unit expansion valves

REMOVAL AND INSTALLATION

1. Disconnect the negative battery cable.
2. Properly discharge the air conditioning system.
3. Disconnect the connector at the low or differential pressure cut off switch. Detach the 3-pin connector for the electronic clutch cycling switch for 1993 Caravan, Voyager and Town & Country.
4. Remove the attaching bolt at the center of the refrigerant plumbing sealing plate.
5. Carefully pull the refrigerant lines away from the expansion valve. Avoid scratching sealing surface with tube pilots. Cover the exposed ends of the lines to minimize contamination.
6. Remove the 2 Torx® screws that mount the expansion valve to the evaporator sealing plate.
7. Remove the valve and discard the gaskets.

To install:

8. Transfer the low pressure cutoff switch to the new valve, if necessary.
9. Coat the new aluminum gasket with wax-free refrigerant oil and install to the evaporator sealing plate.
10. Install the expansion valve and torque the Torx® screws to 100 inch lbs.
11. Lubricate the remaining gasket and install with the refrigerant plumbing to the expansion valve. Torque the attaching bolt to 200 inch lbs.
12. Connect the switch connectors as removed.
13. Evacuate and recharge the air conditioning system.
14. Connect the negative battery cable and check the entire climate control system for proper operation and leaks.

Blower Motor

REMOVAL AND INSTALLATION

Caravan, Voyager and Town & Country

1. Disconnect the negative battery cable.
2. Remove the center bezel by unclipping it from the instrument panel.
3. Remove the accessory switch carrier and the heater/air conditioning control head (after disconnecting vacuum harness and control cable).
4. Remove center or forward console, then remove the attaching screws and remove the lower right instrument panel.
5. Disconnect the blower motor lead under the right side of the instrument panel.
6. Remove the attaching screws, remove the blower motor assembly.
7. The installation is the reverse of the removal procedure.
8. Connect the negative battery cable and check the blower motor for proper operation.

Dakota

1. Disconnect the negative battery cable.
2. Remove the steering column cover, intermittent wiper control and the lower instrument panel module retaining screw to the right of the steering column.
3. Remove the center distribution duct retaining screws and panel support screw at the bottom of the module.
4. Remove the courtesy light at the lower right corner of the module and the screw near the ashtray.
5. Open the glove box and remove the screws along the top edge.
6. Move the instrument panel out and down far enough to unclip the wiring harness and antenna cable. Disconnect the glove box light wire and remove the instrument panel from the vehicle.
7. If equipped with air conditioning, disconnect the 2 vacuum lines from the recirculating air door actuator and disconnect the blower lead wires.
8. Remove 2 screws at the top of the blower housing, 5 screws from around the housing and remove the blower housing from the unit.
9. Remove 3 screw attaching the blower to the unit and remove the blower from the vehicle.
10. Remove the fan wheel from the blower motor, if needed.

To install:

11. Install the fan wheel to the blower motor and secure the clip.
12. Install the blower to the unit and install the blower housing.

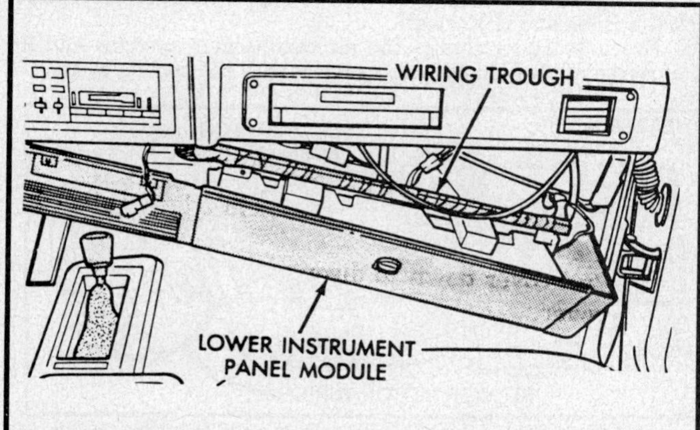

Removing lower instrument panel module—Dakota

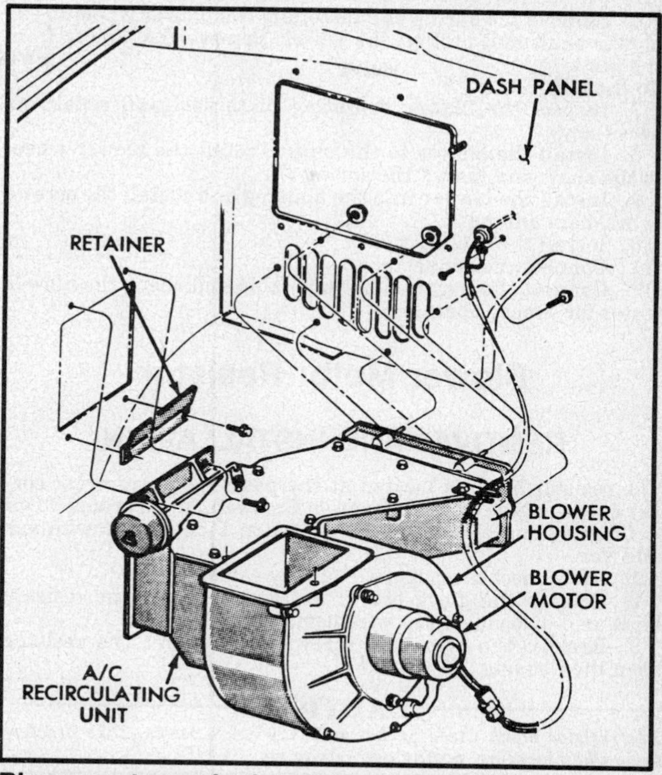

Blower motor and related components—Van

13. Connect the 2 vacuum lines from the recirculating air door actuator, if equipped, and connect the blower lead wires.
14. Hold the module in position and clip the wiring harness and antenna cable in place. Connect the monaural radio speaker wire, if equipped. Connect the glove box light wire.
15. Install the retaining screws along the top of the inside of the glove box.
16. Install the courtesy light at the lower right corner of the module and the screw near the ash receiver.
17. Install the panel support screw at the bottom of the module and the center distribution duct retaining screws.
18. Install the lower instrument panel module retaining screw to the right of the steering column, intermittent wiper control and the steering column cover.
19. Connect the negative battery cable and check the blower motor for proper operation.

Van

1. Disconnect the negative battery cable.
2. Remove the air intake duct and top half of the shroud. Disconnect the blower connector.
3. Remove the blower motor cooling tube.
4. Remove the retaining nuts.
5. If equipped with A/C, pull refrigerant lines inward and upward while removing blower assembly from the housing.
6. Remove the blower motor assembly from the housing.
7. Installation is the reverse of the removal procedure. Check blower operation.

Pick-Up and Ramcharger

1. Disconnect the negative battery cable.
2. Disconnect the blower connector.
3. Remove the blower motor cooling tube.
4. Remove the screws or retaining nuts retaining the blower plate to the housing.
5. Remove the assembly from the housing.

6. Remove the spring clip fastening the blower wheel to the blower shaft and pull off the wheel. Remove the blower from the plate.

To install:

7. Inspect the blower mounting plate seal and repair, as necessary.
8. Install the blower to the plate. Install the blower wheel to the shaft and install the spring clip.
9. Install the blower into the housing and install the screws or washers and nuts.
10. Install the cooling tube.
11. Connect the connector.
12. Connect the negative battery cable and check the blower motor for proper operation.

Blower Motor Resistor

REMOVAL AND INSTALLATION

The resistor block is located at the passenger's side rear corner of the engine compartment on Caravan, Voyager and Town & Country and behind the glove box on Pick-up, Ramcharger and Van.

1. Disconnect the negative battery cable.
2. Remove the glove box, if necessary. Locate the resistor block and disconnect the wire harness.
3. Remove the attaching screws and remove the resistor from the housing.

CAUTION

The resistor block could be hot and may cause burns. Take precautions when locating, testing and removing.

4. Make sure there is no contact between any of the coils before installing.
5. The installation is the reverse of the removal procedure. Make sure the foam seal is in good condition.
6. Connect the negative battery cable and check the blower system for proper operation.

Heater Core and Evaporator

REMOVAL AND INSTALLATION

Caravan, Voyager and Town & Country

1. Disconnect the negative battery cable. Properly discharge the air conditioning system. Disconnect all A/C lines from the connection at the firewall. Plug all openings to minimize contamination of the system.
2. Drain the cooling system, detach the heater hoses from the connection at the firewall. Plug heater hose openings to minimize coolant leakage.
3. Remove the steering column cover and left and right side under panel silencers.
4. Remove the center bezel by unclipping it from the instrument panel.
5. Remove the accessory switch carrier, detach the vacuum harness and control cable from the control unit and then remove the heater/air conditioning control unit from the instrument panel.
6. Remove storage bin and lower right instrument panel.
7. Disconnect the blower motor lead under the right side of the instrument panel.
8. Remove the right side 40-pin connector wiring bracket.
9. Remove the lower right reinforcement, body computer bracket and mid-to-lower reinforcement as an assembly.
10. Disconnect any instrument panel wiring which may be in the way and temporarily re-route it.
11. In the engine compartment, remove the condensation tube. Then, remove the 4 nuts from the firewall retaining the A/C heater unit.

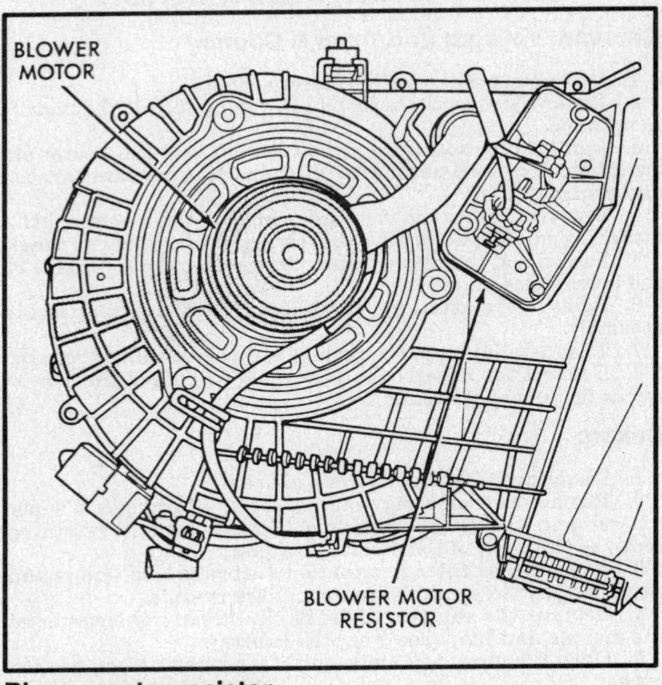

Blower motor resistor

12. Inside the vehicle, pull the unit back until its mounting studs are free of the firewall, lower the unit and take it from the vehicle.

To install:

13. Position the A/C-heater unit to its position, ensuring the mounting studs are through the firewall.
14. In the engine compartment, attach the nuts to the mounting studs. Reinstall the condensation tube.
15. Properly route and connect any instrument panel wiring previously removed. Reinstall the reinforcements and brackets as removed.
16. Install the right lower instrument panel assembly, then the storage bin.
17. Attach the vacuum harness and control cable while installing the A/C-heater control panel. Install the accessory switch carrier and the center panel bezel.
18. Connect the heater hoses to the core tubes.
19. Using new gaskets to restore A/C line connections, reattach the lines at the firewall.
20. Evacuate and recharge the air conditioning system. Add 2 oz. of refrigerant oil during the recharge. Fill the cooling system.

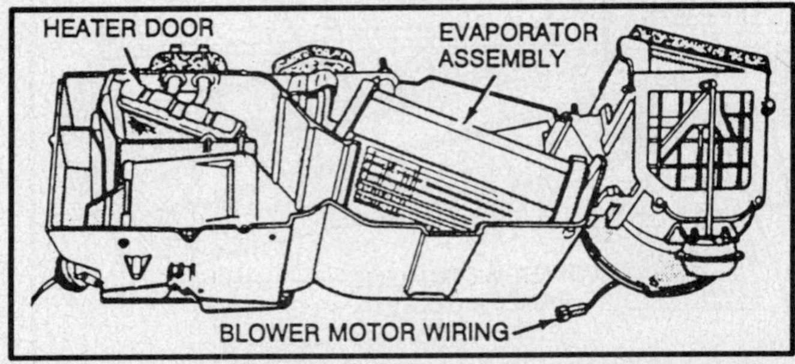

Heater core/evaporator housing and internal arts—Caravan, Voyager and Town & Country

21. Connect the negative battery cable and check the entire climate control system for proper operation and leaks.

NOTE: Refrigerant oil R-134a refrigerant, used in 1993 models, is unique. Be sure to check you are using the proper oil for this system to avoid system operating failures.

Dakota

1. Disconnect the negative battery cable. Properly discharge the air conditioning system. Drain the coolant.
2. Remove the steering column cover, intermittent wiper control and the lower instrument panel module retaining screw to the right of the steering column.
3. Remove the center distribution duct retaining screws and panel support screw at the bottom of the module.
4. Remove the courtesy light at the lower right corner of the module and the screw near the ashtray.
5. Open the glove box and remove the screws along the top edge.
6. Move the instrument panel out and down far enough to unclip the wiring harness and antenna cable. Disconnect the glove box light wire and remove the instrument panel from the vehicle.
7. Remove the center air distribution duct.
8. Remove the antenna wire from retaining clip at the right end of the heater unit.
9. Detach the blower motor connector and remove the thermal insulator retainer from the heater unit.
10. Disconnect the defroster hoses from the adapter at the top of the A/C-heater unit.
11. Disconnect the vacuum harness connector from the A/C control panel, and the vacuum feed line from the check valve.
12. Disconnect the temperature control cable from the heater unit and remove the adjusting clip from the blend air door crank.
13. Disconnect the heater hoses from the core tubes and plug them.
14. Disconnect the refrigerant lines at the H-valve, remove the valve and plug the openings to minimize system contamination. Remove the condensation drain tube, if equipped.
15. Remove 4 heater/air conditioning housing attaching nuts from the rear engine compartment dash panel.
16. Remove the housing support attaching screw and rotate the brace aside.
17. Remove the heater/air conditioning housing from the vehicle.

To install:

18. Assemble the unit, if disassembled, making sure all vacuum tubing is properly routed.
19. Install the assembly to the vehicle and connect the vacuum harness. Install the nuts to the firewall and install the condensation tube. Install the support brace to the housing.
20. Connect the demister hoses to the adaptor at the top of the heater unit.
21. Connect the blower motor connector and install the thermal insulator retainer to the heater unit.
22. Connect the vacuum harness connector to the air conditioning control hose and vacuum feed line to the check valve.
23. Connect the temperature control cable flag retainer to the heater unit and install the adjusting clip from the blend air door crank.
24. Install the center air distribution duct.
25. Install the antenna wire from retaining clip at the right end of the heater unit.
26. Install the instrument panel module and all related parts.
27. Connect the heater hoses to the core tubes.
28. Using new gaskets, install the H-valve and connect the refrigerant lines.
29. Evacuate and recharge the air conditioning system. If the evaporator was replaced, add 2 oz. of refrigerant oil during the recharge. Fill the cooling system.
30. Connect the negative battery cable and check the entire climate control system for proper operation and leaks.

Pick-Up and Ramcharger

WITHOUT AIR CONDITIONING

1. Disconnect the negative battery cable.
2. Drain the cooling system. Remove and plug the heater core hoses.
3. Remove the right side cowl trim panel, if equipped. Remove the glove box assembly by removing base screws and swinging box out from the bottom. Remove the structural brace through the glove box opening.
4. Remove the right half of the instrument panel lower reinforcement and disconnect the ground strap.
5. Disconnect the control cables from the heater housing and the blower motor wires on the engine side.
6. Remove the retaining screw between the package to cowl side sheetmetal.
7. Remove the 6 heater housing retaining nuts on the engine side of the heater assembly and remove the heater housing assembly.
8. Remove the heater housing cover retaining screws and the mode door crank. Separate the cover from the housing.
9. Carefully lift the heater core from the heater housing.

To install:

10. Clean the inside of the housing. Install the heater core into the housing.
11. Install the housing cover. Inspect the dash panel seal for damage and repair, as required.
12. Install the assembly to the dash panel and install the retaining nuts.
13. Install the cowl side retaining screws.
14. Connect the blower motor connector.
15. Connect the control cables.
16. Install the right lower instrument panel reinforcement, structural brace, glove box and cowl side trim panel, if equipped.
17. Connect the heater hoses.
18. Refill the radiator.
19. Connect the negative battery cable, run the vehicle until the thermostat opens, fill the radiator completely and check the operation of the heater.
20. Once the vehicle has cooled, recheck the coolant level.

AIR CONDITIONING

1. Disconnect the negative battery cable. Properly discharge the air conditioning system. Drain the cooling system. Disconnect and plug the heater hoses and the refrigerant lines.
2. Remove the condensation tube from the housing.
3. Move the transfer case and gear shift levers away from the instrument panel.
4. Remove the right side cowl trim panel, if equipped. Remove the glove box lower screws and swing it out from the bottom.
5. Remove the structural brace from the through hole in the glove box opening. Remove the ash tray.
6. Remove the right lower half of the dash reinforcement by removing the retaining screws holding it to the instrument panel and to the cowl side trim panel.
7. Disconnect the radio ground strap. Remove the center and floor air distribution ducts.
8. Disconnect the temperature control cable from the assembly and tape it aside.
9. Disconnect the vacuum lines from the extension on the control unit and unclip the vacuum lines from the defroster duct.
10. Remove the wiring connector from the resistor block. Remove the blower motor electrical connector from the engine side of the assembly.
11. Disconnect the vacuum lines on the engine side and make sure the grommet is free from the dash panel.

12. Remove the evaporator housing nuts on the engine side. Remove the screw that retains the assembly to the cowl side of the sheetmetal.
13. Remove the assembly from the vehicle (instrument panel may have to flex outward slightly during removal).
14. Remove the vacuum actuators, door crank levers, evaporator case cover retaining nuts and screws and the heater core retaining screws. Lift the cover off of the assembly and remove the heater core from its mounting.

To install:

15. Clean the inside of the housing. Install the heater core into the housing.
16. Install the housing cover, retaining screws and nuts, levers and actuators.
17. Inspect the dash panel seals for damage and repair, as required.
18. Feed the vacuum lines through the hole in the dash panel, install the assembly to the dash panel and install all retaining nuts and screws.
19. Connect the resistor block and blower motor.
20. Connect the vacuum lines to the extension on the control unit and clip the vacuum lines to the defroster duct.
21. Connect the temperature control cable to the assembly.
22. Connect the radio ground strap. Install the center and floor air distribution ducts.
23. Install the dash reinforcement, structural brace, glove box and right side cowl trim panel, if equipped. Install the ash tray.
24. Install the condensation tube.
25. Connect the heater hoses and vacuum lines.
26. Install a new gasket and connect the refrigerant lines.
27. Evacuate and recharge the air conditioning system. Refill the radiator.
28. Connect the negative battery cable and check the entire climate control system for proper operation and leaks.

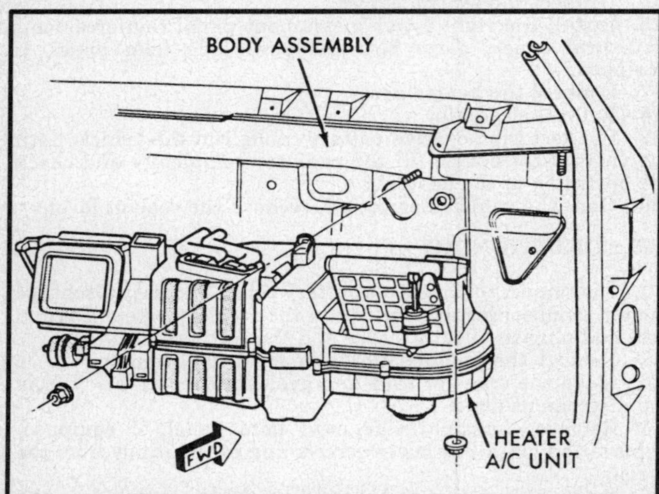

Heater-A/C Housing—Pick-Up and Ramcharger

Van

WITHOUT AIR CONDITIONING

1. Disconnect the negative battery cable.
2. Drain the cooling system. Disconnect and plug the heater hoses.
3. Disconnect the temperature control cable from the heater core cover and the blend door crank. Disconnect the vent cable.
4. Disconnect the blower motor connector.
5. Remove the screws retaining the heater assembly to the side cowl and the nuts fastening the heater assembly to the dash panel.

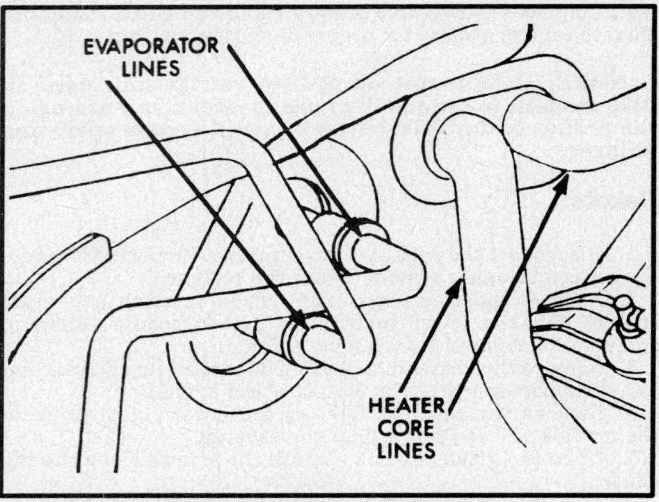

Evaporator and Heater Core Lines—Van

6. Remove the heater unit from the vehicle.
7. Remove the back plate and remove the screws holding the heater core cover to the heater housing.
8. Remove the heater core retaining screws from the heater core and remove the core from the heater housing.

To install:

9. Clean out the inside of the housing. Place the heater core into the housing and fasten.
10. Position the blend air door and right vent door in the housing and fasten the heater core cover to the housing.
11. Check the dash panel and side cowl seals for breaks and lack of adhesion. Repair as required.
12. Install the heater assembly to the vehicle.
13. Connect the blower connector.
14. Connect the cables.
15. Connect the heater hoses.
16. Refill the radiator.
17. Connect the negative battery cable, run the vehicle until the thermostat opens, fill the radiator completely and check the operation of the heater.
18. Once the vehicle has cooled, recheck the coolant level.

AIR CONDITIONING

1. Disconnect the negative battery cable. Properly discharge the air conditioning system completely.
2. Disconnect the freeze control connector from the wire harness at the H-valve.
3. Drain the cooling system. Place a layer of non-conductive waterproof material over the alternator to prevent coolant from spilling on it when disconnecting the heater hoses. Clamp off, then disconnect and cap the heater hoses.
4. Slowly disconnect the refrigerant plumbing from the H-valve. Cap all refrigerant line and H-valve openings. Remove the 2 screws from the filter drier bracket and swing the plumbing aside towards the center of the vehicle.
5. Remove the temperature control cable from the cover.
6. Working from inside the vehicle, remove the glove box, spot cooler bezel and the appearance shield. Working through the glove box opening and under the instrument panel, remove the screws and nuts attaching the evaporator core housing to the dash panel.
7. Remove the 2 screws from the flange connection to the blower housing. Separate the evaporator core housing from the blower housing.
8. Carefully remove the evaporator assembly from the vehicle.
9. Remove the cover from the housing and remove the screw retaining the strap to heater core. Remove the heater core from the housing.

10. Remove the freeze control probe from the evaporator fins, then remove screws beneath A/C line attaching plate and pull evaporator core from housing.

To install:

11. Clean the inside of the housing. Place the evaporator core and heater core into the housing and install the retaining strap and screw.
12. Install the housing cover.
13. Install the blower housing to the evaporator housing.
14. Inspect all air seals and mating surfaces for possible breaks and leaks. Repair as required.
15. Install the assembly to the dash panel and from inside the vehicle, install the screws and nuts attaching it to the dash panel.
16. Install the appearance shield, spot cooler bezel and glove box.
17. Attach the temperature control cable to the cover.
18. Position the plumbing and install the 2 screws onto the filter drier bracket.
19. Install a new gasket and connect the refrigerant lines to the H-valve.
20. Connect the heater hoses and remove the waterproof material from the alternator. Connect the freeze control wire harness, if equipped.
21. Evacuate and recharge the air conditioning system. Refill the radiator.
22. Connect the negative battery cable, run the vehicle until the thermostat opens, fill the radiator completely and check the operation of the entire climate control system.
23. Once the vehicle has cooled, recheck the coolant level.

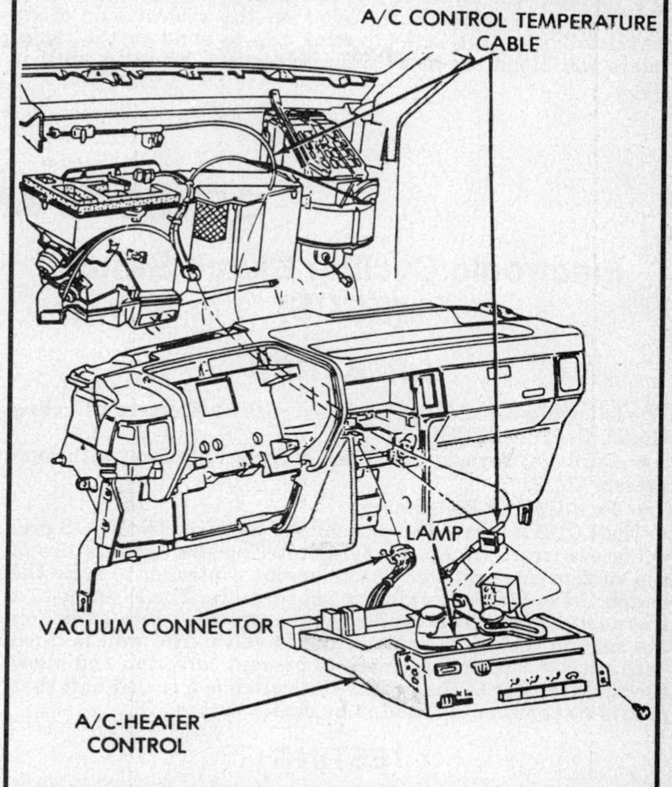

Showing A/C-heater controls—Caravan, Voyager and Town & Country

Refrigerant Lines

REMOVAL AND INSTALLATION

1. Disconnect the negative battery cable.
2. Properly discharge the air conditioning system.
3. Remove the nuts or bolts that attach the refrigerant line sealing plates to the adjoining components. If the lines are connected with flare nuts, use a back-up wrench when disassembling. Cover the exposed ends of the lines to minimize contamination.
4. Remove the lines and discard the gaskets or O-rings.

To install:

5. Coat the new gaskets or O-rings with wax-free refrigerant oil and install. Connect the refrigerant lines to the adjoining components and tighten the nuts or bolts.
6. Evacuate and recharge the air conditioning system.
7. Connect the negative battery cable and check the entire climate control system for proper operation and leaks.

Manual Control Head

REMOVAL AND INSTALLATION

1. Disconnect the negative battery cable.
2. Remove the necessary bezel(s) in order to gain access to the control head.
3. Remove the screws that fasten the control head to the instrument panel.
4. Pull the unit out and unplug the electrical and vacuum connectors. Disconnect the temperature control cable by pushing the flag clip in (on the air door) and pulling the end from its seat.
5. Remove the control head from the instrument panel.
6. The installation is the reverse of the removal procedure.
7. Connect the negative battery cable and check the entire climate control system for proper operation.

Manual Control Cable

ADJUSTMENT

All control cables are self-adjusting. If the cable is not functioning properly, check for kinks and lubricate dry moving parts. The cable cannot be disassembled; replace if faulty.

REMOVAL AND INSTALLATION

1. Disconnect the negative battery cable.
2. Remove the necessary bezel(s) in order to gain access to the control head.
3. Remove the screws that fasten the control head to the instrument panel.
4. Pull the unit out and disconnect the temperature control cable by pushing the flag clip in (on the air door) and pulling the end from its seat.
5. The temperature control cable end is located at the bottom of the heater/air conditioning housing. Disconnect the cable end by pushing the flag in and pulling the end from its seat.
6. Disconnect the self-adjusting clip from the blend air or mode door crank.
7. Take note of the cable's routing and remove the from the vehicle.

To install:

8. Install the cable by routing it in exactly the same position as it was prior to removal.
9. Connect the self-adjusting clip to the door crank and click the flag into the seat.

10. Connect the upper end of the cable to the control head.
11. Place the temperature lever on the coolest side of its travel. Allowing the self-adjusting clip to slide on the cable, rotate the blend air door counterclockwise by hand until it stops.
12. Cycle the lever back and forth a few times to make sure the cable moves freely.
13. Connect the negative battery cable and check the entire climate control system for proper operation.

SENSORS AND SWITCHES

Electronic Cycling Clutch Switch (ECCS)

OPERATION

The following vehicles are equipped with an Electronic Cycling Clutch Switch (ECCS):

- Caravan, Voyager and Town & Country (except with compressor 6C17)
- Pick-Up and Ramcharger

The ECCS is located on or near the H-valve. The ECCS prevents evaporator freeze-up by monitoring the temperature of the suction line and signals the engine controller to cycle the clutch ON or OFF according to temperature. The ECCS uses a thermistor probe in a capillary tube, inserted into a well on the suction line or the side of the H-valve. The well is filled with special conductive grease to prevent corrosion and allow thermal transfer to the probe. The switch is a sealed unit that should be replaced if found to be defective.

TESTING

The compressor clutch coil should cycle 2-3 times per minute at ambient temperatures of 68-90°F (20-32°C). At temperatures above 90°F (32°C), the coil may not cycle at all.

Caravan, Voyager and Town & Country (with fixed displacement compressor)

1. Test the switch in an area with ambient temperature of at least 70°F (21°C).
2. Disconnect the switch connector. Supply 12 volts to pin 2, and ground pin 4 of the ECCS connector.
3. Check for continuity between pins 1 and 3.
4. If continuity is not detected, the switch is faulty and should be replaced.
5. If there is continuity, inspect the rest of the system for an open circuit.

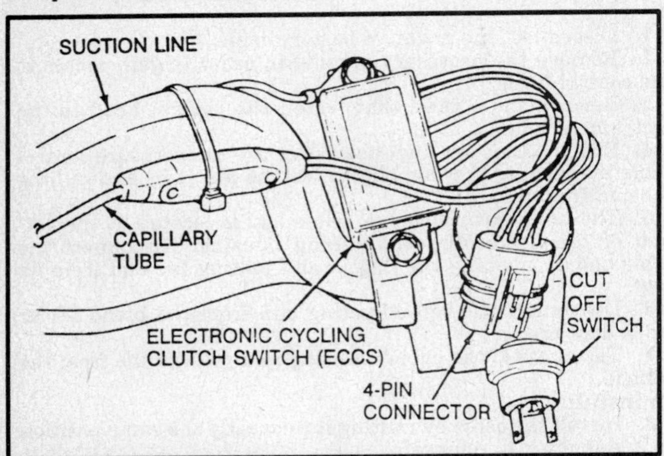

Typical electronic cycling clutch switch

1993 Caravan, Voyager and Town & Country (with variable displacement compressor)

1. Test the switch in an area with ambient temperature of at least 70°F (21°C).
2. Supply 12 volts to pin 2 and the 3-pin ECCS connector. Ground pin 3 and connected Pin 1 (output) through a 390-ohm resistance to the positive (+) 12-volt battery supply.
3. Output voltage (pin 1), when referenced to switch ground, should be 0.75 volt or less. If voltage is higher, replace ECCS.

Pick-Up and Ramcharger

1. Remove the boot connector from the switch. Check for continuity at switch connections. Above 45°F, continuity should exist. If not, replace the switch.
2. If continuity exists (contacts closed), set temperature lever to MAX cool position, blower on LOW speed and activate the A/C button.
3. Operate the engine at 1300 RPM for about 5 minutes. Verify a full refrigerant charge in the sight glass.
4. If the compressor clutch cycles 3-10 times per minute with the ambient temperature between 68-95°F, switch is normal.
5. If clutch fails to engage, check for continuity in switch to clutch circuit. Repair circuit as required.

REMOVAL AND INSTALLATION

1. Disconnect the negative battery cable.
2. Disconnect the ECCS connector.
3. Remove the plastic wire tie holding the bulb against the suction line, as applicable.
4. Remove the mounting screw on the refrigerant line manifold plate at the H-valve.
5. Rotate the switch to separate it from the refrigerant manifold and pull the capillary tube out of the capillary tube well on the suction line or H-valve.

NOTE: The capillary tube well is filled with special temperature conductive grease. If reusing the switch, try to save all the grease. If replacing the switch, new grease will be supplied in the replacement switch package.

To install:

6. Fill the well with the special grease and insert the capillary tube.
7. Mount the switch, with a new O-ring (if applicable) to the refrigerant manifold.
8. Tie the bulb with a new wire tie, if removed.
9. Connect the ECCS connector.
10. Connect the negative battery cable and check the entire climate control system for proper operation.

Fin Sensing Cycling Clutch Switch

OPERATION

The following vehicles are equipped with a fin sensing cycling clutch switch:

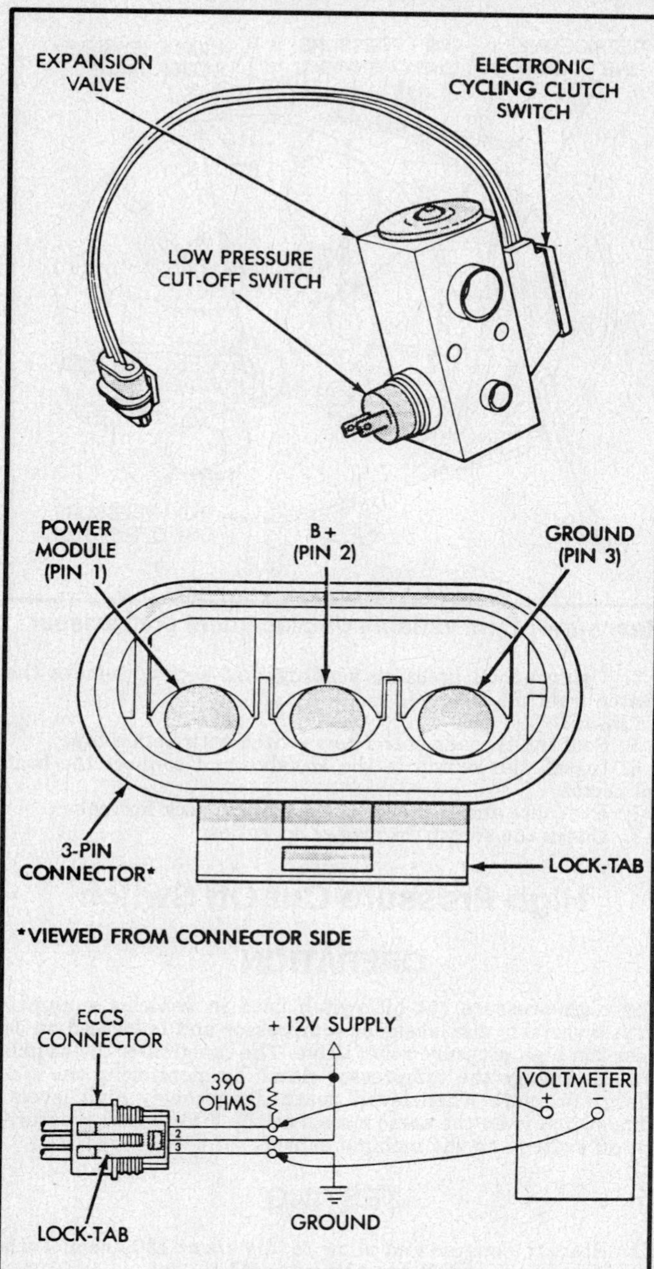

Electronic clutch cycling switch identification and testing—1993 Caravan, Voyager and Town & Country

- Dakota
- Van

The Fin Sensor Clutch Switch (FSCS) is located in the heater/air conditioning housing near the blower motor and has a sensing probe inserted into the evaporator fins. The FSCS prevents evaporator freeze-up by cycling the compressor clutch coil off when the evaporator temperature drops below freezing point. The coil will be cycled back on when the temperature rises above the freeze point. The FSCS uses a thermistor probe in a capillary tube inserted between the evaporator fins. The switch is a sealed unit that should be replaced if found to be defective.

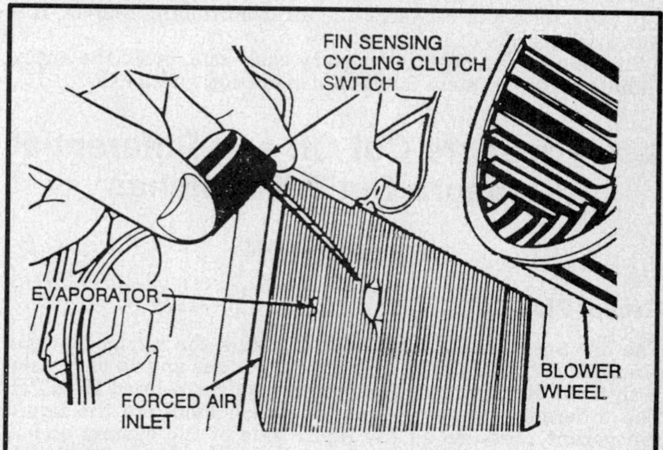

Installing the fin-sensing cycling clutch switch

TESTING

The compressor clutch coil should cycle 2-3 times per minute at ambient temperatures of 68-90°F (20-32°C). At temperatures above 90°F (32°C), the coil may be constantly engaged.

1. Test the switch in an area with ambient temperature of at least 70°F (21°C).
2. Disconnect the switch connector, located behind the glove box. Use a suitable jumper wire to jump between the outer wires of the harness connector.
3. If the compressor clutch engages, remove and replace the switch.
4. With jumper removed and connector reattached to the switch, and with ambient temperature between 68-90°F, clutch should engage 2-3 times per minute. If the compressor clutch does not engage, inspect the rest of the system for an open circuit.

REMOVAL AND INSTALLATION

1. Disconnect the negative battery cable.
2. On Dakota, remove the blower housing. On Vans, remove the heater/air conditioning housing and disassemble.
3. Disconnect the connector, push the wire grommet through the housing and feed the connector through the unit housing.
4. Remove the switch from the evaporator by pulling it through the air inlet opening.
5. The installation is the reverse of the removal procedure.

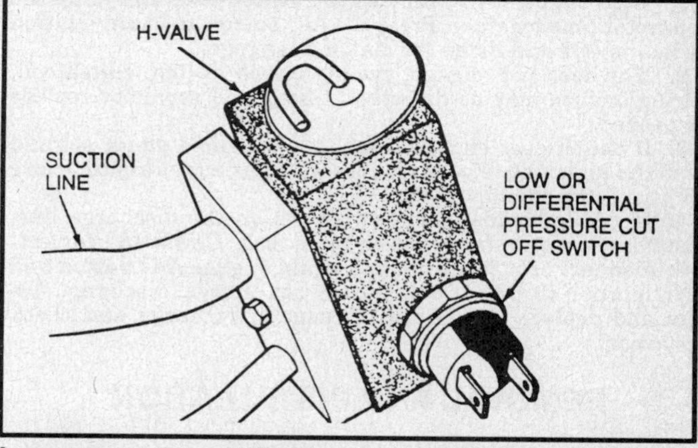

Low pressure or differential pressure cut off switch location

6. Evacuate and recharge the air conditioning system, if it was discharged.
7. Connect the negative battery cable and check the entire climate control system for proper operation and leaks.

Low Pressure Cut Off and Differential Pressure Cut Off Switches

OPERATION

Except Pick-Up

The low pressure cut off switch monitors the refrigerant gas pressure on the suction side of the system and is only used with fixed displacement compressors (silver colored H-valve). The differential pressure cut off switch monitors the liquid refrigerant pressure on the liquid side of the system and is only used with variable displacement compressors (black colored H valve). The switches operate similarly in that they turn off voltage to the compressor clutch coil when the monitored pressure drops to levels that could damage the compressor. The switches are sealed units that must be replaced, if faulty.

TESTING

Except Van

1. Connect a charging station or manifold gauge set to the system. Make sure ambient temperature is above 50°F. Start engine and idle.
2. Disconnect the **LPCO** or **DPCO** switch connector and use a jumper wire to jump between terminals inside the connector boot.
3. If the compressor clutch does not engage, inspect the system for an open circuit or faulty relay, ambient switch or high pressure cut off switch (if equipped).
4. If the clutch engages, connect an air conditioning manifold gauge to the system.
5. Read the low pressure gauge. The low pressure cut off switch should complete the clutch circuit at pressures of at least 14 psi. The differential pressure switch will complete the clutch circuit at pressure of at least 41 psi. Check the system for leaks if the pressures are too low or recharge if needed.
6. If the clutch does not engage when connector is installed and switch connection is jumped, the cut off switch is faulty and should be replaced.

Van

1. With engine **OFF**, remove the switch boot and jump the connector pins together. Press the A/C button and turn ignition switch to **ON** and listen for clutch to engage.
2. If it does not engage, cycling clutch switch, clutch coil, wiring or fuse may be defective. Check and repair or replace as needed.
3. If clutch does engage, connect a manifold gauge set and read the high side (discharge) pressure. At any pressure above 16 psi, clutch should engage.
4. If system reads less than 16 psi on the discharge line, system is low on refrigerant or has a leak. Check and correct.
5. Connect boot to switch and again engage **A/C** button and turn ignition to **ON**. If clutch does not engage, discharge system and replace the switch. Evacuate, recharge and check operation.

REMOVAL AND INSTALLATION

1. Disconnect the negative battery cable.
2. Properly discharge the air conditioning system.
3. Unplug the boot connector from the switch.

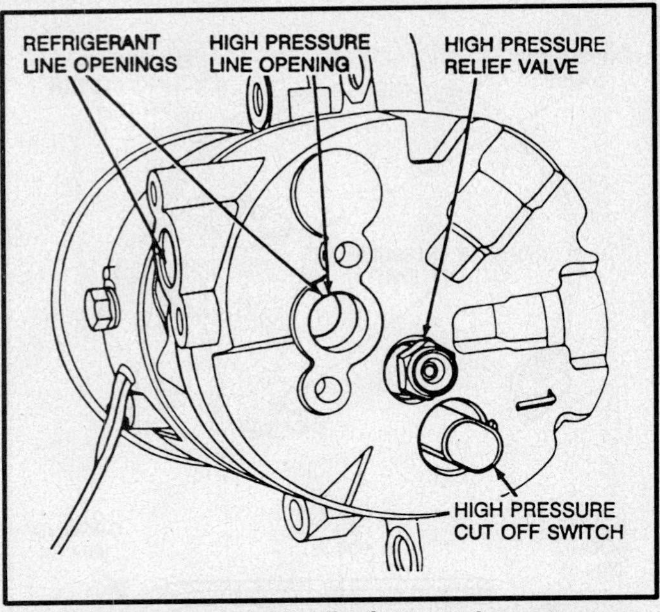

Rear view of the variable displacement compressor

4. Using an oil pressure sending unit socket, remove the switch from the H-valve.

To install:

5. Seal the threads of the new switch with Teflon tape.
6. Install the switch to the H-valve and connect the boot connector.
7. Evacuate and recharge the system. Check for leaks.
8. Check the switch for proper operation.

High Pressure Cut Off Switch

OPERATION

The high pressure cut off switch used in vehicles equipped with a variable displacement compressor and is located on or near the high pressure relief valve. The function of the switch is to disengage the compressor clutch by monitoring the discharge pressure when levels reach dangerously high levels. This switch is on the same circuit as the differential pressure cut off switch and the ambient sensor.

TESTING

1. Start the engine and allow to idle about 1300 rpm. Turn the air conditioner **ON** and blower to **HI**.
2. Connect an air conditioning manifold gauge to the system. The clutch should be engaged when high gauge pressure below 430 psi.
3. Without allowing the engine to overheat, block the flow of air to the condenser with a cover. When the high pressure reaches 450 psi, the clutch should disengage.
4. Remove the cover. When the gauge reading falls below 265 psi, the clutch should cycle back **ON**.
5. Replace the switch, if it does not operate properly.

REMOVAL AND INSTALLATION

1. Disconnect the negative battery cable.
2. Properly discharge the air conditioning system.
3. Disconnect the connector from the switch.
4. Remove the snapring that retains the switch in the compressor.

5. Pull the switch straight from the compressor and discard the O-ring.

To install:

6. Replace the O-ring and lubricate with refrigerant oil before installing.
7. Install the switch to the compressor and secure with a new snapring (use same color snapring as original).
8. Evacuate and recharge the system. Check for leaks.
9. Check the switch for proper operation.

Ambient Temperature Switch

OPERATION

The ambient switch is used in vehicles equipped with a variable displacement compressor and is located behind the grille and in front of condenser. The ambient sensor prevents the compressor clutch from engaging when the ambient temperature is below 50°F (10°C). The ambient switch is a sealed unit and should be replaced, if defective.

TESTING

1. Disconnect the ambient switch connector.
2. Check the continuity across the switch terminals. At ambient temperatures above 50°F (10°C), the circuit should be complete.
3. Chill the switch to below 50°F (10°C) and recheck for continuity. The switch should be open (no continuity) below the specified temperature.
4. Replace the switch, if it is found to be defective.

REMOVAL AND INSTALLATION

1. Disconnect the switch connector.
2. Remove the mounting screw and the switch.
3. Install in reverse of removal procedure.

Condenser Fan Control Switch

OPERATION

The condenser fan control switch is used in vehicles with a variable displacement compressor and is located on the discharge line at the compressor. This switch turns the condenser fan **ON** and **OFF** by monitoring the compressor discharge pressure. The radiator top tank sensor can override this switch and cycle the fan any time the engine temperature gets too high.

TESTING

CAUTION

Keep away from fan blades. Fan can start at any time.

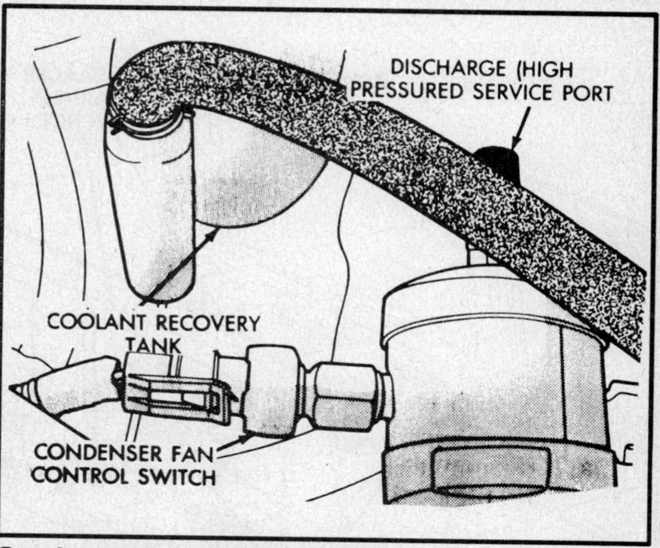

Condenser fan control switch location

1. Disconnect the fan control switch connector.
2. Connect an air conditioning manifold gauge to the system.
3. Jump across the terminals in the wire connector with a jumper wire.
4. Connect an ohmmeter to the switch terminals.
5. Start the engine and allow to idle at 1300 rpm. The radiator fan should run constantly.
6. Turn **ON** the air conditioner and set blower to high speed.
7. If the high pressure reads below 160 psi, the switch should be open (no continuity).
8. Without allowing the engine to overheat, block the flow of air to the condenser with a cover. When the high pressure reaches 230 psi, the switch should close (continuity).
9. Remove the cover. When the pressure drops to below 160 psi, the switch should open again.
10. Replace the switch, if it is defective.

REMOVAL AND INSTALLATION

NOTE: System discharging is not necessary to remove the condenser fan control switch; only a small amount of refrigerant will escape as the switch is being rotated. Take the proper precautions.

1. Disconnect the negative battery cable.
2. Disconnect the connector from the switch.
3. Loosen and quickly rotate the switch counterclockwise to separate the switch from the high pressure line.
4. The installation is the reverse of the removal procedure. Check the switch for proper operation.

REAR AUXILIARY SYSTEM

Expansion Valve

REMOVAL AND INSTALLATION

Caravan, Voyager and Town & Country

1. Disconnect the negative battery cable.
2. Properly discharge the air conditioning system and relieve pressure from cooling system.
3. Remove the middle bench, if equipped. Remove the interior left quarter trim panel as follows:
   - Remove the ashtray and screw behind the ashtray.
   - Pull bottom of quarter trim insert outward to detach retaining clips.

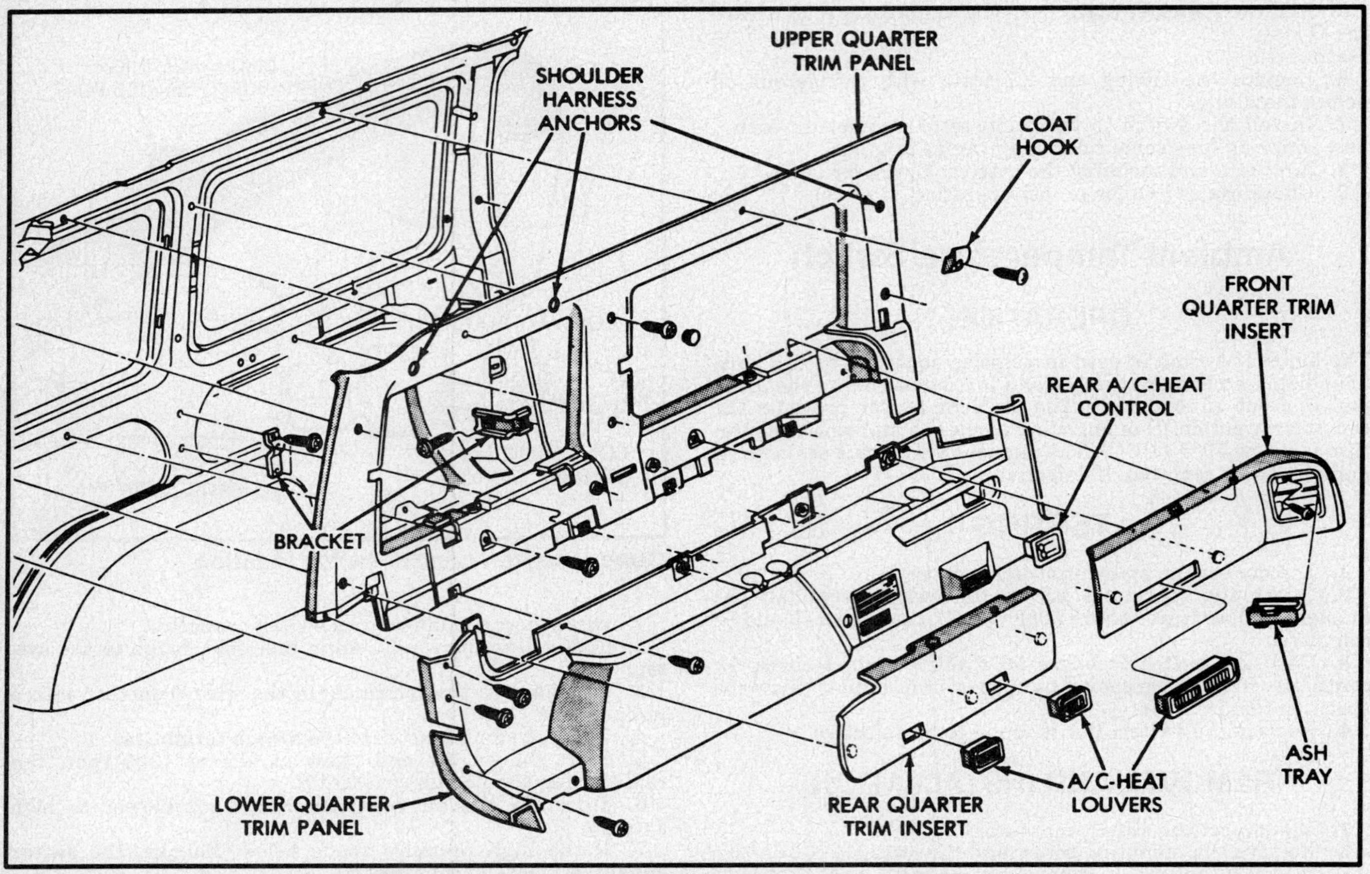

Interior left quarter trim components—Caravan, Voyager and Town & Country

- Lift quarter trim insert up and remove from the vehicle.
- Remove the lower quarter trim from the vehicle.
- Remove cover and bolts attaching the shoulder harness to upper quarter panel. Then remove outboard seat belt anchor bolt from floor. Remove seat belt retractors.
- Remove coat hook and screws holding upper quarter trim to inner quarter panel. Remove panel from the vehicle.

4. Remove the fan-A/C distribution duct.
5. Remove the A/C unit cover.
6. Remove the bolt that secures the refrigerant lines to the expansion valve. Then carefully pull the evaporator and expansion valve straight out of the housing, so as not to scratch the sealing surfaces with the tubes.
7. Remove and discard the aluminum gasket. Cover the exposed ends of the lines to minimize contamination.
8. Remove the Torx® screws and remove the expansion valve from the evaporator. Discard the gasket.

To install:

9. Lubricate the gasket with wax-free refrigerant oil and assemble the expansion valve and evaporator.
10. Lubricate the gasket with wax-free refrigerant oil and carefully install the evaporator and expansion valve assembly to the refrigerant lines and install the bolt.
11. Install the unit cover and air distribution duct.
12. Install the interior trim cover and middle bench.
13. Evacuate and recharge the air conditioning system.
14. Connect the negative battery cable and check the entire climate control system for proper operation and leaks.

Van

1. Disconnect the negative battery cable.

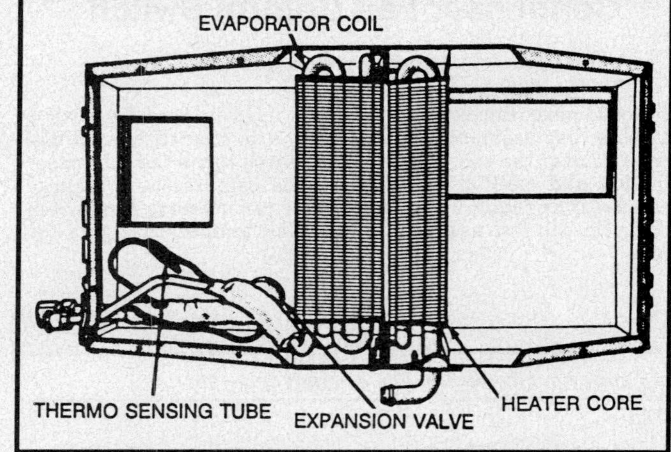

Rear air conditioning components—Van

2. Properly discharge the air conditioning system.
3. Raise and support the vehicle. From underneath, disconnect the refrigerant lines to the rear unit and remove the lower cover. Cover exposed ends of the lines to minimize contamination.
4. Disconnect the lines from the expansion valve. Detach the capillary tube from the refrigerant line and pull the thermo sensing bulb from the well.
5. The installation is the reverse of the removal procedure.
6. Evacuate and recharge the air conditioning system.

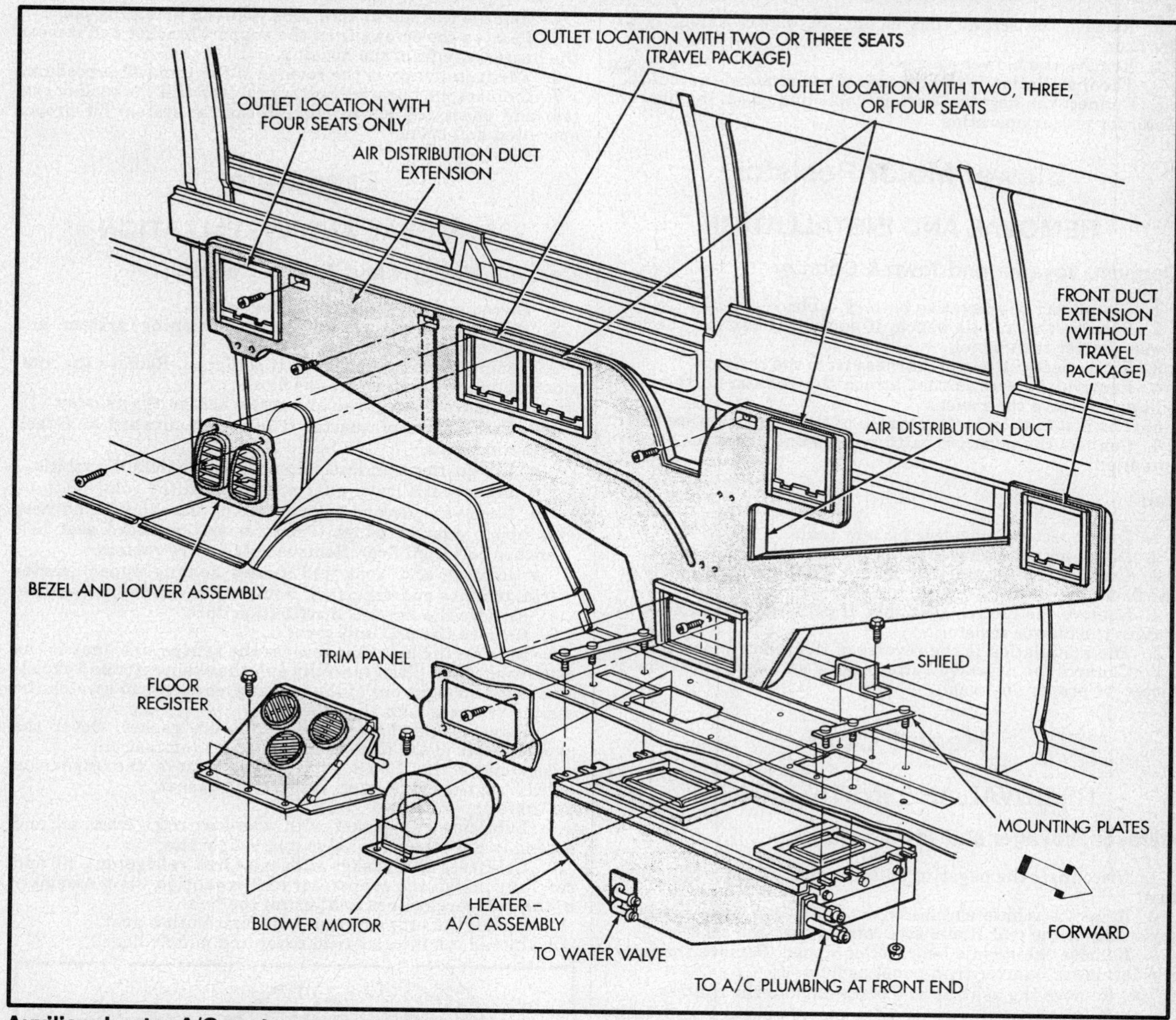

Auxiliary heater-A/C system components—Van

7. Connect the negative battery cable and check the entire climate control system for proper operation and leaks.

Blower Motor

REMOVAL AND INSTALLATION

Caravan, Voyager and Town & Country

1. Disconnect the negative battery cable.
2. Remove the middle bench, if equipped. Remove the left lower quarter trim panel as follows:
   - Remove the ashtray and screw behind the ashtray.
   - Pull bottom of quarter trim insert outward to detach retaining clips.
   - Lift quarter trim insert up and remove from the vehicle.
   - Remove the lower quarter trim from the vehicle.
   - Remove cover and bolts attaching the shoulder harness to upper quarter panel. Then remove outboard seat belt anchor bolt from floor. Remove seat belt retractors.
   - Remove coat hook and screws holding upper quarter trim to inner quarter panel. Remove panel from the vehicle.
3. Remove 1 blower cover to floor screw and 7 cover to unit screws.
4. Rotate the blower scroll cover from under the unit.
5. Compress the clamp at the center of the blower wheel and pull wheel from blower shaft.
6. Remove the 3 motor attaching screws and remove the motor from the unit.
7. The installation is the reverse of the removal procedure.
8. Connect the negative battery cable and check the blower motor for proper operation.

Van

1. Disconnect the negative battery cable.
2. Disconnect the blower motor connectors.

3. Remove the screws that mount the blower assembly to the floor.
4. Remove the blower assembly.
5. The installation is the reverse of the removal procedure.
6. Connect the negative battery cable and check the blower motor for proper operation.

Blower Motor Resistor

REMOVAL AND INSTALLATION

Caravan, Voyager and Town & Country

1. Disconnect the negative battery cable.
2. Remove the middle bench, if equipped. Remove the left lower quarter trim panel.
3. Disconnect the wiring harness from the resistor.
4. Remove the screws that attach the resistor to the rear unit and remove the resistor.
5. The installation is the reverse of the removal procedure.
6. Connect the negative battery cable and check for proper operation.

Van

1. Disconnect the negative battery cable.
2. Disconnect the blower motor connectors.
3. Remove the screws that mount the blower assembly to the floor.
4. Remove the blower assembly. If possible, disassemble to service the blower resistor.
5. The installation is the reverse of the removal procedure.
6. Connect the negative battery cable and check the blower motor for proper operation.

Heater Core

REMOVAL AND INSTALLATION

Caravan, Voyager and Town & Country

1. Disconnect the negative battery cable. Drain cooling system.
2. Raise the vehicle and disconnect the heater hoses from the underbody to the rear heater core tubes. Lower the vehicle.
3. Remove the middle bench, if equipped. Remove the interior left lower quarter trim panel as follows:
   - Remove the ashtray and screw behind the ashtray.
   - Pull bottom of quarter trim insert outward to detach retaining clips.
   - Lift quarter trim insert up and remove from the vehicle.
   - Remove the lower quarter trim from the vehicle.
   - Remove cover and bolts attaching the shoulder harness to upper quarter panel. Then remove outboard seat belt anchor bolt from floor. Remove seat belt retractors.
   - Remove coat hook and screws holding upper quarter trim to inner quarter panel. Remove panel from the vehicle.
4. Remove the air distribution duct.
5. Remove the heater unit cover.
6. Pull the heater core straight up and out of the unit.
7. The installation is the reverse of the removal procedure.
8. Connect the negative battery cable and check for leaks.

Van

1. Disconnect the negative battery cable. Drain the cooling system.
2. Raise the vehicle. From underneath, disconnect the inlet and outlet hoses from the heater core tubes.
3. Remove the auxiliary unit lower cover.
4. Remove the heater core tube seal and mounting plate.
5. Remove the screws from the support bracket and remove the heater core from the housing.
6. The installation is the reverse of the removal procedure.
7. Connect the negative battery cable. Refill the cooling system and check the entire climate control system for proper operation and leaks.

Evaporator

REMOVAL AND INSTALLATION

Caravan, Voyager and Town & Country

1. Disconnect the negative battery cable.
2. Properly discharge the air conditioning system and relieve pressure from cooling system.
3. Remove the middle bench, if equipped. Remove the interior left quarter trim panel as follows:
   - Remove the ashtray and screw behind the ashtray.
   - Pull bottom of quarter trim insert outward to detach retaining clips.
   - Lift quarter trim insert up and remove from the vehicle.
   - Remove the lower quarter trim from the vehicle.
   - Remove cover and bolts attaching the shoulder harness to upper quarter panel. Then remove outboard seat belt anchor bolt from floor. Remove seat belt retractors.
   - Remove coat hook and screws holding upper quarter trim to inner quarter panel. Remove panel from the vehicle.
4. Remove the fan-A/C distribution duct.
5. Remove the A/C unit cover.
6. Remove the bolt that secures the refrigerant lines to the expansion valve. Then carefully pull the evaporator and expansion valve straight out of the housing, so as not to scratch the sealing surfaces with the tubes.
7. Remove and discard the aluminum gasket. Cover the exposed ends of the lines to minimize contamination.
8. Remove the Torx® screws and remove the expansion valve from the evaporator. Discard the gasket.

To install:

9. Lubricate the gasket with wax-free refrigerant oil and assemble the expansion valve and evaporator.
10. Lubricate the gasket with wax-free refrigerant oil and carefully install the evaporator and expansion valve assembly to the refrigerant lines and install the bolt.
11. Install the unit cover and air distribution duct.
12. Install the interior trim cover and middle bench.

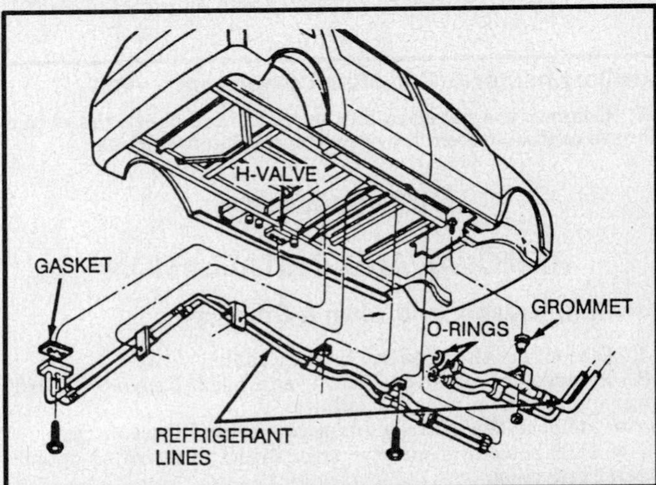

Rear air conditioning underbody plumbing—1993 Caravan, Voyager and Town & Country

13. Evacuate and recharge the air conditioning system.
14. Connect the negative battery cable and check the entire climate control system for proper operation and leaks.

PUSH-ON
COUPLINGS
HOSE
CLAMPS
HEATER
HOSES
HOSE
CLAMPS
REAR HEATER A/C
ENGINE COOLANT TUBING

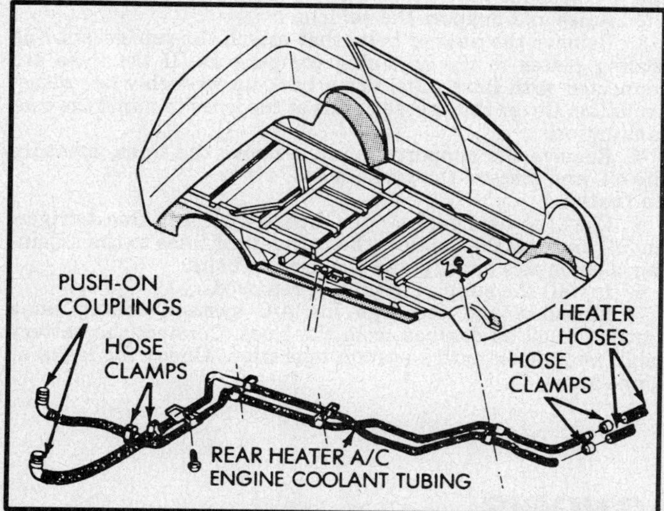

Rear heater underbody plumbing—1994–95 Caravan, Voyager and Town & Country

Van

1. Disconnect the negative battery cable.
2. Properly discharge the air conditioning system.
3. Raise the vehicle and support safely.
4. Disconnect the refrigerant lines and remove the auxiliary unit lower cover. Cover the exposed ends of the lines to minimize contamination.
5. Remove the seal and cover plate. Remove the evaporator from the rear unit.

To install:

6. The installation is the reverse of the removal procedure. Replace the O-rings when installing.
7. Evacuate and recharge the air conditioning system. If the evaporator was replaced, measure the amount of oil that was in the original evaporator and add that amount during the recharge.
8. Connect the negative battery cable and check the entire climate control system for proper operation and leaks.

Refrigerant Lines

REMOVAL AND INSTALLATION

Caravan, Voyager and Town & Country

1. Disconnect the negative battery cable.
2. Properly discharge the air conditioning system.
3. Raise the vehicle and support safely.

NOTE: As each refrigerant line is disconnected, openings should always be capped as soon as possible to minimize contamination.

4. Remove the bolt from the unified plumbing block (left side near fuel tank). Carefully pull lines down, being carefully not to scratch sealing surfaces. Remove and discard aluminum gasket. Cover the sealing surface.

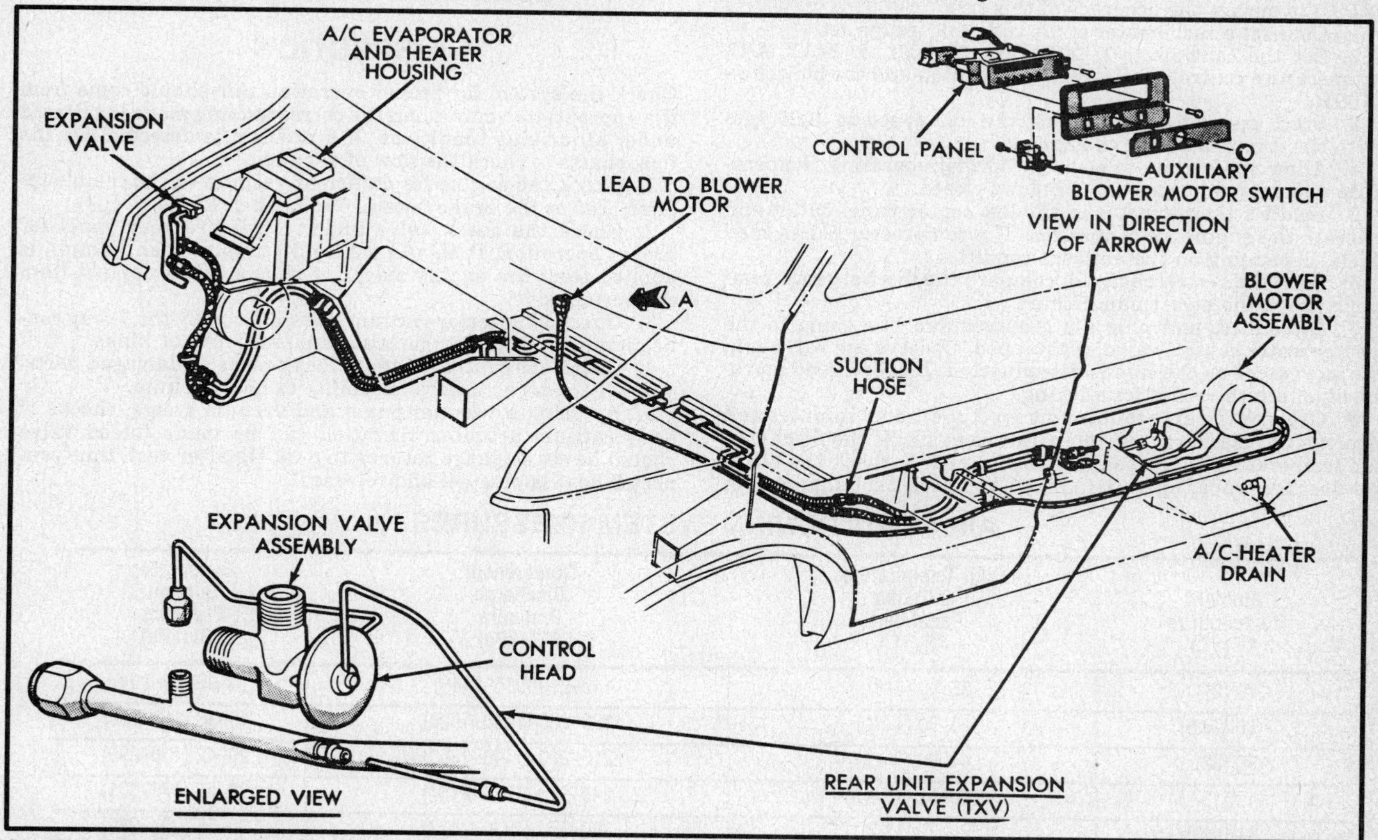

A/C EVAPORATOR
AND HEATER
HOUSING
EXPANSION
VALVE
CONTROL PANEL
AUXILIARY
BLOWER MOTOR SWITCH
LEAD TO BLOWER
MOTOR
A
VIEW IN DIRECTION
OF ARROW A
BLOWER
MOTOR
ASSEMBLY
SUCTION
HOSE
A/C-HEATER
DRAIN
EXPANSION VALVE
ASSEMBLY
CONTROL
HEAD
ENLARGED VIEW
REAR UNIT EXPANSION
VALVE (TXV)

Auxiliary heater-A/C system components—Van

5. Remove 2 screws holding plumbing to the floor pan.
6. Disconnect the parking brake at the hook above the muffler and the cable connection near the support rails.
7. Pull the nylon tubing and unified plumbing block above the muffler support member. Remove the refrigerant lines from the vehicle.

To install:

NOTE: If installing new lines, do not remove shipping caps until actually joining lines to protect the ends.

8. Coat the new gaskets or O-rings with wax-free refrigerant oil and install. Connect the refrigerant lines to the adjoining components and tighten the nuts or bolts.
9. Install the support mount.
10. Evacuate and recharge the air conditioning system. Adjust oil level, adding same amount as drained from lines upon removal.
11. Connect the negative battery cable and check the entire climate control system for proper operation and leaks.

Van

1. Disconnect the negative battery cable. Properly discharge the A/C system.
2. Raise and support the vehicle.
3. Remove the nuts or bolts that attach the refrigerant line sealing plates to the adjoining components. If the lines are connected with flare nuts, use a back-up wrench when disassembling. Cover the exposed ends of the lines to minimize contamination.
4. Remove the support mount. Remove the lines, measure the oil, and discard the gaskets or O-rings.

To install:

5. Coat the new gaskets or O-rings with wax-free refrigerant oil and install. Connect the refrigerant lines to the adjoining components and tighten the nuts or bolts.
6. Install the support mount, if removed.
7. Evacuate and recharge the A/C system, adding same amount of oil as drained from the lines. Connect the battery cable and check entire system operation. Check for leaks at connections.

SYSTEM DIAGNOSIS

Air Conditioning Performance

PERFORMANCE TEST

Air temperature in the testing area must be at least 70°F (21°C) to ensure the accuracy of this test.

1. Connect a tachometer and a manifold gauge set.
2. Set the controls to **RECIRC** or **PANEL** or **MAX A/C**, temperature control level on **COOL** position and the blower on **HIGH**.
3. Start the engine and adjust the idle speed to 1000 rpm with the compressor clutch engaged.
4. Allow the engine to come to normal operating temperature and keep all doors and windows closed.
5. Insert a thermometer in the left center panel outlet and operate the engine for 5 minutes. The compressor clutch may cycle, depending on the ambient conditions.
6. With the clutch engaged, compare the discharge air temperature to the performance chart.
7. Disconnect and plug the gray vacuum line going to the heater water control valve, if equipped. Observe the valve arm for movement as the line is disconnected. If there is no movement, check the valve for sticking.
8. Operate the air conditioning for 2 additional minutes and observe the discharge air temperature again. If the discharge air temperature increased by more than 5°F, check the blend air door for proper operation. If not, compare the temperature, suction and discharge pressures to the chart. Reconnect the gary vacuum line.
9. If the values do not meet specifications, check system components for proper operation.

Vacuum Actuating System

INSPECTION

Check the system for proper operation. Air should come from the appropriate vents when the corresponding mode is selected under all driving conditions. If a problem is detected use the flow-charts to check the flow of vacuum.

1. Check the engine for sufficient vacuum at the main supplier hose at the brake booster for leaks or kinks.
2. Check the check valve under the instrument panel for proper operation. It should not hold vacuum when vacuum is applied from the engine side, but should when applied from the system side.
3. Check all interior vacuum lines, especially the 7-way connection behind the instrument panel for leaks or kinks.
4. Check the control head for leaky ports or damaged parts.
5. Check all actuators for ability to hold vacuum.
6. By using a vacuum pump and vacuum gauge, checks of each vacuum actuator operation can be made (bleed valve should be set so gauge returns to 8 in. Hg after each time connector hose is plugged and released).

AIR CONDITIONING SYSTEM PRESSURES

Ambient Temperature °F (°C)	Air Temperature at Center Panel Vent °F (°C)	Compressor Discharge Pressure PSI (kPa)	Evaporator Suction Pressure PSI (kPa)
70 (21)	35–46 (2–8)	140–210 (965–1448)	10–35 (69–241)
80 (26.5)	39–50 (4–10)	180–235 (1240–1620)	16–38 (110–262)
90 (32)	44–50 (7–13)	210–270 (1448–1860)	20–42 (138–290)
100 (37.5)	50–62 (10–17)	240–310 (1655–2137)	25–48 (172–331)
110 (43)	56–70 (13–21)	280–350 (1930–2413)	30–55 (207–379)

7. Disconnect source vacuum at brake booster unit and connect hose to vacuum pump and gauge. Start test in **FLOOR** position. Watch vacuum gauge drop until actuator moves to position. It should then return to 7.25-8 in. Hg.
8. Repeat procedure for all other panel selections. Each time vacuum should drop then return to 7.25-8 in. Hg.
9. If vacuum drops below 7.25 in. Hg after each test, inspect 7-port hose connector for proper connections and leaks. If okay, plug port 3 of connector (source vacuum) with finger and use vacuum pump hose to alternately test each of the other ports.
10. If vacuum returns to 8 in. Hg after each port check, there are no leaks, but the control switch is faulty and must be replaced.
11. If vacuum drops below 7.25 in. Hg at one or more ports, isolate the faulty hose or actuator and replace as needed.

Air Conditioning Compressor

COMPRESSOR NOISE

Noises that develop during air conditioning operation can be misleading. A noise that sounds like serious compressor damage may only be a loose belt, mounting bolt or clutch assembly. Improper belt tension can also emit a noise that can be mistaken for more serious problems. Check and adjust all possible causes of the noise before replacing the compressor.

COMPRESSOR CLUTCH INOPERATIVE

The air conditioning compressor clutch electrical circuit is controlled by the engine (powertrain) controller (SMEC or SBEC) located in the engine compartment. If the compressor clutch does not engage, check for proper belt tension, tight mounting bolts, and compressor oil level (if there is evidence of an oil leak), etc. If these appear okay, continue on to the diagnostic charts.

NOTE: Do not use a 12 volt test light to probe wires or damage to the on-board computer may result.

CLUTCH COIL TESTING

1. Verify battery charge. Connect an ammeter (0-10 ampere scale) in series with the clutch coil terminal. Use a voltmeter (0-20 volt scale) with clip leads measuring voltage across the battery and A/C clutch.
2. With A/C control at **A/C** and blower at **LOW** speed, start the engine and run at normal idle.
3. The A/C clutch should engage immediately and clutch voltage should be within 2.0 volts of the battery voltage. If clutch does not engage, check the fuse. Test the fusible link with front wheel drive vehicles.
4. If current draw is 2.0-3.7 amperes at 11.5-12.5 volts at the clutch coil, coil is acceptable.
5. If voltage is more than 12.5 volts, add electrical loads by turning on accessories until voltage drops below 12.5 volts.
6. If clutch coil voltage is 0, the coil is open and should be replaced. If ammeter reading is 4 amps or more, the coil is shorted and should be replaced.
7. If coil voltage is not within 2 volts of the battery voltage, test clutch coil feed circuit for excessive voltage drop.

VACUUM SCHEMATICS

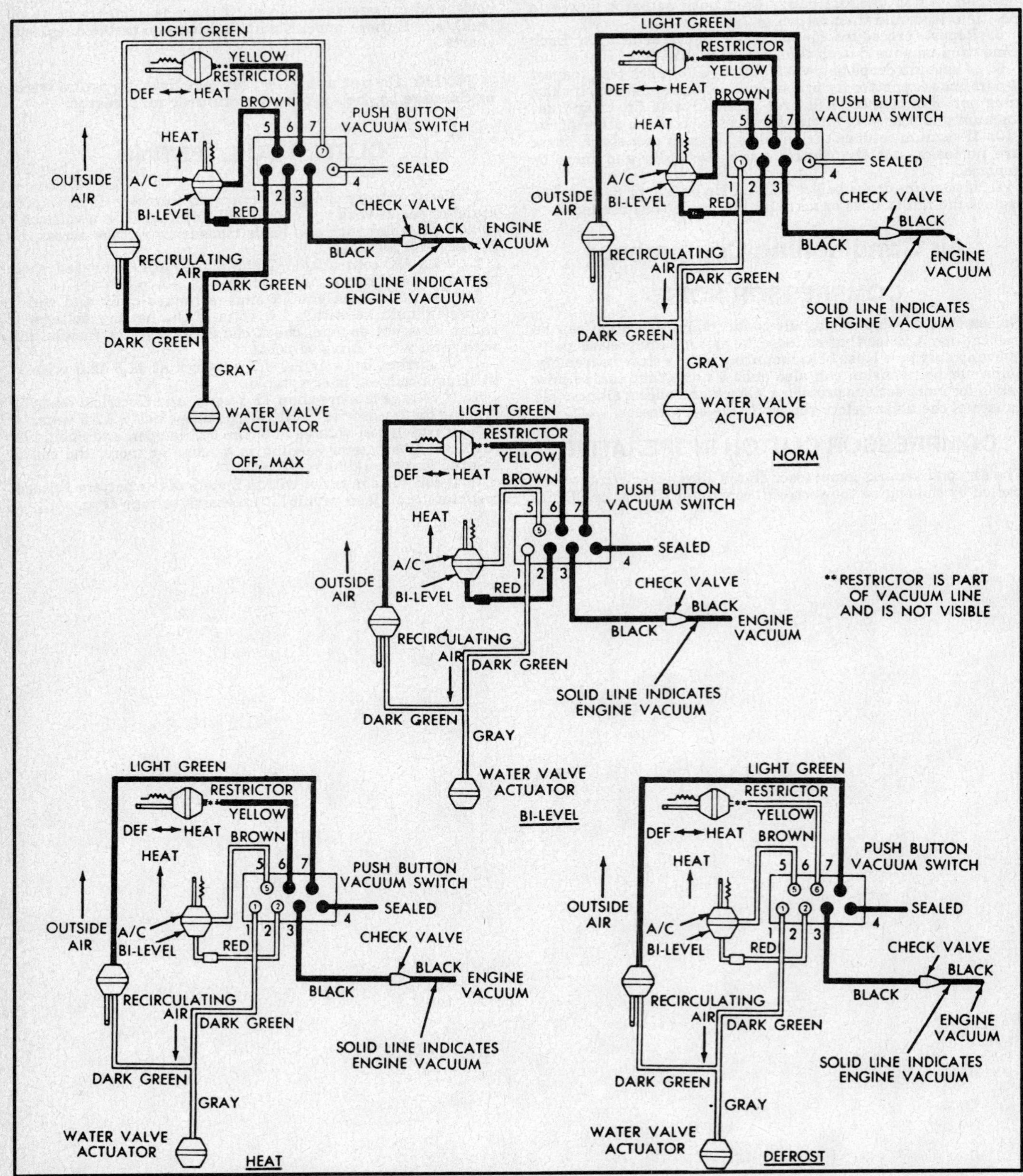

Vacuum schematic—Caravan, Voyager and Town & Country

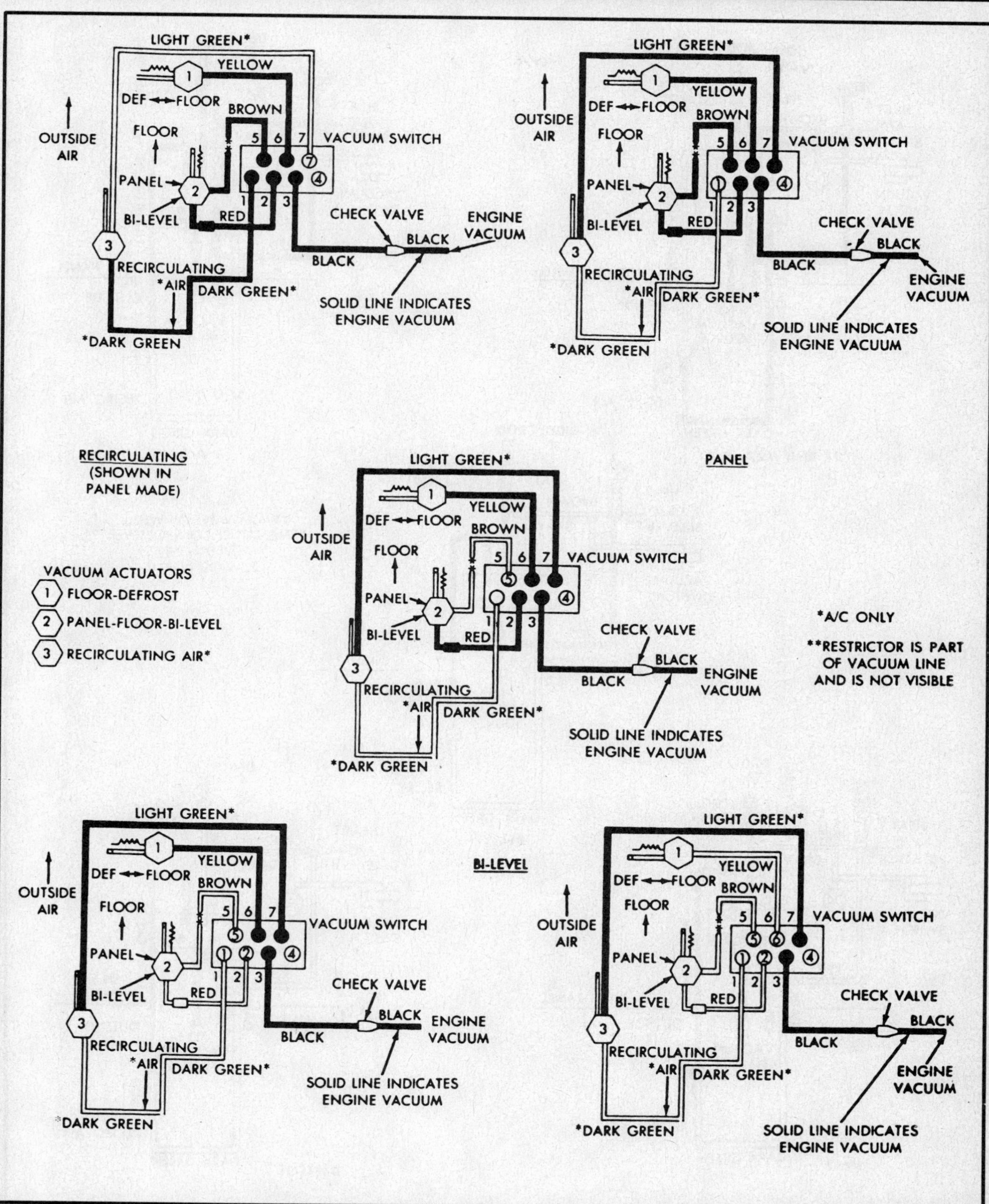

Vacuum schematic—Dakota

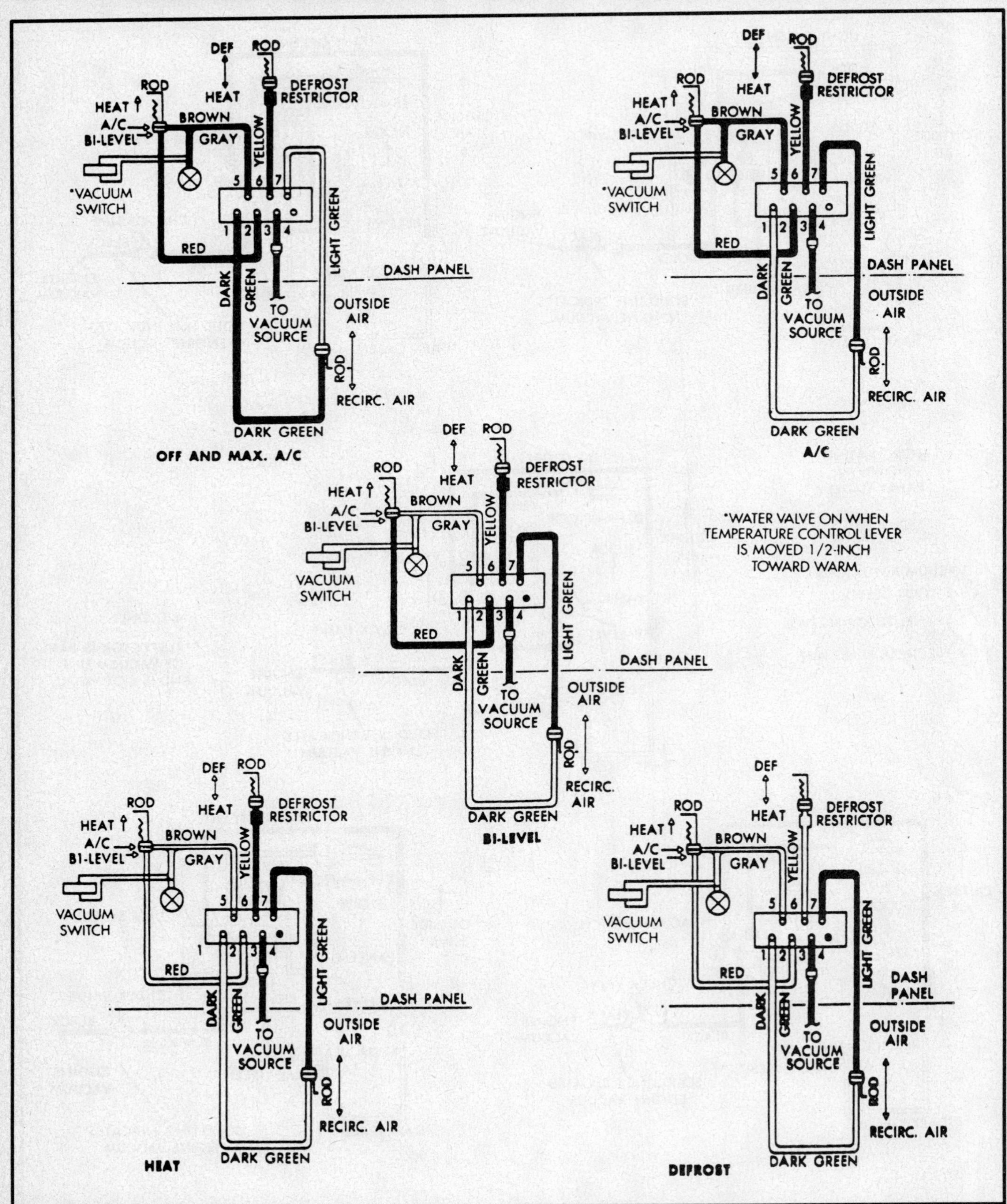

Vacuum schematic—Van

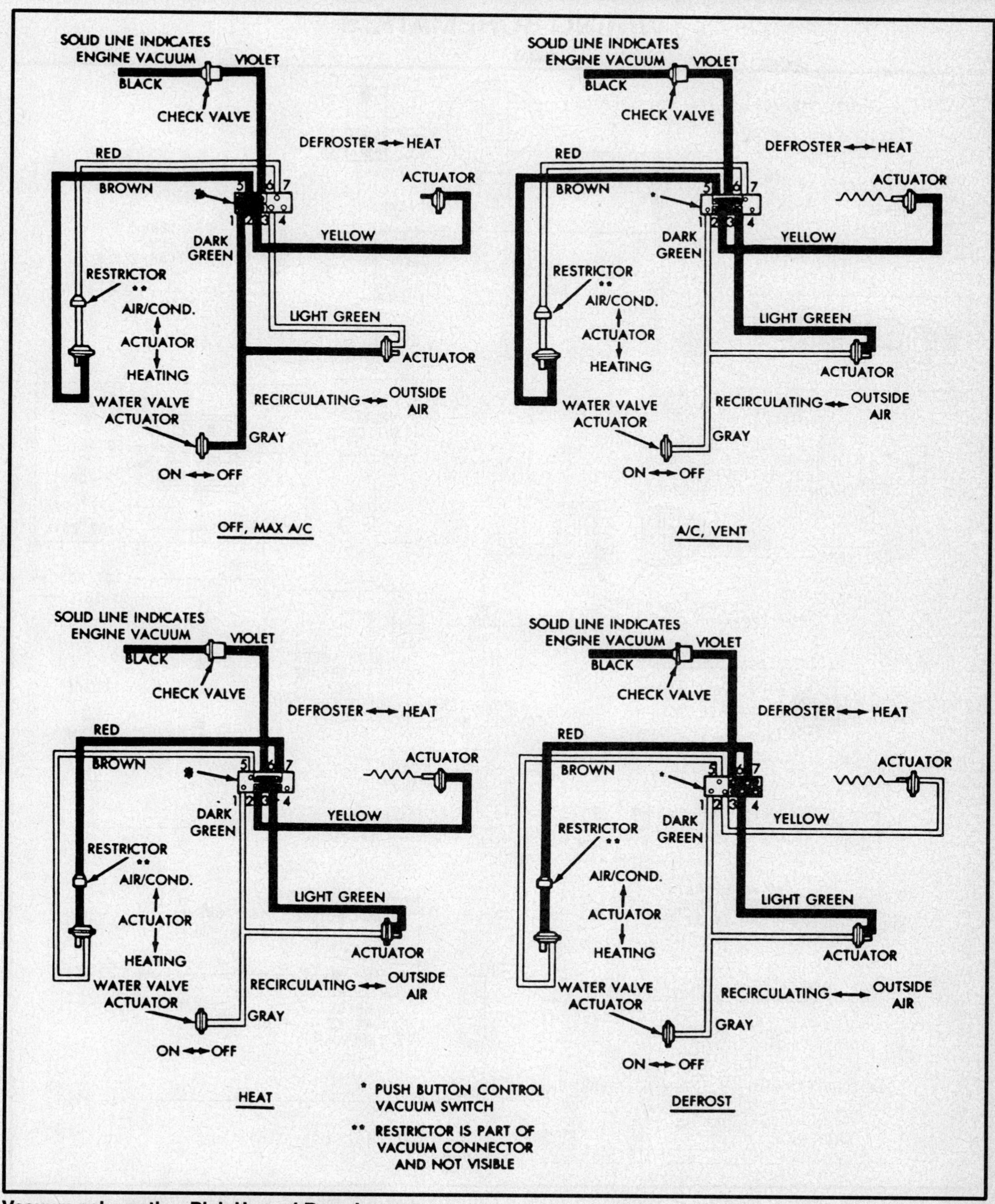

Vacuum schematic—Pick-Up and Ramcharger

WIRING SCHEMATICS

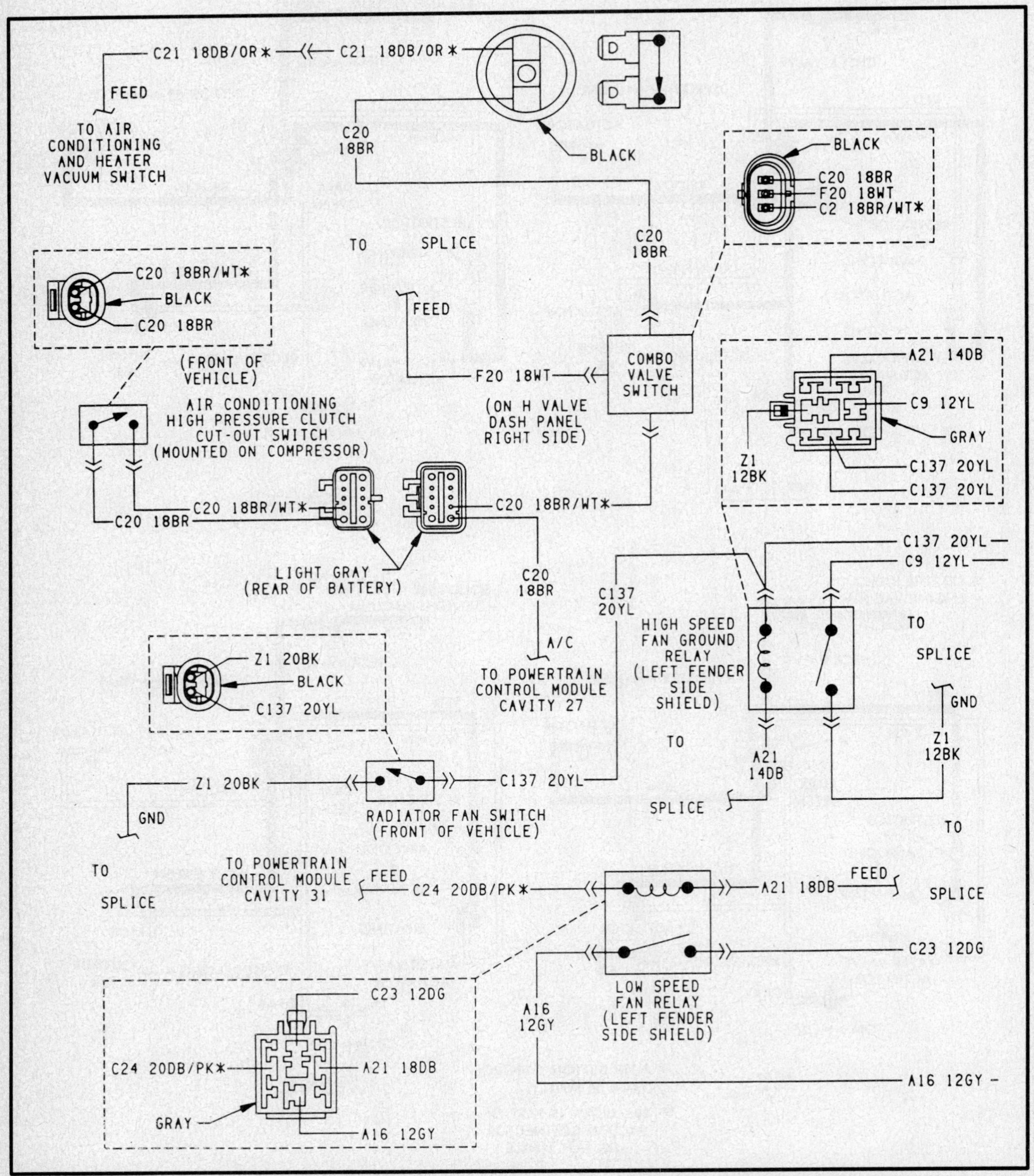

Wiring schematic—1993 Caravan, Voyager and Town & Country with A/C system with 2.5L engine

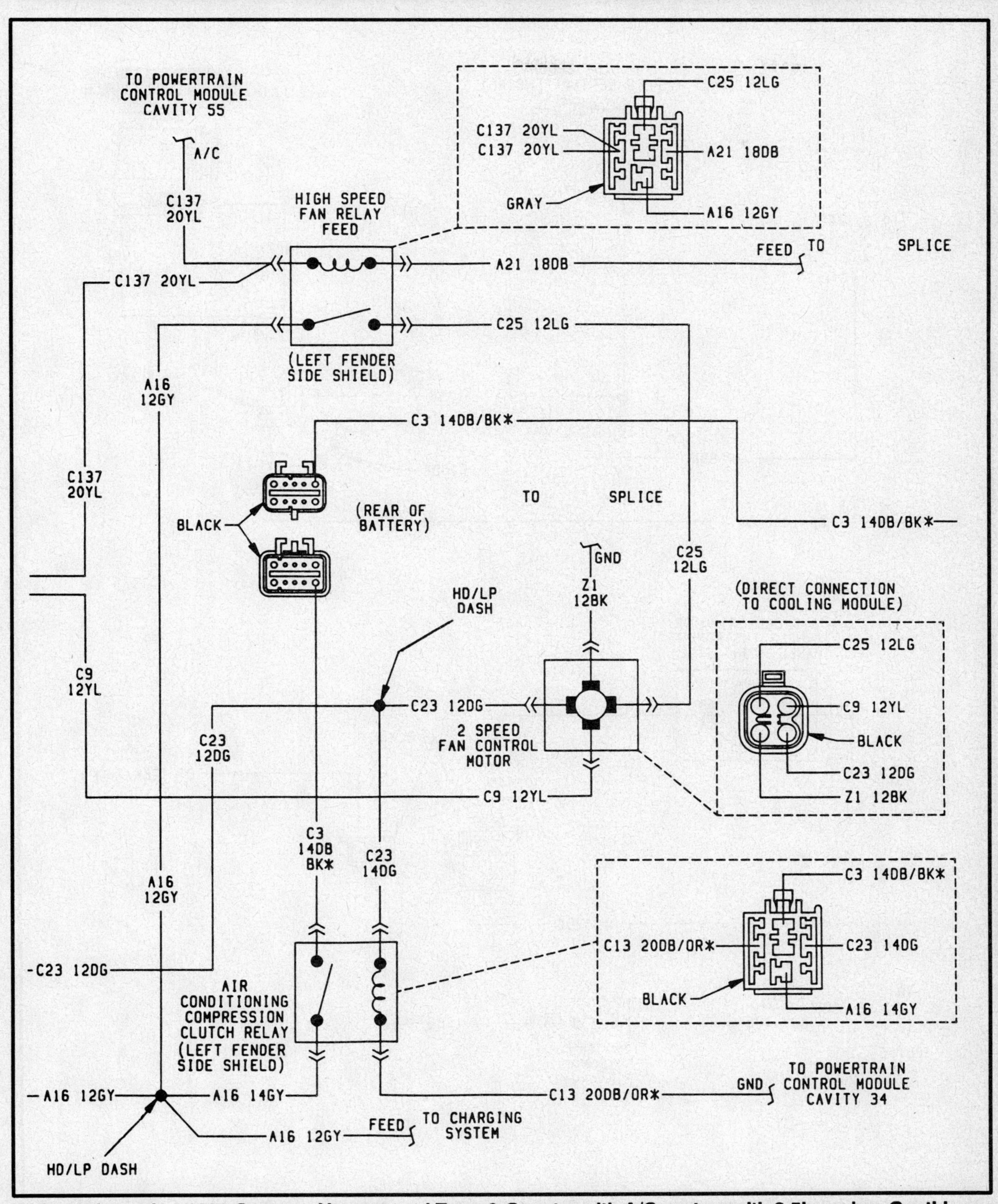

Wiring schematic—1993 Caravan, Voyager and Town & Country with A/C system with 2.5L engine, Cont'd

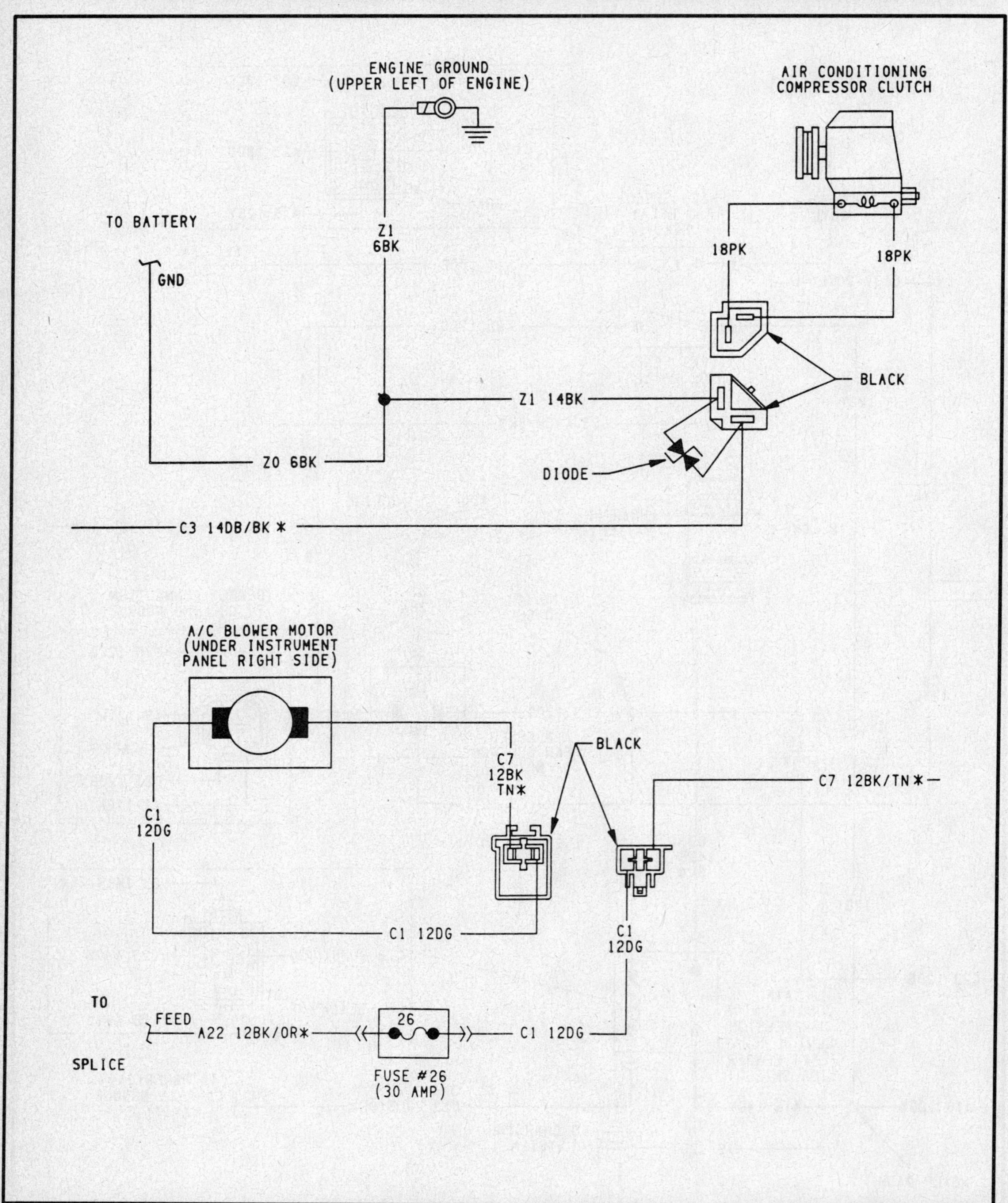

Wiring schematic—1993 Caravan, Voyager and Town & Country with A/C system with 2.5L engine, Cont'd

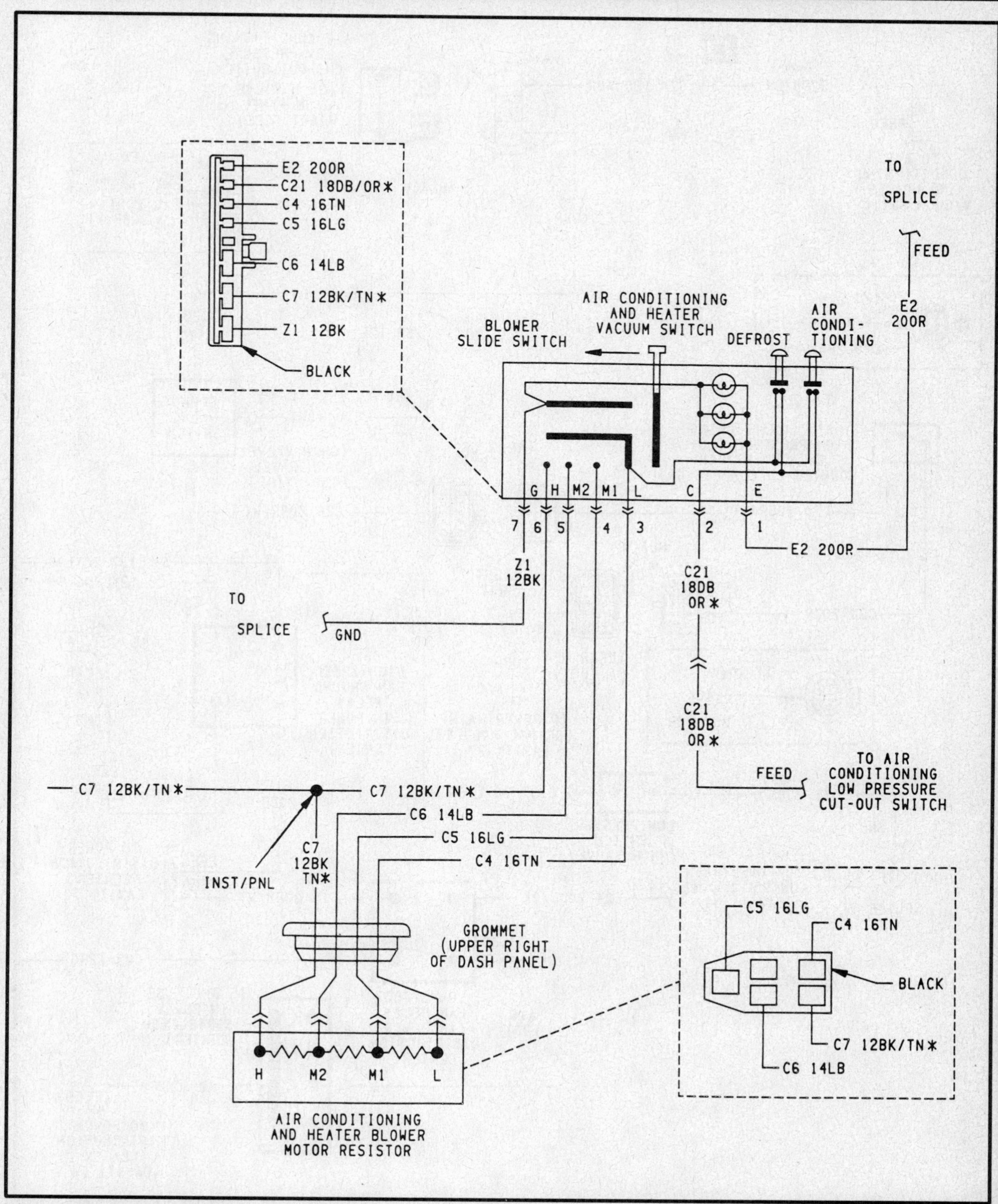

Wiring schematic—1993 Caravan, Voyager and Town & Country with A/C system with 2.5L engine, Cont'd

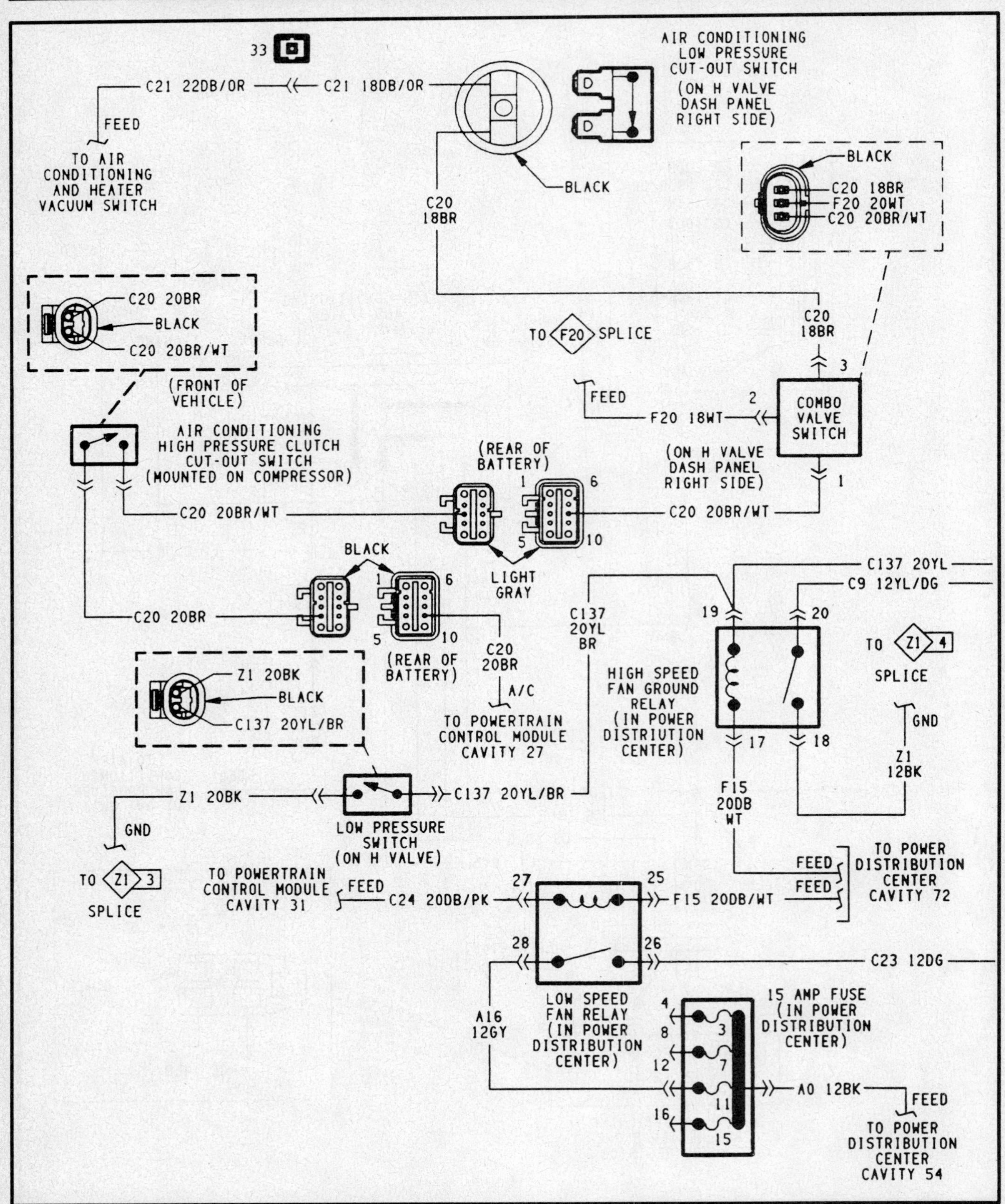

Wiring schematic—1994–95 Caravan, Voyager and Town & Country with heater-A/C system with 2.5L engine

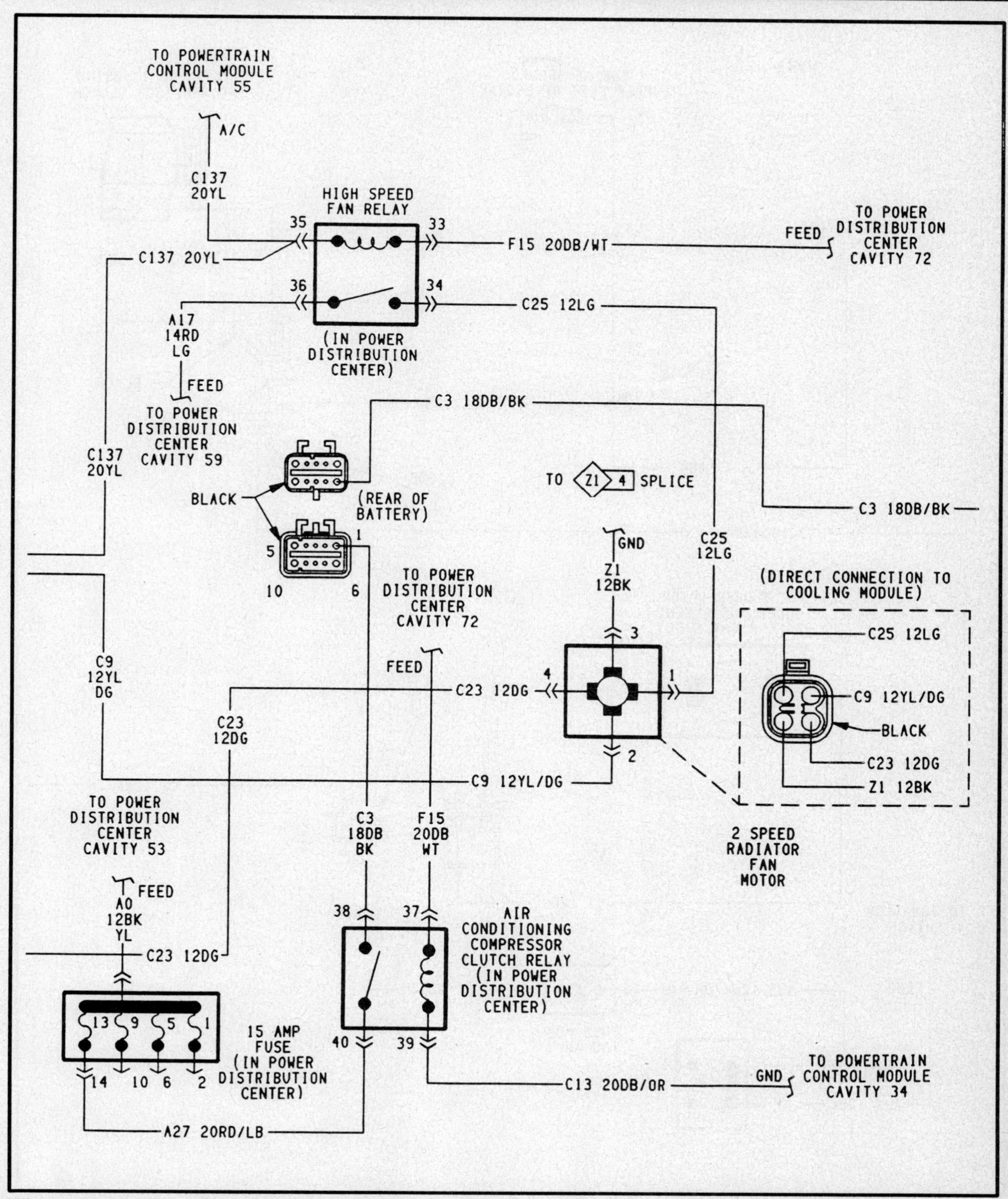

Wiring schematic—1994–95 Caravan, Voyager and Town & Country with heater-A/C system with 2.5L engine, Cont'd

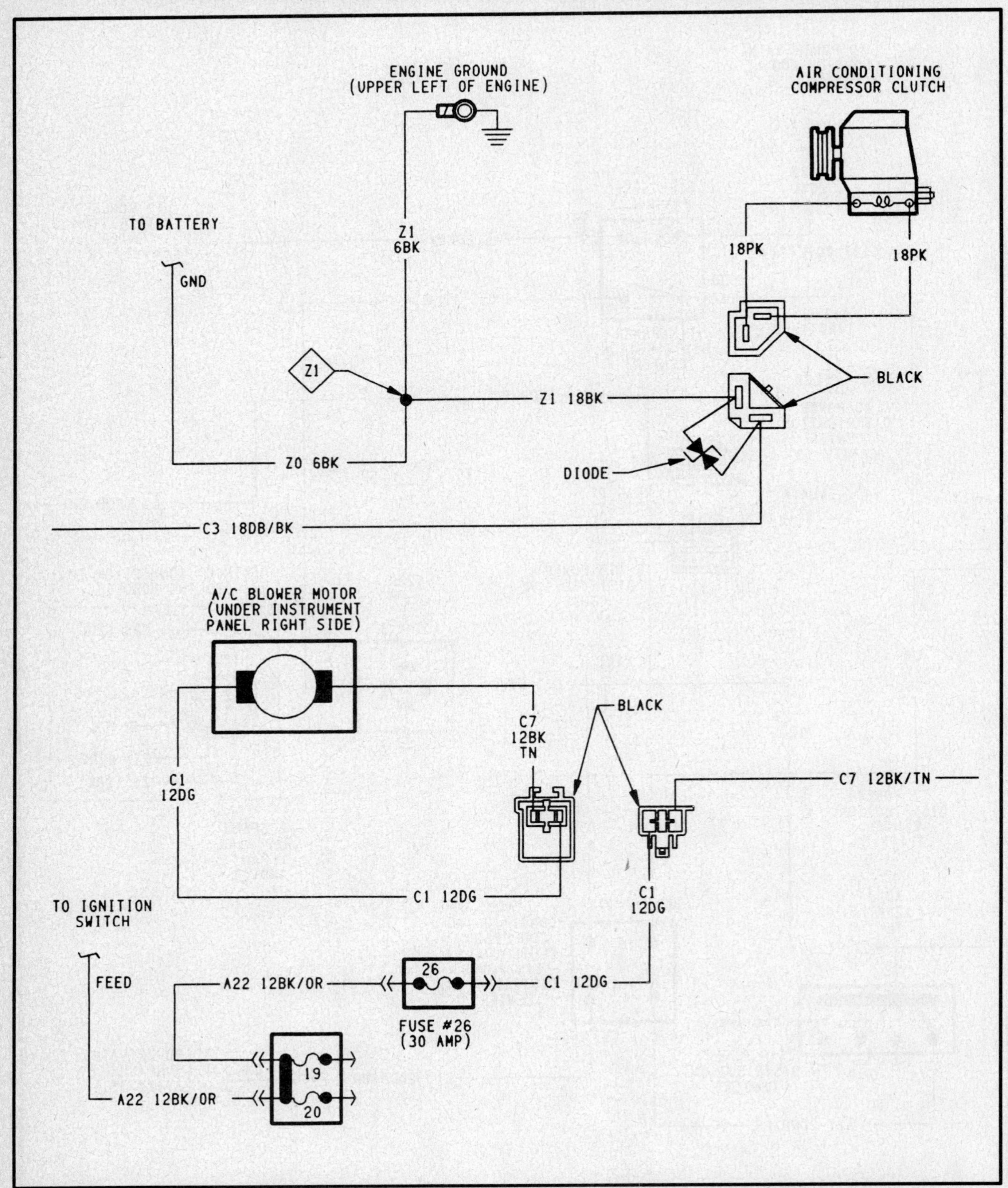

Wiring schematic—1994–95 Caravan, Voyager and Town & Country with heater-A/C system with 2.5L engine, Cont'd

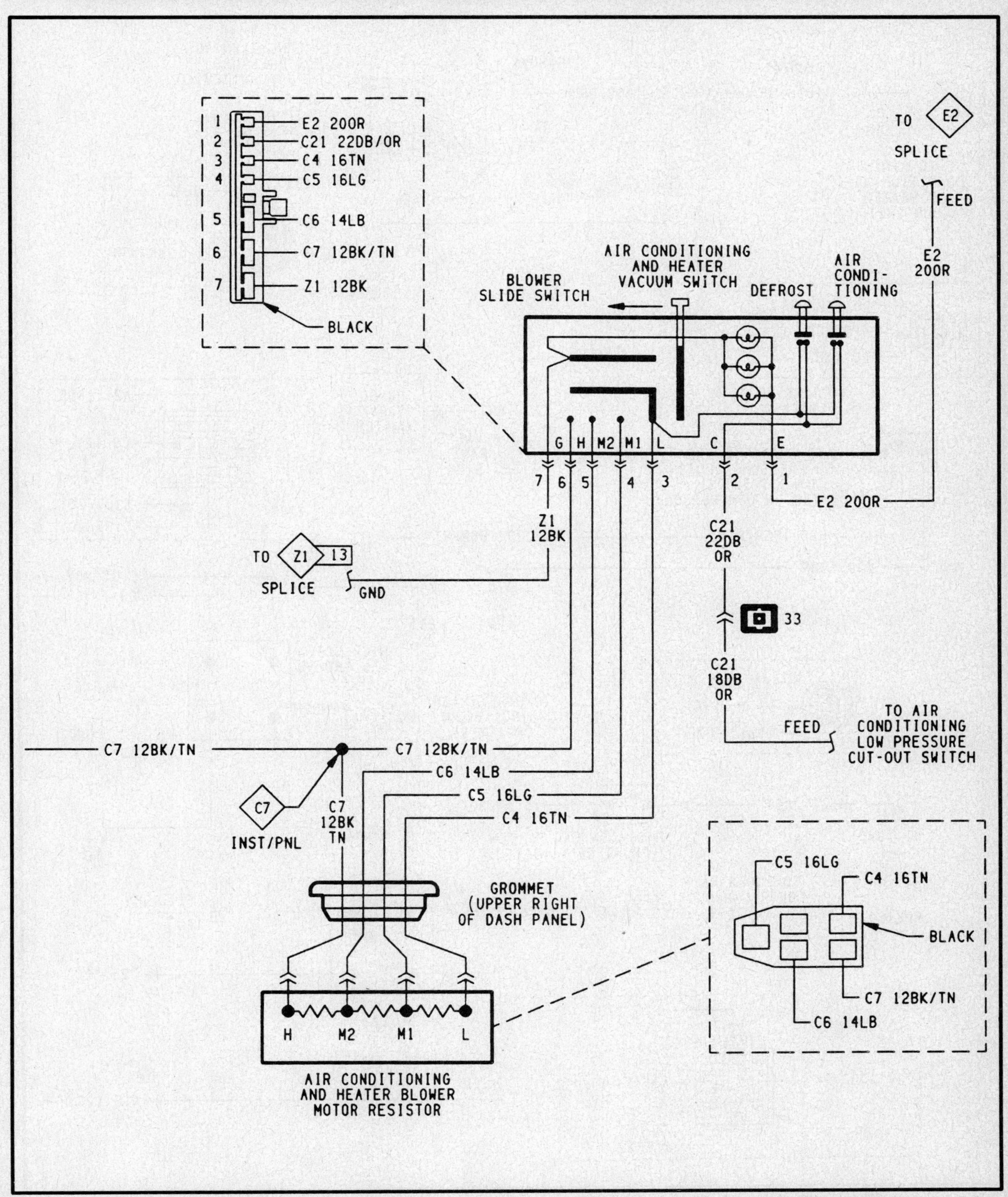

Wiring schematic—1994–95 Caravan, Voyager and Town & Country with heater-A/C system with 2.5L engine, Cont'd

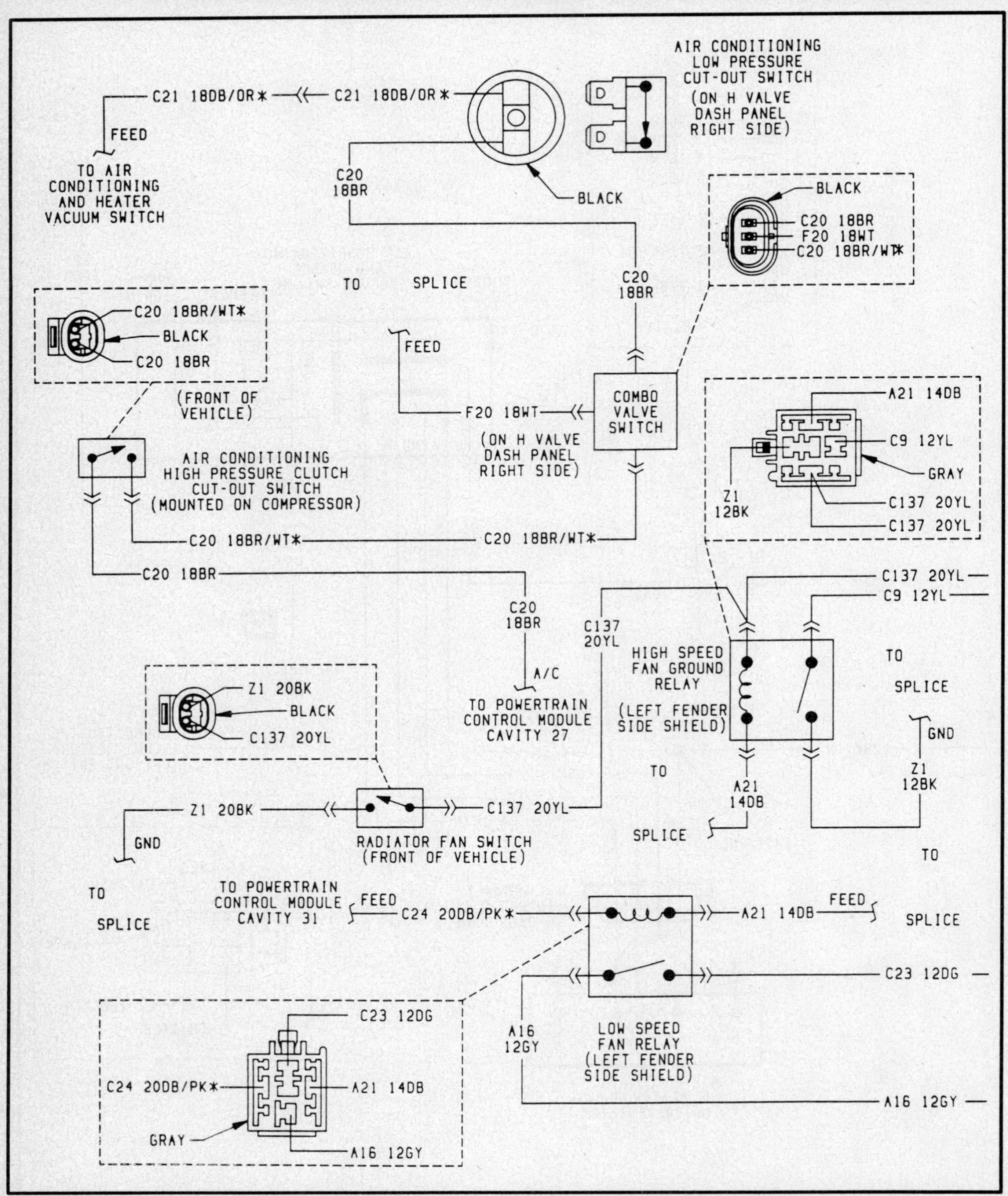

Wiring schematic—1993 Caravan, Voyager and Town & Country with heater-A/C system with 3.0L engine without electronic transaxle

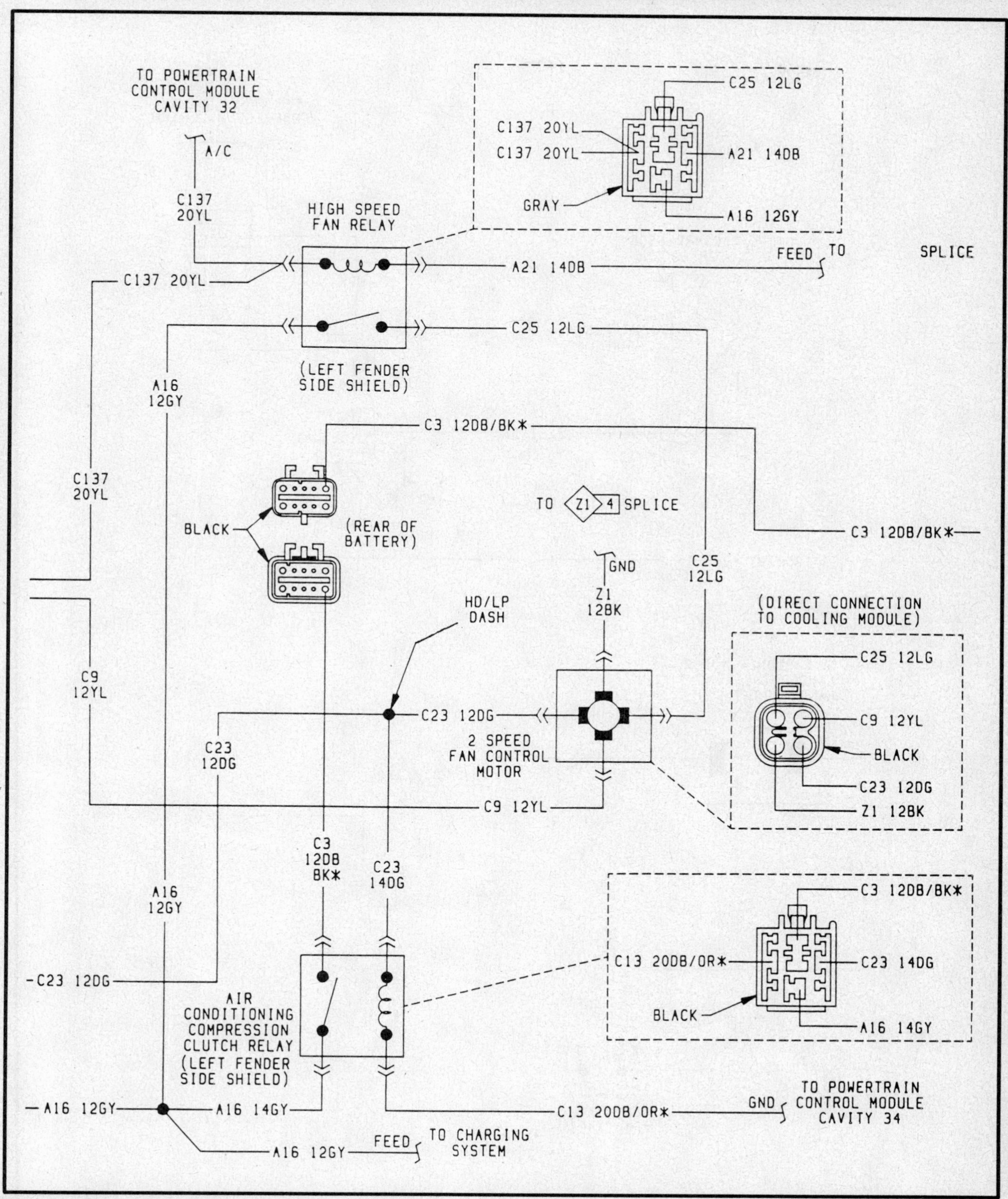

Wiring schematic—1993 Caravan, Voyager and Town & Country with heater-A/C system with 3.0L engine without electronic transaxle, Cont'd

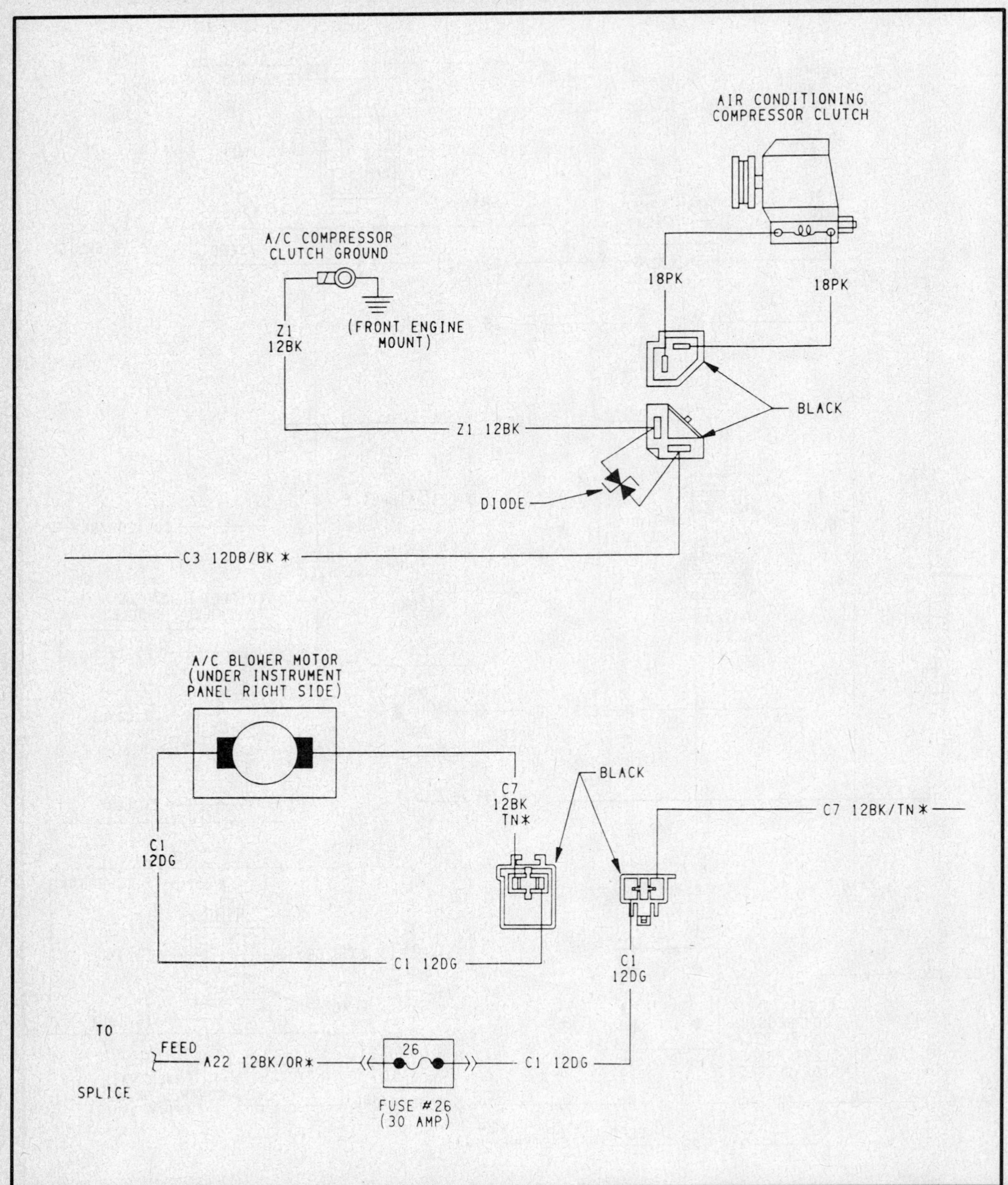

Wiring schematic—1993 Caravan, Voyager and Town & Country with heater-A/C system with 3.0L engine without electronic transaxle, Cont'd

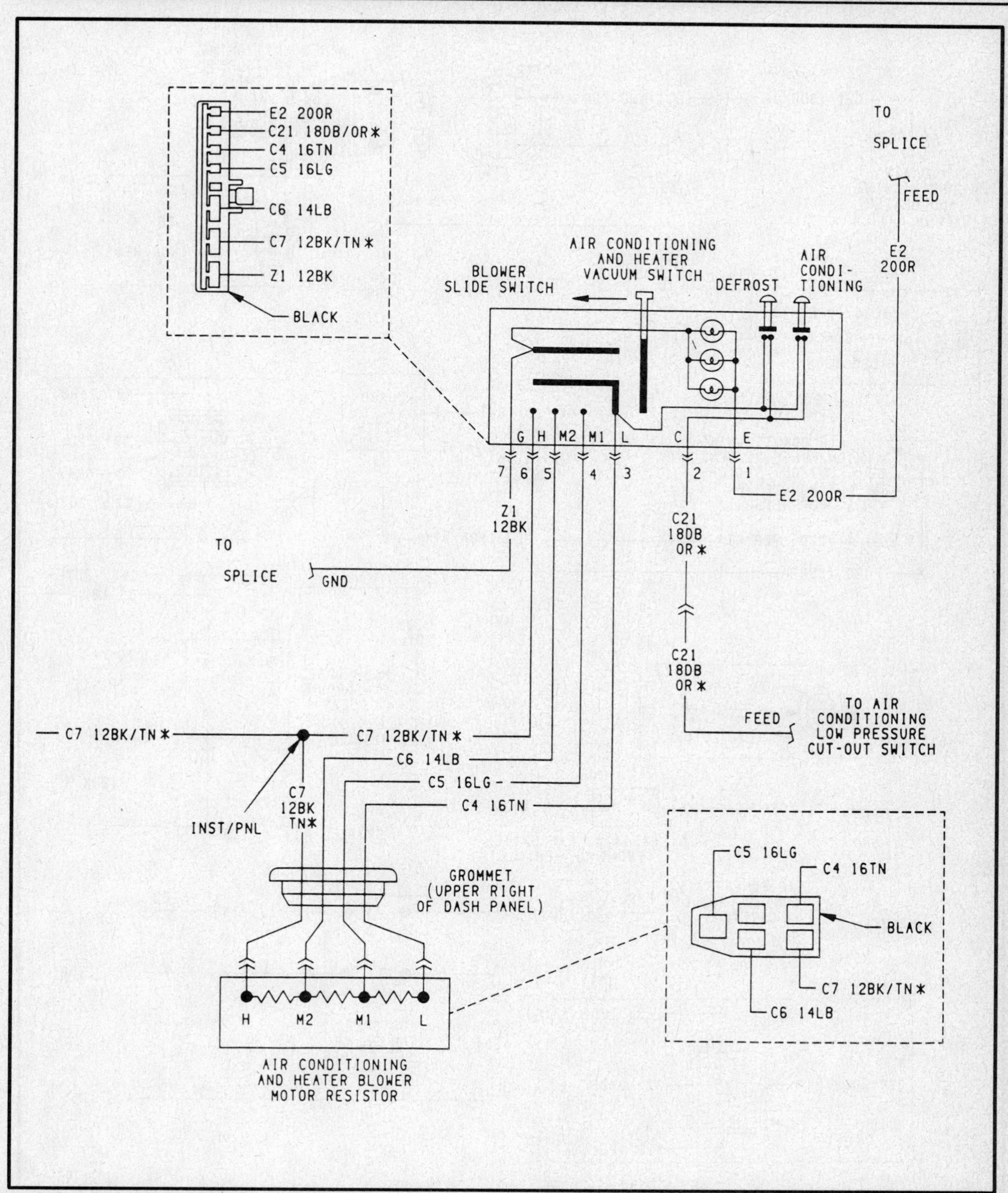

Wiring schematic—1993 Caravan, Voyager and Town & Country with heater-A/C system with 3.0L engine without electronic transaxle, Cont'd

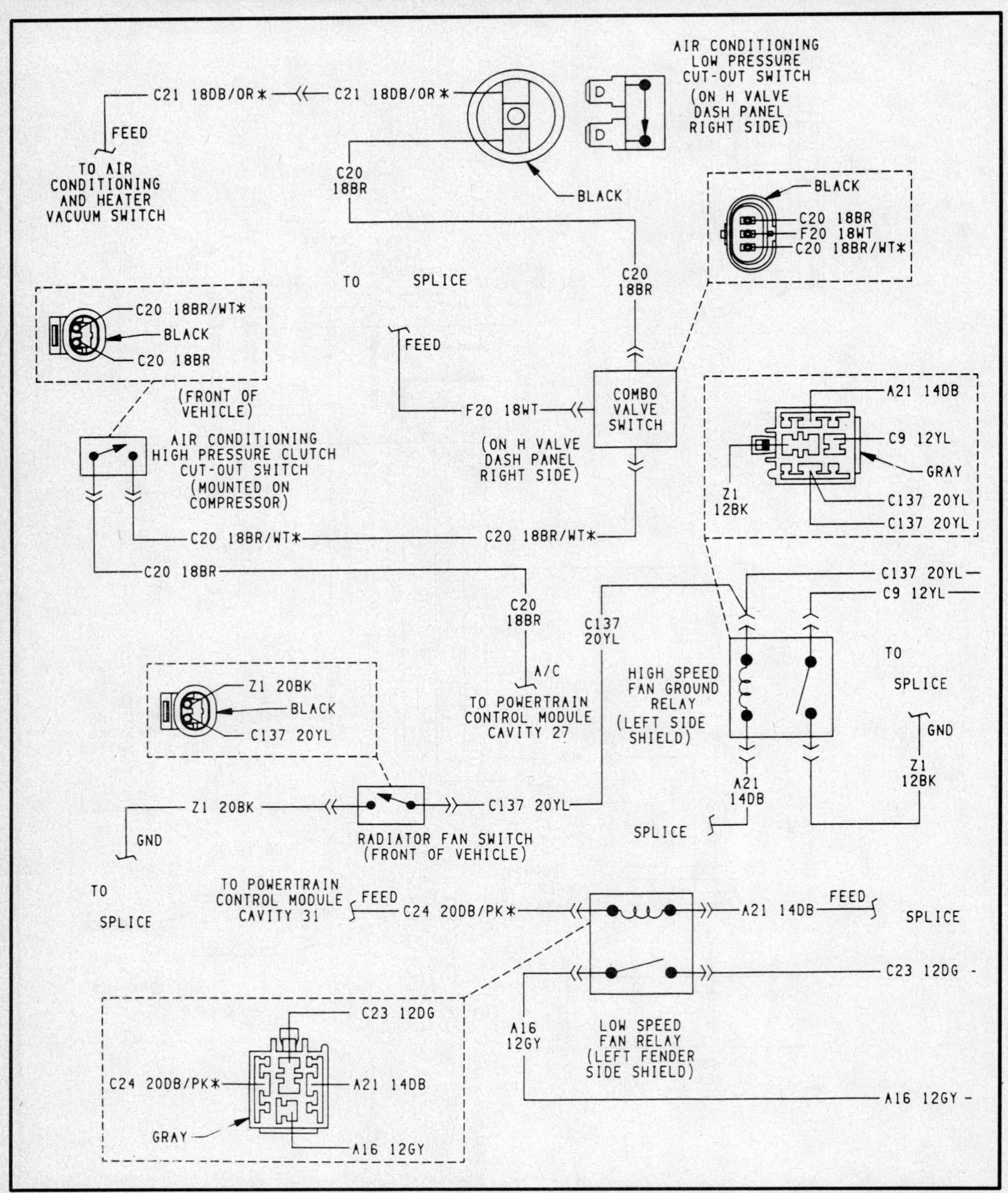

Wiring schematic—1993 Caravan, Voyager and Town & Country with heater-A/C system with 3.0L engine with electronic transaxle

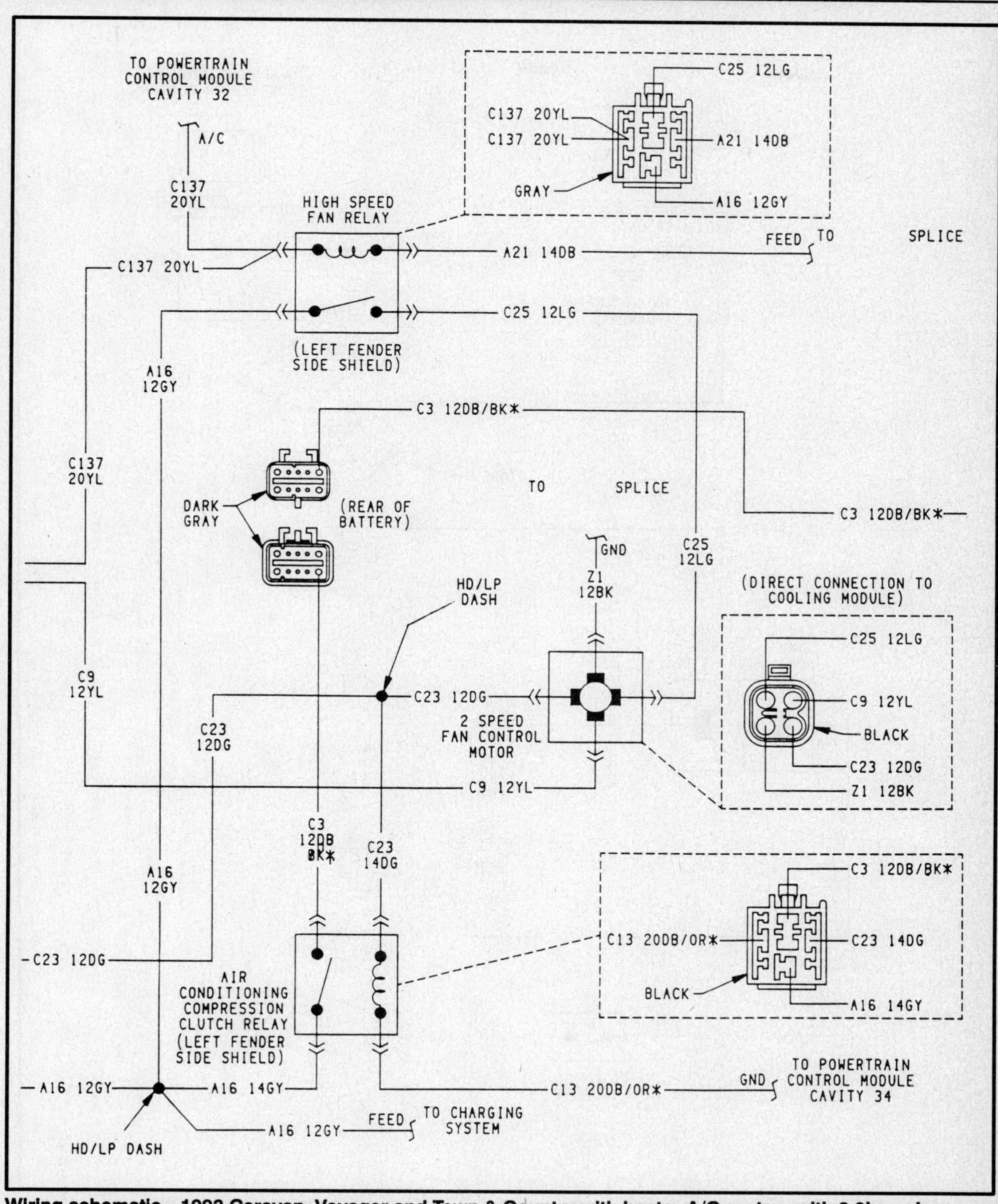

Wiring schematic—1993 Caravan, Voyager and Town & Country with heater-A/C system with 3.0L engine with electronic transaxle, Cont'd

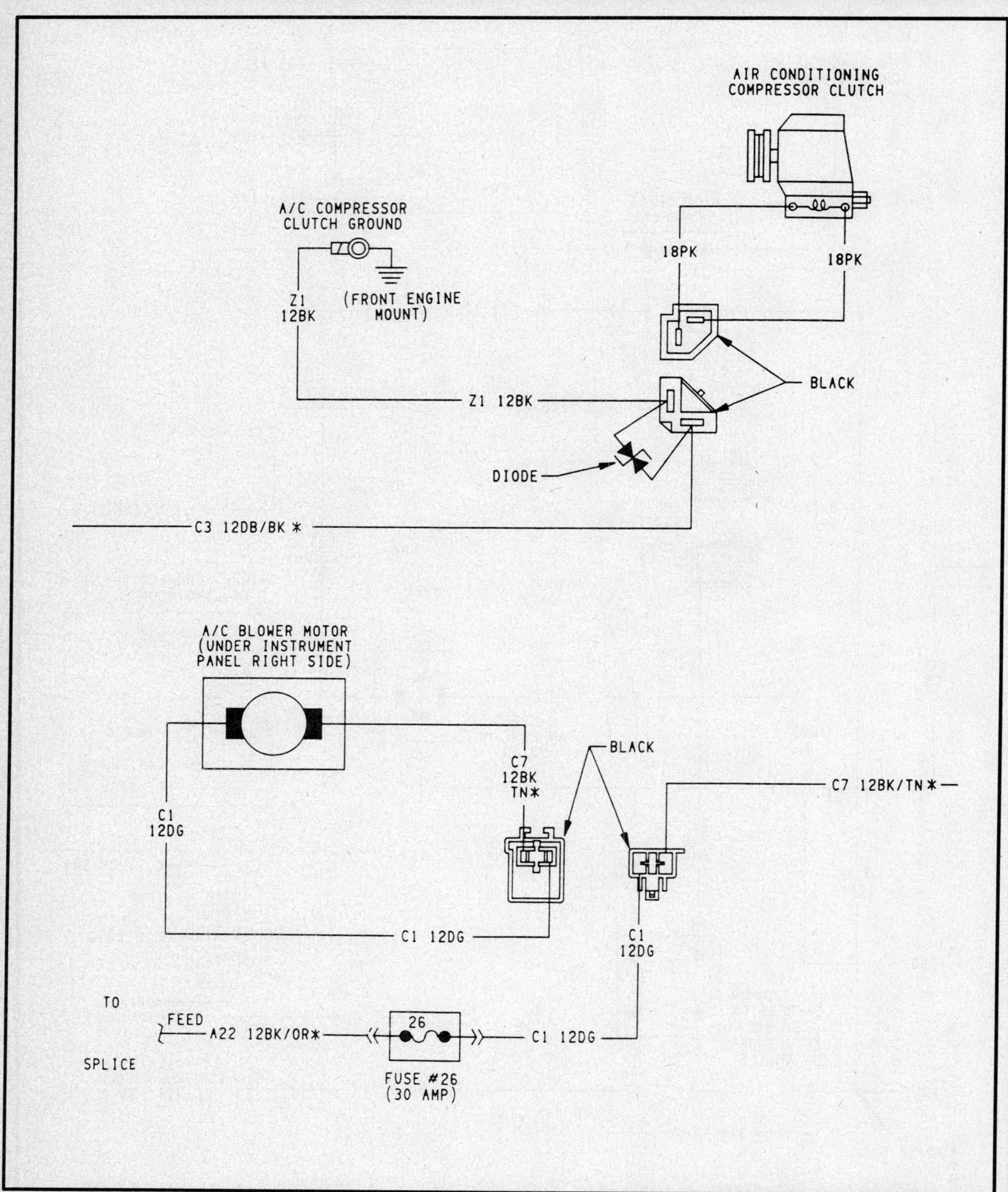

Wiring schematic—1993 Caravan, Voyager and Town & Country with heater-A/C system with 3.0L engine with electronic transaxle, Cont'd

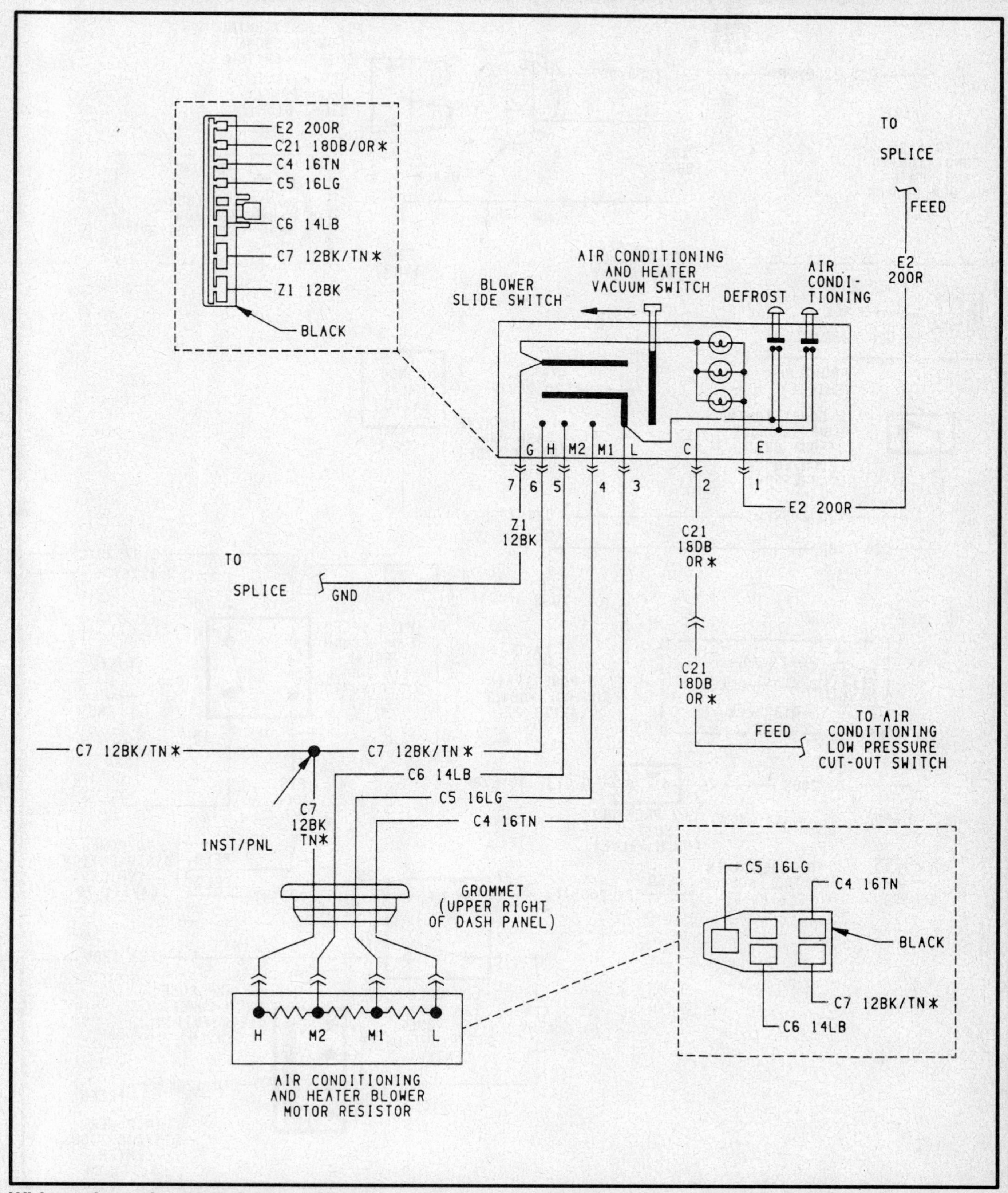

Wiring schematic—1993 Caravan, Voyager and Town & Country with heater-A/C system with 3.0L engine with electronic transaxle, Cont'd

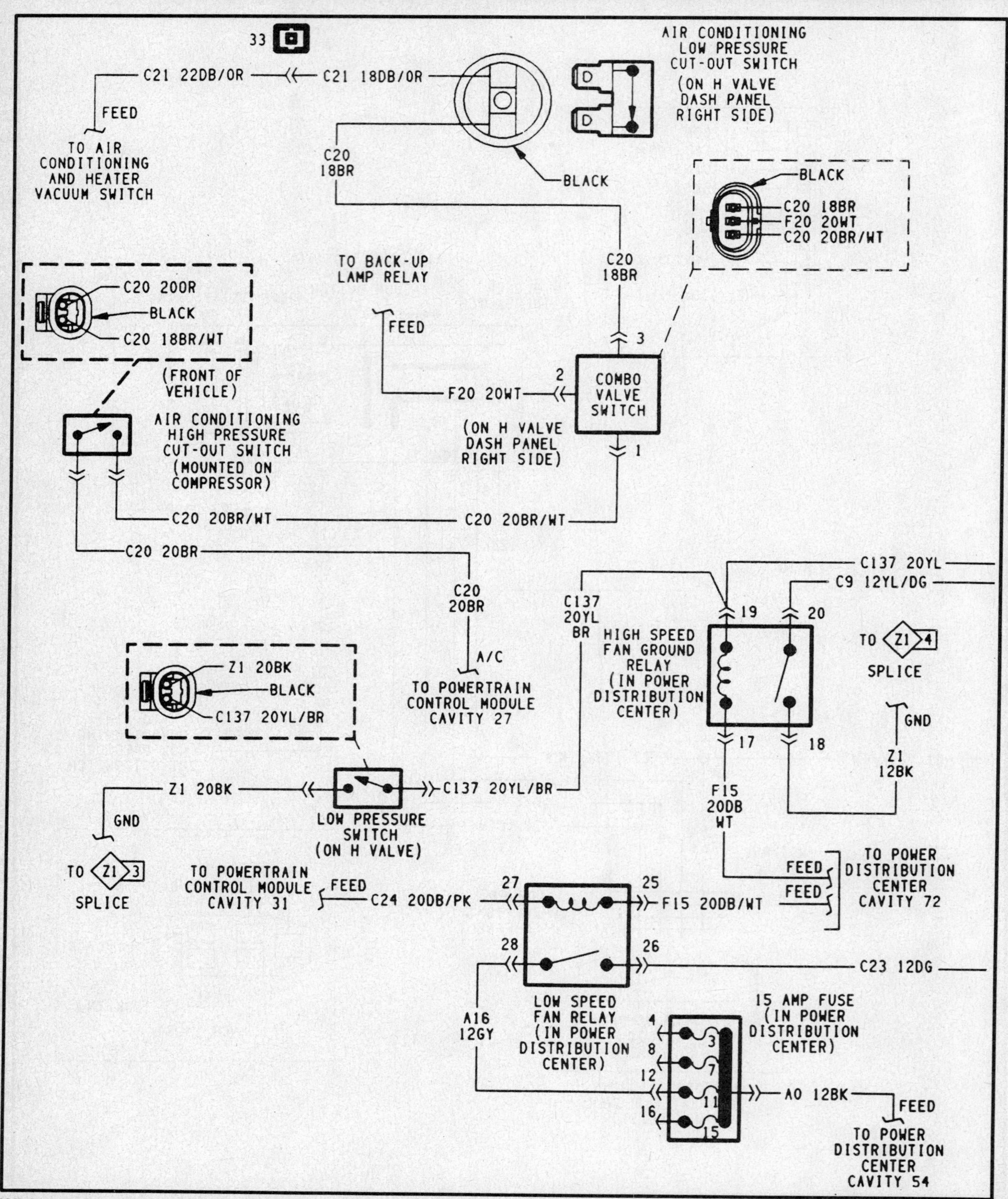

Wiring schematic—1994–95 Caravan, Voyager and Town & Country with heater-A/C system with 3.0L engine with electronic transaxle

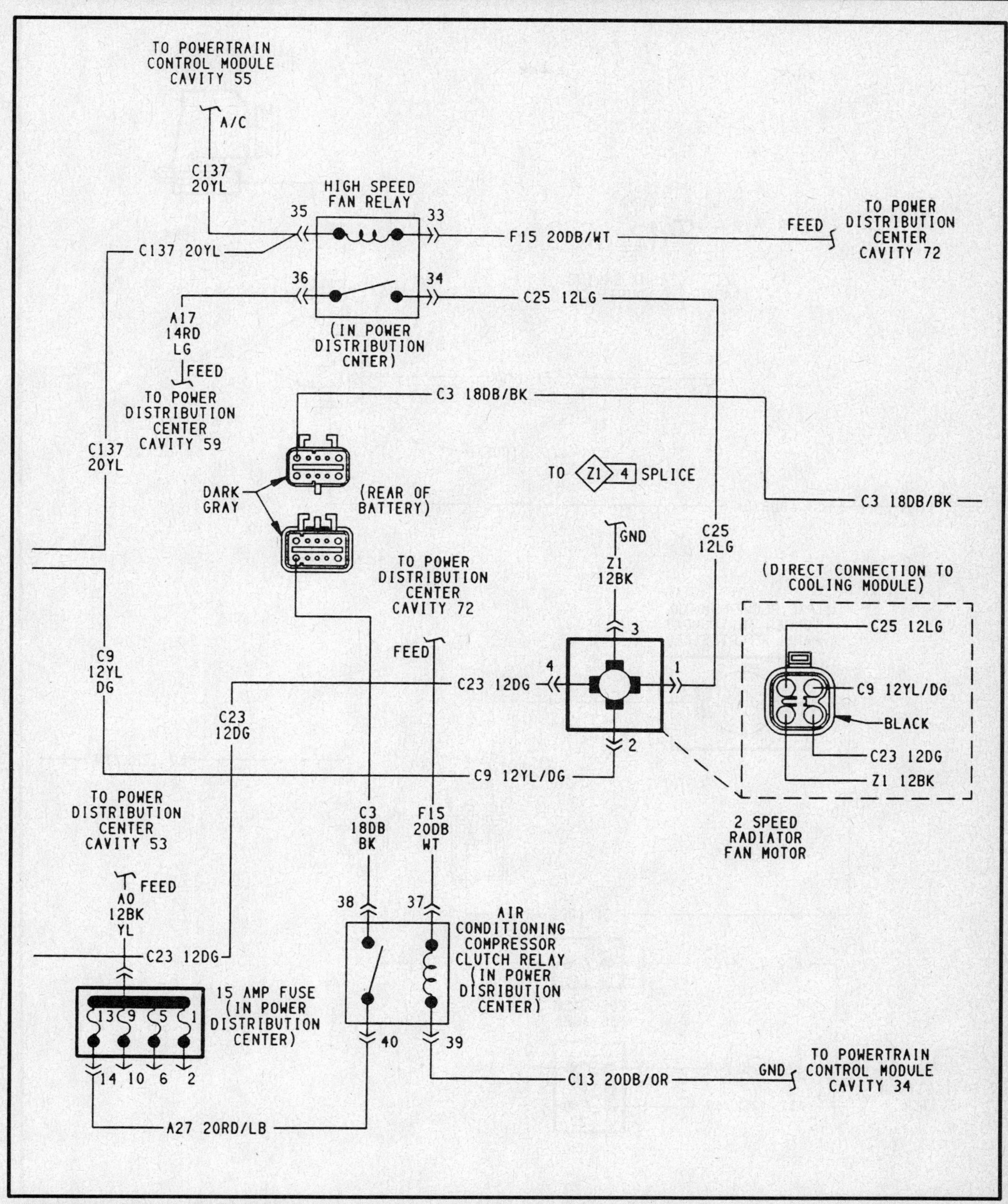

Wiring schematic—1994–95 Caravan, Voyager and Town & Country with heater-A/C system with 3.0L engine with electronic transaxle, Cont'd

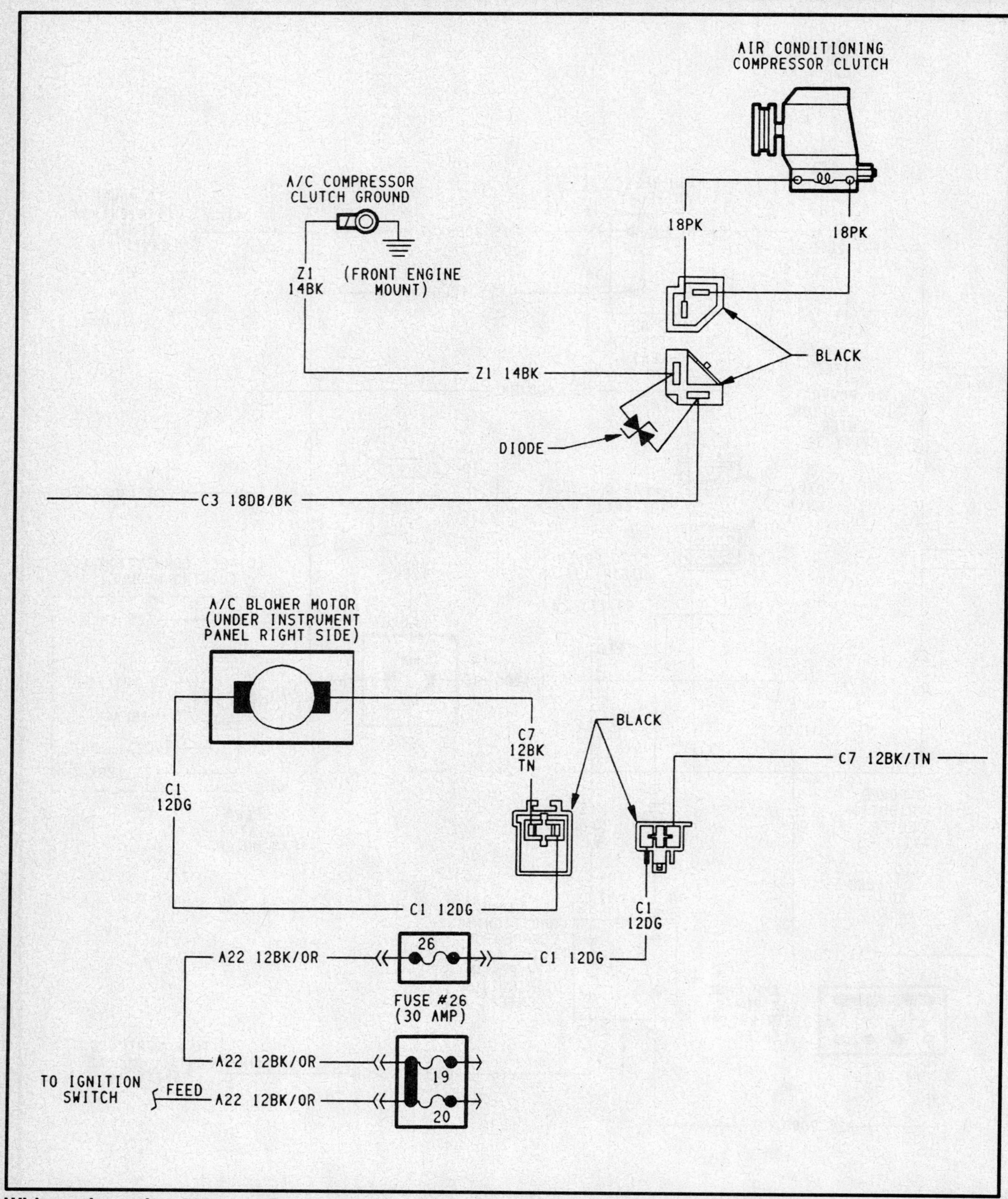

Wiring schematic—1994–95 Caravan, Voyager and Town & Country with heater-A/C system with 3.0L engine with electronic transaxle, Cont'd

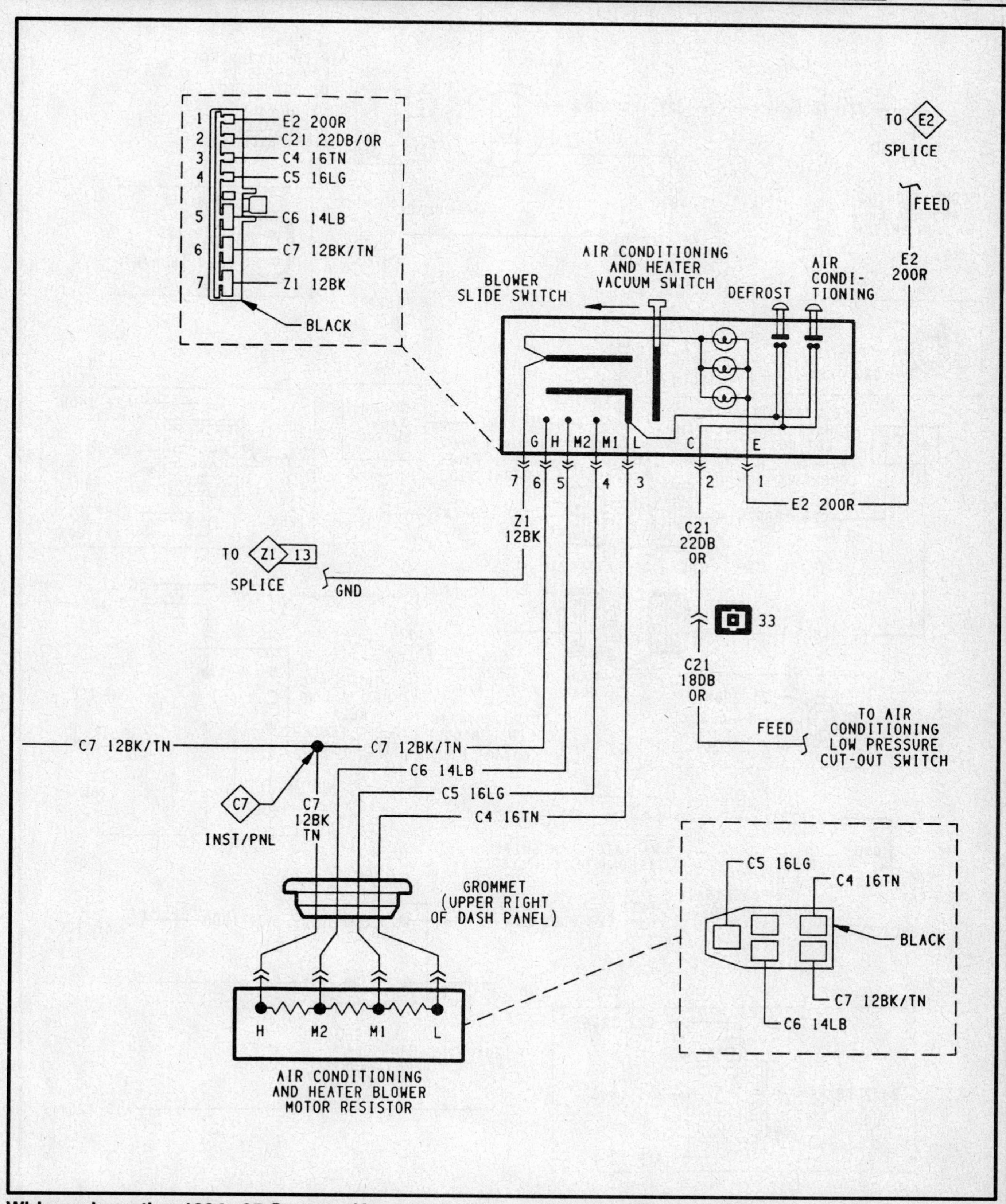

Wiring schematic—1994–95 Caravan, Voyager and Town & Country with heater-A/C system with 3.0L engine with electronic transaxle, Cont'd

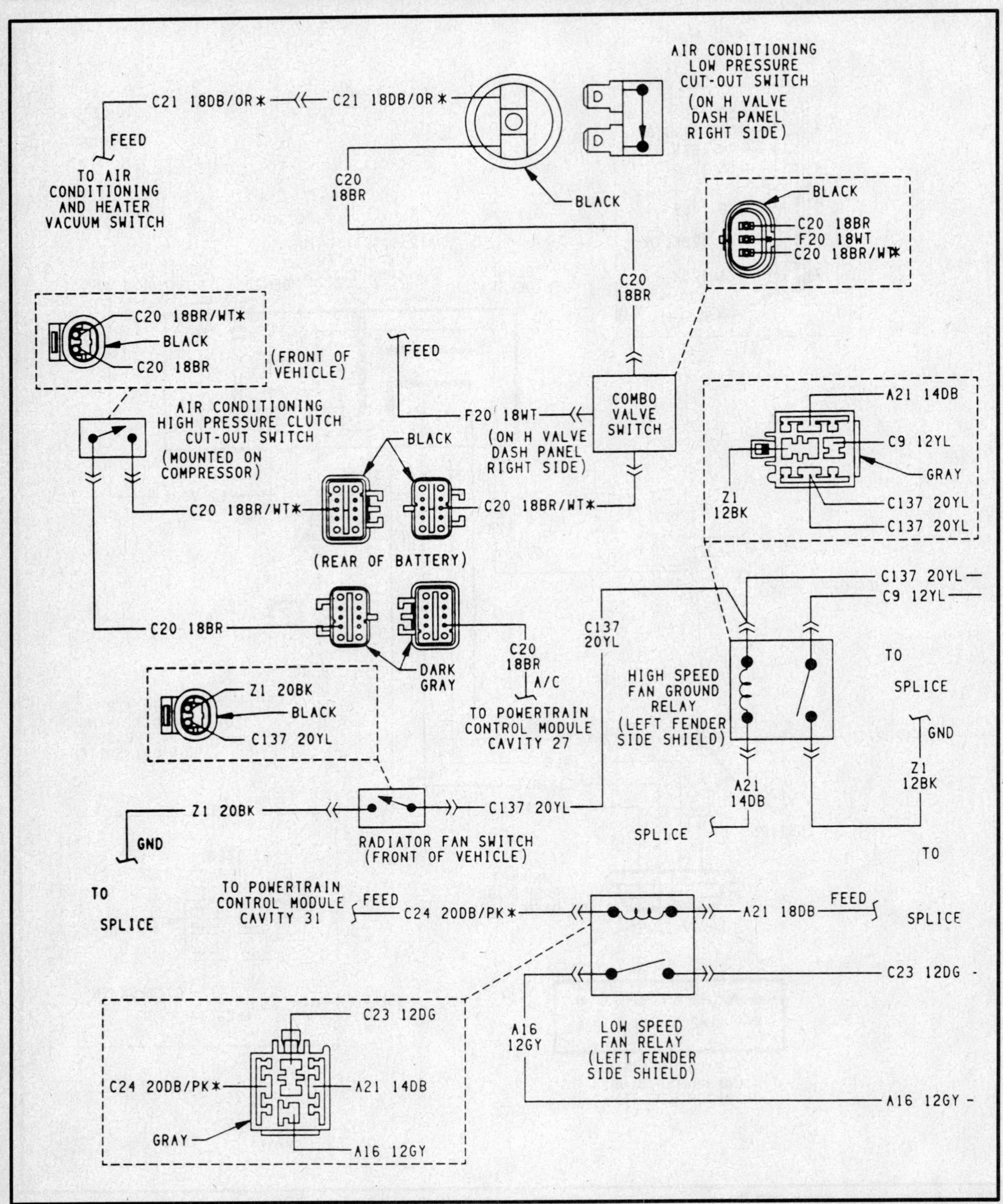

Wiring schematic—1993 Caravan, Voyager and Town & Country with heater-A/C system with 3.3L engine

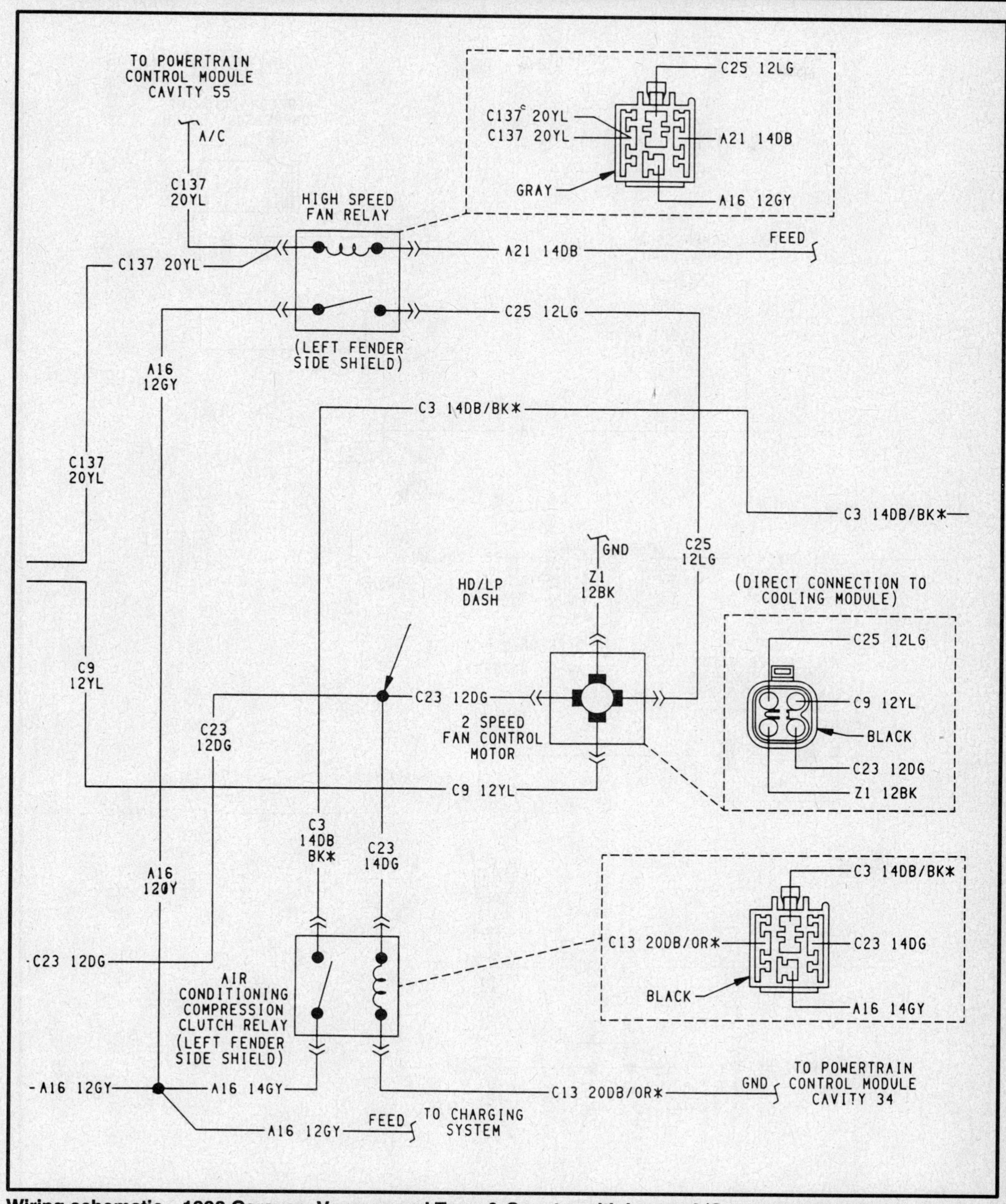

Wiring schematic—1993 Caravan, Voyager and Town & Country with heater-A/C system with 3.3L engine, Cont'd

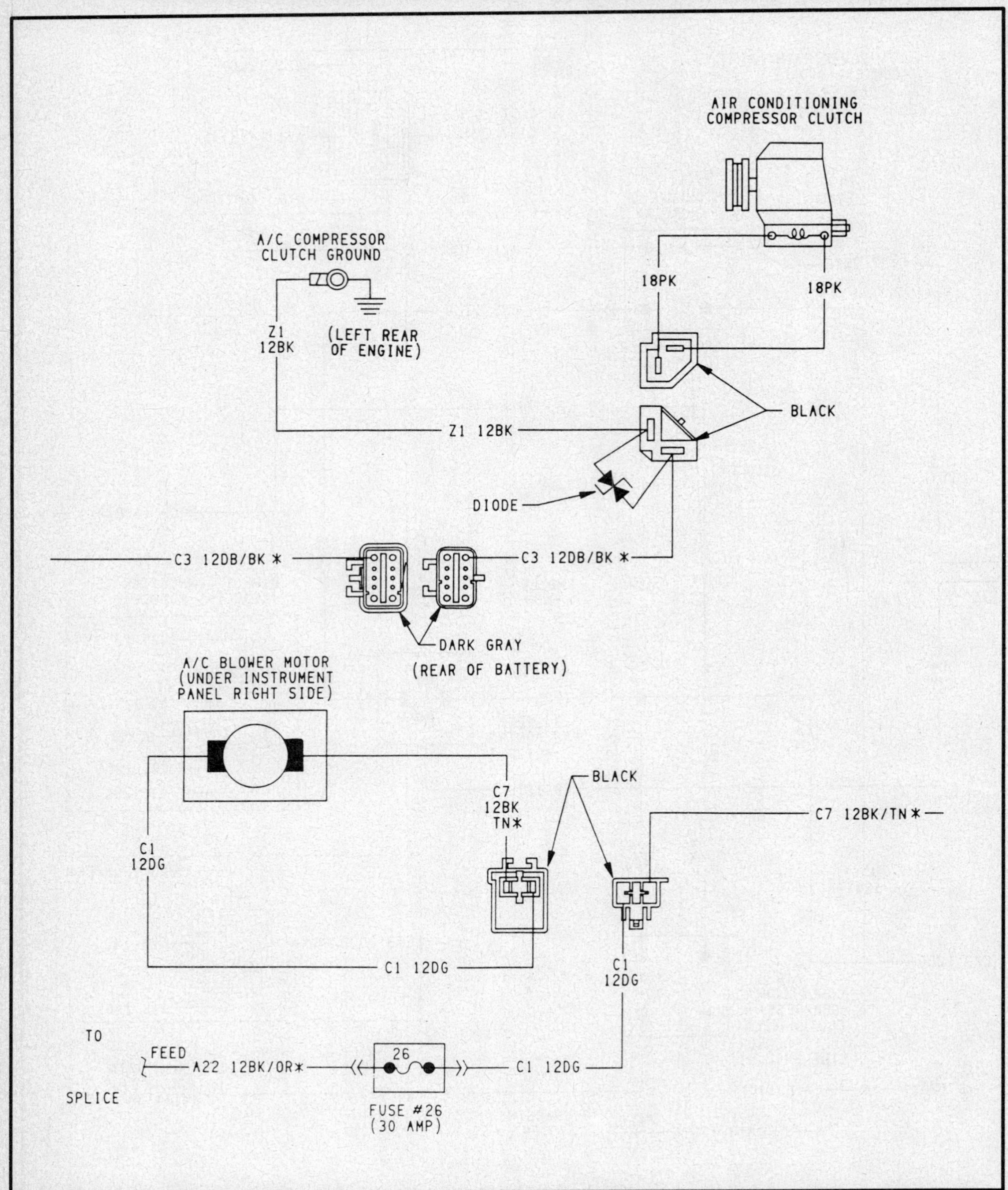

Wiring schematic—1993 Caravan, Voyager and Town & Country with heater-A/C system with 3.3L engine, Cont'd

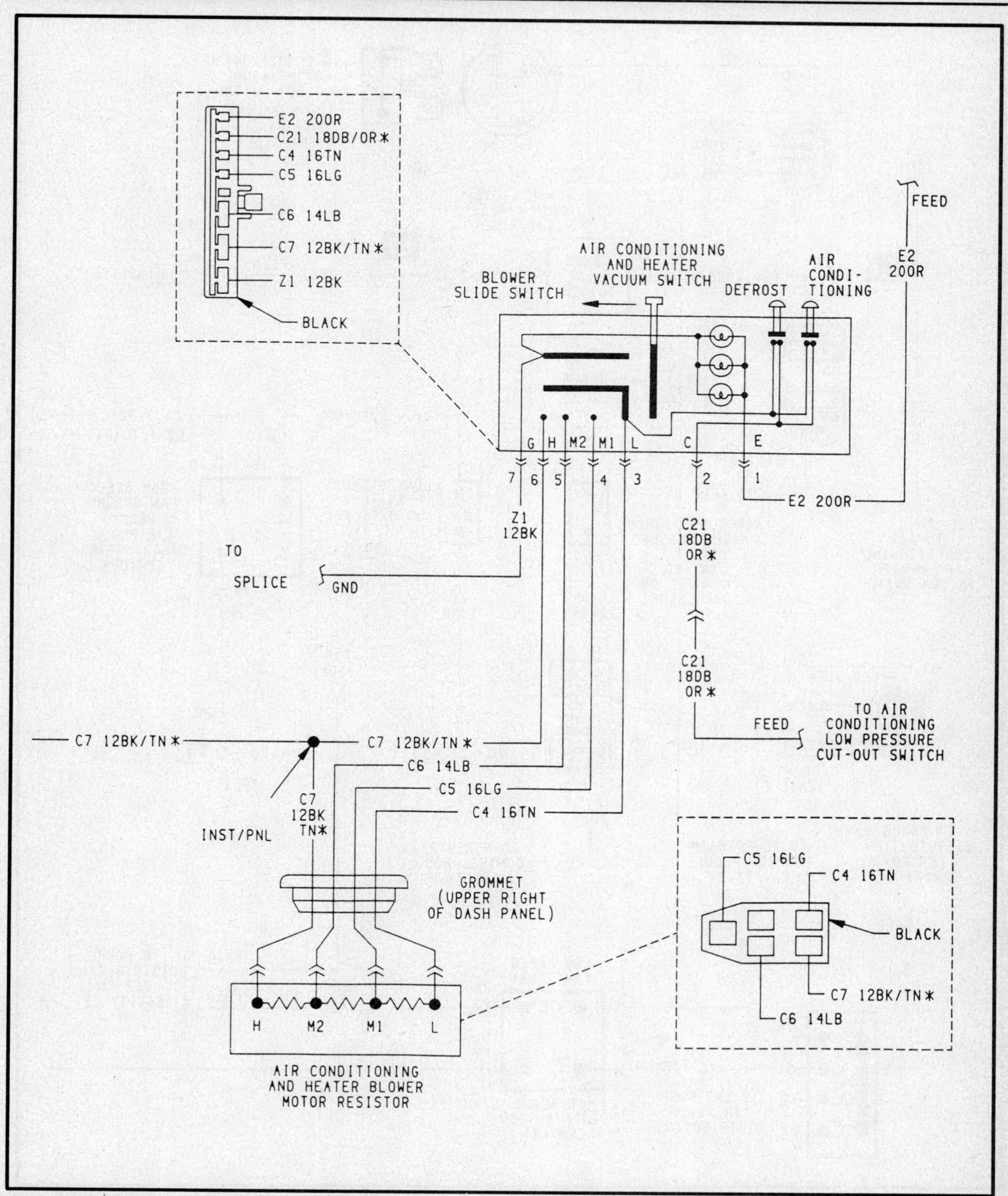

Wiring schematic—1993 Caravan, Voyager and Town & Country with heater-A/C system with 3.3L engine, Cont'd

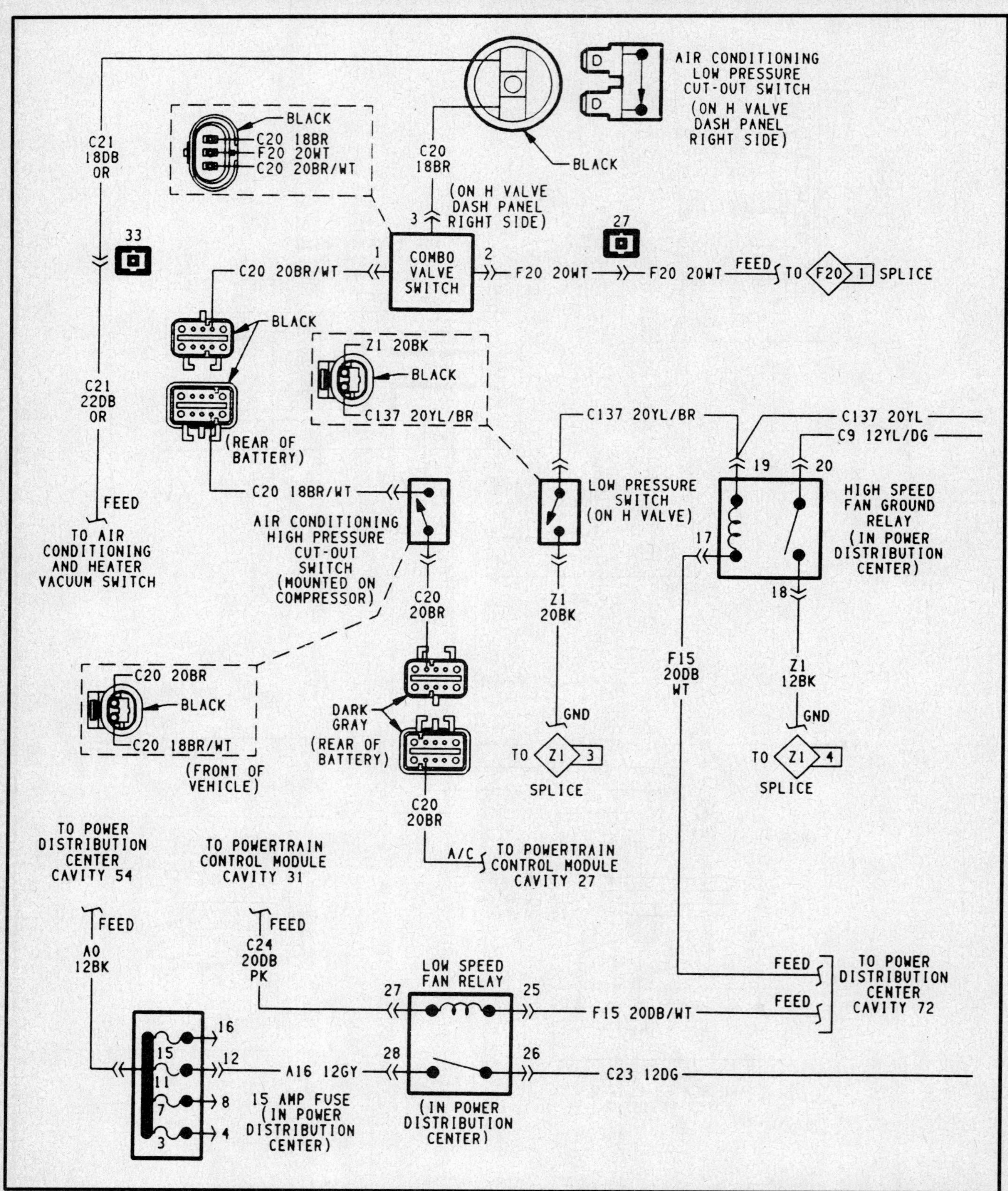

Wiring schematic—1994–95 Caravan, Voyager and Town & Country with heater-A/C system with 3.3L and 3.8L engine

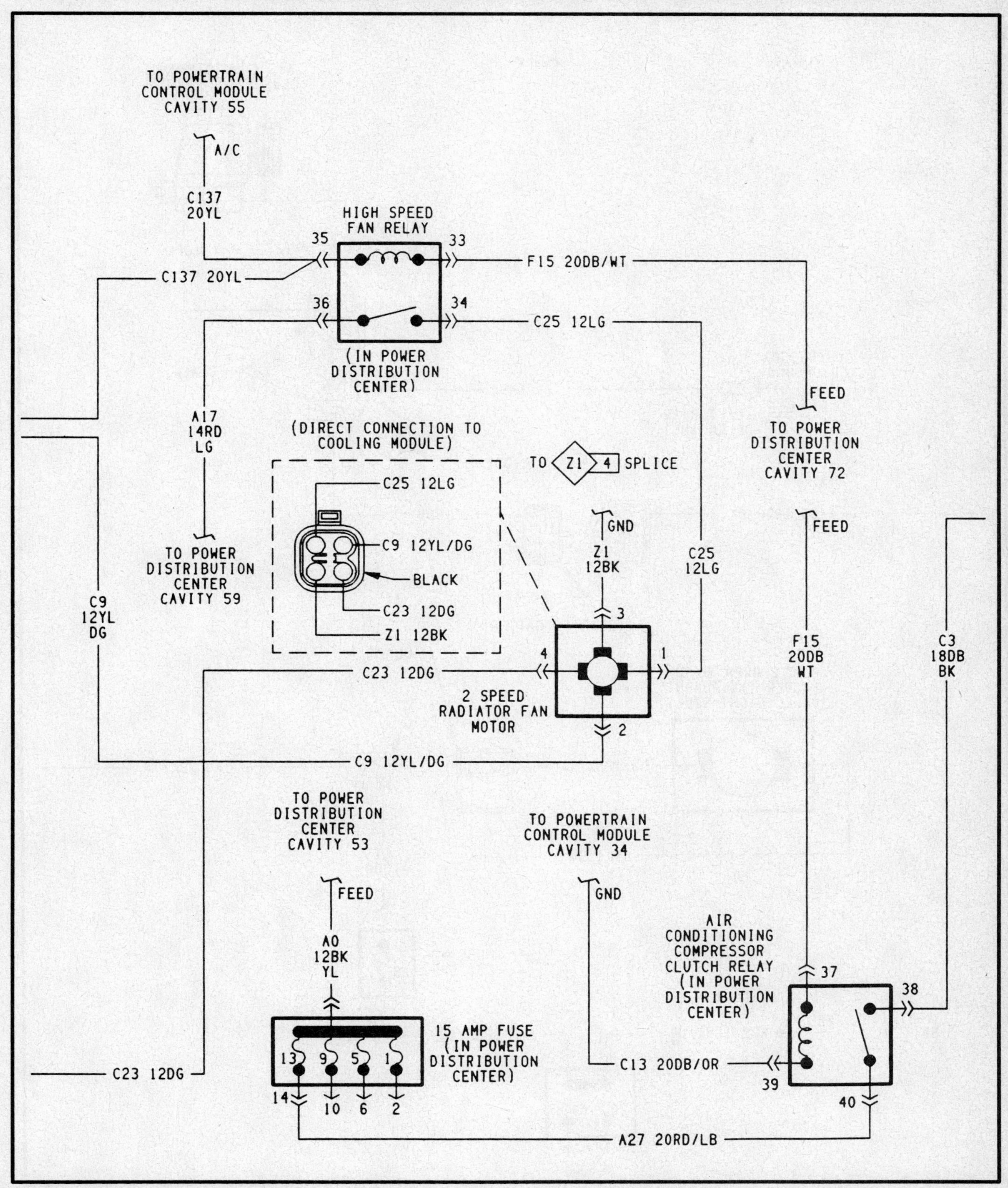

Wiring schematic—1994–95 Caravan, Voyager and Town & Country with heater-A/C system with 3.3L and 3.8L engine, Cont'd

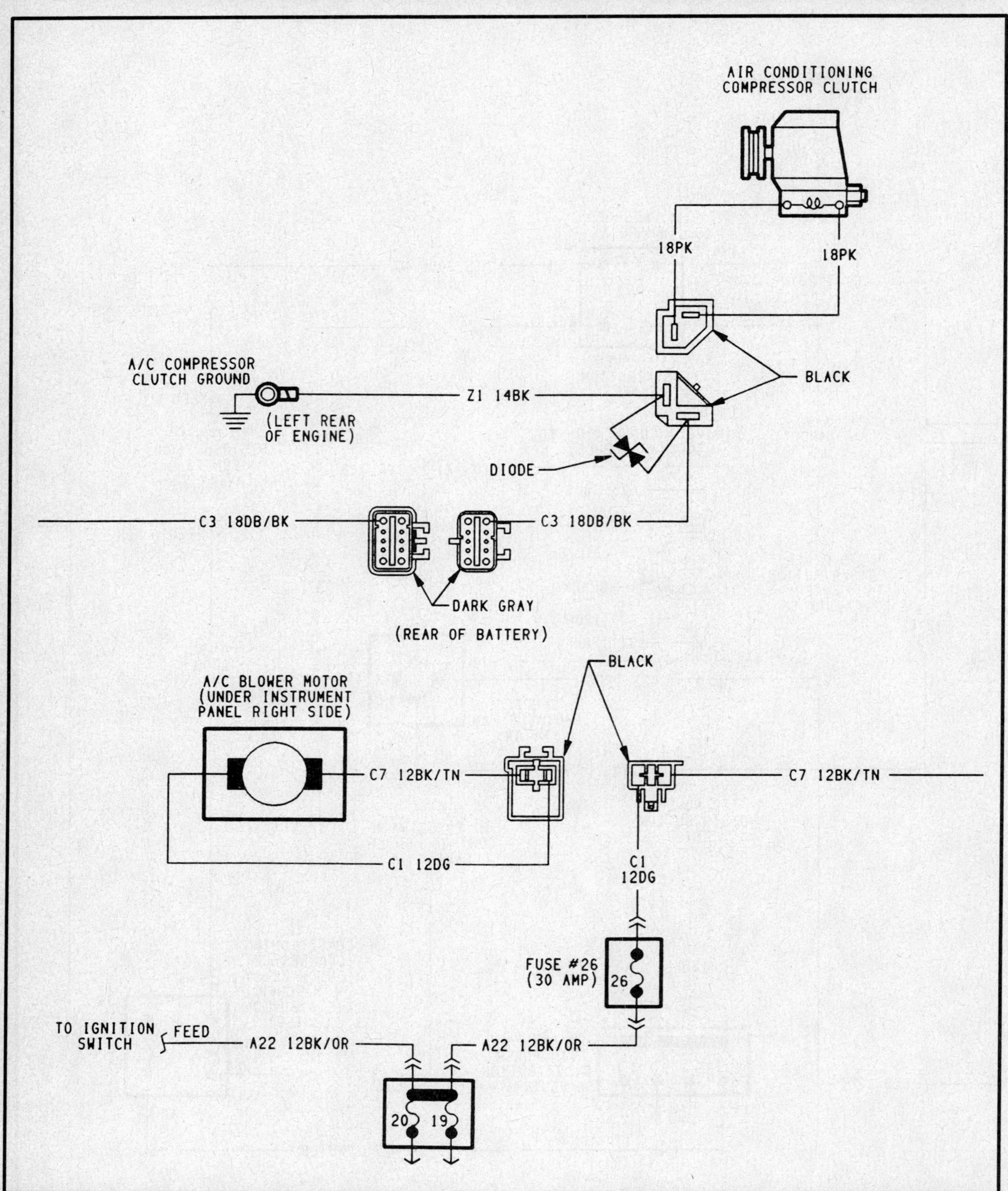

Wiring schematic—1994–95 Caravan, Voyager and Town & Country with heater-A/C system with 3.3L and 3.8L engine, Cont'd

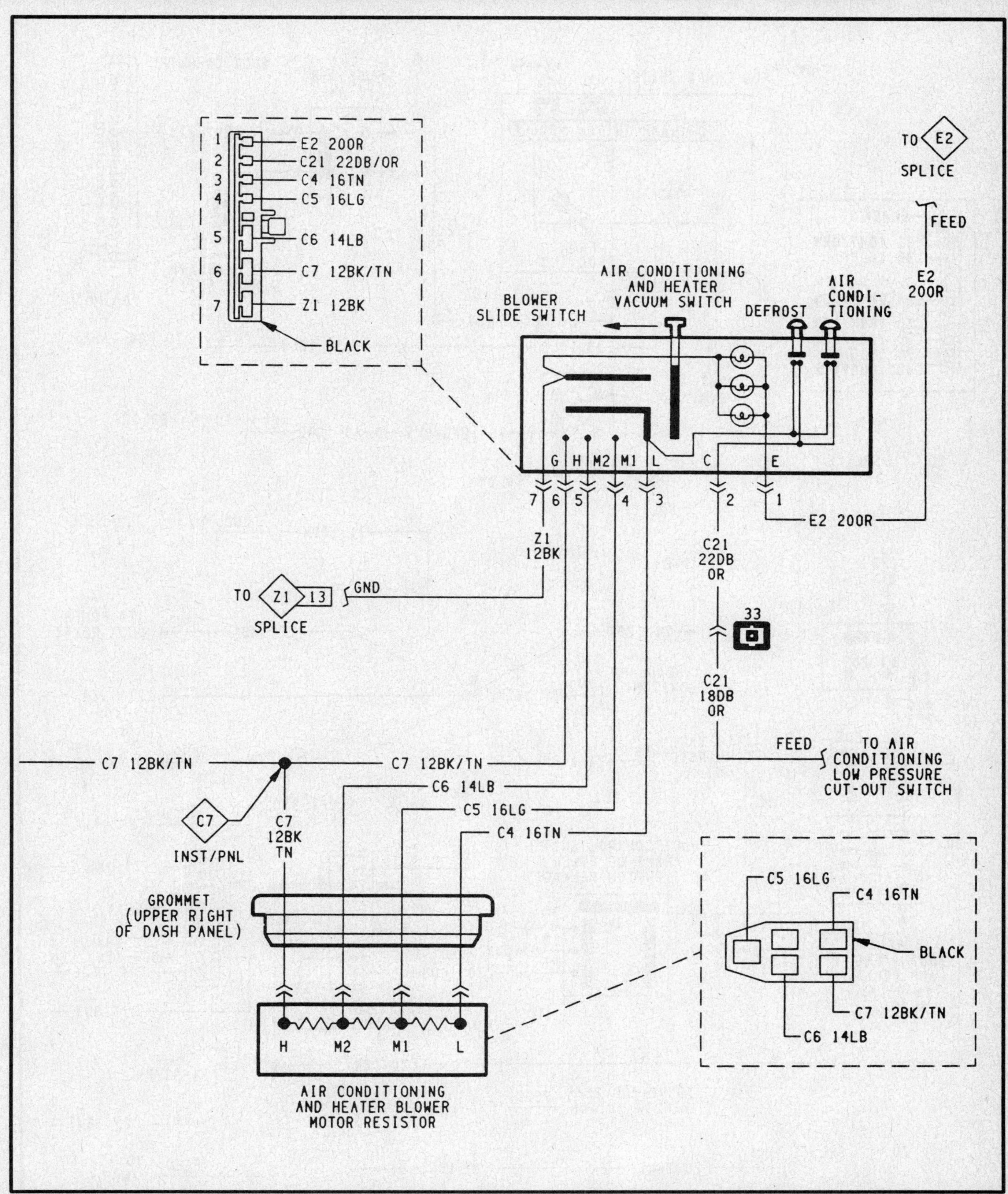

Wiring schematic—1994–95 Caravan, Voyager and Town & Country with heater-A/C system with 3.3L and 3.8L engine, Cont'd

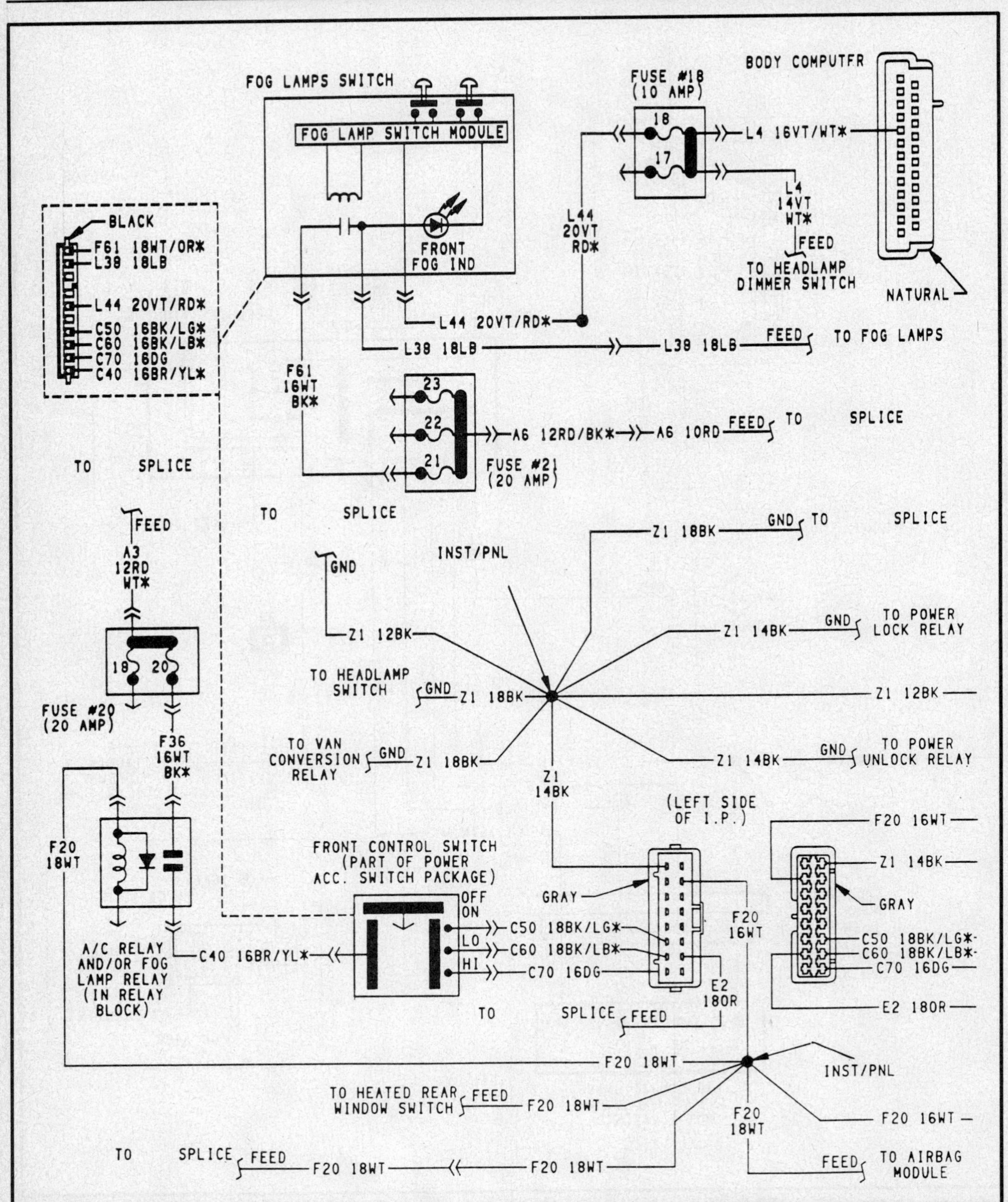

Wiring schematic—1993 Caravan, Voyager and Town & Country with rear heater-A/C system

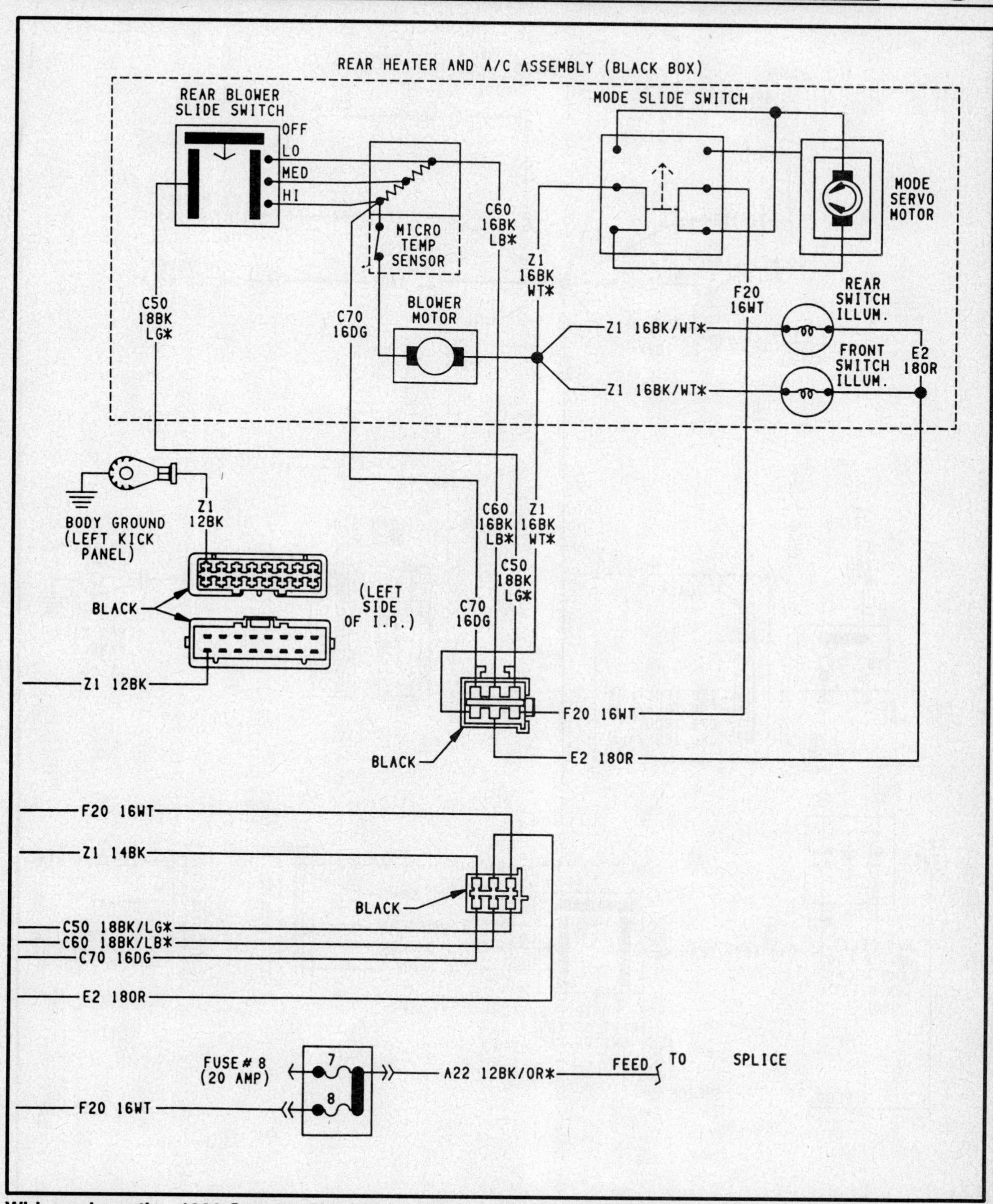

Wiring schematic—1993 Caravan, Voyager and Town & Country with rear heater-A/C system, Cont'd

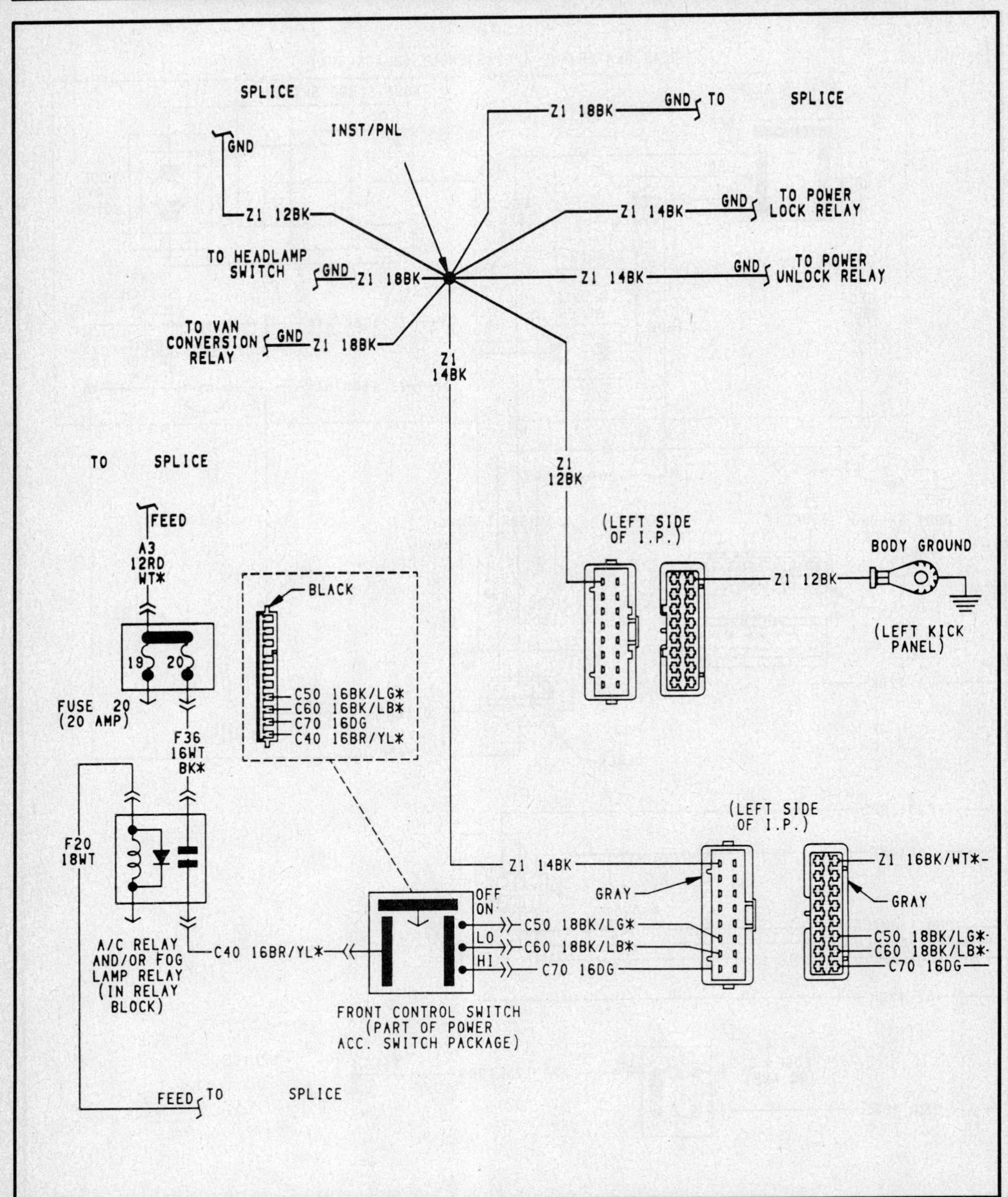

Wiring schematic—1993 Caravan, Voyager and Town & Country with rear heater only

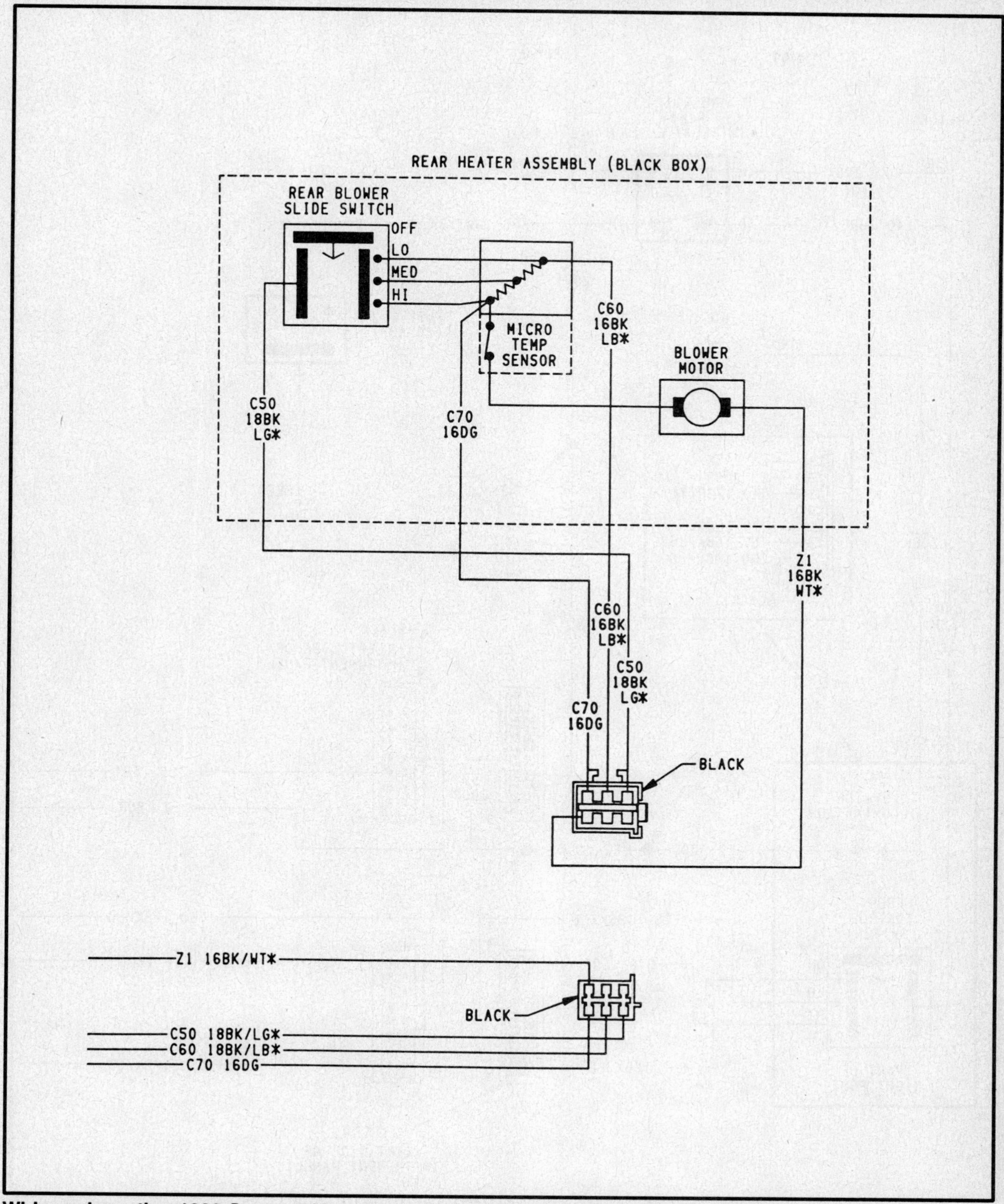

Wiring schematic—1993 Caravan, Voyager and Town & Country with rear heater only, Cont'd

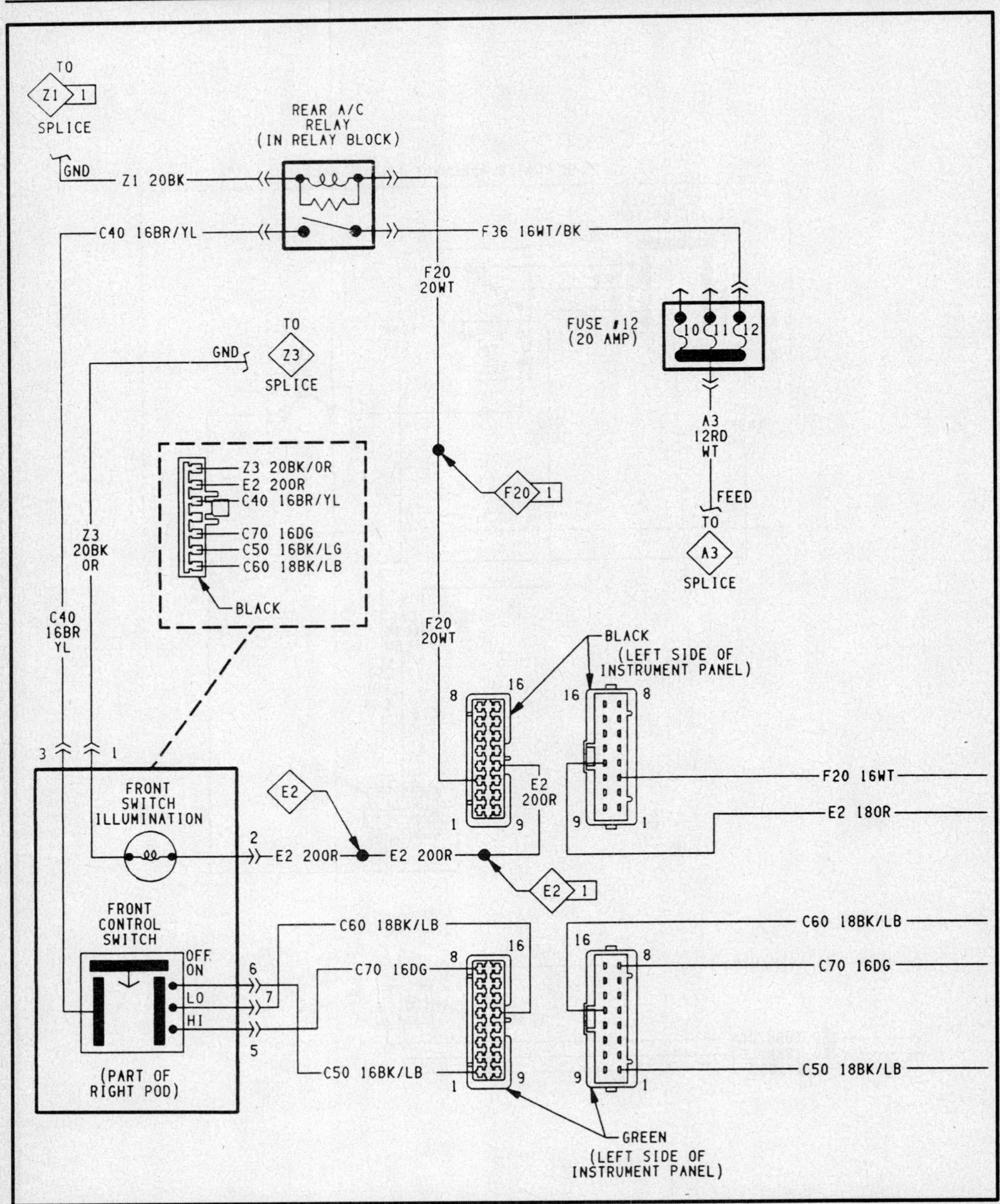

Wiring schematic—1994–95 Caravan, Voyager and Town & Country with rear heater-A/C system

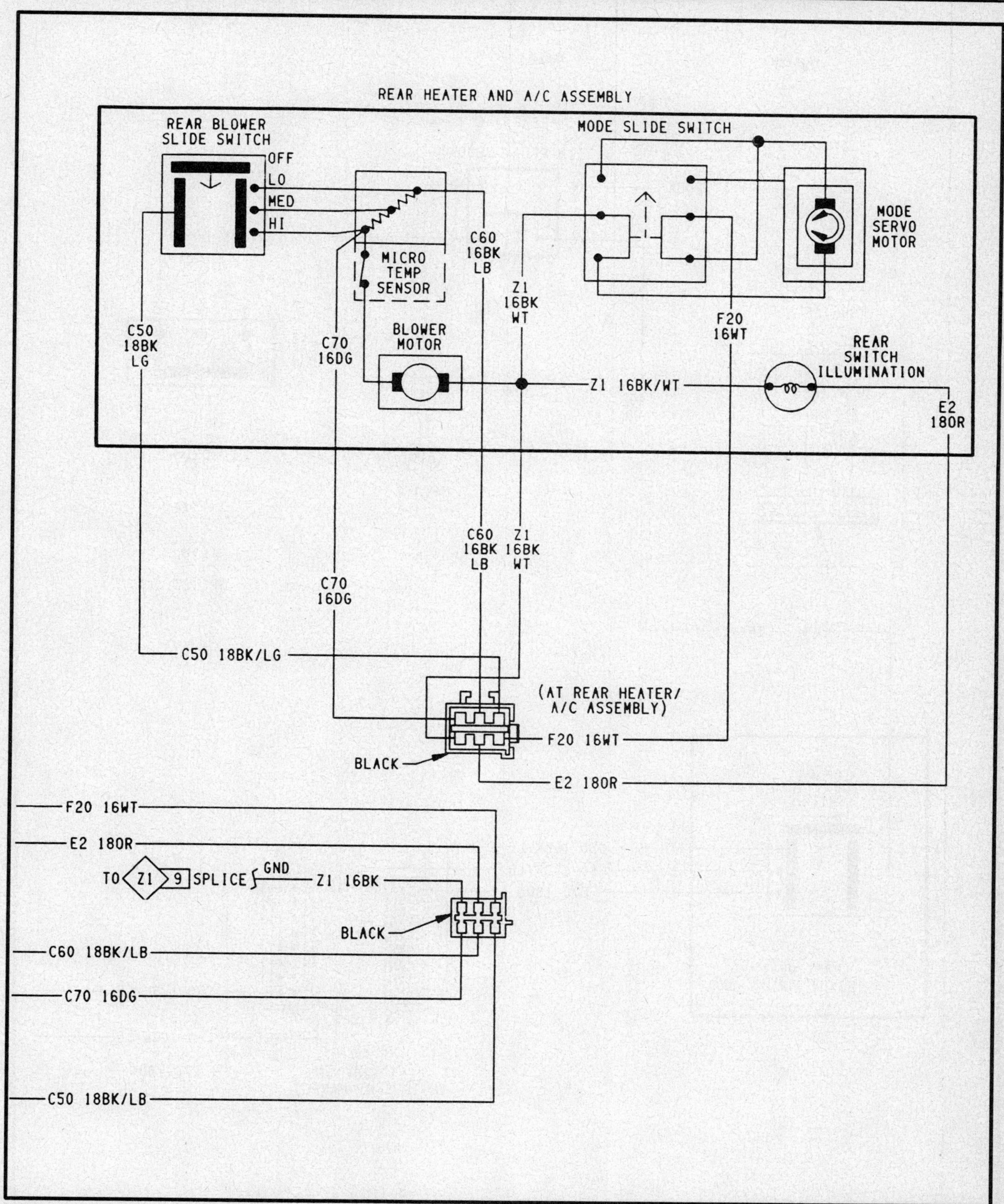

Wiring schematic—1994–95 Caravan, Voyager and Town & Country with rear heater-A/C system, Cont'd

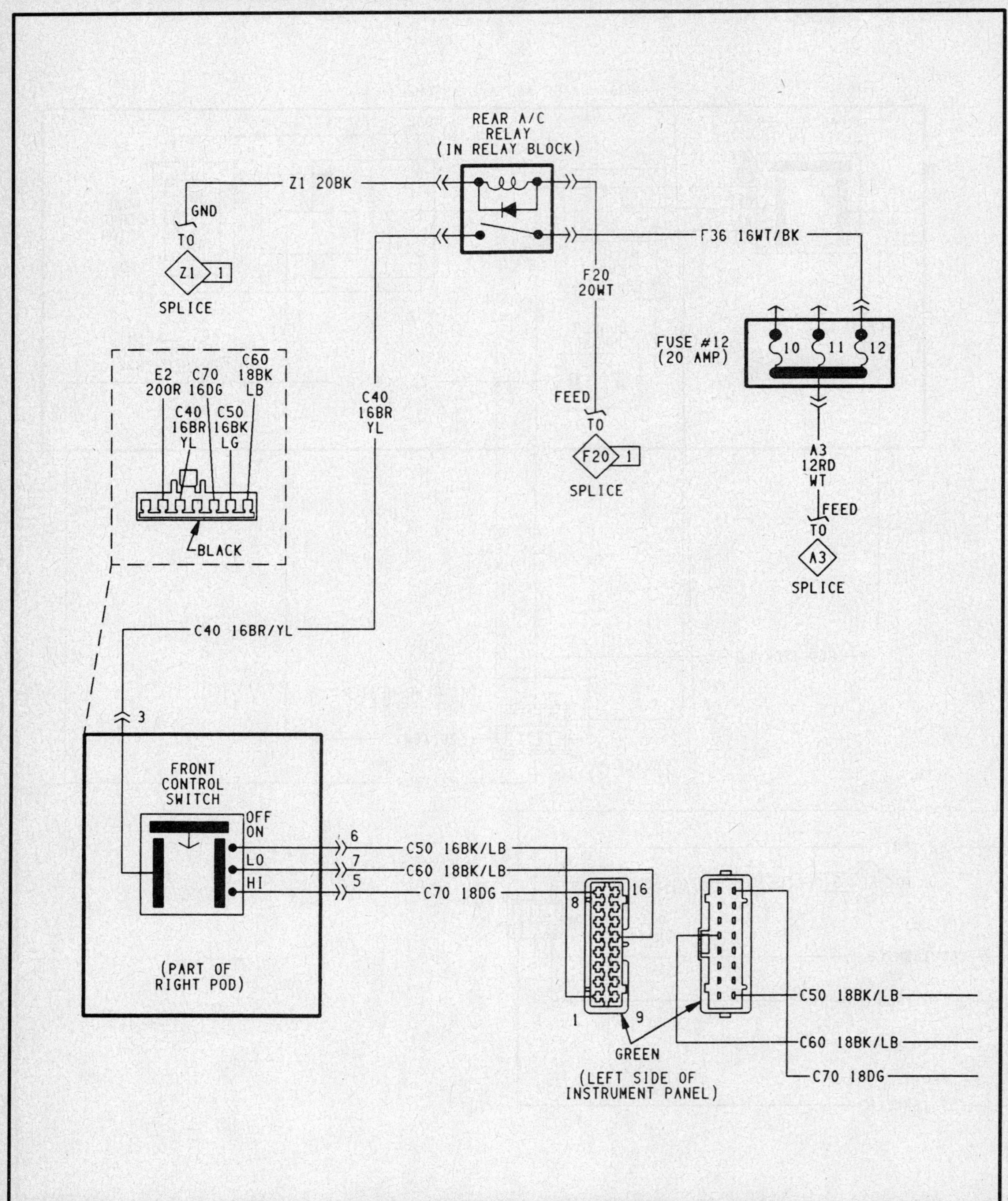

Wiring schematic—1994–95 Caravan, Voyager and Town & Country with rear heater only

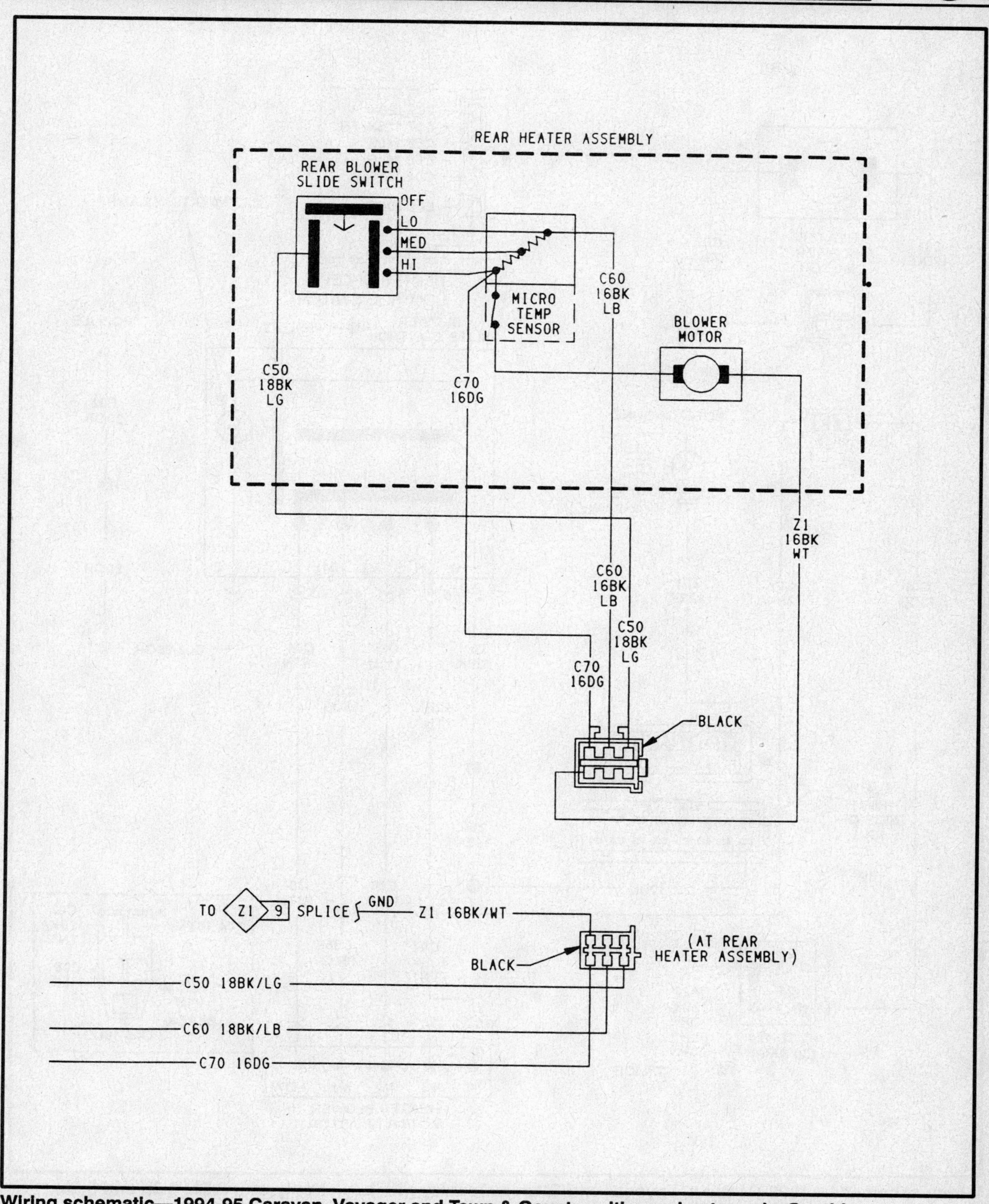

Wiring schematic—1994-95 Caravan, Voyager and Town & Country with rear heater only, Cont'd

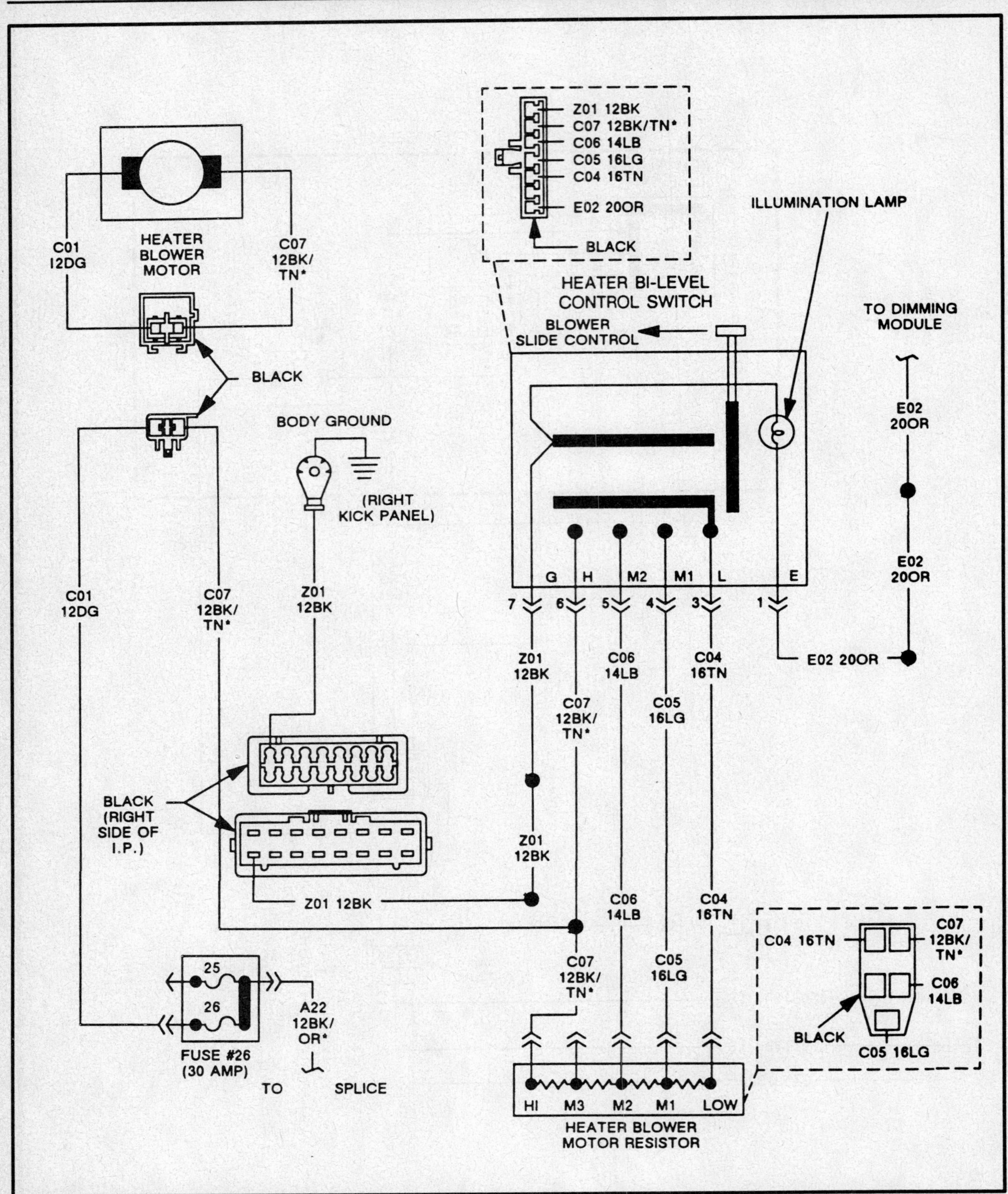

Wiring schematic—1993 Caravan, Voyager and Town & Country with heater only with 2.5L, 3.0L and 3.3L engine

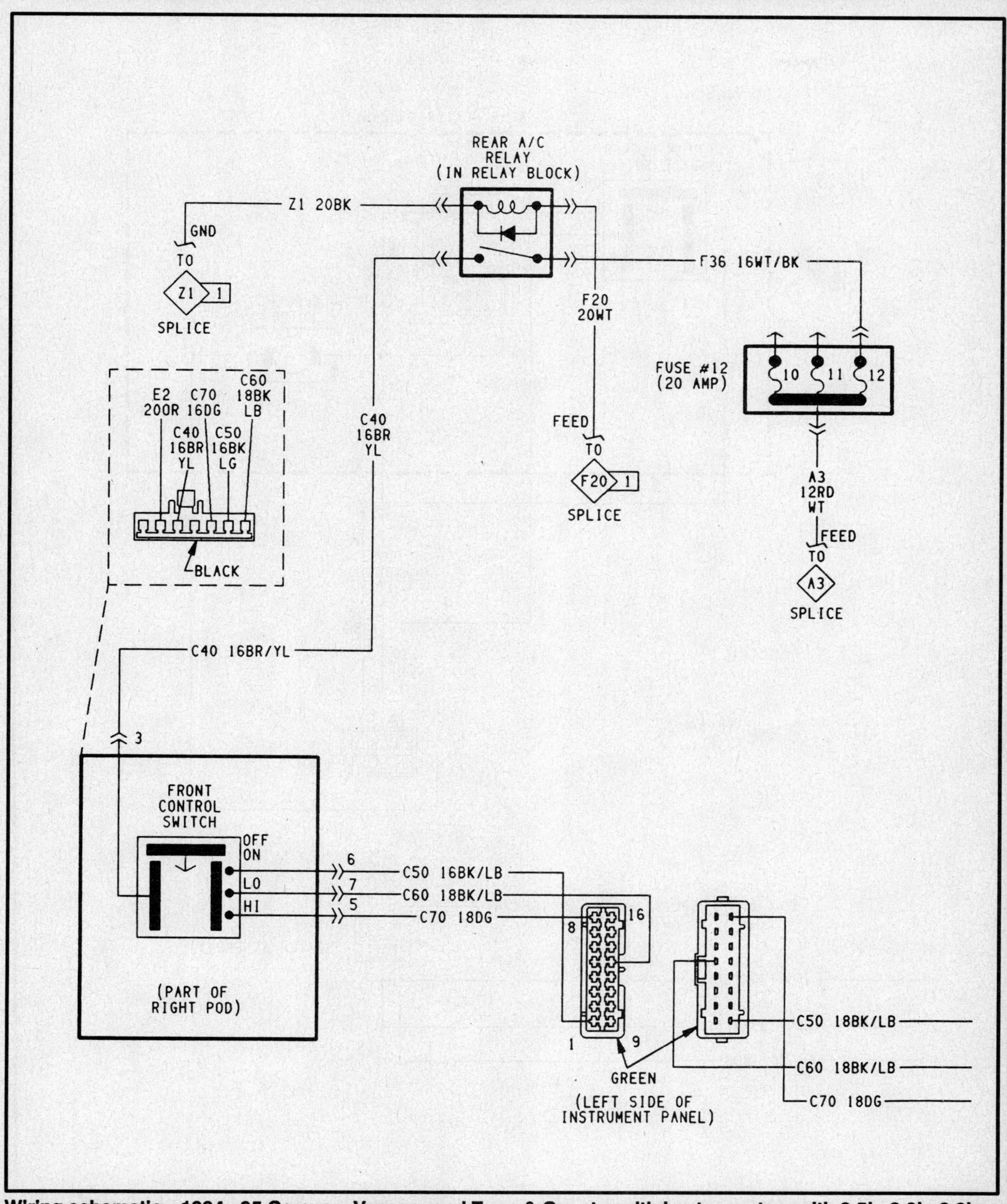

Wiring schematic—1994–95 Caravan, Voyager and Town & Country with heater system with 2.5L, 3.0L, 3.3L and 3.8L engine

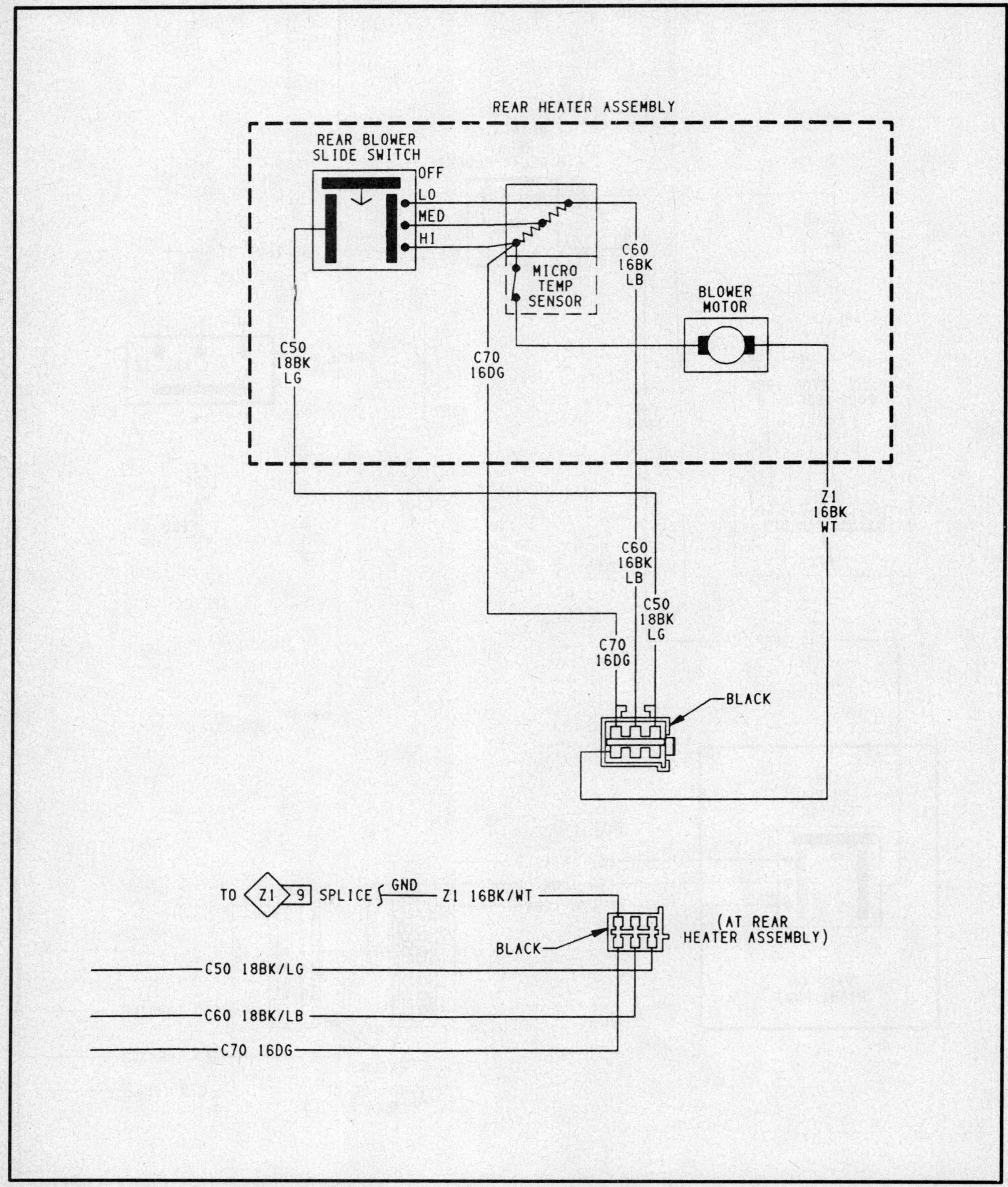

Wiring schematic—1994-95 Caravan, Voyager and Town & Country with heater system with 2.5L, 3.0L, 3.3L and 3.8L engine, Cont'd

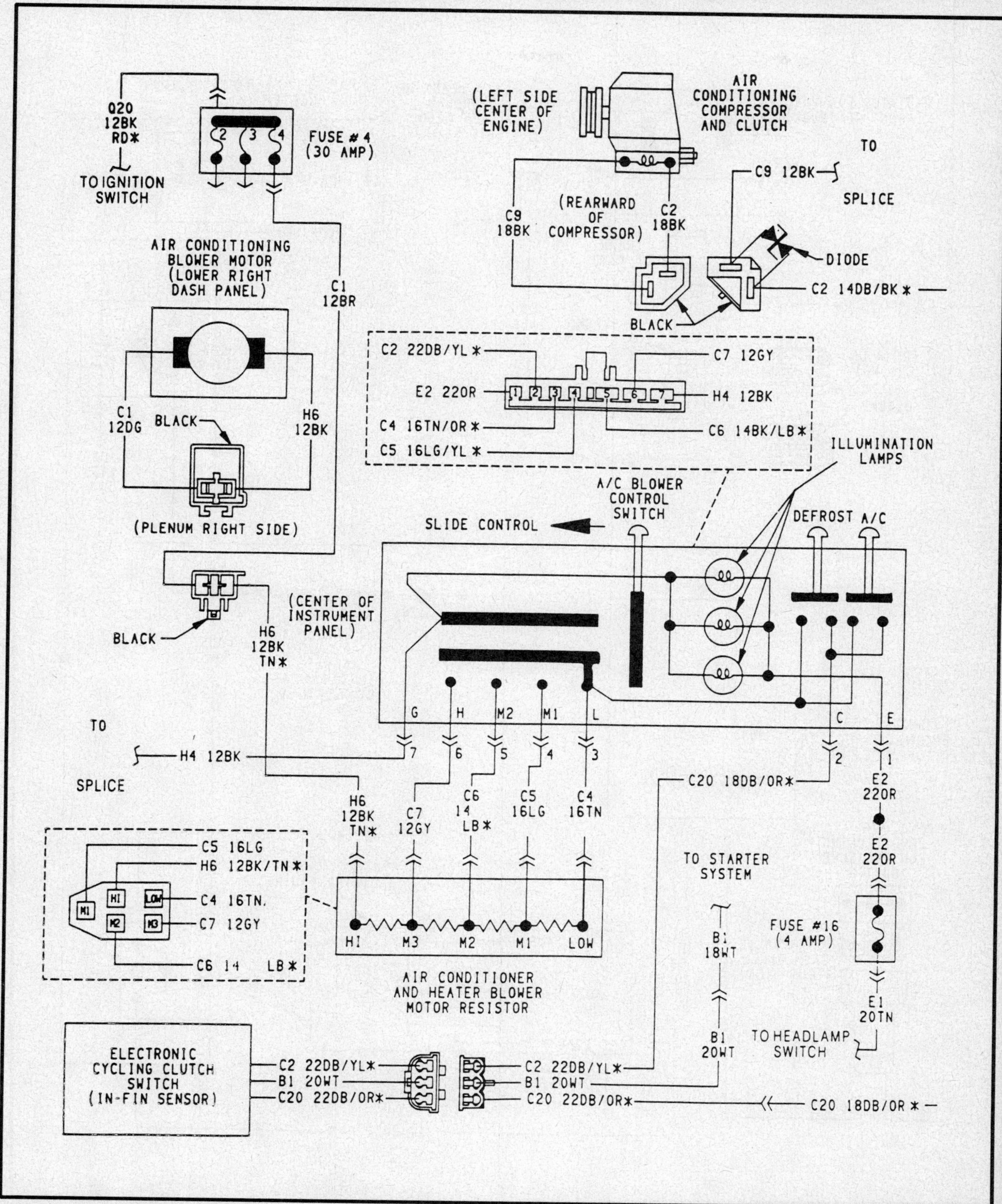

Wiring schematic—1993 Dakota with heater-A/C system with 2.5L engine

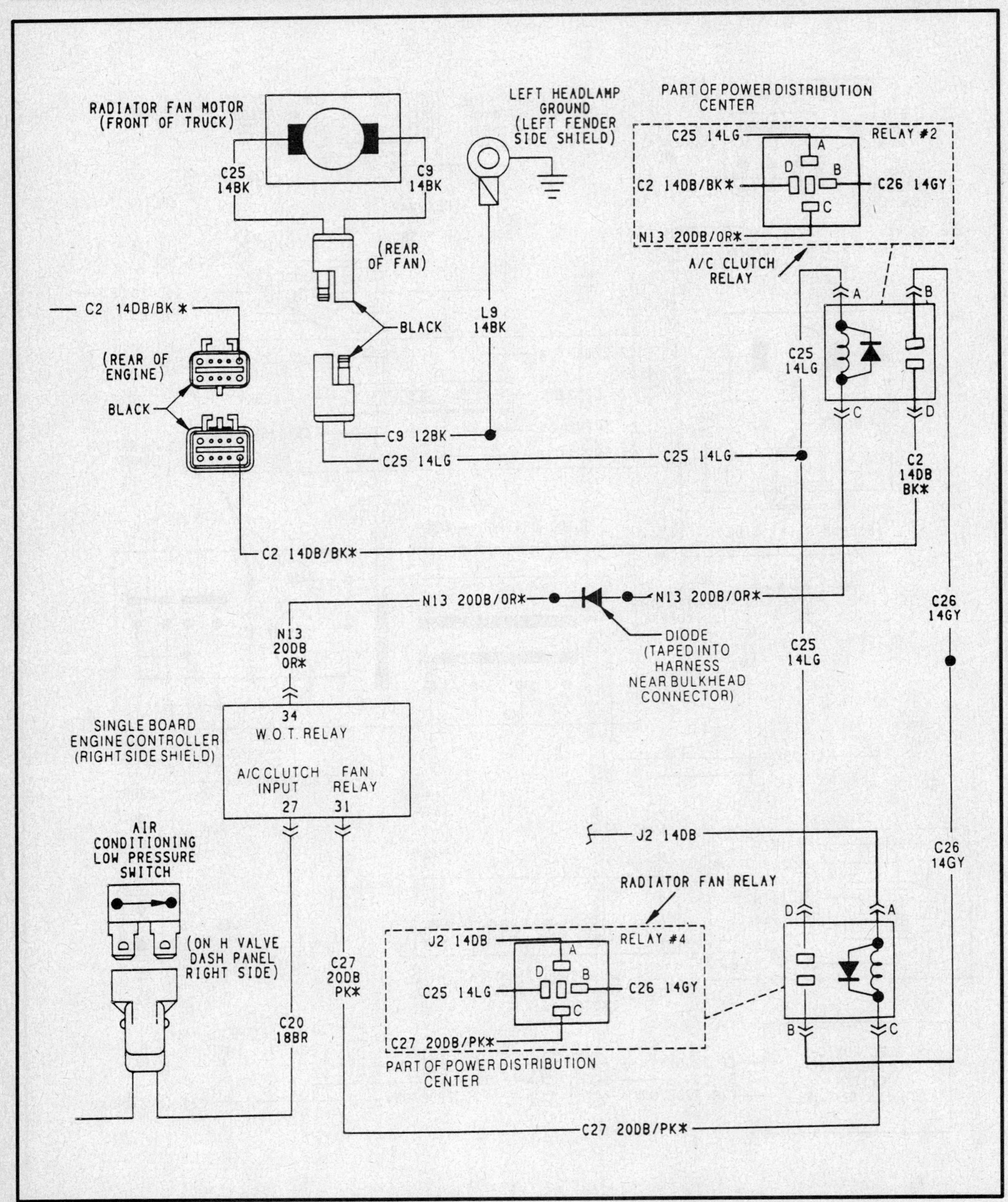

Wiring schematic—1993 Dakota with heater-A/C system with 2.5L engine, Cont'd

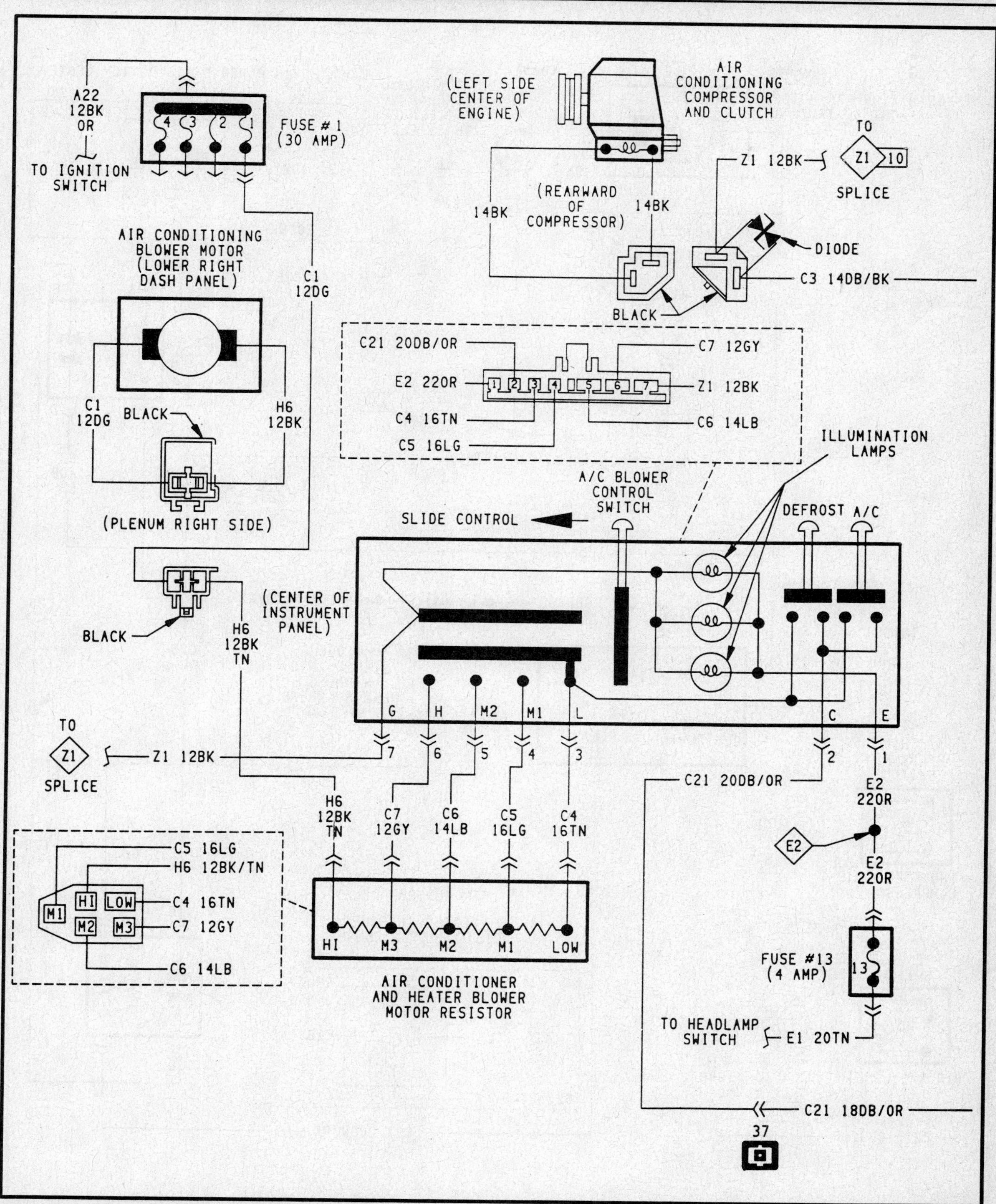

Wiring schematic—1994–95 Dakota with heater-A/C system with 2.5L engine

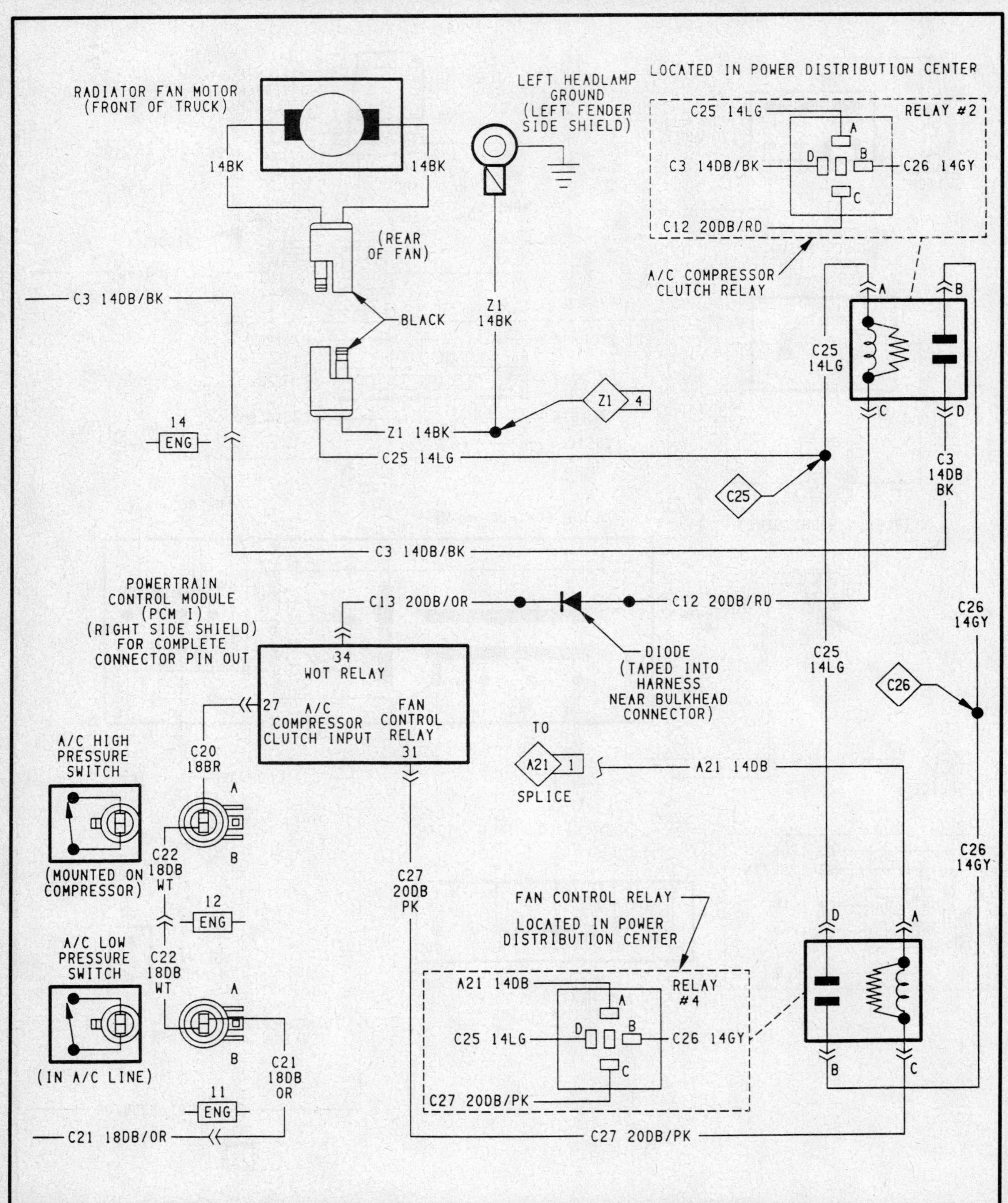

Wiring schematic—1994–95 Dakota with heater-A/C system with 2.5L engine, Cont'd

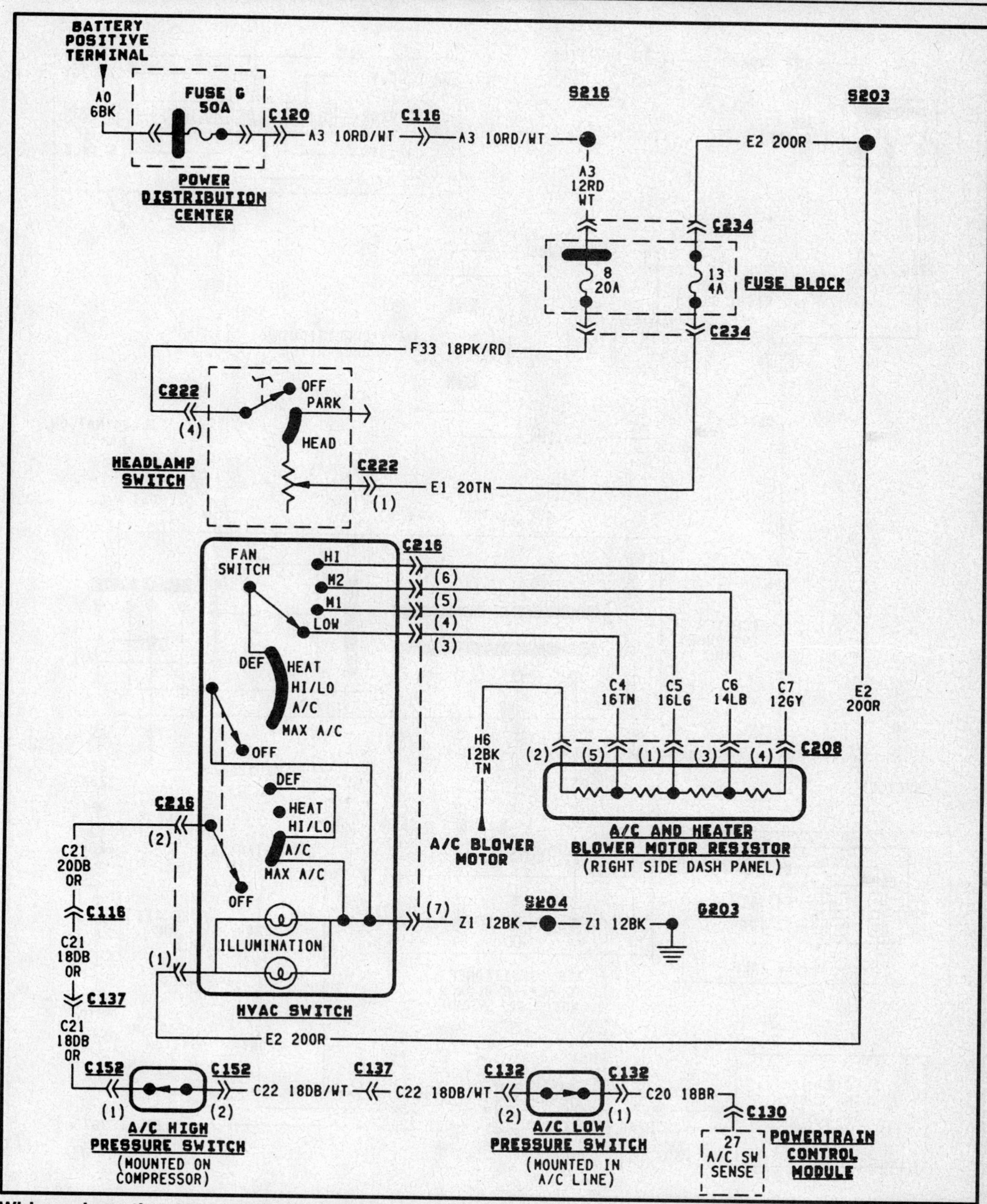

Wiring schematic—1994–95 Dakota with heater-A/C system with 2.5L engine, Cont'd

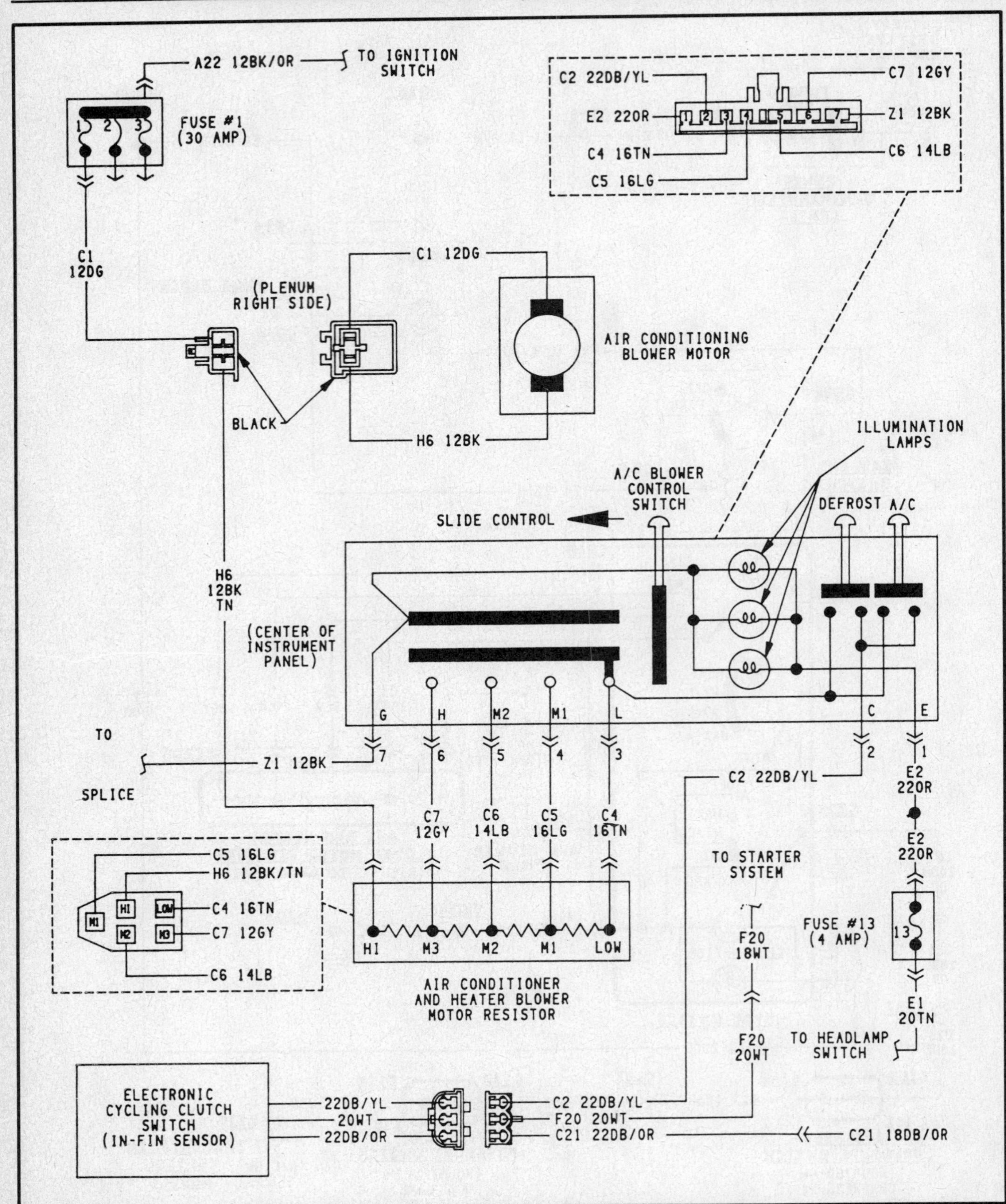

Wiring schematic—1993 Dakota with heater-A/C system with 3.9L and 5.2L engine

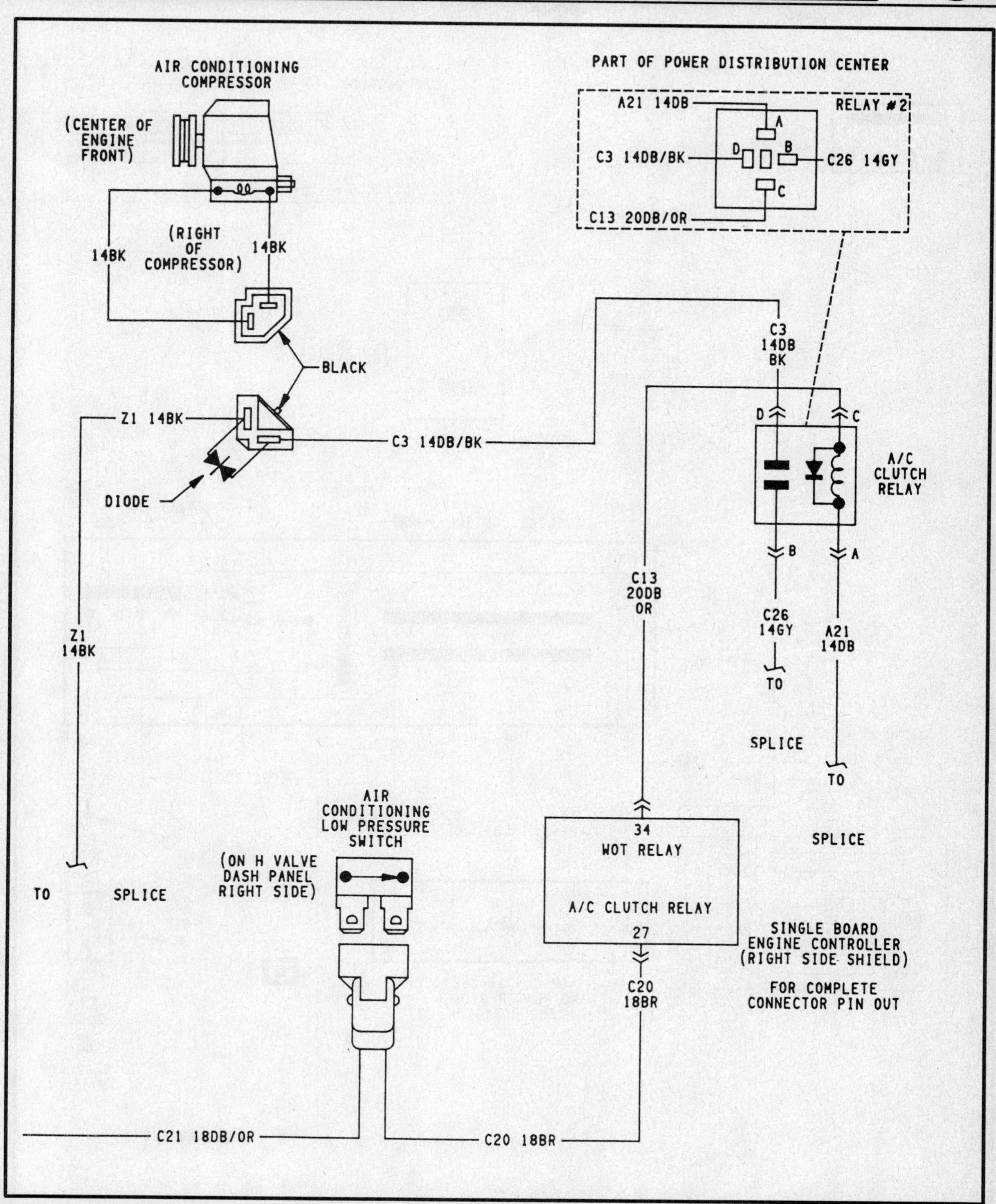

Wiring schematic—1993 Dakota with heater-A/C system with 3.9L and 5.2L engine, Cont'd

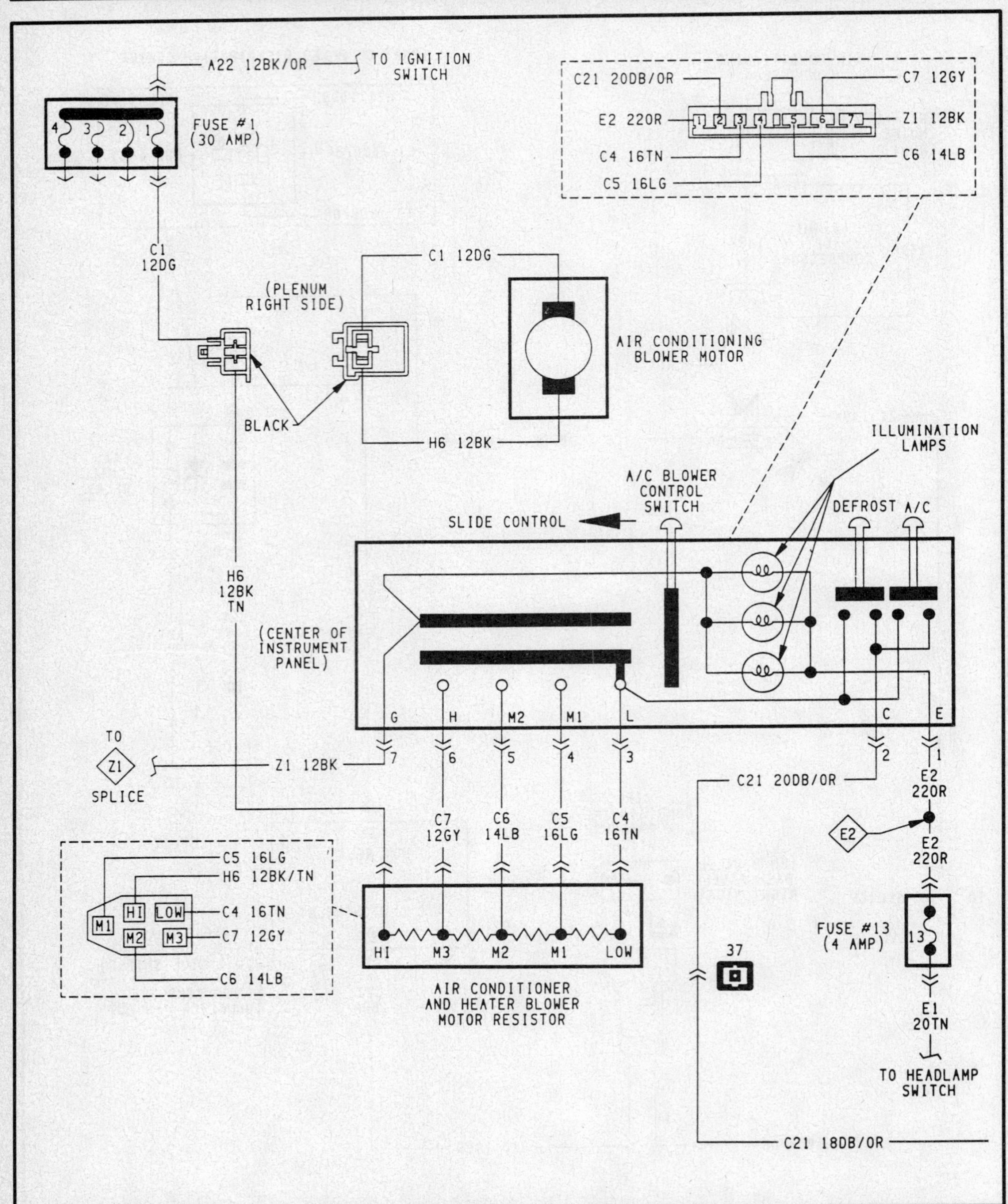

Wiring schematic—1994 Dakota with heater-A/C system with 3.9L and 5.2L engine

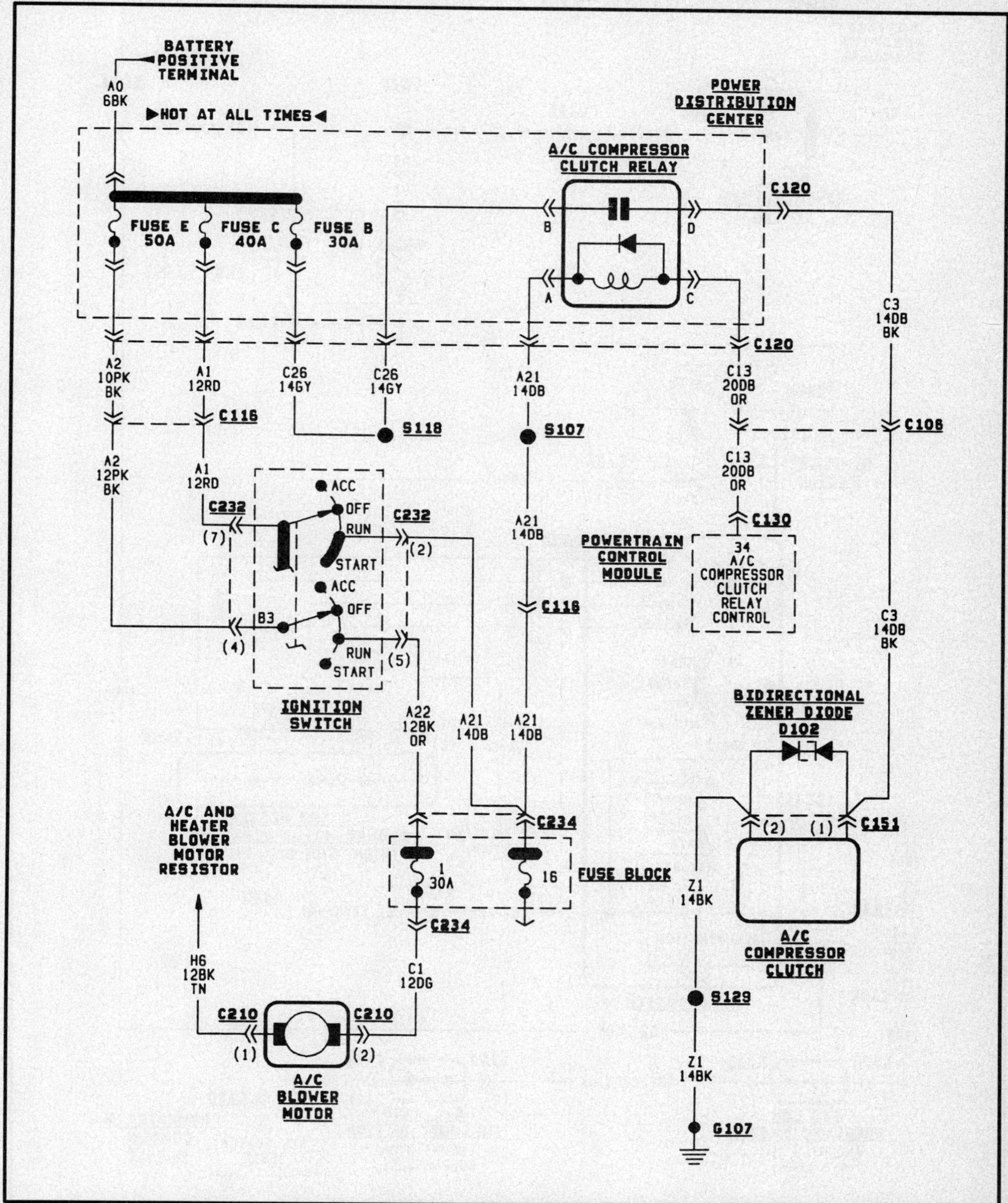

Wiring schematic—1995 Dakota with heater-A/C system with 3.9L and 5.2L engine, Cont'd

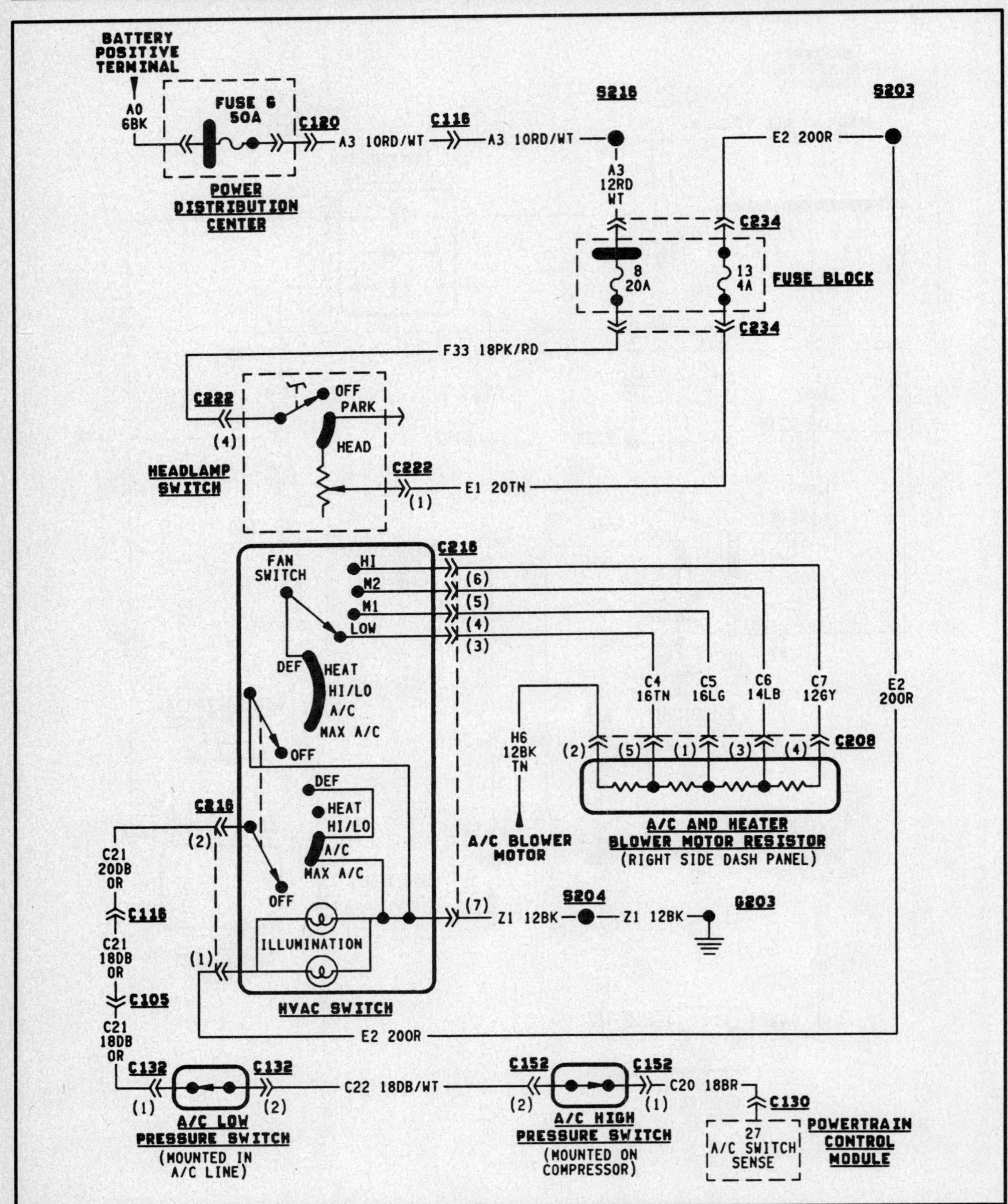

Wiring schematic—1995 Dakota with heater-A/C system with 3.9L and 5.2L engine, Cont'd

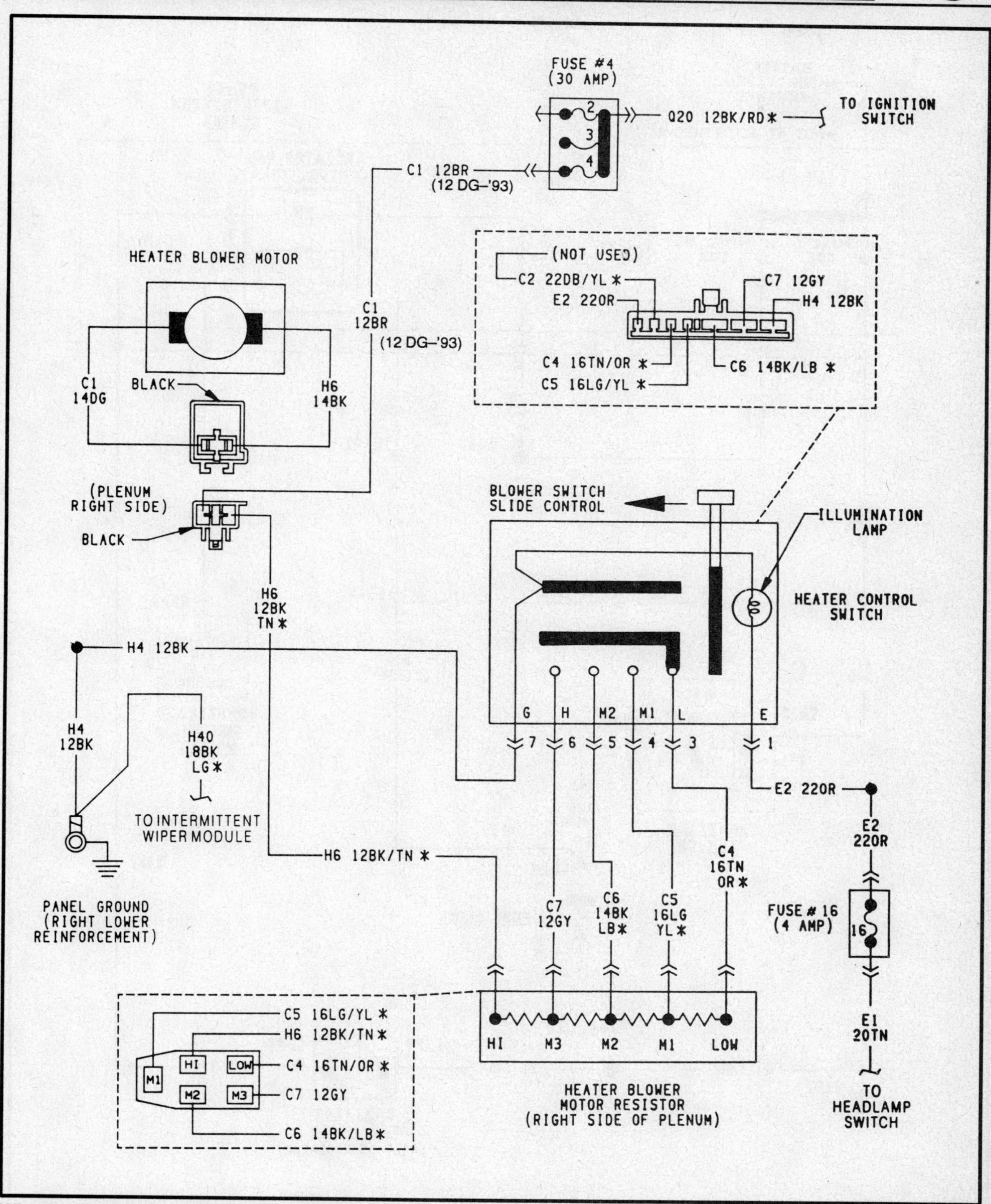

Wiring schematic—1993 Dakota with heater only

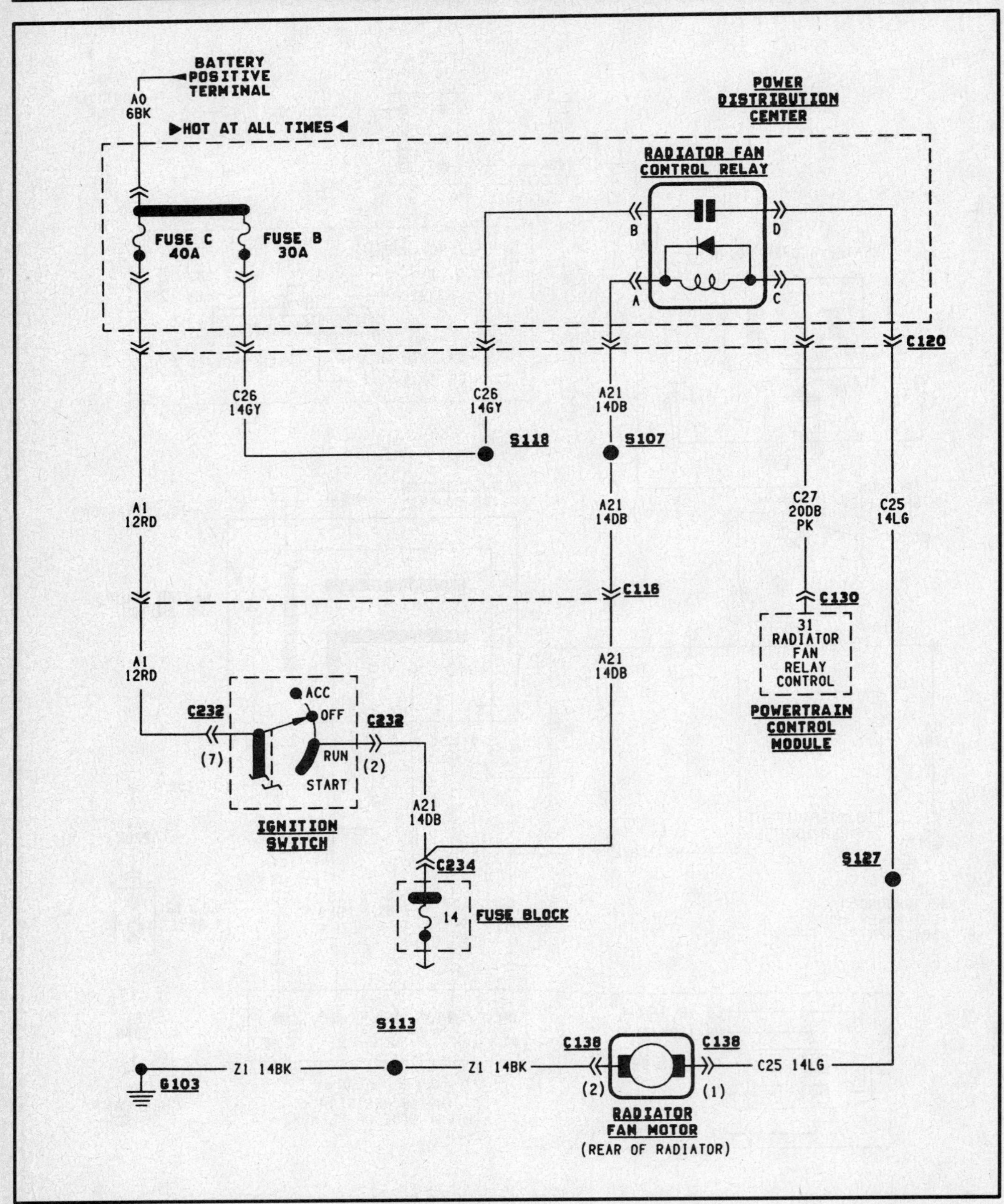

Wiring schematic—1994–95 Dakota with heater only

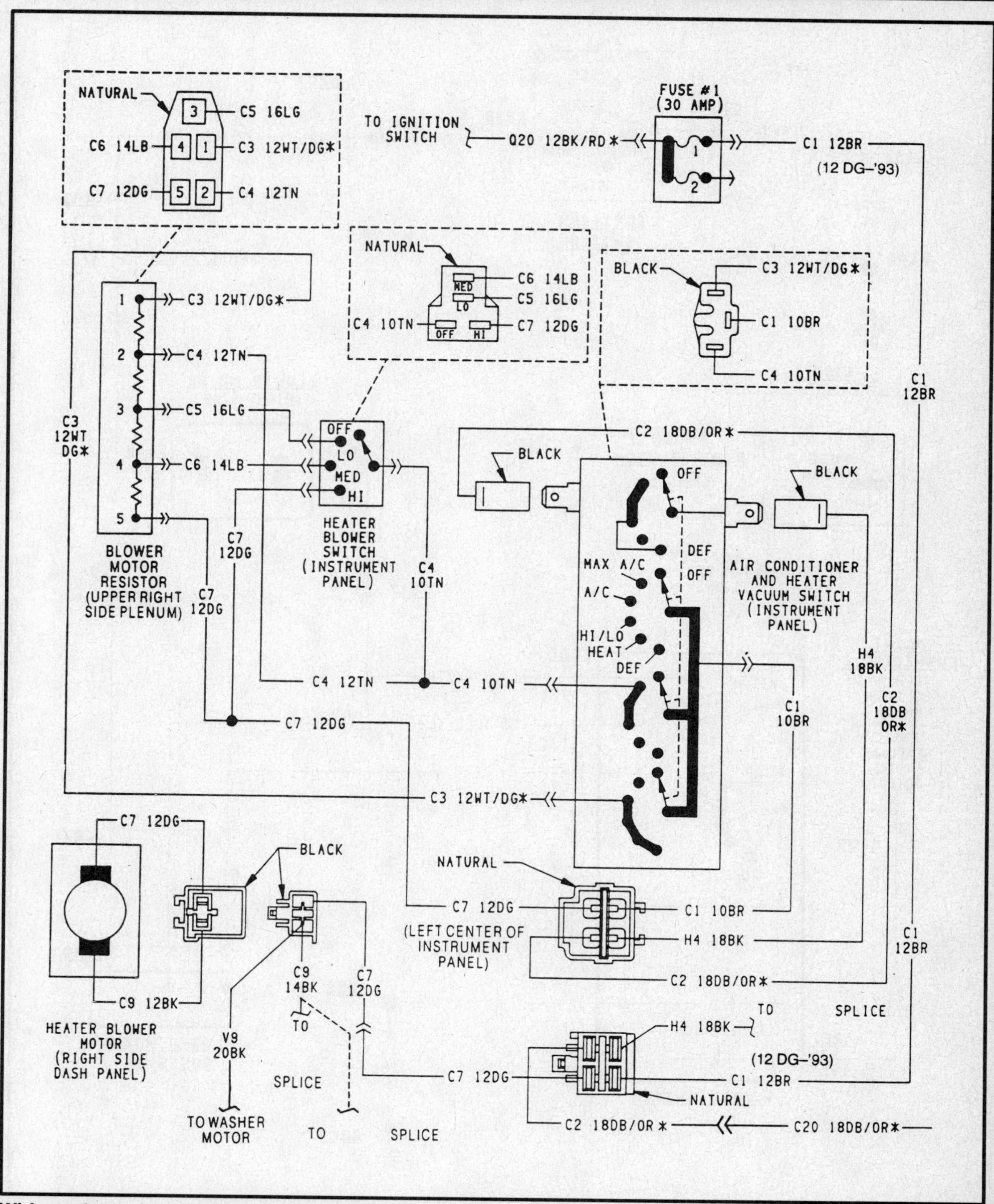

Wiring schematic—Pick-Up with heater-A/C system with gasoline engine

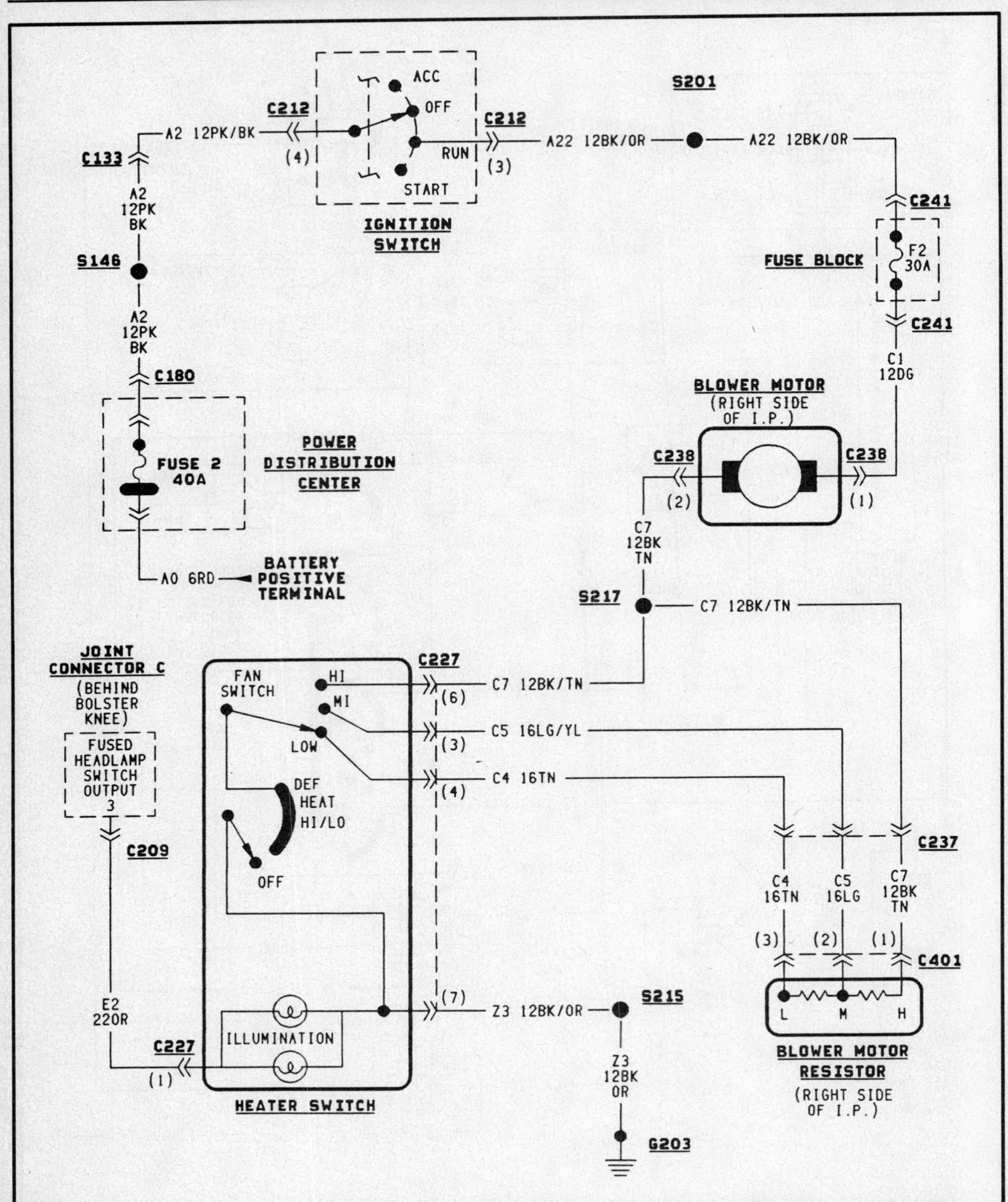

Wiring schematic—Pick-Up and Ramcharger with heater-A/C system with gasoline engine

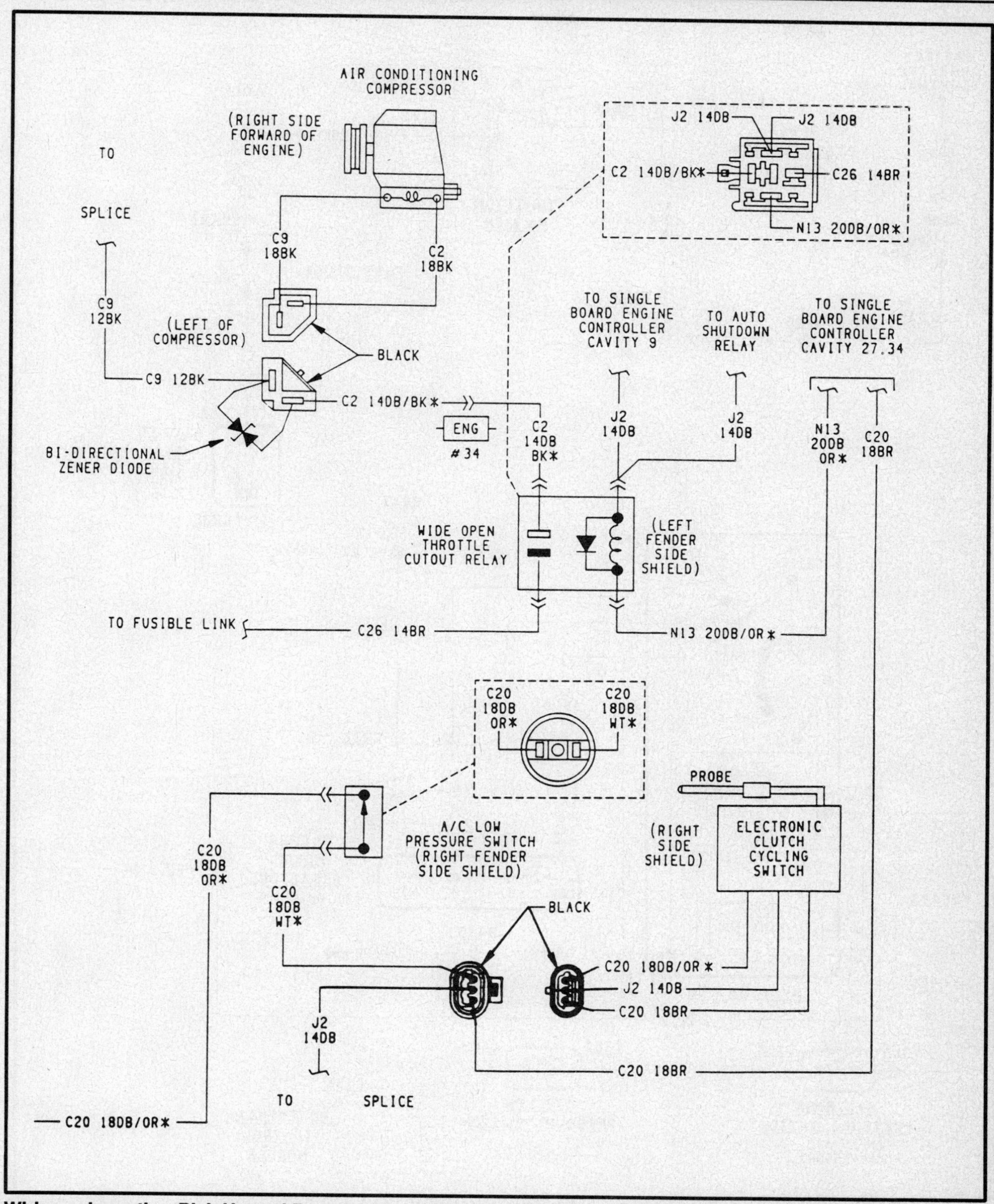

Wiring schematic—Pick-Up and Ramcharger with heater-A/C system with gasoline engine, Cont'd

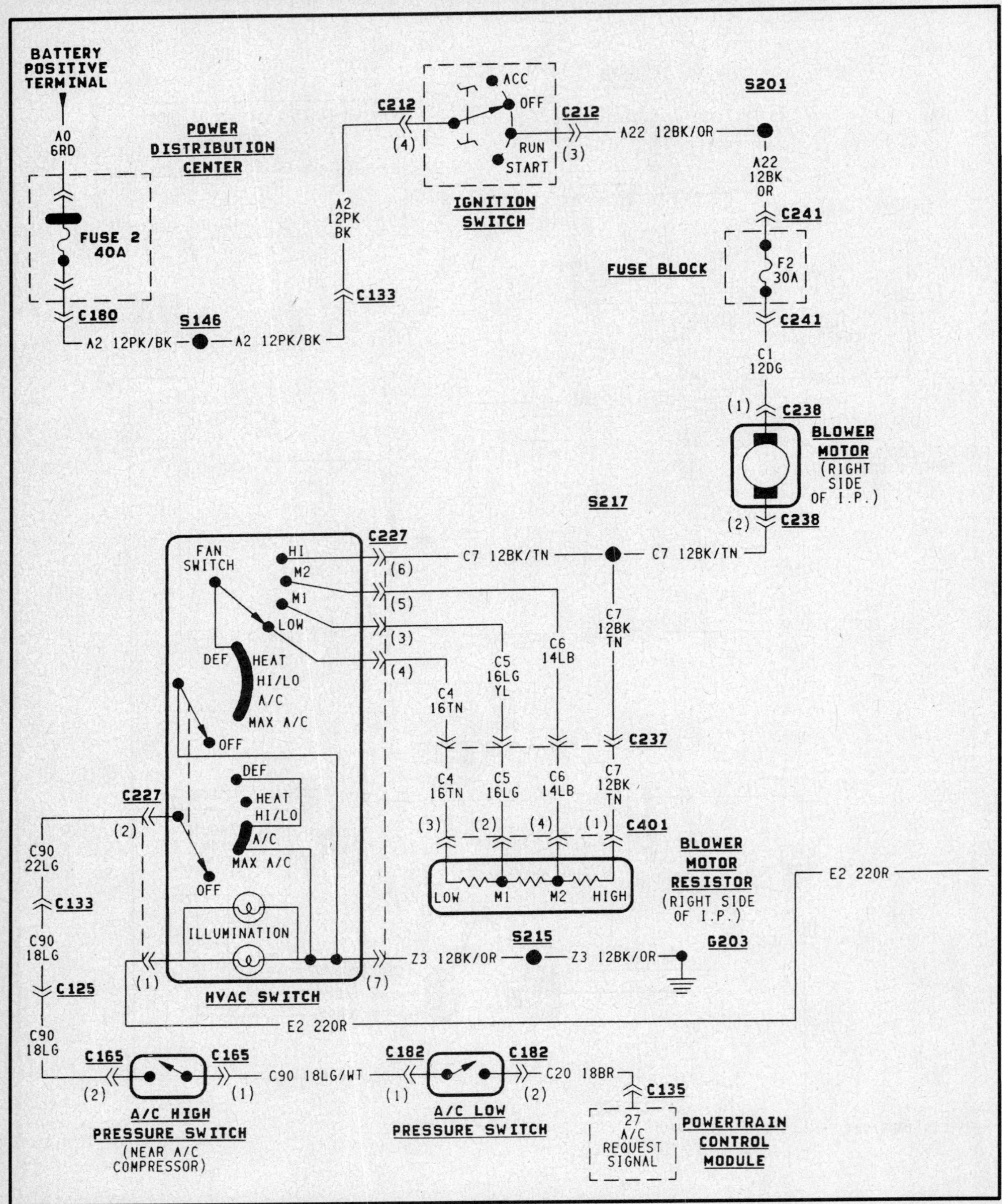

Wiring schematic—Pick-Up with heater-A/C system with gasoline engine

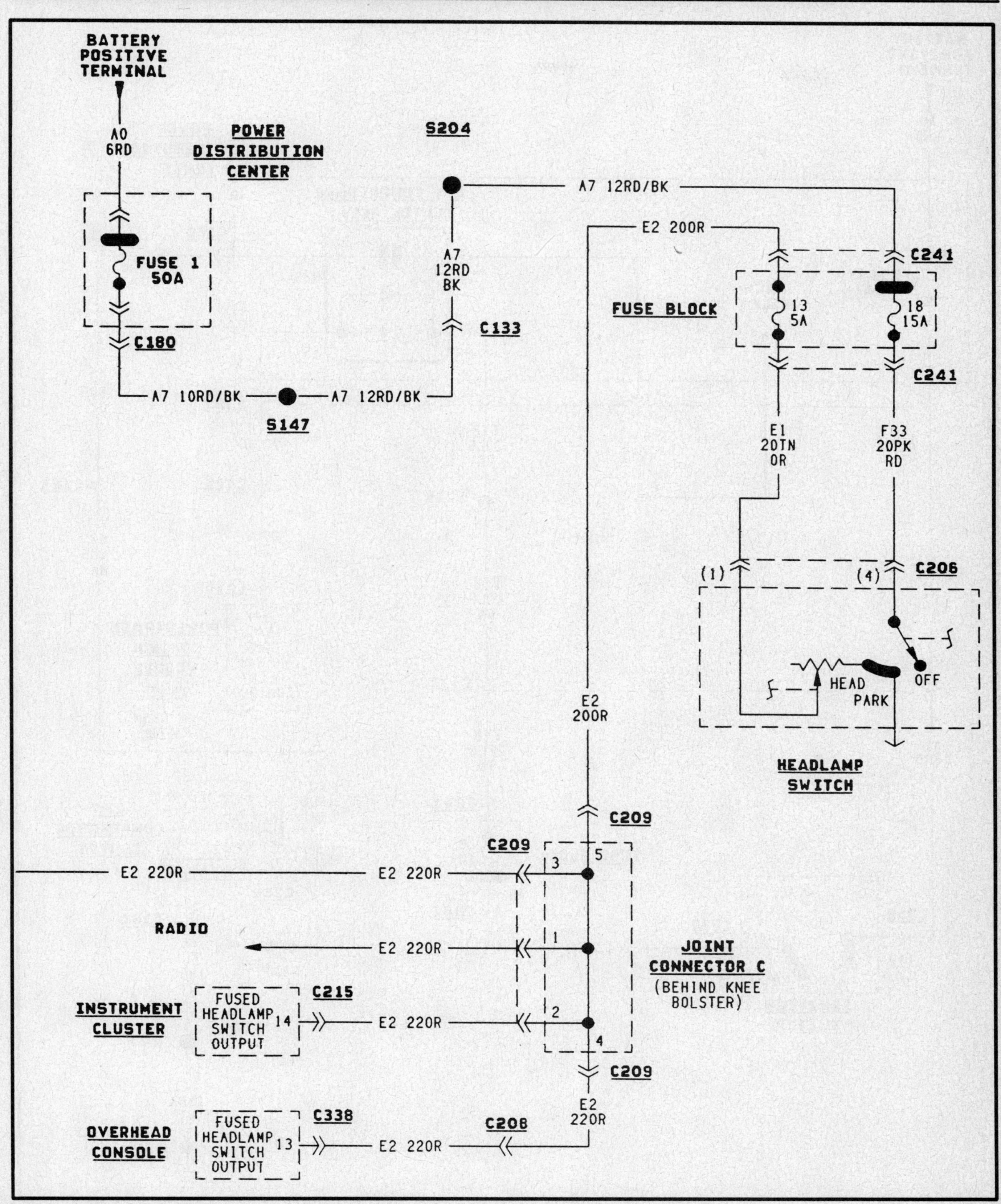

Wiring schematic—Pick-Up with heater-A/C system with gasoline engine, Cont'd

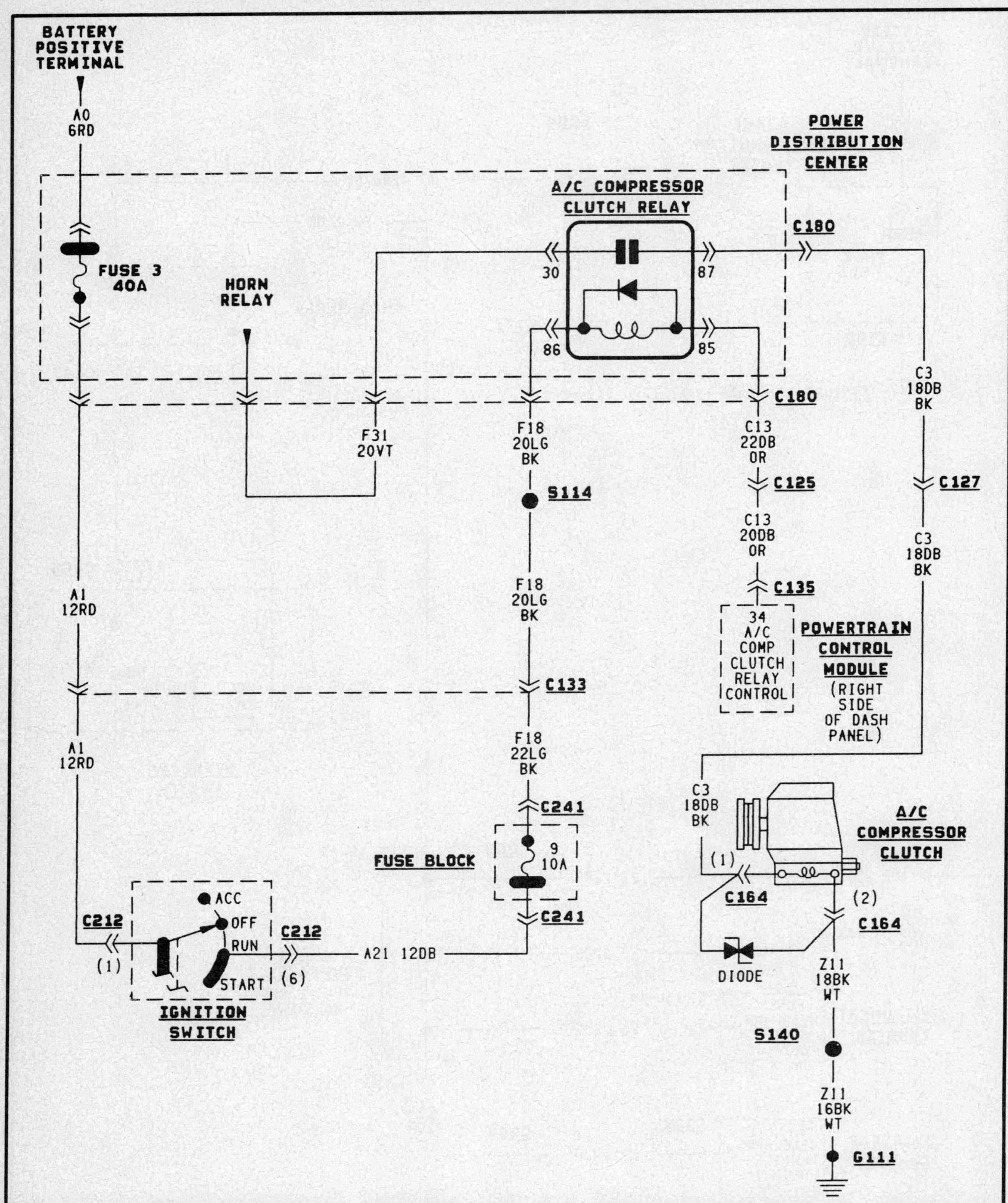

Wiring schematic—Pick-Up with heater-A/C system with gasoline engine, Cont'd

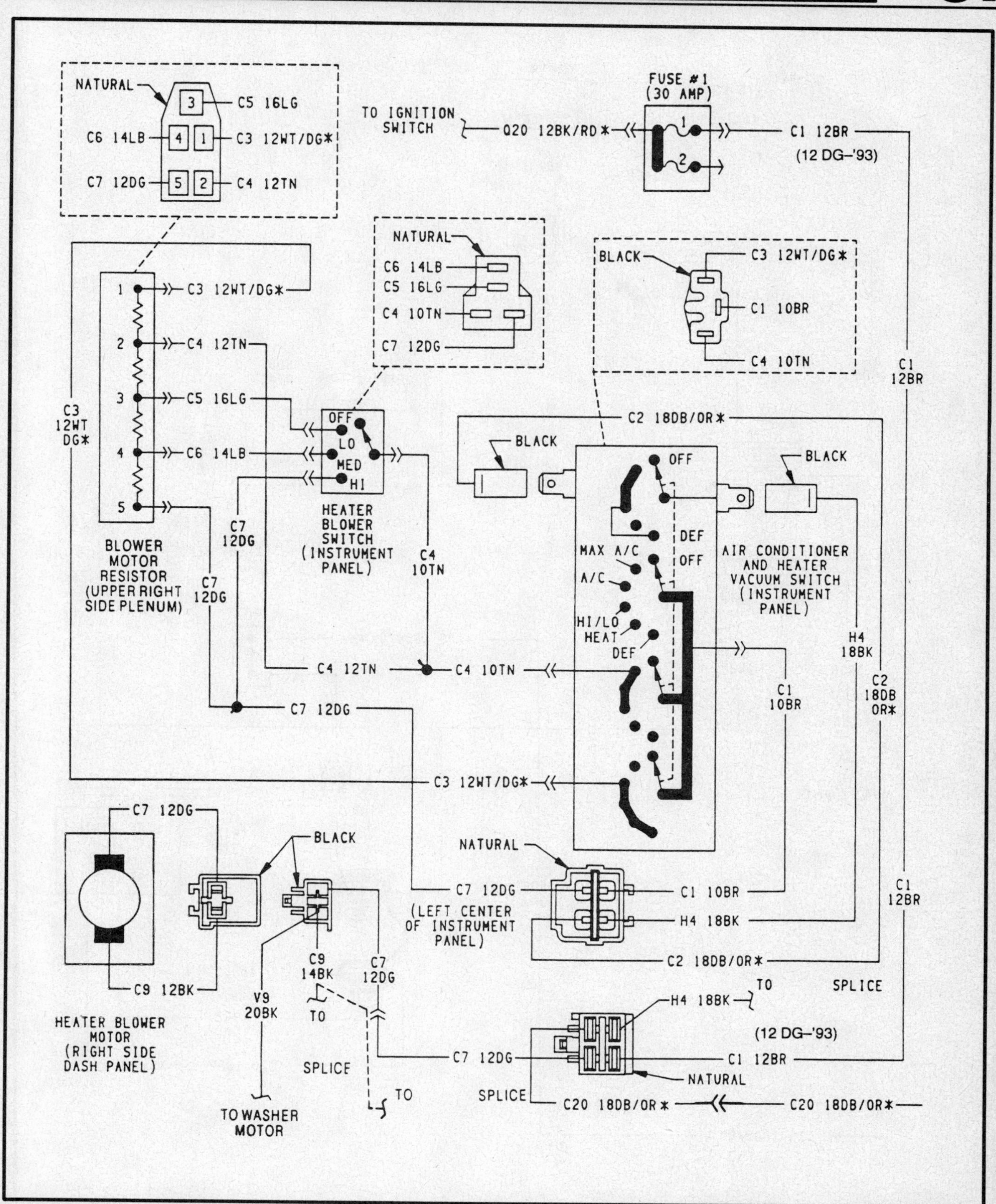

Wiring schematic—Pick-Up and Ramcharger with heater-A/C system with diesel engine

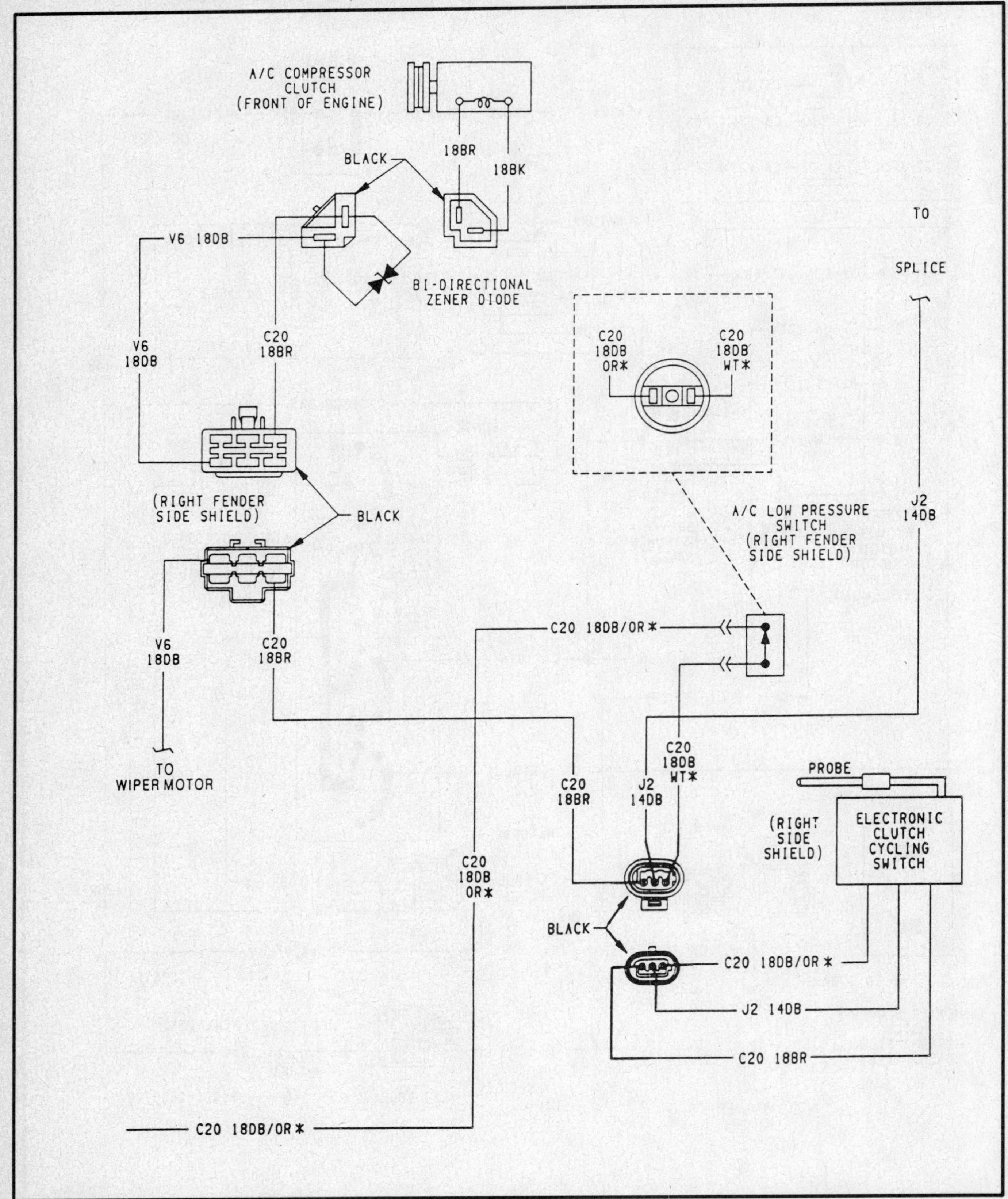

Wiring schematic—Pick-Up and Ramcharger with heater-A/C system with diesel engine, Cont'd

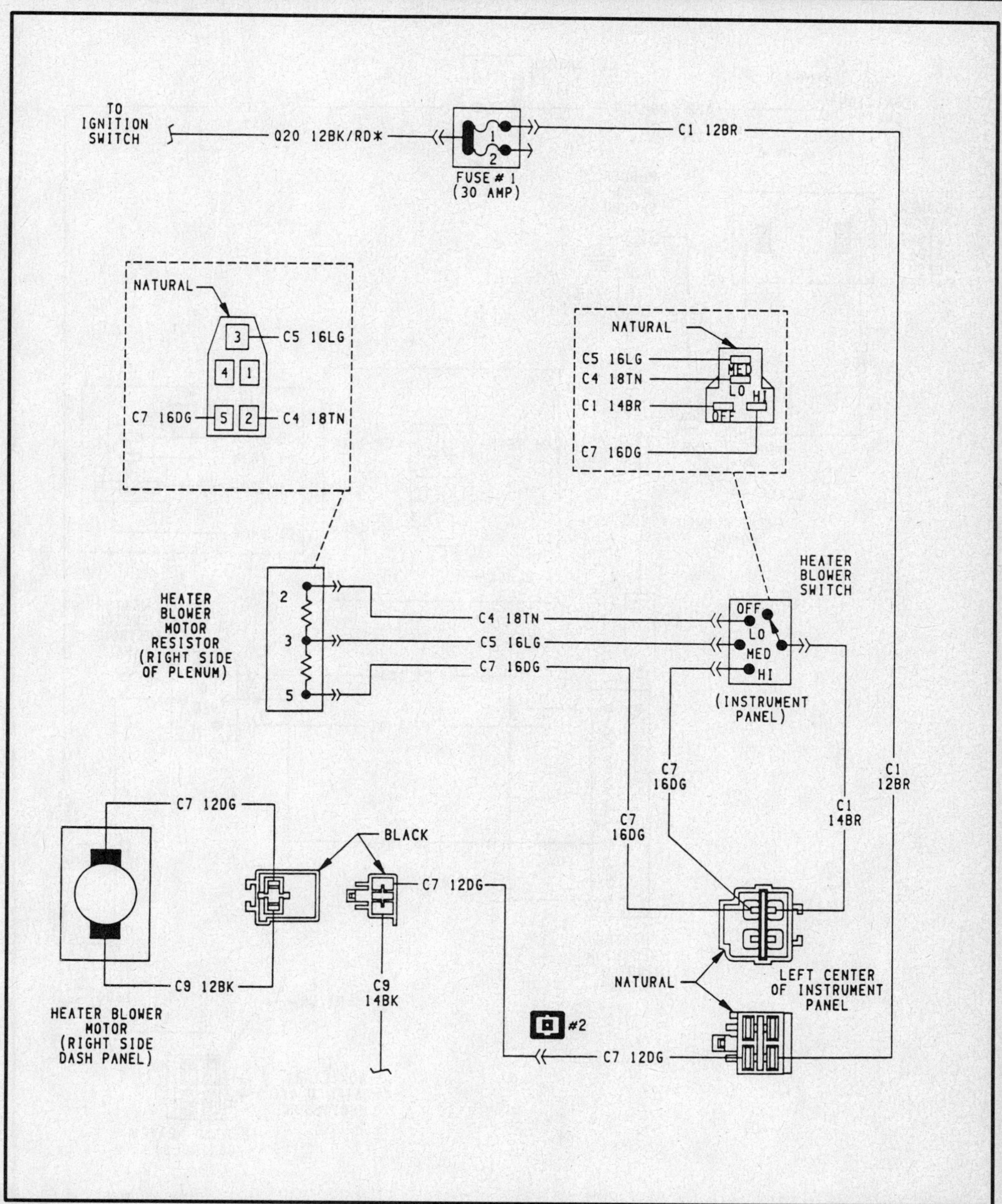

Wiring schematic—Pick-Up and Ramcharger with heater only

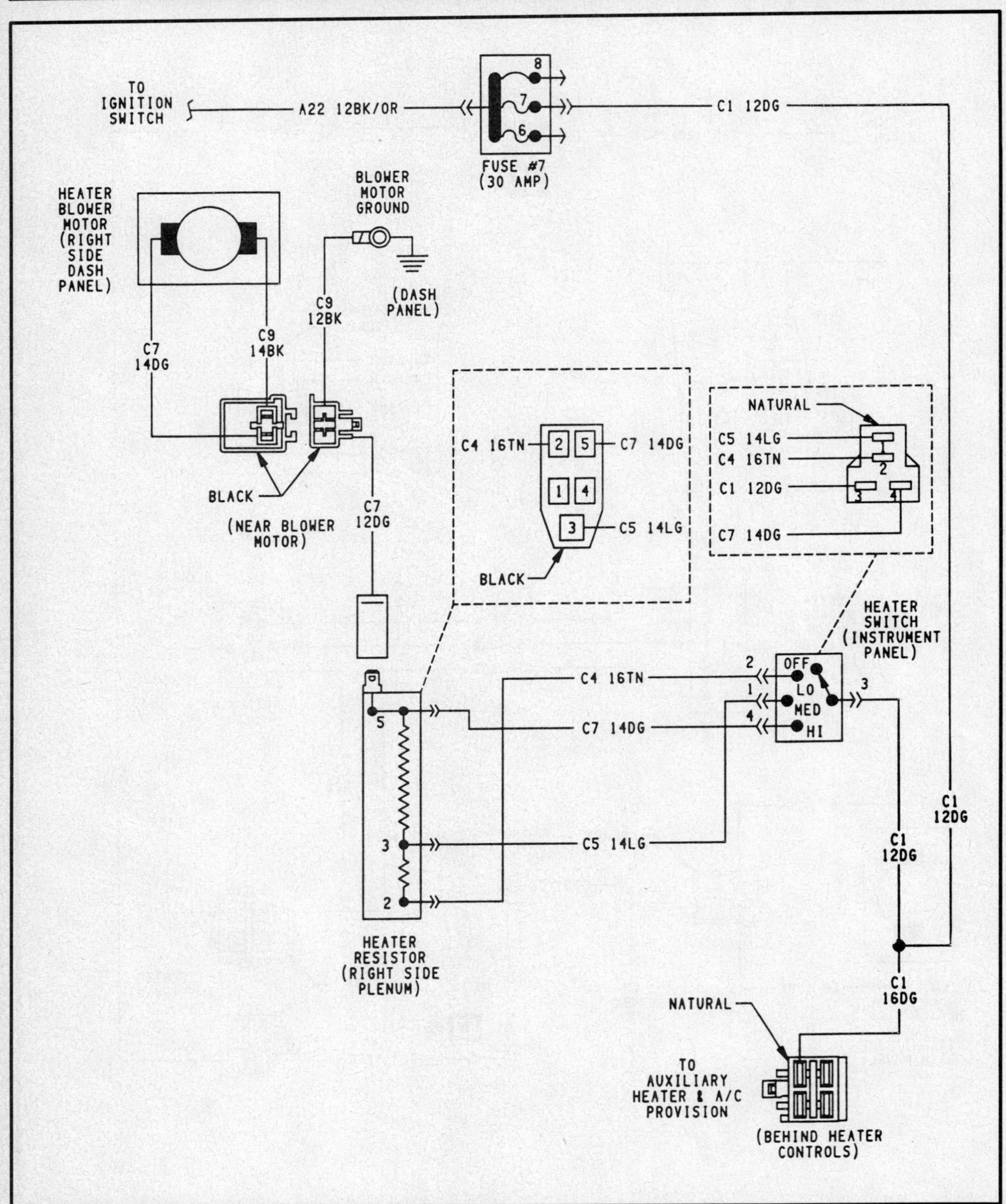

Wiring schematic—Van with heater only

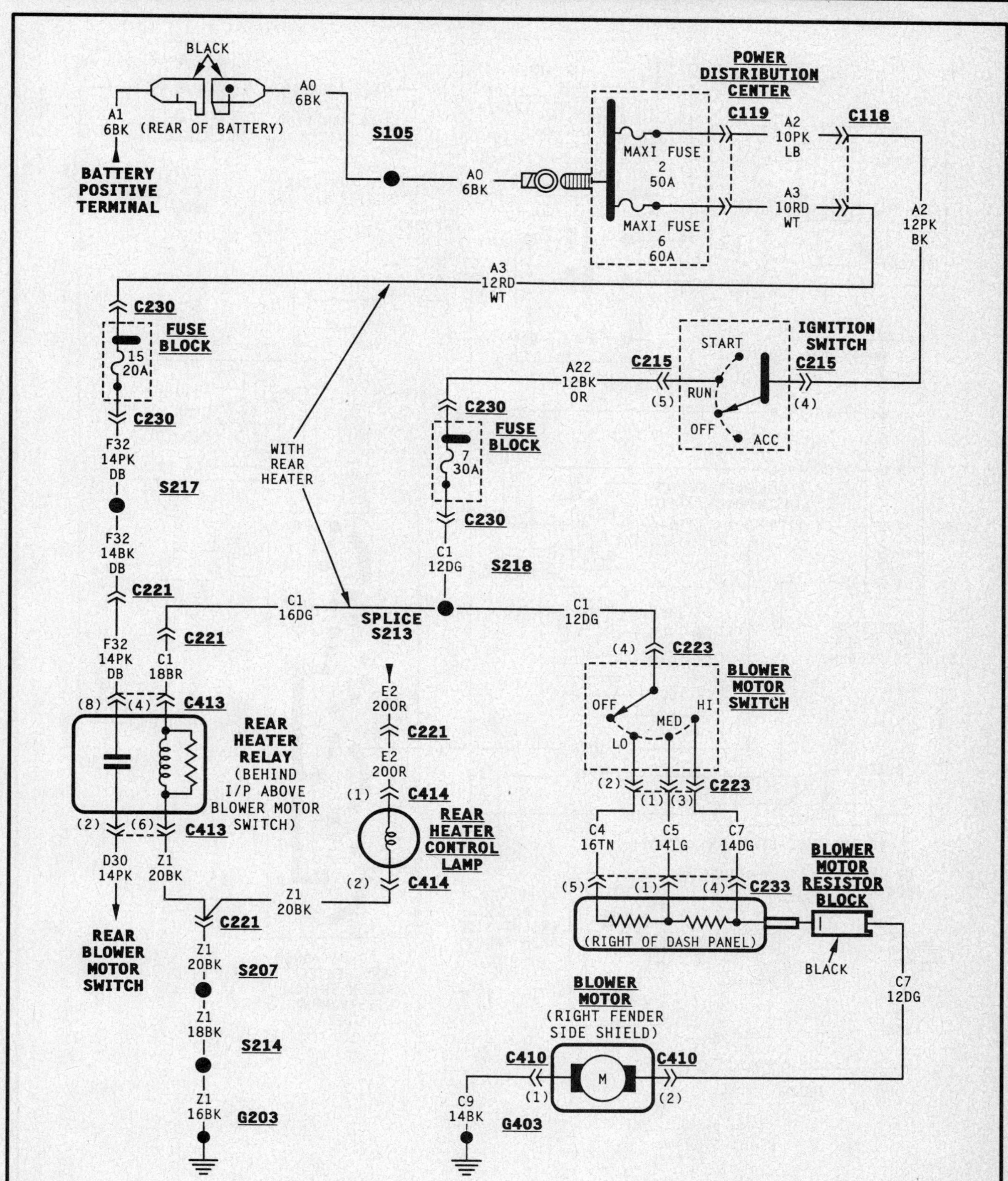

Wiring schematic—Van with heater only, Cont'd

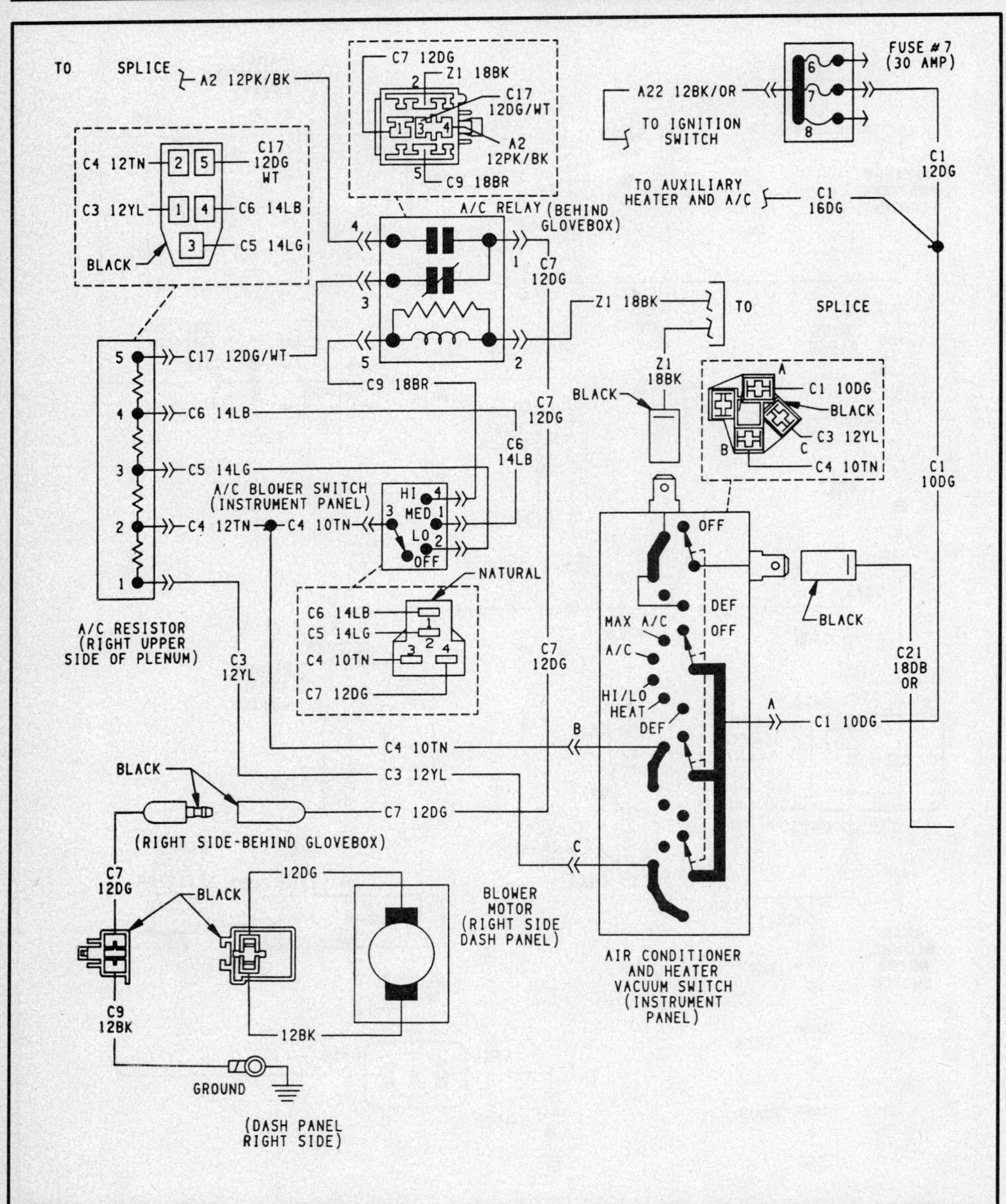

Wiring schematic—1993 Van with heater-A/C system

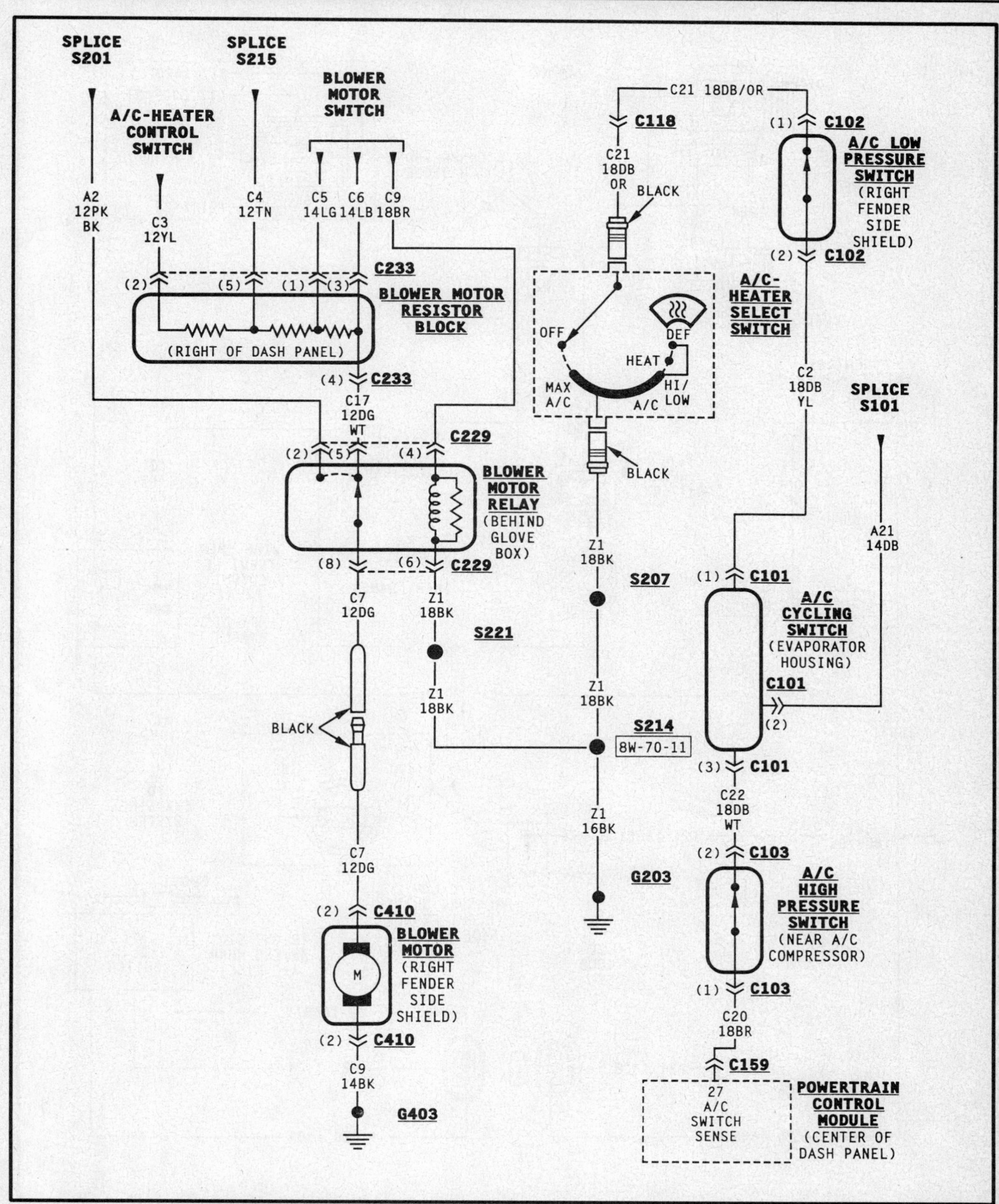

Wiring schematic—Van with heater-A/C system, Cont'd

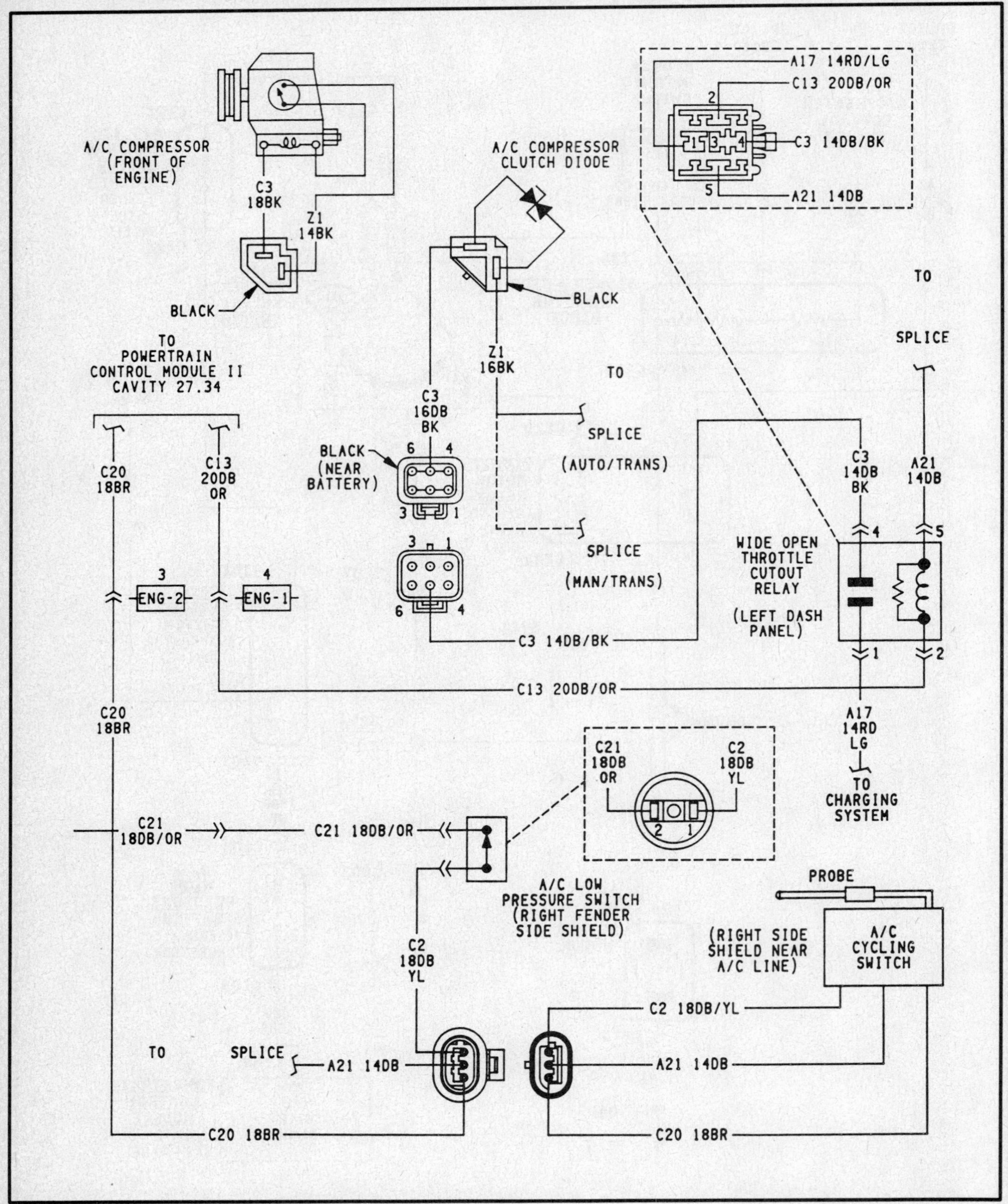

Wiring schematic—1993 Van with heater-A/C system, Cont'd

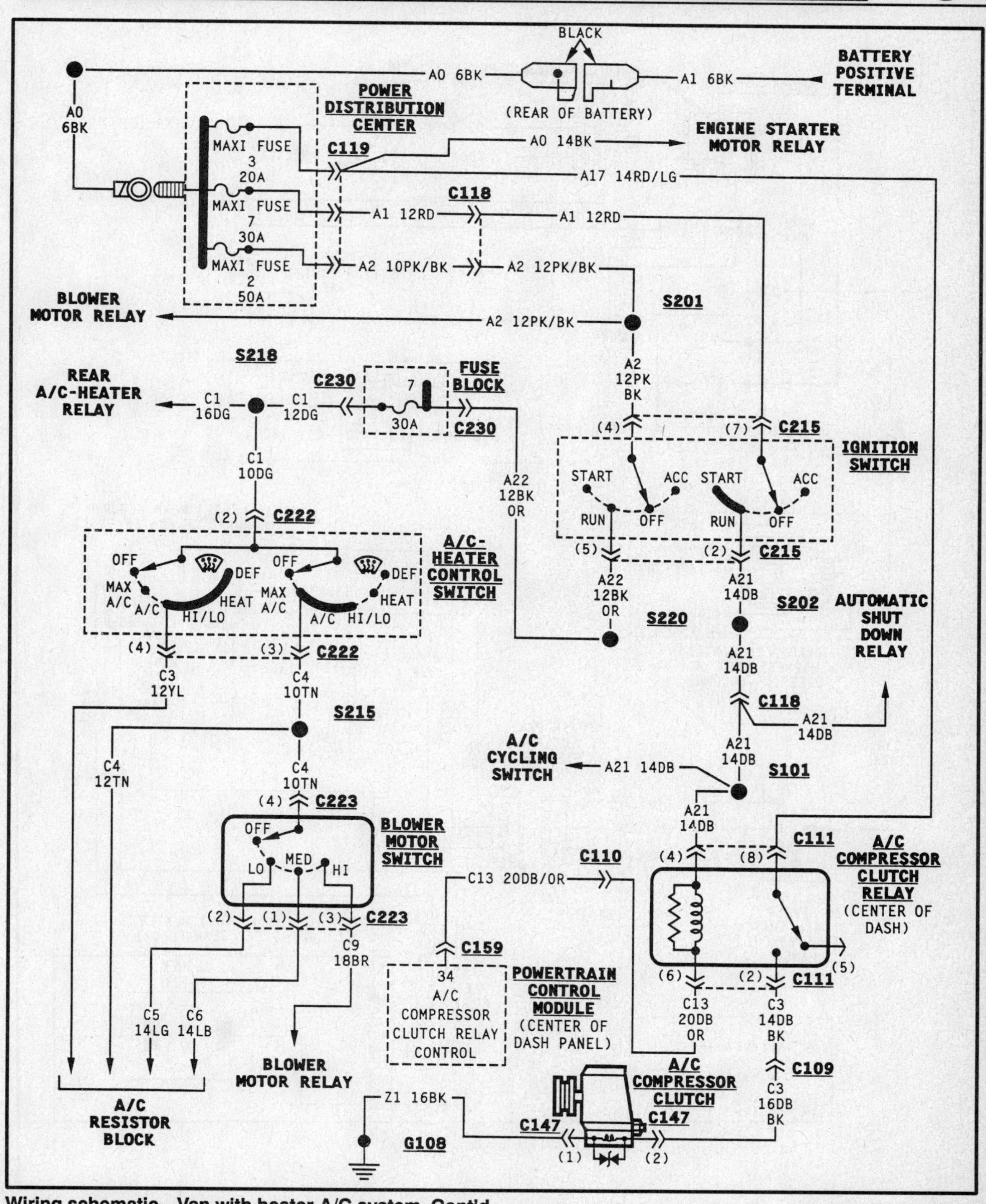

Wiring schematic—Van with heater-A/C system, Cont'd

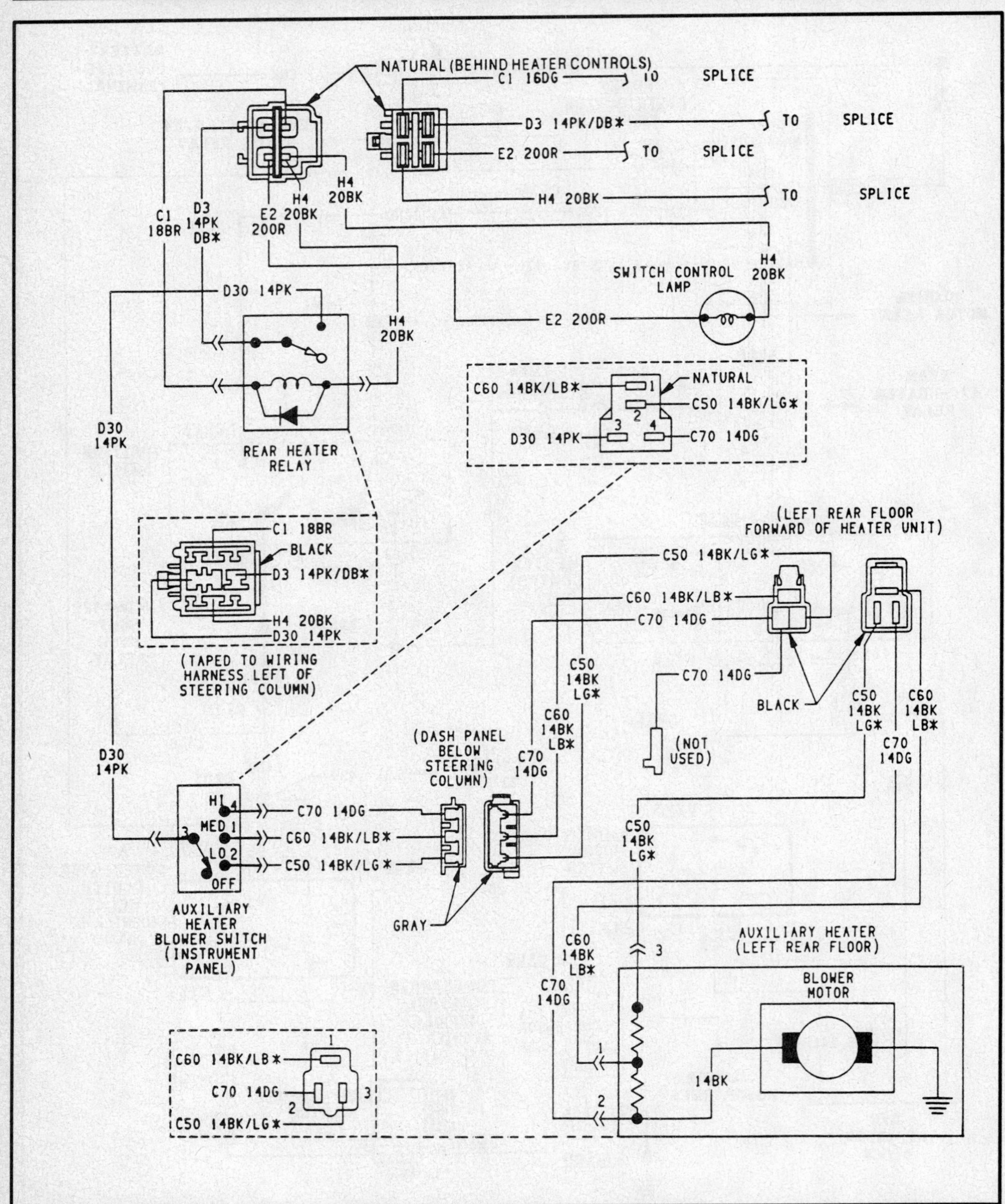

Wiring schematic—Van with rear heater only

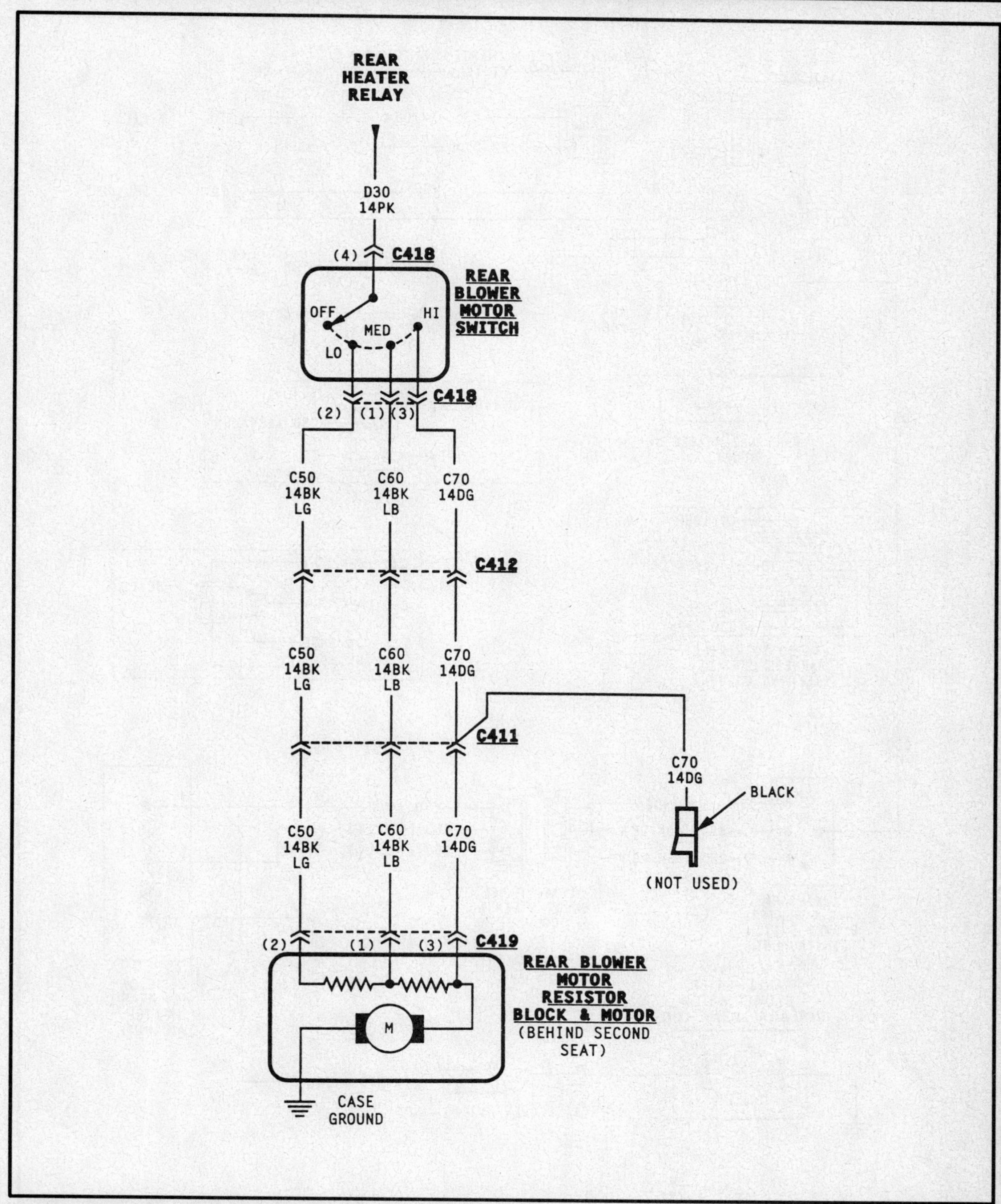

Wiring schematic—Van with rear heater only, Cont'd

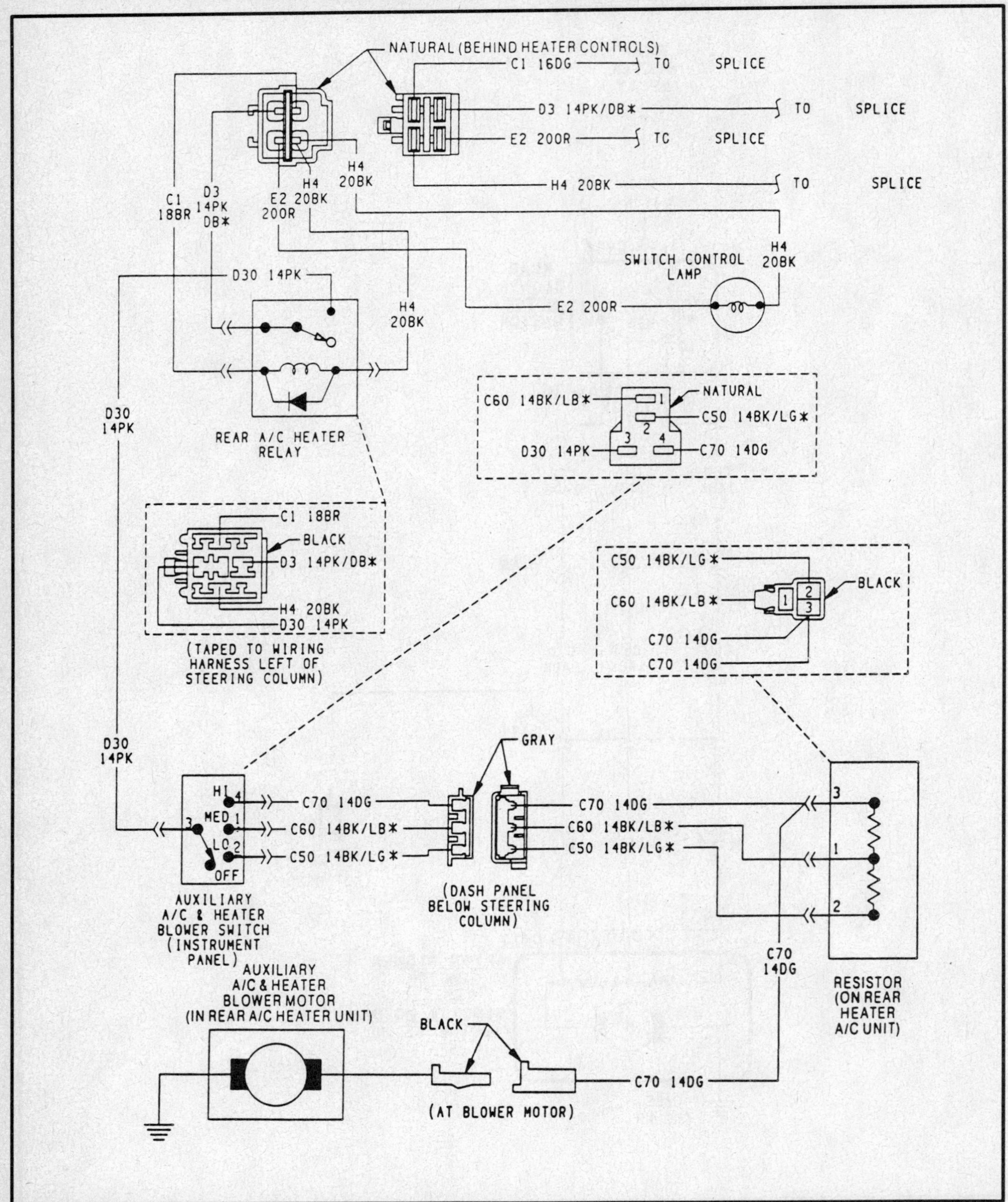

Wiring schematic—Van with rear heater-A/C system

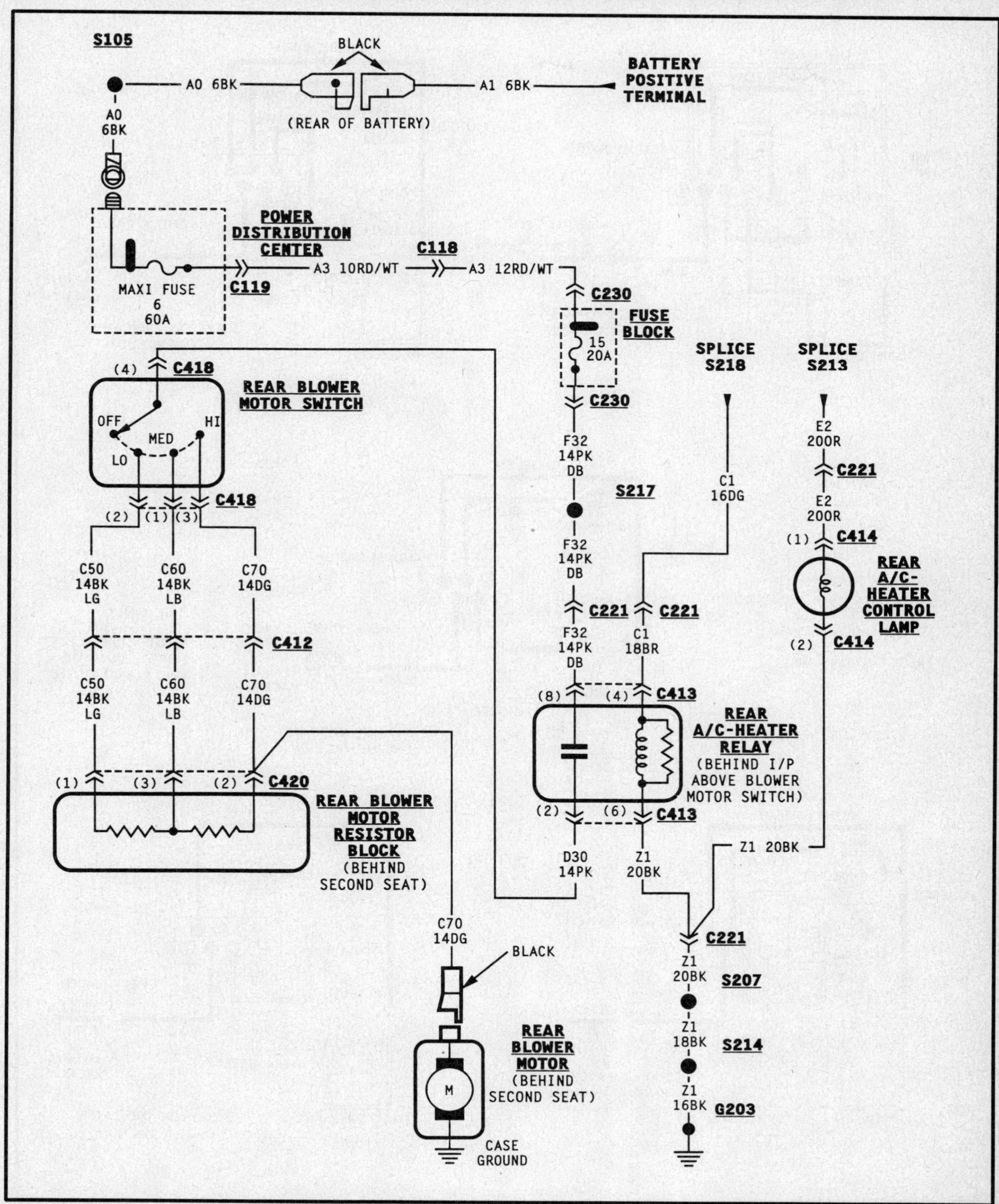

Wiring schematic—Van with rear heater-A/C system, Cont'd

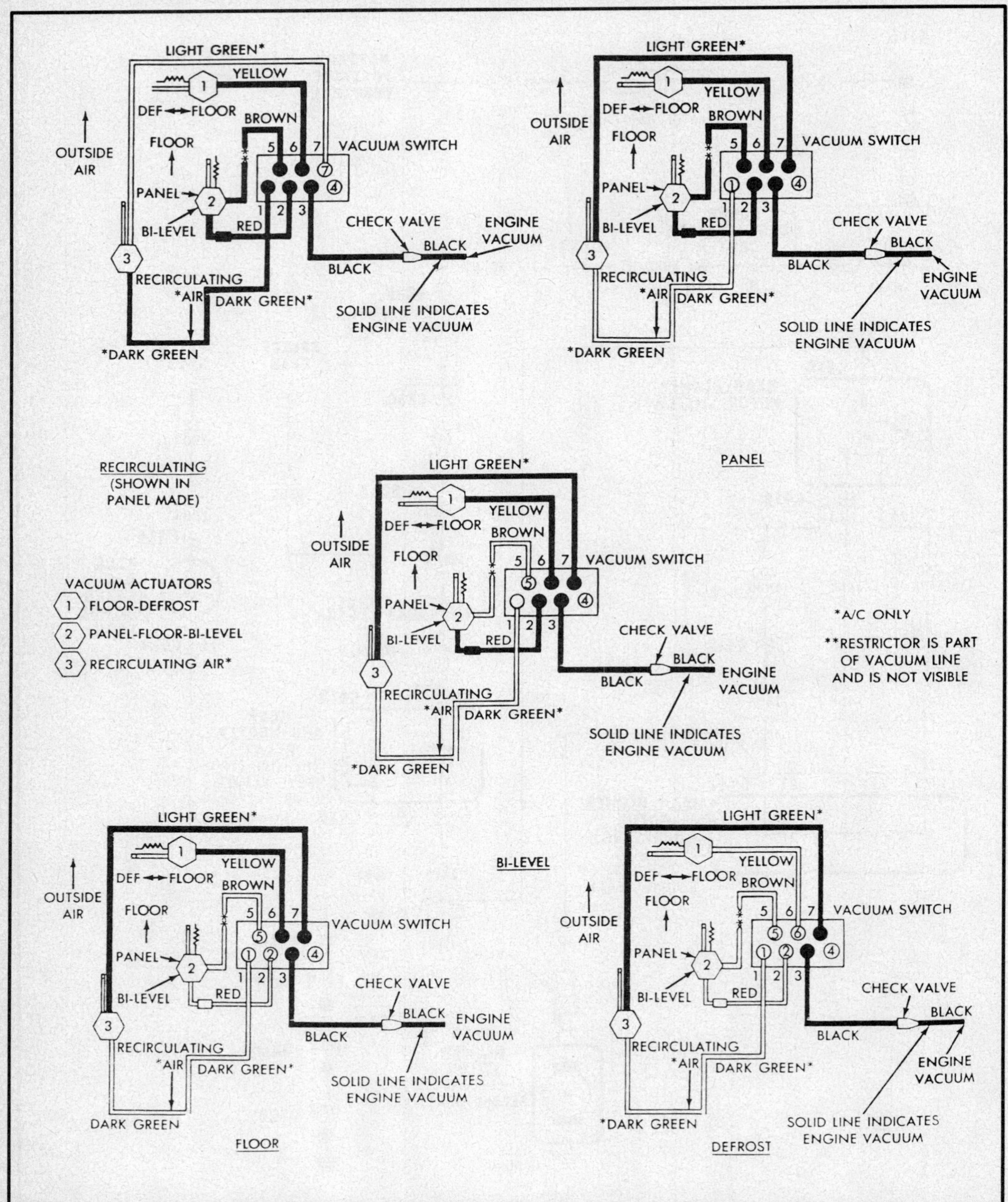

Wiring schematic—Dakota with heater and A/C controls

4 JEEP 4

CHEROKEE • GRAND CHEROKEE • GRAND WAGONEER • WRANGLER

SPECIFICATIONS

ENGINE IDENTIFICATION

Year	Model	Engine Displacement Liters (cc)	Engine Series (ID/VIN)	Fuel System	No. of Cylinders	Engine Type
1993	Cherokee	2.5 (2400)	P	MPI	4	OHV
	Cherokee	4.0 (3878)	S	MPI	6	OHV
	Wrangler	2.5 (2400)	P	MPI	4	OHV
	Wrangler	4.0 (3878)	S	MPI	6	OHV
	Grand Cherokee	4.0 (3878)	S	MPI	6	OHV
	Grand Cherokee	5.2 (5211)	Y	MPI	8	OHV
	Grand Wagoneer	5.2 (5211)	Y	MPI	8	OHV
1994	Cherokee	2.5 (2400)	P	MPI	4	OHV
	Cherokee	4.0 (3878)	S	MPI	6	OHV
	Wrangler	2.5 (2400)	P	MPI	4	OHV
	Wrangler	4.0 (3878)	S	MPI	6	OHV
	Grand Cherokee	4.0 (3878)	Y	MPI	6	OHV
	Grand Cherokee	5.2 (5211)	Y	MPI	8	OHV
1995	Cherokee	2.5 (2400)	P	MPI	4	OHV
	Cherokee	4.0 (3878)	S	MPI	6	OHV
	Wrangler	2.5 (2400)	P	MPI	4	OHV
	Wrangler	4.0 (3878)	S	MPI	6	OHV
	Grand Cherokee	4.0 (3878)	Y	MPI	6	OHV
	Grand Cherokee	5.2 (5211)	Y	MPI	8	OHV

MPI Multi–Point Injection
OHV Overhead Valves

REFRIGERANT CAPACITIES

Year	Model	Refrigerant (oz.)	Oil (fl. oz.)	Compressor Type
1993	Cherokee	38	4.6	SD–709
	Wrangler	32	4.6	SD–709
	Grand Cherokee	28①	7.75①	10PA17
	Grand Wagoneer	28①	7.75①	10PA17
1994	Cherokee	32①	4.6①	SD–709
	Wrangler	32①	4.6①	SD–709
	Grand Cherokee	28①	7.75①	10PA17
1995	Cherokee	32①	4.6①	SD7H15
	Wrangler	32①	4.6①	SD7H15
	Grand Cherokee	28①	7.75①	10PA17

① System uses R–134a non–CFC refrigerant and corresponding oil (ND8 PAG)

AIR CONDITIONING BELT TENSION

Year	Model	Engine Liters (cc)	Belt Type	Specifications New (lbs.)	Specifications Used (lbs.)
1993	Cherokee	2.5 (2400)	Serpentine	180–200	140–160
	Cherokee	4.0 (3878)	Serpentine	180–200	140–160
	Wrangler	2.5 (2400)	Serpentine	180–200	140–160
	Wrangler	4.0 (3878)	Serpentine	180–200	140–160
	Grand Cherokee	4.0 (3878)	Serpentine	180–200	140–160
	Grand Cherokee	5.2 (5211)	Serpentine	①	①
	Grand Wagoneer	5.2 (5211)	Serpentine	①	①
1994	Cherokee	2.5 (2400)	Serpentine	180–200	140–160
	Cherokee	4.0 (3878)	Serpentine	180–200	140–160
	Wrangler	2.5 (2400)	Serpentine	180–200	140–160
	Wrangler	4.0 (3878)	Serpentine	180–200	140–160
	Grand Cherokee	4.0 (3878)	Serpentine	180–200	140–160
	Grand Cherokee	5.2 (5211)	Serpentine	①	①
1995	Cherokee	2.5 (2400)	Serpentine	180–200	140–160
	Cherokee	4.0 (3878)	Serpentine	180–200	140–160
	Wrangler	2.5 (2400)	Serpentine	180–200	140–160
	Wrangler	4.0 (3878)	Serpentine	180–200	140–160
	Grand Cherokee	4.0 (3878)	Serpentine	180–200	140–160
	Grand Cherokee	5.2 (5211)	Serpentine	①	①

① Automatic tensioner; no adjustment.

SYSTEM DESCRIPTION

General Information

Cherokee

The climate control system is an integrated assembly combining air conditioning, heating and fresh air ventilating. Vehicles without air conditioning use a similar assembly minus the air conditioning components. Both systems basically consist of the blower and air inlet assembly and the heater core and air distribution assembly, which may be removed and serviced separately.

The heater system is a blend air type in which fresh air is heated and blended with cooler outside air in varying amounts to produce the desired temperature. The heater coolant valve provides variable coolant flow to the heater core for differing climate conditions.

The air conditioning system adds an evaporator for cooling and dehumidifying. The evaporator does not operate at ambient temperatures below 30°F (–1°C). Evaporator temperature is determined by a fixed setting thermostat switch which cycles the compressor clutch to avoid evaporator freezing. The blower automatically operates except in the **OFF** mode, in which case the blower and outside air are shut off.

Wrangler

A blend air heater system is used, providing constant coolant flow through the heater core. The temperature of heated air entering the passenger compartment is controlled by regulating the amount of air that flows through the heater core. The air control lever operates a door in the fresh air intake duct which controls the amount of air flow into the heater housing. The temperature control lever determines air flow through the heater core by operating the heater housing blend air door.

The air conditioning system is a dual flow unit. Cooling air can be drawn from outside the vehicle or recirculated from inside. The evaporator, blower fan and motor, thermostat, expansion valve, capillary tube, air outlets and system control are located in the evaporator housing. A rotary type compressor and magnetically operated clutch pulley is used for the system.

Grand Cherokee and Grand Wagoneer

These models may be equipped with heater only, manual air conditioning or automatic air conditioning. All vehicles are equipped with a common heater-A/C unit. On heater-only systems, the evaporator assembly is omitted and replace with an air restrictor plate. A typical blend-air type heater system is the basic component. On air conditioned systems, an A/C switch and **RECIRC** position are added to the panel controls. On automatic systems, a digital display is featured.

This system also uses an accumulator and fixed orifice tube instead of the receiver/drier and expansion valve as on other Jeep systems. The accumulator is mounted on the right side of the engine compartment and connects to the evaporator outlet tube and to the compressor inlet line. A clutch cycling switch is mounted on top of the accumulator. The fixed orifice tube is an integral part of the liquid line near the condenser. A high pressure cutout switch on the compressor will stop compressor operation if the discharge pressure reaches 450 psi or more, and a compressor high pressure relief valve bleed system pressure if it senses more than 500 psi.

The Grand Cherokee and Grand Wagoneer model systems are designed to use R-134a refrigerant instead of R-12. R-134a is a non-CFC refrigerant and is not compatible in any amount in R-12. Likewise, the respective refrigerant oils are not compatible. Therefore, never attempt to intermix these chemicals or any service equipment (manifold gauge set, recycling/charging stations, leak detectors, etc.) that may possibly contaminate the R-134a system with any R-12 trace amounts.

Service Port Location

Cherokee and Wrangler

The high pressure service port is located on the discharge line near the compressor. The low pressure service port is located on the suction line near the compressor.

The low side service port is located at the right rear of the engine compartment in the condenser to evaporator line. The high side port is located on the underside of the 10PA17 compressor manifold. This system uses R-134a refrigerant and has special service valve fittings that require the use of dedicated service equipment.

NOTE: Never try to attach the low pressure hose to the clutch cycling pressure switch port on the accumulator.

System Discharging

For the 1993 Cherokee and Wagoneer, R-12 refrigerant is a chlorofluorocarbon which, when mishandled, can contribute to the depletion on the ozone layer in the upper atmosphere. Ozone filters out harmful radiation from the sun. In order to protect the ozone layer, an approved R-12 Recovery/Recycling machine that meets SAE standard J1991 should be employed when discharging the system. Follow the operating instructions provided with the approved equipment exactly to properly discharge the system.

All others use R-134a non-CFC refrigerant. The application is identified by a series of "R-134a" stickers on the key components and refrigeration lines. This refrigerant and its oil are not compatible in any amount with R-12; therefore, special precautions must be taken when servicing these vehicles. Dedicated service equipment (manifold gauge sets, recycling/recharging stations, leak testers) are required with this system.

System Evacuating

If the air conditioning system has been opened to the atmosphere, it should be air and moisture free before being recharged with refrigerant. Moisture and air mixed with refrigerant will raise the compressor head pressure, possibly damage the system's components and will reduce the performance of the system. Moisture will boil at normal room temperature when exposed to a vacuum. To evacuate the system, perform the following procedure:

NOTE: On models except 1993 Cherokee and Wagoneer, use R-134a refrigerant, use only dedicated service equipment designed for this application and that meets SAE standard J2210. Never try to attach the low pressure hose to the clutch cycling pressure switch port on the accumulator.

1. Leak test the system and repair any leaks found.
2. Connect an approved charging station, Recovery/Recycling machine or manifold gauge set and vacuum pump to the discharge and suction ports. The red hose is normally connected to the discharge (high pressure) line and the blue hose is connected to the suction (low pressure) line.
3. Open the discharge and suction ports and start the vacuum pump. If the pump is not able to pull at least 26 in. Hg of vacuum, there is a leak that must be repaired before evacuation can occur.
4. Once the system has reached at least 26 in. Hg of vacuum, allow the system to evacuate for at least 10 minutes. The longer the system is evacuated, the more contaminants will be removed.
5. Close all valves and turn the pump off. If the system loses more than 2 in. Hg of vacuum after 15 minutes, there is a leak that should be repaired.

System Charging

NOTE: On all models except 1993 Cherokee and Wagoneer, use R-134a refrigerant, use only dedicated service equipment designed for this application and that meets SAE standard J2210. Never try to attach the low pressure hose to the clutch cycling pressure switch port on the accumulator.

1. Connect an approved charging station, Recovery/Recycling machine or manifold gauge set to the discharge and suction ports. The red hose is normally connected to the discharge (high pressure) line and the blue hose is connected to the suction (low pressure) line.
2. Follow the instructions provided with the equipment and charge the system with the specified amount of refrigerant.
3. Perform a leak test.

Compressor Oil Level Checking

1993–94 Cherokee and Wrangler

Compressor oil level must be checked and adjusted whenever rapid discharge occurs or system component is replaced. If a replacement compressor is installed it must be filled with new refrigerant oil (Suniso 5GS or equivalent). Total system oil capacity is 4.6 oz. System must not be overfilled. Two procedures are necessary whether replacing a compressor and normal system discharge (Procedure "A") or routine maintenance following system component replacement (Procedure "B").

NOTE: If rapid refrigerant loss has occurred, totally evacuate and purge the system, then fill the compressor oil level.

PROCEDURE A

1. With compressor removed, remove the oil filler plug, discharge cap and suction port cap from the original and replacement compressor.
2. From the new replacement compressor, drain the oil into a clean, calibrated container. Rotate the compressor clutch several times to push out any remaining oil.
3. Repeat the procedure for the oil from the original compressor.
4. Fill the new replacement compressor with the same amount as drained from the original compressor, plus 1 oz.

PROCEDURE B

1. Run the engine and operate the A/C system at idle for about 10 minutes to return maximum amount of oil to the compressor.

MOUNTING ANGLE (DEGREE)	ACCEPTABLE OIL LEVEL INCREMENTS	MOUNTING ANGLE (DEGREE)	ACCEPTABLE OIL LEVEL INCREMENTS
0	3–5	40	7–9
10	4–6	50	8–10
20	5–7	60	9–11
30	6–8	90	10–12

Oil Level Checking Chart

2. Stop the engine and disconnect the clutch coil wire. Frontseat the discharge and suction service valves to isolate the compressor.
3. Lay an angle gauge across the flats of the front mounting ears, center the bubble and read the angle. It should be 0 degrees.
4. Remove the oil filler plug. Rotate the front plate counterweight to 30 degrees angle. Insert the dipstick to its stop. Remove the dipstick and count the oil increments. Add or subtract oil to match the oil level table.

Grand Cherokee, Grand Wagoneer and 1995 Cherokee and Wrangler

Verify oil level, after proper compressor removal procedure, by draining compressor oil into clean, calibrated container. Add same amount to the replacement compressor, minus any additional amount for other components to be replaced (accumulator 4 oz.; condenser 1 oz.; evaporator 2 oz.).

SYSTEM COMPONENTS

Radiator

REMOVAL AND INSTALLATION

Cherokee and Wrangler

1. Disconnect the negative battery cable.
2. Drain the coolant (on 4.0L engines attach a 24 inch hose to draincock to allow cleaner drainage). Remove the radiator grille to access draincock on 4.0L engines (except Wrangler) and to access condenser to radiator mounting screws on 2.5L engines (except Wrangler).
3. Remove the upper and lower hoses and coolant reserve tank hose from the radiator.
4. Remove the alignment dowel E-clip from the lower radiator mounting bracket (except 4.0L engine and Wrangler).
5. Disconnect the overflow tube from the radiator. Remove the electric cooling fan or fan shroud mounting bolts and pull the fan shroud back to the engine.
6. If equipped, disconnect and plug the transmission cooler lines.
7. Remove the radiator mounting bolts.
8. If equipped, remove the condenser to radiator mounting bolts and remove the radiator from the vehicle.

To install:

9. Slide the radiator into position behind the condenser, if equipped. Align the dowel pin with the bottom mounting bracket and install the E-clip if removed.
10. Tighten the condenser-to-radiator bolts to 55 inch lbs. (6.2 Nm).
11. Install the grille if removed. Install and tighten the radiator mounting bolts.
12. Connect the transmission cooler lines, if equipped. Install the fan shroud or electric cooling fan.
13. Connect the radiator hoses and fill with coolant.
14. Connect the negative battery cable and check for leaks.

Grand Cherokee and Grand Wagoneer

NOTE: When removing the radiator or condenser for any reason, note the location of all rubber air seals. To prevent overheating, these seals must be installed to their original positions.

1. Disconnect negative battery cable. Properly drain the cooling system.
2. On 4.0L engine, remove 4 fan hub to water pump pulley mounting nuts and carefully remove the fan from the water pump pulley and position it to the center of the fan shroud (belt removal is not required). Do not attempt to remove the fan assembly from the vehicle at this time.
3. On 5.2L engine, remove the fan/viscous fan drive assembly from the water pump by turning the mounting nut counterclockwise (right hand threads). Place a bar between water pump pulley bolts to prevent rotation during removal. Belt removal is not required. Do not attempt to remove the fan assembly from the vehicle at this time.
4. Remove 2 fan shroud upper mounting nuts. Now remove the shroud and fan assembly together.
5. Disconnect and plug the transmission cooling lines from the radiator.
6. Mark the position of the radiator upper crossmember. Pry up outer clips and remove the upper rubber seal. Remove grille opening mounting bolts now exposed.
7. Remove the grille. Remove the upper brace bolt from the 2 radiator braces.
8. Remove the 2 crossmember to radiator mounting nuts.
9. Through the grille opening, remove the lower bracket bolt from the lower part of the hood latch support bracket.
10. Remove 4 bolts holding radiator upper crossmember to the body. Leave hood latch and cable in place. Lift crossmember up and lay out of the way.
11. Remove 2 side radiator mounting bolts (also used to hold side rubber air seals to the radiator and condenser bracket).
12. Disconnect coolant reserve tank hose at the radiator. Remove the upper radiator hose.
13. On 4.0L engine, remove the lower radiator hose at the water pump. Lift radiator slightly if needed to gain access to lower radiator hose clamp and remove the hose (all engines).

NOTE: With auxiliary transmission oil cooler, do not tear the rubber seal holding the cooler line to the radiator.

14. Gently lift up and remove the radiator. Avoid damaging fins of the radiator or hitting or moving the condenser.

To install:

15. Carefully lower radiator into position on the guide dowels and if equipped through the condenser support brackets. Holes of the L-shaped brackets must be positions between bottom of rubber air seals and top of rubber grommets. Make sure dowels are fully seated in the rubber grommets.
16. Connect the lower radiator hose to the radiator(position tangs on hose clamp straight down) and connect lower radiator hose to the water pump 4.0L engine. Connect the upper radiator hose.
17. With A/C, install 2 condenser to radiator bolts (also retaining the rubber seals to the sides of the radiator). Without A/C, install 2 bolts retaining the rubber air seal to the sides of the radiator.
18. Install the overflow tank hose.
19. Install rubber isolator to radiator, position the upper radiator crossmember and (through the grille opening) install the hood latch support lower retaining bolt.
20. Install 4 bolts securing crossmember to the body and 2 nuts holding crossmember to the radiator. Install the upper bolt to each radiator brace.
21. Install the grille, then the upper rubber seal (with clips).
22. Install the transmission cooler lines, the fan assembly and shroud (note alignment tabs on lower shroud), and mount the shroud to the upper radiator crossmember. Install fan assembly to water pump. Rotate the fan by hand and check for interference.
23. Refill the cooling system. Connect the battery cable. Run engine and check for leaks and proper operation.

COOLING SYSTEM BLEEDING

Air trapped in the system will prevent proper filling and leave the radiator coolant level low, causing a risk of overheating.

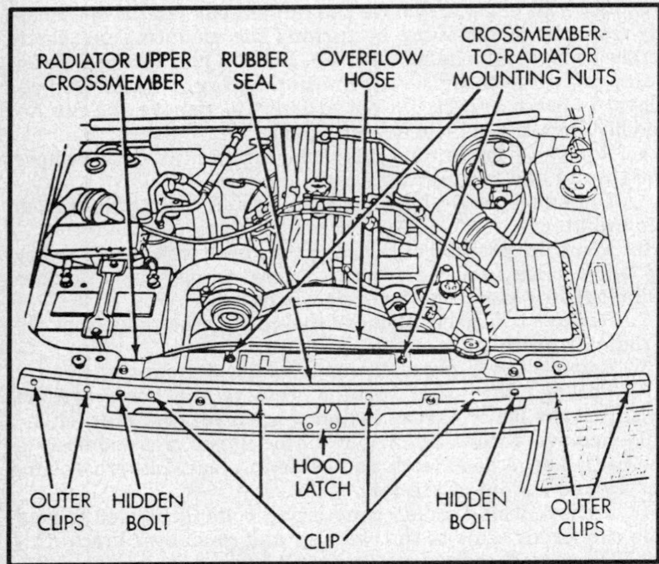

Location of key components for radiator removal—Grand Cherokee and Grand Wagoneer

1. To bleed the system, start with the system cool, the radiator cap off and the radiator filled to about an inch below the filler neck.
2. Start the engine and run it at slightly above normal idle speed. This will ensure adequate circulation. If air bubbles appear and the coolant level drops, fill the system with coolant to bring the level back to the proper level.
3. Run the engine until the thermostat opens; coolant will move abruptly across the top of the radiator and the temperature of the radiator will suddenly rise.
4. At this point, air is expelled and the level may drop. Keep refilling the system until the level is near the top of the radiator and remains constant.
5. Fill the radiator up to the filler neck. Replace the radiator filler cap.

Electric Cooling Fan

Cherokee and Wagoneer with 4.0L engine and air conditioning and/or heavy duty cooling are equipped with an auxiliary electric fan. The engine controller ground the cooling fan relay when the coolant temperature is above 190°F and the fan is **ON**. The fan is also energized whenever the A/C is **ON**.

TESTING

The powertrain control module (or engine controller) will enter a diagnostic trouble code in memory if a fault is detected in the cooling relay or circuit.

1. Access the code through a DRB II diagnostic tool, or by cycling the ignition switch **ON-OFF-ON-OFF-ON** within 5 seconds. The code can then be read via the Check Engine light.
2. Code **35** indicates an open or shorted condition in the relay control circuit. Use the wiring schematic to trace the circuit and resolve the problem in the wiring or replace the cooling fan relay.

REMOVAL AND INSTALLATION

1. Disconnect the negative battery cable. Remove the fan retaining screws from the radiator upper crossmember.
2. Disconnect the electrical lead from the fan assembly.
3. Lift the fan assembly straight up to remove.
4. The installation is the reverse of the removal procedure.

Condenser

REMOVAL AND INSTALLATION

NOTE: All but 1993 Cherokee and Wrangler operate with R-134a refrigerant and special components for this application. Use only dedicated service equipment, replacement parts, refrigerant and refrigerant oil when servicing the system or replacing components.

Cherokee

1. Disconnect the negative battery cable.
2. Properly discharge the air conditioning system. Properly drain the cooling system for 2.5L engine.
3. Disconnect the fan shroud, radiator hoses and automatic transmission cooler lines, if equipped. Unplug the low pressure switch for 2.5L engine.
4. Disconnect the refrigerant lines from the condenser. Cover the exposed ends of the lines to minimize contamination.
5. On 2.5L engine, remove the condenser and radiator as an assembly and disassemble on a workbench.
6. On 4.0L engine, remove the condenser attaching hardware and brackets (note position of rubber air seals), and remove the condenser from the vehicle.

To install:

7. The installation is the reverse of the removal procedure. Use new lubricated O-rings when assembling.
8. Evacuate and recharge the air conditioning system. If the condenser was replaced, add 1 oz. of refrigerant oil during the recharge.
9. Connect the negative battery cable and check the entire climate control system for proper operation and leaks.

Wrangler

1. Disconnect the negative battery cable.
2. Properly discharge the air conditioning system.
3. Drain the coolant and remove the radiator.
4. Disconnect the pressure line from the condenser. Cover the exposed end of the line to minimize contamination. Remove the mounting screws and tilt the bottom of the condenser toward the engine.
5. From the underside of the vehicle, disconnect the evaporator line from the receiver/drier.
6. Remove the condenser and receiver/drier and disassemble on a workbench.

To install:

7. The installation is the reverse of the removal procedure. Use new lubricated O-rings when assembling.
8. Evacuate and recharge the air conditioning system. If the condenser was replaced, add 1 oz. of refrigerant oil during the recharge.
9. Connect the negative battery cable and check the entire climate control system for proper operation and leaks.

Grand Cherokee and Grand Wagoneer

1. Disconnect the negative battery cable. Properly discharge the air conditioning system. Using the spring-lock disconnect tool and procedure, disconnect the refrigerant hoses from the condenser and plug all openings immediately.
2. Remove the grille (8 screws).
3. Remove the upper brace bolts from 2 radiator braces and remove the 2 crossmember to radiator nuts.
4. Remove the lower bolt from the hood latch support brace.
5. Mark the position of the radiator upper crossmember before removal. Remove remaining crossmember bolts, leave hood latch and cable attached, and lift crossmember up and lay to the side.
6. Remove 4 lower condenser bolts, 2 upper condenser bolts and remove the condenser.

To install:

7. Position condenser and secure with 2 upper and 4 lower bolts.
8. Align the crossmember to its position marks and install retaining bolts. Install radiator mounting bolts.
9. Install lower hood latch support bolt. Install the grille.
10. Reconnect the refrigerant hoses to the condenser, using new O-rings where applicable.
11. Evacuate, recharge and leak test the air conditioning system. Connect the battery cable and check system operation.

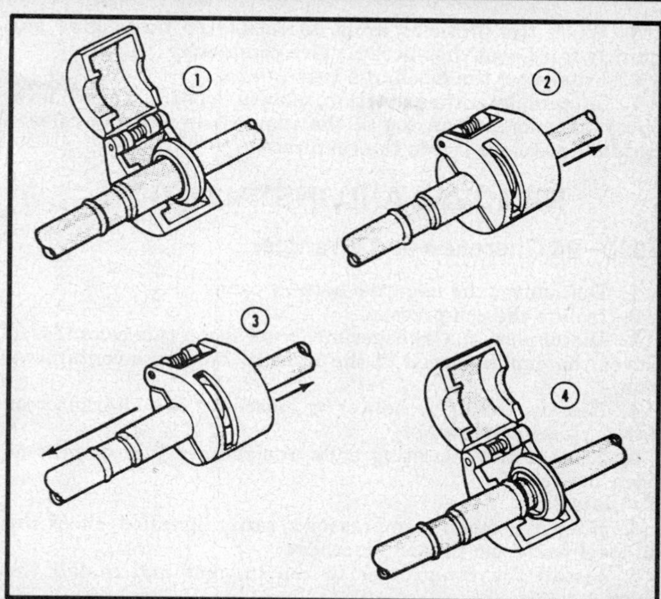

Refrigerant line spring lock coupling disconnect—Grand Cherokee and Grand Wagoneer

Compressor

COMPRESSOR ISOLATION

1993–94 Cherokee and Wrangler

It is not necessary to discharge the air conditioning system for compressor removal. The compressor can be isolated from the remainder of the system, thereby eliminating the need for recharging when assembling.

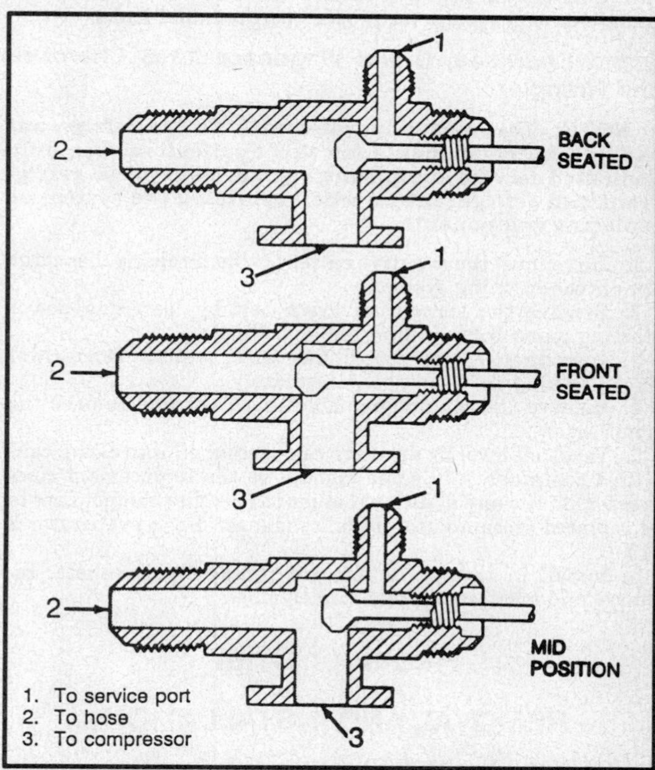

Service valve seating positions for compressor isolation

1. Connect a manifold gauge set with hand valves closed.
2. Place both service valves at mid-position.
3. Start the engine and operate the air conditioning system.
4. Turn the suction service valve (the valve below the larger line) slowly clockwise toward the front-seated position.

5. When the pressure drops to zero, stop the engine and quickly front-seat the suction valve completely.
6. Front-seat the discharge valve.
7. To complete the isolation, slowly loosen the oil level check plug located on top of the compressor body to release residual pressure inside the compressor.

REMOVAL AND INSTALLATION

1993–94 Cherokee and Wrangler

1. Disconnect the negative battery cable.
2. Isolate the compressor.
3. Disconnect the refrigerant lines from the compressor. Cover the exposed ends of the lines to minimize contamination.
4. Remove the drive belt(s) by loosening the alternator or power steering pump.
5. Remove the mounting bolts and remove the compressor from the vehicle.

To install:

6. If a replacement compressor is being installed, check the oil level using the proper procedure.
7. Install the compressor to the bracket and install the bolts.
8. Install the belt(s) and adjust the specification.
9. Connect the refrigerant lines to the compressor. Use new lubricated O-rings when assembling.
10. Connect the negative battery cable and check the entire climate control system for proper operation and leaks.

Grand Cherokee, Grand Wagoneer, 1995 Cherokee and Wrangler

NOTE: This model operates with R-134a refrigerant and special components for this application. Use only dedicated service equipment, replacement parts, refrigerant and refrigerant oil when servicing the system or replacing components.

1. Disconnect the negative battery cable. Properly discharge the air conditioning system.
2. Remove the serpentine drive belt by loosening power steering pump bolts or idler pulley bolts.
3. Disconnect compressor clutch wire. Remove refrigerant lines and plug the openings immediately.
4. Remove the compressor mounting bolts and remove the compressor.
5. Verify oil level by draining compressor oil into clean, calibrated container. Add same amount to the replacement compressor, minus any additional amount for other components to be replaced (accumulator 4 oz.; condenser 1 oz.; evaporator 2 oz.).
6. Install in reverse of removal procedure. Evacuate, recharge and leak test system connections.

Receiver/Drier

REMOVAL AND INSTALLATION

NOTE: All but 1993 Cherokee and Wrangler operate with R-134a refrigerant and special components for this application. Use only dedicated service equipment, replacement parts, refrigerant and refrigerant oil when servicing the system or replacing components.

Cherokee and Wrangler

2.5L Engine

1. Disconnect the negative battery cable.
2. Properly discharge the air conditioning system.
3. Drain the coolant.
4. Disconnect the fan shroud and the radiator hoses.
5. Disconnect the transmission cooler lines as required.
6. Unplug the harness from the low pressure switch.
7. Remove the radiator and condenser as an assembly.
8. Remove the retaining bolts and separate the condenser from the radiator.
9. Remove the receiver/drier from the condenser and plug all openings to prevent moisture from entering the receiver/drier.

To Install:

10. To install, reverse the removal procedure.
11. Evacuate, recharge and leak test system. Check system operation.

4.0L Engine

1. Disconnect the negative battery cable.
2. Properly discharge the air conditioning system.
3. Remove the refrigerant lines from the receiver/drier assembly.
4. Cover the exposed ends of the lines to minimize contamination.
5. Unplug the low pressure switch wiring.
6. Remove the receiver/drier from the engine compartment.

To install:

7. Coat the new O-rings with refrigerant oil and install. Connect the refrigerant lines to the receiver/drier.
8. Evacuate and recharge the air conditioning system. Add 1 oz. of refrigerant oil during the recharge if the receiver/drier was replaced. Check for leaks.

Accumulator

REMOVAL AND INSTALLATION

Grand Cherokee and Grand Wagoneer

NOTE: This model operates with R-134a refrigerant and special components for this application. Use only dedicated service equipment, replacement parts, refrigerant and refrigerant oil when servicing the system or replacing components.

1. Disconnect the negative battery cable. Properly discharge the air conditioning system.
2. Disconnect the refrigerant hoses from the compressor and from the evaporator. Plug all openings immediately.
3. Unplug the low pressure switch wiring.
4. Loosen the accumulator bracket screw and remove the accumulator.
5. To install, reverse the removal procedure, using new O–rings on the refrigerant fittings where applicable. Add 4 oz. of new refrigerant oil to the replacement accumulator.
6. Evacuate, recharge and leak test system. Check system operation.

Expansion Valve

REMOVAL AND INSTALLATION

Cherokee

1. Disconnect the negative battery cable.
2. Properly discharge the air conditioning system.
3. Remove the coolant reservoir and bracket.
4. Disconnect the refrigerant lines from the expansion valve, located on the firewall near the blower motor. Cover the exposed ends of the lines to minimize contamination.
5. Disconnect the expansion valve from the evaporator and remove from the vehicle.

6. The installation is the reverse of the removal procedure. Use new lubricated O-rings when assembling.
7. Evacuate and recharge the air conditioning system.
8. Connect the negative battery cable and check the entire climate control system for proper operation and leaks.

Wrangler

1. Disconnect the negative battery cable.
2. Properly discharge the air conditioning system.
3. Remove the evaporator housing assembly. Cover the exposed ends of the lines to minimize contamination.
4. Remove the insulation wrapped around the suction line and expansion valve. Mark the capillary tube location on the suction line.
5. Disconnect the inlet and outlet connections, capillary tube clamp and equalizer tube.

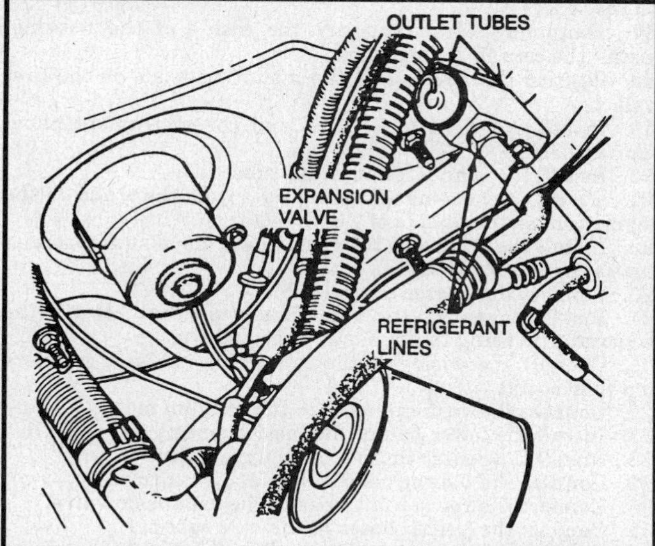

Expansion valve location—Cherokee and Wagoneer

6. Remove the expansion valve from the housing.

To install:

7. Clean the suction line to provide positive engagement with the replacement expansion valve's capillary tube.
8. Connect the inlet and outlet connections. Clamp the capillary tube at the marked position and connect the equalizer tube. Make sure the capillary tube is clamped securely so firm contact with the suction line is achieved.
9. Wrap the expansion valve and suction line with the insulation.
10. Install the evaporator housing.
11. Evacuate and recharge the air conditioning system.
12. Connect the negative battery cable and check the entire climate control system for proper operation and leaks.

Fixed Orifice Tube

REMOVAL AND INSTALLATION

Grand Cherokee and Grand Wagoneer

NOTE: This model operates with R-134a refrigerant and special components for this application. Use only dedicated service equipment, replacement parts, refrigerant and refrigerant oil when servicing the system or replacing components.

1. Disconnect the negative battery cable. Properly discharge the air conditioning system.
2. Disconnect the spring-lock couplings to remove the liquid line from the condenser and from the evaporator.
3. Install by reversing the removal procedure. Evacuate, recharge and leak test the system.

Blower Motor

REMOVAL AND INSTALLATION

Cherokee

2.5L ENGINE

1. Disconnect the negative battery cable.
2. Disconnect the blower motor wiring, located near the firewall.
3. Remove the blower motor mounting screws.
4. Remove the blower and fan assembly.
5. Remove the fan from the motor shaft to gain access to the motor attaching nuts.
6. The installation is the reverse of the removal procedure.
7. Connect the negative battery cable and check the blower for proper operation.

4.0L ENGINE

1. Disconnect the negative battery cable.
2. Remove the coolant reservoir strap, move the reservoir aside and remove the bracket as required.
3. Remove the washer fluid tank as required.
4. If equipped with anti-lock brakes, remove the brake pump and bracket together and position aside.
5. Disconnect the blower motor wiring.
6. Remove the blower motor mounting screws.
7. Remove the blower and fan assembly.
8. Remove the fan from the motor shaft to gain access to the motor attaching nuts.

To install:

9. Assemble the motor and fan. The 2 ears of the retainer clip must be positioned over the flat surface of the motor shaft.
10. Install the motor assembly to the firewall and connect the wiring.
11. Install the anti-lock brake and coolant reservoir components.
12. Connect the negative battery cable and check the blower for proper operation.

Wrangler

1. Disconnect the negative battery cable.
2. If equipped with air conditioning, lower the evaporator housing. If not, remove the heater housing.
3. Remove the blower to housing attaching screws and remove the blower from the housing.
4. The installation is the reverse of the removal procedure.
5. Connect the negative battery cable and check the entire climate control system for proper operation.

Grand Cherokee and Grand Wagoneer

1. Disconnect the negative battery cable. Disconnect the blower motor cooling tube.
2. Remove the blower motor wiring connector from the retainer and disconnect the connector.
3. Remove the blower motor assembly mounting screws and remove the assembly.
4. Remove the blower motor wheel retainer clip and pull the wheel off the blower motor shaft.
5. Installation is the reverse of the removal procedure.

Blower Motor Resistor

REMOVAL AND INSTALLATION

Cherokee

1. Disconnect the negative battery cable.
2. Remove the vacuum motor cover.
3. Disconnect the resistor connector and remove the resistor.
4. The installation is the reverse of the removal procedure.
5. Connect the negative battery cable and check the system for proper operation.

Grand Cherokee and Grand Wagoneer

On the Grand Cherokee and Grand Wagoneer, the resistor is located under the glove box.

1. Disconnect the negative battery cable.
2. Disconnect the resistor connector.
3. Remove the resistor.
4. The installation is the reverse of the removal procedure.
5. Connect the negative battery cable and check the system for proper operation.

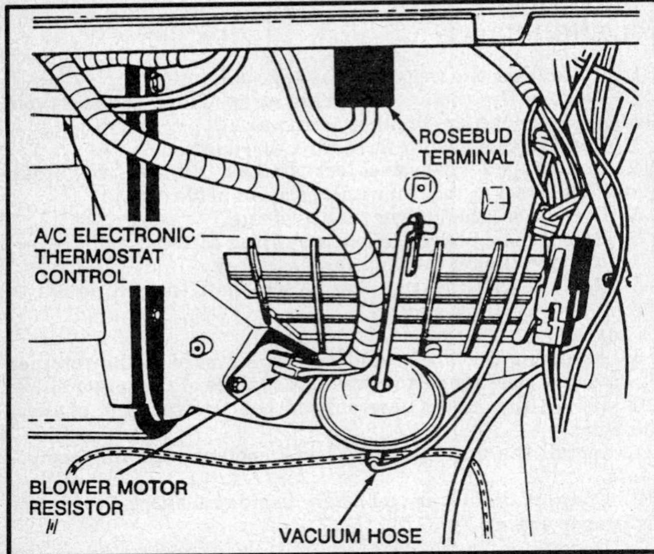

Blower motor resistor location—Cherokee and Wagoneer

Heater Core

REMOVAL AND INSTALLATION

Cherokee

1. Disconnect the negative battery cable. Drain the coolant.
2. Disconnect the heater hoses at the core tubes.
3. If equipped with air conditioning, discharge the refrigerant.
4. Disconnect the refrigerant lines from the expansion valve. Cover the exposed ends of the lines to minimize contamination.
5. Disconnect the blower motor wires and vent tube.
6. Remove the center console, if equipped.
7. Remove the lower half of the instrument panel.
8. Disconnect the wiring at the air conditioning relay, blower motor resistors and air conditioning thermostat. Disconnect the vacuum hoses at the vacuum motor.
9. Cut the plastic retaining strap that retains the evaporator housing to the heater core housing.
10. Disconnect and remove the heater control cable.
11. Remove the 3 clips at the rear blower housing flange and remove the retaining screws.
12. Remove the housing attaching nuts from the studs on the engine compartment side of the firewall.
13. Remove the condensation drain tube.
14. Remove the right kick panel and the instrument panel support bolt.
15. Gently pull out on the right side of the instrument panel and rotate the housing down and toward the rear to disengage the mounting studs from the firewall. Remove the housing.
16. Unbolt and remove the core from the housing.

To install:

17. Thoroughly clean and dry the inside of the housing. Install the core in the housing.
18. Position the housing on the mounting studs on the firewall.
19. Install the right kick panel and the instrument panel support bolt.
20. Install the condensation drain tube.
21. Install the housing attaching nuts from the studs on the engine compartment side of the firewall.
22. Install the 3 clips at the rear blower housing flange and install the retaining screws.
23. Connect the heater control cable.
24. Install a new plastic retaining strap that retains the evaporator housing to the heater core housing.
25. Connect the wiring at the relay, blower motor resistors and thermostat.
26. Connect the vacuum hoses to the vacuum motor.
27. Install the lower half of the instrument panel.
28. Install the center console, if equipped.
29. Connect the blower motor wires and vent tube.
30. Connect the refrigerant lines to the expansion valve.
31. Connect the heater hoses to the core tubes.
32. Fill the cooling system.
33. Evacuate and recharge the air conditioning system.
34. Connect the negative battery cable and check the entire climate control system for proper operation and leaks.

Wrangler

1. Disconnect the negative battery cable.
2. Drain the coolant.
3. Disconnect the heater hoses from the core tubes.
4. Disconnect the vent door cables.
5. Disconnect the blower motor wiring.
6. Disconnect the defroster duct.
7. Remove the nuts that attach the heater housing studs to the engine compartment side of the firewall.
8. To remove the heater housing assembly, tilt it downward to disengage it from the defroster duct, and pull it rearward and out from beneath the instrument panel.
9. Remove the cover from the housing and remove the heater core from the housing.

To install:

10. Thoroughly clean and dry the inside of the housing. Install the core in the housing and install the cover.
11. Install the seals on the heater core tubes and over the blower motor housing.
12. Install the housing to the dash panel. Make sure all studs extend through the sheetmetal.
13. Install the attaching nuts to the studs.
14. Connect the defroster duct.
15. Connect the blower motor wiring and vent door cables.
16. Connect the heater hoses to the core tubes.

17. Fill the cooling system.
18. Connect the negative battery cable and check the entire climate control system for proper operation and leaks.

Grand Cherokee and Grand Wagoneer

NOTE: This procedure requires discharging and recharging the air conditioning system (if equipped). This model operates with R-134a refrigerant and special components for this application. Use only dedicated service equipment, replacement parts, refrigerant and refrigerant oil when servicing the system or replacing components.

1. Disconnect the negative battery cable. Properly discharge the air conditioning system. Disconnect and plug the A/C lines from the evaporator, using the spring lock disconnect tool.
2. Properly drain the cooling system, then disconnect the heater hoses from the heater core tubes. Plug openings to prevent coolant leakage. Remove the coolant reservoir tank.
3. Remove the powertrain control module (PCM) and set it aside. Do not disconnect the 60-way connector.
4. Remove the heater-A/C unit attaching nuts from the firewall. Remove the instrument panel as follows:
   - Remove the defroster duct grille and the speaker grilles.
   - Remove 4 upper panel retaining nuts, 3 screws at lower left side panel, and the instrument panel mounting bolt at left side cowl.
   - Fold down carpet at the left side of the console and remove the 2 mounting screws.
   - Remove 3 lower column cover screws and 6 screws at knee panel. Remove the tilt lever and both column covers. Detach column wiring. Remove 2 nuts and lower the steering column.
   - Remove instrument panel bolt above center of the column.
   - Detach bulkhead connector and cluster wiring at left side of the panel.
   - Remove right side kick panel door and detach wiring.
   - Pull back and lower the instrument panel. Disconnect the A/C vacuum lines and antenna. Remove the instrument panel.
5. Remove the defroster duct and disconnect the rear floor duct from the center duct connector.
6. Disconnect electrical connections, remove attaching nuts at the dash panel and remove the heater-A/C assembly.
7. Remove the heater core retaining screws and pull the heater core out of its housing.

To install:

8. Install the core and position the clips over the heater core tubes. Install retaining screws.
9. Position the heater-A/C assembly in place, putting drain tube through its hole. Install retaining nuts at dash panel, torquing to 40 inch-lbs. (4.5 Nm), then install retaining nuts from firewall side and torque to 60 inch-lbs. (7 Nm).
10. Install heater hoses to heater tubes and connect A/C lines to evaporator tubes.
11. Install the reservoir tank and reconnect the PCM.
12. Install the defrost duct, rear floor duct and connect the heater-A/C assembly electrical connectors.
13. Install the instrument panel in reverse of the removal procedure.
14. Refill the cooling system. Evacuate, recharge and leak test the air conditioning system. Connect the battery cable.
15. Start the vehicle and check system operations.

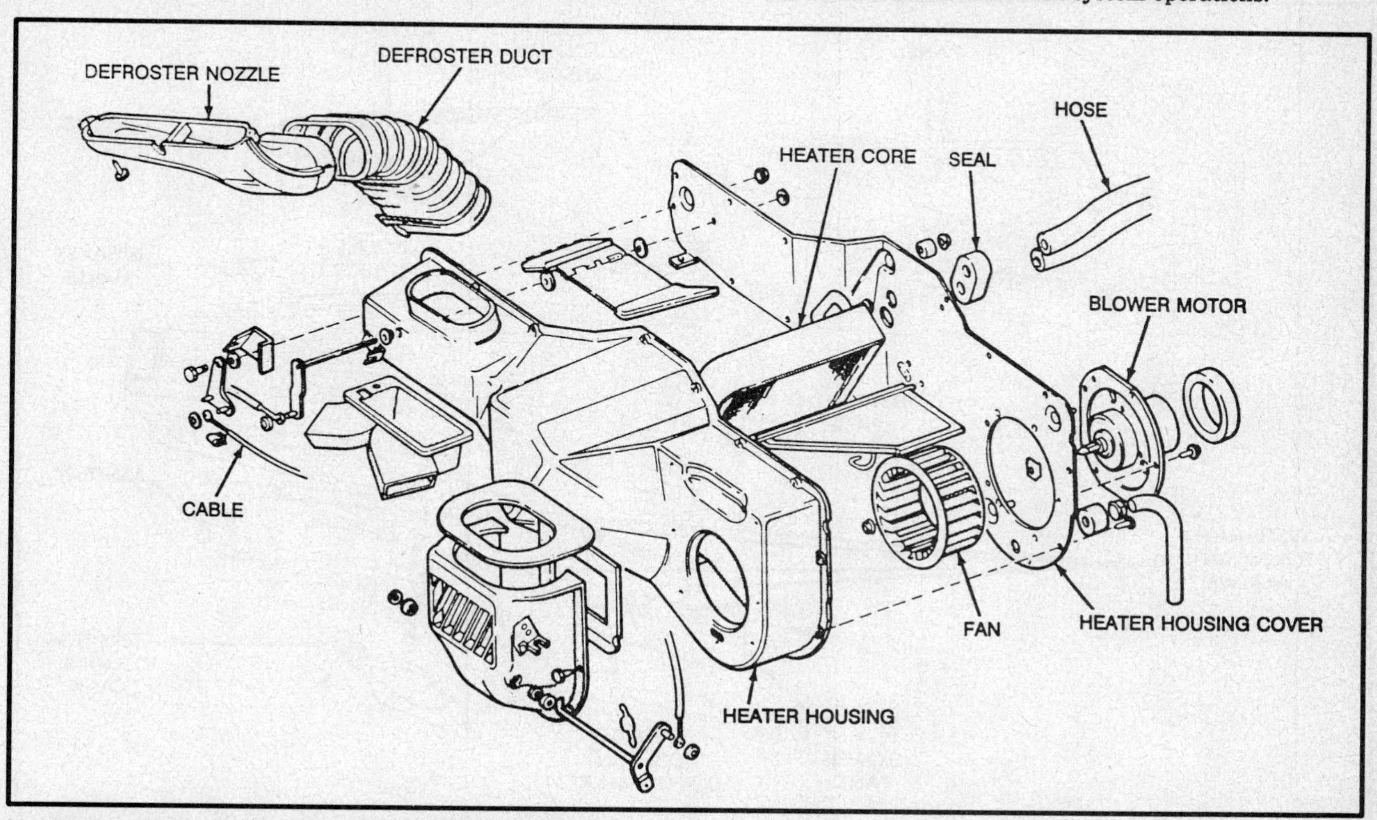

Heater housing and related components—Wrangler

Evaporator

REMOVAL AND INSTALLATION

Cherokee

1. Disconnect the negative battery cable. Drain the coolant.
2. Disconnect the heater hoses at the core tubes.
3. Discharge the refrigerant.
4. Disconnect the refrigerant lines from the expansion valve. Cover the exposed ends of the lines to minimize contamination.
5. Disconnect the blower motor wires and vent tube.
6. Remove the center console, if equipped.
7. Remove the lower half of the instrument panel.
8. Disconnect the wiring at the air conditioning relay, blower motor resistors and air conditioning thermostat. Disconnect the vacuum hoses at the vacuum motor.
9. Cut the plastic retaining strap that retains the evaporator housing to the heater core housing.
10. Disconnect and remove the heater control cable.
11. Remove the 3 clips at the rear blower housing flange and remove the retaining screws.
12. Remove the housing attaching nuts from the studs on the engine compartment side of the firewall.
13. Remove the condensation drain tube.
14. Remove the right kick panel and the instrument panel support bolt.
15. Gently pull out on the right side of the instrument panel and rotate the housing down and toward the rear to disengage the mounting studs from the firewall. Remove the housing.
16. Unbolt and remove the evaporator from the housing.

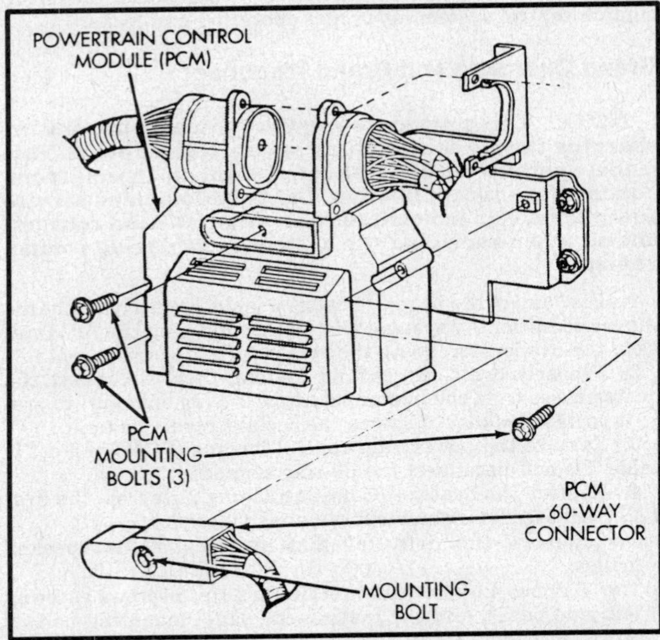

Powertrain control module—Grand Cherokee and Grand Wagoneer

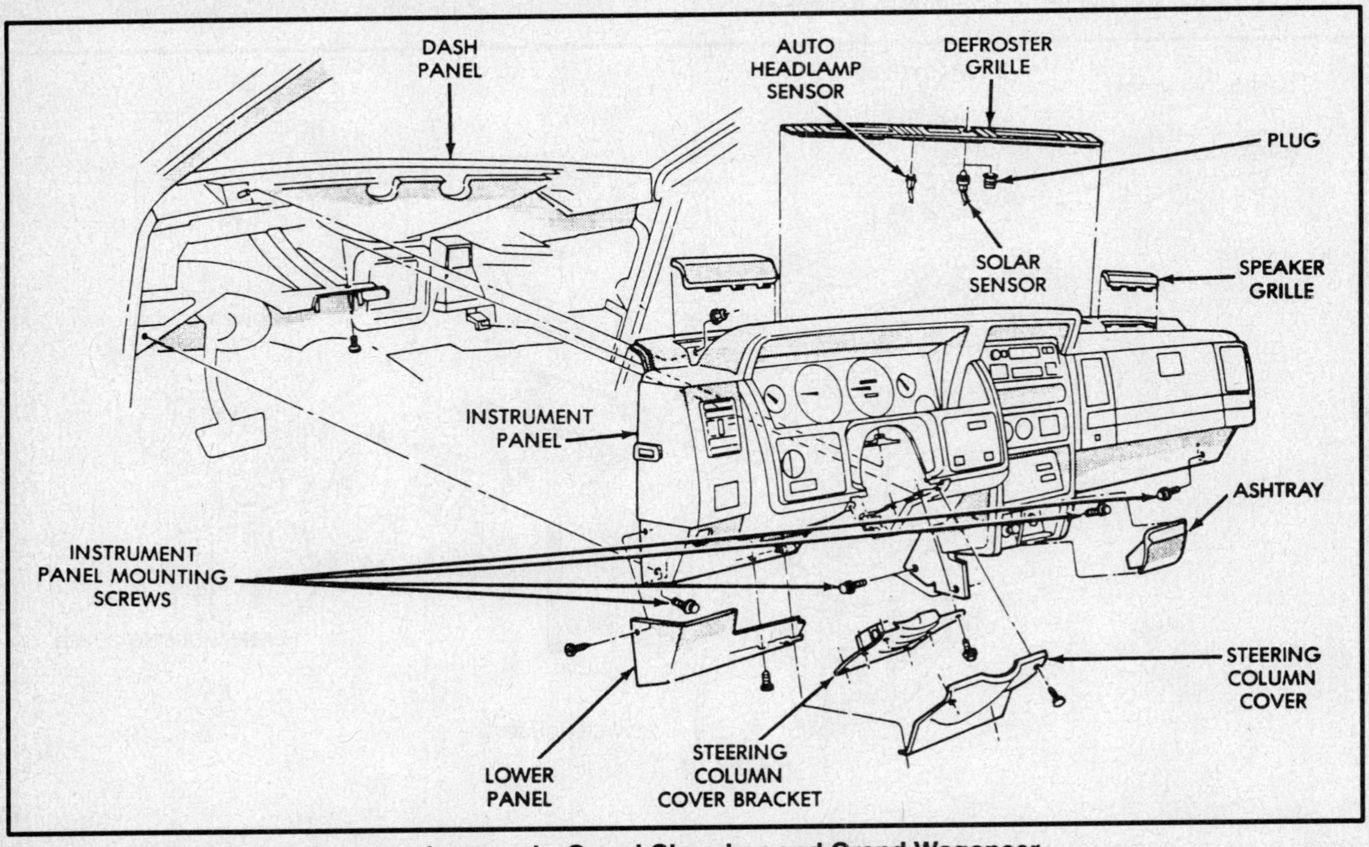

Exploded view of instrument panel removal—Grand Cherokee and Grand Wagoneer

To install:

17. Thoroughly clean and dry the inside of the housing. Install the evaporator in the housing.
18. Position the housing on the mounting studs on the firewall.
19. Install the right kick panel and the instrument panel support bolt.
20. Install the condensation drain tube.
21. Install the housing attaching nuts from the studs on the engine compartment side of the firewall.
22. Install the 3 clips at the rear blower housing flange and install the retaining screws.
23. Connect the heater control cable.
24. Install a new plastic retaining strap that retains the evaporator housing to the heater core housing.
25. Connect the wiring at the relay, blower motor resistors and thermostat.
26. Connect the vacuum hoses to the vacuum motor.
27. Install the lower half of the instrument panel.
28. Install the center console, if equipped.

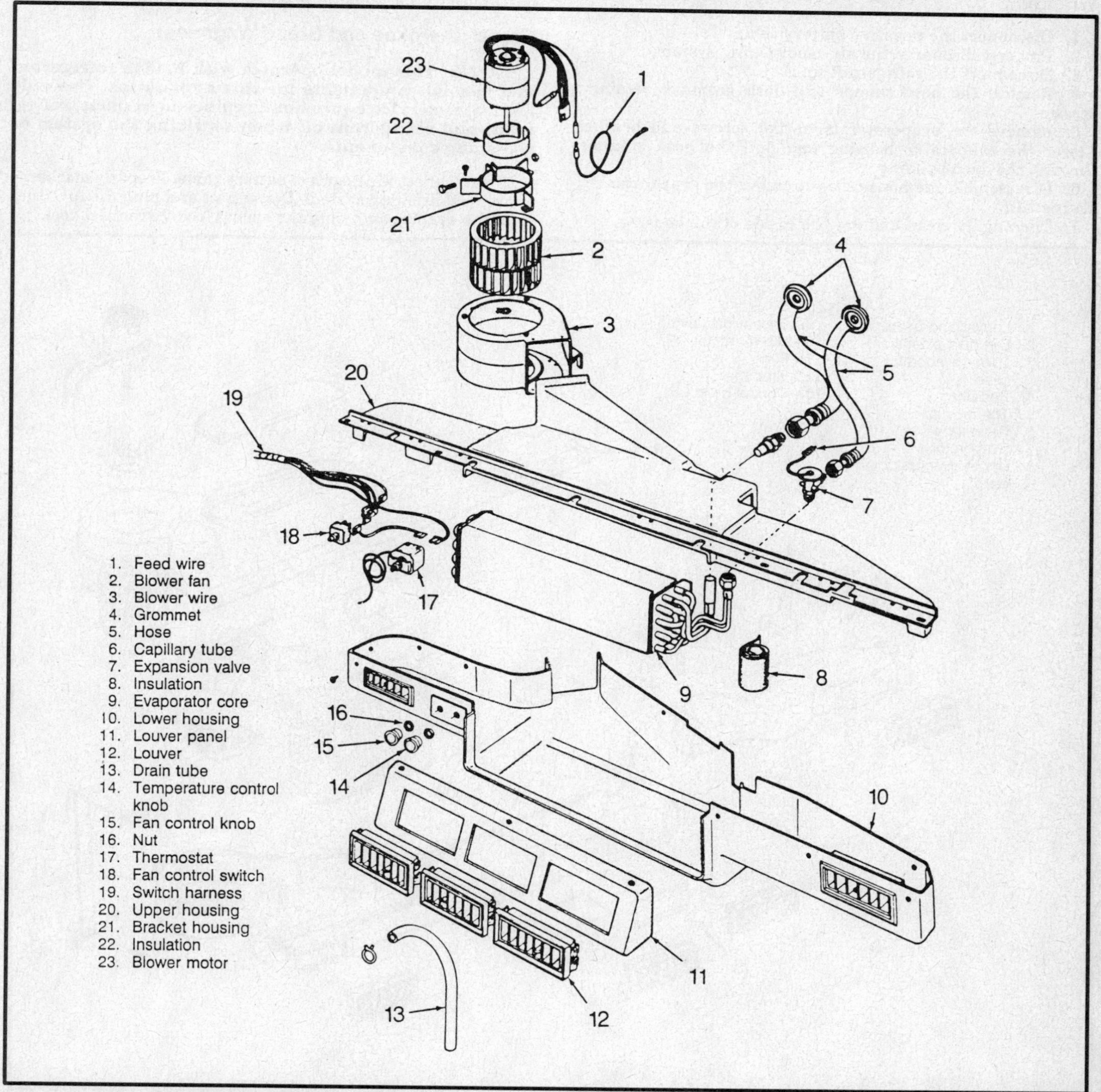

Evaporator housing and related components—Wrangler

29. Connect the blower motor wires and vent tube.
30. Connect the refrigerant lines to the expansion valve.
31. Connect the heater hoses to the core tubes.
32. Fill the cooling system.
33. Evacuate and recharge the air conditioning system. If the evaporator was replaced, add 1 oz. of refrigerant oil during the recharge.
34. Connect the negative battery cable and check the entire climate control system for proper operation and leaks.

Wrangler

1. Disconnect the negative battery cable.
2. Properly discharge the air conditioning system.
3. Disconnect the refrigerant lines.
4. Remove the hose clamps and dash grommet retaining screws.
5. Remove the evaporator mounting screws and bracket. Lower the evaporator housing and pull the hose grommet through the dash opening.
6. Disassemble the housing and remove the evaporator.

To install:

7. Thoroughly clean and dry the inside of the housing.
8. Install the evaporator to the housing and assemble.
9. Install the housing to the vehicle and install the mounting screws.
10. Install the dash grommet retaining screw and hose clamp.
11. Connect the refrigerant lines.
12. Evacuate and recharge the air conditioning system. Add 1 oz. of refrigerant oil during the recharge if the evaporator was replaced.
13. Connect the negative battery cable and check the entire climate control system for proper operation and leaks.

Grand Cherokee and Grand Wagoneer

NOTE: This model operates with R-134a refrigerant and special components for this application. Use only dedicated service equipment, replacement parts, refrigerant and refrigerant oil when servicing the system or replacing components.

1. Disconnect the negative battery cable. Properly discharge the air conditioning system. Disconnect and plug the A/C lines from the evaporator, using the spring lock disconnect tool.

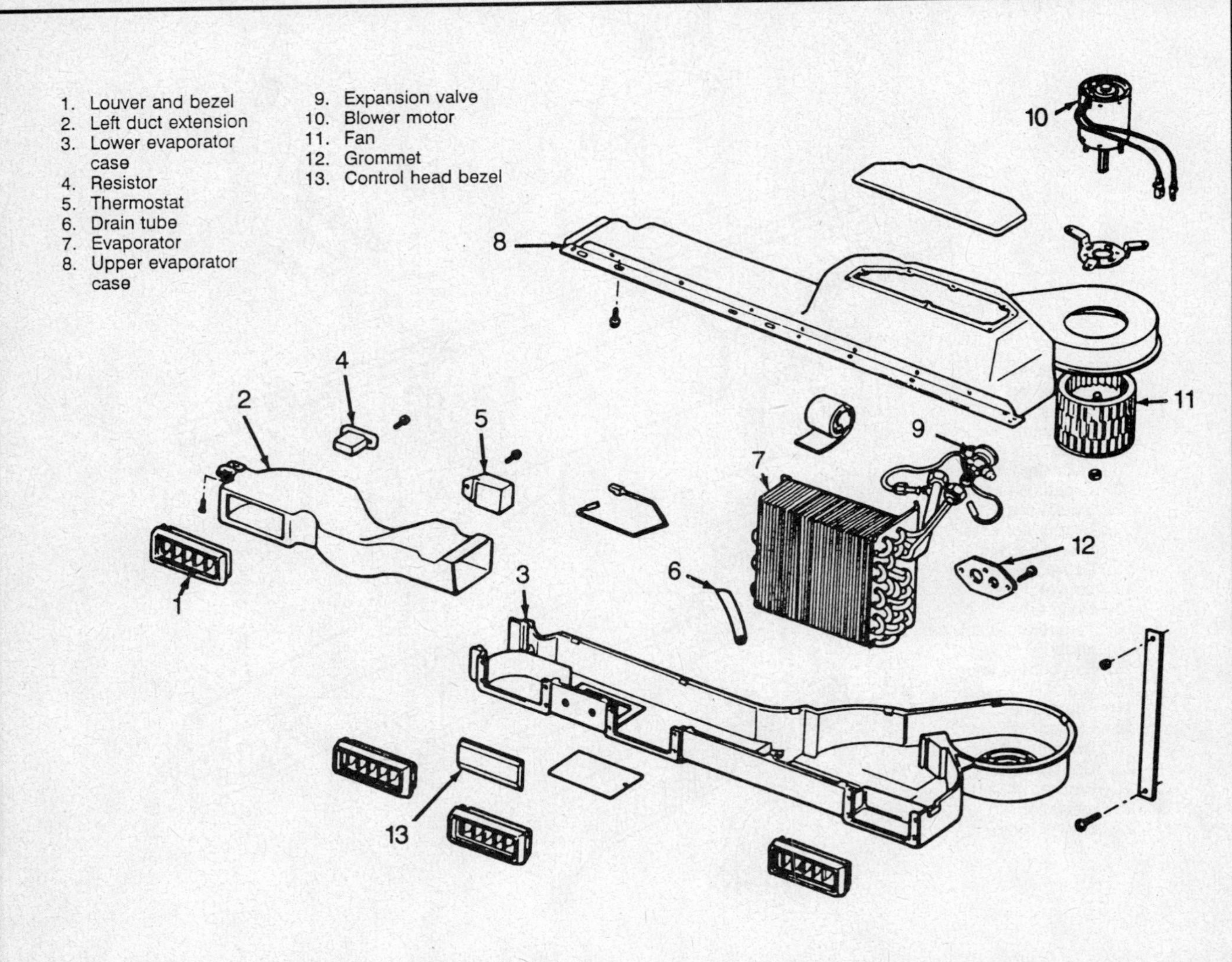

Evaporator housing and related components—Grand Wagoneer

2. Properly drain the cooling system, then disconnect the heater hoses from the heater core tubes. Plug openings to prevent coolant leakage. Remove the coolant reservoir tank.
3. Remove the powertrain control module (PCM) and set it aside. Do not disconnect the 60-way connector.
4. Remove the heater-A/C unit attaching nuts from the firewall. Remove the instrument panel as follows:
   - Remove the defroster duct grille and the speaker grilles.
   - Remove 4 upper panel retaining nuts, 3 screws at lower left side panel, and the instrument panel mounting bolt at left side cowl.
   - Fold down carpet at the left side of the console and remove the 2 mounting screws.
   - Remove 3 lower column cover screws and 6 screws at knee panel. Remove the tilt lever and both column covers. Detach column wiring. Remove 2 nuts and lower the steering column.
   - Remove instrument panel bolt above center of the column.
   - Detach bulkhead connector and cluster wiring at left side of the panel.
   - Remove right side kick panel door and detach wiring.
   - Pull back and lower the instrument panel. Disconnect the A/C vacuum lines and antenna. Remove the instrument panel.
5. Remove the defroster duct and disconnect the rear floor duct from the center duct connector.
6. Disconnect electrical connections, remove attaching nuts at the dash panel and remove the heater-A/C assembly.
7. Turn the heater-A/C unit upside-down. Remove screws holding case halves together. Remove center adaptor heat duct and remove the screw. Turn unit back over, take off the top half the remove the evaporator core.

To install:

8. Install the core and position the top case half, turn the unit over, install the retaining screws. Snap on adaptor heat duct.
9. Position the heater-A/C assembly in place, putting drain tube through its hole. Install retaining nuts at dash panel, torquing to 40 inch-lbs. (4.5 Nm), then install retaining nuts from firewall side and torque to 60 inch-lbs. (7 Nm).
10. Install heater hoses to heater tubes and connect A/C lines to evaporator tubes.
11. Install the reservoir tank and reconnect the PCM.
12. Install the defrost duct, rear floor duct and connect the heater-A/C assembly electrical connectors.
13. Install the instrument panel in reverse of the removal procedure.
14. Refill the cooling system. Evacuate, recharge and leak test the air conditioning system. Connect the battery cable.
15. Start the vehicle and check system operations.

Refrigerant Lines

REMOVAL AND INSTALLATION

1. Disconnect the negative battery cable.
2. Properly discharge the air conditioning system.
3. Unscrew the desired line (or use spring lock coupling disconnect) from its adjoining component. If the lines are connected with flare nuts, use a backup wrench when disassembling. Cover the exposed ends of the lines to minimize contamination.
4. Remove the lines and discard the O-rings.

To install:

5. Coat the O-rings with refrigerant oil and install. Connect the refrigerant lines to the adjoining components and tighten.
6. Evacuate and recharge the air conditioning system.
7. Connect the negative battery cable and check the entire climate control system for proper operation and leaks.

Manual Control Head

REMOVAL AND INSTALLATION

NOTE: On Grand Cherokee and Grand Wagoneer with automatic temperature control, the following procedure is also applicable.

1. Disconnect the negative battery cable.
2. Remove the ashtray (Grand Cherokee and Grand Wagoneer) and the instrument panel bezel.
3. On Cherokee and Wagoneer, remove the radio.
4. Remove the manual control head retaining screws and pull the unit out of the instrument panel.
5. Disconnect all electrical connections, actuating cables and vacuum hoses from the unit and remove from the instrument panel.
6. The installation is the reverse of the removal procedure.
7. Connect the negative battery cable and check the entire climate control system for proper operation.

Manual Control Cables

NOTE: On Grand Cherokee and Grand Wagoneer, all doors are vacuum operated.

ADJUSTMENT

All control cables are self-adjusting. If any cable is not functioning properly, check for kinks and lubricate dry moving parts. Since these cables cannot be disassembled, replace if faulty.

REMOVAL AND INSTALLATION

1. Disconnect the negative battery cable.
2. Remove the necessary bezel in order to gain access to the control head.
3. Remove the screws that fasten the control head to the instrument panel.
4. Pull the unit out and disconnect the temperature control cable.
5. Disconnect the cable end from the air conditioning housing.
6. Take note of the cable's routing and remove the control head from the vehicle.

To install:

7. Install the cable by routing it in exactly the same position as it was prior to removal.
8. Connect the self-adjusting clip to the door crank and secure the cable.
9. Connect the upper end of the cable to the control head.
10. Place the temperature lever on the coolest side of its travel. Allowing the self-adjusting clip to slide on the cable, rotate the door counterclockwise by hand until it stops.
11. Cycle the lever back and forth a few times to make sure the cable moves freely.
12. Connect the negative battery cable and check the entire climate control system for proper operation.

SENSORS AND SWITCHES

Low Pressure Cut Off Switch

OPERATION

The low pressure cut off switch monitors the refrigerant gas pressure on the suction side of the system. The switch turns OFF voltage to the compressor clutch coil when the monitored pressure drops to a level that may damage the compressor. The switch is a sealed unit that must be replaced if faulty.

The switch is located above the receiver/drier on Cherokee and Wrangler.

TESTING

1. Verify system has correct refrigerant charge.
2. Turn ignition switch to **RUN**, A/C blower switch to **ON** and control set to **MAX**.
3. Unplug pressure cut off switch and test feed circuit from select switch. It should be battery voltage if not, repair open to select switch.
4. Test for continuity between the switch terminals. If continuity is not present recover refrigerant from the system. Replace switch, evacuate and recharge system.

REMOVAL AND INSTALLATION

1. Disconnect the negative battery cable.
2. Properly discharge the air conditioning system.
3. Unplug the connector from the switch.
4. Unscrew the switch from the component on which it is mounted.

To install:

5. Seal the threads of the new switch with teflon tape.
6. Install the switch and connect the connector.
7. Evacuate and recharge the system. Check for leaks.
8. Check the switch for proper operation.

Temperature Control Thermostat

OPERATION

The temperature control thermostat is located on the evaporator housing and is equipped with a probe inserted into the evaporator fins. The function of the thermostat is to prevent evaporator freeze-up by cycling the compressor clutch coil off when the evaporator temperature drops below freezing point. The coil will be cycled back on when the temperature rises above the freeze point. The thermostat is a sealed, specially calibrated unit and should be replaced if faulty.

TESTING

1. Test the switch in an area with ambient temperature of at least 70°F(21°C).
2. Turn the ignition switch to the **RUN** position. Turn the air conditioning and blower switches **ON**.
3. Measure the voltage at terminal **A** of the thermostat connector. If no voltage is detected, repair the open from the blower switch.
4. If 12 volts was detected, measure the voltage at the other terminal. If voltage is not detected, replace the thermostat.
5. If 12 volts was detected, measure the voltage at the low pressure cut off switch connector. If no voltage was detected, repair the open.

REMOVAL AND INSTALLATION

Cherokee

1. Disconnect the negative battery cable.
2. Remove the center console, if equipped.
3. Remove the lower instrument panel assembly.
4. Pull the rosebud terminal out of the housing.
5. Disconnect the electrical connector from the thermostat.
6. Remove the wires from the retaining clip.
7. Carefully remove the thermostat probe/thermostat electric cycling switch from the tube guide hole.

To install:

8. Carefully insert the thermostat probe into the tube guide hole until the thermostat electric cycling switch body contacts the housing.
9. Connect the rosebud terminal and snap into the hole in the housing.
10. Connect the wiring and secure the wires with the retaining clip.
11. Install the lower instrument panel and center console.
12. Connect the negative battery cable and check the entire climate control system for proper operation.

Wrangler

1. Disconnect the negative battery cable.
2. Lower the evaporator housing.
3. Remove the attaching screws holding the 2 halves of the housing together and separate the housings.
4. Remove the thermostat from the evaporator housing.

To install:

5. Install the thermostat. Be sure to insert the probe at least 2 in. into the evaporator coil. Do not bend or kink the tube excessively when installing.
6. Assemble the evaporator housing and install.
7. Connect the negative battery cable and check the entire climate control system for proper operation.

Ambient Air Temperature Sensor

Grand Cherokee and Grand Wagoneer

The ambient air temperature sensor is used only on automatic temperature control systems. It is mounted behind the grille to sense exterior temperature and provide a temperature signal to the ATC controller.

TESTING

Perform the ATC system diagnostics for testing and diagnosis.

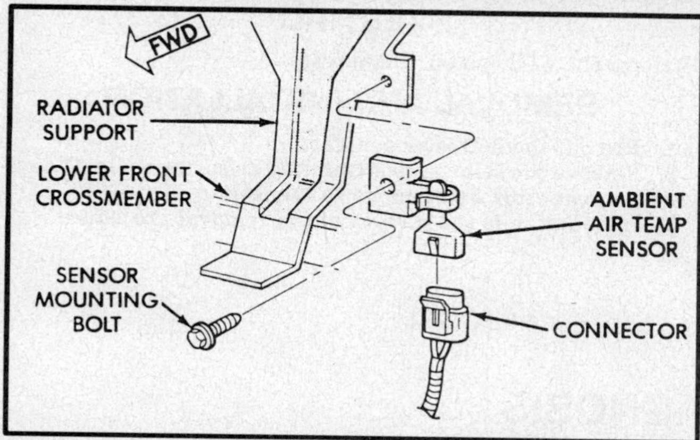

Removing ambient air temperature sensor—Grand Cherokee and Grand Wagoneer with ATC

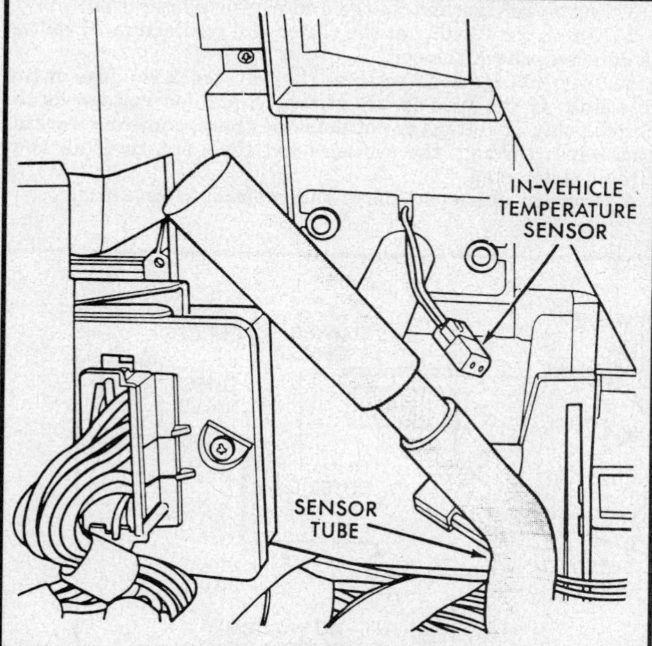

Location of in-vehicle sensor—Grand Cherokee and Grand Wagoneer with ATC

REMOVAL AND INSTALLATION

1. Remove the grille.
2. Disconnect the ambient air temperature sensor connector.
3. Remove the sensor mounting bolt and remove the sensor.
4. Install in reverse of the removal procedure.

In-Vehicle Temperature Sensor

Grand Cherokee and Grand Wagoneer

The in-vehicle temperature sensor is used only on ATC systems and is mounted under the instrument panel on the heater-A/C housing assembly. It senses interior temperature and sends this signal to the ATC controller to compare to the ambient temperature signal and the solar sensor signal. Adjustments are then made by the controller to maintain the preset desired temperature.

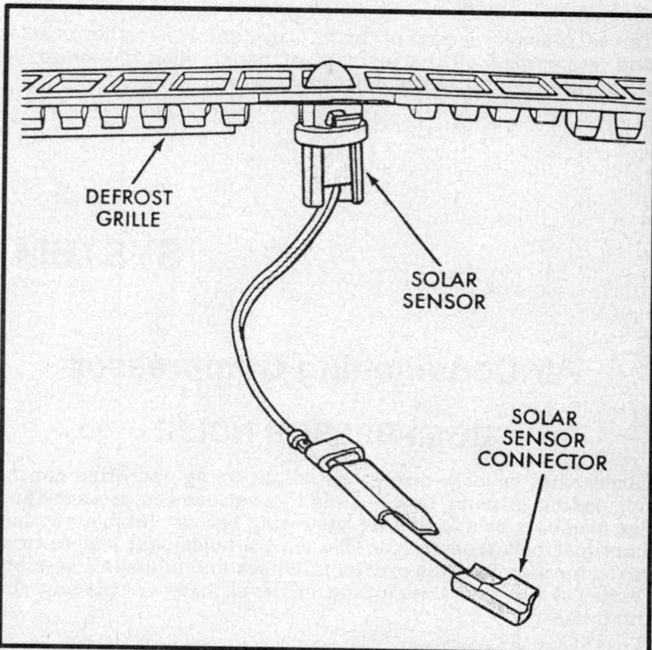

Location of solar sensor—Grand Cherokee and Grand Wagoneer with ATC

TESTING

Perform the ATC system diagnostics for testing and diagnosis.

REMOVAL AND INSTALLATION

1. Disconnect the negative battery cable.
2. Remove the instrument panel as follows:
   - Remove the defroster duct grille and the speaker grilles.
   - Remove 4 upper panel retaining nuts, 3 screws at lower left side panel, and the instrument panel mounting bolt at left side cowl.
   - Fold down carpet at the left side of the console and remove the 2 mounting screws.
   - Remove 3 lower column cover screws and 6 screws at knee panel. Remove the tilt lever and both column covers. Detach column wiring. Remove 2 nuts and lower the steering column.
   - Remove instrument panel bolt above center of the column.
   - Detach bulkhead connector and cluster wiring at left side of the panel.
   - Remove right side kick panel door and detach wiring.
   - Pull back and lower the instrument panel. Disconnect the A/C vacuum lines and antenna. Remove the instrument panel.
3. Disconnect the sensor tube from the sensor assembly and the heater-A/C unit. Remove the sensor screws from the instrument panel bracket and remove the sensor.
4. Installation is the reverse of the removal procedure.

Solar Sensor

Grand Cherokee and Grand Wagoneer

The solar sensor is part of the ATC system. It is amber in color and is mounted on the instrument panel, with the sensor in the right of center of the defroster grille.

TESTING

Perform the ATC system diagnostics.

REMOVAL AND INSTALLATION

1. Pop out the defroster grille.
2. Remove the solar sensor from the defroster grille. Disconnect the connector and remove the sensor.
3. Installation is the reverse of the removal procedure.

SYSTEM DIAGNOSIS

Air Conditioning Compressor

COMPRESSOR NOISE

Noises that develop during air conditioning operation can be misleading. A noise that sounds like serious compressor damage may only be a loose belt, mounting bolt or clutch assembly. Improper belt tension can also emit a noise that can be mistaken for more serious problems. Check and adjust all possible causes of the noise, including oil level, before replacing the compressor.

COMPRESSOR CLUTCH INOPERATIVE

1. Verify refrigerant charge and charge as required.
2. Check for 12 volts at the clutch coil connection. If voltage is detected, check the coil.
3. If no voltage is detected at the coil, check the fuse or fusible link. If the fuse is not blown, check for voltage at the clutch relay. If voltage is not detected there, continue working backwards through the system's switches, etc. until an open circuit is detected.
4. Inspect all suspect parts and replace, as required.

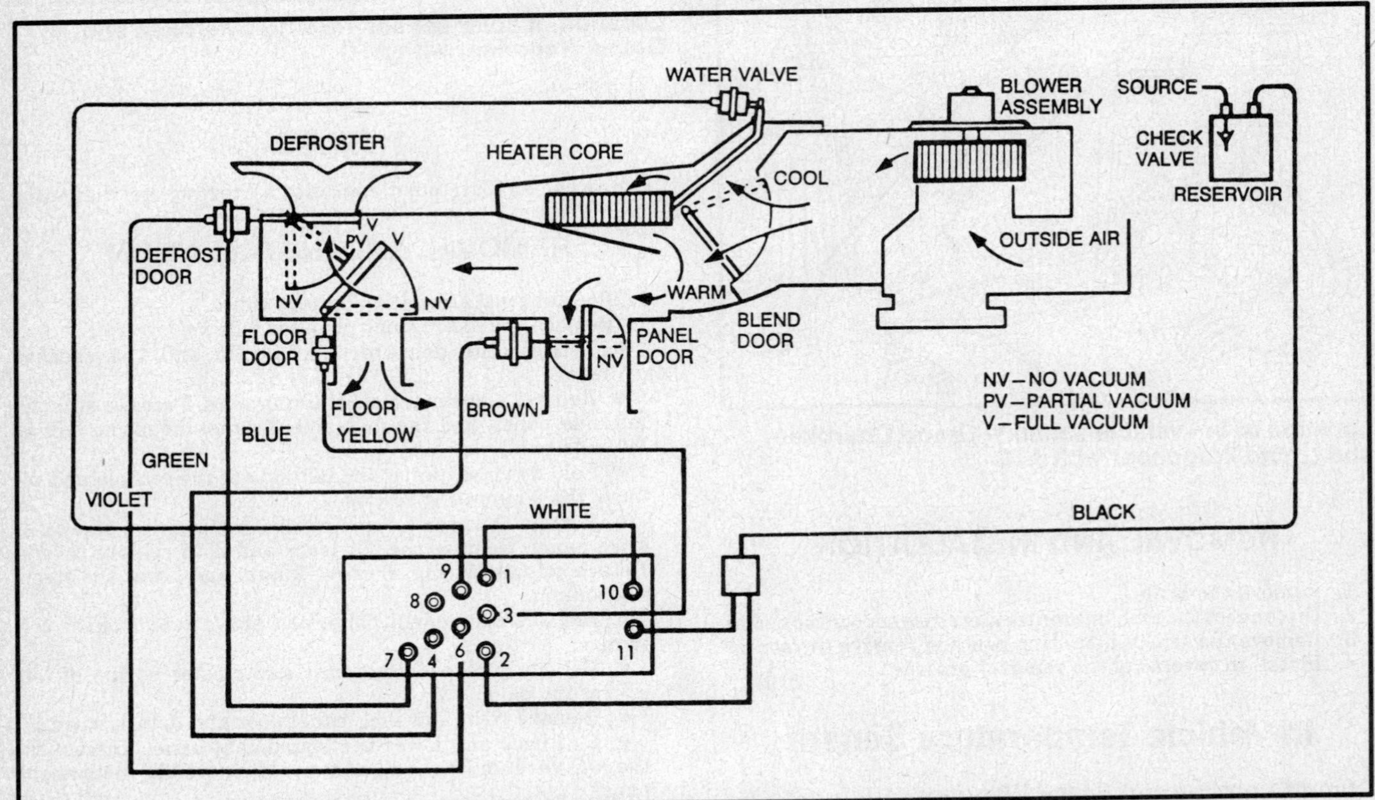

Vacuum schematic—Cherokee with heater only

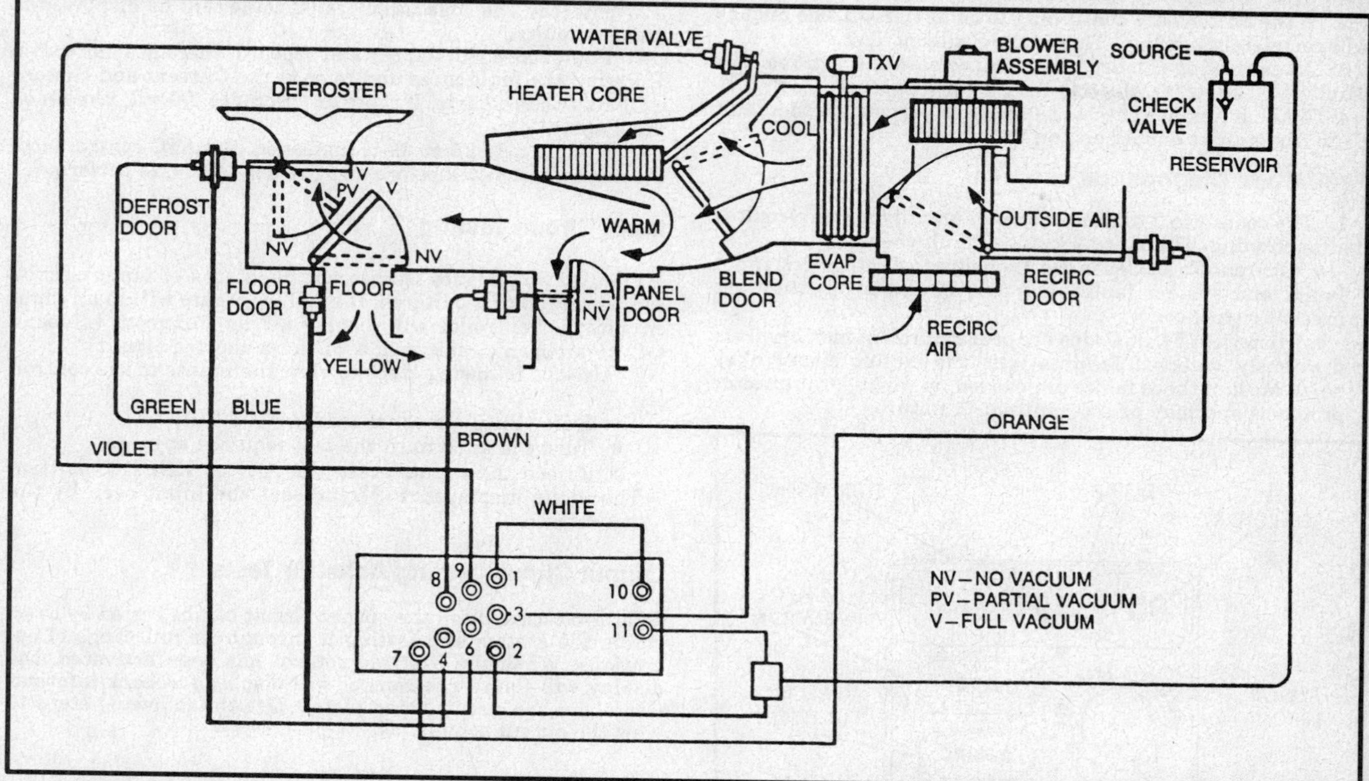

Vacuum schematic—Cherokee with air conditioning

Vacuum Actuating System

INSPECTION

Check the system for proper operation. Air should come from the appropriate vents when the corresponding mode is selected under all driving conditions. If a problem is detected, use the vacuum diagrams to check the flow of vacuum.

1. Check the engine for sufficient vacuum. Check the main supplier hose at the reservoir leaks or kinks.
2. Check the reservoir's check valve for ability to hold vacuum in 1 direction.
3. Check all interior vacuum lines, especially the 11-way connection behind the instrument panel for leaks or kinks.
4. Check the control head for leaky ports or damaged parts.
5. Check all actuators for ability to hold vacuum.

AUTOMATIC TEMPERATURE CONTROL

Diagnostics

The ATC controller, mounted in the control panel, is designed with on-board diagnostics which is capable of diagnosing each input and output circuit of the controller. When a fault is detected and in memory, an **Er** message is momentarily displayed on the control panel, but only once during each ignition cycle.

There are three different groups of testing features this system is capable of:

- Fault codes
- Input circuit testing
- Output circuit testing/actuator tests

Diagnostic Test Selector

The test selector uses the same display as the temperature control point. It is used to display fault codes, identify the test selection mode and to show the value of each circuit being tested.

1. If the **FLOOR** arrow is showing, the test selector value will be a range of number below 0.
2. If the stickman shows no arrows, the test selector value will be a range of numbers between **0** and **99**.
3. If the panel (middle) arrow is showing, the test selector value will be between **100** and **199**.
4. If the panel (middle) arrow and the defrost (top) arrows are both showing, the test selector value will be between **200** and **255**.
5. During diagnostics you may return to the test selector mode simply by turning the temperature dial 1 click in either direction. The stickman and arrows will not be shown in the test selector mode. Another circuit may optionally be monitored or tested.

Entering Diagnostics

1. Depress and hole the **A/C** and **RECIRC** buttons at the same time. Rotate the temperature dial clockwise (to the right) 1 click.

2. If the buttons are continuing to be held down, the display will completely light up. This is the Segment Test.

3. After viewing the Segment Test, release the buttons. The display will show **00** which is the Select Test level.

4. While a number of tests can now be performed, the Fault Code Diagnostics should be performed first.

Fault Code Diagnostics

1. The codes are 2-digit numbers to identify which circuit is malfunctioning. There are 2 kinds of fault codes:

- Current Fault Codes are divided into 2 categories: input faults and system faults. Current Faults mean they are present right now.
- Historical Fault Codes are codes stored in memory from previously detected failures (but the circuit shows okay now). Most of these faults are caused by wiring or connector problems and may be intermittent in nature.

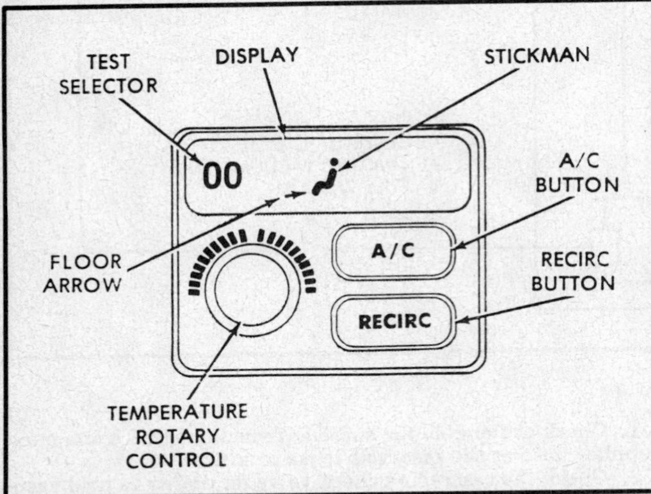

Showing ATC control panel for system diagnostics—Grand Cherokee and Grand Wagoneer with ATC

NOTE: Disconnecting the battery will erase all fault codes. Record the codes as they are viewed prior to moving on to any further procedures which may require battery disconnect.

2. While **00** is displayed, push either **A/C** or **RECIRC** button. The stickman will appear indicating the fault section is now entered. The code numbers **00** to **64** will be displayed to indicate faults.

3. Fault codes will appear and repeat if there are more than 1. Record the fault codes and refer to the Current and Historical Fault Code Charts. If there are no codes, **00** will remain on the display.

4. If fault code **25** or **29** is displayed, the ATC control module must be replaced before any further testing is performed.

Input Circuit Testing

1. After diagnostics is entered, the status of input circuits can be viewed or monitored. If a failure occurs within an input circuit, the controller will display a **?** for unknown values; a **OC** for an open circuit; and a **SC** for a shorted circuit.

2. Use the following steps to view the inputs to the controller:

- Enter the diagnostics mode.
- Turn the knob until the test required appears.
- To see the input, press the **A/C** or **RECIRC** button.

The digits displayed will represent the input seen by the controller.

Output Circuit Testing/Actuator Tests

A failure occurring in the output circuit can be tested by overriding the system and testing it through its full range of operations. When the override control has been activated, the display will flash. The control will display feedback information about the circuit being tested. Use the following steps to view the output commands:

1. Enter the diagnostics mode.
2. Turn the knob until the test required appears.
3. Press **A/C** or **RECIRC** to display the output from the controller.
4. Enter the actuator test by pressing **A/C** or **RECIRC**. When the display blinks, the actuator test mode is activated.
5. Manual tests are those requiring continuing pressing of the **A/C** or **RECIRC** buttons to control the output. Press either of these buttons once to run the automatic tests.

Clearing Fault Codes

Current faults are cleared whenever the problem goes away or is repaired.

To clear historical faults, press and hold either the **A/C** or **RECIRC** button for 3 seconds. The faults have cleared when 2 horizontal bars appear in the display screen.

ATC CURRENT FAULTS CODE CHART

Fail Code/Description	Circuit Description
00 = No Faults	
01 = Circuit open	Ambient Temperature Sensor
02 = Circuit open	In-Vehicle Temperature Sensor
03 = Circuit open	Solar Sensor Input Circuit
04 = Circuit open	Front Panel Blower/Fan Control Input
05 = Circuit open	Front Panel Mode Control Input
06 = Circuit open	Blend Air Door Feedback Circuit
07 = Circuit open	Mode Door Feedback Circuit
08 = Feedback too high	Blower/Fan Feedback Circuit
09 = Circuit shorted	Ambient Temperature Sensor
10 = Circuit shorted	In-Vehicle Temperature Sensor
11 = Circuit shorted	Solar Sensor Input Circuit
12 = Circuit shorted	Front Panel Blower/Fan Control Input
13 = Circuit shorted	Front Panel Mode Control Input
14 = Circuit shorted	Blend Air Door Feedback Circuit
15 = Circuit shorted	Mode Door Feedback Circuit
16 = Feedback too low	Blower/Fan Feedback Circuit
17 = Dimming input error	Pulse Width Dimming PWD Input
19 = Door not responding	Mode Door Feedback Circuit
20 = Door not responding	Blend Air Door Actuator Drive Circuit
21 = Door travel range too small	Mode Door Feedback Circuit
22 = Door travel range too large	Mode Door Feedback Circuit
23 = Door travel range too small	Blend Air Door Actuator Drive Circuit
24 = Door travel range too large	Blend Air Door Actuator Drive Circuit
25 = Calibration data error	Calibration and CPU Data
26 = Coolant temp message missing	Collision Detection C2D BUS Inputs
27 = Vehicle speed message missing	Collision Detection C2D BUS Inputs
28 = Engine RPM message missing	Collision Detection C2D BUS Inputs
29 = CPU error	Calibration and CPU Data
30 = Reserved	
31 = Reserved	
32 = Reserved	

ATC HISTORICAL FAULTS CODE CHART

Fail Code/Description	Circuit Description
33 = Circuit was open	Ambient Temperature Sensor
34 = Circuit was open	In-Vehicle Temperature Sensor
35 = Circuit was open	Solar Sensor Input Circuit
36 = Circuit was open	Front Panel Blower/Fan Control Input
37 = Circuit was open	Front Panel Mode Control Input
38 = Circuit was open	Blend Air Door Feedback Circuit
39 = Circuit was open	Mode Door Feedback Circuit
40 = Feedback was too high	Blower/Fan Feedback Circuit
41 = Circuit was shorted	Ambient Temperature Sensor
42 = Circuit was shorted	In-Vehicle Temperature Sensor
43 = Circuit was shorted	Solar Sensor Input Circuit
44 = Circuit was shorted	Front Panel Blower/Fan Control Input
45 = Circuit was shorted	Front Panel Mode Control Input
46 = Circuit was shorted	Blend Air Door Feedback Circuit
47 = Circuit was shorted	Mode Door Feedback Circuit
48 = Feedback was too low	Blower/Fan Feedback Circuit
49 = Dimming input was in error	Pulse Width Dimming PWD Input
51 = Door was not responding	Mode Door Feedback Circuit
52 = Door was not responding	Blend Air Door Actuator Drive Circuit
53 = Door travel range was too small	Mode Door Feedback Circuit
54 = Door travel range was too large	Mode Door Feedback Circuit
55 = Door travel range was too small	Blend Air Door Actuator Drive Circuit
56 = Door travel range was too large	Blend Air Door Actuator Drive Circuit
57 = Calibration data was in error	Calibration and CPU Data
58 = Coolant temp message was missing	Collision Detection C2D BUS Inputs
59 = Vehicle speed message was missing	Collision Detection C2D BUS Inputs
60 = Engine RPM message was missing	Collision Detection C2D BUS Inputs
61 = CPU was in error	Calibration and CPU Data
62 = Reserved	
63 = Reserved	
64 = Reserved	

ATC CIRCUIT TESTING CHART

Test No.	Test Item	Test Type	System Tested	Displayed Values
01	Blower Control Switch (A/D)	I	Blower System	"?" "OC" "SC" 00-255
02	Blower Feedback	I	Blower System	"?" 00-255
03	Blower Speed	O/A	Blower System	00-255
04	Hi Blower Relay	O/A	Blower System	00 = OFF 01 = ON
05	Mode Control A/D	I	Mode Door System	"OC" "SC" 00-255
06	Mode Door Feedback	I	Mode Door System	"OC" "SC" 00-255
07	Panel Stop	I	Mode Door System	"?" 00-255 If "?" is displayed, activate Mode 11 to find panel stop position.
08	Defrost Stop	I	Mode Door System	"?" 00-255 If "?" is displayed, activate Mode 11 to find defrost stop position.
09	A/C Request	O/A	A/C System	00 = OFF 01 = ON
10	Mode Door Position	O/A	Mode Door System	00-255 It is possible to command the door position beyond the stops. The motor will try to move there.
11	Mode Motor	O/A	Mode Door System	Pressing A/C or RECIRC button for 3 sec. begins reinitialization. 00 = searching for panel stop 01 = searching for defrost stop 02 = moving toward panel 03 = moving toward defrost 04 = in position 05 = stalled moving toward panel 06 = stalled moving toward defrost 07 = feedback error
12	Mode Motor Drive Lines	O	Mode Door System	00 = stopped (lines low) 01 = toward defrost 02 = toward panel 03 = stopped (lines high)
13	Recirc Door	O/A	Recirc Door System	00 = continuous operation (lines grounded) 01 = fresh 02 = recirc. 03 = stopped (lines open)
14	In-Vehicle Temp. A/D	I	Temperature Inputs	"OC" "SC" 00-255
15	Ambient Sensor A/D	I	Temperature Inputs	"OC" "SC" 00-255
16	Blend Door Feedback	I	Blend Door System	"OC" "SC" 00-255
17	Blend Door Cold Stop	I	Blend Door System	"?" 00-255
18	Blend Door Hot Stop	I	Blend Door System	"?" 00-255

TEST TYPE: I = Input 0 = Output O/A = Output/Actuator

ATC CIRCUIT TESTING CHART, CONT'D

Test No.	Test Item	Test Type	System Tested	Displayed Values
19	In-Vehicle Temperature	I	Temperature Inputs	"OC" "SC" −40 to +60 C (−40 to +140 F)
20	Ambient Sensor	I	Temperature Inputs	"OC" "SC" −40 to +60 C (−40 to +140 F)
21	Solar Sensor A/D	I	Sun Intensity Input	"OC" "SC" 00-255
22	Engine Coolant	I	CCD	"?" −40 to +185 C (−40 to +260 F)
23	Vehicle Speed (MPH/KPM)	I	CCD	"?" 00-255
24	Engine RPM (x100)	I	CCD	00-82
25	Blend Door Motor	O/A	Blend Door System	Pressing A/C or RECIRC button for 3 sec. begins reinitialization.
				00 = searching for hot stop 01 = searching for cold stop 02 = moving to warmer 03 = moving to cooler 04 = in position 05 = stalled moving to warmer 06 = stalled moving to cooler 07 = feedback error
26	Blend Door Motor	O/A	Blend Door System	00-255
				It is possible to command the door position beyond the stops. The motor will try to move there.
27	Blend Door Motor Lines	O/A	Blend Door System	00 = stopped (lines low) 01 = toward cold 02 = toward hot 03 = stopped (lines high)
28	Lights On	I	Headlight Switch	00 = OFF 01 = ON
29	Dimming	I	PWD System	"?" 00-255
30	Dimming Level	O/A	Dimming System	"?" 00-255
31	ROM & EEPROM			00-FF
32	ROM & EEPROM			00-FF
33	ROM & EEPROM			00-FF
34	ROM & EEPROM			00-FF
35	ROM & EEPROM			00-FF
36	ROM & EEPROM			00-FF
37	ROM & EEPROM			00-FF
38	ROM & EEPROM			00-FF

TEST TYPE: I = Input O = Output O/A = Output/Actuator

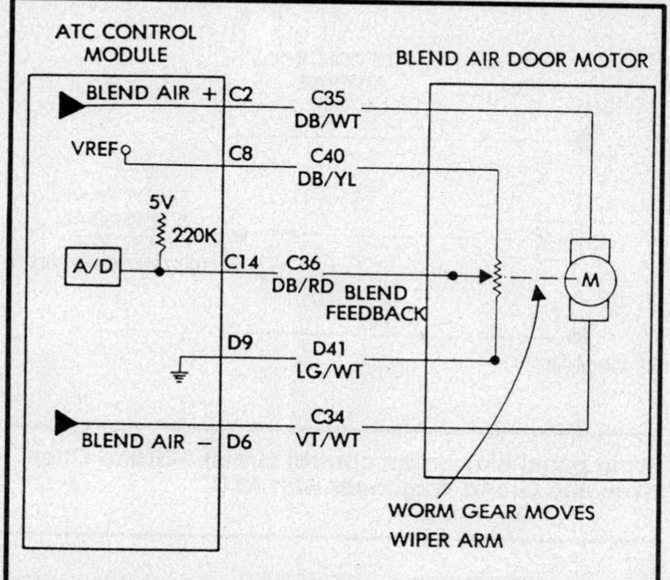

Blend air door actuator drive circuit—Grand Cherokee and Grand Wagoneer with ATC

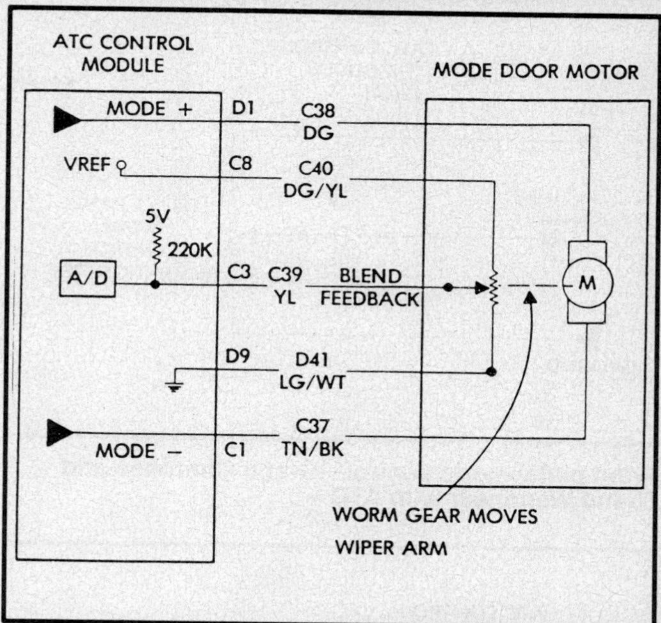

Mode door actuator drive circuit—Grand Cherokee and Grand Wagoneer with ATC

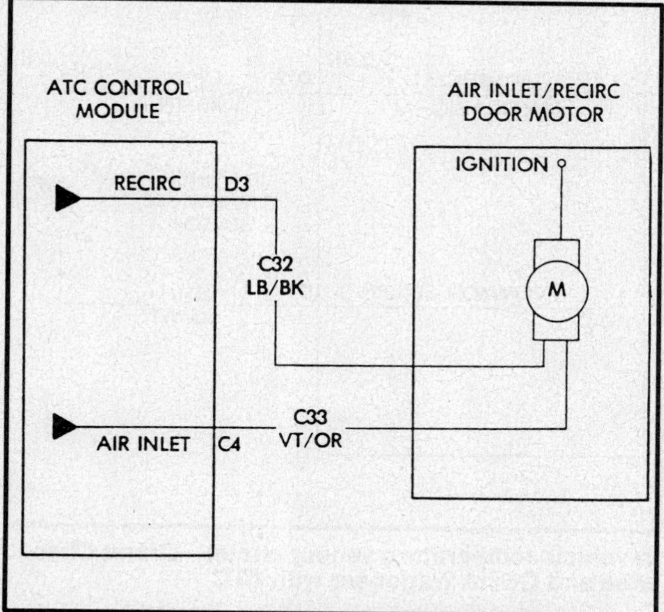

Air inlet/recirc door actuator drive circuit—Grand Cherokee and Grand Wagoneer with ATC

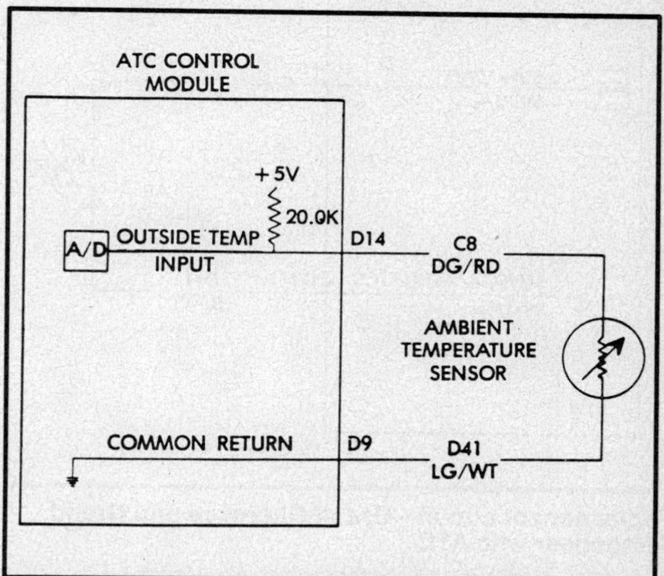

Ambient temperature sensor circuit—Grand Cherokee and Grand Wagoneer with ATC

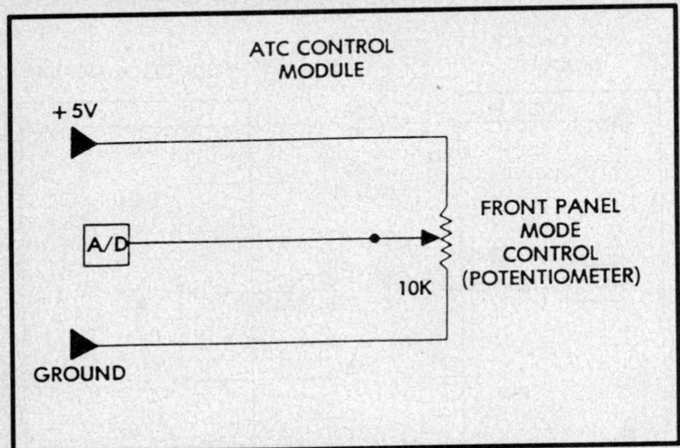

Front panel mode control—Grand Cherokee and Grand Wagoneer with ATC

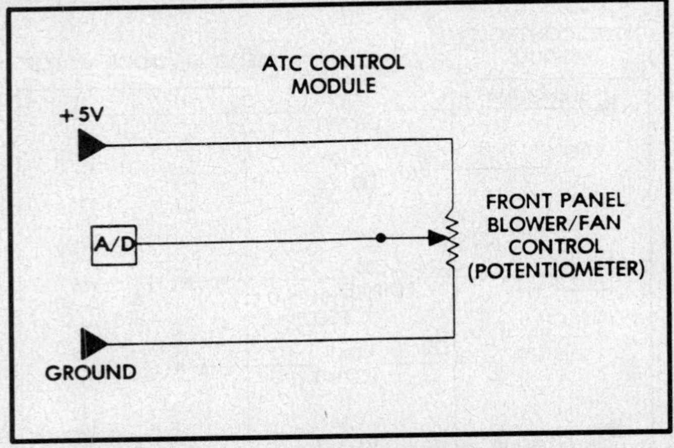

Front panel blower/fan control circuit—Grand Cherokee and Grand Wagoneer with ATC

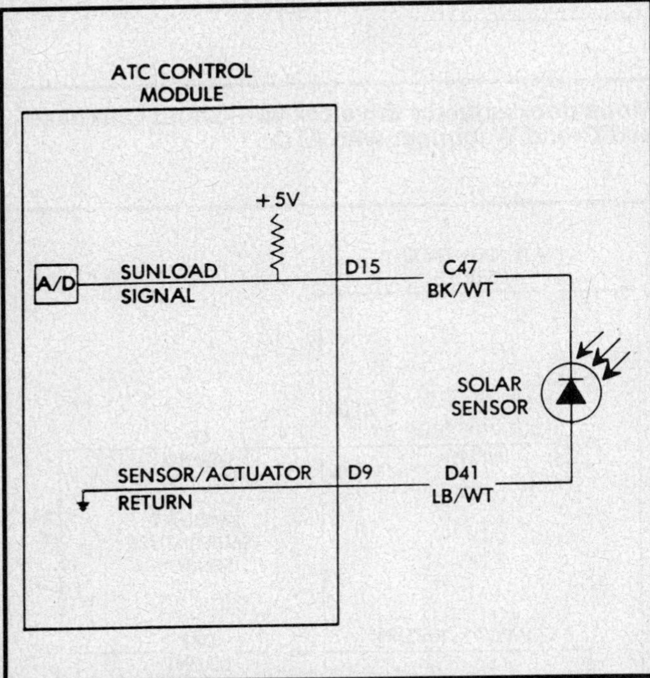

Solar sensor circuit—Grand Cherokee and Grand Wagoneer with ATC

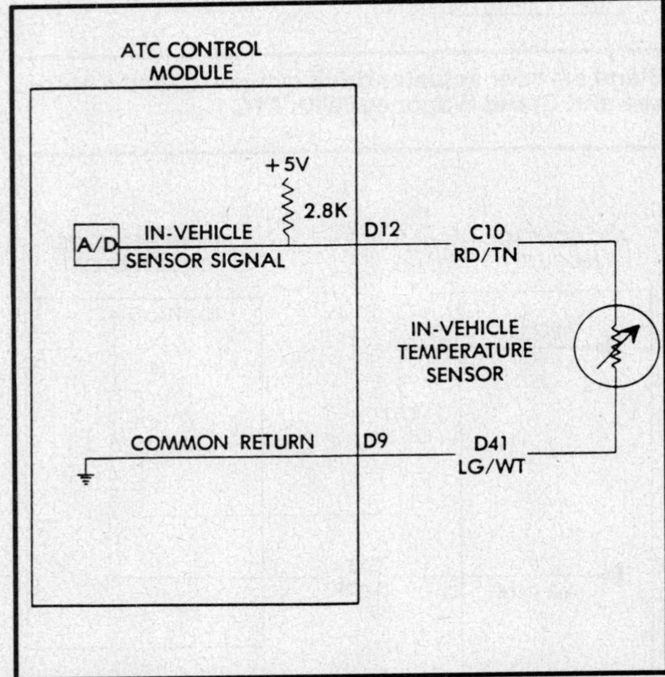

In-vehicle temperature sensor circuit—Grand Cherokee and Grand Wagoneer with ATC

WIRING SCHEMATICS

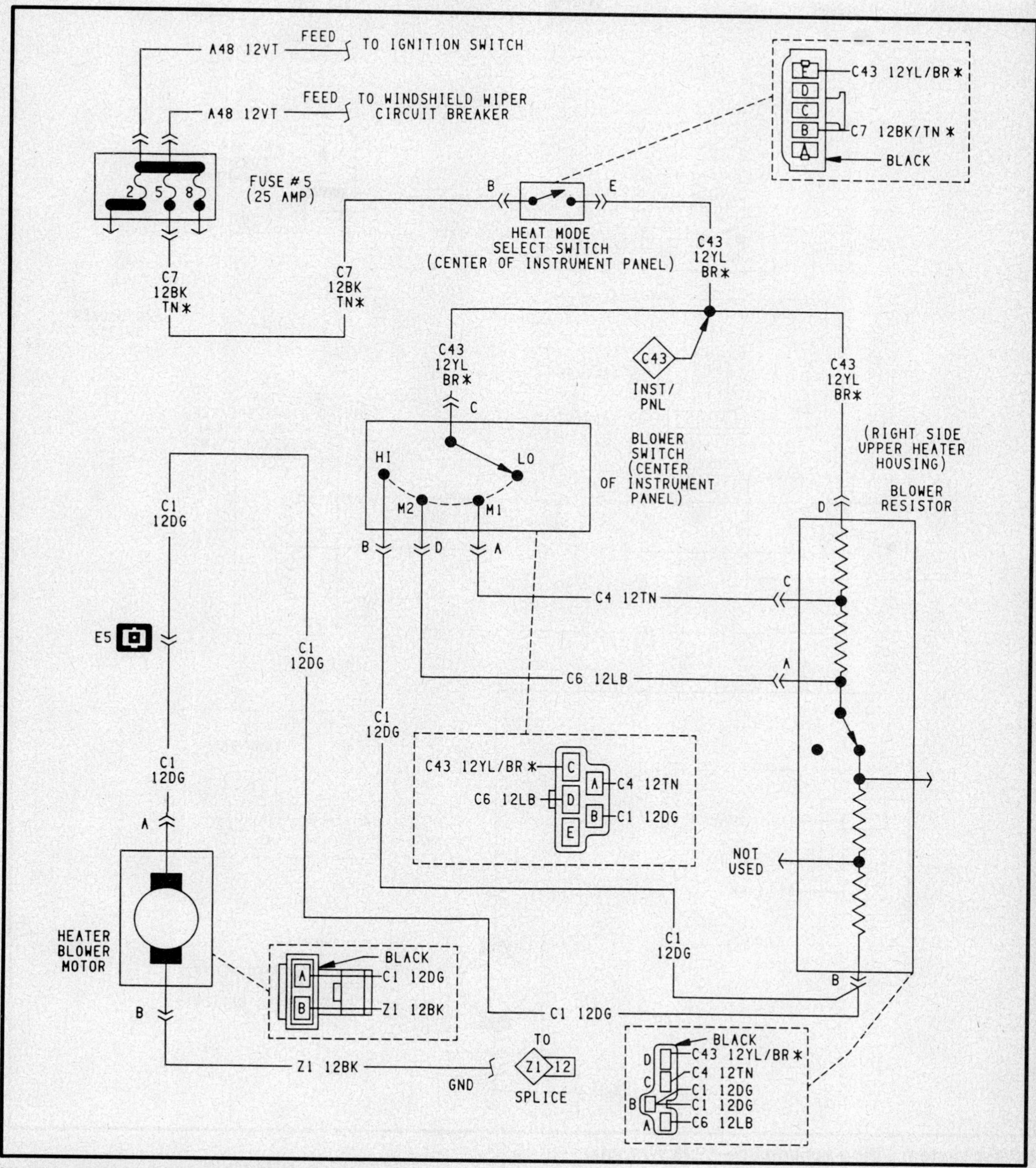

Heater system wiring schematic—Cherokee

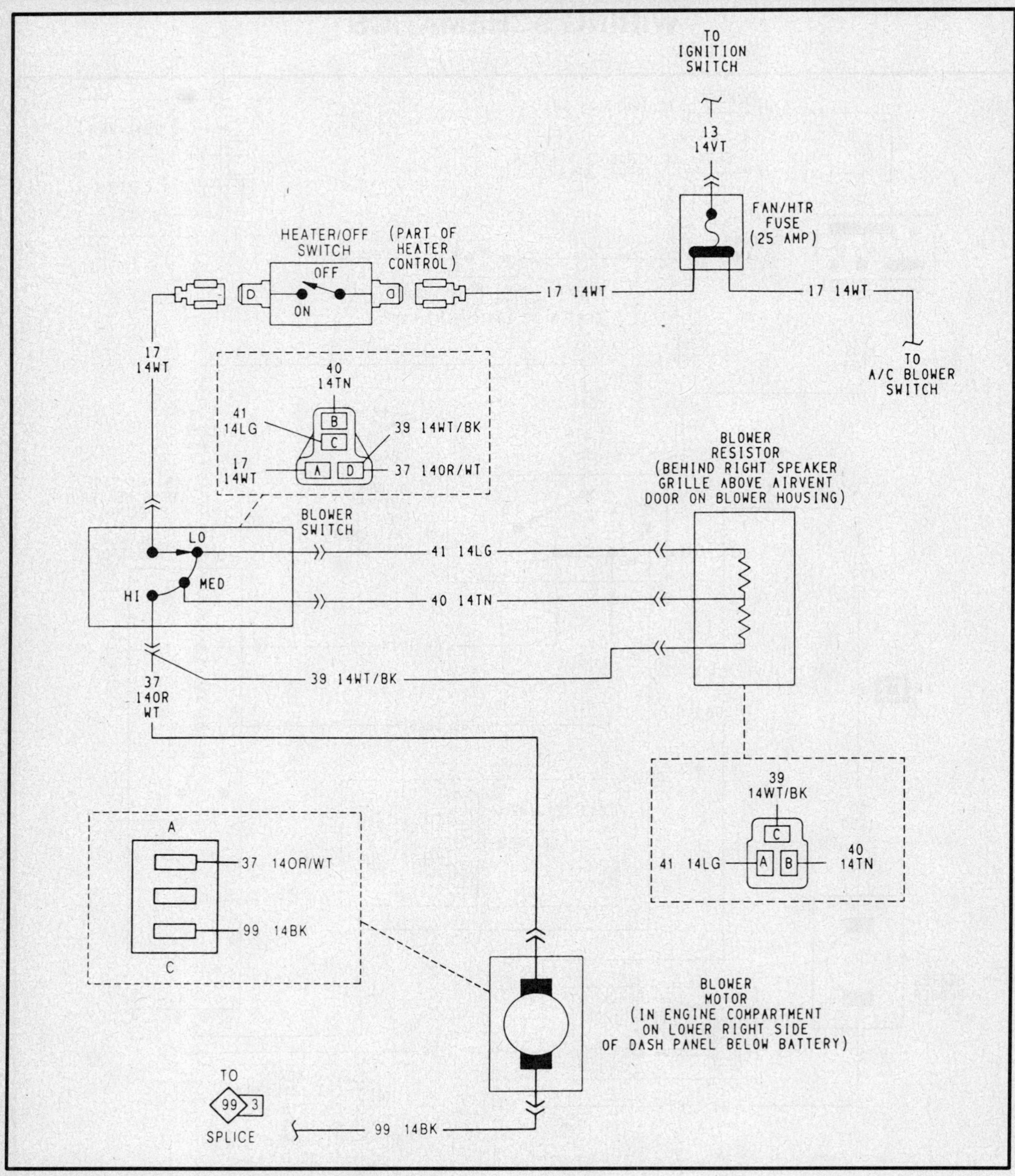

Heater system wiring schematic—1993 Wrangler

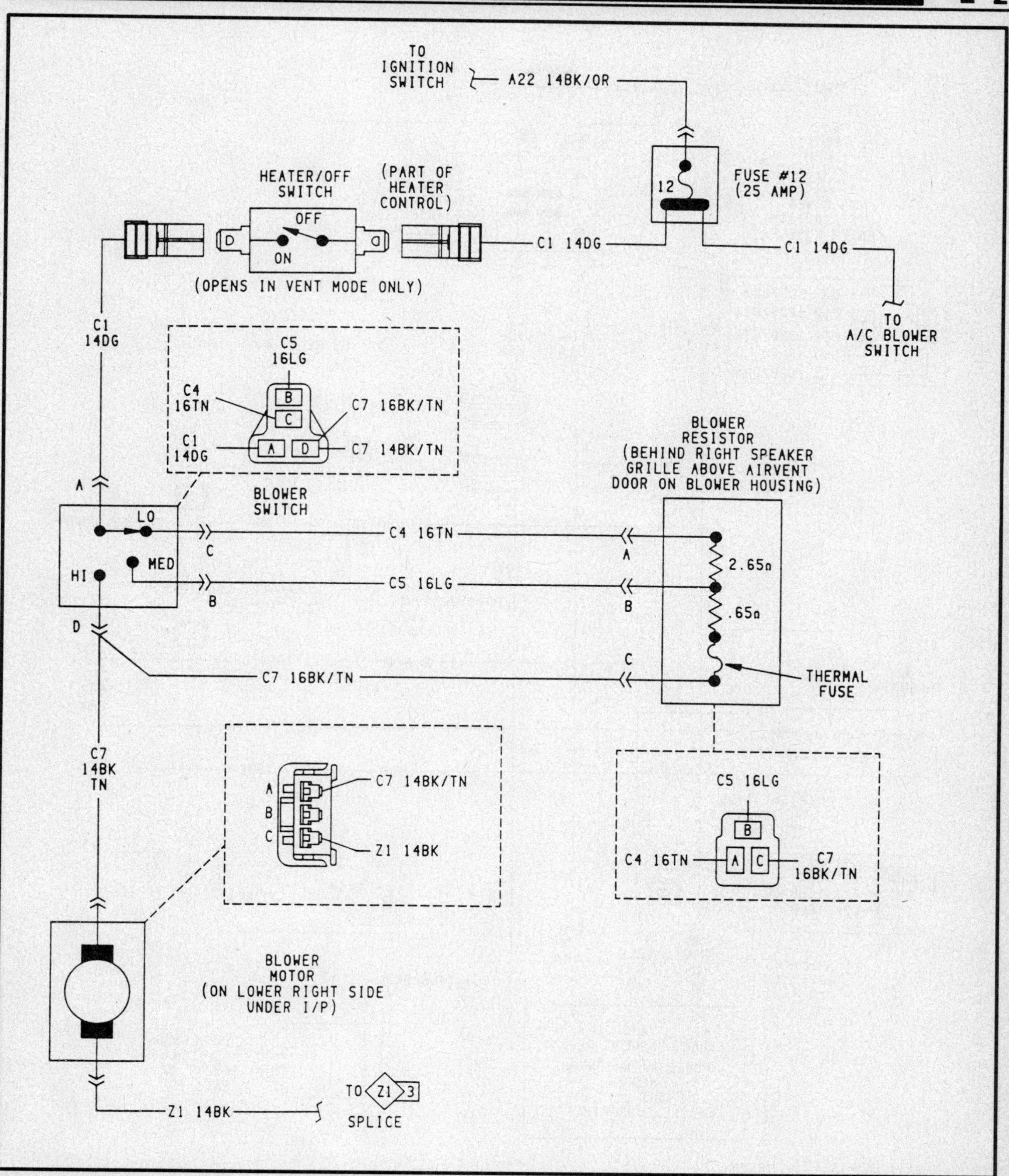

Heater system wiring schematic—1994–95 Wrangler

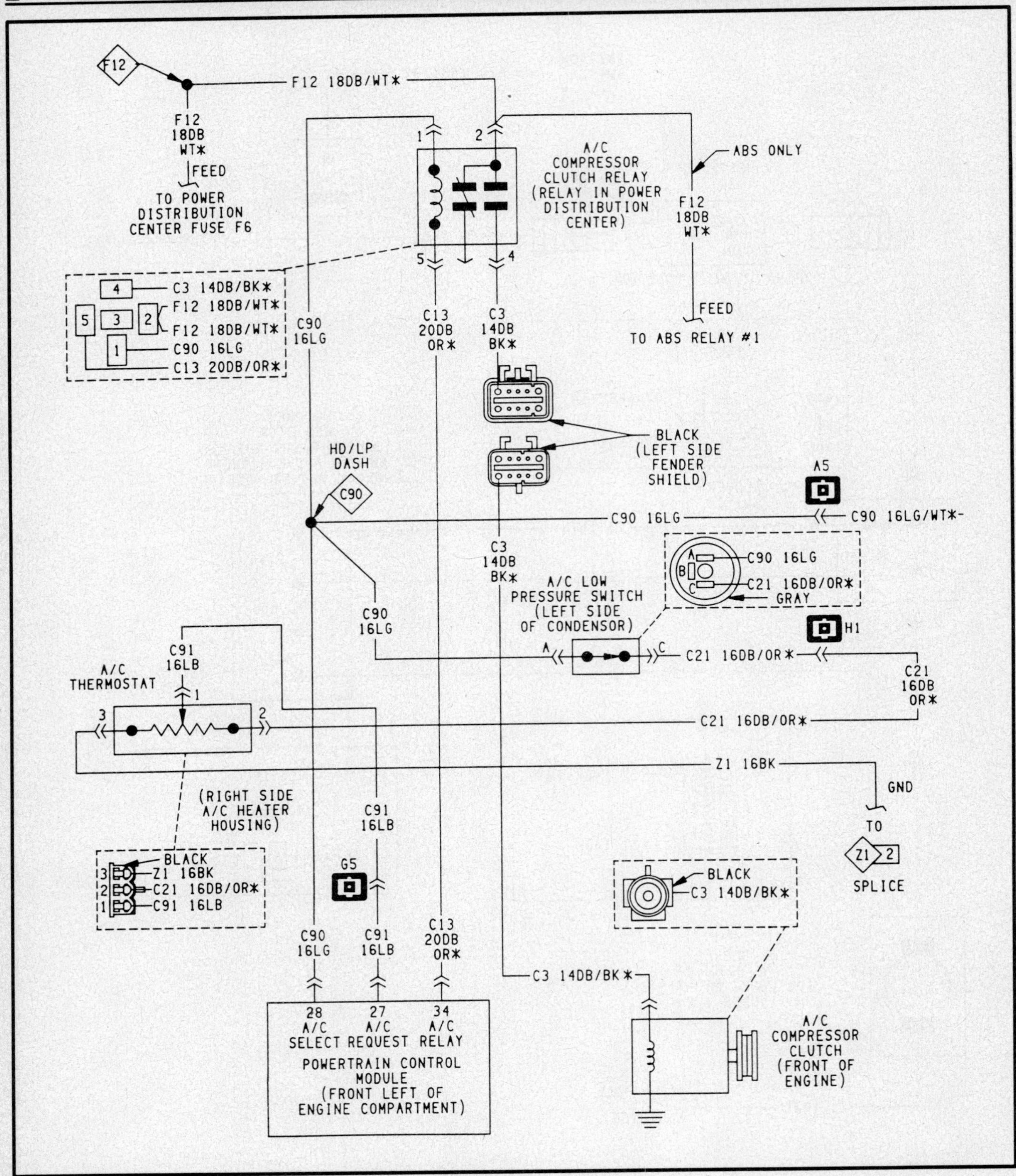

Air conditioning system wiring schematic—1993 Cherokee

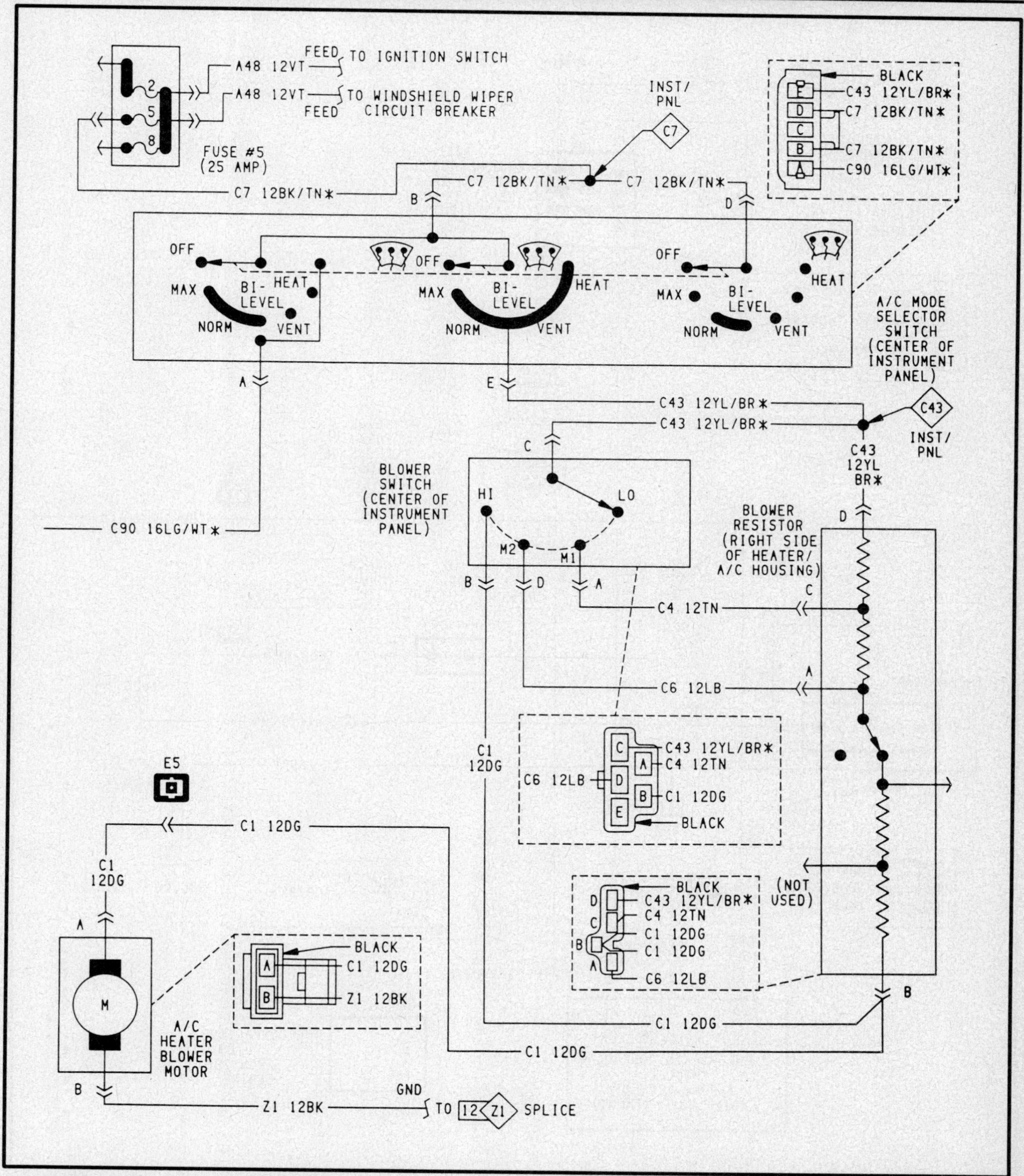

Air conditioning system wiring schematic—1993 Cherokee, Cont'd

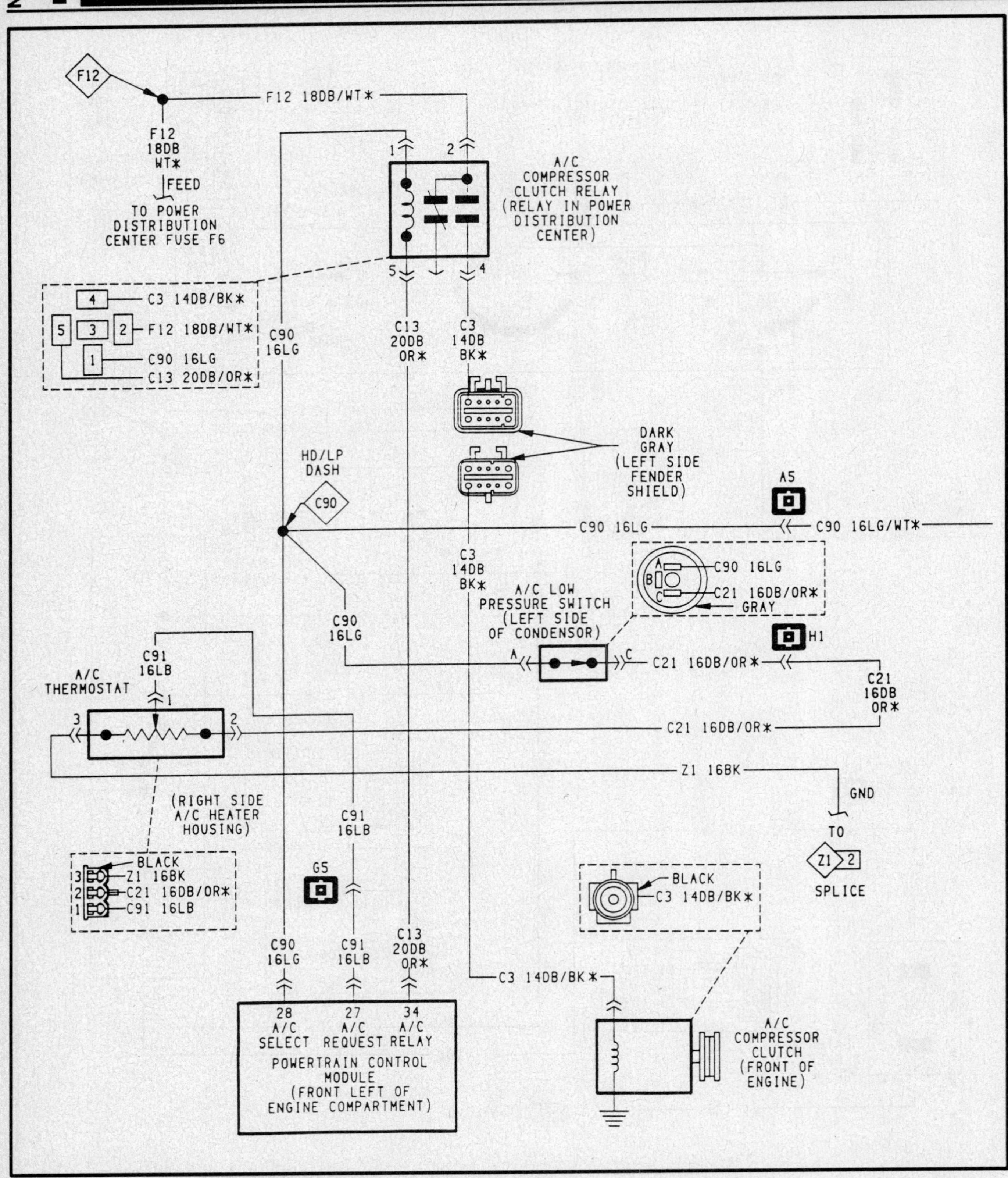

Air conditioning system wiring schematic—1994–95 Cherokee

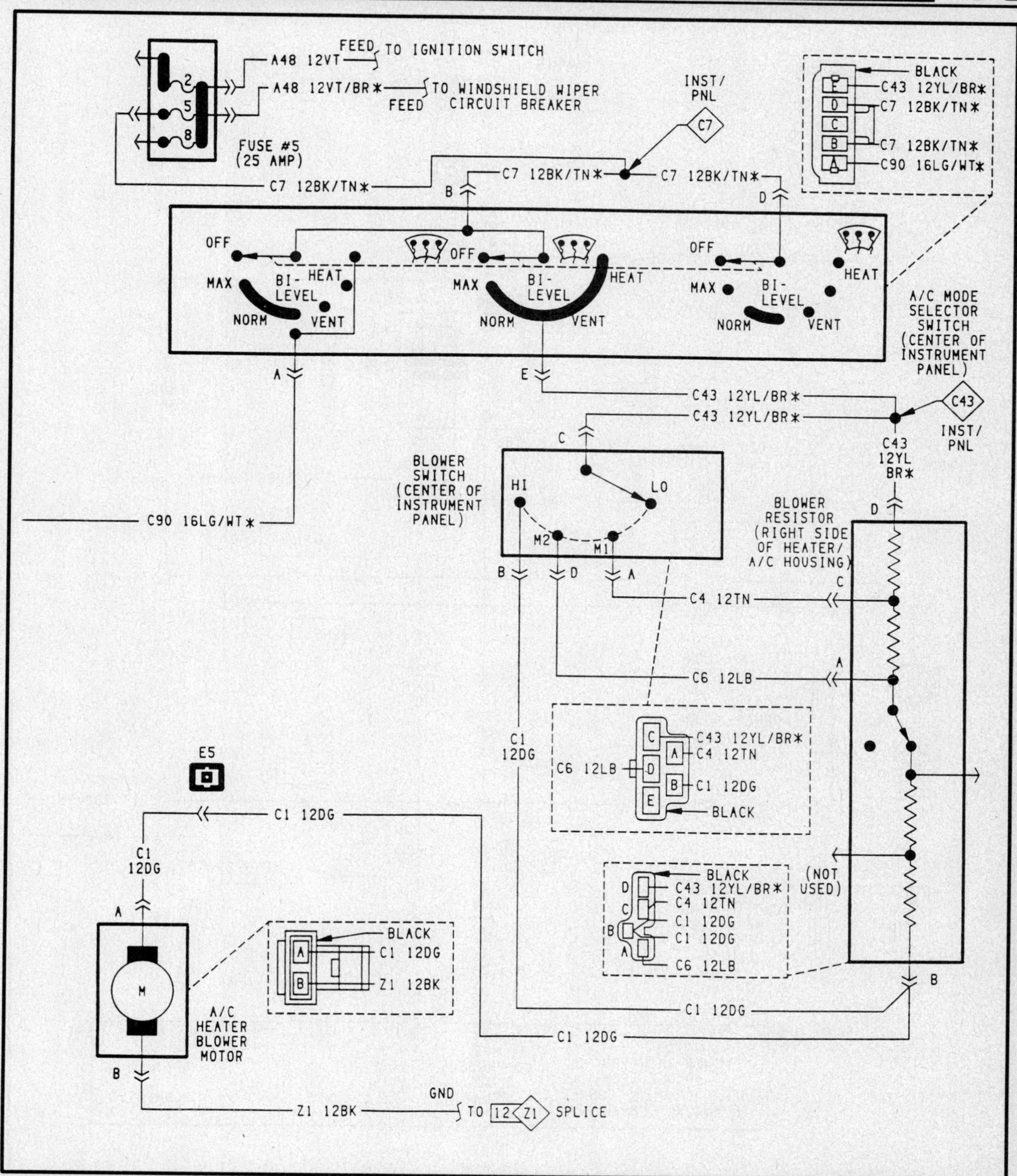

Air conditioning system wiring schematic—1994–95 Cherokee, Cont'd

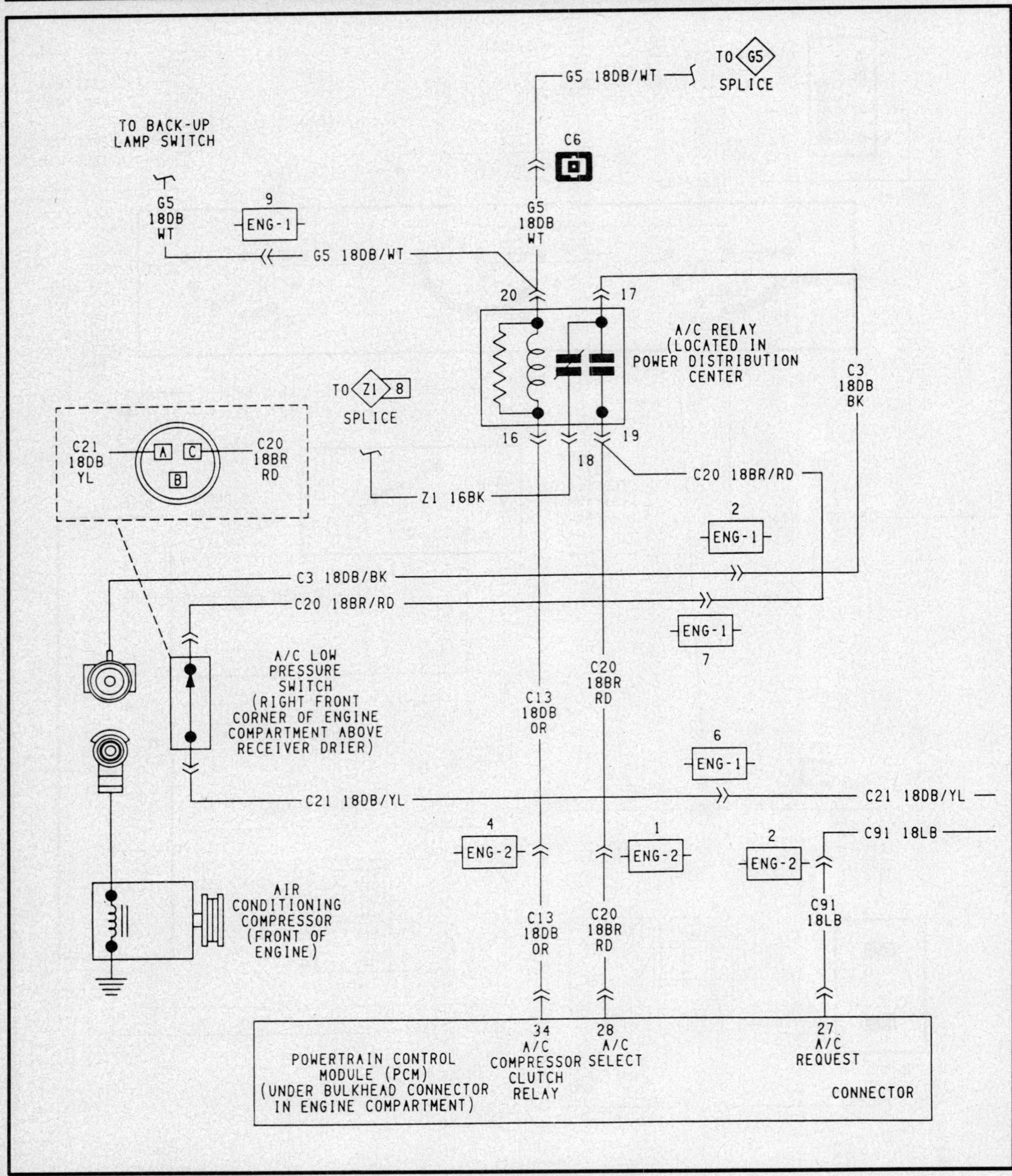

Air conditioning system wiring schematic—Wrangler with 4.0L engine

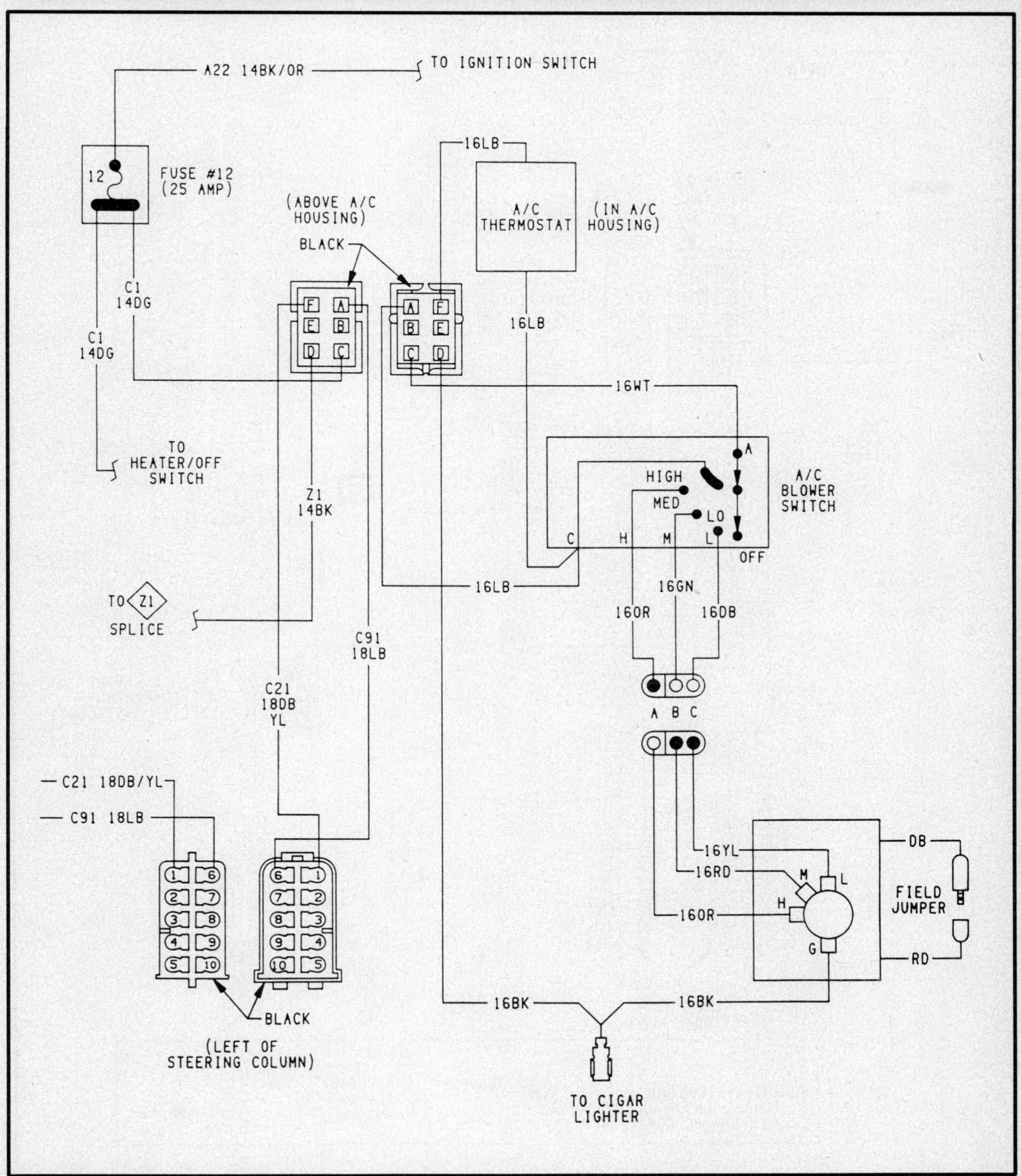

Air conditioning system wiring schematic—Wrangler with 4.0L engine, Cont'd

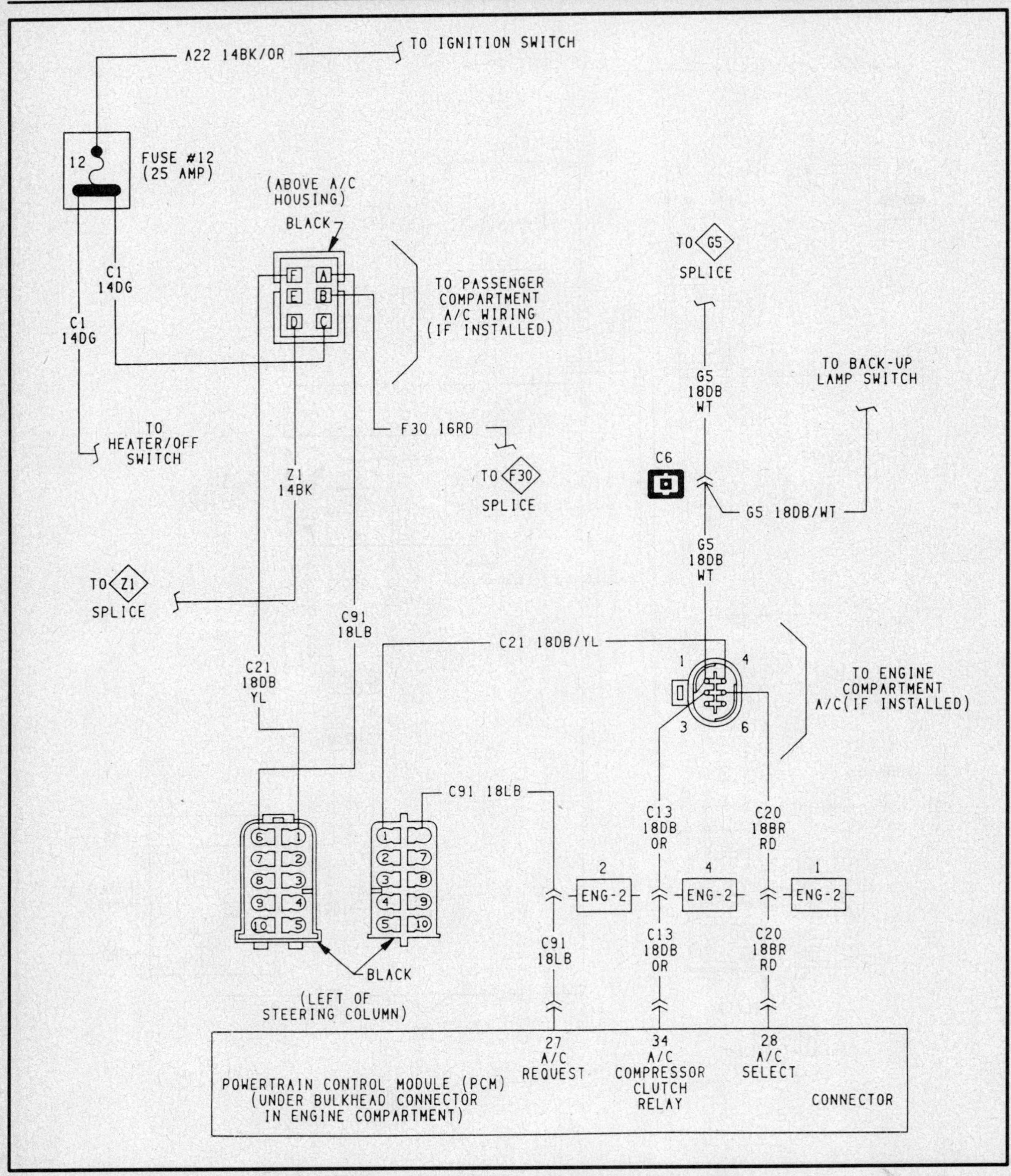

Air conditioning system wiring schematic provisions—Wrangler with 2.5L engine

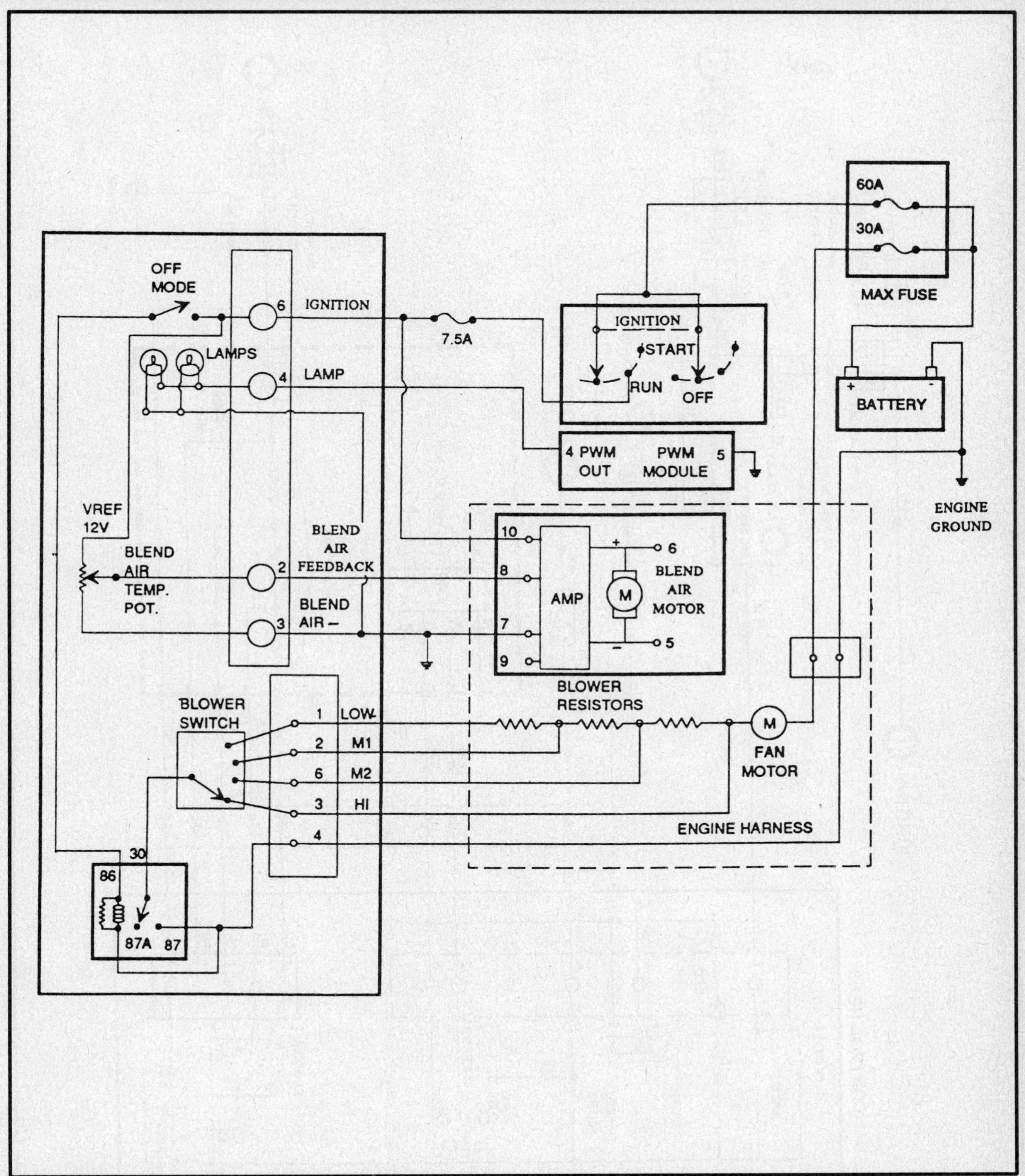

Heater system wiring schematic—Grand Cherokee and Grand Wagoneer

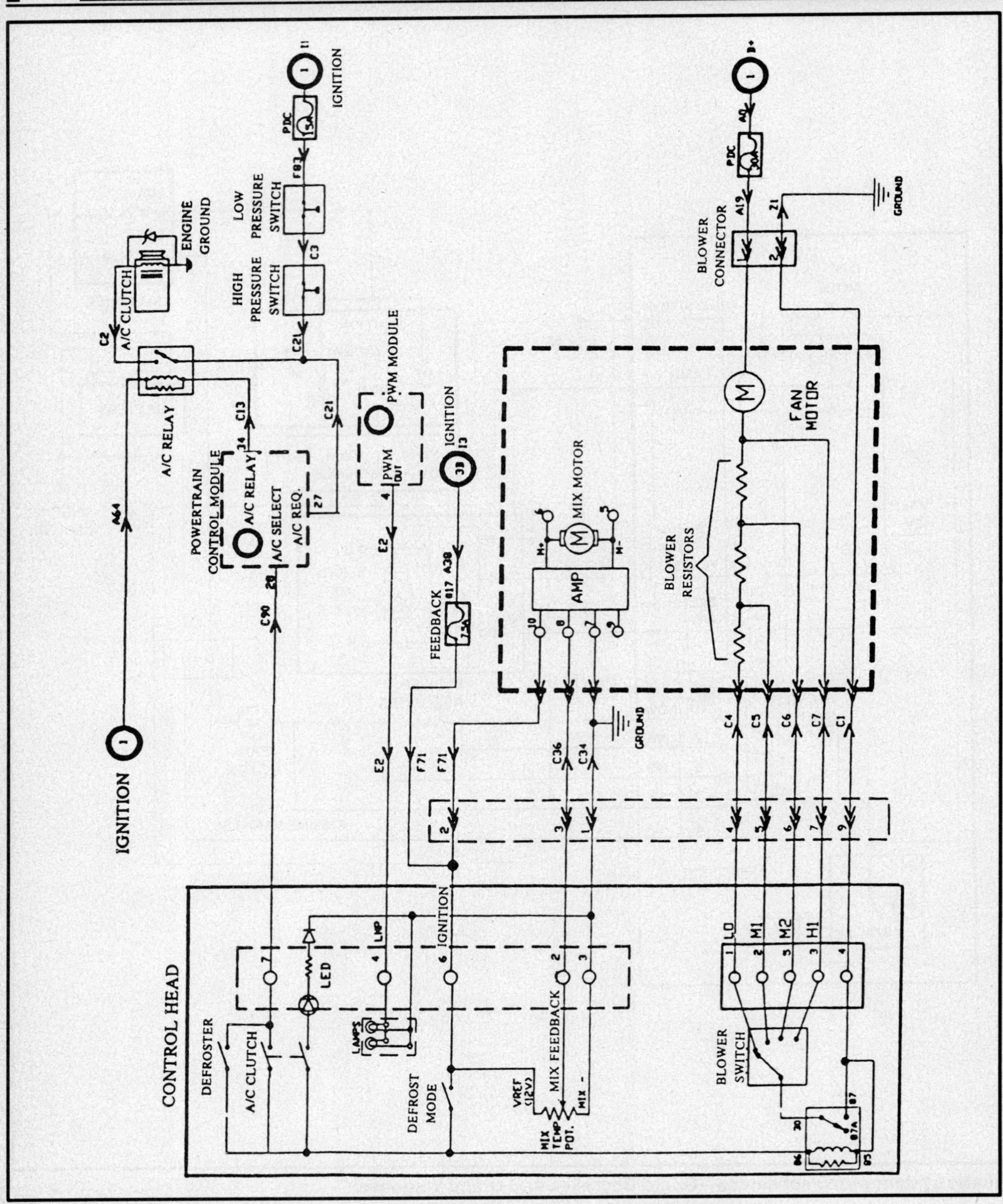

Air conditioning system wiring schematic—Grand Cherokee and Grand Wagoneer

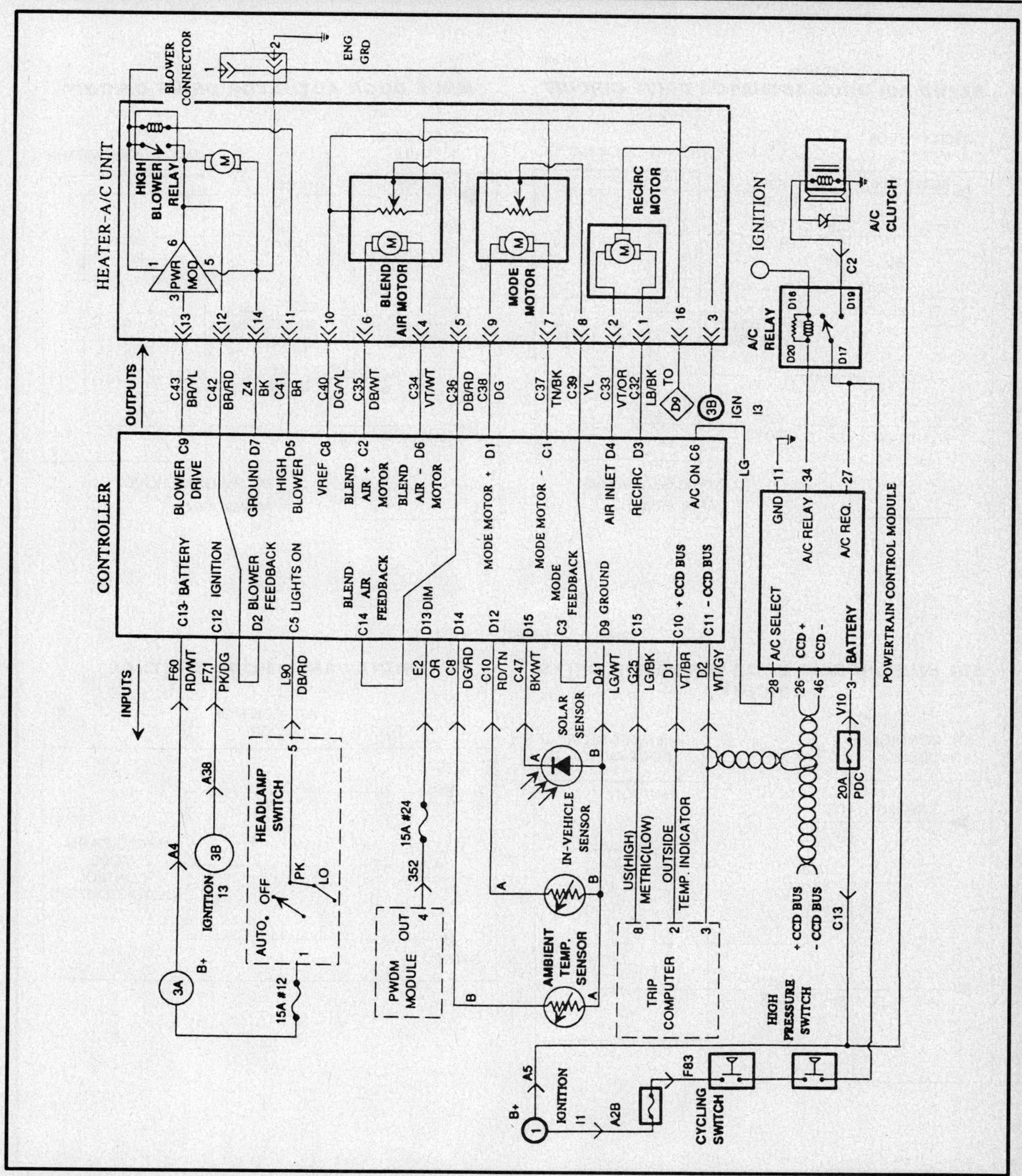

Automatic temperature control system wiring schematic—Grand Cherokee and Grand Wagoneer with ATC

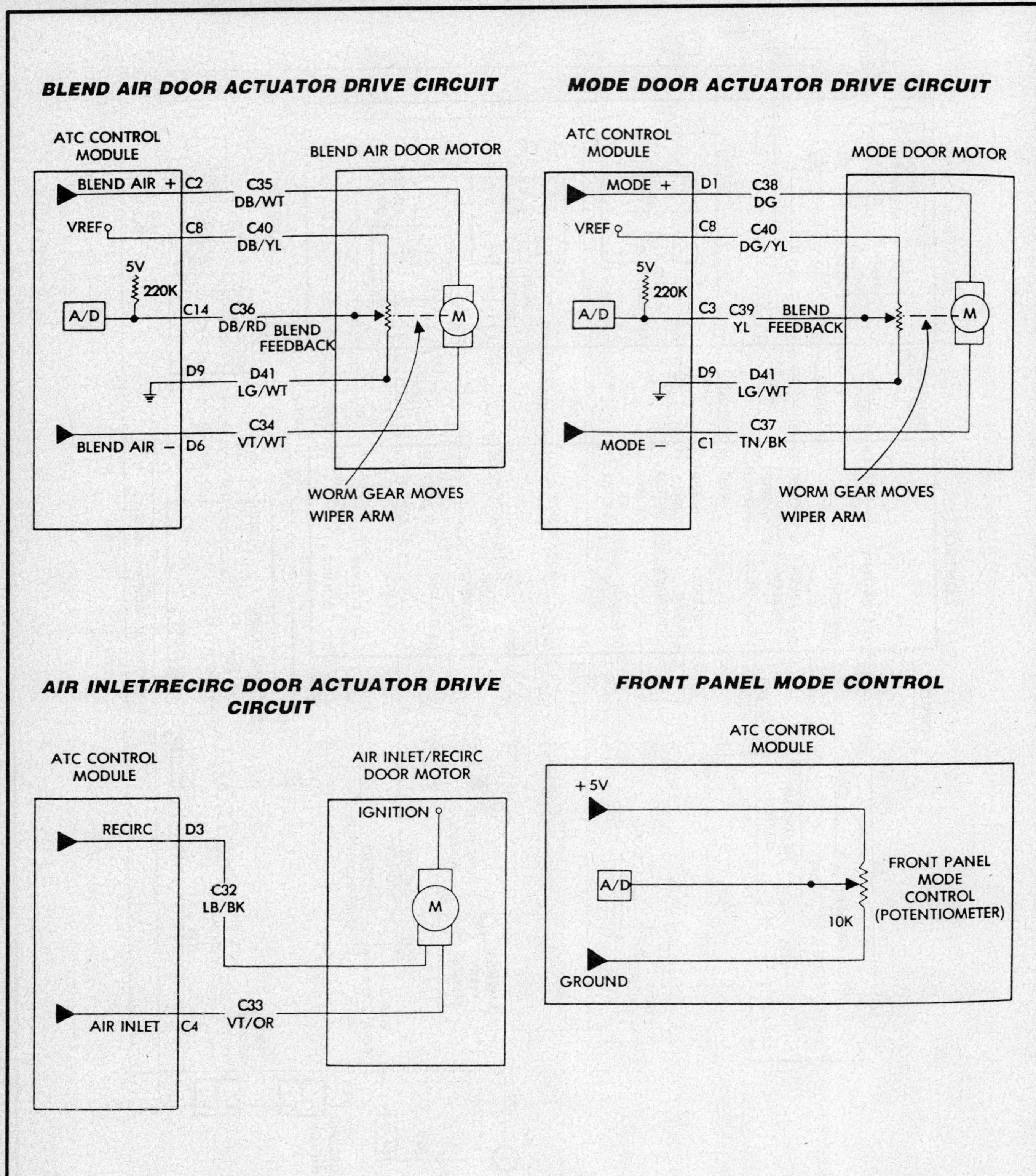
BLEND AIR DOOR ACTUATOR DRIVE CIRCUIT
ATC CONTROL MODULE
BLEND AIR DOOR MOTOR
BLEND AIR +
C2
C35
DB/WT
VREF
C8
C40
DB/YL
5V
220K
A/D
C14
C36
DB/RD
BLEND FEEDBACK
M
D9
D41
LG/WT
C34
VT/WT
BLEND AIR –
D6
WORM GEAR MOVES WIPER ARM
MODE DOOR ACTUATOR DRIVE CIRCUIT
ATC CONTROL MODULE
MODE DOOR MOTOR
MODE +
D1
C38
DG
VREF
C8
C40
DG/YL
5V
220K
A/D
C3
C39
YL
BLEND FEEDBACK
M
D9
D41
LG/WT
C37
TN/BK
MODE –
C1
WORM GEAR MOVES WIPER ARM
AIR INLET/RECIRC DOOR ACTUATOR DRIVE CIRCUIT
ATC CONTROL MODULE
AIR INLET/RECIRC DOOR MOTOR
IGNITION
RECIRC
D3
C32
LB/BK
M
C33
VT/OR
AIR INLET
C4
FRONT PANEL MODE CONTROL
ATC CONTROL MODULE
+5V
A/D
FRONT PANEL MODE CONTROL (POTENTIOMETER)
10K
GROUND

Air door actuator drive circuits—Grand Cherokee and Grand Wagoneer

5 FORD/LINCOLN/MERCURY 5

ASPIRE • CAPRI • CONTINENTAL • CONTOUR • ESCORT • FESTIVA • PROBE • SABLE • TAURUS • TEMPO • TOPAZ • TRACER • MYSTIQUE

SPECIFICATIONS

ENGINE IDENTIFICATION

Year	Model	Engine Displacement Liters (cc)	Engine Series (ID/VIN)	Fuel System	No. of Cylinders	Engine Type
1993	Festiva	1.3 (1319)	H	MFI	4	SOHC
	Capri	1.6 (1597)	Z, 6 ①	MFI	4	DOHC
	Escort	1.8 (1844)	8	EFI	4	DOHC
	Tracer	1.8 (1844)	8	EFI	4	DOHC
	Escort	1.9 (1859)	J	SFI	4	SOHC
	Tracer	1.9 (1859)	J	SFI	4	SOHC
	Tempo	2.3 (2326)	X	EFI	4	OHV
	Topaz	2.3 (2326)	X	EFI	4	OHV
	Tempo	3.0 (2971)	U	EFI	6	OHV
	Topaz	3.0 (2971)	U	EFI	6	OHV
	Taurus	3.0 (2971)	U	EFI	6	OHV
	Sable ②	3.0 (2971)	U	EFI	6	OHV
	Taurus SHO	3.0 (2980)	Y	SFI	6	DOHC
	Taurus SHO	3.2 (3196)	P	SFI	6	DOHC
	Taurus	3.8 (3801)	4	SFI	6	OHV
	Sable	3.8 (3801)	4	SFI	6	OHV
	Probe	2.0 (1993)	A	EFI	4	DOHC
	Probe GT	2.5 (2501)	B	EFI	6	DOHC
	Continental	3.8 (3801)	4	SFI	6	OHV
1994	Aspire	1.3 (1319)	H	SFI	4	SOHC
	Escort	1.8 (1839)	8	MFI	4	DOHC
	Tracer	1.8 (1839)	8	MFI	4	DOHC
	Escort	1.9 (1859)	J	SFI	4	SOHC
	Tracer	1.9 (1859)	J	SFI	4	SOHC
	Tempo	2.3 (2326)	X	SFI	4	OHV
	Topaz	2.3 (2326)	X	SFI	4	OHV
	Tempo	3.0 (2971)	U	EFI	6	OHV
	Topaz	3.0 (2971)	U	EFI	6	OHV
	Probe	2.0 (1993)	A	EFI	4	DOHC
	Probe	2.5 (2501)	B	EFI	6	DOHC
	Taurus	3.0 (2971)	U	EFI	6	OHV
	Sable	3.0 (2971)	U	EFI	6	OHV
	Taurus SHO	3.0 (2980)	Y	EFI	6	DOHC
	Taurus SHO	3.2 (3196)	P	EFI	6	DOHC
	Taurus	3.8 (3801)	4	EFI	6	OHV
	Sable	3.8 (3801)	4	EFI	6	OHV
	Continental	3.8 (3801)	4	SFI	6	OHV
1995	Aspire	1.3 (1319)	4	SFI	4	SOHC
	Escort	1.8 (1839)	8	MFI	4	DOHC
	Tracer	1.8 (1839)	8	SFI	4	DOHC
	Escort	1.9 (1859)	J	SFI	4	SOHC

ENGINE IDENTIFICATION

Year	Model	Engine Displacement Liters (cc)	Engine Series (ID/VIN)	Fuel System	No. of Cylinders	Engine Type
1995	Tracer	1.9 (1859)	J	SFI	4	SOHC
	Contour	2.0 (1988)	A	SFI	4	DOHC
	Contour	2.5 (2543)	B	SFI	6	DOHC
	Probe	2.0 (1993)	A	EFI	4	DOHC
	Probe	2.5 (2501)	B	EFI	6	DOHC
	Mystique	2.0 (1988)	A	SFI	4	DOHC
	Mystique	2.5 (2543)	B	SFI	6	DOHC
	Taurus	3.0 (2971)	U	EFI	6	OHV
	Taurus SHO	3.0 (2980)	Y	EFI	6	DOHC
	Taurus SHO	3.2 (3196)	P	EFI	6	DOHC
	Taurus	3.8 (3801)	4	EFI	6	OHV
	Sable	3.8 (3801)	4	EFI	6	OHV
	Continental	4.6 (4601)	V	SFI	8	DOHC

DOHC – Dual Overhead Cam
OHV – Overhead Valves
SOHC – Single Overhead Cam
EFI – Electronic Fuel Injection
MFI – Multi-Point Fuel Injection
SFI – Sequential Fuel Injection
① Vin 6 = Turbo
② Also applicable to Taurus with flexible fuel

REFRIGERANT CAPACITIES

Year	Model	Refrigerant (oz.)	Oil (fl. oz.)	Compressor Type
1993	Festiva	23	10	Nippondenso 10cyl①
	Capri	22.2–25.8	2.4–3.0	10T13F
	Escort w/1.8L	36	7.75	10P13
	Tracer w/1.8L	36	7.75	10P13
	Escort w/1.9L	36	7	FX-15
	Tracer w/1.9L	36	7	FX-15
	Probe	14	6.8	Panasonic vane type①
	Tempo w/2.3L	35–37	7	FX-15
	Topaz w/2.3L	35–37	7	FX-15
	Tempo w/3.0L	35–37	8	10P15C
	Topaz w/3.0L	35–37	8	10P15C
	Taurus	31–33	7	FX-15
	Sable	31–33	7	FX-15
	Taurus SHO	31–33	8	10P15F
	Continental	39–41	7	FX-15
1994	Aspire	24.9	N/A	Panasonic
	Capri	22.2–25.8	2.4–3.0	10T13F
	Escort w/1.8L	28	7.75	10P13
	Tracer w/1.8L	28	7.75	10P13

REFRIGERANT CAPACITIES

Year	Model	Refrigerant (oz.)	Oil (fl. oz.)	Compressor Type
1994	Escort w/1.9L	28	8	FS-10
	Tracer w/1.9L	28	8	FS-10
	Probe	40	6.8	Panasonic vane type①
	Tempo	31–33	8	10P15C
	Topaz	31–33	8	10P15C
	Taurus	31–33	7②	FS–10
	Sable	31–33	7②	FS–10
	Taurus SHO	31–33	8	10P15F
	Continental	39–41	7	FX–15
1995	Aspire	24.9	N/A	Panasonic①
	Escort	36	7.75	10P13
	Tracer	36	7.75	10P13
	Escort w/1.9L	28	8	FS-10
	Tracer w/1.9L	28	8	FS-10
	Probe	40	6.8	Panasonic vane type①
	Contour	34	7	FS–10
	Mystique	34	7	FS–10
	Taurus	31–33	7	FS–10
	Sable	31–33	7	FS–10
	Taurus SHO	31–33	8	10P15F
	Continental	34	7	FS–10

① Model number not specified by manfacturer
② 10 oz. with auxiliary system

AIR CONDITIONING BELT TENSION

Year	Model	Engine Liters (cc)	Belt Type	Specifications New (lbs.)	Specifications Used (lbs.)
1993	Festiva	1.3(1319)	V–ribbed	110–125	95–110
	Capri	1.6(1597)	V–ribbed	110–132	110–132
	Escort	1.8(1844)	V–ribbed	110–132	95–110
	Tracer	1.8(1844)	V–ribbed	110–132	95–110
	Escort	1.9(1859)	V–ribbed	①	①
	Tracer	1.9(1859)	V–ribbed	①	①
	Probe	2.0((1993)	V–ribbed	140–170	110–150
	Probe	2.5(2501)	V–ribbed	160–190	110–150
	Taurus	3.0(2890)	V–ribbed	①②	①③
	Sable	3.0(2890)	V–ribbed	①	①
	Taurus	3.2(3196)	V–ribbed	①	①
	Sable	3.2(3196)	V–ribbed	①	①
	Taurus	3.8(3801)	V–ribbed	①	①
	Sable	3.8(3801)	V–ribbed	①	①
	Continental	3.8(3801)	V–ribbed	①	①
1994	Aspire	1.3(1319)	V–ribbed	110–125	95–110
	Capri	1.6(1597)	V–ribbed	110–132	110–132

AIR CONDITIONING BELT TENSION

Year	Model	Engine Liters (cc)	Belt Type	Specifications	
				New (lbs.)	Used (lbs.)
1994	Escort	1.8(1839)	V–ribbed	110–132	95–110
	Tracer	1.8(1839)	V–ribbed	110–132	95–110
	Escort	1.9(1859)	V–ribbed	①	①
	Tracer	1.9(1859)	V–ribbed	①	①
	Probe	2.2(2189)	V–ribbed	154–198	132–176
	Probe	3.0(2971)	V–ribbed	①	①
	Tempo	2.3(2326)	V–ribbed	①	①
	Topaz	2.3(2326)	V–ribbed	①	①
	Tempo	3.0(2971)	V–ribbed	①	①
	Topaz	3.0(2971)	V–ribbed	①	①
	Taurus	3.0(2971)	V–ribbed	①	①
	Sable	3.0(2971)	V–ribbed	①	①
	Taurus SHO	3.0 (2980)	V–ribbed	220–285	148–192
	Taurus SHO	3.0 (3196)	V–ribbed	①	①
	Taurus	3.8(3801)	V–ribbed	①	①
	Sable	3.8(3801)	V–ribbed	①	①
	Continental	3.8(3801)	V–ribbed	①	①
1995	Aspire	1.8L(1319)	V–ribbed	110–125	95–110
	Escort	1.8(1839)	V–ribbed	110–132	95–110
	Tracer	1.8(1839)	V–ribbed	110–132	95–110
	Escort	1.9(1859)	V–ribbed	①	①
	Tracer	1.9(1859)	V–ribbed	①	①
	Probe	2.2(2189)	V–ribbed	154–198	132–176
	Probe	3.0(2971)	V–ribbed	①	①
	Contour	2.0L	V–ribbed	①	①
	Mystique	2.0L	V–ribbed	①	①
	Contour	2.5L	V–ribbed	①	①
	Mystique	2.5L	V–ribbed	①	①
	Taurus	3.0 (2971)	V–ribbed	①	①
	Sable	3.0 (2971)	V–ribbed	①	①
	Taurus SHO	3.0 (2980)	V–ribbed	220–285	148–192
	Taurus SHO	3.0 (3196)	V–ribbed	①	①
	Taurus	3.8(3801)	V–ribbed	①	①
	Sable	3.8(3801)	V–ribbed	①	①
	Continental	4.66(28LCID)	V–ribbed	①	①

① Automatic tensioner, no adjustment required
② 3.0L SHO: 220–265 lbs. new.
③ 3.0L SHO: 148–192 lbs. used.

SYSTEM DESCRIPTION

General Information

Ford front wheel drive vehicles use a fixed orifice tube. Ford front wheel drive vehicles are equipped with a suction accumulator/drier connected between the evaporator and the compressor.

The remaining components of the air conditioning systems, the compressor, condenser and evaporator, are common to all Ford front wheel drive vehicles.

Electronic Climate Control Systems

In addition to the normal air conditioning and heating system components, some Probe, Taurus and Sable models use automatic temperature control systems as optional equipment and is standard on Continental. These system operate by adding a series of sensors and switches throughout the system which provide various feedback inputs to the climate control computer. The computer, in turn, sends output signals to adjust blower speed, air door positions and mode operations to maintain the preset temperature adjustment on the panel. Among the major sensors are the ambient temperature sensor, in-car sensor and sunload sensor. These provide key information on outside and interior temperatures.

R-134a Systems

Some Taurus 3.0L models use A/C systems with non-CFC refrigerant 134a. These systems can be identified by a series of **R-134a** tags on key components of the system and on the general air conditioning tag on the radiator cover. Be aware that the use of R-134a is not compatible with R-12. Avoid mixing any amounts of these different refrigerants in the same system or system operating difficulties and possible system damage will occur. Note also that the refrigerant oil used with R-134a systems is different from the oil used with R-12 systems. Be sure to check for proper application before installing either the refrigerant or refrigerant oil. Do not interchange components from these 2 systems, either. Use only dedicated testing, gauge sets, charging stations and leak detectors for the R-134a system.

Service Valve Location

The air conditioning system has a high pressure (discharge) and a low pressure (suction) gauge port valve. These are Schrader valves which provide access to both the high and low pressure sides of the system for service hoses and a manifold gauge set so that system pressures can be read. The high pressure gauge port valve is located between the compressor and the condenser, in the high pressure vapor (discharge) line. The low pressure gauge port valve is located between the suction accumulator/drier and the compressor, in the low pressure vapor (suction) line.

High side adapter set D81L–19703–A or tool YT-354, YT-355 or equivalent is required to connect a manifold gauge set or charging station to the high pressure gauge port valve. Service tee fitting D87P–19703–A, which may be mounted on the clutch cycling pressure switch fitting, is available for use in the low pressure side of fixed orifice tube systems, to be used in place of the low pressure gauge port valve.

System Discharging

The use of refrigerant recovery systems and recycling stations makes possible the recovery and reuse of refrigerant after contaminants and moisture have been removed. If a recovery system or recycling station is used, the following general procedures should be observed, in addition to the operating instructions provided by the equipment manufacturer.

1. Connect the refrigerant recycling station hose(s) to the vehicle air conditioning service ports and the recovery station inlet fitting.

NOTE: Hoses should have shut off devices or check valves within 12 inches of the hose end to minimize the introduction of air into the recycling station and to minimize the amount of refrigerant released when the hose(s) is disconnected.

2. Turn the power to the recycling station **ON** to start the recovery process. Allow the recycling station to pump the refrigerant from the system until the station pressure goes into a vacuum. On some stations the pump will be shut off automatically by a low pressure switch in the electrical system. On other units it may be necessary to manually turn **OFF** the pump.

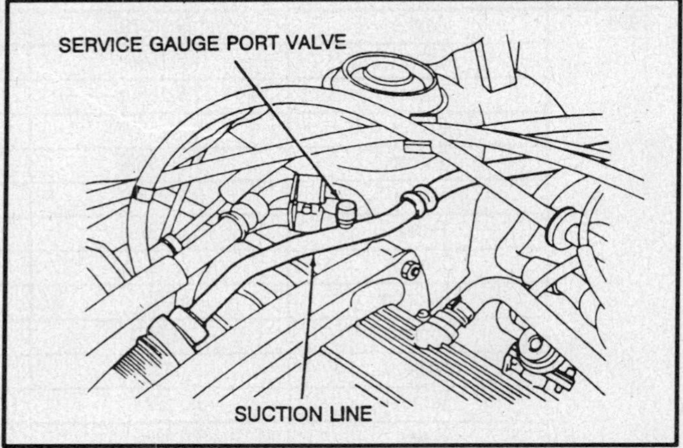

Low pressure service gauge port valve location—Escort and Tracer

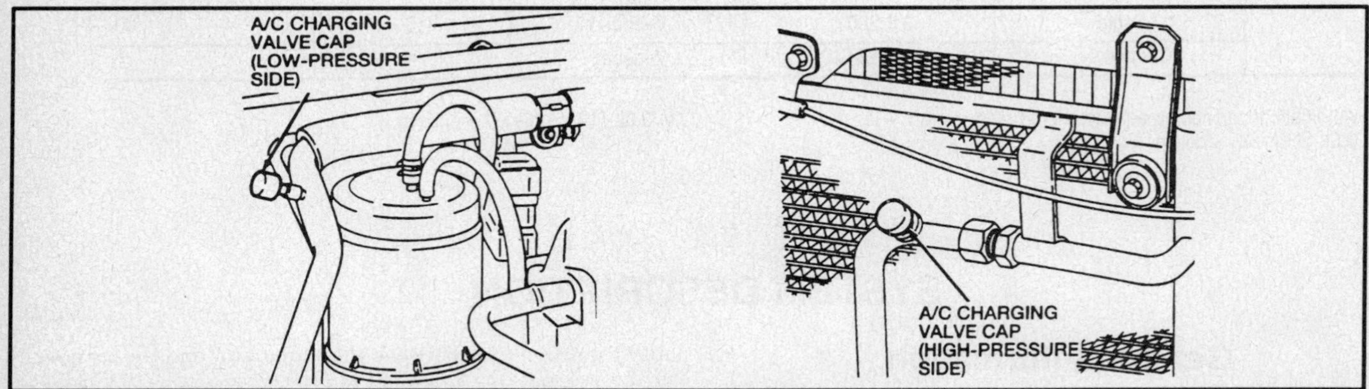

Service gauge port valve locations—Aspire

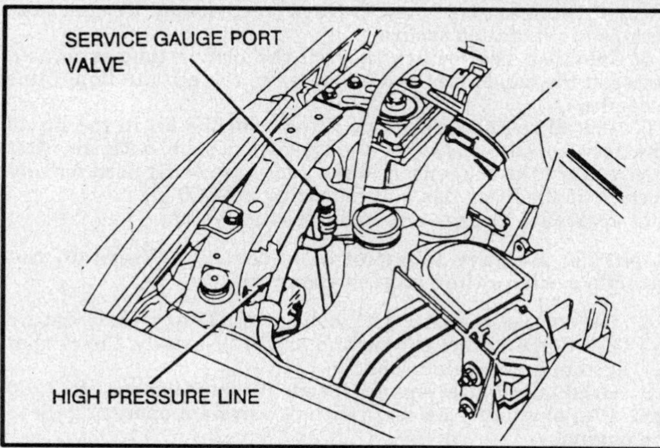

High pressure service gauge port valve location—Escort and Tracer

3. Once the recycling station has evacuated the vehicle air conditioning system, close the station inlet valve, if equipped. Then switch **OFF** the electrical power.
4. Allow the vehicle air conditioning system to remain closed for about 2 minutes. Observe the system vacuum level as shown on the gauge. If the pressure does not rise, disconnect the recycling station hose(s).
5. If the system pressure rises, repeat Steps 2, 3 and 4 until the vacuum level remains stable for 2 minutes.

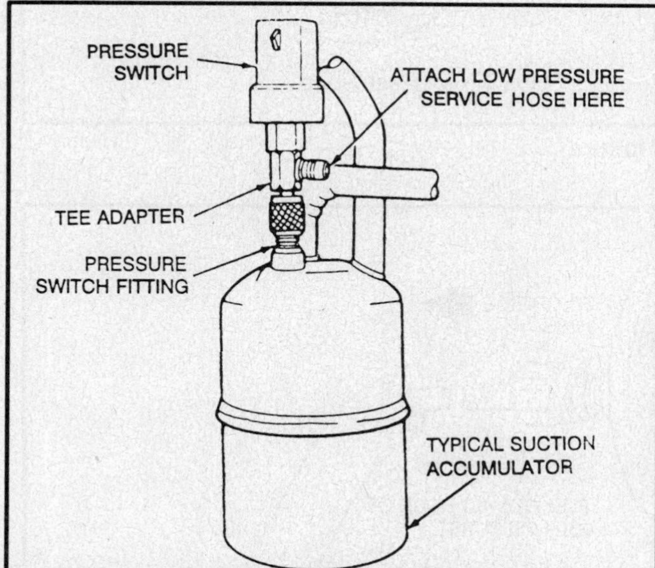

Tee adapter tool installation—fixed orifice tube system

System Flushing

A refrigerant system can become badly contaminated for a number of reasons:

- The compressor may have failed due to damage or wear.
- The compressor may have been run for some time with a severe leak or an opening in the system.
- The system may have been damaged by a collision and left open for some time.

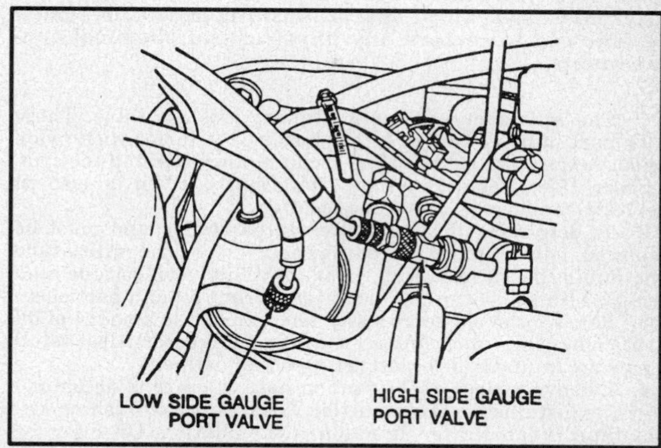

Service gauge port valve locations—Capri

- The system may not have been cleaned properly after a previous failure.
- The system may have been operated for a time with water or moisture in it.
- The system may have had the wrong type refrigerant or refrigerant oil installed.

A badly contaminated system contains water, carbon and other decomposition products. When this condition exists, the system must be flushed with a special flushing agent using equipment designed specially for this purpose.

Flushing Agents

To be suitable as a flushing agent, a refrigerant must remain in liquid state during the flushing operation in order to wash the inside surfaces of the system components. Refrigerant vapor will not remove contaminant particles. They must be flushed with a liquid.

R-113 will do the best job and is recommended as a flushing refrigerant. Both R-11 and R-113 require a propellant or pump type flushing equipment due to their low closed container pressures. R-12 can be used as a propellant with either flushing refrigerant (except in R-134a systems). R-11 is available in pressurized containers. Although not recommended for regular use, it may become necessary to use R-11 if special flushing equipment is not available. R-11 is more toxic than other refrigerants and should be handled with extra care.

Special Flushing Equipment

Special refrigerant system flushing equipment is available from a number of air conditioning equipment manufacturers and usually comes in kit form. A flushing kit, such as model 015–00205, or equivalent, consists of a cylinder for the flushing agent, a nozzle to introduce the flushing agent into the system and a connecting hose.

A second type of equipment, which must be connected into the system, allows for the continuous circulation of the flushing agent through the system. Contaminants are trapped by an external filter/drier. If this equipment is used, follow the manufacturer's instructions and observe all safety precautions.

Flushing After Compressor Failure (Fixed Orifice Tube Systems)

NOTE: A new flushing procedure has been developed to be used whenever a compressor failure occurs due to internal causes. These special flushing procedures must be followed to remove any physical and chemical contaminants.

1. The manufacturer has 2 filtering kits available. Those with part number suffix "A" are hosed on vehicles with nylon lined suction hose between the accumulator/drier and the compressor. If kit has part number with suffix "B", it is used on rubber-lined hose at this same location.
2. To determine if the compressor has failed and must be replaced, follow proper procedures and remove the orifice tube and liquid line, if necessary. Look for a dirty orifice tube and/or a liquid line containing black refrigerant oil and particles.
3. Remove the old compressor and adjust the amount of oil in the new compressor. Install the new compressor. Also install a new accumulator/drier, including oil adjustment.
4. Remove a piece of the suction hose in order to accommodate the installation of the suction filter from the flushing kit. The filter is labeled for direction of installation. On filter for nylon lined hose, use 2 new O-rings on each end. Be sure hose clamps are installed securely.
5. Install a new orifice tube (if the orifice tube is located between the condenser and evaporator, replace the liquid line assembly).
6. Install the pancake style filter from the kit in the liquid line between the condenser and the orifice tube, with the filter inlet toward the condenser. Make sure hose being used for connection of the filter has a burst rating of 2500 psi.
7. Evacuate, charge and leak test the system.

NOTE: Be sure location of hoses and filters do not interfere with other engine components.

8. Set control to **MAX A/C**, blower on **HI** and temperature to FULL COOL. Start engine and let it idle briefly. Check that A/C system is working properly.
9. Gradually raise engine speed, in short stages, to 1200 rpm. Run engine for an hour with A/C system operating. Stop the engine.
10. Allow the engine to cool. Discharge the system properly. Remove the fittings, flexible hoses and pancake filter. Discard the pancake filter.
11. Properly reconnect the liquid line back into the system. Again, evacuate, charge and leak test the system. Check system operation.

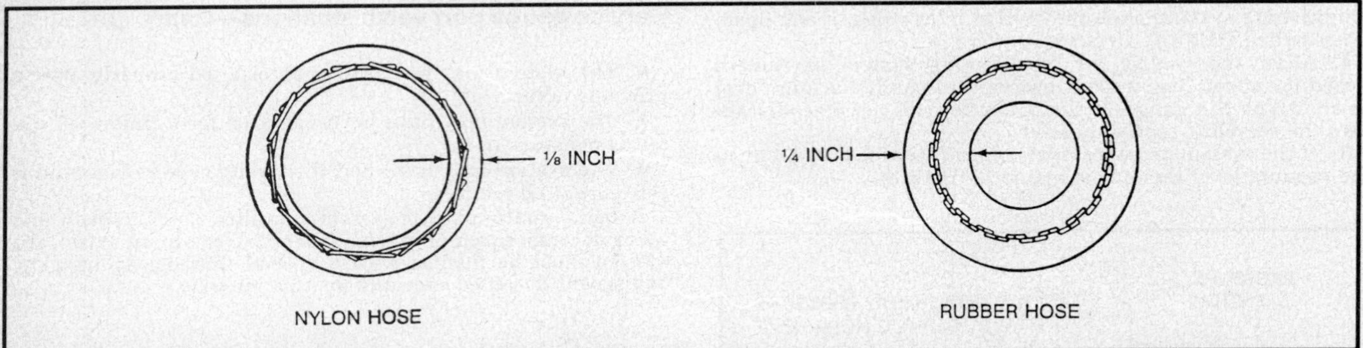

Identifying suction hose type for flushing after compressor failure

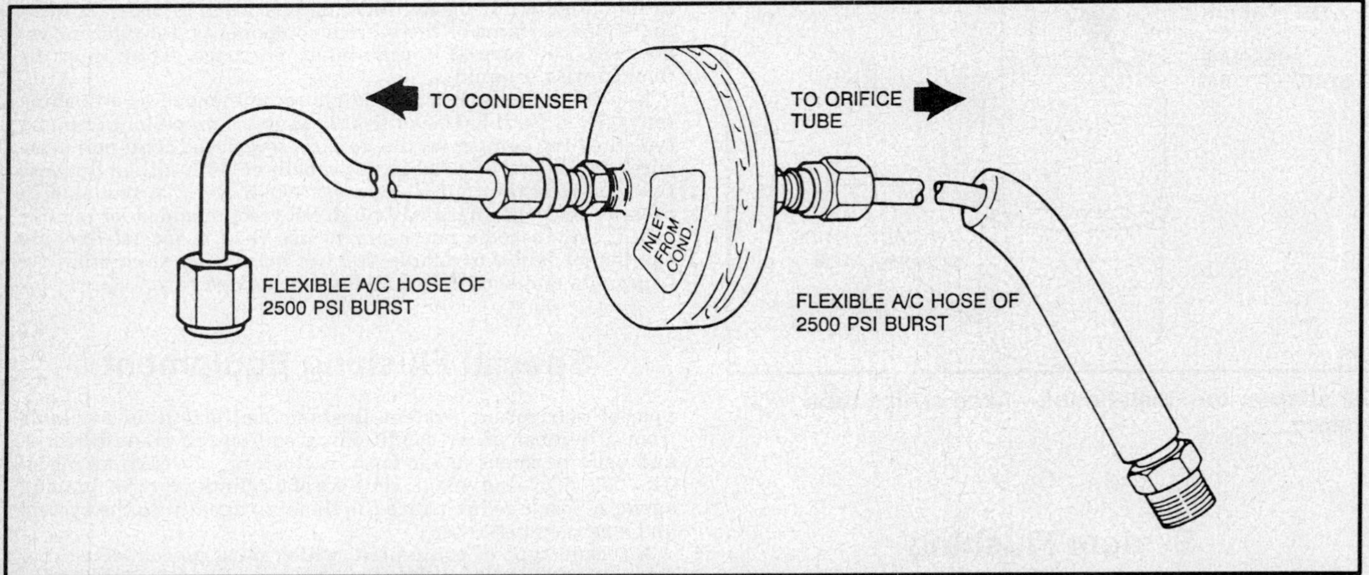

Pancake filter installation for flushing after compressor failure

System Evacuating

1. Connect a manifold gauge set as follows:
   - Turn both manifold gauge set valves fully to the right, to close the high and low pressure hoses to the center manifold and hose.
   - Remove the caps from the high and low pressure service gauge port valves.
   - If the manifold gauge set hoses do not have valve depressing pins in them, install fitting adapters T71P–19703–S and R or equivalent, which have pins, on the low and high pressure hoses.
   - Connect the high and low pressure hoses, or adapters, to the respective high and low pressure service gauge port valves. High side adapter set D81L–19703–A or tool YT-354 or 355 or equivalent is required to connect a manifold gauge set or charging station to the high pressure gauge port valve.

NOTE: Service tee fitting D87P–19703–A, which may be mounted on the clutch cycling pressure switch fitting, is available for use in the low pressure side of fixed orifice tube systems, to be used in place of the low pressure gauge port valve.

2. Leak test all connections and components with flame-type leak detector 023–00006 or equivalent, or electronic leak detector 055–00014, 055–00015 or equivalent.

CAUTION

Fumes from flame-type leak detectors are noxious, avoid inhaling fumes or personal injury may result.

NOTE: Good ventilation is necessary in the area where air conditioning leak testing is to be done. If the surrounding air is contaminated with refrigerant gas, the leak detector will indicate this gas all the time. Odors from other chemicals such as anti-freeze, diesel fuel, disc brake cleaner or other cleaning solvents can cause the same problem. A fan, even in a well ventilated area, is very helpful in removing small traces of air contamination that might affect the leak detector.

Standard tracer dyes cannot be used with R-134a systems. Be sure to check leak dye applications prior to using.

3. Properly discharge the refrigerant system.
4. Make sure both manifold gauge valves are turned fully to the right. Make sure the center hose connection at the manifold gauge is tight.
5. Connect the manifold gauge set center hose to a vacuum pump.
6. Open the manifold gauge set valves and start the vacuum pump.
7. Evacuate the system with the vacuum pump until the low pressure gauge reads at least 25 in. Hg or as close to 30 in. Hg as possible. Continue to operate the vacuum pump for 15 minutes. If a part of the system has been replaced, continue to operate the vacuum pump for another 20–30 minutes.
8. When evacuation of the system is complete, close the manifold gauge set valves and turn the vacuum pump **OFF**.
9. Observe the low pressure gauge for 5 minutes to ensure that system vacuum is held. If vacuum is held, charge the system. If vacuum is not held for 5 minutes, leak test the system, service the leaks and evacuate the system again.

System Charging

NOTE: Be sure to use dedicated equipment while charging systems using R-134a refrigerant.

1. Connect a manifold gauge set according to the proper procedure. Properly discharge and evacuate the system.
2. With the manifold gauge set valves closed to the center hose, disconnect the vacuum pump from the manifold gauge set.
3. Connect the center hose of the manifold gauge set to a refrigerant drum or a small can refrigerant dispensing valve tool YT-280, YT-1034 or equivalent. If a small can dispensing valve is used, install the small can(s) on the dispensing valve.

NOTE: Use only a safety type dispensing valve. Manufacturer does not recommend the use of small cans for charging as exact level of refrigerant charge cannot be managed with small cans.

4. Loosen the center hose at the manifold gauge set and open the refrigerant drum valve or small can dispensing valve. Allow the refrigerant to escape to purge air and moisture from the center hose. Then, tighten the center hose connection at the manifold gauge set.
5. Disconnect the wire harness snap lock connector from the clutch cycling or low pressure switch and install a jumper wire across the 2 terminals of the connector.
6. Open the manifold gauge set low side valve to allow refrigerant to enter the system. Keep the refrigerant can in an upright position.

CAUTION

Do not open the manifold gauge set high pressure (discharge) gauge valve when charging with a small container. Opening the valve can cause the small refrigerant container to explode, which can result in personal injury.

7. When no more refrigerant is being drawn into the system, start the engine and set the control assembly for **MAX COLD** and **HI** blower to draw the remaining refrigerant into the system. If equipped, press the air conditioning switch. Continue to add refrigerant to the system until the specified weight is in the system. Then close the manifold gauge set low pressure valve and the refrigerant supply valve.
8. Remove the jumper wire from the clutch cycling or low pressure switch snap lock connector. Connect the connector to the pressure switch.
9. Operate the system until pressures stabilize to verify normal operation and system pressures.
10. In high ambient temperatures, it may be necessary to operate a high volume fan positioned to blow air through the radiator and condenser to aid in cooling the engine and prevent excessive refrigerant system pressures.
11. When charging is completed and system operating pressures are normal, disconnect the manifold gauge set from the vehicle. Install the protective caps on the service gauge port valves.

SYSTEM COMPONENTS

Radiator

REMOVAL AND INSTALLATION

Taurus, Sable and Continental with 3.0L, 3.2L or 3.8L Engine

1. Disconnect the negative battery cable.
2. Properly drain the cooling system.

3. Remove the rubber overflow tube from the coolant recovery bottle and detach it from the radiator.
4. Remove 2 upper shroud retaining screws and lift the shroud from the lower retaining clips.
5. Disconnect the electric cooling fan motor wires and remove the fan and shroud assembly.
6. Loosen the upper and lower radiator hoses.
7. If equipped with an automatic transaxle, disconnect the transmission oil cooling lines from the radiator fittings using disconnect tool T82L-9500-AH or equivalent.
8. If equipped with 3.0L SHO engine, remove 2 radiator upper retaining screws. If equipped with the 3.8L engine, remove 2 hex nuts from the right radiator support bracket and 2 screws from the left radiator support bracket and remove the brackets.
9. Tilt the radiator rearward approximately 1 in. and lift it directly upward, clear of the radiator support.
10. Remove the radiator lower support rubber pads, if pad replacement is necessary.

To install:

11. Position the radiator lower support rubber pads to the lower support, if previously removed.
12. Position the radiator into the engine compartment and to the radiator support. Insert the molded pins at the bottom of each tank through the slotted holes in the lower support rubber pads.
13. Make sure the plastic pads on the bottom of the radiator tanks are resting on the rubber pads. Install 2 upper retaining bolts to attach the radiator to the radiator support. Tighten the bolts to 46–60 inch lbs. (5–7 Nm). If equipped with the 3.8L engine, tighten the bolts to 13–20 ft. lbs. (17–27 Nm).
14. If equipped with the 3.8L engine, fasten the left radiator support bracket to the radiator support with 2 screws. Tighten the screws to 8.7–17.7 ft. lbs. (11.8–24 Nm). Attach the right support bracket to the radiator support with 2 hex nuts. Tighten the nuts to 8.7–17.7 ft. lbs. (11.8–24 Nm).
15. Attach the radiator upper and lower hoses to the radiator. Position the hose on the radiator connector so the index arrow on the hose is in line with the mark on the connector. If equipped with the 3.8L engine, install constant tension hose clamps between the alignment marks on the hoses.
16. If equipped with automatic transaxles, connect the transmission cooler lines using oil resistant pipe sealer.
17. Install the fan and shroud assembly by connecting the fan motor wiring and positioning the assembly on the lower retainer clips. Attach the top of the shroud to the radiator with 2 screw, nut and washer assemblies. Tighten to 35 inch lbs. (4 Nm).
18. Attach the rubber overflow tube to the radiator filler neck overflow nipple and coolant recovery bottle.
19. Refill the cooling system. If the coolant is being replaced, refill with a 50/50 mixture of water and anti-freeze. Connect the negative battery cable. Operate the engine for 15 minutes and check for leaks. Check the coolant level and add, as required.

Continental with 4.6L Engine

NOTE: When the battery has been disconnected or reconnected, some abnormal drive symptoms may occur while the powertrain control module (PCM) relearns its adaptive strategy. The vehicle may need to be driven 10 miles (18 km) or more to relearn the strategy.

1. Drain the engine cooling system. Disconnect the battery ground cable.
2. Remove the engine air cleaner.
3. Remove the upper radiator hose from the water bypass tube.
4. Remove the radiator overflow hose from the radiator and fan shroud.

NOTE: Loosen the transmission oil cooler tubes while holding the radiator connector with a back-up wrench.

5. Remove the transmission oil cooler tube from the oil cooler inlet fitting.
6. Remove the nuts retaining the A/C condenser core to the radiator.
7. Disconnect the engine control sensor wiring from the cooling fan motors and the CCRM.
8. Raise the vehicle on a hoist.
9. Remove the splash shield from the lower radiator support and front sub-frame.
10. Remove the lower radiator hose from the radiator.

NOTE: Loosen transmission oil cooler tubes while holding radiator connector with a back-up wrench.

11. Remove the oil cooler tube from the oil cooler outlet fitting on radiator.
12. Remove the retaining screws for the power steering/transaxle oil cooler and position the cooler aside.
13. Support the fan shroud, radiator and A/C condenser core with a suitable jack stand. Remove the lower radiator support.
14. Position the jack stand aside and carefully remove the radiator and fan shroud.
15. Remove 2 retaining bolts for the fan shroud at the top of the radiator and remove the fan shroud from the radiator.
16. Remove the upper radiator hose from the radiator.
17. Installation is the reverse of the removal procedure.
    - Tighten the fan shroud bolts and A/C condenser core nuts to the radiator to 24–48 inch lbs. (2.7–5.4 Nm).
    - Tighten the lower radiator support retaining bolts to 71–97 inch lbs. (8–11 Nm).
    - Tighten the transmission oil cooler tubes to the fittings to 18–21 inch lbs. (24.4–28.5 Nm).
    - Tighten the power steering/transaxle oil cooler and splash shield retaining screws securely.

Tempo and Topaz

1. Remove the negative battery cable.
2. Drain coolant from cooling system. Retain coolant in a suitable container for reuse.
3. Remove upper hose from radiator.
4. Remove 2 fasteners retaining upper end of fan shroud to radiator and sight shield.
5. If equipped with air conditioning, remove nut and screw retaining upper end of fan shroud to radiator at cross support, and nut and screw at inlet end of tank.
6. Disconnect electric cooling fan motor wires and air conditioning discharge line, if equipped, from shroud and remove fan shroud from vehicle.
7. Disconnect lower hose from radiator.
8. Disconnect overflow hose from radiator filler neck.
9. If equipped with an automatic transaxle, disconnect oil cooler hoses at transaxle using a quick-disconnect tool. Cap oil tubes and plug oil cooler hoses.
10. Remove 2 nuts retaining top of radiator to radiator support. If stud loosens, ensure it is tightened before radiator is installed. Tilt the top of radiator rearward to allow clearance with upper mounting stud and lift radiator from vehicle. Ensure mounts do not stick to radiator lower mounting brackets.

To install:

11. Ensure that lower radiator mounts are installed over bolts on the radiator support.
12. Position radiator to radiator support making sure radiator lower brackets are positioned properly on lower mounts.
13. Position top of radiator to mounting studs on radiator support and install 2 retaining nuts. Tighten to 5–7 ft. lbs. (7–9.5 Nm).
14. Connect radiator lower hose to engine water pump inlet tube. Install constant tension hose clamp between alignment marks on the hose.

15. Check to ensure radiator lower hose is properly positioned on outlet tank and install constant tension hose clamp. The stripe on lower hose should be indexed with rib on tank outlet.
16. Connect oil cooler hoses to automatic transaxle oil cooler lines, if equipped. Use an appropriate oil resistant sealer.
17. Position fan shroud to radiator lower mounting bosses. If with air conditioning, insert lower edge of shroud into clip at lower center of radiator. Install 2 nuts and bolts retaining upper end of fan shroud to radiator. Tighten nuts to 31–41 inch lbs. (3.5–4.6 Nm). Do not overtighten.
18. Connect electric cooling fan motor wires to wire harness.
19. Connect upper hose to radiator inlet tank fitting and install constant tension hose clamp.
20. Connect overflow hose to nipple just below radiator filler neck.
21. Install air intake tube or sight shield.
22. Connect negative battery cable.
23. Refill cooling system. Start engine and allow to come to normal operating temperature. Check for leaks. Confirm operation of electric cooling fan.

Contour and Mystique

1. Drain the engine cooling system.
2. Disconnect the battery ground cable.
3. Remove the upper radiator hose from radiator.
4. On 2.5L engine equipped vehicles, remove the radiator overflow hose from the radiator.
5. Remove the transmission oil cooler tube from oil cooler inlet fitting (if equipped).
6. Remove the nuts retaining the fan shroud to the radiator.
7. Raise the vehicle on a hoist.
8. Remove the lower radiator hose from the radiator.

NOTE: Loosen transmission oil cooler tubes while holding radiator connector with a back-up wrench.

9. Remove the oil cooler tube from the oil cooler outlet fitting on radiator (if equipped).
10. Support the fan shroud, radiator and A/C condenser core with a suitable jack stand. Remove the lower radiator supports from front sub-frame and radiator.
11. Remove 2 retaining bolts for the A/C condenser core from brackets at bottom of radiator.
12. Position the jack stand aside and carefully remove the radiator.
13. Installation is the reverse of the removal procedure.
    - Tighten the fan shroud nuts and A/C condenser core bolts to radiator to 24–48 inch lbs. (2.7–5.4 Nm).
    - Tighten the lower radiator support retaining bolts to 71–97 inch lbs. (8–11 Nm).
    - If equipped, tighten the transmission oil cooler tube to the fitting to 18–29 ft. lbs. (24–31 Nm).

Escort, Tracer and Aspire

1. Disconnect the negative battery cable.
2. Raise and safely support the vehicle. Drain the cooling system.
3. Remove the right side and front splash shields and remove the lower radiator hose.
4. If equipped with automatic transaxle, remove the lower oil cooler line from the radiator. Remove the oil cooler line brackets from the bottom of the radiator.
5. Lower the vehicle.
6. If equipped with automatic transaxle and air conditioning, remove the seal located between the radiator and fan shroud.
7. If equipped with automatic transaxle, remove the upper oil cooler line from the radiator.
8. If equipped with 1.8L engine, remove the resonance duct from the radiator mounts.
9. Disconnect the cooling fan motor electrical connector and the cooling fan thermoswitch electrical connector.
10. Remove the 3 fan shroud attaching bolts and remove the shroud assembly by pulling it straight up.
11. On 1.9L equipped vehicles with A/C, remove the upper radiator air deflector from the radiator and position it out of the way.
12. Remove the upper radiator hose and the 2 upper radiator isomounts. Remove the radiator by lifting it straight up.

To install:

13. Make sure the radiator lower isomounts are installed over the bolts on the radiator support.
14. Position the radiator to the radiator support, making sure the radiator lower brackets are positioned properly on the lower isomounts.
15. Install the radiator upper isomounts, making sure the radiator locating pegs are positioned correctly. Install the upper radiator hose.
16. On 1.9L equipped vehicles with A/C, position the upper radiator air deflector on the radiator.
17. Lower the cooling fan shroud assembly into place and install the 3 shroud attaching bolts.
18. Connect the cooling fan motor electrical connector and thermoswitch electrical connector.
19. If equipped with 1.8L engine, install the resonance duct on the radiator isomounts.
20. Install the upper oil cooler line on the radiator.
21. If equipped with automatic transaxle and air conditioning, install the seal between the radiator and fan shroud.
22. Raise and safely support the vehicle. Install the lower oil cooler line on the radiator.
23. Install the lower radiator hose and install the right side and front splash shields.
24. Lower the vehicle and fill the cooling system.
25. Connect the negative battery cable, start the engine and check for coolant leaks.

Probe

1. Disconnect the negative battery cable and the cooling fan wiring harness connectors.
2. Remove the radiator pressure cap from the filler neck.

CAUTION

If the system is hot and pressurized, be careful to release the pressure before removing the cap fully.

3. On 2.0L and 2.5L engines, remove the air duct. Disconnect the overflow tube from the filler neck (except 2.5L engines).
4. Properly drain the cooling system.
5. On 2.5L engines, disconnect the expansion tank upper and lower hoses from the radiator and remove the overflow hose from the expansion tank. Remove the expansion tank.
6. Disconnect the upper and lower radiator hoses.
7. Disconnect and plug the cooler lines, if equipped with an automatic transaxle.
8. Remove the radiator mounting bolts.
9. Remove the radiator and the cooling fan as a complete assembly.
10. Remove the fan shroud mounting bolts.
11. Remove the fan and shroud assembly from the radiator.

To install:

12. Install the fan and shroud assembly. Tighten the mounting bolts to 61–87 inch lbs. (7–10 Nm).
13. Install the radiator, making sure the lower tank engages the insulators.
14. Install the upper radiator insulators and tighten the retaining bolts to 69–95 inch lbs. (8–11 Nm).
15. Unplug and connect the cooler lines, if required.
16. Reattach the wiring harness and install the upper and lower radiator hoses to the radiator.

17. Connect the overflow tube to the radiator and connect the cooling fan wiring connectors. Reinstall the expansion tank, if removed.
18. Close the radiator drain valve and fill the system with coolant.
19. Warm the engine to pressurize the system and check for leaks.
20. Recheck the coolant level and refill if necessary.

Capri

1. Disconnect the negative battery cable and the cooling fan wire harness connector.
2. Remove the radiator pressure cap from the filler neck. If the system is hot and pressurized, be careful to release the pressure before fully opening. Drain the cooling system at the draincock, located at the bottom left end of the radiator.
3. Disconnect the radiator upper and lower hoses from the radiator inlet and outlet.
4. Disconnect the overflow tube from the filler neck and disengage the wiring harness from the routing clips attached to the cooling fan shroud.
5. If equipped with automatic transaxle, disconnect and plug the cooler lines.
6. Remove the 6 bolts retaining the radiator upper tank brackets to the radiator core support. Remove the radiator and cooling fan as an assembly.
7. Remove the 4 bolts attaching the fan shroud assembly and remove the fan and shroud assembly.

To install:

8. Place the fan and shroud assembly against the rear of the radiator and secure with the 4 bolts. Tighten the bolts to 23–33 ft. lbs. (31–46 Nm).
9. Make sure the radiator insulators are positioned on the radiator supports. Position the radiator, making sure the lower tank engages the insulators.
10. Install the 6 radiator retaining bolts through the top tank mounting brackets into the core support. Make sure the insulators are aligned.
11. Unplug and connect the automatic transaxle oil cooler lines, if equipped.
12. Secure the wire harness in the routing clips.
13. Connect the upper and lower hoses to the radiator inlet and outlet. Connect the overflow tube to the radiator filler neck.
14. Close the radiator draincock and fill the cooling system. Install the pressure cap.
15. Connect the cooling fan harness connector and the negative battery cable. Start the engine and check for leaks.
16. Check the coolant level and fill as necessary.

Festiva

1. Disconnect the negative battery cable. Properly drain the cooling system.
2. Disconnect the coolant recovery hose from the filler neck.
3. Remove the upper radiator hose.
4. Disconnect the cooling fan wiring harness connector. Disengage the wiring harness from the routing clamp on the cooling fan shroud.
5. Remove the lower radiator hose.
6. Support the radiator by hand and remove the 4 bolts attaching the radiator support brackets to the vehicle body. Raise the radiator/cooling fan/shroud assembly from the crossmember mounting insulator supports and remove from vehicle. Disconnect the cooling fan and shroud from the radiator as required.

To install:

7. Lower the radiator into the normal operating position making certain the mounting insulators engage with their supports. Attach the radiator to the support brackets with the 4 bolts.
8. Connect the upper and lower radiator hoses. Connect the overflow hose. Connect the fan wiring connectors.
9. Close the drain valve and lower the vehicle. Connect the negative battery cable. Fill the cooling system to the proper level.
10. Start the engine and allow to reach normal operating temperature. Inspect for coolant leaks and correct as required.

COOLING SYSTEM BLEEDING

When the entire cooling system is drained, the following procedure should be used to ensure a complete fill.

1. Install the block drain plug, if removed, and close the draincock. With the engine OFF, add anti-freeze to the radiator to a level of 50 percent of the total cooling system capacity. Then add water until it reaches the radiator filler neck seat.
2. Install the radiator cap to the first notch to keep spillage to a minimum.
3. Start the engine and let it idle until the upper radiator hose is warm. This indicates that the thermostat is open and coolant is flowing through the entire system.
4. Carefully remove the radiator cap and top off the radiator with water. Install the cap on the radiator securely.
5. Fill the coolant recovery reservoir to the FULL COLD mark with anti-freeze, then add water to the FULL HOT mark. This will ensure that a proper mixture is in the coolant recovery bottle.
6. Check for leaks at the draincock and block plug.

Cooling Fan

TESTING

Taurus, Sable and Continental

1. Disconnect the wiring connector from the fan motor.
2. Connect a jumper wire from the positive terminal of the battery to one of the terminals in the cooling fan electrical connector.
3. Ground the other connector terminal.
4. If the cooling fan does not function, it must be replaced.
5. If the cooling fan functions, but does not run during normal engine operation, check the cooling fan temperature sensor and the integrated relay control assembly.

Tempo and Topaz

1. Check fuse or circuit breaker for power to cooling fan motor.
2. Remove connector(s) at cooling fan motor(s). Connect jumper wire and apply battery voltage to the positive terminal of the cooling fan motor.
3. Using an ohmmeter, check for continuity in cooling fan motor.

NOTE: Remove the cooling fan connector at the fan motor before performing continuity checks. Perform continuity check of the motor windings only. The cooling fan control circuit is connected electrically to the ECM through the cooling fan relay center. Ohmmeter battery voltage must not be applied to the ECM.

4. Ensure proper continuity of cooling fan motor ground circuit at chassis ground connector.

Escort, Tracer and Aspire

1. Make sure the ignition key is **OFF**.
2. Apply 12 volts to the **Y** wire at the cooling fan motor on all except 1.8L vehicles equipped with 4EAT automatic transaxle or 1.9L vehicles equipped with air conditioning. Replace the motor if it does not run.
3. On 1.8L vehicles equipped with 4EAT automatic transaxle or 1.9L vehicles equipped with air conditioning, apply 12

volts to the **BL** wire (1.8L) or the **LG/Y** wire (1.9L) at the cooling fan motor. Replace the motor if it does not run.

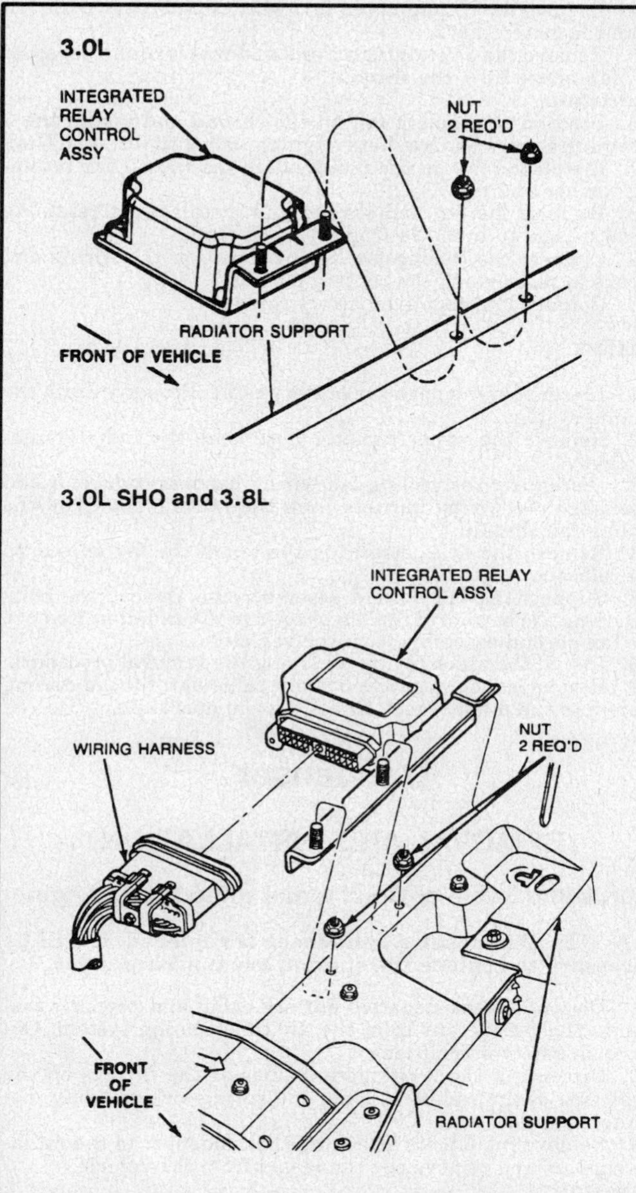

Integrated relay control module location—Taurus and Sable

Probe

With the key **ON** and the engine warmed, disconnect the coolant temperature switch and ground the connector BK/GRN terminal. The fan should operate, if not, check the motor.

Capri

1. Make sure the ignition switch is **OFF**.
2. Locate the cooling fan motor connector and ground the **Y/GN** wire at the connector.
3. If the cooling fan motor does not turn ON, replace it.

Festiva

RADIATOR FAN SWITCH

The cooling fan temperature switch is threaded into the front side of the thermostat housing. The thermoswitch continuity test should be conducted when the coolant temperature is above and below the normal cut-in point of the switch (207°F).

CAUTION

To avoid the possibly of personal injury or damage to the vehicle, make certain that the ignition switch is in the OFF position before disconnecting the wire from the cooling fan temperature switch. If the wire is disconnected from the switch with the ignition switch in the ON position, the cooling fan may turn ON. The maximum amount of time the engine is allowed to operate with the thermo switch disconnected is 2 minutes.

1. Turn the ignition switch to the **OFF** position. With the engine coolant below 207°F, disconnect the thermo switch connector.
2. Using a test meter, check for continuity across the green wire terminal of the switch and ground. At this temperature, continuity should be read across the switch.
3. Connect the thermo switch connector. Start the engine and allow the coolant to reach normal operating temperature (above 207°F).
4. Disconnect the thermo switch connector and check for continuity across the switch as described in Step 2. At this temperature, there should be no continuity across the switch.
5. Secure the engine and connect the thermo switch connector. Replace the thermo switch as required.

Contour and Mystique

COOLING FAN RELAY

The cooling fan relay is located in the left front corner of the engine compartment between the battery and the headlight. The relay is surrounded by a protective boot and is secured to the inner fender panel.

1. Turn the ignition switch to the **OFF** position.
2. Using a test meter, check for continuity across the green/yellow and black/red wire terminals. If continuity is not present, replace the cooling fan relay.

REMOVAL AND INSTALLATION

Taurus, Sable and Continental

1. Disconnect negative battery cable. Remove radiator sight shield.
2. Disconnect the wiring connector from the fan motor. Remove the integrated relay control assembly from the radiator support. If fan wiring is clipped to the shroud, free it for removal.
3. On Continental, remove the air bag sensor.
4. Unbolt the fan and shroud assembly from the radiator. Rotate the fan and shroud assembly and remove upwards past the radiator.
5. Remove the retaining U-clip from the motor shaft and remove the fan.

NOTE: A metal burr may be present on the motor shaft after the retaining clip has been removed. If necessary, remove the burr to facilitate fan removal.

6. Unbolt and withdraw the fan motor from the shroud.
7. Install in the reverse order of removal.

Tempo and Topaz

NOTE: Fan motors on 2.3L and 3.0L engines are similar in design, but cannot be interchanged. Improper application could cause vehicle to overheat or early motor burnout.

1. Disconnect negative battery cable.
2. Disconnect the wiring connector from the fan motor. Disconnect the wire loom from the clip on the shroud by pushing down on the lock fingers and pulling the connector from the motor end.
3. Remove the nuts retaining the fan motor and shroud assembly and remove from the vehicle.
4. Remove the retaining clip from the motor shaft and remove the fan.

NOTE: A metal burr may be present on the motor shaft after the retaining clip has been removed. If necessary, remove burr to facilitate fan removal.

5. Unbolt and withdraw the fan motor from the shroud.

To install:

6. Install the fan motor in position in the fan shroud. Install the retaining nuts and washers and tighten to 44–66 inch lbs.
7. Position the fan assembly on the motor shaft and install the retaining clip.
8. Position the fan, motor and shroud as an assembly in the vehicle. Install the retaining nuts and tighten to 31–41 inch lbs.
9. Install the fan motor wire loom in the clip provided on the fan shroud. Connect the wiring connector to the fan motor. Be sure the lock fingers on the connector snap firmly into place.
10. Reconnect battery cable.
11. Check the fan for proper operation.

Escort, Tracer and Aspire

1. Disconnect the negative battery cable.
2. On 1.8L engine equipped vehicles, remove the resonance duct from the radiator isomounts.
3. Disconnect the cooling fan motor electrical connector.
4. Remove the 3 shroud attaching bolts and remove the cooling fan shroud assembly by pulling it straight up.
5. Working on a bench, remove the cooling fan retainer clip. Remove the cooling fan from the motor shaft.
6. Unclip the cooling fan motor electrical harness retainers and remove the harness from the retainers.
7. Remove the cooling fan motor attaching screws and remove the cooling fan motor from the shroud assembly.
8. To install, reverse the removal procedure.

Probe

NOTE: Probe models require radiator removal before fan assemblies can be removed from the radiator.

1. Disconnect the negative battery cable.
2. Disconnect the cooling fan electrical connectors.
3. Remove the fan shroud-to-radiator screws and the fan/shroud assembly.
4. If removing the fan motor from the shroud, perform the following:
   - Remove the fan blade-to-motor nut and washer.
   - Remove the fan motor-to-shroud bolts and the motor.
5. To install, reverse the removal procedures.

Capri

1. Disconnect the negative battery cable.
2. Disengage the fan wiring harness from the routing clamps and separate the cooling fan wiring connector.
3. Remove the 4 screws retaining the fan shroud to the radiator and remove the fan and shroud.
4. Remove the retaining nut and washer and remove the fan from the motor shaft.
5. Remove the 3 retaining screws and washers and separate the fan motor from the shroud.

To install:

6. Position the cooling fan on the shroud and install the 3 retaining screws and washers. Tighten to 3–4 ft. lbs. (4–6 Nm).
7. Install the fan on the motor shaft and install the retaining washer and nut.
8. Position the fan and shroud and install the 4 retaining screws. Tighten to 23–34 ft. lbs. (31–46 Nm).
9. Connect the cooling fan wiring. Position the wiring and secure in place using the routing clamps.
10. Connect the negative battery cable.

Festiva

1. Disconnect the negative battery cable. Properly drain the cooling system.
2. Remove the upper radiator hose from the radiator connection.
3. Disconnect the cooling fan wiring harness connector and disengage the wiring harness from the routing clamp on the cooling fan shroud.
4. Remove the bolts attaching the top of the fan shroud to the radiator.
5. Support the fan shroud assembly and remove the bolts attaching the bottom of the fan shroud to the radiator. Remove the fan shroud assembly from the vehicle.
6. Install the assembly by reversing the removal procedure.
7. Reconnect the negative battery cable and fill the cooling system to the proper level. Check system operation.

Condenser

REMOVAL AND INSTALLATION

Taurus and Sable or Continental without 4.6L Engine

NOTE: Whenever a condenser is replaced, it will be necessary to replace the suction accumulator/drier.

1. Disconnect the negative battery cable and properly discharge the refrigerant from the air conditioning system. Observe all safety precautions.
2. Disconnect the 2 refrigerant lines at the fittings on the right side of the radiator, using the spring-lock coupling disconnect procedure.
3. Remove the 4 bolts attaching the condenser to the radiator support and remove the condenser from the vehicle.

To install:

NOTE: Some models use R-134a refrigerant. System components, refrigerant, refrigerant oil and testing and recharging equipment are not compatible with similar items from R-12 systems. Be sure to use only the proper components, refrigerant, oil or equipment when servicing these systems.

4. Add 1 oz. (30 ml) of clean refrigerant oil if installing a new replacement condenser.
5. Position the condenser assembly to the radiator support brackets and install the attaching bolts.
6. Connect the refrigerant lines to the condenser assembly. Perform the spring-lock coupling connection procedure.
7. Leak test, evacuate and charge the refrigerant system following the proper procedures. Observe all safety precautions.

Continental with 4.6L Engine

NOTE: Whenever the air conditioner condenser core is replaced, it is necessary that the suction accumulator/drier also be replaced.

If an air conditioner condenser core leak is suspected, the condenser core must be leak-tested before it is removed from the vehicle.

1. Remove the radiator upper sight shield.

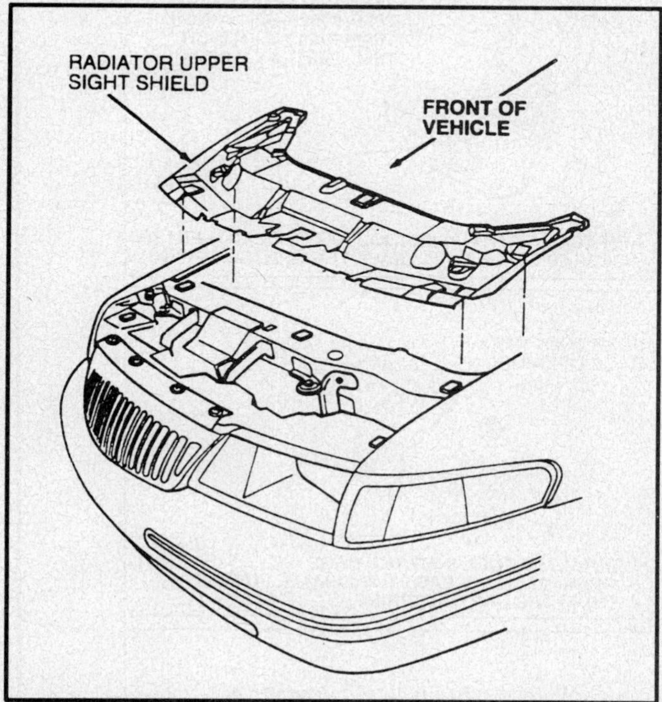

Radiator upper sight shield—Continental

2. Discharge the refrigerant from system at the service access gauge port valve location on the suction line. Observe all safety precautions.
3. Remove 2 nuts retaining the air conditioner condenser core to radiator.
4. Use mechanic's wire to temporarily suspend the radiator from the upper radiator support.
5. Raise the vehicle on a hoist.
6. Remove the radiator air deflector.
7. Remove 4 screws retaining the power steering/transaxle oil cooler to the lower radiator support and position the cooler aside.
8. Remove 6 retaining screws and lower the radiator support from vehicle.
9. Disconnect the condenser-to-evaporator tube from the condenser core outlet tube using Spring Lock Coupling Disconnect Tool T81P–19623–G2. Plug the lines to prevent dirt and excessive moisture from entering.
10. Disconnect the compressor-to-condenser discharge line from A/C manifold and tube using Spring Lock Coupling Disconnect Tool T81P–19623–G1. Plug the lines to prevent dirt and excessive moisture from entering.
11. Lift the condenser core off the support brackets on the radiator and lower the condenser core out of the vehicle.

To install:

12. If the air conditioner condenser core is to be replaced, add 1 oz (2.9 ml) of clean Motorcraft YN–12b refrigerant oil or equivalent meeting Ford specification WSH–M1C231–B to the condenser core.
13. Install the condenser core to radiator.
14. Remove the plugs from the 2 refrigerant lines and install new O-ring seals after dipping into clean refrigerant oil.
15. Connect the compressor-to-condenser discharge line to the manifold and tube and the condenser-to-evaporator tube to the condenser core outlet tube.
16. Install the lower radiator support with 6 retaining screws.
17. Install the power steering/transaxle oil cooler to the lower radiator support with 4 retaining screws.
18. Install the radiator air deflector.
19. Lower the vehicle to the floor.
20. Remove mechanic's wire temporarily securing the radiator to the upper radiator support and install 2 nuts retaining the air conditioner condenser core to radiator.
21. Leak-test, evacuate and charge the refrigerant system. Observe all safety precautions.
22. Install the radiator upper sight shield.
23. Check the air conditioning system for proper operation.

Tempo, Topaz, Contour and Mystique

NOTE: Whenever a condenser is replaced, it will be necessary to replace the suction accumulator/drier.

1. Disconnect the negative battery cable and properly discharge the refrigerant system. Observe all safety precautions.
2. Properly drain the cooling system.
3. Remove the ignition coil from the engine.
4. Remove the radiator from the vehicle.
5. Disconnect the liquid line and compressor discharge line. Perform the spring-lock coupling disconnect procedure.
6. Remove the condenser upper bracket attaching screws and remove the condenser from the vehicle.

To install:

7. Add 1 oz. (30 ml) of clean refrigerant oil if installing a new replacement condenser.
8. Position the condenser to the lower mounts. Move the top of the condenser forward and push the condenser into the radiator opening. Install the upper mounting brackets.
9. Using new special O-rings E1ZZ–19B596–A or E35Y–19D690–A or equivalent, lubricated with clean refrigerant oil, connect the liquid line and the compressor discharge line to the condenser.
10. Install the radiator.
11. Install the ignition coil on the engine.
12. Fill the cooling system to the correct level.
13. Leak test, evacuate and charge the refrigerant system. Observe all safety precautions.

Escort and Tracer

NOTE: If the condenser is replaced, it will be necessary to replace the suction accumulator/drier.

1. Disconnect the negative battery cable. Discharge the refrigerant from the air conditioning system.
2. Drain the cooling system and remove the radiator. Remove the radiator grille.
3. Disconnect the refrigerant lines from the condenser using the spring-lock coupling disconnect procedure. Plug all ports to prevent the entrance of dirt and moisture.
4. Remove the condenser mounting nuts from the mounting bracket and remove the condenser.

To install:

5. Add 1 oz. (30ml) of clean refrigerant oil if installing a new replacement condenser.
6. Position the condenser and install the mounting nuts.
7. Using new O-rings lubricated with clean refrigerant oil, connect the refrigerant lines to the condenser using the spring-lock coupling connect procedure.
8. Install the radiator grille. Install the radiator and fill the cooling system.
9. Connect the negative battery cable. Leak test, evacuate and charge the system. Observe all safety precautions.

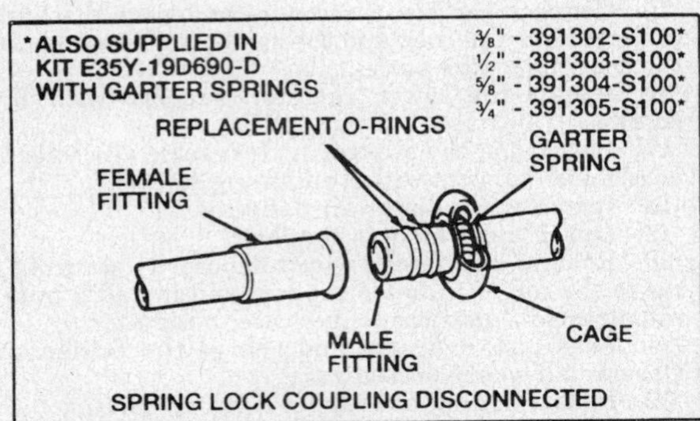

*ALSO SUPPLIED IN

TO CONNECT COUPLING

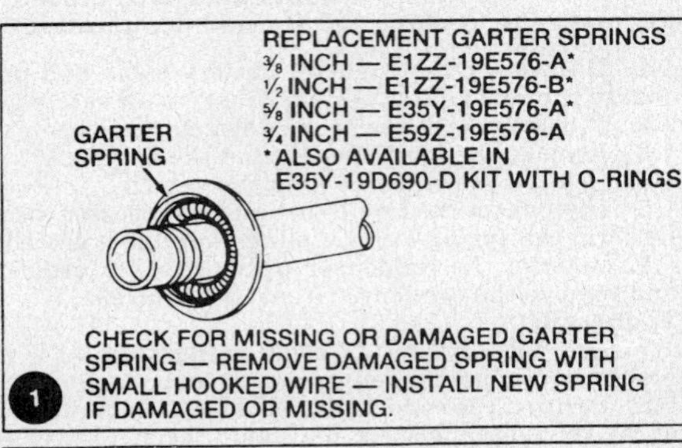

REPLACEMENT GARTER SPRINGS
3/8 INCH — E1ZZ-19E576-A*
1/2 INCH — E1ZZ-19E576-B*
5/8 INCH — E35Y-19E576-A*
3/4 INCH — E59Z-19E576-A
*ALSO AVAILABLE IN
E35Y-19D690-D KIT WITH O-RINGS
GARTER
SPRING

1. CHECK FOR MISSING OR DAMAGED GARTER SPRING — REMOVE DAMAGED SPRING WITH SMALL HOOKED WIRE — INSTALL NEW SPRING IF DAMAGED OR MISSING.

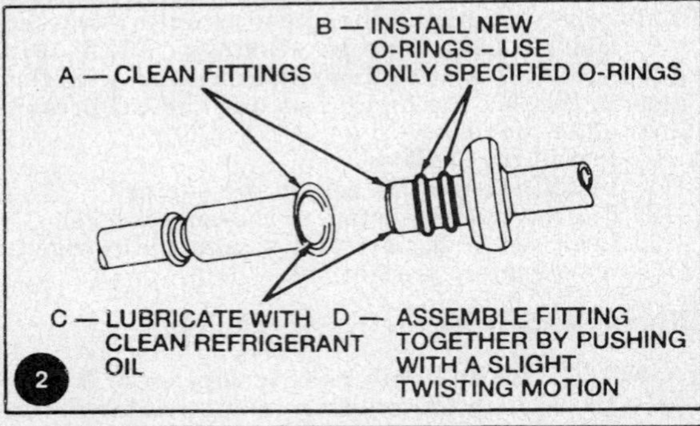

A — CLEAN FITTINGS

O-RINGS - USE
ONLY SPECIFIED O-RINGS
C — LUBRICATE WITH

D — ASSEMBLE FITTING
TOGETHER BY PUSHING
WITH A SLIGHT

2.

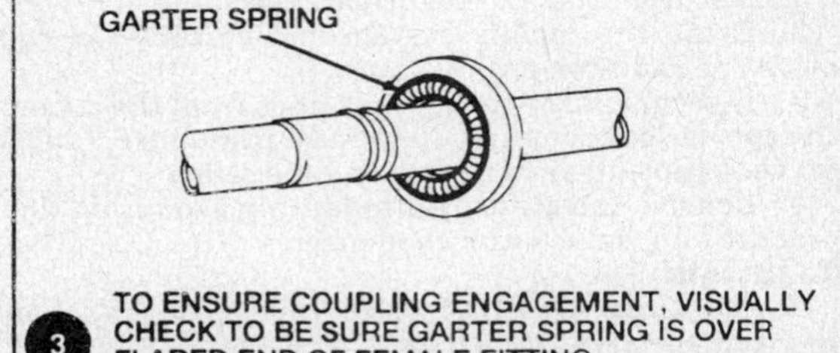

3. TO ENSURE COUPLING ENGAGEMENT, VISUALLY CHECK TO BE SURE GARTER SPRING IS OVER FLARED END OF FEMALE FITTING.

TO DISCONNECT COUPLING

CAUTION — DISCHARGE SYSTEM BEFORE DISCONNECTING COUPLING

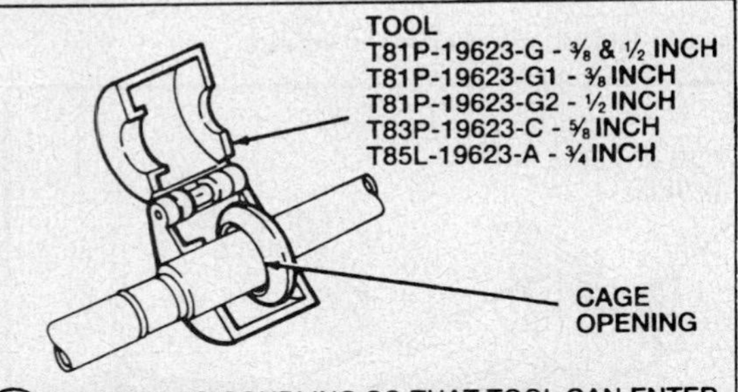

1. FIT TOOL TO COUPLING SO THAT TOOL CAN ENTER CAGE OPENING TO RELEASE THE GARTER SPRING.

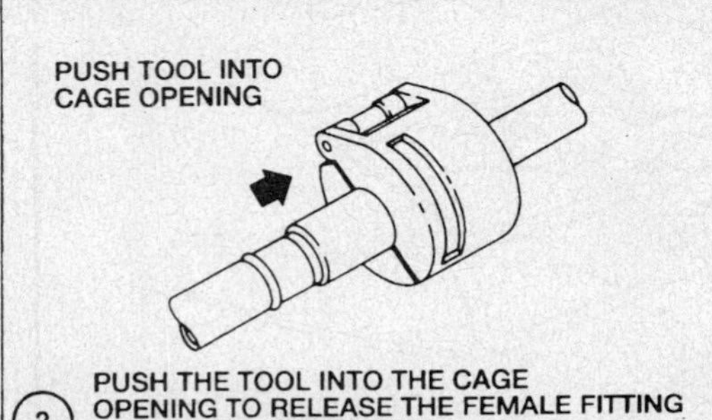

PUSH TOOL INTO

2. PUSH THE TOOL INTO THE CAGE OPENING TO RELEASE THE FEMALE FITTING FROM THE GARTER SPRING.

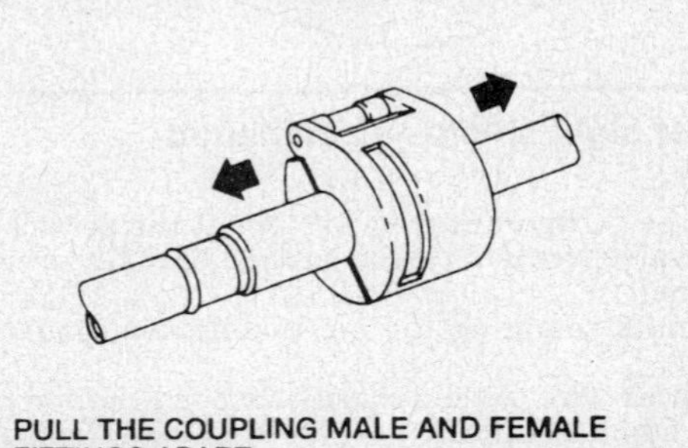

3. PULL THE COUPLING MALE AND FEMALE FITTINGS APART.

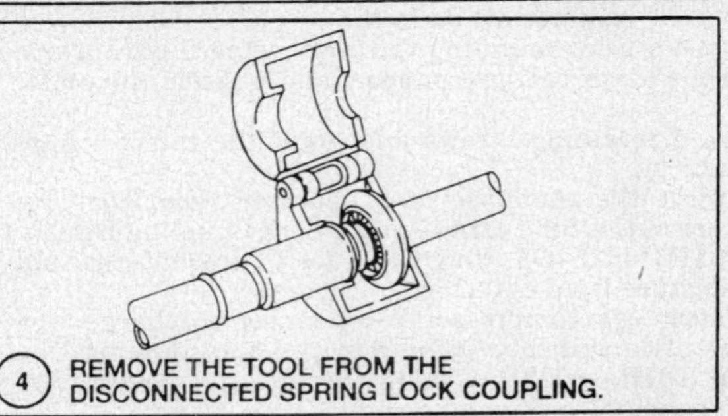

4. REMOVE THE TOOL FROM THE DISCONNECTED SPRING LOCK COUPLING.

Spring lock coupling disconnect and reconnect procedure

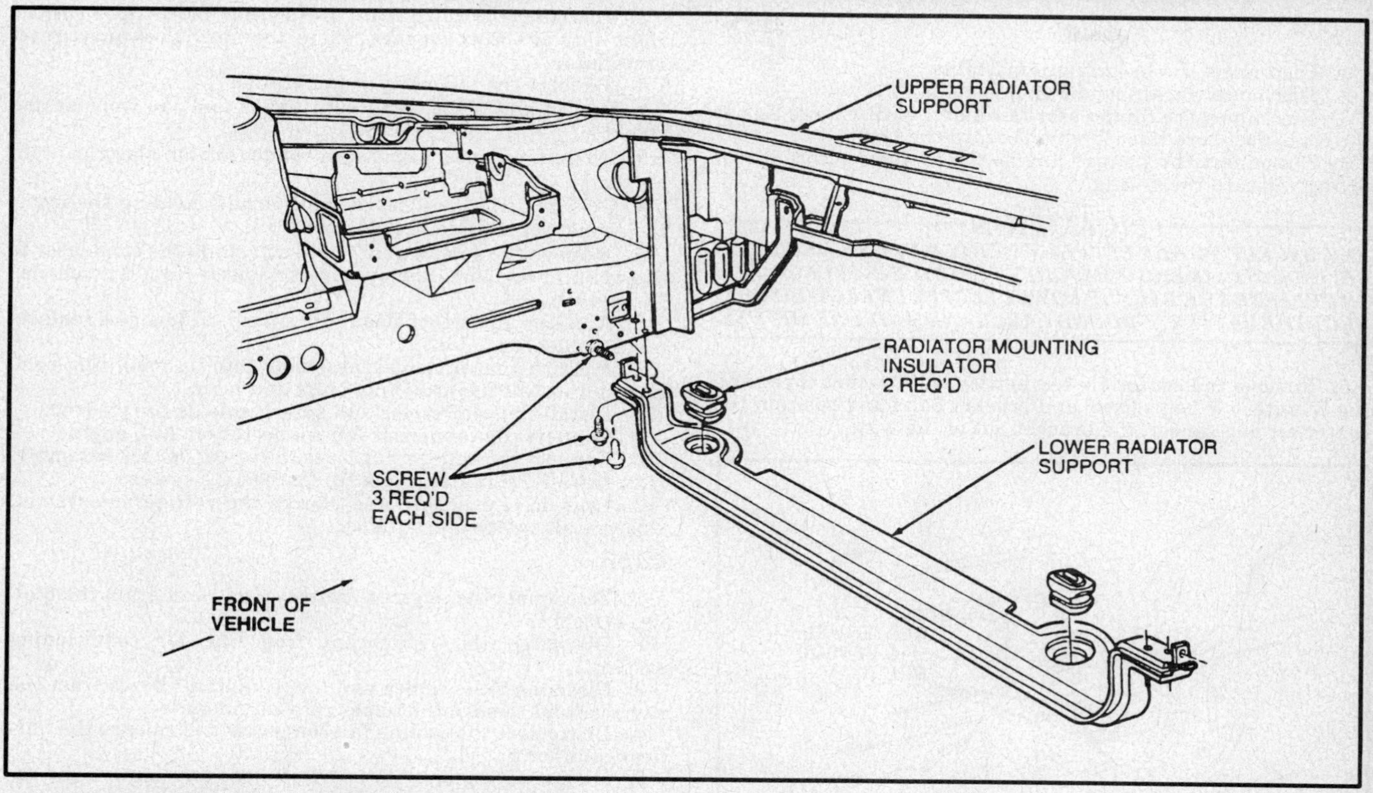

UPPER RADIATOR SUPPORT
RADIATOR MOUNTING INSULATOR 2 REQ'D
LOWER RADIATOR SUPPORT
SCREW 3 REQ'D EACH SIDE
FRONT OF VEHICLE

Lower radiator support installation—Continental

FRONT OF VEHICLE
RADIATOR AIR DEFLECTOR
SCREW 3 REQ'D TIGHTEN TO 40-55 INCH-LBS. (4.5-6.3 Nm)
REUSABLE PUSH PIN 5 REQ'D

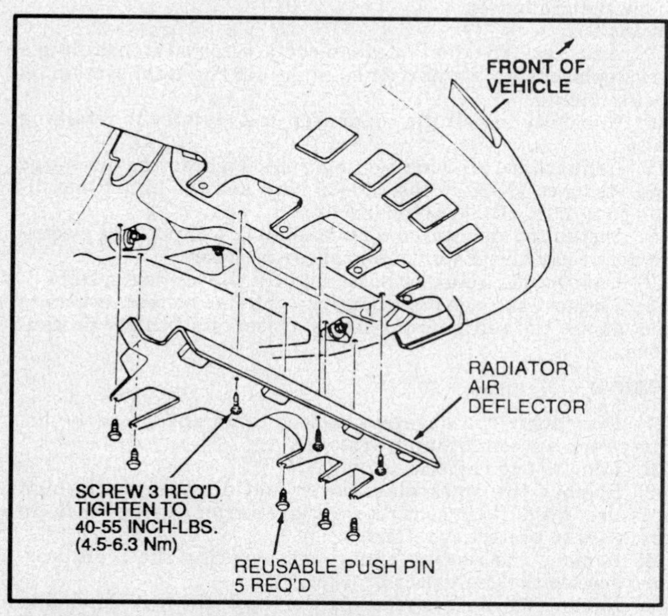

Radiator air deflector—Continental

FRONT OF VEHICLE

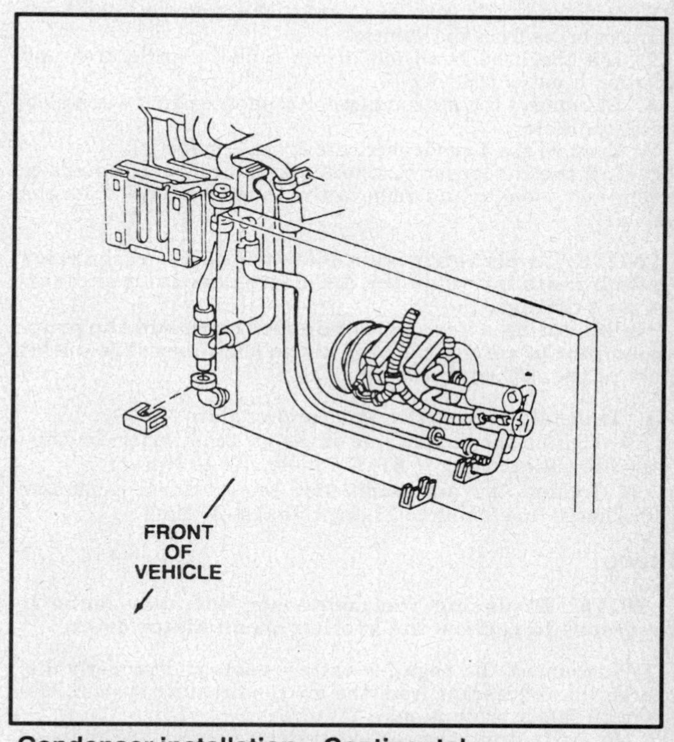

Condenser installation—Continental

Aspire

1. Disconnect the battery ground cable.
2. Discharge the air conditioner system.
3. Disconnect the compressor-to-condenser discharge line at the condenser core inlet fitting. Discard the O-ring.
4. Disconnect the jumper line at the condenser core outlet fitting. Discard the O-ring.

CAUTION

THE BACKUP POWER SUPPLY ENERGY MUST BE DEPLETED BEFORE ANY AIR BAG COMPONENT SERVICE IS PREFORMED. TO DEPLETE THE BACKUP POWER SUPPLY ENERGY, DISCONNECT THE BATTERY GROUND CABLE AND WAIT ONE MINUTE.

5. Remove the center air bag sensor and bracket cover and the 2 center air bag sensor and bracket bolts and position the center air bag sensor and bracket out of the way.

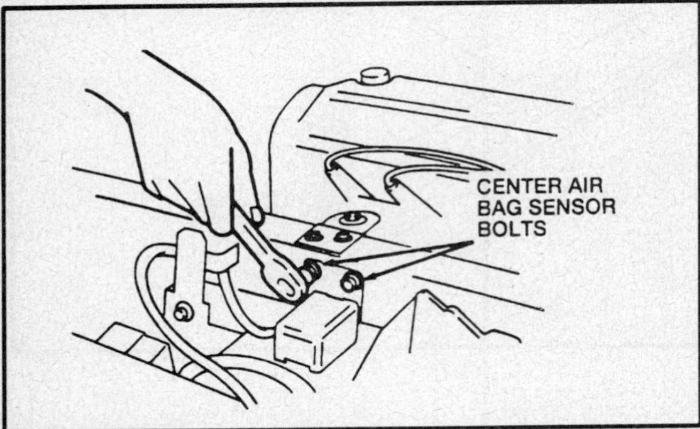

Center air bag sensor—Aspire

6. Remove the 2 bolts, nut, screw, clip, and the hood latch support brace from the vehicle.
7. Lift the hood latch out of the radiator grille area and position it out of the way.
8. Disconnect the air conditioner condenser fan switch electrical connector.
9. Remove the 4 condenser core bracket bolts.
10. Lift the condenser core to allow the condenser studs to clear their mounts and remove the condenser core from the vehicle.

NOTE: Apply refrigerant oil to the new O-rings prior to their installation on the A/C condenser inlet and outlet port fittings.

In installing a new A/C condenser core, add the proper amount of refrigerant oil to the high-pressure outlet port of the A/C compressor.

11. To install, reverse the removal procedure.
    - Tighten the jumper line at the air conditioner condenser core outlet fitting to 87–174 in–lb (10–19 Nm).
    - Tighten the air conditioner compressor-to-condenser discharge line fitting to 11–18 ft–lb (15–24 Nm).

Probe

NOTE: Replacing the condenser will also make it necessary to replace the suction accumulator/drier

1. Disconnect the negative battery cable and properly discharge the refrigerant from the air conditioning system. Observe all safety precautions.
2. Properly drain the cooling system. Remove the radiator from the vehicle.
3. Disconnect 2 refrigerant lines from the fittings on the right side of the condenser, using the springlock disconnect procedure.
4. Perform the following as applicable:
    - Loosen and place aside both upper and the front splash shield .
    - On 2.2L engines, disconnect condenser fan electrical connector.
    - On 2.2L turbo engines, remove 4 nuts holding the intercooler and set it aside.
5. Remove the 4 bolts and 2 nuts attaching the condenser to the radiator support. Remove the condenser from the vehicle.

To install:

6. Add 1 oz. (30 ml) of clean refrigerant oil to a new replacement condenser.
7. Position the condenser assembly into its mounting position and install the attaching bolts and nuts.
8. Install the intercooler and splash shields as removed.
9. Connect the condenser fan connector on 2.2L engine.
10. Connect the refrigerant lines to the condenser assembly.
11. Install the radiator and fill the cooling system.
12. Leak test, evacuate and charge the refrigerant system. Observe all safety precautions.

Capri

1. Disconnect the negative battery cable and drain the cooling system.
2. Discharge the refrigerant from the air conditioning system.
3. Disconnect the upper and lower radiator hoses from the radiator and remove the upper radiator mounts.
4. Disconnect the cooling fan connector and release the harness retainer.
5. Disconnect the coolant overflow hose and remove the radiator and fan assembly.
6. Disconnect the air conditioning lines and plug them to prevent moisture from entering the system.
7. Position the wiring harness aside.
8. Remove the condenser retaining bolts and carefully remove the condenser.

To install:

9. Add 1 oz. (25–30ml) of clean compressor oil if installing a new replacement compressor to maintain the total system oil requirements.
10. Carefully install the condenser and install the retaining bolts.
11. Connect the air conditioning lines. Tighten the discharge line fitting to 15–18 ft. lbs. (20–25 Nm) and the liquid line fitting to 9–11 ft. lbs. (12–15 Nm).
12. Install the radiator and fan assembly. Connect the electrical connector and install the harness retainer.
13. Connect the radiator hoses and fill the cooling system.
14. Connect the negative battery cable. Leak test, evacuate and charge the refrigerant system. Observe all safety precautions.

Festiva

1. Disconnect the negative battery cable and properly discharge the air conditioning system.
2. Remove the radiator grille.
3. Remove the sight glass cover and disconnect the high pressure hose fitting at the receiver/drier, using back-up wrenches to protect the fittings.
4. Remove the routing clamp bolt securing the high pressure hose to the condenser bracket.
5. Remove the 2 bolts securing the top of the hood latch and center brace. Remove the bolt securing the bottom of the hood latch center brace.
6. Lift the hood latch from the grille area and lay it back across the engine.
7. Remove the 2 nuts attaching the condenser to the radiator core support. Lift the condenser to allow the mounting grommets to clear their mounts and remove the condenser.

8. If necessary, remove the condenser fan on automatic transaxle equipped vehicles. If necessary, remove the receiver/drier.

To install:

9. Add 1 fluid oz. (30 ml) of clean refrigerant oil if installing a new replacement condenser.
10. If removed, install the receiver/drier. If removed, install the condenser fan on automatic transaxle equipped vehicles.
11. Make sure the mounting grommets are in position and install the condenser. Make sure the mounting insulators are properly seated in the radiator core support crossmember.
12. Make sure the upper rubber mounts are secure on the condenser mounting studs.
13. Install and tighten the 2 nuts to secure the condenser to the radiator core support.
14. Position the center brace and hood latch and install the center brace attaching bolts.
15. Install a new O-ring on the compressor discharge hose fitting and connect it to the condenser.
16. Install and tighten the routing clamp attaching bolt.
17. Install a new O-ring and connect the high pressure hose fitting to the receiver/drier.
18. Install the radiator grille, evacuate, charge and test the system.

Compressor

REMOVAL AND INSTALLATION

Taurus, Sable and Continental

EXCEPT 3.8L AND 4.6L ENGINE

NOTE: Whenever a compressor is replaced, it will be necessary to replace the suction accumulator/drier.

Some models use R-134a refrigerant. System components, refrigerant, refrigerant oil and testing and recharging equipment are not compatible with similar items from R-12 systems. Be sure to use only the proper components, refrigerant, oil or equipment when servicing these systems.

1. Disconnect the negative battery cable and properly discharge the air conditioning system.
2. Disconnect the compressor clutch wires at the field coil connector on the compressor.
3. Loosen the drive belt and disconnect the hose assemblies from the condenser and suction line.
4. Remove the mounting bolts and remove the compressor and manifold and tube assembly from the vehicle as a unit. Remove the assembly from the top; it will not clear through the bottom.
5. Remove the manifold and tube assembly as an on-bench operation.
6. If the compressor is to be replaced, remove the clutch and field coil assembly.

To install:

NOTE: New service replacement 10P15F and FX-15 compressors contain a full capacity of refrigerant oil. Before replacement compressor installation, drain 4 oz. (120 ml) of refrigerant oil from the compressor. New FS-10 compressors are shipped without oil. Drain and measure oil from the old compressor. Add the measured amount plus 1 oz. to the new compressor. This will maintain the total system oil charge within the specified limits. On FS-10 R-134a system, use only the proper oil intended for these systems.

7. Install the manifold and tube assembly on the air conditioning compressor.
8. Install the compressor and manifold and tube assembly on the air conditioning mounting bracket.
9. Using new O-rings lubricated with clean refrigerant oil, connect the suction line to the compressor manifold and tube assembly. Attach the discharge line to the air conditioning condenser.
10. Connect the clutch wires to the field coil connector.
11. Install the drive belt.
12. Leak test, evacuate and charge the system. Observe all safety precautions.
13. Check the system for proper operation.

3.8L ENGINE

NOTE: Whenever a compressor is replaced, it will be necessary to replace the suction accumulator/drier.

1. Disconnect the negative battery cable and properly discharge the air conditioning system.
2. Properly drain the cooling system. Save the coolant for reuse.
3. Disconnect and remove the integrated relay controller.
4. Disconnect and remove the fan and shroud assembly.
5. Disconnect the upper and lower radiator hoses and remove the radiator.
6. Disconnect the air conditioning compressor magnetic clutch wire at the field coil connector on the compressor.
7. Remove the top 2 compressor mounting bolts.
8. Raise and safely support the vehicle.
9. Loosen and remove the compressor drive belt.
10. Disconnect the Heated Oxygen Sensor (HO_2S) wire connector and remove the air conditioning muffler supporting strap bolt from the sub-frame.
11. Disconnect the air conditioning system hose from the condenser and suction accumulator/drier using the spring-lock coupling tool or equivalent. Immediately install protective caps on the open lines.
12. Remove the bottom 2 compressor mounting bolts. Make sure the compressor is properly supported as the bolts are removed.
13. Remove the compressor, manifold and tube assemblies from the vehicle as a unit. The assembly can be removed from the bottom using care not to scrape against the condenser.
14. Remove the manifold and tube assemblies from the compressor.
15. If the compressor is to be replaced, remove the clutch and field coil assembly.

To install:

NOTE: A new service replacement FX-15 compressor contains 8 oz. (240 ml) of refrigerant oil. Before installing a new compressor, drain 4 oz. (120 ml) of refrigerant oil from the compressor. New FS-10 compressors are shipped without oil. Drain and measure oil from the old compressor. Add the measured amount plus 1 oz. to the new compressor. This will maintain total system oil charge within specified limits.

16. Using new O-rings, lubricated with clean refrigerant oil, install the manifold and tube assemblies onto the new compressor.
17. Install the compressor, manifold and tube assemblies onto the compressor mounting bracket.
18. Using new O-rings lubricated with clean refrigerant oil, connect the suction line to the compressor and manifold assembly.
19. Using new O-rings lubricated with clean refrigerant oil, connect the discharge line to the compressor and manifold assembly.
20. Install the muffler support onto the sub-frame and connect the Heated Oxygen Sensor (HO_2S) wire connector.
21. Install the compressor drive belt and lower the vehicle.
22. Install the radiator and connect the radiator hoses.
23. Install the fan and shroud assembly and connect the integrated relay connector.
24. Connect the negative battery cable and fill the radiator with the coolant that was saved.

25. Leak test, evacuate and charge the system. Check the system for proper operation.

Continental

4.6L Engine

NOTE: If A/C compressor is inoperative, due to internal causes, clean the refrigerant system to remove any debris or contaminants to prevent damage to the replacement A/C compressor.

Replacement of the suction accumulator/drier is necessary when the A/C compressor is replaced.

The A/C evaporator core orifice should be replaced whenever the A/C compressor is replaced for lack of performance.

1. Disconnect the negative battery cable and discharge the refrigerant from the system following the recommended service procedures. Observe all safety precautions.
2. Remove the radiator upper right shield.
3. Raise the vehicle on a hoist.
4. Remove the radiator air deflector.
5. Loosen the idler pulley to remove the tension from the drive belt. Remove the drive belt from the air conditioner clutch pulley.
6. Remove the air conditioner manifold and tube from the compressor.
7. Disconnect the compressor clutch wires at the wire connector.
8. Remove 3 compressor retaining bolts and remove the compressor.

To install:

NOTE: A new service replacement FS-10 compressor is shipped without compressor oil.

Service the replacement FS-10 compressor with the correct amount of clean Motorcraft YN-12b refrigerant oil or equivalent meeting Ford specification WSH-M1C231-B.

9. Position the compressor to the mounting brackets. Install the three retaining bolts.
10. Lubricate new O-ring seals with clean Motorcraft YN-12b refrigerant oil or equivalent meeting Ford specification WSH-M1C231-B and position them in O-ring seal grooves of the compressor manifold and tube.
11. Apply Pipe Sealant with Teflon D8AZ-19554-A or equivalent meeting Ford specification WSK-M2G350-A2 to threads of manifold retaining bolt.

NOTE: When replacing an FS-10 compressor, use original manifold bolt from the removed compressor to retain the manifold and tube to the new compressor. Do not use the shipping cap bolts.

Position the manifold and tube with O-ring seals to the compressor. Install retaining bolt and tighten to 13–17 ft. lbs. (17–23 Nm).

12. Connect the compressor clutch wires at the harness connector.
13. Install the drive belt on the compressor clutch pulley.
14. Install the radiator air deflector.
15. Leak test, evacuate and charge the system.
16. Install the radiator upper sight shield.
17. Connect the negative battery cable.
18. Check the system for proper operation.

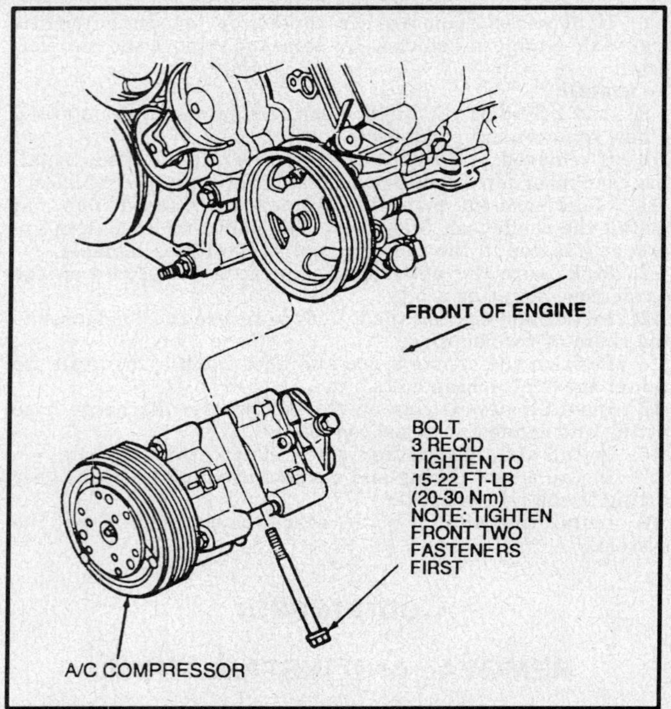

Compressor installation—4.6L engine

Tempo and Topaz

NOTE: Whenever a compressor is replaced, it will be necessary to replace the suction accumulator/drier.

1. Disconnect the negative battery cable and properly discharge the refrigerant system.
2. Disconnect the compressor clutch wires at the field coil connector on the compressor.
3. Remove the discharge line from the manifold and tube assembly.
4. Remove the suction line from the suction manifold using a back-up wrench on each fitting.
5. Loosen 2 idler attaching screws and release the compressor belt tension.
6. Raise and safely support the vehicle. Remove the 4 bolts attaching the compressor to the mounting bracket.
7. Remove the 2 screws attaching the heater water return tube to the underside of the engine supports.
8. Remove the compressor from the underside of the vehicle.

To install:

NOTE: A new service replacement compressor contains a full capacity of refrigerant oil. Prior to installing the replacement compressor, drain the refrigerant oil from the removed compressor into a calibrated container. Then, drain the refrigerant oil from the new compressor into a clean calibrated container. If the amount of oil drained from the removed compressor was between 3–5 oz. (90–148 ml), pour the same amount of clean refrigerant oil into the new compressor. If the amount of oil that was removed from the old compressor is greater than 5 oz. (148 ml), pour 5 oz. (148 ml) of clean refrigerant oil into the new compressor. If the amount of refrigerant oil that was removed from the old compressor is less than 3 oz. (90 ml), pour 3 oz. (90 ml) of clean refrigerant oil into the new compressor.

9. Position the compressor to the compressor bracket and install the 4 bolts.

10. Attach 2 screws attaching the heater water return tube to the underside of the engine supports.
11. Attach the compressor belt and tighten the 2 idler screws.
12. Install the suction line to the suction manifold using a backup wrench on each fitting. Use new O-rings lubricated with clean refrigerant oil.
13. Install the discharge line spring lock fitting to the manifold and tube assembly. Use new O-rings lubricated with clean refrigerant oil.
14. Connect the compressor clutch wire connector to the field coil connector at the compressor.
15. Leak test, evacuate and charge the system. Check the system for proper operation.

Contour and Mystique

1. Disconnect the negative battery cable and properly discharge the system. Observe all safety precautions.
2. Raise the vehicle.
3. Remove the right front wheel.
4. Remove 2 retaining screws and engine and transmission splash shield.

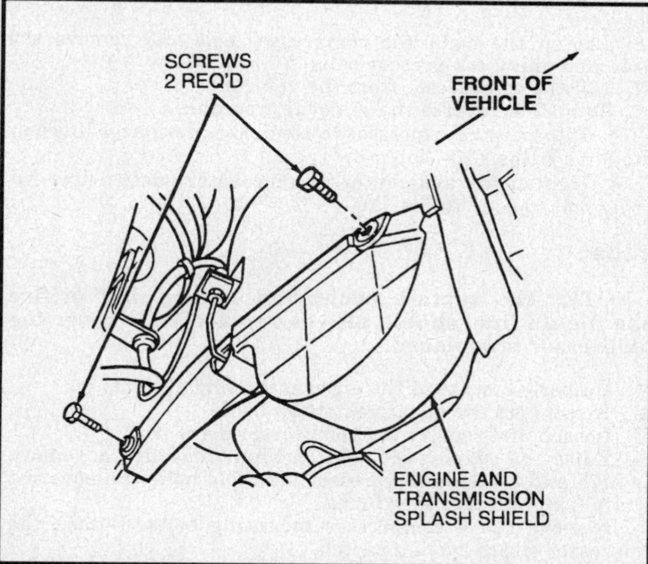

Splash shield—Contour and Mystique

5. Remove the drive belt.
6. Remove the radiator air deflector.
7. On 2.5L engine only, remove 3 retaining nuts and 2 heat shields from oil pan retaining studs.
8. On 2.0L engine only, drain the cooling system.
9. On 2.0L engine only, disconnect the lower radiator hose from radiator and position the hose to improve access to the compressor retaining bolts.
10. Disconnect the air conditioner clutch wire connector from the clutch.
11. Loosen the manifold retainer bolt and remove from the manifold and tube. Cap the manifold and tube and the compressor to prevent the entrance of dirt and moisture.
12. Remove the compressor retaining bolts.
13. Remove the compressor from the vehicle.

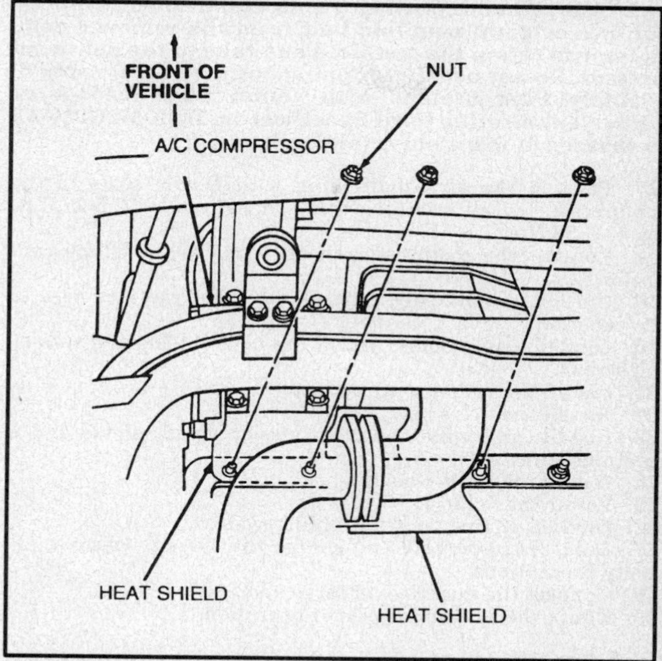

Heat shields—Contour and Mystique

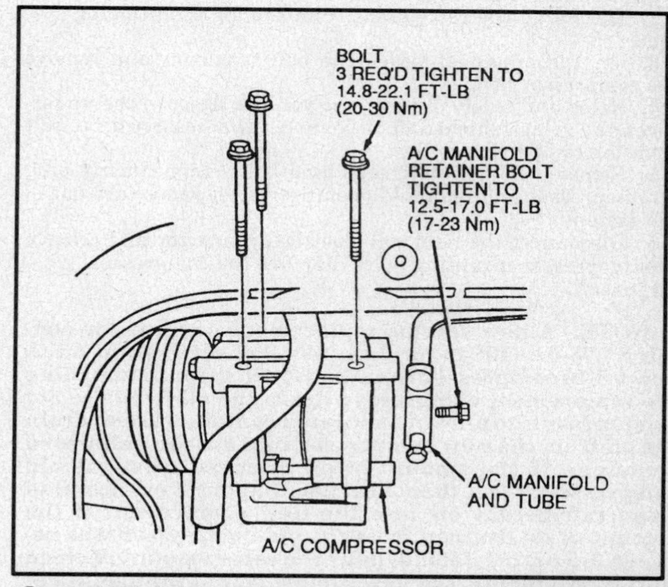

Compressor installation—Contour and Mystique

To install:

14. Service the replacement air conditioner compressor with the correct amount of clean Motorcraft YN-12b refrigerant oil or equivalent meeting Ford specification WSH-M1C231-B as outlined.
15. Install A/C compressor and retaining bolts. Tighten compressor retaining bolts to (14.8–22.1 ft–lb) 20–30 Nm.
16. Lubricate new O-ring seals with clean Motorcraft YN-12b refrigerant oil or equivalent meeting Ford Specification WSH-M1C231-B and position them in O-ring seal grooves of the A/C compressor.

NOTE: When replacing the air conditioner compressor, use original manifold bolt from the removed compressor to retain the manifold and tube to the new compressor. Do not use the shipping bolts.

Apply Pipe Sealant with Teflon D8AZ-19554-A or equivalent meeting Ford Specification WSK-M2G350-A2 to threads of manifold retaining bolt.

17. Position the air conditioning with O-ring seals to the compressor. Install retaining bolt and tighten to 12.5-17.0 ft. lbs. (17–23 Nm).
18. Connect the compressor clutch wires to the clutch connector.
19. On 2.0L engine only, connect the lower radiator hose to the radiator.
20. On 2.5L engine only, install the heat shields and retaining screws.
21. Install the radiator air deflector.
22. Install the drive belt.
23. Install the engine and transmission splash shield and 2 retaining screws.
24. Install the front wheel.
25. Lower the vehicle.
26. On 2.0L engine only, fill cooling system.
27. Leak test, evacuate and charge the system. Observe all safety precautions.
28. Connect the negative battery cable.
29. Check the system for proper operation.

Escort and Tracer

NOTE: Whenever the compressor is replaced, replace the suction accumulator/drier and the fixed orifice tube.

1. Disconnect the negative battery cable.
2. Discharge the refrigerant from the air conditioning system.
3. On 1.9L engines, loosen the belt tensioner and remove the compressor belt.
4. Raise and safely support the vehicle. Remove the undercover and splash shield and disconnect the accessory drive belt from the compressor pulley.
5. Remove the manifold attaching bolts. Immediately plug all compressor and manifold openings to keep moisture out of the system.
6. Disconnect the field coil electrical connector and remove the compressor mounting bolts. Remove the compressor.

To install:

NOTE: A new service replacement compressor contains 7.75 oz. (10P13) or 7 oz. FX-15 of refrigerant oil. A new FS-10 compressor contains no oil. Prior to installing the replacement compressor, drain the oil from the old compressor into a clean calibrated container. Then drain the oil from the new compressor into a clean calibrated container. If the amount of oil removed from the old compressor is less than 3 oz. (90ml), pour 3 oz. (90ml) of clean refrigerant oil into the new compressor. If the amount of oil drained from the old compressor was between 3–5 oz. (90–150ml), pour the same amount of clean refrigerant oil into the new compressor. If the amount of oil removed from the old compressor is greater than 5 oz. (150ml), pour 5 oz. (150ml) of clean oil into the new compressor. This will maintain the total system oil charge requirements.

7. Position the compressor and install the mounting bolts. Tighten the bolts to 15–22 ft. lbs. (10P13) or 31–44 ft. lbs. (FX-15 or FS-10 on 1.9L engines).
8. Connect the field coil electrical connector.
9. Remove all plugs, then install new O-rings lubricated with clean refrigerant oil on the manifolds. Position the manifolds and install the attaching bolts. Tighten the bolts to 13–17 ft. lbs. (18–23 Nm).
10. Attach the accessory drive belt to the compressor pulley and install the splash shield and undercover.
11. Lower the vehicle. Check the accessory drive belt for proper tension. On 1.9L engines, replace the compressor drive belt after the vehicle is lowered.

NOTE: The air conditioning system should be flushed whenever a compressor is replaced.

12. Connect the negative battery cable. Leak test, evacuate and charge the system. Observe all safety precautions.

Aspire

1. Disconnect the negative battery cable and discharge the air conditioner system.
2. Remove the compressor-to-condenser discharge line bolt. Plug the compressor outlet fitting to prevent moisture from entering the system.
3. Disconnect the compressor-to-condenser discharge line from the compressor.
4. Remove the evaporator-to-compressor suction line fitting bolt from the compressor. Plug the compressor inlet fitting to prevent moisture from entering the system.
5. Loosen the tensioner pulley and blet from the compressor.

NOTE: Do not remove the right front A/C compressor bolt from the compressor so that the right front bolt will clear the radiator upon compressor removal.

6. Loosen the right top compressor bolt and remove the three remaining compressor bolts.
7. Lift the compressor from the vehicle.
8. To install, reverse the removal procedure.
   - Tighten the compressor-to-condenser discharge line bolt to 8–11 ft. lbs. (10–15 Nm).
   - Tighten the evaporator-to-compressor suction line fitting bolt to 8–11 ft. lbs. (10–15 Nm).

Probe

NOTE: The suction accumulator/drier and orifice tube (liquid line) should also be replaced whenever the compressor is replaced.

1. Properly discharge the air conditioning system.
2. Disconnect the negative battery cable.
3. Loosen and remove the compressor drive belt.
4. Raise and support the vehicle. From underneath, remove the high and low side compressor manifold bolts. Remove the manifold and discard the O-rings.
5. Remove the 4 compressor mounting bolts. Detach the compressor clutch cycling switch.
6. Remove the compressor.

To install:

NOTE: The replacement compressor is filled with refrigerant oil. However, to maintain the proper amount of oil throughout the system, pour the oil from the replacement compressor into a clean container. Now pour the oil from the old compressor into another clean, calibrated container. Pour the same amount of new refrigerant oil into the replacement compressor as removed from the old compressor, plus, add 0.67 oz. more.

7. Position the compressor and install the 4 mounting bolts.
8. Connect the clutch cycling switch.
9. Reattach the manifold, installing new O-rings.
10. Lower the vehicle and install the compressor drive belt, adjusting for proper tension.
11. Connect the battery cable. Evacuate and recharge the air conditioning system. Perform a leak test. Check entire system operation.

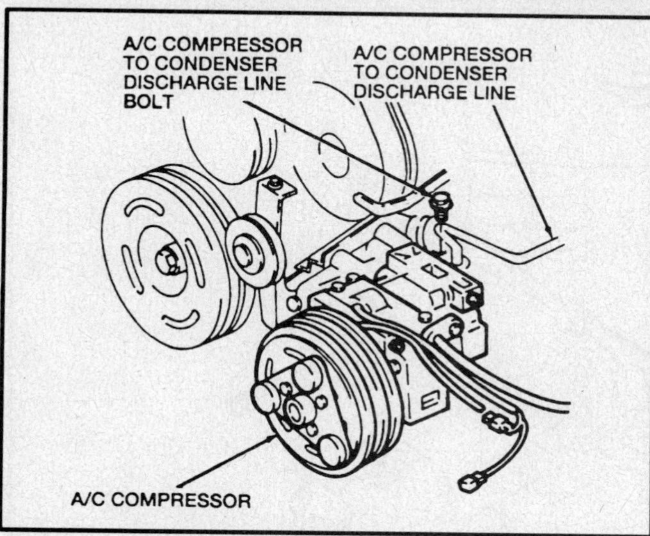

Compressor location—Aspire

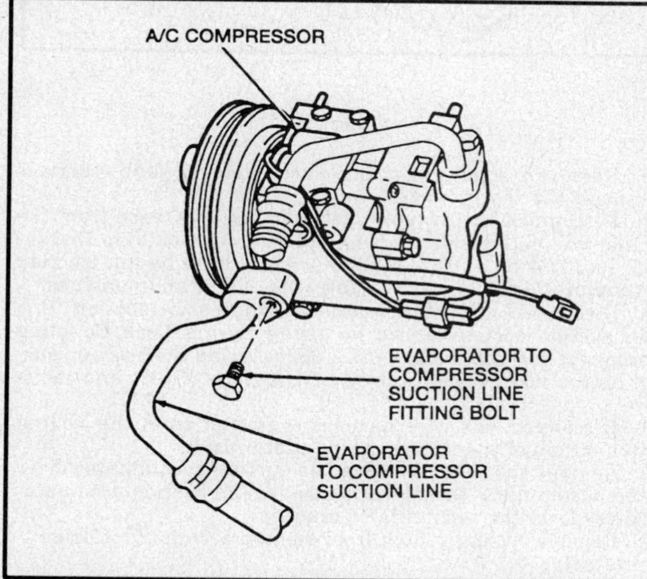

Compressor and lines—Aspire

Capri

1. Run the engine at fast idle with the air conditioner **ON** for 10 minutes, then shut the engine **OFF**.
2. Disconnect the negative battery cable.
3. Discharge the refrigerant from the air conditioning system.
4. Remove the compressor drive belt.
5. Raise and safely support the vehicle.
6. Remove the underbody covers and disconnect the magnetic clutch electrical connector.
7. Disconnect the suction and discharge hose assembly from the compressor. Cap the open fittings to keep moisture and dirt out of the system.
8. Remove the compressor mounting bolts and remove the compressor.

To install:

9. Add 2.05–3.38 oz. (61–100ml) of clean refrigerant oil to a new replacement compressor to maintain total system oil requirements.
10. Position the compressor and install the retaining bolts. Tighten to 30–40 ft. lbs. (39–54 Nm).
11. Connect the suction and discharge hose assembly to the compressor.
12. Connect the magnetic clutch electrical connector and install the underbody covers.
13. Lower the vehicle.
14. Install the compressor drive belt and connect the negative battery cable.
15. Leak test, evacuate and charge the system. Observe all safety precautions.

Festiva

1. Disconnect the negative battery cable and properly discharge the refrigerant system.
2. Remove the compressor drive belt and disconnect the clutch coil wire.
3. Disconnect the suction and discharge fittings from the compressor. Cap the open fittings immediately to keep moisture from the system.
4. Remove the suction and discharge manifold bolts and remove the manifolds. Remove the compressor mounting bolts and the compressor.

To install:

NOTE: A new service replacement compressor contains 2.1–3.5 oz. (60–100 ml) of the specified refrigerant oil. Prior to installing the replacement compressor, drain 1.2 oz. (30 ml) of refrigerant oil from the compressor. This will maintain the system total oil charge within the specified limits.

5. Position the compressor on the mounting bracket and start the bolts.
6. Install the manifolds to 13–17 ft. lbs., connect the refrigerant hoses and the clutch wire.
7. Tighten the compressor mounting bolts to 30–40 ft. lbs. (39–54 Nm) and adjust the tension of the drive belt.
8. Connect the negative battery cable and properly leak test, evacuate and charge the system.

Accumulator/Drier

REMOVAL AND INSTALLATION

Taurus and Sable or Continental without 4.6L Engine

1. Disconnect the negative battery cable and discharge the refrigerant from the air conditioning system. Observe all safety precautions.
2. Disconnect the suction hose at the compressor. Cap the suction hose and the compressor to prevent entrance of dirt and moisture.
3. Disconnect the accumulator/drier inlet tube from the evaporator core outlet, using the spring-lock coupling disconnect procedure.
4. Disconnect the wire harness connector from the pressure switch on top of the accumulator/drier.
5. Remove the screw holding the accumulator/drier in the accumulator bracket and remove the accumulator/drier.

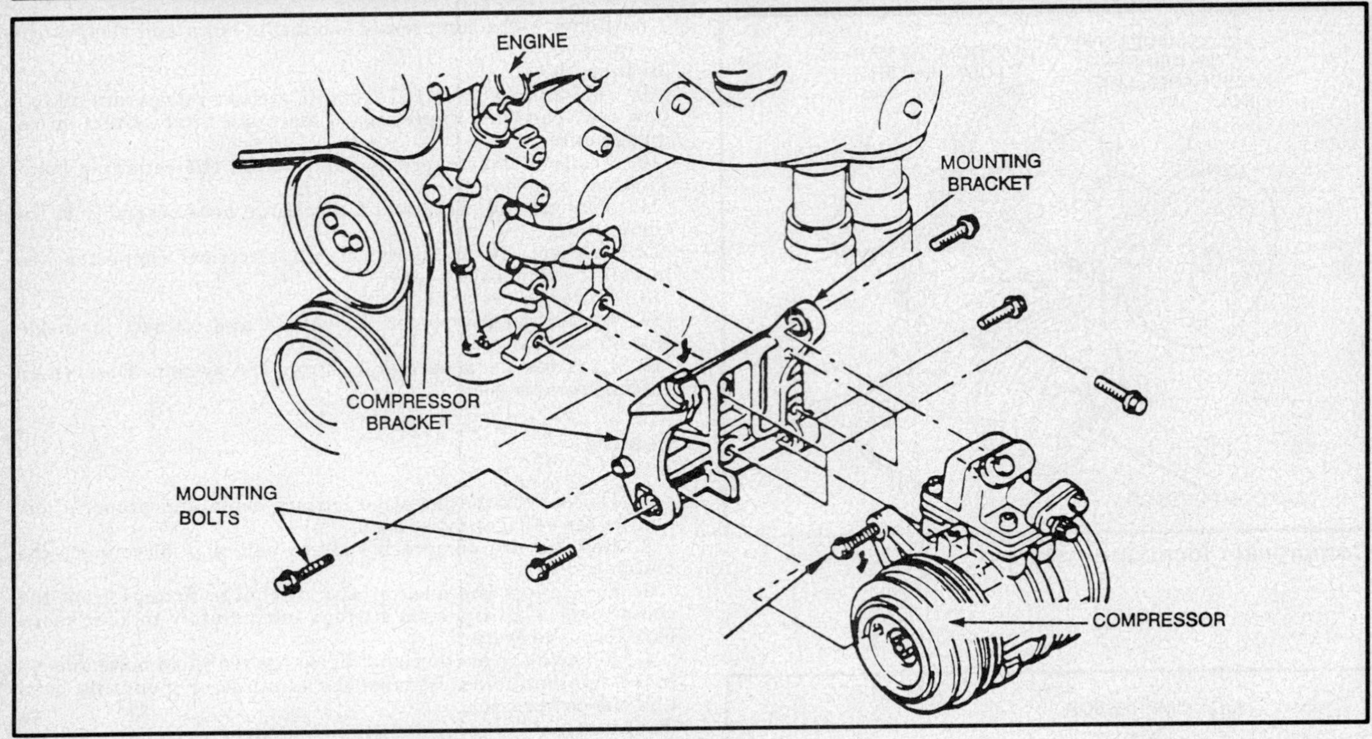

Compressor installation—1.3L engine

To install:

NOTE: Some models use R-134a refrigerant. System components, refrigerant, refrigerant oil and testing and recharging equipment are not compatible with similar items from R-12 systems. Be sure to use only the proper components, refrigerant, oil or equipment when servicing these systems.

6. Drain the oil from the removed accumulator/drier through the Schrader valve fitting. Add the same amount of oil as drained (on Continental, manufacturer recommends same amount plus 2 oz.) of clean refrigerant oil.
7. Position the accumulator/drier on the vehicle and route the suction hose to the compressor.
8. Using a new O-ring lubricated with clean refrigerant oil, connect the accumulator/drier inlet tube to the evaporator core outlet.
9. Install the screw in the accumulator/drier bracket.
10. Using new O-rings lubricated with clean refrigerant oil, connect the suction hose to the compressor.
11. Leak test, evacuate and charge the system. Check the system for proper operation.

Continental with 4.6L Engine

NOTE: The compressor oil from vehicles equipped with an FS-10 A/C compressor may have a dark color while maintaining a normal oil viscosity. This is normal for this A/C compressor because carbon from the A/C compressor piston rings will discolor the oil.

1. Disconnect the negative battery cable.
2. Remove radiator upper sight shield to access suction accumulator/drier.
3. Discharge refrigerant from the system following recommended service procedures. Observe all safety precautions.
4. Remove 2 screws retaining the windshield washer fluid reservoir filler to brace.
5. Remove 2 retaining screws and the brace from vehicle.
6. Remove 2 screws from the power steering fluid reservoir and move the reservoir aside.
7. Disconnect the evaporator-to-accumulator tube from the suction accumulator/drier using Spring Lock Coupling Disconnect Tool (3/4 inch) T85L-19623-A. Cap the tube and suction accumulator/drier to prevent entrance of dirt and moisture.
8. Disconnect the evaporator-to-compressor suction line from suction accumulator/drier using Spring Lock Coupling Disconnect Tool (3/4 inch) T85L-19623-A. Cap the line and suction accumulator/drier to prevent entrance of dirt and moisture.
9. Disconnect the wire harness connector from the cycling switch on top of the suction accumulator/drier.
10. Remove the screw holding the suction accumulator/drier in the accumulator bracket and remove the suction accumulator/drier form the accumulator bracket.
11. Remove cycling switch from suction accumulator/drier.

To install:

12. Drill 2 holes in the bottom and drain the oil from the removed accumulator/drier. Add the same amount of oil as drained plus 2 oz. of clean refrigerant oil.
13. Install A/C cycling switch on suction accumulator/drier.
14. Position suction accumulator/drier in A/C accumulator bracket.
15. Using new O-ring seals lubricated with clean refrigerant oil, connect evaporator to compressor suction line and evaporator to accumulator tube to suction accumulator/drier.
16. Install screw in A/C accumulator bracket.
17. Connect wire harness connector to A/C cycling switch.
18. Install power steering fluid reservoir with 2 retaining screws.
19. Install brace with 2 retaining screws.
20. Install windshield washer fluid reservoir filler to brace with 2 retaining screws.
21. Leak test, evacuate and charge the system. Observe all safety precautions.
22. Install radiator upper sight shield.

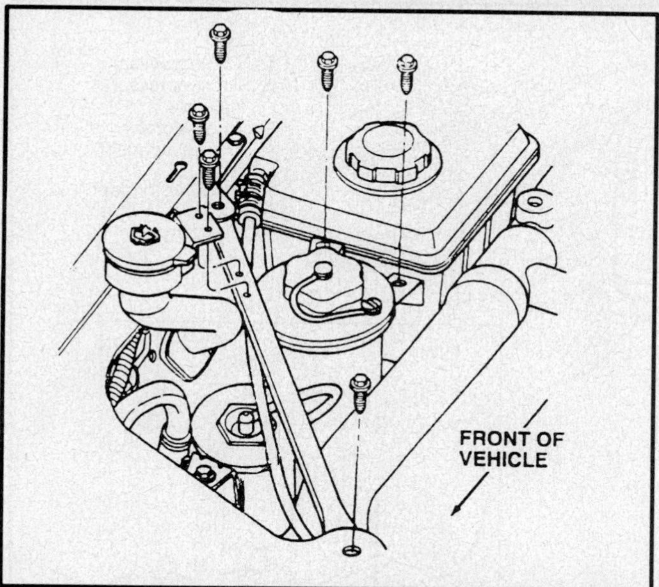

Windshield washer and power steering reservoirs—Continental with 4.6L engine

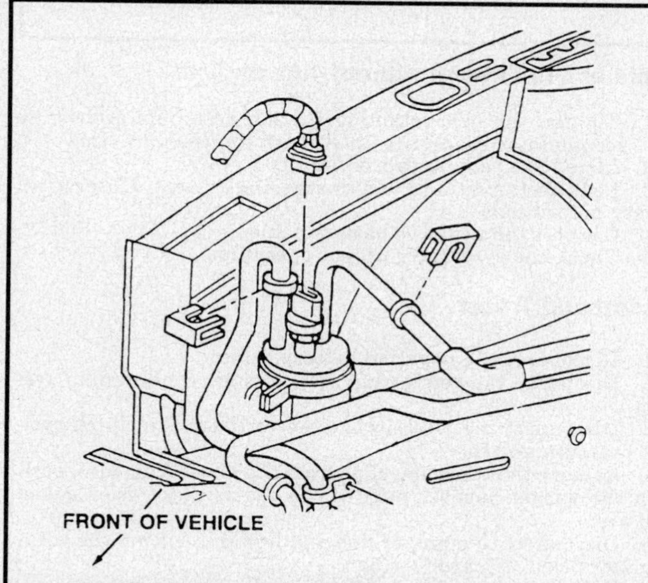

Suction accumulator/drier connections—Continental with 4.6L engine

23. Connect the negative battery cable.
24. Check system for proper operation.

Tempo and Topaz

1. Disconnect the negative battery cable. Properly discharge the refrigerant from the air conditioning system, observing all safety precautions.
2. Disconnect the suction hose at the accumulator.
3. Disconnect the accumulator/drier inlet tube from the evaporator core outlet.
4. Disconnect the wire harness connector from the pressure switch on top of the accumulator/drier.
5. Remove the nut and screw that retain the accumulator/drier to the dash panel and remove the assembly.

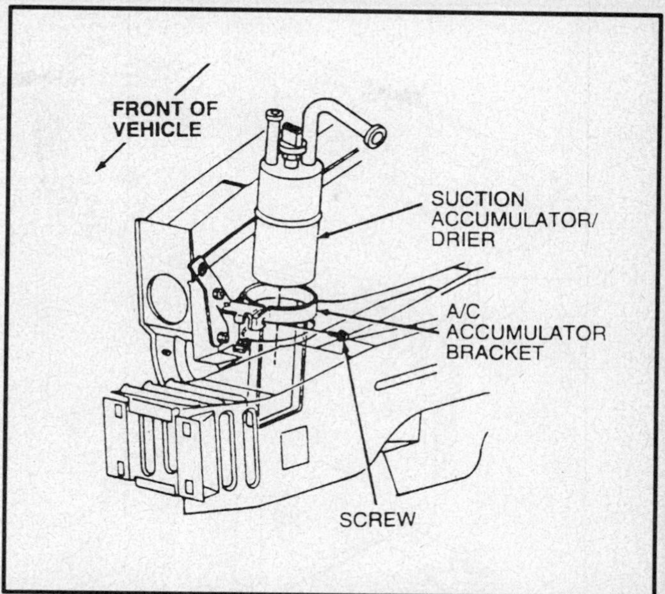

Suction accumulator/drier and bracket—Continental with 4.6L engine

To install:

6. Drain the oil from the old accumulator/drier. Add the same amount of oil removed, plus 2 oz. (60 ml) of clean refrigerant oil to the new accumulator.
7. Position the accumulator/drier in the mounting bracket.
8. Using new O-rings lubricated with clean refrigerant oil, connect the accumulator/drier inlet tube to the evaporator core outlet.
9. Position the accumulator/drier mounting bracket over the evaporator case stud and secure with the retaining nut. Install the screw through the slot in the lower leg of the mounting bracket.
10. Using a new special O-ring lubricated with clean refrigerant oil, connect the suction hose to the suction accumulator at the spring-lock coupling.

NOTE: Use only O-rings contained in kit E35Y-19D690-A or equivalent. The use of any other O-ring will allow the connection to leak.

11. Leak test, evacuate and charge the system. Observe all safety precautions.
12. Check the system for proper operation.

Contour and Mystique

NOTE: The compressor oil from vehicles equipped with an FS-10 A/C compressor may have a dark color while maintaining a normal oil viscosity. This is normal for this A/C compressor because carbon from the A/C compressor piston rings will discolor the oil.

1. Disconnect the negative battery cable.
2. Recover the refrigerant from the A/C system. Observe all safety precautions.
3. Disconnect wire harness connector from A/C cycling switch.
4. Disconnect the A/C manifold and tube using Spring Lock Coupling Disconnect Tool T83-19623-C or equivalent at the suction accumulator/drier. Cap the A/C manifold and tube and suction accumulator/drier to prevent the entrance of dirt and moisture.
5. Raise and safely support the vehicle.
6. Remove the radiator air deflector.
7. Remove 2 bolts retaining the A/C accumulator bracket to the front sub-frame.

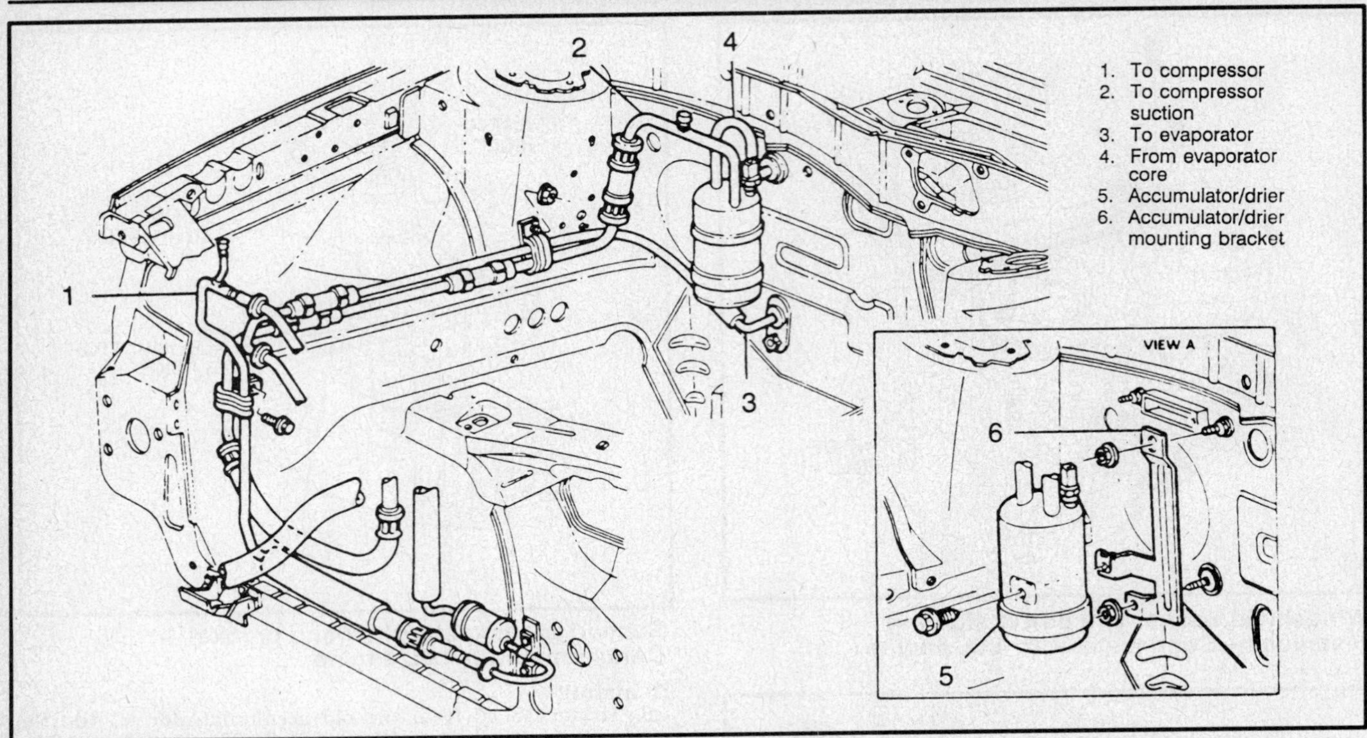

Accumulator/drier removal and installation—Taurus and Sable or Continental without 4.6L engine

8. Pull suction accumulator/drier down along side front subframe to improve access to evaporator to compressor suction line.
9. Unscrew the A/C cycling switch from the top of the suction accumulator/drier.
10. Disconnect evaporator-to-compressor suction line using Spring Lock Coupling Disconnect Tool T83-P-19623-C or equivalent at the suction accumulator/drier. Cap the line and suction accumulator/drier to prevent the entrance of dirt and moisture.
11. Remove the suction accumulator/drier from the vehicle.
12. Loosen the bolt retaining the suction accumulator/drier to the accumulator bracket and remove the accumulator from the bracket.

To install:

13. Drain the oil from the old accumulator/drier. Add the same amount of oil removed, plus 2 oz. (60 ml) of clean refrigerant oil to the new accumulator.
14. Position the suction accumulator/drier into the A/C accumulator bracket. Do not tighten clamp bolt at this time.
15. Lubricate the O-ring seal on the suction accumulator/drier nipple with clean Motorcraft YN-12b refrigerant oil or equivalent meeting Ford Specification WSH-M1C231-B.
16. Screw the A/C cycling switch on the suction accumulator/drier nipple and hand–tighten.
17. Using a new O-ring lubricated with clean Motorcraft YN-12b refrigerant oil or equivalent meeting Ford Specification WSH-M1C231-B, connect the suction accumulator/drier inlet tube to the evaporator to compressor suction line.
18. Install the A/C accumulator bracket to the front sub–frame with two retaining bolts. Tighten bolts to 58–83 inch lbs. (6.6–9.4 Nm).
19. Using a new O-ring seal lubricated with clean Motorcraft YN-12b refrigerant oil or equivalent meeting Ford specification WSH-M1C231-B, connect the A/C manifold and tube to the suction accumulator/drier.
20. Connect wiring harness connector to A/C electronic door actuator motor.
21. Tighten the bolt retaining suction accumulator/drier to A/C accumulator bracket to 58–83 inch lbs. (6.6–9.4 Nm).
22. Install the radiator air deflector.
23. Leak test, evacuate and charge the system. Observe all safety precautions.
24. Connect the negative battery cable.
25. Check the system for proper operation.

Escort and Tracer

1. Disconnect the negative battery cable.
2. Discharge the refrigerant from the air conditioning system.
3. Disconnect the electrical connector from the clutch cycling pressure switch.
4. Remove the retaining clips from the liquid line; also, position the wiring harness next to the accumulator/drier out of the way.
5. Disconnect the jumper line and liquid line from the accumulator/drier. Discard O–ring.
6. Disconnect the suction line from the accumulator/drier.
7. Remove the mounting strap bolt (1 bolt on 1.8L; 2 bolts on 1.9L).
8. Disconnect the accumulator/drier from the evaporator outlet tube. Remove the accumulator/drier.

To install:

NOTE: If the accumulator/drier is to be replaced, drill a 1/2 in. (12.7mm) hole in the old accumulator body and drain the oil from the accumulator into a clean calibrated container. Add the same amount of oil as removed, plus 2 oz. (60ml) of clean refrigerant oil to a new accumulator/drier.

9. Using new O-rings lubricated with clean refrigerant oil, connect the suction accumulator/drier to the evaporator outlet tube.
10. Install the mounting strap bolt(s).

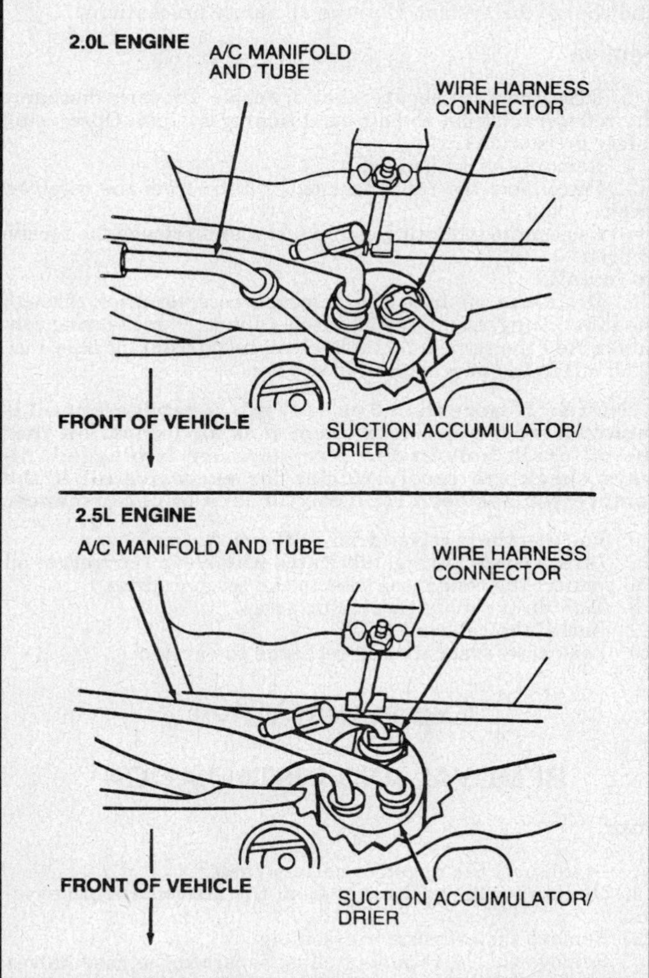

Accumulator/drier locations—Contour and Mystique

11. Reconnect the wiring harness near the accumulator/drier.
12. Using new O-rings lubricated with clean refrigerant oil, connect the suction line to the accumulator/drier.
13. Reconnect the clutch cycling pressure switch.
14. Connect the negative battery cable. Leak test, evacuate and charge the system. Observe all safety precautions.

Probe

1. Disconnect the negative battery cable. Properly discharge the refrigerant from the air conditioning system. Observe all safety precautions.
2. Remove the carbon canister.
3. Disconnect the clutch cycling pressure switch electrical connector from the switch.
4. Remove the 2 mounting bolts from the accumulator/drier mounting bracket and carefully remove the accumulator/drier from the vehicle.

To install:

5. Drain the oil from the removed accumulator/drier. Add the same amount plus 1 oz. (30 ml) of clean refrigerant oil to the new accumulator.
6. Position the accumulator/drier onto the mounting bracket and install the mounting bolts.

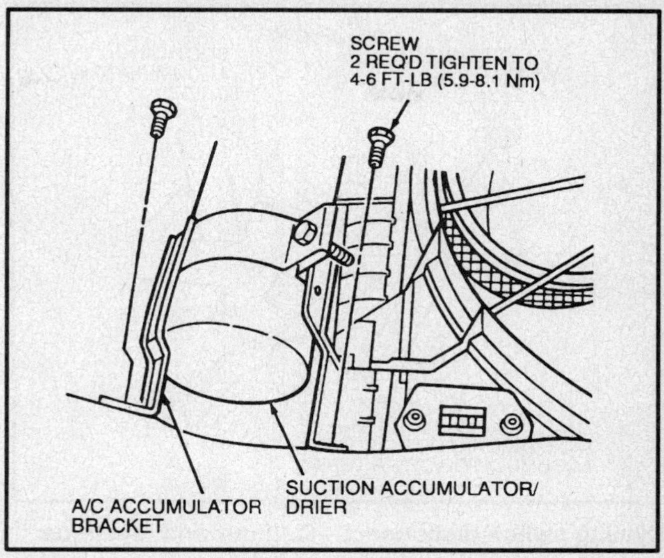

Accumulator/drier bracket removal—Contour and Mystique

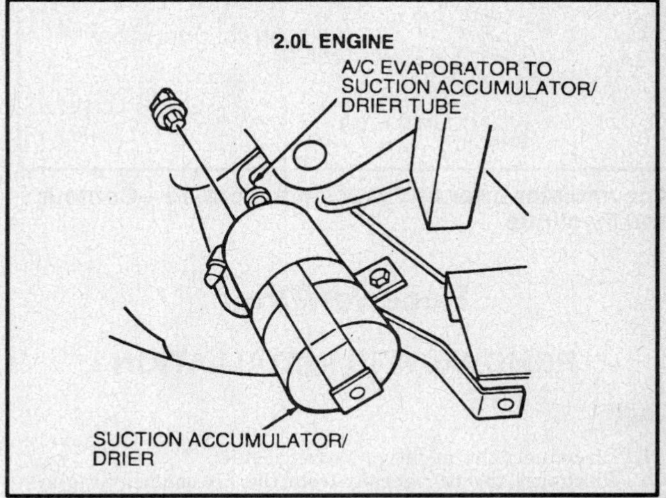

Accumulator/drier lines disconnect—Contour and Mystique

7. Connect the suction line to the evaporator core, as removed.
8. Connect the compressor suction line to the accumulator/drier assembly.
9. Connect the clutch cycling pressure switch electrical connector and install the carbon canister.
10. Connect the negative battery cable. Leak test, evacuate and charge the refrigerant system. Observe all safety precautions.

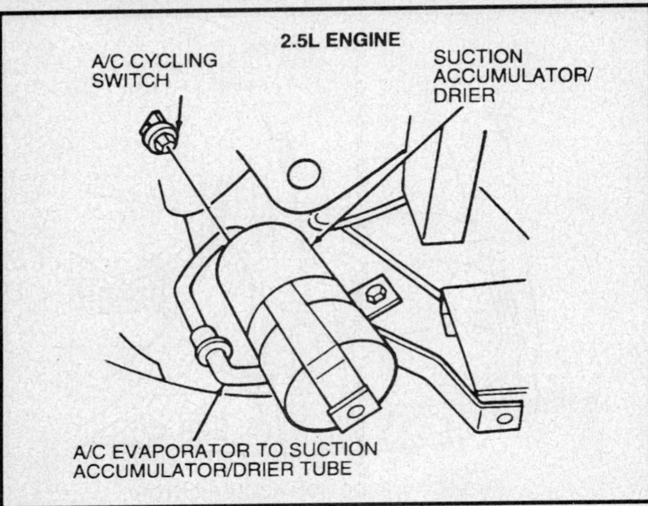

Cycling switch disconnect—Contour and Mystique

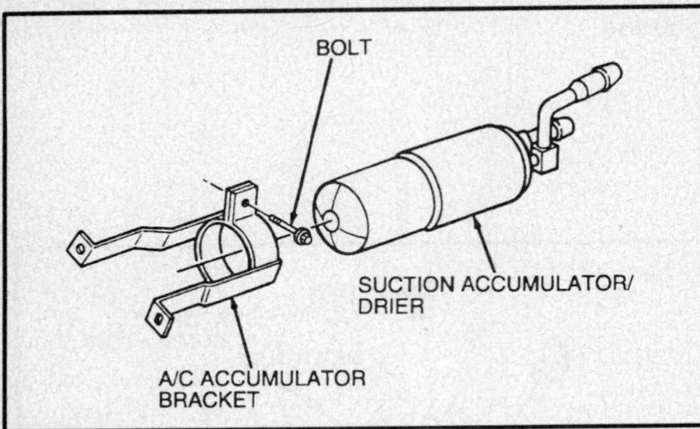

Accumulator drier and bracket separated—Contour and Mystique

Receiver/Drier

REMOVAL AND INSTALLATION

Capri

1. Disconnect the negative battery cable.
2. Discharge the refrigerant from the air conditioning system.
3. Remove the air cleaner assembly and front mounting bracket.
4. Disconnect the air conditioning lines from the receiver/drier and plug the ends to prevent dirt and moisture from entering the system.
5. Loosen the bracket and remove the receiver/drier.

To install:

6. Add 0.50–0.65 oz. (15–20ml) of clean refrigerant oil to a new replacement receiver/drier to maintain total system oil requirements.
7. Install the receiver/drier into the bracket.
8. Connect the air conditioning lines making sure to connect the line coming from the condenser to the port marked **IN**. Tighten the line connection retaining screws to 9–11 ft. lbs. (12–15 Nm).
9. Install the air cleaner assembly and mounting bracket.
10. Connect the negative battery cable. Leak test, evacuate and charge the system. Observe all safety precautions.

Festiva

1. Disconnect the negative battery cable. Properly discharge the refrigerant from the air conditioning system. Observe all safety precautions.
2. Remove the condenser.
3. Disconnect the condenser outlet tube from the receiver/drier.
4. Loosen the mounting clamp screw and remove the receiver/drier.

To install:

5. Drain the oil from the removed receiver/drier through the inlet fitting. Drain the oil into a calibrated measuring container. Add the same amount of clean refrigerant oil plus 1 oz. (29.5 ml) to the new accumulator drier.

NOTE: If more than 5 oz. (147 ml) of refrigerant oil is removed from a receiver/drier, it is an indication that the oil drain hole in the receiver/drier is plugged. Always check the receiver/drier for excessive oil if the compressor has been replaced for lack of performance.

6. Position the receiver/drier in the mounting clamp.
7. Install a new O-ring, lubricated with clean refrigerant oil and connect the condenser tube to the receiver/drier.
8. Tighten the mounting clamp screw.
9. Install the condenser.
10. Leak test, evacuate and recharge the system.

Expansion Valve

REMOVAL AND INSTALLATION

Capri

1. Disconnect the negative battery cable.
2. Discharge the refrigerant from the air conditioning system.
3. Remove the evaporator assembly.
4. Remove the 10 retaining clips, separate the case halves and remove the evaporator.
5. Remove the de-ice thermostat and disconnect the liquid tube from the inlet fitting of the expansion valve.
6. Remove the capillary tube from the evaporator outlet and remove the expansion valve from the inlet fitting of the evaporator.

To install:

7. Install the expansion valve to the inlet fitting of the evaporator. Tighten the fitting to 9–11 ft. lbs. (12–15 Nm).
8. Connect the liquid tube to the inlet fitting of the expansion valve. Tighten the fitting to 9–11 ft. lbs. (12–15 Nm).
9. Install the packing to fix the capillary tube of the expansion valve to the outlet of the evaporator.
10. Install the de-ice switch and assemble the case halves with the 10 retaining clips.
11. Install the evaporator assembly.
12. Connect the negative battery cable. Leak test, evacuate and charge the system according. Observe all safety precautions.

Festiva and Aspire

1. Disconnect the negative battery cable. Properly discharge the refrigerant from the air conditioning system.
2. Remove the evaporator housing.
3. Remove the air inlet duct.
4. Remove the staples and the capillary tube insulation. Remove the capillary tube clamp.
5. Disconnect the expansion valve at the evaporator tube fitting and inlet tube fitting and remove the expansion valve.

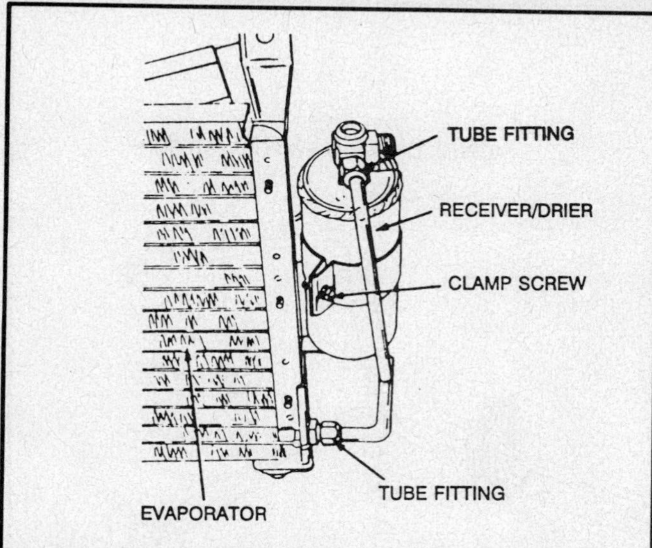

Receiver/drier location—Festiva

To install:

6. Install new O-rings on the evaporator and inlet tube fittings.
7. Connect the evaporator tube and inlet tube fittings.
8. Install the capillary tube and clamp, then install the insulation and staple it into position.
9. Install the air inlet duct and install the evaporator housing.
10. Leak test, evacuate and recharge the system.

Fixed Orifice Tube

The fixed orifice tube is located in the liquid line near the condenser and is an integral part of the liquid line. If it is necessary to replace the orifice tube, the liquid line must be replaced or fixed orifice tube replacement kit E5VY–190695–A or equivalent, must be installed. The fixed orifice tube is removed and installed using fixed orifice tube remover/replacer T83L–19990–A or equivalent.

The fixed orifice tube should be replaced whenever a compressor is replaced. If high pressure reads extremely high and low pressure is almost a vacuum, the fixed orifice is plugged and must be replaced.

REMOVAL AND INSTALLATION

NOTE: Whenever a refrigerant line is replaced, it will be necessary to replace the accumulator/drier. Replace the fixed orifice tube whenever the compressor is being replaced for failure.

Except Escort and Tracer

WITHOUT FIXED ORIFICE TUBE REPLACEMENT KIT

1. Disconnect the negative battery cable. Properly discharge the air conditioning system.
2. Disconnect and remove the liquid line from the vehicle.
3. To install, position the new line with protective caps installed. Install new O-rings in each position. After line is in place with retaining clamps, remove protective caps one at a time and attach each end of the line.
4. Evacuate, recharge and leak test the system. Check for proper operation.

FIXED ORIFICE TUBE REPLACEMENT KIT

1. Disconnect the negative battery cable.
2. Discharge the refrigerant from the air conditioning system.
3. Remove the liquid line from the vehicle.
4. Locate the orifice tube by 3 indented notches or a circular depression in the metal portion of the liquid line. Note the angular position of the ends of the liquid line so that it can be reassembled in the correct position.
5. Cut a 2–1/2 in. (63.5mm) section from the tube at the orifice tube location. Do not cut closer than 1 in. (25.4mm) from the start of the bend in the tube.
6. Remove the orifice tube from the housing using pliers. An orifice tube removal tool cannot be used.
7. Flush the 2 pieces of liquid line to remove any contaminants.
8. Lubricate the O-rings with clean refrigerant oil and assemble the orifice tube kit, with the orifice tube installed, to the liquid line. Make sure the flow direction arrow is pointing toward the evaporator end of the liquid line and the taper of each compressor ring is toward the compressor nut.

NOTE: The inlet tube will be positioned against the orifice tube tabs when correctly assembled.

9. While holding the hex of the tube in a vise, tighten each compression nut to 65–70 ft. lbs. (88–94 Nm) with a crow foot wrench.
10. Assemble the liquid line to the vehicle using new O-rings lubricated with clean refrigerant oil.
11. Leak test, evacuate and charge the system. Observe all safety precautions.
12. Check the system for proper operation.

Escort and Tracer

1. Disconnect the negative battery cable.
2. Discharge the refrigerant from the air conditioning system.
3. Disconnect the spring-lock coupling next to the fixed orifice tube according to the spring-lock coupling disconnect procedure. Discard the O-rings.
4. Remove as many refrigerant line retaining nuts and bolts as necessary to permit access to the open end of the refrigerant line.
5. Using fixed orifice tube remover/replacer T83L–19990–A or equivalent, remove the fixed orifice tube from the refrigerant line.

To install:

6. Install the fixed orifice tube using the orifice tube remover/replacer.
7. Install the refrigerant line retaining nuts and bolts.
8. Using new O-rings lubricated with clean refrigerant oil, connect the spring-lock coupling.
9. Connect the negative battery cable. Leak test, evacuate and charge the system. Observe all safety precautions.

Blower Motor

REMOVAL AND INSTALLATION

Taurus and Sable or Continental without 4.6L engine

1. Disconnect the negative battery cable.

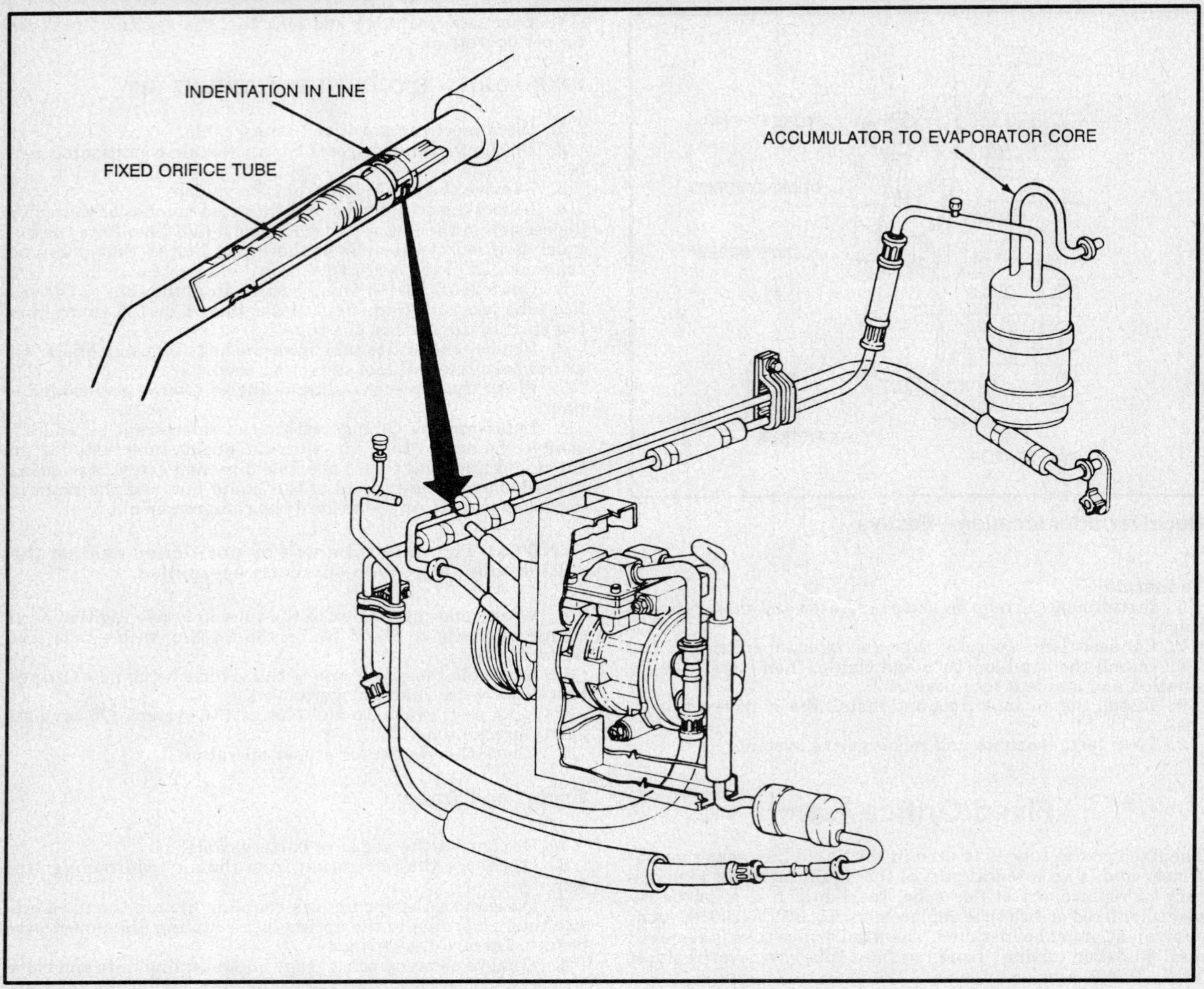

INDENTATION IN LINE
FIXED ORIFICE TUBE
ACCUMULATOR TO EVAPORATOR CORE

Fixed orifice tube location—Continental

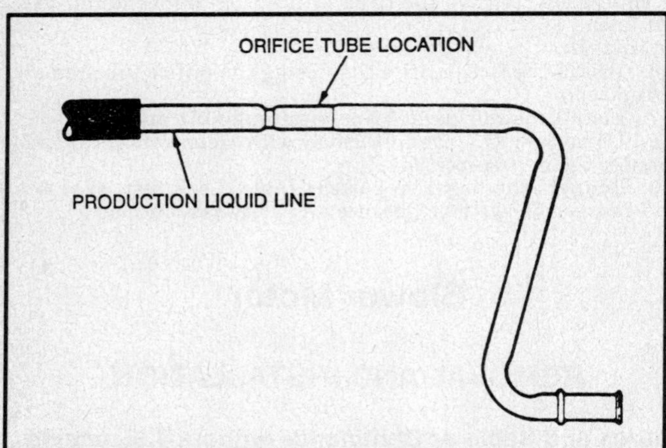

Fixed orifice tube location—typical

2. Open the glove compartment door, release the door retainers and lower the door.
3. Remove the screw attaching the recirculation duct support bracket to the instrument panel cowl.
4. Remove the vacuum connection to the recirculation door vacuum motor. Remove the screws attaching the recirculation duct to the heater assembly.
5. Remove the recirculation duct from the heater assembly, lowering the duct from between the instrument panel and the heater case.
6. Disconnect the blower motor electrical lead. Remove the blower motor wheel clip and remove the blower motor wheel.
7. Remove the blower motor mounting plate screws and remove the blower motor from the evaporator case.
8. Complete the installation of the blower motor by reversing the removal procedure.

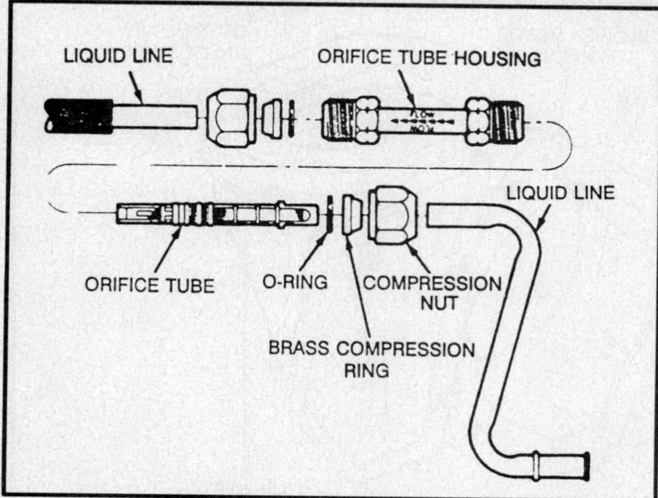

Orifice tube kit disassembled

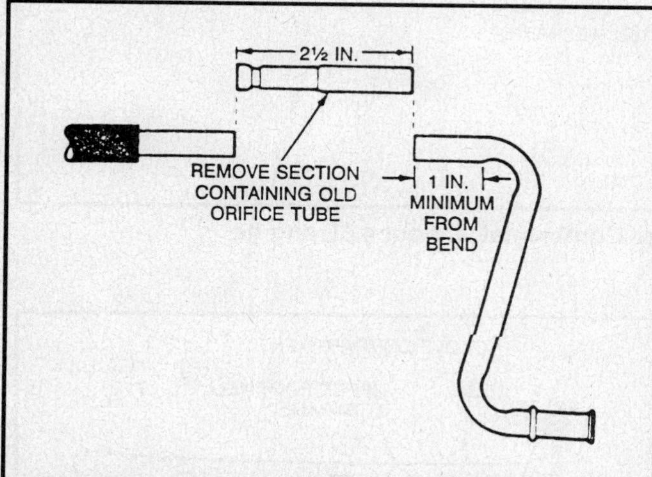

Orifice tube section removed from liquid line

Continental with 4.6L engine

1. Disconnect the negative battery cable.
2. Disengage two push pins retaining instrument panel insulator to instrument panel. Disconnect courtesy lamp from instrument panel insulator.
3. Remove passenger door trim panel, pull back carpet and reposition main wire harness connector and bracket to improve access to blower motor.
4. Working from under instrument panel, disconnect electrical harness connector from blower motor.
5. Remove 3 heater blower motor mounting plate screws. Remove blower motor from A/C evaporator housing.
6. To install, reverse removal procedures.

Tempo and Topaz

1. Disconnect the negative battery cable.
2. Remove the glove compartment assembly.
3. Disconnect the blower motor wires from the blower motor resistor.
4. Loosen the instrument panel lower right side.
5. Remove 4 screws holding the blower motor to the heater case.

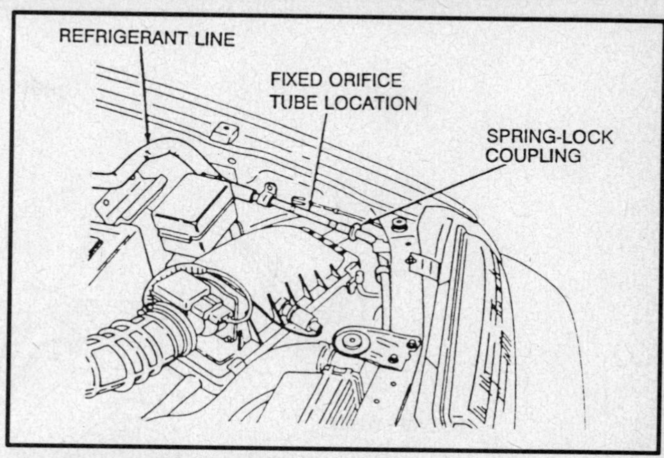

Fixed orifice tube location—Escort and Tracer

6. Rotate the motor until the mounting plate flats clear the edge of the glove compartment opening. Remove the motor and mounting plate.
7. Remove the motor and seal from the mounting plate. Check that plate surface is clean. Remove the pushnut and take the wheel off the motor shaft.

To install:

8. Position the blower wheel on the motor shaft and install the pushnut. With new seal in place, position the motor and plate to the heater case.
9. Install 4 mounting screws and the lower right instrument panel bolt.
10. Connect blower motor wires. Connect the negative battery cable and check blower operation. Install the glove compartment.

Contour and Mystique

1. Disconnect the negative battery cable.
2. Working from inside vehicle, remove push pins and upper footwell trim panel from the passenger side.
3. Disconnect the wire harness electrical connector from the blower motor.
4. Carefully lift retaining lug on A/C blower motor flange and rotate blower motor counterclockwise approximately 30 degrees to disengage it from the A/C evaporator housing.
5. Pull the blower motor out of the A/C evaporator housing.

To install:

6. Insert blower motor into A/C evaporator housing and turn clockwise until realining lug engages.
7. Connect wiring connector to blower motor.
8. Install upper footwell trim panel.
9. Connect the negative battery cable.

Escort, Tracer and Aspire

1. Disconnect the negative battery cable.
2. Remove the trim panel below the glove compartment.
3. Remove the wiring bracket and bolt and disconnect the blower motor electrical connector.
4. Remove the 3 blower motor mounting bolts and remove the blower motor.
5. Remove the blower wheel retaining clip and remove the blower wheel from the blower motor.

To install:

6. Install the blower wheel and the retaining clip.
7. Position the blower motor and install the mounting bolts.
8. Connect the electrical connector and install the wiring bracket and bolt.
9. Install the trim panel and connect the negative battery cable.

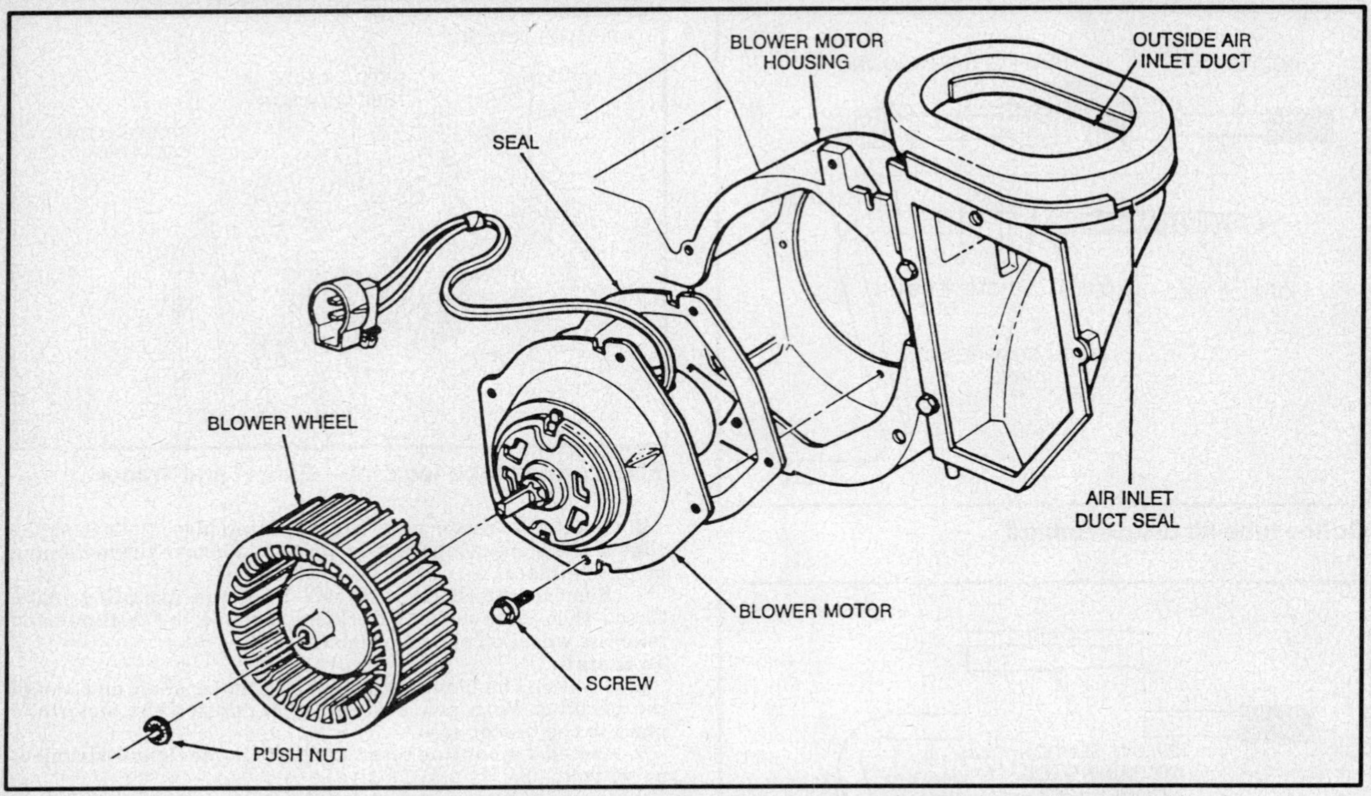

Blower motor removal and installation—Taurus and Sable or Continental without 4.6L engine

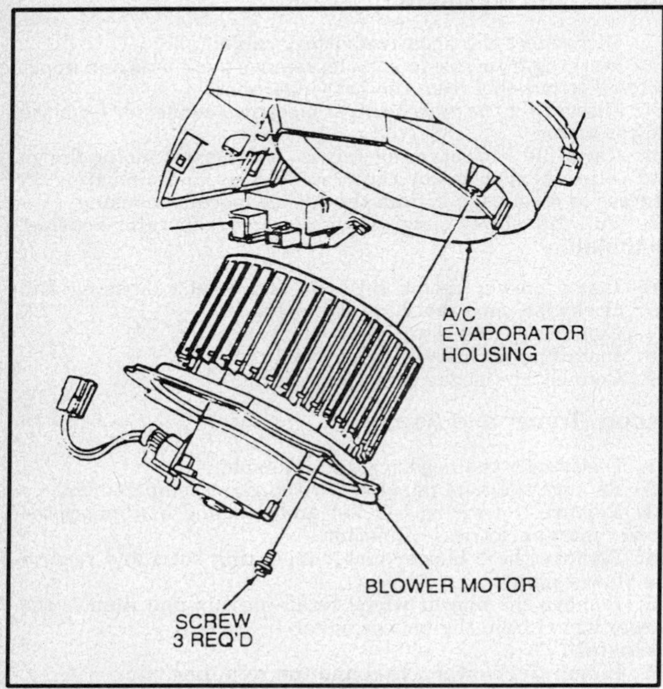

Blower motor removal and installation—Continental with 4.6L engine

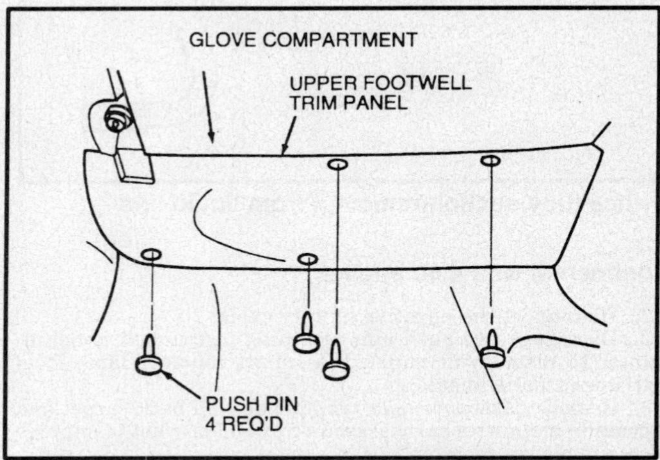

Footwell trim panel removal and installation—Contour and Mystique

Probe

1. Disconnect the negative battery cable.
2. Remove the sound deadening panel from the passenger side.
3. If required, remove the glove box assembly and the brace.
4. If required, remove the cooling hose from the blower motor assembly.

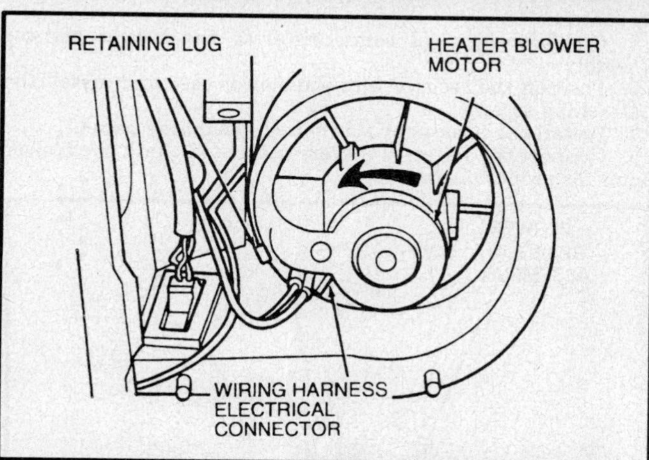

Blower motor removal and installation—Contour and Mystique

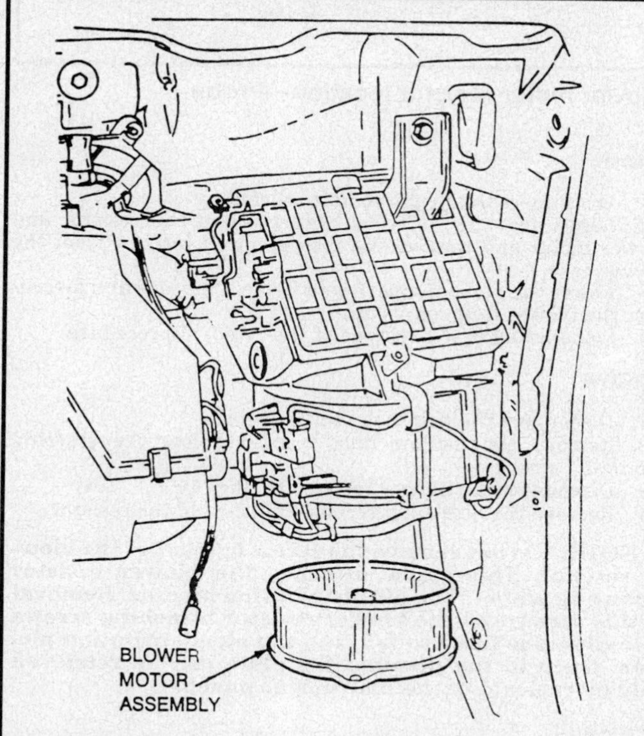

Blower motor assembly removal and installation—Probe

5. Disconnect the electrical connector from the blower motor.
6. Remove the blower motor-to-blower motor housing screws and blower motor.
7. If necessary, remove the blower wheel-to-blower motor clip and the wheel.
8. To install, reverse the removal procedures and check the blower motor operation.

Capri

1. Disconnect the negative battery cable.
2. Disconnect the electrical connector at the blower motor and remove the 3 screws retaining the motor and cover to the blower case.
3. Remove the cover, cooling tube and blower motor.
4. Remove the nut retaining the blower wheel to the blower motor and remove the blower wheel.
5. Remove the gasket from the blower motor.

To install:

6. Position the gasket onto the blower motor and install the blower wheel onto the blower motor. Install the attaching nut.
7. Position the blower motor, cooling tube and cover into the blower case. Install the 3 screws.
8. Connect the electrical connector to the blower motor and connect the negative battery cable. Check the operation of the blower motor.

Festiva

1. Disconnect the negative battery cable.
2. Locate the instrument panel spacer brace below the steering column and remove it, if installed.
3. Disconnect and lower the length of flexible air discharge hose from below the steering column.
4. Disconnect the blower motor wiring.
5. Remove the blower motor-to-air distribution plenum attaching screws and pull the blower motor with blower wheel away from the heater housing.
6. Remove the blower wheel retaining nut from the motor shaft and remove the blower wheel. Remove the washer from the motor shaft.

To install:

7. Assemble the blower wheel to the new blower motor by reversing the removal procedure.
8. Position the blower assembly onto the air distribution plenum and install the attaching screws. Connect the blower wiring.
9. Raise and connect the length of flexible hose. Install the support brace.
10. Connect the negative battery cable. Check the blower operation.

Blower Motor Resistor

REMOVAL AND INSTALLATION

Taurus and Sable

1. Disconnect the negative battery cable.
2. Open the glove compartment door and release the glove compartment retainers so that the glove compartment hangs down.
3. Disconnect the wire harness connector from the resistor assembly.
4. Remove the 2 resistor attaching screws and remove the resistor from the evaporator case.

To install:

5. Position the resistor assembly in the evaporator case opening and install 2 attaching screws. Do not apply sealer to the resistor assembly mounting surface.
6. Connect the wire harness connector to the resistor.
7. Connect the negative battery cable, check the operation of the blower motor and close the glove compartment door.

Tempo and Topaz

1. Disconnect the negative battery cable.
2. Pull the sides of the glove compartment liner inward and pull the liner from the opening. Allow the glove compartment and door to hang on the hinges.
3. Disconnect the wire connector from the resistor assembly.
4. Remove the 2 resistor attaching screws and remove the resistor assembly.

To install:

5. Position the resistor assembly in the opening and install the 2 attaching screws.

6. Connect the wire harness connectors to the resistor assembly.
7. Connect the negative battery cable and check for proper operation of the blower motor in all blower speeds.
8. Install the glove compartment in the glove compartment opening.

Contour and Mystique

1. Disconnect the negative battery cable.
2. Working from inside the vehicle, disengage clips and remove upper footwell trim panel from the passenger side.
3. Disconnect wire harness from heater blower motor switch resistor.
4. Insert screwdriver approximately 0.2 in. (5 mm) under edge of heater blower motor switch resistor to disengage retainer and remove heater blower motor switch resistor.

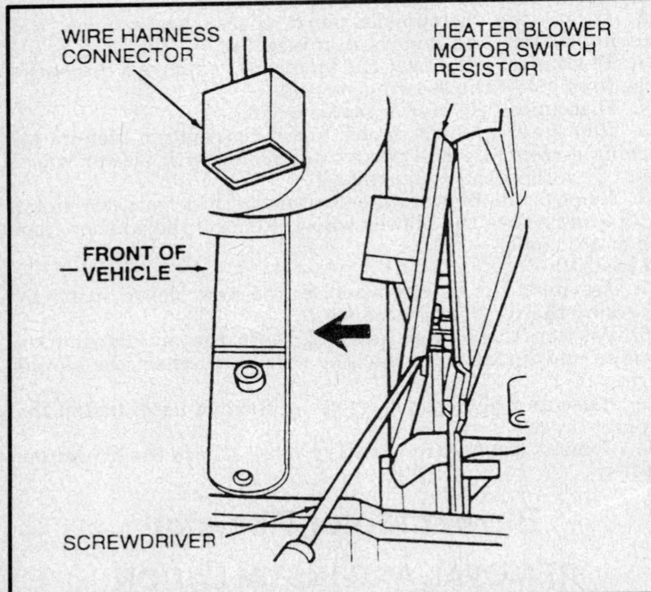

Blower motor switch resistor—Contour and Mystique

To install:

5. Position heater blower motor switch resistor on A/C evaporator housing and snap into place.
6. Connect wiring harness.
7. Install upper footwell trim panel.
8. Connect the negative battery cable.
9. Check blower motor for proper operation at all speeds.

Escort, Tracer and Aspire

1. Disconnect the negative battery cable.
2. Disconnect the 2 resistor assembly electrical connectors.
3. Remove the 2 attaching bolts and remove the resistor assembly.
4. Installation is the reverse of the removal procedure.

Probe

1. Disconnect the negative battery cable.
2. Remove the passenger side sound deadening panel.
3. Disconnect the electrical connector(s) from the blower resistor assembly.
4. Remove the attaching screws from the blower resistor assembly at the bottom of the blower case and remove the resistor from the blower case.

To install:

5. Connect electrical connector(s) to the blower resistor assembly.
6. Position the resistor into the blower case and install the 2 attaching screws.
7. Install the passenger side sound deadening panel.
8. Connect the negative battery cable and check the blower motor for proper operation.

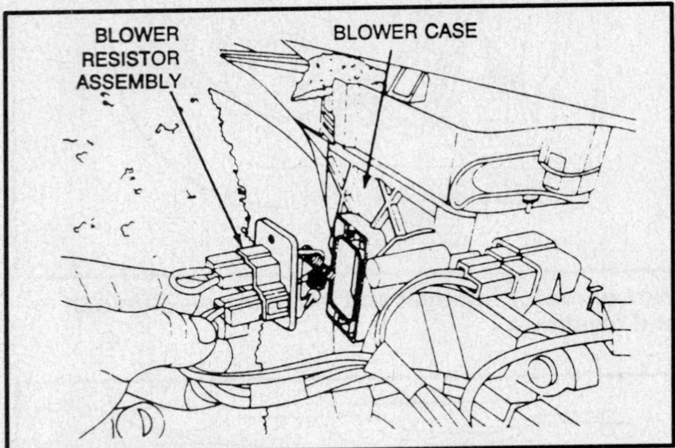

Blower motor resistor location—Probe

Capri

1. Disconnect the negative battery cable.
2. Disconnect the electrical connectors at the resistor and blower motor and remove the 2 screws and resistor from the blower case.
3. Lower the glove compartment below the stops and disconnect the blower feed connector.
4. Installation is the reverse of the removal procedure.

Festiva

1. Disconnect the negative battery cable.
2. Remove the airflow duct located below the steering column.
3. Disconnect the blower resistor wiring.
4. Remove the attaching screws and the blower resistor.

NOTE: Do not remove the screw in front of the blower resistor. This screw attaches the blower resistor mounting plate to the air distribution plenum. Removal of this screw and the blower resistor attaching screws will allow the plate to fall into the air distribution plenum. Once in the plenum, the plate can be retrieved only by removal of the instrument panel.

To install:

5. Position the resistor on the plenum and install the attaching screws.
6. Connect the blower resistor wiring and install the airflow duct.
7. Connect the negative battery cable and check the blower motor operation.

Heater Core

REMOVAL AND INSTALLATION

Taurus, Sable and Continental

1. Disconnect the negative battery cable.
2. Drain the cooling system.

3. Disconnect the heater hoses from the heater core.
4. Remove the instrument panel assembly and lay it on the front seat.
5. Remove the evaporator case if equipped with air conditioning. If equipped with heater only, remove heater case as follows:
- Remove the screw holding instrument panel shake brace to the heater case. Remove the brace.
- Remove the floor register and rear floor ducts from the bottom of the heater case.
- In the engine compartment, remove 3 nuts holding heater case to the dash panel.
- Remove 2 screws attaching brackets to the cowl top panel. Remove the heater case.
6. Remove the vacuum source line from the heater core tube seal.
7. Remove the seal from the heater core tubes.
8. On Continental, remove the screws attaching the blend door actuator to the door shaft on the evaporator case. Remove the actuator from the case.
9. Remove the heater core access cover and foam seal from the evaporator case.
10. Lift the heater core with 3 foam seals from the evaporator case. Transfer the foam seals to the new heater core.
11. Installation is the reverse of the removal procedure.

Tempo and Topaz

1. Disconnect the negative battery cable.
2. Drain the cooling system.
3. Disconnect the heater hoses from the heater core.
4. From inside the vehicle, remove the 2 screws retaining floor duct to the plenum. Remove 1 screw retaining floor duct to instrument panel. Remove floor duct.
5. Remove the 4 screws attaching the heater core cover to the heater case assembly.
6. Remove the heater core and cover from the plenum.
7. Installation is the reverse of the removal procedure.

Contour and Mystique

1. Disconnect the negative battery cable.
2. Remove the heater outlet floor duct.
3. Raise and safely support the vehicle.
4. Disconnect the heater water hoses from heater core inlet and outlet tubes. Plug the heater water hose and cap the heater core tubes to prevent coolant loss during removal of heater core.
5. Disconnect the vacuum supply hose (black) from vacuum service in engine compartment.
6. Disconnect the vacuum supply hose (black) from A/C vacuum reservoir tank and bracket inside vehicle.
7. Release 4 retaining tabs and remove heater core, heater core cover and vacuum hose form vehicle.
8. Remove the heater dash panel seal and vacuum hose from heater core cover.
9. Remove the retaining screw and heater core mounting bracket from the heater core cover.
10. Remove the heater core from the heater core cover.
11. Remove the heater core case seal from the heater core.
12. Installation is the reverse of the removal procedure.

Escort, Tracer and Aspire

1. Disconnect the negative battery cable and drain the cooling system.
2. Disconnect the heater hoses at the bulkhead.
3. Remove the instrument panel as follows:
- Remove the 4 bolts securing the steering column to the instrument panel frame. Lower the steering column.
- Remove the cap screws securing the instrument cluster bezel to the instrument panel and remove the instrument cluster bezel.
- Disconnect the speedometer cable at the transaxle by pulling the cable out of the vehicle speed sensor.
- Remove the screws and bolts securing the instrument cluster to the instrument panel. Pull the instrument cluster out slightly and disconnect the electrical connectors from the rear of the instrument cluster.
- Disconnect the speedometer cable from the instrument cluster. Remove the instrument cluster from the instrument panel.
- Detach the hood release cable from the left lower dash trim panel. Carefully pry out both dash side panels.
- Remove the 4 retaining screws and the left lower dash trim panel. Disconnect all necessary electrical connectors.
- Remove the 2 hinge-to-instrument panel retaining screws and remove the glove compartment.
- Remove the climate control assembly and the ash tray.
- Remove the 7 accessory console retaining screws. Disconnect the radio antenna, radio wire connectors and cigarette lighter connector.
- Remove the retaining screws and the right lower dash trim panel. Disconnect the 3 amplifier wire connectors.
- Remove the 4 bolts attaching the instrument panel frame to the floor pan. Remove the bolt from both of the lower instrument panel mounts.
- Remove the 2 bolts from both of the upper instrument panel mounts. Remove the retaining screw and the defroster duct bezel.
- Remove the 3 mounting bolts that attach the upper instrument panel to the cowl and remove the instrument panel from the vehicle.

NOTE: Use care to prevent any damage to the instrument panel or the surrounding interior trim.

4. Disconnect the mode selector and temperature control cables from the cams and retaining clips.
5. Remove the necessary defroster duct screws and loosen the capscrew that secures the heater-to-blower clamp.
6. Remove the 3 heater unit mounting nuts and disconnect the antenna lead from the retaining clip. Remove the heater unit.
7. Remove the insulator and the 4 brace capscrews. Remove the brace.
8. Remove the heater core from the heater unit.

To install:

9. Install the heater core into the heater unit and install the brace.
10. Install the brace capscrews and the insulator.

NOTE: If a new heater unit is being installed, save the keys that are found on the new unit for mode selector and temperature control cable adjustment.

11. Position the heater unit and attach the defroster and floor ducting. Install the heater unit mounting nuts.
12. Tighten the heater-to-blower clamp capscrew and install the defroster duct screws. Connect the antenna lead to the retaining clip.
13. Install the instrument panel by reversing the removal procedure.
14. Connect and adjust the mode selector and temperature control cables. Connect the heater hoses at the bulkhead.
15. Fill the cooling system and connect the negative battery cable. Start the engine and check for leaks. Check the coolant level and fill as necessary.

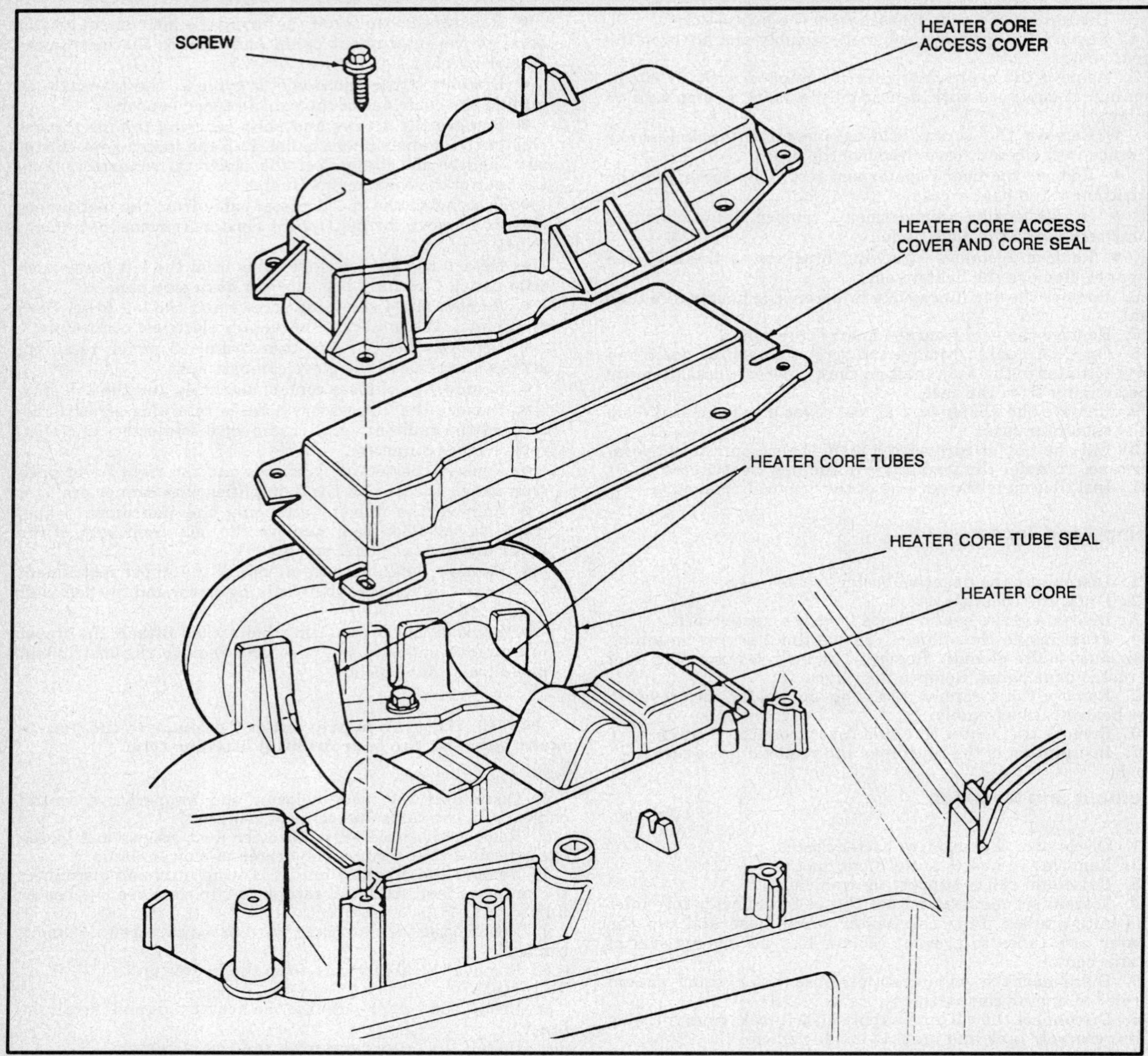

Heater core access cover removal—Taurus, Sable and Continental

Probe

1. Disconnect the negative battery cable. Remove the instrument panel as follows:
   - Remove the upper and lower steering column covers, detach the steering column and lower it to the seat.
   - Remove the instrument cluster.
   - Remove the floor console.
   - Remove the glove compartment.
   - Remove the hush panel, console kick panels and side kick panels.
   - Remove the climate control assembly.
   - Remove the radio assembly and trip computer, if equipped.
   - If required, remove dash panel access cover to gain access to the center instrument panel to dash mounting nut.
   - Remove the 2 instrument panel side covers.
   - Remove the instrument panel mounting bolts.
   - Remove the door pillar trim.
   - Lift the panel up and to the rear, disconnect all remaining electrical harnesses and remove the panel from the vehicle.
2. Drain the cooling system to a level below the heater core.
3. Disconnect and plug the hoses from the heater core.
4. If equipped with air conditioning, remove the evaporator assembly. Remove the main air duct from the heater case.

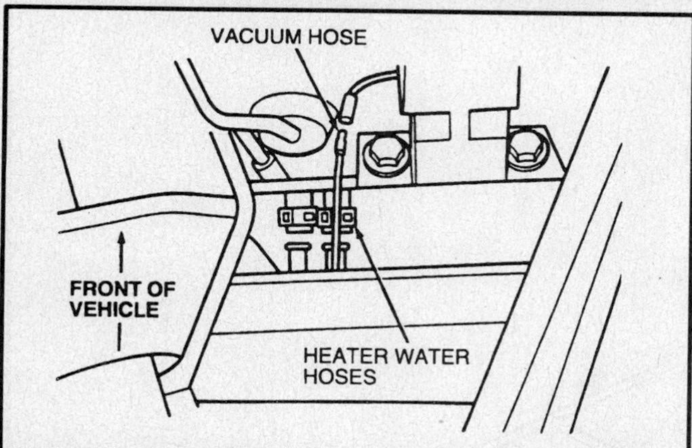

Heater water and vacuum hoses—Contour and Mystique

5. Loosen the upper left evaporator/blower unit nut to allow for removal of the heater case. Remove the heater wire harness screw.
6. Remove the heater case attaching screws and pull the heater case straight out; be careful not to damage the heater core extension tubes.
7. Remove the heater core tube braces-to-heater case screws and the tube braces. Lift the heater core straight up and from the heater case.
8. Installation is the reverse of the removal procedure.

Capri

1. Disconnect the negative battery cable and drain the cooling system.
2. Remove the floor console as follows:
   - Slide the front seats completely forward and remove the screws retaining the rear of the console.
   - Slide the front seat completely rearward and remove the screws retaining the rear console to the front console.
   - Raise the parking lever as far as it will go, raise the rear of the console and pull backwards to remove.
   - Disconnect the wiring harness from the mirror switch and headlight motor switch.
   - If equipped with an automatic transaxle, loosen the jam nut and unscrew the shift handle.
   - Raise the ashtray, disconnect the wiring beneath it and remove the center carpet panels. Remove the brackets, if necessary.
   - If equipped with a manual transaxle, remove the screws retaining the manual shift lever boot to the bottom of the front console and remove the screws and front console leaving the shift knob and boot on the shift lever. Unscrew the shift knob with the boot and remove from the shift lever, if necessary.
   - If equipped with an automatic transaxle, remove the screws and shift quadrant. Disconnect the shift quadrant light connector.
3. Remove the instrument panel as follows:
   - Remove the left and right lower cowl trim panels.
   - Remove the heater/radio bezel, trim covers, instrument cluster bezel and storage compartment.
   - Remove the instrument cluster and the steering column.
   - Loosen the nut retaining the hood release cable to the lower instrument panel and position the cable aside.
   - Remove the radio and the heater control panel.
   - Tag and remove all wiring harness retainers and connectors from the instrument panel.
   - Remove the 3 screws, lockwashers and plain washers located near the base of the windshield. Remove the 2 bolts and washers from each side of the instrument panel. An access panel is provided for the upper bolts.
   - Remove the 2 screws and lockwashers retaining the instrument panel to the center floor bracket. Remove the 2 screws retaining the instrument panel to the steering column support.
   - With the help of an assistant, gently slide the instrument panel outward. Disconnect the ducts and wiring during removal.
4. Disconnect and plug the heater hoses at the extension tubes.
5. Remove the plastic rivets and both defroster hoses. Remove the main air duct connecting the heater case to the blower case or air conditioning unit, if equipped.
6. Roll back the carpet to gain access to the lower duct and lower mounting bolts. It may be necessary to remove the carpet fasteners.
7. Disconnect the lower duct for the rear seat supply from the heater case.
8. Remove the cable ends from the heater case, if still connected and remove the wiring harness.
9. Remove the 2 lower bolts, 2 upper nuts and 1 center retaining nut from the blower case and remove the heater case.
10. Remove the 3 screws attaching the heater core cover to the heater case and remove the cover. Remove the screws securing the tube braces.
11. Loosen the clamps and remove the extension tubes from the heater core. Remove the O-ring from the outlet tube.
12. Remove the heater core by pulling it straight out. Remove the extension tubes and grommets, if necessary.

To install:

13. Install the grommets and extension tubes, if removed. Make sure the grommets are flush with the engine compartment wall.
14. Install the heater core into the heater case and install a new O-ring onto the outlet extension tube. Connect the extension tubes to the heater core and tighten the clamps.
15. Secure the extension tube braces with the screws and install the heater core cover with the 3 screws.
16. Position the heater case onto the mounting studs and guide the extension tubes through the dash panel. Make sure the grommets are sealed around the extension tubes.
17. Install 2 upper nuts, 1 center retaining nut and 2 lower bolts. Tighten all fasteners to 5–7 ft. lbs. (7–10 Nm).
18. Install the lower duct onto the heater case. Reposition the carpet and install the fasteners, if removed.
19. Attach the wiring harness and connect the defroster hoses and main air duct to the heater case. Install the plastic retaining rivets.
20. Connect the heater hoses and tighten the clamps to 3–4 ft. lbs. (4–6 Nm).
21. Install the instrument panel by reversing the removal procedure. Connect the control cable to the heater case and adjust the cable.
22. Install the floor console by reversing the removal procedure.
23. Fill the cooling system and connect the negative battery cable. Operate the heater and check for leaks.

Festiva

1. Disconnect the negative battery cable. Drain the cooling system.
2. Remove the instrument panel as follows:
   - Remove the steering wheel and combination switch.

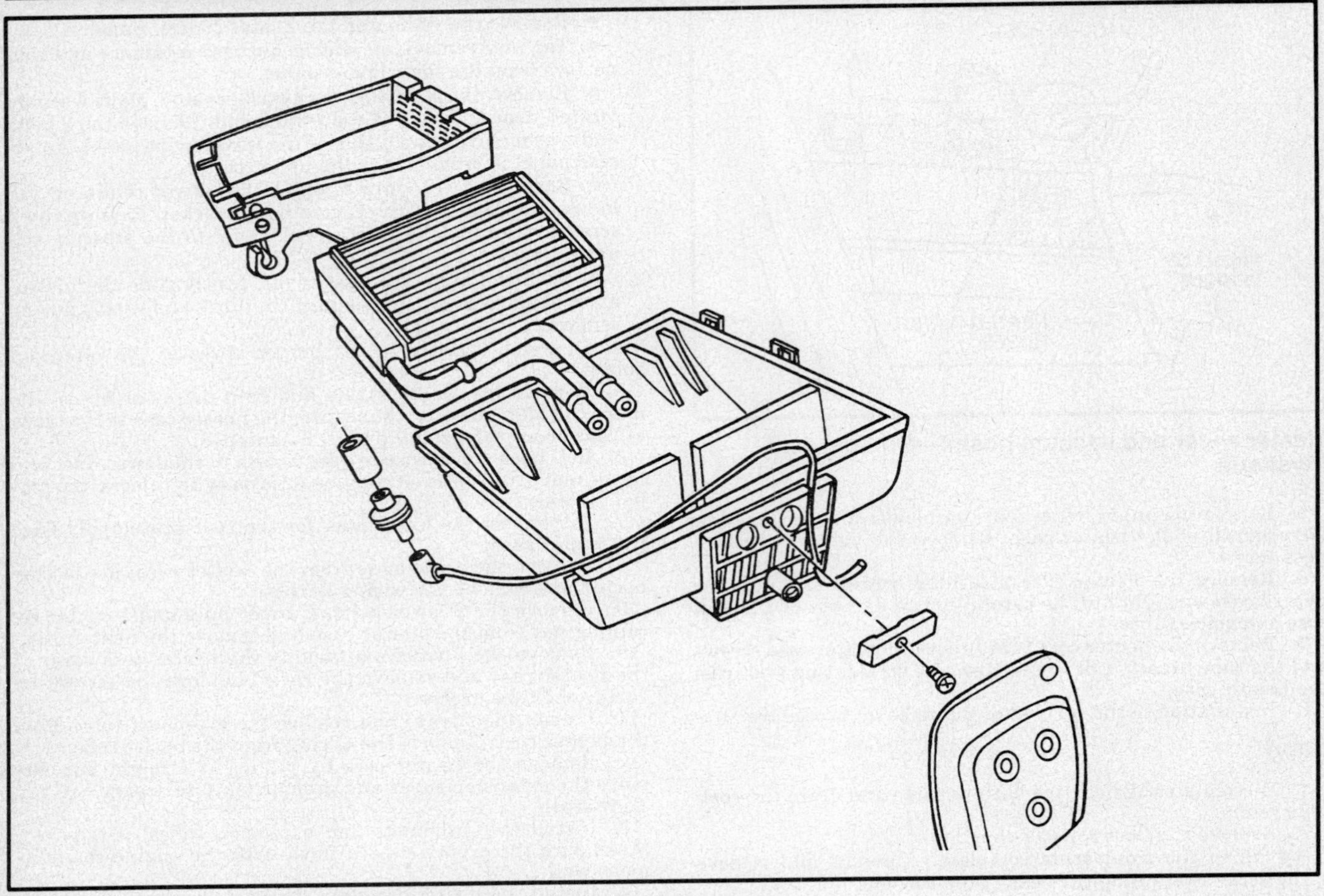

Heater core removal and installation—Contour and Mystique

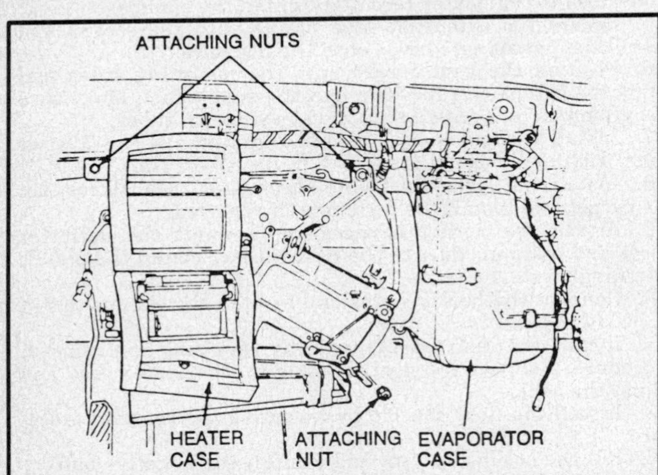

Heater case attaching screw locations—Probe with air conditioning

- Remove instrument cluster bezel and disconnect electrical connectors.
- Remove left and right heater ducts. Disconnect speedometer cable from the transaxle.
- Loosen instrument cluster, pull it out slightly, lift lock tab and detach 2 cluster electrical connectors, then press the lock tab and detach the speedometer cable. Remove the instrument cluster.
- Remove steering column shield and bracket.
- Remove the glove box.
- Open fuse box cover and remove 2 top screws.
- Remove floor console. Remove support bracket below the ashtray.
- Remove the radio and heater-A/C control panel.
- Remove the snap in covers to expose instrument panel retaining bolts. Remove all bolts, disconnect wiring connectors and remove the instrument panel.

3. Remove the air distribution plenum by performing the following steps:
   - Disconnect the heater hoses from inside the engine compartment.
   - Disconnect the blower motor and blower resistor wiring.
   - Disengage the wiring harness and antenna lead from the routing bracket on the front of the air distribution housing.
   - Loosen the clamp screw securing the connector duct to the air inlet housing.
   - Remove the upper and lower plenum attaching nuts. Disengage the plenum from the defroster ducts and remove from the vehicle.
4. Disconnect the link from the 2 defroster doors.
5. Locate and remove the screws just above and to the right of the blower resistor. Turn the plenum around and remove the screw located to the left of the blower motor opening.

6. Remove the retaining clips that secure the plenum halves. Separate the plenum halves.
7. Remove the heater core and tube insert/stiffener. Remove the tube insert/stiffener from the heater core and transfer to the new unit. Install the new heater core.
8. Installation is the reverse of the removal procedure.

Evaporator

REMOVAL AND INSTALLATION

Taurus and Sable or Continental without 4.6L engine

NOTE: Whenever an evaporator is removed, it will be necessary to replace the accumulator/drier.

1. Disconnect the negative battery cable.
2. Properly drain and recover the coolant.
3. Properly discharge the air conditioning system.
4. Disconnect the heater hoses from the heater core. Plug the heater core tubes.
5. Disconnect the vacuum supply hose from the in-line vacuum check valve in the engine compartment.
6. Disconnect the liquid line and the accumulator from the evaporator core at the dash panel. Cap the refrigerant lines and evaporator core to prevent entrance of dirt and moisture.
7. Remove the instrument panel and place it on the front seat.
8. Remove the screw holding the instrument panel shake brace to the evaporator case and remove the instrument panel shake brace.
9. Remove the 2 screws attaching the floor register and rear seat duct to the bottom of the evaporator case.
10. Disconnect the vacuum line, electrical connections and aspirator hose from the evaporator case.
11. Remove the 3 nuts attaching the evaporator case to the dash panel in the engine compartment.
12. Remove the 2 screws attaching the support brackets to the cowl top panel.
13. Carefully pull the evaporator assembly away from the dash panel and remove the evaporator case from the vehicle.
14. Disconnect and remove the vacuum harness.
15. Remove the 6 screws attaching the recirculation duct and remove the duct from the evaporator case.
16. Remove the 2 screws from the air inlet duct and remove the duct from the evaporator case.
17. Remove the support bracket from the evaporator case.
18. If equipped with automatic temperature control, remove the screws holding the electronic connector bracket to the recirculation duct and remove the blend door actuator and cold engine lock out switch, which is held on by spring tension at the outermost heater core tube.
19. Remove the molded seals from the evaporator core tubes.
20. Drill a 3/16 in. (4.75mm) hole in both upright tabs on top of the evaporator case.
21. Using a suitable tool, cut the top of the evaporator case between the raised outline. Fold the cutout cover back from the opening and lift the evaporator core from the case.

To install:

NOTE: Add 3 oz. (90 ml) of clean refrigerant oil to a new replacement evaporator core to maintain total system refrigerant oil requirements. On some Taurus 3.0L models, the air conditioning system is charged with R-134a refrigerant and corresponding oil. Do not intermix chemicals or components from R-12 systems.

22. Transfer the foam core seals to the new evaporator core.
23. Position the evaporator core in the case and close the cutout cover.
24. Install a spring nut on each of the 2 upright tabs with 2 holes drilled in the front flange. Make sure the holes in the spring nuts are aligned with the 3/16 in. (4.75mm) holes drilled in the tab and flange. Install and tighten the screw in each spring nut to secure the cutout cover in the closed position.
25. Install caulking cord to seal the evaporator case against leakage along the cut line.
26. Install the air inlet duct to the evaporator case and tighten the 2 screws. Install the recirculation duct to the evaporator case and tighten 6 screws.
27. If equipped with automatic temperature control, install the electrical connector bracket to the recirculation duct, install the speed controller connector to the bracket and attach the blend door actuator to the evaporator case. Install the electrical connector to the bracket. Attach the cold engine lock out switch by snapping the spring clip in place on the outermost heater core tube.
28. Install the vacuum harness to the evaporator case and install the foam seals over the evaporator tubes. Assemble the support bracket to the evaporator case.
29. Position the evaporator case assembly to the dash panel and cowl top panel at the air inlet opening. Install the 2 screws attaching the support brackets to the top cowl panel.
30. Install the 3 nuts in the engine compartment attaching the evaporator case to the dash panel.
31. Connect the vacuum line, electrical connections and aspirator hose at the evaporator case.
32. Install the floor register and rear seat duct to the evaporator case and tighten the 2 attaching screws.
33. Install the instrument panel shake brace and screw to the evaporator case.
34. Install the instrument panel.
35. Connect the liquid line and accumulator/drier to the evaporator core and connect the heater hoses to the heater core.
36. Connect the black vacuum supply hose to the vacuum check valve in the engine compartment.
37. Fill the radiator to the correct level with the previously removed coolant.
38. Connect the negative battery cable and leak test, evacuate and charge the air conditioning system.
39. Check the system for proper operation.

Continental with 4.6L engine

NOTE: If an A/C evaporator core leak is suspected, the A/C evaporator core must be leak tested before it is removed from the vehicle.

1. Record User 1 and User 2 preset radio frequencies for reprogramming following installation.
2. Disconnect the battery ground cable.
3. Drain coolant from radiator into a clean container.
4. Discharge the refrigerant from A/C system. Observe all safety precautions.
5. Disconnect heater water hoses from the heater core. Plug the heater core tubes, or blow any coolant from the heater core with low-pressure air.
6. Disconnect the vacuum supply hose (black) from the in-line A/C vacuum check valve in the engine compartment.
7. Disconnect condenser-to-evaporator tube and evaporator-to-accumulator tube from the evaporator core at dash panel. Cap the refrigerant lines and the evaporator core to prevent entrance of dirt and moisture.
8. Remove the instrument panel.
9. Remove 2 screws retaining the heater outlet floor duct to bottom of the evaporator housing.
10. Disconnect the electrical connections from the A/C evaporator housing.
11. Remove 3 nuts retaining the evaporator housing to the dash panel in engine compartment.
12. Remove 2 screws retaining the support brackets to the cowl top panel in passenger compartment.

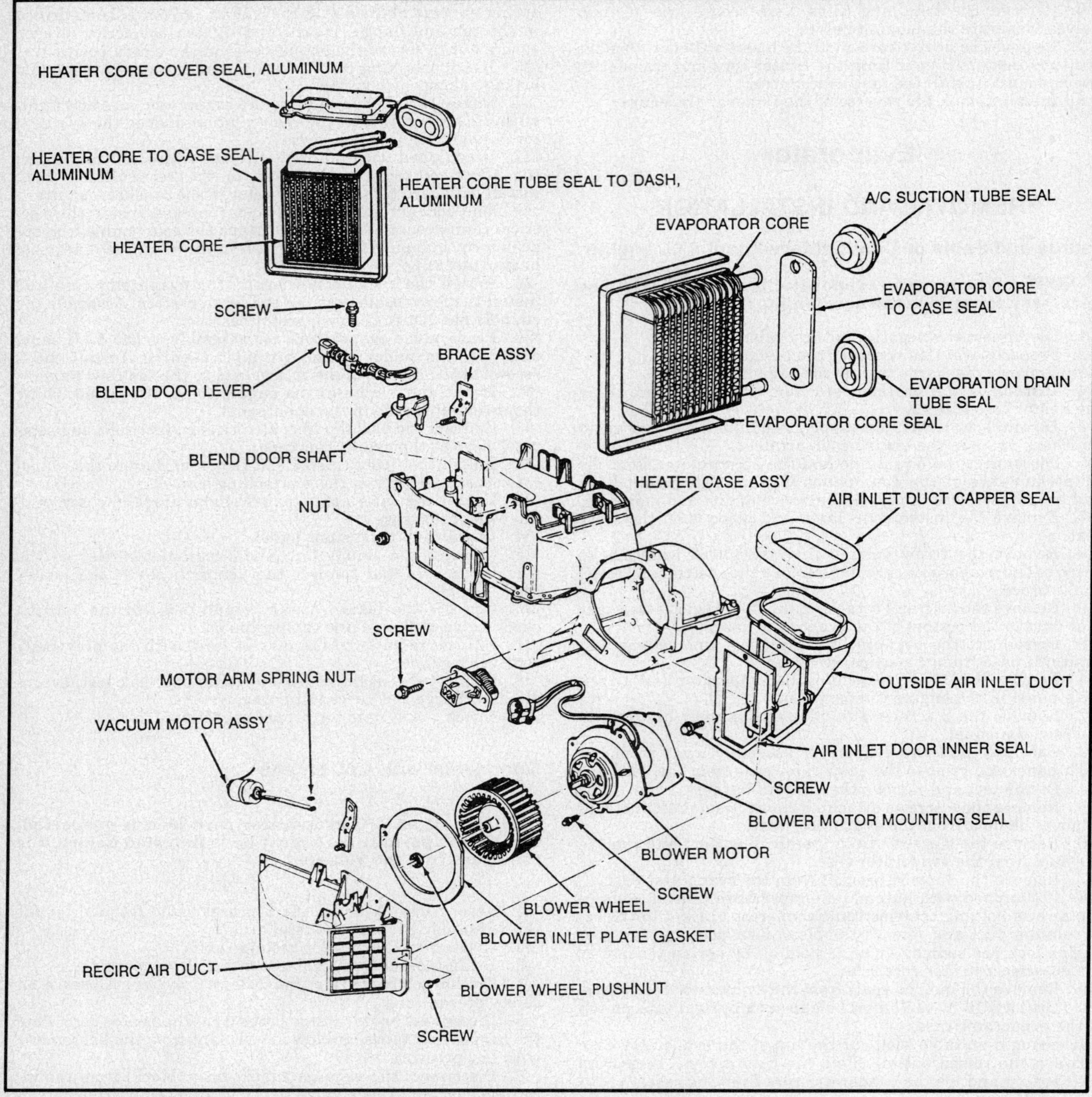

Exploded view of heater and evaporation assembly—Taurus and Sable

13. Carefully pull the evaporator housing away from the dash panel and remove the evaporator case from the vehicle.
14. Remove foam seals from the evaporator core tubes.
15. Remove 2 retaining screws and metal cover from the evaporator housing.
16. Remove 3 remaining retaining screws and the electronic door actuator motor from the evaporator housing.
17. Disengage the spring from the heater core cover and remove spring from lever.

NOTE: Do not attempt to bend any part of the lever, it is brittle and will break.

Gently depress locking ramp and remove lever from secondary A/C air temperature control door end.

18. Rotate the primary A/C air temperature control door shaft down, then swing metal link and remove from pin.
19. Remove retaining screws from around flange joint of A/C evaporate housing.

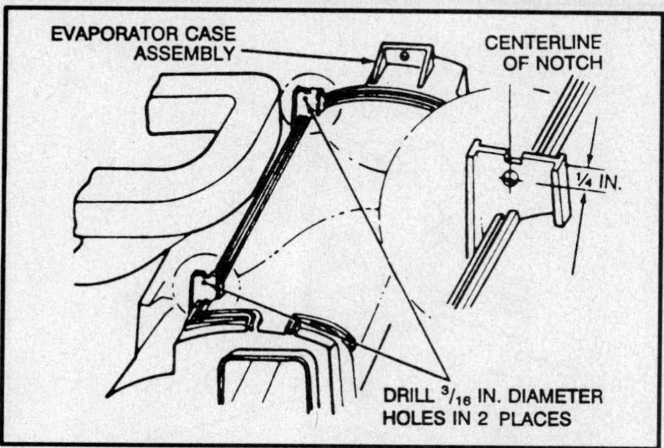

Drilling holes in evaporator case tabs—Taurus, Sable and Continental

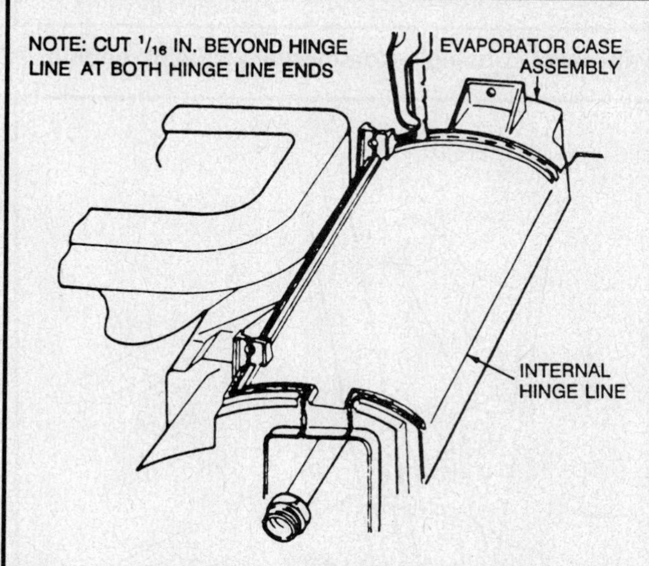

Evaporator case cutting—Taurus, Sable and Continental

20. With side cutters (or equivalent), cut all snap loops around flange joint of A/C evaporator housing.
21. Remove the upper evaporator housing case from the lower evaporator case housing.
22. Remove the evaporator core from the lower evaporator case housing.

To install:

23. Transfer 3 foam seals to the new A/C evaporator core.
24. Position the evaporator core in the lower evaporator case housing.
25. Install the upper evaporator case housing to the lower evaporator case housing, making sure heater air damper door lower post is positioned in pivot hole in lower evaporator case housing.
26. Install retaining screws around flange joint of A/C evaporator housing.
27. Install metal link over pin on primary A/C air temperature control door shaft.
28. Install secondary A/C air temperature control door lever on metal link.

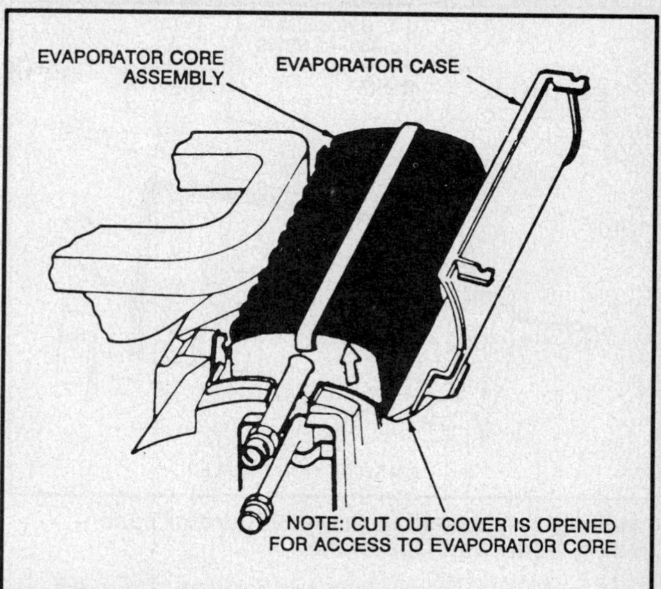

Evaporator core removal—Taurus, Sable and Continental

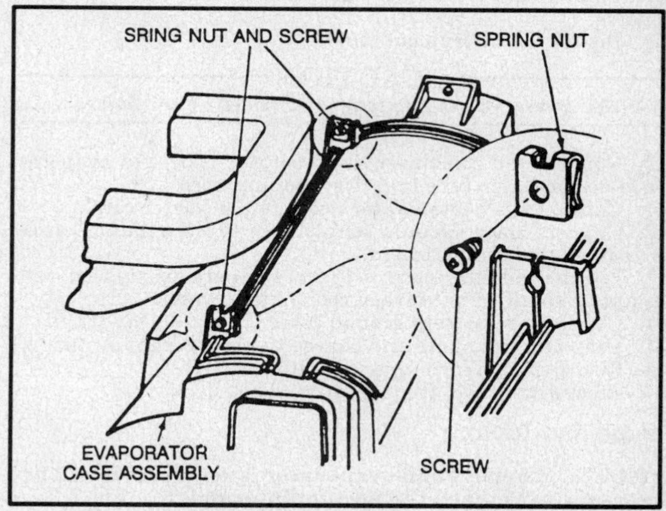

Securing cutout evaporator case cover in closed position—Taurus, Sable and Continental

29. Install secondary A/C air temperature control door lever to secondary A/C air temperature control door end.
30. Engage spring to the heater core cover and secondary A/C air temperature control door lever.
31. Install A/C electronic door actuator motor to the evaporator housing with 3 retaining screws.
32. Install the metal cover to the evaporator housing with 2 retaining screws.
33. Install foam seals over evaporator tubes.
34. Install A/C evaporator housing assembly.

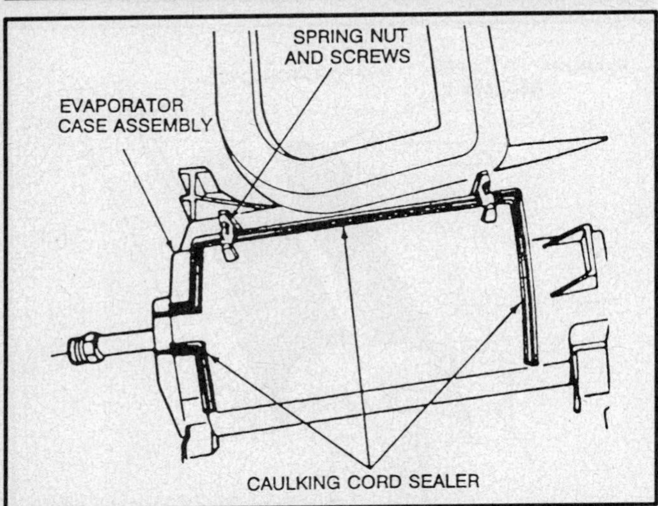

Caulking cord installation on evaporator case—Taurus, Sable and Continental

NOTE: Install screw and washer assembly first to properly position housing to cowl.

35. Position the evaporator housing assembly against the dash panel and cowl top panel at air inlet opening. Install 2 screws retaining support brackets to cowl top panel.
36. Install 3 nuts in engine compartment retaining the evaporator housing to dash panel.
37. Install the heater outlet floor duct to the evaporator housing and tighten 2 retaining screws.
38. Connect the electrical connections at the A/C evaporator housing.
39. Install the instrument panel.

CAUTION

Make sure correct type O–ring seals are installed on A/C fittings.

40. Connect the condenser-to-evaporator tube and evaporator-to-accumulator tube to A/C evaporator core.
41. Connect the heater water hoses to the heater core.
42. Connect black vacuum supply hose to the vacuum check valve in engine compartment.
43. Fill the radiator to correct level with previously removed coolant or specified mixture of coolant and water.
44. Connect the battery ground cable.
45. Leak test, evacuate and charge the refrigerant system.
46. Check system for proper operation.
47. Reprogram radio frequencies and set clock.

Tempo and Topaz

NOTE: Whenever an evaporator is removed, it will be necessary to replace the accumulator/drier.

1. Disconnect the negative battery cable.
2. Drain the coolant from the radiator into a clean container.
3. Properly discharge the refrigerant from the air conditioning system.
4. Disconnect the heater hoses from the heater core. Plug the heater core tubes.
5. Disconnect the liquid line and the accumulator/drier inlet tube from the evaporator core at the dash panel. Cap the refrigerant lines and evaporator core to prevent the entrance of dirt and excess moisture.
6. Remove the instrument panel and lay it on the front seat as follows:
   - Detach the speedometer cable from the transaxle.

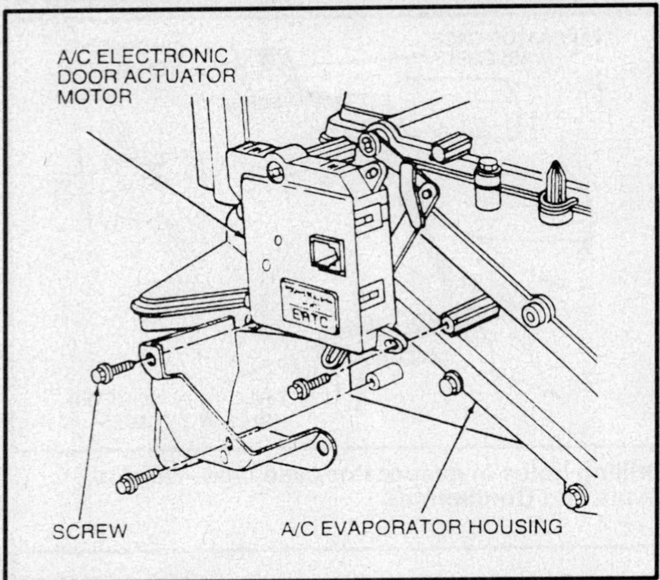

Evaporator housing—Continental with 4.6L engine

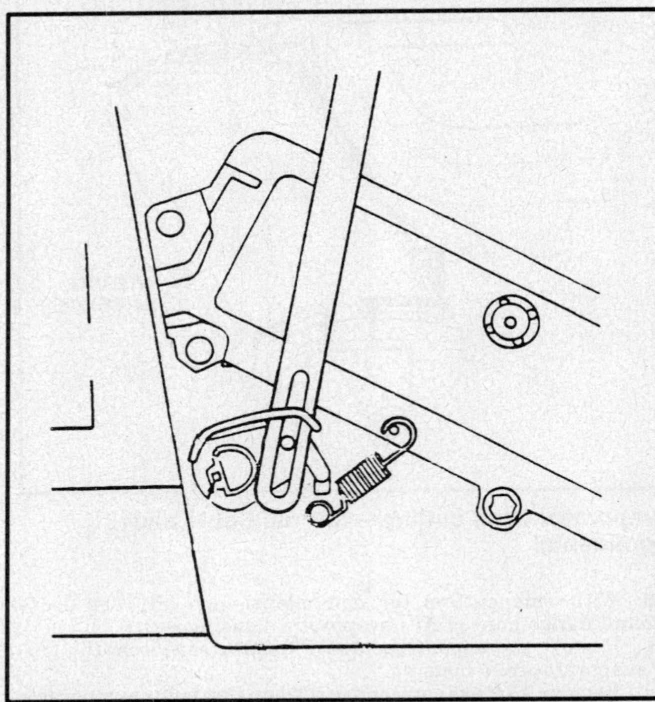

Heater core lever—Continental with 4.6L engine

   - Remove the lower cluster finish panels. Remove 4 cluster opening finish panel screws and pull panel rearward.
   - Remove the column opening reinforcement, speed control module (if equipped) and lower steering column shroud.
   - Loosen, but do not remove, 2 nuts and bolts retaining steering column. Remove the upper column cover.
   - Disconnect the combination switch wiring. On console shift, remove interlock cable screw and detach cable from the steering column (automatic transaxle only).
   - Loosen steering column to intermediate shaft clamp. Remove steering column from the support bracket. Pry open the shaft clamp enough to easily disengage shafts.

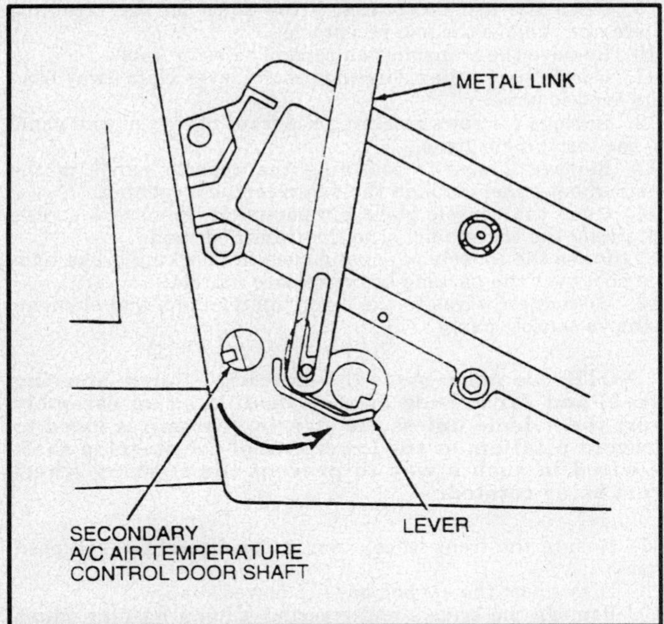

Control door—Continental with 4.6L engine

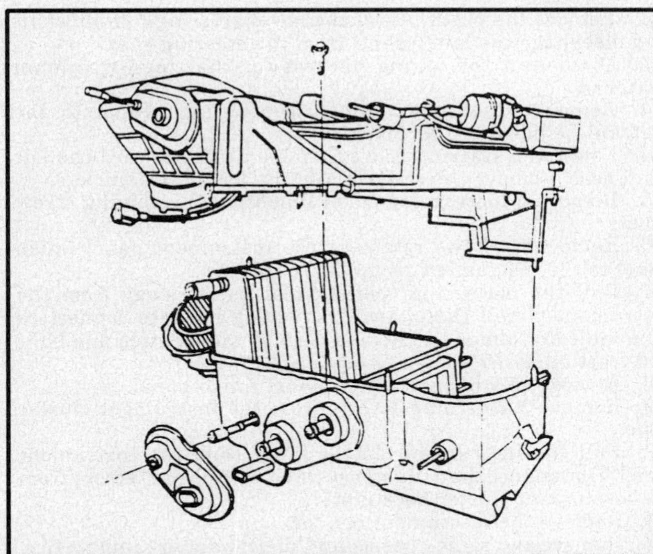

Evaporator housing—Continental with 4.6L engine

NOTE: If steering column bracket clips are bent or distorted, they must be replaced.

- Remove instrument cluster screws and pull it back enough to detach speedometer cable. Loosely install cluster screws to keep it in place during instrument panel removal.
- Let glove box door hang down. Detach all vacuum and electrical connections and heater and radio cables.
- In the engine compartment, disconnect the main wiring loom and push wiring and grommet through the firewall.
- Through steering column opening, remove 1 panel to column support bracket retaining nut.
- Remove 2 lower panel to cowl side retaining screws (both sides).

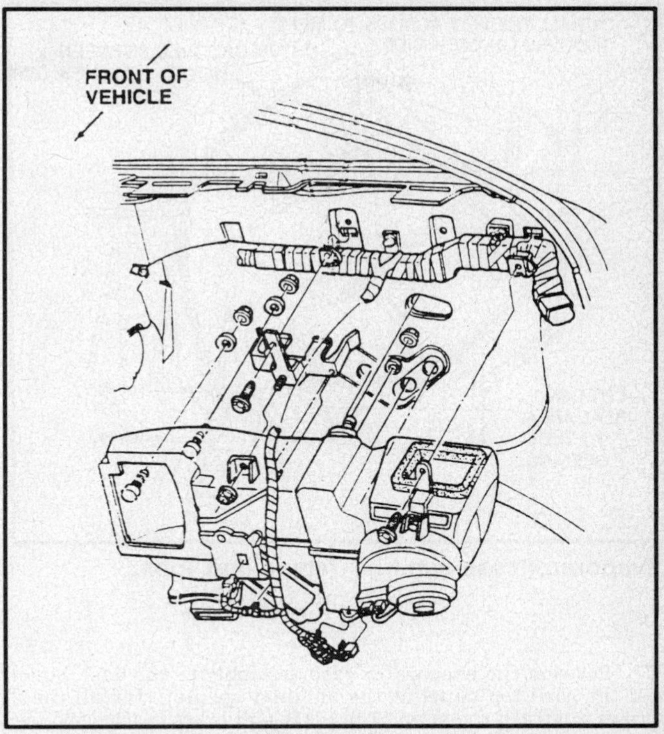

Evaporator case installation—Continental with 4.6L engine

- On left side of panel, remove vertical brace nuts. Remove 4 upper panel retaining screws at cowl and remove instrument panel.

7. Disconnect the wire harness connector from the blower motor resistor.
8. Remove 1 screw attaching the bottom of the evaporator case to the dash panel and remove the instrument panel brace from the cowl top panel.
9. Remove the 2 nuts attaching the evaporator case to the dash panel in the engine compartment.
10. Loosen the sound insulation from the cowl top panel in the area around the air inlet opening.
11. Remove the 2 screws attaching the support bracket and the brace to the cowl top panel.
12. Remove the 4 screws attaching the air inlet duct to the evaporator case and remove the air inlet duct.
13. Remove the evaporator-to-cowl seals from the evaporator tubes.
14. Perform the following procedure:
    - Using a suitable tool, and following guidelines in illustration, cut the top from the evaporator case completely.
    - Remove the cover from the case and lift the evaporator core from the case.
    - Use a suitable tool to remove any rough edges from the case that may have been caused by the cutting.
15. Remove the evaporator core.

To install:

NOTE: Add 3 oz. (90 ml) of clean refrigerant oil to a new replacement evaporator core to maintain total system refrigerant oil requirements.

16. Install the new evaporator core and cover according to the instructions in the new evaporator core kit, E83H–19850–BB or equivalent.

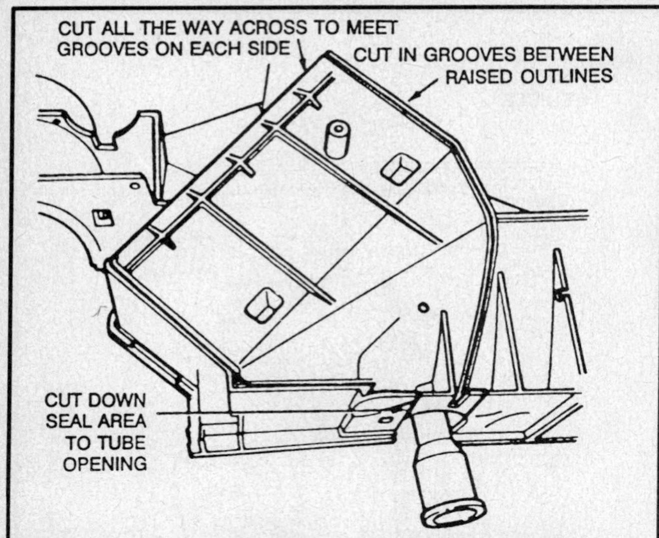
CUT ALL THE WAY ACROSS TO MEET GROOVES ON EACH SIDE
CUT IN GROOVES BETWEEN RAISED OUTLINES
CUT DOWN SEAL AREA TO TUBE OPENING

Evaporator case cutting—Tempo and Topaz

17. Position the evaporator case assembly to the dash panel and the cowl top panel at the air inlet opening. Install the 2 screws to attach the support bracket and brace to the cowl top panel.
18. Install the 2 nuts in the engine compartment to attach the evaporator case to the dash panel. Inspect the evaporator drain tube for a good seal and that the drain tube is through the opening and not obstructed.
19. Position the sound insulation around the air inlet duct on the cowl top panel.
20. Install the instrument panel.
21. Install 1 screw to attach the bottom of the evaporator assembly to the dash panel.
22. Connect the heater hoses to the heater core.
23. Using new O-rings lubricated with clean refrigerant oil, connect the liquid line and the accumulator/drier inlet tube to the evaporator core. Tighten each connection using a backup wrench to prevent component damage.
24. Fill the radiator to the correct level with the removed coolant and connect the negative battery cable.
25. Leak test, evacuate and charge the air conditioning system. Check the system for proper operation.

Contour and Mystique

NOTE: Whenever an A/C evaporator core is replaced, it will be necessary to replace the suction accumulator/ drier.

Before an A/C evaporator core is replaced, it must be leak-tested in the vehicle to verify that it is leaking.

1. Disconnect the battery ground cable.
2. Remove right and left windshield wiper pivot arms.
3. Remove plastic screw covers and 5 top screws retaining cowl vent screen.
4. Raise and properly support the hood.
5. Pull the hood pad straight up away from the cowl vent screen.
6. Remove 5 side screws retaining the cowl vent screen to the body.
7. Remove the cowl vent screen. The right half of the cowl vent screen must be removed before the left half.
8. Disconnect the upper speedometer cable from the lower speedometer cable.
9. Open the ash receptacle, press down on the retaining plate and remove the ash receptacle.
10. Remove the transmission control selector knob.
11. Carefully pry the transaxle control lever plate away from the console panel.
12. Remove 4 screws retaining the front of the console panel to the instrument panel.
13. Remove 2 screws retaining the console panel to the instrument panel through the ash receptacle opening.
14. Open the console glove compartment. Remove 3 screws retaining the console panel to the front floor pan.
15. Raise the console panel and ease the parking brake handle boot over the parking brake release handle.
16. Disconnect wires to the cigar lighter knob and element. Remove console panel.

NOTE: Do not remove the steering column, steering wheel and driver side air bag module as an assembly from the vehicle unless the steering column is loced to prevent rotation, or the lower end of the steering shaft is wired in such a way to prevent the steering wheel from being rotated.

17. Ensure the front wheels are in the straight-ahead position.
18. Disconnect the air bag backup power supply.
19. Remove the screws and steering column opening finish panel.
20. Remove the screws retaining the upper and lower steering column shrouds. Remove the upper and lower steering column shrouds.
21. Remove the pinch bolt at the lower steering column shaft and disengage the lower shaft from the steering gear.
22. Disconnect the wiring harness for the steering column switches.
23. Remove 4 bolts retaining the steering column to the instrument panel reinforcement.
24. Lower the steering column and slide the toward the left front seat. Remove the steering column from the vehicle.
25. Remove 3 instrument panel finish panel retaining screw covers.
26. Remove 6 screws retaining the instrument panel finish panel to the instrument panel.
27. Pull the instrument panel finish panel away from the instrument panel. Disconnect the wiring harness connectors from indicator lamps and heated back window switch and light and traction assist switch, if equipped.
28. Remove cluster instrument panel finish panel.
29. Remove 5 retaining screws from the instrument cluster panel.
30. Pull the instrument cluster away from the instrument panel. Disconnect the 3 cluster printed circuit connectors from the instrument cluster back plate.
31. Remove the instrument cluster.
32. Remove the radio chassis and digital audio compact disc player if equipped.
33. Remove the heater and air conditioner control.
34. Remove the left switch plate finish panel.
35. Remove the glove compartment.
36. Remove the right center body pillar inside lower finish panel.
37. Disconnect the wiring harness connectors and ground connections at the right side cowl panel. Disconnect one ground wire from under the right floor carpet.
38. Pull the front door opening weatherstrip off at the instrument panel location. Remove the main mounting bolt cover on the right side.
39. Remove 2 instrument panel retaining screws at the left side of the glove compartment opening.
40. Disconnect 2 main wiring harness connectors at the instrument panel fuse junction panel.
41. Disconnect 5 wiring harness connectors at the rear of the fuse junction panel.

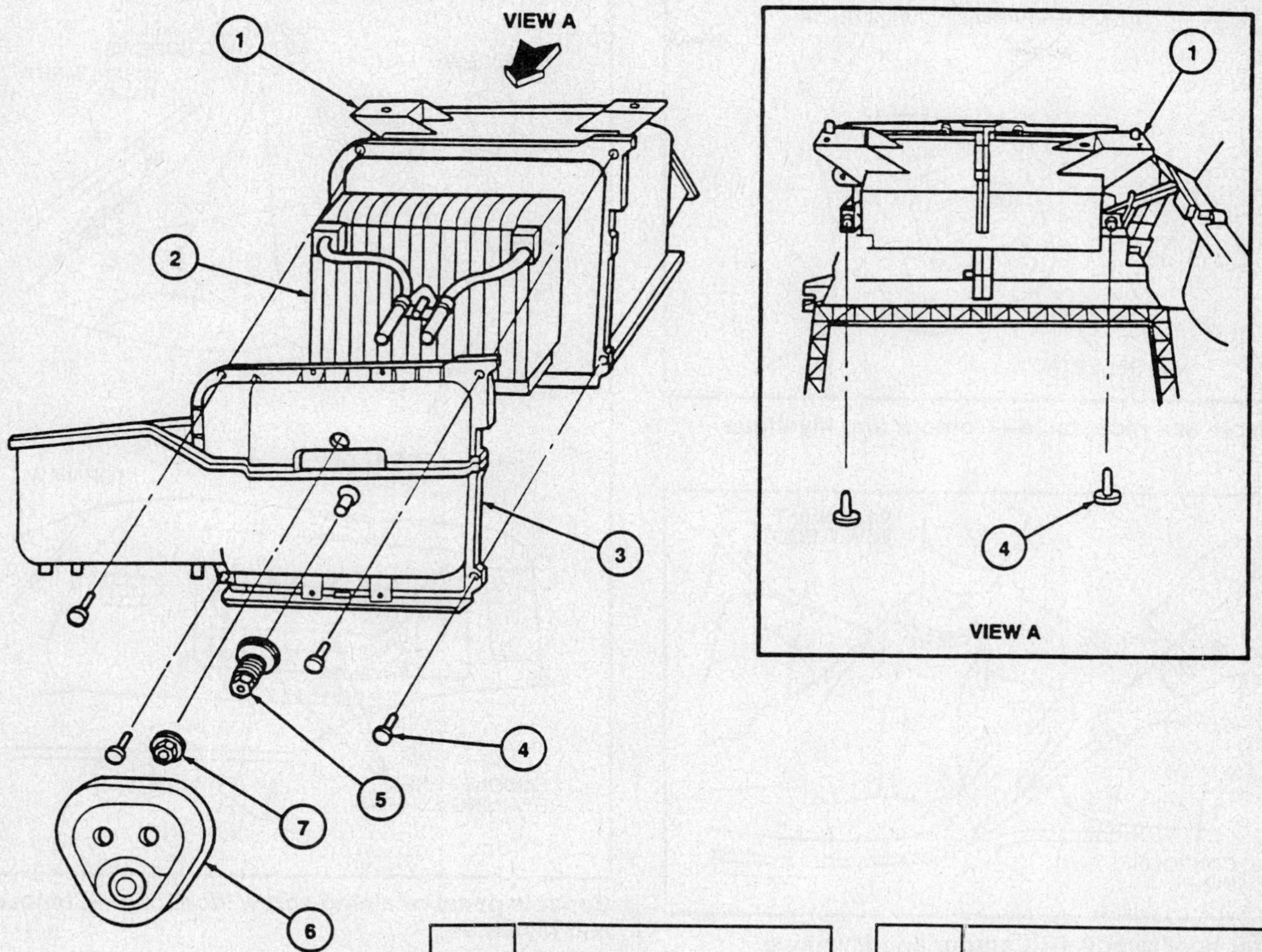

VIEW A

VIEW A

Item	Description
1	A/C Evaporator Housing
2	A/C Evaporator Core
3	Evaporator Core Cover

Item	Description
4	Screw (6 Req'd)
5	Threaded Adapter
6	Heater Dash Panel Seal
7	Nut (1 Req'd)

Evaporator case removal and installation—Contour and Mystique

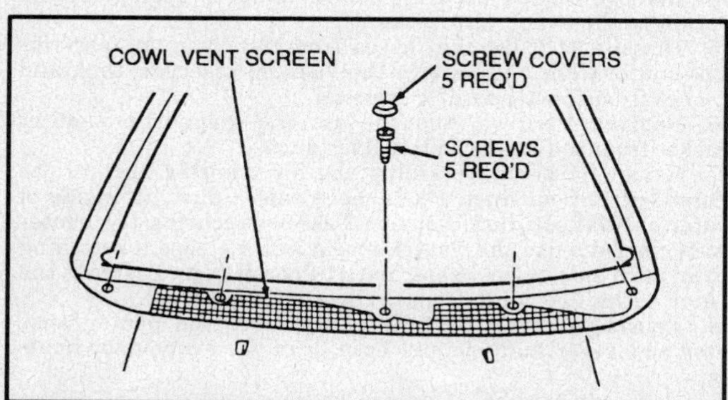

Cowl vent screens—Contour and Mystique

42. Disconnect 3 wiring connectors for the stoplamp switch.
43. Remove the rubber grommet from the upper speedometer cable at the dash panel.
44. From under the instrument panel pry the upper speedometer cable out of the center bracket at the dash panel.
45. Remove 3 screws retaining the instrument panel at the steering column tube opening.
46. Pull the front door opening weatherstrip off at the instrument panel location. Remove the left main mounting bolt cover.

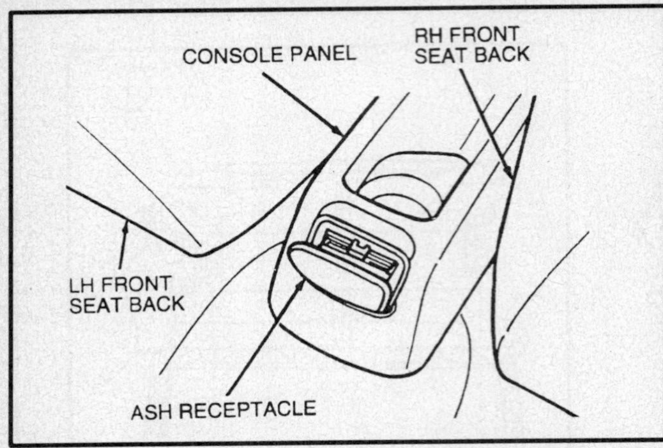

Console ash receptacle—Contour and Mystique

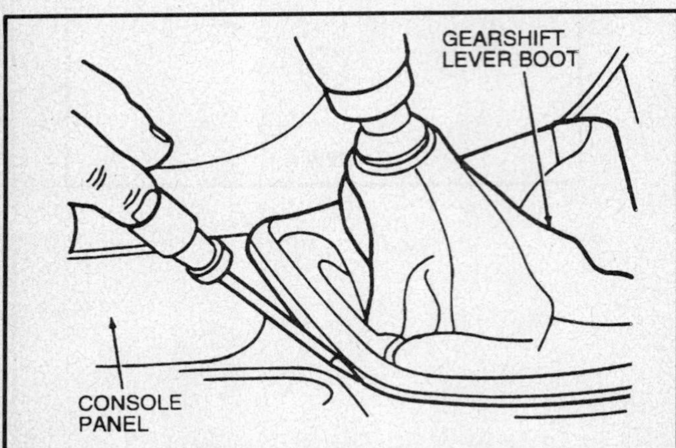

Shifter boot removal—Contour and Mystique

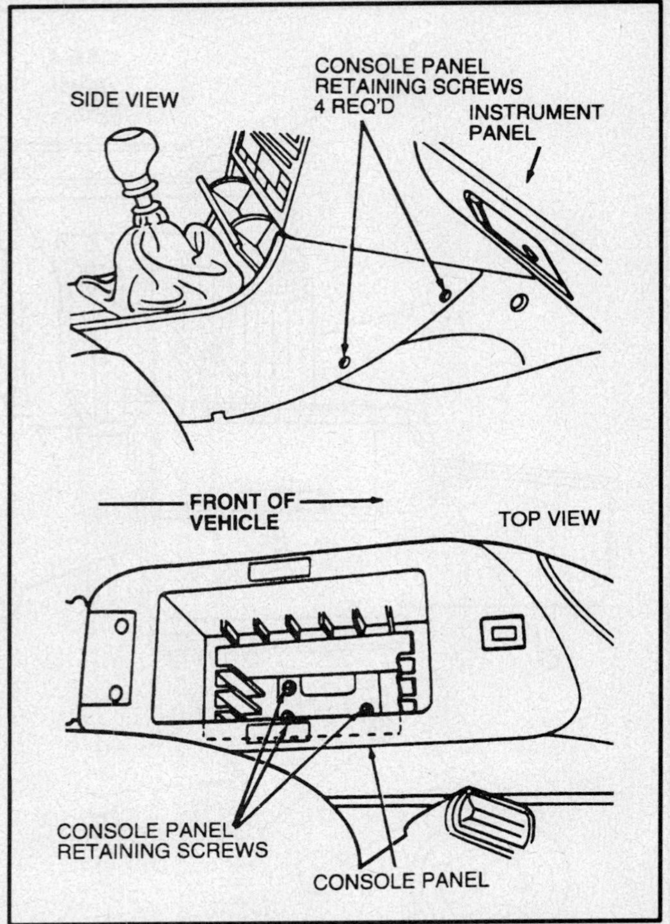

Console panel retaining screw locations—Contour and Mystique

47. Remove 2 bolts retaining the passenger side air bag to the instrument panel reinforcement.
48. Disconnect the radio antenna from the radio chassis.
49. Cut the wire ties retaining the demister hoses to the instrument panel reinforcement.
50. Disconnect the wiring harness for the radio amplifier.

NOTE: Removal and installation of the instrument panel is best accomplished by 2 people.

51. Remove 4 instrument panel mounting bolts (2 each side).
52. Gently lift the instrument panel away from the dash panel. Remove the instrument panel.
53. Place a drain pan or suitable container under the heater water hose connections at the cowl panel.
54. Discharge refrigerant from the air conditioner system at the service access gauge port valve located on the suction line. Observe all safety precautions.
55. Raise and safely support vehicle.
56. Disconnect the heater water hoses from the heater core inlet and outlet tubes. Plug the hoses and cap the tubes to prevent coolant loss.
57. Disconnect the vacuum supply hose (black) from the vacuum source in the engine compartment.
58. Disconnect the discharge line and the evaporator-to-compressor suction line (2.0L engine) or jumper line (2.5L engine) from the evaporator core inlet and outlet tubes at the cowl panel.
59. Remove 1 nut retaining the evaporator housing to the cowl panel.
60. Working from inside the vehicle, remove 1 nut from the upper crossmember brace.
61. Remove 1 bolt from the bottom mounting bracket and remove the crossmember brace.
62. Pull off the plenum demister adapter from the right and left sides of the evaporator housing.
63. Remove 2 screws retaining the ram air intake duct to the evaporator housing. Release 3 retaining clips and remove the ram air intake duct from the evaporator housing.
64. Remove 1 screw securing the vacuum reservoir tank and bracket to the evaporator housing.
65. Disconnect 2 vacuum hoses from the vacuum reservoir tank and bracket and remove the vacuum reservoir tank and bracket from the evaporator housing.
66. Remove 4 screws and the air bag diagnostic monitor bracket from the heater outlet floor duct.
67. Remove 1 screw retaining the air transfer duct to the heater outlet floor duct. Push the transfer duct up inside of heater outlet floor duct. Remove 3 screws securing the heater outlet floor duct to the heater core cover. Release a retaining tab on each side of the heater outlet floor duct and remove the heater outlet floor duct from the heater core cover.
68. Release 4 retaining tabs and remove the heater core, heter core cover and vacuum hose from the evaporator housing.

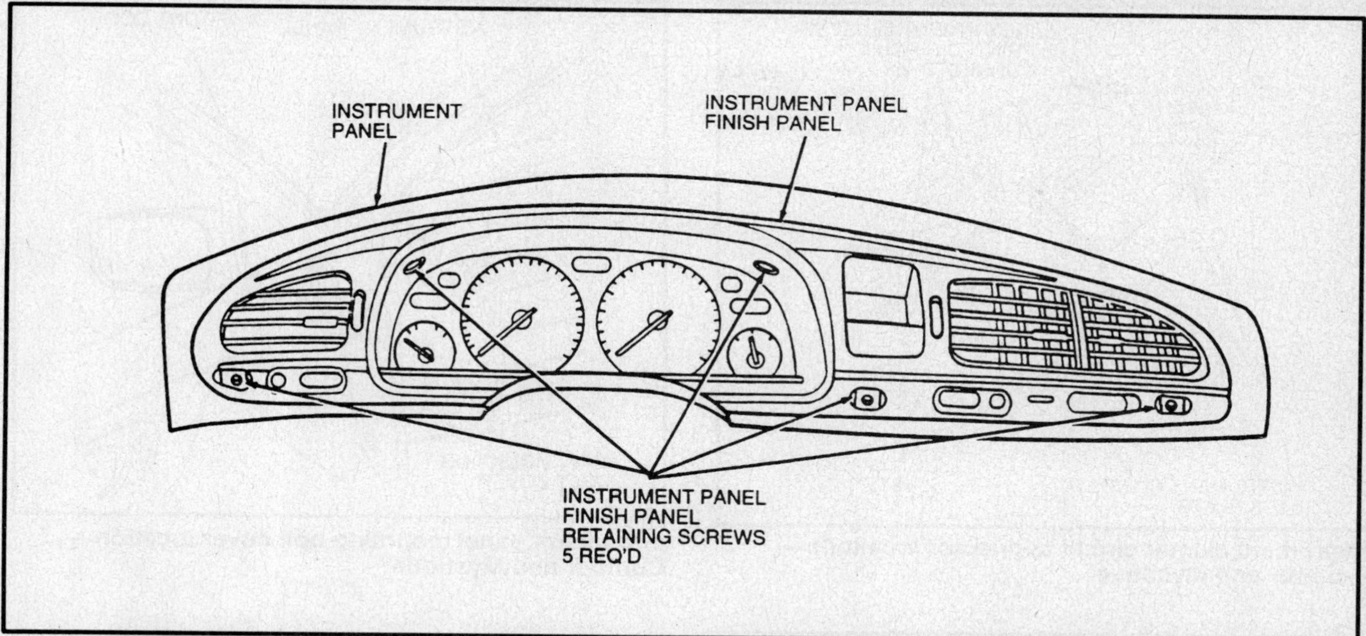

Instrument panel finish panel—Contour and Mystique

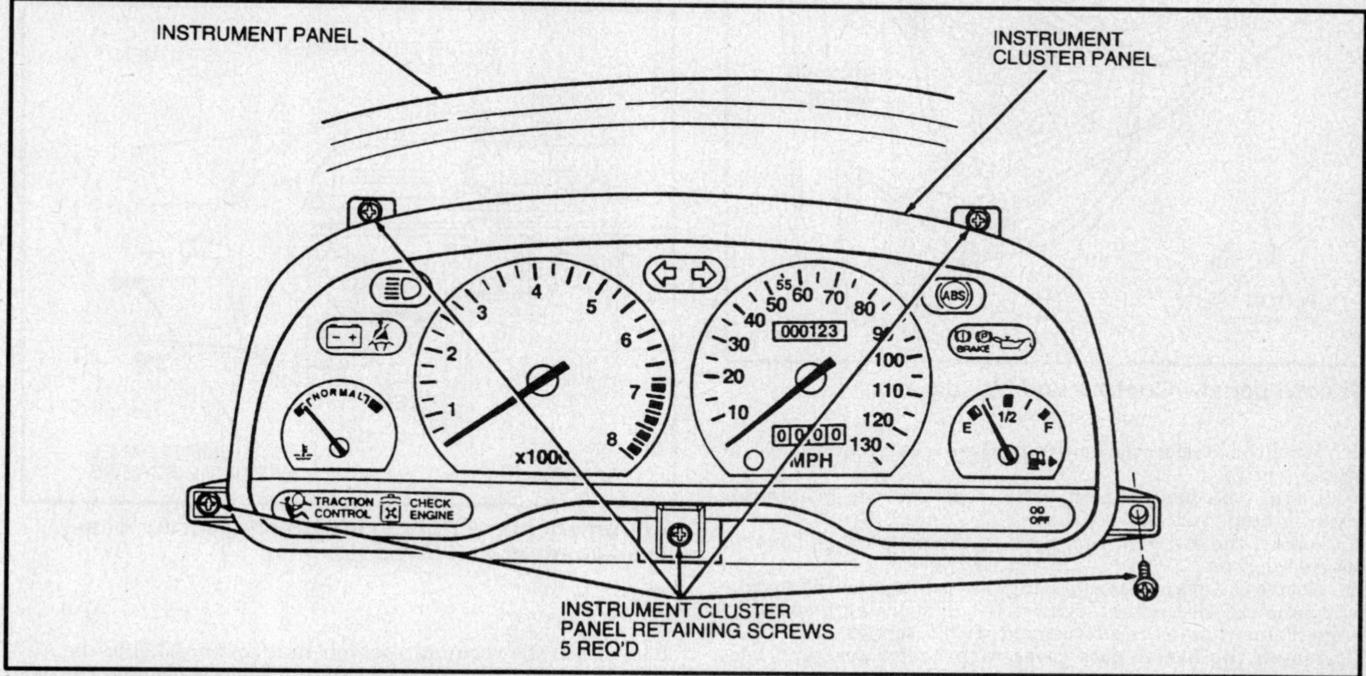

Instrument cluster—Contour and Mystique

69. Remove 3 screws, amplifier and radio power booster equalizer amplifier bracket from the vehicle, if equipped.
70. Remove 5 screws retaining the evaporator housing to the instrument panel reinforcement. Rotate the evaporator housing away from the instrument panel reinforcement and remove the evaporator housing from the vehicle.
71. Remove vacuum line from the recirculating air vacuum control motor.
72. Remove metal clips and disengage lugs retaining the recirculating air duct to the evaporator housing.
73. Remove the recirculating air duct.
74. Remove the heater dash panel seal and evaporator retaining nut.
75. Remove 2 screws from the rear of the evaporator housing.
76. Remove 4 screws from the front of the evaporator housing.
77. Separate the evaporator housing and remove the evaporator core.

To install:

78. Position the evaporator core in the evaporator housing.

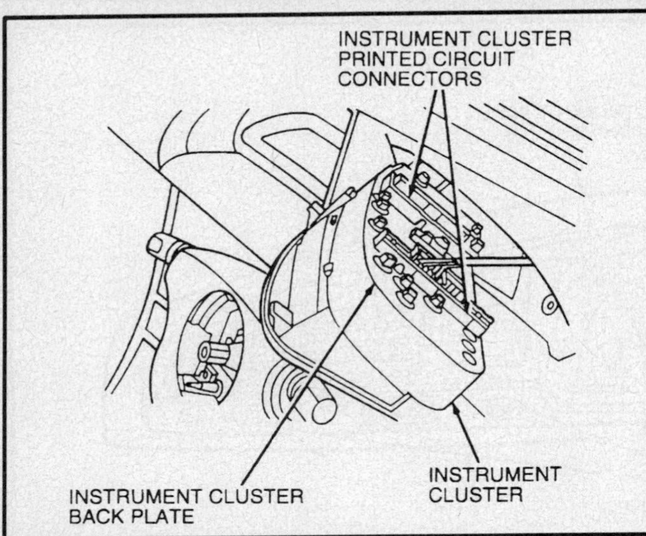

Instrument cluster circuit connector locations—Contour and Mystique

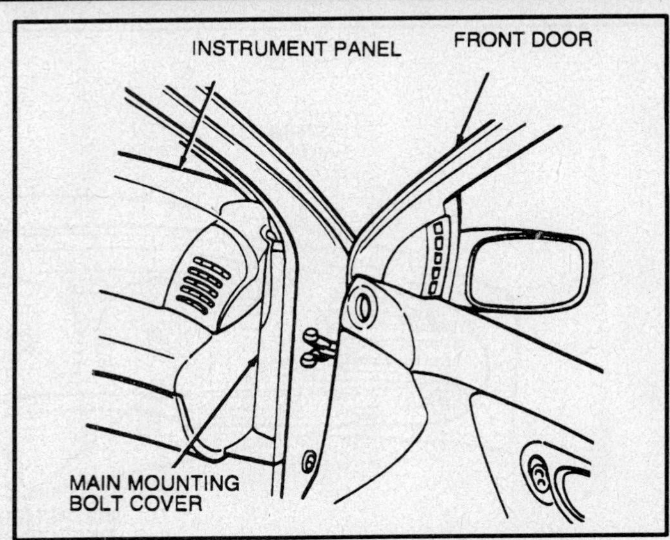

Instrument panel mounting bolt cover location—Contour and Mystique

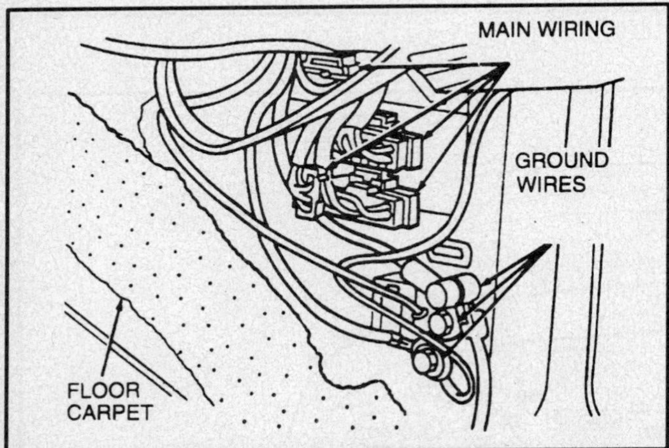

RH cowl panel—Contour and Mystique

79. Mate the evaporator housing halves and install the 6 connecting screws.
80. Install the heater dash panel seal and the evaporator retaining nut.
81. Attach the recirculating duct to the evaporator housing with metal clips.
82. Rotate the evaporator housing into position on the instrument panel reinforcement. Secure the evaporator housing to the instrument panel reinforcement with 5 screws.
83. Install the heater core cover with heater core and vacuum hose to the evaporator housing. Use additional metal service clips if required.
84. Install the heater outlet floor duct to the heater core cover. Secure with 3 screws and additional metal service clips. Slide the air transfer duct down to engage with the rear seat air flow duct. Secure the air transfer duct in this position with 1 screw.
85. Attach the air bag diagnostic monitor bracket to the heater outlet floor duct with 4 retaining screws.
86. Install the ram air intake duct to the evaporator housing and secure with 2 screws.
87. Install the right and left plenum demister adapters to the evaporator housing.

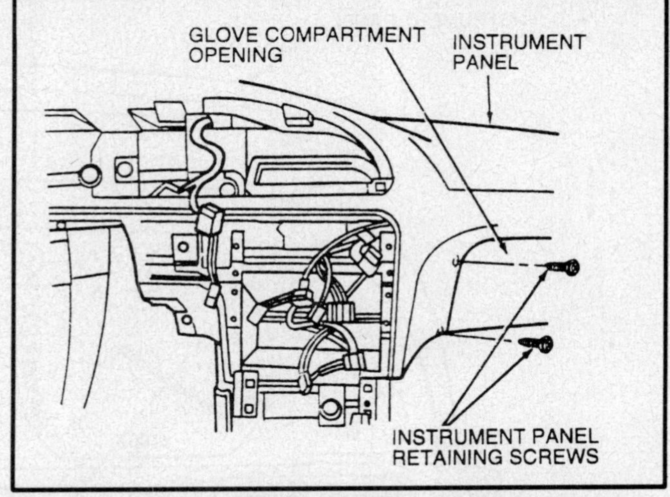

Instrument panel right side retaining screw location—Contour and Mystique

88. Install the vacuum reservoir tank and bracket to the A/C evaporator housing and secure with 1 screw. Connect 2 vacuum hoses and the vacuum check valve to the vacuum reservoir tank and bracket.
89. Install the radio power booster equalizer amplifier bracket with 3 retaining screws, if equipped.
90. Secure the upper crossmember brace with 1 nut.
91. Secure the bottom mounting bracket with 1 bolt.
92. Install the instrument panel in reverse order of removal.
93. Working from inside engine compartment, install 1 nut retaining the evaporator housing to cowl panel.
94. Connect the discharge line and evaporator to the compressor suction line (2.0L engine) or jumper line (2.5L engine) to the evaporator core tubes at the cowl panel.

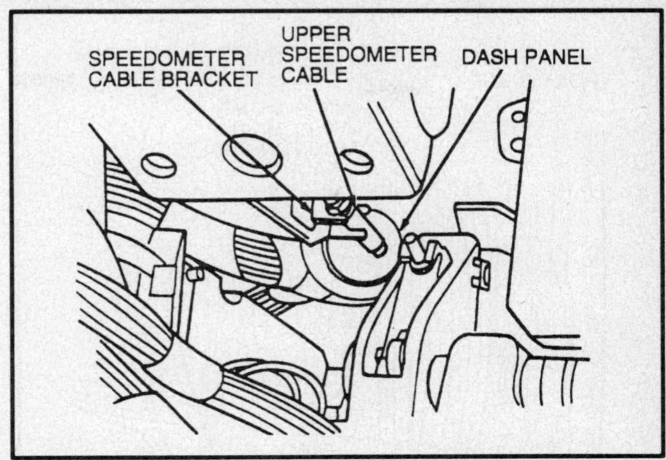

Speedometer cable disconnect—Contour and Mystique

LOCATION FOR INSTRUMENT PANEL WIRING
FUSE JUNCTION PANEL

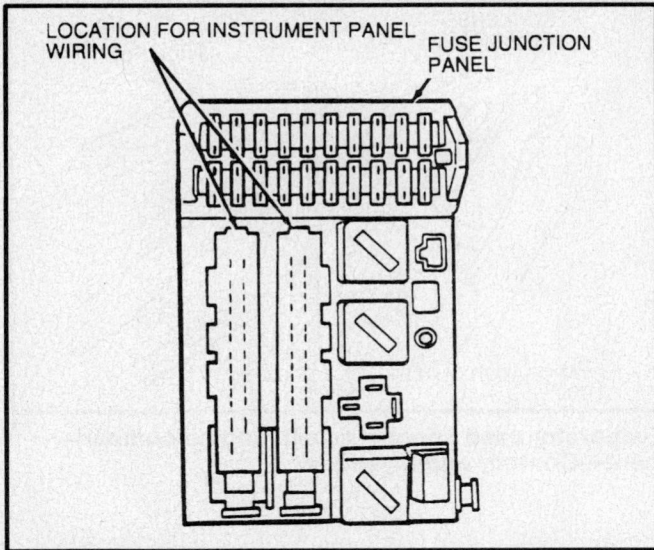

Instrument panel wiring connector locations—Contour and Mystique

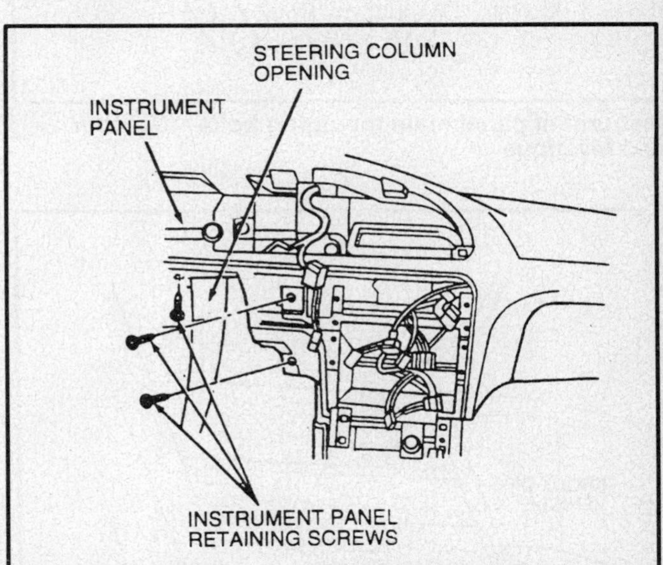

Instrument panel left side retaining screws—Contour and Mystique

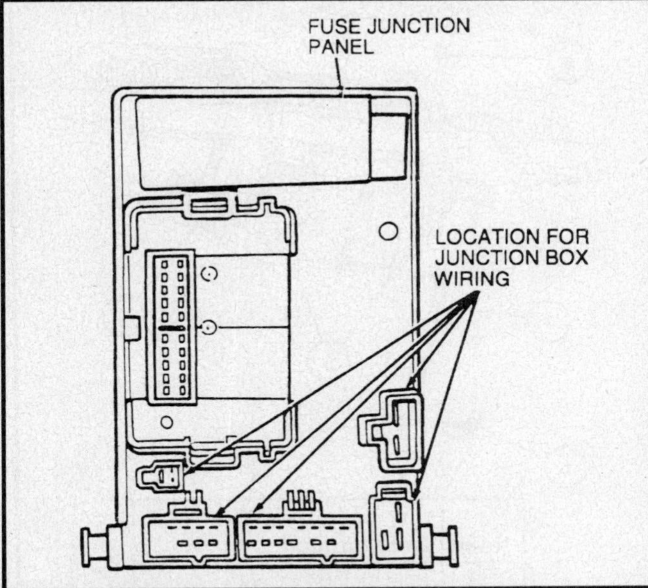

Fuse junction panel—Contour and Mystique

95. Raise and safely support vehicle.
96. Connect the heater water hoses to the heater core tubes.
97. Connect the vacuum source line and service coolant system.
98. Connect the battery ground cable.
99. Charge the refrigerant system. Observe all safety precautions.
100. After service, check the engine coolant level in the radiator coolant recovery reservoir. Fill as required with the recommended coolant mixture.

Escort and Tracer

NOTE: Do not disassemble the evaporator/blower unit. If the evaporator core needs to be replaced, replace the evaporator/blower unit as an assembly. If the evaporator/blower unit is replaced, it will also be necessary to replace the accumulator/drier.

1. Disconnect the negative battery cable.
2. Discharge the refrigerant from the air conditioning system.
3. Disconnect the high pressure line and the accumulator/drier inlet tube from the evaporator core at the bulkhead, using the spring-lock coupling disconnect procedure. Plug all ports to prevent the entrance of dirt and moisture.
4. Remove the glove compartment. If necessary, remove the trim panel below the glove compartment.
5. Disconnect the 2 electrical connectors from the resistor assembly and the electrical connector from the blower motor.
6. Remove the right end panel from the instrument panel and the trim panel just below it.
7. Remove the support bar and the support plate.

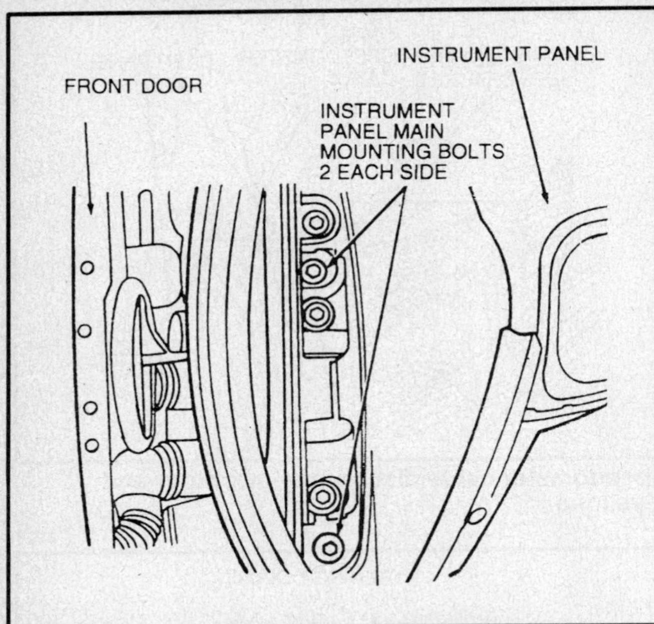

Instrument panel main mounting bolts—Contour and Mystique

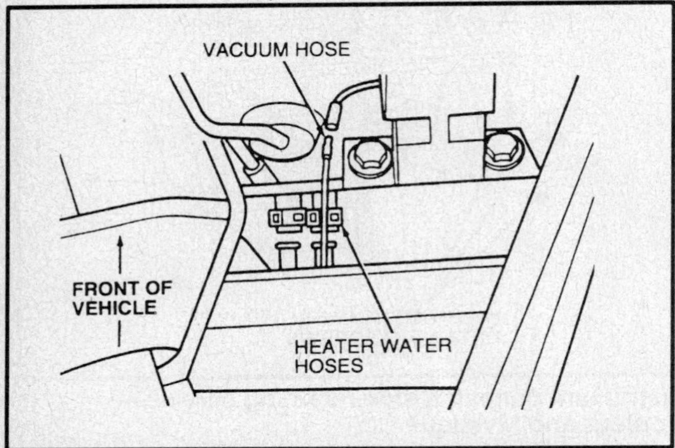

Vacuum and heater water hoses—Contour and Mystique

8. Disconnect the cable from the recirc/fresh air cam and retaining clip. Loosen the capscrew that secures the evaporator-to-heater clamp.
9. Remove the 4 mounting nuts from the evaporator/blower unit and remove the evaporator/blower unit.

To install:

NOTE: Make sure 3 oz. (90ml) of clean refrigerant oil is contained in the evaporator core of the replacement evaporator/blower unit.

10. Position the evaporator/blower unit and install the mounting nuts.
11. Tighten the capscrew that secures the evaporator-to-heater clamp. Connect the cable to the recirc/fresh air cam and adjust the cable.
12. Install the support plate and the support bar.
13. Install the right lower dash trim panel and the 3 capscrews. Install the right dash side panel.

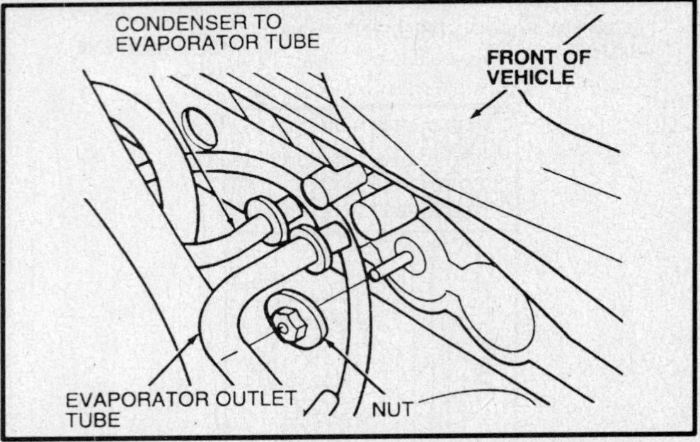

Evaporator case connections in engine compartment—Contour and Mystique

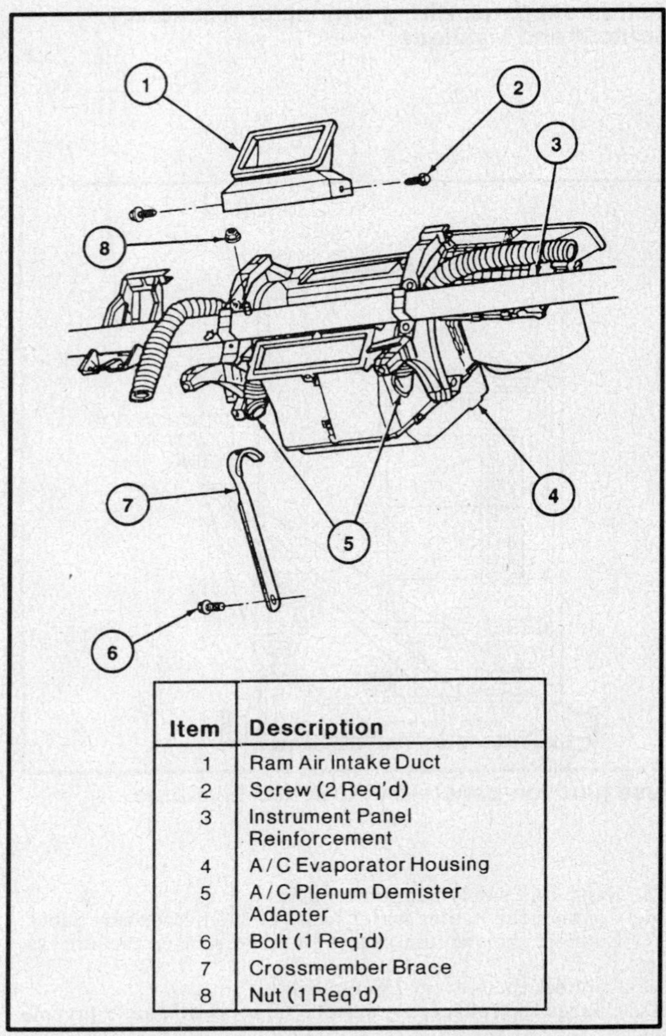

Item	Description
1	Ram Air Intake Duct
2	Screw (2 Req'd)
3	Instrument Panel Reinforcement
4	A/C Evaporator Housing
5	A/C Plenum Demister Adapter
6	Bolt (1 Req'd)
7	Crossmember Brace
8	Nut (1 Req'd)

Ram air intake duct—Contour and Mystique

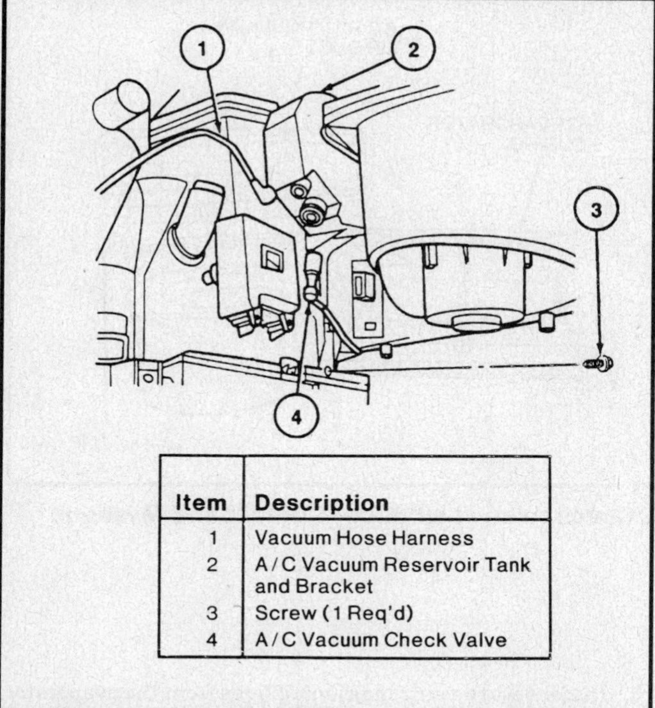

Item	Description
1	Vacuum Hose Harness
2	A / C Vacuum Reservoir Tank and Bracket
3	Screw (1 Req'd)
4	A / C Vacuum Check Valve

Evaporator case vacuum disconnects—Contour and Mystique

14. Connect the blower motor electrical connector and the 2 resistor assembly electrical connectors.
15. If necessary, install the trim panel below the glove compartment. Install the glove compartment.
16. Using new O-rings lubricated with clean refrigerant oil, connect the high pressure line and the accumulator/drier inlet tube to the evaporator core at the bulkhead.
17. Connect the negative battery cable. Leak test, evacuate and charge the system. Observe all safety precautions.

Probe

1. Disconnect the negative battery cable. Properly discharge the air conditioning system.
2. Disconnect the high pressure and low pressure line fittings at the firewall. Disconnect the source vacuum line.
3. Remove the instrument panel as follows:
   - Remove the upper and lower steering column covers, detach the steering column and lower it to the seat.
   - Remove the instrument cluster.
   - Remove the floor console.
   - Remove the glove compartment.
   - Remove the hush panel, console kick panels and side kick panels.
   - Remove the climate control assembly.
   - Remove the radio assembly and trip computer, if equipped.
   - Remove the 2 instrument panel side covers.
   - Remove the instrument panel mounting bolts.
   - Remove the door pillar trim.
   - Lift the panel up and to the rear, disconnect all remaining electrical harnesses and remove the panel from the vehicle.
4. Disconnect the blower motor and the blower resistor wiring.
5. Remove 2 nuts and blots from the evaporator/blower assembly brace and remove the brace.

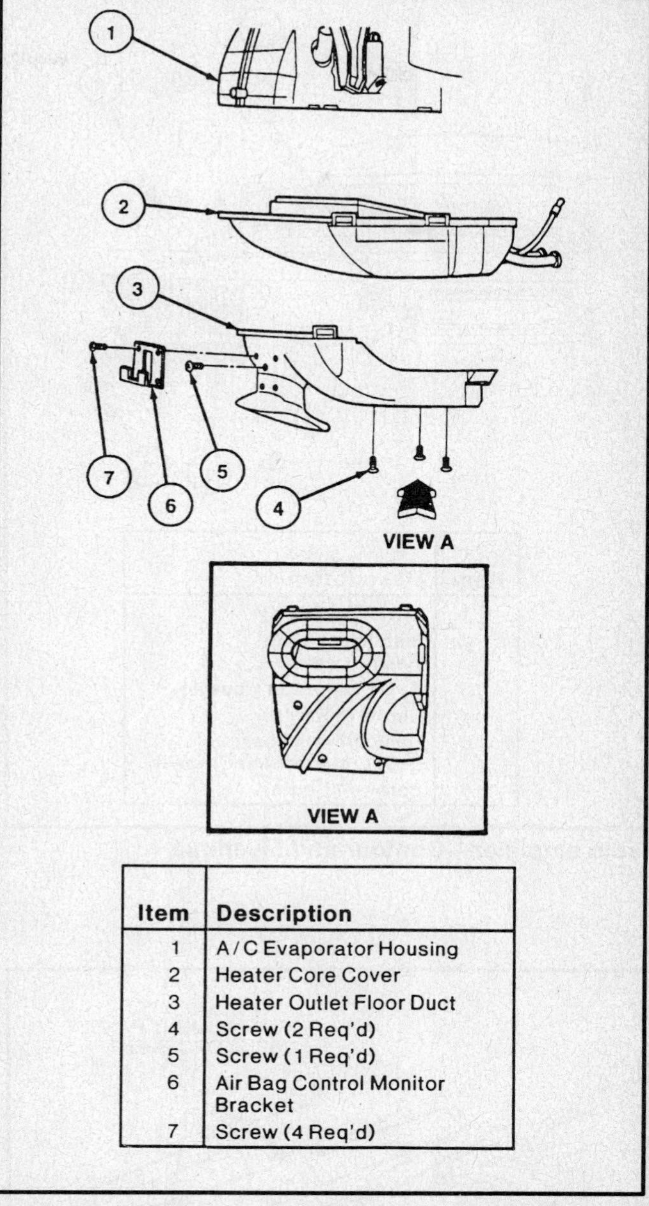

Item	Description
1	A / C Evaporator Housing
2	Heater Core Cover
3	Heater Outlet Floor Duct
4	Screw (2 Req'd)
5	Screw (1 Req'd)
6	Air Bag Control Monitor Bracket
7	Screw (4 Req'd)

Evaporator/heater case components—Contour and Mystique

6. Remove 3 nuts and 1 bolt from the evaporator/blower assembly. Remove the assembly.

To install:

7. Reverse the removal procedures to install the evaporator/blower assembly and the instrument panel.
8. Reconnect the high and low pressure lines. Evacuate, recharge and leak test the system. Check system operation.

Capri

1. Disconnect the negative battery cable.
2. Discharge the refrigerant from the air conditioning system.

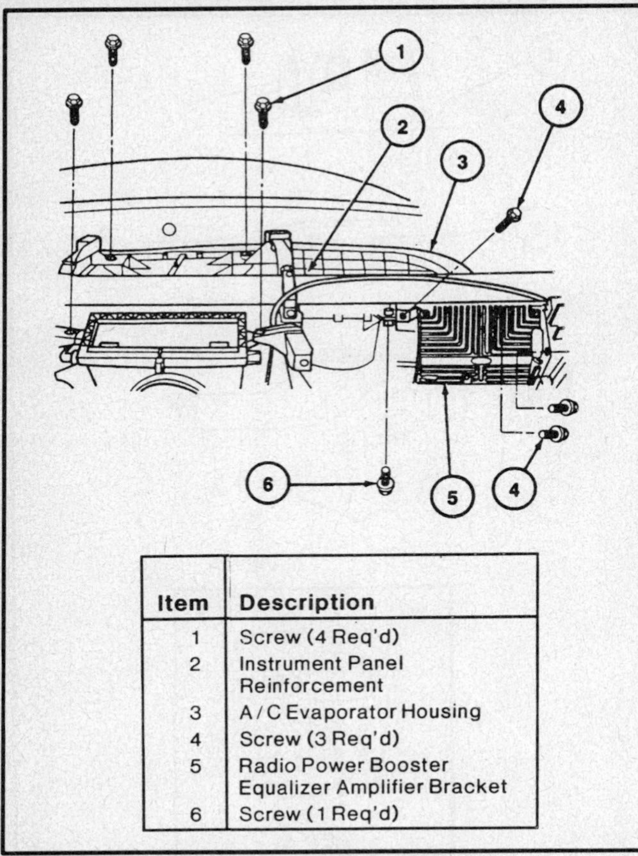

Item	Description
1	Screw (4 Req'd)
2	Instrument Panel Reinforcement
3	A/C Evaporator Housing
4	Screw (3 Req'd)
5	Radio Power Booster Equalizer Amplifier Bracket
6	Screw (1 Req'd)

Radio amplifier—Contour and Mystique

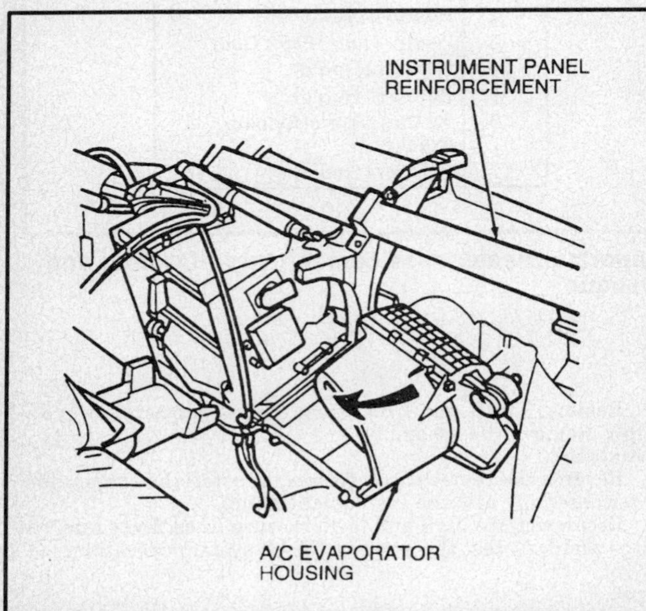

Removing the evaporator housing—Contour and Mystique

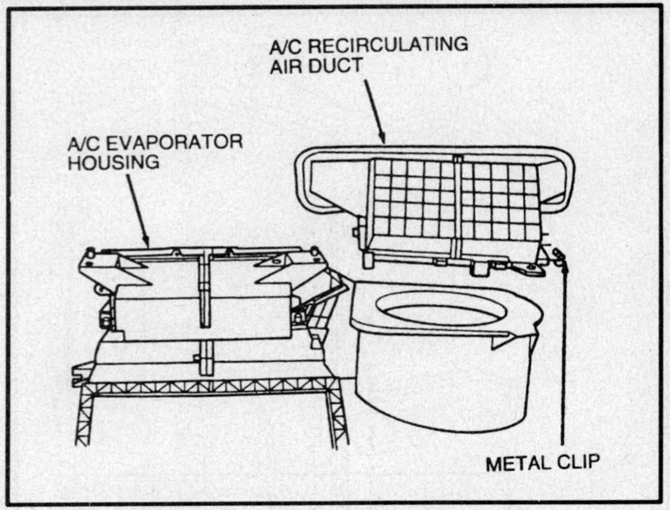

A/C recirculating air duct—Contour and Mystique

3. Disconnect the air conditioning lines from the evaporator in the engine compartment and plug the ends to prevent dirt and moisture from entering the system.
4. Remove the glove compartment and the glove compartment upper panel. Remove the upper panel bracket.
5. Disconnect the electrical connectors and release the harness retainers.
6. Remove the defroster tube, air duct bands and the drain hose.
7. Remove the evaporator mount bolts and nuts and carefully remove the evaporator.
8. Remove the 10 retaining clips, separate the case halves and remove the evaporator.
9. Remove the de-ice thermostat and disconnect the liquid tube from the inlet fitting of the expansion valve.
10. Remove the capillary tube from the evaporator outlet and remove the expansion valve from the inlet fitting of the evaporator.

To install:

11. Install the expansion valve to the inlet fitting of the evaporator. Tighten the fitting to 9–11 ft. lbs. (12–15 Nm).
12. Connect the liquid tube to the inlet fitting of the expansion valve. Tighten the fitting to 9–11 ft. lbs. (12–15 Nm).
13. Install packing to fix the capillary tube of the expansion valve to the outlet of the evaporator. Install the de-ice switch.
14. Assemble the case halves with the 10 retaining clips.
15. Add 0.845–1.014 oz. (25–30ml) of clean refrigerant oil to the replacement evaporator.
16. Carefully position the evaporator assembly and install the retaining bolts and nuts. Make sure the evaporator grommet in the dash panel is in the proper position.
17. Install the air duct bands and the drain hose.
18. Connect the electrical connector and install the harness retainers.
19. Install the defroster tube.
20. Install the glove compartment upper panel bracket, the glove compartment upper panel and the glove compartment.
21. Unplug the liquid line and connect it to the evaporator inlet. Tighten the fitting to 9–11 ft. lbs. (12–15 Nm).
22. Unplug the suction line and connect it to the evaporator outlet. Tighten the fitting to 22–25 ft. lbs. (30–35 Nm).
23. Connect the negative battery cable. Leak test, evacuate and charge the system. Observe all safety precautions.

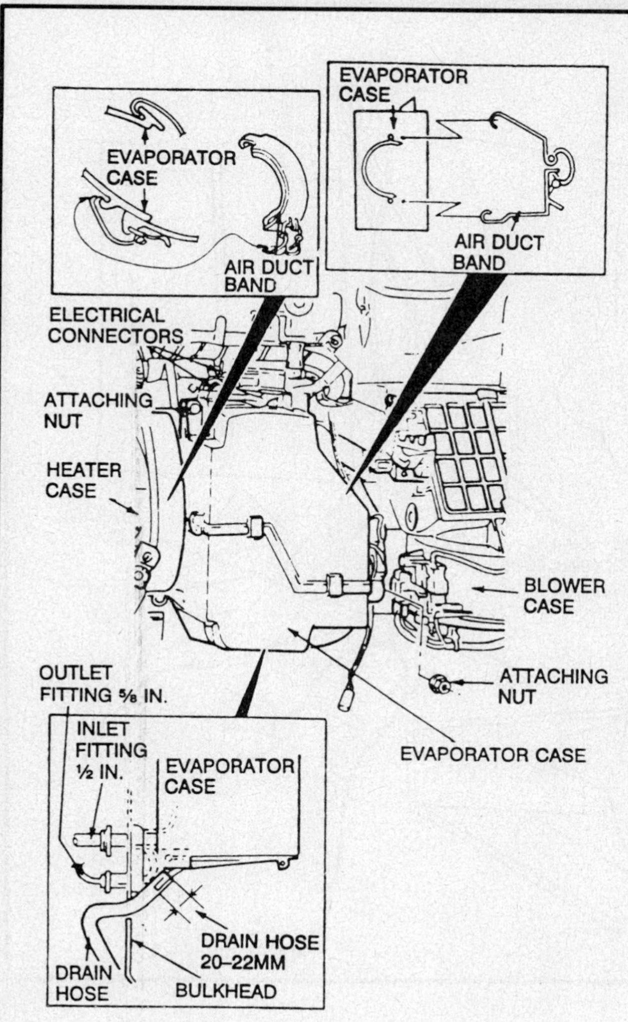

Evaporator case assembly—Probe

Festiva and Aspire

1. Disconnect the negative battery cable.
2. Properly discharge the refrigerant from the air conditioning system.
3. Disconnect the suction line from the evaporator outlet fitting and the high pressure line from the evaporator inlet fitting.
4. Remove the attaching screws and the glove box.
5. Disconnect the 2 electrical connectors and the cable from the thermostat.
6. Disengage the wiring harness routing clamps from the evaporator housing.
7. Loosen the clamp screw securing the connector duct to the evaporator housing.
8. Disconnect the drain hose from the evaporator housing and remove the air inlet duct attaching bolt.
9. Remove the bolt attaching the base of the evaporator housing to the dash panel.
10. Remove the nuts attaching the top of the evaporator housing to the dash panel and remove the evaporator housing.
11. Remove the 10 clips securing the upper evaporator housing to the lower evaporator housing and remove the upper evaporator housing.
12. Remove the attaching screws and the thermostat. Pull the sensing tube from between the evaporator core fins as the thermostat is removed.
13. Remove the evaporator from the lower housing and remove the tube insert from between the inlet and outlet tubes.
14. Remove the staples securing the capillary tube insulator over the expansion valve capillary tube and suction tube.
15. Remove the clamp securing the expansion valve capillary tube to the suction tube.
16. Disconnect the evaporator tube fitting and remove the expansion valve.

To install:

NOTE: Add 3 oz. (90 ml) of clean refrigerant oil to a new replacement evaporator core to maintain total system refrigerant oil requirements.

17. Install a new O-ring on the evaporator tube fittings, then install the expansion valve.
18. Position the capillary tube and install the clamp. Install the capillary tube insulation and staple it in position.
19. Install the tube insert between the inlet and outlet tubes and position the evaporator in the lower evaporator housing.
20. Carefully push the thermostat sensing tube into position between the evaporator core fins.
21. Place the upper evaporator housing onto the lower evaporator housing and install the 10 clips.
22. Position the evaporator housing under the instrument panel.
23. Install and tighten the 2 nuts securing the top of the evaporator housing to the dash panel and the bolt securing the base of the evaporator housing to the dash panel.
24. Install the air inlet duct attaching bolt and connect the drain hose to the evaporator housing.
25. Tighten the connecting duct clamp screw and attach the wiring harness routing clamps to the evaporator housing.
26. Connect the cable and the 2 electrical connectors to the thermostat.
27. Position the glove box and install the attaching screws.
28. Slide the suction and liquid tube grommets onto their tubes.
29. Install a new O-ring, lubricated with clean refrigerant oil and connect the suction line to the evaporator outlet. Install a new O-ring, lubricated with clean refrigerant oil and connect the high pressure hose to the evaporator inlet fitting.
30. Connect the negative battery cable. Evacuate, charge and test the system.

Refrigerant Lines

REMOVAL AND INSTALLATION

NOTE: Whenever a refrigerant line is replaced, it will be necessary to replace the accumulator/drier on fixed orifice tube systems.

All Except Aspire

1. Disconnect the negative battery cable.
2. Properly discharge the refrigerant from the air conditioning system.

NOTE: On Contour and Mystique equipped with a 2.0L engine, the windshield wiper arms must be positioned away from the cowl vent screen. This can be accomplished by switching OFF the ignition switch when the cycling windshield wipers are at the top of their arc on the windshield.

3. On Contour and Mystique with 2.0L engine only, position windshield wiper arms away from cowl vent screen.
4. On Contour and Mystique with 2.0L engine only, remove plastic screw covers and three top screws retaining RH half of cowl vent screen.

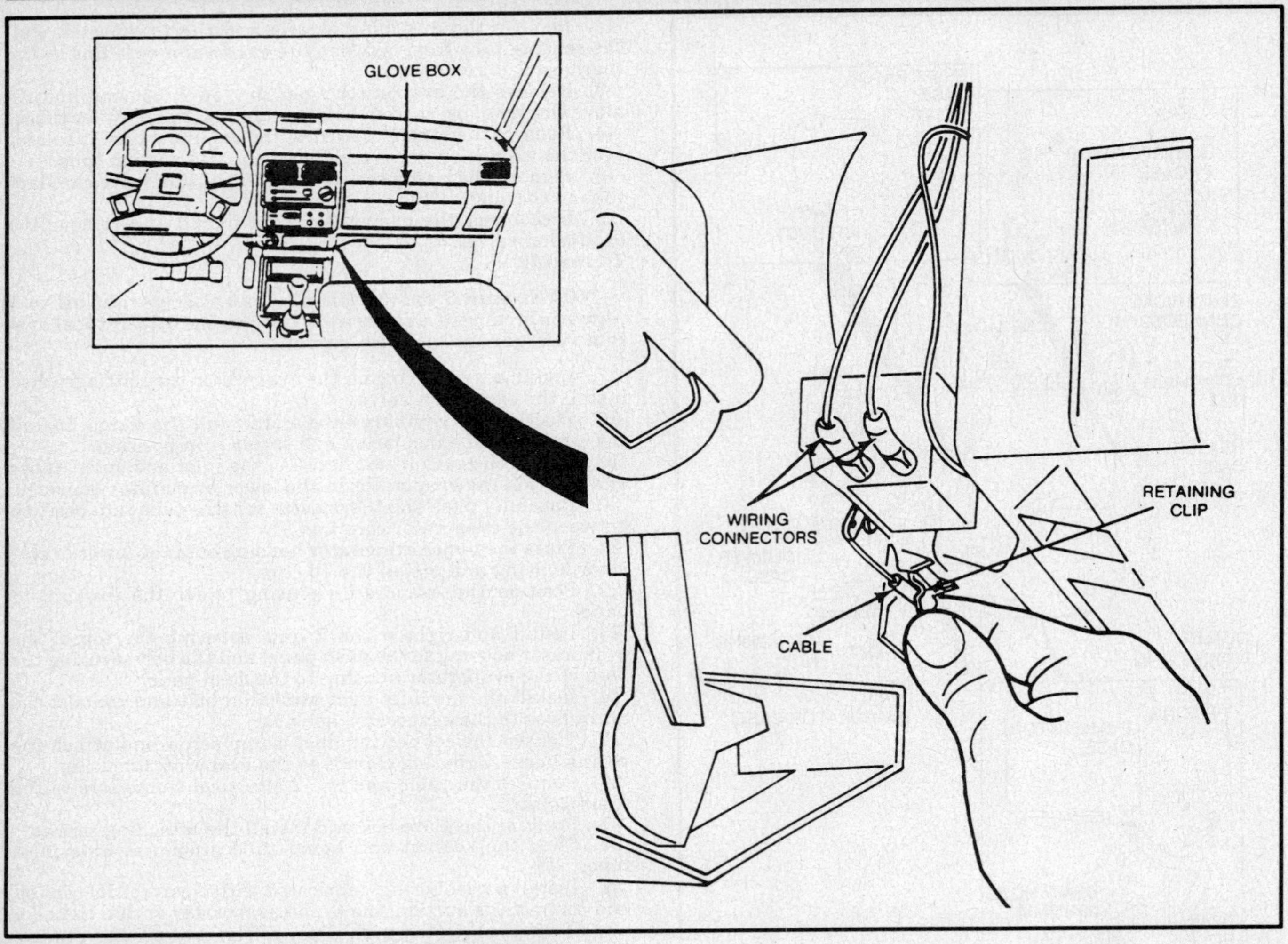

Disconnecting wiring from the thermostat—Festiva

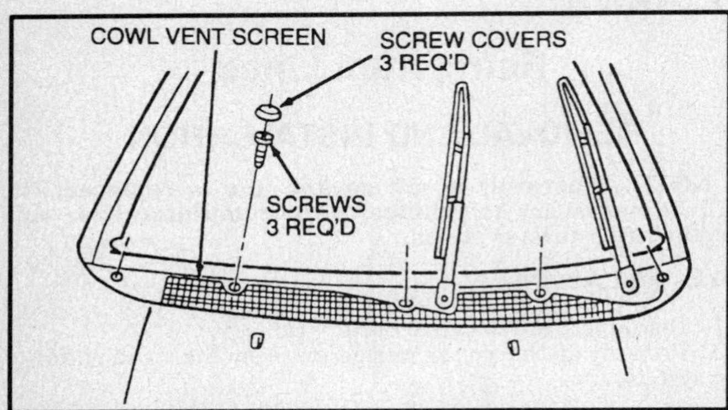

Cowl vent installation—Contour and Mystique

5. On Contour and Mystique with 2.0L engine only, remove 2 screws retaining electrical accessory mounting plate to cowl and position plate to improve access.
6. Disconnect and remove the refrigerant line using a wrench on each side of the tube O-fittings. If the refrigerant line has a spring-lock coupling, disconnect the fitting.
7. Route the new refrigerant line with the protective caps installed.
8. On Contour and Mystique with 2.5L engine, route new jumper line with protected caps.
9. Connect the new refrigerant line into the system using new O-rings lubricated with clean refrigerant oil. Use 2 wrenches when tightening the tube O-fittings or perform the spring-lock coupling connect procedure.
10. On Contour and Mystique with 2.0L engine only, install electrical accessory mounting plate to cowl with 2 screws. Install cowl vent screen and hood pad.
11. Connect the negative battery cable. On Contour and Mystique with 2.0L engine only, switch ignition switch to RUN and park windshield wipers. Leak test, evacuate and charge the refrigerant system.

Aspire

1. Properly discharge the refrigerant from the air conditioning system.
2. Remove the battery and remove the radiator coolant recovery reservoir.
3. Disconnect the evaporator-to-compressor suction line at the front evaporator-to-compressor suction line fitting.
4. Remove the 2 evaporator-to-compressor suction line bracket nuts and the bolt from the 3 evaporator-to-compressor suction line brackets.
5. Disconnect the evaporator-to-compressor suction line at the evaporator core outlet fitting. Plug the evaporator core outlet fitting to prevent moisture from entering the system.

6. Disconnect the 3 vacuum hoses from the Exhaust Gas Recirculation (EGR) solenoid valve assembly.
7. Remove the evaporator-to-compressor suction line bracket nut from the chassis below the A/C condenser core.
8. Remove the evaporator-to-compressor suction line fitting bolt from the compressor. Plug the compressor inlet fitting to prevent moisture from entering the system.
9. Remove the front evaporator-to-compressor suction line from the vehicle.

NOTE: The liquid line is in 2 pieces – the rear liquid line runs along the bulkhead, from the A/C evaporator core inlet fitting to the LH side of the bulkhead, below the windshield wiper motor. The front liquid line runs along the LH side of the engine compartment, from the rear liquid line to the suction accumulator/drier outlet fitting. This procedure covers the removal of both portions of the liquid line.

10. Remove the 2 liquid line bracket nuts and the bolt from the 3 liquid line brackets.
11. Remove the rear liquid line from the A/C evaporator core inlet fitting. Plug the A/C evaporator core inlet fitting to prevent moisture from entering the system.
12. Disconnect the rear line at the front liquid line fitting. Remove the rear liquid line from the vehicle.
13. Remove the liquid line fitting from the suction accumulator/drier outlet fitting. Plug the suction accumulator/drier outlet fitting to prevent moisture from entering the system.
14. Remove the front liquid line from the vehicle.

To install:

NOTE: Apply clean refrigerant oil to the O-rings prior to installation.

15. Installation is the reverse of the removal procedure.
    - Tighten the liquid line at the suction accumulator outlet fitting to 69–104 in lb (8–11 Nm).
    - Tighten the liquid line at the A/C evaporator core inlet fitting to 87–174 in lb (10–19 Nm).
    - Tighten the rear liquid line to front liquid line fitting to 9.4–10.4 ft lb (12.8–14.2 Nm).

Jumper Lines

REMOVAL AND INSTALLATION

1. Properly discharge the refrigerant from the air conditioning system.
2. Remove the jumper line at the condenser core outlet fitting. Plug the condenser core outlet fitting to prevent moisture from entering the system.
3. Disconnect the jumper line at the suction accumulator/drier inlet fitting. Plug the receiver/drier tank inlet fitting to prevent moisture from entering the system.
4. Remove the jumper line from the vehicle.

NOTE: Apply clean refrigerant oil to the O-rings prior to installation.

5. To install, reverse the removal procedure.
6. Tighten the jumper line at the suction accumulator/drier inlet fitting to 69–104 in–lb (8–11 Nm).
7. Tighten the jumper line at the A/C condenser core outlet fitting to 87–174 in–lb (10–19 Nm).

Manual Control Head

REMOVAL AND INSTALLATION

Taurus and Sable

1. Disconnect the negative battery cable.
2. Remove the instrument panel finish applique.

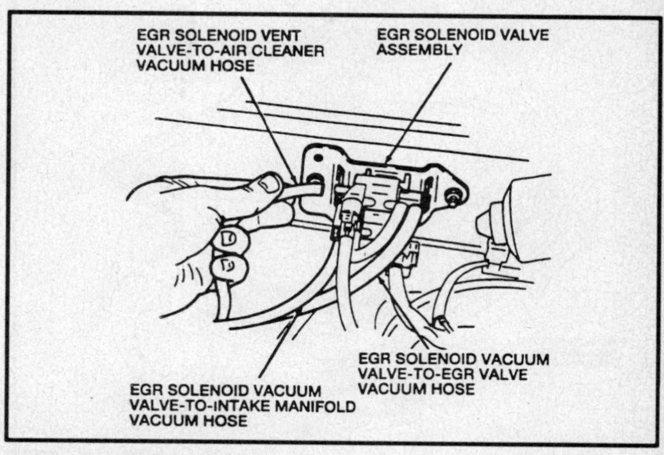

EGR Solenoid—Aspire

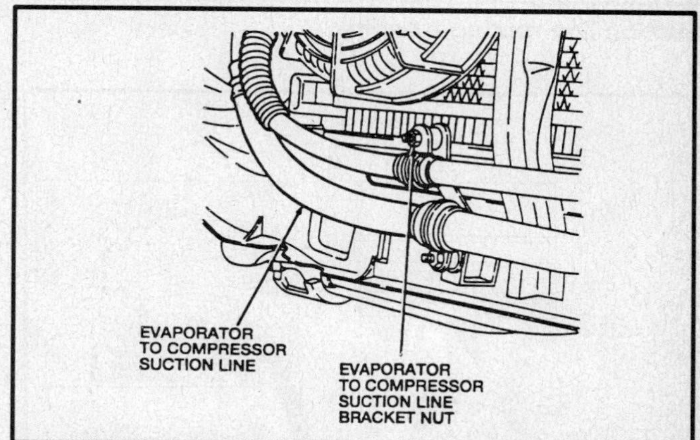

Suction line bracket—Aspire

3. Remove the 4 screws attaching the control assembly to the instrument panel. Remove 4 Torx® screws retaining control head.
4. Pull the control assembly from the instrument panel opening and disconnect the wire connectors from the control assembly.
5. Disconnect the vacuum harness and temperature control cable from the control assembly. Discard the used pushnut from the vacuum harness.

To install:

6. Connect the temperature cable to the control assembly.
7. Connect the wire connectors and vacuum harness to the control assembly using new pushnuts.

NOTE: Push on the vacuum harness retaining nuts. Do not attempt to screw them onto the post.

8. Position the control assembly to the instrument panel opening and install 4 attaching screws.
9. Install the instrument panel finish applique.
10. Connect the negative battery cable and check the system for proper operation.

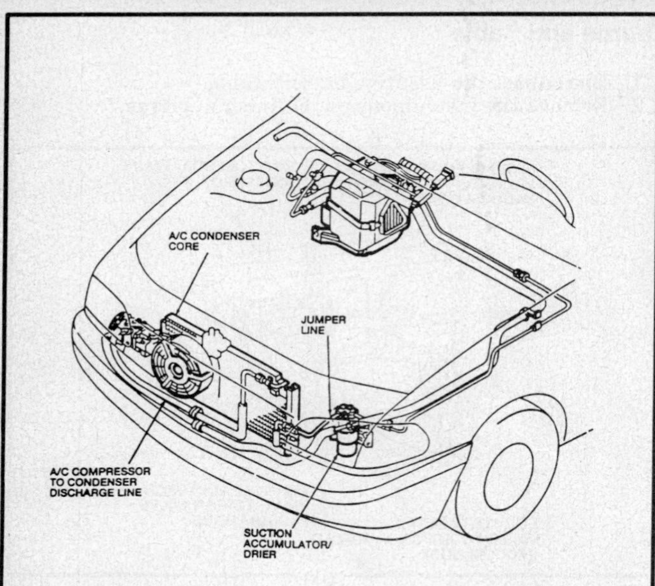

Suction line routing—Aspire

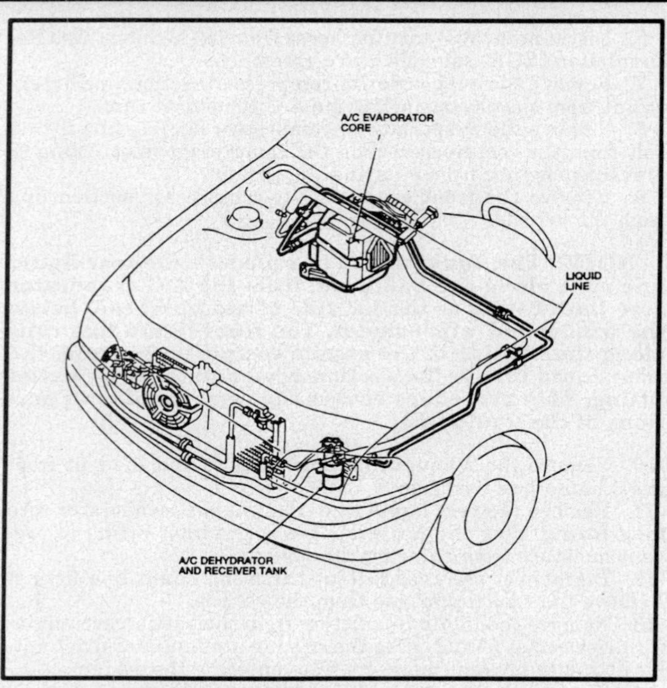

Accumulator/drier—Aspire

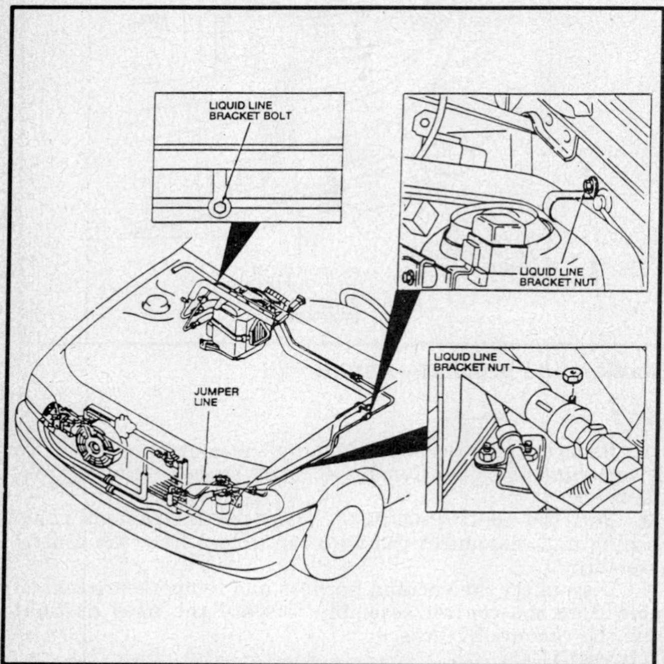

Suction line installation—Aspire

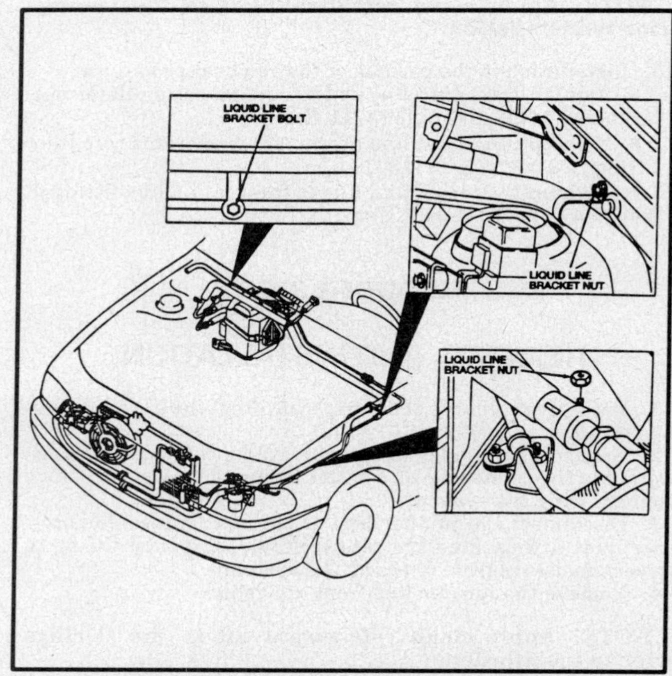

Jumper line installation—Aspire

Tempo and Topaz

1. Disconnect the negative battery cable.
2. Move the temperature control lever to the **COOL** position. Disconnect the temperature control cable housing end retainer from the air conditioning case bracket using control cable removal tool T83P–18532–AH or equivalent. Disconnect the cable from the temperature door crank arm.
3. Insert 2 suitable tools into the 3.5mm holes provided in the bezel. Apply a light inboard force at each side of the control. The spring clips will become depressed, releasing the air conditioner control from the register housing.
4. Pull the control assembly out from the register housing. Disconnect the temperature cable housing from the control mounting bracket using the control cable removal tool.
5. Remove the twist off cap from the temperature control lever and remove the temperature control cable.

6. Remove the temperature cable wire from the control lever and disconnect the electrical connectors from the control assembly.

7. Remove the 2 spring nuts that attach the vacuum harness assembly to the control assembly and remove the assembly.

To install:

8. Position the control assembly near the instrument panel opening. Connect the vacuum harness to the control assembly. Install the 2 spring nuts. Connect the electrical connectors to the control assembly.

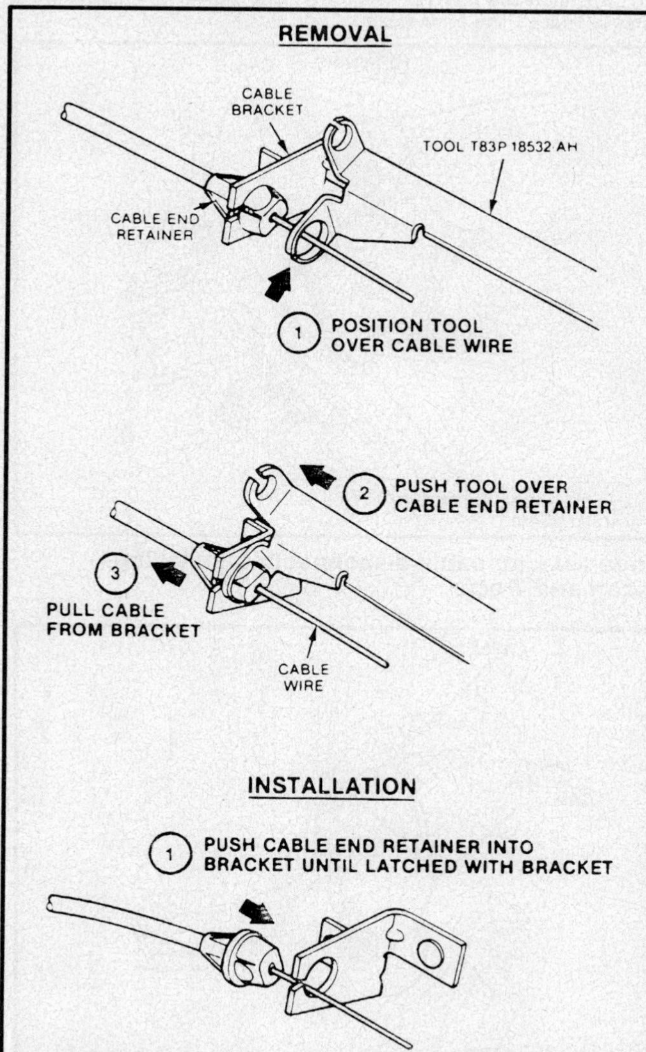
REMOVAL
CABLE BRACKET
TOOL T83P 18532 AH
CABLE END RETAINER
1 POSITION TOOL OVER CABLE WIRE
2 PUSH TOOL OVER CABLE END RETAINER
3
PULL CABLE FROM BRACKET
CABLE WIRE
INSTALLATION
1 PUSH CABLE END RETAINER INTO BRACKET UNTIL LATCHED WITH BRACKET

Control cable removal and installation using special tool—Tempo and Topaz

9. Move the temperature control lever to the **COOL** position.

10. Connect the temperature control cable to the control.

11. Position the control assembly to the register housing. Align the locking tabs on the control bracket with the metal slide track in the instrument panel.

12. Slide the aligned control assembly down the metal track until the spring clips on the control have snapped in, indicating that the control is locked in the register housing.

13. Move the temperature control lever to the **COOL** position.

14. Connect the self-adjusting clip of the temperature control cable to the temperature door crank arm.

15. Slide the cable housing end retainer into the evaporator case bracket and engage the tabs of the cable and retainer with the bracket.

16. Move the temperature control lever to the **WARM** position to adjust the cable assembly.

17. Check for proper operation of the temperature control lever.

Contour and Mystique

NOTE: Record pre-set radio frequencies.

1. Disconnect battery ground cable.

CAUTION

Do not use excessive force when installing removing tool This will damage retaining clips, making radio chassis or digital audio compact disc player removal difficult.

2. Install Radio Removing Tool T87P–19061–A into radio faceplate or digital audio compact disc player face plate.

3. Apply a slight spreading force on tool and pull radio chassis or digital audio compact disc player from instrument panel.

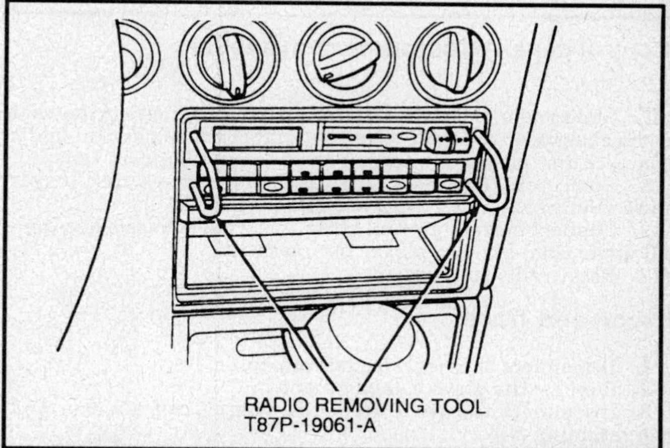
RADIO REMOVING TOOL
T87P-19061-A

Radio removing tool

NOTE: On Mystique, remove both radio chassis and digital audio compact disc player. On Contour remove radio chassis only.

4. Disconnect the connectors and remove the radio chassis and or digital audio compact disc player.

5. Open ash receptacle and remove 2 screws retaining control opening finish panel to instrument panel (Mystique only). Snap finish panel away from instrument panel.

6. Disconnect light switch rheostat resistor wiring connector.

7. Remove 2 screws and heater control from the instrument panel (Contour only).

8. Disconnect wire connectors from the heater control.

9. Disconnect vacuum hose harness from heater control.

10. Remove 4 screws and heater control from finish panel (Mystique only).

11. Position heater control in control opening finish panel and install retaining screws (Mystique only).

12. Connect wire connector(s) and vacuum hose harness to heater control.

13. Position heater control in control opening finish panel and install retaining screws (Contour only).

14. Connect dash dimmer switch wiring connector.

15. Install control opening finish panel by snapping it into place. Secure finish panel with 2 screws (Mystique only).

16. Connect wiring connectors and antenna cable to radio chassis.

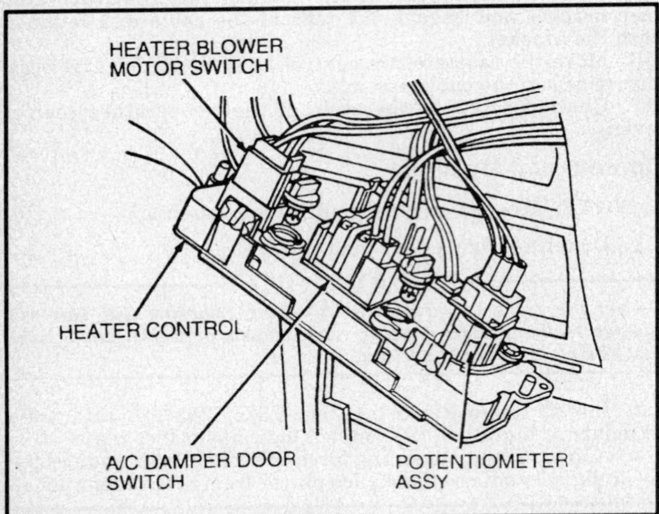

Control panel—Contour and Mystique

17. Slide radio chassis into instrument panel, ensuring that radio chassis or rear radio chassis support of the digital audio compact disc player is engaged on the upper support rail.
18. Push radio chassis or digital audio compact disc player inward until retaining clips are fully engaged.
19. Connect battery ground cable. Test radio chassis and digital audio compact disc player for operation.
20. Reset radio stations.

Escort and Tracer

1. Disconnect the negative battery cable.
2. Remove the glove compartment.
3. Disconnect the cable from the recirc/fresh air cam and the retaining clip.
4. Disconnect the cable from the mode selector cam and the retaining clip.

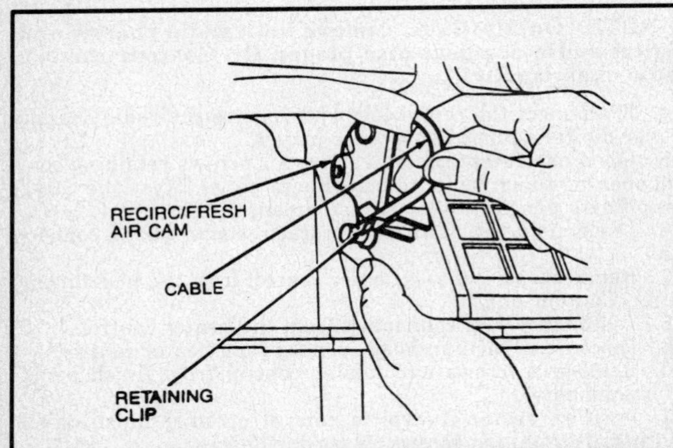

Fresh/recirc cable disconnecting/installing—Escort and Tracer

5. Disconnect the cable from the temperature control cam and the retaining clip.
6. Remove the trim bezel and remove the 4 retaining screws from the control assembly. Carefully pull the control assembly out of the accessory console.
7. Disconnect the blower and air conditioning switch electrical connector and disconnect the illumination light electrical connector.
8. Remove the control assembly.

To install:

9. Route each control cable to it's appropriate cam.
10. Connect the illumination light electrical connector and the blower and air conditioning switch electrical connector.
11. Position the control assembly and install the 4 retaining screws. Install the trim bezel.

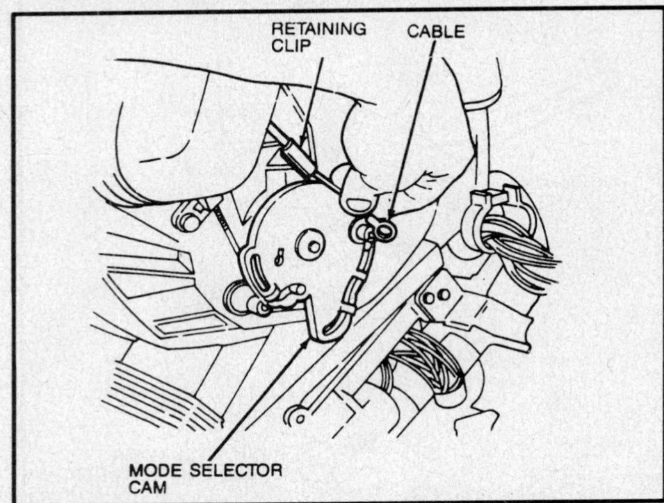

Mode selector cable disconnecting/installing—Escort and Tracer

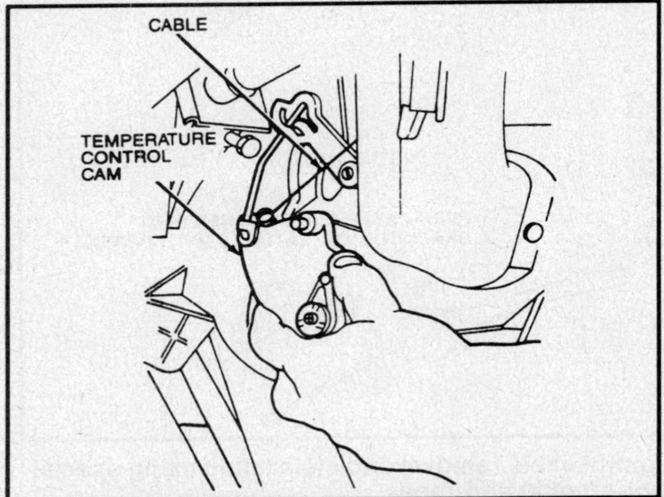

Temperature control cable disconnecting/installing—Escort and Tracer

12. Adjust the temperature control cable, the mode selector cable and the recirc/fresh air cable.
13. Install the glove compartment and connect the negative battery cable.

Probe

1. Disconnect the negative battery cable. Remove the floor console assembly as follows:

- Remove the armrest (if equipped).
- If manual transaxle, unscrew the shifter knob. If automatic transaxle, remove the emergency override key switch cover.
- Engage the parking brake. Gently pull up on top half of console to separate it from the lower half.
- Disconnect the cigar lighter wiring and the light element wiring. Remove the ashtray bulb.
- Remove control console bezel. Remove the screw and push pin from both floor heater duct covers.
- Remove 6 lower console retaining screws and remove the console.

2. Remove 3 control panel screws. Disconnect the mode selector electrical connection.
3. Remove 2 mode selector vacuum harness nuts and pull off the vacuum harness.
4. Detach blower motor electrical connector and control panel bulb connector.
5. Disengage the temperature control cable from the control panel (pull panel out to reach cable attachment) and actuator. Remove the control panel.
6. Installation is the reverse of the removal procedures. Adjust temperature cable, if needed.

Capri

1. Disconnect the negative battery cable.
2. Remove the storage compartment.
3. Remove the control panel/radio bezel and remove the control panel retaining screws.
4. Lower the glove compartment past it's stop and remove the glove compartment upper support.
5. Disconnect the air door control cable.
6. Disconnect the function selector cable at the heater assembly.
7. Remove the left center carpet panel.
8. Disconnect the temperature control cable at the heater assembly.
9. Pull the control panel from the instrument panel far enough to gain access to the electrical connectors and disconnect. Use caution so as not to damage the control cables.
10. Remove the 2 screws and the control panel assembly with the cables attached.

To install:

11. Route the cables into the instrument panel and position the control panel in the instrument panel. Connect the electrical connectors.
12. Install the control panel with the retaining screws.
13. Connect the temperature control cable, function selector cable and air door control cable. Check and adjust the control cables.
14. Install the left center carpet panel.
15. Install the glove compartment upper support and return the glove compartment to the closed position.
16. Install the control panel/radio trim bezel and storage compartment.
17. Connect the negative battery cable and check for proper operation.

Festiva and Aspire

1. Disconnect the negative battery cable.
2. Remove the bezel screws and accessory bezel.
3. Remove the radio.
4. Remove the 4 screws securing the control assembly to the instrument panel.
5. Remove the attaching screws and the glove box.
6. Remove the retaining clip and disconnect the fresh/recirc air door cable at the door operating lever. The cable end is accessible through the glove box opening.
7. Disconnect the mode selector cable at the function control lever. Disconnect the temperature control cable.
8. Pull the control assembly away from the instrument panel.
9. Disconnect the blower motor switch, air conditioning switch and illumination lamp wiring connectors.
10. Remove the control assembly.

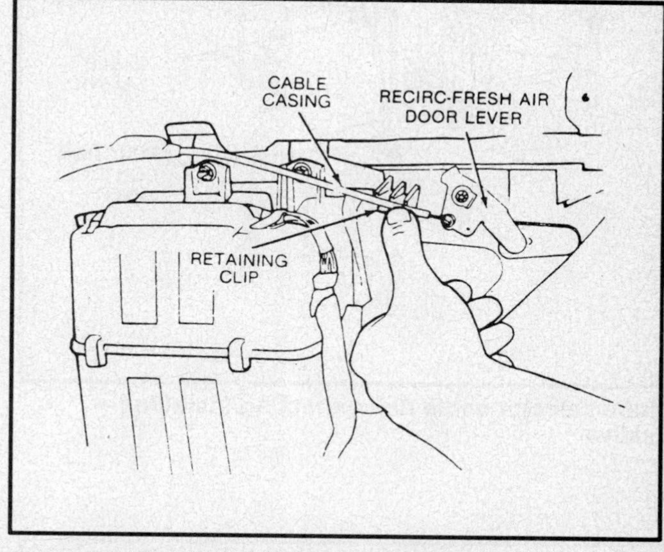

Fresh/recirc cable disconnecting/installing—Festiva

To install:

11. Feed the control cables through the instrument panel opening and position the control assembly in the opening. Route the cables in the general direction of the levers while positioning the control assembly.
12. Route the cables and connect to the levers.
13. Connect the blower motor, air conditioning switch and illumination lamp wiring connectors.
14. Position the control assembly and install the attaching screws.
15. Check and adjust the control cables, if necessary.
16. Position the glove box and install the attaching screws.
17. Install the radio and the accessory bezel.
18. Connect the negative battery cable and check for proper control assembly operation.

Manual Control Cables

ADJUSTMENT

Taurus and Sable

The temperature control cable is self-adjusting when the temperature selector knob is rotated to it's fully CLOCKWISE (RED) position, as marked on the face of the control assembly. A preset adjustment should be made before attempting to perform the self-adjustment operation, to prevent kinking the control wire. The preset adjustment can be performed either with the cable installed in the vehicle or before cable installation.

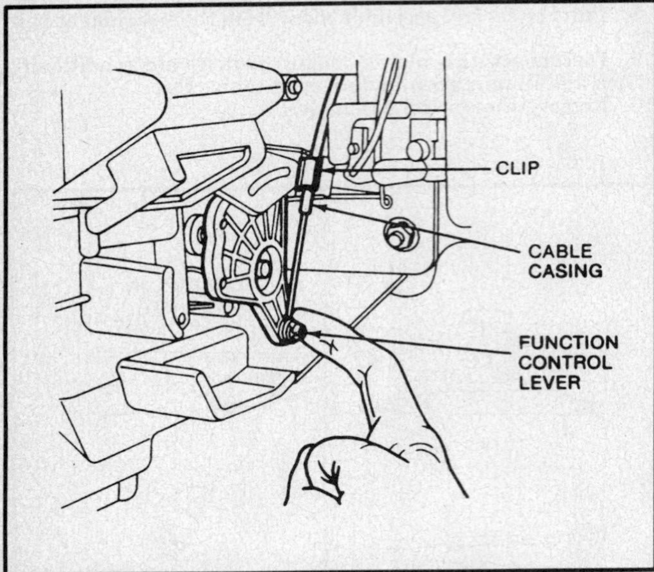

Mode selector cable disconnecting/installing—Festiva

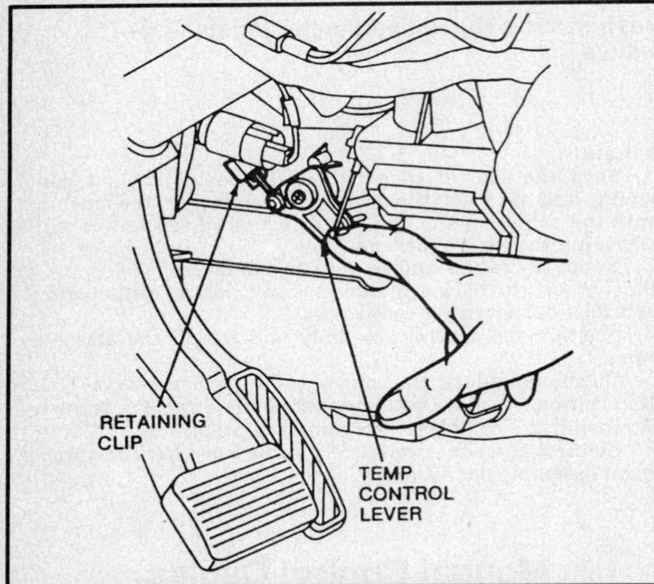

Temperature control cable disconnecting/installing—Festiva

BEFORE CABLE INSTALLATION

1. Insert the end of a suitable tool in the end loop of the temperature control cable.
2. Slide the self-adjusting clip down the control wire, away from the loop, approximately 1 in. (25.4mm).
3. Install the cable assembly.
4. Rotate the temperature selector knob to the CLOCKWISE (RED) position marked on the control assembly face to position the self-adjusting clip.
5. Check for proper control operation.

AFTER CABLE INSTALLATION

1. Move the selector knob clockwise to the **COOL** position.
2. Hold the crank arm firmly in position and insert a suitable tool into the wire loop. Pull the cable wire through the self-adjusting clip until there is a space of approximately 1 in. (25.4mm) between the clip and the wire end loop.
3. Rotate the selector knob clockwise to allow positioning of the self-adjusting clip.
4. Check for proper control operation.

Tempo and Topaz

The temperature control cable is self-adjusting with the movement of the temperature lever to the end of the slot in the bezel face of the control assembly. A preset adjustment must be made before attempting to perform the self-adjustment operation, to prevent kinking of the control wire during cable installation. The preset adjustment may be performed either with the cable installed at the control assembly or before cable installation.

1. Grasp the temperature control cable and the adjusting clip with suitable tools.
2. Slide the self-adjusting clip down the control wire, away from the end, approximately 1 in. (25mm).
3. With the selector lever in the maximum DOWN position, insert the cable housing into the mounting bracket hole and push to snap into place. Attach the self-adjusting clip to the door crank arm.
4. Move the selector lever to the end of the slot in the bezel face of the control assembly to position the self-adjusting clip.
5. Check for proper control operation.

Escort and Tracer

TEMPERATURE CONTROL CABLE

1. Move the temperature control lever to the **COLD** position on the control assembly.
2. To secure the cam in the proper position, insert cable locating key PNE7GH–18C408–A or equivalent, through the cam key slot to the heater case key boss opening.
3. Disconnect the cable from the retaining clip next to the temperature control cam.

NOTE: The temperature control cam is located on the left side of the heater unit.

4. Connect the cable to the retaining clip and remove the cable locating key.
5. Make sure the temperature control lever moves it's full stroke.

MODE SELECTOR CABLE

1. Move the mode selector lever to the **DEFROST** position on the control assembly.
2. Insert cable locating key PNE7GH–18C408–A or equivalent, through the mode cam key slot and heater case key boss opening, to secure the cam in the proper position.
3. Remove the trim panel below the glove compartment, if equipped.
4. Disconnect the cable from the retaining clip next to the mode selector cam.

NOTE: The mode selector cam is located on the right side of the heater unit.

5. Make sure the mode selector lever is in the **DEFROST** position.
6. Connect the cable straight to the retaining clip.

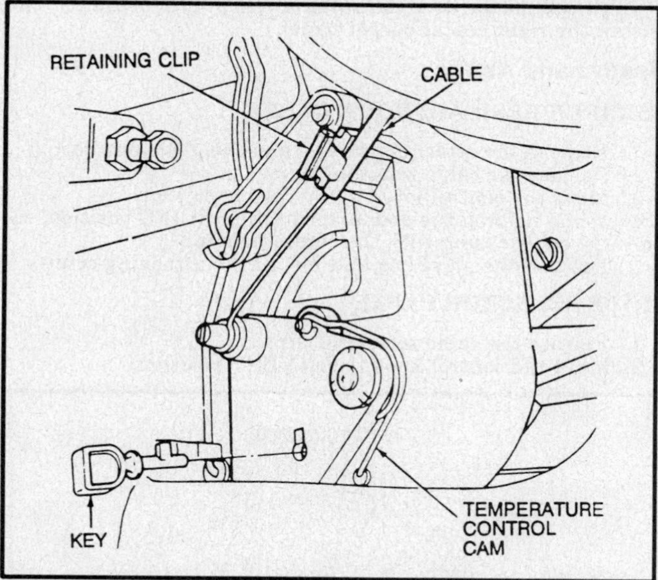

Temperature control cable adjustment—Escort and Tracer

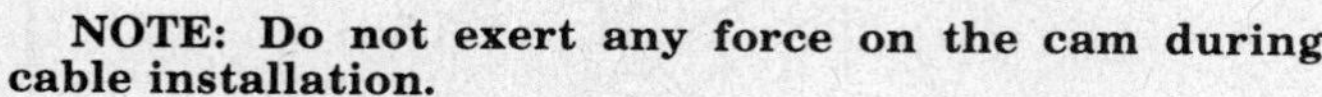

NOTE: Do not exert any force on the cam during cable installation.

7. Remove the cable locating key.
8. Install the trim panel, if equipped.
9. Make sure the mode selector lever moves it's full stroke.

RECIRC/FRESH AIR CABLE

1. Move the recirc/fresh air lever to the **FRESH** position on the control assembly.
2. Remove the glove compartment.
3. Insert cable locating key PNE7GH–18C408–A or equivalent, through the fresh air door cam key slot and recirc door key boss opening to secure the cam in the proper position.
4. Disconnect the cable from the retaining clip next to the recirc/fresh air cam.
5. Connect the cable to the retaining clip and remove the cable locating key.
6. Install the glove compartment.
7. Make sure the recirc/fresh air lever moves it's full stroke.

Probe

The control cables should be adjusted every time they are removed to assure maximum travel of the air control doors.

TEMPERATURE CONTROL CABLE

1. Position the temperature control lever in the **MAX-WARM** position.
2. Remove the glove compartment.
3. Remove the cable located on the right side of the heater case from the cable housing brace.
4. With the cable end on the door lever pin, push the door lever down to it's extreme stop.
5. Secure the cable into the cable housing brace.
6. Check the temperature control lever for proper operation.
7. Install the passenger's side sound deadening panel or the glove box, as removed.

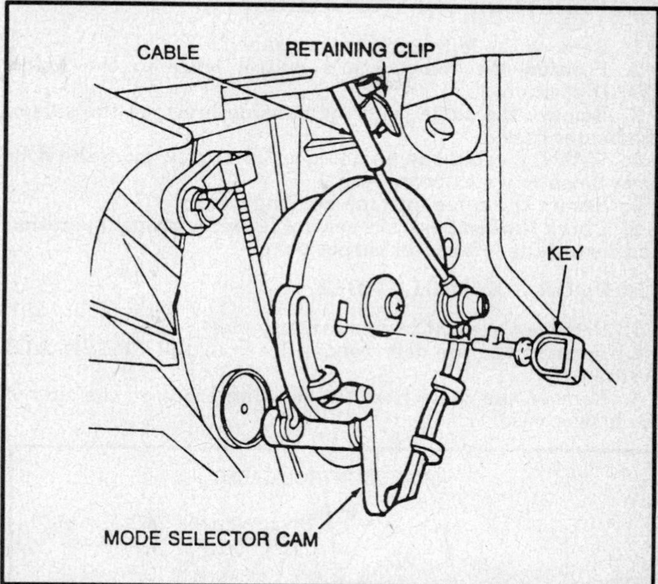

Mode selector cable adjustment—Escort and Tracer

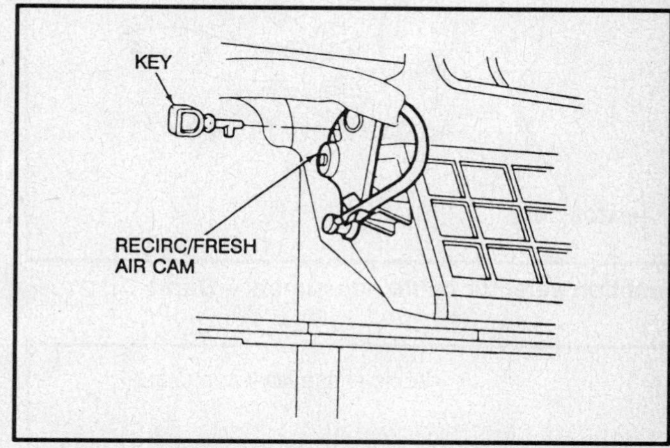

Fresh/recirc selector cable adjustment—Escort and Tracer

Capri

FUNCTION SELECTOR CABLE

1. Remove the right center carpet panel.
2. Position the function selector lever in the **DEFROST** position.
3. Release the cable from the housing brace located on the side of the heater case.
4. With the cable end on the door lever pin, push the door lever down to it's extreme stop.
5. Secure the cable into the cable housing brace and adjust the function selector rod as follows:
   - Remove the rod from the retaining clip at the heater case.
   - Push the door lever downward to it's extreme stop.
   - Adjust the rod to align with the clip in the heater case lever and secure the rod into the retaining clip.
   - Check the lever for proper operation and install the right center carpet panel.

TEMPERATURE CONTROL CABLE

1. Remove the left center carpet panel.
2. Position the temperature control lever in the **MAX-COLD** position.
3. Remove the cable from the housing brace on the side of the heater case.
4. With the cable end on the door lever pin, push the door lever down to it's extreme stop.
5. Secure the cable into the housing brace.
6. Check the temperature control lever for proper operation and install the left center carpet panel.

AIR DOOR CONTROL CABLE

1. Remove the right center carpet panel.
2. Position the air door control lever in the **FRESH AIR** position.
3. Remove the cable from the housing brace on the side of the blower case.

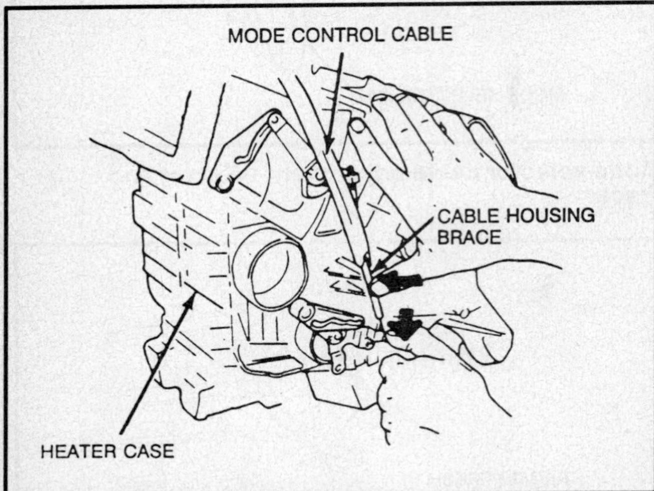

Function selector cable adjustment—Capri

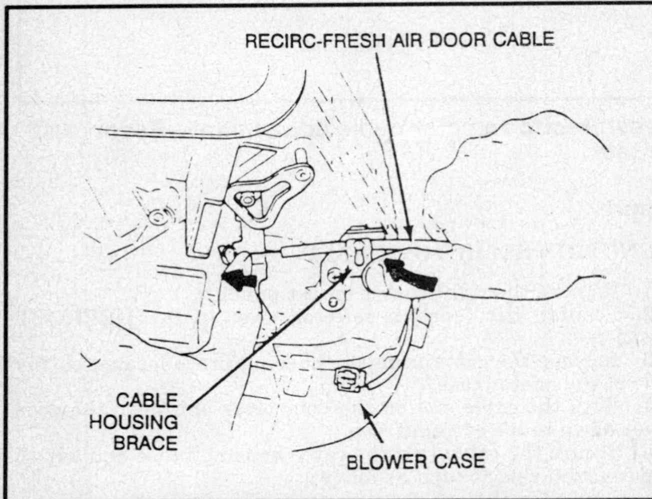

Air door control cable adjustment—Capri

4. With the cable end on the door lever pin, push the door lever forward to it's extreme stop.
5. Secure the cable into the housing brace.
6. Check the air door control lever for proper operation and install the right center carpet panel.

Festiva and Aspire

RECIRC/FRESH AIR DOOR CABLE

1. Remove the attaching screws and the glove box door.
2. Release the cable retaining clip.
3. Move the control lever to the recirc position.
4. While holding the door lever in the RECIRC position, secure the cable casing with the retaining clip.
5. Position the glove box and install the attaching screws.

MODE SELECTOR CABLE

1. Release the cable retaining clip.
2. Move the control knob to the VENT position.

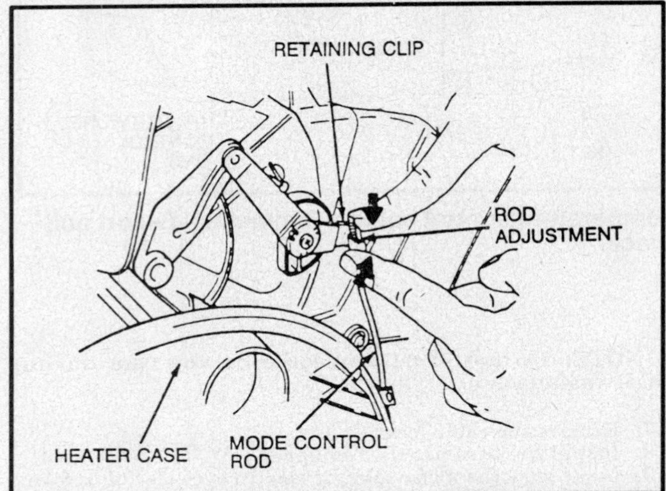

Function selector rod adjustment—Capri

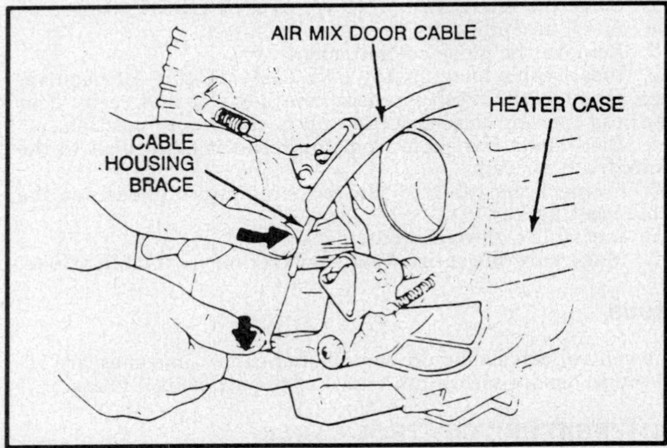

Temperature control cable adjustment—Capri

3. While holding the function control lever downward against it's stop, secure the cable casing with the retaining clip.

TEMPERATURE CONTROL CABLE

1. Release the cable from the retaining clip.
2. Move the temperature control lever to the **MAX-COLD** position.

3. While holding the temperature control lever upward against it's stop, secure the linkage to the retaining clip.

REMOVAL AND INSTALLATION

Taurus and Sable

TEMPERATURE CONTROL CABLE

1. Remove the control assembly from the instrument panel.
2. Disconnect the cable retainer and wire from the control assembly.
3. Disconnect the temperature cable from the plenum temperature blend door crank arm and cable mounting bracket.

To install:

4. Check to make sure the self-adjusting clip is at least 1 in. (25.4mm) from the end loop of the control cable.
5. Route the cable behind the instrument panel and connect the control cable to the mounting bracket on the plenum.
6. Install the self-adjusting clip on the temperature blend door crank arm.
7. Snap the cable housing into place at the control assembly. Connect the "S" bend end of the control cable to the temperature lever arm on the control assembly.
8. Install the control assembly into the instrument panel.

Tempo and Topaz

TEMPERATURE CONTROL CABLE

1. Move the temperature control lever to the **COOL** position. Disconnect the temperature control cable housing and retainer from the air conditioning bracket using control cable removal tool T83P–18532–AH or equivalent. Disconnect the cable from the temperature door crank arm.
2. Insert 2 suitable tools into the 3.5mm holes provided in the bezel. Apply a light inboard force at each side of the control to depress the spring clips and release the air conditioning control from the register housing.
3. Pull the control assembly from the register housing. Move the temperature control lever to **COOL**.
4. Disconnect the temperature cable housing from the control mounting bracket using the control cable removal tool.
5. Remove the twist-off cap from the temperature control lever and remove the temperature control cable.

To install:

6. Position the self-adjusting clip on the control cable.
7. Insert the self-adjusting clip end of the temperature control cable through the control assembly opening of the instrument panel and down to the left side of the evaporator case.
8. Connect the cable wire and housing to the control assembly.
9. Install the twist-off cap by pushing it on.
10. Align the locking tabs of the control bracket with the metal slide track on the instrument panel.
11. Slide the aligned control assembly down the metal track until the metal clips on the control have snapped in, indicating that the control is locked in the register housing.
12. Install the temperature control cable on the air conditioning case.
13. Check the system for proper operation.

Escort and Tracer

1. Disconnect the negative battery cable.
2. Remove the glove compartment.
3. Disconnect the cable from the recirc/fresh air cam and the retaining clip.
4. Disconnect the cable from the mode selector cam and the retaining clip.
5. Disconnect the cable from the temperature control cam and the retaining clip.
6. Remove the trim bezel and remove the 4 retaining screws from the control assembly. Carefully pull the control assembly out of the accessory console.
7. Disconnect the blower and air conditioning switch electrical connector and disconnect the illumination light electrical connector.
8. Remove the control assembly.
9. Disconnect the cable(s) to be replaced from the control assembly.

To install:

10. Attach the replacement cable(s) to the control assembly.
11. Route each control cable to it's appropriate cam.
12. Connect the illumination light electrical connector and the blower and air conditioning switch electrical connector.
13. Position the control assembly and install the 4 retaining screws. Install the trim bezel.
14. Adjust the temperature control cable, the mode selector cable and the recirc/fresh air cable.
15. Install the glove compartment and connect the negative battery cable.

Probe

1. Remove the control panel assembly.
2. Remove the applicable cable housing brace and remove the cable.

To install:

3. Insert the cable end into the hole of the control lever.
4. Position the cable housing into it's seat.
5. Install the cable housing brace.
6. Install the control panel assembly and check for proper control cable operation.

Capri

1. Disconnect the negative battery cable.
2. Remove the storage compartment.
3. Remove the control panel/radio bezel and remove the control panel retaining screws.
4. Lower the glove compartment past it's stop and remove the glove compartment upper support.
5. Disconnect the air door control cable.
6. Disconnect the function selector cable at the heater assembly.
7. Remove the left center carpet panel.
8. Disconnect the temperature control cable at the heater assembly.
9. Pull the control panel from the instrument panel far enough to gain access to the electrical connectors and disconnect. Use caution so as not to damage the control cables.
10. Remove the 2 screws and the control panel assembly with the cables attached.
11. Remove the cable(s) to be replaced from the control panel assembly.

To install:

12. Attach the replacement cable(s) to the control panel assembly.
13. Route the cables into the instrument panel and position the control panel in the instrument panel. Connect the electrical connectors.
14. Install the control panel with the retaining screws.
15. Connect the temperature control cable, function selector cable and air door control cable. Check and adjust the control cables.
16. Install the left center carpet panel.
17. Install the glove compartment upper support and return the glove compartment to the closed position.
18. Install the control panel/radio trim bezel and storage compartment.
19. Connect the negative battery cable and check for proper operation.

Festiva

1. Disconnect the negative battery cable.

2. Remove the bezel screws and accessory bezel.
3. Remove the radio.
4. Remove the 4 screws securing the control assembly to the instrument panel.
5. Remove the attaching screws and the glove box.
6. Remove the retaining clip and disconnect the recirculate/fresh air door cable at the door operating lever. The cable end is accessible through the glove box opening.
7. Disconnect the mode selector cable at the function control lever. Disconnect the temperature control cable.
8. Pull the control assembly away from the instrument panel.
9. Disconnect the blower motor switch, air conditioning switch and illumination lamp wiring connectors.
10. Remove the control assembly with the control cables.

To install:

11. Feed the control cables through the instrument panel opening and position the control assembly in the opening. Route the cables in the general direction of the levers while positioning the control assembly.
12. Route the cables and connect to the levers.
13. Connect the blower motor, air conditioning switch and illumination lamp wiring connectors.
14. Position the control assembly and install the attaching screws.
15. Check and adjust the control cables, if necessary.
16. Position the glove box and install the attaching screws.
17. Install the radio and the accessory bezel.
18. Connect the negative battery cable and check for proper control assembly operation.

Electronic Control Head

REMOVAL AND INSTALLATION

Taurus and Sable or Continental without 4.6L Engine

1. Disconnect the negative battery cable.
2. On Taurus and Sable, perform the following procedure:
   - Pull out the lower left and lower right instrument panel snap-on finish panel inserts. Remove the 8 screws retaining the upper finish panel.
   - Pull the lower edge of the upper finish panel away from the instrument panel. It is best to grasp the finish panel from the lower left corner and pull the panel away by walking the hands around the panel in a clockwise direction.
3. On Continental, perform the following procedure:
   - Pry the left and right instrument panel shelf molding up to disengage the clips and remove the moldings.
   - Remove the instrument panel cluster opening finish panel retaining screws and remove the panel.
4. On all vehicles, remove the 4 Torx® head screws retaining the control assembly. Pull the control assembly away from the instrument panel into a position which provides access to the rear connections.
5. Disconnect the 2 harness connectors from the control assembly by depressing the latches at the top of the connectors and pulling.
6. Remove the nuts retaining the vacuum harness to the control assembly.

To install:

7. Connect the 2 electrical harness connectors to the control assembly. Push the keyed connectors in until a click is heard.
8. Attach the vacuum harness to the vacuum port assembly. Secure the harness by tightening the 2 nuts.
9. Position the control assembly into the instrument panel opening and install the 4 attaching Torx® head screws. Make sure, as the control is positioned, the locating posts are correctly aligned with their respective holes.
10. Carefully place the instrument panel applique into it's assembly position. Make sure the spring clips are aligned with their proper holes. Press the applique into place. Make sure all spring clips and screws are secure.
11. On Taurus and Sable, install the 8 screws retaining the upper finish panel. Insert the lower left and lower right instrument panel snap-on finish panel inserts.
12. On Continental, install the left and right shelf moldings.
13. Connect the negative battery cable and check the system operation.

Continental with 4.6L Engine

1. Record User 1 and User 2 preset radio frequencies for reprogramming following installation.
2. Disconnect the negative battery cable.

CAUTION

Do not use excessive force when installing Radio Removing Tool. This will damage retaining clips, making radio chassis removal difficult.

3. Install Radio Removing Tool T87P–19061–A into radio faceplate.
4. Apply a slight spreading force on tools and pull the front control unit from instrument panel.
5. Disconnect wiring connectors and remove the front control unit from the vehicle.

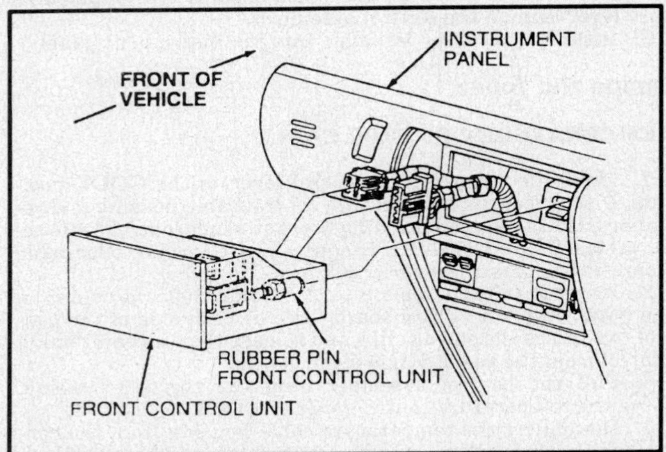

Front control unit—Continental

NOTE: The instrument panel moulding is retained by snap-in tabs.

6. Remove the instrument panel moulding.
7. Remove 3 screws retaining the bottom of the instrument panel steering column cover to the instrument panel.
8. Pull on instrument panel steering column cover to unsnap the 4 clips across the top of the instrument panel steering column cover.
9. Remove 3 screws retaining the side of the instrument panel finish panel to the instrument panel.
10. Pull the instrument panel finish panel to release 2 clips to right of EATC control assembly, disconnect rear window defroster switch wire connector and remove instrument panel finish panel from vehicle.
11. Remove 4 screws retaining EATC control assembly and pull the control out of the instrument panel.
12. Remove 2 harness connectors from EATC control assembly.
13. Remove nuts retaining vacuum hose harness to EATC control assembly. Remove EATC control assembly from instrument panel.

To install:

14. Connect 2 electrical harness connectors to EATC control assembly.
15. Attach vacuum hose harness to EATC control assembly. Secure harness by tightening two nuts.

16. Position EATC control assembly into instrument panel and secure with 4 screws.
17. Connect the rear window defroster switch wire connector and install the instrument panel finish panel to instrument panel with 3 retaining screws.
18. Install instrument panel steering column cover to instrument panel and secure with 3 retaining screws.
19. Install instrument panel moulding to instrument panel.
20. Connect front control unit wiring connectors and install front control unit into instrument panel.
21. Connect the battery ground cable and check system operation.
22. Program radio frequencies and set clock.

SENSORS AND SWITCHES

Clutch Cycling Pressure Switch

OPERATION

The clutch cycling pressure switch is a safety device that opens and closes on pressure changes in the refrigerant. The switch shuts the compressor off when refrigerant pressure is not within the range specified for the vehicle. The clutch cycling pressure switch is located on top of the accumulator/drier on fixed orifice tube systems and in the liquid line between the evaporator and receiver/drier on expansion valve systems.

REMOVAL AND INSTALLATION

1. Disconnect the negative battery cable.
2. On Capri and Festiva, properly discharge the air conditioning system.
3. Disconnect the wire harness connector from the pressure switch.
4. Unscrew the pressure switch from the accumulator/drier.

To install:

5. Lubricate the O-ring on the accumulator nipple with clean refrigerant oil.
6. Screw the pressure switch on the accumulator nipple.
7. Connect the wire connector to the pressure switch.
8. On Capri and Festiva, evacuate, recharge and leak test system.
9. Check the pressure switch installation for refrigerant leaks.
10. Connect the negative battery cable and check the system for proper operation.

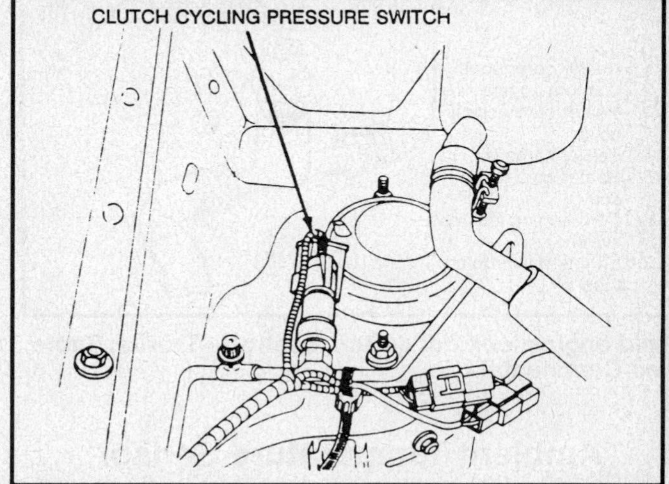

Clutch cycling pressure switch location—Festiva

Cold Engine Lock Out Switch

OPERATION

The cold engine lock out switch is used in the automatic temperature control system on Taurus, Sable and Continental. It prevents the air conditioning compressor from running when the engine is cold. The switch is located in the heater core inlet tube in the engine compartment.

In ambient temperatures below approximately 45°F (7°C), the air conditioner cycling switch on Contour and Mystique will not allow compressor operation because of low system pressures.

REMOVAL AND INSTALLATION

Taurus, Sable and Continental

1. Disconnect the negative battery cable.
2. Disconnect the 2 wire connector from the switch.
3. Partially drain the coolant from the radiator.
4. Remove the threaded switch from the heater tube.

To install:

5. Apply sealer to the switch threads and install it into the fitting in the heater tube. Tighten to 8–14 ft. lbs. (11–19 Nm).
6. Attach the electrical connector to the top of the switch.
7. Refill the radiator with the removed coolant to the proper level.
8. Connect the negative battery cable.

Contour and Mystique

1. Remove the cover from the power distribution box.
2. Pull the clutch control relay from power distribution box.
3. To install, reverse the removal procedures.

Wide-Open Throttle Relay

OPERATION

The air conditioner Wide-Open Throttle (WOT) relay controls clutch operation through the clutch control relay based on information received from the cycling switch, the pressure cutoff switch and the powertrain control module.

REMOVAL AND INSTALLATION

Contour and Mystique

1. Remove the cover from the power distribution box.
2. Pull Wide-Open Throttle (WOT) relay out of the power distribution box.
3. To install, reverse removal procedures.

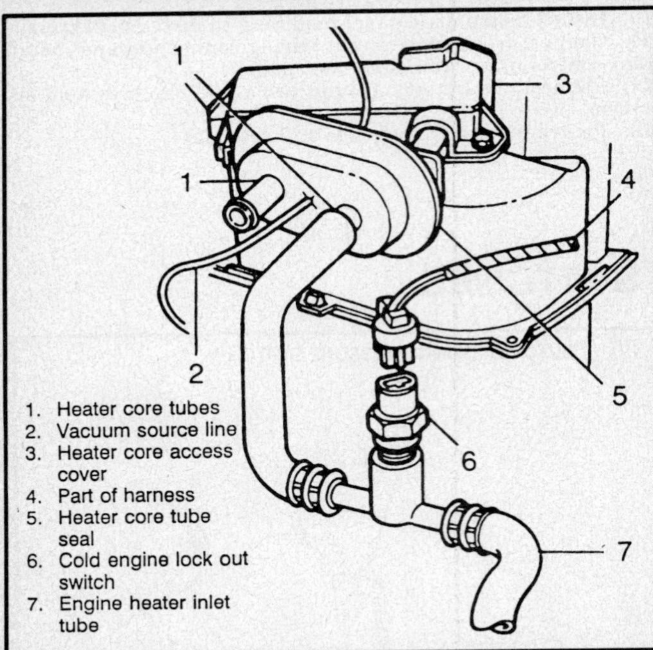

Cold engine lock out switch location—Taurus, Sable and Continental

Ambient Temperature Sensor

OPERATION

The ambient temperature sensor is used in the automatic temperature control system on Taurus, Sable and Continental. It contains a thermistor which measures the temperature of the outside air. The sensor is located in front of the condenser on the left side of the vehicle.

REMOVAL AND INSTALLATION

Taurus, Sable and Continental

1. Disconnect the negative battery cable.
2. Remove the ambient sensor mounting nut and remove the sensor.
3. Disconnect the electrical connector from the ambient sensor.

To install:

4. Connect the electrical connector to the ambient sensor.
5. Position the ambient sensor and install the mounting nut. Tighten to 55–65 inch lbs. (6.2–7.3 Nm). On Continental with 4.6L engine, tighten to 23–33 inch lbs (2.6–3.8 Nm).
6. Connect the negative battery cable and check the system for proper operation.

In-Vehicle Temperature Sensor

OPERATION

The in-vehicle temperature sensor is used in the automatic temperature control system on Taurus, Sable and Continental. It contains a thermistor which measures the temperature of the air inside the passenger compartment. The sensor is located behind the instrument panel above the glove compartment.

REMOVAL AND INSTALLATION

Taurus, Sable and Continental

1. Disconnect the negative battery cable.
2. Disengage the glove compartment door stops and allow the door to hang by the hinge.
3. Working through the glove compartment opening, unclip the sensor from the retainer by squeezing the side tabs.
4. Pull the sensor down into the glove compartment, then disconnect the electrical connector and aspirator flex hose from the sensor.

To install:

5. Connect the electrical connector and aspirator flex hose to the sensor.
6. Working through the glove compartment opening, attach the sensor to the retaining clip.
7. Engage the glove compartment door stops and close the door.
8. Connect the negative battery cable.

Sunload Sensor

OPERATION

The sunload sensor is used in the automatic temperature control system on Taurus, Sable and Continental. It contains a photovoltaic (sensitive to sunlight) diode that provides input to the system microcomputer. The sensor is located in the left radio speaker grille assembly on Taurus and Sable and in the right speaker grille assembly on Continental.

REMOVAL AND INSTALLATION

Taurus, Sable and Continental

1. Disconnect the negative battery cable.
2. On Taurus and Sable, remove the left-hand speaker grille assembly. On Continental, remove the right-hand speaker grille assembly.

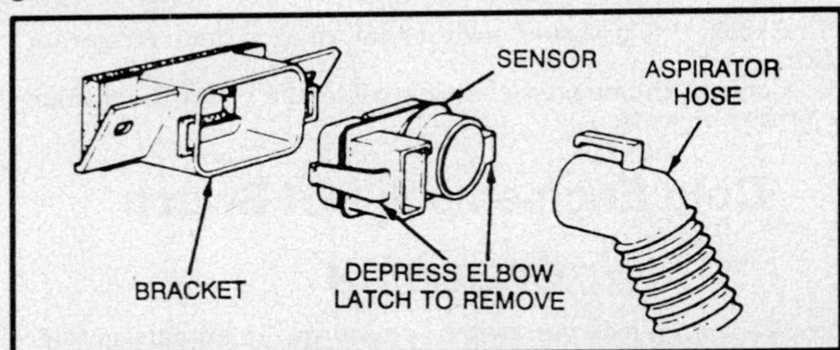

In-vehicle sensor installation—Taurus, Sable and Continental

3. Remove the sunload sensor assembly from the 2 mounting studs and disconnect the electrical connector.

To install:

4. Connect the electrical connector to the sunload sensor.
5. Install the sensor to the speaker grille by pushing the sensor firmly over the 2 mounting studs.
6. Install the speaker grille assembly and connect the negative battery cable.

Blower Speed Controller

OPERATION

The blower speed controller is used on Taurus, Sable, Continental and Probe with automatic temperature control. It converts the base current received from the electronic control assembly into high current, variable ground feed to the blower motor. The blower fan speed is therefore infinitely variable. The blower speed controller is located in the evaporator case, upstream of the evaporator core on Taurus, Sable and Continental. On Probe, the blower speed controller is known as the power transistor and is located under the instrument panel in the blower case.

REMOVAL AND INSTALLATION

Taurus, Sable and Continental

1. Disconnect the negative battery cable.
2. Disengage the glove compartment door stops and allow the door to hang by the hinge.
3. Working through the glove compartment opening, disconnect the electrical snap-lock connector and aspirator hose at the blower motor controller. Also, disconnect the snap-lock connector from it's mounting bracket.
4. Remove the 2 screws attaching the blower controller to the evaporator case and remove the controller. Do not touch the fins of the controller until it has had a sufficient time to cool.

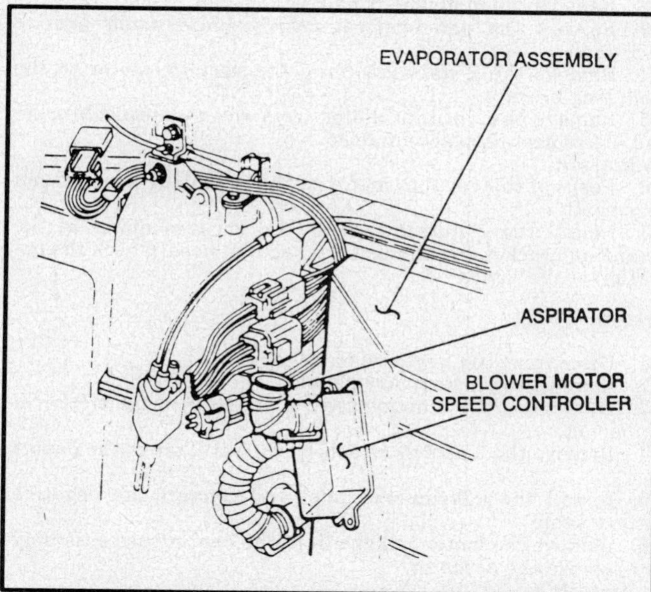

Blower motor speed controller location—Taurus, Sable and Continental

To install:

5. Position the blower controller on the evaporator case and install the 2 attaching screws.
6. Connect the wire connector and aspirator hose to the blower controller. Install the connector on the mounting bracket.
7. Close the glove compartment door, connect the negative battery cable and check the system for proper operation.

Probe

1. Disconnect the negative battery cable.
2. Remove the instrument panel.
3. Remove the blower case assembly.
4. Disconnect the power transistor electrical connector and remove the power transistor assembly from the blower case air outlet.

To install:

5. Install the power transistor assembly into the blower case and connect the electrical connector.
6. Install the blower case assembly.
7. Install the instrument panel.
8. Connect the negative battery cable and check for proper blower motor operation.

Temperature Blend Door Actuator Motor

OPERATION

The temperature blend door actuator is used on Taurus, Sable and Continental with automatic temperature control. The actuator controls blend door movement on command from the control assembly. The blend door actuator is located on top of the evaporator assembly.

REMOVAL AND INSTALLATION

Taurus, Sable and Continental

1. Disconnect the negative battery cable.
2. Loosen the instrument panel and pull back from the cowl.
3. Remove the blend door actuator electrical connector and plastic clamp from the bracket on the evaporator case. Remove the 3 actuator attaching screws.
4. Lift the actuator vertically for a distance of approximately 1/2 in. (12mm) to disengage it from the bracket and blend door shaft. Pull the actuator back toward the passenger compartment.

NOTE: The mounting bracket remains in place on the evaporator case.

To install:

5. Insert the blend door actuator horizontally over the actuator bracket on the evaporator case.
6. Insert the actuator shaft into the blend door. Manually moving the door will help engage the shaft.
7. Attach the actuator bracket with the 3 attaching screws.
8. Attach the actuator electrical connector and plastic clamp to the bracket on the evaporator case.
9. Install the instrument panel and connect the negative battery cable.

NOTE: After replacement of the blend door actuator, the system must be recalibrated for proper operation. To recalibrate, disconnect the positive battery cable from the battery, wait 30 seconds and reconnect the battery cable. Calibration will be performed automatically when the automatic temperature control electronic control assembly is energized.

Contour and Mystique

1. Remove 2 lower retaining screws from the electronic door actuator motor.
2. Open the glove compartment, push in on the sides of glove compartment to bypass stops and lower the door to floor.
3. Disconnect wire harness connector from the electronic door actuator motor.
4. Remove 2 upper retaining screws and the electronic door actuator motor from the evaporator housing.
5. To install, reverse removal procedures.

Recirc/Fresh Air Selector Door Vacuum Actuator Motor

OPERATION

The recirc/fresh air selector door actuator motor is used on Taurus, Sable and Continental with automatic temperature control. The motor controls the position of the door which allows fresh air or recirculated air, or a combination of the 2, into the vehicle. On Taurus, Sable and Continental, the motor is mounted on the recirculate/fresh air duct.

REMOVAL AND INSTALLATION

Taurus, Sable and Continental

1. Lower the glove compartment door to provide access to the recirculation duct assembly.
2. Disconnect the vacuum hose from the end of the vacuum motor and the motor arm retainer from the door crank arm.
3. Remove the 2 nuts retaining the vacuum motor to the recirculation duct and remove the motor.

To install:

4. Position the vacuum motor to the fresh air/recirculate door crank arm, position the motor to the recirculation duct and install the 2 retaining nuts.
5. Install the retainer on the door crank arm.
6. Connect the white vacuum hose to the vacuum motor and check the operation of the vacuum motor.
7. Close the glove compartment door.

Function Control Actuator Motor

OPERATION

The function control actuator motor is used on Taurus, Sable, Continental and Probe with automatic temperature control. The motor controls the door which directs the flow of air to the defroster ducts, instrument panel ducts or floor ducts. On Taurus, Sable and Continental, 2 motors are used to perform the control function and they are both located on the plenum. On Probe the motor is located on the heater case.

REMOVAL AND INSTALLATION

Continental

1. Disconnect the negative battery cable.
2. Remove the steering column and the instrument panel assemblies.

NOTE: The plenum assembly will be attached to the instrument panel. The vacuum line connector will be disconnected from its mating connector from the vacuum control valve.

3. If the panel-defrost door motor is being removed, perform the following procedure:
   - Disconnect the vacuum hose from the motor.
   - Remove the 2 nuts attaching the motor to it's mounting bracket.
   - Compress the end of the pin on the door crank and lift the motor arm off the crank. This will release the motor assembly from the plenum.
4. If the panel-floor door vacuum motor is being removed. perform the following procedure:
   - Disconnect both vacuum hoses from the motor.
   - Remove the 2 screws which attach the motor arm shield to the plenum and remove the shield.
   - Remove the 2 nuts securing the motor to it's mounting bracket.
   - Compress the end of the pin on the door crank and lift the motor arm off the crank. This will release the motor assembly from the plenum.
5. Installation is the reverse of the removal procedure.

Taurus and Sable

PANEL/FLOOR DOOR VACUUM MOTOR

1. Disconnect the negative battery cable.
2. Remove the instrument panel.
3. Depress the tabs and disconnect the vacuum motor arm from the door shaft.
4. Remove the 2 screws retaining the vacuum motor to the mounting bracket.
5. Remove the vacuum motor from the mounting bracket and disconnect the vacuum hose.

To install:

6. Position the vacuum motor on the mounting bracket and door shaft.
7. Install the 2 screws attaching the vacuum motor to the mounting bracket.
8. Connect the vacuum hose to the vacuum motor and check the operation of the motor.
9. Install the instrument panel and connect the negative battery cable.

PANEL/DEFROST DOOR VACUUM MOTOR

1. Disconnect the negative battery cable.
2. Remove the instrument panel.
3. Remove the panel-defrost door vacuum motor arm to door shaft.
4. Remove the 2 nuts retaining the vacuum motor to the mounting bracket.
5. Remove the vacuum motor from the mounting bracket and disconnect the vacuum hose.

To install:

6. Position the vacuum motor to the mounting bracket and door shaft.
7. Install the 2 nuts attaching the vacuum motor to the mounting bracket and connect the vacuum hose. Check the operation of the motor.

Probe

1. Disconnect the negative battery cable.
2. Remove the instrument panel.
3. Disconnect the function control actuator motor electrical connector.
4. Remove the 3 screws attaching the actuator to the heater case.
5. Install the instrument panel and connect the negative battery cable.
6. Remove the motor linkage from the heater case assembly and remove the actuator.

To install:

7. Position the function control actuator motor onto the heater case and reconnect the motor linkage.
8. Install the attaching screws to the actuator at the heater case and connect the actuator electrical connector.
9. Install the instrument panel and connect the negative battery cable.
10. Check for proper actuator motor operation.

Ventilation – Fresh Air

OPERATION

Outside air is drawn into the vehicle through the cowl-mounted pollen filter. The pollen filter consists of 3 layers of polyester and polycarbonate non-woven fabric in a frame of the same material. It restricts particles larger than 3 microns, completely blocking pollen and dust which range in size from 7 to 100 microns. Air distribution within the vehicle is controlled by the climate control system.

Passenger compartment air is exhausted from the vehicle through open windows or luggage compartment air vents.

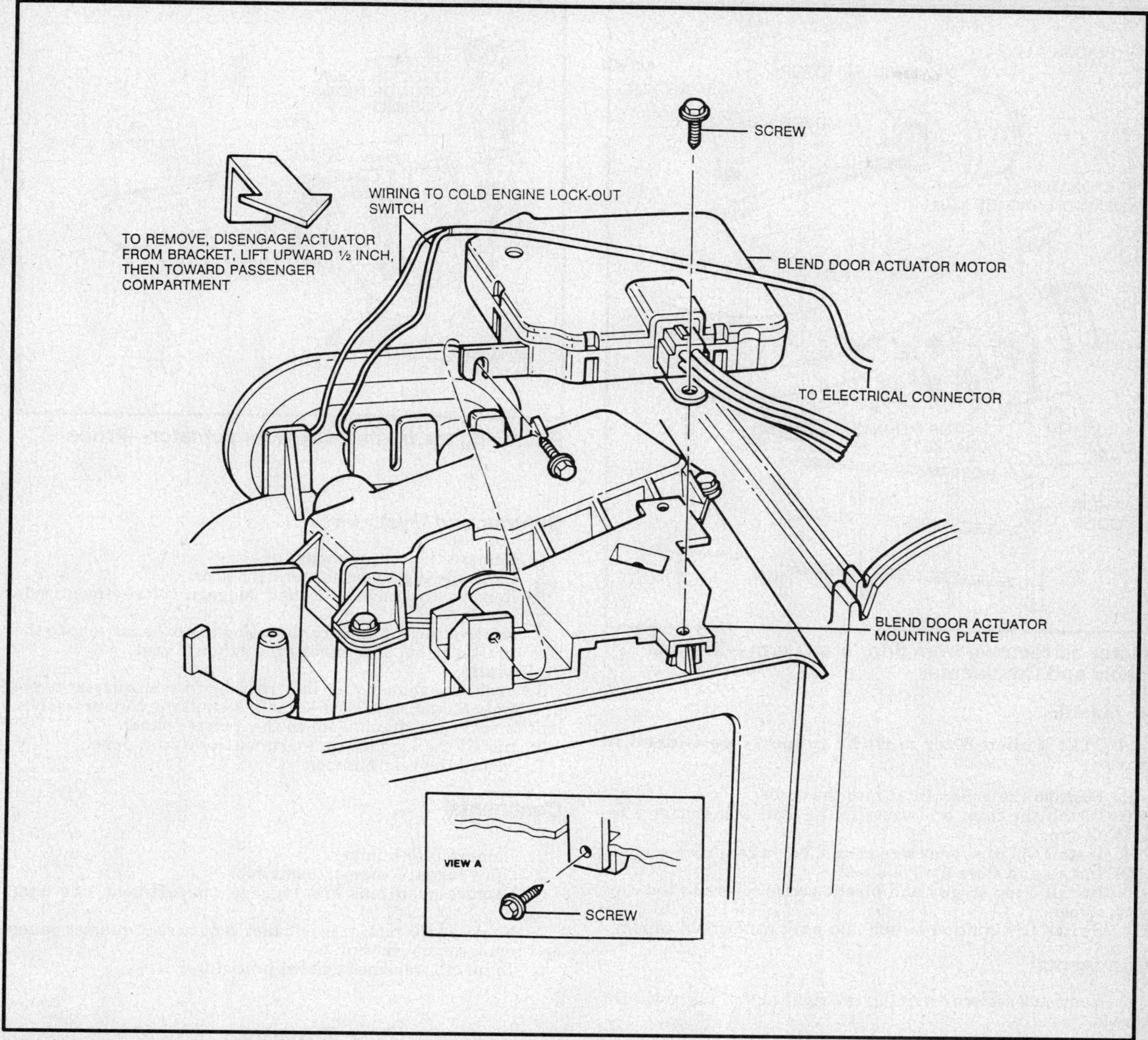

Electric blend air door actuator removal—Taurus, Sable and Continental

Pollen Filter

REMOVAL AND INSTALLATION

Contour and Mystique

NOTE: The windshield wiper arms must be positioned away from the cowl vent screen to access pollen filter. This can be accomplished by switching off the ignition switch when the cycling windshield wipers are at the top of their arc on the windshield.

1. Position windshield wiper arms away from cowl vent screen.
2. Remove plastic screw covers and three top screws retaining right half of cowl vent screen.
3. Raise and support the hood.
4. Pull the hood pad straight up away from cowl vent screen.
5. Remove 3 side screws retaining the right half of cowl vent screen.
6. Remove right half of the cowl vent screen from the vehicle.
7. Disengage the clips retaining the pollen filter cover.
8. Remove the cover and filter from the vehicle and remove the filter from the cover.

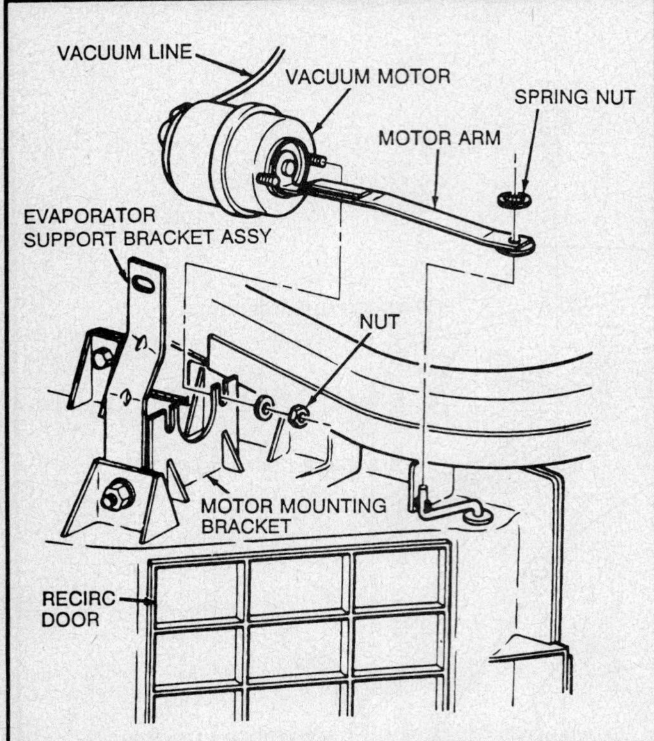

Motor air removal from door crank arm—Taurus, Sable and Continental

To install:

NOTE: Pollen filter must be properly positioned in cover.

9. Position the pollen filter into the cover.
10. Install the filter and cover to the cowl and engage 2 retaining clips.
11. Install the cowl vent screen and 3 side retaining screws.
12. Install and close the hood pad.
13. Install 3 top screws and plastic screw covers to the cowl vent screen.
14. Switch **ON** ignition switch and park windshield wipers.

Continental

1. Remove 2 screws retaining the right half of the cowl vent screen.
2. Raise and support the hood.
3. Pull the hood pad away from the cowl vent screen.
4. Remove the right half of the cowl vent screen.
5. Remove the filter from the housing.

To install:

NOTE: The pollen filter must be properly positioned in the housing.

6. Install the pollen filter into the housing.
7. Install the right half of the cowl vent screen and hood pad.
8. Close the hood.
9. Install 2 screws to cowl vent screen. Tighten to 30–42 in. lbs. (3.4–4.8 Nm).

Exhaust Vent

REMOVAL AND INSTALLATION

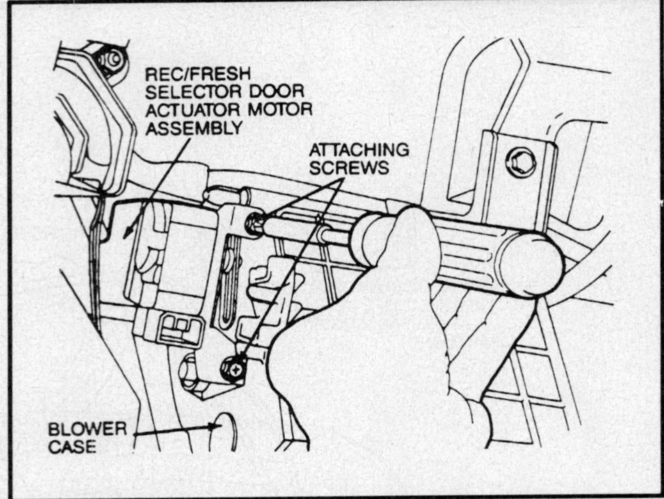

Removing the fresh/recirc door actuator—Probe

Contour and Mystique

1. Remove the rear bumper.
2. Open the luggage compartment door.
3. Remove the push pins and luggage compartment side trim panel.
4. Remove the caulking cord sealing the exhaust vent to the rear quarter panel and remove the exhaust vent.

To install:

5. Position exhaust vent into opening in rear quarter panel and apply Motorcraft D6AZ–19560–A caulking cord or equivalent to seal the exhaust vent to the quarter panel.
6. Install the luggage compartment side trim panel.
7. Install the rear bumper.

Continental

1. Remove rear bumper.
2. Open luggage compartment door.
3. Remove push pins and luggage compartment side trim panel.
4. Release tabs retaining exhaust vent to rear quarter panel and remove exhaust vent.
5. To install, reverse removal procedure.

Relays

OPERATION

Tempo, Topaz, Taurus and Sable

These models, with transverse mounted engines, need an electric engine cooling fan. Instead of separate relays, these models use an Integrated Relay Control Module (ICRM) or Constant Control Relay Module (CCRM). This module has circuit control for various engine functions, including the cooling fan and A/C compressor clutch. If an A/C function is chosen, the compressor clutch coil will be energized through the relay module only when the cooling fan is operating. The module will disengage the A/C compressor clutch during wide open throttle, very high or too low engine speed, engine cranking or coolant temperatures above 245°F (118°C).

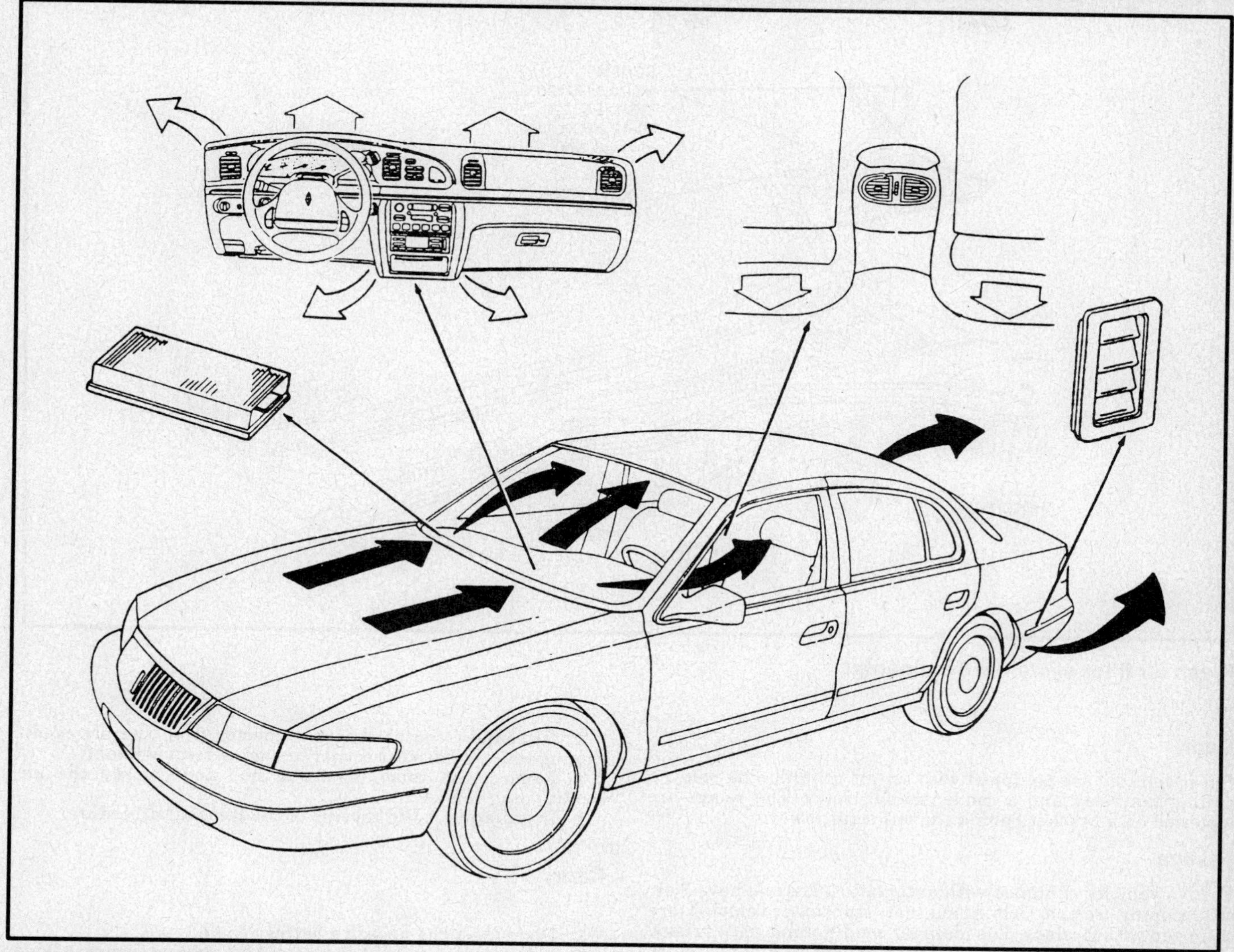

Fresh air distribution—Continental

Escort and Tracer

Escort and Tracer vehicles are equipped with an air conditioning relay. When the air conditioning switch is pressed, the air conditioning relay closes. The relay energizes the magnetic clutch allowing the engine to drive the compressor. Also at this time, the cooling fan relay is closed and the cooling fan is energized. Escort and Tracer equipped with the 1.9L engine are equipped with a WAC relay. This relay is controlled by the electronic control unit and prevents the air conditioning system from operating when the vehicle is operated at full throttle. The air conditioning relay and WAC relay are both located in the right rear corner of the engine compartment.

Probe

BLOWER MOTOR RELAYS

Probe vehicles use 2 blower relays: one between the bumper and radiator is activated when the ignition is ON and blower switch is in any position except OFF; the other relay is activated when the ignition is ON and the blower is in MEDIUM or HIGH position.

Probe vehicles equipped with automatic temperature control have a blower motor ON relay and a blower motor HIGH relay (mounted on the blower case), and a blower motor relay (mounted near the battery). When the blower switch is moved from the **OFF** position, the ON relay is energized and the contacts close. This allows the circuitry within the control amplifier to flow base current to the blower speed controller (power transistor) so the blower operates. When the blower switch is placed in the **MAX** position, the HIGH relay is energized and the contacts within the relay close. This relay then creates a short circuit in the blower speed controller (power transistor), thereby bypassing the transistor and the blower motor will operate at maximum speed. Power is supplied to the ON and HIGH relays by the blower motor relay.

CONDENSER FAN AND COOLING FAN RELAYS

Probe vehicles use high and low speed condenser fan relays (in left engine compartment fuse box) and high and low speed cooling fan relays (front of radiator support).

A/C RELAY

Probe vehicles use an A/C relay (in the left engine compartment fuse box). The relay is energized through the fuses and the power control module and applies battery voltage to the A/C clutch field coil when A/C is ON and ignition is in ACC or RUN.

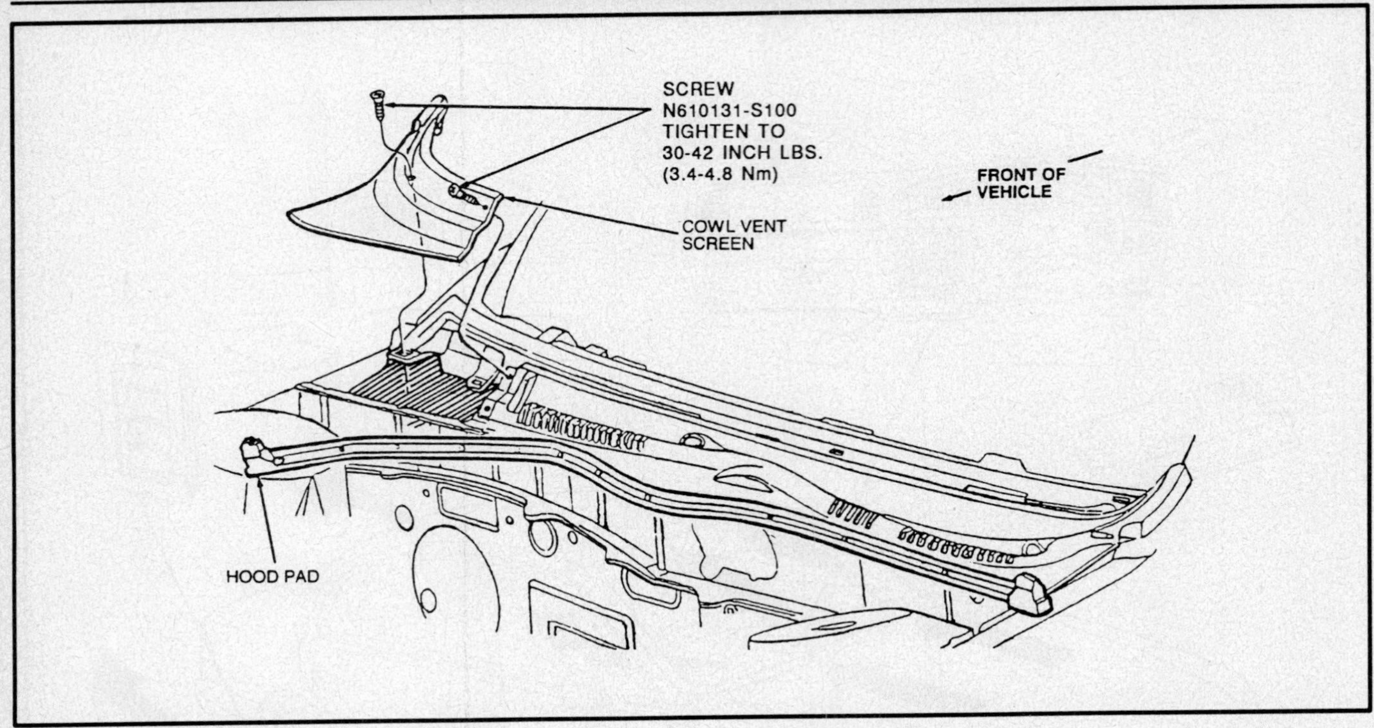

Fresh air filter system—Continental

Capri

Capri vehicles are equipped with an air conditioning relay, a cooling fan relay and a condenser fan relay. The relays are mounted on a bracket behind the left strut tower.

Festiva

Festiva vehicles equipped with automatic transaxle have 3 air conditioning relays, while manual transaxle vehicles are equipped with 2 relays. The main air conditioning relay is used on all Festiva vehicles. It grounds the engine cooling fan motor so that it will operate constantly with the air conditioning ON. It also sends a signal to the electronic control unit indicating the additional alternator load caused by the fan operation. The air conditioning relay is closed whenever the air conditioning is ON and the blower is ON. The Wide Open Throttle Air Conditioning Cut-Off Relay (WAC) is used on all Festiva vehicles. It supplies power to the compressor clutch and the condenser fan relay on automatic transaxle equipped vehicles. It is controlled by the electronic control unit and operates to cut off the air conditioning during wide open throttle driving or to cycle the compressor clutch. The condenser fan relay is used on Festiva vehicles with automatic transaxle only. When refrigerant pressure is high in the condenser and the pressure switch is closed, the relay contacts close and the condenser fan motor runs. All Festiva air conditioning relays are located in the left front corner of the engine compartment between the battery and the radiator core support near the rear of the left headlight.

REMOVAL AND INSTALLATION

Escort and Tracer

AIR CONDITIONING RELAY AND WAC RELAY

1. Disconnect the negative battery cable.
2. Disconnect the electrical connector from the air conditioning relay (right rear corner of engine compartment).
3. Remove the relay mounting nut and remove the air conditioning relay.
4. Installation is the reverse of the removal procedure.

Capri

1. Disconnect the negative battery cable.
2. Lift the relay to be replaced and it's rubber retaining boot from the bracket.
3. Disconnect the relay electrical connector and remove the relay from the retaining boot.
4. Installation is the reverse of the removal procedure.

Probe

BLOWER MOTOR RELAY NO. 1

1. Disconnect negative battery cable. Remove 5 air flow shield screws.
2. Slide the relay off the bracket and push back the relay boot. Disconnect the blower motor relay No. 1 connector.
3. Installation is the reverse of the removal procedure.

BLOWER MOTOR RELAY NO. 2

1. Disconnect the negative battery cable.
2. Remove the 2 hush panel screws and disconnect illumination bulb from its socket.
3. Remove 2 relay screws and remove the relay.
4. Installation is the reverse of the removal procedure.

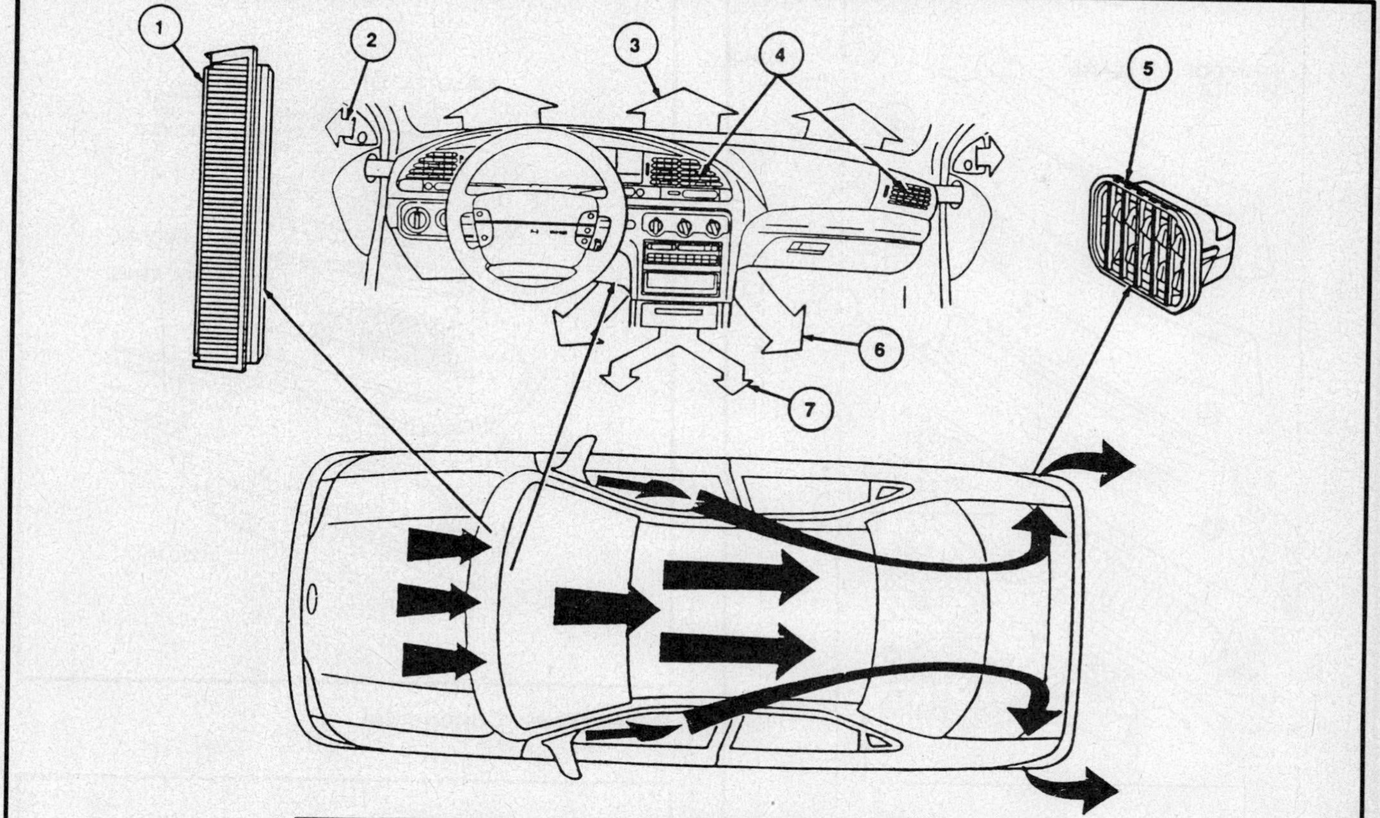

Item	Description
1	Pollen Filter
2	Side Window Demister Air Flow
3	Defroster Nozzle Air Flow

Item	Description
4	Instrument Panel Registers
5	Exhaust Vent
6	Floor Register Air Flow
7	Rear Seat Air Flow

Fresh air distribution—Contour and Mystique

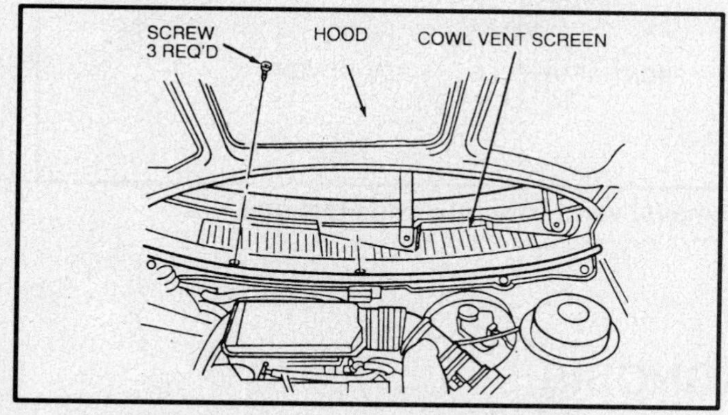

Cowl vent installation—Contour and Mystique

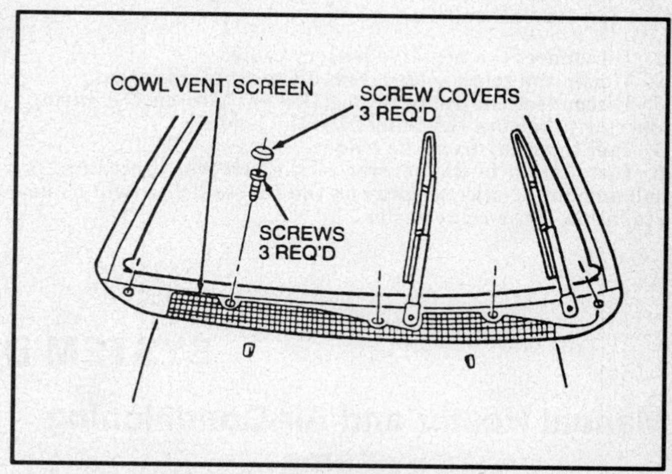

Cowl vent screen—Contour and Mystique

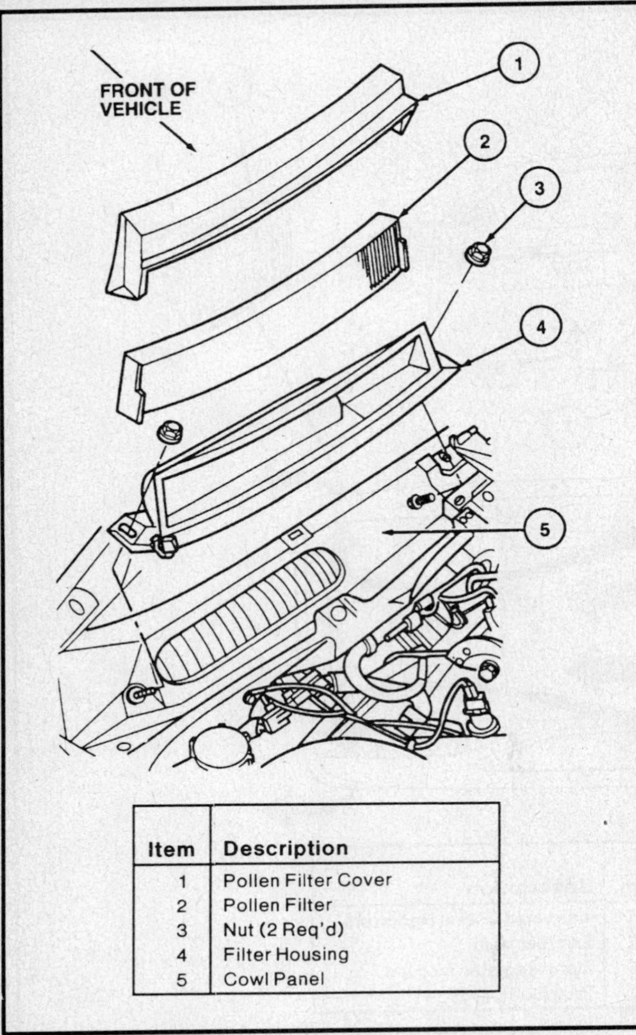

Item	Description
1	Pollen Filter Cover
2	Pollen Filter
3	Nut (2 Req'd)
4	Filter Housing
5	Cowl Panel

Pollen filter assembly—Contour and Mystique

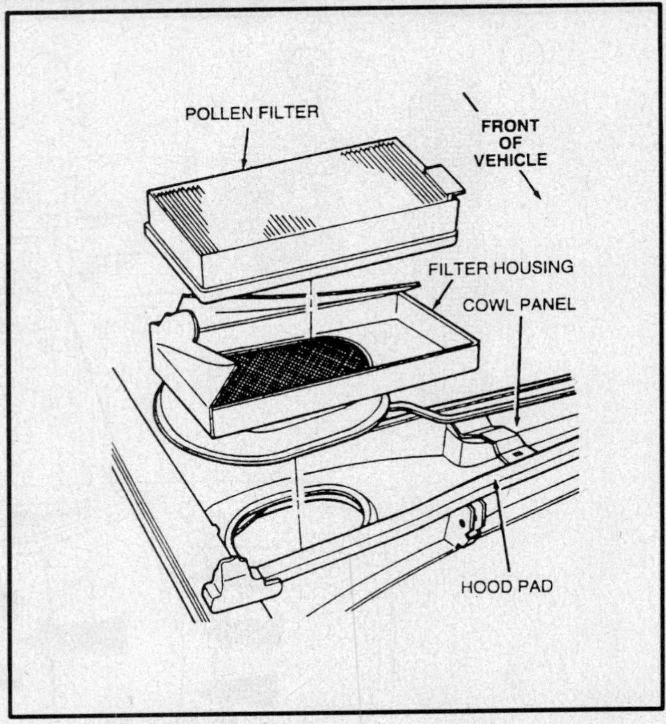

Pollen filter—Continental

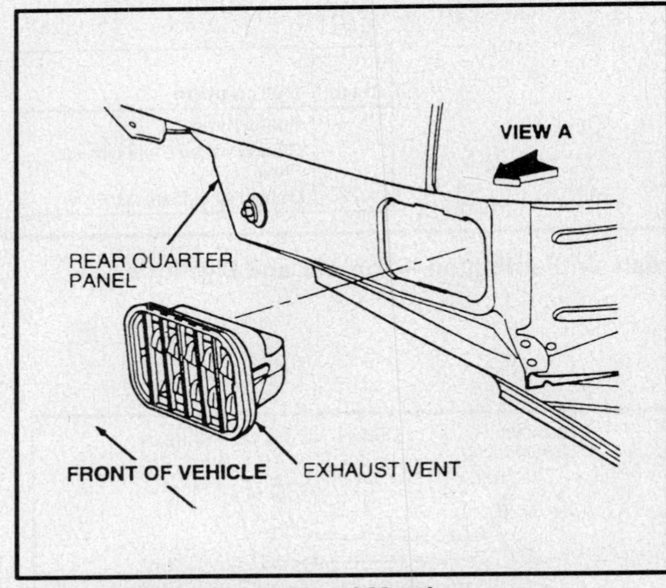

Exhaust vent—Contour and Mystique

Festiva

NOTE: The removal and installation procedure is the same for 1 or all relays.

1. Disconnect the negative battery cable.
2. Unclip the relay holder from it's mounting bracket.
3. Disconnect the relay wiring. Do not pull on the wiring connector to remove the relay from the holder.
4. Pull the relay from the holder.
5. Installation is the reverse of the removal procedure. A small amount of silicone spray on the rubber holder will make installation of the relay easier.

SYSTEM DIAGNOSIS

Manual Heater and Air Conditioning Systems

DIAGNOSTIC PROCEDURE

1. Verify condition with vehicle driver and attempt to recreate the condition prior to further action.

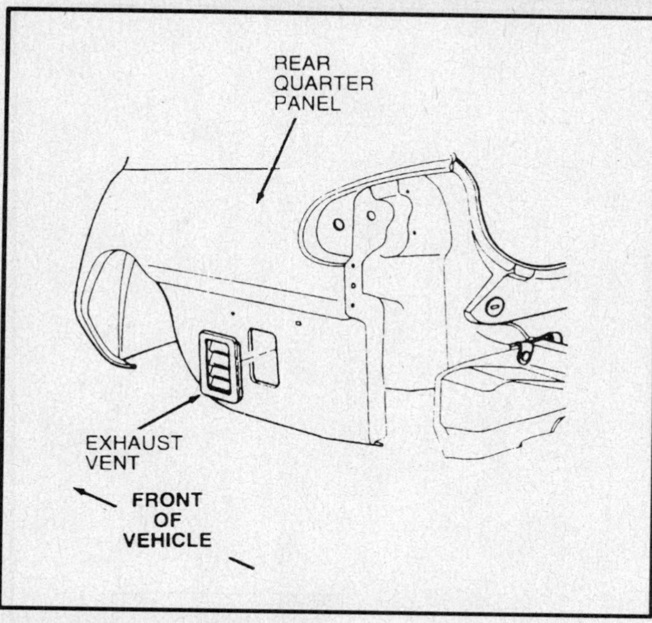

Exhaust vent—Continental

2. Check for full battery charge, good electrical and vacuum connections.
3. Check for proper adjustment of control cables and proper operation of air door cranks and/or vacuum actuators.
4. Check cooling system for proper coolant level, operation of thermostat, cooling fans and water valve.
5. Check A/C system for proper refrigerant charge.
6. Follow specific diagnostic procedures in the following charts and use the wiring schematics for circuit information.

Automatic Temperature Control System

DIAGNOSTIC PROCEDURE

Taurus, Sable and Continental

1. Perform the Self Diagnostic Test. Record all error codes displayed during the test.
2. If error codes appear during the Self Diagnostic Test, follow the diagnostic procedures indicated in the Error Code Key.
3. If a malfunction exists but no error code appears during the Self Diagnostic Test, perform the Functional Test and consult the No Error Code Found Diagnosis and Testing chart.

SELF DIAGNOSTIC TEST

The control assembly will detect electrical malfunctions occurring during the self test.

1. Make sure the coolant temperature is at least 120°F (49°C).
2. To display error codes, push the OFF and FLOOR buttons simultaneously and then the AUTOMATIC button within 2 seconds. The test may run as long as 20 seconds, during which time the display will be blank. If the display is blank for more than 20 seconds, consult the No Error Code Found Diagnosis and Testing chart.
3. The Self Diagnostic Test can be initiated at any time with the resulting error codes being displayed. Normal operation of the system stops when the Self Diagnostic Test is activated. To exit the self test and restart the system, push the COOLER button. The self test should be deactivated before powering the system down.

FUNCTIONAL TEST

The Functional Test is designed to catch those system failures that the self test is unable to test.

1. Make sure the engine is cold.
2. The in-vehicle temperature should be greater than 50°F (10°C) for proper evaluation of system response.
3. Follow the instructions in each step of the Functional Test.

VACUUM SYSTEM DIAGNOSIS

To test the automatic temperature control vacuum system, start the engine and depress the function buttons slowly from 1 position to another. A momentary hiss should be heard as each button is depressed from 1 position to another, indicating that vacuum is available at the control assembly. A continuous hiss at the control assembly indicates a major leak somewhere in the system. It does not necessarily indicate that the leak is at the control assembly.

If a momentary hiss cannot be heard as each function button is depressed from 1 position to another, check for a kinked, pinched or disconnected vacuum supply hose. Also, inspect the check valve between the vacuum intake manifold and the vacuum reservoir to ensure it is working properly.

If a momentary hiss can be heard as each function button is depressed from 1 position to another, vacuum is available at the control assembly. Cycle the function buttons through each position with the blower on HI and check the location(s) of the discharge air. The airflow schematic and vacuum control chart shows the vacuum motors applied for each function selection along with an airflow diagram of the system. The airflow diagram shows the position of each door when vacuum is applied and their no-vacuum position. With this chart, airflow for each position of the control assembly can be determined. If a vacuum motor fails to operate, the motor can readily be found because the airflow will be incorrect.

If a vacuum motor is inoperative, check the operation of the motor with a vacuum tester. If the vacuum motor operates properly, the vacuum hose is probably kinked, pinched, disconnected or has a leak.

If the function system functions normally at idle, but goes to defrost during acceleration, a small leak exists in the system. The leak can best be located by shutting **OFF** the engine and using a gauge to check for vacuum loss while selectively blocking off vacuum hoses.

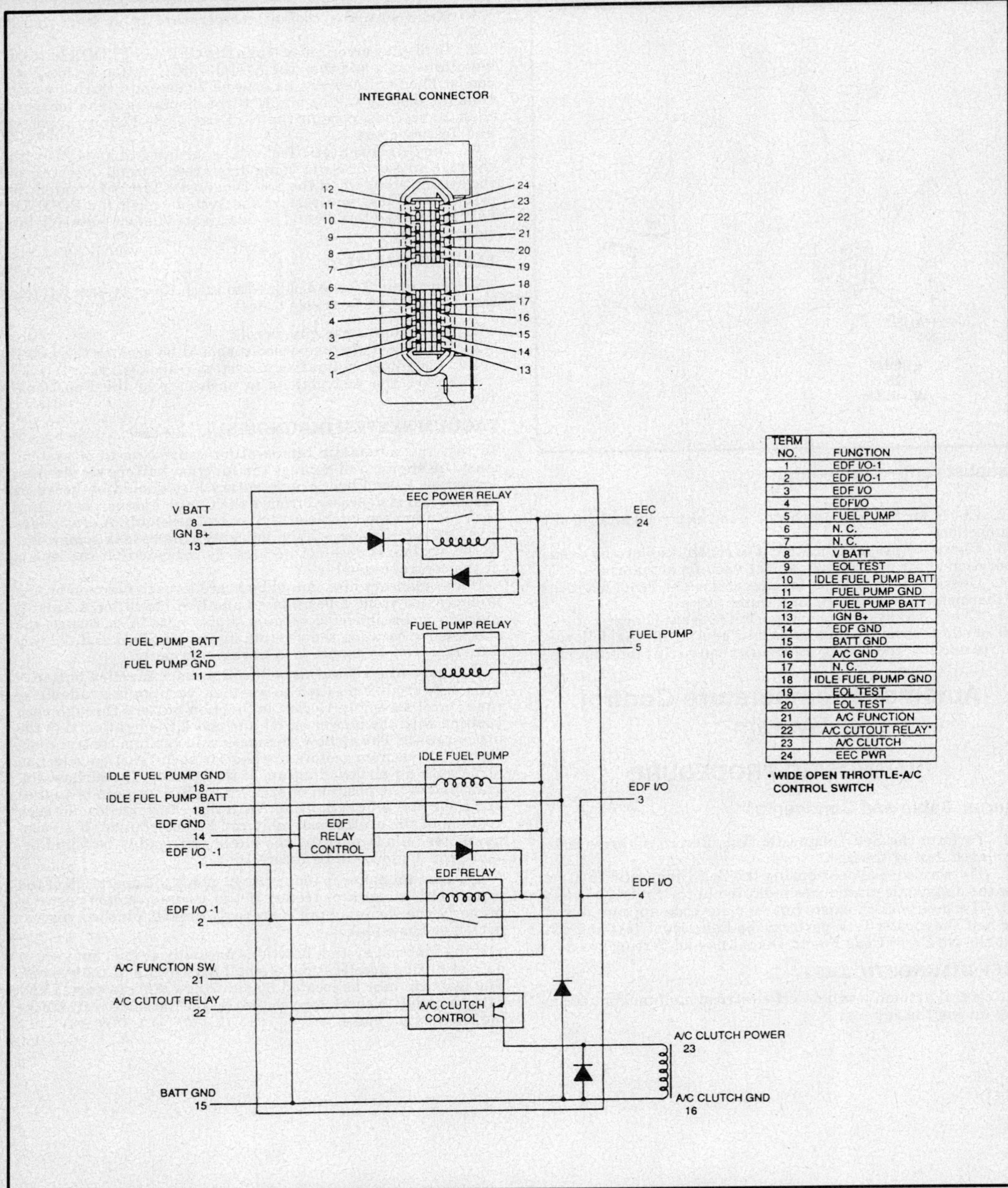

TERM NO.	FUNCTION
1	EDF I/O-1
2	EDF I/O-1
3	EDF I/O
4	EDFI/O
5	FUEL PUMP
6	N. C.
7	N. C.
8	V BATT
9	EOL TEST
10	IDLE FUEL PUMP BATT
11	FUEL PUMP GND
12	FUEL PUMP BATT
13	IGN B+
14	EDF GND
15	BATT GND
16	A/C GND
17	N. C.
18	IDLE FUEL PUMP GND
19	EOL TEST
20	EOL TEST
21	A/C FUNCTION
22	A/C CUTOUT RELAY*
23	A/C CLUTCH
24	EEC PWR

• WIDE OPEN THROTTLE-A/C CONTROL SWITCH

Constant Control Relay Module (CCRM) circuit and pin references—Taurus 3.0L SHO

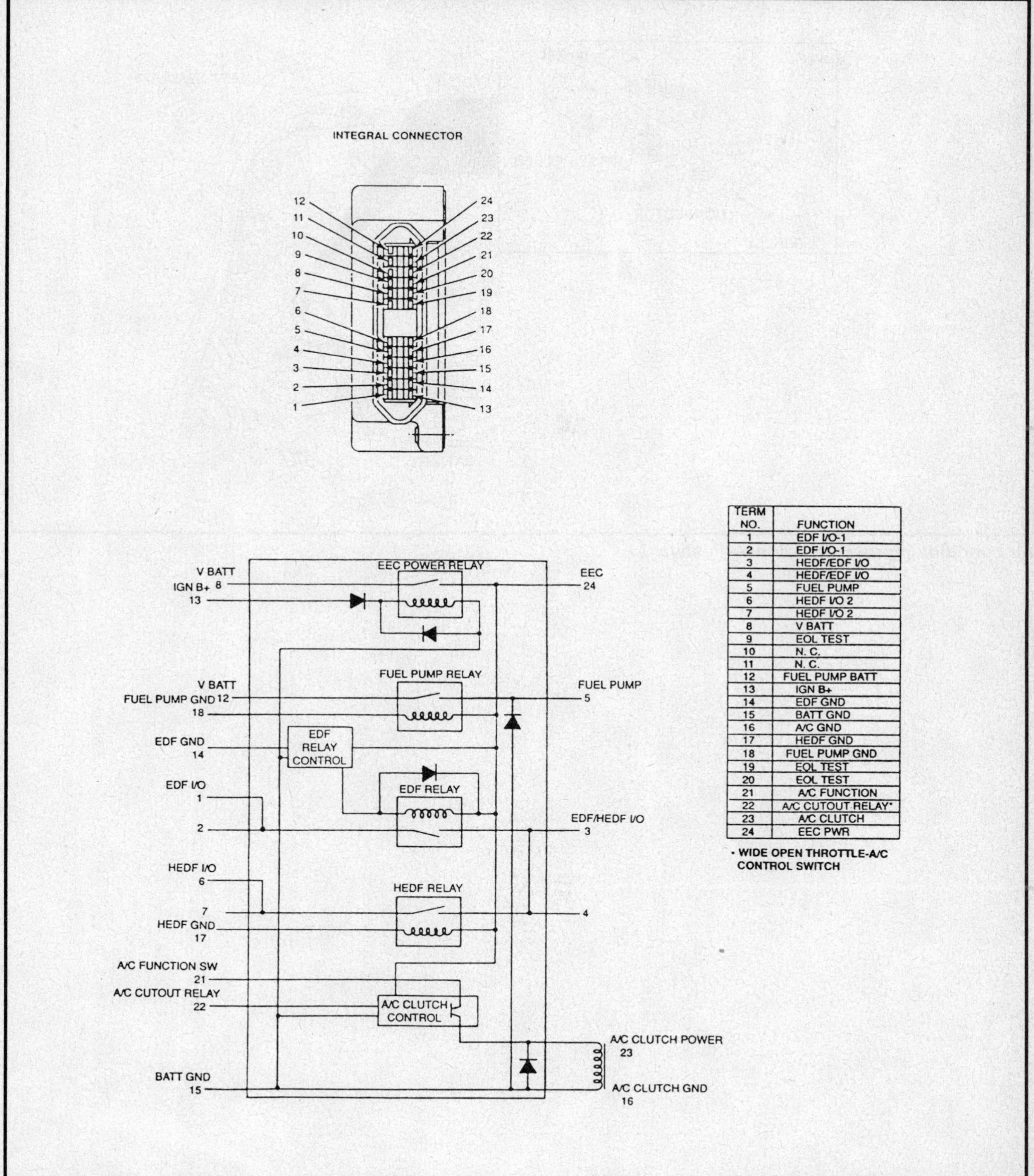

TERM NO.	FUNCTION
1	EDF I/O-1
2	EDF I/O-1
3	HEDF/EDF I/O
4	HEDF/EDF I/O
5	FUEL PUMP
6	HEDF I/O 2
7	HEDF I/O 2
8	V BATT
9	EOL TEST
10	N. C.
11	N. C.
12	FUEL PUMP BATT
13	IGN B+
14	EDF GND
15	BATT GND
16	A/C GND
17	HEDF GND
18	FUEL PUMP GND
19	EOL TEST
20	EOL TEST
21	A/C FUNCTION
22	A/C CUTOUT RELAY*
23	A/C CLUTCH
24	EEC PWR

* WIDE OPEN THROTTLE-A/C CONTROL SWITCH

Constant Control Relay Module (CCRM) circuit and pin references—Tempo, Topaz, Taurus and Sable

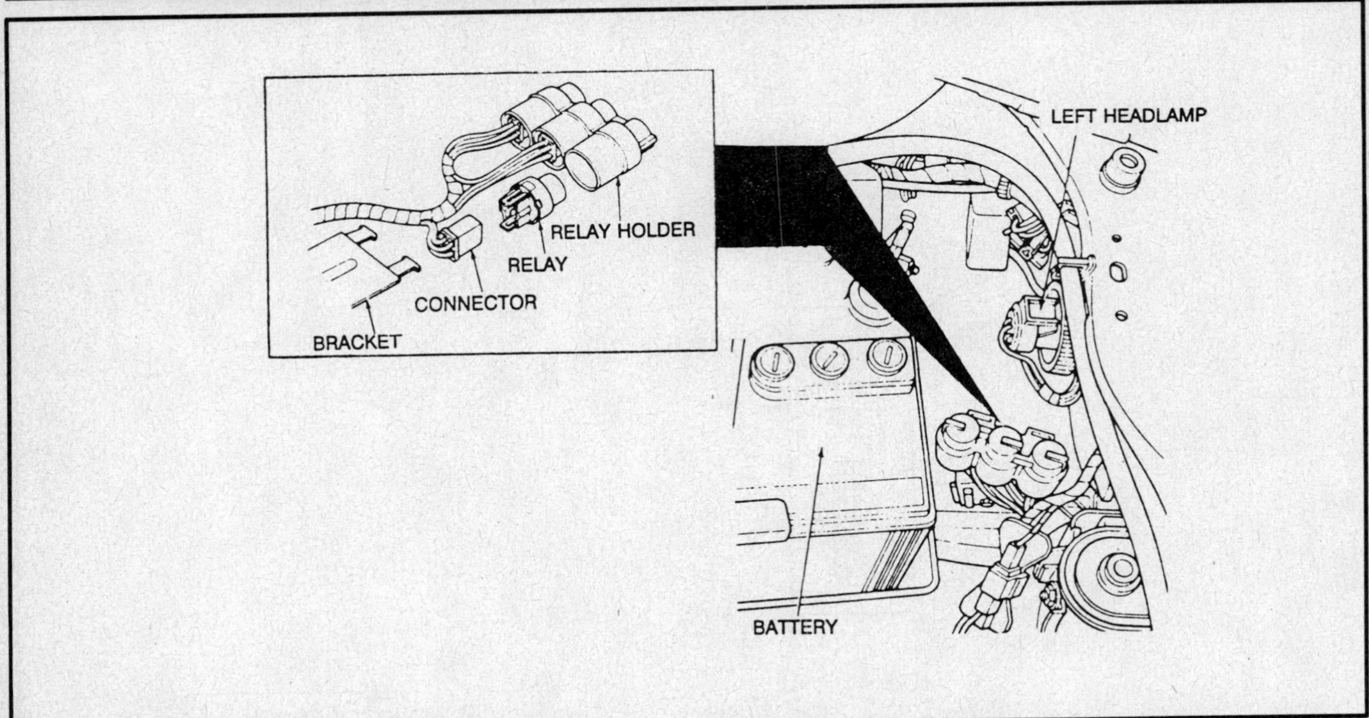

Air conditioning relay locations—Festiva

DIAGNOSIS AND TESTING—CONTOUR AND MYSTIQUE

CLIMATE CONTROL SYSTEM

CONDITION	POSSIBLE SOURCE	ACTION
• Vent Does Not Operate	• No vacuum to A/C control. • Damaged vacuum control motor. • Damaged/kinked vacuum hose.	• GO to Pinpoint Test A.
• Heat Does Not Operate	• No vacuum to A/C control. • Damaged vacuum control motor. • Damaged/kinked vacuum hose. • Damaged/plugged heater core.	• GO to Pinpoint Test B.
• Defrost Does Not Operate	• No vacuum to A/C control. • Damaged vacuum control motor. • Damaged/kinked vacuum hose. • Damaged/plugged heater core.	• GO to Pinpoint Test C.
• A/C Does Not Operate	• Blown fuse. • Circuitry short/open. • A/C cycling switch damaged. • A/C system discharged. • Starter motor cutout relay damaged. • Damaged relays.	• GO to Pinpoint Test D.
• Blower Motor Does Not Operate	• Blown fuse. • Circuitry open/shorted. • Heater blower motor switch damaged. • A/C heater blower relay. • Blower motor.	• GO to Pinpoint Test E.
• Engine Cooling Fan Does Not Operate When A/C is Activated	• Low speed fan control relay damaged. • Circuitry damaged. • Cooling fan motor damaged.	• GO to Pinpoint Test F.
• Insufficient A/C Cooling	• Malfunctioning temperature blend door. • Restricted A/C evaporator core orifice. • Low refrigerant level. • Insufficient vent operation. • Malfunctioning A/C cycling switch. • Inoperative relays.	• GO to Refrigerant System Tests, under Service Procedures.
• No Operation In All Temperature Settings • No Operation In All Function Settings • Improper Operation In Function Settings	• Malfunctioning temperature blend door. • No vacuum to A/C control. • Damaged vacuum control motor. • Damaged/kinked vacuum hose.	
• Noise While Operating Climate Control System	• A/C compressor. • A/C clutch. • Damaged drive belt.	• REFER to A/C Compressor or A/C Clutch Description and Operation. REPLACE drive belt as required.
• Noise While Not Operating Climate Control System	• A/C clutch. • Damaged drive belt.	• REFER to A/C Clutch Description and Operation REPLACE drive belt as required.

DIAGNOSIS AND TESTING—CONTOUR AND MYSTIQUE, CONT'D

Pinpoint Tests

PINPOINT TEST A: VENT DOES NOT OPERATE

	TEST STEP	RESULT	▶ ACTION TO TAKE
A1	CHECK SYSTEM AIRFLOW		
	• With engine running and heater blower motor switch on high, check system airflow in each A/C damper door switch position to determine which position(s) have incorrect air flow. Refer to vacuum application chart for correct system air flow. • **Is airflow from the defroster outlets for all positions?**	Yes No	▶ GO to **A2**. ▶ GO to **A13**.
A2	CHECK VACUUM SUPPLY HOSE CONNECTION		
	• Check vacuum supply hose to be sure it is connected to both the engine manifold and A/C vacuum check valve. • **Is hose disconnected?**	Yes No	▶ RECONNECT hose. RESTORE vehicle. RETEST system. ▶ GO to **A3**.
A3	CHECK VACUUM SUPPLY HOSE FOR LEAKS		
	• Disconnect vacuum supply hose from engine manifold fitting and from A/C vacuum check valve. Plug one end of hose and leak test with vacuum pump. • **Does hose leak?**	Yes No	▶ SERVICE or REPLACE vacuum hose. RESTORE vehicle. RETEST system. ▶ CONNECT hose to manifold fitting. GO to **A4**.
A4	CHECK VACUUM CHECK VALVE FOR CORRECT INSTALLATION		
	NOTE: Engine must be running for this test. • Check A/C vacuum check valve for correct installation by removing the vacuum hose harness from check valve and check for vacuum. → DIRECTION OF FREE AIRFLOW • **Is vacuum available at the check valve port?**	Yes No	▶ RECONNECT both hoses. GO to **A6**. ▶ GO to **A5**.
A5	INSPECT VACUUM CHECK VALVE FOR OBSTRUCTIONS		
	• Inspect A/C vacuum check valve for an obstruction and proper operation. Air flow through the A/C vacuum check valve should be in the direction from engine. • **Is check valve plugged or obstructed?**	Yes No	▶ REPLACE A/C vacuum check valve. RESTORE vehicle. RETEST system. ▶ GO to **A6**.

DIAGNOSIS AND TESTING—CONTOUR AND MYSTIQUE, CONT'D

PINPOINT TEST A: VENT DOES NOT OPERATE (Continued)

TEST STEP		RESULT	ACTION TO TAKE
A6	LEAK TEST VACUUM CHECK VALVE		
	• Remove A/C vacuum check valve from vehicle. Connect a hose to the outlet port of check valve. Connect Rotunda Vacuum Tester 021-00014 or equivalent to other end of hose. DIRECTION OF FREE AIRFLOW 021-00014 • Pump 11.34 kPa (15 inches) vacuum on A/C vacuum check valve and observe gauge reading. If vacuum loss exceeds 3.37 kPa (1 inch) per minute, remove A/C vacuum check valve from tester and plug vacuum hose. Pull a vacuum with the tester to be certain hose and tester are not cause of leak. PLUG 021-00014 • If tester and hose do not leak, check valve for cause of leak. • **Does check valve lose more than 3.37 kPa (1 inch) vacuum in one minute?**	Yes ▶ No ▶	REPLACE A/C vacuum check valve. RESTORE vehicle. RETEST system. REINSTALL A/C vacuum check valve and GO to **A7**.
A7	CHECK VACUUM RESERVOIR		
	• Connect Rotunda Vacuum Tester 021-00014 or equivalent to A/C vacuum reservoir tank and bracket and leak test reservoir. Reservoir must hold vacuum. • **Does reservoir leak?**	Yes ▶ No ▶	REPLACE A/C vacuum reservoir tank and bracket. RESTORE vehicle. RETEST system. CONNECT hose to A/C vacuum reservoir tank and bracket. GO to **A8**.
A8	CHECK SUPPLY HOSE		
	• Disconnect and plug BLACK supply hose at A/C control. Disconnect other end of supply hose from A/C vacuum check valve and leak test hose with vacuum tester. • **Does supply hose leak?**	Yes ▶ No ▶	SERVICE or REPLACE hose. RESTORE vehicle. RETEST system. REMOVE plug and RECONNECT vacuum hoses. GO to **A9**.
A9	CHECK CONTROL ASSEMBLY		
	• Disconnect vacuum hose harness at in-line multiple connector near A/C control. Plug all vacuum hoses except BLACK. Connect Vacuum Tester to BLACK hose. Select each function position, apply 11.34 kPa (15 inches) vacuum and check for vacuum drop. Drop should not exceed 3.37 kPa (1 inch) vacuum per minute for any function position. • **Does drop exceed 3.37 kPa (1 inch) vacuum per minute?**	Yes ▶ No ▶	NOTE Function positions where vacuum drops. GO to **A10**. GO to **A11**.

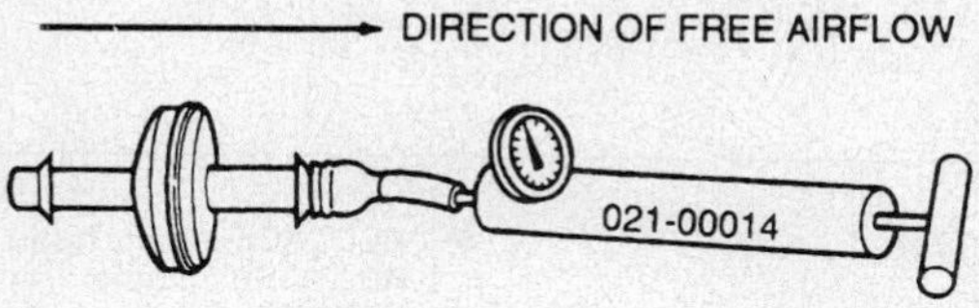

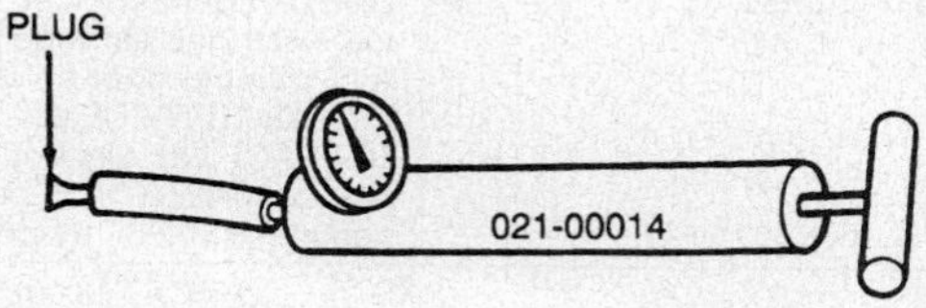

DIAGNOSIS AND TESTING—CONTOUR AND MYSTIQUE, CONT'D

PINPOINT TEST A: VENT DOES NOT OPERATE (Continued)

	TEST STEP	RESULT	▶ ACTION TO TAKE
A10	LEAK TEST CONTROL ASSEMBLY		
	• Remove vacuum hose harness from A/C control. Connect Vacuum Tester to control supply port and plug control port that indicated a leak in step A9. Select function positions noted in Step A9 and apply 11.34 kPa (15 inches) vacuum after selecting each position. Vacuum drop should not exceed 1.68 kPa (1/2 inch) per minute. • **Does vacuum drop exceed 1.68 kPa (1/2 inch) in one minute?**	Yes No	▶ REPLACE A/C damper door switch. RESTORE vehicle. RETEST system. ▶ GO to **A12**.
A11	CHECK SUPPLY HOSE FOR BLOCKAGE		
	• Disconnect BLACK supply hose from A/C vacuum check valve. Connect Vacuum Tester to supply hose and operate tester as if pulling a vacuum. If tester can pull a vacuum, hose is plugged. If tester pulls a partial vacuum, hose is restricted. • **Is hose plugged or restricted?**	Yes No	▶ REPLACE supply hose. RESTORE vehicle. RETEST system. ▶ GO to **A15**.
A12	LEAK TEST JUMPER VACUUM HARNESS		
	• Plug one end of vacuum hose that indicated a leak in step A9. Apply 11.34 kPa (15 inches) vacuum to hose and observe vacuum gauge. Vacuum should not drop. • **Does vacuum drop?**	Yes No	▶ SERVICE or REPLACE vacuum hose harness. RESTORE vehicle. RETEST system. ▶ CHECK connection of vacuum hose harness to A/C damper door switch for leak. SERVICE or REPLACE vacuum hose harness. RESTORE vehicle. RETEST system.
A13	EVALUATE SYSTEM AIR FLOW		
	• **Is the air flow in step A1 correct for each function position?**	Yes No	▶ GO to **A14**. ▶ GO to **A15**.
A14	ISOLATE LEAKING VACUUM CIRCUIT		
	• Repeat step A1 and accelerate engine speed for each function position. • **Does air flow go to defrost during acceleration?**	Yes No	▶ GO to **A19**. ▶ GO to **A15**.
A15	REVIEW VEHICLE HISTORY		
	• **Did system function properly prior to this complaint?**	Yes No	▶ GO to **A18**. ▶ GO to **A16**.
A16	CHECK VACUUM HOSES FOR OBSTRUCTION		
	• Check each vacuum hose to be sure it is not plugged. • **Is a hose plugged?**	Yes No	▶ REPLACE vacuum hose harness. RESTORE vehicle. RETEST system. ▶ GO to **A17**.
A17	CHECK VACUUM HARNESS		
	• Compare vacuum hose colors in each vacuum harness to the vacuum schematic. • **Do the hose colors agree with the schematics?**	Yes No	▶ GO to **A18**. ▶ REPLACE vacuum hose harness. RESTORE vehicle. RETEST system.
A18	CHECK VACUUM CIRCUIT FOR PINCH OR KINK		
	• Check vacuum circuit for pinched or kinked vacuum hose. • **Is hose pinched or kinked?**	Yes No	▶ REPLACE vacuum hose harness. RESTORE vehicle. RETEST system. ▶ GO to **A19**.

DIAGNOSIS AND TESTING—CONTOUR AND MYSTIQUE, CONT'D

PINPOINT TEST A: VENT DOES NOT OPERATE (Continued)

TEST STEP		RESULT ▶	ACTION TO TAKE
A19	CHECK VACUUM CIRCUIT CONNECTIONS		
	• Check each vacuum hose connection to determine if it is partially connected or disconnected. • **Is a vacuum hose connection disconnected or partially connected?**	Yes ▶	RECONNECT hose. RESTORE vehicle. RETEST system.
		No ▶	GO to **A20**.
A20	CHECK VACUUM HOSE FOR LEAKS		
	• Disconnect both ends of vacuum hose in suspected circuit. Plug one end and leak test with vacuum tester. • **Does vacuum hose leak?**	Yes ▶	SERVICE or REPLACE hose. RESTORE vehicle. RETEST system.
		No ▶	GO to **A21.**
A21	CHECK VACUUM CONTROL MOTOR		
	• Check vacuum control motor for leaks with vacuum tester. • **Does vacuum control motor hold vacuum?**	Yes ▶	GO to **A22.**
		No ▶	REPLACE vacuum control motor. RESTORE vehicle. RETEST system.
A22	CHECK VACUUM CONTROL MOTOR INSTALLATION		
	• Check attachment of vacuum motor arm to damper door. • **Is vacuum control motor arm attached to door or door crank arm?**	Yes ▶	CHECK for binding or damaged damper door. SERVICE or REPLACE damper door. RESTORE vehicle. RETEST system.
		No ▶	CONNECT vacuum control motor arm to door and / or crank arm and check operation. RESTORE vehicle. RETEST system.

PINPOINT TEST B: HEAT DOES NOT OPERATE

TEST STEP		RESULT ▶	ACTION TO TAKE
B1	CHECK FOR VACUUM TO FUNCTION CONTROL		
	• Start engine and allow engine to idle. • Disconnect A / C, heater vacuum source tube (black). Check for vacuum. • **Is vacuum present?**	Yes ▶	GO to **B2.**
		No ▶	SERVICE vacuum source tube (black) as required. RESTORE vehicle. RETEST system.
B2	CHECK FLOOR PANEL DOOR OPERATION		
	• Actuate A / C damper door switch to the floor position. • Locate heater air damper door vacuum control motor. • Check for vacuum at yellow tube and red tube. • **Is vacuum present at each vacuum tube?**	Yes ▶	REPLACE vacuum control motor. GO to **B3.**
		No ▶	SERVICE suspect hose for cut or damage. RESTORE vehicle. RETEST system.
B3	CHECK HEATER FOR PROPER TEMPERATURE		
	• Allow engine to run until operating temperature is achieved. • Move A / C damper door switch to FLOOR position. • Actuate temperature knob to full heat position. • Actuate heater blower motor switch. • **Is heater temperature OK?**	Yes ▶	GO to **B4.**
		No ▶	GO to A / C electronic door actuator motor diagnosis.
B4	CHECK BLOWER MOTOR OPERATION		
	• Actuate heater blower motor switch in all positions. • **Did blower motor operate properly?**	Yes ▶	RESTORE vehicle. RETEST system.
		No ▶	GO to Pinpoint Test E.

DIAGNOSIS AND TESTING—CONTOUR AND MYSTIQUE, CONT'D

PINPOINT TEST C: DEFROST DOES NOT OPERATE

TEST STEP		RESULT	ACTION TO TAKE
C1	CHECK FOR VACUUM TO FUNCTION CONTROL		
	• Start engine and allow engine to idle. • Disconnect A/C, heater vacuum source tube (black). Check for vacuum. • **Is vacuum present?**	Yes ▶ No ▶	GO to **C2.** SERVICE vacuum source tube (black) as required. RESTORE vehicle. RETEST system.
C2	CHECK DEFROST DOOR OPERATION		
	• Actuate A/C damper door switch to the defrost position. • Locate windshield defroster door vacuum control motor. • Check for vacuum at blue and gray vacuum tubes. • **Is vacuum present at each vacuum tube?**	Yes ▶ No ▶	REPLACE A/C damper door switch. GO to **C3.**
C3	CHECK DEFROSTER TEMPERATURE		
	• Allow engine to run until operating temperature is achieved. • Move A/C damper door switch to DEFROST position. • Actuate temperature knob to full-heat position. • Actuate heater blower motor switch. • **Is defrost temperature OK?**	Yes ▶ No ▶	GO to **C4.** GO to A/C electronic door actuator motor diagnosis.
C4	CHECK BLOWER MOTOR OPERATION		
	• Actuate heater blower motor switch in all positions. • **Did blower motor operate properly?**	Yes ▶ No ▶	RESTORE vehicle. RETEST system. GO to Pinpoint Test E.

PINPOINT TEST D: A/C DOES NOT OPERATE

TEST STEP		RESULT	ACTION TO TAKE
D1	CHECK A/C CLUTCH		
	• Prepare vehicle as follows: — Set A/C damper door switch at MAX A/C. — Set heater blower motor switch on HIGH. — Set temperature lever at full COOL. — Close doors and windows. — Run engine at approximately 1500 rpm. • **Does A/C clutch operate?**	Yes ▶ No ▶	GO to **D32.** GO to **D2.**
D2	CHECK VOLTAGE SUPPLY FROM THE A/C DAMPER DOOR SWITCH		
	• Turn engine off. Leave ignition switch in RUN position. • Actuate A/C damper door switch to MAX A/C. • Using a test lamp connected to a known good ground, check for voltage at A/C damper door switch connector Pin 2, Circuit 14S (P/O). • **Did test lamp illuminate?**	Yes ▶ No ▶	GO to **D12.** GO to **D3.**
D3	CHECK VOLTAGE SUPPLY TO SWITCH		
	• Using a test lamp, check voltage at A/C damper door switch connector Pin 1, Circuit 14S (P). • **Did test lamp illuminate?**	Yes ▶ No ▶	REPLACE A/C damper door switch. RESTORE vehicle. RETEST system. GO to **D4.**
D4	CHECK CIRCUIT 14S (P) FOR OPEN		
	• Using a test lamp, check for voltage output from A/C-heater blower relay, fuse junction panel connector A, Pin 4, Circuit 14S (P/BL). • **Did test lamp illuminate?**	Yes ▶ No ▶	SERVICE Circuit 14S (P) for open circuit. RESTORE vehicle. RETEST system. GO to **D5.**

DIAGNOSIS AND TESTING—CONTOUR AND MYSTIQUE, CONT'D

PINPOINT TEST D: A/C DOES NOT OPERATE (Continued)

TEST STEP		RESULT ▶	ACTION TO TAKE
D5	CHECK VOLTAGE SUPPLY TO BLOWER RELAY		
	• Using a test lamp, check output side of Fuse 37 (30A) for voltage. • **Did test lamp illuminate?**	Yes ▶ No ▶	GO to **D6.** REPLACE Fuse 37 (30A). RESTORE vehicle. RETEST system.
D6	CHECK CIRCUIT 14S (P/BL) FOR VOLTAGE INPUT		
	• Using a test lamp, check fuse junction panel connector A, Pin 2, Circuit 14S (P/BL) for voltage. • **Did test lamp illuminate?**	Yes ▶ No ▶	GO to **D7.** GO to **D8.**
D7	CHECK FOR GROUND TO BLOWER RELAY		
	• Using an ohmmeter connected to a known good ground, connect the second lead to fuse junction panel connector Pin B5 and check for a ground. • **Is resistance 5 ohms or less?**	Yes ▶ No ▶	REPLACE A/C-heater blower relay. RESTORE vehicle. RETEST system. SERVICE ground circuit for open circuit. RESTORE vehicle. RETEST system.
D8	CHECK VOLTAGE SUPPLY FROM PIN 3 OF A/C DAMPER DOOR SWITCH		
	• Using a test lamp connected to a known good ground, check for voltage output at Pin 3, Circuit 14S (P/BL) of A/C damper door switch. • **Did test lamp illuminate?**	Yes ▶ No ▶	SERVICE Circuit 14S (P/BL) for open circuit. RESTORE vehicle. RETEST system. GO to **D9.**
D9	CHECK VOLTAGE SUPPLY TO PIN 4		
	• Using a test lamp, check for voltage input to A/C damper door switch Pin 4, Circuit 14 (P/W). • **Did test lamp illuminate?**	Yes ▶ No ▶	REPLACE A/C, A/C damper door switch. RESTORE vehicle. RETEST system. GO to **D10.**
D10	CHECK CIRCUIT 14 (P/W) AND 14 (P/BL) FOR OPEN CIRCUITS		
	• Using a test lamp, check output voltage of Fuse 23 (15A). • **Did test lamp illuminate?**	Yes ▶ No ▶	SERVICE Circuit 14 (P/BL) and 14 (P/W) for open circuit. RESTORE vehicle. RETEST system. GO to **D11.**
D11	CHECK CIRCUITS 14 (P/BL), 14 (P/W) AND 14 (P/BK) FOR SHORT CIRCUIT		
	• Remove Fuse 23 (15A). • Disconnect A/C damper door switch. • Disconnect A/C electronic door actuator motor. • Using an ohmmeter, connect one lead to the output side of Fuse 23 (15A). Connect second lead to a known good ground. • **Is resistance 5 ohms or less?**	Yes ▶ No ▶	SERVICE Circuits 14 (P/BL), 14 (P/W) or 14 (P/BK) for short to ground. REPLACE Fuse 23 (15A). RESTORE vehicle. RETEST system. REPLACE Fuse 23 (15A). RESTORE vehicle. RETEST system.
D12	CHECK FOR VOLTAGE TO A/C CYCLING SWITCH		
	• Using a test lamp, check for voltage at A/C cycling switch, Circuit 14S (P/O). • **Did test lamp illuminate?**	Yes ▶ No ▶	GO to **D13.** SERVICE Circuit 14S (P/O) for open circuit. RESTORE vehicle. RETEST system.

DIAGNOSIS AND TESTING—CONTOUR AND MYSTIQUE, CONT'D

PINPOINT TEST D: A/C DOES NOT OPERATE (Continued)

TEST STEP		RESULT	► ACTION TO TAKE
D13	CHECK A/C CYCLING SWITCH		
	• Disconnect A/C cycling switch. • Start engine, A/C should be in MAX A/C mode. • Using a jumper wire, connect one end to Pin 1 at A/C cycling switch connector. Connect second lead to Pin 2 at A/C cycling switch. • Observe A/C clutch. • **Did A/C clutch engage?**	Yes No	► REPLACE A/C cycling switch. NOTE: Do not discharge system. A/C cycling switch has a Schrader valve. RESTORE vehicle. RETEST system. ► GO to **D14.**
D14	CHECK VOLTAGE INPUT TO A/C PRESSURE CUT-OFF SWITCH		
	• Using a test lamp, check for voltage at A/C pressure cut-off switch connector Pin D, Circuit 14S (P). • **Did test lamp illuminate?**	Yes No	► GO to **D15.** ► SERVICE Circuit 14S (P) for open circuit. RESTORE vehicle. RETEST system.
D15	CHECK A/C PRESSURE CUT-OFF SWITCH		
	• Disconnect A/C pressure cut-off switch. • Start engine, A/C should be in MAX A/C mode. • Using a jumper wire, connect one end to Pin D of the A/C pressure cut-off switch connector. Connect the other end of jumper wire to Pin C. • Observe A/C clutch. • **Did A/C clutch engage?**	Yes No	► REPLACE A/C pressure cut-off switch. RESTORE vehicle. RETEST system. ► GO to **D16.**
D16	CHECK VOLTAGE INPUT TO A/C WIDE OPEN THROTTLE (WOT) RELAY		
	NOTE: WOT relay is located in the power distribution box. • Remove power distribution box cover. • Using a screwdriver, carefully unlock the tabs holding the two fuse blocks in place. • Carefully lift both fuse blocks from the power distribution box to gain access to the electrical connectors. • Using a test lamp, check voltage at WOT relay connector Pin 3, Circuit 14S (P/BL). • **Did test lamp illuminate?**	Yes No	► GO to **D17.** ► SERVICE Circuit 14S (P/BL) for open circuit. RESTORE vehicle. RETEST system.
D17	CHECK VOLTAGE FROM A/C WIDE OPEN THROTTLE (WOT) RELAY		
	• Using a test lamp, check for voltage at Pin 5, Circuit 14S (P/BL) of the A/C WOT relay. • **Did test lamp illuminate?**	Yes No	► GO to **D18.** ► GO to **D21.**
D18	CHECK VOLTAGE AT A/C CLUTCH FIELD COIL		
	• Using a test lamp, check for voltage at A/C clutch field coil Circuit 14S (P/Y). • **Did test lamp illuminate?**	Yes No	► GO to **D19.** ► SERVICE Circuit 14S (P/BL) and 14S (P/Y) for open circuit. RESTORE vehicle. RETEST system.
D19	CHECK A/C CLUTCH GROUND CIRCUIT		
	• Using an ohmmeter connected to a known good ground, check ground Circuit 31 (BK) at A/C clutch field coil with the second test lead. • **Is resistance 5 ohms or less?**	Yes No	► GO to **D20.** ► SERVICE A/C clutch field coil ground Circuit 31 (BK) for open circuit. RESTORE vehicle. RETEST system.

DIAGNOSIS AND TESTING—CONTOUR AND MYSTIQUE, CONT'D

PINPOINT TEST D: A/C DOES NOT OPERATE (Continued)

	TEST STEP	RESULT ▶	ACTION TO TAKE
D20	CHECK A/C CLUTCH CIRCUIT FOR SHORT CIRCUIT		
	• Disconnect A/C clutch field coil. • Disconnect A/C wide open throttle (WOT) relay. • Using an ohmmeter, connect one lead to Pin 5 of the A/C WOT relay connector. Connect the second lead to a known good ground. • **Is resistance 5 ohms or less?**	Yes ▶	SERVICE A/C clutch field coil harness, including A/C clutch diode, for short circuit. REPLACE A/C clutch field coil. RESTORE vehicle. RETEST system.
		No ▶	REPLACE A/C clutch field coil. RESTORE vehicle. RETEST system.
D21	CHECK FOR GROUND SIGNAL TO A/C WOT RELAY		
	• Using an ohmmeter connected to a known good ground, connect the second lead to A/C WOT relay connector Pin 2, Circuit 91S (BK/Y) and check for a ground. • **Is resistance 5 ohms or less?**	Yes ▶	GO to **D22.**
		No ▶	SERVICE Circuit 91S (BK/Y) for an open circuit. If circuit is not open, GO to Powertrain Control/Emissions Diagnosis
D22	CHECK FOR VOLTAGE TO A/C WOT RELAY		
	• Using a test lamp connected to a known good ground, check voltage at A/C WOT relay connector Pin 1, Circuit 95 (GN/Y). • **Did test lamp illuminate?**	Yes ▶	REPLACE A/C wide open throttle (WOT) relay. RESTORE vehicle. RETEST system.
		No ▶	GO to **D23.**
D23	CHECK CIRCUIT 95 (GN/Y) FOR OPEN CIRCUIT		
	• Using a test lamp, check for voltage from powertrain control module relay at power distribution box connector D9, Circuit 95 (GN/Y). • **Did test lamp illuminate?**	Yes ▶	SERVICE Circuit 95 (GN/Y) for open circuit. RESTORE vehicle. RETEST system.
		No ▶	GO to **D24.**
D24	CHECK POWER SUPPLY		
	• Using a test lamp, check output side of power distribution box Fuse 9 (20A) for voltage. • **Did test lamp illuminate?**	Yes ▶	GO to **D25.**
		No ▶	REPLACE Fuse 9 (20A) in the power distribution box. RESTORE vehicle. RETEST system.
D25	CHECK FOR VOLTAGE AT POWERTRAIN CONTROL MODULE RELAY		
	• Using a test lamp, check for voltage from Fuse 4 (20A) to power distribution box connector Pin E3. • **Did test lamp illuminate?**	Yes ▶	GO to **D26.**
		No ▶	GO to **D27.**
D26	CHECK FOR POWERTRAIN CONTROL MODULE RELAY GROUND		
	• Using an ohmmeter connected to a known good ground, check for ground at power distribution box connector Pin D10 with the second lead. • **Is resistance 5 ohms or less?**	Yes ▶	REPLACE powertrain control module relay. RESTORE vehicle. RETEST vehicle.
		No ▶	SERVICE ground circuit for open circuit. RESTORE vehicle. RETEST system.
D27	CHECK SUPPLY TO FUSE 4 (20A)		
	• Using a test lamp connected to a known good ground, check voltage input to Fuse 4 (20A), Circuit 14 (P/BL). • **Did test lamp illuminate?**	Yes ▶	REPLACE Fuse 4 (20A). RESTORE vehicle. RETEST system.
		No ▶	GO to **D28.**

DIAGNOSIS AND TESTING—CONTOUR AND MYSTIQUE, CONT'D

PINPOINT TEST D: A/C DOES NOT OPERATE (Continued)

TEST STEP	RESULT	ACTION TO TAKE
D28 CHECK VOLTAGE OUTPUT FROM IGNITION RELAY		
• Using a test lamp, check for voltage at fuse junction panel connector M2, Circuit 15 (GN)/14 (P/BL). • **Did test lamp illuminate?**	Yes ▶ No ▶	SERVICE Circuit 15 (GN)/14 (P/BL) for open circuit. RESTORE vehicle. RETEST system. GO to **D29.**
D29 CHECK SUPPLY TO IGNITION RELAY		
• Using a test lamp, check for voltage input at fuse junction panel connector L2. • **Did test lamp illuminate?**	Yes ▶ No ▶	GO to **D30.** SERVICE incoming B+ circuit for open circuit. RESTORE vehicle. RETEST system.
D30 CHECK FOR IGNITION RELAY GROUND		
• Using an ohmmeter connected to a known good ground, connect the second lead to fuse junction panel connector B5. • **Is resistance 5 ohms or less?**	Yes ▶ No ▶	GO to **D31.** SERVICE incoming ground circuit for open circuit. RESTORE vehicle. RETEST system.
D31 CHECK FOR IGNITION SWITCH SIGNAL		
• Using a test lamp connected to a known good ground, with ignition switch in RUN position, check for voltage at fuse junction panel connector N4. • **Did test lamp illuminate?**	Yes ▶ No ▶	REPLACE ignition relay. RESTORE vehicle. RETEST system. SERVICE incoming ignition switch circuit for open circuit. CHECK fuse junction panel 3A (D2) diode and SERVICE as necessary. RESTORE vehicle. RETEST system.
D32 CHECK A/C CLUTCH CYCLING		
• Prepare vehicle as follows: — Hook up manifold gauge set. — Set function control at MAX A/C. — Set heater blower motor switch on HIGH. — Set temperature knob full COOL. — Close doors and windows. — Use a thermostat to check temperature at center discharge register, record outside temperature. — Run engine at approximately 1500 rpm with A/C clutch engaged. — Stabilize with above conditions for 10-15 minutes. • Check A/C clutch OFF/ON time with timing device, such as wristwatch. • Refer to Refrigerant System Tests under Service Procedures. • **Did A/C clutch cycle very rapidly?**	Yes ▶ No ▶	GO to **D33.** **REFER to Air Conditioning.**
D33 CHECK A/C CYCLING SWITCH OPERATION		
• Using a jumper wire, bypass A/C cycling switch. • Feel A/C evaporator inlet and outlet tubes. • **Is outlet tube approximately same temperature (between -2°C and 4°C [28°F-40°F]) or slightly colder than inlet tube?**	Yes ▶ No ▶	REPLACE A/C cycling switch. NOTE: Do not discharge system. A/C cycling switch has a Schrader valve. RESTORE vehicle. RETEST system. Discharge system and SERVICE. RETEST system.

DIAGNOSIS AND TESTING—CONTOUR AND MYSTIQUE, CONT'D

PINPOINT TEST E: BLOWER MOTOR DOES NOT OPERATE

	TEST STEP	RESULT	▶	ACTION TO TAKE
E1	CHECK VOLTAGE SUPPLY			
	• Remove A/C heater control. • Turn ignition switch to RUN. • Using a test lamp connected to a known good ground, check Pin 4 Circuit 14 (P/W) at A/C heater control connector. • **Did test lamp illuminate?**	Yes No	▶ ▶	GO to **E4.** GO to **E2.**
E2	CHECK VOLTAGE SUPPLY CIRCUIT FOR VOLTAGE			
	• Using a test lamp, check output side of Fuse 23 (15A) in battery junction panel. • **Did test lamp illuminate?**	Yes No	▶ ▶	SERVICE Circuit 14 (P/BL) for open circuit. RESTORE vehicle. RETEST system. GO to **E3.**
E3	CHECK CIRCUIT 14 (P/BL) and 14 (P/W) FOR SHORT			
	• Remove Fuse 23 (15A). • Disconnect A/C and heater control connector. • Using ohmmeter connected to a known good ground, connect second lead to Pin 4 Circuit 14 (P/W). Measure resistance. • **Is resistance 5 ohms or less?**	Yes No	▶ ▶	SERVICE Circuit 14 (P/W) and 14 (P/BL) for short to ground. REPLACE Fuse 23 (15A). RESTORE vehicle. RETEST system. REPLACE Fuse 23 (15A). GO to **E4.**
E4	CHECK A/C-HEATER SWITCH, VOLTAGE OUTPUT			
	• Disconnect blower motor at connector A in the battery junction panel. • Reconnect A/C damper door switch. • Actuate A/C damper door switch to any ON position. • Using a test lamp, check Pin 3 Circuit 14S (P/BL) at A/C damper door switch for voltage. • **Did test lamp illuminate?**	Yes No	▶ ▶	GO to **E5.** REPLACE A/C damper door switch. RESTORE vehicle. RETEST system.
E5	CHECK CIRCUIT 14S (P/BL) FOR OPEN			
	• Make sure that the A/C damper door switch is actuated to any ON position. • Using a test lamp, check A/C blower relay Pin A2, Circuit 14S (P/BL) on junction panel connector A for voltage. • **Did test lamp illuminate?**	Yes No	▶ ▶	GO to **E6.** SERVICE Circuit 14S (P/BL) for open circuit. RESTORE vehicle. RETEST system.
E6	CHECK BLOWER RELAY GROUND CIRCUIT			
	• Using an ohmmeter connected to a known good ground, connect second lead to blower relay connector Pin B5 on the junction panel and check for a ground. • **Is resistance 5 ohms or less?**	Yes No	▶ ▶	GO to **E7.** SERVICE ground circuit for open circuit. RESTORE vehicle. RETEST system.
E7	CHECK BLOWER RELAY VOLTAGE SUPPLY			
	• Using a test lamp connected to a known good ground, check for blower relay voltage supply at and from Fuse 37 (30A). • **Did test lamp illuminate?**	Yes No	▶ ▶	GO to **E8.** REPLACE Fuse 37 (30A). RESTORE vehicle. RETEST system.
E8	TEST BLOWER RELAY			
	• Using a test lamp, back-probe blower relay for voltage output at connector Pin A4. • **Did test lamp illuminate?**	Yes No	▶ ▶	GO to **E9.** REPLACE blower motor relay. RESTORE vehicle. RETEST system.

DIAGNOSIS AND TESTING—CONTOUR AND MYSTIQUE, CONT'D

PINPOINT TEST E: BLOWER MOTOR DOES NOT OPERATE (Continued)

TEST STEP		RESULT	▶ ACTION TO TAKE
E9	CHECK CIRCUIT 14S (P/BK) • Disconnect heater blower motor switch connector. • Using a test lamp connected to a known good ground, check Circuit 14S (P/BK) for voltage from blower motor relay. • **Did test lamp illuminate?**	Yes No	▶ GO to **E10.** ▶ SERVICE Circuit 14S (P/BL) and 14 (P/BK) for open circuit. RESTORE vehicle. RETEST system.
E10	CHECK CIRCUIT 14S (P) FOR OPEN • Using a test lamp, check A/C damper door switch connector Pin 1, Circuit 14S (P) for voltage. • **Did test lamp illuminate?**	Yes No	▶ GO to **E11.** ▶ SERVICE Circuit 14S (P) for open circuit. RESTORE vehicle. RETEST system.
E11	CHECK CIRCUIT 14S (P/W) TO BLOWER MOTOR RESISTOR • Disconnect blower motor. • Disconnect heater blower motor switch resistor. • Disconnect heater blower motor switch. • Using an ohmmeter, check resistance of Circuit 14S (P/BK) at blower motor harness connector Pin 4, Circuit 14S (P/W) at heater blower motor switch resistor. • **Is resistance 5 ohms or less?**	Yes No	▶ GO to **E12.** ▶ SERVICE Circuit 14S (P/W) for open circuit. RESTORE vehicle. RETEST system.
E12	CHECK CIRCUIT 14S (P/Y) • Using an ohmmeter, check resistance of Circuit 14S (P/Y) from heater blower motor switch to heater blower motor switch resistor. • **Is resistance 5 ohms or less?**	Yes No	▶ GO to **E13.** ▶ SERVICE Circuit 14S (P/Y) for open circuit. RESTORE vehicle. RETEST system.
E13	CHECK CIRCUIT 14S (P/BL) • Using an ohmmeter, check resistance of Circuit 14S (P/BL) from heater blower motor switch to heater blower motor switch resistor. • **Is resistance 5 ohms or less?**	Yes No	▶ GO to **E14.** ▶ SERVICE Circuit 14S (P/BL) for open circuit. RESTORE vehicle. RETEST system.
E14	CHECK THERMAL LIMITER CIRCUIT 14S (P/BL) • Using an ohmmeter, check resistor of Circuit 14S (P/BL) from heater blower motor switch to heater blower motor switch resistor connector Pin 1. • **Is resistance 5 ohms or less?**	Yes No	▶ GO to **E15.** ▶ SERVICE Circuit 14S (P/BL) for open circuit. RESTORE vehicle. RETEST system.
E15	CHECK HEATER BLOWER MOTOR SWITCH RESISTOR • Remove heater blower motor switch resistor and inspect resistor coils. • Using an ohmmeter, check for proper resistance values at all resistor terminals (see Electrical Schematics). Also check thermal limiter for continuity. • **Is there continuity at all terminals and are the resistance values as specified in Electrical Schematics?**	Yes No	▶ GO to **E16.** ▶ REPLACE heater blower motor switch resistor assembly. RESTORE vehicle. RETEST system.
E16	CHECK CIRCUIT 14S (P/O) TO BLOWER MOTOR • Using a test lamp connected to a known good ground, check for voltage at B+ terminal of blower motor, Circuit 14S (P/O). • **Did test lamp illuminate?**	Yes No	▶ GO to **E17.** ▶ SERVICE Circuit 14S (P/O) for open circuit. RESTORE vehicle. RETEST system.

DIAGNOSIS AND TESTING—CONTOUR AND MYSTIQUE, CONT'D

PINPOINT TEST E: BLOWER MOTOR DOES NOT OPERATE (Continued)

TEST STEP		RESULT ▶	ACTION TO TAKE
E17	CHECK A/C BLOWER MOTOR		
	• Reconnect blower motor. • Using a No. 10 gauge jumper wire, connect one end to battery negative. Connect other end of jumper to black wire negative lead at blower motor. • **Did blower motor operate?**	Yes ▶ No ▶	GO to **E18.** REPLACE blower motor. RESTORE vehicle. RETEST system.
E18	BLOWER MOTOR SWITCH TEST		
	• Use chart below to test heater blower motor switch. (See TESTING PROCEDURE below) • **Did heater blower motor switch test OK?**	Yes ▶ No ▶	System operational. RESTORE vehicle. RETEST system. REPLACE heater blower motor switch. RESTORE vehicle. RETEST system.

TESTING PROCEDURE

To Test	Connect Self-Powered Test Lamp or Ohmmeter to Terminals	Move Heater Blower Motor Switch to These Positions	A Good Heater Blower Motor Switch Will Indicate
Medium-Lo Speed	14S (P/BK) and 14S (P/Y) Pin 4 to Pin 1	Lo Medium Lo Medium Hi Hi	Open Circuit Closed Circuit Open Circuit Open Circuit
Medium-Hi Speed	14S (P/BK) and 14S (P/BL) Pin 4 to Pin 2	Lo Medium Lo Medium Hi Hi	Open Circuit Open Circuit Closed Circuit Open Circuit
Hi Speed	14S (P/BK) and 14S (P/O) and 14S (P/BL) to Thermal Limiter Pin 4 to Pin 3	Lo Medium Lo Medium Hi Hi	Open Circuit Open Circuit Open Circuit Closed Circuit

PINPOINT TEST F: ENGINE COOLING FAN DOES NOT OPERATE WHEN A/C IS ACTIVATED

TEST STEP		RESULT ▶	ACTION TO TAKE
F1	CHECK FOR VOLTAGE SUPPLY FROM A/C DAMPER DOOR SWITCH		
	• Remove power distribution box cover. • Using a screwdriver, carefully unlock the tabs holding the two fuse blocks in place. • Carefully lift both fuse blocks from the power distribution box to gain access to the electrical connectors. • Using a test lamp connected to a known good ground, check for voltage at power distribution box connector Pin E3. • **Did test lamp illuminate?**	Yes ▶ No ▶	GO to **F2.** GO to **D2.**
F2	CHECK POWERTRAIN CONTROL MODULE RELAY POWER SUPPLY		
	• Using a test lamp, check output side of Fuse 9 (20A) for voltage. • **Did test lamp illuminate?**	Yes ▶ No ▶	GO to **F3.** REPLACE Fuse 9 (20A). RESTORE vehicle. RETEST system.
F3	CHECK VOLTAGE OUTPUT FROM POWERTRAIN CONTROL MODULE RELAY		
	• Using a test lamp, check voltage output from power distribution box connector Pin D9. • **Did test lamp illuminate?**	Yes ▶ No ▶	GO to **F4.** GO to **D26.**

DIAGNOSIS AND TESTING—CONTOUR AND MYSTIQUE, CONT'D

PINPOINT TEST F: ENGINE COOLING FAN DOES NOT OPERATE WHEN A/C IS ACTIVATED (Continued)

	TEST STEP	RESULT	► ACTION TO TAKE
F4	CHECK CIRCUIT 95 (GN/Y)/95 (GN/BL) FOR OPEN CIRCUIT		
	• Using a test lamp, check for voltage at engine cooling fan relay connector Pin 6, Circuit 95 (GN/BL). • **Did test lamp illuminate?**	Yes No	► GO to **F5.** ► SERVICE Circuit 95 (GN/Y)/95 (GN/BL) for open circuit. RESTORE vehicle. RETEST system.
F5	CHECK GROUND CIRCUIT 31 (BK/W)		
	• Using a voltmeter connected to a known B+, connect second lead to low speed fan control relay connector Pin 1 in power distribution box, Circuit 31 (BK/W) and check for a ground signal from powertrain control module. • **Is powertrain control module sending a ground signal?**	Yes No	► GO to **F6.** ► CHECK Circuit 31 (BK/W) for open circuit. If circuit is not open, GO to Powertrain Control/Emissions Diagnosis.
F6	CHECK POWER SUPPLY TO LOW SPEED FAN CONTROL RELAY		
	• Using a test lamp connected to a known good ground, check low speed fan control relay connector Pin 3 in power distribution box, Circuit 30 (R) for voltage. • **Did test lamp illuminate?**	Yes No	► GO to **F8.** ► GO to **F7.**
F7	CHECK CIRCUIT 30 (R) FOR OPEN CIRCUIT		
	• Using a test lamp, check output voltage side of Fuse 2 (60A). • **Did test lamp illuminate?**	Yes No	► SERVICE Circuit 30 (R) for open circuit. RESTORE vehicle. RETEST system. ► REPLACE Fuse 2 (60A). RESTORE vehicle. RETEST system.
F8	CHECK RELAY GROUND CIRCUIT 31 (BK) FOR OPEN CIRCUIT		
	• Using an ohmmeter connected to a known good ground, connect second lead to engine cooling fan relay connector Pin 7 and check for a ground. • **Is resistance 5 ohms or less?**	Yes No	► GO to **F9.** ► SERVICE Circuit 31 (BK) for open circuit. RESTORE vehicle. RETEST system.
F9	CHECK RELAY VOLTAGE OUTPUT		
	• Using a test lamp connected to a known good ground, check for voltage output of low speed fan control relay at connector Pin 5. • **Did test lamp illuminate?**	Yes No	► GO to **F10.** ► REPLACE engine cooling fan relay. RESTORE vehicle. RETEST system.
F10	CHECK CIRCUIT 13 (GN/W) FOR OPEN CIRCUIT		
	• Using a test lamp, check for voltage at engine cooling fan resistor, Circuit 13 (GN/W). • **Did test lamp illuminate?**	Yes No	► GO to **F11.** ► SERVICE Circuit 13 (GN/W) for open circuit. RESTORE vehicle. RETEST system.
F11	CHECK RESISTOR VOLTAGE OUTPUT		
	• Using a test lamp, check for voltage from fan control resistor, Circuit 15 (GN/BL). • **Did test lamp illuminate?**	Yes No	► GO to **F12.** ► REPLACE fan control resistor. RESTORE vehicle. RETEST system.

DIAGNOSIS AND TESTING—CONTOUR AND MYSTIQUE, CONT'D

PINPOINT TEST F: ENGINE COOLING FAN DOES NOT OPERATE WHEN A/C IS ACTIVATED (Continued)

TEST STEP		RESULT	ACTION TO TAKE
F12	CHECK CIRCUIT 15 (GN/Y) FOR OPEN CIRCUIT		
	• Using a test lamp, check for voltage at fan control motor, Circuit 15 (GN/Y). • **Did test lamp illuminate?**	Yes ▶	GO to **F13.**
		No ▶	SERVICE Circuit 15 (GN/Y) for open circuit. RESTORE vehicle. RETEST system.
F13	CHECK COOLING FAN GROUND		
	• Using an ohmmeter connected to a known good ground, check for ground at fan control motor, Circuit 31 (BK) using the second test lead. • **Did test lamp illuminate?**	Yes ▶	REPLACE fan control motor. RESTORE vehicle. RETEST system.
		No ▶	SERVICE Circuit 31 (BK) for open circuit. RESTORE vehicle. RETEST system.

Component Tests

Heater Core

Plugged Heater Core

Check to see that the engine coolant is at the proper level. Start the engine and turn on the heater. When the engine coolant reaches operating temperature, carefully feel the outlet hose of the heater core. If it is not hot, the heater core may have an air pocket or may be plugged.

1. Before **heater core pressure test**, inspect for visible evidence of coolant leakage at the heater water hose to heater core attachments. A coolant leak at the heater water hose could follow the heater core tube to the heater core and appear as a leak in the heater core.
2. Check the system for loose hose clamps. The hose clamps should be tightened to 15-21 inch lbs. (1.7-2.4 Nm).
3. If leakage is found and hose clamps are over-tightened, remove heater water hose and check heater core tube for damage. Service damaged or deformed heater core tube, replace hose clamp and tighten to 15-21 inch lbs. (1.7-2.4 Nm). An over-tightened hose clamp may cause leakage at hose connection.

Pressure Test

1. NOTE: Due to space limitations in the engine compartment, a bench test is recommended for heater core pressure testing.

   Drain the coolant from the cooling system.
2. Disconnect the heater water hoses from the heater core tubes.
3. Install a short piece of heater water hose, approximately 101 mm (4 inches) long, on each heater core tube.
4. Fill the heater core and heater water hoses with water and install Plug BT-7422-B and Adapter BT-7422-A from Rotunda Radiator/Heater Core Pressure Tester 021-00012 or equivalent in the heater water hose ends. Secure the heater water hoses, plug and adapter with hose clamps.
5. Attach the pump and gauge assembly from Rotunda Radiator/Heater Core Pressure Tester 021-00012 or equivalent to the adapter.
6. Close the bleed valve at the base of the gauge and pump 207 kPa (30 psi) of air pressure into the heater core.
7. Observe the pressure gauge for a minimum of three minutes. The pressure should not drop.
8. If the pressure does not drop, no leaks are indicated.
9. If the pressure drops, check the hose connections to the core tubes for leaks. If the hoses do not leak, remove the heater core from the vehicle and bench test the heater core as outlined:

   - For the bench test, remove heater core from A/C evaporator housing.
   - Drain all coolant from the heater core.
   - Connect the 101 mm (4-inch) test hoses with plug and adapter to the core tubes. Then connect the air pump and gauge assembly to the adapter.
   - Apply 207 kPa (30 psi) of air pressure to the heater core with Rotunda Radiator/Heater Core Pressure Tester 021-00012 or equivalent, and submerge the heater core in water.
   - If a leak is observed, service or replace the heater core as necessary.

HEATING SYSTEM DIAGNOSIS—TAURUS, SABLE, TEMPO AND TOPAZ

INSUFFICIENT, ERRATIC, OR NO HEAT OR DEFROST

Possible Source	Action
Low radiator coolant due to: • Coolant leaks	Fill to level. Pressure test for engine cooling system and heater system leaks. Service as required.
• Engine overheating	Remove bugs, leaves, etc. from radiator and/or condenser fins. Check for: Sticking thermostat Incorrect ignition timing Water pump impeller damage Restricted cooling system Slipping belt Cooling fan inoperative Service as required.
Plugged or partially plugged heater core	Clean and backflush engine cooling system and heater core separately.
Improperly adjusted control cables	Readjust as specified.
Airflow control doors sticking or binding	Check to see if cable operated doors respond properly to movements of the Control Levers. If hesitation in movement is noticed, determine cause and service sticking or binding door as required.
Kinked, clogged, collapsed, soft, swollen, or decomposed engine cooling system or heater system hoses	Replace damaged hoses and backflush engine cooling system, then heater core, until all particles have been removed.
Blocked air inlet	Check cowl air inlet for leaves, foreign material, etc. Remove as required.

NO HI-OUTPUT HEATING

Possible Source	Action
Fuse (Hi-Output Switch)	Replace if required.
Water Valve	Check if sticking — closed — service as required.
Vacuum Line Leak	Check vacuum lines to and from solenoid.
Hi-Output Switch	Check for power and continuity.
Open Circuit at Electro/Vacuum Solenoid	Check for voltage at Hi-output solenoid. Also check for a good circuit to ground at solenoid.

BLOWER MOTOR INOPERATIVE

Possible Source	Action
Blown fuse	Check fuse for continuity. Replace fuse as necessary
Thermal limiter	Check thermal limiter for an open condition
Open circuit	Check for voltage at blower motor. Also check for a good circuit to ground at the blower motor
Blower motor	Check blower motor operation by grounding ground side lead to a good ground.
Blower switch	Perform a continuity check on the blower switch

BLOWER MOTOR OPERATES ON HIGH SPEED ONLY

Possible Source	Action
Blower motor resistor	a. Check resistor for open circuit with a self-powered test lamp. Replace if open. b. Check to be sure wire harness connector makes good contact with resistor spade terminals. Service as required.
Blower motor wire harness	Check wire harness from resistor assembly to blower switch for a short to ground. Service as necessary.

HEATING SYSTEM DIAGNOSIS AND SYMPTOMS—FESTIVA

CONDITION	POSSIBLE SOURCE	ACTION
• Blower Motor Does Not Operate	• Fuse. • Circuit. • Blower motor. • Blower motor resistor. • Blower motor switch.	• GO to BM1.
• Blower Motor Runs Constantly	• Circuit. • Blower motor. • Blower motor resistor. • Blower motor switch.	• GO to BM6.
• Low Position Does Not Operate	• Circuit. • Blower motor resistor. • Blower motor switch.	• GO to BM8.
• Med Position Does Not Operate	• Circuit. • Blower motor resistor. • Blower motor switch.	• GO to BM8.
• High Position Does Not Operate	• Circuit. • Blower motor switch.	• GO to BM8.

HEATING SYSTEM DIAGNOSIS AND PINPOINT TESTS—FESTIVA, CONT'D

	TEST STEP	RESULT	▶	ACTION TO TAKE
BM1	CHECK FUSE			
	• Key OFF. • Check 15A HEATER fuse located in the interior fuse panel. • **Is the fuse OK?**	Yes No	▶ ▶	GO to BM4. GO to BM2.
BM2	CHECK SYSTEM			
	• Key OFF. • Replace the 15A HEATER fuse. • Key ON. • **Does the fuse fail again?**	Yes No	▶ ▶	GO to BM3. GO to BM4.
BM3	CHECK FOR SHORT TO GROUND			
	• Key OFF. • Remove the 15A HEATER fuse. • Disconnect the blower motor connector. • Measure the resistance of the "BL / Y" wire between the bottom terminal of the 15A HEATER fuse holder and ground. • **Is the resistance less than 5 ohms?**	Yes No	▶ ▶	SERVICE the "BL / Y" wire between the interior fuse panel and the blower motor connector. REPLACE the 15A HEATER fuse. GO to BM4.

HEATING SYSTEM DIAGNOSIS AND PINPOINT TESTS— FESTIVA, CONT'D

	TEST STEP	RESULT	▶	ACTION TO TAKE
BM4	CHECK POWER SUPPLY TO BLOWER MOTOR			
	• Key OFF. • Disconnect the blower motor connector. • Key ON. • Measure the voltage of the "BL / Y" wire at the blower motor connector. • **Is the voltage greater than 10 volts?**	Yes No	▶ ▶	GO to BM5. SERVICE the "BL / Y" wire between the interior fuse panel and the blower motor.
BM5	CHECK BLOWER MOTOR			
	• Key OFF. • Disconnect the blower motor connector. • Apply 12 volts to the "BL / Y" wire terminal and apply ground to the "BL / R" wire terminal on the blower motor. • **Does the blower motor run at high speed?**	Yes No	▶ ▶	GO to BM6. REPLACE the blower motor.
BM6	CHECK WIRE BETWEEN BLOWER MOTOR AND BLOWER MOTOR RESISTOR			
	• Key OFF. • Disconnect the blower motor connector and the blower motor resistor connector. • Measure the the resistance of the "BL / R" wire between the blower motor connector and the blower motor resistor connector. • Measure the resistance of the "BL / R" wire between the blower motor connector and ground. • **Is the resistance less than 5 ohms between the blower motor connector and the blower motor resistor connector, and greater than 10,000 ohms between the blower motor connector and ground?**	Yes No	▶ ▶	GO to BM7. SERVICE the "BL / R" wire between the blower motor resistor and the blower motor.
BM7	CHECK BLOWER MOTOR CONTROL SWITCH GROUND			
	• Key OFF. • Disconnect the blower motor control switch connector. • Measure the resistance of the "BK" wire between the blower motor control switch connector and ground. • **Is the resistance less than 5 ohms?**	Yes No	▶ ▶	GO to BM8. SERVICE the "BK" wire between the blower motor control switch and ground.
BM8	CHECK BLOWER MOTOR CONTROL SWITCH			
	• Key OFF. • Disconnect the blower motor control switch connector. • Measure the resistance between the following wire terminals on the blower motor control switch:	Yes No	▶ ▶	GO to BM9. REPLACE the blower motor control switch.

Switch Position	Wires	Resistance
OFF	BK-BL / W BK-BL / Y BK-BL / BK	Greater than 10,000 ohms Greater than 10,000 ohms Greater than 10,000 ohms
1	BK-BL / W	Less than 5 ohms
2	BK-BL / Y	Less than 5 ohms
3	BK-BL / BK	Less than 5 ohms

• **Are the resistances OK?**

HEATING SYSTEM DIAGNOSIS AND PINPOINT TESTS— FESTIVA, CONT'D

	TEST STEP	RESULT	▶	ACTION TO TAKE
BM9	CHECK WIRES BETWEEN BLOWER MOTOR RESISTOR AND BLOWER MOTOR CONTROL SWITCH			
	• Key OFF. • Disconnect the blower motor resistor connector and the blower motor control switch connector. • Measure the resistance of the following wires between the blower motor resistor connector and the blower motor control switch connector.	Yes No	▶ ▶	REPLACE the blower motor resistor. SERVICE the wire(s) in question between the blower motor resistor and the blower motor control switch.

Wire
BL / W
BL / Y
BL / BK

• Measure the resistance of these same wires between the blower motor control switch connector and ground.
• **Are the resistances less than 5 ohms between the blower motor resistor connector and the blower motor control switch connector, and greater than 10,000 ohms between the blower motor control switch connector and ground?**

AIR CONDITIONING DIAGNOSIS AND TESTING— EXCEPT PROBE, FESTIVA, ASPIRE, TRACER AND ESCORT

INSUFFICIENT OR NO A/C COOLING — FIXED ORIFICE TUBE CYCLING CLUTCH SYSTEM

TEST STEP		RESULT ▶	ACTION TO TAKE
A1	VERIFY THE CONDITION		
	• Check system operation	System cooling properly ▶	INSTRUCT vehicle owner on proper use of the system
		System not cooling properly ▶	GO to **A2**
A2	CHECK COOLING FAN		
	• Does vehicle have an electro-drive cooling fan?	Yes ▶	GO to **A3**
		No ▶	GO to **A5**
A3	CHECK A/C COMPRESSOR CLUTCH		
	• Does the A/C compressor clutch engage?	Yes ▶	GO to **A4**
		No ▶	REFER to clutch circuit diagnosis
A4	CHECK OPERATION OF COOLING FAN		
	• Check to ensure electro-drive cooling fan runs when the A/C compressor clutch is engaged	Yes ▶	GO to **A5**
		No ▶	REFER to engine cooling fan circuit diagnosis.
A5	COMPONENT CHECK		
	Under-hood check of the following • Loose, missing or damaged compressor drive belt • Loose or disconnected A/C clutch or clutch cycling pressure switch wires/connectors • Disconnected resistor assembly • Loose vacuum lines or misadjusted control cables Inside vehicle check for • Blown fuse/proper blower motor operation • Vacuum motors/temperature door movement — full travel • Control electrical and vacuum connections	OK but still not cooling ▶	GO to **A7**
		Not OK ▶	REPAIR and GO to **A6**
A6	CHECK SYSTEM		
	• Check system operation	(OK) ▶	Condition Corrected GO to **A1**
		(NOT OK) ▶	GO to **A7**

AIR CONDITIONING DIAGNOSIS AND TESTING— EXCEPT PROBE, FESTIVA, ASPIRE, TRACER AND ESCORT, CONT'D

INSUFFICIENT OR NO A/C COOLING — FIXED ORIFICE TUBE CYCLING CLUTCH SYSTEM — Continued

TEST STEP		RESULT ▶	ACTION TO TAKE
A7	CHECK COMPRESSOR CLUTCH		
	• Use refrigerant system pressure/clutch cycle rate and timing evaluation charts. After preparing vehicle as follows: 1. Hook up manifold gauge set. 2. Set function control at max. A/C 3. Set blower switch on high 4. Set temperature lever full cold 5. Close doors and windows 6. Use a thermometer to check temperature at center discharge register, record outside temperature. 7. Run engine at approximately 1500 rpm with compressor clutch engaged. 8. Stabilize with above conditions for 10-15 minutes. • Check compressor clutch off/on time with watch. Refer to charts for normal clutch cycle timing rates	Compressor cycles very rapidly (1 second on) (1 second off) ▶	GO to **A8**
		Compressor runs continuously (normal operation in ambient temperature above 27°C (80°F) depending on humidity conditions) ▶	GO to **A9**
		Compressor cycles slow ▶	GO to **A8**
A8	CHECK CLUTCH CYCLING PRESSURE SWITCH		
	• Bypass clutch cycling pressure switch with jumper wire. Compressor on continuously. • Hand feel evaporator inlet and outlet tubes	Outlet tube same temperature approximately -2°C - 4°C (28°F - 40°F) or slightly colder than inlet tube (after fixed orifice) ▶	REPLACE clutch cycling pressure switch. Do not discharge system. Switch fitting has Schrader Valve. GO to **A9**
		Inlet tube warm or (after fixed orifice) colder than outlet tube ▶	GO to **A10**
A9	CHECK SYSTEM PRESSURES		
	• Compare readings with normal system pressure ranges.	Clutch cycles within limits, system pressure within limits ▶	System OK GO to **A1**
		Compressor runs continuously (normal operation in ambient temperature above 27°C (80°F) depending on humidity conditions) ▶	GO to **A11**
		Compressor cycles high or low ON above 259 kPa (52 psi) OFF below 144 kPa (20 psi) ▶	REPLACE clutch cycling pressure switch. Do not discharge system. Switch fitting has Schrader valve. CHECK system. OK — GO to **A1**. NOT OK — REINSTALL original switch. GO to **A10**.

AIR CONDITIONING DIAGNOSIS AND PINPOINT TEST B—EXCEPT PROBE, FESTIVA, TRACER, ASPIRE, ESCORT AND CAPRI

TEST STEP		RESULT	▶	ACTION TO TAKE
B1	CHECK SYSTEM OPERATION			
	• Start engine. • Set the A/C control MAX A/C. Check battery voltage (if not 12.5 volts or more, refer to Charging System Diagnosis). • **Does clutch engage?**	Yes	▶	Circuit functioning properly
		No	▶	GO to **B2.**
B2	BY-PASS PRESSURE SWITCH			
	• Disconnect electrical connector from pressure switch on accumulator. Jumper the harness connector pins. Engine must be running and system set at MAX A/C. • **Does clutch engage?**	Yes	▶	GO to **B3.**
		No	▶	GO to **B4.**
B3	CHECK REFRIGERANT SYSTEM PRESSURES			
	• Connect gauge set to service ports and observe pressure. • **Does pressure measure above 50 psi?**	Yes	▶	REPLACE clutch cycling pressure switch. GO to **B1.**
		No	▶	CHECK refrigerant system for leaks. SERVICE leak test and charge as necessary. GO to **B1.**
B4	CHECK VOLTAGE AT PRESSURE SWITCH			
	• Check for battery voltage at pressure switch electrical connector 348 circuit (LG/P wire) to ground. • **Is there battery voltage?**	Yes	▶	GO to **B8.**
		No	▶	GO to **B5.**
B5	CHECK A/C CONTROL SWITCH			
	• Check for battery voltage at the A/C control switch 348 circuit (LG/P wire). • **Is there voltage?**	Yes	▶	SERVICE wiring as necessary. GO to **B1.**
		No	▶	GO to **B6.**
B6	CHECK EATC OR CONTROL ASSEMBLY OUTPUT VOLTAGE			
	• Check for battery voltage at: EATC Control Assembly Pin 25 (clutch output signal). A/C Control Assembly output. • **Is there voltage?**	Yes	▶	CHECK circuit between control assembly and pressure switch for open. SERVICE as necessary. GO to **B1.**
		No	▶	GO to **B6.**
B7	CHECK FUSE			
	• Check for voltage at fuse panel 295 circuit (LB/PK wire). Ignition switch must be in the run position. • Ignition switch must be in the run position. • **Is there voltage?**	Yes	▶	SERVICE wiring between control assembly and fuse. GO to **B1.**
		Less than 10 volts	▶	CHECK charging system operation and for high resistance in clutch circuit.
		No	▶	CHECK fuse. SERVICE circuit as required. CHECK diode in IRCM for short. (Pins 16 and 23). GO to **B1.**

AIR CONDITIONING DIAGNOSIS AND PINPOINT TEST B—EXCEPT PROBE, FESTIVA, TRACER, ASPIRE, ESCORT AND CAPRI, CONT'D

TEST STEP		RESULT	▶	ACTION TO TAKE
B8	CHECK CLUTCH CIRCUITS			
	• Check for voltage across harness connector at clutch field coil. — A minimum of 10 volts is required. • **Are there 10 volts or more?**	Yes	▶	GO to **B9.**
		No	▶	GO to **B11.**
B9	JUMP FIELD COIL			
	• Disconnect field coil and jump battery voltage and ground to clutch field coil. • **Does clutch engage?**	Yes	▶	CLEAN coil electrical terminals and RETEST.
		No	▶	GO to **B10.**
B10	CHECK CLUTCH AIR GAP			
	• Check air gap between clutch hub and pulley. • **Is air gap within specified limits?**	Yes	▶	REPLACE clutch field coil.
		No	▶	RESET clutch air gap GO to **B10.**
B11	CHECK IRCM OUTPUT VOLTAGE			
	• Check for voltage between Pins 16 and 23 of the IRCM. — A minimum of 10 volts is required. • **Is voltage present?**	Yes	▶	CHECK clutch coil wiring harness for open circuit. SERVICE as necessary. GO to **B1.**
		No	▶	GO to **B12.**
B12	CHECK CLUTCH SIGNAL AT IRCM			
	• Check for minimum of 11 volts at Pin 21 of the IRCM (clutch input signal). • **Is voltage present?**	Yes	▶	GO to **B13.**
		No	▶	CHECK circuit between pressure switch and Pin 21 of IRCM for open. SERVICE as necessary.
B13	CHECK A/C CUT-OUT SIGNAL			
	• Remove RED wire from Pin 22 of IRCM harness connector. Start engine and set system set at MAX A/C. • **Does the clutch energize?**	No	▶	REPLACE the IRCM.
		Yes	▶	GO to **B14.**
B14	CHECK POWERTRAIN CONTROL MODULE (PCM) 12A650 INPUT SIGNAL			
	• Check for minimum of 11 volts at Pin 10 of PCM. • **Is there voltage?**		▶	The PCM is causing the CCRM to energize and interrupt the compressor circuit. Any of the following can be cause. REFER to PCM diagnosis in Service Manual. — **Throttle Position Sensor** - Sending WOT signal PCM. Disconnect electrical connector to remove sensor from circuit. Clutch will engage if sensor is sending WOT cut-out signal. — **Hot Engine Coolant** - Sensor sending hot coolant signal to PCM. Disconnect electrical connector from sensor. Clutch will engage if sensor is sending hot coolant signal to PCM. — **A/C On Circuit to PCM Open** - If this circuit is open, PCM will not receive signal from pressure switch to turn A/C clutch on.

HEATING SYSTEM DIAGNOSIS AND TESTING—CAPRI

CONDITION	POSSIBLE SOURCE	ACTION
• Insufficient, Erratic, or No Heat or Defrost	• Low coolant due to coolant leaks	• Fill system to proper level. Pressure test system and radiator cap. Service as required
	• Engine overheating	• Check water pump drive belt • Remove debris from radiator and/or condenser cooling fins • Check electric cooling fan for proper operation • Check thermostat for proper operation • Check water pump for damage or restricted cooling system or heater core
	• Blocked air inlet	• Check air inlet for leaves, etc. Clean as required
	• Heater flaps sticking or inoperative	• Check heater control unit operation. Service as required • Check cable operation. Service as required • Disconnect cable(s). Check control unit and flap operation. Service as required
• Air Comes Out Defroster Outlet Only, or Air Distribution Not Controllable	• Cables disconnected or out of adjustment	• Inspect control unit and cables. Service as required

CONDITION	POSSIBLE SOURCE	ACTION
• Vent System Leaks Air When in OFF Position	• Vent / Recirc. door not sealing	• Check door for obstructions, damaged seal. Service as required • Check control cable for proper adjustment and operation. Service as required
Blower Motor Does Not Run, or Blower Motor Does Not Run at Selected Speed	• No power to blower motor, blower motor switch	• Check blower circuit breaker, fuse, wiring. Service as required
	• No ground to blower motor	• Check ground circuit. Service as required
	• Blower switch worn or damaged	• Check Blower switch. Service as required
	• Blower resistor damaged	• Check blower resistor. Bypass resistor with jumper wire. If blower runs, replace resistor
	• Blower motor damaged	• Connect fused jumper lead to power and "hot" side of blower motor. If motor does not run, connect jumper from ground to ground of blower motor. If blower does not run with both jumpers connected, replace blower motor

HEATING SYSTEM DIAGNOSIS AND TESTING—CAPRI, CONT'D

TEST STEP	RESULT ►	ACTION TO TAKE
IC3 REFRIGERANT CHARGE — CHECK FOR INSUFFICIENT REFRIGERANT		
• Connect the manifold gauge set. • Operate the engine at 2000 rpm and set the A/C to maximum cooling. • Measure the low- and high-side pressures. • If insufficient refrigerant, the pressures should be: Low-side: Below 785 kPa (0.8 kg/cm², 11.4 psi) High-side: 785-883 kPa (8-9 kg/cm², 114-128 psi) • If the pressure is low, check for leakage as evidenced by oil stains at connections. • If no oil stains are evident, check for leakage at the following connections using a gas leak detector (observe warning and safety precautions): Inlet and outlet of; condenser, suction accumulator/drier, compressor, sight glass, cooling unit. • Is the refrigerant pressure low and is leakage present?	Yes (And leakage present) ►	REPLACE O-rings at leaking connectors and RETORQUE, then EVACUATE the system, RECHARGE and RETEST.
	Yes (No leaks present) ►	EVACUATE, RECHARGE, and RETEST the system. (Leakage occurred slowly over a long time.)
	No (But cooling is erratic) ►	GO to IC5

TEST STEP	RESULT ►	ACTION TO TAKE
IC4 REFRIGERANT CHARGE — CHECK FOR EXCESSIVE REFRIGERANT		
• Connect the manifold gauge set. • Operate the engine at 2000 rpm and set the A/C to maximum cooling. • Measure the low-and high-side pressures. • If excessive refrigerant, the pressures should be: Low-side: Above 245 kPa (2.5 kg/cm², 35.6 psi) High-side: Above 1,962 kPa (20 kg/cm², 284 psi) • If the pressure is high, check the condenser for bent fins or other damage. • Is the refrigerant pressure high?	Yes ►	REPAIR condenser fins or other damage, DISCHARGE the excess refrigerant, until RETEST shows the low and high sides to be within normal specification.
	No (But cooling is erratic) ►	GO to IC5

HEATING SYSTEM DIAGNOSIS AND TESTING—CAPRI, CONT'D

TEST STEP	RESULT ►	ACTION TO TAKE
IC5 REFRIGERANT CHARGE — CHECK FOR AIR IN SYSTEM		
• Connect the manifold gauge set. • Operate the engine at 2000 rpm and set the A/C to maximum cooling. • Measure the low-and high-side pressures. • If air is in the refrigerant, the pressures should be: Low-side: Above 245 kPa (2.5 kg/cm², 35.6 psi) High-side: Above 2256 kPa (23 kg/cm², 327 psi) • Do the pressures indicate air in the refrigerant charge?	Yes ►	DISCHARGE, EVACUATE and RECHARGE the system with fresh refrigerant R-12 to the correct amount GO to IC2 RECHECK the low- and high-side pressures, and if they are still too high, REPLACE the suction accumulator/drier, RECHARGE and RECHECK pressures.
	No (But cooling still erratic) ►	GO to IC6

TEST STEP	RESULT ►	ACTION TO TAKE
IC6 REFRIGERANT CHARGE — CHECK FOR REFRIGERANT CIRCULATION		
• Connect the manifold gauge set. • Operate the engine at 2000 rpm and set the A/C to maximum cooling. • Measure the low-and high-side pressures. • If there is no circulation of refrigerant in the system, the pressures should be: Low-side: 76 cm-Hg (3.0 in-Hg) vacuum. High-side: Below 589 kPa (kg/cm², 85 psi) of pressure. • If the pressures indicate no refrigerant circulation, turn the A/C OFF for 10 minutes. • Turn the A/C ON to determine whether the blockage is due to moisture or solid material. • After turning the system ON, does it operate normally?	Yes (But cooling is erratic) ►	GO to IC7 (Moisture in system freezes, then melts and relieves blockage.)
	No ►	REPLACE the fixed orifice, EVACUATE the system and RECHARGE the system with fresh refrigerant R-12 to the correct amount GO to IC2 RECHECK the low-and high-side pressures.

HEATING SYSTEM DIAGNOSIS AND TESTING—CAPRI, CONT'D

CONDITION	POSSIBLE SOURCE	ACTION
• Blower Motor Does Not Operate	• Main fuse. • Resistor. • Blower motor. • Blower motor control switch. • Circuit.	• Go to **HP1**. • Go to **HP7**. • Go to **HP5**. • Go to **HP12**. • Go to **HP4**.
• Blower Motor Runs Constantly	• Resistor. • Blower motor control switch. • Circuit.	• Go to **HP7**. • Go to **HP12**. • Go to **HP4**.
• Blower Motor Does Not Run in All Speeds	• Resistor. • Blower motor control switch. • Circuit.	• Go to **HP7**. • Go to **HP12**. • Go to **HP4**.

CONDITION	POSSIBLE SOURCE	ACTION
• Intermittent Blower Motor Operation	• Resistor • Blower motor control switch • Circuit	• Go to **HP12**. • Go to **HP12**. • Go to **HP4**.
• Improper Air Circulation (Air Comes Out of Wrong Duct)	• Temperature control levers. • Temperature control cables. • Air distribution doors.	• Go to **V2**. • Go to **V1**. • Go to **V2**.
• No Heat (Blower Motor Functioning Properly)	• Coolant level. • Heater hoses. • Engine thermostat. • Heater core. • Temperature blend cable.	• Visually inspect level • Visually inspect hoses • Go to **NH1**. • Go to **NH2**. • Go to **NH4**.

HEATING SYSTEM DIAGNOSIS AND TESTING— CAPRI, CONT'D

TEST STEP	RESULT ▶	ACTION TO TAKE
HP1 CHECK FUSE		
• Access main fuse panel	Yes ▶	GO to **HP4**.
• Check the 60 amp main fuse.	No ▶	GO to **HP2**.
• Is the fuse good?		
HP2 CHECK SYSTEM		
• Replace blown 60 amp main fuse.	Yes ▶	GO to **HP3**.
• Key ON.	No ▶	GO to **HP4**.
• Did the fuse blow again?		
HP3 CHECK FOR SHORT TO GROUND		
• Key OFF.	Yes ▶	SERVICE BL wire.
• Disconnect the BL wire from the main fuse.	No ▶	GO to **HP4**.
• Measure the resistance of the BL wire between the fuse panel and ground.		
• Is resistance less than 5 ohms?		
HP4 CHECK SUPPLY TO BLOWER MOTOR		
• Disconnect the blower motor connector.	Yes ▶	GO to **HP5**.
• Key ON.	No ▶	SERVICE BL wire.
• Measure the voltage on the BL wire at the connector.		
• Reconnect the blower motor connector.		
• Is the voltage greater than 10 volts?		
HP5 CHECK BLOWER MOTOR		
• Key OFF.	Yes ▶	GO to **HP6**.
• Disconnect blower motor connector.	No ▶	SERVICE/REPLACE blower motor.
• Apply 12 volts to the BL terminal.		
• Ground the BL/W terminal.		
• Reconnect blower motor.		
• Does the blower motor run?		

HEATING SYSTEM DIAGNOSIS AND TESTING— CAPRI, CONT'D

TEST STEP	RESULT ▶	ACTION TO TAKE
HP6 CHECK LEAD TO RESISTOR		
• Locate the resistor connector.	Yes ▶	GO to **HP7**
• Measure the resistance of the BL/W wire between the motor and the resistor.	No ▶	SERVICE the BL/W wire.
• Is the resistance less than 5 ohms?		
HP7 CHECK RESISTOR		
• Measure the resistance from the BL/W wire at the connector to the following wires at the connector:	Yes ▶	GO to **HP8**.
WIRE — RESISTANCE BL/Y — 2.6 ohms BL — 1.2 ohms BL/R — 6 ohms BL/W — 1 ohms	No ▶	REPLACE resistor.
• Are the resistances correct?		
HP8 CHECK LEADS TO BLOWER MOTOR CONTROL SWITCH		
• Locate the blower motor control switch connector.	Yes ▶	GO to **HP9**.
• Measure the resistance of the following wires between the resistor and the blower motor control switch: WIRE BL/Y BL BL/R BL/W	No ▶	SERVICE wire in question.
• Are the resistances less than 5 ohms?		
HP9 CHECK LEAD TO A/C SWITCH		
• Locate the A/C switch connector.	Yes ▶	GO to **HP10**.
• Measure the resistance of the BL/Y wire between the A/C switch and the blower motor control switch.	No ▶	SERVICE the BL/Y wire.
• Is the resistance less than 5 ohms?		

HEATING SYSTEM DIAGNOSIS AND TESTING—CAPRI, CONT'D

TEST STEP	RESULT ▶	ACTION TO TAKE
HP10 CHECK LEAD TO ELECTRICAL LOAD CONTROL SWITCH		
• Measure the resistance of the BL/GN wire between blower motor control switch and the electrical load control switch • Is the resistance less than 5 ohms?	Yes ▶ No ▶	GO to **HP11**. SERVICE BL/GN wire.
HP11 CHECK BLOWER MOTOR CONTROL SWITCH GROUND		
• Measure the resistance of the BK wire between the blower motor control switch and ground • Is the resistance less than 5 ohms?	Yes ▶ No ▶	GO to **HP12**. SERVICE BK wire.
HP12 CHECK BLOWER MOTOR CONTROL SWITCH		
• Disconnect the blower motor control switch. • Measure the resistance between ground and the wire colors listed below at the following switch positions	Yes ▶ No ▶	RETURN to condition chart. SERVICE/REPLACE blower motor control switch.

SWITCH POSITION	WIRE COLOR	RESISTANCE
OFF	All Colors	Greater than 10,000 ohms
1	BL/Y	Less than 5 ohms
	All Others	Greater than 10,000 ohms
2	BL	Less than 5 ohms
	All Others	Greater than 10,000 ohms
3	BL/R	Less than 5 ohms
	All Others	Greater than 10,000 ohms
4	BL/W	Less than 5 ohms
	All Others	Greater than 10,000 ohms

• Reconnect the blower motor control switch.

• Are the resistances correct?

HEATING SYSTEM DIAGNOSIS AND TESTING—CAPRI, CONT'D

TEST STEP	RESULT ▶	ACTION TO TAKE
V1 CHECK CABLE OPERATION		
• Access the control panel. • Slide the temperature control lever, air intake control lever and the airflow control lever back and forth. • Do the levers slide smoothly?	Yes ▶ No ▶	GO to **V2**. CHECK control panel and cables for damage, SERVICE/REPLACE as required.
V2 AIRFLOW SELECTOR SYSTEM FUNCTION		
• With the ignition switch ON and the blower control switch set to position 4 for maximum airflow, change the position settings of the airflow selector. Verify that they conform to the specified airflow patterns as listed.	Yes ▶ No ▶	GO to **V3**. SERVICE, ADJUST, or REPLACE the heater or its outlet door or components as required.

Airflow Selector Position	Specified Airflow Pattern (Exit Locations Shown)
Panel	Ventilator outlets
Hi-Lo	Ventilator and floor outlets
Floor	Floor outlets and small amount to defroster outlets
Mix	Floor and defroster outlets
Def	Defroster outlets

• Do the airflow patterns conform to the specified patterns for each of the tested selector positions?

HEATING SYSTEM DIAGNOSIS AND TESTING— CAPRI, CONT'D

Panel

Hi-Lo

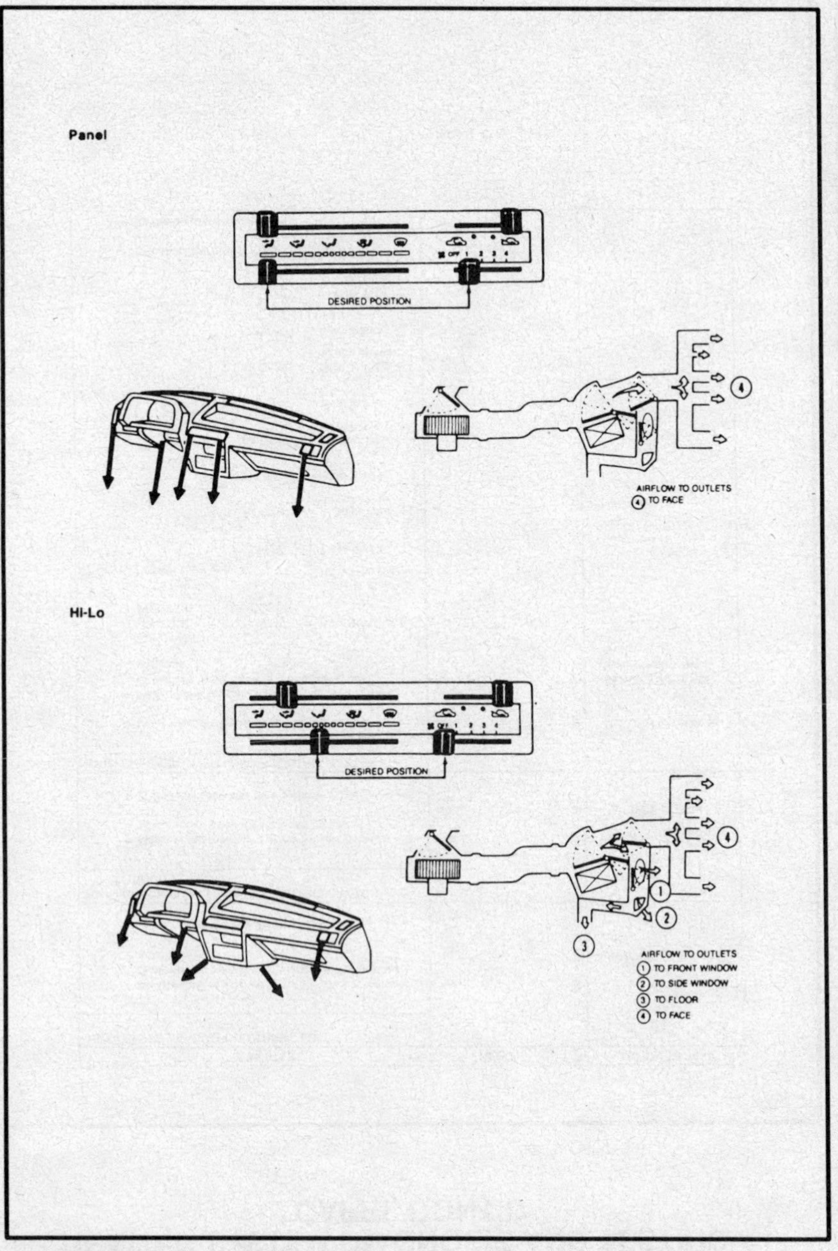

HEATING SYSTEM DIAGNOSIS AND TESTING— CAPRI, CONT'D

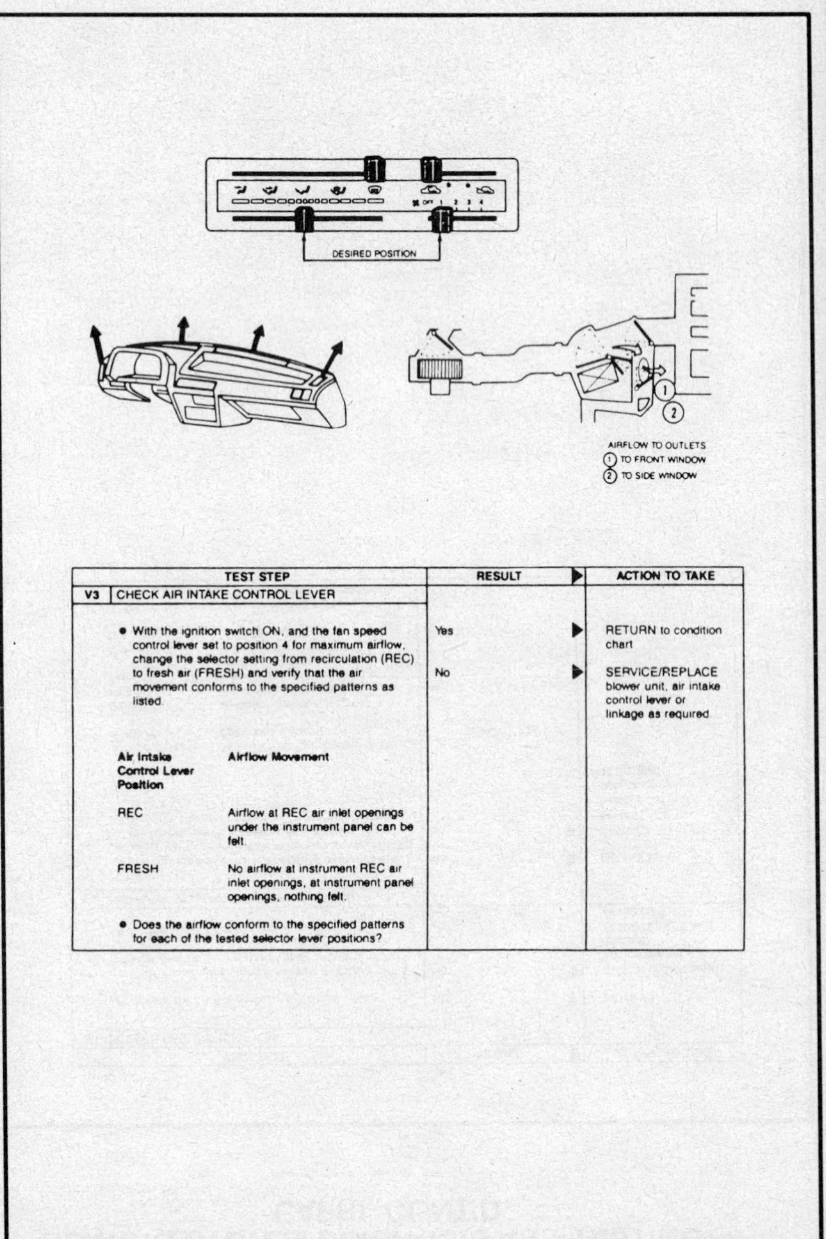

TEST STEP		RESULT	ACTION TO TAKE
V3	CHECK AIR INTAKE CONTROL LEVER		
	• With the ignition switch ON, and the fan speed control lever set to position 4 for maximum airflow, change the selector setting from recirculation (REC) to fresh air (FRESH) and verify that the air movement conforms to the specified patterns as listed.	Yes ▶	RETURN to condition chart
		No ▶	SERVICE/REPLACE blower unit, air intake control lever or linkage as required
	Air Intake Control Lever Position — **Airflow Movement**		
	REC — Airflow at REC air inlet openings under the instrument panel can be felt.		
	FRESH — No airflow at instrument REC air inlet openings, at instrument panel openings, nothing felt.		
	• Does the airflow conform to the specified patterns for each of the tested selector lever positions?		

HEATING SYSTEM DIAGNOSIS AND TESTING—CAPRI, CONT'D.

TEST STEP	RESULT	▶ ACTION TO TAKE
NH1 ENGINE THERMOSTAT FUNCTION		
• Check engine coolant level. • Start and warm up the engine until the coolant temperature stabilizes. • Verify the reported condition by checking the heater for adequate heat output (temperature blend lever to extreme right, airflow selector lever at panel, blower at position 4). • Is the heat output inadequate?	Yes No	▶ GO to **NH2.** ▶ Check cooling system
NH2 HEATER CORE — CHECK FOR AIRFLOW BLOCKAGE		
• Check the heater core blower motor housing and connecting air passages for blockage (such as leaves, paper, etc) • Is the heater core and its connecting air passages free of blockage?	Yes No	▶ GO to **NH3.** ▶ REMOVE components and clean as required.
NH3 HEATER CORE — CHECK FOR COOLANT BLOCKAGE		
• Back flush the heater core to remove core sand, etc. • Is the heater core free of blockage to coolant flow?	Yes No	▶ GO to **NH4.** ▶ REPLACE heater core.
NH4 TEMPERATURE BLEND FUNCTION		
• Start and warm up the engine to normal operating temperature. • Set the blower control to position 4. • Set the airflow selector lever to panel. • Move the temperature blend lever gradually from extreme left to extreme right and verify that the air temperature gradually increases from cold to hot. • Does the temperature blend function properly and is the air hot with the lever at its extreme right?	Yes No	▶ RETURN to condition chart. ▶ ADJUST the temperature blend cable to close off all bypass air around the heater core when the temperature blend lever is set to the extreme right.

AIR CONDITIONING DIAGNOSIS AND PINPOINT TEST B—CAPRI

TEST STEP	RESULT	▶ ACTION TO TAKE
B1 CHECK SYSTEM INTEGRITY		
• Check for fully charged battery. • Check for blown fuses, corrosion, poor electrical connections, signs of opens, shorts or damage to the wiring harness. NOTE: If a blown fuse is replaced and fails immediately, there is a short to ground in the system. • Key ON, engine idling. • A/C ON. • Blower ON. • Shake the wiring harness vigorously and look for signs of opens or shorts. • Tap each connector and look for signs of bad connections. • **Does system appear to be in good condition?**	Yes No	▶ GO to **B2.** ▶ SERVICE or REPLACE damaged components as required.
B2 CHECK FOR CLUTCH VOLTAGE		
• Engine ON. • A/C ON, blower ON. • Measure voltage on the BK/W wire at the compressor clutch connector. • **Is voltage greater than 10 volts?**	Yes No	▶ GO to **B3.** ▶ GO to **B4.**
B3 CHECK CLUTCH RESISTANCE		
• Key OFF, A/C OFF. • Allow engine to cool. • Disconnect compressor clutch connector. • Measure resistance between compressor clutch connector (clutch side) and compressor clutch case. • **Is resistance between 2.7 and 3.5 ohms?**	Yes No	▶ CHECK condition of drive belt, clutch material and compressor. SERVICE as required. ▶ SERVICE compressor clutch ground. If all OK, REPLACE compressor clutch.
B4 CHECK FOR SHORT IN CLUTCH WIRE		
• Key OFF. • Disconnect compressor clutch and WAC relay. • Measure resistance between BK/W wire at WAC relay connector and ground. • **Is resistance less than 5 ohms?**	Yes No	▶ SERVICE BK/W wire from WAC relay to compressor clutch. ▶ GO to **B5.**
B5 CHECK COMPRESSOR CLUTCH WIRE		
• Key OFF. • Disconnect compressor clutch and WAC relay. • Measure resistance of BK/W wire between WAC relay and compressor clutch. • **Is resistance less than 5 ohms?**	Yes No	▶ GO to **B6.** ▶ SERVICE BK/W wire.
B6 CHECK FOR VOLTAGE FROM WAC RELAY		
• Engine idling. • A/C ON, blower ON. • Measure voltage on BK/W wire at WAC relay. • **Is voltage greater than 10 volts?**	Yes No	▶ GO to **B12.** ▶ GO to **B7.**
B7 CHECK HEATER CIRCUIT BREAKER		
• Locate interior fuse panel. • Check 30 amp heater circuit breaker • **Is the reset button on circuit breaker sticking out?**	Yes No	▶ GO to **B8.** ▶ GO to **B9.**
B8 CHECK SYSTEM		
• Push in reset button on the heater circuit breaker. • Key ON. • **Did reset button pop out again?**	Yes No	▶ SERVICE the BL wire at the interior fuse panel for a short to ground. ▶ GO to **B9.**

AIR CONDITIONING DIAGNOSIS AND PINPOINT TEST B— CAPRI, CONT'D

	TEST STEP	RESULT	▶ ACTION TO TAKE
B9	CHECK IN-LINE COOLER FUSE		
	• Check 15 amp in-line COOLER fuse. • **Is fuse OK?**	Yes No	▶ GO to **B11.** ▶ GO to **B10.**
B10	CHECK SYSTEM		
	• Replace 15 amp in-line COOLER fuse. • Key ON. • **Does fuse fail again?**	Yes No	▶ SERVICE BL wire between the in-line fuse and WAC relay for a short to ground. ▶ GO to **B11.**
B11	CHECK FOR VOLTAGE TO WAC RELAY		
	• Key ON. • Measure voltage on BL wire at the WAC relay connector. • **Is voltage greater than 10 volts?**	Yes No	▶ GO to **B12.** ▶ SERVICE BL wire.
B12	CHECK FUSE		
	• Check 15 amp AIR COND fuse. • **Is fuse OK?**	Yes No	▶ GO to **B15.** ▶ GO to **B13.**
B13	CHECK SYSTEM		
	• Replace 15 amp AIR COND fuse. • Key ON. • **Does fuse fail again?**	Yes No	▶ GO to **B14.** ▶ GO to **B15.**
B14	CHECK FOR SHORT(S) TO GROUND		
	• Key OFF. • Locate and disconnect interior fuse panel connector. • Locate and disconnect following components: — A/C switch — WAC relay — Condenser fan motor — Condenser fan relay • Measure resistance between the BL wire at the interior fuse panel connector and ground. • **Is resistance less than 5 ohms?**	Yes No	▶ SERVICE BL wire(s) for short(s) to ground. ▶ GO to **B15.**
B15	CHECK POWER SUPPLY TO WAC RELAY		
	• Key ON. • Measure voltage on BL/BK wire at the connector. • **Is voltage greater than 10 volts?** NOTE: The BL/BK wire changes to a BL wire at a splice before the interior fuse panel (See electrical schematic).	Yes No	▶ GO to **B16.** ▶ SERVICE BL/BK wire between the interior fuse panel and WAC relay.
B16	CHECK WAC RELAY OPERATION		
	• Key ON. • Ground the W wire at WAC relay with a jumper wire. • Measure voltage on BK/W wire at WAC relay. • **Is voltage greater than 10 volts with W wire grounded and less than 1 volt with W wire open?**	Yes No	▶ GO to **B17.** ▶ REPLACE WAC relay.
B17	CHECK VOLTAGE TO PCM		
	• Locate and disconnect PCM connector. • Key ON. • Measure voltage on W wire at PCM connector. • **Is voltage greater than 10 volts?**	Yes No	▶ GO to **B18.** ▶ SERVICE W wire between WAC relay and PCM.
B18	CHECK FUSE		
	• Check 20 amp COOLING FAN fuse. • **Is fuse OK?**	Yes No	▶ GO to **B21.** ▶ GO to **B19.**

AIR CONDITIONING DIAGNOSIS AND PINPOINT TEST B— CAPRI, CONT'D

	TEST STEP	RESULT	▶ ACTION TO TAKE
B19	CHECK SYSTEM		
	• Replace COOLING FAN fuse[1]. • Key ON. • Check fuse. • **Did the fuse fail again?**	Yes No	▶ GO to **B20.** ▶ GO to **B21.**
B20	CHECK FOR SHORT TO GROUND		
	• Key OFF. • Locate and disconnect the interior fuse panel connector. • Locate and disconnect the cooling fan motor and A/C control module. • Measure the resistance between the Y wire at the interior fuse panel connector and ground. • **Is resistance less than 5 ohms?**	Yes No	▶ SERVICE Y wire(s). ▶ GO to **B21.**
B21	CHECK POWER SUPPLY TO A/C CONTROL MODULE		
	• Disconnect A/C control module connector. • Key ON, A/C OFF. • Measure voltage on Y wire at A/C control module connector. • **Is voltage greater than 10 volts?**	Yes No	▶ GO to **B22.** ▶ SERVICE Y wire between the interior fuse panel and A/C control module.
B22	CHECK A/C CONTROL MODULE OPERATION		
	• Checks are made at harness side of the A/C control module connector with module connected. • Check A/C control module voltages as listed below with: (see table below) • **Are measured voltages correct?**	Yes No	▶ GO to **B23.** ▶ REPLACE A/C control module.
B23	CHECK WIRE TO A/C SWITCH AND CONDENSER FAN RELAY		
	• Key OFF. • Disconnect A/C switch, A/C control module and condenser fan relay. • Measure resistance between GN wire at A/C control module to A/C switch and condenser fan relay. • **Is resistance less than 5 ohms?**	Yes No	▶ GO to **B24.** ▶ SERVICE GN wire(s) in question.
B24	CHECK THERMISTOR CIRCUIT		
	• Key OFF. • Disconnect A/C control module and thermistor. • Measure resistance of each wire between A/C control module and thermistor. Two W/BL wires. One Y/GN wire. • **Is resistance less than 5 ohms on each wire?**	Yes No	▶ GO to **B25.** ▶ SERVICE each wire between A/C control module and thermistor as required.

B22 voltage table:

Key ON, A/C OFF: Blower OFF:	Key ON, A/C OFF: Blower ON:
R: Greater than 10V	2.2V
Y: Greater than 10V	Greater than 10V
GN: Greater than 10V	1.5V
W/BL: Greater than 10V	3.3V
W/BL: Greater than 10V	3.3V
Y/GN: Greater than 10V	1.5V

AIR CONDITIONING DIAGNOSIS AND PINPOINT TEST B—CAPRI, CONT'D.

TEST STEP		RESULT	▶ ACTION TO TAKE
B25	CHECK THERMISTOR		
	• Remove thermistor. • Measure resistance between W / BL and Y / GN wire terminals on the thermistor. • Apply liquid freon or other cooling liquid to sensing bulb on switch to bring temperature of the sensing bulb below 32°F. • **Is resistance less than 1,500 ohms with sensing bulb warm (above 77°F) and more than 4,500 ohms with sensing bulb cold (32 °F or below)?**	Yes No	▶ GO to **B26.** ▶ REPLACE thermistor.
B26	CHECK POWER SUPPLY TO A / C SWITCH		
	• Disconnect A / C switch. • Key ON. • Measure voltage on BL / BK wire at A / C switch connector. • **Is reading greater than 10 volts?**	Yes No	▶ GO to **B27.** ▶ SERVICE the BL / BK wire.
B27	CHECK A / C SWITCH OPERATION		
	• Key ON, A / C ON. • Check A / C switch voltages at harness side of connector with:	Yes No	▶ GO to **B28.** ▶ REPLACE A / C switch.

Key ON, A / C ON: Blower ON:	Key ON, A / C OFF: Blower OFF:
GN: Less than 2V	Greater than 10V
BL / BK: Greater than 10V	Greater than 10V
BL / Y: Less than 1V	Greater than 10V

• **Are measured voltages the same?**

TEST STEP		RESULT	▶ ACTION TO TAKE
B28	CHECK WIRE TO BLOWER MOTOR CONTROL SWITCH AND BLOWER MOTOR RESISTOR		
	• Key OFF. • Measure resistance of BL / Y wire(s) between A / C switch, blower motor control switch and blower motor resistor. • **Is resistance less than 5 ohms?**	Yes No	▶ GO to **B29.** ▶ SERVICE BL / Y wire(s) in question.
B29	CHECK WIRE BETWEEN A / C CONTROL MODULE AND CLUTCH CYCLING PRESSURE SWITCH		
	• Key OFF. • Disconnect clutch cycling pressure switch and A / C control module connectors. • Measure resistance of R wire between clutch cycling pressure switch connector and A / C control module connector. • **Is resistance less than 5 ohms?**	Yes No	▶ GO to **B31.** ▶ SERVICE the R wire.
B30	CHECK CLUTCH CYCLING PRESSURE SWITCH		
	• Connect a manifold set to the service gauge port valves. • Disconnect the clutch cycling pressure switch connector. • Measure resistance between R wire terminals of the clutch cycling pressure switch. • **Is resistance less than 5 ohms when the system high side pressure is above 206 ± 20 kPa (30 ± 3 psi)?**	Yes No	▶ GO to **B31.** ▶ REPLACE clutch cycling pressure switch. NOTE: If high side pressure is below 206 ± 20 kPa (30 ± 3 psi) CHECK refrigerant system. REFER to test step **A1.**
B31	CHECK WIRE BETWEEN CLUTCH CYCLING PRESSURE SWITCH AND PCM		
	• Key OFF. • Disconnect PCM and clutch cycling pressure switch. • Measure resistance of R wire between clutch cycling pressure switch and PCM. • **Is resistance less than 5 ohms?**	Yes No	▶ REFER to Powertrain Control / Emissions Diagnosis for diagnosis of the PCM. ▶ SERVICE R wire.

CONDENSER FAN SYSTEM DIAGNOSIS AND PINPOINT TEST C—CAPRI

TEST STEP		RESULT	▶ ACTION TO TAKE
C1	SYSTEM INTEGRITY CHECK		
	• Check for fully charged battery. • Check for blown fuses, corrosion, poor electrical connections, signs of opens, shorts or damage to the wiring harness. NOTE: If a blown fuse is replaced and fails immediately there is a short to ground in the circuit. • Key ON, engine idling. • A / C ON. • Blower ON. • Shake wiring harness vigorously from the condenser fan motor to the condenser fan relay and the refrigerant pressure switch. Look for signs of opens or shorts. • Tap each connector and look for signs of bad connections. • **Does system appear to be in good condition?**	Yes No	▶ GO to **C2.** ▶ SERVICE or REPLACE damaged components as required.
C2	CHECK FUSE		
	• Check 15 amp AIR COND fuse. • **Is fuse OK?**	Yes No	▶ GO to **C5.** ▶ GO to **C3.**
C3	CHECK SYSTEM		
	• Replace 15 amp AIR COND fuse. • Key ON. • **Does fuse fail again?**	Yes No	▶ GO to **C4.** ▶ GO to **C5.**
C4	CHECK FOR SHORT(S) TO GROUND		
	• Locate and disconnect the interior fuse panel connector. • Locate and disconnect the condenser fan motor, condenser fan relay, WAC relay, and A / C Switch connectors. • Measure the resistance between the BL wire at the interior fuse panel connector and ground. • **Is the resistance less than 5 ohms?**	Yes No	▶ SERVICE the BL wire(s) in question. ▶ GO to **C5.**
C5	CHECK FUSE		
	• Check COOLING FAN fuse[3]. • **Is fuse OK?**	Yes No	▶ GO to **C8.** ▶ GO to **C6.**
C6	CHECK SYSTEM		
	• Replace COOLING FAN fuse[3]. • Key ON. • **Does fuse fail again?**	Yes No	▶ GO to **C7.** ▶ GO to **C8.**

CONDENSER FAN SYSTEM DIAGNOSIS AND PINPOINT TEST C—CAPRI, CONT'D

	TEST STEP	RESULT	ACTION TO TAKE
C7	CHECK FOR SHORT(S) TO GROUND		
	• Locate and disconnect the interior fuse panel connector. • Locate and disconnect the A/C control module and cooling fan motor connectors. • Measure the resistance between the Y wire at the interior fuse panel connector and ground. • **Is the resistance less than 5 ohms?**	Yes ▶ No ▶	SERVICE the Y wire(s). GO to C8.
C8	CHECK POWER SUPPLY TO CONDENSER FAN MOTOR		
	• Key ON. • Measure voltage on BL wire at condenser fan motor. • **Is voltage greater than 10 volts?**	Yes ▶ No ▶	GO to **C9.** SERVICE BL wire between condenser fan motor and interior fuse panel.
C9	CHECK POWER SUPPLY TO CONDENSER FAN RELAY		
	• Key ON. • Measure voltage on BL/BK wire at condenser fan relay connector. • **Is voltage greater than 10 volts?**	Yes ▶ No ▶	GO to **C10.** SERVICE BL/BK wire between condensor fan relay and interior fuse panel.
C10	CHECK CONDENSER FAN RELAY CONTROL CIRCUIT		
	• Key OFF. • Disconnect A/C control module, condenser fan relay, and A/C switch. • Measure resistance of GN wire between each of the above components. • **Is resistance less than 5 ohms?**	Yes ▶ No ▶	GO to **C11.** SERVICE GN wire(s) in question.
C11	CHECK CONDENSER FAN MOTOR OPERATION		
	• Key OFF. • Disconnect condenser fan motor. • Apply 12 volts to BL wire terminal at the condenser fan motor. • Ground GN/R wire terminal at the condenser fan motor. • **Does the condenser fan motor run?**	Yes ▶ No ▶	GO to **C12.** REPLACE condenser fan motor.
C12	CHECK WIRE TO CONDENSER FAN RELAY		
	• Key ON. • Disconnect condenser fan relay. • Measure resistance of GN/R wire between condenser fan relay and condenser fan motor. • **Is resistance less than 5 ohms?**	Yes ▶ No ▶	GO to **C13.** SERVICE GN/R wire.
C13	CHECK CONDENSER FAN RELAY GROUND (CONDENSER FAN MOTOR)		
	• Disconnect condenser fan relay connector. • Measure resistance between BK wire at the condenser fan relay connector and ground. • **Is resistance less than 5 ohms?**	Yes ▶ No ▶	GO to **C14.** SERVICE BK wire.
C14	CHECK CONDENSER FAN RELAY		
	• Disconnect condenser fan relay. • Measure resistance between GN/R wire terminal and BK wire terminal of relay. • **Is resistance greater than 10,000 ohms?** • Apply 12 volts to BL/BK wire terminal and ground GN wire terminal. • Measure resistance between GN/R terminal and BK terminal. • **Is resistance less than 5 ohms?**	Yes ▶ No ▶	RETURN to condition chart. REPLACE condenser fan relay.

MANUAL AIR CONDITIONING DIAGNOSIS AND TESTING—PROBE

	TEST STEP	RESULT	ACTION TO TAKE
A1	CHECK SYSTEM PRESSURES		
	• Connect a manifold gauge set. • Run the engine at 2,000 rpm. • Place the blower motor on high (position 4). • Set the temperature control at cool. • If the compressor clutch does not engage jump a battery power to the "GN/BK" wire at the clutch connector. • Wait until the air conditioning system stabilizes and check the readings of HI and LO gauges. — Normal HI: 199-228 psi (1373-1570 kPa) — Normal LO: 28-43 psi (196-294 kPa) • Is the pressure normal? MANIFOLD GAUGE SET 063-00010	Yes ▶ No ▶	GO to CC1 GO to A2
A2	CHECK FOR INSUFFICIENT REFRIGERANT		
	• Read the HI and the LO gauges on the manifold set. • Check for low pressure on both HI and LO gauges. Gauge: HI — Pressure: 114-128 psi (785-883 kPa) (8-9 kg/cm²) Gauge: LO — Pressure: 11.4 psi (78 kPa) (0.8 kg/cm²) • Are both of the pressures low?	Yes ▶ No ▶	LEAK CHECK the system and RECHARGE with proper amount of refrigerant GO to A3

MANUAL AIR CONDITIONING DIAGNOSIS AND TESTING—PROBE, CONT'D

A3 CHECK FOR EXCESSIVE REFRIGERANT

- Read the HI and the LO gauges on the manifold set.
- Check for high pressure on both HI and LO gauges.

Gauge	Pressure
HI	284 psi or greater (1962 kPa or greater) (20 kg/cm^2 or greater)
LO	35.6 psi or greater (245 kPa or greater) (2.5 kg/cm^2 or greater)

- Are both of the pressures high?

RESULT	▶	ACTION TO TAKE
Yes	▶	RECHARGE the system with the proper amount of oil and refrigerant.
No	▶	GO to A4.

A4 CHECK FOR AIR IN SYSTEM

- Read the HI and LO gauges on the manifold set.
- Check for warm low-pressure piping during operation.
- Check for high pressure on both Hi and LO gauges.

Gauge	Pressure
HI	327 psi or greater (2257 kPa or greater) (23 kg/cm^2 or greater)
LO	35.6 psi or greater (245 kPa or greater) (2.5 kg/cm^2 or greater)

- Is the low side piping warm and both pressures high?

RESULT	▶	ACTION TO TAKE
Yes	▶	EVACUATE and RECHARGE the system. CHECK the compressor oil for contamination. REPLACE the receiver/drier.
No	▶	GO to A5.

A5 CHECK FOR MOISTURE IN SYSTEM

- Read the HI and the LO gauges on the manifold set.

Gauge	Pressure
HI	687-1472 kPa (7-15 kg/cm^2) (100-213 psi)
LO	50 cmHg (20 inHg) of Vacuum - 147 kPa (1.5 kg/cm^2, 21.3 psi)

- Check for fluctuating high-pressure side and low-pressure side becoming vacuum and pressure.
- Are the pressures fluctuating?

RESULT	▶	ACTION TO TAKE
Yes	▶	EVACUATE the system. REPLACE the receiver/drier. RECHARGE the system.
No	▶	GO to A6.

A6 CHECK FOR POOR CIRCULATION

- Read the HI and the LO gauges on the manifold set.
- Check for frost buildup on piping near the receiver and the fixed orifice tube.
- Check for low pressure on the HI gauge and very low pressure on LO gauge.

Gauge	Pressure
HI	85-95 psi (586-655 kPa) (5.97-6.67 kg/cm^2)
LO	30 in-Hg vacuum (76 cm-Hg vacuum)

- Is a frost buildup present and are both pressures low?

RESULT	▶	ACTION TO TAKE
Yes	▶	EVACUATE the system. REPLACE the receiver/drier. CLEAN or REPLACE the fixed orifice tube as required; RECHARGE the system.
No	▶	GO to A7.

A7 CHECK FOR FAULTY COMPRESSOR

- Read the HI and LO gauges on the manifold set.
- Check for HI pressure gauge reading too low and LO pressure gauge reading too high.

Gauge	Pressure
HI	99-143 psi (686-981 kPa) (7-10 Kg/cm^2)
LO	57-85 psi (392-589 kPa) (4-6 kg/cm^2)

- Is the HI gauge too low and LO gauge to high?

NOTE: To prevent the replacement of good components, be aware that the following components may be at fault:

— Compressor clutch circuit
— Ventilation system (blockage)
— Air ducting
— Manual controls/cables/air duct doors

RESULT	▶	ACTION TO TAKE
Yes	▶	SERVICE the compressor as required.
No	▶	OPERATE the system for 15-20 minutes longer. CYCLE the temperature control from cold to hot, back to cold and RE-CHECK the pressures.

A/C COMPRESSOR CLUTCH DIAGNOSIS AND TESTING— PROBE

TEST STEP		RESULT	▶	ACTION TO TAKE
CC1	CHECK POWER TO COMPRESSOR CLUTCH			
	• Turn the key to ON, run the engine at idle. • Turn the A/C ON. • Turn the blower ON. • Set the temperature on COLD. • Does the compressor engage? • Measure the voltage at the compressor clutch connector "GN/BK" wire. • Is the voltage greater than 10 volts while the compressor clutch is engaged?	Yes	▶	INSPECT ground of the clutch, and condition of the drive belt and the clutch material.
		No 2.2L	▶	GO to CC2.
		No 3.0L	▶	GO to CC5.

A/C COMPRESSOR CLUTCH DIAGNOSIS AND TESTING— PROBE, CONT'D

TEST STEP		RESULT	▶	ACTION TO TAKE
CC2	CHECK "GN/BK" FOR OPENS			
	• Turn the key to OFF. • Disconnect the condenser fan relay. • Disconnect the condenser fan motor. • Measure the resistance between the compressor clutch "GN/BK" terminal and the condenser fan relay "GN/BK" terminal. • Is the resistance less than 5 ohms?	Yes	▶	GO to CC3.
		No	▶	SERVICE the "GN/BK" wire for opens.
CC3	CHECK "GN/BK" FOR SHORTS			
	• Turn the key to OFF. • Disconnect the compressor clutch. • Disconnect the condenser fan relay. • Disconnect the condenser fan motor. • Measure the resistance between the condenser fan relay "GN/BK" terminal and ground. • Measure the resistance between the condenser fan relay "GN/BK" terminal and "BK/W" terminal. • Are both resistances greater than 10,000 ohms?	Yes	▶	RECONNECT the compressor clutch and the condenser fan motor. GO to CC4.
		No	▶	SERVICE the "GN/BK" wire for shorts to ground or to key power.
CC4	CHECK CONDENSER FAN RELAY GROUND			
	• Turn the key to OFF. • Disconnect the condenser fan relay. • Measure the resistance between the condenser fan relay "BK" terminal and ground. • Is the resistance less than 5 ohms?	Yes	▶	GO to CC9.
		No	▶	SERVICE the "BK" wire for open.
CC5	CHECK COMPRESSOR CONNECTION (3.0L LX ONLY)			
	• Turn the key to OFF. • Disconnect the integral relay controller. • Disconnect the compressor clutch. • Measure the resistance of the following wires. (see table below) • Are the resistances OK?	Yes	▶	LEAVE the compressor clutch and integral relay controller disconnected. GO to CC6.
		No	▶	SERVICE the wire in question.
CC6	CHECK FOR SHORTS			
	• Turn the key to OFF. • Measure the resistance from the compressor clutch connector "GN/BK" and "GN/BL" wires to ground. • Are both resistances greater than 10,000 ohms?	Yes	▶	RECONNECT the compressor clutch. GO to CC7.
		No	▶	SERVICE the wire in question.

CC5 resistance table:

From	To	Resistance
Compressor Clutch GN/BK	Integral Relay Controller GN/BK	0-5 ohms
Compressor Clutch GN/BL	Integral Relay Controller GN/BL	0-5 ohms

A/C COMPRESSOR CLUTCH DIAGNOSIS AND TESTING— PROBE, CONT'D

TEST STEP	RESULT ▶	ACTION TO TAKE
CC7 CHECK POWER TO INTEGRAL RELAY CONTROLLER		
• Turn the key to ON. • Turn the A/C ON, turn the blower ON. • Measure the voltage at the integral relay controller connector "PK/BK" terminal. • Is voltage greater than 10 volts?	Yes ▶ No ▶	REFER to the Powertrain Control/Emissions Diagnosis for integral relay controller diagnosis. RECONNECT the integral relay controller. GO to CC8.
CC8 CHECK POWER TO CLUTCH CYCLING PRESSURE SWITCH (CCPS)		
• Turn the key to ON. • Turn the A/C ON, turn the Blower ON. • Disconnect the Clutch Cycling Pressure Switch (CCPS). • Measure the voltage at the CCPS connector "BL/BK" terminal. • Is the voltage greater than 10 volts?	Yes ▶ No ▶	GO to CC16. RECONNECT the CCPS. GO to CC9.
CC9 CHECK A/C RELAY (3.0L) OR CONDENSER FAN RELAY (2.2L) POWER		
• Disconnect the A/C relay (3.0L). • Disconnect the condenser fan relay (2.2L). • Turn the key to ON. • Turn the A/C to ON. • Turn the blower ON. • Measure the voltage at the relay "BK/W" and "GN" terminals. • Is the voltage greater than 10 volts?	Yes, 2.2L ▶ Yes, 3.0L ▶ No ▶	RECONNECT the condenser fan relay. GO to CC10. RECONNECT the A/C relay. GO to CC11. SERVICE the wire in question.
CC10 CHECK CONDENSER FAN RELAY (2.2L ONLY)		
• Turn the key to ON. • Turn the blower ON. • Measure the voltage at the condenser fan relay "GN/BK" terminal. • Ground the condenser fan relay "BL/BK" terminal. • Is the voltage greater than 10 volts with the "BL/BK" terminal grounded and less than 1 volt with the terminal open?	Yes ▶ No ▶	GO to CC12. REPLACE the condenser fan relay.
CC11 CHECK VOLTAGE AT CLUTCH CYCLING PRESSURE SWITCH (3.0L ONLY)		
• Turn the key to ON. • Switch the A/C ON and OFF. • Measure the voltage at the clutch cycling pressure switch "BL/BK" terminal. • Does the voltage jump between 0 volts and 10-12 volts?	Yes ▶ No Equipped with manual air conditioning ▶ No Equipped with electronic air conditioning ▶	SERVICE "BL/BK" terminal between the A/C relay and the clutch cycling pressure switch. GO to CC12. GO to ATC module diagnosis.

A/C COMPRESSOR CLUTCH DIAGNOSIS AND TESTING— PROBE, CONT'D

TEST STEP	RESULT ▶	ACTION TO TAKE
CC12 CHECK A/C SWITCH		
• Turn the key to OFF. • Disconnect the blower control switch connector. • Using an analog VOM, connect the negative (-) lead to the "BL/GN" wire and the positive (+) lead to the "BL/O" wire at the blower control switch. • Switch the A/C button ON and OFF. • Does the resistance jump from greater than 10,000 ohms to 0-5 ohms?	Yes ▶ No ▶	GO to CC13. REPLACE the blower control switch.
CC13 CHECK SWITCH GROUND		
• Turn the key to OFF. • Disconnect the blower control switch. • Measure the resistance between blower control switch "BK" terminal and ground. • Is resistance less than 5 ohms?	Yes, 3.0L ▶ Yes, 2.2L ▶ No ▶	SERVICE the "BL/GN" wire from the A/C relay to blower control switch. GO to CC14. SERVICE the "BK" wire to ground.
CC14 CHECK CCPS CONNECTION		
• Turn the key to OFF. • Turn the A/C OFF. • Disconnect the blower control switch. • Disconnect the clutch cycling pressure switch. • Measure the resistance between the blower control switch "BL/GN" terminal and the clutch cycling pressure switch "BL/GN" terminal. • Is resistance less than 5 ohms?	Yes ▶ No ▶	GO to CC15. SERVICE the "BL/GN" wire for opens.
CC15 CHECK FOR SHORTS		
• Turn the key to OFF. • Turn the A/C OFF. • Leave the blower control switch and clutch cycling pressure switch disconnected. • Measure the resistance from the blower control switch connector "BL/GN" wire to ground. • Is the resistance greater than 10,000 ohms?	Yes ▶ No ▶	GO to CC16. SERVICE the "BL/GN" wire for shorts.
CC16 CHECK CCPS OPERATION		
• Turn the key to ON, run the engine at idle. • Turn the A/C ON, turn the blower ON. • Disconnect the Clutch Cycling Pressure Switch (CCPS). • Jump the terminals of the CCPS connector together. • Does the compressor operate with the terminals jumped and stop with the terminals open?	Yes ▶ No (2.2L) ▶ No (3.0L) ▶	REPLACE the clutch cycling pressure switch. REFER to the Powertrain Control/Emissions Diagnosis SERVICE the "PK/BK" wire from the CCPS to the integral relay controller.

COOLING FAN DIAGNOSIS AND TESTING—PROBE

TEST STEP	RESULT	▶	ACTION TO TAKE
CFM1 CHECK FUSES			
• Check the 20 amp A/C fuse and the 15 amp COOLING FAN fuse. • Are the fuses OK?	Yes No	▶ ▶	GO to CFM4. GO to CFM2.
CFM2 CHECK SYSTEM			
• Replace the fuse(s). • Turn the key to ON. • Does the fuse(s) blow again?	Yes No	▶ ▶	GO to CFM3. GO to CFM4.
CFM3 CHECK FOR SHORTS TO GROUND			
• Turn the key to OFF. • Disconnect the condenser fan relay. • Measure the resistance of the following wires between the fuse panel and ground. (see table below) • Is the resistances less than 5 ohms?	Yes No	▶ ▶	SERVICE the wire in question for shorts. GO to CFM4.
CFM4 CHECK CONDENSER FAN MOTOR OPERATION			
• Turn the key to OFF. • Disconnect the condenser fan motor. • Apply battery power to the condenser fan motor "GN/BK" terminal (motor side). • Ground the condenser fan motor "BK" terminal (motor side). • Does the motor operate?	Yes No	▶ ▶	GO to CFM5. REPAIR the motor side of the harness for opens or shorts, if all OK, REPLACE the motor.

Wire Color	Fuse
"GN"	A/C fuse (main fuse panel)
"BK/W"	COOLING FAN fuse (interior fuse panel)

GN/BK
BK
BATTERY

COOLING FAN DIAGNOSIS AND TESTING—PROBE, CONT'D

TEST STEP	RESULT	▶	ACTION TO TAKE
CFM5 CHECK VOLTAGE AT CONDENSER FAN RELAY			
• Turn the key to ON. • Set the VOM on the 20 volt scale. • Measure the voltage at the relay "GN" and "BK/W" terminals. • Are both readings greater than 10 volts?	Yes No	▶ ▶	GO to CFM6. REPAIR the wire in question ("GN" to the main fuse panel or "BK/W" to the interior fuse panel).
CFM6 CHECK RELAY OPERATION			
• Turn the key to ON. • Measure the voltage at the condenser fan relay "GN/BK" terminal. • Ground the condenser fan relay "BL/BK" terminal. • Does the voltage jump up to 10-12 volts when the "BL/BK" terminal is grounded?	Yes No	▶ ▶	GO to CFM7. REPLACE the relay.
CFM7 CHECK CONDENSER FAN RELAY GROUND			
• Turn the key to OFF. • Disconnect the battery. • Measure the resistance at the condenser fan relay. (see table below) • Are the resistances OK?	Yes No	▶ ▶	GO to CFM8. SERVICE the wire in question.
CFM8 CHECK FOR OPENS			
• Turn the key to OFF. • Disconnect the condenser fan motor. • Disconnect the condenser fan relay. • Measure the resistance between the condenser fan motor "GN/BK" wire and relay "GN/BK" wire. • Is the resistance less than 5 ohms?	Yes No	▶ ▶	GO to CFM9. SERVICE the "GN/BK" wire.

GN
BK/W

Voltmeter (+)	Voltmeter (-)	Resistance
BK	Ground	0-5 ohms
BK	BK/W	Over 10,000 ohms
BK	GN	Over 10,000 ohms

COOLING FAN DIAGNOSIS AND TESTING—PROBE, CONT'D

	TEST STEP	RESULT	▶	ACTION TO TAKE
CFM9	CHECK FOR SHORTS			
	• Turn the key to OFF. • Disconnect the condenser fan motor. • Disconnect the condenser fan relay. • Disconnect the compressor clutch. • Disconnect the battery. • Measure the resistance from the "GN/BK" terminal to the "GN" terminal and ground. • Are both resistances greater than 10,000 ohms?	Yes	▶	Problem is with the ECA, the "BL/R" wire at condenser fan relay (4EAT), "BK/GN" wire at condenser fan relay (MTX), or ECA.
		No	▶	SERVICE the wire.

	TEST STEP	RESULT	▶	ACTION TO TAKE
CF1	CHECK FUSES			
	• Locate the main fuse panel and the interior fuse panel. • Check the 20 amp A/C fuse, the 15 amp COOLING FAN fuse and the 60 amp COOLING FAN fuse. • Are the fuses OK?	Yes	▶	GO to CF4.
		No	▶	GO to CF2.
CF2	CHECK A/C SYSTEM			
	• Replace the fuse(s). • Turn the key to ON. • Does the fuse(s) blow again?	Yes	▶	GO to CF3.
		No	▶	GO to CF4.
CF3	CHECK FOR SHORTS TO GROUND			
	• Replace the fuse(s). • Disconnect the integral relay controller and the A/C relay. • Measure the resistance of the following wires between the fuse panel and ground. (see table below) • Are the resistances less than 5 ohms?	Yes	▶	SERVICE the wire in question.
		No	▶	GO to CF4.
CF4	CHECK FOR POWER TO A/C RELAY			
	• Turn the key to ON. • Set the VOM on 20 volt scale. • Measure the voltage at the A/C relay "GN" and "BK/W" terminals. • Are both readings greater than 10 volts?	Yes	▶	GO to CF5.
		No	▶	SERVICE the wire in question.

Wire Color	Fuse
"GN"	A/C fuse (main fuse panel)
"BK/W"	COOLING FAN fuse (interior fuse panel)
"BK/R"	COOLING FAN fuse (main fuse panel)

COOLING FAN DIAGNOSIS AND TESTING—PROBE, CONT'D

	TEST STEP	RESULT	▶	ACTION TO TAKE
CF5	CHECK FOR POWER TO THE INTEGRAL RELAY CONTROLLER			
	• Set the VOM on 20 volt scale. • Measure the voltage of the integral relay controller "BK/R" terminal. • Is the voltage greater than 10 volts?	Yes	▶	GO to CF6.
		No	▶	SERVICE the "BK/R" wire.
CF6	CHECK OPERATION OF COOLING FAN MOTOR			
	• Disconnect the cooling fan motor. • Apply 12 volts to the "BL/Y" wire (motor side). • Ground the "BK" wire (motor side). • Does the cooling fan motor operate correctly? • Apply 12 volts to the "BL/BK" wire (motor side). • Ground the "BK" wire (motor side). • Does the cooling fan motor operate correctly?	Yes	▶	GO to CF7.
		No	▶	REPAIR the motor side of the harness for opens or shorts, if all OK, REPLACE the cooling fan motor.
CF7	CHECK GROUND OF THE COOLING FAN MOTOR			
	• Leave the cooling fan motor disconnected. • Measure the resistance between the "BK" wire and ground of the cooling fan motor. • Is the resistance less than 5 ohms?	Yes	▶	RETURN to the Symptom Chart.
		No	▶	SERVICE the "BK" wire to ground.

BLOWER MOTOR SYSTEM DIAGNOSIS AND SYMPTOMS—1993 PROBE

CONDITION	POSSIBLE SOURCE	ACTION
• Blower Motor Does Not Operate	• Fuse(s). • Circuit. • Blower motor relay # 1. • Blower motor. • Mode selector switch. • Blower motor resistor.	• GO to BM1.
• Blower Motor Always Runs or Always Runs With Key ON and Mode Selector Switch OFF	• Circuit. • Blower motor relay # 1.	• GO to BM10.
• Blower Motor Does Not Operate Higher than LO Speed	• Circuit. • Blower motor resistor. • Blower switch.	• GO to BM13.
• Blower Motor Stays at LO Speed in Second Blower Switch Position	• Circuit.	• GO to BM15.
• Blower Motor Stays at Second Speed in Third Blower Switch Position	• Fuse. • Circuit. • Blower motor relay # 2.	• GO to BM16.
• Blower Motor Stays at Third Speed in HI Blower Switch Position	• Circuit.	• GO to BM15.
• Blower Motor Always at Third Speed Until in HI Blower Switch Position	• Circuit. • Blower motor relay # 2.	• GO to BM20.

BLOWER MOTOR SYSTEM DIAGNOSIS AND PINPOINT TESTING—1993 PROBE

	TEST STEP	RESULT	▶ ACTION TO TAKE
BM1	CHECK FUSES		
	• Check the 15A ENGINE fuse in the interior fuse panel and the 40A HEATER fuse in the main fuse panel. • **Are the fuses OK?**	Yes No	▶ GO to BM4. ▶ GO to BM2.
BM2	CHECK SYSTEM		
	• Key OFF. • Replace the blown fuse(s). • Key ON. • **Do any of the fuses fail again?**	Yes No	▶ GO to BM3. ▶ GO to BM4.
BM3	CHECK FOR SHORTS TO GROUND		
	• Key OFF. • Disconnect the 10-pin interior fuse panel connector and remove the 40A HEATER fuse from the main fuse panel. • Disconnect the blower motor relay # 1 connector near the right front of the radiator. • Measure the resistance of the "BK / W" wire between the 10-pin interior fuse panel connector and ground. • Measure the resistance of the "BL" wire between the left terminal of the 40A HEATER fuse holder and ground. • **Are any resistances less than 5 ohms?**	Yes No	▶ SERVICE wire(s) in question. ▶ RECONNECT the 10-pin interior fuse panel connector. REPLACE the 40A HEATER fuse and / or the 15A ENGINE fuse. RECONNECT the blower motor relay # 1. GO to BM4.

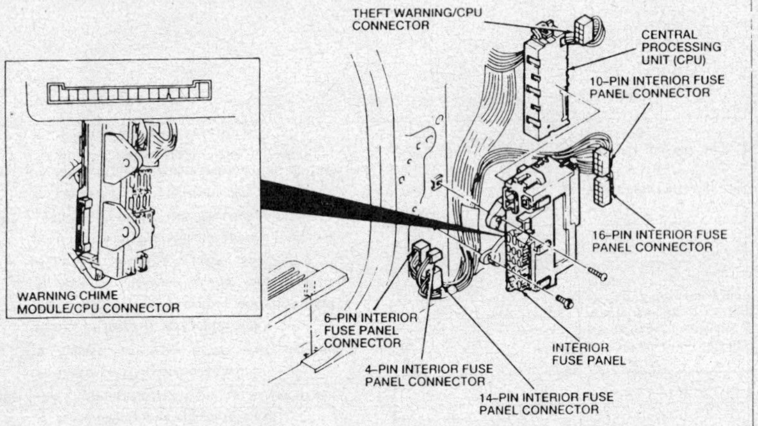

THEFT WARNING/CPU CONNECTOR
CENTRAL PROCESSING UNIT (CPU)
10–PIN INTERIOR FUSE PANEL CONNECTOR
16–PIN INTERIOR FUSE PANEL CONNECTOR
WARNING CHIME MODULE/CPU CONNECTOR
6–PIN INTERIOR FUSE PANEL CONNECTOR
INTERIOR FUSE PANEL
4–PIN INTERIOR FUSE PANEL CONNECTOR
14–PIN INTERIOR FUSE PANEL CONNECTOR

	TEST STEP	RESULT	▶ ACTION TO TAKE
BM4	CHECK VOLTAGE AT BLOWER MOTOR		
	• Key OFF. • Disconnect the blower motor connector on the blower assembly. • Key ON. • Measure the voltage on the "R" wire at the blower motor connector. • **Is the voltage greater than 10 volts?**	Yes No	▶ GO to BM8. ▶ GO to BM5.
BM5	CHECK POWER TO BLOWER MOTOR RELAY # 1		
	• Key OFF. • Disconnect the blower motor relay # 1 connector near the right front of the radiator. • Key ON. • Measure the voltage on the "BK / W" wire and the "BL" wire at the blower motor relay # 1 connector. • **Are the voltages greater than 10 volts?**	Yes No	▶ GO to BM6. ▶ SERVICE the "BK / W" and / or "BL" wire(s).

BLOWER MOTOR SYSTEM DIAGNOSIS AND PINPOINT TESTING—1993 PROBE, CONT'D

TEST STEP	RESULT	▶ ACTION TO TAKE
BM6 CHECK BLOWER MOTOR RELAY # 1		
• Key OFF. • Disconnect the blower motor relay # 1 connector. • Measure the resistance between the "BL" and "W" wire terminals on the relay. • Apply 12 volts to the "BK/W" wire terminal and ground to the "BK/R" wire terminal on the relay. • Measure the resistance between the "BL" wire terminal and the "W" wire terminal on the relay. • **Is the resistance less than 5 ohms when 12 volts and ground are applied, and greater than 10,000 ohms when 12 volts and ground are not applied?**	Yes No	▶ GO to BM7. ▶ REPLACE the blower motor relay # 1.
BM7 CHECK BLOWER MOTOR RELAY # 1 GROUND CIRCUIT		
• Key OFF. • Disconnect the blower motor relay # 1 connector. • Measure the resistance of the "BK/R" wire between the blower motor relay # 1 connector and ground. • **Is the resistance less than 5 ohms?**	Yes No	▶ SERVICE the "W" "R" wire between the blower motor relay # 1 and the blower motor. ▶ SERVICE the "BK/R" wire between the blower motor relay # 1 and the starter motor.
BM8 CHECK BLOWER MOTOR		
• Key OFF. • Disconnect the blower motor connector. • Apply 12 volts to the "R" wire terminal and ground to the "BL/O" wire terminal at the blower motor. • **Does the motor operate at HI speed?**	Yes No	▶ GO to BM9. ▶ REPLACE the blower motor.
BM9 CHECK MODE SELECTOR SWITCH GROUND		
• Key OFF. • Disconnect the mode selector switch connector. • Measure the resistance of the "BK" wire (circuit 52) between the mode selector switch connector and ground. • **Is the resistance less than 5 ohms?**	Yes No	▶ GO to BM10. ▶ SERVICE the "BK" wire.
BM10 CHECK MODE SELECTOR SWITCH		
• Key OFF. • Disconnect the mode selector switch connector. • Measure the resistance between the "BL/Y" terminal and the "BK" wire terminal (circuit 52) wire at the mode selector switch with the switch in the following positions: (see table below) • **Are the resistances as specified?**	Yes No	▶ GO to BM11. ▶ REPLACE the mode selector switch.

Mode Selector Switch Position	Resistance (ohms)
OFF	greater than 10,000 ohms
VENT	less than 5 ohms
FLOOR	less than 5 ohms
MIX	less than 5 ohms
DEF	less than 5 ohms
NORM A C (If equipped)	less than 5 ohms
MAX A C (If equipped)	less than 5 ohms

BLOWER MOTOR SYSTEM DIAGNOSIS AND PINPOINT TESTING—1993 PROBE, CONT'D

TEST STEP	RESULT	▶ ACTION TO TAKE
BM11 CHECK WIRE BETWEEN MODE SELECTOR SWITCH AND BLOWER MOTOR RESISTOR		
• Key OFF. • Disconnect the mode selector switch connector. • Disconnect the blower motor resistor connector on the blower assembly, the blower motor relay #2 connector and the blower switch connector. • Measure the resistance between the "BL/Y" wire at the mode selector switch connector and the "GN/R" wire at the blower motor resistor connector. • Measure the resistance of the "BL/Y" wire between the mode selector switch connector and ground. • **Is the resistance less than 5 ohms between the mode selector switch connector and the blower motor resistor connector, and greater than 10,000 ohms between the mode selector switch connector and ground?**	Yes No	▶ GO to BM12. ▶ SERVICE the "BL/Y" - "GN/R" wire.
BM12 CHECK WIRE BETWEEN BLOWER MOTOR AND BLOWER MOTOR RESISTOR		
• Key OFF. • Disconnect the blower motor connector. • Disconnect the blower motor resistor connector on the blower assembly. • Disconnect the blower switch connector. • Measure the resistance between the "BL/O" wire at the blower motor connector and "BL/W" wire at blower motor resistor connector. • Measure the resistance of the "BL/O" wire between the blower motor connector and ground. • **Is the resistance less than 5 ohms between the blower motor connector and the blower motor resistor connector, and greater than 10,000 ohms between the blower motor connector and ground?**	Yes No	▶ GO to BM13. ▶ SERVICE the "BL/O"-"BL/W" wire.
BM13 CHECK BLOWER MOTOR RESISTOR		
• Key OFF. • Disconnect the blower motor resistor connector on the blower assembly. • Measure the resistance between the terminals of the blower motor resistor as indicated: (see table below) • **Are the resistances approximately as indicated?**	Yes No	▶ GO to BM14. ▶ REPLACE the blower motor resistor.

Terminals	Resistance (ohms)
BL/W and GN/R	2.76 ohms
BL/W and BL	1.07 ohms
BL/W and R/BK	0.38 ohms

BLOWER MOTOR SYSTEM DIAGNOSIS AND PINPOINT TESTING—1993 PROBE, CONT'D

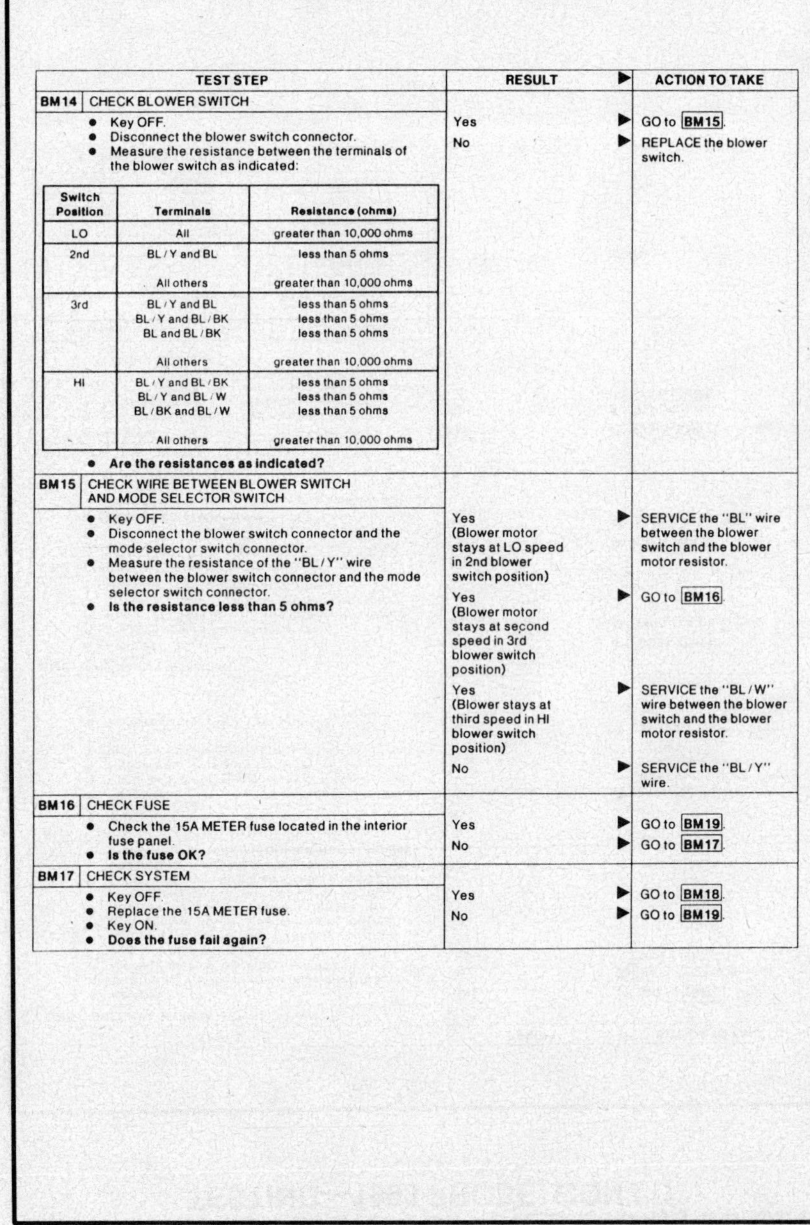

TEST STEP	RESULT ▶	ACTION TO TAKE
BM14 CHECK BLOWER SWITCH		
• Key OFF. • Disconnect the blower switch connector. • Measure the resistance between the terminals of the blower switch as indicated:	Yes ▶ No ▶	GO to BM15. REPLACE the blower switch.

Switch Position	Terminals	Resistance (ohms)
LO	All	greater than 10,000 ohms
2nd	BL / Y and BL	less than 5 ohms
	All others	greater than 10,000 ohms
3rd	BL / Y and BL	less than 5 ohms
	BL / Y and BL / BK	less than 5 ohms
	BL and BL / BK	less than 5 ohms
	All others	greater than 10,000 ohms
HI	BL / Y and BL / BK	less than 5 ohms
	BL / Y and BL / W	less than 5 ohms
	BL / BK and BL / W	less than 5 ohms
	All others	greater than 10,000 ohms

• **Are the resistances as indicated?**

TEST STEP	RESULT ▶	ACTION TO TAKE
BM15 CHECK WIRE BETWEEN BLOWER SWITCH AND MODE SELECTOR SWITCH		
• Key OFF. • Disconnect the blower switch connector and the mode selector switch connector. • Measure the resistance of the "BL / Y" wire between the blower switch connector and the mode selector switch connector. • **Is the resistance less than 5 ohms?**	Yes (Blower motor stays at LO speed in 2nd blower switch position) ▶ Yes (Blower motor stays at second speed in 3rd blower switch position) ▶ Yes (Blower stays at third speed in HI blower switch position) ▶ No ▶	SERVICE the "BL" wire between the blower switch and the blower motor resistor. GO to BM16. SERVICE the "BL / W" wire between the blower switch and the blower motor resistor. SERVICE the "BL / Y" wire.
BM16 CHECK FUSE		
• Check the 15A METER fuse located in the interior fuse panel. • **Is the fuse OK?**	Yes ▶ No ▶	GO to BM19. GO to BM17.
BM17 CHECK SYSTEM		
• Key OFF. • Replace the 15A METER fuse. • Key ON. • **Does the fuse fail again?**	Yes ▶ No ▶	GO to BM18. GO to BM19.

BLOWER MOTOR SYSTEM DIAGNOSIS AND PINPOINT TESTING—1993 PROBE, CONT'D

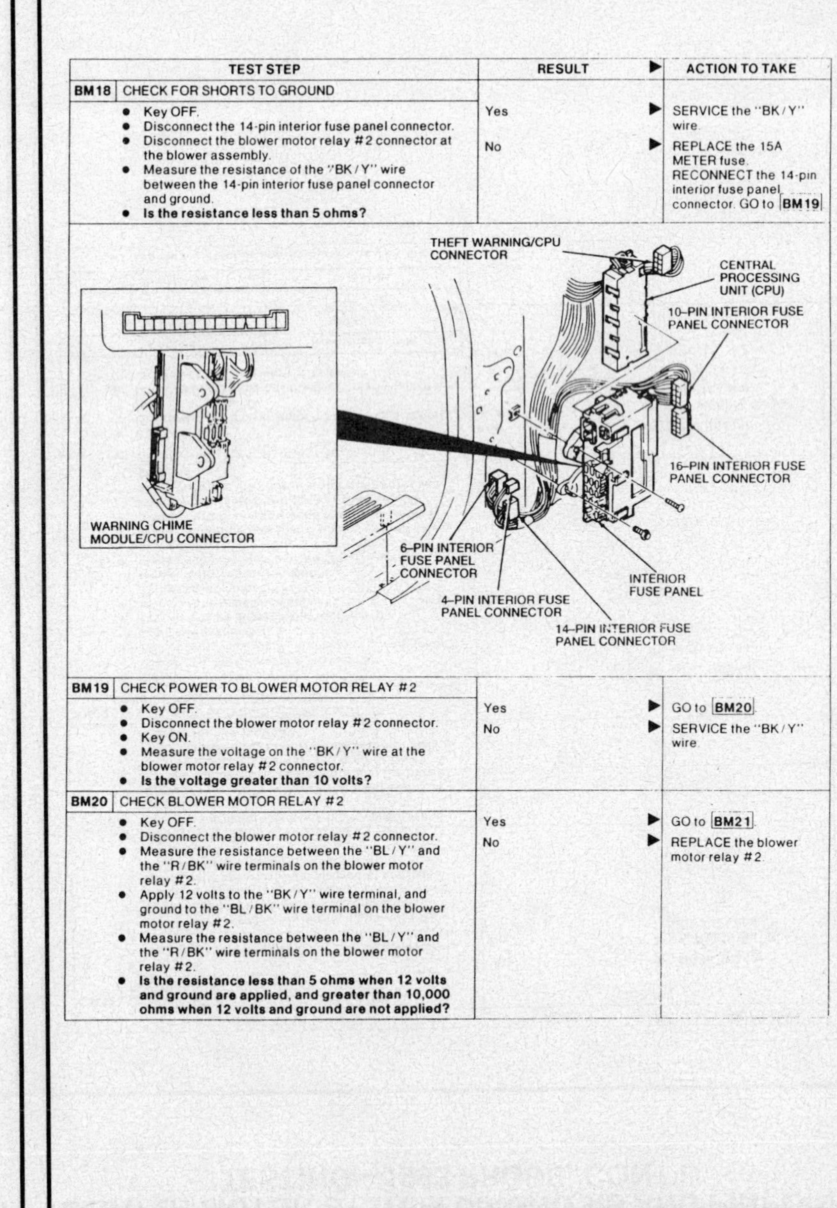

TEST STEP	RESULT ▶	ACTION TO TAKE
BM18 CHECK FOR SHORTS TO GROUND		
• Key OFF. • Disconnect the 14-pin interior fuse panel connector. • Disconnect the blower motor relay #2 connector at the blower assembly. • Measure the resistance of the "BK / Y" wire between the 14-pin interior fuse panel connector and ground. • **Is the resistance less than 5 ohms?**	Yes ▶ No ▶	SERVICE the "BK / Y" wire. REPLACE the 15A METER fuse. RECONNECT the 14-pin interior fuse panel connector. GO to BM19.
BM19 CHECK POWER TO BLOWER MOTOR RELAY #2		
• Key OFF. • Disconnect the blower motor relay #2 connector. • Key ON. • Measure the voltage on the "BK / Y" wire at the blower motor relay #2 connector. • **Is the voltage greater than 10 volts?**	Yes ▶ No ▶	GO to BM20. SERVICE the "BK / Y" wire.
BM20 CHECK BLOWER MOTOR RELAY #2		
• Key OFF. • Disconnect the blower motor relay #2 connector. • Measure the resistance between the "BL / Y" and the "R / BK" wire terminals on the blower motor relay #2. • Apply 12 volts to the "BK / Y" wire terminal, and ground to the "BL / BK" wire terminal on the blower motor relay #2. • Measure the resistance between the "BL / Y" and the "R / BK" wire terminals on the blower motor relay #2. • **Is the resistance less than 5 ohms when 12 volts and ground are applied, and greater than 10,000 ohms when 12 volts and ground are not applied?**	Yes ▶ No ▶	GO to BM21. REPLACE the blower motor relay #2.

BLOWER MOTOR SYSTEM DIAGNOSIS AND PINPOINT TESTING—1993 PROBE, CONT'D

TEST STEP		RESULT	▶	ACTION TO TAKE
CF4	CHECK VOLTAGE FROM MOTOR			
	• Disconnect the condenser fan relay. • Measure the voltage on the "GN/R" wire at the condenser fan relay connector. • Is the voltage greater than 10 volts?	Yes No	▶ ▶	GO to CF5. SERVICE the "GN/R" wire from condenser fan motor to the condenser fan relay.
CF5	CHECK RELAY OPERATION			
	• Remove the condenser fan relay. • Jump battery power to the relay A-terminal. • Measure the resistance between the B-terminal and the C-terminal on the relay. • Ground the D-terminal on the relay. • Is the resistance greater than 10,000 ohms with the D-terminal open and less than 5 ohms with the D-terminal grounded? (GN/R) B A (W) (BK) C D (BK)	Yes No	▶ ▶	GO to CF6. REPLACE the condenser fan relay.
CF6	CHECK CONDENSER FAN RELAY GROUND			
	• Measure the resistance of the "BK" wire at the condenser fan relay to ground. • Is the resistance less than 5 ohms?	Yes No	▶ ▶	GO to CF7. SERVICE the "BK" wire to ground.
CF7	CHECK VOLTAGE AT REFRIGERANT PRESSURE SWITCH			
	• Key ON, engine idling. • A/C ON. • Blower ON. • Measure the voltage on the "BK" wire at the refrigerant pressure switch connector. • Is the voltage greater than 10 volts?	Yes No	▶ ▶	GO to CF8. GO to CC4.
CF8	CHECK REFRIGERANT PRESSURE SWITCH OPERATION			
	• Install a Manifold Gauge Set. • Key ON, engine idling. • A/C ON. • Blower ON. • Verify that the pressure in the discharge line is below 1965 kPa (285 psi). • Measure the voltage on the "W" wire at the refrigerant pressure switch connector. • Is the voltage greater than 10 volts?	Yes No	▶ ▶	REPLACE the refrigerant pressure switch. GO to CF9.
CF9	CHECK REFRIGERANT PRESSURE SWITCH OPERATION			
	• Install a Manifold Gauge Set. • Key ON, engine idling. • A/C ON. • Blower ON. • Run the A/C system until the high pressure gauge reads above 2350 kPa (340 psi). • Measure the voltage on the "W" wire at the refrigerant pressure switch connector. • Is the voltage greater than 10 volts?	Yes No	▶ ▶	SERVICE the "W" wire between the refrigerant pressure switch and the cooling fan relay. REPLACE the refrigerant pressure switch.

AIR CONDITIONING DIAGNOSIS AND SYMPTOMS—1993 FESTIVA

CONDITION	POSSIBLE SOURCE	ACTION
• Magnetic Clutch Does Not Engage	• Fuse(s). • Circuit. • A/C switch. • Pressure switch. • Thermostatic switch. • WAC relay. • Magnetic clutch. • Insufficient refrigerant.	• GO to AC1. • GO to RF1.
• Magnetic Clutch Is Engaged Constantly (No Cycling)	• Circuit. • Thermostatic switch. • WAC relay.	• GO to AC9.
• No Cooling or Insufficient Cooling	• Insufficient refrigerant. • Expansion valve. • Moisture, air, excessive oil or refrigerant in system. • Blocked evaporator or condenser. • Clogged refrigerant circulation system. • Compressor.	• GO to RF1.
• Intermittent Cooling	• Insufficient refrigerant. • Excessive moisture in system. • Expansion valve. • Compressor. • Magnetic clutch slipping.	• GO to RF1.
• Blows Frost Out Of Ducts (After Several Minutes Of Operation)	• Excessive refrigerant. • Plugged evaporator drain line. • Thermostatic switch.	• GO to RF1. • GO to AC11.
• Cooling Fan Does Not Operate When A/C Is Activated	• Fuse. • Circuit. • A/C relay.	• GO to AC1.
• Condenser Fan Never Runs (ATX Only)	• Fuse. • Circuit. • Condenser fan motor. • Condenser fan relay. • Pressure switch.	• GO to AC21.
• Condenser Fan Operates Continuously	• Circuit. • Condenser fan relay. • Pressure switch.	• GO to AC28.
• A/C On Indicator Does Not Illuminate	• Circuit. • A/C switch. • A/C switch bulb.	• GO to AC4.
• A/C On Indicator Illuminates Constantly	• Circuit. • A/C switch.	• GO to AC9.

DIAGNOSIS AND TESTING—ASPIRE

Symptom Chart — Climate Control System

NOTE: Use Rotunda 73 Digital Multimeter 105-00051 or equivalent to perform electrical Pinpoint Tests.

CLIMATE CONTROL SYSTEM

CONDITION	POSSIBLE SOURCE	ACTION
• Heat Always On	• Climate control assembly. • Loose or broken heater air cable.	• GO to Pinpoint Test A1.
• Insufficient Heat	• Water thermostat. • Coolant level. • Heater water hoses. • Heater core. • Heater air cable. • Temperature control door.	• GO to Pinpoint Test B1.
• Insufficient A/C Cooling	• Insufficient refrigerant. • Refrigerant leak(s). • Heater air cable. • Temperature control door.	• GO to Pinpoint Test C1.
• No Operation In All Temperature Settings	• Temperature control door. • Loose or broken heater air cable. • Ducts broken or leaking.	• GO to Pinpoint Test D1.
• Blower Motor Does Not Operate	• Fuse. • Circuit breaker. • Circuit. • Blower motor relay. • Blower motor. • Heater blower motor switch.	• GO to Pinpoint Test E1.
• Blower Motor Runs Constantly	• Circuit. • Heater blower motor switch.	• GO to Pinpoint Test F1.
• Blower Motor Does Not Operate Properly	• Circuit. • Heater blower motor switch. • A/C blower motor resistor.	• GO to Pinpoint Test G1.
• No Operation in Low Blower Setting	• Circuit. • A/C blower motor resistor. • Heater blower motor switch.	• GO to Pinpoint Test H1.
• No Operation in Medium Blower Setting	• Circuit. • A/C blower motor resistor. • Heater blower motor switch.	• GO to Pinpoint Test J1.
• No Operation in High Blower Setting	• Circuit. • Heater blower motor switch.	• GO to Pinpoint Test K1.
• A/C Compressor Clutch Does Not Engage	• Insufficient refrigerant. • Fuse(s). • Circuit. • A/C compressor clutch control relay. • Thermal protection switch. • A/C compressor clutch. • A/C pressure cut-off switch.	• GO to Pinpoint Test L1.
• A/C Compressor Clutch Does Not Disengage	• Circuit. • A/C compressor clutch control relay. • A/C compressor clutch.	• GO to Pinpoint Test M1.
• A/C Compressor Clutch Cycles Rapidly	• Insufficient refrigerant. • A/C compressor clutch. • A/C compressor clutch control relay.	• GO to Pinpoint Test N1.
• A/C Compressor Clutch Slippage	• A/C compressor clutch. • A/C compressor.	• INSPECT the A/C drive belt tension. ADJUST or REPLACE A/C drive belt if necessary. Otherwise, REPLACE the A/C compressor.
• Noise While Operating Climate Control System	• Bearings. • Refrigerant components. • Insufficient refrigerant. • Excessive refrigerant.	• GO to Pinpoint Test P1.

DIAGNOSIS AND TESTING—ASPIRE, CONT'D

CLIMATE CONTROL SYSTEM (Continued)

CONDITION	POSSIBLE SOURCE	ACTION
• A/C Condenser Cooling Fan Never Runs	• Fuse(s). • Circuit. • Condenser fan relay. • A/C condenser cooling fan.	• GO to Pinpoint Test Q1.
• A/C Condenser Cooling Fan Operates Continuously	• Circuit. • Condenser fan relay. • A/C condenser cooling fan. • Engine coolant temperature sensor.	• GO to Pinpoint Test R1.
• A/C Indicator Not Operating Properly	• Ignition switch. • A/C on indicator miniature bulb.	• GO to Pinpoint Test S1.
• A/C On Indicator Illuminates Constantly	• A/C switch.	• REPLACE the A/C switch.
• Heater and A/C Air Inlet Duct Door Does Not Operate	• Heater air cable. • Temperature control door.	• INSPECT the heater air cable for kinks or breaks. REPAIR or REPLACE the heater air cable as necessary. Otherwise, SERVICE the temperature control door.
• One or More Modes Do Not Work (Air Outlet Does Not Change)	• Climate control assembly. • Loose or broken air flow control cable. • Air flow control doors. • Ducts blocked or leaking.	• INSPECT the air flow control cable for kinks or breaks. REPAIR or REPLACE the air flow control cable as necessary. Otherwise, SERVICE the air flow control door.
• Engine Cooling Fan Motor Does Not Operate When A/C is Activated	• Circuit.	• REFER to PC/ED
• No Air Circulation or Improper Air Circulation (Blower Motor Operates)	• Air flow control door(s). • Heater and ventilation intake duct blocked. • Ducts blocked or leaking.	• INSPECT, ADJUST or REPLACE air flow control door(s) as necessary. • CLEAR the blockage. • CLEAR the blockage or REPAIR leakage.
• Frost Being Blown out of Ducts	• Evaporator box drain tube. • Refrigerant system.	• INSPECT and CLEAN the evaporator case drain tube as necessary. PERFORM the Refrigerant System Tests.

Pinpoint Tests — Climate Control System

PINPOINT TEST A: HEAT ALWAYS ON

TEST STEP		RESULT	►	ACTION TO TAKE
A1	CHECK TEMPERATURE CONTROL CABLE			
	• Inspect the heater air cable for kinks or breaks. • **Is the heater air cable OK?**	Yes	►	SERVICE the temperature control door.
		No	►	SERVICE the heater air cable.

PINPOINT TEST B: INSUFFICIENT HEAT

TEST STEP		RESULT	►	ACTION TO TAKE
B1	CHECK COOLING SYSTEM			
	• Inspect the cooling system. • **Is the cooling system OK?**	Yes	►	GO to **B2**.
		No	►	SERVICE the cooling system as necessary.

DIAGNOSIS AND TESTING—ASPIRE, CONT'D

PINPOINT TEST B: INSUFFICIENT HEAT (Continued)

TEST STEP		RESULT	ACTION TO TAKE
B2	CHECK HEATER CORE		
	• Perform the Plugged Heater Core tests in this section. • **Is the heater core OK?**	Yes ▶ No ▶	GO to **B3**. SERVICE the heater core.
B3	CHECK TEMPERATURE CONTROL CABLE		
	• Inspect the heater air cable for kinks or breaks. • **Is the heater air cable OK?**	Yes ▶ No ▶	SERVICE the temperature control door. REPLACE the heater air cable.

PINPOINT TEST C: INSUFFICIENT A/C COOLING

TEST STEP		RESULT	ACTION TO TAKE
C1	CHECK REFRIGERANT		
	• Perform the Refrigerant System Tests in this section. • **Is the refrigerant system OK?**	Yes ▶ No ▶	GO to **C2**. REPAIR as necessary.
C2	CHECK TEMPERATURE CONTROL CABLE		
	• Inspect the heater air cable for kinks or breaks. • **Is the heater air cable OK?**	Yes ▶ No ▶	SERVICE the temperature control door. REPLACE the heater air cable.

PINPOINT TEST D: NO OPERATION IN ALL TEMPERATURE SETTINGS

TEST STEP		RESULT	ACTION TO TAKE
D1	CHECK TEMPERATURE CONTROL CABLE		
	• Inspect the heater air cable for kinks or breaks. • **Is the heater air cable OK?**	Yes ▶ No ▶	SERVICE the temperature control door. SERVICE the heater air cable.

PINPOINT TEST E: BLOWER MOTOR DOES NOT OPERATE

TEST STEP		RESULT	ACTION TO TAKE
E1	CHECK FUSE		
	• Key OFF. • Check the 15A R. WIPER fuse located in the interior fuse junction panel. • **Is the fuse OK?**	Yes ▶ No ▶	GO to **E4**. GO to **E2**.
E2	CHECK SYSTEM		
	• Key OFF. • Replace the blown fuse. • Key ON. • **Does the fuse fail again?**	Yes ▶ No ▶	GO to **E3**. GO to **E4**.
E3	CHECK FOR SHORT TO GROUND		
	• Key OFF. • Remove the 15A R. WIPER fuse. • Disconnect the blower motor relay connector. • Measure the resistance of the "BL/GN" wire between the top terminal of the 15A R. WIPER fuse holder and ground. • **Is the resistance less than 5 ohms?**	Yes ▶ No ▶	SERVICE the "BL/GN" wire. REPLACE the 15A R. WIPER fuse. RECONNECT the blower motor relay. GO to **E4**.
E4	CHECK CIRCUIT BREAKER		
	• Key OFF. • Check the 30A BLOWER circuit breaker located in the interior fuse junction panel. • **Is the circuit breaker OK?**	Yes ▶ No ▶	GO to **E7**. GO to **E5**.

DIAGNOSIS AND TESTING—ASPIRE, CONT'D

PINPOINT TEST E: BLOWER MOTOR DOES NOT OPERATE (Continued)

	TEST STEP	RESULT	▶	ACTION TO TAKE
E5	CHECK SYSTEM			
	• Reset circuit breaker. • **Does the circuit breaker fail again?**	Yes No	▶ ▶	GO to **E6**. GO to **E7**.
E6	CHECK FOR SHORT TO GROUND			
	• Remove the 30A BLOWER circuit breaker. • Disconnect the blower motor relay connector. • Measure the resistance of the "W / GN" wire between the top terminal of the 30A BLOWER circuit breaker holder and ground. • **Is the resistance greater than 10,000 ohms?**	Yes No	▶ ▶	REPLACE the 30A BLOWER circuit breaker. SERVICE the "W / GN" wire.
E7	CHECK BLOWER MOTOR			
	• Perform the Blower Motor component test in this section. • **Is the blower motor OK?**	Yes No	▶ ▶	GO to **E8**. REPLACE the blower motor.
E8	CHECK HEATER BLOWER MOTOR SWITCH			
	• Perform the Heater Blower Motor Switch component test in this section. • **Is the heater blower motor switch OK?**	Yes No	▶ ▶	GO to **E9**. REPLACE the heater blower motor switch.
E9	CHECK HEATER BLOWER MOTOR SWITCH GROUND			
	• Disconnect the heater blower motor switch connector. • Measure the resistance of the "BK" wire between the heater blower motor switch connector and ground. • **Is the resistance less than 5 ohms?**	Yes No	▶ ▶	GO to **E10**. SERVICE the "BK" wire.
E10	CHECK BLOWER MOTOR RELAY			
	• Key OFF. • Locate and disconnect the blower motor relay connector. • Apply 12 volts to the "BL / GN" wire terminal at the blower motor relay. • Ground the "BK" wire terminal at the blower motor relay. • Measure the resistance between the "W / GN" wire and "R" wire terminals on the blower motor relay. • **Is the resistance less than 5 ohms?**	Yes No	▶ ▶	GO to **E11**. REPLACE the blower motor relay.
E11	CHECK POWER TO BLOWER MOTOR RELAY			
	• Key OFF. • Disconnect the blower motor relay connector. • Key ON. • Measure the voltage on the "BL / GN" and "W / GN" wires at the blower motor relay connector. • **Are the voltages greater than 10 volts?**	Yes No	▶ ▶	GO to **E12**. SERVICE the wire(s) in question.
E12	CHECK BLOWER MOTOR RELAY GROUND			
	• Key OFF. • Disconnect the blower motor relay connector. • Measure the resistance of the "BK" wire between the blower motor relay connector and ground. • **Is the resistance less than 5 ohms?**	Yes No	▶ ▶	RECONNECT the blower motor relay. GO to **E13**. SERVICE the "BK" wire.
E13	CHECK WIRE BETWEEN BLOWER MOTOR RELAY AND BLOWER MOTOR			
	• Key OFF. • Disconnect the blower motor connector. • Key ON. • Measure the voltage on the "R" wire at the blower motor connector. • **Is the voltage greater than 10 volts?**	Yes No	▶ ▶	SERVICE the "BL / W" wire between the blower motor and the heater blower motor switch. SERVICE the "R" wire.

DIAGNOSIS AND TESTING—ASPIRE, CONT'D

PINPOINT TEST F: BLOWER MOTOR RUNS CONSTANTLY

TEST STEP		RESULT	▶ ACTION TO TAKE
F1	CHECK HEATER BLOWER MOTOR SWITCH		
	• Key OFF. • Locate and disconnect the heater blower motor switch connector. • Heater blower motor switch OFF. • Measure the resistance between the "BL/W" and the "BK" wire terminals on the heater blower motor switch. • **Is the resistance greater than 10,000 ohms?**	Yes ▶ No ▶	SERVICE the "BL/W" wire for shorts to ground. REPLACE the heater blower motor switch.

PINPOINT TEST G: BLOWER MOTOR DOES NOT OPERATE PROPERLY

TEST STEP		RESULT	▶ ACTION TO TAKE
G1	CHECK HEATER BLOWER MOTOR SWITCH		
	• Perform the Heater Blower Motor Switch component test in this section. • **Is the heater blower motor switch OK?**	Yes ▶ No ▶	GO to **G2**. REPLACE the heater blower motor switch.
G2	CHECK A/C BLOWER MOTOR RESISTOR		
	• Perform the A/C Blower Motor Resistor component test in this section. • **Is the A/C blower motor resistor OK?**	Yes ▶ No ▶	SERVICE the "BL/W" wire between the blower motor, the heater blower motor switch, and the A/C blower motor resistor. REPLACE the A/C blower motor resistor.

PINPOINT TEST H: NO OPERATION IN LOW BLOWER SETTING

TEST STEP		RESULT	▶ ACTION TO TAKE
H1	CHECK HEATER BLOWER MOTOR SWITCH		
	• Perform the Heater Blower Motor Switch component test in this section. • **Is the heater blower motor switch OK?**	Yes ▶ No ▶	GO to **H2**. REPLACE the heater blower motor switch.
H2	CHECK A/C BLOWER MOTOR RESISTOR		
	• Perform the A/C Blower Motor Resistor component test in this section. • **Is the A/C blower motor resistor OK?**	Yes ▶ No ▶	SERVICE the "BL/Y" wire between the A/C blower motor resistor and the heater blower motor switch. REPLACE the A/C blower motor resistor.

PINPOINT TEST J: NO OPERATION IN MEDIUM BLOWER SETTING

TEST STEP		RESULT	▶ ACTION TO TAKE
J1	CHECK HEATER BLOWER MOTOR SWITCH		
	• Perform the Heater Blower Motor Switch component test in this section. • **Is the heater blower motor switch OK?**	Yes ▶ No ▶	GO to **J2**. REPLACE the heater blower motor switch.
J2	CHECK A/C BLOWER MOTOR RESISTOR		
	• Perform the A/C Blower Motor Resistor component test in this section. • **Is the A/C blower motor resistor OK?**	Yes ▶ No ▶	SERVICE the "BL" wire between the A/C blower motor resistor and the heater blower motor switch. REPLACE the A/C blower motor resistor.

DIAGNOSIS AND TESTING—ASPIRE, CONT'D

PINPOINT TEST K: NO OPERATION IN HIGH BLOWER SETTING

TEST STEP		RESULT ▶	ACTION TO TAKE
K1	CHECK HEATER BLOWER MOTOR SWITCH		
	• Perform the Heater Blower Motor Switch component test in this section. • **Is the heater blower motor switch OK?**	Yes ▶ No ▶	SERVICE the "BL/W" wire between the blower motor and the heater blower motor switch. REPLACE the heater blower motor switch.

PINPOINT TEST L: A/C COMPRESSOR CLUTCH DOES NOT ENGAGE

TEST STEP		RESULT ▶	ACTION TO TAKE
L1	CHECK REFRIGERANT SYSTEM		
	• Perform the Refrigerant System Tests in this section. • **Is the refrigerant pressure OK?**	Yes ▶ No ▶	GO to **L2**. SERVICE the refrigerant system as necessary.
L2	CHECK FUSES		
	• Key OFF. • Check the 20A WIPER fuse located in the interior fuse junction panel and the 30A COOLING FAN fuse located in the main fuse junction panel. • **Are the fuses OK?**	Yes ▶ No ▶	GO to **L5**. GO to **L3**.
L3	CHECK SYSTEM		
	• Key OFF. • Replace the blown fuse(s). • Key ON. • **Do(es) the fuse(s) fail again?**	Yes ▶ No ▶	GO to **L4**. GO to **L5**.
L4	CHECK FOR SHORT(S) TO GROUND		
	• Key OFF. • Remove the fuse that blew during L3. • Disconnect the A/C compressor clutch control relay connector. • Measure the resistance of the "BL" wire between the top terminal of the 20A WIPER fuse holder and ground. • Measure the resistance of the "W/BK" wire between the left terminal of the 30A COOLING FAN fuse holder and ground. • **Are the resistances less than 5 ohms?**	Yes ▶ No ▶	SERVICE the wire(s) in question. REPLACE the 20A WIPER fuse and/or the 30A COOLING FAN fuse. GO to **L5**.

DIAGNOSIS AND TESTING—ASPIRE, CONT'D

PINPOINT TEST L: A/C COMPRESSOR CLUTCH DOES NOT ENGAGE (Continued)

TEST STEP		RESULT	ACTION TO TAKE
L5	CHECK A/C COMPRESSOR CLUTCH OPERATION		
	• Key OFF. • Disconnect the A/C compressor clutch connector from the thermal protection switch. THERMAL PROTECTION SWITCH (PART OF 19703) / TO A/C CLUTCH FIELD COIL / FROM THERMAL PROTECTION TO A/C CLUTCH FIELD COIL / THERMAL PROTECTION SWITCH HARNESS CONNECTOR • Apply 12 volts to the "BK" wire at the A/C compressor clutch connector leading to the A/C compressor clutch. • Disconnect the 12 volt supply to the A/C compressor clutch. • **Does the A/C compressor clutch hub pull in when 12 volts is applied, and release when 12 volts is removed?**	Yes ▶ No ▶	GO to **L6**. REPLACE the A/C compressor clutch.
L6	CHECK THERMAL PROTECTION SWITCH		
	• Key OFF. • Disconnect both of the thermal protection switch connectors. See illustration in test step L5. • Measure the resistance of the thermal protection switch between the "BK" wires of the thermal protection switch connectors. • **Is the resistance less than 5 ohms?**	Yes ▶ No ▶	GO to **L7**. REPLACE the A/C compressor.
L7	CHECK A/C COMPRESSOR CLUTCH CONTROL RELAY		
	• Key OFF. • Remove the A/C compressor clutch control relay. • Apply 12 volts to the "BL" wire terminal and the "W/BK" wire terminal on the A/C compressor clutch control relay. • Measure the voltage on the "GN/W" wire terminal on the A/C compressor clutch control relay during the following conditions: (see table below) • **Are the voltages OK?**	Yes ▶ No ▶	GO to **L8**. REPLACE the A/C compressor clutch control relay.

BL/O Wire Terminal	Voltage on GN/W Wire Terminal
Open	Less than 1 volt
Grounded	Greater than 10 volts

DIAGNOSIS AND TESTING—ASPIRE, CONT'D

PINPOINT TEST L: A/C COMPRESSOR CLUTCH DOES NOT ENGAGE (Continued)

	TEST STEP	RESULT	▶ ACTION TO TAKE
L8	CHECK POWER SUPPLY		
	• Key OFF. • Remove the A/C compressor clutch control relay. • Key ON. • Measure the voltage on the "BL" wire and the "W/BK" wire at the A/C compressor clutch control relay connector. • **Are the voltages greater than 10 volts?**	Yes ▶ No ▶	GO to **L9**. SERVICE the wire(s) in question for open.
L9	CHECK A/C SWITCH		
	• Key OFF. • Locate and disconnect the A/C switch connector. • Turn the A/C switch off. • Measure the resistance of the A/C switch between the "BL/Y" wire and the "GN/BK" wire terminal at the A/C switch. • Turn the A/C switch on. • **Is the resistance less than 5 ohms with the A/C switch on, and greater than 10,000 ohms with the A/C switch off?**	Yes ▶ No ▶	GO to **L10**. REPLACE the A/C switch.
L10	CHECK A/C SWITCH GROUND		
	• Key OFF. • Disconnect the A/C switch connector. • Turn the heater blower motor switch to the low speed position. • Measure the resistance of the "BL/Y" wire between the A/C switch connector and ground. • **Is the resistance less than 5 ohms?**	Yes ▶ No ▶	GO to **L11**. SERVICE the "BL/Y" wire for open.
L11	CHECK WIRE BETWEEN A/C SWITCH AND A/C EVAPORATOR TEMPERATURE CONTROL THERMOSTAT		
	• Key OFF. • Disconnect the A/C switch connector. • Locate and disconnect the A/C evaporator temperature control thermostat connectors. • Measure the resistance of the "GN/BK" wire between the A/C switch connector and the A/C evaporator temperature control thermostat connector. • **Is the resistance less than 5 ohms?**	Yes ▶ No ▶	GO to **L12**. SERVICE the "GN/BK" wire for open.
L12	CHECK A/C EVAPORATOR TEMPERATURE CONTROL THERMOSTAT		
	• Key OFF. • Disconnect the A/C evaporator temperature control thermostat connectors. • Measure the resistance between the terminals of the A/C evaporator temperature control thermostat. • **Is the resistance less than 5 ohms?**	Yes ▶ No ▶	GO to **L13**. REPLACE the A/C evaporator temperature control thermostat.
L13	CHECK WIRE BETWEEN A/C EVAPORATOR TEMPERATURE CONTROL THERMOSTAT AND A/C PRESSURE CUT-OFF SWITCH		
	• Key OFF. • Disconnect the A/C evaporator temperature control thermostat connectors. • Locate and disconnect the A/C pressure cut-off switch connector. • Measure the resistance of the "GN/R" wire between the A/C pressure cut-off switch connector and the A/C evaporator temperature control thermostat connector. • **Is the resistance less than 5 ohms?**	Yes ▶ No ▶	GO to **L14**. SERVICE the "GN/R" wire for open.

DIAGNOSIS AND TESTING—ASPIRE, CONT'D

PINPOINT TEST L: A/C COMPRESSOR CLUTCH DOES NOT ENGAGE (Continued)

TEST STEP		RESULT	ACTION TO TAKE
L14	CHECK A/C PRESSURE CUT-OFF SWITCH		
	• Key OFF. • Disconnect the A/C pressure cut-off switch connector. • Measure the resistance between the terminals of the A/C pressure cut-off switch. • **Is the resistance less than 5 ohms?**	Yes No	▶ GO to **L15**. ▶ REPLACE the A/C pressure cut-off switch.
L15	CHECK WIRE BETWEEN A/C COMPRESSOR CLUTCH CONTROL RELAY AND A/C COMPRESSOR CLUTCH		
	• Key OFF. • Remove the A/C compressor clutch control relay. • Disconnect the A/C compressor clutch connector. • Measure the resistance of the "GN/W" wire between the A/C compressor clutch control relay connector and A/C clutch connector. • Measure the resistance of the "GN/W" wire between the A/C compressor clutch control relay connector and ground. • **Is the resistance less than 5 ohms between the A/C compressor clutch control relay and the A/C compressor clutch, and greater than 10,000 ohms between the A/C compressor clutch control relay and ground?**	Yes No	▶ REFER to the PC/ED Manual, diagnose the A/C compressor clutch control relay circuit. ▶ SERVICE the "GN/W" wire.

PINPOINT TEST M: A/C COMPRESSOR CLUTCH DOES NOT DISENGAGE

TEST STEP		RESULT	ACTION TO TAKE
M1	CHECK REFRIGERANT SYSTEM		
	• Perform the Refrigerant System Tests in this section. • **Is the refrigerant system performance OK?**	Yes No	▶ GO to **M2**. ▶ SERVICE the refrigerant system as necessary.
M2	CHECK A/C COMPRESSOR CLUTCH		
	• Key OFF. • Locate and disconnect the A/C compressor clutch connector. • Start engine. • **Does the A/C compressor clutch disengage?**	Yes No	▶ GO to **M3**. ▶ REPLACE the A/C compressor clutch.
M3	CHECK A/C COMPRESSOR CLUTCH CONTROL RELAY		
	• Key OFF. • Remove the A/C compressor clutch control relay. • Apply 12 volts to the "BL" wire terminal and the "W/BK" wire terminal on the A/C compressor clutch control relay. • Measure the voltage on the "GN/W" wire terminal on the A/C compressor clutch control relay during the following conditions: BL/O Wire Terminal — Voltage on GN/W Wire Terminal Open — Less than 1 volt Grounded — Greater than 10 volts • **Are the voltages OK?**	Yes No	▶ GO to **M4**. ▶ REPLACE the A/C compressor clutch control relay.

BL/O Wire Terminal	Voltage on GN/W Wire Terminal
Open	Less than 1 volt
Grounded	Greater than 10 volts

DIAGNOSIS AND TESTING—ASPIRE, CONT'D

PINPOINT TEST M: A/C COMPRESSOR CLUTCH DOES NOT DISENGAGE (Continued)

TEST STEP		RESULT ▶	ACTION TO TAKE
M4	CHECK A/C MODE SELECTOR SWITCH		
	• Key OFF. • Locate and disconnect the A/C switch connector. • Turn the A/C switch off. • Measure the resistance of the A/C switch between the "GN/BK" wire terminal and "BL/Y" wire terminal at the A/C switch. • Turn the A/C switch on. • **Is the resistance less than 5 ohms with the A/C switch on, and greater than 10,000 ohms with the A/C switch off?**	Yes ▶ No ▶	GO to **M5**. REPLACE the A/C switch.
M5	CHECK WIRE BETWEEN A/C SWITCH AND A/C EVAPORATOR TEMPERATURE CONTROL THERMOSTAT		
	• Key OFF. • Disconnect the A/C switch connector. • Locate and disconnect the A/C evaporator temperature control thermostat connector. • Measure the resistance of the "GN/BK" wire between the A/C evaporator temperature control thermostat connector and ground. • **Is the resistance greater than 10,000 ohms?**	Yes ▶ No ▶	GO to **M6**. SERVICE the "GN/BK" wire for short.
M6	CHECK WIRE BETWEEN A/C EVAPORATOR TEMPERATURE CONTROL THERMOSTAT AND A/C PRESSURE CUT-OFF SWITCH		
	• Key OFF. • Disconnect the A/C evaporator temperature control thermostat connector. • Locate and disconnect the A/C pressure cut-off switch connector. • Measure the resistance of the "GN/R" wire between the A/C pressure cut-off switch connector and ground. • **Is the resistance greater than 10,000 ohms?**	Yes ▶ No ▶	GO to **M7**. SERVICE the "GN/R" wire for short.
M7	CHECK WIRE BETWEEN A/C COMPRESSOR CLUTCH CONTROL RELAY AND POWERTRAIN CONTROL MODULE		
	• Key OFF. • Remove the A/C compressor clutch control relay. • Locate and disconnect the powertrain control module connectors. • Measure the resistance of the "BL/O" wire between the A/C compressor clutch control relay connector and ground. • **Is the resistance greater than 10,000 ohms?**	Yes ▶ No ▶	REFER to the PC/ED to diagnose the A/C pressure cut-off switch and A/C compressor clutch control circuits. SERVICE the "BL/O" wire for short.

PINPOINT TEST N: A/C COMPRESSOR CLUTCH CYCLES RAPIDLY

TEST STEP		RESULT ▶	ACTION TO TAKE
N1	CHECK REFRIGERANT SYSTEM		
	• Perform the Refrigerant System Tests in this section. • **Is the refrigerant system performance OK?**	Yes ▶ No ▶	REFER to the PC/ED to diagnose the A/C pressure cut-off switch. SERVICE the refrigerant system as necessary.

DIAGNOSIS AND TESTING—ASPIRE, CONT'D

PINPOINT TEST P: NOISE WHILE OPERATING CLIMATE CONTROL SYSTEM

	TEST STEP	RESULT ▶	ACTION TO TAKE
P1	CHECK A/C COMPRESSOR		
	• Run the engine at a constant 3000-4000 rpm. • Alternately switch the A/C compressor on and off by turning the A/C switch on and off. • **Does the noise disappear?**	Yes ▶	If the system was recently recharged, A/C compressor is OK. Otherwise PERFORM the Refrigerant System Tests.
		No ▶	GO to **P2**.
P2	RECHECK A/C COMPRESSOR		
	• Turn engine off and let engine sit for 1-2 minutes. • Run engine and hold the speed at 3000-4000 rpm. • Cycle the A/C compressor on and off as in step P1. • **Does the noise disappear?**	Yes ▶	PERFORM the A/C Compressor service procedures.
		No ▶	REPLACE the A/C compressor.

PINPOINT TEST Q: A/C CONDENSER COOLING FAN NEVER RUNS

	TEST STEP	RESULT ▶	ACTION TO TAKE
Q1	CHECK A/C CONDENSER FAN OPERATION		
	• Key OFF. • Locate and disconnect the A/C condenser fan switch connector. • Key ON, engine running. • Turn the A/C switch on. • Jump the "PK" wire and the "BK" wire at the A/C condenser fan switch connector. • **Does the A/C condenser fan operate when the "PK" wire is grounded?**	Yes ▶	CHECK the A/C system high pressure. If the high pressure is above 220 psi, REPLACE the A/C condenser fan switch. Otherwise, A/C condenser operation is normal. RETURN to Symptom Chart to SERVICE any other concerns.
		No ▶	GO to **Q2**.
Q2	CHECK FUSES		
	• Key OFF. • Check the 20A WIPER fuse located in the interior fuse junction panel, and the 30A COOLING FAN fuse located in the main fuse junction panel. • **Are the fuses OK?**	Yes ▶	GO to **Q5**.
		No ▶	GO to **Q3**.
Q3	CHECK SYSTEM		
	• Key OFF. • Replace the blown fuse(s). • Key ON. • **Do(es) the fuse(s) fail again?**	Yes ▶	GO to **Q4**.
		No ▶	GO to **Q5**.
Q4	CHECK FOR SHORT(S) TO GROUND		
	• Key OFF. • Remove the 30A COOLING FAN fuse and the 20A WIPER fuse. • Locate and disconnect the condenser fan relay connector. • Measure the resistance of the "BL" wire between the top terminal of the 15A R.WIPER fuse holder and ground. • Measure the resistance of the "W/BK" wire between the left terminal of the 30A COOLING FAN fuse holder and ground. • **Are the resistances less than 5 ohms?**	Yes ▶	SERVICE the wire(s) in question.
		No ▶	REPLACE the 30A COOLING FAN fuse and/or 20A WIPER fuse. RECONNECT the condenser fan relay. GO to **Q5**.

DIAGNOSIS AND TESTING—ASPIRE, CONT'D

PINPOINT TEST Q: A/C CONDENSER COOLING FAN NEVER RUNS (Continued)

	TEST STEP	RESULT ▶	ACTION TO TAKE
Q5	CHECK A/C CONDENSER COOLING FAN		
	• Key OFF. • Disconnect the A/C condenser cooling fan connector. • Apply 12 volts to the "BL/BK" wire terminal and ground to the "BK" wire terminal. • **Does the A/C condenser cooling fan operate?**	Yes ▶ No ▶	GO to **Q6**. REPLACE the A/C condenser cooling fan.
Q6	CHECK A/C CONDENSER COOLING FAN GROUND		
	• Key OFF. • Disconnect the A/C condenser cooling fan connector. • Measure the resistance of the "BK" wire between the A/C condenser cooling fan connector and ground. • **Is the resistance less than 5 ohms?**	Yes ▶ No ▶	GO to **Q7**. SERVICE the "BK" wire.
Q7	CHECK POWER TO CONDENSER FAN RELAY		
	• Key OFF. • Disconnect the condenser fan relay connector. • Key ON. • Measure the voltage on the "BL" and "W/BK" wires at the condenser fan relay connector. • **Are the voltages greater than 10 volts?**	Yes ▶ No ▶	GO to **Q8**. SERVICE the wire(s) in question.
Q8	CHECK A/C CONDENSER FAN SWITCH GROUND		
	• Key OFF. • Disconnect the A/C condenser fan switch connector. • Measure the resistance of the "BK" wire between the A/C condenser fan switch connector and ground. • **Is the resistance less than 5 ohms?**	Yes ▶ No ▶	REFER to the PC/ED Manual, diagnose the condenser fan relay control circuit. SERVICE the "BK" wire.

PINPOINT TEST R: A/C CONDENSER COOLING FAN OPERATES CONTINUOUSLY

	TEST STEP	RESULT ▶	ACTION TO TAKE
R1	CHECK CONDENSER FAN RELAY		
	• Key OFF. • Locate and disconnect the condenser fan relay. • Measure the resistance between the "W/BK" and "BL/BK" wire terminals on the condenser fan relay. • **Is the resistance greater than 10,000 ohms?**	Yes ▶ No ▶	GO to **R2**. REPLACE the condenser fan relay.
R2	CHECK WIRE BETWEEN CONDENSER FAN RELAY AND POWERTRAIN CONTROL MODULE		
	• Key OFF. • Disconnect the condenser fan relay connector. • Locate and disconnect the powertrain control module connectors. • Measure the resistance of the "LG" wire between the condenser fan relay connector and ground. • **Is the resistance greater than 10,000 ohms?**	Yes ▶ No ▶	REFER to the PC/ED Manual, diagnose the condenser fan relay control circuit. SERVICE the "LG" wire.

PINPOINT TEST S: A/C INDICATOR NOT OPERATING PROPERLY

	TEST STEP	RESULT ▶	ACTION TO TAKE
S1	CHECK A/C ON INDICATOR MINIATURE BULB		
	• Key OFF. • Locate and remove the A/C on indicator miniature bulb. • Check the continuity between the terminals of the A/C on indicator miniature bulb. • **Does continuity exist?**	Yes ▶ No ▶	GO to **S2**. REPLACE the A/C on indicator miniature bulb.

AIR CONDITIONING DIAGNOSIS AND PINPOINT TESTING—FESTIVA

TEST STEP		RESULT ▶	ACTION TO TAKE
RF1	CHECK REFRIGERANT SYSTEM PRESSURES		
	• Connect a Rotunda Standard Side Wheel Manifold Set 023-R0014, or equivalent to the A/C system. • Key ON, engine idling at 2000 rpm. • Blower on position 3. • Turn the A/C switch on, and turn the temperature blend lever to the extreme left (cool position). • Wait 5 minutes for the system to stabilize. • Observe the gauges and feel the temperatures of the suction and pressure lines near the compressor. • Look for a buildup of condensation on the A/C plumbing near the compressor and receiver/drier. • Turn the A/C switch off and observe the sight glass, then turn the A/C switch back on. • Compare the gauge readings and system temperatures to the chart in RF2.		

AIR CONDITIONING DIAGNOSIS AND PINPOINT TESTING—FESTIVA, CONT'D

TEST STEP		RESULT ▶	ACTION TO TAKE
RF2	REFRIGERANT SYSTEM PRESSURES		

Gauge Reading	Pressure Side Plumbing	Suction Side Plumbing	Sight Glass	Possible Cause	Action To Take
HI: 1372-1517 kPa (199-220 psi) LO: 131-172 kPa (19-25 psi)	Warm and dry	Cool and dry	Bubbles only after shutoff	• Normal operation	• Return to the Symptom Chart.
HI: 786-883 kPa (114-128 psi) LO: 0-83 kPa (0-12 psi) (too low)	Warm and dry	Warm and dry	Bubbles all the time Never bubbles	• Insufficient refrigerant • Empty system	• Test for leaks. Evacuate and recharge the system.
HI: 1620-1931 kPa (235-280 psi) LO: 234-303 kPa (34-44 psi) (too high)	Warm and dry	Cool and dry	No bubbles after shutoff	• Excessive refrigerant • System oil level is too low • Condenser obstruction • Condenser fan not operating	• Evacuate and recharge the system. • Put in the proper amount of oil. • Clear the obstruction. • Return to the Symptom Chart.
HI: 1793-2000 kPa (260-290 psi) (too high) LO: 172-241 kPa (25-35 psi) (too high)	Warm	Heavy dew or frost buildup	No bubbles after shutoff	• Expansion valve stuck open • Heat sensing bulb improperly installed	• Repair or replace the expansion valve as required. • Reinstall bulb properly.
HI: 1862-2275 kPa (270-330 psi) (too high) LO: 172-241 kPa (25-35 psi)	Warm	Warm	—	• Air in the system • Oil contamination	• Evacuate and recharge. If the same symptom is present after recharge, repair or replace the receiver/drier.
HI: Fluctuates LO: Fluctuates between vacuum & normal pressure	Warm	Fluctuates between cool and warm	—	• Moisture in system	• Evacuate, repair or replace the receiver/drier and recharge.
HI: 483-1034 kPa (70-150 psi) (too low) LO: Vacuum (too low)	Warm	Frost or dew near expansion valve	—	• Dirt or moisture in system is blocking the expansion valve or equalizer tube	• Evacuate, repair or replace the expansion valve and receiver/drier, and recharge.
HI: 483-1034 kPa (70-150 psi) (too low) LO: 172-241 kPa (25-35 psi) (too high)	Warm	Warm	—	• Faulty compressor	• Repair or replace the compressor.

AIR CONDITIONING DIAGNOSIS AND PINPOINT TESTING—FESTIVA, CONT'D

	TEST STEP	RESULT	▶	ACTION TO TAKE
AC1	CHECK FUSES			
	• Key OFF. • Check 15A HEATER fuse and the 20A C.FAN fuse located in the interior fuse panel. • **Are the fuses OK?**	Yes No	▶ ▶	GO to AC4. GO to AC2.
AC2	CHECK SYSTEM			
	• Key OFF. • Replace the blown fuse(s). • Key ON. • **Do(es) the fuse(s) fail again?**	Yes No	▶ ▶	GO to AC3. GO to AC4.
AC3	CHECK FOR SHORT(S) TO GROUND			
	• Key OFF. • Remove the 15A HEATER fuse and the 20A C.FAN fuse. • Disconnect the A/C switch connector, the A/C relay, the cooling fan motor connector and the WAC relay. • Measure the resistance of the "Y" wire between the bottom terminal of the 20A C.FAN fuse holder and ground. • Measure the resistance of the "BL/Y" wire between the bottom terminal of the 15A HEATER fuse holder and ground. • **Are either of the resistances less than 5 ohms?**	Yes No	▶ ▶	SERVICE the wire(s) in question between the interior fuse panel and the component(s). REPLACE the 15A HEATER fuse and/or the 20A C.FAN fuse. GO to AC4.
AC4	CHECK POWER SUPPLY TO A/C SYSTEM			
	• Key OFF. • Disconnect the WAC relay, the A/C relay, the cooling fan motor connector and the A/C switch connector. • Key ON. • Measure the voltage of the "BL" wire at the A/C switch connector and the A/C relay connector. • Measure the voltage of the "Y" wire at the cooling fan motor connector and the WAC relay connector. • Measure the voltage of the "BL/R" wire at the WAC relay connector. • **Is each voltage greater than 10 volts?**	Yes (Cooling fan does not operate) Yes (A/C on indicator does not illuminate) Yes (Magnetic clutch does not operate) No (No voltage on the "BL/R" wire) No (No voltage on other wires)	▶ ▶ ▶ ▶ ▶	GO to AC33. GO to AC15. GO to AC9. GO to AC5. SERVICE the wire(s) in question.
AC5	CHECK WIRE BETWEEN IGNITION SWITCH AND WAC RELAY			
	• Key OFF. • Disconnect the ignition switch connector and the WAC relay. • Measure the resistance of the "BL/R" wire between the ignition switch connector and the WAC relay connector. • **Is the resistance less than 5 ohms?**	Yes No	▶ ▶	REFER to diagnosis of the ignition switch. GO to AC6.
AC6	CHECK WIRE BETWEEN IGNITION SWITCH AND 10A IN-LINE FUSE			
	• Key OFF. • Disconnect the ignition switch connector. • Remove the 10A in-line fuse. • Measure the resistance of the "BL/R" wire between the ignition switch connector and the 10A in-line fuse connector. • **Is the resistance less than 5 ohms?**	Yes No	▶ ▶	GO to AC7. SERVICE the "BL/R" wire between the ignition switch and the 10A in-line fuse.

AIR CONDITIONING DIAGNOSIS AND PINPOINT TESTING—FESTIVA, CONT'D

	TEST STEP	RESULT	▶	ACTION TO TAKE
AC7	CHECK 10A IN-LINE FUSE			
	• Key OFF. • Remove the 10A in-line fuse. • Check the 10A in-line fuse. • **Is the fuse OK?**	Yes No	▶ ▶	SERVICE the "BL/R" wire between the 10A in-line fuse and the WAC relay for an open. GO to AC8.
AC8	CHECK WIRE BETWEEN 10A IN-LINE FUSE AND WAC RELAY			
	• Key OFF. • Disconnect the WAC relay. • Remove the 10A in-line fuse. • Measure the resistance of the "BL/R" wire between the 10A in-line fuse connector (WAC relay side) and ground. • **Is the resistance less than 5 ohms?**	Yes No	▶ ▶	SERVICE the "BL/R" wire between the 10A in-line fuse and the WAC relay for a short. REPLACE the 10A in-line fuse. GO to AC20.
AC9	CHECK A/C CONTROL CIRCUIT TO PCM			
	• Key OFF. • Reconnect the WAC relay, the A/C relay, the cooling fan motor connector and the A/C switch connector. • Disconnect the blower motor connector and the Powertrain Control Module (PCM) connectors. • Remove the 15A HEATER fuse. • Turn the blower switch to the 1, 2 or 3 position. • Turn the A/C switch on. • Measure the resistance of the "GN" wire between the Powertrain Control Module connector (Pin 1Q) and ground. • Turn the A/C switch off. • Measure the resistance of the "GN" wire between the PCM connector (Pin 1Q) and ground. • **Is the resistance less than 5 ohms with the A/C switch on, and greater than 10,000 ohms with the A/C switch off?**	Yes No	▶ ▶	GO to AC19. GO to AC10.
AC10	CHECK WIRE BETWEEN PCM AND THERMOSTATIC SWITCH			
	• Key OFF. • Reconnect the blower motor connector and the 15A HEATER fuse. • Disconnect the PCM connectors, the thermostatic switch connector, and the A/C relay. • Measure the resistance of the "GN" wire between the PCM connector (Pin 1Q) and the thermostatic switch connector. • Measure the resistance of the "GN" wire between the thermostatic switch connector and ground. • **Is the resistance less than 5 ohms between the PCM connector and the thermostatic switch connector, and greater than 10,000 ohms between the thermostatic switch connector and ground?**	Yes No	▶ ▶	GO to AC11. SERVICE the "GN" wire between the PCM and the thermostatic switch.

AIR CONDITIONING DIAGNOSIS AND PINPOINT TESTING—FESTIVA, CONT'D

TEST STEP		RESULT	▶	ACTION TO TAKE
AC11	CHECK THERMOSTATIC SWITCH			
	• Key OFF. • Reconnect the PCM connector and the A/C relay. • Disconnect and remove the thermostatic switch. • Measure the resistance between the "GN" wire terminal and the "BK/W" wire terminal on the thermostatic switch with the thermostatic sensing bulb above 25°C (77°F). • Apply liquid freon or other cooling liquid to the thermostatic sensing bulb on the thermostatic switch to bring the temperature below 0°C (32°F). • Measure the resistance between the "GN" wire terminal and the "BK/W" wire terminal on the thermostatic switch. • **Is the resistance less than 5 ohms when the temperature is above 25°C (77°F), and greater than 10,000 ohms when the temperature is below 0°C (32°F)?**	Yes (Magnetic clutch operates continuously) Yes (Magnetic clutch does not engage) No	▶ ▶ ▶	GO to AC19. GO to AC12. REPLACE the thermostatic switch.
AC12	CHECK WIRE BETWEEN THERMOSTATIC SWITCH AND PRESSURE SWITCH			
	• Key OFF. • Disconnect the thermostatic switch connector and the pressure switch connector. • Measure the resistance of the "BK/W" wire between the thermostatic switch connector and the pressure switch connector. • Measure the resistance of the "BK/W" wire between the thermostatic switch connector and ground. • **Is the resistance less than 5 ohms between the thermostatic switch connector and the pressure switch connector, and greater than 10,000 ohms between the thermostatic switch connector and ground?**	Yes No	▶ ▶	GO to AC13. SERVICE the "BK/W" wire between the thermostatic switch and the pressure switch.
AC13	CHECK PRESSURE SWITCH			
	• Key OFF. • Reconnect the thermostatic switch connector. • Disconnect the pressure switch connector. • With the system at normal operating pressure, measure the resistance between the "BK/W" wire terminal and the "Y/GN" wire terminal on the pressure switch. • **Is the resistance less than 5 ohms?**	Yes No	▶ ▶	GO to AC14. REPLACE the pressure switch.
AC14	CHECK WIRE BETWEEN PRESSURE SWITCH AND A/C SWITCH			
	• Key OFF. • Disconnect the pressure switch connector and the A/C switch connector. • Measure the resistance of the "Y/GN" wire between the pressure switch connector and the A/C switch connector. • Measure the resistance of the "Y/GN" wire between the pressure switch connector and ground. • **Is the resistance less than 5 ohms between the pressure switch connector and the A/C switch connector, and greater than 10,000 ohms between the pressure switch connector and ground?**	Yes No	▶ ▶	GO to AC15. SERVICE the "Y/GN" wire between the pressure switch and the A/C switch.

AIR CONDITIONING DIAGNOSIS AND PINPOINT TESTING—FESTIVA, CONT'D

TEST STEP		RESULT	▶	ACTION TO TAKE
AC15	CHECK A/C SWITCH			
	• Key OFF. • Reconnect the pressure switch connector. • Disconnect the A/C switch connector. • A/C switch off. • Measure the resistance between the "Y/GN" wire terminal and the "BL/W" terminal on the A/C switch. • A/C switch on. • Measure the resistance between the "Y/GN" wire terminal and the "BL/W" wire terminal on the A/C switch. • **Is the resistance less than 5 ohms with the A/C switch on, and greater than 10,000 ohms with the A/C switch off?**	Yes (A/C lamp does not illuminate) Yes (Magnetic clutch does not operate) No	▶ ▶ ▶	GO to AC16. GO to AC18. REPLACE the A/C switch.
AC16	CHECK POWER SUPPLY TO A/C SWITCH BULB			
	• Key OFF. • Reconnect the A/C switch connector. • Remove the A/C switch bulb. • Key ON. • Measure the voltage at the A/C switch bulb connector. • **Is the voltage greater than 10 volts?**	Yes No	▶ ▶	GO to AC17. REPLACE the A/C switch.
AC17	CHECK A/C SWITCH BULB CONTROL CIRCUIT			
	• Key OFF. • Disconnect the A/C switch connector. • Remove the A/C switch bulb. • Measure the resistance between the "Y/GN" wire terminal on the A/C switch and the A/C switch bulb connector. • **Is the resistance less than 5 ohms?**	Yes No	▶ ▶	REPLACE the A/C switch bulb. REPLACE the A/C switch.
AC18	CHECK WIRE BETWEEN BLOWER MOTOR SWITCH AND A/C SWITCH			
	• Key OFF. • Disconnect the blower motor switch connector and the A/C switch connector. • Measure the resistance of the "BL/W" wire between the blower motor switch connector and the A/C switch connector. • **Is the resistance less than 5 ohms?**	Yes No	▶ ▶	REFER to diagnosis of the blower motor system. SERVICE the "BL/W" wire between the blower motor switch and the A/C switch.
AC19	CHECK WAC RELAY			
	• Key OFF. • Reconnect the A/C relay, the cooling fan motor connector and the A/C switch connector. • Reconnect the PCM connectors and the blower motor connector. • Install the 15A HEATER fuse. • Disconnect the WAC relay. • Apply 12 volts to the "BL/R" wire terminal and the "Y" wire terminal on the WAC relay. • Measure the voltage of the "BK/W" wire terminal on the WAC relay. • Apply ground to the "GN/Y" wire terminal on the WAC relay. • Measure the voltage of the "BK/W" wire terminal on the WAC relay. • **Is the voltage less than 1 volt with ground not applied, and greater than 10 volts with ground applied?**	Yes No	▶ ▶	GO to AC20. REPLACE the WAC relay.

AIR CONDITIONING DIAGNOSIS AND PINPOINT TESTING—FESTIVA, CONT'D

TEST STEP		RESULT	ACTION TO TAKE
AC20	CHECK WIRE BETWEEN THE WAC RELAY AND MAGNETIC CLUTCH		
	• Key OFF. • Disconnect the WAC relay, the magnetic clutch connector and the pressure switch connector (ATX only). • Measure the resistance of the "BK" wire (ATX) ["BK/W" wire (MTX)] between the WAC relay connector and the magnetic clutch connector. • Measure the resistance of the "BK" wire (ATX) ["BK/W" wire (MTX)] between the WAC relay connector and ground. • **Is the resistance less than 5 ohms between the WAC relay connector and the magnetic clutch connector, and greater than 10,000 ohms between the WAC relay connector and ground?**	Yes ▶ No ▶	REPLACE the magnetic clutch. SERVICE the "BK" wire (ATX) ["BK/W" (MTX)] between the WAC relay and the magnetic clutch.
AC21	CHECK POWER SUPPLY TO CONDENSER FAN MOTOR		
	• Key OFF. • Disconnect the condenser fan motor connector. • Measure the voltage of the "Y" wire at the condenser fan motor connector. • **Is the voltage greater than 10 volts?**	Yes ▶ No ▶	GO to AC27. GO to AC22.
AC22	CHECK FUSE		
	• Key OFF. • Check the 25A MAIN fuse link located in the main fuse panel. • **Is the fuse link OK?**	Yes ▶ No ▶	GO to AC25. GO to AC23.
AC23	CHECK SYSTEM		
	• Key OFF. • Replace the 25A MAIN fuse link. • **Does the fuse link fail again?**	Yes ▶ No ▶	GO to AC24. GO to AC25.
AC24	CHECK FOR SHORT TO GROUND		
	• Key OFF. • Remove the 25A MAIN fuse link. • Disconnect the 15A in-line fuse connector. • Measure the resistance of the "W" wire between the rear terminal of the 25A MAIN fuse link holder and ground. • **Is the resistance less than 5 ohms?**	Yes ▶ No ▶	SERVICE the "W" wire between the main fuse panel and the 15A in-line fuse. REPLACE the 25A MAIN fuse link. GO to AC25.
AC25	CHECK POWER SUPPLY TO 15A IN-LINE FUSE		
	• Key OFF. • Disconnect the 15A in-line fuse. • Measure the voltage of the "W" wire at the 15A in-line fuse connector. • **Is the voltage greater than 10 volts?**	Yes ▶ No ▶	GO to AC26. SERVICE the "W" wire between the main fuse panel and the 15A in-line fuse.
AC26	CHECK 15A IN-LINE FUSE		
	• Key OFF. • Remove the 15A in-line fuse. • Check the 15A in-line fuse. • **Is the fuse OK?**	Yes ▶ No ▶	SERVICE the "Y" wire between the 15A in-line fuse and the cooling fan motor for an open. SERVICE the "Y" wire for a short to ground. REPLACE the 15A in-line fuse.
AC27	CHECK CONDENSER FAN MOTOR		
	• Key OFF. • Disconnect the condenser fan motor connector. • Apply 12 volts to the "Y" wire terminal of the condenser fan motor. • Apply ground to the "GN/R" wire terminal of the condenser fan motor. • **Does the condenser fan motor operate?**	Yes ▶ No ▶	GO to AC28. REPLACE the condenser fan motor.

AIR CONDITIONING DIAGNOSIS AND PINPOINT TESTING—FESTIVA, CONT'D

TEST STEP		RESULT	ACTION TO TAKE
AC28	CHECK WIRE BETWEEN CONDENSER FAN MOTOR AND CONDENSER FAN RELAY		
	• Key OFF. • Disconnect the condenser fan motor connector and the condenser fan relay connector. • Measure the resistance of the "GN/R" wire between the condenser fan relay connector and the condenser fan motor connector. • Measure the resistance of the "GN/R" wire between the condenser fan motor connector and ground. • **Is the resistance less than 5 ohms between the condenser fan motor connector and the condenser fan relay connector, and greater than 10,000 ohms between the condenser fan motor connector and ground?**	Yes ▶ No ▶	GO to AC29. SERVICE the "GN/R" wire between the condenser fan motor and the condenser fan relay.
AC29	CHECK CONDENSER FAN RELAY		
	• Key OFF. • Disconnect the condenser fan relay. • Apply ground to the "BK" wire terminals on the condenser fan relay. • Measure the resistance between the "GN/R" wire terminal on the condenser fan relay and ground. • Apply 12 volts to the "W" wire terminal on the condenser fan relay. • Measure the resistance between the "GN/R" wire terminal on the condenser fan relay and ground. • **Is the resistance less than 5 ohms with 12 volts applied, and greater than 10,000 ohms with 12 volts not applied?**	Yes ▶ No ▶	GO to AC30. REPLACE the condenser fan relay.
AC30	CHECK CONDENSER FAN RELAY GROUND		
	• Key OFF. • Disconnect the condenser fan relay. • Measure the resistance of the "BK" wires between the condenser fan relay connector and ground. • **Are the resistances less than 5 ohms?**	Yes ▶ No ▶	GO to AC31. SERVICE the "BK" wire(s) between the condenser fan relay and ground.
AC31	CHECK WIRE BETWEEN CONDENSER FAN RELAY AND PRESSURE SWITCH		
	• Key OFF. • Disconnect the condenser fan relay connector and the pressure switch connector. • Measure the resistance of the "W" wire between the condenser fan relay connector and the pressure switch connector. • Measure the resistance of the "W" wire between the pressure switch connector and ground. • **Is the resistance less than 5 ohms between the condenser fan relay connector and the pressure switch connector, and greater than 10,000 ohms between the pressure switch connector and ground?**	Yes ▶ No ▶	GO to AC32. SERVICE the "W" wire between the pressure switch and the condenser fan relay.
AC32	CHECK WIRE BETWEEN PRESSURE SWITCH AND MAGNETIC CLUTCH		
	• Key OFF. • Reconnect the condenser fan relay. • Disconnect the pressure switch connector and the magnetic clutch connector. • Measure the resistance of the "BK" wire between the pressure switch connector and the magnetic clutch connector. • **Is the resistance less than 5 ohms?**	Yes ▶ No ▶	REPLACE the pressure switch. SERVICE the "BK" wire between the pressure switch and magnetic clutch.

AIR CONDITIONING DIAGNOSIS AND PINPOINT TESTING—FESTIVA, CONT'D

TEST STEP		RESULT ▶	ACTION TO TAKE
AC33	CHECK WIRE BETWEEN A/C RELAY AND THERMOSTATIC SWITCH		
	• Key OFF. • Disconnect the A/C relay connector and the thermostatic switch connector. • Measure the resistance of the "GN" wire between the A/C relay connector and the thermostatic switch connector. • **Is the resistance less than 5 ohms?**	Yes ▶ No ▶	GO to AC34. SERVICE the "GN" wire between the A/C relay and the thermostatic switch.
AC34	CHECK WIRE BETWEEN THE COOLING FAN MOTOR AND THE A/C RELAY		
	• Key OFF. • Disconnect the cooling fan motor connector and the A/C relay. • Measure the resistance of the "Y/R" wire between the cooling fan motor connector and the A/C relay connector. • **Is the resistance less than 5 ohms?**	Yes ▶ No ▶	GO to AC35. SERVICE the "Y/R" wire between the cooling fan motor and the A/C relay.
AC35	CHECK A/C RELAY		
	• Key OFF. • Disconnect the A/C relay. • Apply 12 volts to the "Y/R" wire terminal and the "BL" wire terminal on the A/C relay. • Measure the voltage of the "BK" wire terminal on the A/C relay. • Apply ground to the "GN" wire terminal on the A/C relay. • Measure the voltage of the "BK" wire terminal on the A/C relay. • **Is the voltage less than 1 volt with ground not applied, and greater than 10 volts with ground applied?**	Yes ▶ No ▶	SERVICE the "BK" wire between the A/C relay and ground for an open. REPLACE the A/C relay.

HEATING SYSTEM DIAGNOSIS AND TESTING—ESCORT AND TRACER

TEST STEP		RESULT ▶	ACTION TO TAKE
NH1	ENGINE THERMOSTAT FUNCTION		
	• If engine overheating is reported or is present, refer to the cooling system diagnostics for servicing the engine thermostat. • If failure to reach normal operating temperature is a reported symptom, start and warm up the engine until the coolant temperature stabilizes. • Verify the reported symptom by checking the heater for adequate heat output (temperature control lever to the extreme right, mode selector lever at panel, blower at Position 4). • If the heater output is inadequate, remove the engine thermostat and check it for "start to open" temperature setting. • Is the "start to open" temperature setting within specification? • Specification: "start-to-open" temperature setting: 83.5-86.5°C (182-188°F)	Yes ▶ No ▶	GO to NH2. REPLACE the engine thermostat

TEST STEP		RESULT ▶	ACTION TO TAKE
NH2	HEATER CORE — CHECK FOR AIR FLOW BLOCKAGE		
	• Check the heater core and connecting air passages for blockage, such as leaves, paper, etc. • Remove the blockage as required. • Are the heater core and its connecting air passages free of blockage?	Yes ▶ No ▶	GO to NH3. CLEAN, REPAIR or REPLACE components as required.

HEATING SYSTEM DIAGNOSIS AND TESTING—ESCORT AND TRACER, CONT'D

TEST STEP	RESULT ►	ACTION TO TAKE
NH3 HEATER CORE — CHECK FOR COOLANT BLOCKAGE		
• Refer to the engine cooling system diagnostics for the correct heater core block flush procedure. • Back flush the heater core to remove core sand, etc., following cooling system diagnostics. • Reassemble the cooling system components using "Installation" instructions. • Is the heater core free of blockage to coolant flow?	Yes ► No ►	GO to NH4. REPLACE the heater core.

TEST STEP	RESULT ►	ACTION TO TAKE
NH4 TEMPERATURE CONTROL AND CABLES FUNCTION		
• Start and warm up the engine to its normal operating temperature. • Set the blower switch to Position 4. • Set the mode selector lever to panel. • Move the temperature control lever gradually from the extreme left to the extreme right and verify that the air temperature gradually increases from cold to hot. • Is the temperature control lever functioning properly and is the air hot when the lever is at the extreme right?	Yes ► No ►	RETURN to symptom chart. ADJUST the temperature control cable to close off all bypass air around the heater core when the temperature control lever is set to the extreme right.

TEST STEP	RESULT ►	ACTION TO TAKE
HP1 CHECK FUSE		
• Check the 30 amp "Heater" fuse. • Is the fuse good?	Yes ► No ►	GO to HP4. GO to HP2.

HEATING SYSTEM DIAGNOSIS AND TESTING—ESCORT AND TRACER, CONT'D

TEST STEP	RESULT ►	ACTION TO TAKE
HP2 CHECK SYSTEM		
• Replace the blown 30 amp "Heater" fuse. • Key ON. • Did the fuse blow again?	Yes ► No ►	GO to HP3. GO to HP4.

TEST STEP	RESULT ►	ACTION TO TAKE
HP3 CHECK FOR SHORT TO GROUND		
• Key OFF. • Disconnect the "BL/W" wire from the "Heater" fuse. • Measure the resistance of the "BL/W" wire between the fuse panel and ground. • Is the resistance less than 5 ohms?	Yes ► No ►	SERVICE the "BL/W" wire. GO to HP4.

TEST STEP	RESULT ►	ACTION TO TAKE
HP4 CHECK SUPPLY TO BLOWER MOTOR		
• Disconnect the blower motor connector. • Key ON. • Measure the voltage on the "BL/W" wire at the connector. • Reconnect the blower motor connector. • Is the voltage greater than 10 volts?	Yes ► No ►	GO to HP5. SERVICE the "BL/W" wire.

HEATING SYSTEM DIAGNOSIS AND TESTING—ESCORT AND TRACER, CONT'D

TEST STEP	RESULT ►	ACTION TO TAKE
HP5 CHECK BLOWER MOTOR		
• Key OFF. • Disconnect the blower motor connector. • Apply 12 volts to the "BL/W" terminal. • Ground the "BL/BK" terminal. • Reconnect the blower motor. • Did the blower motor run?	Yes ► No ►	GO to HP6. SERVICE/REPLACE the blower motor.

TEST STEP	RESULT ►	ACTION TO TAKE
HP6 CHECK LEAD TO RESISTOR		
• Locate the resistor connector. • Measure the resistance of the "BL/BK" wire between the motor and the resistor. • Is the resistance less than 5 ohms?	Yes ► No ►	GO to HP7. SERVICE the "BL/BK" wire.

TEST STEP	RESULT ►	ACTION TO TAKE
HP7 CHECK RESISTOR		
• Measure the resistance from the "BL/BK" wire at the connector to the following wires at the connector.	Yes ► No ►	GO to HP8. REPLACE the resistor.

Wire	Resistance
"BL/Y"	2.6 ohms
"BL"	1.2 ohms
"BL/R"	.6 ohm
"BL/W"	.1 ohm

• Are the resistances correct?

HEATING SYSTEM DIAGNOSIS AND TESTING—ESCORT AND TRACER, CONT'D

TEST STEP	RESULT ►	ACTION TO TAKE
HP8 CHECK LEADS TO BLOWER MOTOR CONTROL SWITCH		
• Locate the blower motor control switch connector. • Measure the resistance of the following wires between the resistor and the blower motor control switch. **Wire** "BL/Y" "BL" "BL/R" "BL/W" • Are the resistances less than 5 ohms?	Yes ► No ►	GO to HP9. SERVICE the wire in question.

TEST STEP	RESULT ►	ACTION TO TAKE
HP9 CHECK THE BLOWER MOTOR CONTROL SWITCH GROUND		
• Measure the resistance of the "BK" wire between the blower motor control switch and ground. • Is the resistance less than 5 ohms?	Yes ► No ►	GO to HP10. SERVICE the "BK" wire.

TEST STEP	RESULT ►	ACTION TO TAKE
HP10 CHECK THE BLOWER MOTOR CONTROL SWITCH		
• Disconnect the blower motor control switch. • Measure the resistance between ground and the wire colors listed below at the following switch positions.	Yes ► No ►	RETURN to the Symptom Chart. SERVICE/REPLACE the blower motor control switch.

Switch Position	Wire Color	Resistance
OFF	All Colors	Greater than 10,000 ohms
1	"BL/Y"	Less than 5 ohms
	All Others	Greater than 10,000 ohms
2	"BL"	Less than 5 ohms
	All Others	Greater than 10,000 ohms
3	"BL/R"	Less than 5 ohms
	All Others	Greater than 10,000 ohms
4	"BL/W"	Less than 5 ohms
	All Others	Greater than 10,000 ohms

• Reconnect the blower motor control switch.
• Are the resistances correct?

HEATING SYSTEM DIAGNOSIS AND TESTING—ESCORT AND TRACER, CONT'D

TEST STEP	RESULT ►	ACTION TO TAKE
V1 AIR FLOW SELECTOR SYSTEM FUNCTION		
• With the ignition switch ON and the blower switch set to Position 4 for maximum air flow, check the air flow patterns resulting from the following position settings of the mode selector. Verify that they conform to the specified air flow patterns as listed:	Yes ►	GO to V2 .
	No ►	REPAIR, ADJUST or REPLACE the heater or its outlet door or components as required.

Air Flow Selector Position	Specified Air Flow Pattern (Exit Locations Shown)
PANEL	Ventilator outlets
HI-LO	Ventilator and floor outlets
FLOOR	Floor outlets and small amount to the defroster outlets
MIX	Floor and defroster outlets
DEF	Defroster outlets

• Do the air flow patterns conform to the specified patterns for each of the tested selector positions?

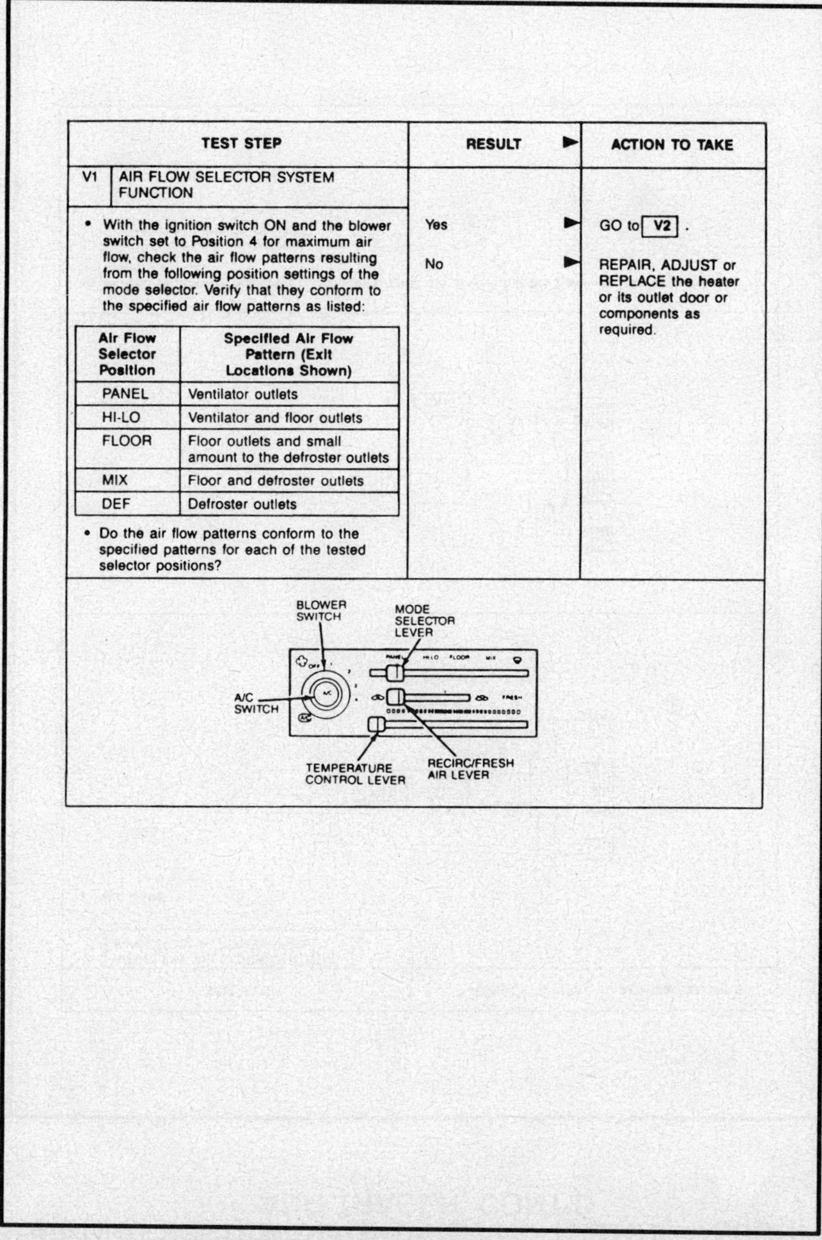

HEATING SYSTEM DIAGNOSIS AND TESTING—ESCORT AND TRACER, CONT'D

TEST STEP	RESULT ►	ACTION TO TAKE
V1 AIR FLOW SELECTOR SYSTEM FUNCTION — CONTINUED		

PANEL MODE

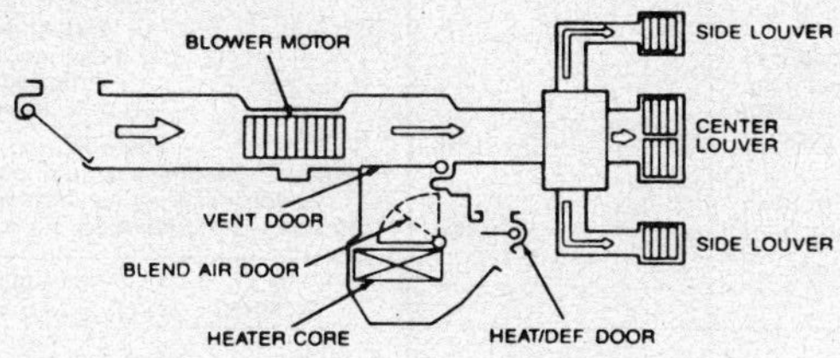

BLOWER MOTOR
SIDE LOUVER
CENTER LOUVER
SIDE LOUVER
VENT DOOR
BLEND AIR DOOR
HEATER CORE
HEAT/DEF DOOR

HI-LO MODE

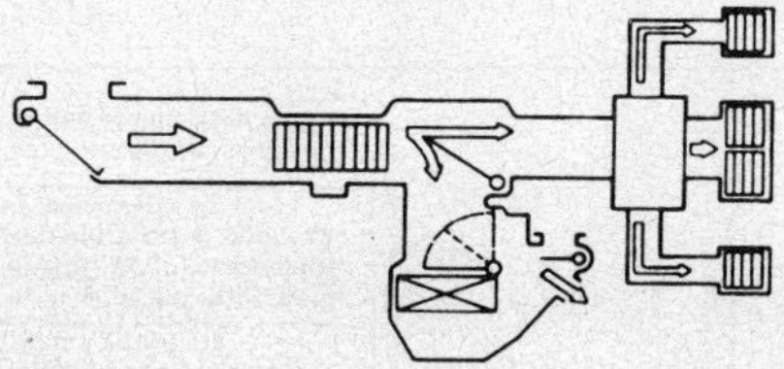

FLOOR MODE

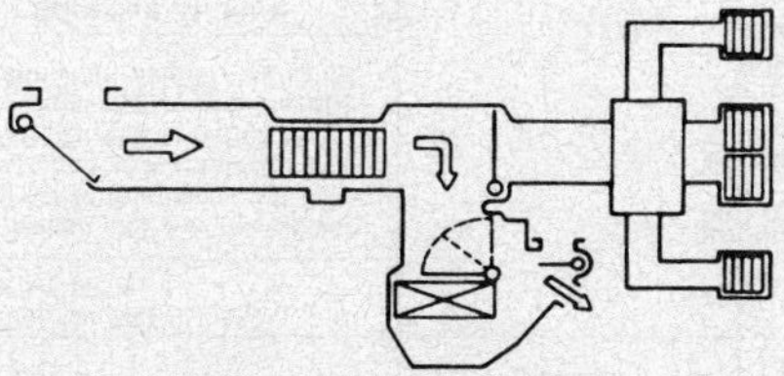

HEATING SYSTEM DIAGNOSIS AND TESTING—ESCORT AND TRACER, CONT'D

TEST STEP	RESULT ►	ACTION TO TAKE
V1 AIR FLOW SELECTOR SYSTEM FUNCTION — CONTINUED		

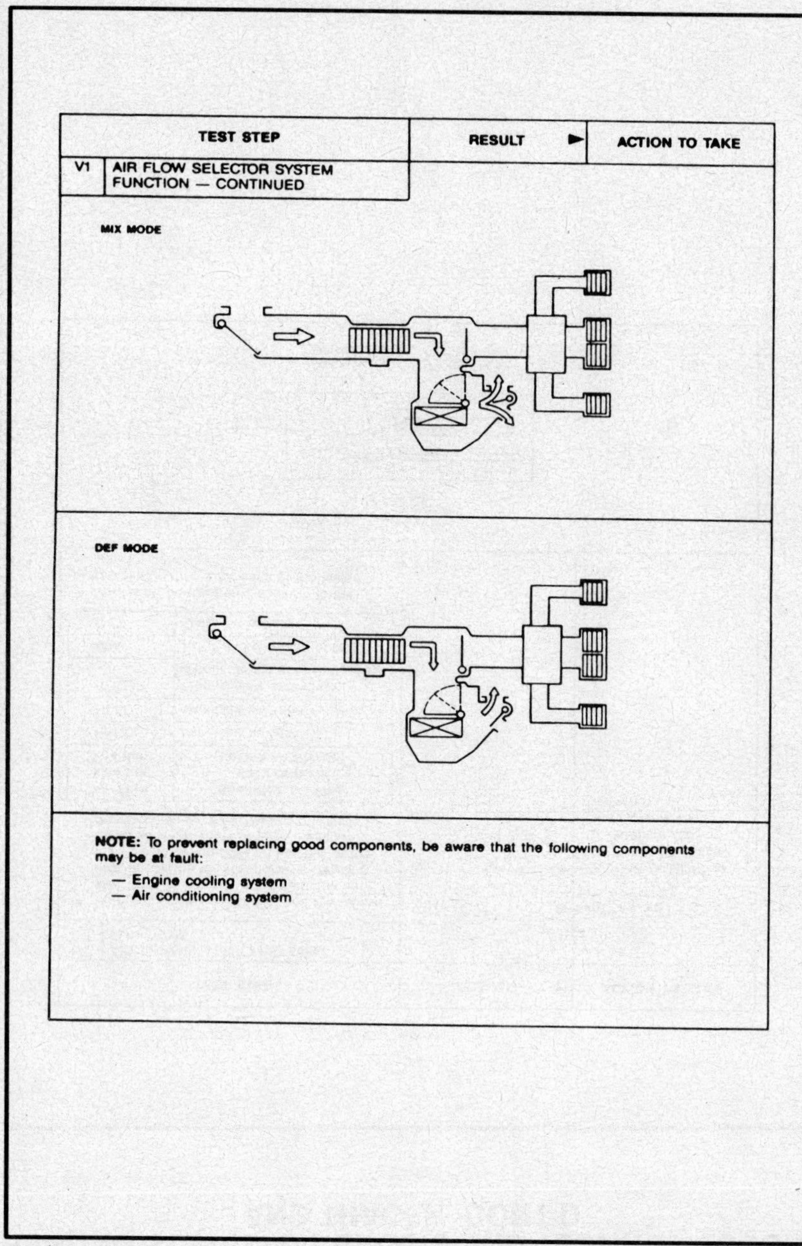

NOTE: To prevent replacing good components, be aware that the following components may be at fault:

— Engine cooling system
— Air conditioning system

HEATING SYSTEM DIAGNOSIS AND TESTING—ESCORT AND TRACER, CONT'D

TEST STEP	RESULT ►	ACTION TO TAKE
V2 RECIRCULATION — FRESH AIR SELECTOR FUNCTION		
• With the ignition switch ON and the blower fan speed control set to Position 4 for maximum air flow, change the selector setting from RECIRCULATION (REC) to FRESH AIR. Verify that the air movement conforms to the specified patterns as listed:	Yes ►	GO to V3.
	No ►	REPAIR, ADJUST or REPLACE the blower unit or the rec-fresh selector door or linkage as required.
• Does the air flow conform to the specified patterns for each of the tested selector lever positions?		

Recirc/Fresh Air Lever Position	Specified Air Flow Movement (Air Intake)
Extreme Left (Recirc)	Air flow at REC air inlet openings under the instrument panel can be felt and heard (whistling)
Extreme Right (Fresh)	No air flow at the instrument panel REC air inlet openings, at instrument panel openings; no whistling-type air noise.

TEST STEP	RESULT ►	ACTION TO TAKE
V3 VENTILATION SYSTEM — CHECK FOR BLOCKAGE		
• Disassemble the following components of the ventilation system for inspection as required, and remove any foreign material causing air flow blockage: Blower motor Blower housing Recirculation inlet (paper, etc.) Fresh inlet (leaves, etc.) Main air duct (no A/C) Evaporator (with A/C) Heater core inlet side Air outlets at floor, panel and defroster • Is the air flow adequate in all selector modes for both recirculation and fresh air modes?	Yes ►	RETURN to symptom chart. System OK.
	No ►	ADJUST recirculation-fresh air door, heat door, defroster door or vent door as required.

AIR CONDITIONING DIAGNOSIS AND TESTING—ESCORT AND TRACER

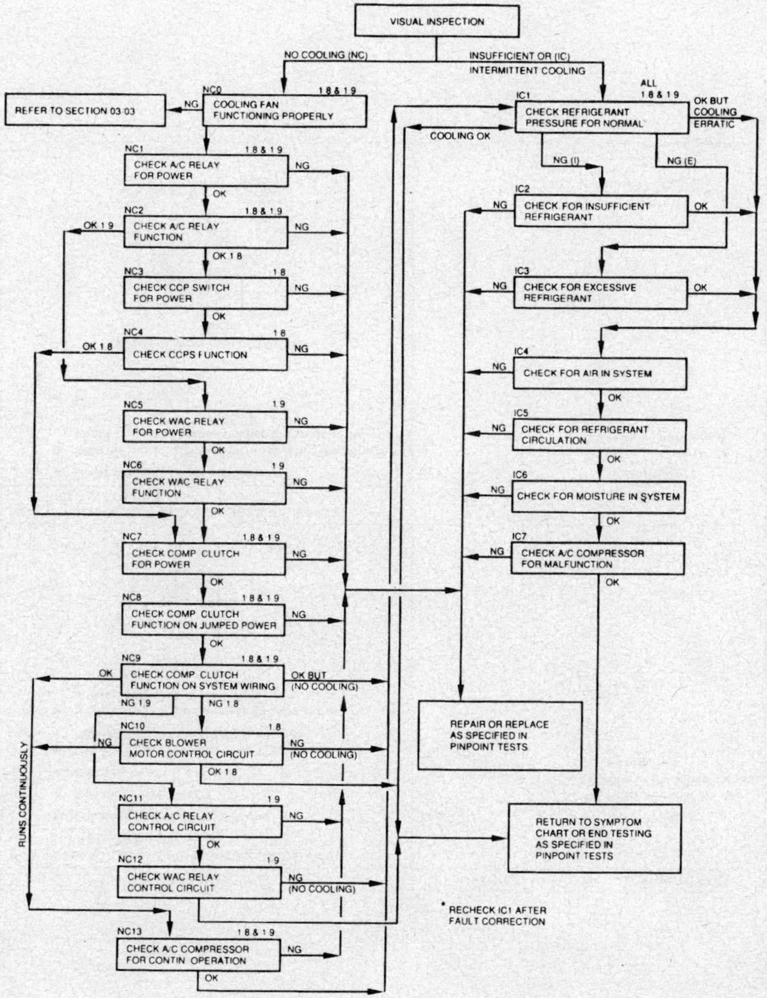

VISUAL INSPECTION

NO COOLING (NC) — INSUFFICIENT OR (IC) INTERMITTENT COOLING

- NC0 (1.8 & 1.9) COOLING FAN FUNCTIONING PROPERLY — NG: REFER TO SECTION 03-03
- NC1 (1.8 & 1.9) CHECK A/C RELAY FOR POWER — NG / OK
- NC2 (1.8 & 1.9) CHECK A/C RELAY FUNCTION — NG / OK 1.8 / OK 1.9
- NC3 (1.8) CHECK CCP SWITCH FOR POWER — NG / OK
- NC4 (1.8) CHECK CCPS FUNCTION — NG / OK 1.8
- NC5 (1.9) CHECK WAC RELAY FOR POWER — NG / OK
- NC6 (1.9) CHECK WAC RELAY FUNCTION — NG / OK
- NC7 (1.8 & 1.9) CHECK COMP. CLUTCH FOR POWER — NG / OK
- NC8 (1.8 & 1.9) CHECK COMP. CLUTCH FUNCTION ON JUMPED POWER — NG / OK
- NC9 (1.8 & 1.9) CHECK COMP. CLUTCH FUNCTION ON SYSTEM WIRING — OK / OK BUT (NO COOLING) / NG 1.9 / NG 1.8
- NC10 (1.8) CHECK BLOWER MOTOR CONTROL CIRCUIT — NG / NG (NO COOLING) / OK 1.8
- NC11 (1.9) CHECK A/C RELAY CONTROL CIRCUIT — NG / OK
- NC12 (1.9) CHECK WAC RELAY CONTROL CIRCUIT — NG (NO COOLING) / OK
- NC13 (1.8 & 1.9) CHECK A/C COMPRESSOR FOR CONTIN. OPERATION — NG / OK

RUNS CONTINUOUSLY

- IC1 (ALL 1.8 & 1.9) CHECK REFRIGERANT PRESSURE FOR NORMAL* — COOLING OK / OK BUT COOLING ERRATIC / NG (I) / NG (E)
- IC2 CHECK FOR INSUFFICIENT REFRIGERANT — NG / OK
- IC3 CHECK FOR EXCESSIVE REFRIGERANT — NG / OK
- IC4 CHECK FOR AIR IN SYSTEM — NG / OK
- IC5 CHECK FOR REFRIGERANT CIRCULATION — NG / OK
- IC6 CHECK FOR MOISTURE IN SYSTEM — NG / OK
- IC7 CHECK A/C COMPRESSOR FOR MALFUNCTION — NG / OK

REPAIR OR REPLACE AS SPECIFIED IN PINPOINT TESTS

RETURN TO SYMPTOM CHART OR END TESTING AS SPECIFIED IN PINPOINT TESTS

* RECHECK IC1 AFTER FAULT CORRECTION

AIR CONDITIONING DIAGNOSIS AND TESTING—ESCORT AND TRACER, CONT'D

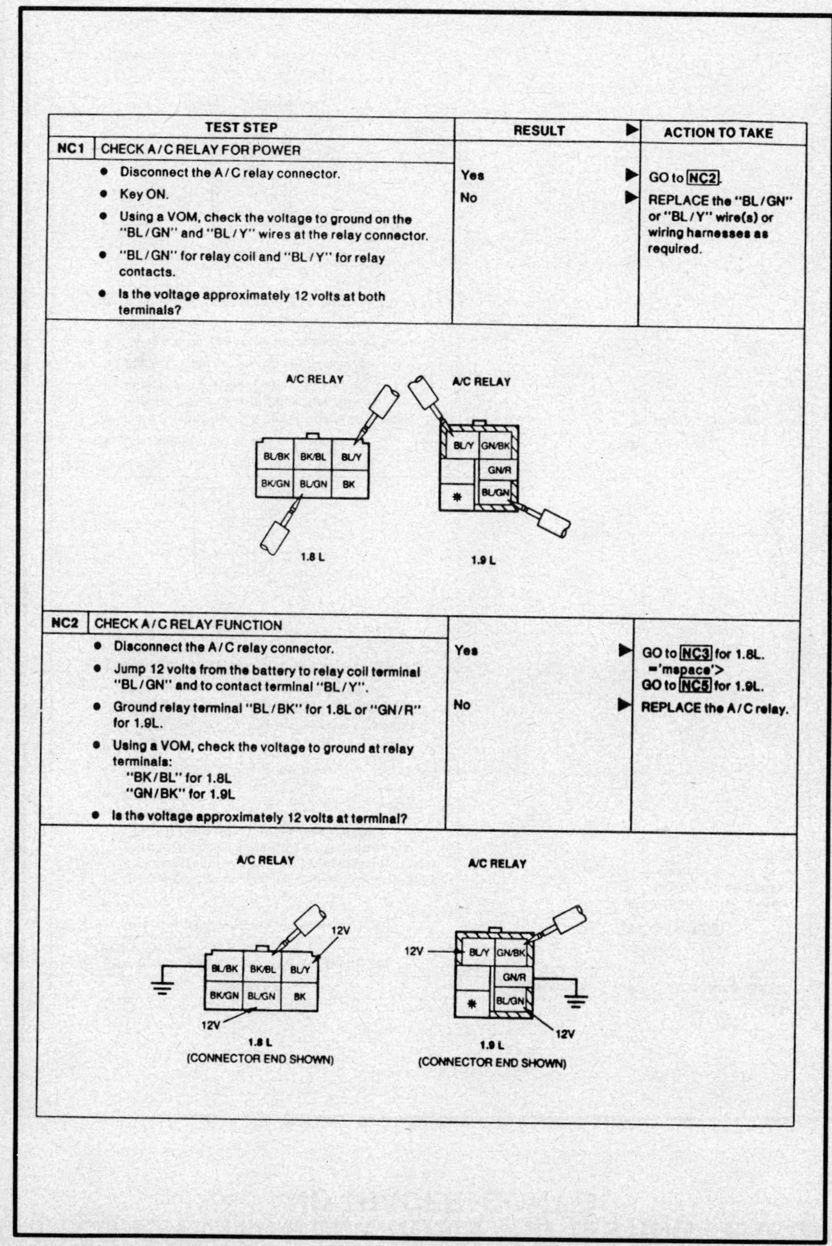

	TEST STEP	RESULT ▶	ACTION TO TAKE
NC1	CHECK A/C RELAY FOR POWER		
	• Disconnect the A/C relay connector. • Key ON. • Using a VOM, check the voltage to ground on the "BL/GN" and "BL/Y" wires at the relay connector. • "BL/GN" for relay coil and "BL/Y" for relay contacts. • Is the voltage approximately 12 volts at both terminals?	Yes ▶ No ▶	GO to NC2. REPLACE the "BL/GN" or "BL/Y" wire(s) or wiring harnesses as required.
NC2	CHECK A/C RELAY FUNCTION		
	• Disconnect the A/C relay connector. • Jump 12 volts from the battery to relay coil terminal "BL/GN" and to contact terminal "BL/Y". • Ground relay terminal "BL/BK" for 1.8L or "GN/R" for 1.9L. • Using a VOM, check the voltage to ground at relay terminals: "BK/BL" for 1.8L "GN/BK" for 1.9L • Is the voltage approximately 12 volts at terminal?	Yes ▶ No ▶	GO to NC3 for 1.8L. ='mspace'> GO to NC5 for 1.9L. REPLACE the A/C relay.

AIR CONDITIONING DIAGNOSIS AND TESTING—ESCORT AND TRACER, CONT'D

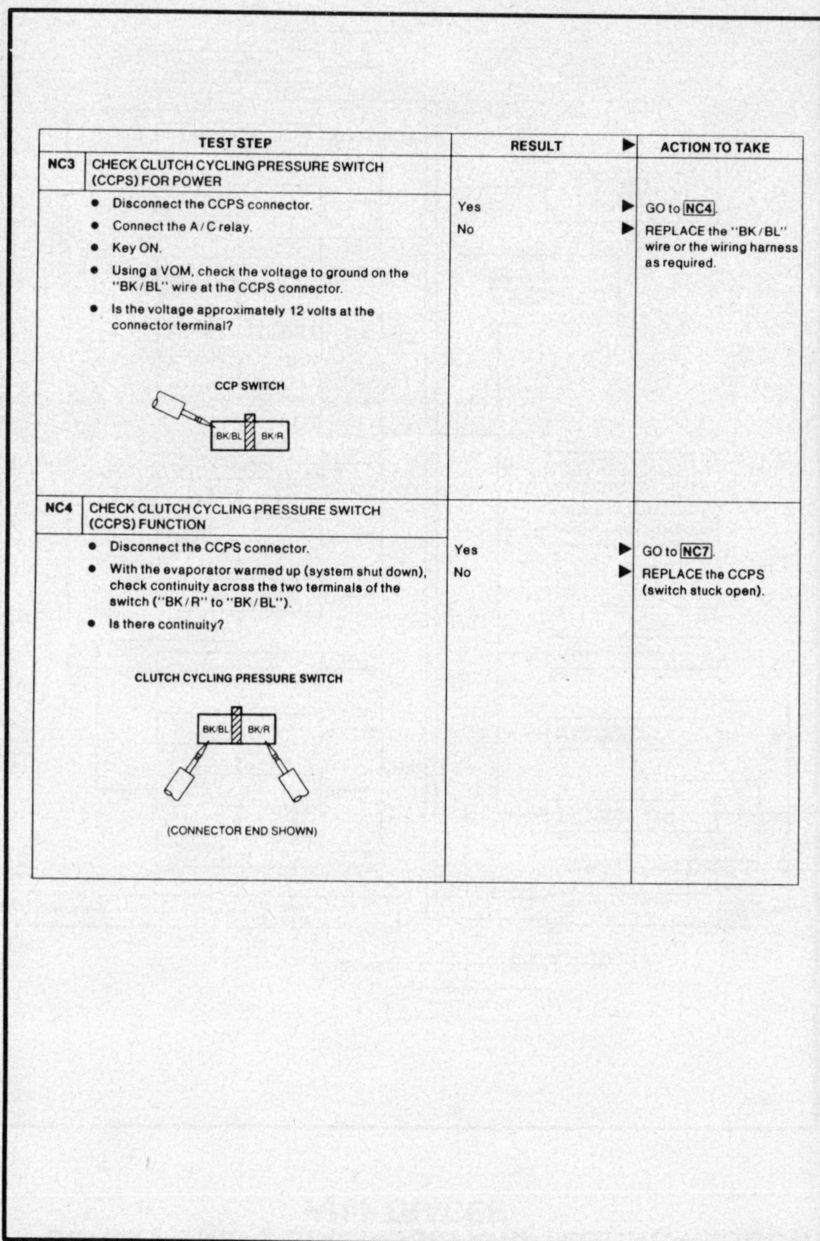

	TEST STEP	RESULT ▶	ACTION TO TAKE
NC3	CHECK CLUTCH CYCLING PRESSURE SWITCH (CCPS) FOR POWER		
	• Disconnect the CCPS connector. • Connect the A/C relay. • Key ON. • Using a VOM, check the voltage to ground on the "BK/BL" wire at the CCPS connector. • Is the voltage approximately 12 volts at the connector terminal? CCP SWITCH BK/BL BK/R	Yes ▶ No ▶	GO to NC4. REPLACE the "BK/BL" wire or the wiring harness as required.
NC4	CHECK CLUTCH CYCLING PRESSURE SWITCH (CCPS) FUNCTION		
	• Disconnect the CCPS connector. • With the evaporator warmed up (system shut down), check continuity across the two terminals of the switch ("BK/R" to "BK/BL"). • Is there continuity? CLUTCH CYCLING PRESSURE SWITCH BK/BL BK/R (CONNECTOR END SHOWN)	Yes ▶ No ▶	GO to NC7. REPLACE the CCPS (switch stuck open).

	TEST STEP	RESULT ▶	ACTION TO TAKE
NC5	CHECK WIDE OPEN THROTTLE A/C (WAC) RELAY FOR POWER		
	• Disconnect the WAC relay connector. • Key ON. • Using a VOM, verify that the voltage to ground at the connector terminal "BL/GN" is approximately 12 volts before going further. If it is not, replace the "BL/GN" wire or harness as required before proceeding. • Key OFF. • Disconnect the CCPS connector. • Key ON. • Ground the "GN/R" wire at the CCPS connector. • Using a VOM, check the voltage to ground at the WAC relay connector terminal "GN/BK". • Is the voltage at the "GN/BK" connector terminal approximately 12 volts? * GN/BK BL/BK BL/W BL/GN	Yes ▶ No ▶	GO to NC6. REPLACE the "GN/BK" wire or wiring harness as required.
NC6	CHECK WAC RELAY FUNCTION (1.9L ONLY)		
	• Disconnect the WAC relay connector. • Jump 12 volts from the battery to the WAC relay terminal "BL/GN" and ground the "BL/BK" terminal to open the relay. • Apply 12 volts to "GN/BK" terminal. • Using a VOM, check the voltage at the WAC relay terminal "BL/W". • Is the voltage zero at WAC relay terminal "BL/W"? WAC RELAY * GN/BK BL/BK BL/W BL/GN 12V (CONNECTOR END SHOWN)	Yes ▶ No ▶	GO to NC7. REPLACE the WAC relay.

AIR CONDITIONING DIAGNOSIS AND TESTING—ESCORT AND TRACER, CONT'D

TEST STEP	RESULT ▶	ACTION TO TAKE
NC7 CHECK COMPRESSOR CLUTCH FOR POWER		
• Disconnect the A/C relay connector. • Jump 12 volts from the battery to the A/C relay terminals "BL/GN" and "BL/Y" and ground relay terminal "BL/BK" for 1.8L or terminal "GN/R" for 1.9L, to close the relay. • Verify that the CCPS for 1.8L is closed (A/C system shut down and warmed up). • Jump the A/C relay terminal "BK/BL" to the relay connector "BK/BL" (1.8L). • Disconnect the compressor clutch connector. • Using a VOM, measure the voltage to ground at the compressor clutch connector terminal "BK/R" for 1.8L, or "BL/W" for 1.9L. • Is the voltage approximately 12 volts at the clutch connector?	Yes ▶ No ▶	GO to NC8. REPLACE the wire "BK/R" for 1.8L or "BL/W" for 1.9L, or the wiring harness as required.
BK R — 1.8 L; BL/W — 1.9 L		
NC8 CHECK COMPRESSOR CLUTCH FUNCTION ON JUMPED POWER		
• Disconnect the compressor clutch connector. • Start the engine. • Jump 12 volts from the battery to the compressor clutch power terminal "BK/R" (1.8L) or "BL/W" (1.9L) with the engine running and note the clutch engagement. • Does the clutch engage instantly and pick up the compressor very rapidly without screeching or squealing?	Yes ▶ No ▶	GO to NC9. REPLACE the compressor clutch.
12V BK R — 1.8 L; 12V BL/W — 1.9 L		

AIR CONDITIONING DIAGNOSIS AND TESTING—ESCORT AND TRACER, CONT'D

TEST STEP	RESULT ▶	ACTION TO TAKE
NC9 CHECK COMPRESSOR CLUTCH FUNCTION ON SYSTEM WIRING		
• Reconnect all connectors previously disconnected. • Remove all jumper wiring. • Start the engine. • Press the A/C switch and turn on the blower control. • Note whether the compressor clutch engages and drives the compressor. • Does the compressor clutch operate on system wiring satisfactorily?	Yes But compressor runs continuously ▶ Yes Compressor cycles on and off but cooling not satisfactory ▶ No ▶	GO to NC13. GO to IC1. GO to NC10 for 1.8L. GO to NC11 for 1.9L. (control circuit malfunction).

1.8L Engine

TEST STEP	RESULT ▶	ACTION TO TAKE
NC10 CHECK BLOWER MOTOR CONTROL CIRCUIT		
• Key OFF. • Blower motor switch ON (position 1, 2, 3, or 4). • A/C switch depressed ON. • Using a VOM, check continuity from the "GN/BK" wire at the ECA to the "BK" wire at the blower motor switch. • Check the continuity from the "BL/BK" wire at the ECA to the "BL/GN" terminal at the A/C relay. • If any of the above checks show no continuity, repair or replace the wires, wiring harnesses or connectors as required before proceeding. • If the above checks meet the specification for continuity, attempt to operate the A/C with the engine running. • Does the A/C system operate and is it cooling satisfactorily?	Yes ▶ No System operates but cooling not satisfactory ▶ No Compressor runs continuously ▶	End of testing. GO to IC1. GO to NC13. (Shorted control circuit)

1.9L Engine

TEST STEP	RESULT ▶	ACTION TO TAKE
NC11 CHECK A/C RELAY CONTROL CIRCUIT		
• Key OFF. • Blower motor switch ON. • A/C switch depressed ON. • Using a VOM, check continuity from the "BL/GN" terminal on the A/C relay to the "GN/R" terminal at the CCPS. • Check continuity from the "R/Y" terminal at the CCPS to the "BK" terminal at the blower motor switch. • Is there continuity?	Yes ▶ No ▶	GO to NC12. REPAIR or REPLACE the wire, wires or harness as required, including connectors.

AIR CONDITIONING DIAGNOSIS AND TESTING—ESCORT AND TRACER, CONT'D

TEST STEP		RESULT	▶	ACTION TO TAKE
NC12	CHECK WAC RELAY CONTROL CIRCUIT			
	• Using a VOM, check continuity from the "BL/GN" terminal at the WAC relay to the "BL/BK" terminal at the ECA. Also check the continuity from the "GN/BK" terminal on the WAC relay to the "GN/BK" terminal on the ECA. • If any of these checks show no continuity, repair or replace the wires, wiring harnesses or connectors as required before proceeding. • If the above checks meet the specification for continuity, attempt to operate the A/C system with the engine running. • Does the A/C system operate and is it cooling satisfactorily?	Yes	▶	End of testing.
		No System operates but cooling not satisfactory	▶	GO to IC1.
		No Compressor runs continuously	▶	GO to NC13. (Shorted control circuit)

1.8L, 1.9L Engines

TEST STEP		RESULT	▶	ACTION TO TAKE
NC13	CHECK A/C COMPRESSOR			
	• Using a VOM, check for opens and/or shorts to ground in each control circuit wire as follows, referring as required to the 1.8L or 1.9L wiring diagram: **1.8L and 1.9L:** "BL/Y", "BL", "BL/R", "BL/W" (blower switch to resistor), "BL/BK" (resistor to blower motor). **1.8L only:** "BL/BK" (A/C relay to ECA), "GN/BK" and "R/Y" (ECA to A/C switch), "O/BL" (blower switch to ECA). **1.9L only:** "GN/R" (A/C relay to CCPS), "R/Y" (CCPS to A/C switch). • Check for stuck closed contact points by testing for continuity as follows: 1.8L A/C relay — "BL/Y" to "BK/BL" 1.9L A/C relay — "BL/Y" to "GN/BK" 1.9L CCP switch — "GN/R" to "R/Y" Remove the CCPS from the suction accumulator to obtain sufficiently low pressure to open the switch. • Is the cause of continuous compressor operation corrected?	Yes	▶	GO to IC1.
		No	▶	REPAIR or REPLACE any damaged or shorted wiring, wiring harnesses, connectors or components as required. RETEST after repairs.

AIR CONDITIONING DIAGNOSIS AND TESTING—ESCORT AND TRACER, CONT'D

TEST STEP		RESULT	▶	ACTION TO TAKE
IC1	CHECK REFRIGERANT PRESSURE CHART			
	• Connect a manifold gauge set. • Run the engine at fast idle. • Operate the A/C at maximum cooling for a few minutes with blower on speed III. • Observe A/C system pressure on the high and low sides of the gauge. • Compare the gauge readings to the pressure specifications listed below.	Cooling is still erratic	▶	GO to IC4.
		No Insufficient	▶	GO to IC2.
		No Excessive	▶	GO to IC3.

Description	Specification
Normal Refrigerant Pressure Low-Side Pressure	147-294 kPa (1.5-3.0 kg/cm², 21-43 psi)
High-Side Pressure	1,177-1,619 kPa (12.0-16.5 kg/cm², 171-235 psi)

• Is the A/C pressure reading OK?

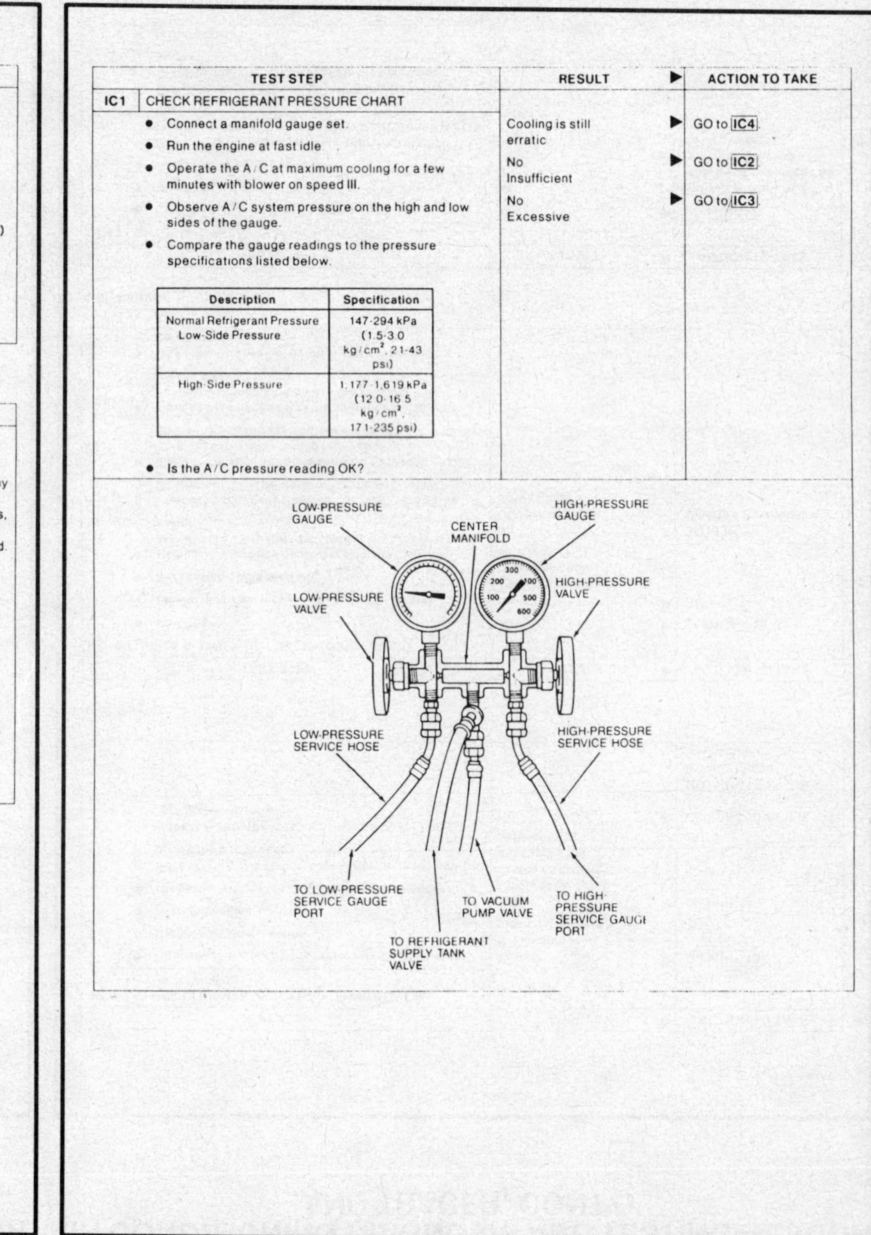

AIR CONDITIONING DIAGNOSIS AND TESTING—ESCORT AND TRACER, CONT'D

	TEST STEP	RESULT	ACTION TO TAKE
IC2	CHECK FOR INSUFFICIENT REFRIGERANT		
	• Connect the manifold gauge set. • Operate the engine at 2000 rpm and set the A/C to maximum cooling. • Measure the low-side and high-side pressures. • If insufficient refrigerant, the pressures should be: Low-side: Below 7.85 kPa (0.8 kg/cm², 11.4 psi) High-side: 785-883 kPa (8-9 kg/cm², 114-128 psi) • If the pressure is low, check for leakage as evidenced by oil stains at connections. • If no oil stains are evident, check for leakage at the following connections using a gas leak detector (observe warning and safety precautions): Inlet and outlet of; condenser, suction accumulator/drier, compressor, sight glass, cooling unit. • Is the refrigerant pressure low and is leakage present?	Yes (And leakage present) ▶	REPLACE O-rings at leaking connectors and RETORQUE, then EVACUATE the system, RECHARGE and RETEST.
		Yes (No leaks present) ▶	EVACUATE, RECHARGE, and RETEST the system. (Leakage occurred slowly over a long time.)
		No (But cooling is erratic) ▶	GO to IC4.
IC3	CHECK FOR EXCESSIVE REFRIGERANT		
	• Connect the manifold gauge set. • Operate the engine at 2000 rpm and set the A/C to maximum cooling. • Measure the low-side and high-side pressures. • If excessive refrigerant, the pressures should be: Low-side: Above 245 kPa (2.5 kg/cm², 35.6 psi) High-side: Above 1,962 kPa (20 kg/cm², 284 psi) • If the pressure is high, check the condenser for bent fins or other damage. • Is the refrigerant pressure high?	Yes ▶	REPAIR condenser fins or other damage, DISCHARGE the excess refrigerant, until RETEST shows the low and high sides to be within normal specification.
		No (But cooling is erratic) ▶	GO to IC4.
IC4	CHECK FOR AIR IN SYSTEM		
	• Connect the manifold gauge set. • Operate the engine at 2000 rpm and set the A/C to maximum cooling. • Measure the low-side and high-side pressures. • If air is in the refrigerant, the pressures should be: Low-side: Above 245 kPa (2.5 kg/cm², 35.6 psi) High-side: Above 2256 kPa (23 kg/cm², 327 psi) • Do the pressures indicate air in the refrigerant charge?	Yes ▶	DISCHARGE, EVACUATE and RECHARGE the system with fresh refrigerant R-12 to the correct amount. GO to IC1. RECHECK the low-side and high-side pressures, and if they are still too high, REPLACE the suction accumulator/drier, RECHARGE and RECHECK pressures.
		No (But cooling still erratic) ▶	GO to IC5.

AIR CONDITIONING DIAGNOSIS AND TESTING—ESCORT AND TRACER, CONT'D

	TEST STEP	RESULT	ACTION TO TAKE
IC5	CHECK FOR REFRIGERANT CIRCULATION		
	• Connect the manifold gauge set. • Operate the engine at 2000 rpm and set the A/C to maximum cooling. • Measure the low-side and high-side pressures. • If there is no circulation of refrigerant in the system, the pressures should be: Low-side: 76 cm-Hg (3.0 in-Hg) vacuum. High-side: Below 589 kPa (kg/cm², 85 psi) of pressure. • If the pressures indicate no refrigerant circulation, turn the A/C OFF for 10 minutes. • Turn the A/C ON to determine whether the blockage is due to moisture or solid material. • After turning the system ON, does it operate normally?	Yes (But cooling is erratic) ▶	GO to IC6. (Moisture in system freezes, then melts and relieves blockage.)
		No ▶	REPLACE the fixed orifice, EVACUATE the system and RECHARGE the system with fresh refrigerant R-12 to the correct amount. GO to IC1. RECHECK the low-side and high-side pressures.
IC6	CHECK FOR MOISTURE IN SYSTEM		
	• Connect the manifold gauge set. • Operate the engine at 2000 rpm and set the A/C to maximum cooling. • Measure the low-side and high-side pressures. • If moisture is in the refrigerant, the pressures should be: Low-side: 50 cm-Hg (2.0 in-Hg) of vacuum to 147 kPa (1.5 kg/cm², 21.3 psi) of pressure. High-side: 687-1,472 kPa (7-15 Kg/cm², 100-213 psi) • Do the pressures indicate moisture in the refrigerant system?	Yes ▶	DISCHARGE, EVACUATE and RECHARGE the system with fresh refrigerant R-12 to the correct amount. GO to IC1. RECHECK the low-side and high-side pressures and if still too high, REPLACE the suction accumulator/drier, RECHARGE and RECHECK pressures.
		No ▶	GO to IC7.
IC7	CHECK A/C COMPRESSOR FOR MALFUNCTION		
	• Connect the manifold gauge set. • Operate the engine at 2000 rpm and set the A/C to maximum cooling. • Measure the low-side and high-side pressures. • If the A/C compressor is malfunctioning (not pumping properly) the pressures should be: Low-side: 392-589 kPa (4-6 kg/cm², 57-85 psi) High-side: 687-981 kPa (7-10 kg/cm², 100-142 psi) • If the pressures indicate a faulty compressor or slipping clutch, operate the system for 20 minutes, cycling the temperature control from hot to cold to hot several times. • Recheck the pressures. • Do the pressures indicate a faulty compressor or clutch?	Yes Clutch slipping ▶	REPAIR or REPLACE the clutch as required.
		Yes Clutch not slipping ▶	REPLACE the A/C compressor, EVACUATE the system and RECHARGE with R-12 refrigerant to the correct amount.
		No ▶	GO to IC1. RECHECK the low-side and high-side pressures.

AUTOMATIC TEMPERATURE CONTROL ERROR CODE KEY—TAURUS, SABLE AND CONTINENTAL

ERROR CODE KEY

Error Code	Detected Condition	Troubleshooting/Repair Procedure
01	Replace control head	
02	Blend door problem	• Refer to Blend Door Actuator Diagnosis
03	In-car temp sensor open or short	• Refer to In-Car Temp Sensor Diagnosis
04	Ambient temp sensor open or short	• Refer to Ambient Temp Sensor Diagnosis
05	Sunload sensor short	• Refer to Sunload Sensor Diagnosis
888	Testing complete — no test failure (all segments on)	• Refer to EATC System Functional Check

	TEST STEP	RESULT	ACTION TO TAKE
1	Turn ignition switch to the RUN position. Press the AUTO button. Set control at 90°F setting.	Control powers up	GO to 2.
		Control does not light	REFER to Diagnosis When Self-Test And Functional Test Indicate No Errors Found.
2	Verify that the blower does not come on. (Engine coolant temp. < 120°F)	Blower off	GO to 3.
		Blower on	REFER to CELO Inoperative.
3	Ensure that engine is warm (coolant temp. > 120°F). Set control at 75 setting.	Blower on	GO to 4.
		Blower off	REFER to Blower Speed Controller Diagnosis-No Blower.
4	Rotate blower thumbwheel fully down.	Blower goes to low blower	GO to 5.
			CHECK battery voltage. If voltage is below 10 volts, refer to Charging System Diagnosis.
		Blower does not go to low blower	REFER to Blower Speed Controller Diagnosis.
5	Rotate blower thumbwheel fully up.	Blower goes to high blower	GO to 6.
		Blower does not go to high blower	REFER to Blower Speed Controller Diagnosis.
6	Press the DEFROST button.	Verify that air is discharged from defroster nozzle with small bleed through the side window demistors. Verify that the outside air/recirc door is in the outside air position.	GO to 7.
		Air is not discharged through the defroster or side window demistors.	REFER to Vacuum System Diagnosis.

AUTOMATIC TEMPERATURE CONTROL FUNCTIONAL TEST—TAURUS, SABLE AND CONTINENTAL

	TEST STEP	RESULT	ACTION TO TAKE
7	Press the FLOOR button.	Verify that the air is discharged through the floor ducts.	GO to 8.
		Air is not discharged through the floor ducts.	REFER to Vacuum System Diagnosis.
8	Press the VENT button.	Verify that the air is discharged through the panel ducts.	GO to 9.
		Air is not discharged through the panel ducts.	REFER to Vacuum System Diagnosis.
9	Make sure that the ambient temperature is greater than 40°F. Press the MAX A/C button.	Verify that the outside air/recirc door is in the recirc position.	GO to 10.
		Outside air/Recirc door is not in the recirc position.	REFER to Vacuum System Diagnosis.
10	Press the VENT button.	Verify that the VENT display is lit. Verify that the clutch is off.	GO to 11.
		A/C clutch is still on	REFER to Clutch Does Not Disengage When In OFF Diagnosis.
11	Press the MAX A/C button again.	Verify that the MAX A/C display is lit and that the clutch is on.	GO to 12.
		A/C clutch is off.	REFER to No Clutch Operation Diagnosis.
12	Press the AUTO button.	Verify that the AUTO display is lit	REFER to Diagnosis When Self-Test And Functional Test Indicate No Errors Found.

AUTOMATIC TEMPERATURE CONTROL NO ERROR CODE FOUND DIAGNOSIS AND TESTING—TAURUS, SABLE AND CONTINENTAL

CONDITION	POSSIBLE SOURCE	ACTION
• Cool Discharge Air When System is Set to Auto/90°F	• Heater system malfunction. • Blend door not in max. heat.	• REFER to heater system operating principles • CHECK position of blend door. • CHECK coolant level. • CHECK shaft attachment. • TEST per Blend Door Actuator Diagnosis (assume 2 was displayed in the Self-Test).
• Warm Discharge Air in Auto/60°F	• Clutch circuit malfunction. • Check refrigerant. • Blend door not in max. A/C position. • Outside/Recirc door not in recirc.	• TEST clutch circuit per No Clutch Operation Diagnosis. • CHECK position of blend door. • CHECK shaft attachment. • TEST per Blend Door Actuator Diagnosis (assume 2 was displayed in the Self-Test). • TEST per Vacuum System Diagnosis.
• Cool Air in 85°F, Max. Heat in 90°F • Heat in 65°F Max. Cool in 60°F	• Sensor shorted. • Sensor open.	• TROUBLESHOOT according to Sensor Diagnosis. • TROUBLESHOOT according to Sensor Diagnosis.
• No Blower	• Damaged CELO switch/wiring. • Damaged blower controller. • Damaged control head. • Damaged blower motor. • Damaged wiring.	• TEST per No Blower Section of Blower Speed Controller.
• High Blower Only	• Damaged control head. • Damaged blower controller. • Damaged wiring.	• TEST per High Blower Only Section of Blower Speed Controller.
• Clutch is On in Off Mode	• Damaged control head. • Damaged wiring or interface components.	• TEST according to "Clutch does not Disengage when in OFF mode".

AUTOMATIC TEMPERATURE CONTROL NO ERROR CODE FOUND DIAGNOSIS AND TESTING—TAURUS, SABLE AND CONTINENTAL, CONT'D

CONDITION	POSSIBLE SOURCE	ACTION
• Control Assembly Digits and VFD Do Not Light Up Blower Off	• Fuse. • Ignition Circuit No. 298 open. • Ignition Circuit No. 797 open. • Ground Circuit No. 57A open. • Damaged control head.	• Replace fuse. • Check Circuit No. 298. • Check Circuit No. 797. • Check Circuit No. 57A. • Change control assembly.
• Cold Air is Delivered During Heating when Engine is Cold.	• Damaged wiring. • Damaged or inoperative engine temperature switch.	• Place system at 90°F/Auto. With ignition off, (ignition must be off when grounding Circuit No. 244 for valid results) ground Circuit No. 244 at engine temp. switch. Start vehicle. If blower is off, replace cold engine lockout (CELO). If blower is on, check wiring. If OK, replace control assembly. • Replace engine temperature switch.
• Temperature Set Point Does Not Repeat After Turning Off Ignition	• Circuit No. 797 not connected to control head. • Damaged or inoperative control assembly.	• Remove control assembly connector. With ignition off, check for 12 volts at Pin 12 (Driver's side connector VA). • If no voltage, check fuse/wiring. If voltage, replace control head.
• Control Head Temperature Display Will Not Switch From Fahrenheit To Centigrade When the E/M Trip Computer Button is Pushed	• Damaged or inoperative wiring, trip minder or control head.	• **CAUTION: ACCIDENTAL SHORTING OF THE WRONG PIN COULD DESTROY THE CONTROL HEAD.** Short Pin 20 of connector VA (Circuit No. 506) to ground. Turn on ignition. If the display does not switch from F to C, Circuit No. 506 is open at the control assembly and the control assembly is damaged. Otherwise check the wiring and the trip minder.
• System Does Not Control Temperature	• Sensor hose not connected to aspirator or sensor. • Aspirator not secured to evaporator case. • Sensor seal(s) missing or not installed properly. • Aspirator or sensor hose blocked with foreign material or kinked. • Damaged aspirator hose.	• Inspect and service. • Inspect and service. • Inspect and service. • Inspect and service. • Inspect and service.
• EATC Control Head Turns On and Off Erratically. No Control of System.	• Damaged charging system. EATC will not function with too low or too high battery voltage.	• Check battery voltage. If battery voltage is less than 10 volts or greater than 16 volts, refer to charging system diagnosis. Do not replace EATC control head.

AUTOMATIC TEMPERATURE CONTROL IN–CAR TEMPERATURE SENSOR DIAGNOSIS AND TESTING—TAURUS, SABLE AND CONTINENTAL

CONDITION	POSSIBLE SOURCE	ACTION
• Self-Diagnostics Error Code 03 (Warm Air Discharge at 65°F or Cool Air Discharge at 85°F)	1. Sensor open or shorted.	• Disconnect wire harness connector at sensor. Measure resistance across sensor terminals and compare with Sensor Resistance Table below. • If resistance is out of specifications shown in Table, replace sensor. If sensor is okay, go to Step 2.
	2. Wire harness open or shorted.	• Disconnect battery cables. Disconnect wire harness connector from sensor and disconnect both connectors from control head. • Check for continuity and for possible shorting between the two wires (pin 2 and pin 17). Repair if necessary. Reconnect wire harness and battery cables.

SENSOR RESISTANCE TABLE

APPROXIMATE TEMPERATURE	SENSOR RESISTANCE ACCEPTABLE RANGE
10°C to 20°C (50°F to 68°F)	37K to 58K ohms
20°C to 30°C (68°F to 86°F)	24K to 37K ohms
30°C to 40°C (86°F to 104°F)	16K to 24K ohms

AUTOMATIC TEMPERATURE CONTROL AMBIENT SENSOR DIAGNOSIS AND TESTING—TAURUS, SABLE AND CONTINENTAL

CONDITION	POSSIBLE SOURCE	ACTION
• Self-Diagnostics Error Code 04 and Outside Temperature Display is Reading – 40°F or 140°F (Warm Air Discharge at 65°F or Cool Air Discharge at 85°F)	1. Sensor open or shorted.	• Disconnect battery cables (this is necessary to reset outside temperature display memory). Disconnect the wire harness connector at sensor. Measure resistance across sensor terminal and compare with Sensor Resistance Table in In-Car Temperature Sensor Diagnosis Chart. • If resistance is out of specifications shown in Sensor Resistance Table, replace sensor. If sensor is okay, go to Step 2. Reconnect battery cables. NOTE: Install sensor and electrical connections before battery is reconnected
• Intermittent Heating and Cooling. Outside Temperature Display Sometimes Inaccurate	2. Sensor wire harness open or shorted.	• Disconnect battery cables. Disconnect wire harness connector from sensor and disconnect both connectors from the control head. • Inspect for crimped terminals. • Check for continuity and for possible shorting between the two wires (pins 1 and 2). Service if necessary. Reconnect wire harness and battery cables.

AUTOMATIC TEMPERATURE CONTROL SUNLOAD SENSOR DIAGNOSIS AND TESTING—TAURUS, SABLE AND CONTINENTAL

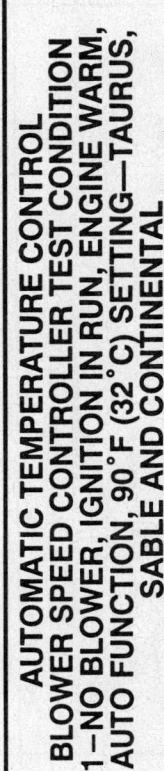

CONDITION	POSSIBLE SOURCE	ACTION
• Self-Diagnostics Error Code 05	1. Sensor shorted.	• Disconnect battery cables. Disconnect wire harness connector at sensor and disconnect both connectors from control head.* Check for continuity and for possible shorting between the two wires (pin 3 and pin 16). Repeat if necessary. Reconnect battery cables.

* NOTE: Check the sensor for a short using an ohmmeter. Since the sensor is a Photodiode, there should be some unspecified resistance across the terminals dependent upon the available light in the area. The only test that should be made is for a short circuit (zero resistance). If resistance is zero ohms, replace the sensor.

AUTOMATIC TEMPERATURE CONTROL NO CLUTCH DIAGNOSIS AND TESTING—TAURUS, SABLE AND CONTINENTAL

	TEST STEP	RESULT	▶	ACTION TO TAKE
A	Jump the LB/PK and LG/P wires Pin 26 and Pin 25 of driver side connector VA.	Clutch engages	▶	REPLACE control assembly.
		Clutch does not engage	▶	(Damaged wiring, integrated controller or EEC-IV module, damaged pressure switch.)
		15A fuse blows	▶	Clutch is shorted. CHECK diode in wiring harness across clutch in particular. Service short, then test to see if the control head will turn the clutch off and on. If not, replace control assembly.

AUTOMATIC TEMPERATURE CONTROL CLUTCH DOES NOT ENGAGE WHEN IN OFF POSITION DIAGNOSIS AND TESTING—TAURUS, SABLE AND CONTINENTAL

	TEST STEP	RESULT	▶	ACTION TO TAKE
A	Disconnect connector VA (driver's side) from control assembly.	Clutch disengages	▶	CHANGE control assembly.
		Clutch stays on	▶	(Faulty wiring, faulty integrated controller or EEC-IV module, faulty pressure switch.)

AUTOMATIC TEMPERATURE CONTROL BLOWER SPEED CONTROLLER TEST CONDITION 1–NO BLOWER, IGNITION IN RUN, ENGINE WARM, AUTO FUNCTION, 90°F (32°C) SETTING—TAURUS, SABLE AND CONTINENTAL

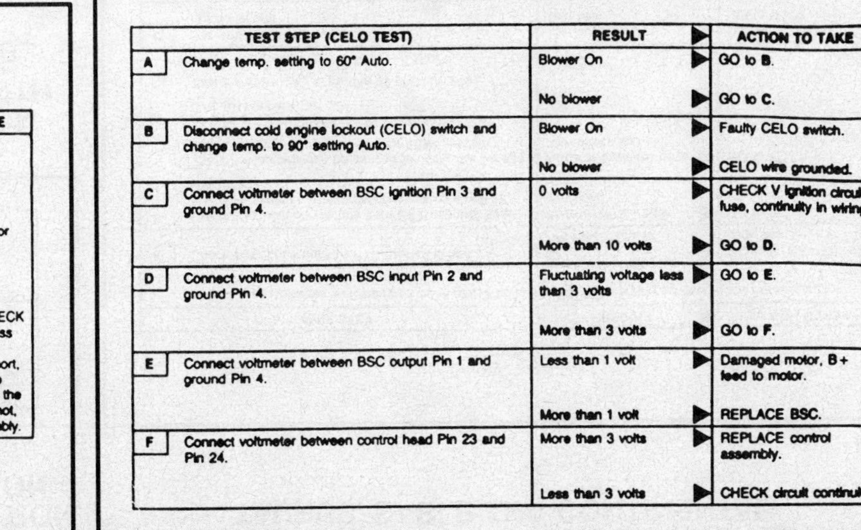

	TEST STEP (CELO TEST)	RESULT	▶	ACTION TO TAKE
A	Change temp. setting to 60° Auto.	Blower On	▶	GO to B.
		No blower	▶	GO to C.
B	Disconnect cold engine lockout (CELO) switch and change temp. to 90° setting Auto.	Blower On	▶	Faulty CELO switch.
		No blower	▶	CELO wire grounded.
C	Connect voltmeter between BSC ignition Pin 3 and ground Pin 4.	0 volts	▶	CHECK V ignition circuit fuse, continuity in wiring.
		More than 10 volts	▶	GO to D.
D	Connect voltmeter between BSC input Pin 2 and ground Pin 4.	Fluctuating voltage less than 3 volts	▶	GO to E.
		More than 3 volts	▶	GO to F.
E	Connect voltmeter between BSC output Pin 1 and ground Pin 4.	Less than 1 volt	▶	Damaged motor, B+ feed to motor.
		More than 1 volt	▶	REPLACE BSC.
F	Connect voltmeter between control head Pin 23 and Pin 24.	More than 3 volts	▶	REPLACE control assembly.
		Less than 3 volts	▶	CHECK circuit continuity.

AUTOMATIC TEMPERATURE CONTROL BLOWER SPEED CONTROLLER TEST CONDITION 2–HIGH BLOWER ONLY, NO BLOWER AUTO FUNCTION, BLOWER THUMBWHEEL TURNED TO LOW POSITION—TAURUS, SABLE AND CONTINENTAL

	TEST STEP (Voltmeter Connections)	RESULT ▶	ACTION TO TAKE
A	Disconnect HBR and BSC electronic connections.	Blower in high ▶	Faulty blower motor or blower wire circuit.
		Blower OFF ▶	GO to B.
B	Reconnect BSC and connect voltmeter between BSC input Pin 2 and ground Pin 4 (auto function). Rotate blower switch from high to low blower.	Less than 7 volts fluctuating ▶	REPLACE control assembly.
		More than 7 volts fluctuating ▶	REPLACE BSC.

AUTOMATIC TEMPERATURE CONTROL BLOWER SPEED CONTROLLER TEST CONDITION 3–BLOWER OPERATES BUT DOES NOT VARY WITH BLOWER CONTROL SWITCH—TAURUS, SABLE AND CONTINENTAL

	TEST STEP (Voltmeter Connection)	RESULT ▶	ACTION TO TAKE
A	Connect voltmeter between BSC input Pin 2 and ground Pin 4 (Auto mode). Rotate blower switch from min. to max. then back to min.	Voltage fluctuation from below 7 volts to above 7 volts then back below 7 volts ▶	GO to B.
		No change in voltage ▶	Replace control head assy.
B	Connect voltmeter between BSC output Pin 1 and ground Pin 4 (Auto mode). Rotate blower switch from min. to max.	Voltage changes from less than 1 volt to 7 volts ▶	Faulty blower motor, or B+ feed to motor.
		No change in voltage ▶	Replace BSC.

AUTOMATIC TEMPERATURE CONTROL AUTOMATIC TEMPERATURE CONTROL BLOWER SPEED CONTROLLER TEST CONDITION 4–COLD ENGINE LOCK OUT (CELO) INOPERATIVE: BLOWER TURNS ON IMMEDIATELY IN AUTO, 90°F (32°C) SETTING, WITH COLD ENGINE—TAURUS, SABLE AND CONTINENTAL

	TEST STEP	RESULT ▶	ACTION TO TAKE
A	Cold engine (engine coolant temp. below 120°) control set at auto 90°.	Blower on ▶	CHECK coolant and retest. If blower turns on again with a cold engine, REPLACE CELO.
		Blower off ▶	CELO OK.

AUTOMATIC TEMPERATURE CONTROL BLEND DOOR ACTUATOR DIAGNOSIS AND TESTING—TAURUS, SABLE AND CONTINENTAL

	TEST STEP	RESULT ▶	ACTION TO TAKE
	Letters in parentheses indicate (wire color, circuit no.). See Fig. 11 for wiring schematic and connector pin diagrams.		
A	Check error code during EATC functional test.	02 Any other number ▶	GO to B. REVIEW error code key
B	Disconnect both connectors from EATC control head and drive actuator in both directions using any 9-12 volt battery.	Actuator drives both directions ▶	GO to C.
	The following pins can be jumped to utilize the vehicle battery. Insure the ignition is in the RUN position. All pins are located on the LEFT connector (E6DB-14489-VA). Trial 1: Pin 24 (BK, 57) to Pin 22 (DB/LG, 249) Trial 2: Pin 24 (BK, 57) to Pin 21 (0,250)	Actuator does not drive both directions ▶	GO to F.
C	Reconnect control head and test according to EATC functional test.	Test successful Test fails ▶	Done GO to D.
D	Disconnect both connectors from EATC control assembly. Measure resistance as shown below at the control assembly connector with the connector disconnected.	All resistances OK ▶	GO to E.
	All pins are located on the RIGHT connector (E6DB-14489-UA). Pin 15 (LG/O, 243) to Pin 6 (O/BK, 776) 5000-7000 ohms Pin 5 (O/W, 351) to Pin 6 (O/BK, 776) 300-7300 ohms Pin 5 (O/W, 351) to Pin 15 (LG/O, 243) 300-7300 ohms	Any resistance not OK ▶	GO to F.
E	Change control head and test according to EATC functional test.	Test successful Test fails ▶	Done GO to A.
F	Check vehicle wiring harness and connector continuity as shown below. Disconnect connectors from both control assembly and blend door actuator. Blend door actuator connector is accessible through glove compartment.	Continuity bad ▶	GO to H.
	PIN / COLOR/CIRCUIT / FUNCTION 1 (DB/LG, 249) Motor CCW 2 (LG/O, 243) Feedback Pot. (−) 3 (O/W, 351) Feedback Pot. (Wiper) 4 (O/BK, 776) Feedback Pot. (+) 5 (O, 250) Motor CW 6 (BK, 57) Ground 7 — No Connection 8 (LB/PK, 295) Voltage In Reconnect all three connectors at end of this test.	Continuity good ▶	GO to G.
G	Change blend door actuator and test according to EATC functional test.	Test successful Test fails ▶	Done GO to A.
H	Fix/replace wiring harness, connect and test according to EATC functional test.	Test successful Test fails ▶	Done GO to A.

WIRING SCHEMATICS

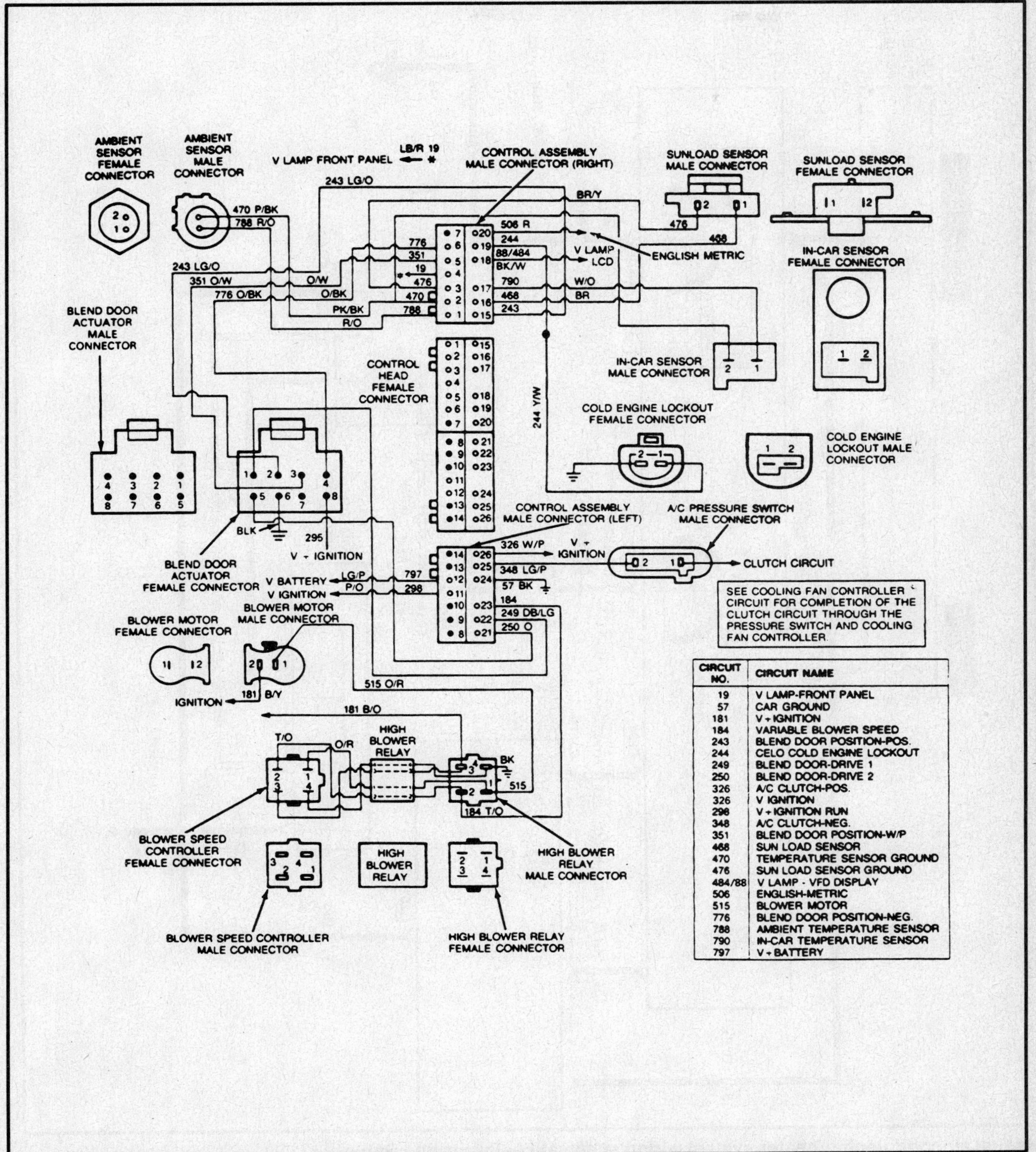

SEE COOLING FAN CONTROLLER CIRCUIT FOR COMPLETION OF THE CLUTCH CIRCUIT THROUGH THE PRESSURE SWITCH AND COOLING FAN CONTROLLER.

CIRCUIT NO.	CIRCUIT NAME
19	V LAMP-FRONT PANEL
57	CAR GROUND
181	V + IGNITION
184	VARIABLE BLOWER SPEED
243	BLEND DOOR POSITION-POS.
244	CELO COLD ENGINE LOCKOUT
249	BLEND DOOR-DRIVE 1
250	BLEND DOOR-DRIVE 2
326	A/C CLUTCH-POS.
326	V IGNITION
298	V + IGNITION RUN
348	A/C CLUTCH-NEG.
351	BLEND DOOR POSITION-W/P
468	SUN LOAD SENSOR
470	TEMPERATURE SENSOR GROUND
476	SUN LOAD SENSOR GROUND
484/88	V LAMP - VFD DISPLAY
506	ENGLISH-METRIC
515	BLOWER MOTOR
776	BLEND DOOR POSITION-NEG.
788	AMBIENT TEMPERATURE SENSOR
790	IN-CAR TEMPERATURE SENSOR
797	V + BATTERY

Automatic temperature control system wiring schematic—Taurus, Sable and Continental

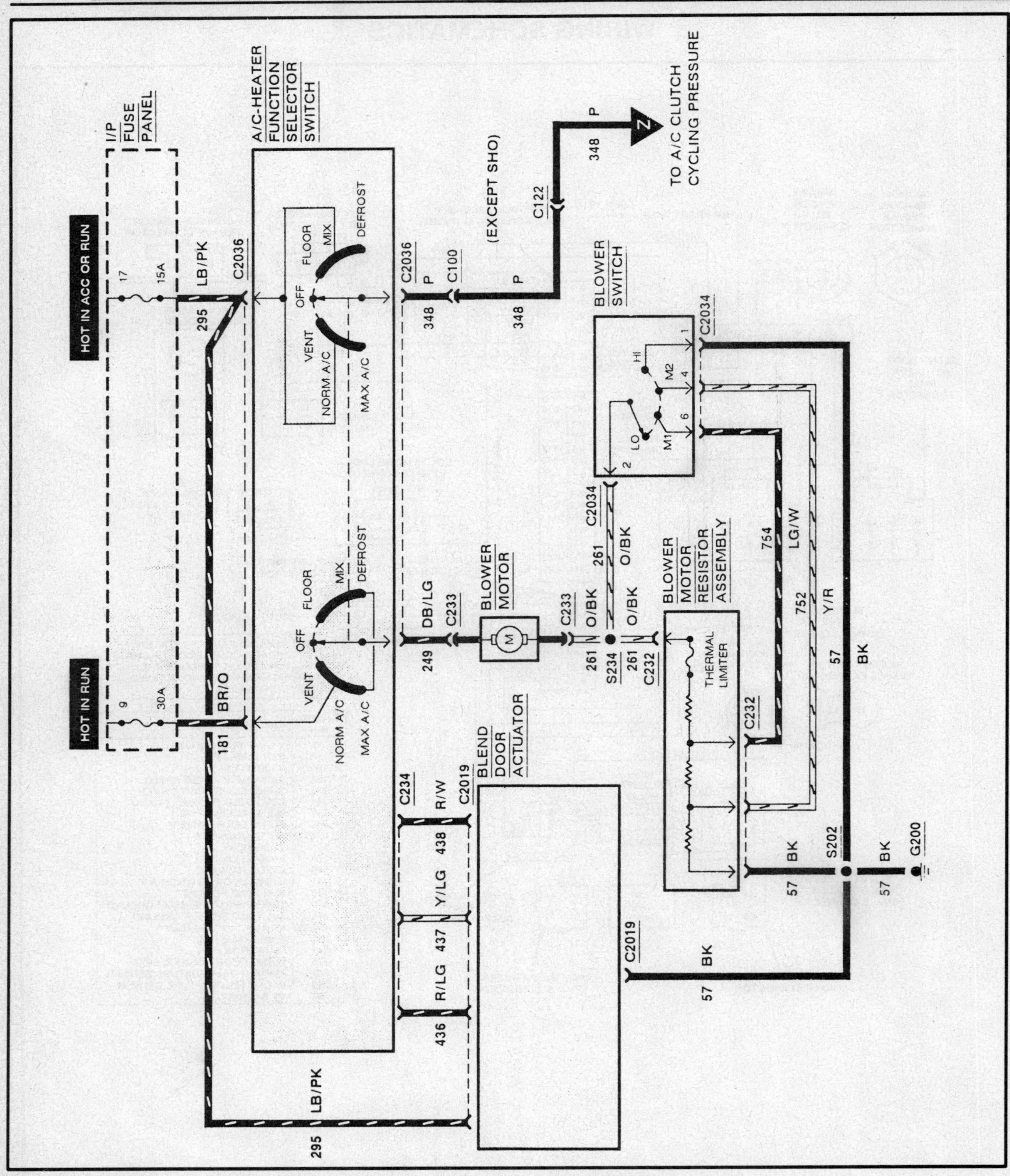

Manual air conditioning/heater system wiring schematic—Taurus and Sable

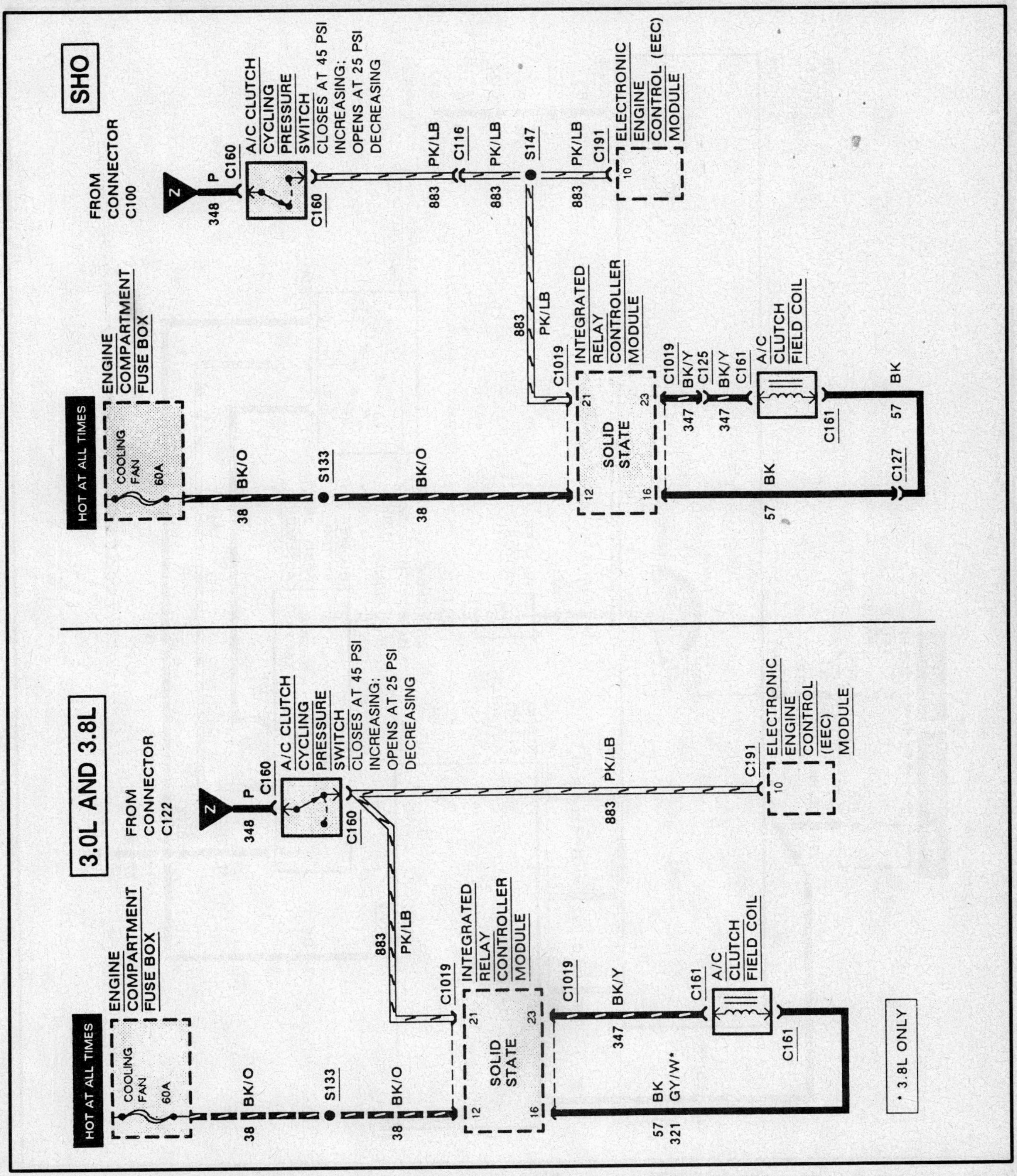

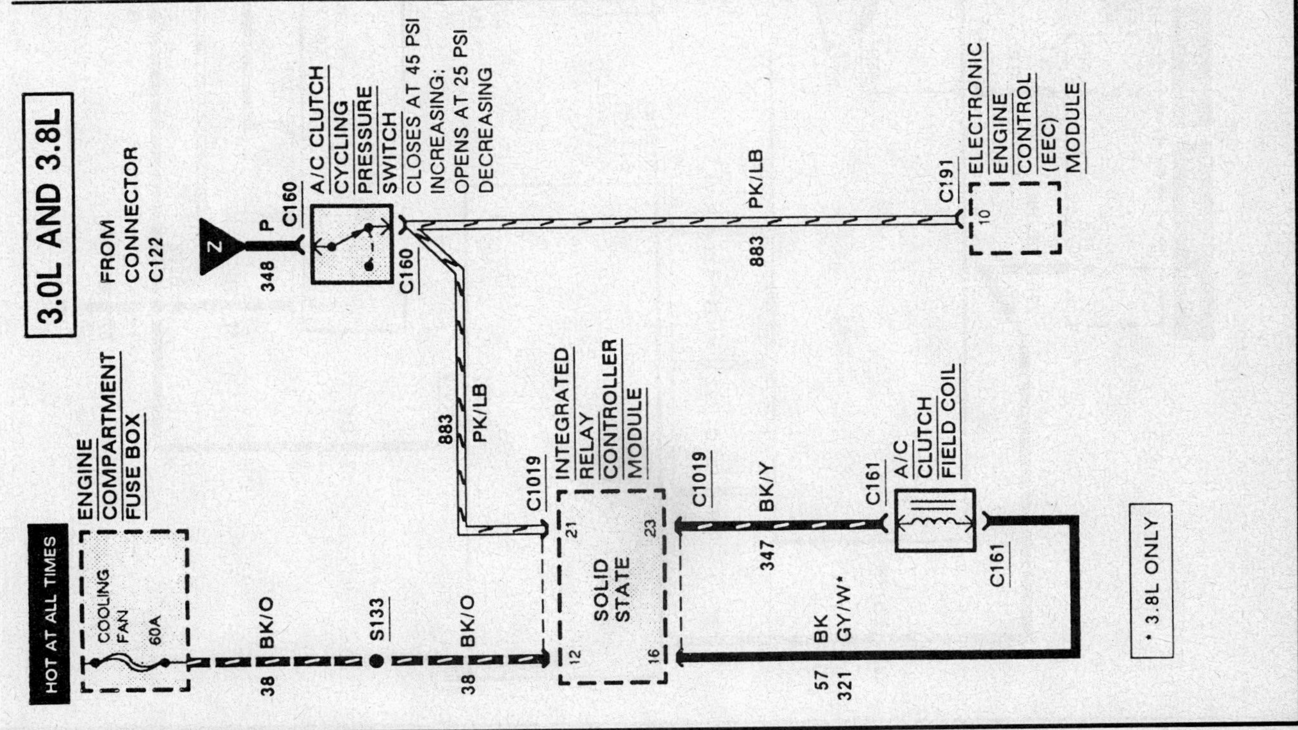

Manual air conditioning/heater system wiring schematic—Taurus and Sable, Cont'd

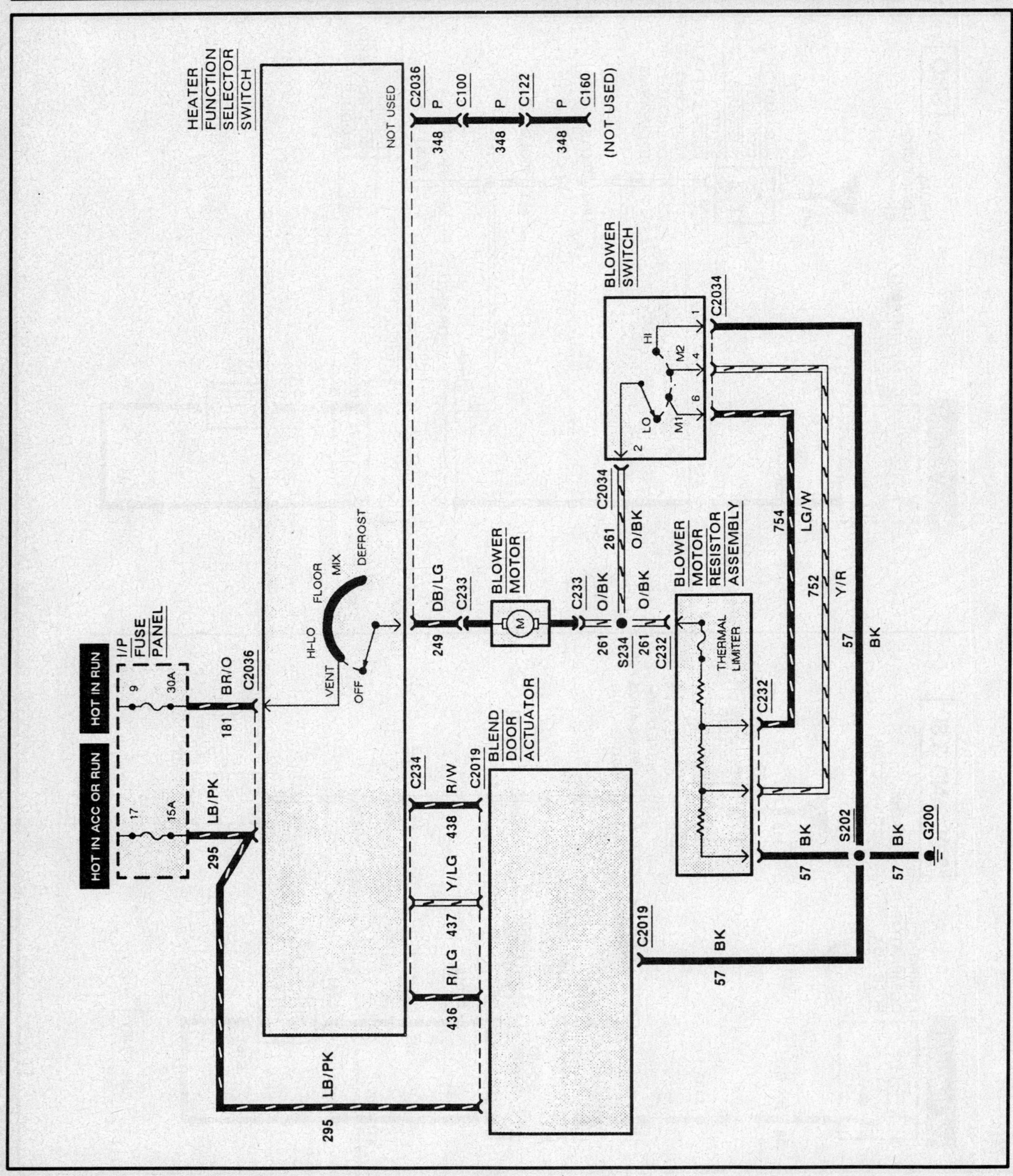

Heater only system wiring schematic—Taurus and Sable

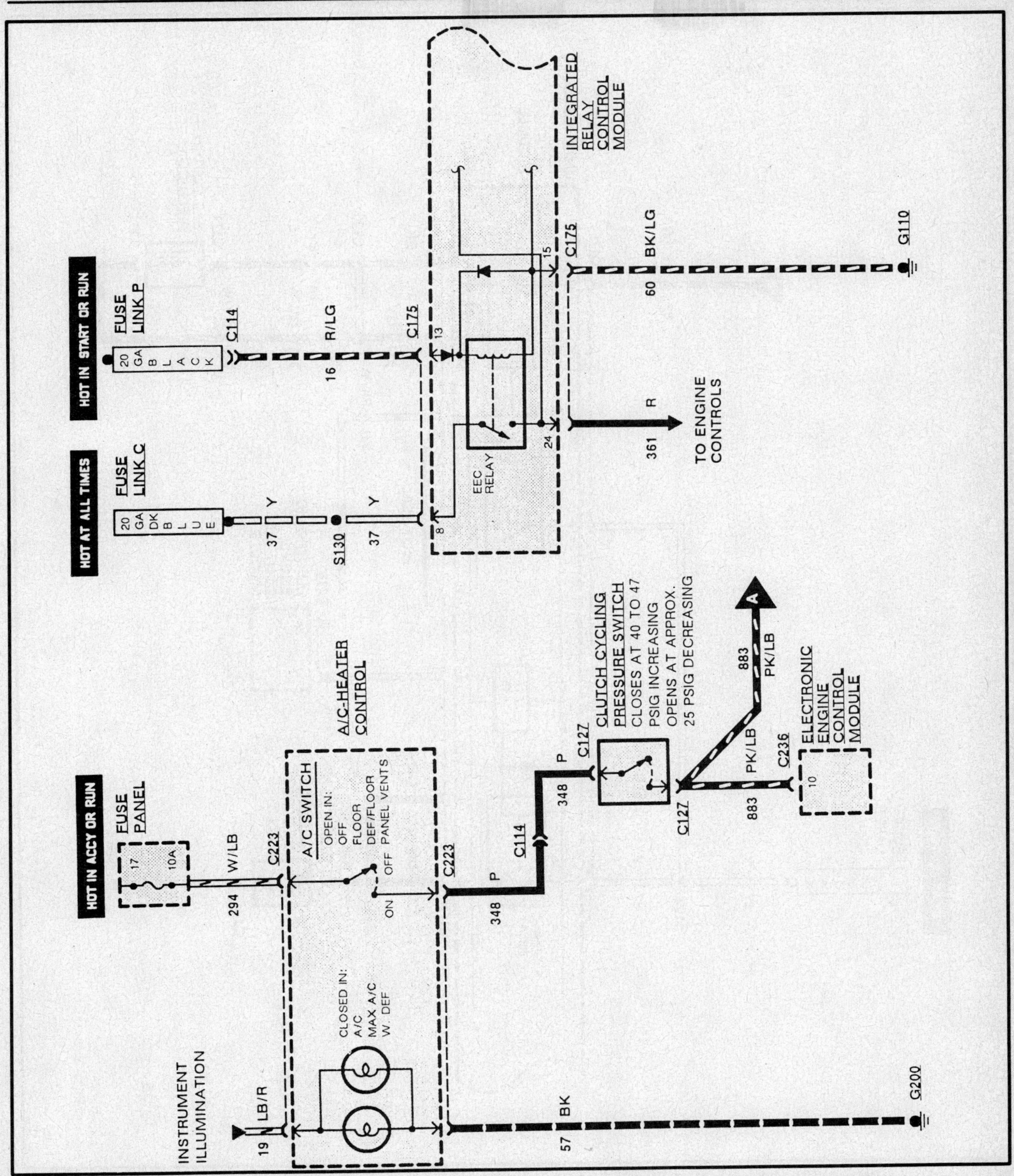

Manual air conditioning/heater system wiring schematic—Tempo and Topaz with 2.3L engine

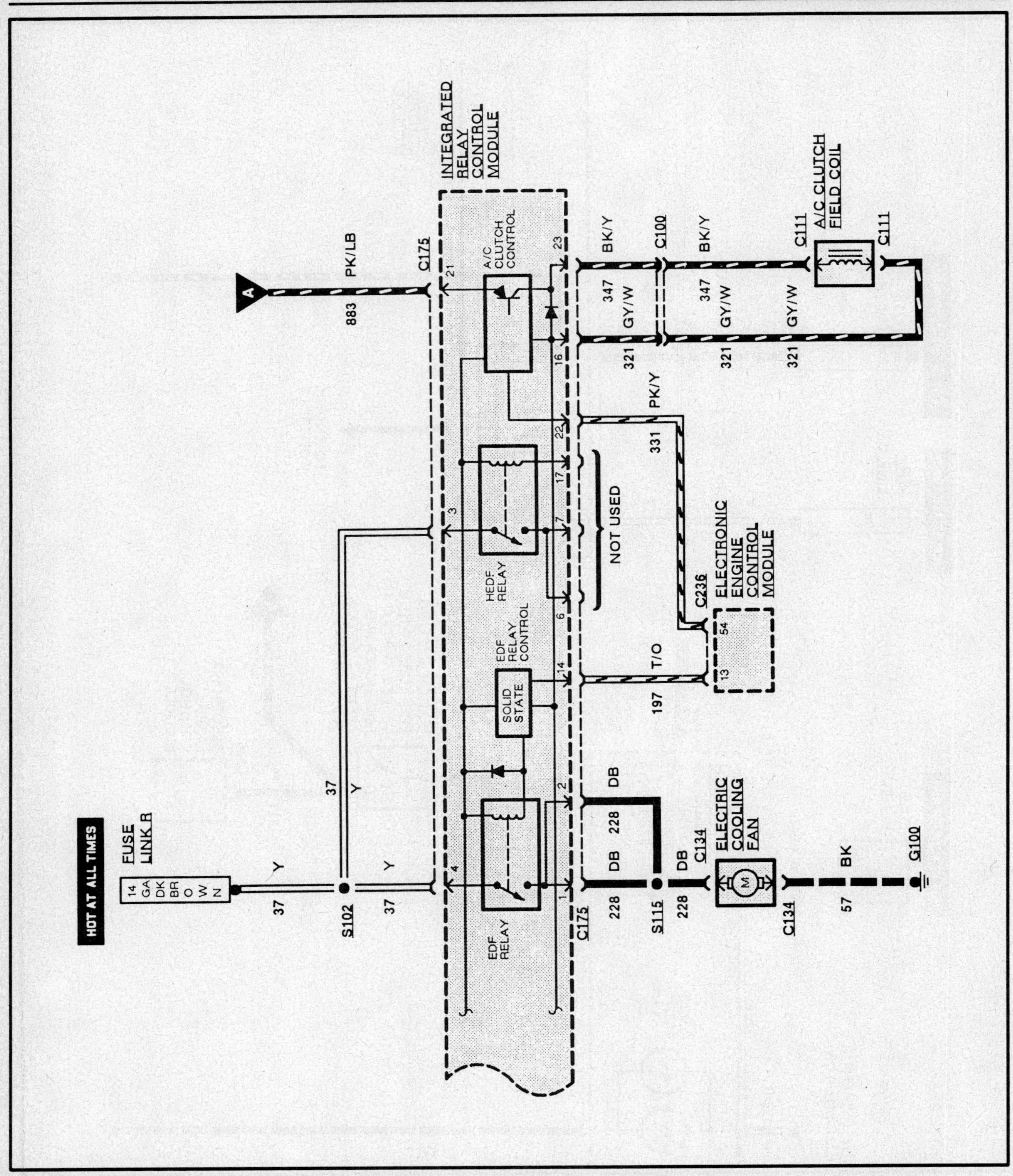

Manual air conditioning/heater system wiring schematic—Tempo and Topaz with 2.3L engine, Cont'd

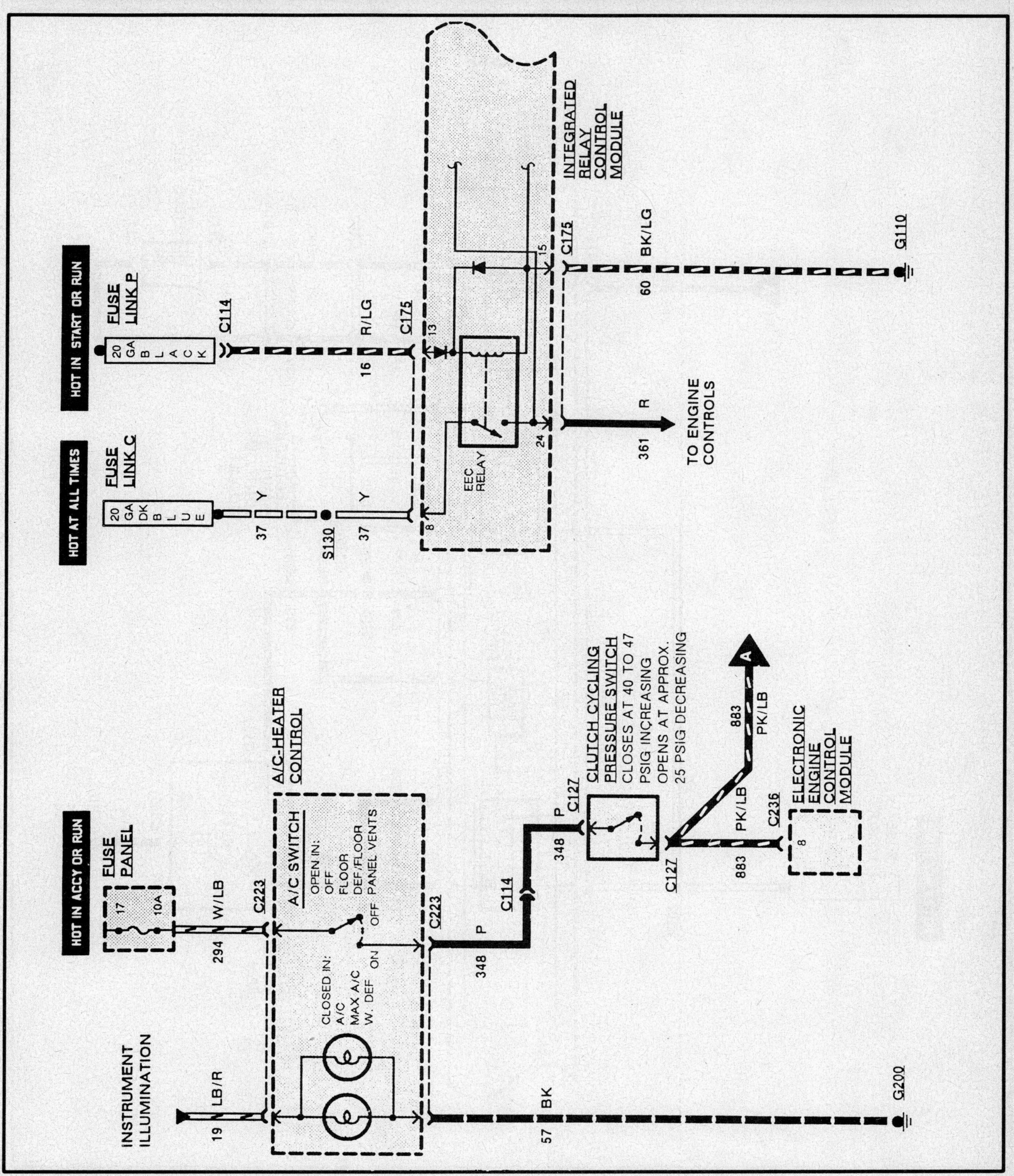

Manual air conditioning/heater system wiring schematic—Tempo and Topaz with 3.0L engine

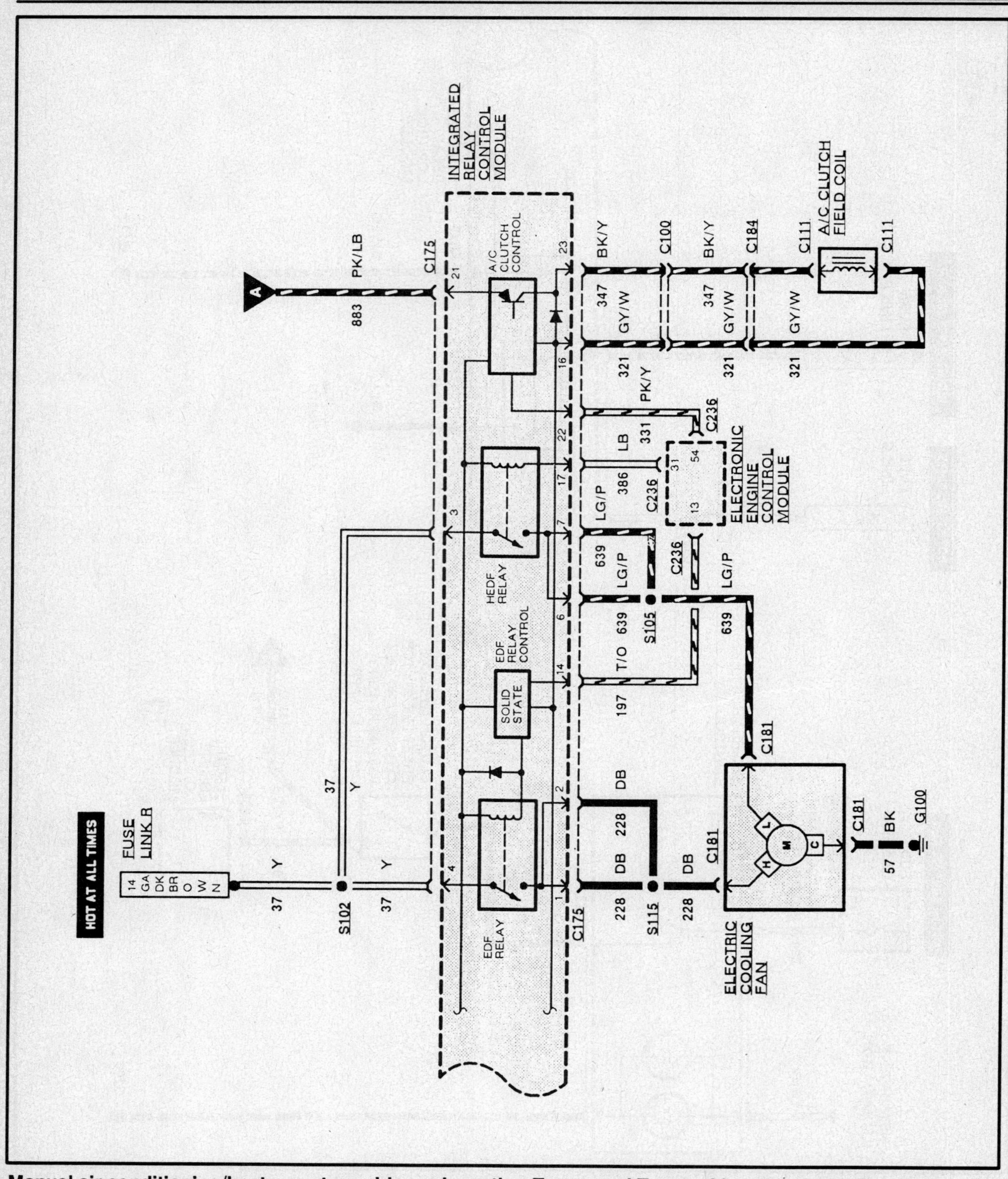

Manual air conditioning/heater system wiring schematic—Tempo and Topaz with 3.0L engine, Cont'd

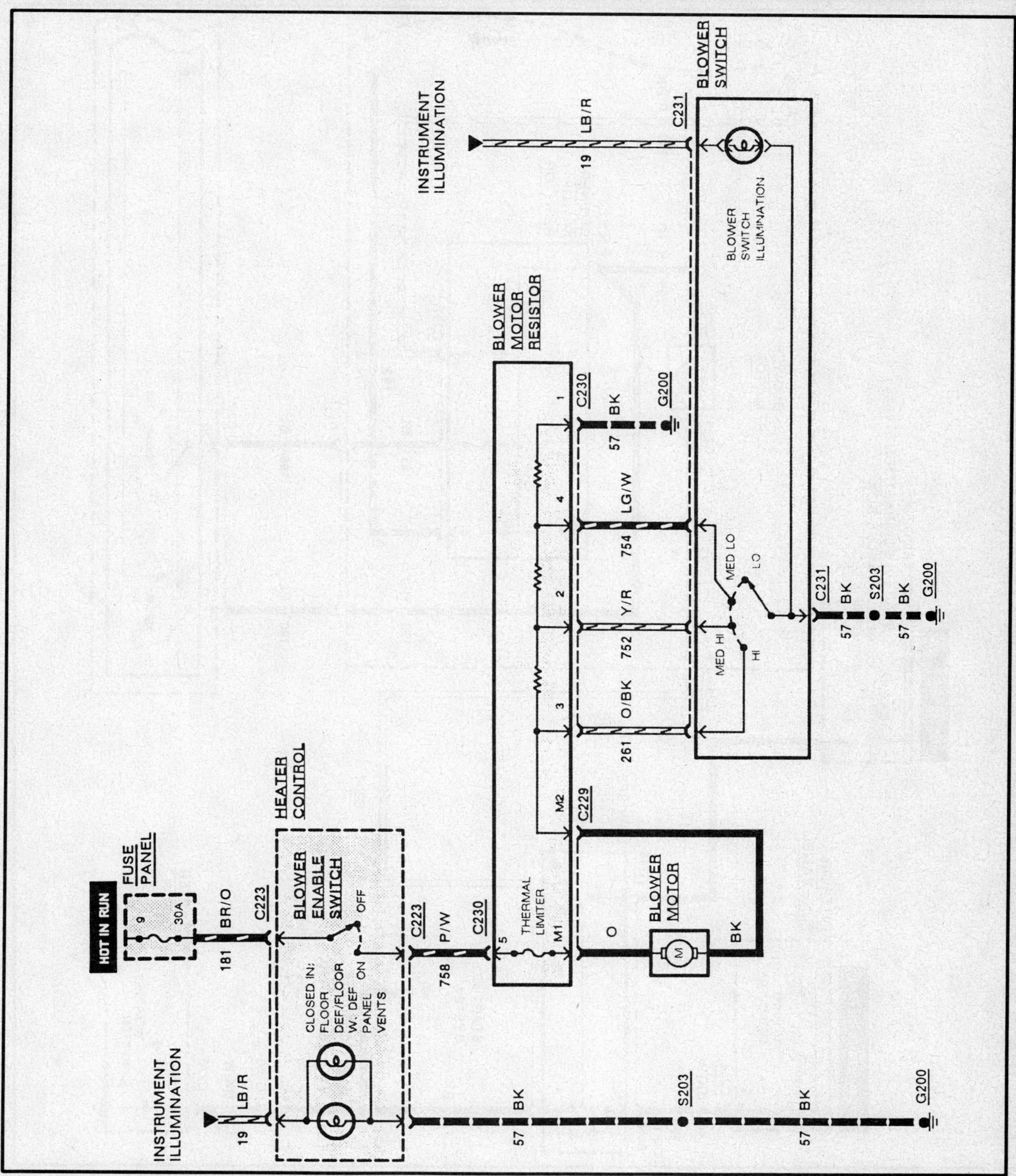

Heater only system wiring schematic—Tempo and Topaz

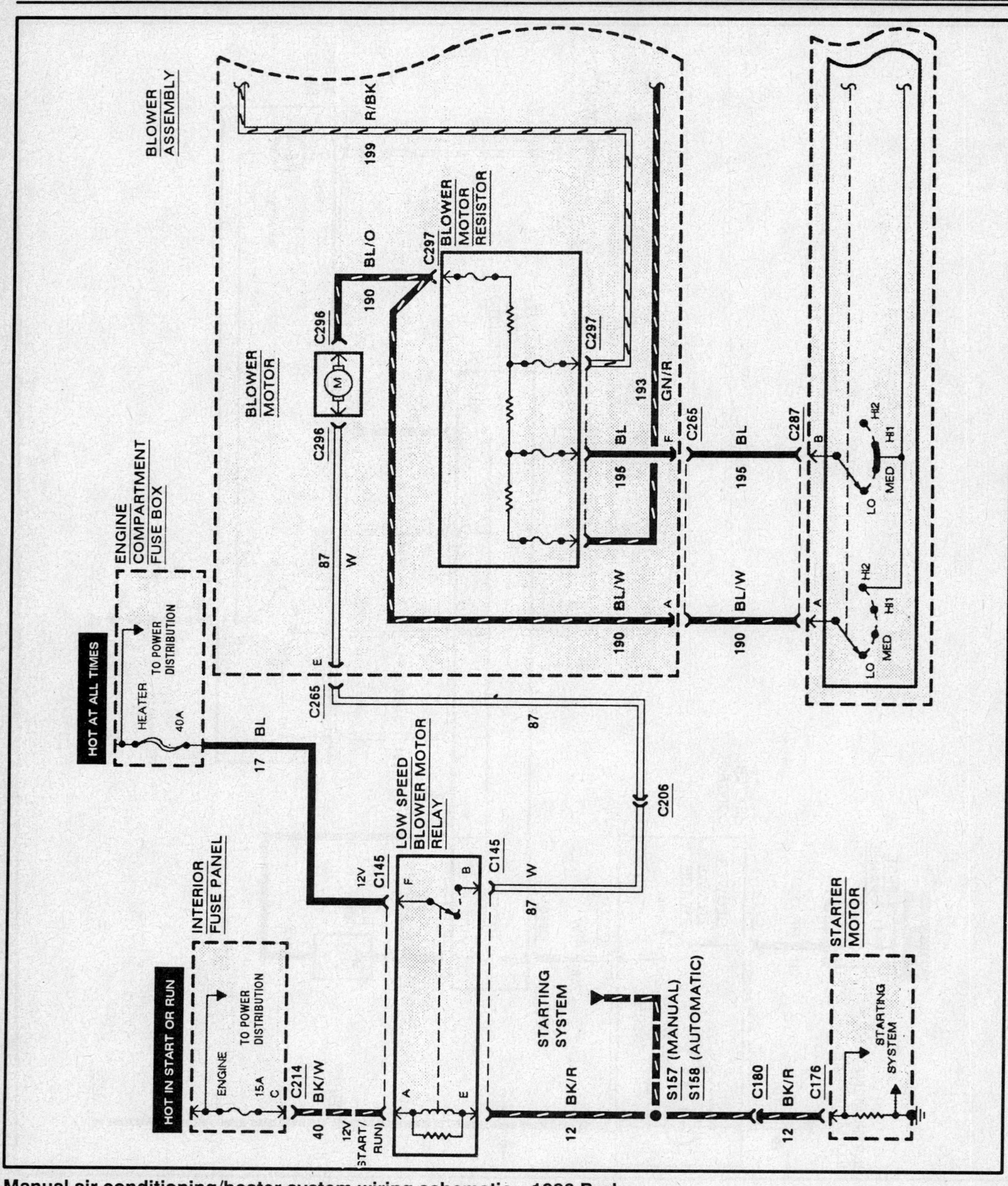

Manual air conditioning/heater system wiring schematic—1993 Probe

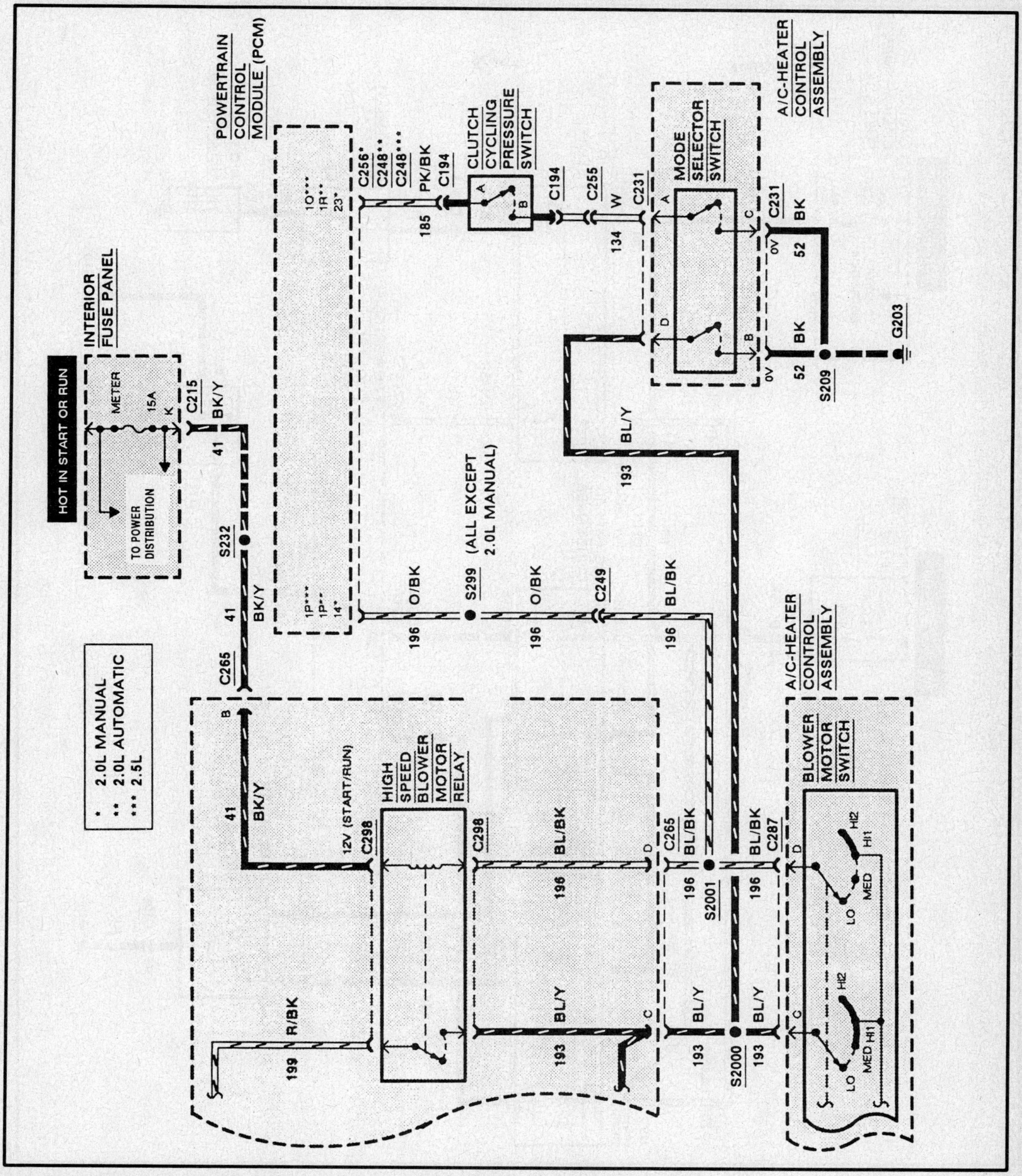

Manual air conditioning/heater system wiring schematic—1993 Probe, Cont'd

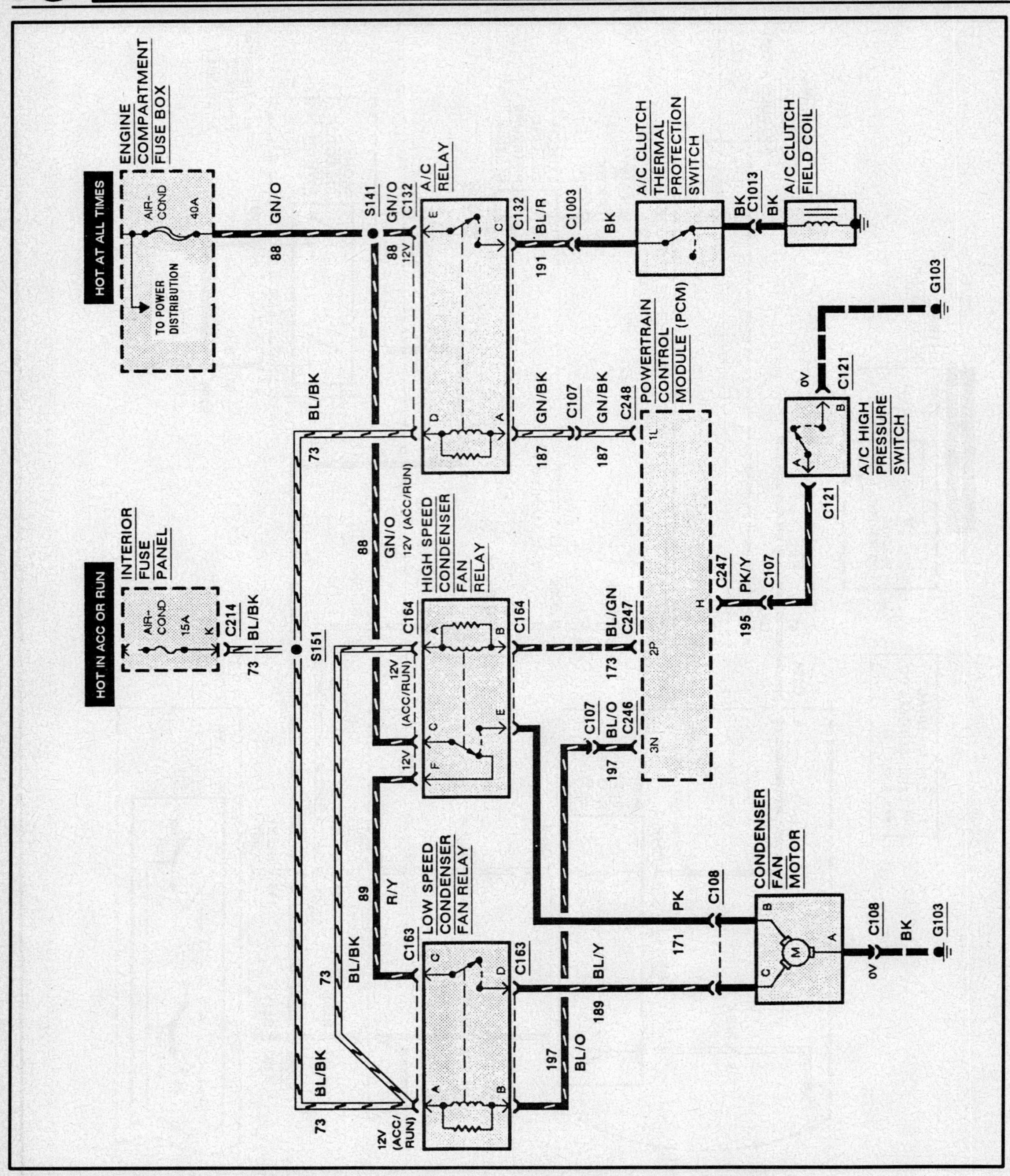

Manual air conditioning/heater system wiring schematic—1993 Probe with 2.5L engine

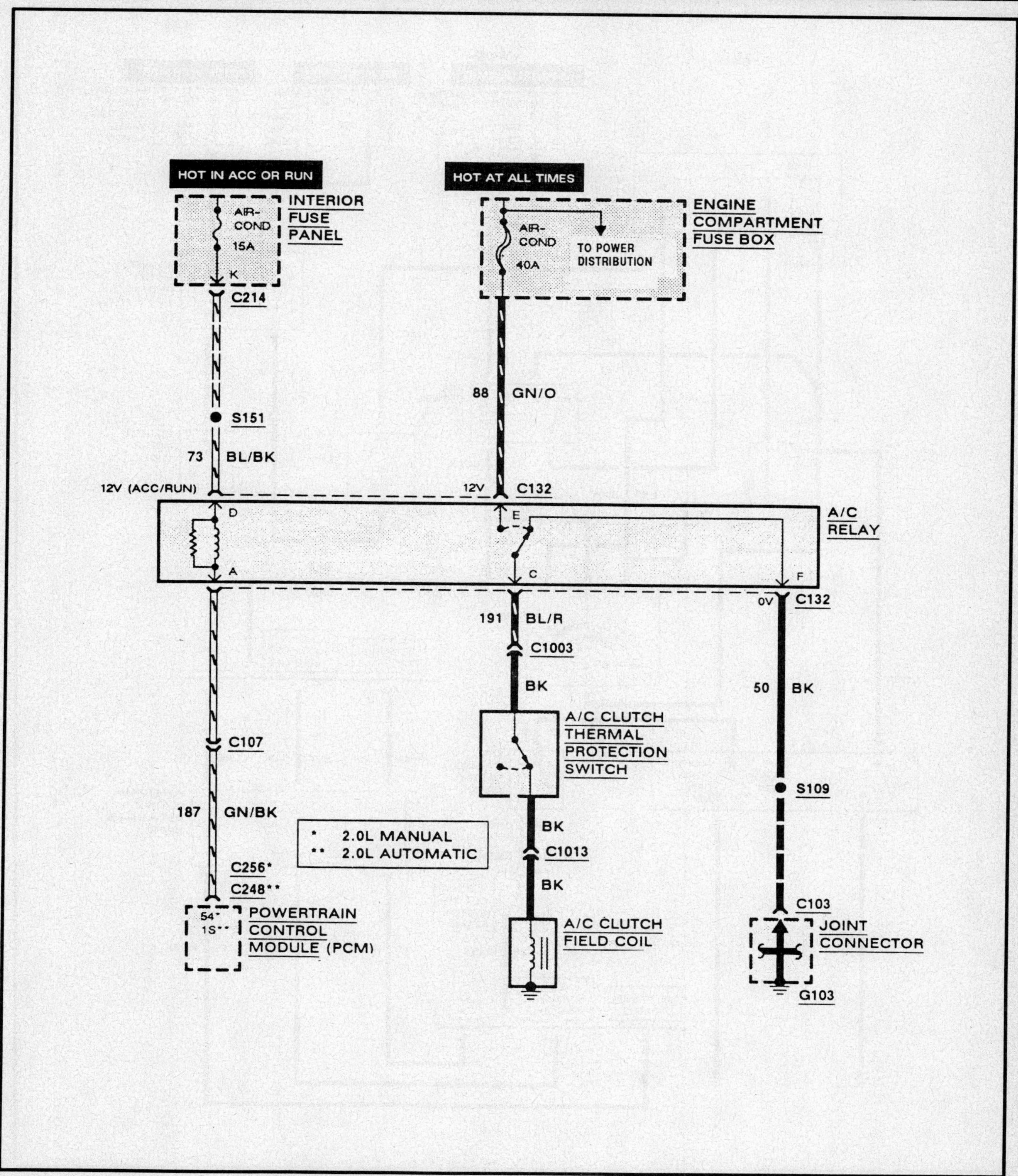

Manual air conditioning/heater system wiring schematic—1993 Probe with 2.0L engine

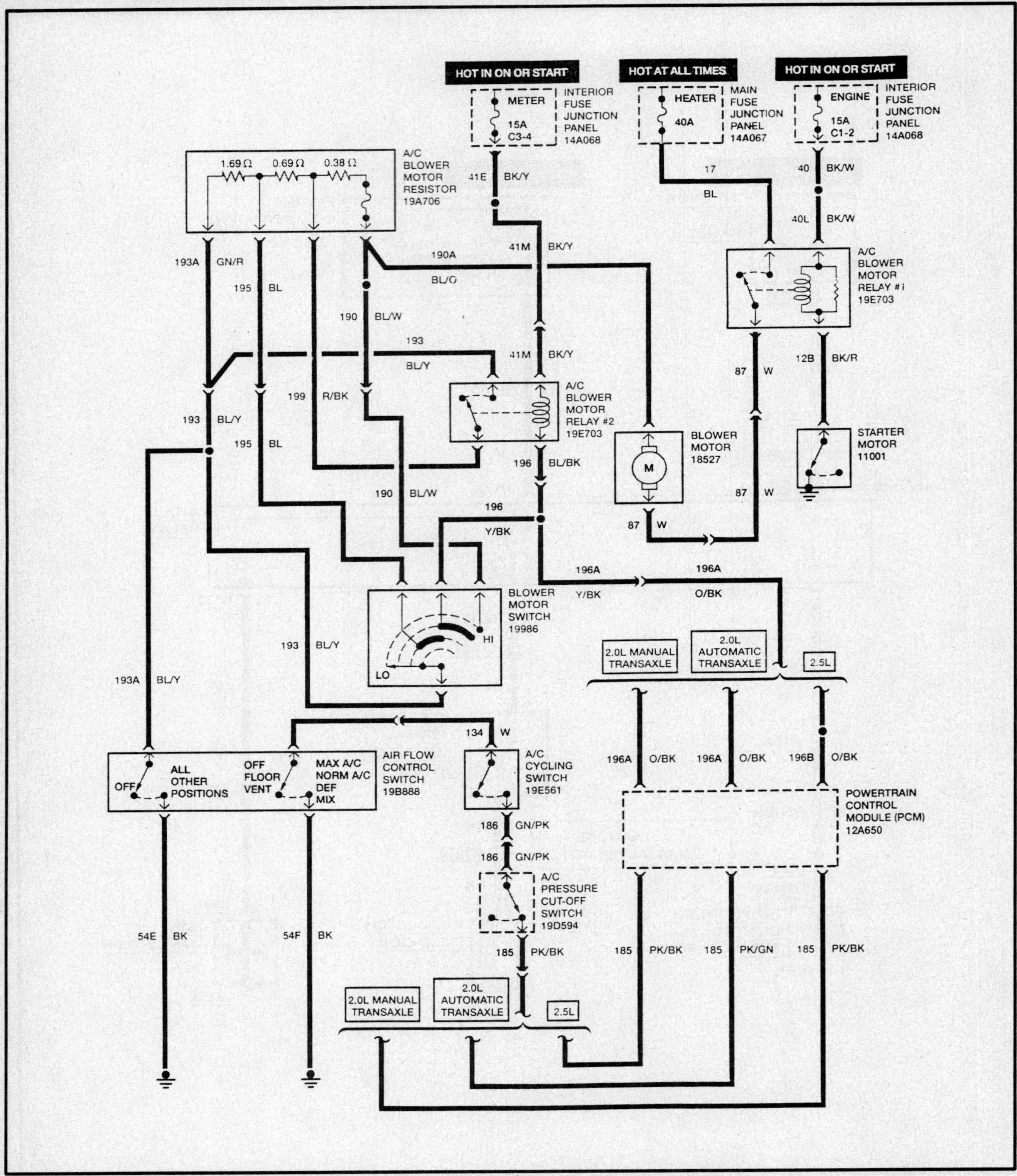

Manual air conditioning/heater system wiring schematic—1994–95 Probe

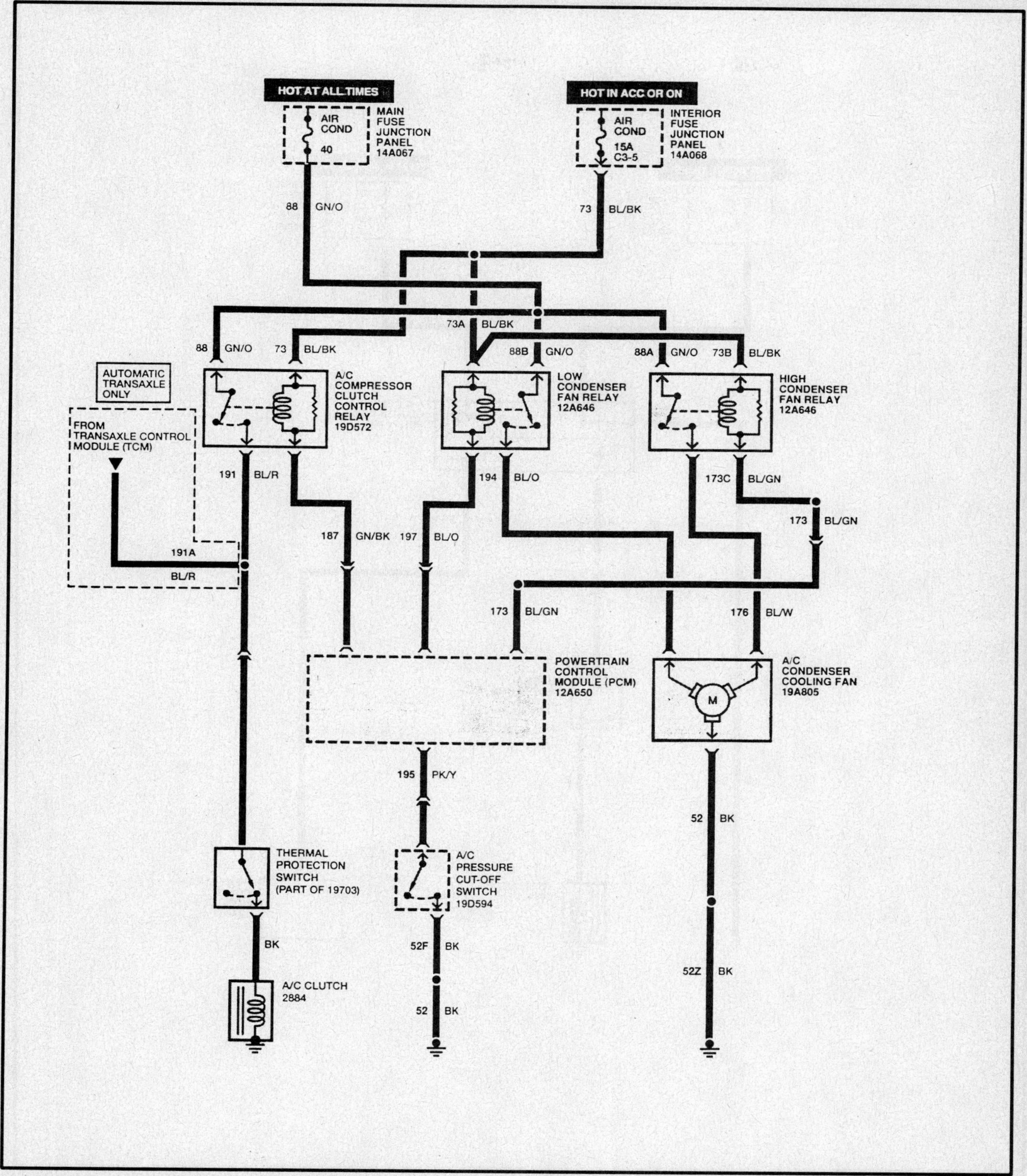

Manual air conditioning/heater system wiring schematic—1994–95 Probe, Cont'd

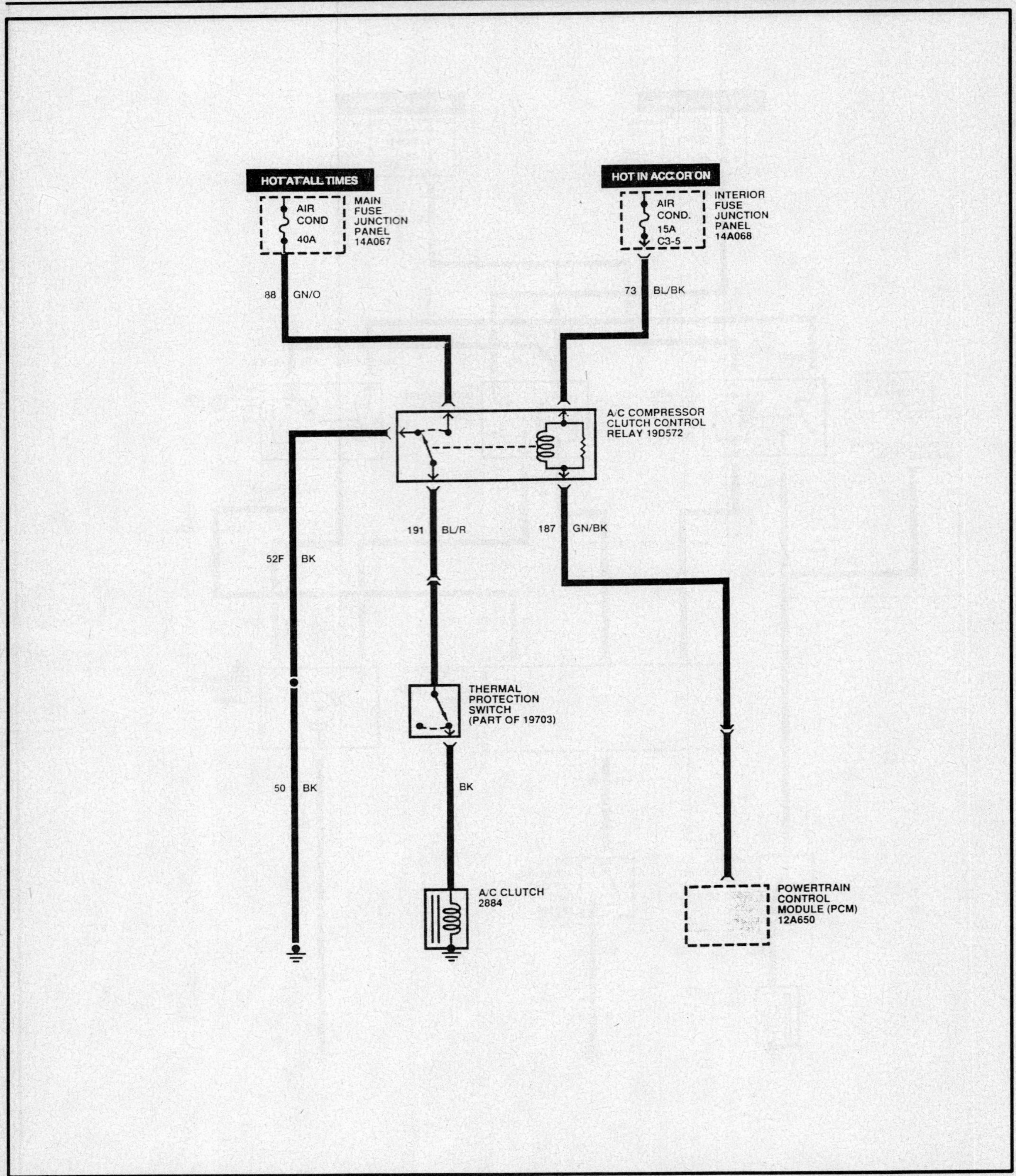

Manual air conditioning/heater system wiring schematic—1994–95 Probe, Cont'd

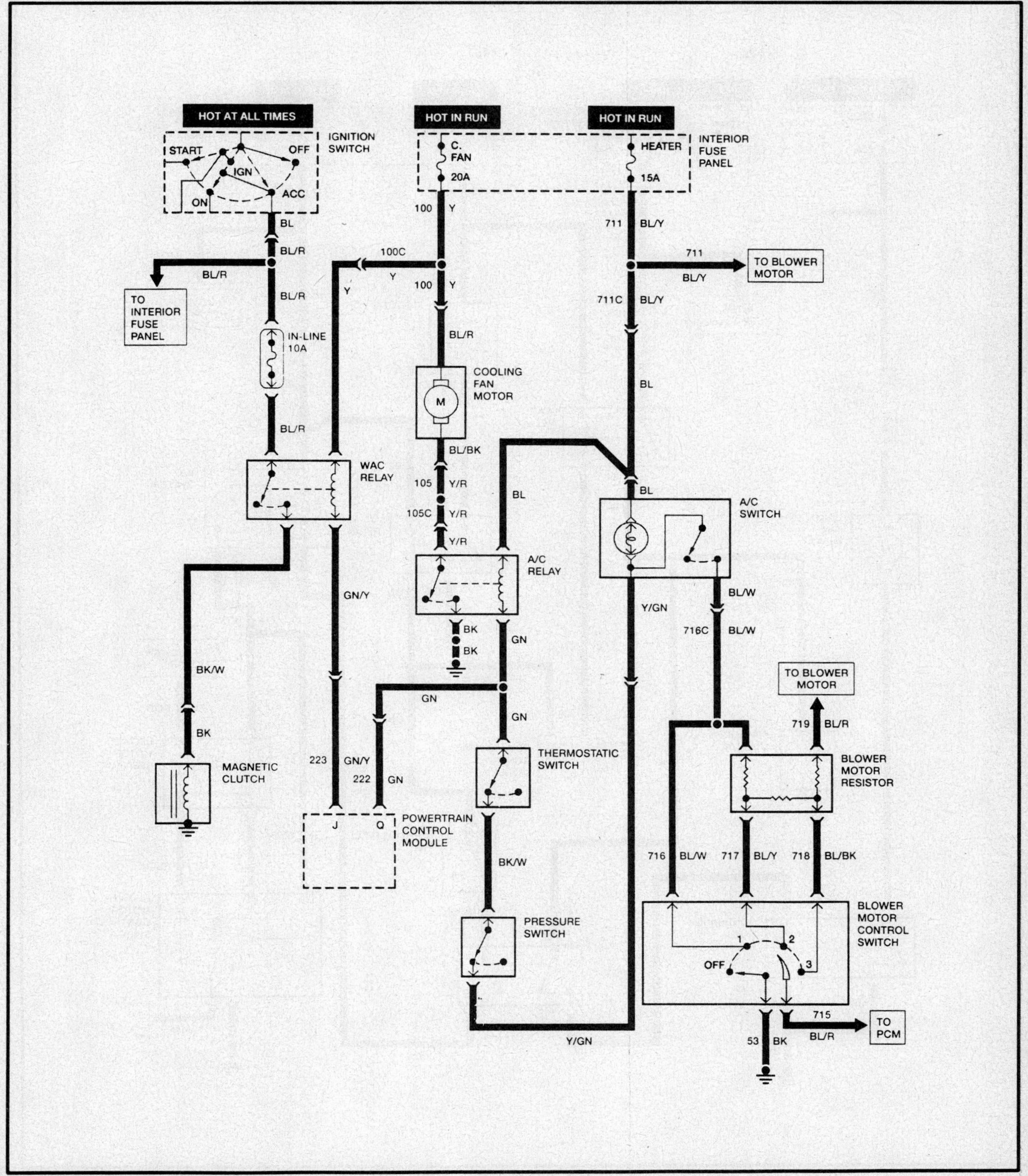

Manual air conditioning/heater system wiring schematic—Festiva with manual transaxle

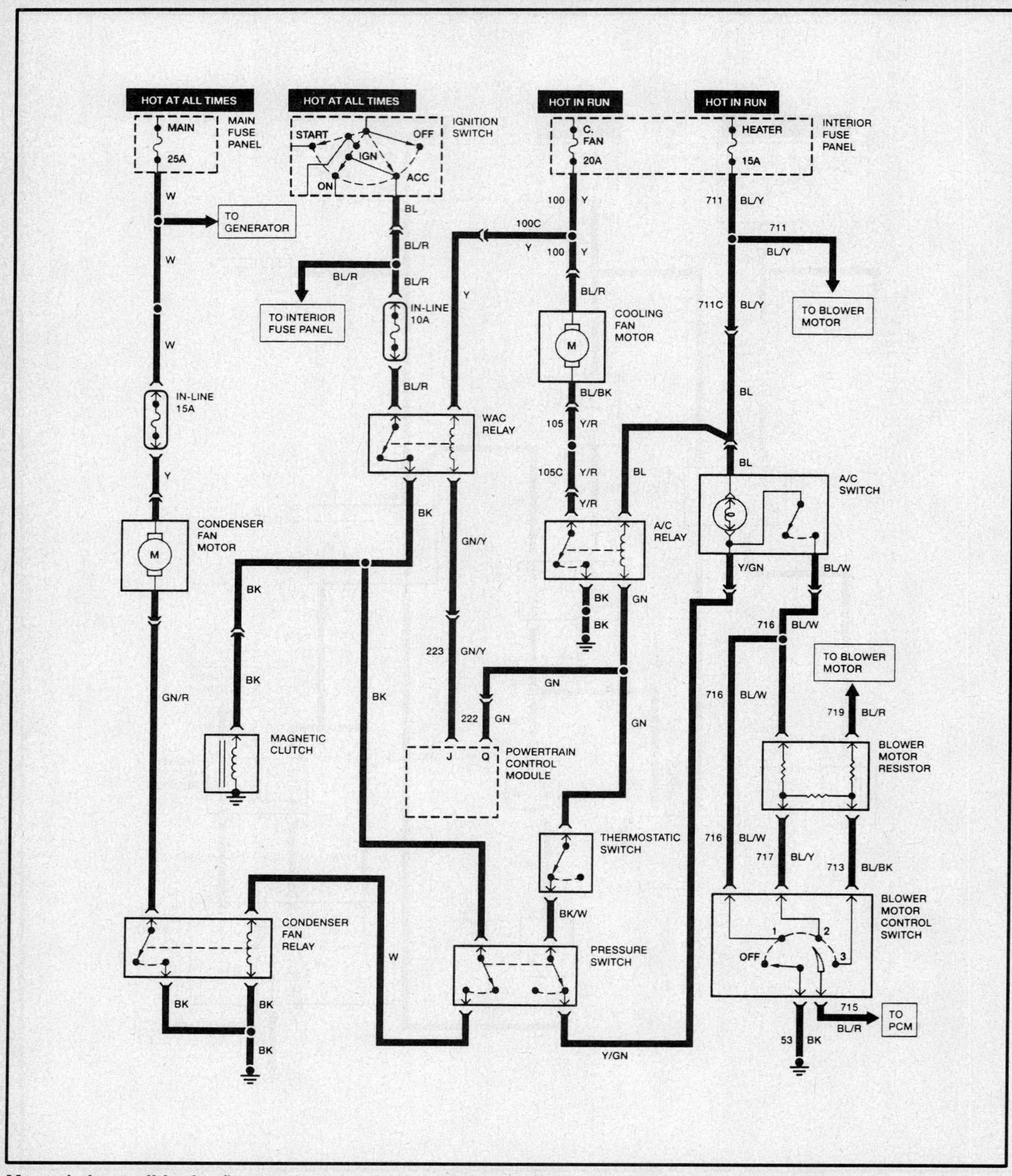

Manual air conditioning/heater system wiring schematic—Festiva with automatic transaxle

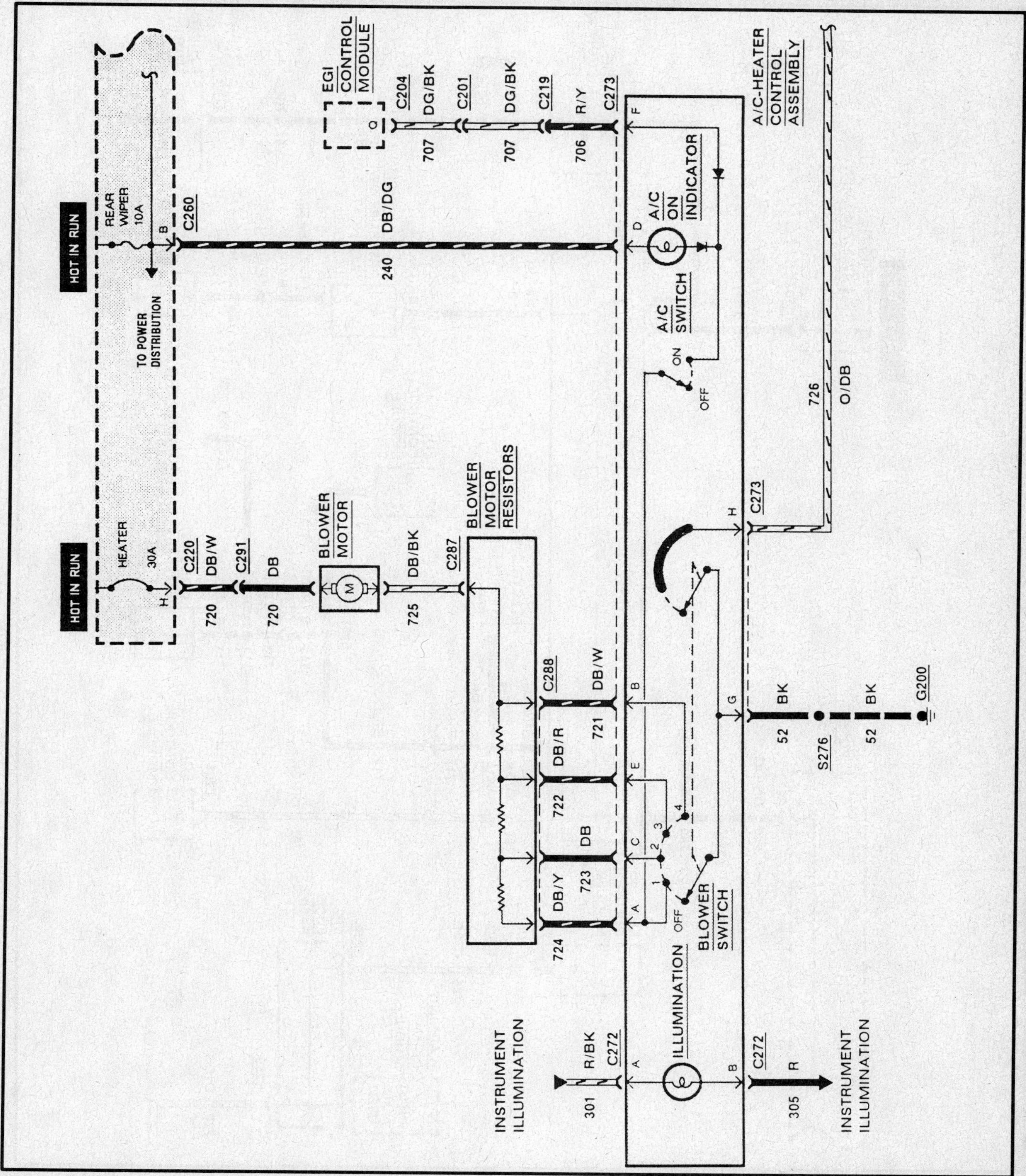

Manual air conditioning/heater system wiring schematic—Escort and Tracer with 1.8L engine

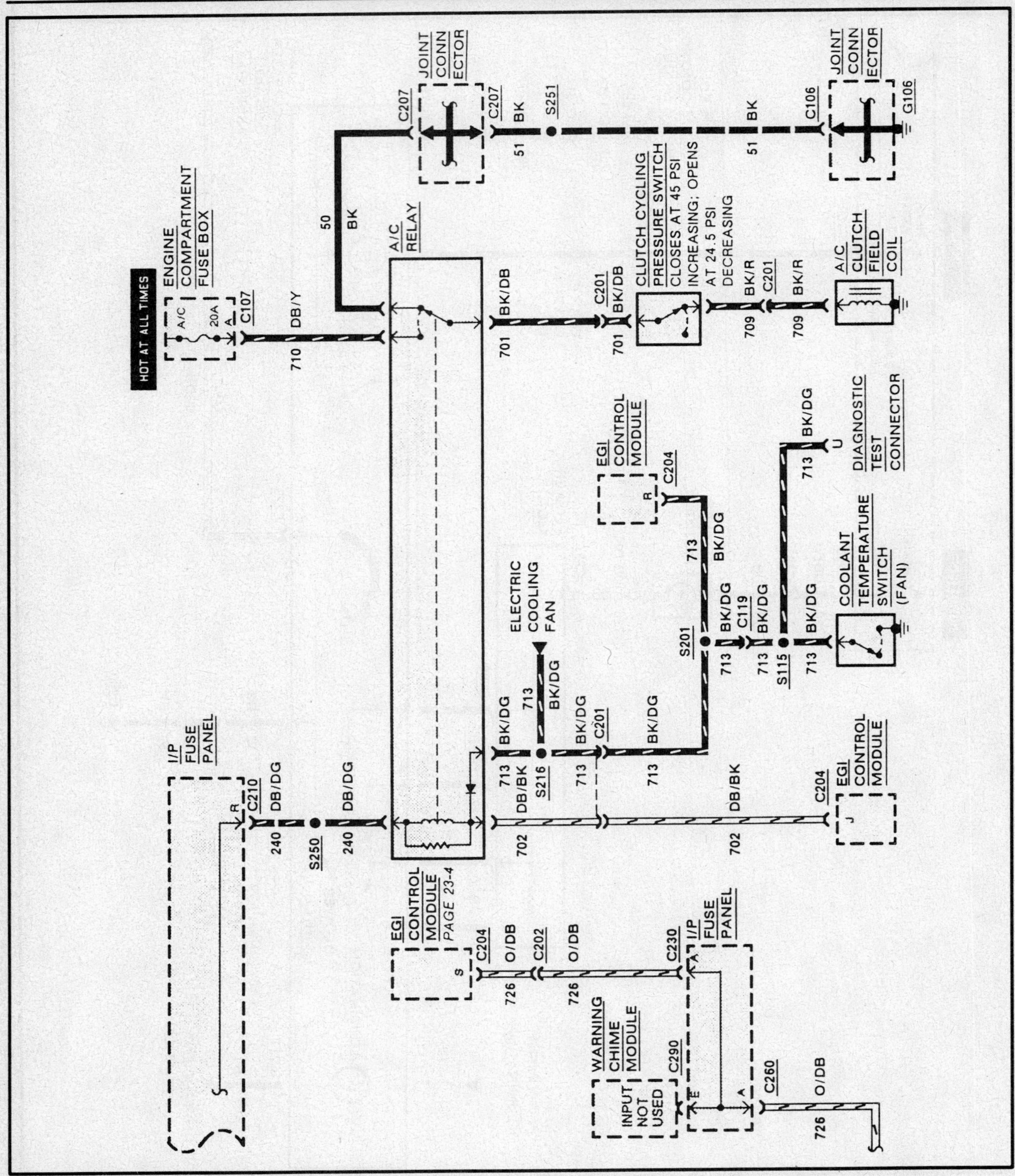

Manual air conditioning/heater system wiring schematic—Escort and Tracer with 1.8L engine, Cont'd

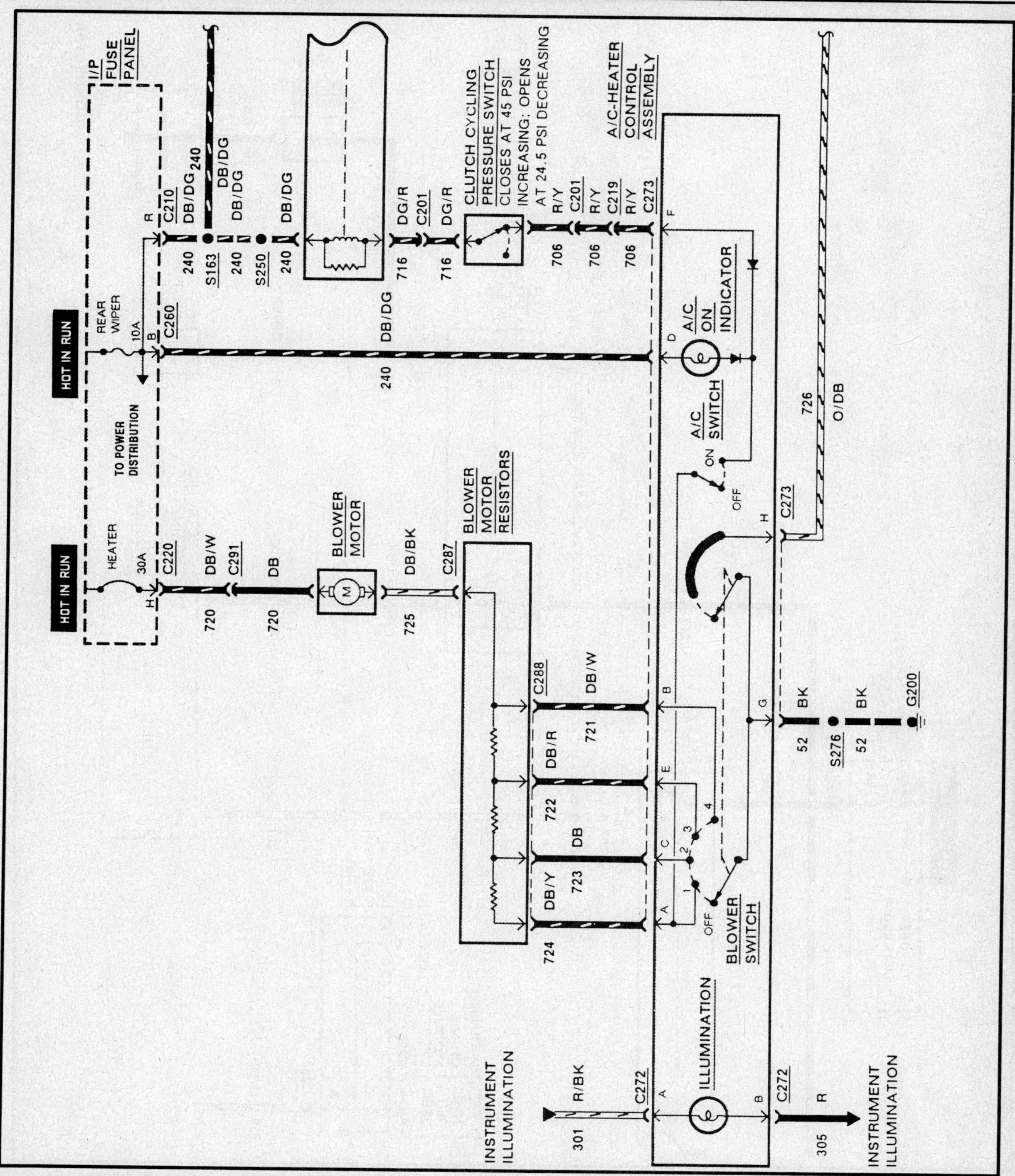

Manual air conditioning/heater system wiring schematic—Escort and Tracer with 1.9L engine

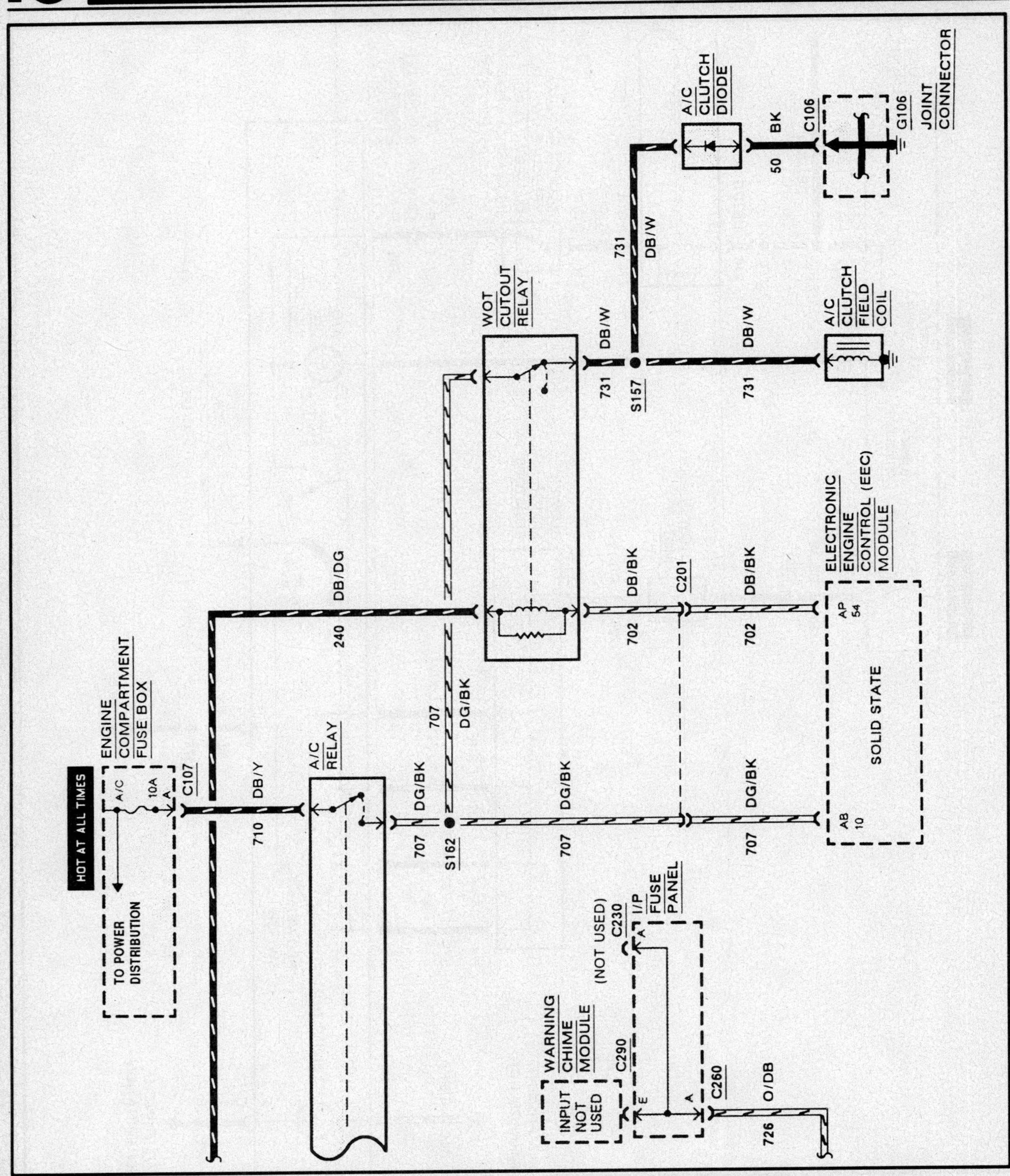

Manual air conditioning/heater system wiring schematic—Escort and Tracer with 1.9L engine, Cont'd

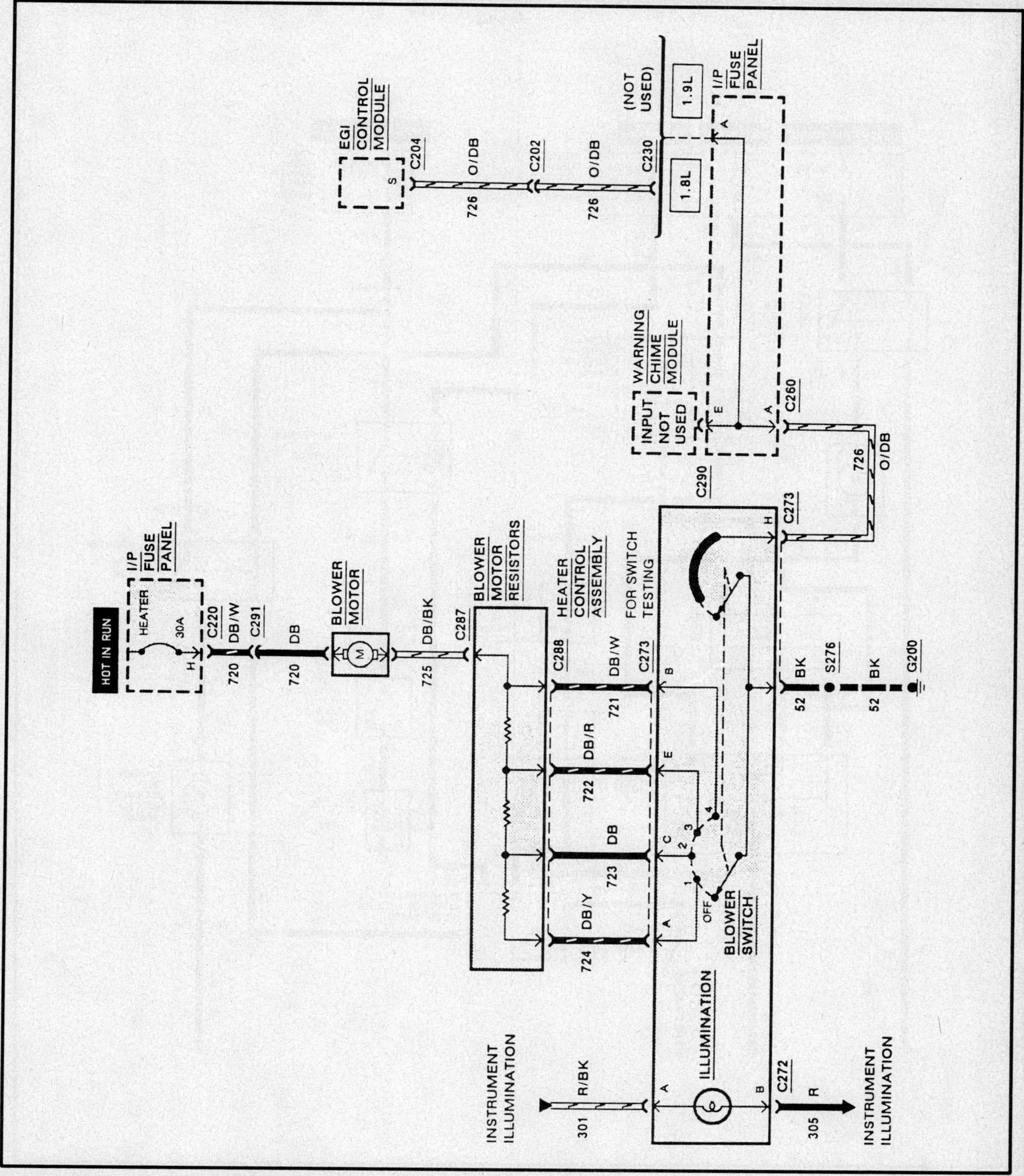

Heater only system wiring schematic—Escort and Tracer

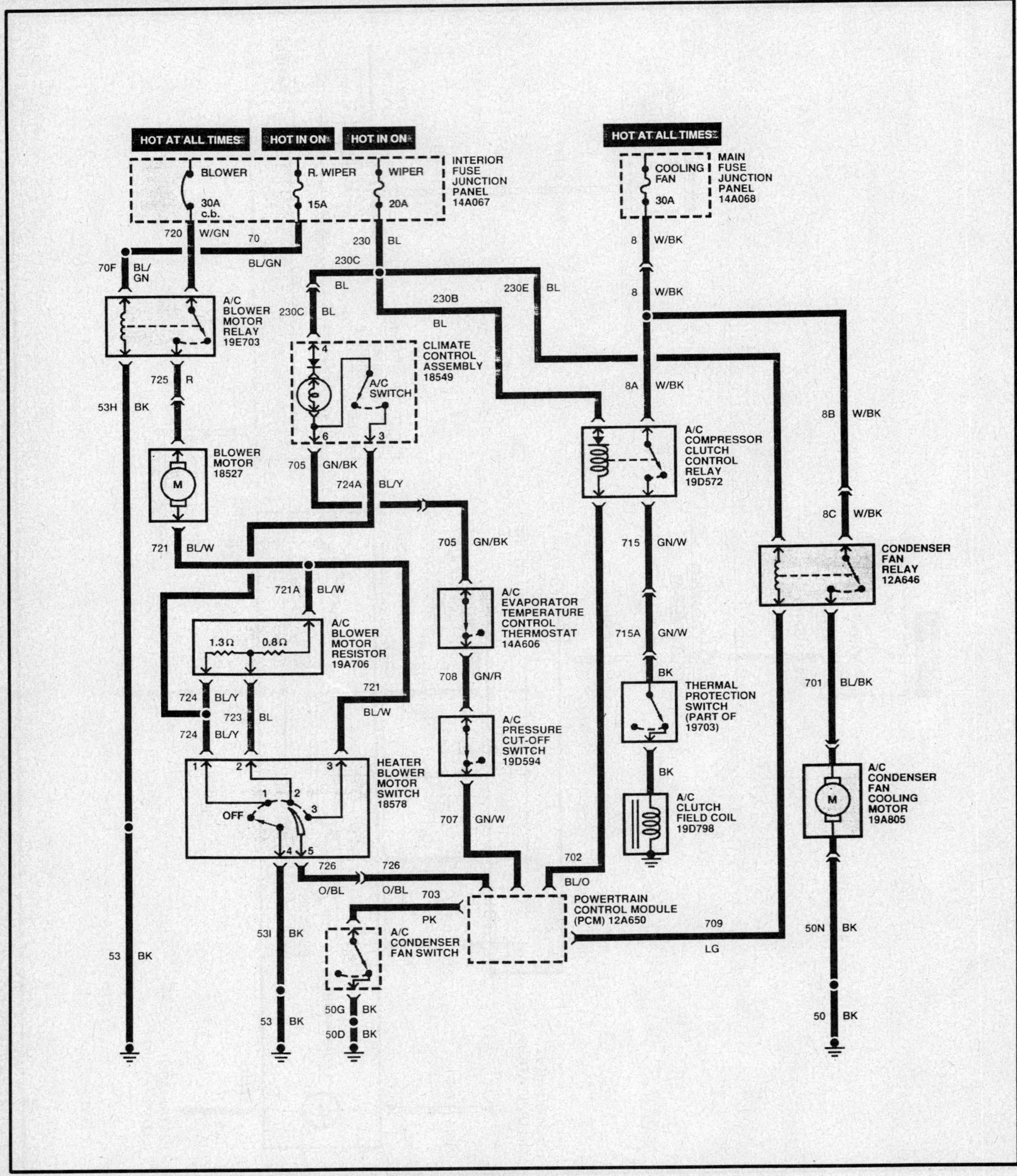

Manual air conditioning/heater system wiring schematic—Aspire

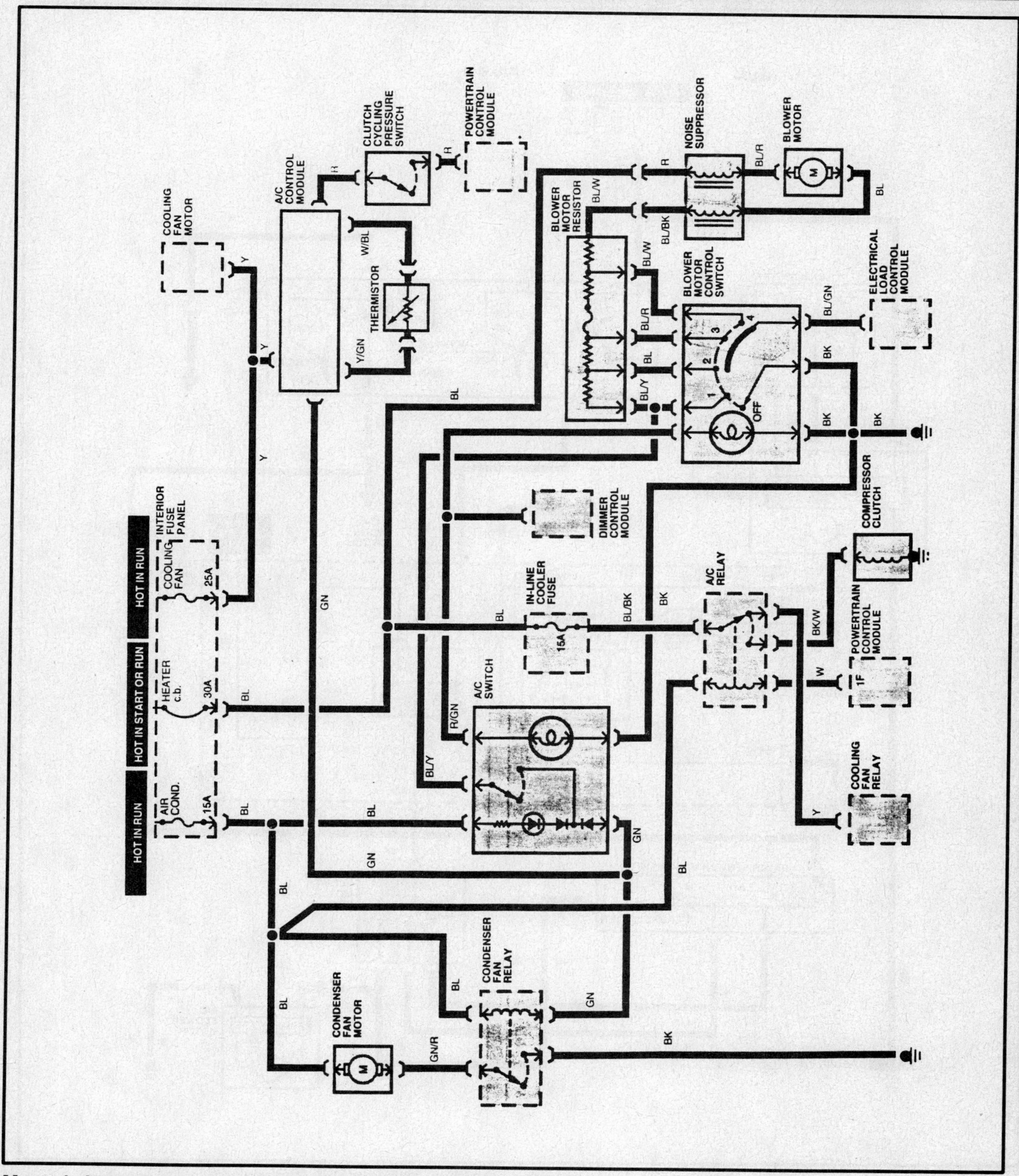

Manual air conditioning/heater system wiring schematic—Capri

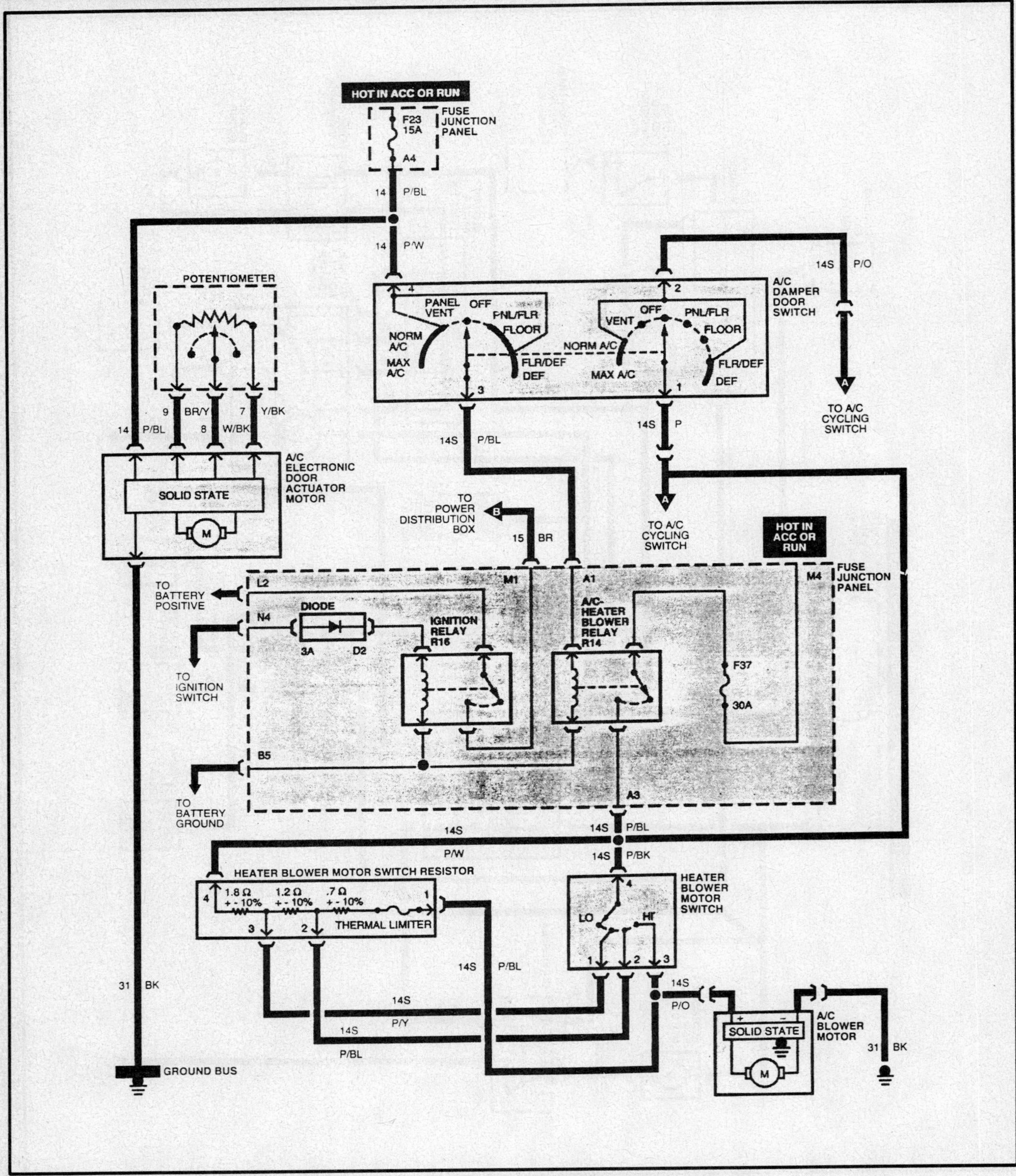

Manual air conditioning/heater system wiring schematic—Contour and Mystique

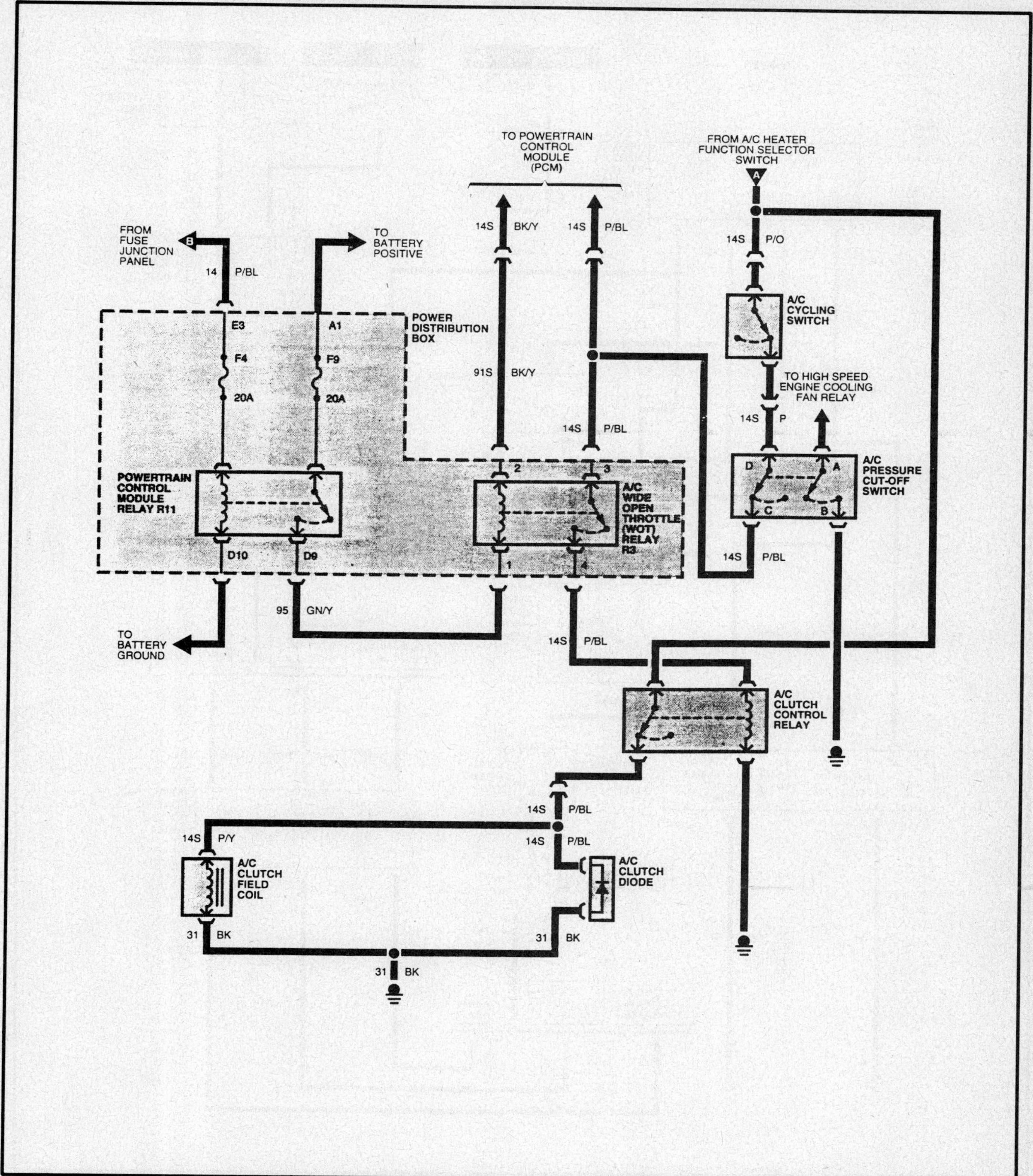

Manual air conditioning/heater system wiring schematic—Contour and Mystique, Cont'd

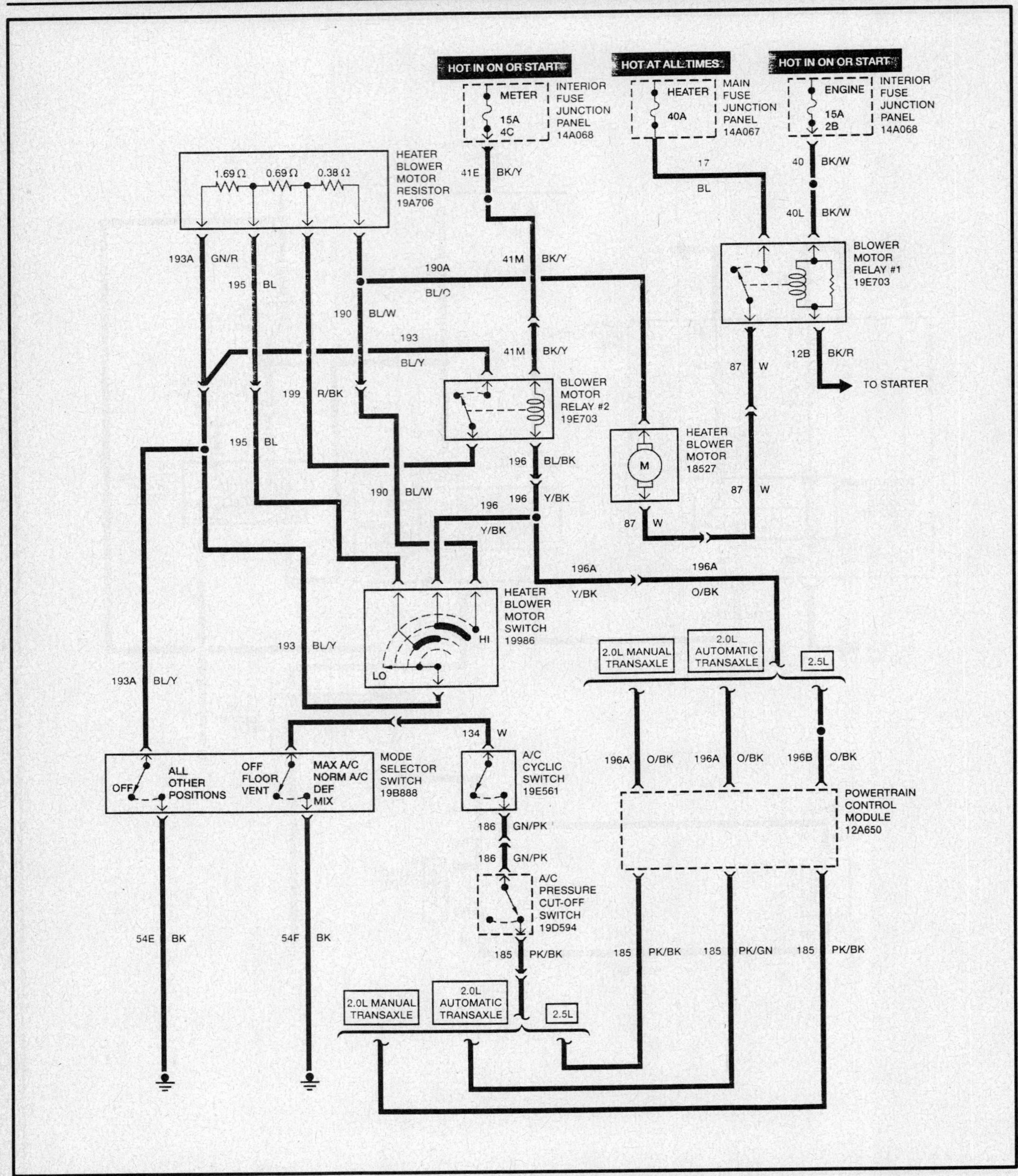

Manual air conditioning/heater system wiring schematic—1994–95 Probe

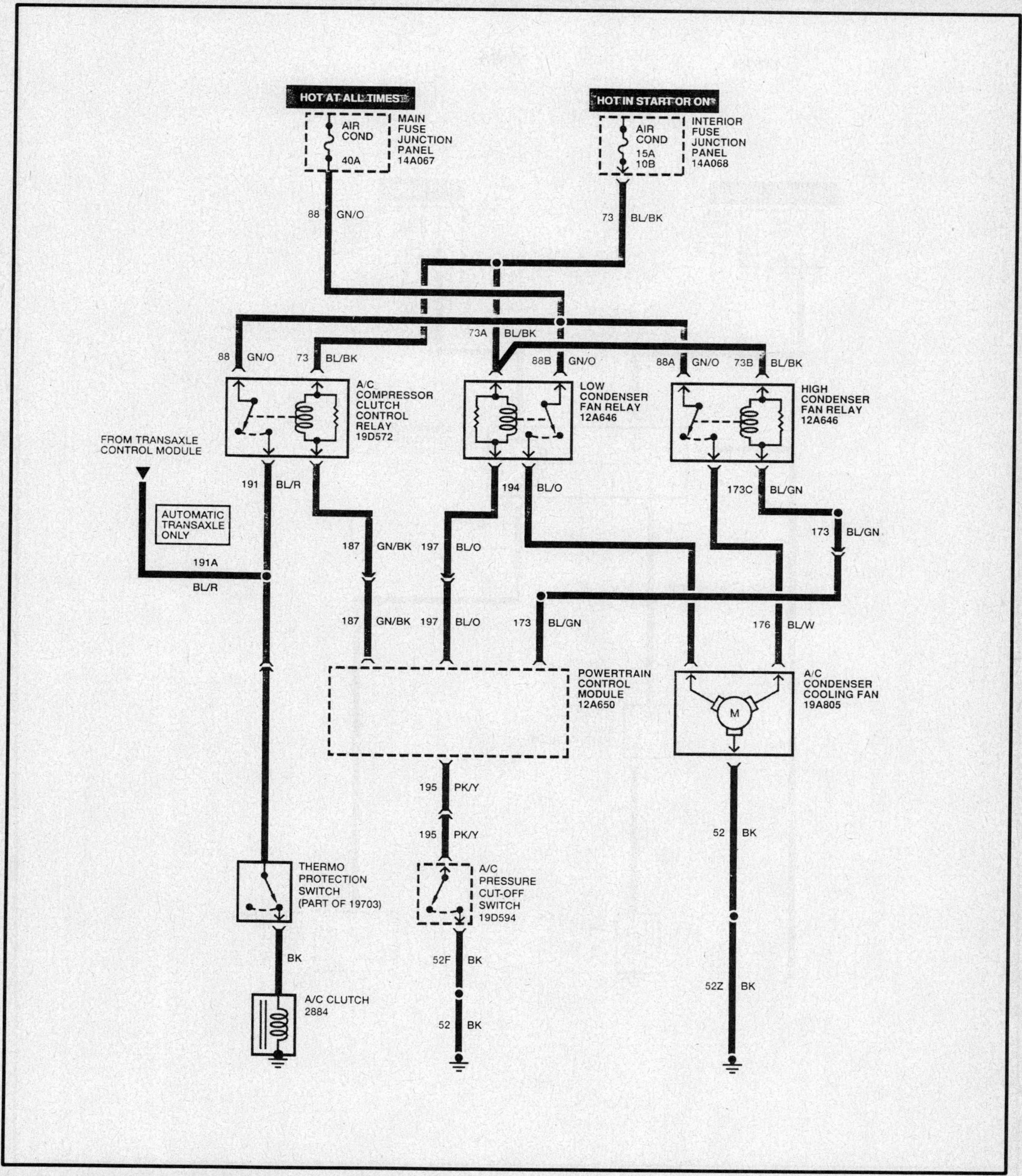

Manual air conditioning/heater system wiring schematic—1994–95 Probe, Cont'd

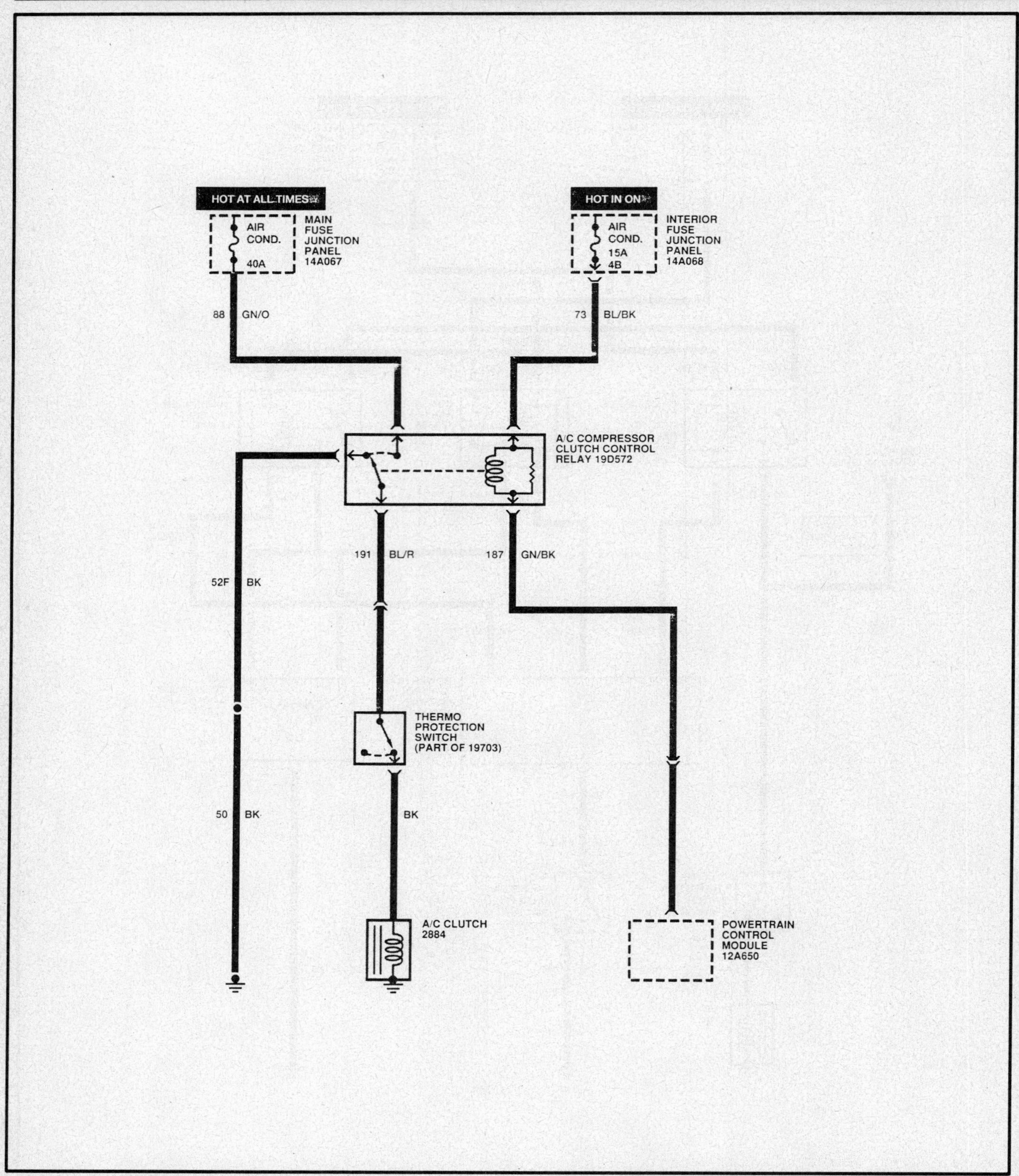

Manual air conditioning/heater system wiring schematic—1994–95 Probe, Cont'd

6 FORD/LINCOLN/MERCURY 6

COUGAR • CROWN VICTORIA • GRAND MARQUIS • MARK VIII • MUSTANG • THUNDERBIRD • TOWN CAR

SPECIFICATIONS

ENGINE IDENTIFICATION

Year	Model	Engine Displacement Liters (cc)	Engine Series (ID/VIN)	Fuel System	No. of Cylinders	Engine Type
1993	Mustang	2.3 (2295)	M	EFI	4	OHC
	Mustang	5.0 (4943) HO	E	SEFI	8	OHV
	Thunderbird	3.8 (3801)	4	SEFI	6	OHV
	Cougar	3.8 (3801)	4	SEFI	6	OHV
	Thunderbird	3.8 (3801) SC	R	SEFI	6	OHV
	Thunderbird	5.0 (4943) HO	T	SEFI	8	OHV
	Cougar	5.0 (4943) HO	T	SEFI	8	OHV
	Mark VIII	4.6 (4593) 4V	W	SEFI	8	DOHC
	Crown Victoria	4.6 (4593) 2V	W	SEFI	8	OHC
	Grand Marquis	4.6 (4593) 2V	W	SEFI	8	OHC
	Town Car	4.6 (4593) 2V	W	SEFI	8	OHC
1994	Mustang	3.8 (3801)	4	SEFI	6	OHV
	Mustang	5.0 (4943) HO	T	SEFI	8	OHV
	Mustang	5.0 (4943) SHP	D	SEFI	8	OHV
	Thunderbird	3.8 (3801)	4	SEFI	6	OHV
	Cougar	3.8 (3801)	4	SEFI	6	OHV
	Thunderbird	3.8 (3801) SC	R	SEFI	6	OHV
	Thunderbird	4.6 (4593) 2V	W	SEFI	8	OHC
	Cougar	4.6 (4593) 2V	W	SEFI	8	OHV
	Mark VIII	4.6 (4593) 4V	W	SEFI	8	DOHC
	Crown Victoria	4.6 (4593) 2V	W	SEFI	8	OHC
	Grand Marquis	4.6 (4593) 2V	W	SEFI	8	OHC
	Town Car	4.6 (4593) 2V	W	SEFI	8	OHC
1995	Mustang	3.8 (3801)	4	SEFI	6	OHV
	Mustang	5.0 (4943) HO	T	SEFI	8	OHV
	Mustang	5.0 (4943) SHP	D	SEFI	8	OHV
	Thunderbird	3:8 (3801)	4	SEFI	6	OHV
	Cougar	3.8 (3801)	4	SEFI	6	OHV
	Thunderbird	3.8 (3801) SC	R	SEFI	6	OHV
	Thunderbird	4.6 (4593) 2V	W	SEFI	8	OHC
	Cougar	4.6 (4593) 2V	W	SEFI	8	OHV
	Mark VIII	4.6 (4593) 4V	W	SEFI	8	DOHC
	Crown Victoria	4.6 (4593) 2V	W	SEFI	8	OHC
	Grand Marquis	4.6 (4593) 2V	W	SEFI	8	OHC
	Town Car	4.6 (4593) 2V	W	SEFI	8	OHC

OHC – Overhead Cam
OHV – Overhead Valves
EFI – Electronic Fuel Injection
SEFI – Sequential Electronic Fuel Injection
DOHC – Dual Overhead Cam
HO – High Output
SC – Supercharged
SHP Special High Performance (Cobra)

AIR CONDITIONING BELT TENSION

Year	Model	Engine Liters (cc)	Belt Type	Specifications	
				New (lbs.)	Used (lbs.)
1993	Mustang	2.3 (2295)	Poly–V	①	①
	Mustang	5.0 (4943) HO	Serpentine	①	①
	Thunderbird	3.8 (3801)	Serpentine	①	①
	Cougar	3.8 (3801)	Serpentine	①	①
	Thunderbird	3.8 (3801) SC	Serpentine	①	①
	Thunderbird	5.0 (4943) HO	Serpentine	①	①
	Cougar	5.0 (4943) HO	Serpentine	①	①
	Mark VIII	4.6 (4593)	Serpentine	①	①
	Crown Victoria	4.6 (4593)	Serpentine	①	①
	Grand Marquis	4.6 (4593)	Serpentine	①	①
	Town Car	4.6 (4593)	Serpentine	①	①
1994	Mustang	3.8 (3801)	Serpentine	①	①
	Mustang	5.0 (4943) HO	Serpentine	①	①
	Mustang	5.0 (4943) SHP	Serpentine	①	①
	Thunderbird	3.8 (3801)	Serpentine	①	①
	Cougar	3.8 (3801)	Serpentine	①	①
	Thunderbird	3.8 (3801) SC	Serpentine	①	①
	Thunderbird	4.6 (4593)	Serpentine	①	①
	Cougar	4.6 (4593)	Serpentine	①	①
	Mark VIII	4.6 (4593)	Serpentine	①	①
	Crown Victoria	4.6 (4593)	Serpentine	①	①
	Grand Marquis	4.6 (4593)	Serpentine	①	①
	Town Car	4.6 (4593)	Serpentine	①	①
1995	Mustang	3.8 (3801)	Serpentine	①	①
	Mustang	5.0 (4943) HO	Serpentine	①	①
	Mustang	5.0 (4943) SHP	Serpentine	①	①
	Thunderbird	3.8 (3801)	Serpentine	①	①
	Cougar	3.8 (3801)	Serpentine	①	①
	Thunderbird	3.8 (3801) SC	Serpentine	①	①
	Thunderbird	4.6 (4593)	Serpentine	①	①
	Cougar	4.6 (4593)	Serpentine	①	①
	Mark VIII	4.6 (4593)	Serpentine	①	①
	Crown Victoria	4.6 (4593)	Serpentine	①	①
	Grand Marquis	4.6 (4593)	Serpentine	①	①
	Town Car	4.6 (4593)	Serpentine	①	①

① Automatic belt tensioner
HO – High Output
SC – Supercharged
SHP – Special High Performance

REFRIGERANT CAPACITIES

Year	Model	Refrigerant (oz.)	Oil (fl. oz.)	Compressor Type
1993	Mustang (2.3)	38–42	8	10P15C
	Mustang (5.0)	38–42	10	6P148
	Thunderbird	38–42	7	FX–15
	Cougar	38–42	7	FX–15
	Mark VIII	33–35	7①	FX–15
	Crown Victoria	38–39	7①	FX–15
	Grand Marquis	38–39	7①	FX–15
	Town Car	36–37	7①	FX–15
1994	Mustang	33–35	7	FS–10
	Thunderbird	35–37	7	FS–10
	Cougar	35–37	7	FS–10
	Mark VIII	33–35	7①	FS–10
	Crown Victoria	40–41	7①	FS–10
	Grand Marquis	40–41	7①	FS–10
	Town Car	38–39	7①	FS–10
1995	Mustang	34	7	FS–10
	Thunderbird	35–37②	7	FS–10
	Cougar	35–37②	7	FS–10
	Mark VIII	33–35	7	FS–10
	Crown Victoria	34	7	FS–10
	Grand Marquis	34	7	FS–10
	Town Car	34	7	FS–10

① 10 oz. with auxiliary A/C

② 33–35 oz. with Semi–Automatic Temperature Control

SYSTEM DESCRIPTION

General Information

The air conditioning system used on Ford rear wheel drive vehicles is the fixed orifice tube-cycling clutch type. The system components consist of the compressor, magnetic clutch, condenser, evaporator, suction accumulator/drier and the necessary connecting refrigerant lines. The fixed orifice tube assembly is a fixed restriction between the high and low pressure liquid refrigerant and meters the flow of liquid refrigerant into the evaporator core. Evaporator temperature is controlled by sensing the pressure within the evaporator with the clutch cycling pressure switch. The pressure switch controls compressor operation as necessary to maintain the evaporator pressure within specified limits.

An electronic automatic temperature control system is standard equipment on Mark VIII and Town Car; it is optional on all other models except Mustang. This system uses a series of sensors and an electronic control unit to monitor sensor inputs and vary system operations to maintain a preset temperature. It will automatically vary heating and cooling operations as well as mode controls as needed.

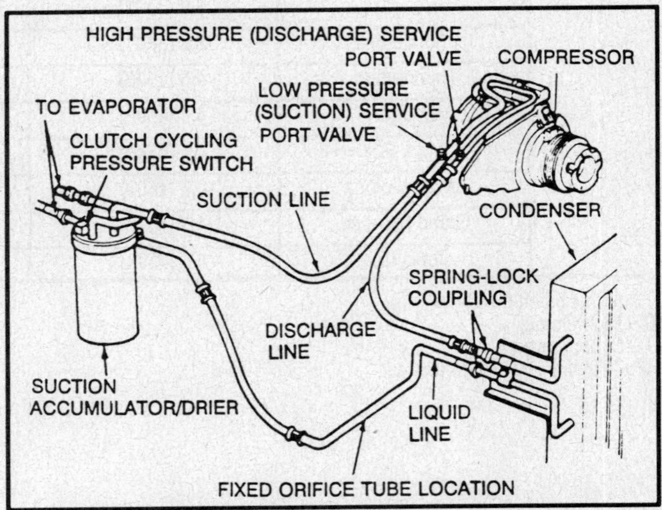

Fixed orifice tube air conditioning system—typical

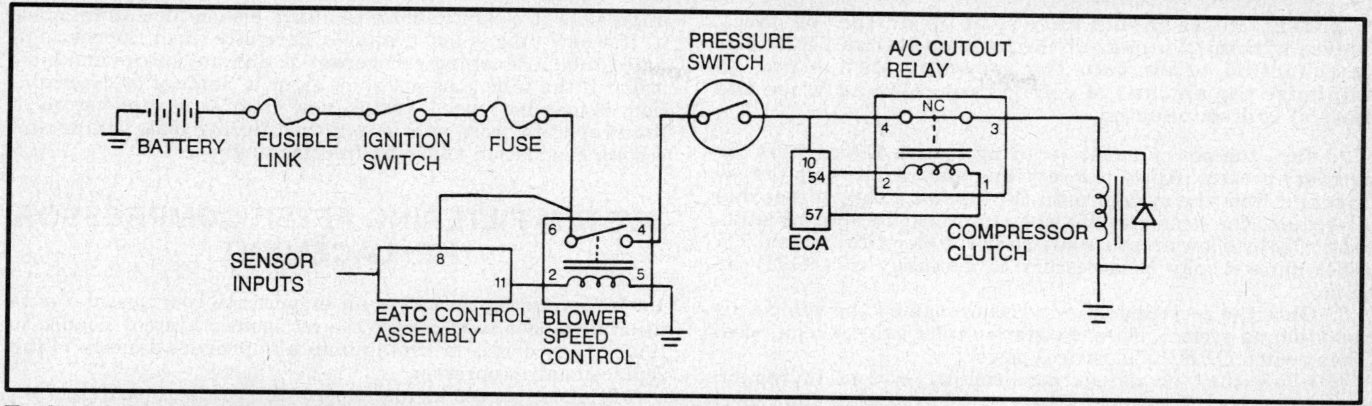

Typical system wiring diagram with Automatic Temperature Control (ATC)

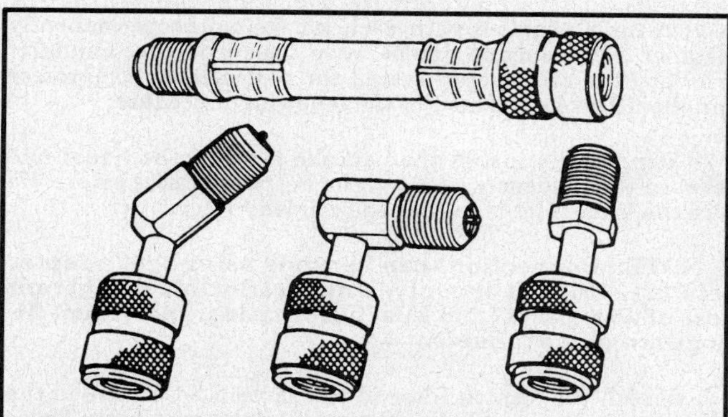
High pressure gauge port valve adapters

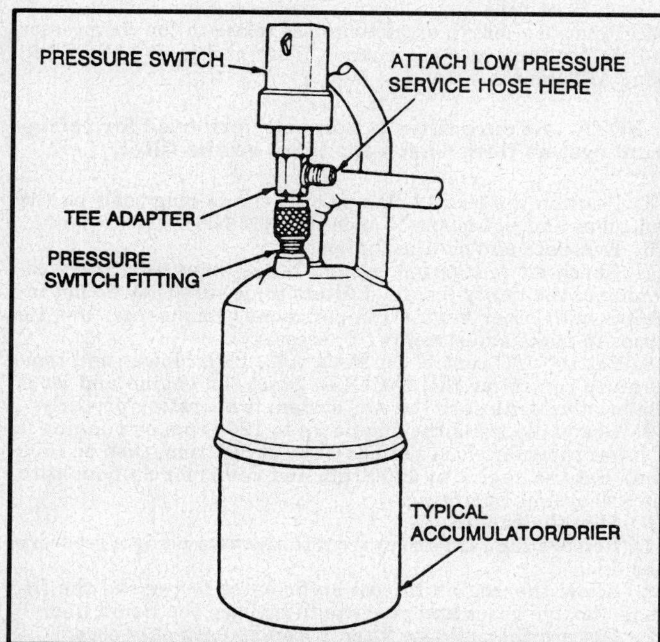

Tee adapter tool installation

Some models are manufactured to use R-134a refrigerant and R-134a type refrigerant oil. These systems are clearly marked with "R-134a" tags on key components and refrigerant lines. The characteristics of R-134a require that the clutch cycling switch be calibrated to slightly higher ON and OFF cycling points. In addition, a new refrigerant containment switch has been added to the discharge line to prevent refrigerant from discharging to the atmosphere through the pressure relief valve. It operates by increasing the speed of the engine cooling fan and cutting off compressor operation when certain high pressure is reached. All other components function virtually the same as on R-12 systems; however, the refrigerant, oil, components and service equipment cannot be intermixed between R-134a systems and R-12 systems.

Service Valve Location

The air conditioning system has a high pressure (discharge) and a low pressure (suction) gauge port valve. These are Schrader valves which provide access to both the high and low pressure sides of the system for service hoses and a manifold gauge set so system pressures can be read. The high pressure gauge port valve is located between the compressor and the condenser, in the high pressure vapor (discharge) line. The low pressure gauge port valve is located between the suction accumulator/drier and the compressor, in the low pressure vapor (suction) line.

High side adapter set D81L–19703–A or tool YT–354, 355 or equivalent, is required to connect a manifold gauge set or charging station to the high pressure gauge port valve. Service tee fitting D87P–19703–A, which may be mounted on the clutch cycling pressure switch fitting, is available for use in the low pressure side, to be used in place of the low pressure gauge port valve.

On Mark VIII models with R-134a systems, new service valves with quick-disconnect feature and female fittings are used to prevent introduction of R-12 into the system in error.

System Discharging

NOTE: The use of dedicated manifold gauge set, recycling/recharging stations and leak detectors is required with R-134a. Mixing of any amounts of R-12 with R-134a or their respective refrigerant oils will cause harm to the system operation and components.

The use of refrigerant recovery systems and recycling stations makes possible the recovery and reuse of refrigerant after contaminants and moisture have been removed. The reuse of refrigerant will minimize the discharge of ozone depleting chlorofluorocarbons into the atmosphere. When a recovery system or recycling station is used, the following general procedures should be observed, in addition to the operating instructions provided by the equipment manufacturer.

1. Connect the refrigerant recycling station hose(s) to the vehicle air conditioning service ports and the recovery station inlet fitting.

NOTE: Hoses should have shut off devices or check valves within 12 inches of the hose end to minimize the introduction of air into the recycling station and to minimize the amount of refrigerant released when the hose(s) is disconnected.

2. Turn the power to the recycling station **ON** to start the recovery process. Allow the recycling station to pump the refrigerant from the system until the station pressure goes into a vacuum. On some stations the pump will be shut off automatically by a low pressure switch in the electrical system. On other units it may be necessary to manually turn **OFF** the pump.
3. Once the recycling station has evacuated the vehicle air conditioning system, close the station inlet valve, if equipped. Then switch **OFF** the electrical power.
4. Allow the vehicle air conditioning system to remain closed for about 2 minutes. Observe the system vacuum level as shown on the gauge. If the pressure does not rise, disconnect the recycling station hose(s).
5. If the system pressure rises, repeat Steps 2, 3 and 4 until the vacuum level remains stable for 2 minutes.

System Flushing

A refrigerant system can become badly contaminated and in need of flushing for a number of reasons:

- The compressor may have failed due to damage or wear.
- The compressor may have been run for some time with a severe leak or an opening in the system.
- The system may have been damaged by a collision and left open for some time.
- The system may not have been cleaned properly after a previous failure.
- The system may have been operated for a time with water or moisture in it.

A badly contaminated system contains water, carbon and other decomposition products. When this condition exists, the system must be flushed with a special flushing agent (R-11 or R-113) using equipment designed specially for this purpose.

FLUSHING AGENTS

To be suitable as a flushing agent, a refrigerant must remain in liquid state during the flushing operation in order to wash the inside surfaces of the system components. Refrigerant vapor will not remove contaminant particles. They must be flushed with a liquid. R-11 is more toxic than other refrigerants and should be handled with extra care.

SPECIAL FLUSHING EQUIPMENT

Special refrigerant system flushing equipment is available from a number of air conditioning equipment suppliers and usually comes in kit form. A flushing kit, such as model 015–00205 or equivalent, consists of a cylinder for the flushing agent, a nozzle to introduce the flushing agent into the system and a connecting hose.

A second type of equipment, which must be connected into the system, allows for the continuous circulation of the flushing agent through the system. Contaminants are trapped by an external filter/drier. If this equipment is used, follow the manufacturer's instructions and observe all safety precautions.

SYSTEM CLEANING AND FLUSHING

NOTE: Use extreme care and adhere to all safety precautions related to the use of refrigerants when flushing a system.

When it is necessary to flush a refrigerant system, the accumulator/drier must be removed and replaced, because it is impossible to clean. Remove the fixed orifice tube and replace it. If a new tube is not available, carefully wash the contaminated tube in flushing refrigerant or mineral spirits and blow it dry. If the tube does not show signs of damage or deterioration, it may be reused. Install new O-rings. Any moisture in the evaporator core will be removed during leak testing and system evacuation following the cleaning job.

SYSTEM FILTERING AFTER COMPRESSOR REPLACEMENT

1994–95 vehicles that have an inoperative compressor due to internal causes should have the refrigerant system cleaned to remove any debris or contaminants to prevent damage to the replacement compressor.

A filter kit should be installed in the refrigerant system before replacing the compressor. The pancake filter supplied with each kit should be temporarily installed in the liquid line between the condenser core and the evaporator core orifice. The suction filter supplied with each kit should be permanently installed in the suction line between the suction accumulator/drier and the compressor. Install the replacement compressor and the filters as outlined in the following procedure:

1. Temporarily install the pancake filter in the liquid line between the condenser core and the evaporator core orifice. Be sure the filter inlet is toward the condenser core.

NOTE: Connections can be made using Test Adapter Set D93L–19703–B or equivalent, and flexible refrigerant hose of 2500 psi (17,238 kPa) burst rating. Individual fittings are also available.

2. Install the suction filter in the suction hose close to the compressor. Suction filter is for nylon–lined core hose. These filters have 2 grooves in the end tubes to accommodate O–ring seals.
3. On the filter for nylon–lined hose, install O–ring seals, 2 on each filter tube.
4. Remove a length of suction hose (close to the compressor end) to accommodate the suction filter and install the filter, using A/C clamps.

NOTE: Be sure filter is correctly oriented for refrigerant system flow. Check the label on the filter.

5. Position the size 12 clamps over the O–ring seals on the end tubes and tighten to 55 inch lbs. (6.2 Nm).
6. Evacuate and charge the system.
7. Check all refrigerant system hoses, lines, and the positioning of the newly installed filters to be sure they do not interfere with other engine compartment components. Use tie straps to make adjustments (if necessary).
8. Set the A/C control on **MAX A/C**, high blower and temperature control at FULL–COLD. Start the engine and let it idle briefly. Make sure the A/C system is operating properly.
9. Gradually bring the engine up to 1200 rpm by running it at lower rpms for short periods (first at 800 rpm, then at 1000 rpm). Set the engine at 1200 rpm and run it for an hour with the A/C system operating.
10. Stop the engine.
11. Remove the refrigerant from the system using a recovery machine.
12. Allow the engine to cool sufficiently to remove the fittings, flexible hoses and pancake filter from the liquid line.
13. Discard the pancake filter. It can be used only once.
14. Reconnect the liquid line back into the system.
15. Evacuate, charge and leak test the system. Make any necessary adjustments.
16. Check the operation of the system in all control function selector lever positions.

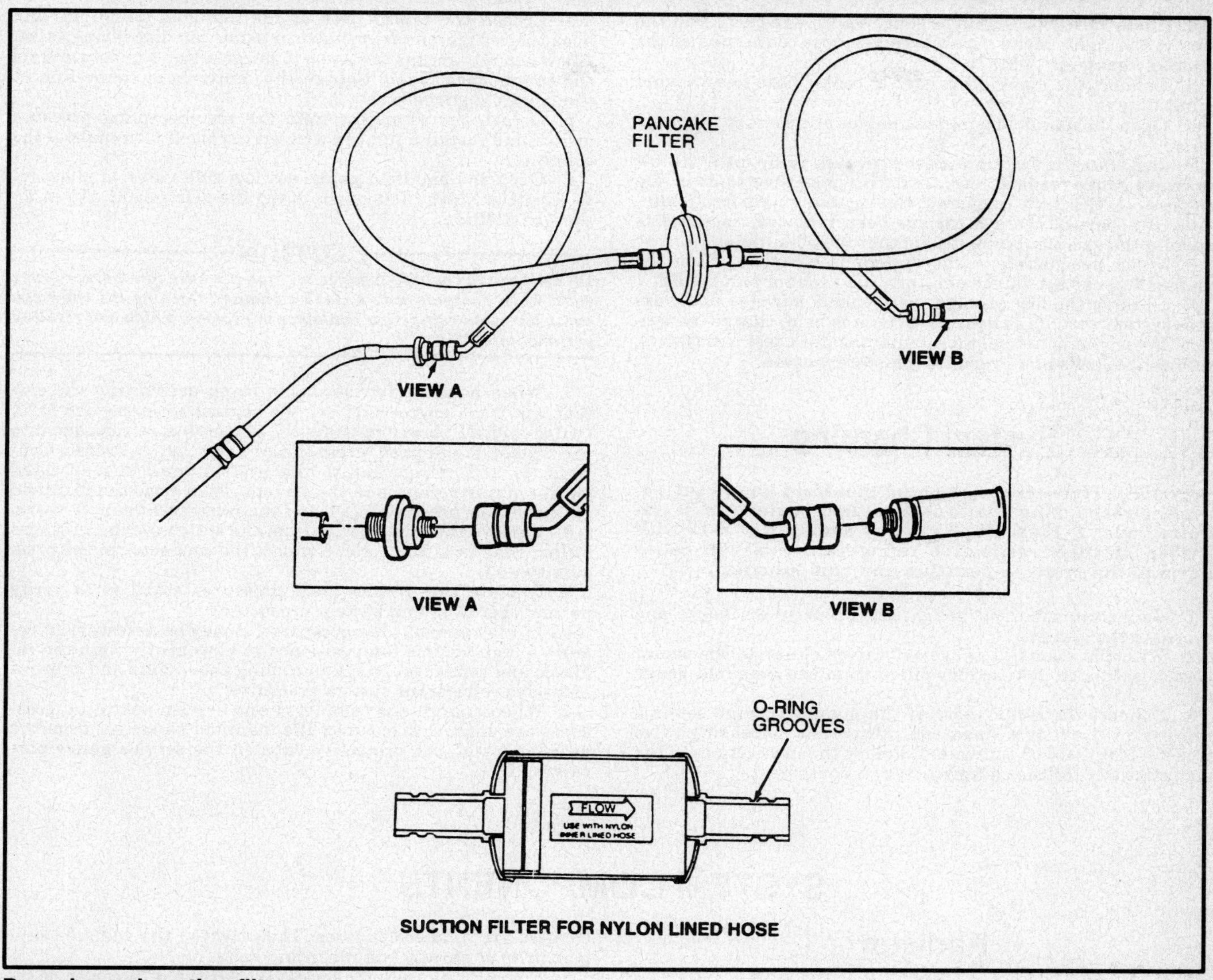

Pancake and suction filters

System Evacuating

NOTE: The use of dedicated manifold gauge set, recycling/recharging stations and leak detectors is required with R-134a. Mixing of any amounts of R-12 with R-134a or their respective refrigerant oils will cause harm to the system operation and components.

1. Connect a manifold gauge set as follows:
   - Turn both manifold gauge set valves all the way to the right, to close the high and low pressure hoses to the center manifold and hose.
   - Remove the caps from the high and low pressure service gauge port valves.
   - If the manifold gauge set hoses do not have valve depressing pins in them, install fitting adapters T71P–19703–S and R or equivalent, which have pins, on the low and high pressure hoses.
   - Connect the high and low pressure hoses or adapters, to the respective high and low pressure service gauge port valves. High side adapter set D81L–19703–A or tool YT–354 or 355 or equivalent is required to connect a manifold gauge set or charging station to the high pressure gauge port valve.

NOTE: Service tee fitting D87P–19703–A, which may be mounted on the clutch cycling pressure switch fitting, is available for use in the low pressure side, to be used in place of the low pressure gauge port valve.

2. Leak test all connections and components with flame-type leak detector 023–00006, electronic leak detector 055–00014 or 055–00015 or equivalent.

CAUTION

Fumes from flame-type leak detectors are noxious, avoid inhaling them or personal injury may result. Good ventilation is necessary in the area where air conditioning leak testing is to be done. If the surrounding air is contaminated with refrigerant gas, the leak detector will indicate this gas all the time. Odors from other chemicals such as anti-freeze, diesel fuel, disc brake cleaner or other cleaning solvents can cause the same problem. (A fan, even in a well ventilated area, is very helpful in removing small traces of air contamination that might affect the leak detector.)

3. Properly discharge the refrigerant system.

4. Make sure both manifold gauge valves are turned all the way to the right. Make sure the center hose connection at the manifold gauge is tight.
5. Connect the manifold gauge set center hose to a vacuum pump.
6. Open the manifold gauge set valves and start the vacuum pump.
7. Evacuate the system with the vacuum pump until the low pressure gauge reads at least 25 in. Hg or as close to 30 in. Hg as possible. Continue to operate the vacuum pump for 15 minutes. If a part of the system has been replaced, continue to operate the vacuum pump for another 20–30 minutes.
8. When evacuation of the system is complete, close the manifold gauge set valves and turn the vacuum pump **OFF**.
9. Observe the low pressure gauge for 5 minutes to ensure that system vacuum is held. If vacuum is held, charge the system. If vacuum is not held for 5 minutes, leak test the system, service the leaks and evacuate the system again.

System Charging

NOTE: The use of dedicated manifold gauge set, recycling/recharging stations and leak detectors is required with R-134a. Mixing of any amounts of R-12 with R-134a or their respective refrigerant oils will cause harm to the system operation and components.

1. Connect a manifold gauge set. Properly discharge and evacuate the system.
2. With the manifold gauge set valves closed to the center hose, disconnect the vacuum pump from the manifold gauge set.
3. Connect the center hose of the manifold gauge set to a refrigerant drum or a small can refrigerant dispensing valve tool YT–280, 1034 or equivalent. Follow the instructions of the manufacturer for the charging station equipment.
4. Loosen the center hose at the manifold gauge set and open the refrigerant drum valve or small can dispensing valve. Allow the refrigerant to escape to purge air and moisture from the center hose. Then, tighten the center hose connection at the manifold gauge set.
5. Detach the connector from the clutch cycling pressure switch and install a jumper wire across the 2 terminals of the connector.
6. Open the manifold gauge set low side valve to allow refrigerant to enter the system. Keep the refrigerant can in an upright position.

CAUTION

Do not open the manifold gauge set high pressure (discharge) gauge valve when charging with a small container. Opening the valve can cause the small refrigerant container to explode, which can result in personal injury.

7. When no more refrigerant is being drawn into the system, start the engine and set the control assembly for MAX COLD and HI blower to draw the remaining refrigerant into the system. If equipped, press the air conditioning switch. Continue to add refrigerant to the system until the specified weight of refrigerant is in the system. Then close the manifold gauge set low pressure valve and the refrigerant supply valve.
8. Remove the jumper wire from the clutch cycling pressure switch snap lock connector. Connect the connector to the pressure switch.
9. Operate the system until pressures stabilize to verify normal operation and system pressures.
10. In high ambient temperatures, it may be necessary to operate a high volume fan positioned to blow air through the radiator and condenser to aid in cooling the engine and prevent excessive refrigerant system pressures.
11. When charging is completed and system operating pressures are normal, disconnect the manifold gauge set from the vehicle. Install the protective caps on the service gauge port valves.

SYSTEM COMPONENTS

Radiator

REMOVAL AND INSTALLATION

1. Disconnect the negative battery cable. Drain the cooling system. If equipped with supercharger, remove the inter cooler from the radiator.
2. Disconnect the upper, lower and overflow hoses at the radiator.
3. On automatic transmission equipped vehicles, disconnect the fluid cooler lines at radiator.
4. Depending on model; remove the 2 top mounting bolts and remove radiator and shroud assembly or remove the shroud mounting bolts and position the shroud aside. If the air conditioner condenser is attached to the radiator, remove the retaining bolts and position the condenser aside. Do not disconnect the refrigerant lines.
5. Remove the radiator attaching bolts or top brackets and lift out the radiator.

To install:

6. If a new radiator is to be installed, transfer the petcock from the old radiator to the new one. If equipped with an automatic transmission, transfer the fluid cooler line fittings from the old radiator.
7. Position the radiator and install, do not tighten the radiator support bolts. If equipped with an automatic transmission, connect the fluid cooler lines. Then tighten the radiator support bolts or shroud and mounting bolts.
8. Connect the radiator hoses. Install the intercooler, if removed.
9. Close the radiator petcock. Fill and bleed the cooling system. Start the engine and bring to operating temperature. Check for leaks.
10. If equipped with an automatic transmission, check the cooler lines for leaks and interference. Check the transmission fluid level.

COOLING SYSTEM BLEEDING

When the entire cooling system is drained, the following procedure should be used to ensure a complete fill.

1. Install the block drain plug, if removed and close the draincock. With the engine off, add anti-freeze to the radiator to a level of 50 percent of the total cooling system capacity. Then add water until it reaches the radiator filler neck seat.
2. On Mustang equipped with the 2.3L engine, disconnect the heater hose at the connection on the thermostat housing. Fill the radiator until coolant (50/50 mix of coolant and water) is visible at the connection in the thermostat housing or the coolant level in the radiator reaches the radiator filler neck seat. Install the heater hose and tighten the hose clamps.
3. Install the radiator cap to the first notch to keep spillage to a minimum.

4. Start the engine and let it idle until the upper radiator hose is warm. This indicates that the thermostat is open and coolant is flowing through the entire system.
5. Carefully remove the radiator cap and top off the radiator with water. Install the cap on the radiator securely.
6. Fill the coolant recovery reservoir to the FULL COLD mark with anti-freeze, then add water to the FULL HOT mark. This will ensure that a proper mixture is in the reservoir.

Electric Cooling Fan

TESTING

1. Disconnect the electrical connector at the cooling fan motor.
2. Connect a jumper wire between the negative motor lead and ground.
3. Connect another jumper wire between the positive motor lead and the positive terminal of the battery.
4. If the cooling fan motor does not run, it must be replaced.

REMOVAL AND INSTALLATION

Mustang

1. Disconnect the negative battery cable.
2. Remove the fan wiring harness from the routing clip. Disconnect the wiring harness from the fan motor connector by pulling up on the single lock finger to separate the connectors.
3. Remove the 4 mounting bracket attaching screws and remove the fan assembly from the vehicle.
4. Remove the retaining clip from the end of the motor shaft and remove the fan.

NOTE: A metal burr may be present on the motor after the retaining clip is removed. Deburring of the shaft may be required to remove the fan.

5. Remove the nuts attaching the fan motor to the mounting bracket.
6. Installation is the reverse of the removal procedure. Tighten the fan motor-to-mounting bracket attaching nuts to 48.5–62.0 inch lbs. (5.5–7.0 Nm) and the mounting bracket attaching screws to 70–95 inch lbs. (8.0–10.5 Nm).

Thunderbird

3.8L SC ENGINE

1. Disconnect the negative battery cable.
2. Disconnect the fan motor wiring connector at the side of the fan shroud. Remove the male terminal connector retaining clip from the shroud mounting tab.
3. Remove the overflow hose from the fan shroud retaining clip (1993 only).
4. Remove the 2 shroud upper retaining bolts at the radiator support.
5. Lift the cooling fan module past the radiator, disengaging the shroud from the 2 lower retaining clips.
6. Installation is the reverse of the removal procedure. Tighten the shroud retaining bolts to 36 inch lbs. (4 Nm) on 1993 models or 27–53 inch lbs. (3–6 Nm) on 1994–95 models.

Crown Victoria, Grand Marquis and Town Car

1995

1. Turn the lower fan shroud in the upper fan shroud to allow clearance for fan shroud removal.
2. Disconnect the electric auxiliary cooling fan motor wiring connector at the right side of the fan shroud.
3. Remove the radiator upper sight shield.
4. Loosen the fan shroud from the radiator mounting and remove the lower radiator hose from the supports on the fan shroud.
5. Lift the fan shroud out of the vehicle.

To install:

6. Position the fan shroud on the radiator lower mounting clips. Install the two retaining screws and tighten to 24–48 inch lbs. (2.7–5.4 Nm).
7. Position the lower radiator hose onto the supports on the fan shroud.
8. Turn the lower fan shroud in the upper fan shroud to the closed position.

Thunderbird and Cougar without Supercharger and 1994–95 Mark VIII

1. Disconnect the negative battery cable.
2. Remove the 2 fan shroud retaining bolts.
3. Separate the lower radiator hose from the fan shroud (Mark VIII only).
4. Disconnect the cooling fan motor wire harness at the cooling fan motor.
5. Lift the cooling fan assembly out of the vehicle.
6. Installation is the reverse of the removal procedure. Tighten the shroud retaining bolts to 24–48 inch lbs. (2.7–5.4 Nm) on Mark VIII or 46–64 inch lbs. on Thunderbird and Cougar.

Condenser

REMOVAL AND INSTALLATION

Crown Victoria, Grand Marquis and Town Car

NOTE: Whenever the condenser is replaced, it will be necessary to replace the suction accumulator/drier.

1. Disconnect the battery cables and remove the battery.
2. Properly drain the engine coolant. Save the coolant for reuse.

NOTE: 1995 models have the condenser attached to the radiator. The condenser and the radiator must be handled as a unit.

3. Disconnect the upper radiator hose, the lower radiator hose and the de–aeration hose from the radiator. (On 1993–94 models, disconnect only the upper radiator hose.)
4. Using a back–up wrench to hold the radiator fitting, disconnect the transmission cooler lines. Plug or cap the lines and fittings to prevent contamination. (On 1993–94 models, do not disconnect.)
5. Discharge the refrigerant from the air conditioning system.
6. Disconnect the 2 refrigerant lines at the fittings near the radiator on the right side of the vehicle using the spring-lock coupling disconnect procedure. Plug the lines to prevent dirt and excessive moisture from entering.
7. If necessary, remove the 2 retaining screws from the air intake duct and position it away from the radiator/condenser area.
8. Remove the 2 retaining screws from the fan shroud and position it rearward away from the radiator/condenser area.
9. Remove the screw from each of the 2 radiator brackets and remove the radiator brackets.
10. On 1993–94 models, tilt the radiator rearward, remove the 2 retaining screws from the top rear of the condenser core and lift the condenser core from the vehicle. Remove and retain the 4 corner mounts.
11. On 1995 models, lift the radiator and the condenser core from the vehicle as an assembly. Remove the upper condenser mounting bracket bolts and separate the condenser core from the radiator.

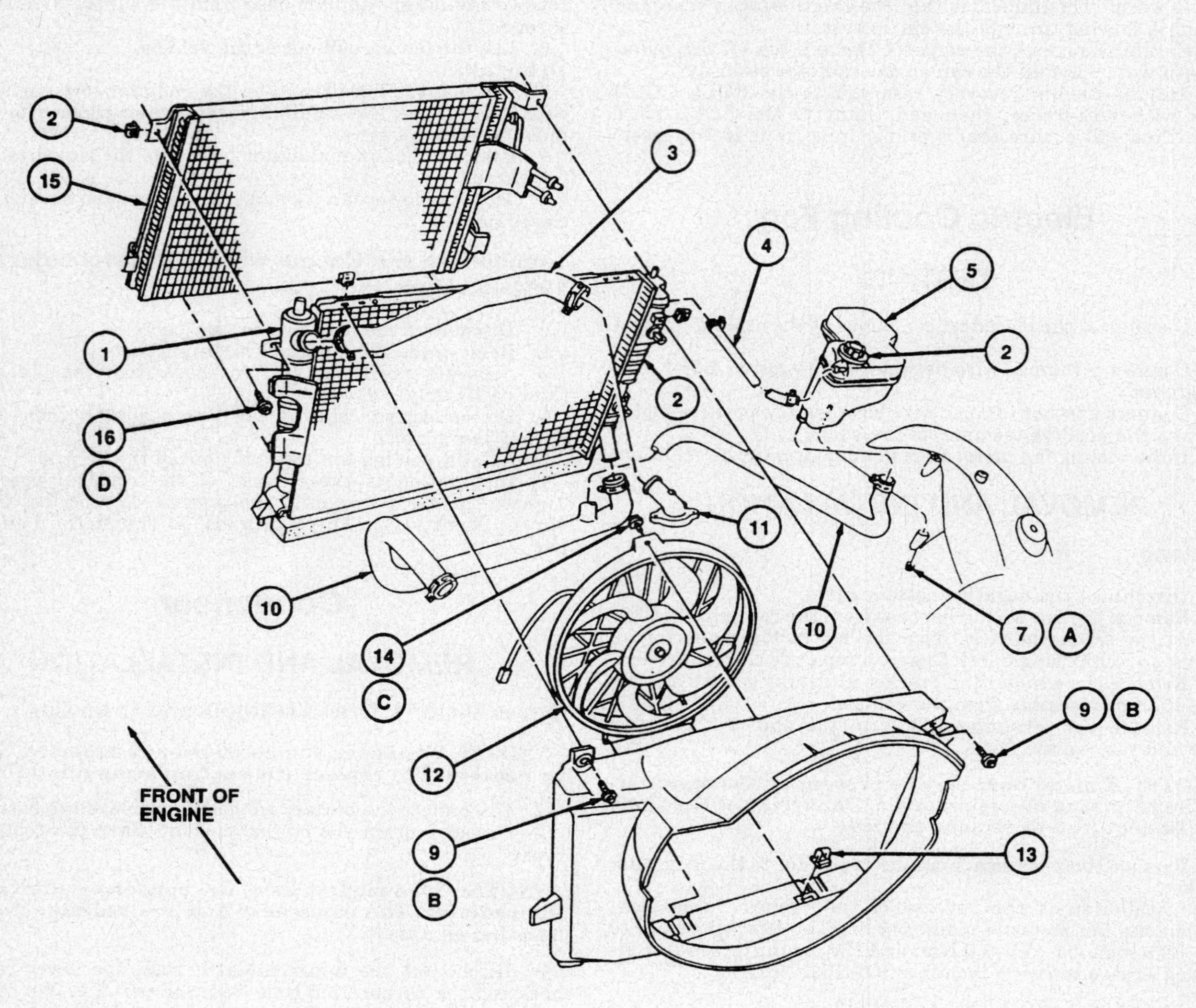

Item	Description
1	Radiator
2	Clip (4 Req'd)
3	Upper Radiator Hose
4	Radiator Overflow Hose
5	Radiator Coolant Recovery Reservoir
6	Pressure Relief Cap
7	Nut (3 Req'd)
8	Fan Shroud
9	Screw (2 Req'd)
10	Lower Radiator Hose

Item	Description
11	Water Hose Connection
12	Cooling Fan Motor / Fan Blade and Fan Shroud
13	Clip (3 Req'd)
14	Screw (2 Req'd)
15	A / C Condenser Core
16	Screw (2 Req'd)
A	Tighten to 4-5 ft. lbs. (5.5-7.0 N·m).
B	Tighten to 24-48 inch lbs. (2.7-5.4 N·m).
C	Tighten to 27-53 inch lbs. (3-6 N·m).
D	Tighten to 71-97 inch lbs. (8-11 N·m).

Electric Fan System and Related Components—Crown Victoria, Grand Marquis and Town Car

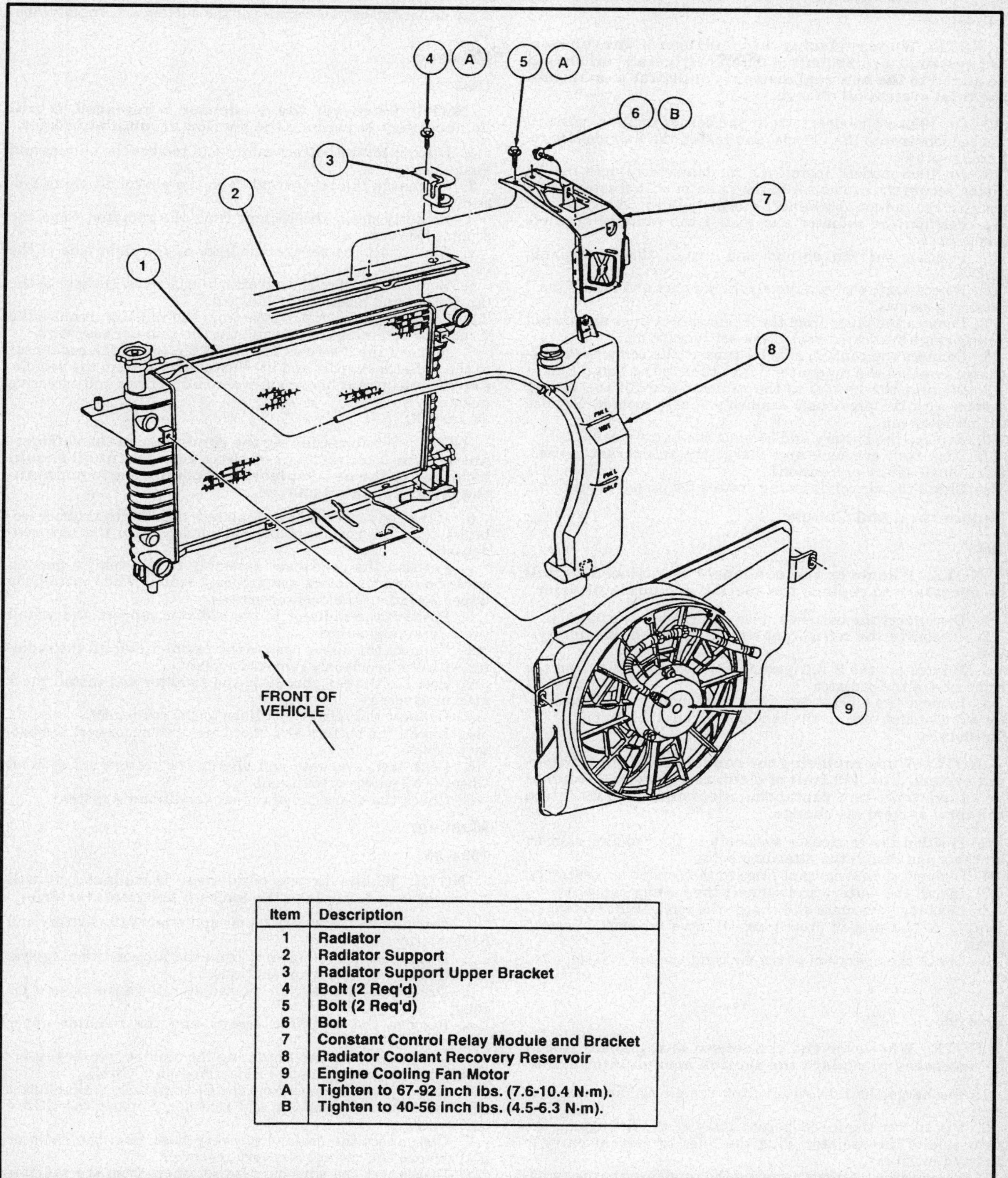

Item	Description
1	Radiator
2	Radiator Support
3	Radiator Support Upper Bracket
4	Bolt (2 Req'd)
5	Bolt (2 Req'd)
6	Bolt
7	Constant Control Relay Module and Bracket
8	Radiator Coolant Recovery Reservoir
9	Engine Cooling Fan Motor
A	Tighten to 67-92 inch lbs. (7.6-10.4 N·m).
B	Tighten to 40-56 inch lbs. (4.5-6.3 N·m).

Electric Fan System and Related Components—1994–95 Mustang

To install:

NOTE: When replacing the condenser in the refrigerant system, 1 oz. (29.5ml) of clean refrigerant oil should be added to the new replacement condenser to maintain the total system oil charge.

12. On 1993–94 models, attach the corner mounts, position the condenser into the vehicle, and install the 2 condenser retaining screws.
13. On 1995 models, install the condenser core onto the radiator, secure the condenser to the radiator with 2 screws, and position the radiator/condenser assembly in the vehicle.
14. Position the radiator and install the radiator brackets and 2 screws.
15. Position the fan shroud and install the 2 retaining screws.
16. If necessary, position the air intake duct and install the 2 retaining screws.
17. Remove the plugs from the 2 refrigerant lines and install new O-rings lubricated with clean refrigerant oil.
18. Connect the condenser inlet tube to the compressor discharge line and the condenser outlet tube to the liquid line.
19. Connect the hose(s) to the radiator and fill the cooling system with the previously drained radiator coolant. Replace the radiator cap.
20. Replace the battery and connect the battery cables.
21. Leak test, evacuate and charge the refrigerant system. Observe all safety precautions.
22. Check the air conditioning system for proper operation.

Thunderbird and Cougar

1993

NOTE: Whenever the condenser is replaced, it will be necessary to replace the suction accumulator/drier.

1. Disconnect the battery cables and remove the battery.
2. Discharge the refrigerant from the air conditioning system.
3. Disconnect the 2 refrigerant lines at the fittings on the right side of the radiator.
4. Remove the 4 bolts attaching the condenser to the radiator support and remove the condenser from the vehicle.

To install:

NOTE: When replacing the condenser in the refrigerant system, 1 oz. (29.5ml) of clean refrigerant oil should be added to the new replacement condenser to maintain the total system oil charge.

5. Position the condenser assembly to the radiator support brackets and install the attaching bolts.
6. Connect the refrigerant lines to the condenser assembly.
7. Install the battery and connect the battery cables.
8. Leak test, evacuate and charge the refrigerant system according to the proper procedure. Observe all safety precautions.
9. Check the operation of the air conditioning system.

1994–95

NOTE: Whenever the condenser is replaced, it will be necessary to replace the suction accumulator/drier.

1. Discharge the refrigerant from the air conditioning system.
2. Disconnect the 2 refrigerant lines at the fittings on the right side of the radiator. Plug the lines to prevent entry of dirt and moisture.
3. Remove the 2 screws securing the condenser to the radiator support and lift condenser from vehicle.
4. Installation is the reverse of the removal procedure. If installing a new condenser core, add 1 oz. (30ml) of refrigerant oil to either the condenser core or the suction accumulator/drier.

Mustang

1993

NOTE: Whenever the condenser is replaced, it will be necessary to replace the suction accumulator/drier.

1. Disconnect the battery cables and remove the battery and heat shield.
2. Discharge the refrigerant from the air conditioning system.
3. Properly drain the coolant from the radiator. Save the coolant for reuse.
4. Disconnect the refrigerant lines at the right side of the radiator.
5. Remove the 2 fan shroud attaching screws. Disengage the fan shroud and position it rearward.
6. Disconnect the upper hose from the radiator, remove the 2 radiator retaining clamps and tilt the radiator rearward.
7. Remove the 2 screws attaching the top of the condenser to the radiator support and lift the condenser from the vehicle. Cap the refrigerant lines to prevent entry of dirt and excessive moisture.

To install:

NOTE: When replacing the condenser in the refrigerant system, 1 oz. (29.5ml) of clean refrigerant oil should be added to the new replacement condenser to maintain the total system oil charge.

8. If the condenser is to be replaced, transfer the rubber isolators from the bottom of the old condenser to the new condenser.
9. Position the condenser assembly to the vehicle making sure the lower isolators are properly seated. Then install the upper 2 condenser attaching screws.
10. Position the radiator to the radiator support and install the 2 retaining clamps.
11. Connect the upper hose to the radiator and fill the radiator with the previously removed coolant.
12. Position the fan shroud to the radiator and install the 2 attaching screws.
13. Connect the refrigerant lines to the condenser.
14. Install the battery and heat shield, then connect the battery cables.
15. Leak test, evacuate and charge the refrigerant system. Observe all safety precautions.
16. Check the operation of the air conditioning system.

Mustang

1994–95

NOTE: Whenever the condenser is replaced, it will be necessary to replace the suction accumulator/drier.

1. Disconnect the battery cables and remove the battery and battery tray.
2. Discharge the refrigerant from the air conditioning system. Observe all safety precautions.
3. Drain the coolant from the radiator. Save the coolant for reuse.
4. Remove the retaining screws and the radiator upper sight shield.
5. Remove the 1 screw retaining the coolant recovery reservoir to the Constant Control Relay Module (CCRM).
6. Remove the 2 screws from the CCRM bracket. Disconnect the wire harness connector and retainer. Remove the CCRM and bracket.
7. Disconnect the coolant recovery hose from the radiator and remove the coolant recovery reservoir.
8. Disconnect the wire harness retainers from the radiator support.
9. Disconnect the wire harness connectors from the anti–lock brake control module and the engine cooling fan.

10. Disconnect the refrigerant lines at the right side of the condenser. Cap the lines to prevent entry of dirt and moisture.
11. Disconnect the upper radiator hose, remove the 2 retaining screws and 2 radiator support upper brackets and tilt the radiator rearward.
12. Remove the 2 retaining screws and the 2 condenser mounting brackets from the radiator support. Lift the condenser core from the vehicle.

To install:

NOTE: When replacing the condenser in the refrigerant system, 1 oz. (29.5ml) of clean refrigerant oil should be added to the new replacement condenser to maintain the total system oil charge.

13. Position the condenser in the vehicle with the lower isolators properly seated on the condenser mounting brackets. Then install the 2 mounting brackets and the 2 attaching screws.
14. Position the radiator to the radiator support, install the 2 radiator support upper brackets and the 2 retaining screws and connect the upper radiator hose.
15. Using new O–rings lubricated with clean refrigerant oil, connect the refrigerant lines to the condenser.
16. Connect the wire harness connectors to the anti–lock brake control module and the engine cooling fan. Install the harness retainers into the radiator support.
17. Install the coolant recovery reservoir into the lower bracket and connect the coolant recovery hose to the radiator.
18. Install the Constant Control Relay Module (CCRM) and bracket assembly with the 2 retaining screws. Connect the CCRM wiring connector and wire harness retainer.
19. Install the 1 screw retaining the coolant recovery reservoir to the CCRM bracket.
20. Install the radiator upper sight shield and the retaining screws.
21. Install the battery tray and the battery. Connect the battery cables, positive cable first.
22. Refill the cooling system.
23. Leak test, evacuate and charge the refrigerant system. Observe all safety precautions.
24. Check the operation of the air conditioning system.

Mark VIII

NOTE: Whenever the condenser is replaced, it will be necessary to replace the suction accumulator/drier.

1. Discharge the refrigerant from the air conditioning system.
2. Disconnect the 2 refrigerant lines at the fittings on the right side of the radiator. Plug the lines to prevent entry of dirt and moisture.
3. Remove the 2 screws securing the condenser to the radiator support and lift condenser from vehicle.
4. Installation is the reverse of the removal procedure. If installing a new condenser core, add 1 oz. (30 ml) of refrigerant oil to either the condenser core or the suction accumulator/drier.

Compressor

REMOVAL AND INSTALLATION

Crown Victoria, Grand Marquis and Town Car

NOTE: The suction accumulator/drier and the fixed orifice tube should also be replaced whenever the compressor is replaced. Special filtering and flushing should be done to the system if compressor has failed (identified by dirty orifice tube and/or black refrigerant, with particles, in the liquid line).

1. Disconnect the negative battery cable.
2. Discharge the refrigerant from the air conditioning system.
3. Remove the drive belt from the clutch pulley.
4. Disconnect the compressor clutch wires at the wire connectors.
5. Remove the manifold and tube retaining bolt from the rear of the compressor. Separate the manifold and tube and plug the openings to prevent entry of dirt and moisture.
6. Remove the 3 compressor lower retaining bolts and remove the compressor.
7. Remove the bracket from the compressor.

To install:

NOTE: A new service replacement FX–15 compressor contains 7 oz. (207ml) of refrigerant oil. A new service replacement FS–1Q compressor shipped during 1994 contains 7 oz. of refrigerant oil; those shipped after 1994 contain no oil. Prior to installing the replacement compressor, drain the refrigerant oil from the removed compressor into a calibrated container. Then, drain the refrigerant oil from the new compressor into a clean calibrated container. If the amount of oil drained from the removed compressor was 3–5 oz (90–148ml), pour the same amount of clean refrigerant oil into the new compressor (for FS–1Q compressors, add 1 oz.). If the amount of oil removed from the old compressor is greater than 5 oz. (148ml), pour 5 oz. (148ml) of clean refrigerant oil into the new compressor. If the amount of refrigerant oil removed from the old compressor is less than 3 oz. (90ml), pour 3 oz. (90ml) of clean refrigerant oil into the new compressor. This will maintain the total system oil charge within specification.

8. Service the replacement compressor with the correct amount of clean refrigerant oil.
9. Install the bracket on the compressor.
10. Position the compressor on the engine and install the 3 retaining bolts.
11. Using new O–rings lubricated with clean refrigerant oil, position the manifold and tube on the compressor.
12. Coat the threads of the original bolt with Teflon pipe seal, install the bolt to the manifold, and tighten to 12.5–17 ft. lbs. (17–23 Nm)
13. Connect the compressor clutch wires at the wire connector and attach the connector to the compressor front bracket.
14. Install the belt on the compressor clutch pulley.
15. Leak test, evacuate and charge the system. Observe all safety precautions.
16. Check the operation of the air conditioning system.

Mark VIII

NOTE: The suction accumulator/drier and the fixed orifice tube should also be replaced whenever the compressor is replaced. Special filtering and flushing should be done to the system if compressor has failed (identified by dirty orifice tube and/or black refrigerant, with particles, in the liquid line).

1. Disconnect the negative battery cable.
2. Discharge the refrigerant from the air conditioning system.
3. Properly drain the coolant from the radiator. Save the coolant for reuse.
4. Disconnect the transmission oil cooler lines while holding the radiator connector with a back–up wrench. Plug the lines and connectors to prevent contamination.
5. Disconnect the upper and lower radiator hoses and the radiator overflow hose from the radiator.
6. Remove the 2 upper fan shroud retaining bolts. Disconnect the cooling fan motor wire harness and remove the cooling fan/shroud assembly.
7. Remove the radiator upper support retaining bolts and remove the supports. Lift the radiator from the vehicle.
8. Disconnect the air conditioner clutch wire and loosen the 3 compressor mounting bolts.

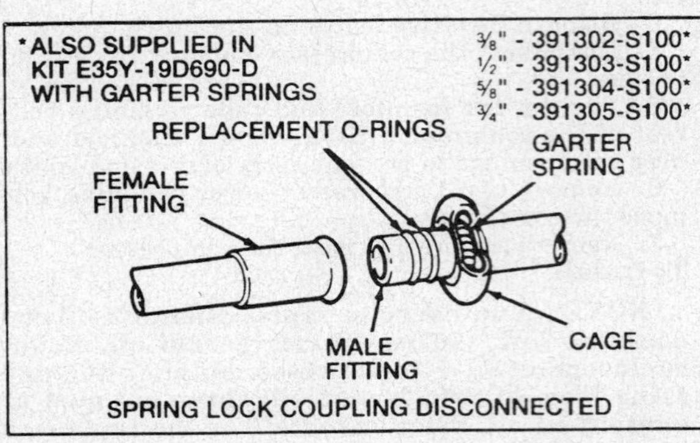

TO CONNECT COUPLING

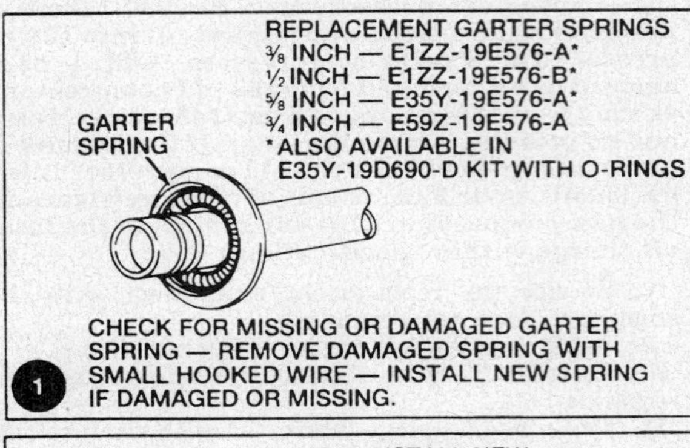

1 CHECK FOR MISSING OR DAMAGED GARTER SPRING — REMOVE DAMAGED SPRING WITH SMALL HOOKED WIRE — INSTALL NEW SPRING IF DAMAGED OR MISSING.

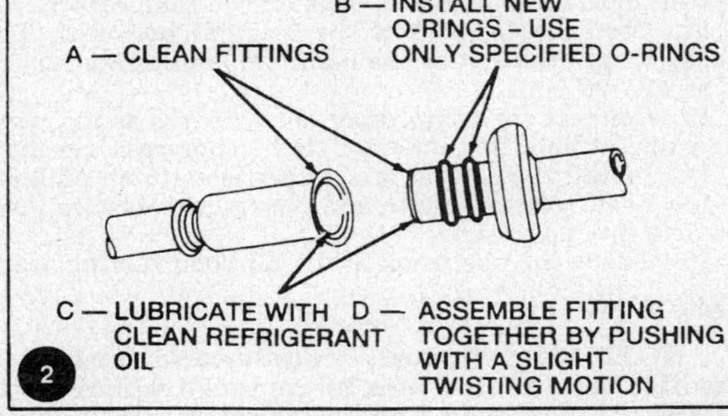

2

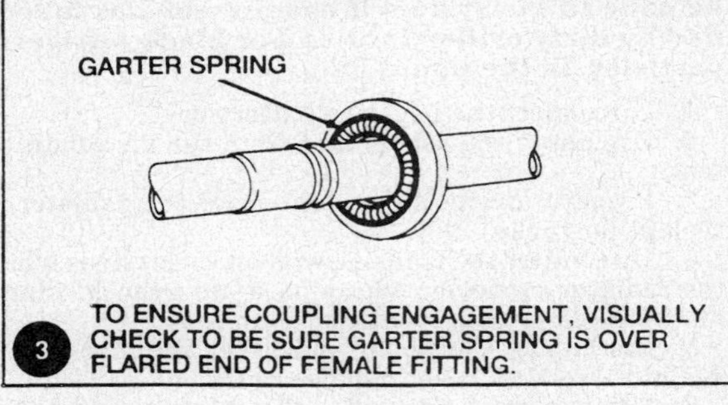

3 TO ENSURE COUPLING ENGAGEMENT, VISUALLY CHECK TO BE SURE GARTER SPRING IS OVER FLARED END OF FEMALE FITTING.

TO DISCONNECT COUPLING

CAUTION — DISCHARGE SYSTEM BEFORE DISCONNECTING COUPLING

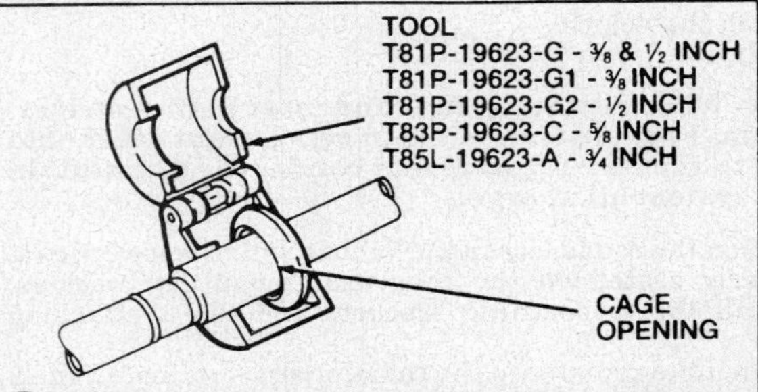

1 FIT TOOL TO COUPLING SO THAT TOOL CAN ENTER CAGE OPENING TO RELEASE THE GARTER SPRING.

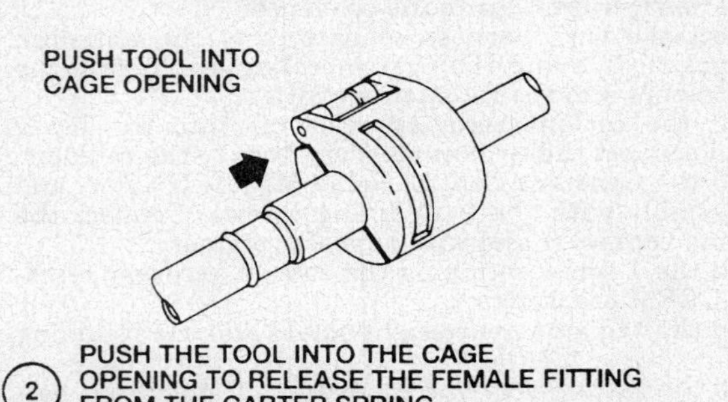

2 PUSH THE TOOL INTO THE CAGE OPENING TO RELEASE THE FEMALE FITTING FROM THE GARTER SPRING.

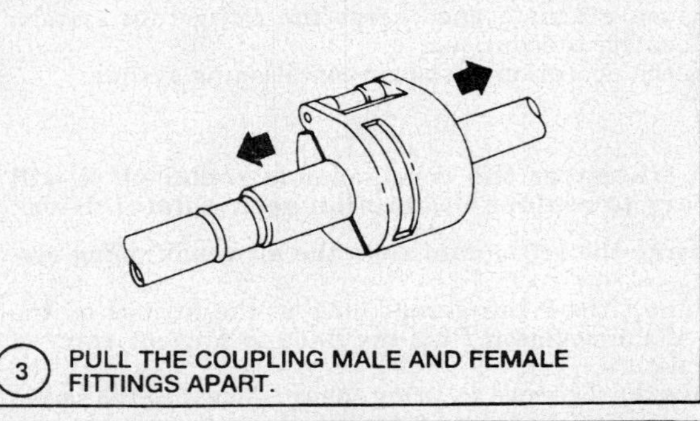

3 PULL THE COUPLING MALE AND FEMALE FITTINGS APART.

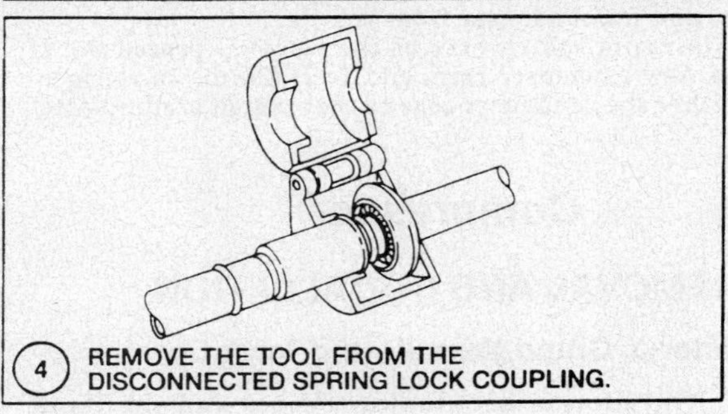

4 REMOVE THE TOOL FROM THE DISCONNECTED SPRING LOCK COUPLING.

Spring lock coupling disconnect and reconnect procedure

9. Loosen and remove the compressor drive belt.
10. Disconnect the heated oxygen sensor wire connector.
11. Remove the air conditioner muffler support bracket screw.
12. Disconnect the air conditioner system hoses from the condenser core and the suction accumulator/drier. Cap the lines and connectors to prevent entry of dirt and moisture.
13. Properly support the air conditioner compressor and remove the 3 compressor mounting bolts.
14. Remove the compressor, manifold and tube assemblies as a unit.
15. Remove the manifold and tube assemblies from the compressor. If the compressor is to be replaced, remove the clutch and field coil assembly.

To install:

NOTE: Prior to installing the replacement compressor, drain the refrigerant oil from the removed compressor into a calibrated container. Then, drain the refrigerant oil if any from the new compressor into a calibrated container. If the amount of oil drained from the removed compressor was 3–5 oz. (90–148ml), pour the same amount of clean refrigerant oil plus 1 oz. (30ml) into the new compressor. If the amount of oil removed from the old compressor is greater than 5 oz. (148ml), pour 5 oz. (148ml) of clean refrigerant oil into the new compressor. If the amount of refrigerant oil removed from the old compressor is less than 3 oz. (90ml), pour 3 oz. (90ml) of clean refrigerant oil into the new compressor. This will maintain the total system oil charge within specification.

16. Using new O–rings lubricated with clean refrigerant oil, install the manifold and tube assemblies on the compressor.
17. Install the compressor, manifold and tube assembly on the compressor mounting bracket. Torque the 3 mounting bolts to 15–22 ft. lbs. (20–30 Nm).
18. Using new O–rings lubricated with clean refrigerant oil, connect the tube assemblies to the condenser core and the suction accumulator/drier spring–lock couplings.
19. Install the air conditioner muffler support bracket on the sub–frame.
20. Connect the heated oxygen sensor wire connector.
21. Install the compressor drive belt.
22. Install the radiator and the fan and shroud assembly.
23. Connect the upper and lower radiator hoses and the radiator overflow hoses. Fill the radiator with coolant.
24. Connect the transmission oil cooler lines. Using a back–up wrench to prevent damage, torque connectors to 18–23 ft. lbs. (24–31 Nm).
25. Leak test, evacuate and charge the system. Observe all safety precautions.
26. Connect negative battery cable.
27. Check the operation of the air conditioning system.

Thunderbird and Cougar

3.8 AND 5.0 ENGINES

NOTE: The suction accumulator/drier and the fixed orifice tube should also be replaced whenever the compressor is replaced. Special filtering and flushing should be done to the system if compressor has failed (identified by dirty orifice tube and/or black refrigerant, with particles, in the liquid line).

1. Disconnect the negative battery cable.
2. Discharge the refrigerant from the air conditioning system.
3. Remove the compressor drive belt and disconnect the compressor clutch wires at the field coil connector on the compressor.
4. Remove the suction and discharge manifold from the compressor. Cap the suction and discharge ports in the manifold and compressor to prevent entry of dirt or moisture.
5. Remove the 4 bolts that secure the compressor to the mounting bracket and remove the compressor.

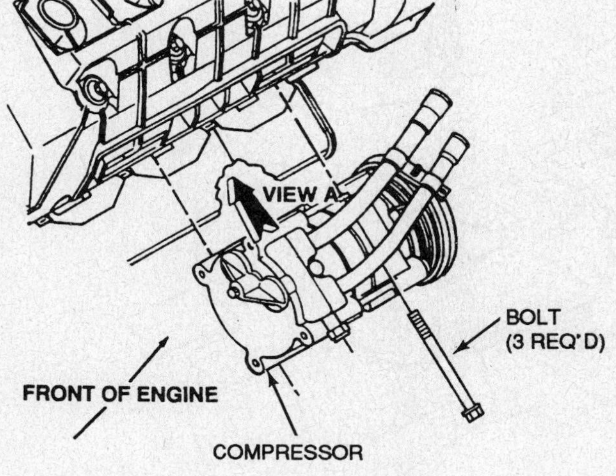

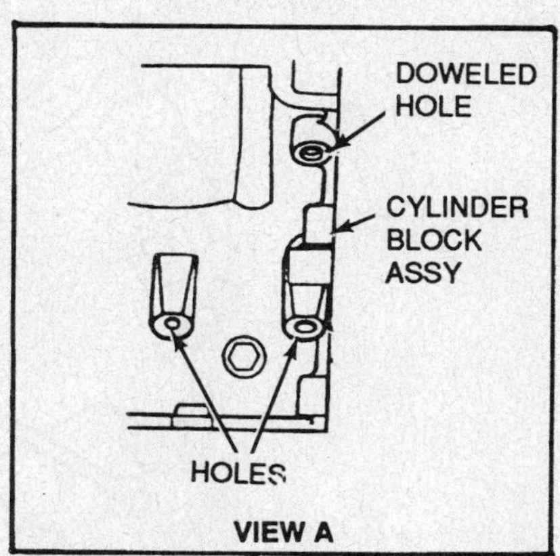

Air conditioning compressor installation—Mark VIII (other 4.6L engines similar)

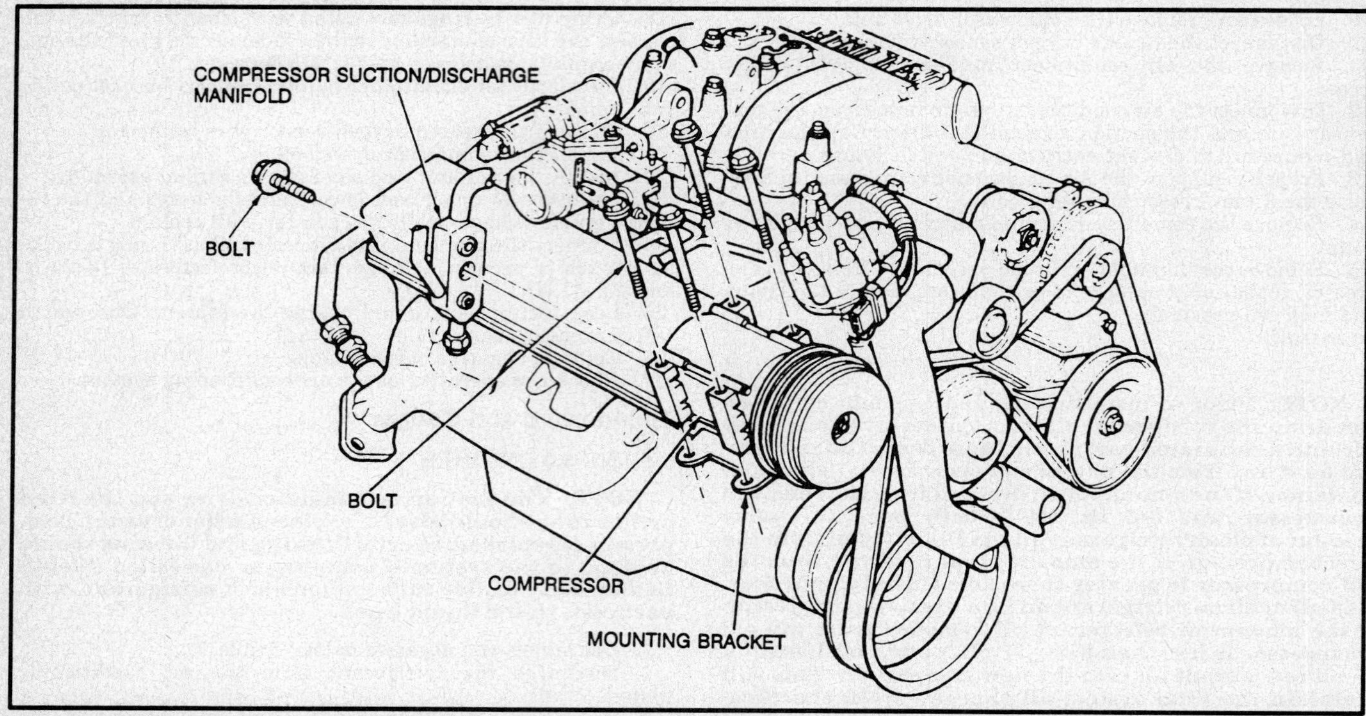

Air conditioning compressor installation—Thunderbird and Cougar except 3.8L SC engine

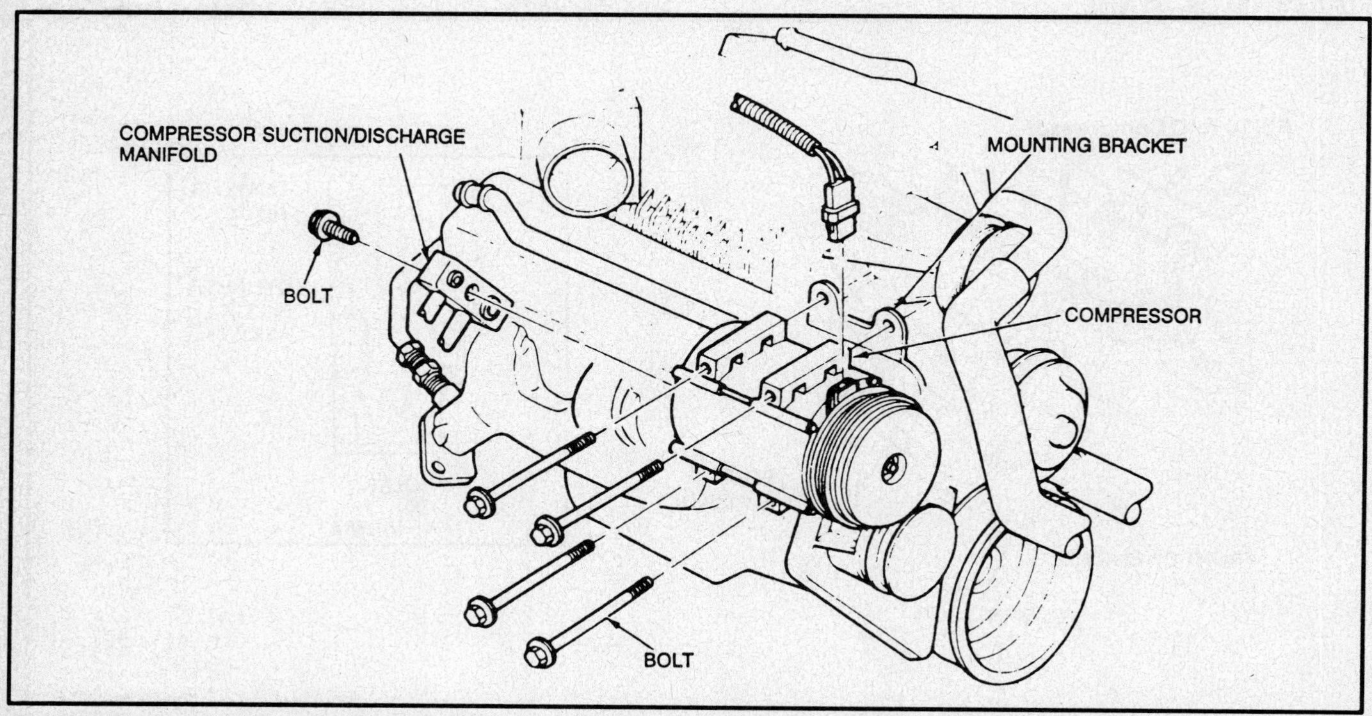

Air conditioning compressor installation—Thunderbird and Cougar with 3.8L SC engine

To install:

NOTE: A new service replacement FX-15 compressor contains 7 oz. (207ml) of refrigerant oil. FS-10 compressor shipped during 1994 contains 7 oz. of refrigerant oil; those shipped after 1994 contain no oil. Prior to installing the replacement compressor, drain the refrigerant oil from the removed compressor into a calibrated container. Then, drain the refrigerant oil if any from the new compressor into a clean calibrated container. If the amount of oil drained from the removed compressor was between 3-5 oz. (90-148ml), pour the same amount of clean refrigerant oil into the new compressor (for FS-10 compressors, add 1 oz.). If the amount of oil that was removed from the old compressor is greater than 5 oz. (148ml), pour 5 oz. (148ml) of clean refrigerant oil into the new compressor. If the amount of refrigerant oil that was removed from the old compressor is less than 3 oz. (90ml), pour 3 oz. (90ml) of clean refrigerant oil into the new compressor. This will maintain the total system oil charge within specification.

6. Position the compressor on the mounting bracket and install the 4 mounting bolts.
7. Remove the protective caps and install the suction and discharge manifold on the compressor.
8. Connect the clutch wires to the field coil connector and install the compressor drive belt.
9. Leak test, evacuate and charge the air conditioning system. Observe all safety precautions.
10. Check the operation of the air conditioning system.

4.6L ENGINE

NOTE: The suction accumulator/drier and the fixed orifice tube should also be replaced whenever the compressor is replaced. Special filtering and flushing should be done to the system if compressor has failed (identified by dirty orifice tube and/or black refrigerant, with particles, in the liquid line).

1. Disconnect the negative battery cable.
2. Properly discharge the refrigerant from the air conditioning system.
3. Disconnect the engine cooling fan wire assembly.
4. Remove the 2 cooling fan retaining screws and remove the cooling fan.
5. Remove the engine drive belt.
6. Disconnect the compressor wire assembly.
7. Remove the upper compressor retaining bolts.
8. Disconnect the knock sensor.
9. Remove the air conditioner manifold and tube. Plug the lines to prevent entry of dirt and moisture.
10. Remove the lower compressor retaining bolts and remove the compressor.

To install:

NOTE: Prior to installing the replacement compressor, drain the refrigerant oil from the removed compressor into a calibrated container. Then, drain the refrigerant oil if any from the new compressor into a calibrated container. If the amount of oil drained from the removed compressor was 3-5 oz. (90-148ml), pour the same amount of clean refrigerant oil plus 1 oz. (30ml) into the new compressor. If the amount of oil removed from the old compressor is greater than 5 oz. (148ml), pour 5 oz. (148ml) of clean refrigerant oil into the new compressor. If the amount of refrigerant oil removed from the old compressor is less than 3 oz. (90ml), pour 3 oz. (90ml) of clean refrigerant oil into the new compressor. This will maintain the total system oil charge within specification.

11. Position the compressor and install the lower compressor retaining bolts. Tighten the bolts to 31–44 ft. lbs. (41–61 Nm).
12. Connect the knock sensor.
13. Connect the compressor wire assembly.
14. Install the air conditioner manifold and tube. Tighten the manifold retaining bolt to 12.5–17 ft. lbs. (17–23 Nm).
15. Install the upper compressor retaining bolts. Tighten the bolts to 31–44 ft. lbs. (41–61 Nm).
16. Position the cooling fan and install the 2 retaining screws. Tighten the screws to 46–64 inch lbs. (5.2–7.2 Nm).
17. Connect the cooling fan wire assembly.
18. Leak test, evacuate and charge the air conditioning system. Observe all safety precautions.
19. Check the operation of the air conditioning system.

Mustang

2.3L ENGINE

NOTE: The suction accumulator/drier and the fixed orifice tube should also be replaced whenever the compressor is replaced. Special filtering and flushing should be done to the system if compressor has failed (identified by dirty orifice tube and/or black refrigerant, with particles, in the liquid line).

1. Disconnect the negative battery cable.
2. Discharge the refrigerant from the air conditioning system.
3. Disconnect the compressor clutch wires at the field coil connector on the compressor.
4. Disconnect the discharge and suction hoses from the compressor manifolds. Cap the refrigerant lines and compressor manifolds to prevent the entrance of dirt and moisture.
5. Remove the screw and washer assembly from the adjusting bracket.
6. Rotate the compressor outward and remove the drive belt.
7. Remove the compressor mounting bolt attaching the bracket to the compressor lower mounting lug.
8. Remove the compressor and adjusting bracket intact.
9. Remove the clutch field coil and adjusting bracket from the compressor, if the compressor is to be replaced.

To install:

NOTE: A new service replacement 10P15C compressor contains 8 oz. (237ml) of refrigerant oil. Prior to installing the replacement compressor, drain the refrigerant oil from the removed compressor into a calibrated container. Then, drain the refrigerant oil from the new compressor into a clean calibrated container. If the amount of oil drained from the removed compressor was between 3-5 oz. (90-148ml), pour the same amount of clean refrigerant oil into the new compressor. If the amount of oil that was removed from the old compressor is greater than 5 oz. (148ml), pour 5 oz. (148ml) of clean refrigerant oil into the new compressor. If the amount of refrigerant oil that was removed from the old compressor is less than 3 oz. (90ml), pour 3 oz. (90ml) of clean refrigerant oil into the new compressor. This will maintain the total system oil charge within specification.

10. Install the clutch field coil and adjusting bracket if it was removed or the compressor was replaced.
11. Install the compressor mounting brackets and drive belt in the reverse order of their removal.
12. Connect the refrigerant lines to the compressor and connect the clutch wires to the field coil connector.

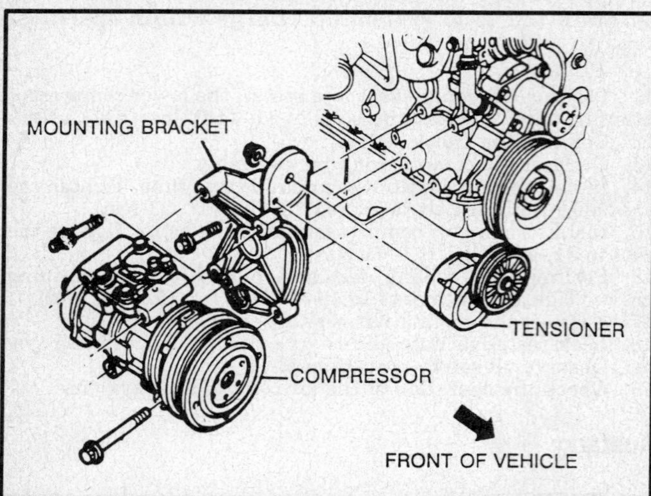

Air conditioning compressor installation—Mustang with 2.3L engine

13. Leak test, evacuate and charge the air conditioning system. Observe all safety precautions.
14. Check the operation of the air conditioning system.

1994–95 3.8L ENGINE

NOTE: The suction accumulator/drier and the fixed orifice tube should also be replaced whenever the compressor is replaced. Special filtering and flushing should be done to the system if compressor has failed (identified by dirty orifice tube and/or black refrigerant, with particles, in the liquid line).

1. Discharge the refrigerant from the air conditioning system. Observe all safety procedures.
2. Unfasten the 2 latches on the engine air tray at the mass air flow (MAF) sensor.
3. Disconnect the negative battery cable; then disconnect the wire harness from the MAF sensor and the intake air temperature (IAT) sensor.
4. Loosen the engine air cleaner tube clamp and remove the MAF sensor and the air cleaner outlet tube.
5. Remove the drive belt.
6. Remove the manifold and tube retaining bolt and separate the manifold and tube from the compressor. Cap all openings to prevent the entry of dirt and moisture.
7. Disconnect the compressor clutch wires at the clutch field coil connector.
8. Remove the compressor retaining bolts and remove the compressor from the vehicle.

To install:

NOTE: Prior to installing the replacement compressor, drain the refrigerant oil from the removed compressor into a calibrated container. Then, drain the refrigerant oil if any from the new compressor into a calibrated container. If the amount of oil drained from the removed compressor was 3–5 oz. (90–148ml), pour the same amount of clean refrigerant oil plus 1 oz. (30ml) into the new compressor. If the amount of oil removed from the old compressor is greater than 5 oz. (148ml), pour 5 oz. (148ml) of clean refrigerant oil into the new compressor. If the amount of refrigerant oil removed from the old compressor is less than 3 oz. (90ml), pour 3 oz. (90ml) of clean refrigerant oil into the new compressor. This will maintain the total system oil charge within specification.

9. Install the compressor and the retaining bolts. Tighten the bolts to 15–22 ft. lbs. (20–30 Nm).
10. Lubricate new O–ring seals with clean refrigerant oil and position the O–rings in the seal grooves of the manifold and tube.
11. Apply Teflon pipe sealant to the original manifold retaining bolt. Position the manifold and tube on the compressor. Install the retaining bolt and tighten to 12.5–17 ft. lbs. (17–23 Nm).
12. Connect the compressor clutch wires to the clutch field coil connector.
13. Install the drive belt.
14. Install the MAF sensor and the air cleaner outlet tube to the engine air tray.
15. Connect the wire harness to the MAF sensor and the IAT sensor. Tighten the air cleaner tube clamp to 21–28 inch lbs. (2.3–3.2 Nm). Connect the negative battery cable.
16. Leak test, evacuate and charge the air conditioning system. Observe all safety precautions.
17. Check the operation of the air conditioning system.

1993 5.0L ENGINE

NOTE: The suction accumulator/drier and the fixed orifice tube should also be replaced whenever the compressor is replaced. Special filtering and flushing should be done to the system if compressor has failed (identified by dirty orifice tube and/or black refrigerant, with particles, in the liquid line).

1. Disconnect the negative battery cable.
2. Discharge the refrigerant from the air conditioning system.
3. Disconnect the compressor clutch wires at the field coil connector on the compressor.
4. Disconnect the discharge and suction hoses from the compressor manifolds. Cap the refrigerant lines and compressor manifolds to prevent the entrance of dirt and moisture.
5. Remove the 2 screws attaching the brace to the rear mounting bracket.
6. Remove the 2 screws attaching the bracket to the compressor lower front mounting lugs.
7. Remove 1 screw attaching the bracket to the compressor upper mounting lug.
8. Remove the compressor/clutch assembly and rear support from the vehicle as a unit.
9. Remove the 2 screws attaching the compressor to the rear support and remove the rear support.
10. If the compressor is to be replaced, remove the clutch and field coil assembly from the compressor.

To install:

NOTE: A new service replacement 6P148 compressor contains 10 oz. (300ml) of refrigerant oil. Prior to installing the replacement compressor, drain the refrigerant oil from the removed compressor into a calibrated container. Then, drain the refrigerant oil from the new compressor into a clean calibrated container. If the amount of oil drained from the removed compressor was between 3–5 oz. (90–148ml), pour the same amount of clean refrigerant oil into the new compressor. If the amount of oil that was removed from the old compressor is greater than 5 oz. (148ml), pour 5 oz. (148ml) of clean refrigerant oil into the new compressor. If the amount of refrigerant oil that was removed from the old compressor is less than 3 oz. (90ml), pour 3 oz. (90ml) of clean refrigerant oil into the new compressor. This will maintain the total system oil charge within specification.

11. Install the compressor and brackets in the reverse order of their removal.
12. Using new O-rings lubricated with clean refrigerant oil, connect the suction and discharge lines to the compressor manifolds. Tighten the suction hose fitting to 21–27 ft. lbs. (28–36 Nm) and the discharge hose fitting to 15–20 ft. lbs. (20–27 Nm).

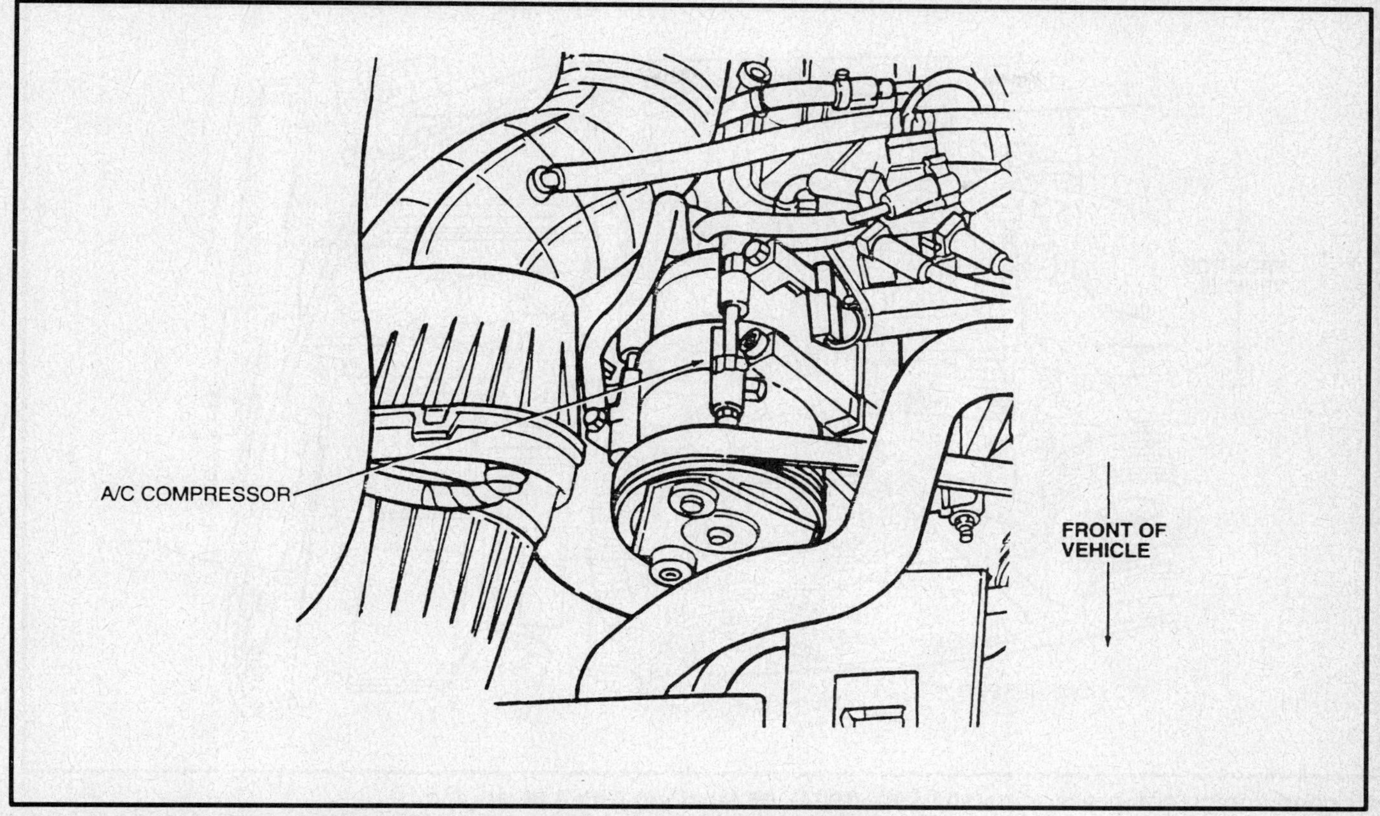

Air conditioning compressor installation—1993 Mustang with 5.0L engine

13. Connect the clutch wires to the field coil connector and install the drive belt.
14. Leak test, evacuate and charge the air conditioning system. Observe all safety precautions.
15. Check the system for proper operation.

1994–95 5.0L ENGINE

NOTE: The suction accumulator/drier and the fixed orifice tube should also be replaced whenever the compressor is replaced. Special filtering and flushing should be done to the system if compressor has failed (identified by dirty orifice tube and/or black refrigerant, with particles, in the liquid line).

1. Discharge the refrigerant from the air conditioning system. Observe all safety procedures.
2. Disconnect both battery cables and remove the battery and the battery tray.
3. Remove the retaining screws and the radiator upper sight shield.
4. Remove the drive belt.
5. Remove the manifold and tube retaining bolt and separate the manifold and tube from the compressor. Cap all openings to prevent the entry of dirt and moisture.
6. Disconnect the compressor clutch wires at the clutch field coil connector.
7. Remove the compressor retaining bolts and remove the compressor from the vehicle.

To install:

NOTE: Prior to installing the replacement compressor, drain the refrigerant oil from the removed compressor into a calibrated container. Then, drain the refrigerant oil if any from the new compressor into a calibrated container. If the amount of oil drained from the removed compressor was 3–5 oz. (90–148ml), pour the same amount of clean refrigerant oil plus 1 oz. (30ml) into the new compressor. If the amount of oil removed from the old compressor is greater than 5 oz. (148ml), pour 5 oz. (148ml) of clean refrigerant oil into the new compressor. If the amount of refrigerant oil removed from the old compressor is less than 3 oz. (90ml), pour 3 oz. (90ml) of clean refrigerant oil into the new compressor. This will maintain the total system oil charge within specification.

8. Install the compressor and the retaining bolts. Tighten the bolts to 15–22 ft. lbs. (20–30 Nm).
9. Lubricate new O–ring seals with clean refrigerant oil and position the O–rings in the seal grooves of the manifold and tube.
10. Apply Teflon pipe sealant to the original manifold retaining bolt. Position the manifold and tube on the compressor. Install the retaining bolt and tighten to 12.5–17 ft. lbs. (17–23 Nm).
11. Connect the compressor clutch wires to the clutch field coil connector.
12. Install the drive belt.
13. Install the radiator upper sight shield and the retaining screws.
14. Install the battery tray and the battery. Connect the battery cables, positive cable first.
15. Leak test, evacuate and charge the air conditioning system. Observe all safety precautions.
16. Check the operation of the air conditioning system.

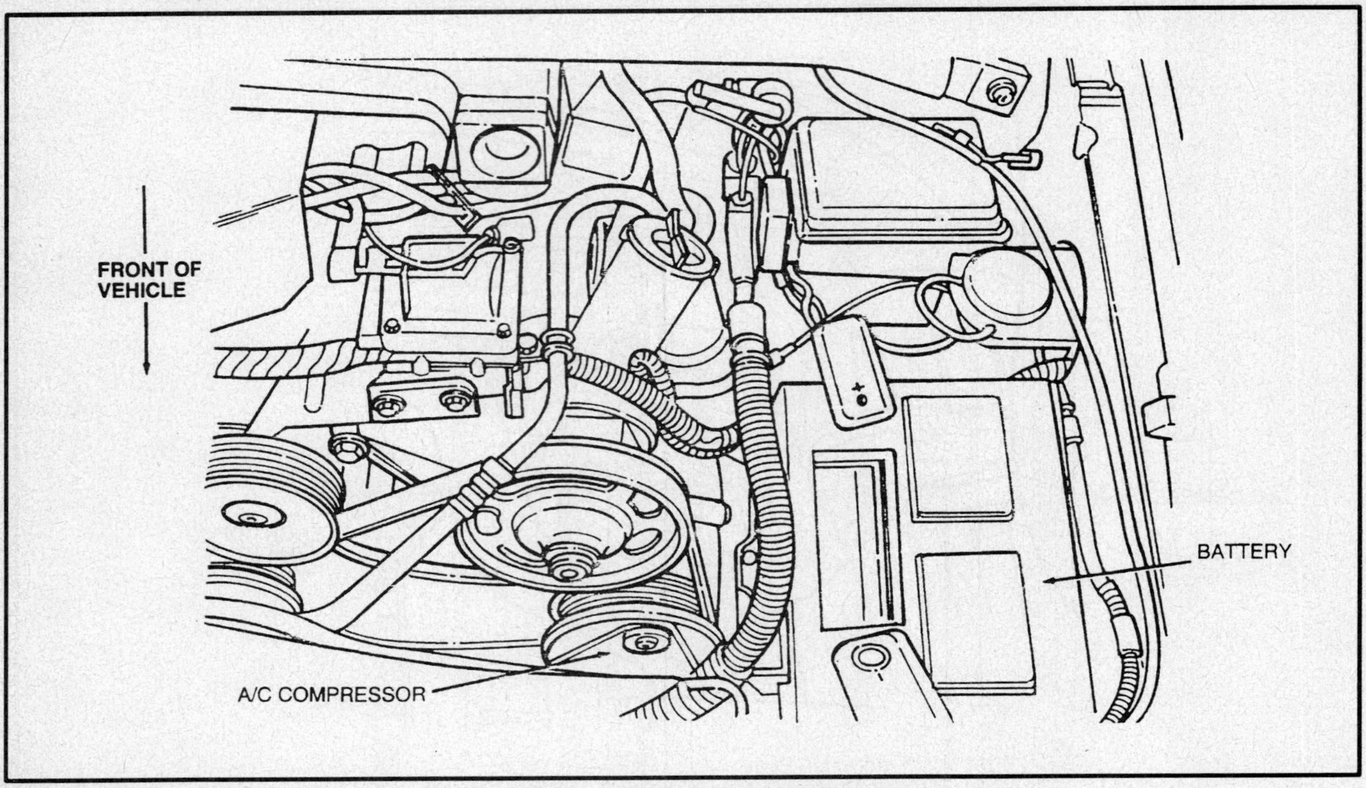

Air conditioning compressor installation—1994–95 Mustang with 3.8L engine

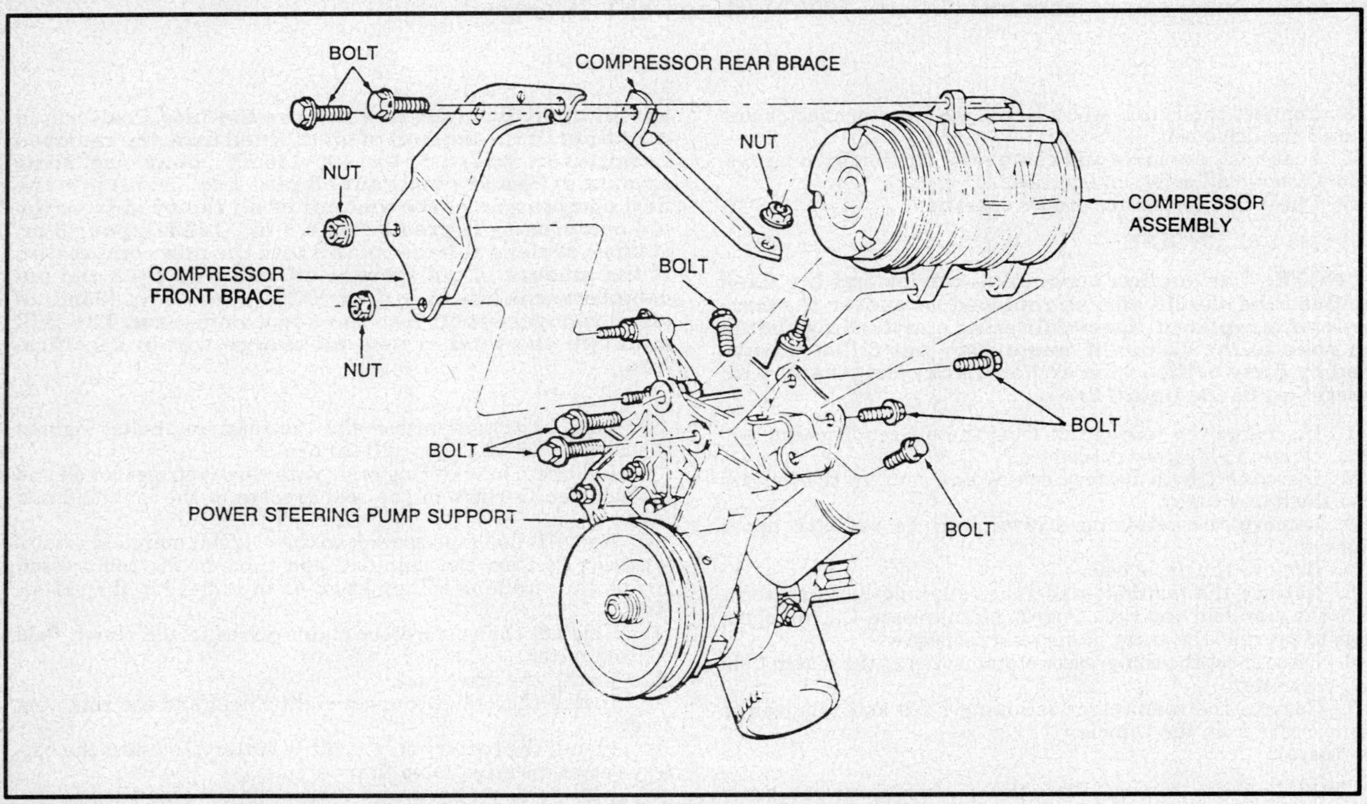

Air conditioning compressor installation—1994–95 Mustang with 5.0L engine

Accumulator/Drier

REMOVAL AND INSTALLATION

NOTE: The use of dedicated manifold gauge set, recycling/recharging stations and leak detectors is required on vehicles with R-134a. Mixing of any amounts of R-12 with R-134a or their respective refrigerant oils will cause harm to the system operation and components. Use only replacement components designed for R-134a applications.

Any time a major component of the air conditioning system is replaced, it is necessary to replace the suction accumulator/drier. A major component would be the condenser, compressor, evaporator or a refrigerant hose/line. A fixed orifice tube or O–ring is not considered a major component but the orifice tube should be replaced whenever the compressor is replaced for lack of performance.

The accumulator/drier should also be replaced, if 1 of the following conditions exist:

- The accumulator/drier is perforated.
- The refrigerant system has been opened to the atmosphere for a period of time longer than required to make a minor repair.
- There is evidence of moisture in the system such as internal corrosion of metal refrigerant lines or the refrigerant oil is thick and dark.

NOTE: The compressor oil from vehicles equipped with an FX-15 or FS–10 compressor may have a dark color while maintaining a normal oil viscosity. This is normal for this compressor because carbon from the compressor piston rings may discolor the oil.

When replacing the suction accumulator/drier, the following procedure must be used to ensure that the total oil charge in the system is correct after the new accumulator/drier is installed.

1. Drain the oil from the removed accumulator/drier into a suitable measuring container. It may be necessary to drill one or two 1/2 in. holes in the bottom of the old accumulator/drier to ensure that all the oil has drained out.
2. Add the same amount of clean new refrigerant oil plus 2 oz. to the new accumulator/drier. Use only the proper type of oil for the vehicle being serviced.

Crown Victoria, Grand Marquis and Town Car

1. Disconnect the negative battery cable.
2. Discharge the refrigerant from the air conditioning system.
3. Disconnect the electrical connector from the pressure switch and remove the switch by unscrewing it from the accumulator/drier.
4. Disconnect the suction hose from the accumulator/drier.
5. Loosen the fitting connecting the accumulator/drier to the evaporator core. Use 2 wrenches to prevent component damage.
6. Remove the screw attaching the accumulator/drier strap to the mounting bracket.
7. Disconnect the accumulator/drier from the evaporator core. Remove the 2 straps from the accumulator/drier.

To install:

8. Using a new O-ring lubricated with clean refrigerant oil, connect the accumulator/drier to the evaporator core tube. Tighten the connection finger-tight only.
9. Position the strap on the accumulator/drier. Align the strap with the mounting bracket and install the mounting screw. Loosen the connection of the accumulator/drier to the evaporator core, if it is necessary to reposition the accumulator to install the strap attaching screw.
10. Tighten the accumulator/drier to evaporator core fitting using 2 wrenches.
11. Using a new O-ring lubricated with clean refrigerant oil, connect the suction hose to the accumulator/drier.
12. Install a new O-ring lubricated with clean refrigerant oil on the pressure switch nipple of the accumulator/drier. Install the pressure switch and tighten the switch finger-tight only.
13. Connect the electrical connector to the pressure switch.
14. Leak test, evacuate and charge the air conditioning system. Observe all safety precautions.
15. Check the system for proper operation.

Mark VIII

1. Disconnect the negative battery cable.
2. Discharge the refrigerant from the air conditioning system.
3. Disconnect the suction hose at the compressor. Cap the hose and compressor to prevent the entrance of dirt and moisture.
4. Disconnect the accumulator/drier inlet tube from the evaporator core outlet.
5. Disconnect the wire harness connector from the pressure switch on top of the accumulator/drier.
6. Remove the screw holding the accumulator/drier in the accumulator bracket and remove the accumulator/drier.

To install:

7. Position the accumulator/drier to the vehicle and route the suction hose to the compressor.
8. Using a new O-ring lubricated with clean refrigerant oil, connect the accumulator/drier inlet tube to the evaporator core outlet.
9. Install the screw in the accumulator/drier bracket.
10. Using a new O-ring lubricated with clean refrigerant oil, connect the suction hose to the compressor.
11. Leak test, evacuate and charge the air conditioning system. Observe all safety precautions.
12. Check the system for proper operation.

Thunderbird and Cougar

1. Disconnect the negative battery cable.
2. Discharge the refrigerant from the air conditioning system.

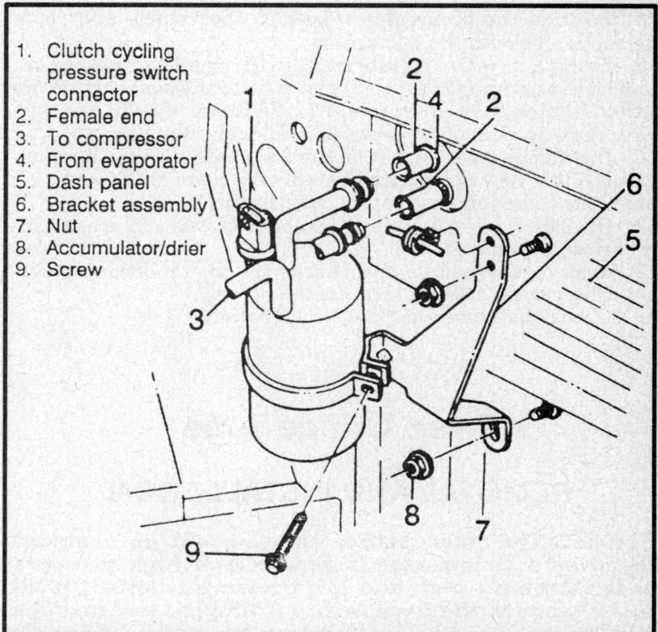

Accumulator/drier installation—Thunderbird, Cougar and Mark VIII

3. Disconnect the suction hose at the accumulator/drier (3.8L SC) or at the compressor (3.8L EFI and 4.6L). Cap the suction hose and compressor openings to prevent the entrance of dirt and moisture.
4. Disconnect the accumulator/drier inlet tube from the evaporator core outlet.
5. Disconnect the wire harness connector from the pressure switch on top of the accumulator/drier.
6. Remove the screw holding the accumulator/drier in the accumulator bracket and remove the accumulator/drier.

To install:

7. Position the accumulator/drier to the vehicle and route the suction hose to the compressor.
8. Using a new O-ring lubricated with clean refrigerant oil, connect the accumulator/drier inlet tube to the evaporator core outlet.
9. Install the screw in the accumulator/drier bracket.
10. Using a new O-ring lubricated with clean refrigerant oil, connect the suction hose to the accumulator/drier or the compressor, as required.
11. Leak test, evacuate and charge the air conditioning system. Observe all safety precautions.
12. Check the system for proper operation.

Mustang

1. Disconnect the negative battery cable.
2. Discharge the refrigerant from the air conditioning system.
3. On 2.3L engine equipped vehicles, remove the speed control servo, if equipped.
4. Disconnect the suction hose at the compressor. Cap the hose and compressor to prevent the entrance of dirt and moisture.
5. Disconnect the accumulator/drier inlet tube from the evaporator core outlet. Use 2 wrenches to prevent component damage.
6. Disconnect the wire harness connector from the pressure switch on top of the accumulator/drier.
7. Remove the screw (1993) or nut (1994–95) holding the accumulator/drier in the accumulator bracket and remove the accumulator/drier.

To install:

8. Position the accumulator/drier to the vehicle and route the suction hose to the compressor.
9. Using a new O-ring lubricated with clean refrigerant oil, connect the accumulator/drier inlet tube to the evaporator core outlet. Tighten the connection to 21–26 ft. lbs. (28–36 Nm). using a back-up wrench to prevent component damage.
10. Install the screw or nut on the accumulator/drier bracket.
11. Using a new O-ring lubricated with clean refrigerant oil, connect the suction hose to the compressor.
12. On 2.3L engine equipped vehicles, install the speed control servo, if removed.
13. Leak test, evacuate and charge the air conditioning system. Observe all safety precautions.
14. Check the system for proper operation.

Fixed Orifice Tube

REMOVAL AND INSTALLATION

NOTE: The fixed orifice tube should be replaced whenever a compressor is replaced. If high pressure reads extremely high and low pressure (suction) is almost a vacuum, the fixed orifice is plugged and must be replaced.

The use of dedicated manifold gauge set, recycling/recharging stations and leak detectors is required on vehicles with R-134a. Mixing of any amounts of R-12 with R-134a or their respective refrigerant oils will cause harm to the system operation and components. Use only replacement components designed for R-134a applications.

Crown Victoria, Grand Marquis and Town Car

The fixed orifice tube is constructed with a plastic body, 2 screens and a small brass tube down the center of the orifice body. Two O-rings are around the orifice tube body to seal against leakage around the body. Do not attempt to remove the fixed orifice tube with pliers or to twist or rotate the orifice tube in the evaporator core tube; to do so will break the fixed orifice tube body in the evaporator core tube. Use only the recommended tool following the recommended service procedures.

1. Discharge the refrigerant from the air conditioning system.
2. Disconnect the liquid line from the evaporator core. Cap the liquid line to prevent the entrance of dirt and excessive moisture.

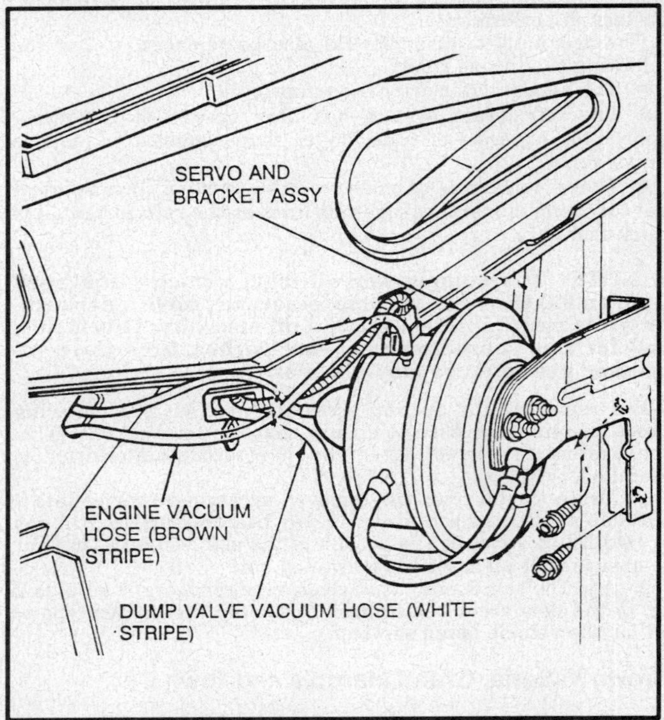

Showing location of speed control servo for removal of accumulator/drier—Mustang with 2.3L engine (speed control optional)

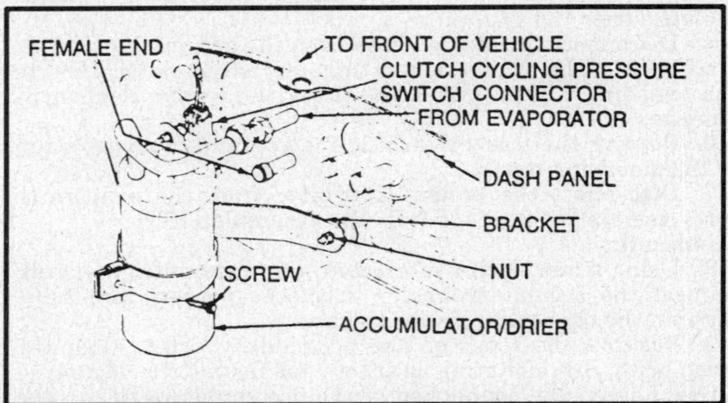

Accumulator/drier installation—Mustang

3. Pour a small amount of clean refrigerant oil into the evaporator core inlet tube to lubricate the tube and orifice O-rings during removal of the fixed orifice tube from the evaporator core tube.
4. Engage the fixed orifice tube remover T83L–19990–A or equivalent, with the 2 tangs on the fixed orifice tube. Do not twist or rotate the fixed orifice tube in the evaporator core tube as it may break off in the evaporator core tube.
5. Hold the T-handle of the fixed orifice tube remover T83L–19990–A or equivalent, to keep it from turning and run the nut on the tool down against the evaporator core tube until the orifice is pulled from the tube.
6. If the fixed orifice tube breaks in the evaporator core tube, it must be removed from the tube with broken orifice tube remover T83L–19990–B or equivalent.
7. To remove a broken orifice tube, insert the screw end of the broken orifice tube remover T83L–19990–B or equivalent, into the evaporator core tube and thread the screw end of the tool into the brass tube in the center of the fixed orifice tube. Pull the fixed orifice tube out.
8. If only the brass center tube is removed during Step 7, insert the screw end of broken orifice tube remover T83L–19990–B or equivalent into the evaporator core tube and screw the end of the tool into the fixed orifice tube body. Pull the fixed orifice tube body out.

To install:

9. Lubricate the O-rings on the fixed orifice tube body liberally with clean refrigerant oil.
10. Place the fixed orifice tube on the fixed orifice tube remover T83L–19990–A or equivalent, and insert the fixed orifice tube into the evaporator core tube until the orifice is seated at the stop.
11. Remove the remover tool from the fixed orifice tube.
12. Using a new O-ring lubricated with clean refrigerant oil, connect the liquid line to the evaporator core tube.
13. Leak test, evacuate and charge the system. Observe all safety precautions.
14. Check the system for proper operation.

Mark VIII, Thunderbird, Cougar and Mustang

If replacement of the fixed orifice tube is necessary, the liquid line must be replaced or orifice tube replacement kit E5VY–19D695–A or equivalent, installed.

1. Discharge the refrigerant from the air conditioning system.
2. Remove the liquid line containing the fixed orifice tube.
3. Locate the orifice tube by the 3 indented notches or a circular depression in the metal portion of the liquid line.
4. Note the angular position of the ends of the liquid line so it can be reassembled in the correct position.
5. Cut a 2 1/2 in. (63.5mm) section from the tube at the orifice tube location. Do not cut closer than 1 in. (25.4mm) from the start of a bend in the tube.
6. Remove the orifice tube from the housing with pliers. The orifice tube removal tool cannot be used.
7. Flush the 2 pieces of liquid line to remove any contaminants.
8. Lubricate the O-rings with clean refrigerant oil and assemble the orifice tube kit, with the orifice tube installed, to the liquid line. Make sure the flow direction arrow is pointing toward the evaporator end of the liquid line and the taper of each compression ring is toward the compression nut.

NOTE: The inlet tube will be positioned against the orifice tube tabs when correctly assembled.

9. While holding the hex of the tube in a suitable vise, tighten each compression nut to 65–70 ft. lbs. (88–94 Nm) with a crow foot wrench.
10. Install the liquid line on the vehicle using new O-rings lubricated with clean refrigerant oil.
11. Leak test, evacuate and charge the system. Observe all safety precautions.
12. Check the system for proper operation.

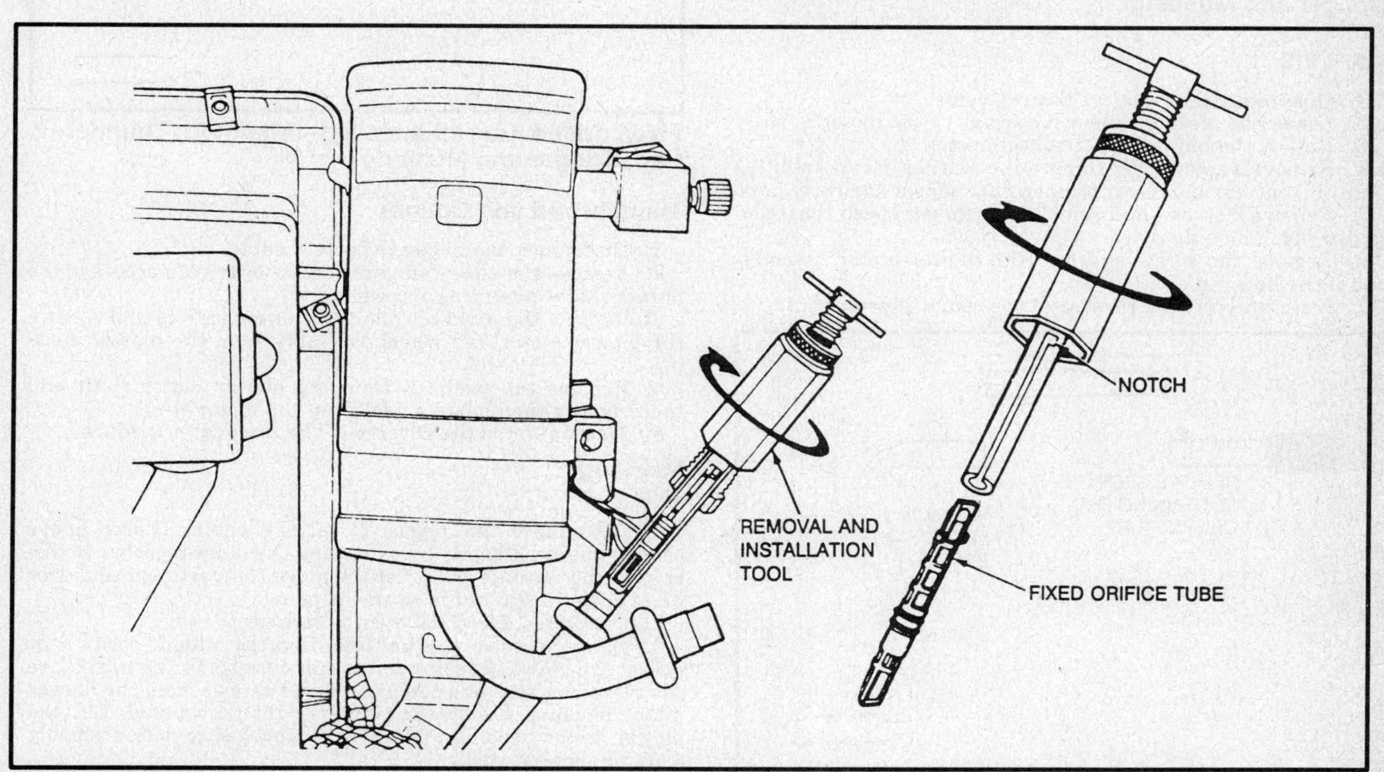

Fixed orifice tube removal—Crown Victoria, Grand Marquis and Town Car

Blower Motor

REMOVAL AND INSTALLATION

Crown Victoria, Grand Marquis and Town Car

1. Disconnect the negative battery cable.
2. Disconnect the blower motor lead connector from the wiring harness connector.
3. Remove the blower motor cooling tube from the blower motor.
4. Remove the 4 retaining screws.
5. Turn the motor and wheel assembly slightly to the right so the bottom edge of the mounting plate follows the contour of the wheel well splash panel. Lift up on the blower and remove it from the blower housing.
6. Installation is the reverse of the removal procedure.

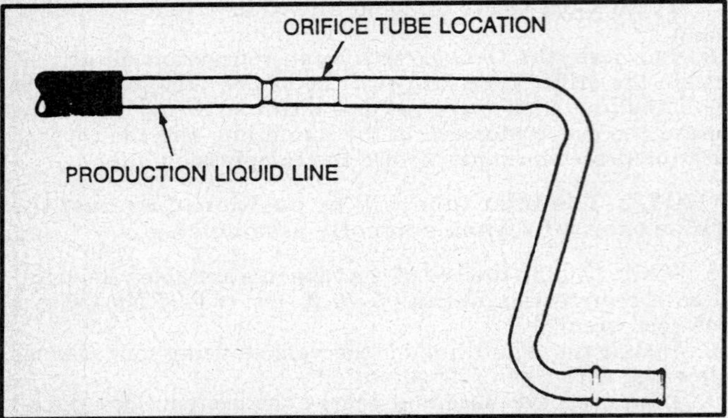

Fixed orifice tube location—Mark VIII, Thunderbird, Cougar and Mustang

Mark VIII

1. Disconnect the negative battery cable.
2. Lower the glove box door for access to the motor.
3. Detach the blower electrical connector.
4. Remove 2 screws and remove the muffler (Evaporator Air Control Venturi) and in-car temperature sensor aspirator hose.
5. Remove 2 screws and remove the blower speed controller (pulse width modulator).
6. Remove the screw and pull the blower motor assembly out of the housing.
7. Installation is the reverse of the removal procedure.

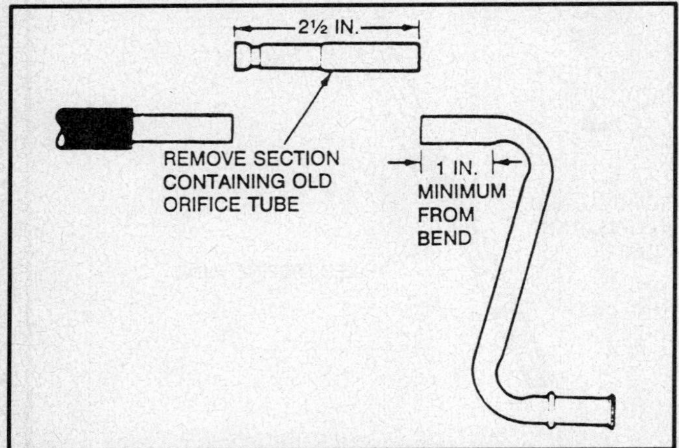

Fixed orifice tube section removed from liquid line—Mark VIII, Thunderbird, Cougar and Mustang

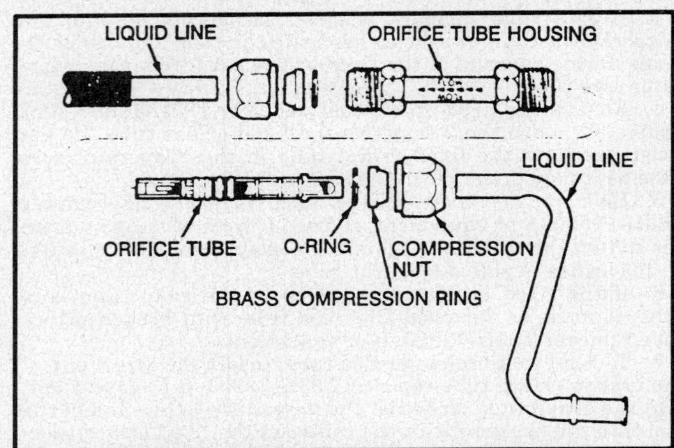

Fixed orifice tube kit disassembled—Mark VIII, Thunderbird, Cougar and Mustang

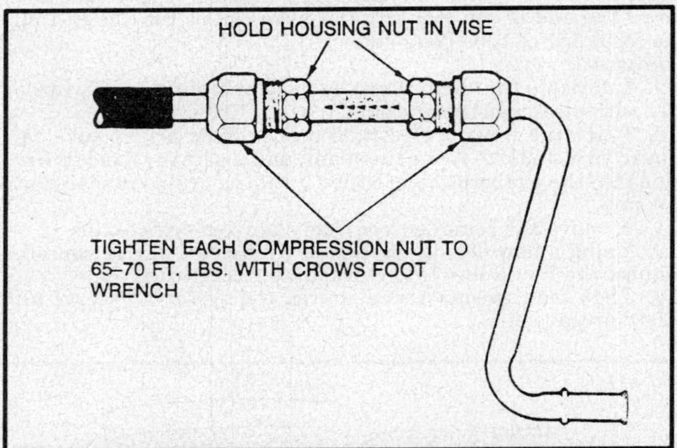

Fixed orifice tube kit installed—Mark VIII, Thunderbird, Cougar and Mustang

Thunderbird and Cougar

1. Disconnect the negative battery cable.
2. Remove the glove compartment liner to gain access to the blower motor mounting screws.
3. Remove the 4 blower motor retaining screws and remove the blower motor and wheel assembly from the blower housing.
4. Remove the pushnut from the blower motor shaft and then remove the blower wheel from the motor shaft.
5. Installation is the reverse of the removal procedure.

Mustang

1993

1. Disconnect the negative battery cable. Loosen glove compartment assembly by squeezing the sides together to disengage the retainer tabs. Let the glove compartment and door hang down in front of instrument panel.
2. Disconnect electrical wiring harness.
3. Disconnect the vacuum line from the outside-recirc door motor, the blower housing to bracket case retaining nut. Close the glove box door and remove 2 lower screws from the blower motor housing. Remove the lower right trim panel. Lift the blower motor housing and air inlet duct-recirc door assembly from the heater case.
4. Disconnect the cooling tube. Remove 4 screws attaching motor to housing. Pull motor and wheel out of housing.
5. Installation is the reverse of the removal procedure.

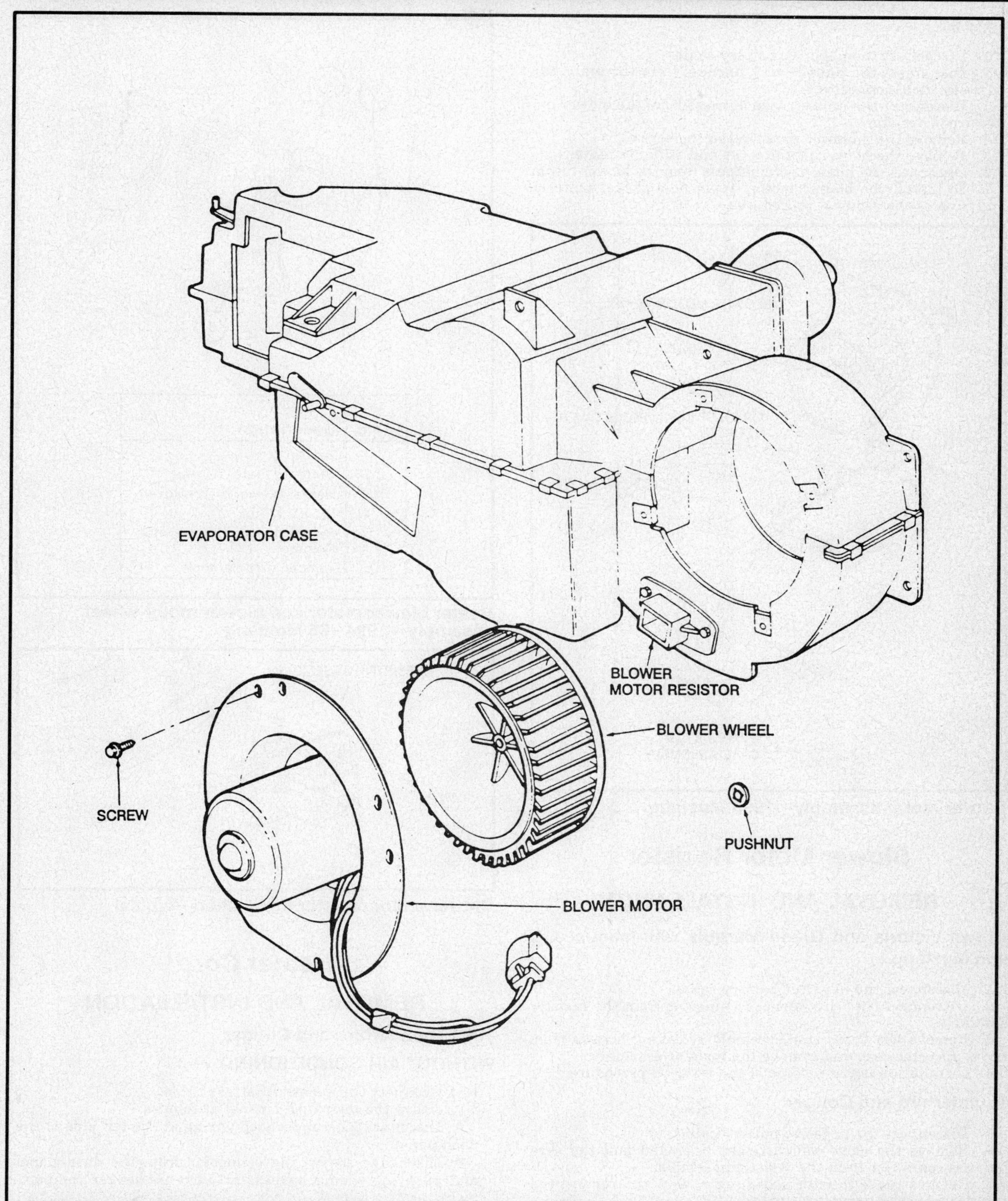

Blower motor assembly removal—Thunderbird and Cougar

1994–95

1. Disconnect the negative battery cable.
2. Disconnect the jumper wire harness from the main harness electrical connector.
3. Disconnect the jumper wire harness from the blower motor switch resistor.
4. Remove the 3 blower motor retaining screws.
5. Remove the blower motor cover and stiffener plate.
6. Disconnect the jumper wire harness from the blower motor.
7. To install the blower motor, apply new gasket material and reverse the removal procedures.

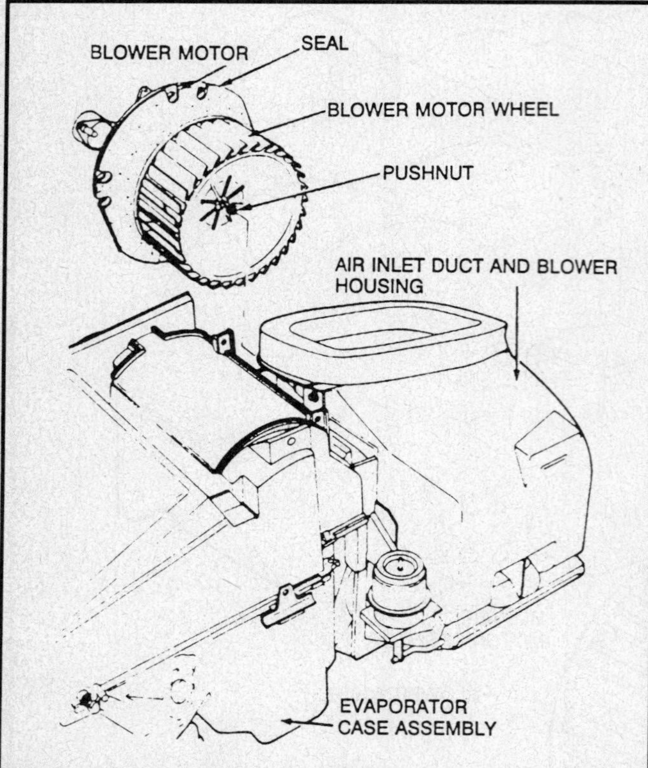

Blower motor assembly—1993 Mustang

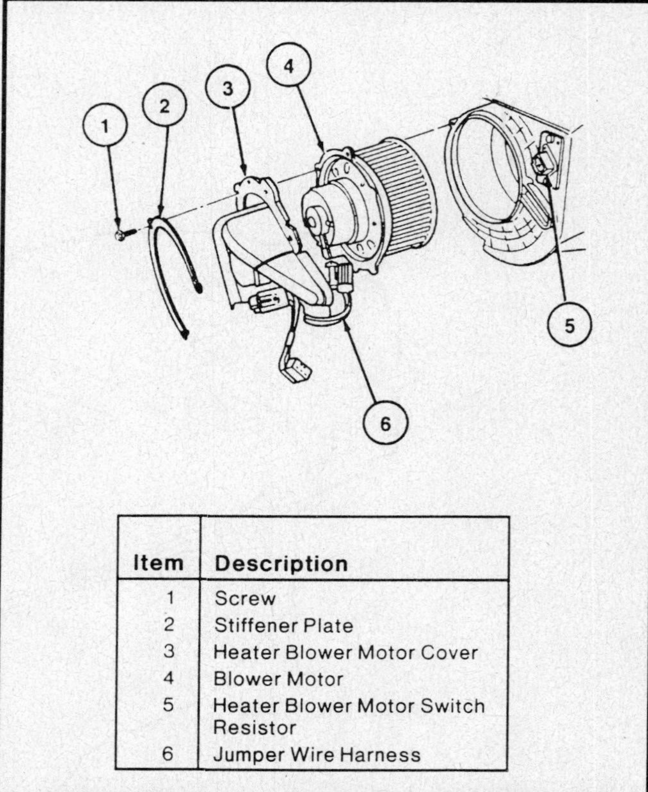

Item	Description
1	Screw
2	Stiffener Plate
3	Heater Blower Motor Cover
4	Blower Motor
5	Heater Blower Motor Switch Resistor
6	Jumper Wire Harness

Heater blower motor and blower motor wheel assembly—1994–95 Mustang

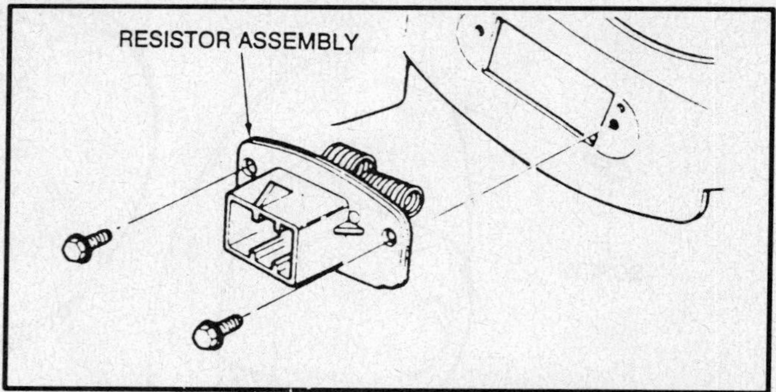

Blower motor resistor installation—typical

Blower Motor Resistor

REMOVAL AND INSTALLATION

Crown Victoria and Grand Marquis with manual A/C and Mustang

1. Disconnect the negative battery cable.
2. Disconnect the wire harness connector from the resistor assembly.
3. Remove the 2 resistor assembly retaining screws from the evaporator case and remove the resistor assembly.
4. Installation is the reverse of the removal procedure.

Thunderbird and Cougar

1. Disconnect the negative battery cable.
2. Remove the glove compartment liner and pull the wire harness connector from the resistor assembly.
3. Remove the 2 resistor attaching screws and remove the resistor from the evaporator case.
4. Installation is the reverse of the removal procedure. Do not apply sealer to the resistor assembly mounting surface.

Heater Core

REMOVAL AND INSTALLATION

1993 Thunderbird and Cougar

WITHOUT AIR CONDITIONING

1. Disconnect the negative battery cable.
2. Remove the instrument panel as follows:
   - Disconnect the underhood wiring at the left side of the dash panel.
   - Disengage the wiring connector from the dash panel and push the wiring harness into the passenger compartment.
   - Remove the steering column lower trim cover by removing the 3 screws at the bottom, 1 screw on the left side

and pulling to disengage the 5 snap-in retainers across the top.

- Remove the steering column lower opening reinforcement. 6 screws retain the reinforcement to the instrument panel.
- Remove the steering column upper and lower shrouds and disconnect the wiring from the steering column.
- Remove the shift interlock switch and disconnect the steering column lower universal joint.
- Support the steering column and remove the 4 nuts retaining the column to the support. Remove the column from the vehicle.
- Remove the 1 screw retaining the left side of the instrument panel to the parking brake bracket.
- Install the steering column lower opening reinforcement using the 4 screws, 1 at each corner. This will prevent the instrument panel from twisting when being removed.
- Remove the right and left cowl side trim panels.
- Remove the console assembly and remove the 2 nuts retaining the center of the instrument panel to the floor.
- Open the glove compartment, squeeze the sides of the bin and lower to the full open position. From under the instrument panel and through the glove compartment opening, disconnect the wiring, vacuum lines and control cables.
- Remove 2 screws from the right side and 2 screws from the left side retaining the instrument panel to the cowl side.
- Remove the right and left upper finish panels by pulling up to disengage the snap-in retainers. There are 3 on the right side, and 4 on the left side.
- Remove the 4 screws retaining the instrument panel to the cowl top. Remove the right and left roof rail trim panel. Remove the door frame weatherstrip.
- Carefully pull the instrument panel away from the cowl and disconnect any remaining wiring or controls.

3. Remove the right instrument panel brace located above the heater case and attached to the cowl.
4. Drain the coolant from the cooling system and remove the hoses from the heater core. Plug the hoses and the core.
5. Disconnect the black vacuum supply hose from the in-line vacuum check valve in the engine compartment.
6. Disconnect the blower motor wire harness from the resistor and motor lead.
7. Working under the hood, remove the 3 nuts retaining the heater assembly to the dash panel.
8. In the passenger compartment, remove the screw attaching the heater assembly support bracket to the cowl top panel.
9. Remove the 1 screw retaining the bracket below the heater assembly to the dash panel.
10. Carefully pull the heater assembly away from the dash panel and remove the heater assembly from the vehicle.
11. Remove the 4 heater core access cover attaching screws and remove the access cover.
12. Remove the seal from the heater core tubes and pull the heater core from the case.

To install:

13. Inspect the heater core sealer in the case and replace, if necessary.
14. Install the heater core in the case with the seals on the outside of the case. Install the heater core tube seal on the heater core tubes.
15. Position the heater core access cover and seal on the case and install the 4 attaching screws.
16. Position the heater assembly in the vehicle. Install the screw attaching the heater assembly support bracket to the cowl top panel.

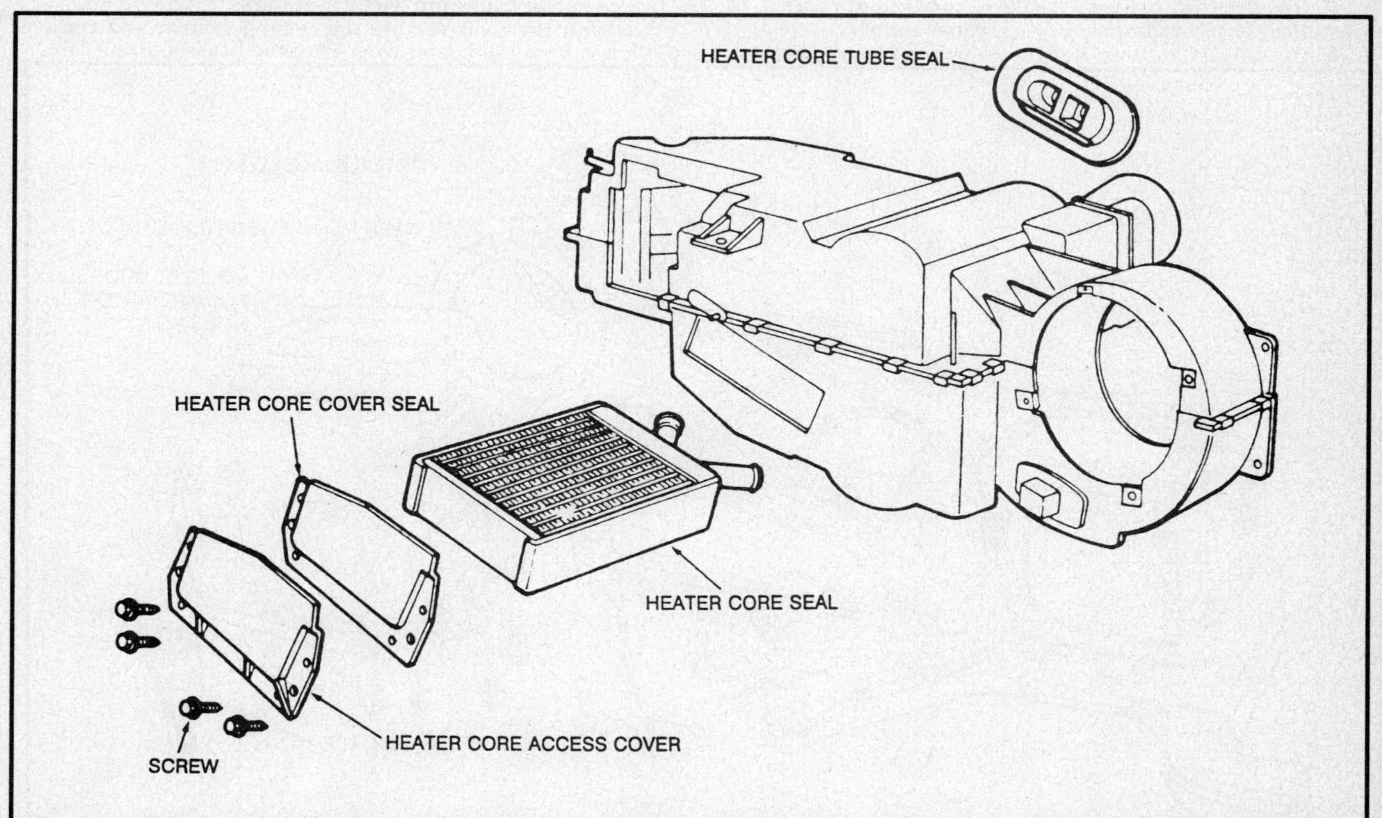

Heater core removal—Thunderbird and Cougar

17. Working under the hood, install the 3 nuts retaining the heater assembly to the dash panel.
18. Install 1 screw to retain the bracket below the heater assembly to the dash panel.
19. Connect the blower motor and the harness to the resistor and blower motor lead.
20. Connect the black vacuum supply hose to the vacuum check valve in the engine compartment.
21. Install the right instrument panel brace and install the instrument panel by reversing the removal procedure.
22. Connect the heater hoses to the heater core and fill the cooling system. Check heater operation.

Mustang

1. Disconnect the negative battery cable.
2. Remove the floor console and instrument panel as follows:
   - Remove the 2 covers at rear of console and remove armrest retaining bolts and remove armrest.
   - Remove the gearshift opening trim panel (snap-fit). On manual transmission models, shift boot is attached to bottom of finish panel; remove the shift knob and slide boot and finish panel up and off the lever.
   - Pull emergency brake handle up, remove 4 screws and lift up top finish panel. Detach wiring.
   - On 1993 models, snap out the front upper finish panel. Remove the radio finish panel.
   - On 1993 models, lower the glove box door and remove the 2 console–to–panel screws.
   - On 1993 models, disconnect all underhood wiring connectors from the main wiring harness. Disengage the rubber grommet seal from the dash panel and push the wiring harness and connectors into the passenger compartment.
   - On 1994–95 models, remove the radio chassis (if installed) or pry radio cover finish panel out of console.
   - On 1994–95 models, flex the glove box bin tabs inward, drop glove box assembly down and remove the 2 console–to–instrument panel screws.
   - On 1994–95 models, remove the 4 console bracket retaining screws and remove the console panel.
   - Remove the 3 bolts attaching the steering column opening cover and reinforcement panel. Remove the cover.
   - Remove the steering column opening reinforcement by removing 2 bolts. Remove the 2 bolts retaining the lower steering column opening reinforcement and remove the reinforcement.
   - Remove the 6 steering column retaining nuts. 2 are retaining the hood release mechanism and 4 retain the column to the lower brake pedal support. Lower the steering column to the floor.
   - Remove the steering column upper and lower shrouds and disconnect the wiring from the multi-function switch.
   - Remove the brake pedal support nut and snap out the defroster grille.
   - On 1994–95 models, remove the steering column through bolt and nut in the engine compartment. Remove the steering column from the vehicle.
   - Remove the screws from the speaker covers. Snap out the speaker covers. Remove the front screws retaining the right and left scuff plates at the cowl trim panel. Remove the right and left side cowl trim panels.
   - Disconnect the wiring at the right and left cowl sides. Remove the cowl side retaining bolts, 1 on each side.
   - Open the glove compartment door and flex the glove compartment bin tabs inward. Drop down the glove compartment door assembly.
   - Remove the 5 cowl top screw attachments. Gently pull the instrument panel away from the cowl. Disconnect the speedometer cable and wire connectors.
3. Drain the coolant from the cooling system and remove the hoses from the heater core. Plug the hoses and the core.

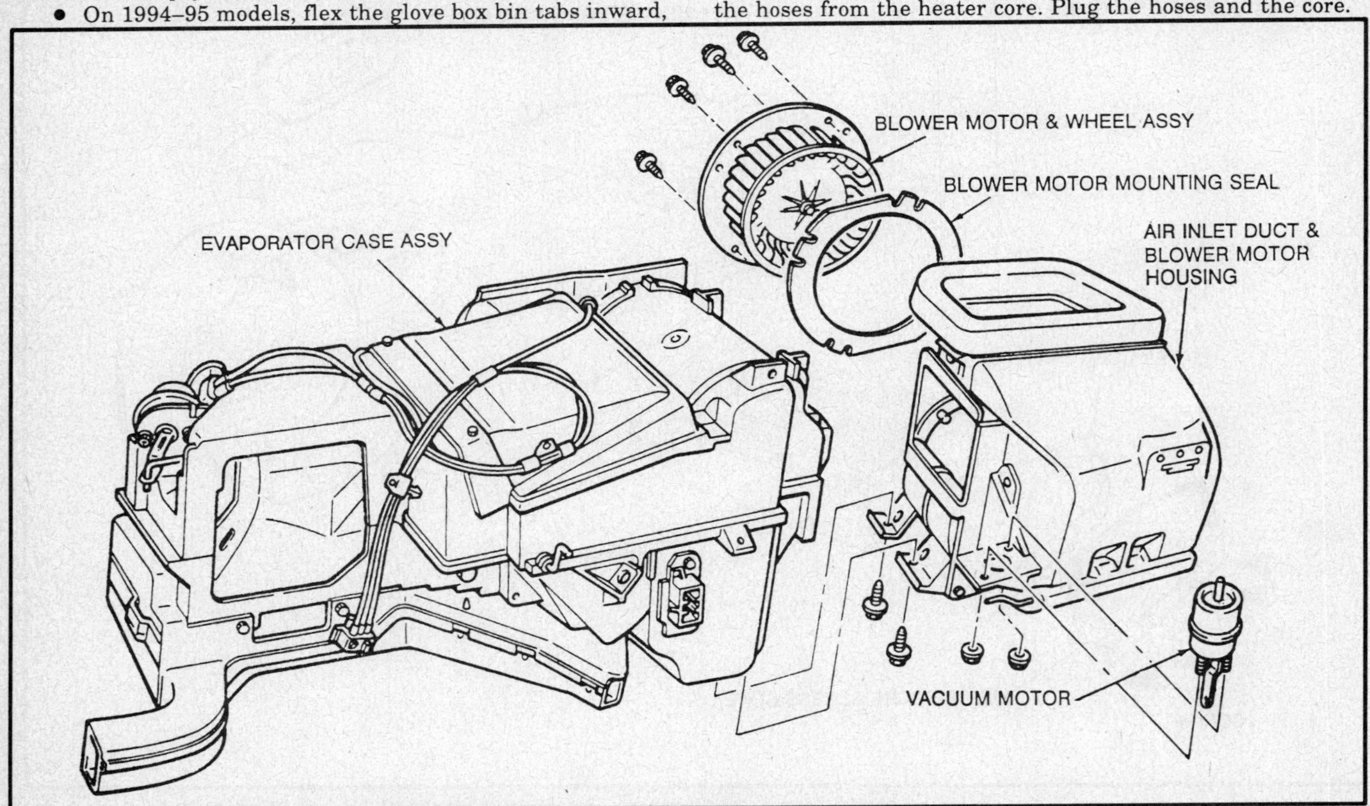

Removing heater case and heater core—Mustang without air conditioning

4. Remove the screw attaching the air inlet duct and blower housing assembly support bracket to the cowl top panel.
5. Disconnect the black vacuum supply hose from the in-line vacuum check valve in the engine compartment.
6. Disconnect the blower motor wire harness from the resistor and motor head.
7. Working under the hood, remove the 2 nuts retaining the heater assembly to the dash panel.
8. In the passenger compartment, remove the screw attaching the heater assembly support bracket to the cowl top panel. Remove the 1 screw retaining the bracket below the heater assembly to the dash panel.
9. Carefully pull the heater assembly away from the dash panel and remove from the vehicle.
10. Remove the 4 heater core access cover attaching screws and remove the access cover from the case.
11. Lift the heater core and seal from the case. Remove the seal from the heater core tubes.

To install:

12. Install the heater core tube seal on the heater core tubes. Inspect the heater core sealer in the heater case and replace, if necessary.
13. Install the heater core in the case with the seals on the outside of the case. Position the heater core access cover on the case and install the 4 attaching screws.
14. Position the heater assembly in the vehicle. Install the screw attaching the heater assembly support bracket to the cowl top panel.
15. Check the heater assembly drain tube to ensure it is through the dash panel and is not pinched or kinked.
16. Working under the hood, install the 2 nuts retaining the heater assembly to the dash panel. Install the air inlet duct and blower housing support bracket attaching screw. Install 1 screw to the retainer bracket below the heater assembly to the dash panel.
17. Connect the blower motor ground wire to ground and the harness to the resistor and blower motor lead.
18. Connect the black vacuum supply hose to the vacuum check valve in the engine compartment.
19. Install the instrument panel and floor console by reversing the removal procedure.
20. Connect the heater hoses to the heater core and fill the cooling system. Check the system for proper operation.

Crown Victoria, Grand Marquis and Town Car

AIR CONDITIONING

1. Disconnect the negative battery cable.
2. Drain the cooling system and disconnect the heater hoses from the heater core tubes. Plug the hoses and the heater core tubes.
3. Remove the 3 nuts located below the windshield wiper motor attaching the left end of the plenum to the dash panel. Remove the 1 nut retaining the upper left corner of the evaporator case to the dash panel.
4. From the engine compartment, disconnect the 2 vacuum supply hoses from the vacuum source. Disconnect the vacuum harness from the thermal blower lockout switch. Push the grommet and vacuum supply hoses into the passenger compartment.
5. Remove the right and left lower instrument panel insulators.

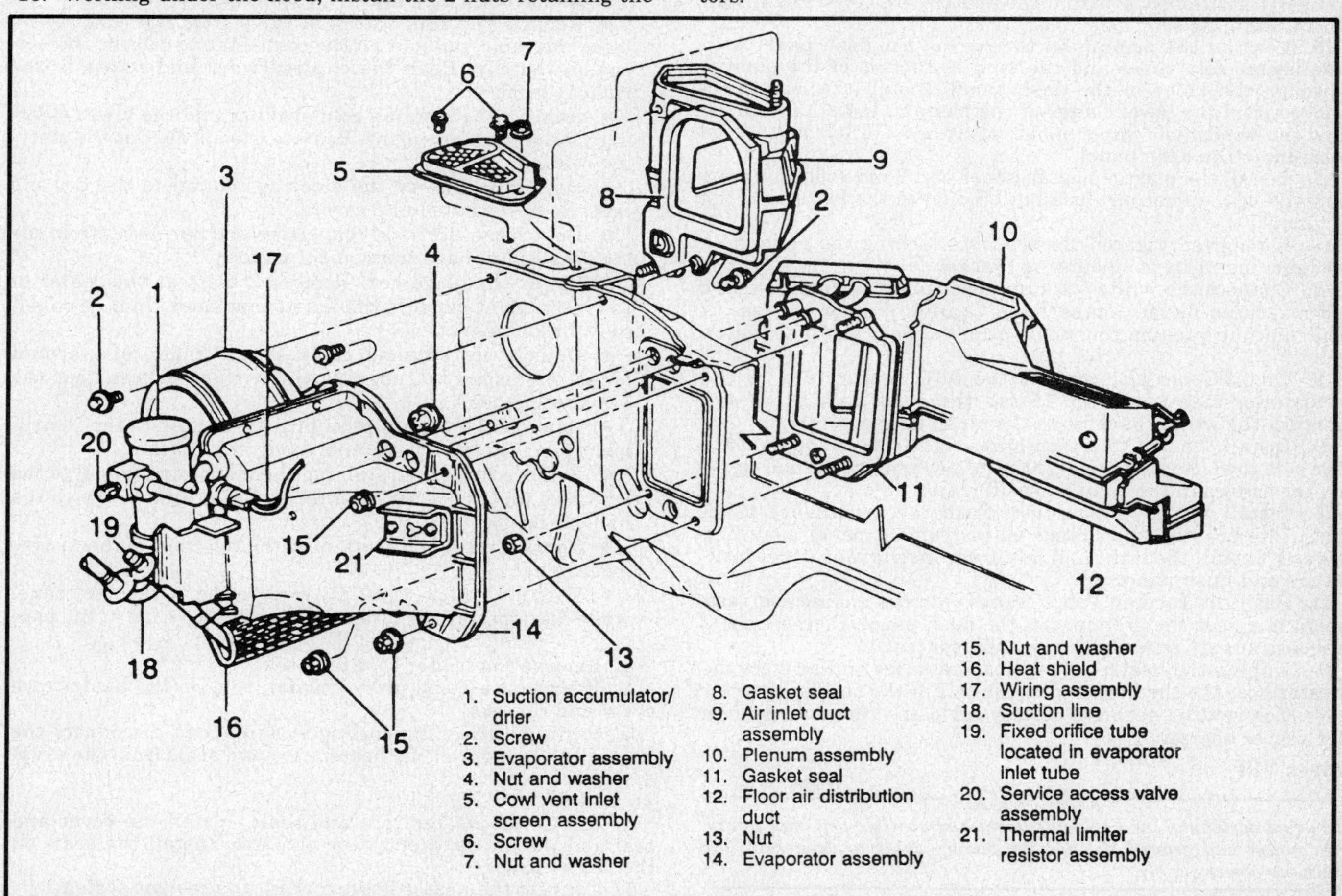

Plenum and evaporator removal—Crown Victoria, Grand Marquis and Town Car

6. Remove all instrument panel mounting screws and pull the instrument panel back as far as it will go without disconnecting the wiring harness.
7. Loosen the right door sill plate and remove the right side cowl trim panel.
8. On ATC equipped models, remove the cross body brace and disconnect the wiring harness from the temperature blend door actuator. Disconnect the ATC sensor tube from the evaporator case connector.
9. Disconnect the vacuum jumper harness at the multiple vacuum connector near the floor air distribution duct. Disconnect the white vacuum hose from the outside-recirc door vacuum motor.
10. Remove 2 hush panels.
11. Remove 1 plastic push fastener retaining the floor air distribution duct to the left end of the plenum and 2 screws on the rear face of the plenum and remove the floor air distribution duct.
12. Remove 2 nuts from the 2 studs along the lower flange of the plenum. Carefully move the plenum rearward to allow the heater core tubes and the stud at the top of the plenum to clear the holes in the dash panel. Remove the plenum from the vehicle by rotating the top of the plenum forward, down and out from under the instrument panel.
13. Remove the 4 retaining screws from the heater core cover and remove the cover from the plenum assembly. Pull the heater core and seal assembly from the plenum assembly.

To install:

14. Carefully install the heater core and seal assembly into the plenum assembly. Visually check to ensure the core seal is properly positioned. Position the heater core cover and install the 4 retaining screws.
15. Position the plenum on the rear of the dash panel with the heater core tubes and the stud at the top of the plenum through the holes in the dash panel. Install the 3 nuts removed from the lower flange of the plenum. Install 3 nuts below the windshield wiper motor at attach the left end of the plenum to the dash panel.
16. Install the plastic push fastener and 2 nuts retaining the left end of the floor air distribution duct to the left end of the plenum.
17. If removed, tighten the screws attaching the panel door vacuum motor to the mounting bracket.
18. Connect the white vacuum hose from the outside-recirc door vacuum motor. Connect the vacuum jumper harness at the multiple vacuum connector near the floor air distribution duct.
19. On ATC models, connect the ATC sensor tube to the evaporator case connector. Install the cross body brace and connect the wiring harness to the blend door actuator.
20. Install the bolt to attach lower right side of the panel to the side cowl. Replace the right side cowl trim panel and tighten the screws in the right door sill plate.
21. Install the glove box door. Push the instrument panel back into position and install all instrument panel mounting screws. Install the right and left lower instrument panel insulators and hush panels.
22. Push the vacuum supply hoses into the engine compartment and seat the grommet in the dash panel. Connect the 2 vacuum supply hoses to the vacuum source.
23. Unplug the heater core hoses and tubes and connect the heater hoses to the heater core tubes. Fill the cooling system.
24. Connect the negative battery cable and check the system for proper operation.

Mark VIII

CAUTION

To avoid accidental air bag deployment and possible personal injury, disconnect and ground the positive battery cable to deenergize the back–up power supply.

1. Disconnect the positive battery cable. Ground the positive cable for 1 minute to deenergize the back-up power supply.
2. Remove the instrument panel as follows:
   - Loosen the main harness connector bolt in the engine compartment at the left side of the dash panel.
   - Remove both door scuff plates and weatherstrip.
   - Remove both roof inner side moldings (held by clips).
   - Lift the rear edge of the defroster grille to detach the 8 clips and remove 2 corner clips. Remove the grille.
   - Remove both under panel sound insulators
   - Remove both kick panels
   - Remove the gear selector handle.
   - Remove the Electronic Automatic Temperature Control (EATC) instrument panel finish panel.
   - Remove the instrument panel finish panel.
   - Remove the 2 screws retaining the console finish panel to the radio control cover.
   - Unsnap the right rear corner of the console finish panel; then disengage the three attaching clips from the left rear corner.
   - Disconnect the cigar lighter socket and retainer, lamp and switch connectors and remove the console finish panel.
   - Remove the 2 screws retaining the console panel to the instrument panel.
   - Open the glove compartment door and remove the cover in the bottom tray to gain access to the retaining screws. Remove the 2 screws.
   - Slide the console panel rearward and up to remove.
   - Remove the air duct at the console.
   - Remove the shift interlock cable from the console, release the cable, pull out on the center tab to release the detent on the clip. Push the clip rearward and rotate to the right to remove.
   - Remove the steering column filler and the lower steering column reinforcement. Remove the air duct at the steering column.
   - Detach and lower the steering column to the driver's seat. Remove the column covers.
   - Detach the electrical connectors and harnesses from the steering column and instrument panel.
   - Lower the glove box. Remove 2 bolts at the center of the instrument panel to the floor tunnel and 1 nut at panel-to-right kick panel.
   - Detach the antenna cable at the radio, all vacuum hoses, the aspirator tube and the wiring harness near the evaporator case.
   - Remove the 2 nuts retaining the center of the instrument panel to the floor tunnel mounting bracket.
   - Remove the 1 nut retaining the instrument panel to the left cowl, and the 1 nut retaining the parking brake to the half car beam.
   - Remove the 6 bolts retaining the top front of the instrument panel.
   - With assistance, carefully remove the instrument panel while disengaging the 9 retainers at the top edge of the panel.
3. Remove the heater core tube seal.
4. Remove the blend door actuator, remove the heater core cover and the seal.
5. Partially drain the cooling system, then disconnect the heater hoses and pull the heater core and seals from the evaporator case.

To install:

6. Install the heater core and seals, install the cover and seal and install the blend door actuator. Install the seals on the heater tubes.
7. Connect the heater hoses and fill the coolant system.

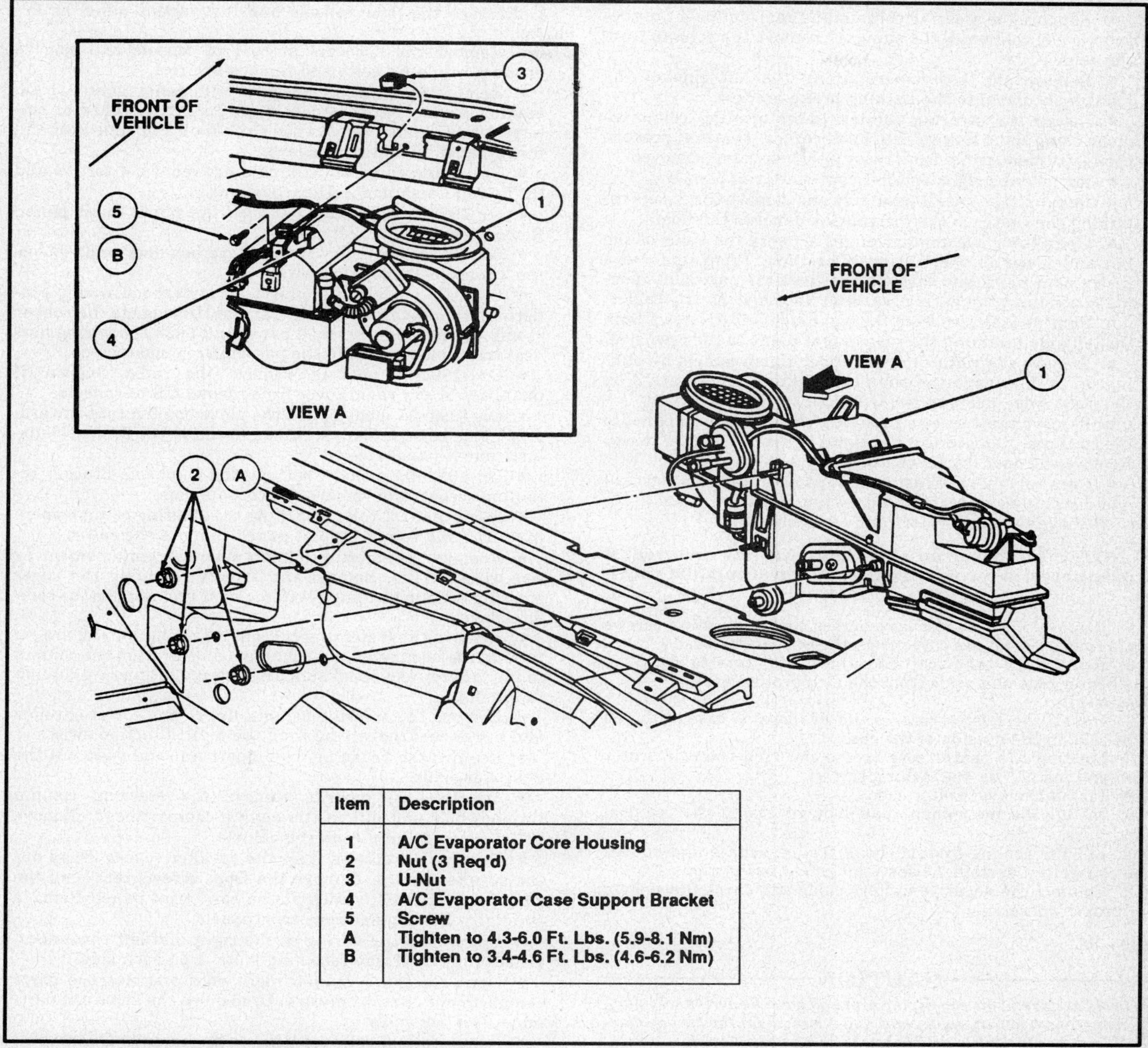

Item	Description
1	A/C Evaporator Core Housing
2	Nut (3 Req'd)
3	U-Nut
4	A/C Evaporator Case Support Bracket
5	Screw
A	Tighten to 4.3-6.0 Ft. Lbs. (5.9-8.1 Nm)
B	Tighten to 3.4-4.6 Ft. Lbs. (4.6-6.2 Nm)

Evaporator assembly installation—Mark VIII

8. Install the instrument panel in reverse order of the removal procedure.
9. Connect the battery cable and check system operation. Verify proper coolant level.

Thunderbird and Cougar

1993

1. Disconnect the negative battery cable and drain the cooling system.
2. Discharge the refrigerant from the air conditioning system.
3. Remove the instrument panel as follows:
   - Disconnect the underhood wiring at the left side of the dash panel.
   - Disengage the wiring connector from the dash panel and push the wiring harness into the passenger compartment.
   - Remove the steering column lower trim cover by removing the 3 screws at the bottom, 1 screw on the left side and pulling to disengage the 5 snap-in retainers across the top.
   - Remove the steering column lower opening reinforcement. Six screws retain the reinforcement to the instrument panel.
   - Remove the steering column upper and lower shrouds and disconnect the wiring from the steering column.
   - Remove the shift interlock switch and disconnect the steering column lower universal joint.

• Support the steering column and remove the 4 nuts retaining the column to the support. Remove the column from the vehicle.
• Remove the 1 screw retaining the left side of the instrument panel to the parking brake bracket.
• Install the steering column lower opening reinforcement using the 4 screws, 1 at each corner. This will prevent the instrument panel from twisting when being removed.
• Remove the right and left cowl side trim panels.
• Remove the console assembly and remove the 2 nuts retaining the center of the instrument panel to the floor.
• Open the glove compartment, squeeze the sides of the bin and lower to the full open position. From under the instrument panel and through the glove compartment opening, disconnect the wiring, vacuum lines and control cables.
• Remove 2 screws from the right side and 2 screws from the left side retaining the instrument panel to the cowl side.
• Remove the right and left upper finish panels by pulling up to disengage the snap-in retainers. There are 3 on the right side, and 4 on the left side.
• Remove the 4 screws retaining the instrument panel to the cowl top. Remove the right and left roof rail trim panel. Remove the door frame weatherstrip.
• Carefully pull the instrument panel away from the cowl and disconnect any remaining wiring or controls.

4. Remove the evaporator case assembly.

NOTE: Whenever an evaporator case is removed, it will be necessary to replace the suction accumulator/drier.

5. Remove the 4 heater core access cover attaching screws and remove the access cover from the evaporator case.
6. Remove the tube seal from the heater core tubes. Slide the heater core and seals from the evaporator case.

To install:

7. Install the heater core in the evaporator case with the tube seal on the outside of the case.
8. Position the heater core access cover on the evaporator case and install the 4 attaching screws.
9. Install the evaporator case.
10. Install the instrument panel by reversing the removal procedure.
11. Fill the cooling system. Leak test, evacuate and charge the refrigerant system. Observe all safety precautions.
12. Connect the negative battery cable and check the system for proper operation.

1994–95

CAUTION

To avoid accidental air bag deployment and possible personnel injury, disconnect both battery cables and wait 1 minute for the air bag diagnostic monitor to deplete the air bag back–up power supply.

1. Disconnect the negative battery cable. Disconnect the positive battery cable and wait 1 minute for the back–up power supply to be deenergized.
2. Partially drain the cooling system.
3. Remove the instrument panel and the evaporator case.
4. Remove the 4 heater core access cover retaining screws and remove the access cover from the evaporator core.
5. Remove the tube gasket from the heater core tubes.
6. Slide the heater core and seals from the evaporator case.
7. Installation is the reverse of the removal procedure.

Mustang

1. Disconnect the negative battery cable and drain the cooling system.
2. Discharge the refrigerant from the air conditioning system.
3. Remove the floor console and instrument panel as follows:

• Remove the 2 covers at rear of console and remove armrest retaining bolts and remove armrest.
• Remove the gearshift opening trim panel (snap-fit). On manual transmission models, shift boot is attached to bottom of finish panel; remove the shift knob and slide boot and finish panel up and off the lever.
• Pull emergency brake handle up, remove 4 screws and lift up top finish panel. Detach wiring.
• On 1993 models, snap out the front upper finish panel. Remove the radio finish panel.
• On 1993 models, lower the glove box door and remove the 2 console–to–panel screws.
• On 1993 models, disconnect all underhood wiring connectors from the main wiring harness. Disengage the rubber grommet seal from the dash panel and push the wiring harness and connectors into the passenger compartment.
• On 1994–95 models, remove the radio chassis (if installed) or pry radio cover finish panel out of console.
• On 1994–95 models, flex the glove box bin tabs inward, drop glove box assembly down and remove the 2 console–to–instrument panel screws.
• On 1994–95 models, remove the 4 console bracket retaining screws and remove the console panel.
• Remove the 3 bolts attaching the steering column opening cover and reinforcement panel. Remove the cover.
• Remove the steering column opening reinforcement by removing 2 bolts. Remove the 2 bolts retaining the lower steering column opening reinforcement and remove the reinforcement.
• Remove the 6 steering column retaining nuts. 2 are retaining the hood release mechanism and 4 retain the column to the lower brake pedal support. Lower the steering column to the floor.
• Remove the steering column upper and lower shrouds and disconnect the wiring from the multi-function switch.
• Remove the brake pedal support nut and snap out the defroster grille.
• On 1994–95 models, remove the steering column through bolt and nut in the engine compartment. Remove the steering column from the vehicle.
• Remove the screws from the speaker covers. Snap out the speaker covers. Remove the front screws retaining the right and left scuff plates at the cowl trim panel. Remove the right and left side cowl trim panels.
• Disconnect the wiring at the right and left cowl sides. Remove the cowl side retaining bolts, 1 on each side.
• Open the glove compartment door and flex the glove compartment bin tabs inward. Drop down the glove compartment door assembly.
• Remove the 5 cowl top screw attachments. Gently pull the instrument panel away from the cowl. Disconnect the speedometer cable and wire connectors.

NOTE: Whenever an evaporator case is replaced, it will be necessary to replace the suction accumulator/drier.

4. Disconnect the liquid line and the accumulator/drier inlet tube for the evaporator core at the dash panel. Cap the refrigerant lines and evaporator core tube to prevent the entrance of dirt and excessive moisture. Remove the high and low pressure hoses. Cap openings.
5. Disconnect the heater hoses from the heater core tubes and plug the hoses and tubes.
6. Remove the screw attaching the air inlet duct and blower housing assembly support brace to the cowl top panel.
7. Disconnect the black vacuum supply hose from the in-line vacuum check valve in the engine compartment. Discon-

nect the blower motor wires from the wire harness and disconnect the wire harness from the blower motor resistor.

8. Working under the hood, remove the 2 nuts retaining the evaporator case to the dash panel. Inside the passenger compartment, remove the 2 screws attaching the evaporator case support brackets to the cowl top panel.

9. Remove the 1 screw retaining the bracket below the evaporator case to the dash panel. Carefully pull the evaporator case away from the dash panel and remove the evaporator case assembly from the vehicle.

10. Remove the 4 heater core access cover attaching screws and remove the cover from the case.

11. Lift the heater core and seal from the case. Remove the seal from the heater core tubes.

To install:

12. Install the heater core tube seal on the heater core tubes.

13. Inspect the heater core sealer in the evaporator case. Replace with suitable caulking cord, if necessary.

14. Install the heater core in the case with the seals on the case and install the 4 attaching screws.

NOTE: When replacing the evaporator, 3 oz. (90ml) of clean refrigerant oil should be added to new evaporator to maintain the total system oil charge.

15. Position the evaporator case assembly in the vehicle. Install the screws attaching the evaporator case support brackets to the cowl top panel. Check the evaporator case drain tube to ensure it is through the dash panel and is not pinched or kinked.

16. Install 1 screw retaining the bracket below the evaporator case to the dash panel. Working under the hood, install the 2 nuts retaining the evaporator case to the dash panel. Tighten the 4 nuts and 2 screws in the engine compartment. Tighten the 2 screws in the passenger compartment and the 2 support bracket attaching screws.

17. Connect the blower motor wire harness to the resistor and blower motor. Connect the black vacuum supply hose to the vacuum check valve in the engine compartment.

18. Using new O-rings lubricated with clean refrigerant oil, connect the liquid line and suction accumulator inlet to the evaporator core tubes, Tighten each connection using a back-up wrench to prevent component damage.

19. Install the instrument panel by reversing the removal procedure.

20. Connect the heater hoses to the heater core and fill the cooling system.

21. Connect the negative battery cable. Leak test, evacuate and charge the refrigerant system. Observe all safety precautions.

22. Check the system for proper operation.

Evaporator

REMOVAL AND INSTALLATION

Crown Victoria, Grand Marquis and Town Car

1. Disconnect the negative battery cable and drain the cooling system. Save the coolant for reuse.

2. Discharge the refrigerant from the air conditioning system.

NOTE: Whenever the evaporator case is removed, it will be necessary to replace the suction accumulator/drier.

3. Disconnect the suction hose from the accumulator/drier. Plug the openings to prevent dirt and excessive moisture from entering. Position the hose away from the evaporator assembly.

4. Disconnect the liquid line from the evaporator inlet tube and plug the openings. Position the liquid line away from the evaporator assembly.

5. Disconnect the connector from the pressure switch on the accumulator/drier.

6. Loosen the heater hose clamps and disconnect the heater hoses from the heater core tubes.

7. On ATC systems, turn the steering wheel to the left so the wheel well support bracket is accessible. Remove the bracket.

8. Remove the 6 screws holding the right side of the hood seal bracket assembly. Remove the copper hood ground clip from underneath the hood seal and fold the hood seal assembly to the left side of the vehicle.

9. Loosen the retaining clamp and disconnect the emission hose that passes over the top of the evaporator case assembly. Position the emission hose and all vacuum hoses and movable wires away from the evaporator case assembly.

10. Disconnect the blower motor wiring connectors. Disconnect the 2 large wire harnesses, which cross the evaporator assembly, at the various connecting points. Position them away from the evaporator assembly.

11. From the passenger side of the dash panel, fold back the carpeting on the right side of the floor. Remove the bottom left screw of the 2 screws that support the inlet recirculation air duct assembly.

12. On ATC systems, from the passenger compartment, disconnect the ambient sensor air tube from the evaporator sensor air tube port.

13. From the engine side of the dash panel, remove 3 nuts, 1 upper and 2 lower, from the 3 evaporator assembly mounting studs. Also remove 2 screws, 1 drill-point and 1 sheet metal, from the blower motor and wheel portion of the case assembly.

14. Pull the bottom of the evaporator case assembly away from the dash panel to disengage the 2 bottom studs. On Automatic Temperature Control (ATC) equipped vehicles, this will also disengage the evaporator ambient sensor air tube port. Move the top of the evaporator assembly away from the dash panel, disengaging it from the top stud and maneuver the case up and over the wheel well splash panel. The splash panel may be pushed downward slightly for additional clearance.

15. Remove the dash panel seal and remove the heat shield from the bottom of the evaporator case.

16. Remove the 6 screws attaching the 2 halves of the evaporator case together. Separate the 2 halves of the evaporator case and remove the evaporator core and suction accumulator/drier assembly.

17. Disconnect the suction accumulator/drier inlet from the evaporator core outlet tube. Remove the retaining screw from the accumulator/drier and evaporator core mounting brackets and remove the accumulator/drier from the evaporator core.

To install:

NOTE: When replacing the evaporator, 3 fluid oz. (90ml) of clean refrigerant oil should be added to the new evaporator to maintain the total system oil charge.

18. Attach the suction accumulator/drier to the evaporator core mounting bracket with the retaining screw. Install a new O-ring lubricated with clean refrigerant oil and connect the accumulator/drier inlet connection to the outlet tube of the evaporator core. Tighten using a back-up wrench to prevent component damage.

19. Position the evaporator core assembly to the right half of the evaporator case. Apply caulking cord or similar sealer to the case flange and around the evaporator core tubes.

20. Position the evaporator case left half and dash panel gasket to the case right half. Install the support strap on the evaporator inlet tube. Install the 7 screws to attach the 2 halves of the case together. The center screw on the front of the case also attaches the support strap.

21. Install the dash panel seal. Install a new heat shield on the bottom of the evaporator case assembly with staples.

22. Position the evaporator assembly near the dash panel by maneuvering it down past the wheel splash panel. If necessary, push the splash panel downward slightly for extra clearance.
23. On Automatic Temperature Control (ATC) equipped vehicles, engage the sensor air tube port into the dash panel port opening. On all vehicles, engage the 2 bottom studs into the evaporator assembly stud holes. Move the top of the evaporator assembly toward the dash panel while engaging the top dash panel stud into the evaporator assembly stud hole. Replace, but do not tighten, the 3 stud nuts.
24. Replace the 2 screws, being careful to return the drill point screw to the correct hole which is located on top of the case and to the right of the blower motor and wheel assembly. Tighten the 3 stud nuts that were previously installed.
25. Position the 2 large wire harnesses across the evaporator case assembly and connect the various connectors. Connect the blower motor electrical connectors.
26. Place the emission hose clamp on the hose, tighten the clamp and position it over the evaporator case assembly along with the vacuum hoses and wires previously removed.
27. Unfold the hood seal bracket assembly and insert the copper hood ground clip under the hood seal. Install the 6 screws which secure the right side of the hood seal bracket assembly.
28. Place the heater core hose clamps onto the heater hoses and carefully connect the hoses to the inlet and outlet heater core tubes. Position and tighten the clamps. Refill the coolant system.
29. Remove the plugs from the evaporator inlet tube and the liquid line and install new O-rings dipped in clean refrigerant oil. Connect the liquid line to the evaporator inlet tube.
30. Remove the plugs from the suction accumulator/drier outlet and the suction hose and install new O-rings dipped in clean refrigerant oil. Connect the suction hose to the accumulator/drier.
31. Connect the electrical connector to the clutch cycling pressure switch and install the wheel well splash panel bracket. From the passenger compartment, install the recirculation air duct assembly screw. On Automatic Temperature Control (ATC) equipped vehicles, connect the ambient air sensor tube to the evaporator air tube port.

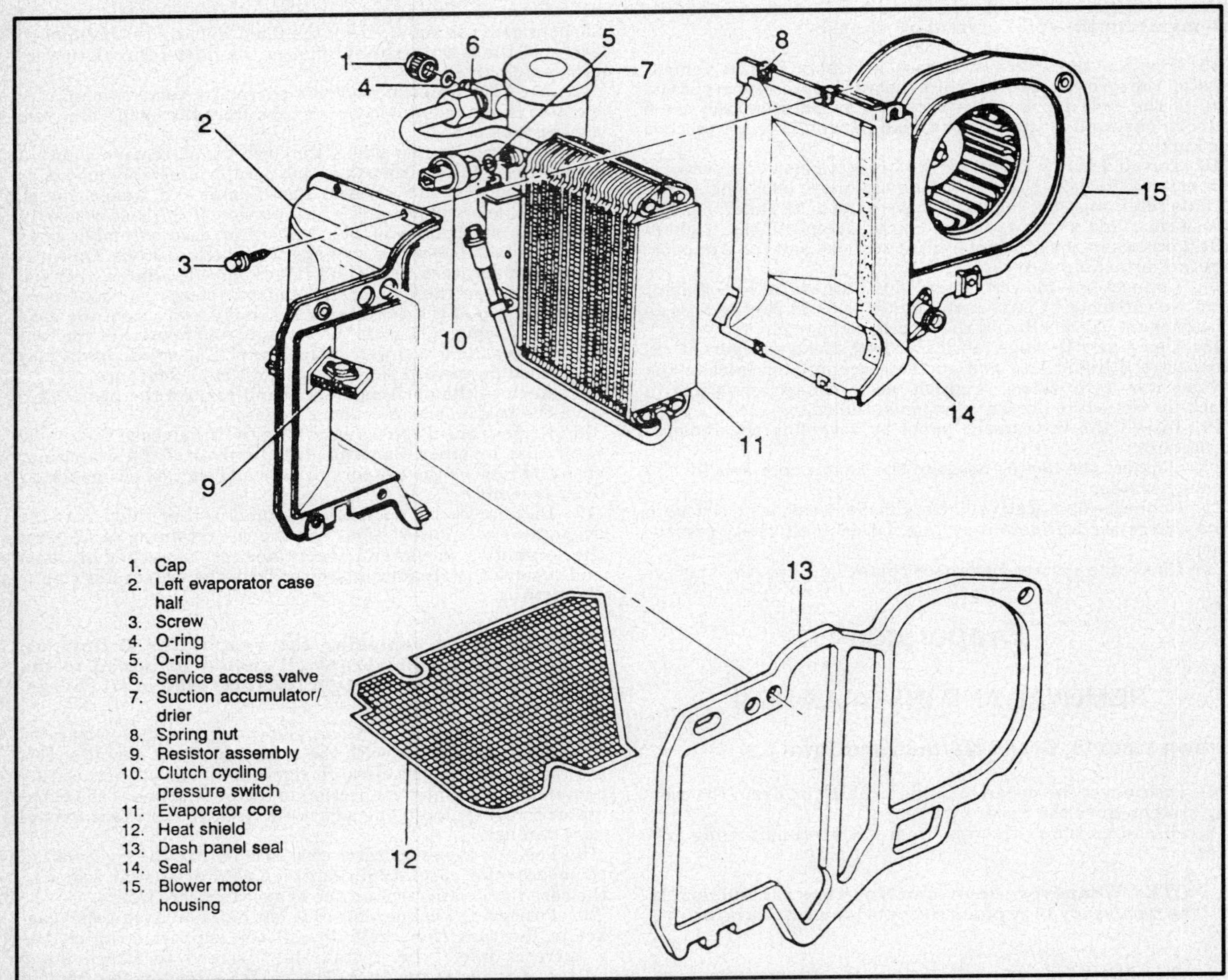

Evaporator core removal—Crown Victoria, Grand Marquis and Town Car

32. Connect the negative battery cable. Leak test, evacuate and charge the refrigerant system. Observe all safety precautions.
33. Check the system for proper operation.

Mark VIII

CAUTION

To avoid accidental air bag deployment and possible personnel injury, disconnect both battery cables and wait 1 minute for the air bag diagnostic monitor to deplete the air bag back–up power supply.

NOTE: If it is necessary to replace an evaporator core, the entire evaporator case assembly must be replaced. After it is removed from the vehicle, transfer all components to the new case.

1. Disconnect the positive battery cable. Ground the positive cable for 1 minute to de–energize the back–up power supply.
2. Properly drain the cooling system and discharge the air conditioning system.
3. Detach and plug the heater hoses from the dash panel and blow any remaining coolant from the heater core with low pressure air. Detach the vacuum hose from the check valve.
4. Disconnect the refrigerant lines (accumulator and evaporator tube). Cap all openings immediately.
5. Remove the instrument panel as follows:
   - Loosen the main harness connector bolt in the engine compartment at the left side of the dash panel.
   - Remove both door scuff plates and weatherstrip.
   - Remove both roof inner side moldings (held by clips).
   - Lift the rear edge of the defroster grille to detach the 8 clips and remove 2 corner clips. Remove the grille.
   - Remove both under panel sound insulators
   - Remove both kick panels
   - Remove the gear selector handle.
   - Remove the Electronic Automatic Temperature Control (EATC) instrument panel finish panel.
   - Remove the instrument panel finish panel.
   - Remove the 2 screws retaining the console finish panel to the radio control cover.
   - Unsnap the right rear corner of the console finish panel; then disengage the 3 attaching clips from the left rear corner.
   - Disconnect the cigar lighter socket and retainer, lamp and switch connectors and remove the console finish panel.
   - Remove the 2 screws retaining the console panel to the instrument panel.
   - Open the glove compartment door and remove the cover in the bottom tray to gain access to the 2 console panel–to–instrument panel console bracket retaining screws. Remove the 2 screws.
   - Slide the console panel rearward and up to remove.
   - Remove the air duct at the console.
   - Remove the shift interlock cable from the console, release the cable, pull out on the center tab to release the detent on the clip. Push the clip rearward and rotate to the right to remove.
   - Remove the steering column cover and the lower steering column reinforcement. Remove the air duct at the steering column.
   - Detach and lower the steering column to the driver's seat. Remove the column shroud.
   - Detach the electrical connectors and harnesses from the steering column and instrument panel.
   - Lower the glove box. Remove 2 bolts at the center of the instrument panel to the floor tunnel and 1 nut at panel–to–right kick panel.
   - Detach the antenna cable at the radio, all vacuum hoses, the aspirator tube and the wiring harness near the evaporator case.
   - Remove the 2 nuts retaining the center of the instrument panel to the floor tunnel mounting bracket.
   - Remove the 1 nut retaining the instrument panel to the right cowl, the 1 nut retaining the instrument panel to the left cowl, and the 1 nut retaining the parking brake to the half car beam.
   - Remove the 6 bolts retaining the top front of the instrument panel.
   - With assistance, carefully remove the instrument panel while disengaging the 9 retainers at the top edge of the panel.
6. Remove the floor register from the bottom of the evaporator case, then remove the screws holding the case to the dash top panel.
7. Disconnect the vacuum and electrical connections. Detach the aspirator hose.
8. In the engine compartment, remove 3 nuts holding the evaporator case to the dash panel.
9. Pull the evaporator case straight away from the dash panel and remove it.

To install:

10. Install the evaporator case (add 3.0 oz. of new refrigerant oil if the evaporator core/case are replaced), install 3 nuts from the engine compartment side.
11. Attach the vacuum and electrical connectors and the aspirator hose. Install the floor register and the top retaining screws.
12. Install the instrument panel in reverse order of the removal procedure.
13. Attach the refrigerant lines. Attach the heater hoses and the vacuum source hose.
14. Refill the cooling system. Evacuate, recharge and leak test the system.
15. Connect the battery cable and check the system for proper operation. Verify the coolant is at the proper level.

Thunderbird and Cougar

1993

NOTE: Whenever an evaporator case is removed, it will be necessary to replace the suction accumulator/drier.

1. Disconnect the negative battery cable and drain the cooling system.
2. Discharge the refrigerant from the air conditioning system.
3. Remove the instrument panel according to the following procedure:
   - Disconnect the underhood wiring at the left side of the dash panel.
   - Disengage the wiring connector from the dash panel and push the wiring harness into the passenger compartment.
   - Remove the steering column lower trim cover by removing the 3 screws at the bottom, 1 screw on the left side and pulling to disengage the 5 snap-in retainers across the top.
   - Remove the steering column lower opening reinforcement. Six screws retain the reinforcement to the instrument panel.
   - Remove the steering column upper and lower shrouds and disconnect the wiring from the steering column.
   - Remove the shift interlock switch and disconnect the steering column lower universal joint.
   - Support the steering column and remove the 4 nuts retaining the column to the support. Remove the column from the vehicle.
   - Remove the 1 screw retaining the left side of the instrument panel to the parking brake bracket.

- Install the steering column lower opening reinforcement using the 4 screws, 1 at each corner. This will prevent the instrument panel from twisting when being removed.
- Remove the right and left cowl side trim panels.
- Remove the console assembly and remove the 2 nuts retaining the center of the instrument panel to the floor.
- Open the glove compartment, squeeze the sides of the bin and lower to the full open position. From under the instrument panel and through the glove compartment opening, disconnect the wiring, vacuum lines and control cables.
- Remove 2 screws from the right side and 2 screws from the left side retaining the instrument panel to the cowl side.
- Remove the right and left upper finish panels by pulling up to disengage the snap-in retainers. There are 3 on the right side, 4 on the left side.
- Remove the 4 screws retaining the instrument panel to the cowl top. Remove the right and left roof rail trim panel. Remove the door frame weather-strip.
- Carefully pull the instrument panel away from the cowl and disconnect any remaining wiring or controls.

4. Disconnect the liquid line and accumulator/drier inlet tube from the evaporator core at the dash panel. Cap the refrigerant lines and evaporator core to prevent the entrance of dirt and excessive moisture.
5. If necessary, remove the throttle cable bracket and position it out of the way. Disconnect the heater hoses from the heater core. Plug the hoses and heater core tubes.
6. Disconnect the black vacuum supply hose from the in-line vacuum check valve in the engine compartment. Disconnect the blower motor wiring.
7. Working under the hood, remove the nuts retaining the evaporator case to the dash panel. In the passenger compartment, remove the screw attaching the evaporator case support bracket to the cowl top panel.
8. Remove 1 nut retaining the bracket below the evaporator case to the dash panel. Carefully pull the evaporator case away from the dash panel and remove the evaporator case assembly from the vehicle.
9. Using a suitable cutting tool, cut the top of the evaporator case to gain access to the evaporator core. Remove the old evaporator core from the case.

To install:

NOTE: When replacing the evaporator, 3 fluid oz. (90ml) of clean refrigerant oil should be added to the new evaporator to maintain the total system oil charge.

10. Make sure all burrs are removed from the sawed edges of the evaporator case. Hold the cover against the case firmly and drill five 3/16 in. diameter holes for the attaching screws.
11. Install the new evaporator in the evaporator case and install the service cover and the 5 attaching screws. Run a bead of caulking cord or other suitable sealer, between the service cover and the evaporator case.
12. Position the evaporator case assembly in the vehicle and install the screw attaching the evaporator case support bracket to the cowl top panel. Check the evaporator case drain tube to make sure it is through the dash panel and is not pinched or kinked.
13. Install 1 nut retaining the mounting bracket at the left end of the evaporator case to the dash panel and another nut to retain the bracket below the evaporator case to the dash panel.
14. Working under the hood, install the 2 nuts retaining the evaporator case to the dash panel. Tighten the 4 nuts, 2 in the engine compartment and 2 in the passenger compartment and the 1 support bracket attaching screw.
15. Connect the blower motor wiring. Connect the black vacuum supply hose to the vacuum check valve in the engine compartment.
16. Using new O-rings lubricated with clean refrigerant oil, connect the liquid line and suction accumulator inlet tube to the evaporator core. Install the throttle cable bracket, if removed.
17. Install the instrument panel by reversing the removal procedure.
18. Connect the heater hoses to the heater core and fill the cooling system.
19. Leak test, evacuate and charge the system. Observe all safety precautions.
20. Check the system for proper operation.

1994–95

CAUTION

To avoid accidental air bag deployment and possible personnel injury, disconnect both battery cables and wait 1 minute for the air bag diagnostic monitor to deplete the air bag back–up power supply.

1. Disconnect the negative battery cable. Disconnect the positive battery cable and wait 1 minute for the back–up power supply to be deenergized.
2. Partially drain the cooling system.
3. Discharge the refrigerant from the air conditioning system. Observe all safety precautions.
4. Remove the instrument panel as follows:

- Loosen the main wiring connector bolt in the engine compartment at the left side of the dash panel and separate the connectors.
- Remove the radio antenna stanchion and disconnect the radio antenna lead–in cable from the base of the stanchion.
- Remove both windshield side garnish moldings.
- Remove both door scuff plates and weatherstrip.
- Remove both kick panels.
- Remove the 3 steering column cover retaining screws and pull on the steering column cover to unsnap the 3 clips across the top of the cover. Remove the instrument panel steering column cover.
- Remove the ignition switch lock cylinder
- Remove the 4 steering column shroud retaining screws and remove the shrouds.
- Install the ignition switch lock cylinder to prevent the steering wheel from turning.
- Disconnect the wiring connectors at the multi–function switch.
- Remove the 1 screw and the evaporator register duct from under the steering column tube
- Disconnect the wiring connectors at the bottom of the steering column tube.
- Remove the steering column lower yoke pinch bolt. Using a screwdriver, spread the yoke slightly.
- While supporting the steering column tube, remove the 4 steering column tube retaining nuts.
- Remove the interlock cable retaining screws and the shift actuator cable fitting.
- Remove the steering column tube.
- Loosen the main wiring connector bolt at the left side of the steering column opening and separate the connectors.
- Disconnect the stop light switch wiring connector and the clutch pedal switch wiring connector (manual transmission).
- Pull back the floor carpet on both sides. Disconnect the window regulator safety relay switch wiring and the power train control module.
- Unsnap the glove compartment door check, remove the 3 door hinge retaining screws and remove the glove compartment from the instrument panel.
- Through the glove compartment opening, disconnect the wiring and vacuum connectors from the evaporator housing.
- Disconnect the main wiring from the speed control amplifier. Remove the amplifier and bracket assembly.

- Open the console glove compartment door, remove the 2 screws from the console finish panel, and lift the rear of the console finish panel to unsnap the retainers.
- Reach under the console finish panel and disconnect the wires to the fog lamp switch, the air suspension drive switch (if equipped) and the cigar lighter.
- Lift the rear of the console finish panel, slide the panel rearward to release and lift off.
- Remove the mat and the center screw from the console glove compartment. Lift the glove compartment from the console panel and disconnect the luggage compartment and fuel filler door switches (if equipped).
- Remove the 2 screws from the bottom of the console glove compartment and the 1 cap and screw from each side. Remove the front sides of the floor console.
- Remove the 2 screws retaining the front of the console to the instrument panel. Disconnect the jumper wire and main wiring and lift off the console

NOTE: Protect the instrument panel surface during the following procedures.

- Insert a putty knife or similar tool under either the left or right corner of the instrument panel upper finish panel and pry up to release one snap clip. Working toward the opposite side of the vehicle, unsnap the remaining 4 clips by hand.
- Remove the 2 instrument panel retaining nuts from the left cowl, the 1 nut from the right cowl, and the 2 nuts and 1 bolt from the console bracket.
- With assistance, remove the 6 bolts retaining the top of the instrument panel to the dash panel and carefully remove the instrument panel while disconnecting any remaining connections. Disengage the radio antenna wire grommet and pull the lead–in cable through the dash panel.

5. Remove the high– and low–pressure hoses. Cap the hoses to prevent the entry of dirt and moisture.
6. Disconnect the liquid line and the accumulator/drier inlet tube from the evaporator core. Cap the lines and the core.
7. Remove the accumulator/drier and the accumulator/drier bracket.
8. Disconnect and plug the heater hoses and heater core tubes.
9. Disconnect the black vacuum supply hose from the vacuum check valve in the engine compartment.
10. Remove the 3 evaporator case retaining nuts in the engine compartment.
11. Remove the 1 screw retaining the evaporator case support bracket to the cowl top panel and the 2 nuts retaining the evaporator case to the dash panel.
12. Pull the evaporator case away from the dash panel and remove the evaporator case.

To install:

NOTE: Whenever an evaporator case is removed, it will be necessary to replace the suction accumulator/drier.

If it is necessary to replace an evaporator core, the entire evaporator case assembly must be replaced. After the evaporator case is removed, transfer the heater core and all vacuum control motors, vacuum lines and air ducts to the replacement case.

13. Position the evaporator case in the vehicle. Ensure that the case drain tube is through the dash panel and is not pinched or kinked.
14. Install the 1 screw retaining the evaporator core support bracket to the cowl top panel and the 2 nuts retaining the evaporator case to the dash panel.
15. Install the 3 evaporator case retaining nuts in the engine compartment.
16. Connect the black vacuum supply hose to the vacuum check valve in the engine compartment.
17. Install the suction accumulator/drier bracket and suction accumulator/drier.
18. Install the throttle cable bracket, if removed.
19. Using new O–rings lubricated with clean refrigerant oil, connect the liquid line and suction accumulator/drier inlet tube to the evaporator core.
20. Connect the high– and low–pressure refrigerant hoses using new O–rings dipped in clean refrigerant oil.
21. Install the instrument panel by reversing the removal procedure.
22. Connect the heater hoses to the heater core and fill the cooling system.
23. Leak test, evacuate and charge the refrigeration system. Observe all safety precautions.
24. Check the system for proper operation.

Mustang

1993

NOTE: Whenever an evaporator core is replaced, it will be necessary to replace the suction accumulator/drier.

1. Disconnect the negative battery cable and drain the cooling system.
2. Discharge the refrigerant from the air conditioning system.
3. Remove the instrument panel according to the following procedure:
   - Remove the 2 covers at rear of console and remove armrest retaining bolts and remove armrest.
   - Remove the gearshift opening trim panel (snap-fit). On manual transmission models, shift boot is attached to bottom of finish panel; remove the shift knob and slide boot and finish panel up and off the lever.
   - Pull emergency brake handle up, remove 4 screws and lift up top finish panel. Detach wiring.
   - Snap out front upper finish panel. Remove the radio finish panel.
   - Lower the glove box door and remove 2 console to panel screws.
   - Disconnect all underhood wiring connectors from the main wiring harness. Disengage the rubber grommet seal from the dash panel and push the wiring harness and connectors into the passenger compartment.
   - Remove the 3 bolts attaching the steering column opening cover and reinforcement panel. Remove the cover.
   - Remove the steering column opening reinforcement by removing 2 bolts. Remove the 2 bolts retaining the lower steering column opening reinforcement and remove the reinforcement.
   - Remove the 6 steering column retaining nuts; 2 are retaining the hood release mechanism and 4 retain the column to the lower brake pedal support. Lower the steering column to the floor.
   - Remove the steering column upper and lower shrouds and disconnect the wiring from the multi-function switch.
   - Remove the brake pedal support nut and snap out the defroster grille.
   - Remove the screws from the speaker covers. Snap out the speaker covers. Remove the front screws retaining the right and left scuff plates at the cowl trim panel. Remove the right and left side cowl trim panels.
   - Disconnect the wiring at the right and left cowl sides. Remove the cowl side retaining bolts, 1 on each side.
   - Open the glove compartment door and flex the glove compartment bin tabs inward. Drop down the glove compartment door assembly.
   - Remove the 5 cowl top screw attachments. Gently pull the instrument panel away from the cowl. Disconnect the speedometer cable and wire connectors.

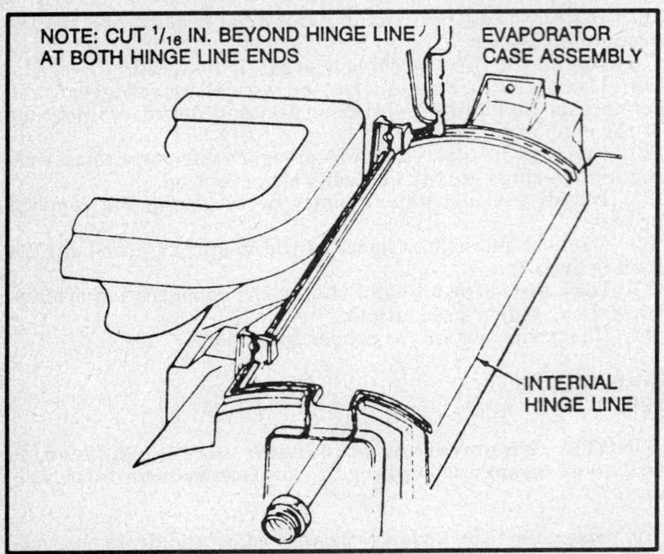

Evaporator case cutting—1993 Mustang

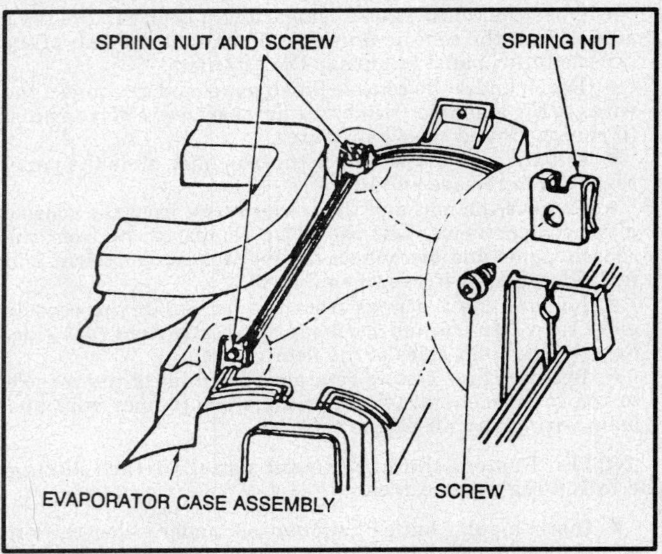

Evaporator core removal—1993 Mustang

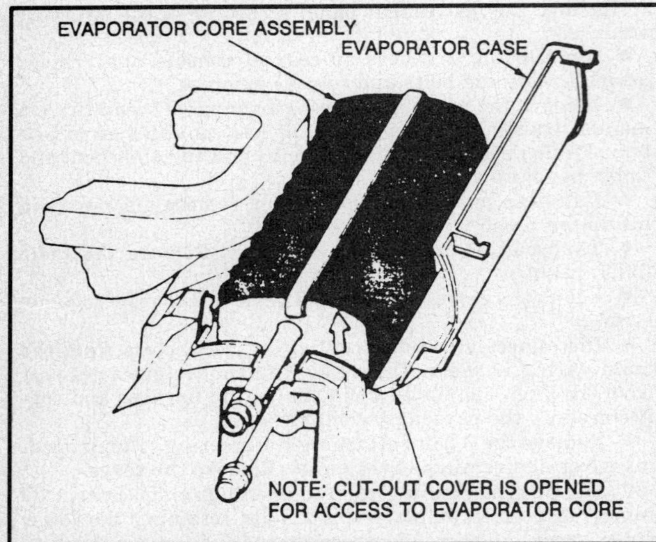

Caulking cord installation—1993 Mustang

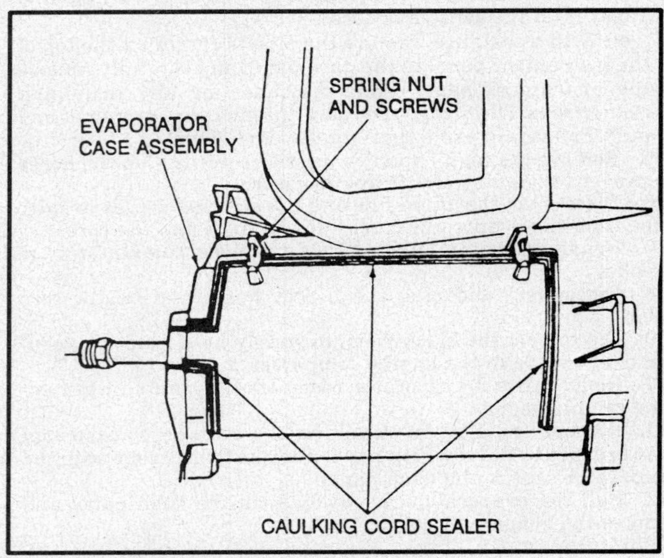

Spring nut installation—1993 Mustang

4. Disconnect the liquid line and the accumulator/drier inlet tube from the evaporator core at the dash panel. Cap the refrigerant lines and evaporator core tube to prevent the entrance of dirt and excessive moisture. Remove the high and low pressure hoses. Cap openings.
5. Disconnect the heater hoses from the heater core tubes and plug the hoses and tubes.
6. Remove the screw attaching the air inlet duct and blower housing assembly support brace to the cowl top panel.
7. Disconnect the black vacuum supply hose from the in-line vacuum check valve in the engine compartment. Disconnect the blower motor wires from the wire harness and disconnect the wire harness from the blower motor resistor.
8. Working under the hood, remove the 2 nuts retaining the evaporator case to the dash panel. Inside the passenger compartment, remove the 2 screws attaching the evaporator case support brackets to the cowl top panel.
9. Remove the 1 screw retaining the bracket below the evaporator case to the dash panel. Carefully pull the evaporator case away from the dash panel and remove the evaporator case assembly from the vehicle.
10. Remove the 4 screws retaining the air inlet duct to the evaporator case and remove the duct. Remove the foam seal from the evaporator core tubes.
11. Drill a 3/16 in. hole in both upright tabs on top of the evaporator case. Using a suitable cutting tool, cut the top of the evaporator case between the raised outlines.
12. Remove the 2 screws retaining the blower motor resistor to the evaporator case and remove the resistor. Fold the cutout flap from the opening and lift the evaporator core from the case.

To install:

NOTE: When replacing the evaporator, 3 oz. (90ml) of clean refrigerant oil should be added to the new evaporator to maintain the total system oil charge.

13. Transfer 2 foam core seals to the new evaporator core. Position the evaporator core in the case and close the cutout cover.
14. Install a spring nut on each of the 2 upright tabs. Make sure the hole in the spring nut is aligned with the hole drilled in the tab. Install and tighten a screw in each spring nut through the hole in the tab to secure the cutout cover in the closed position.
15. Install caulking cord or other suitable sealer, to seal the evaporator case against leakage along the cut line. Using new caulking cord, assemble the air inlet duct to the evaporator case.
16. Install the blower motor resistor and the foam seal over the evaporator core and heater core tubes.
17. Position the evaporator case assembly in the vehicle. Install the screws attaching the evaporator case support brackets to the cowl top panel. Check the evaporator case drain tube to ensure it is through the dash panel and is not pinched or kinked.
18. Install 1 screw retaining the bracket below the evaporator case to the dash panel. Working under the hood, install the 2 nuts retaining the evaporator case to the dash panel. Tighten the 4 nuts and 2 screws in the engine compartment. Tighten the 2 screws in the passenger compartment and the 2 support bracket attaching screws.
19. Connect the blower motor wire harness to the resistor and blower motor. Connect the black vacuum supply hose to the vacuum check valve in the engine compartment.
20. Using new O-rings lubricated with clean refrigerant oil, connect the liquid line and suction accumulator inlet to the evaporator core tubes. Tighten each connection using a back-up wrench to prevent component damage.
21. Install the instrument panel by reversing the removal procedure.
22. Connect the heater hoses to the heater core and fill the cooling system.
23. Connect the negative battery cable. Leak test, evacuate and charge the refrigerant system. Observe all safety precautions.
24. Check the system for proper operation.

1994–95

NOTE: Whenever an evaporator core is replaced, it will be necessary to replace the suction accumulator/drier.

1. Disconnect the negative battery cable.
2. Discharge the refrigerant from the air conditioning system.
3. Remove the instrument panel and the evaporator case .

To install:

NOTE: If it is necessary to replace an evaporator core, the entire evaporator case assembly must be replaced. After the evaporator case is removed, transfer the heater core and all vacuum control motors, vacuum lines and air ducts to the replacement case.

4. Install the evaporator case and the instrument panel.
5. Connect the negative battery cable. Leak test, evacuate and charge the refrigerant system. Observe all safety precautions.
6. Check the system for proper operation.

Refrigerant Lines

REMOVAL AND INSTALLATION

NOTE: Whenever a refrigerant line is replaced, it will be necessary to replace the suction accumulator/drier.

1. Disconnect the negative battery cable. Discharge the refrigerant from the air conditioning system.
2. Disconnect the refrigerant line. Remove the refrigerant line.
3. Route the new refrigerant line with the protective caps installed.
4. Connect the refrigerant line into the system using new O-rings lubricated with clean refrigerant oil.
5. Connect the negative battery cable. Leak test, evacuate and charge the refrigerant system. Observe all safety precautions.

Manual Control Head

REMOVAL AND INSTALLATION

Crown Victoria and Grand Marquis

1993–94

1. Disconnect the negative battery cable.
2. Remove the left and right instrument panel molding assemblies. Remove the cluster finish panel screws that were under the moldings and also the 6 screws along the top surface of the cluster finish panel.
3. Pull off the knob from the headlight auto dim switch. Remove the headlight switch shaft as follows:
   - Locate the headlight switch assembly body under the instrument panel.
   - Push the spring loaded shaft release button located on the side of the switch body and simultaneously pull out the headlight switch shaft.
4. Remove the steering column close out bolster panel by removing the 2 screws on the left side, 1 screw on the right side and 3 screws from the bottom.
5. Remove the 2 screws retaining the steering column close out bolster panel bracket and remove the bracket.
6. Remove the 4 nuts holding the steering column and let the steering column rest on the front seat.
7. Remove the cluster finish panel, removing the electrical connectors from the accessory push button switches.
8. Remove the center finish panel as follows:
   - The center finish panel is retained by 2 screws on the top and 2 snap-in tabs on the bottom.
   - Remove the 2 top screws and gently rock the top back while unsnapping the bottom from the instrument panel.
   - Remove the electrical connector from the clock.
9. Remove the 4 screws from the air conditioning control assembly and pull the control out of the instrument panel. Remove the electrical connectors, the temperature cable and the vacuum connector from the control assembly.

To install:

10. Connect the temperature cable, electrical connectors and the vacuum connector to the control assembly. Position the control assembly in the instrument panel and attach with the 4 screws.
11. Install the electrical connector to the clock on the center finish panel. Install the center finish panel by snapping in the bottom and using the 2 screws on the top.
12. Position the cluster finish panel. Raise the steering column and install the 4 nuts to the steering column bracket.
13. Install the bolt to the steering column shift position indicator bracket and install the shift position indicator cable to the steering column arm, as removed.
14. Position the steering column close out bolster panel bracket and install with the 2 screws. Install the steering column close out bolster panel.

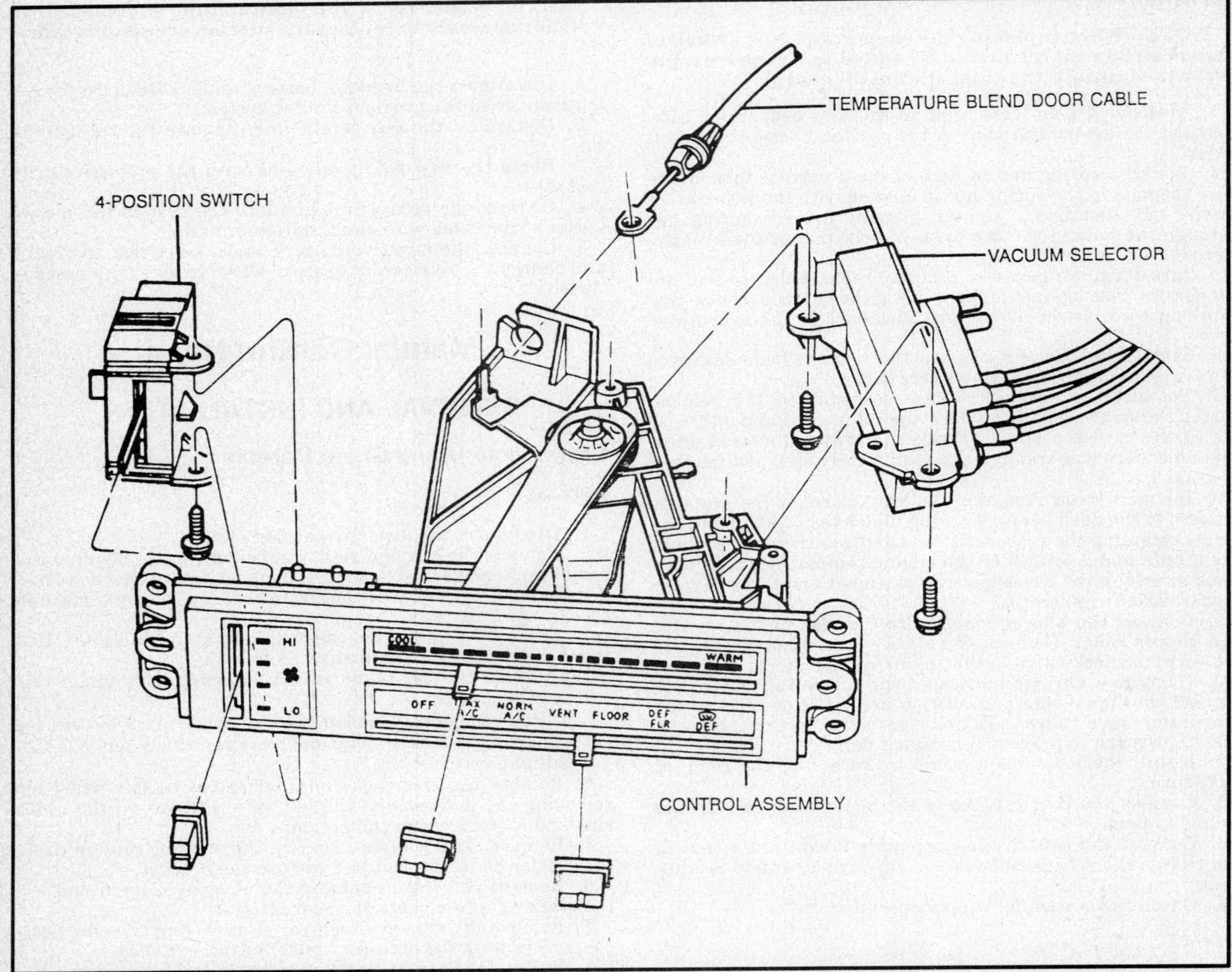

Disassembled view of manual heater–A/C control panel—1993 Crown Victoria and Grand Marquis

15. Install the cluster finish panel screws and snap in the headlight switch knob/shaft assembly. Install the headlight auto dim knob.
16. Position the left and right instrument panel molding assemblies and install by snapping into place.
17. Connect the negative battery cable and check the system for proper operation.

1995

1. Disconnect the negative battery cable.
2. Unsnap the instrument panel upper moulding retaining tabs and remove the moulding.
3. Remove the 4 screws from the control and pull the control head away from the instrument panel.
4. Disconnect the 3 electrical connectors and the vacuum harness from the control head.
5. Installation is the reverse of the removal procedure.

Thunderbird and Cougar

1. Disconnect the negative battery cable.
2. Insert removal tool T87P–19061–A or equivalent, in the retaining clip access holes. Apply a side load away from the control to disengage the clips.
3. Pull the control assembly from the instrument panel opening and disconnect the wire connectors from the control assembly. Disconnect the vacuum harness and the temperature control cable (1993 models only) from the control assembly.

To install:

4. Connect the temperature cable (1993 model only), wire connectors and vacuum harness to the control assembly.

NOTE: Push on the vacuum harness retaining nuts. Do not attempt to screw on to post.

5. Position the control assembly in the instrument panel opening. Engage it in the track in the instrument panel and push it in until it latches firmly in place.
6. Connect the negative battery cable and check the system for proper operation.

Mustang

1993

1. Disconnect the negative battery cable.
2. Remove the snap-in trim molding in the floor console to expose the 4 control assembly attaching screws. Remove the 4 screws attaching the control assembly to the instrument panel.

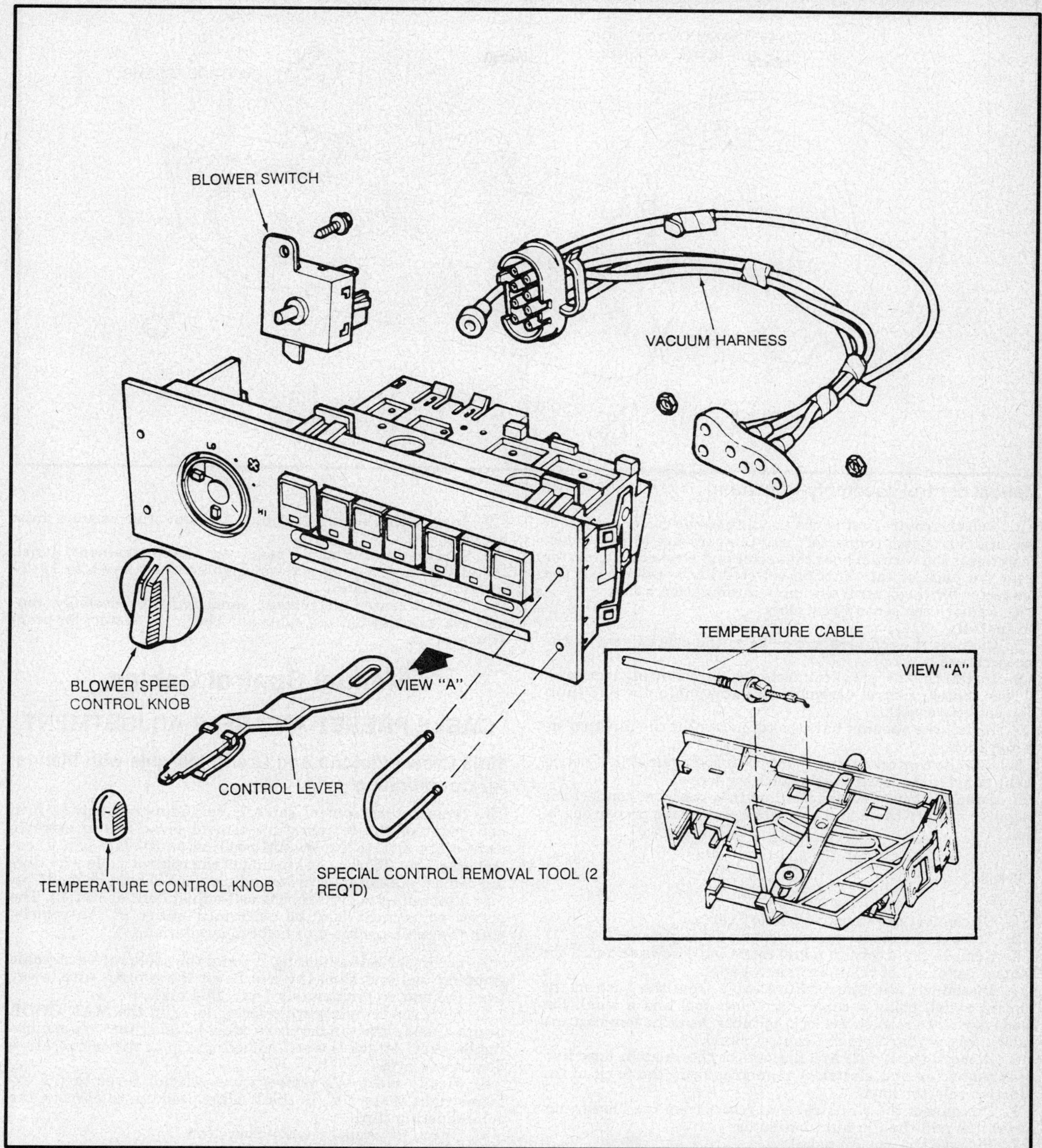

Disassembled view of manual heater–A/C control panel—1993 Thunderbird and Cougar

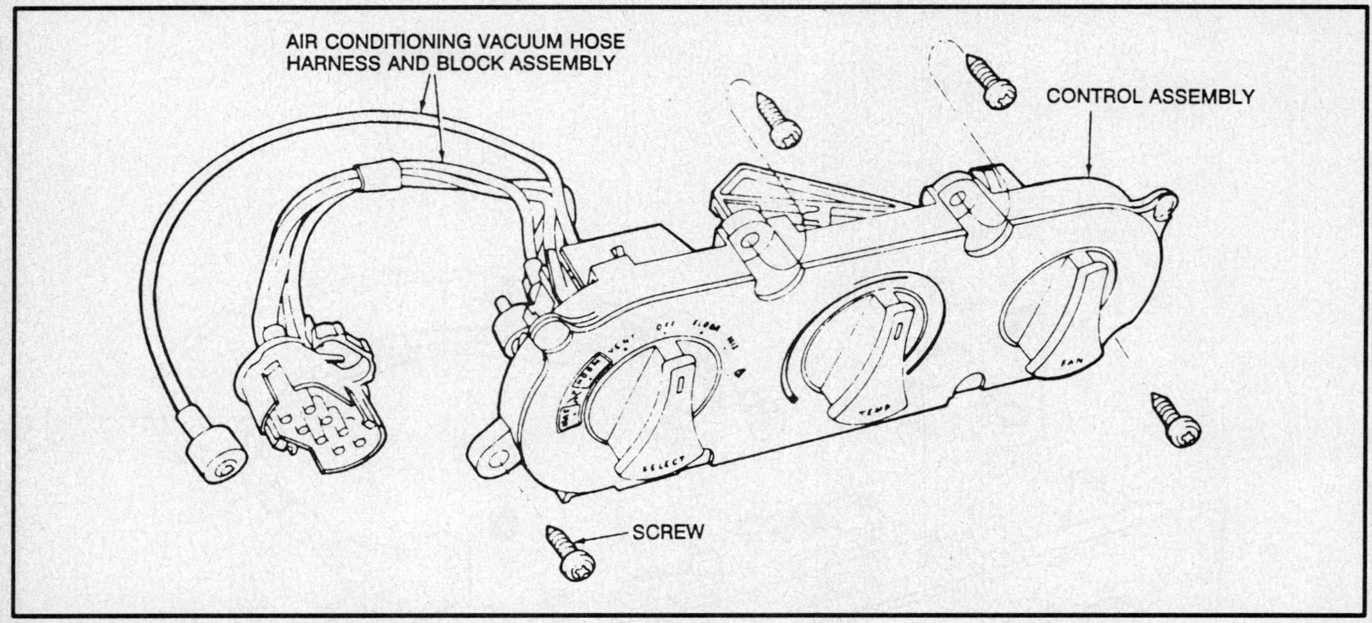

Manual control assembly—Mustang

3. Roll the control out of the opening in the console. Disconnect the fan switch connectors and temperature control cable. Disconnect the vacuum hose connector and electrical connector from the back of the function selector knob. Disconnect the connector for the control assembly illumination bulbs.
4. Remove the control assembly.

To install:

5. Connect the temperature cable to the geared arm on the temperature control.
6. Install the electrical connector at the following locations: blower switch, control assembly illumination bulbs and function selector switch.
7. Install the vacuum harness connector for the function selector knob.
8. Roll the control assembly into position against the instrument panel and install the 4 attaching screws.
9. Snap the console trim molding into position, connect the negative battery cable and check the system for proper operation.

1994–95

1. Disconnect the negative battery cable.
2. Remove the center instrument panel register.
3. Remove the 4 control panel retaining screws and pull the control panel out of the instrument panel.
4. Disconnect the temperature cable from the back of the control panel, using a cable disconnect tool and a small flat blade prybar to release the locking tubes. Pull the temperature cable away prybar from the control panel.
5. Remove the 2 nuts and disconnect the vacuum hose harness connector and electrical connector from the back of the function selector knob.
6. Disconnect the electrical connectors from the blower motor switch and the illumination bulbs.
7. Remove the control panel.

To install:

8. Position the temperature cable to the mid-point of its adjustment, directly between H and C. Position the temperature control knob to its mid-point and connect the temperature cable to the geared arm on the control panel. Rotate the temperature control knob from maximum cool to maximum warm to verify the proper range of rotation.
9. Install the electrical connectors and the vacuum hose harness.
10. Position the control panel on the instrument panel. Install the 4 retaining screws. Tighten the screws to 19–27 inch lbs. (2.1–2.9 Nm).
11. Install center instrument panel register assembly, connect the negative battery cable and check the system for proper operation.

Manual Control Cables

CABLE PRESET AND SELF-ADJUSTMENT

1993 Crown Victoria and Grand Marquis with Manual Air Conditioning

The temperature control cable is self-adjusting with a firm movement of the temperature control lever to the extreme right of the slot, to the **WARM** position, in the face of the control assembly. To prevent kinking of the control cable wire during cable installation, a preset adjustment should be made before attempting to perform the self-adjustment operation. The preset adjustment may be performed either in the vehicle, with the cable installed or before installation.

1. Grasp the self-adjusting clip and the cable with a suitable gripping tool and slide the clip down the control wire, away from the end, approximately 1 in. (25.4mm).
2. With the temperature selector lever in the **MAX COOL** position, snap the temperature cable housing into the mounting bracket. Attach the self-adjusting clip to the temperature door crank arm.
3. Firmly move the temperature selector lever to the extreme right of the slot, to the **WARM** position, to position the self-adjusting clip.
4. Check for proper control operation.

Thunderbird and Cougar

The temperature control cable is self-adjusting with a firm movement of the temperature control lever to the extreme right of the slot, to the **WARM** position, in the face of the control assembly. To prevent kinking of the control cable wire during cable installation, a preset adjustment should be made before attempting to perform the self-adjustment operation. The preset adjustment may be performed either in the vehicle, with the cable installed or before installation.

BEFORE INSTALLATION

1. Grasp the temperature control cable and the adjusting clip with suitable gripping tools.
2. Slide the self-adjusting clip down the control wire, away from the cable end, approximately 3/4 in. (18mm).
3. Install the cable assembly.
4. Move the temperature selector lever to the right end of the slot, to the **WARM** position, in the bezel face of the control assembly to position the self-adjusting clip.
5. Check for proper control operation.

AFTER INSTALLATION

1. Move the selector lever to the **COOL** position.
2. Hold the crank arm firmly in position and grasp the cable end with a suitable gripping tool. Pull the cable wire through the self-adjusting clip until there is a space of approximately 3/4 in. (18mm) between the clip and the cable end.
3. Move the selector lever to the right of the slot to position the self-adjusting clip.
4. Check for proper control operation.

Mustang

The temperature control cable is self-adjusting with the movement of the temperature selector knob to its fully clockwise position in the red band on the face of the control assembly. To prevent kinking of the control wire, a preset adjustment should be made before attempting to perform the self-adjustment operation. The preset adjustment may be performed either with the cable installed in the vehicle or before cable installation.

BEFORE INSTALLATION

1. Insert the end of an awl or pointed tool in the end loop of the temperature control cable, at the temperature door crank arm end.
2. Slide the self-adjusting clip down the control wire, away from the end loop, approximately 1 in. (25mm).
3. Install the cable assembly.
4. Turn the temperature control knob fully clockwise to position the self-adjusting clip.
5. Check for proper control operation.

AFTER INSTALLATION

1. Turn the temperature selector knob to the **COOL** position.
2. Hold the temperature door crank arm firmly in position, insert a suitable tool into the wire end loop and pull the cable wire through the self-adjusting clip until there is a space of approximately 1 in. (25mm) between the clip and the wire end loop.
3. Turn the temperature control knob FULLY CLOCKWISE to position the self-adjusting clip.
4. Check for proper control operation.

REMOVAL AND INSTALLATION

1993 Crown Victoria and Grand Marquis with Manual Air Conditioning

1. Disconnect the negative battery cable.
2. Press the glove compartment door stops inward and allow the door to hang by the hinge.
3. Remove the control assembly from the instrument panel. Disconnect the cable housing from the control assembly and disengage the cable from the temperature control lever.
4. Through the glove compartment opening, disconnect the temperature cable from the plenum temperature blend door crank arm and cable mounting bracket. Note the cable routing and remove the cable from the vehicle.

To install:

5. Check to make sure the self-adjusting clip is at least 1 in. (25.4mm) from the end loop of the control cable.
6. Route the cable behind the instrument panel and connect the control cable to the mounting bracket on the plenum. Install the self-adjusting clip on the temperature blend door crank arm.
7. Connect the other end of the control cable to the temperature lever arm on the control assembly. Snap the cable housing into place at the control assembly.
8. Install the control assembly in the instrument panel and return the glove compartment door to the normal position.
9. Connect the negative battery cable and check the system for proper operation.

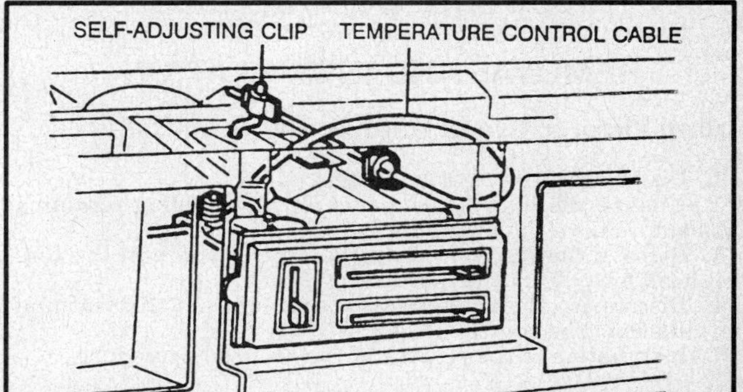

Temperature control cable routing—1993 Crown Victoria and Grand Marquis

1993 Thunderbird and Cougar

1. Disconnect the negative battery cable.
2. Remove the control assembly and disconnect the cable housing from the control assembly.
3. Disconnect the temperature cable from the plenum temperature blend door crank arm and the cable mounting bracket. Note the cable routing and remove the cable from the vehicle.

To install:

4. Check to ensure the self-adjusting clip is at least 3/4 in. (18mm) from the end loop of the control cable.
5. Route the cable behind the instrument panel and connect the control cable to the mounting bracket on the plenum. Install the self-adjusting clip on the temperature blend door crank arm.
6. Connect the cable to the temperature control lever and snap the cable housing into place at the control assembly. Install the control assembly.
7. Move the temperature lever firmly to the extreme right end of the slot, to the **WARM** position, to position the self-adjusting clip on the control cable. Check the temperature selector lever for proper operation.
8. Connect the negative battery cable and check the system for proper operation.

Mustang

1. Disconnect the negative battery cable.
2. Remove the control assembly from the instrument panel.
3. Disengage the temperature control cable from the cable actuator on the control assembly. Disconnect the temperature cable from the plenum temperature blend door crank arm and cable mounting bracket.
4. Note the cable routing and remove the cable from the vehicle.

To install:

5. Check to ensure the self-adjusting clip is at least 1 in. (25.4mm) from the end loop of the control cable.
6. Route the cable behind the instrument panel and connect the control cable to the mounting bracket on the plenum. Install the self-adjusting clip on the temperature blend door crank arm.
7. Engage the cable end with the cable actuator on the control assembly. Install the control assembly in the instrument panel.
8. Turn the temperature control knob all the way to the right, to the **WARM** position, to position the self-adjusting clip on the control cable. Check the temperature control knob for proper operation.
9. Connect the negative battery cable and check the system for proper operation.

Electronic Control Head

REMOVAL AND INSTALLATION

Crown Victoria, Grand Marquis and Town Car

1. Disconnect the negative battery cable.
2. Unsnap the instrument panel upper moulding retaining tabs and remove the moulding.
3. Remove the 4 screws from the control and pull the control head away from the instrument panel.
4. Disconnect the 3 electrical connectors and the vacuum harness from the control head.
5. Installation is the reverse of the removal procedure.

Mark VIII

1. Disconnect the negative battery cable.
2. Remove the instrument panel air conditioning control opening finish panel by unsnapping at the bottom.
3. Remove the 4 screws attaching the control assembly to the instrument panel.
4. Slide the control assembly out from the instrument panel opening and disconnect the 2 harness connectors from the control assembly by disengaging the latches on the top of the control.
5. Remove 2 nuts retaining vacuum hose harness to control assembly. Remove control assembly from instrument panel.

To install:

6. Connect the 2 harness connectors to the control assembly. Push keyed connectors in until a click is heard.
7. Attach vacuum hose harness to vacuum port assembly and secure with 2 nuts.
8. Position the control assembly to the instrument panel opening and install the 4 attaching screws.
9. Position the instrument panel center finish panel on the instrument panel and snap in.
10. Connect the negative battery cable and check the system for proper operation.

Semi–Automatic Control Head

REMOVAL AND INSTALLATION

1994–95 Thunderbird and Cougar

1. Disconnect the negative battery cable.
2. Insert removal tool T87P–19061–A or equivalent, in the retaining clip access holes. Apply a side load away from the control to disengage the clips.
3. Pull the control assembly away from the instrument panel opening and disconnect the wire connectors and the vacuum harness from the control assembly.

To install:

4. Connect the wire connectors and the vacuum harness to the control assembly.
5. Position the control assembly in the instrument panel opening. Engage it in the track in the instrument panel and push it in until it latches firmly in place.
6. Connect the negative battery cable and check the system for proper operation.

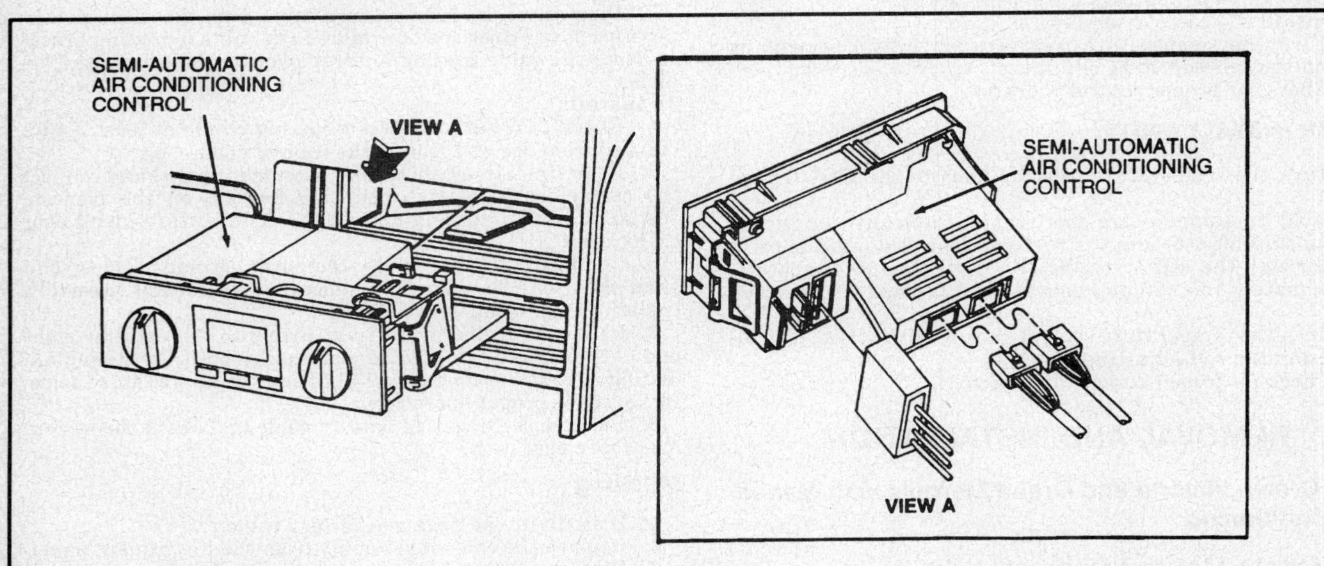

Semi–automatic air conditioning control—1994–95 Thunderbird and Cougar

SENSORS AND SWITCHES

Clutch Cycling Pressure Switch

OPERATION

The clutch cycling pressure switch is mounted on a Schrader valve fitting on top of the suction accumulator/drier. A valve depressor, located inside the threaded end of the pressure switch, presses in on the Schrader valve stem as the switch is mounted and allows the suction pressure inside the accumulator/drier to act on the switch. The electrical switch contacts will open when the suction pressure drops to 22–28 psi. and close when the suction pressure rises to approximately 45 psi. or above. Ambient temperatures below approximately 50°F (10°C) will also open the clutch cycling pressure switch contacts because of the pressure/temperature relationship of the refrigerant in the system. The electrical switch contacts control the electrical circuit to the compressor magnetic clutch coil. When the switch contacts are closed, the magnetic clutch coil is energized and the air conditioning clutch is engaged to drive the compressor. When the switch contacts are open, the compressor magnetic clutch coil is de-energized, the air conditioning clutch is disengaged and the compressor does not operate. The clutch cycling pressure switch, when functioning properly, will control the evaporator core pressure at a point where the plate/fin surface temperature will be maintained slightly above freezing which prevents evaporator icing and the blockage of airflow.

REMOVAL AND INSTALLATION

1. Disconnect the negative battery cable.
2. Disconnect the wire harness connector from the pressure switch.
3. Unscrew the pressure switch from the top of the suction accumulator/drier.

To install:

4. Lubricate the O-ring on the accumulator nipple with clean refrigerant oil.
5. Screw the pressure switch on the accumulator nipple. Hand tighten only.
6. Connect the wire connector to the pressure switch.
7. Check the pressure switch installation for refrigerant leaks. Connect the negative battery cable and check the system for proper operation.

Pressure Cut-Off Switch

OPERATION

The pressure cut-off switch is located on the manifold and tube between the compressor and the condenser core. It contains 2 sets of electrical contacts: one for the compressor circuit and one for the high-speed fan. The contact in the compressor circuit is normally closed. When the compressor head pressure rises to approximately 420 psi (2869 kPa), the contacts open and the compressor is turned OFF. When the head pressure drops to approximately 250 psi (1724 kPa), the contacts close and allow operation of the compressor. The contact in the high speed fan circuit is normally open. When the discharge line pressure reaches approximately 325 psi (2241 kPa), the contact close and engage the high-speed fan control. When the discharge line pressure drops to approximately 275 psi (1896 kPa), the contacts open and the high-speed fan control is disengaged.

REMOVAL AND INSTALLATION

1. Disconnect the negative battery cable.
2. Remove the cut-off switch electrical connector.
3. Remove the pressure cut-off switch from the manifold and tube.
4. To install, use new O-ring seals lubricated with clean refrigerant oil and reverse the removal procedure.

Temperature Control Lock Out Switch (TCLO)

OPERATION

1994–95 Crown Victoria, Grand Marquis and Town Car

The TCLO is used on Crown Victoria, Grand Marquis and Town Car (except 1993) with Automatic Temperature Control (ATC). It is a combination vacuum valve and a single-pole single-throw switch powered by a thermal element. The TCLO is located in the heater supply hose in the engine compartment with the thermal element of the switch in contact with the engine coolant. In the FLOOR function lever position and with a cold engine, the blower is locked out and the outside-recirc door is in the RECIRC position.

When the engine coolant warms up to approximately 120°F (49°C), the electrical switch contacts close permitting the blower to operate and the outside-recirc door to move to the outside position.

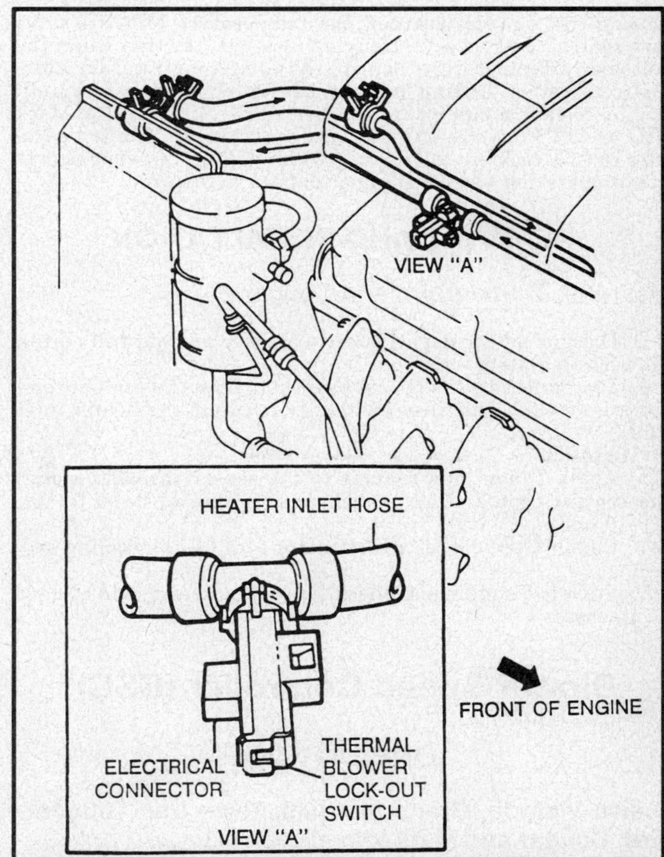

Showing location of thermal blower lock-out switch—Crown Victoria, Grand Marquis and Town Car

REMOVAL AND INSTALLATION

1994–95 Crown Victoria, Grand Marquis and Town Car

1. Disconnect the negative battery cable. Drain the cooling system.
2. Disconnect the electrical and vacuum connectors from the TCLO.
3. Loosen the hose clamps at the TCLO and remove the TCLO from the hose.

To install:

4. Slide the new hose clamps over the ends of the hoses. Apply soapy water to the ends of the hoses.
5. Insert the TCLO in the hose ends and tighten the clamps to 16–22 inch lbs. (1.80–2.48 Nm).
6. Connect the electrical and vacuum connectors to the TCLO. Fill the cooling system.
7. Connect the negative battery cable and check the air conditioning system for proper operation.

Temperature Control Lock Out Valve and Switch

OPERATION

Mark VIII, Thunderbird and Cougar

During cool or cold weather, the temperature lock out valve and switch controls a cold engine lock out function when the Automatic Temperature Control (ATC) system is set for automatic operation. During lock out, the fan will not operate until engine coolant temperature reaches 120°F (49°C) on the Mark VIII or 113°F on the Thunderbird and Cougar. The temperature control lock out valve and switch will not prevent blower motor operation when cooling or defrost is required.

REMOVAL AND INSTALLATION

Mark VIII, Thunderbird and Cougar

1. Disconnect the negative battery cable and partially drain the cooling system.
2. Disconnect the electrical connector from the coolant temperature switch and unscrew the switch from the heater inlet tube.

To install:

3. Apply Teflon pipe sealant to the sensor threads. Install the coolant temperature switch and tighten to 9–14 ft. lbs. (11–19 Nm).
4. Connect the electrical connector and fill the cooling system.
5. Start the engine and check for coolant leaks. Add coolant as necessary.

Blower Speed Controller (BSC)

OPERATION

Crown Victoria, Grand Marquis, Town Car, Thunderbird, Cougar and Mark VIII

The blower speed controller is used on Mark VIII and Thunderbird, Cougar, Crown Victoria, Grand Marquis and Town Car with Automatic Temperature Control (ATC). The BSC is located in the evaporator case (on Mark VIII it is located on the blower motor housing). It converts low current signals from the electronic control assembly to a high current, variable ground feed to the blower motor. Blower motor speed is infinitely variable and is controlled by the electronic control assembly software. A delay function provides a gradual increase or decrease in blower motor speed under all conditions.

NOTE: The system should not be operated with the blower motor disconnected. Damage may occur to the BSC if cooling air is not provided by the blower motor.

Variable blower speed controller—Crown Victoria, Grand Marquis and Town Car

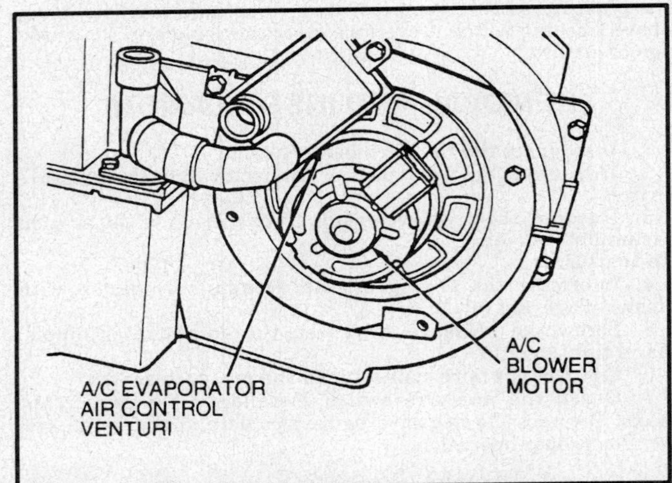

Blower motor and speed controller—Mark VIII

REMOVAL AND INSTALLATION

Crown Victoria, Grand Marquis and Town Car

1. Disconnect the negative battery cable.
2. Disconnect the wire harness connector from the blower speed controller.
3. Remove the 2 retaining screws securing the blower speed controller to the evaporator case and remove the blower speed controller.
4. Installation is the reverse of the removal procedure.

Mark VIII, Thunderbird and Cougar

1. Disconnect the negative battery cable.
2. Lower the glove box for access, then, working through the opening, detach the 2 snap-lock electrical connectors from the blower speed controller (pulse width modulator).
3. Remove 2 screws and remove the controller.
4. Installation is the reverse of the removal procedure.

Ambient Temperature Sensor

OPERATION

The ambient temperature sensor is used on Thunderbird, Cougar, Mark VIII, Crown Victoria, Grand Marquis and Town Car with automatic temperature control. The sensor contains a thermistor which measures the temperature of the outside air and provides an input signal to the control assembly. On Mark VIII, Crown Victoria, Grand Marquis and Town Car, the sensor is located in front of the condenser on the hood latch support brace.

REMOVAL AND INSTALLATION

Mark VIII, Crown Victoria, Grand Marquis and Town Car

1. Disconnect the negative battery cable.
2. Disconnect the electrical connector from the ambient temperature sensor.
3. Remove the mounting screw and remove the ambient temperature sensor and bracket assembly.
4. Installation is the reverse of the removal procedure.

In-Vehicle Sensor

OPERATION

On Mark VIII, Crown Victoria, Grand Marquis and Town Car with Automatic Temperature Control (ATC), and on Thunderbird and Cougar with Semi-Automatic Temperature Control (SATC), the in-vehicle sensor contains a thermistor that senses the passenger compartment air and provides an input signal to the control assembly. A small opening through the instrument panel allows passenger compartment air to enter the in-vehicle sensor. The sensor is located behind the instrument panel directly above the control assembly. On Mark VIII the sensor is located behind the instrument panel message center.

REMOVAL AND INSTALLATION

Crown Victoria, Grand Marquis and Town Car

1993–94

1. Disconnect the negative battery cable and air bag back-up power supply.
2. Remove the left and right instrument panel molding assemblies. Remove the cluster finish panel screws that were under the moldings and also the 6 screws along the top surface of the cluster finish panel.
3. Pull off the knob from the headlight auto dim switch. Remove the headlight switch shaft as follows:
   - Locate the headlight switch assembly body under the instrument panel.
   - Push the spring loaded shaft release button located on the side of the switch body and simultaneously pull out the headlight switch shaft.
4. Remove the steering column close out bolster panel by removing the 2 screws on the left side, 1 screw on the right side and 3 screws from the bottom.
5. Remove the 2 screws retaining the steering column close out bolster panel bracket and remove the bracket.
6. Remove the shift position indicator and cable assembly as follows:
   - Place the shift lever in **1** position.
   - Remove the shift position indicator cable from the steering column arm.
   - Remove the bolt from the steering column shift position indicator bracket.
7. Remove the 4 nuts holding the steering column and let the steering column rest on the front seat.
8. Remove the cluster finish panel.

NOTE: Remove the electrical connectors from the accessory push button switches.

9. Remove the center finish panel as follows:
   - The center finish panel is retained by 2 screws on the top and 2 snap-in tabs on the bottom.
   - Remove the 2 top screws and gently rock the top back while unsnapping the bottom from the instrument panel.
   - Remove the electrical connector from the clock.
10. Grasp the sensor assembly, remove the 2 screws and rotate the sensor down and out of the instrument panel.
11. Disconnect the electrical lead and the air hose from the sensor.

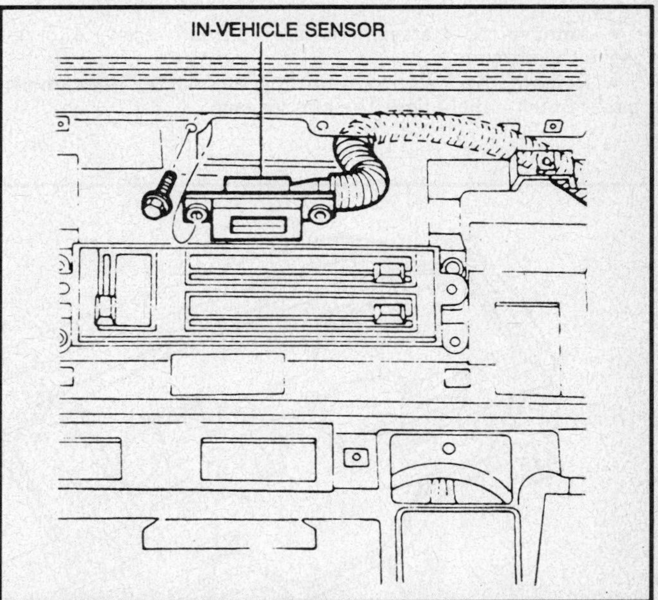

In-vehicle sensor removal—1993–94 Crown Victoria, Grand Marquis and Town Car

To install:

12. Connect the electrical lead and the air hose to the sensor.
13. Position the sensor on the instrument panel and install the 2 attaching screws.
14. Install the electrical connector to the clock on the center finish panel. Install the center finish panel by snapping in the bottom and using the 2 screws on the top.
15. Position the cluster finish panel. Raise the steering column and install the 4 nuts to the steering column bracket.
16. Install the bolt to the steering column shift position indicator bracket and install the shift position indicator cable to the steering column arm.
17. Position the steering column close out bolster panel bracket and install with the 2 screws. Install the steering column close out bolster panel.
18. Install the cluster finish panel screws and snap in the headlight switch knob/shaft assembly. Install the headlight auto dim knob.
19. Position the left and right instrument panel molding assemblies and install by snapping into place.
20. Connect the negative battery cable and check the system for proper operation.

1995

1. Disconnect negative battery cable.
2. Unsnap the instrument panel upper molding tabs and remove the moulding.

3. Remove the attaching screw and slide the temperature control sensor up and out of the instrument panel.
4. Disconnect the electrical lead and the temperature control sensor hose and elbow from the sensor.
5. Installation is the reverse of the removal procedure.

1994–95 Thunderbird and Cougar

1. Disconnect the negative battery cable.
2. Remove the instrument panel finish panel and the cluster instrument panel as follows:
   - Remove the 3 screws along the bottom of the steering column cover. Pull on the steering column cover to unsnap the 3 clips across the top and remove the steering column cover.
   - Remove the 4 steering column shroud screws and remove the shrouds.
   - Remove the 2 screws retaining the cluster instrument panel finish panel above the cluster face.
   - Pull the cluster instrument panel finish panel to unsnap the 1 retaining clip above the left air conditioner register and the 3 retaining clips on the right vertical edge.
   - Pull the cluster instrument panel finish panel away from the instrument panel far enough to disconnect the wiring connectors.
3. Remove the electrical connector and the sensor hose and elbow from the sensor.
4. Remove the 2 screws retaining the automatic temperature control sensor and remove the sensor.
5. Installation is the reverse of the removal procedure.

Mark VIII

1. Disconnect the negative battery cable.
2. Remove the instrument panel message center cover.
3. Unsnap the automatic temperature sensor from the sensor housing.
4. Disconnect the electrical connector and automatic temperature control sensor hose and elbow from the automatic temperature control.
5. Installation is the reverse of the removal procedure.

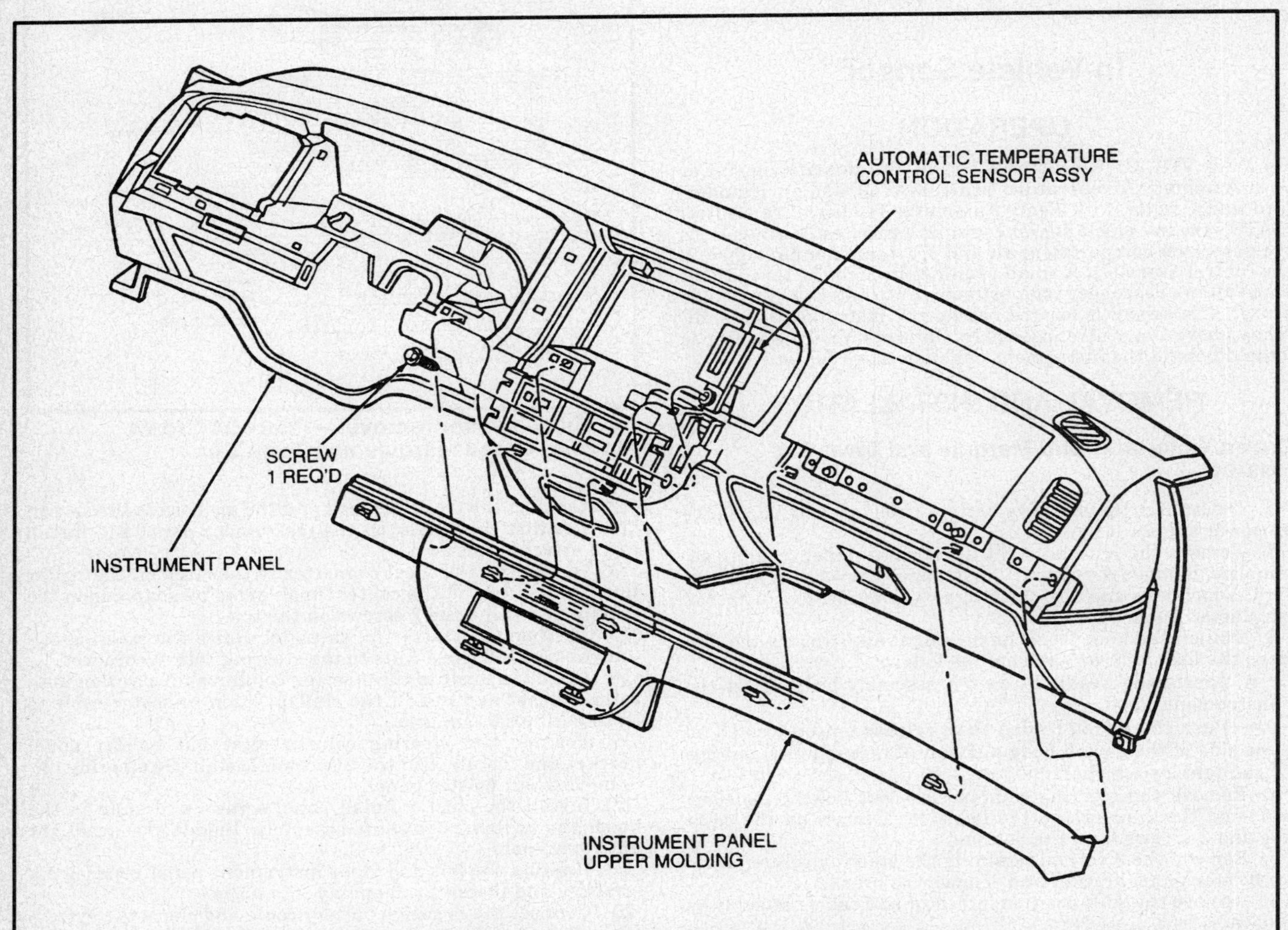

Automatic temperature control sensor—1995 Crown Victoria, Grand Marquis and Town Car

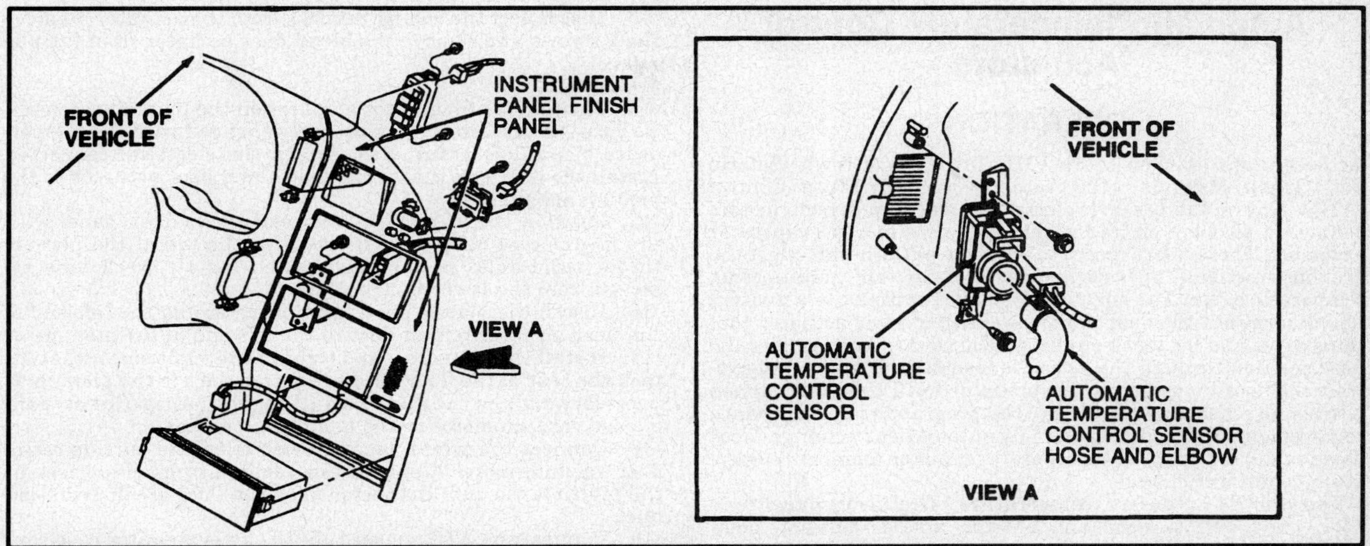

Automatic temperature control sensor—1994–95 Thunderbird and Cougar

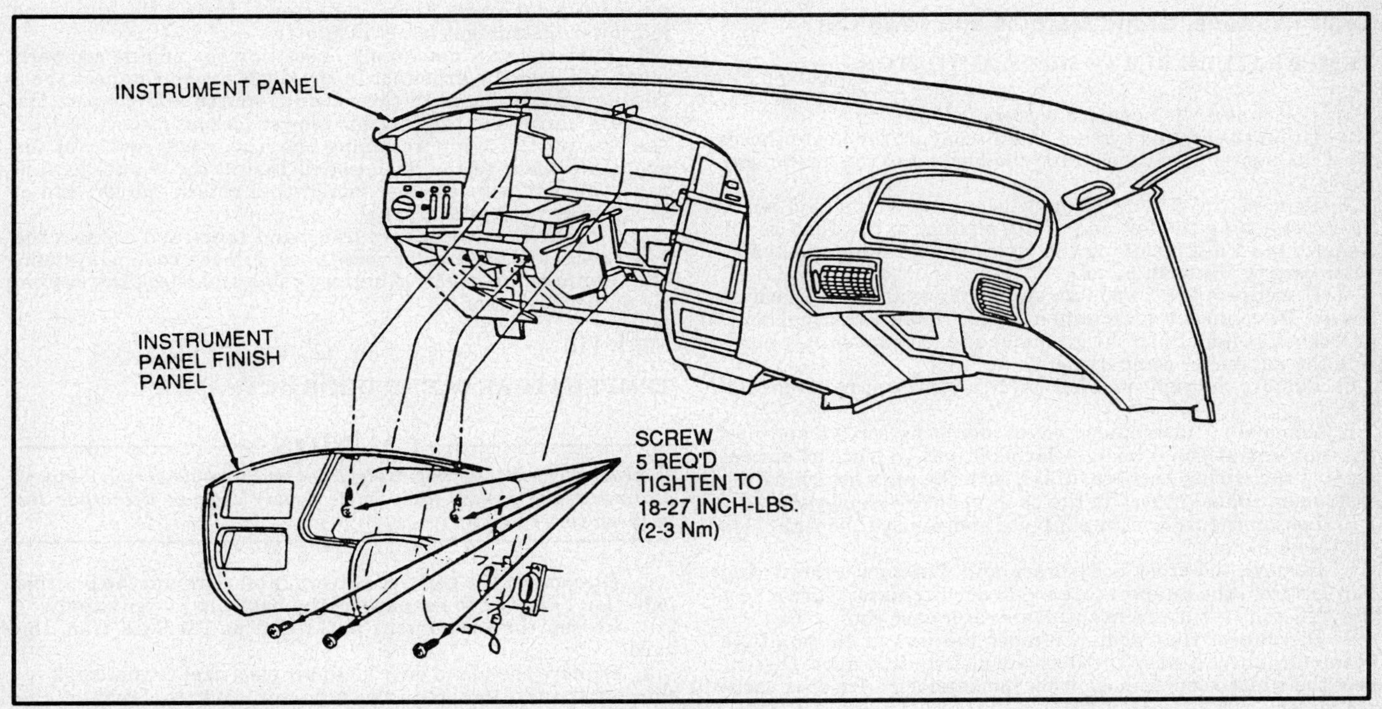

Instrument panel finish panel—1994–95 Thunderbird and Cougar

Sunload Sensor

OPERATION

The sunload sensor is located on the top right side of the instrument panel on the Mark VIII and Town Car and on the Crown Victoria and Grand Marquis with Automatic Temperature Control (ATC). It contains a photovoltaic diode and provides input to the ATC system.

REMOVAL AND INSTALLATION

1. Disconnect the negative battery cable.
2. Remove the instrument panel cover and unsnap the sunload sensor from its mounting studs.
3. Disconnect the electrical connector from the sunload sensor.
4. Installation is the reverse of the removal procedure.

Automatic Temperature Control Actuators

OPERATION

Actuators are used on Mark VIII, Town Car, Crown Victoria and Grand Marquis with Automatic Temperature Control (ATC). The actuators are electric or vacuum-driven motors connected to doors on and within the plenum and evaporator assembly. These doors direct the airflow pattern and enact the system functional operation: heat, defrost, air conditioning, temperature, etc. The control assembly controls the actuators and determines the door positions. Each electric actuator contains drive and feedback circuitry. The control head senses the door position through the actuator feedback circuitry and controls the door by powering the actuator until the programmed position is reached. According to the programmed performance requirements, the control assembly automatically changes door position during operation as operator input or ambient temperature conditions change.

There are 4 actuators: temperature blend door, panel/floor door, panel/defrost door and outside air/recirculation door. Mark VIII, Crown Victoria, Grand Marquis and Town Car have an electronically controlled temperature blend door actuator. Other door actuators are vacuum driven.

REMOVAL AND INSTALLATION

Crown Victoria, Grand Marquis and Town Car

TEMPERATURE BLEND DOOR ACTUATOR

1. Disconnect the negative battery cable.
2. Drain the cooling system and disconnect the heater hoses from the heater core tubes. Plug the hoses and the heater core tubes.
3. Remove the 3 nuts located below the windshield wiper motor attaching the left end of the plenum to the dash panel. Remove the 1 nut retaining the upper left corner of the evaporator case to the dash panel.
4. Disconnect the 2 vacuum supply hoses from the vacuum source. Disconnect the vacuum harness from the thermal blower lockout switch. Push the grommet and vacuum supply hoses into the passenger compartment.
5. Remove the right and left lower instrument panel insulators.
6. Remove all instrument panel mounting screws and pull the instrument panel back as far as it will go without disconnecting the wiring harness. Make sure the nuts attaching the instrument panel braces to the dash panel are removed.
7. Loosen the right door sill plate and remove the right side cowl trim panel.
8. Remove the cross body brace and disconnect the wiring harness from the temperature blend door actuator. Disconnect the ATC sensor tube from the evaporator case connector.
9. Disconnect the vacuum jumper harness at the multiple vacuum connector near the floor air distribution duct. Disconnect the white vacuum hose from the outside-recirc door vacuum motor.
10. Remove the left and loosen the right screw attaching the passenger (rear) side of the floor air distribution duct to the plenum. It may be necessary to remove the 2 screws attaching the partial (lower) panel door vacuum motor to the mounting bracket to gain access to the right screw.
11. Remove 1 plastic push fastener retaining the floor air distribution duct to the left end of the plenum and 2 screws on the rear face of the plenum and remove the floor air distribution duct.
12. Remove 2 nuts from the 2 studs along the lower flange of the plenum. Carefully move the plenum rearward to allow the heater core tubes and the stud at the top of the plenum to clear the holes in the dash panel.
13. Disconnect the wiring harness from the actuator. Remove the 4 screws and remove the blend door actuator from the plenum.

To install:

14. Position the blend door actuator on the plenum assembly. Be sure the actuator cam is properly engaged with the temperature blend door crank arm. Attach the electrical connector. Install the 4 screws that secure the blend door actuator to the plenum assembly.
15. Position the plenum on the rear of the dash panel with the heater core tubes and the stud at the top of the plenum through the holes in the dash panel. Install the 2 nuts removed from the lower flange of the plenum.
16. Install the plastic push fastener retaining the left end of the floor air distribution duct to the left end of the plenum.
17. Install the left screw and tighten the right screw that attach the rear of the floor air distribution duct to the plenum. If necessary, tighten the screws attaching the partial (lower) panel door vacuum motor to the mounting bracket.
18. Connect the white vacuum hose from the outside-recirc door vacuum motor. Connect the vacuum jumper harness at the multiple vacuum connector near the floor air distribution duct.
19. Connect the ATC sensor tube to the evaporator case connector. Install the cross body brace and connect the wiring harness to the blend door actuator.
20. Replace the right side cowl trim panel and tighten the screws in the right door sill plate.
21. Push the instrument panel back into position and install all instrument panel mounting screws. Install the right and left lower instrument panel insulators.
22. Push the vacuum supply hoses into the engine compartment and seat the grommet in the dash panel. Connect the 2 vacuum supply hoses to the vacuum source and connect the vacuum harness to the thermal blower lockout switch.
23. Install the 1 nut retaining the upper left corner of the evaporator case to the dash panel. Install the 3 nuts located below the windshield wiper motor, that attach the left end of the plenum to the dash panel.
24. Unplug the heater core hoses and tubes and connect the heater hoses to the heater core tubes. Fill the cooling system.
25. Connect the negative battery cable and check the system for proper operation.

Mark VIII

TEMPERATURE BLEND DOOR ACTUATOR

CAUTION

To avoid accidental air bag deployment and possible personal injury, disconnect and ground the positive battery cable to deenergize the back-up power supply.

1. Disconnect the positive battery cable. Ground the positive cable for 1 minute to deenergize the back-up power supply.
2. Loosen the instrument panel and pull it back from the cowl.
3. Remove the blend door actuator electrical connector, 3 retaining screws, and pull the actuator from the rear of the evaporator case.
4. Installation is the reverse of the removal procedure.

1994–95 Thunderbird and Cougar

CAUTION

To avoid accidental air bag deployment and possible personal injury, disconnect and ground the positive battery cable to deenergize the back-up power supply.

1. Disconnect the negative battery cable. Disconnect the positive battery cable and wait 1 minute for the back-up power supply to be deenergized.

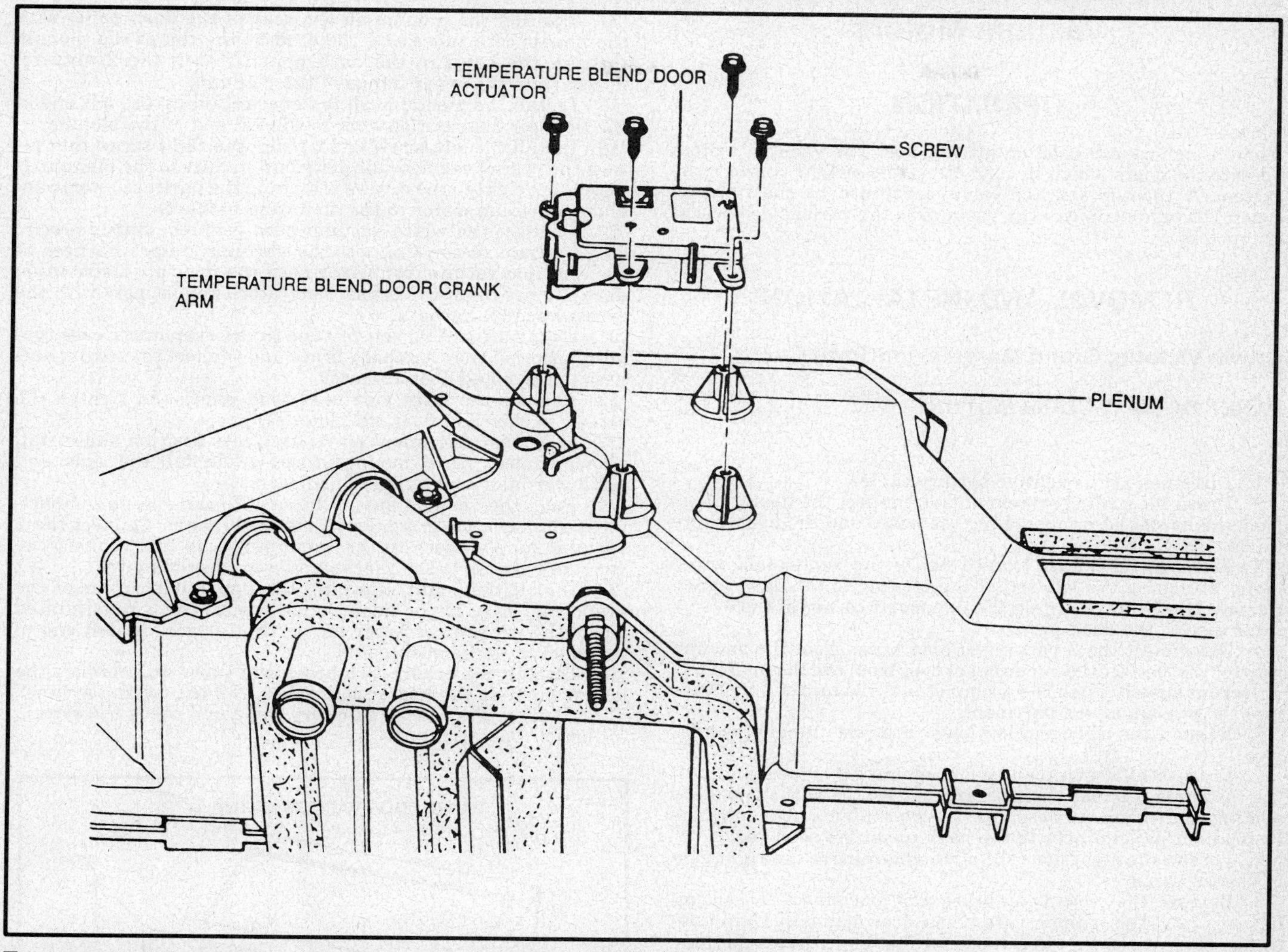

Temperature blend door actuator—Crown Victoria, Grand Marquis and Town Car

2. Remove the instrument panel.
3. Disconnect the electrical connector from the electronic door actuator motor.
4. Remove the 3 actuator motor mounting screws.
5. Disengage the actuator shaft from the temperature control door and remove the actuator motor.

To install:

6. Engage the actuator motor shaft into the temperature control door and align the actuator mounting tabs with the mounting bosses.

CAUTION

Do not drive a fourth screw through the heater core cover. It will interfere with the temperature control door.

7. Install the actuator motor with 3 screws.
8. Connect the actuator motor electrical connector.
9. Install the instrument panel by reversing the removal procedure.
10. Connect the battery cables.

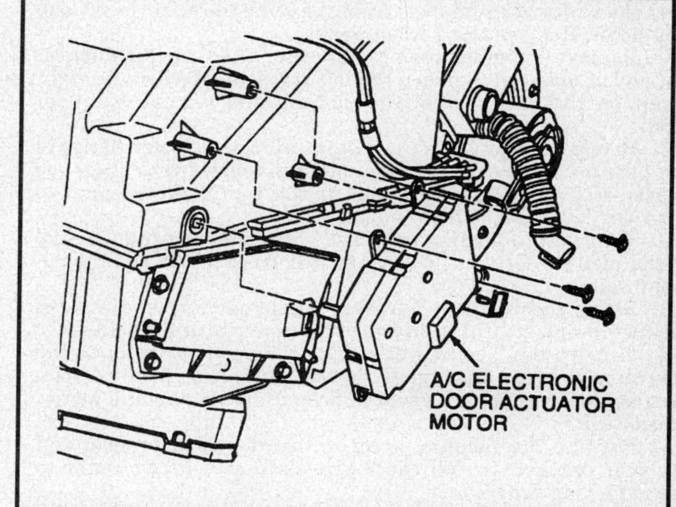

Electronic door actuator motor removal—1994–95 Thunderbird and Cougar

Vacuum Motors

OPERATION

Vacuum motors are used on all vehicles. The vacuum motors operate the doors which in turn direct the airflow through the system. A vacuum selector valve, controlled by the function control lever, distributes the vacuum to the various door vacuum motors.

REMOVAL AND INSTALLATION

Crown Victoria, Grand Marquis and Town Car

PANEL DOOR VACUUM MOTOR

1. Disconnect the negative battery cable.
2. Drain the cooling system and disconnect the heater hoses from the heater core tubes. Plug the hoses and the heater core tubes.
3. Remove the 3 nuts located below the windshield wiper motor attaching the left end of the plenum to the dash panel. Remove the 1 nut retaining the upper left corner of the evaporator case to the dash panel.
4. Disconnect the 2 vacuum supply hoses from the vacuum source. Disconnect the vacuum harness from the thermal blower lockout switch. Push the grommet and vacuum supply hoses into the passenger compartment.
5. Remove the right and left lower instrument panel insulators.
6. Remove all instrument panel mounting screws and pull the instrument panel back as far as it will go without disconnecting the wiring harness. Make sure the nuts attaching the instrument panel braces to the dash panel are removed.
7. Loosen the right door sill plate and remove the right side cowl trim panel.
8. Remove the cross body brace and disconnect the wiring harness from the temperature blend door actuator. On all vehicles, disconnect the ATC sensor tube from the evaporator case connector.
9. Disconnect the vacuum jumper harness at the multiple vacuum connector near the floor air distribution duct. Disconnect the white vacuum hose from the outside-recirc door vacuum motor. Remove the 2 hush panels.
10. Remove 1 plastic push fastener for the floor air duct (at left end of plenum). Remove the left screw and loosen the right screw on the rear face of the plenum and remove the floor duct.
11. Remove 2 nuts from the 2 studs along the lower flange of the plenum. Carefully move the plenum rearward to allow the heater core tubes and the stud at the top of the plenum to clear the holes in the dash panel.
12. Remove the plenum from the vehicle by rotating the top of the plenum forward, down and out from under the instrument panel.
13. Reach through the defroster nozzle opening and remove the sleeve nut attaching the vacuum motor arm to the door.
14. Remove the 2 screws attaching the vacuum motor to the mounting bracket. Disengage the vacuum motor from the plenum and disconnect the vacuum hose from the vacuum motor.

To install:

15. Position the vacuum motor to the mounting bracket and the door bracket. Install the 2 screws to attach the motor to the mounting bracket.
16. Connect the vacuum motor arm to the panel door with a new sleeve nut. Connect the vacuum hose to the vacuum motor. The blue hose connects to the upper vacuum motor and the orange hose connects to the lower vacuum motor.
17. Position the plenum on the rear of the dash panel with the heater core tubes and the stud at the top of the plenum through the holes in the dash panel. Install the 2 nuts removed from the lower flange of the plenum.
18. Install the plastic push fastener retaining the left end of the floor air distribution duct to the left end of the plenum.
19. Install the left screw and tighten the right screw that attach the rear of the floor air distribution duct to the plenum. If necessary, tighten the screws attaching the partial (lower) panel door vacuum motor to the mounting bracket.
20. Connect the white vacuum hose from the outside-recirc door vacuum motor. Connect the vacuum jumper harness at the multiple vacuum connector near the floor air distribution duct. Do not block the sensor aspirator exhaust port with the excess vacuum harness.
21. Connect the ATC sensor tube to the evaporator case connector. Install the cross body brace and connect the wiring harness to the blend door actuator.
22. Replace the right side cowl trim panel and tighten the screws in the right door sill plate.
23. Push the instrument panel back into position and install all instrument panel mounting screws. Install the right and left lower instrument panel insulators.
24. Push the vacuum supply hoses into the engine compartment and seat the grommet in the dash panel. Connect the 2 vacuum supply hoses to the vacuum source and connect the vacuum harness to the thermal blower lockout switch.
25. Install the 1 nut retaining the upper left corner of the evaporator case to the dash panel. Install the 3 nuts located below the windshield wiper motor, that attach the left end of the plenum to the dash panel.
26. Unplug the heater core hoses and tubes and connect the heater hoses to the heater core tubes. Fill the cooling system.
27. Connect the negative battery cable and check the system for proper operation.

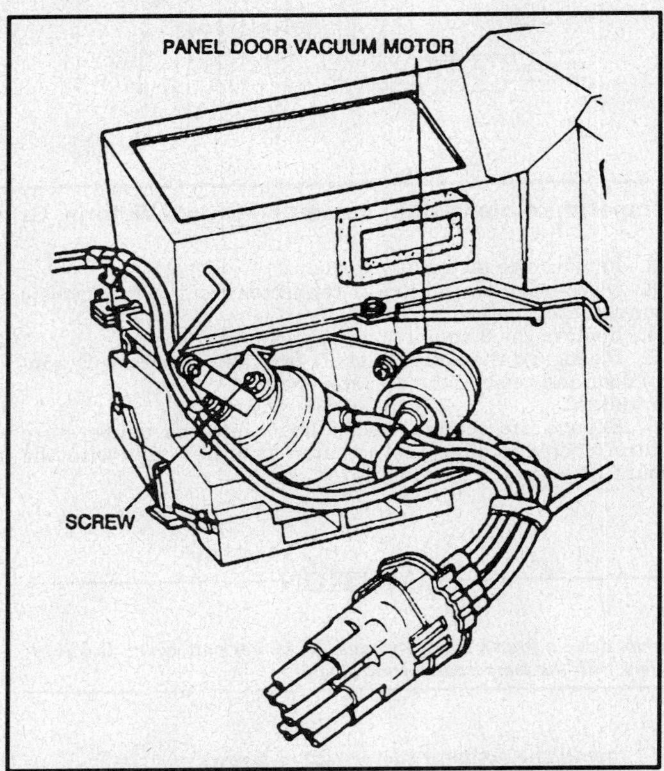

Servo motor assembly removal—Crown Victoria, Grand Marquis and Town Car with ATC

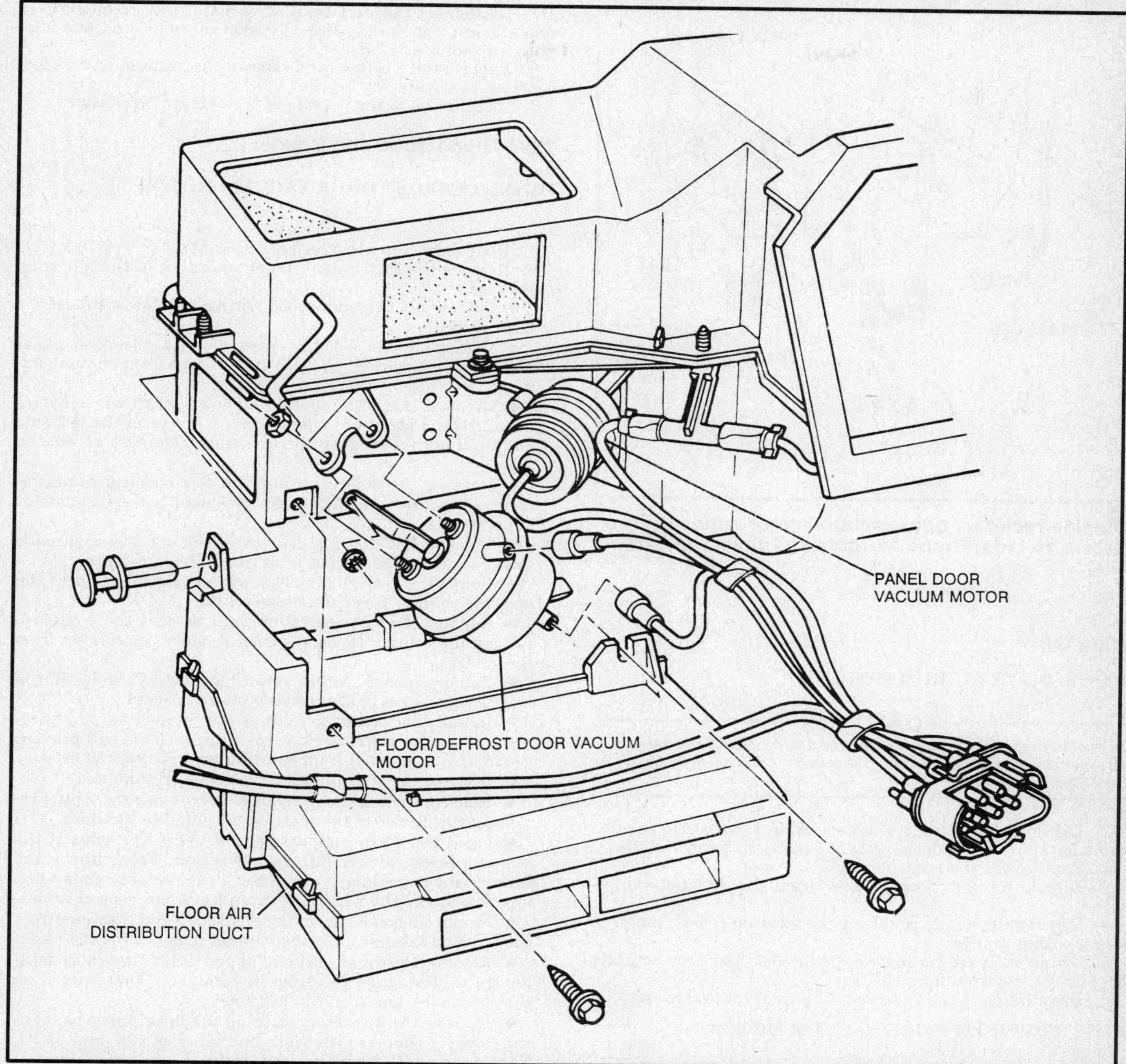

Disassembled view of floor air distribution duct and floor/defrost door vacuum motor—Crown Victoria, Grand Marquis and Town Car with ATC

FLOOR/DEFROST DOOR VACUUM MOTOR

1. Remove the floor air distribution duct assembly.
2. Remove the pushnut retaining the vacuum motor arm to the floor/defrost door crank arm. Remove the 2 nuts retaining the vacuum motor to the motor bracket.
3. Disengage the motor from the mounting bracket and the motor arm from the door crank arm. Remove the motor from the plenum and disconnect the vacuum hoses from the motor.
4. Installation is the reverse of the removal procedure.

OUTSIDE/RECIRCULATING DOOR VACUUM MOTOR

1. Remove the spring nut retaining the outside/recirculating door vacuum motor arm to the outside/recirculating door crank arm.
2. On 1993 models, disengage vacuum motor arm and washer from the crank arm. Disengage the assist spring and second washer from crank arm. Detach white vacuum hose. Remove 2 nuts holding motor and spring bracket to air inlet duct bracket. Remove the motor.
3. Installation is the reverse of the removal procedure.

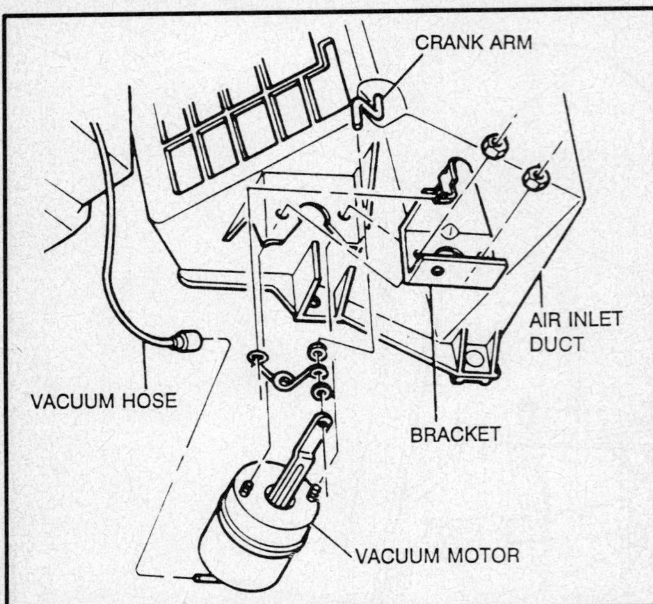

Outside/recirc air door vacuum motor removal—Crown Victoria, Grand Marquis and Town Car with ATC

Mark VIII

PANEL DOOR VACUUM MOTOR

CAUTION

To avoid accidental air bag deployment and possible personal injury, disconnect and ground the positive battery cable to deenergize the back–up power supply.

1. Disconnect the positive battery cable. Ground the positive cable for 1 minute to deenergize the back–up power supply.
2. Remove the instrument panel.
3. Disconnect the vacuum hose from the vacuum control motor.
4. Remove the 2 nuts retaining the vacuum control motor to its mounting bracket.
5. Swing the vacuum control motor until the door actuator arm can be removed from the door.
6. Installation is the reverse of the removal procedure.

FLOOR/DEFROST DOOR VACUUM MOTOR

Removal and installation procedures are the same as for the Panel Door Vacuum Motor.

OUTSIDE/RECIRCULATING DOOR VACUUM MOTOR

CAUTION

To avoid accidental air bag deployment and possible personal injury, disconnect and ground the positive battery cable to deenergize the back–up power supply.

1. Disconnect the positive battery cable. Ground the positive cable for 1 minute to deenergize the back–up power supply.
2. Remove the instrument panel.
3. Remove the evaporator case.
4. Disconnect the vacuum hose from the vacuum control motor.
5. Disconnect the vacuum control motor arm from the door crank arm by squeezing the door arm retainer stud and slipping the motor arm off.
6. Remove the 2 screws and remove the vacuum control motor from the mounting bracket.
7. Installation is the reverse of the removal procedure.

1993 Thunderbird and Cougar

PANEL/DEFROST DOOR VACUUM MOTOR

1. Disconnect the negative battery cable.
2. Remove the instrument panel according to the following procedure:
   - Disconnect the underhood wiring at the left side of the dash panel.
   - Disengage the wiring connector from the dash panel and push the wiring harness into the passenger compartment.
   - Remove the steering column lower trim cover by removing the 3 screws at the bottom, 1 screw on the left side and pulling to disengage the 5 snap-in retainers across the top.
   - Remove the steering column lower opening reinforcement. Six screws retain the reinforcement to the instrument panel.
   - Remove the steering column upper and lower shrouds and disconnect the wiring from the steering column.
   - Remove the shift interlock switch and disconnect the steering column lower universal joint.
   - Support the steering column and remove the 4 nuts retaining the column to the support. Remove the column from the vehicle.
   - Remove the 1 screw retaining the left side of the instrument panel to the parking brake bracket.
   - Install the steering column lower opening reinforcement using the 4 screws, 1 at each corner. This will prevent the instrument panel from twisting when being removed.
   - Remove the right and left cowl side trim panels.
   - Remove the console assembly and remove the 2 nuts retaining the center of the instrument panel to the floor.
   - Open the glove compartment, squeeze the sides of the bin and lower to the full open position. From under the instrument panel and through the glove compartment opening, disconnect the wiring, vacuum lines and control cables.
   - Remove 2 screws from the right side and 2 screws from the left side retaining the instrument panel to the cowl side.
   - Remove the right and left upper finish panels by pulling up to disengage the snap-in retainers. There are 3 on the right side, and 4 on the left side.
   - Remove the 4 screws retaining the instrument panel to the cowl top. Remove the right and left roof rail trim panel. Remove the door frame weather-strip.
   - Carefully pull the instrument panel away from the cowl and disconnect any remaining wiring or controls.
3. Remove the spring nut retaining the panel/defrost door vacuum motor arm to the door shaft.
4. Remove the 2 nuts retaining the vacuum motor to the mounting bracket. Remove the vacuum motor from the mounting bracket and disconnect the vacuum hose.

To install:

5. Position the vacuum motor to the mounting bracket and the door shaft. Install 2 nuts to attach the panel/defrost vacuum motor to the mounting bracket.
6. Connect the vacuum hose to the panel/defrost vacuum motor.
7. Install the instrument panel by reversing the removal procedure.
8. Connect the negative battery cable.

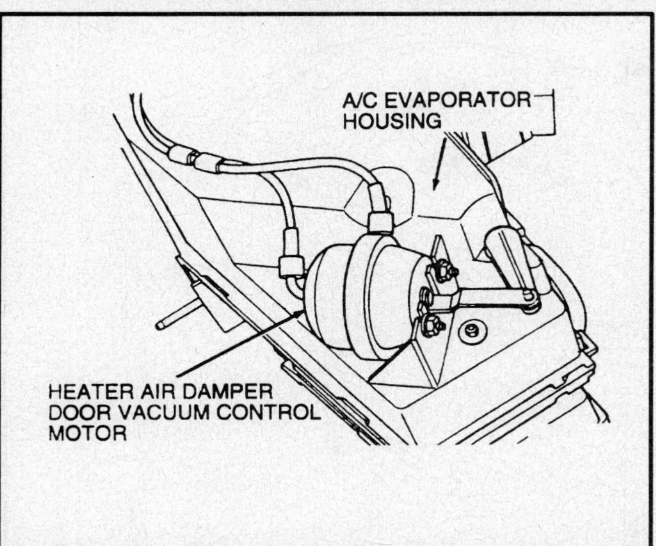

Panel/defrost door vacuum motor—Typical

FLOOR/DEFROST DOOR VACUUM MOTOR

1. Disconnect the negative battery cable.
2. Remove the instrument panel according to the following procedure:
   - Disconnect the underhood wiring at the left side of the dash panel.
   - Disengage the wiring connector from the dash panel and push the wiring harness into the passenger compartment.
   - Remove the steering column lower trim cover by removing the 3 screws at the bottom, 1 screw on the left side and pulling to disengage the 5 snap-in retainers across the top.
   - Remove the steering column lower opening reinforcement. Six screws retain the reinforcement to the instrument panel.
   - Remove the steering column upper and lower shrouds and disconnect the wiring from the steering column.
   - Remove the shift interlock switch and disconnect the steering column lower universal joint.
   - Support the steering column and remove the 4 nuts retaining the column to the support. Remove the column from the vehicle.
   - Remove the 1 screw retaining the left side of the instrument panel to the parking brake bracket.
   - Install the steering column lower opening reinforcement using the 4 screws, 1 at each corner. This will prevent the instrument panel from twisting when being removed.
   - Remove the right and left cowl side trim panels. Remove the console assembly and remove the 2 nuts retaining the center of the instrument panel to the floor.
   - Open the glove compartment, squeeze the sides of the bin and lower to the full open position. From under the instrument panel and through the glove compartment opening, disconnect the wiring, vacuum lines and control cables.
   - Remove 2 screws from the right side and 2 screws from the left side retaining the instrument panel to the cowl side.
   - Remove the right and left upper finish panels by pulling up to disengage the snap-in retainers. There are 3 on the right side, 4 on the left side.
   - Remove the 4 screws retaining the instrument panel to the cowl top. Remove the right and left roof rail trim panel. Remove the door frame weather-strip.
   - Carefully pull the instrument panel away from the cowl and disconnect any remaining wiring or controls.
   - Carefully pull the instrument panel away from the cowl and disconnect any remaining wiring or controls.
3. Remove the 2 nuts retaining the vacuum motor to the mounting bracket.
4. Disconnect the vacuum hoses from the vacuum motor and disengage the motor arm from the floor/defrost door crank arm. Remove the vacuum motor.

To install:

5. Engage the motor arm to the floor/defrost door crank arm. Position the vacuum motor on the mounting bracket and install the 2 retaining nuts.
6. Connect the vacuum hoses.
7. Install the instrument panel by reversing the removal procedure.
8. Connect the negative battery cable.

1994–95 Thunderbird and Cougar

FLOOR/DEFROST DOOR VACUUM MOTOR

CAUTION

To avoid accidental air bag deployment and possible personal injury, disconnect and ground the positive battery cable to deenergize the back-up power supply.

1. Disconnect the negative battery cable. Disconnect the positive battery cable and wait 1 minute for the back-up power supply to be deenergized.
2. Remove the instrument panel.
3. Remove the spring nut retaining the defroster door vacuum control arm motor to the door shaft.
4. Remove the 2 nuts retaining the vacuum control motor to the mounting bracket.
5. Remove the vacuum control motor from the bracket and disconnect the vacuum hose.

To install:

6. Position the vacuum control motor to the mounting bracket and the door shaft. Attach the motor to the door shaft with the spring nut.
7. Install the 2 nuts to attach the vacuum control motor to the mounting bracket.
8. Connect the vacuum hose to the defroster door vacuum control motor.
9. Install the instrument panel by reversing the removal procedure.
10. Connect the battery cables.

PANEL/DEFROST DOOR VACUUM MOTOR

CAUTION

To avoid accidental air bag deployment and possible personal injury, disconnect and ground the positive battery cable to deenergize the back-up power supply.

1. Disconnect the negative battery cable. Disconnect the positive battery cable and wait 1 minute for the back-up power supply to be deenergized.
2. Remove the instrument panel.
3. Remove the 2 nuts retaining the vacuum control motor to the mounting bracket.
4. Disconnect the vacuum hoses from the vacuum control motor and disengage the motor arm from the heater air damper door crank arm. Remove the vacuum control motor.

To install:

5. Engage the motor arm with the heater air damper door crank arm.

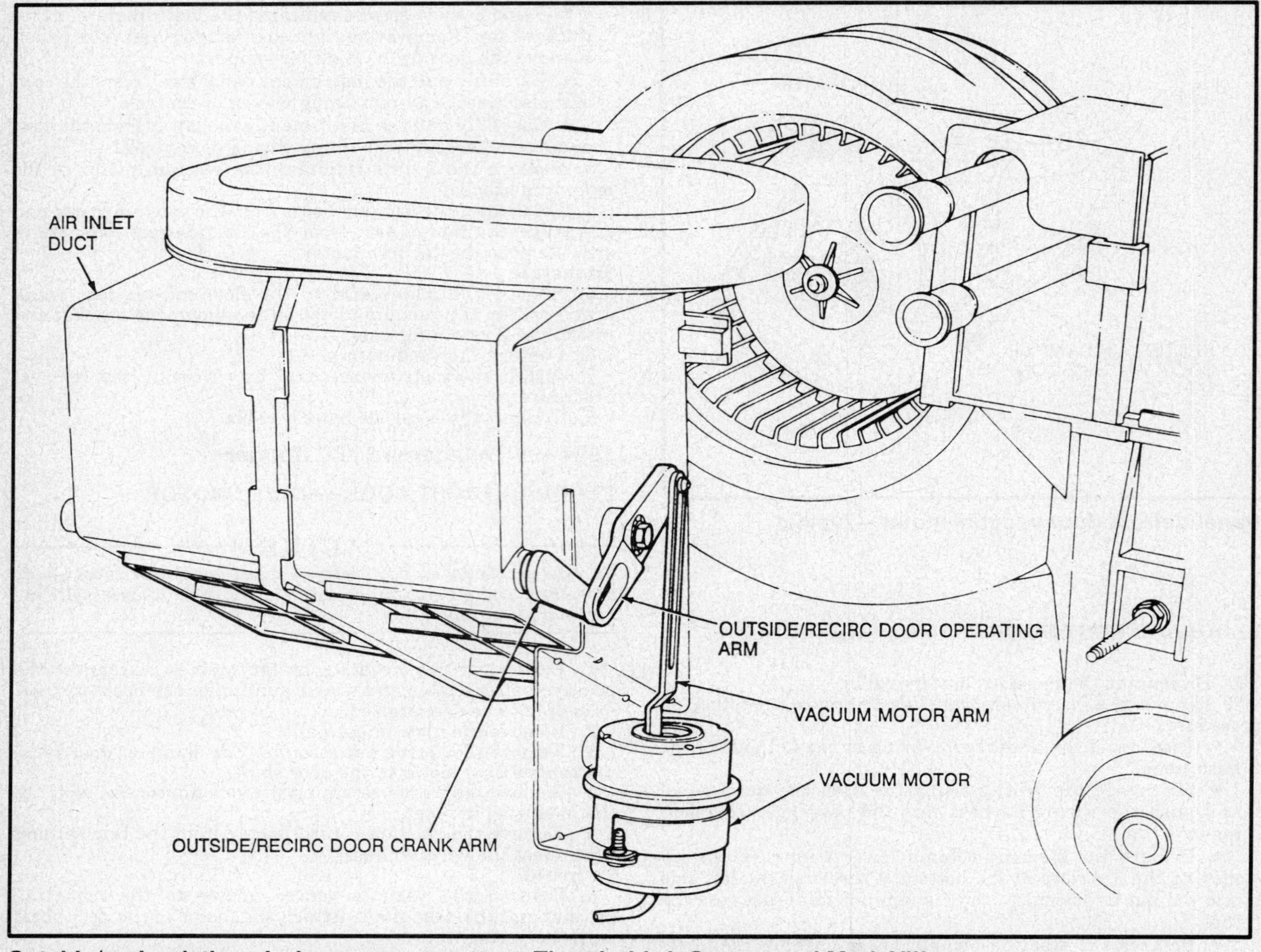

Outside/recirculating air door vacuum motor—Thunderbird, Cougar and Mark VIII

6. Position the vacuum control motor on the mounting bracket and install the 2 retaining nuts.
7. Install the instrument panel by reversing the removal procedure.
8. Connect the battery cables.

OUTSIDE/RECIRCULATING DOOR VACUUM MOTOR

1. Working between the outside/recirculating air inlet duct and the dash panel, remove the 2 screws retaining the vacuum motor to the mounting bracket.
2. Disconnect the vacuum hose from the vacuum motor.
3. Disengage the vacuum motor arm from the outside/recirculating air door operating link and remove the vacuum motor.
4. Installation is the reverse of the removal procedure.

1993 Mustang

PANEL/DEFROST DOOR VACUUM MOTOR

1. Disconnect the negative battery cable.
2. Remove the instrument panel according to the following procedure:
   - Remove the 2 covers at rear of console and remove armrest retaining bolts and remove armrest.
   - Remove the gearshift opening trim panel (snap-fit). On manual transmission models, shift boot is attached to bottom of finish panel; remove the shift knob and slide boot and finish panel up and off the lever.
   - Pull emergency brake handle up, remove 4 screws and lift up top finish panel. Detach wiring.
   - Snap out front upper finish panel. Remove the radio finish panel.
   - Lower the glove box door and remove 2 console to panel screws.
   - Disconnect all underhood wiring connectors from the main wiring harness. Disengage the rubber grommet seal from the dash panel and push the wiring harness and connectors into the passenger compartment.
   - Remove the 3 bolts attaching the steering column opening cover and reinforcement panel. Remove the cover.
   - Remove the steering column opening reinforcement by removing 2 bolts. Remove the 2 bolts retaining the lower steering column opening reinforcement and remove the reinforcement.
   - Remove the 6 steering column retaining nuts. 2 are retaining the hood release mechanism and 4 retain the column to the lower brake pedal support. Lower the steering column to the floor.

- Remove the steering column upper and lower shrouds and disconnect the wiring from the multi-function switch. Remove the brake pedal support nut and snap out the defroster grille.
- Remove the screws from the speaker covers. Snap out the speaker covers. Remove the front screws retaining the right and left scuff plates at the cowl trim panel. Remove the right and left side cowl trim panels.
- Disconnect the wiring at the right and left cowl sides. Remove the cowl side retaining bolts, 1 on each side.
- Open the glove compartment door and flex the glove compartment bin tabs inward. Drop down the glove compartment door assembly.
- Remove the 5 cowl top screw attachments. Gently pull the instrument panel away from the cowl. Disconnect the speedometer cable and wire connectors.

3. Remove the spring nut retaining the panel/defrost door vacuum motor arm to the door shaft.
4. Remove the 2 nuts retaining the vacuum motor to the mounting bracket. Remove the vacuum motor from the mounting bracket and disconnect the vacuum hose.

To install:

5. Position the vacuum motor to the mounting bracket and door shaft. Install 2 nuts to attach the panel/defrost vacuum motor to the mounting bracket.
6. Connect the vacuum hose to the panel/defrost vacuum motor.
7. Install the instrument panel by reversing the removal procedure.
8. Connect the negative battery cable.

FLOOR/DEFROST DOOR VACUUM MOTOR

1. Disconnect the negative battery cable and drain the cooling system.
2. Discharge the refrigerant from the air conditioning system.
3. Remove the instrument panel according to the following procedure:

- Remove the 2 covers at rear of console and remove armrest retaining bolts and remove armrest.
- Remove the gearshift opening trim panel (snap-fit). On manual transmission models, shift boot is attached to bottom of finish panel; remove the shift knob and slide boot and finish panel up and off the lever.
- Pull emergency brake handle up, remove 4 screws and lift up top finish panel. Detach wiring.
- Snap out front upper finish panel. Remove the radio finish panel.
- Lower the glove box door and remove 2 console to panel screws.
- Disconnect all underhood wiring connectors from the main wiring harness. Disengage the rubber grommet seal from the dash panel and push the wiring harness and connectors into the passenger compartment.
- Remove the 3 bolts attaching the steering column opening cover and reinforcement panel. Remove the cover.
- Remove the steering column opening reinforcement by
- removing 2 bolts. Remove the 2 bolts retaining the lower steering column opening reinforcement and remove the reinforcement.
- Remove the 6 steering column retaining nuts; 2 are retaining the hood release mechanism and 4 retain the column to the lower brake pedal support. Lower the steering column to the floor.
- Remove the steering column upper and lower shrouds and disconnect the wiring from the multi-function switch.
- Remove the brake pedal support nut and snap out the defroster grille.
- Remove the screws from the speaker covers. Snap out the speaker covers. Remove the front screws retaining the right and left scuff plates at the cowl trim panel. Remove the right and left side cowl trim panels.
- Disconnect the wiring at the right and left cowl sides. Remove the cowl side retaining bolts, 1 on each side.
- Open the glove compartment door and flex the glove compartment bin tabs inward. Drop down the glove compartment door assembly.
- Remove the 5 cowl top screw attachments. Gently pull the instrument panel away from the cowl. Disconnect the speedometer cable and wire connectors.

4. Disconnect the liquid line and the accumulator/drier inlet tube from the evaporator core at the dash panel. Cap the refrigerant lines and evaporator core tube to prevent the entrance of dirt and excessive moisture.
5. Disconnect the heater hoses from the heater core tubes and plug the hoses and tubes.
6. Remove the screw attaching the air inlet duct and blower housing assembly support brace to the cowl top panel.
7. Disconnect the black vacuum supply hose from the in-line vacuum check valve in the engine compartment. Disconnect the blower motor wires from the wire harness and disconnect the wire harness from the blower motor resistor.
8. Working under the hood, remove the 2 nuts retaining the evaporator case to the dash panel. Inside the passenger compartment, remove the 2 screws attaching the evaporator case support brackets to the cowl top panel.
9. Remove the 1 screw retaining the bracket below the evaporator case to the dash panel. Carefully pull the evaporator case away from the dash panel and remove the evaporator case assembly from the vehicle.
10. Remove the 2 nuts that attach the vacuum motor to the case and disconnect the vacuum hose from the motor.
11. Remove the spring nut that attaches the motor crank arm to the shaft and remove the motor.

To install:

12. Position the motor and install the spring nut that attaches the motor crank arm to the shaft.
13. Connect the vacuum hose to the motor and install the 2 nuts that attach the vacuum motor to the case.
14. Position the evaporator case assembly in the vehicle. Install the screws attaching the evaporator case support brackets to the cowl top panel. Check the evaporator case drain tube to ensure it is through the dash panel and is not pinched or kinked.
15. Install 1 screw retaining the bracket below the evaporator case to the dash panel. Working under the hood, install the 2 nuts retaining the evaporator case to the dash panel. Tighten the 4 nuts and 2 screws in the engine compartment. Tighten the 2 screws in the passenger compartment and the 2 support bracket attaching screws.
16. Connect the blower motor wire harness to the resistor and blower motor. Connect the black vacuum supply hose to the vacuum check valve in the engine compartment.
17. Using new O-rings lubricated with clean refrigerant oil, connect the liquid line and suction accumulator inlet to the evaporator core tubes. Tighten each connection using a back-up wrench to prevent component damage.
18. Install the instrument panel by reversing the removal procedure.
19. Connect the heater hoses to the heater core and fill the cooling system.
20. Connect the negative battery cable. Leak test, evacuate and charge the refrigerant system. Observe all safety precautions.
21. Check the system for proper operation.

OUTSIDE/RECIRCULATING DOOR VACUUM MOTOR

1. Remove the glove compartment. Disconnect the vacuum hose from the vacuum motor.
2. Remove the motor arm retainer from the outside/recirculating door shaft.

3. Remove the 2 nuts retaining the vacuum motor to the mounting bracket and remove the motor.
4. Installation is the reverse of the removal procedure.

1994–95 Mustang

PANEL/DEFROST DOOR VACUUM MOTOR

1. Disconnect the negative battery cable.
2. Remove the instrument panel.
3. Loosen the 2 retaining nuts.
4. Disconnect the vacuum hose.
5. Remove the vacuum motor arm from the door.
6. Remove the vacuum control motor.
7. Installation is the reverse of the removal procedure.

FLOOR/DEFROST DOOR VACUUM MOTOR

1. Disconnect the negative battery cable.
2. Remove the instrument panel.
3. Remove the vacuum motor arm retaining washer.
4. Loosen the 2 retaining nuts.
5. Remove the vacuum control motor. Disconnect the vacuum hose.
6. Installation is the reverse of the removal procedure.

OUTSIDE/RECIRCULATING DOOR VACUUM MOTOR

1. Disconnect the negative battery cable.
2. Remove the instrument panel.
3. Remove the vacuum control motor arm from the door cam.
4. Disconnect the vacuum hose harness from the vacuum control motor.
5. Remove the 2 vacuum motor retaining screws.
6. Remove the vacuum control motor.
7. Installation is the reverse of the removal procedure.

SYSTEM DIAGNOSIS

HEATER AND MANUAL AIR CONDITIONING SYSTEMS

The system is controlled by vacuum actuation of all doors except the temperature blend door (cable controlled). The blower motor is activated by an electrical connection from the panel to the motor via a resistor. Check system basics: battery voltage, cooling system operation, linkages and connections, electrical contacts, grounds and door positions.

AUTOMATIC TEMPERATURE CONTROL SYSTEMS

These systems utilize the basic elements of the manual air conditioning systems, but supplement manual operations with a series of sensors and switches to provide feedback input to the system control unit which, in turn, sends output signals to activate door positions, blower speeds and temperature changes to maintain the pre-set condition.

Some of these systems utilize a digital display control panel which, in addition to temperature read-outs, provides display of self-diagnostic codes to assist in determining cause of system failure.

1993 Thunderbird and Cougar

SELF TEST

If an existing failure is detected by the control assembly, a code (or codes) will appear on the display. Codes beginning with **E** represent an existing error (failure). Codes beginning with **P** indicate an intermittent failure. To identify these errors, perform the self-test as follows:

1. Turn ignition to **ON**. Depress the **FLOOR** button. Slide blower lever to **HIGH**.
2. Push both **COOL** and **WARM** buttons at the same time and hold for 3 seconds. Display — should appear.
3. After about 20 seconds, this will be replaced by an error code starting with **E** or **P**. Refer to the code charts in this section for assistance.
4. If **75°** (or 24°C) is displayed instead, power to the vehicle has been interrupted and must be repaired, then repeat full self-test.
5. To exit the diagnostic mode at any time, turn ignition switch to **OFF** or depress the **OFF** button on the control panel. When the control assembly is turned back **ON**, the temperature door will self-calibrate for 20 seconds.
6. To clear the **P** codes, depress the **COOL** button for 3 seconds. Check the appropriate circuit to be sure the condition has been resolved.

1994–95 Thunderbird and Cougar

1. Turn the ignition switch to **RUN**. Set the function selector to **FLOOR** and the blower control to **AUTO**.
2. Press both **COOL** and **OUTSIDE TEMP** at the same time: then press **WARM** within 2 seconds. The display will show a tracer segment moving counterclockwise.
3. After about 20 seconds, trouble codes for any faults will be displayed. Record the codes.
4. To exit the self test and retain all trouble codes, press **COOL**. To exit the self test and clear all trouble codes, press **OUTSIDE TEMP**, then press **WARM**.
5. Wait 25 seconds for temperature blend door to calibrate before turning ignition switch to **OFF**.

Mark VIII and 1994–95 Crown Victoria, Grand Marquis and Town Car

ON-BOARD DIAGNOSTIC TEST

1. With in-car temperature at least 50°F (10°C) and engine coolant at normal operating temperature, push **OFF** and **FLOOR** at the same time, then push **AUTO** within 2 seconds.
2. The display will go blank for up to 20 seconds as the self-diagnostic test operates.
3. If the display stays blank for more than 20 seconds, go to the "Symptom Chart".
4. To exit the diagnostic routine and restart the system, push the **BLUE** button. The on-board diagnostics should be deactivated before powering the system down.

1993 Crown Victoria and Grand Marquis

DIAGNOSIS AND TESTING

Due to the interactions of all heating, ventilation and air conditioning functions in an automatic temperature control system, it is essential that the entire climate control system be checked to fully analyze the proper failure condition(s) and isolate the inoperative component(s). After a preliminary check to verify the complaint, a check of the supporting systems should be performed:

HEATING SYSTEM DIAGNOSIS AND TESTING

CONDITION	POSSIBLE SOURCE	ACTION
• Air flow changes direction when vehicle is accelerated	• Vacuum system leak (if applicable).	• Check vacuum system with hand vacuum pump from control head connector. Service tubing, or replace damaged components as required.
• Insufficient, erratic, or no heat or defrost	• Kinked, clogged, collapsed, soft, swollen, or decomposed engine cooling system or heater system hoses.	• Replace damaged hoses and back-flush engine cooling system. Then back-flush heater system, until all particles have been removed.
	• Blocked air inlet.	• Check cowl air inlet for leaves, foreign material, etc. Remove as required.
• Air Comes Out of Defroster Outlet in Any Function Selector Lever Position	• Vacuum system (indicates a very bad leak).	• Listen for vacuum system leak. Look for disconnected vacuum hose connector. Use hand-operated vacuum pump, and check vacuum motors for diaphragm leak. Also check for leaking vacuum selector valve on control assembly, check valve, and leaking vacuum reservoir tank. Service hoses, or replace components as required.
• Cowl Ventilation System Leaks Air When in OFF Position	• Recirc door not properly sealing in recirc position.	• Check operation of recirc door for proper seal, kinked, or binding door. Service as required.
• Blower Does Not Operate Properly	• Blower motor.	• Run a #10 gauge jumper wire directly from the (grounded) negative battery terminal to the negative lead (black wire) of the blower motor. If the motor runs, the problem must be external to the motor. If the motor will not run, check the ground connection for good electrical contact. If this connection is good, the motor is inoperative and should be replaced.
	• Blower resistor.	• Check continuity of resistors for opens or check thermal limiter for continuity, if so equipped. (A blown thermal limiter will allow motor operation on Hi blower only). Service or replace as required.
	• Blower wire harness.	• Check for proper installation of harness connector terminal connectors. • Check wire-to-terminal continuity. • Check continuity of wires in harness for shorts (a short to ground will cause motor to operate with no control over the motor), opens, abrasion, etc. • Service as required.
	• Blower switch(es).	• Check blower switch(es) for proper contact. Replace switch(es) as required.
	• Vacuum selector valve.	• Check vacuum selector valve for proper contacts. Replace if required.

HEATING SYSTEM DIAGNOSIS AND TESTING, CONT'D

CONDITION	POSSIBLE SOURCE	ACTION
• Insufficient, Erratic, or No Heat or Defrost	• Low radiator coolant due to: • Coolant leaks.	• Check radiator cap pressure. Replace if below minimum pressure. • Fill to level. Pressure test for engine cooling system and heater system leaks. Service as required.
	• Engine overheating.	• Remove bugs, leaves, etc. from radiator or condenser fins. • Check for: Loose fan belt Sticking thermostat Incorrect ignition timing Water pump impeller damage Restricted cooling system • Service as required.
	• Loose fan belt. • Thermostat.	• Replace if cracked or worn and/or adjust belt tension. • Check coolant temperature at radiator filler neck. If under 170°F, check thermostat.
	• Plugged or partially plugged heater core.	• Clean and backflush engine cooling system and heater core.
	• Loose or improperly adjusted control cables.	• Adjust to specification.
	• Vacuum hoses crossed, collapsed, or kinked (if applicable).	• Check to see if door vacuum motors respond properly to movements of the Function Selector Lever and the Temperature Control Lever. Visually check vacuum hoses, and service as required.
	• Air flow control doors sticking or binding.	• Check to see if door vacuum motors or cable operated blend door respond properly to movements of Function and Temperature Control Levers. If hesitation in movement is noticed, disconnect vacuum motor arm from door crank arm, and move crank arm by hand. Service sticking or binding door as required.
	• Vacuum motor or hose leaks (if applicable).	• Disconnect multiple vacuum connector from back of Control Assembly, and check each connector opening with hand operated vacuum pump. If one line leaks vacuum, test motor by itself before replacing. (Be careful of vacuum hoses that operate two motors at same time.) Service vacuum hose(s), or replace vacuum motor as required.

MANUAL HEATER/A/C SYSTEM VACUUM LEAK DIAGNOSIS

TEST STEP	RESULT ▶	ACTION TO TAKE
A0 CHECK CONNECTORS		
• Check in-line and control assembly multiple connectors for proper installation. • Listen for hiss.	Hiss stops ▶	RECHECK system for proper operation.
	Hiss continues ▶	GO to **A1**.
A1 DETERMINE LEAKING VALVE		
• Move function lever to determine what Selector Valve positions are leaking.	All leak ▶	GO to **A2**.
	Some leak but not all ▶	GO to **A4**
A2 CHECK SOURCE TUBE		
• Check vacuum source tube (black) from reservoir to control assembly for cut or disconnection. • Listen for hiss.	Hiss stops ▶	SERVICE tube. RECHECK system for proper operation.
	Hiss continues ▶	GO to **A3**.
A3 PINCH OFF SOURCE TUBE		
• Pinch off source tube (black) at control assembly. • Listen for hiss.	Hiss stops ▶	REPLACE selector valve. RECHECK system for proper operation.
	Hiss continues ▶	RECHECK source tube (black), connections, reservoir and check valve. SERVICE or REPLACE as required.
A4 DETERMINE LEAKING TUBE(S)		
• Determine what color tube(s) are used in leaking function selector valve position(s). (Refer to air flow schematic and vacuum control chart.) • Pinch off suspect tube(s), one at a time, near each respective vacuum motor. • Listen for hiss.	Hiss stops ▶	CHECK tube connection to vacuum motor and SERVICE and/or RECONNECT if loose or split. RECHECK for hiss. If hiss still continues, REPLACE vacuum motor.* RECHECK system for proper operation.
	Hiss continues ▶	GO to **A5**.
A5 PINCH OFF SUSPECT TUBE(S)		
• Pinch off suspect tube(s), one at a time, near control assembly and/or in-line connector. • Listen for hiss.	Hiss stops ▶	CHECK tube for cut or damage. SERVICE if required. RECHECK system for proper operation.
	Hiss continues ▶	REPLACE function vacuum selector valve.

*Never manually operate any vacuum motor or vacuum motor controlled door — this may cause internal damage to the vacuum motor diaphragm.

AIR CONDITIONING SYSTEM DIAGNOSIS AND TESTING INSUFFICIENT OR NO COOLING

TEST STEP	RESULT ▶	ACTION TO TAKE
A1 VERIFY THE CONDITION		
• Check system operation. Verify the charge in the system.	System cooling properly ▶	INSTRUCT vehicle owner on proper use of the system.
	System not cooling properly ▶	GO to **A2**
A2 CHECK COOLING FAN		
• Does vehicle have an electro-drive cooling fan?	Yes ▶	GO to **A3**
	No ▶	GO to **A5**
A3 CHECK A/C COMPRESSOR CLUTCH		
• Does the A/C compressor clutch engage?	Yes ▶	GO to **A4**
	No ▶	REFER to clutch circuit diagnosis
A4 CHECK OPERATION OF COOLING FAN		
• Check to ensure electro-drive cooling fan runs when the A/C compressor clutch is engaged	Yes ▶	GO to **A5**
	No ▶	Check cooling fan
A5 COMPONENT CHECK		
Underhood check of the following • Loose, missing or damaged compressor drive belt • Loose or disconnected A/C clutch or clutch cycling pressure switch wires/connectors • Disconnected resistor assembly • Loose vacuum lines or misadjusted control cables Inside vehicle check for • Blown fuse/proper blower motor operation • Vacuum motors/temperature door movement — full travel • Control electrical and vacuum connections	OK but still not cooling ▶	GO to **A7**
	Not OK ▶	SERVICE and GO to **A6**
A6 CHECK SYSTEM		
• Check system operation	OK ▶	Condition Corrected GO to **A1**
	Not OK ▶	GO to **A7**

AIR CONDITIONING SYSTEM DIAGNOSIS AND TESTING—INSUFFICIENT OR NO COOLING—CONT'D

TEST STEP	RESULT	ACTION TO TAKE
A7 CHECK COMPRESSOR CLUTCH		
• Use refrigerant system pressure/clutch cycle rate and timing evaluation charts. After preparing vehicle as follows: 1 Hook up manifold gauge set 2 Set function control at max. A/C 3 Set blower switch on high 4 Set temperature lever full cold 5 Close doors and windows 6 Use a thermometer to check temperature at center discharge register, record outside temperature 7 Run engine at approximately 1500 rpm with compressor clutch engaged 8 Stabilize with above conditions for 10-15 minutes. • Check compressor clutch off on time with watch Refer to charts for normal clutch cycle timing rates	Compressor cycles very rapidly (1 second on) (1 second off)	▶ GO to **A8**.
	Compressor runs continuously (normal operation in ambient temperature above 27°C (80°F) depending on humidity conditions)	▶ GO to **A9**.
	Compressor cycles slow	▶ GO to **A8**
A8 CHECK CLUTCH CYCLING PRESSURE SWITCH		
• Bypass clutch cycling pressure switch with jumper wire. Compressor on continuously • Hand feel evaporator inlet and outlet tubes	Outlet tube same temperature approximately −2°C - 4°C (28°F - 40°F) or slightly colder than inlet tube (after fixed orifice)	▶ REPLACE clutch cycling pressure switch. Do not discharge system Switch fitting has Schrader Valve. GO to **A9**
	Inlet tube warm or (after fixed orifice) colder than outlet tube	▶ GO to **A10**.
A9 CHECK SYSTEM PRESSURES		
• Compare readings with normal system pressure ranges	Clutch cycles within limits, system pressure within limits	▶ System OK. GO to **A1**
	Compressor runs continuously (normal operation in ambient temperature above 27°C (80°F) depending on humidity conditions)	▶ GO to **A11**
	Compressor cycles high or low ON above 259 kPa (52 psi) OFF below 144 kPa (20 psi)	▶ REPLACE clutch cycling pressure switch. Do not discharge system. Switch fitting has Schrader valve. CHECK system. OK — GO to **A1**. NOT OK — REINSTALL original switch. GO to **A10**.

AIR CONDITIONING SYSTEM DIAGNOSIS AND TESTING—INSUFFICIENT OR NO COOLING—CONT'D

TEST STEP	RESULT	ACTION TO TAKE
A10 CHECK SYSTEM		
• Leak check system.	Leak found	▶ SERVICE, discharge, evacuate and charge system. System OK, GO to **A1**.
	No leak found	▶ Low refrigerant charge or moisture in system. Discharge, evacuate and charge system. System OK.
A11 CHECK CLUTCH CYCLING		
• Disconnect blower motor wire and check for clutch cycling off at 144 kPa (20 psi) (suction pressure).	Clutch cycles OFF at 144-179 kPa (20-26 psi)	▶ CONNECT blower motor wire. System OK, GO to **A1**
	Pressure falls below 144 kPa (20 psi)	▶ REPLACE clutch cycling pressure switch. Do not discharge system. Switch fitting has Schrader valve. System OK, GO to **A1**.

COMPRESSOR CLUTCH CIRCUIT DIAGNOSIS— MUSTANG WITH 2.3L ENGINE

TEST STEP		RESULT	▶	ACTION TO TAKE
B1	CHECK SYSTEM OPERATION			
	• Start engine. • Set the A/C control to MAX A/C. • Check battery voltage (If not 12.5 volts or more, refer to Charging System Diagnosis. • **Does clutch engage?**	Yes	▶	Circuit functioning properly.
		No	▶	GO to **B2**.
B2	BYPASS PRESSURE SWITCH			
	• Disconnect electrical connector from pressure switch on accumulator. • Jumper harness connector pins. • Engine must be running and system set at MAX A/C. • **Does clutch engage?**	Yes	▶	GO to **B3**.
		No	▶	GO to **B4**.
B3	CHECK REFRIGERANT SYSTEM PRESSURES			
	• Connect gauge set to service ports and observe pressure. Reading should be above 50 psi. • **Is pressure above 50 psi?**	Yes	▶	REPLACE clutch cycling pressure switch. GO to **B1**.
		No	▶	CHECK refrigerant system for leaks. SERVICE as required. GO to **B1**.
B4	CHECK VOLTAGE AT PRESSURE SWITCH			
	• Check for battery voltage at pressure switch electrical connector 883/347 circuit (P/LB and BK/Y). • **Is there battery voltage?**	No	▶	GO to **B9**.
		Yes	▶	GO to **B5**.
B5	CHECK SUPPLY VOLTAGE TO PRESSURE SWITCH			
	• Check for battery voltage at pressure switch Circuit 348 (LG/P). • **Is there battery voltage?**	No	▶	GO to **B6**.
		Yes	▶	VERIFY that system pressure is above 50 psi. If above 50 psi, REPLACE pressure switch.
B6	CHECK FUSE			
	• Check for voltage at fuse panel Circuit 298 (P/O). • Ignition switch must be in the ACC or RUN position. • **Is voltage at least 12.5 volts?**	Yes	▶	GO to **B7**.
		No	▶	CHECK charging system operation and for high resistance in circuit.
		No voltage	▶	CHECK fuse. SERVICE circuit as required. CHECK diodes in IRCM 9Pins 16 and 23) and across clutch coil for short. GO to **B1**.
B7	CHECK A/C SWITCH			
	• Check for battery voltage at the A/C control switch outlet Circuit 348 (LG/P). • **Is there battery voltage?**	Yes	▶	CHECK Circuit 348 between A/C switch and pressure switch for open. SERVICE as necessary.
		No	▶	GO to **B8**.
B8	CHECK POWER TO A/C SWITCH			
	• Check for battery voltage at inlet of A/C switch Circuit 298 (P/O). • **Is there battery voltage?**	Yes	▶	REPLACE A/C switch.
		No	▶	SERVICE wiring as necessary. GO to **B1**.
B9	CHECK CLUTCH CIRCUITS			
	• Check for voltage across harness connector at clutch field coil. • **Is there at least 10 volts?**	Yes	▶	GO to **B11**.
		No	▶	GO to **B10**.

COMPRESSOR CLUTCH CIRCUIT DIAGNOSIS— MUSTANG WITH 2.3L ENGINE, CONT'D

TEST STEP		RESULT	▶	ACTION TO TAKE
B10	CHECK IRCM OUTPUT VOLTAGE			
	• Check for voltage between Pins 16 and 23 of the IRCM. • **Is there at least 10 volts?**	Yes	▶	CHECK clutch coil wiring harness for open circuit. SERVICE as necessary. GO to **B1**.
		No	▶	GO to **C13**.
B11	JUMP FIELD COIL			
	• Disconnect field coil and jump battery voltage and ground to clutch field coil. • **Does clutch engage?**	Yes	▶	SERVICE coil electrical terminals and RETEST.
		No	▶	GO to **B12**.
B12	CHECK CLUTCH AIR GAP			
	• Check air gap between clutch hub and pulley. Air gap must be within specified limits. • **Is air gap within specifications?**	Yes	▶	REPLACE clutch field coil.
		No	▶	RESET air gap.
			▶	GO to **B11**.
B13	CHECK CLUTCH SIGNAL AT IRCM			
	• Check for a minimum of 11 volts at Pin 21 of the IRCM (Clutch input signal) with pressure switch jumped. • **Is there at least 11 volts?**	Yes	▶	GO to **B14**.
		No	▶	Check circuit between A/C control and IRCM for open. SERVICE as necessary.
B14	CHECK A/C CUT-OUT SIGNAL			
	• Remove wire from Pin 22 of IRCM harness connector. Then, start engine and set the EATC system at MAX A/C. • **Does clutch engage?**	No	▶	REPLACE IRCM.
		Yes	▶	GO to **B15**.
B15	CHECK THROTTLE POSITION SENSOR			
	• With engine running and system set at MAX A/C, disconnect throttle position sensor. • **Does clutch engage?**	Yes	▶	ADJUST or REPLACE throttle position sensor.
		No	▶	GO to **B16**.
B16	CHECK ENGINE COOLANT SENSOR			
	• With engine running and system set at MAX A/C, disconnect engine coolant temperature sensor. • **Does clutch engage?**	Yes	▶	REPLACE sensor.
		No	▶	LOCATE and SERVICE open in A/C sense circuit to ECA.

COMPRESSOR CLUTCH CIRCUIT DIAGNOSIS— MUSTANG WITH 3.8L OR 5.0L ENGINE

TEST STEP	RESULT ▶	ACTION TO TAKE
C1 CHECK SYSTEM OPERATION		
• Start engine. • Turn A/C on. • Check battery voltage • Turn blower switch to HI. • **Does compressor clutch engage after 5 second delay?**	Yes ▶ No ▶	Circuit functioning properly. GO to **C2**.
C2 BYPASS PRESSURE SWITCH		
• Disconnect electrical connector from pressure switch on accumulator. • Jumper harness connector pins. • Engine must be running and A/C turned to ON position. • **Does clutch engage?**	Yes ▶ No ▶	GO to **C3**. GO to **C4**.
C3 CHECK REFRIGERANT SYSTEM PRESSURES		
• Connect gauge set to service ports and observe pressure. Reading should be above 50 psi. • **Is pressure above 50 psi?**	Yes ▶ No ▶	REPLACE clutch cycling pressure switch. GO to **C1**. CHECK refrigerant system for leaks. SERVICE as required. GO to **C1**.
C4 CHECK VOLTAGE AT PRESSURE SWITCH		
• Check for battery voltage at pressure switch electrical connector Circuit 348 (LG/P) to ground. • **Is there battery voltage?**	Yes ▶ No ▶	GO to **C8**. GO to **C5**.
C5 CHECK A/C CONTROL SWITCH		
• Check for battery voltage at the A/C control switch 348 control (LG/P). • **Is there battery voltage?**	Yes ▶ No ▶	SERVICE wiring as necessary. GO to **C1**. GO to **C6**.
C6 CHECK CONTROL SUPPLY VOLTAGE		
• Check for battery voltage at Control Assembly 298 Circuit (P/O). • **Is there battery voltage?**	Yes ▶ No ▶	REPLACE Control Assembly. GO to **C7**.
C7 CHECK FUSE		
• Check for voltage at 298 circuit (P/O). • Ignition switch must be in the RUN position. • **Is there battery voltage?**	Yes ▶ No ▶ No voltage ▶	SERVICE wiring between fuse and control assembly. GO to **C1**. CHECK charging system operation for high resistance in clutch circuit. CHECK fuse. If blown CHECK diode for short. SERVICE as required. GO to **C1**.
C8 CHECK CLUTCH CIRCUITS		
• Check for voltage across harness connector at clutch field coil. • **Is there battery voltage?**	Yes ▶ No ▶	GO to **C10**. GO to **C9**.
C9 CHECK CLUTCH VOLTAGE		
• Check for voltage at clutch harness connector between 347 circuit (BK/Y) and ground. • **Is there battery voltage?**	Yes ▶ No ▶	GO to **C12**. GO to **C13**.

COMPRESSOR CLUTCH CIRCUIT DIAGNOSIS— MUSTANG WITH 3.8L OR 5.0L ENGINE, CONT'D

TEST STEP	RESULT ▶	ACTION TO TAKE
C10 JUMP FIELD COIL		
• Disconnect field coil and jump battery voltage and ground to clutch field coil. • **Does clutch engage?**	Yes ▶ No ▶	CLEAN coil electrical terminals and RETEST. GO to **C11**.
C11 CHECK CLUTCH AIR GAP		
• Check air gap between clutch hub and pulley. Air gap must be within specified limits. • **Is air gap within specifications?**	Yes ▶ No ▶ ▶	REPLACE clutch field coil. SET air gap. GO to **C10**.
C12 CHECK CLUTCH GROUND		
• Check Circuit 57 (BK) at clutch harness connector for continuity to ground. • Must have continuity with minimum resistance. • **Is there continuity?**	No ▶ Yes ▶	SERVICE circuit and/or ground connection. CHECK ground connection. CLEAN as required. GO to **C1**.
C13 CHECK VOLTAGE AT A/C CUT-OUT RELAY		
• Check for voltage at the A/C cut-out relay Circuit 883 (PK/LB) to ground. • **Is there voltage?**	No ▶ Yes ▶	**SERVICE open circuit between A/C relay and pressure switch.** GO to **C14**.
C14 CHECK A/C CUT-OUT RELAY		
• Disconnect connector from relay. • Jumper across the connector Circuit 883 (PK/LB) to Circuit 347 (BK/Y). • With engine running and A/C ON, check for clutch engagement. • **Does clutch engage?**	Yes ▶ No ▶	GO to **C15**. **CHECK for shorted diode. SERVICE as required. GO to C1.**
C15 CHECK A/C CUT-OUT RELAY OPERATION		
• **With engine running and A/C ON, reconnect harness connector to A/C cut-out relay and check to see if relay energizes. The clutch circuit will open if the relay energizes.** • **Does relay energize?**	No ▶ Yes ▶	REPLACE A/C cut-out relay. **Engine coolant temperature sensor sending hot coolant signal to ECA, or throttle position sensor sending cut-out signal to ECA. DISCONNECT electrical connector from each sensor. Clutch will engage if sensor is sending incorrect signal.**
C16 CHECK THROTTLE POSITION SENSOR		
• **Does clutch energize?**	Yes ▶ No ▶	ADJUST or REPLACE throttle position sensor GO to **C17**.
C17 CHECK ENGINE COOLANT SENSOR		
• **Does clutch engage?**	Yes ▶ No ▶	REPLACE sensor. LOCATE and SERVICE open in A/C sensor circuit to ECA

COMPRESSOR CLUTCH CIRCUIT DIAGNOSIS—THUNDERBIRD AND COUGAR WITH 3.8L AND 5.0L ENGINES

Compressor Circuit Diagnosis—3.8L and 5.0L

Operation of the A/C compressor clutch is dependent on signals from the engine computer. The system is designed to interrupt compressor operation when certain conditions exist. The A/C compressor clutch can be shut off (or kept off) for several seconds at engine start-up, at high engine speeds, during acceleration, when the engine coolant temperature exceeds a predetermined temperature and during low engine idle conditions. If A/C compressor operation can be restored with a jumper wire across the contact terminals of the A/C cut-out relay harness connector, the powertrain control module (PCM) 12A650 is interrupting compressor operation.

NOTE: The ambient temperature must also be above approximately 10° C (50° F) for A/C compressor operation.

A/C CLUTCH CIRCUIT DIAGNOSIS

	TEST STEP	RESULT ▶	ACTION TO TAKE
B1	CHECK SYSTEM OPERATION		
	• Start engine. • Turn MAX A/C ON. • Check battery voltage • Turn blower switch to HI. • **Does compressor clutch engage after 5 second delay?**	Yes ▶ No ▶	Circuit functioning properly. GO to **B2.**
B2	BY-PASS PRESSURE SWITCH		
	• Disconnect electrical connector from pressure switch on accumulator. • Jumper harness connector pins. • Engine must be running and A/C turned to ON position. • **Does clutch engage?**	Yes ▶ No ▶	GO to **B3.** GO to **B4.**
B3	CHECK REFRIGERANT SYSTEM PRESSURES		
	• Connect gauge set to service ports and observe pressure. Reading should be above 50 psi. • **Is pressure above 50 psi?**	Yes ▶ No ▶	REPLACE clutch cycling pressure switch. GO to **B1.** CHECK refrigerant system for leaks. SERVICE system as required. GO to **B1.**
B4	CHECK VOLTAGE AT PRESSURE SWITCH		
	• Check for battery voltage at pressure switch electrical connector Circuit 348 (LG/P) to ground. • **Is there battery voltage?**	Yes ▶ No ▶	GO to **B6.** GO to **B5.**
B5	CHECK SYSTEM CONTROL MODULE		
	• Check for battery voltage at Pin 2 of the ECC system module. • Ignition switch must be in the run position and system set at an A/C position. • **Is there battery voltage?**	Yes ▶ Less than 10 volts ▶ No ▶	SERVICE wiring between control module and pressure switch. GO to **B6.** CHECK charging system operation and for high resistance in clutch circuit. GO to **B1.** REPLACE ECC system module. CHECK system.

COMPRESSOR CLUTCH CIRCUIT DIAGNOSIS—THUNDERBIRD AND COUGAR WITH 3.8L AND 5.0L ENGINES—CONT'D

	TEST STEP	RESULT ▶	ACTION TO TAKE
B6	CHECK CLUTCH CIRCUITS		
	• Check for voltage across harness connector at clutch field coil. • A minmum of 10 volts is required. • **Is there battery voltage?**	Yes ▶ No ▶	GO to **B8.** GO to **B7.**
B7	CHECK CLUTCH VOLTAGE		
	• Check for voltage at clutch harness connector between Circuit 347 (BK/Y) and ground. • **Is there battery voltage?**	Yes ▶ No ▶	GO to **B10.** GO to **B11.**
B8	JUMP FIELD COIL		
	• Disconnect field coil and jump battery voltage and ground to clutch field coil. • **Does clutch engage?**	Yes ▶ No ▶	CLEAN coil electrical terminals and RETEST system. GO to **B9.**
B9	CHECK CLUTCH AIR GAP		
	• Check air gap between clutch hub and pulley. Air gap must be within specified limits. • **Is air gap within specifications?**	Yes ▶ No ▶	REPLACE clutch field coil. RESET air gap. GO to **B8.**
B10	CHECK CLUTCH GROUND		
	• Check the Circuit 57 (BK) at clutch harness connector for continuity to ground. • Must have continuity with minimum resistance. • **Is there continuity?**	Yes ▶ No ▶	CHECK ground connection. CLEAN as required. GO to **B1.** SERVICE circuit and/or ground connection.
B11	CHECK VOLTAGE AT A/C CUT-OUT RELAY		
	• Check for voltage at the A/C cut-out relay Circuit 883 (PK/LB) to ground. • **Is there voltage?**	Yes ▶ No ▶	GO to **B12.** SERVICE open circuit between A/C relay and pressure switch.
B12	JUMP A/C CUT-OUT RELAY		
	• Disconnect connector from relay. • Jumper across the connector Circuit 883 (PK/LB) to Circuit 347 (BK/Y). • With engine running and A/C on, check for clutch engagement. • **Does clutch engage?**	Yes ▶ No ▶	GO to **B13.** CHECK for shorted diode. SERVICE as required. GO to **B1.**
B13	CHECK A/C CUT-OUT RELAY OPERATION		
	• With engine running and A/C on, reconnect harness connector to A/C cut-out relay and check to see if relay energizes. The clutch circuit will open if the relay energizes. • **Does relay energize?**	Yes ▶ No ▶	The Powertrain Control Module (PCM) is causing IRCM to interrupt compressor circuit. Following are possible causes. ▶ Throttle Position Sensor—Sending cut-out signal to PCM. Disconnect electrical connector to remove sensor from circuit. Clutch will engage if sensor is sending W.O.T. cut-out signal. ▶ Hot Engine Coolant—Sensor sending hot coolant signal to PCM. Disconnect electrical connector from sensor. Clutch will engage if sensor is sending hot coolant signal to PCM. ▶ A/C Senses Circuit to PCM Open—If circuit is open, PCM will not receive signal from pressure switch to turn A/C clutch ON. REPLACE A/C cut-out relay.

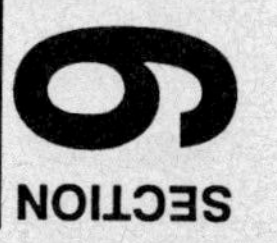

COMPRESSOR CLUTCH CIRCUIT DIAGNOSIS–THUNDERBIRD AND COUGAR WITH 3.8L SC ENGINE

A/C Clutch Circuit Diagnosis, 3.8L SC

Operation of the A/C compressor clutch is dependent on ambient temperature and signals from the engine computer. Strategies are programmed into the engine computer to interrupt A/C compressor operation when certain conditions exist. The A/C compressor clutch can be shut off (or kept off) for several seconds at engine start-up, at high engine speeds, during low engine idle conditions (approx. 200 rpm below low idle specs.)

NOTE: The ambient temperature must also be above approximately 50°F, for A/C compressor operation.

A/C CLUTCH CIRCUIT DIAGNOSIS

	TEST STEP	RESULT ▶	ACTION TO TAKE
C1	CHECK SYSTEM OPERATION		
	• Start engine. • Select MAX A/C on control assembly. • Check battery voltage (if not 12.5 volts or more, check charging system. Refer to Section 14-00). • Turn blower switch to HI. • **Does compressor clutch engage?**	Yes ▶	Circuit functioning properly.
		No ▶	GO to **C2**.
C2	BYPASS PRESSURE SWITCH		
	• Disconnect electrical connector from pressure switch on accumulator. • Jumper the harness connector pins. • Engine must be running and system set at MAX A/C. • **Does clutch engage?**	Yes ▶	GO to **C3**.
		No ▶	GO to **C4**.
C3	CHECK REFRIGERANT SYSTEM PRESSURES		
	• Connect gauge set to service ports and observe pressure. Reading should be above 50 psi. • **Is pressure above 50 psi?**	Yes ▶	REPLACE clutch cycling pressure switch. GO to **C1**.
		No ▶	CHECK refrigerant system for leaks. SERVICE, leak test and charge as necessary. GO to **C1**.
C4	CHECK VOLTAGE AT PRESSURE SWITCH		
	• Check for battery voltage at pressure switch electrical connector 883 circuit P/LB wire) to ground. • **Is there battery voltage?**	Yes ▶	GO to **C9**.
		No ▶	GO to **C5**.
C5	CHECK SUPPLY VOLTAGE TO PRESSURE SWITCH		
	• Check for battery voltage (348 circuit to ground) at pressure switch. • **Is there battery voltage?**	Yes ▶	VERIFY that system pressure is above 50 psi. If above, REPLACE pressure switch. GO to **C1**.
		No ▶	GO to **C6**.
C6	CHECK CONTROL MODULE		
	• Check for battery voltage at Pin 20 of ECC module. • Ignition switch must be in RUN and A/C system set at MAX A/C. • **Is there battery voltage?**	Yes ▶	CHECK wiring for open between control module and pressure switch. SERVICE as necessary. GO to **C7**.
		Voltage less than 12.5 volts ▶	CHECK charging system operation and for high resistance in circuit.
		No ▶	REPLACE control module. CHECK system.
C7	CHECK A/C SWITCH		
	• Check for battery voltage at A/C switch outlet (348 circuit PINK wire). • **Is there battery voltage at A/C switch outlet?**	Yes ▶	CHECK circuit 348 between A/C switch and pressure switch for open. SERVICE as necessary.
		No ▶	GO to **C8**.

COMPRESSOR CLUTCH CIRCUIT DIAGNOSIS–THUNDERBIRD AND COUGAR WITH 3.8L SC ENGINE—CONT'D

	TEST STEP	RESULT ▶	ACTION TO TAKE
C8	CHECK POWER TO A/C SWITCH		
	• Check for battery voltage at inlet of A/C switch (298 circuit P/O wire). • **Is there battery voltage at inlet of A/C switch?**	Yes ▶	REPLACE control assembly.
		No ▶	SERVICE wiring as necessary. GO to **C1**.
C9	CHECK CLUTCH CIRCUITS		
	• Check for voltage across harness connector at clutch field coil. A minimum of 10 volts is required. • **Is there voltage across connector?**	Yes ▶	GO to **C11**.
		No ▶	GO to **C10**.
C10	CHECK IRCM OUTPUT VOLTAGE		
	• Check for voltage between Pins 16 and 23 of the IRCM. A minimum of 10 volts is required. • **Is there voltage?**	Yes ▶	CHECK clutch coil wiring harness for open circuit. SERVICE as necessary. GO to **C1**.
		No ▶	GO to **C13**.
C11	JUMP FIELD COIL		
	• Disconnect field coil and jump battery voltage and ground to clutch field coil. • **Does clutch engage?**	Yes ▶	CLEAN coil electrical terminals and RETEST.
		No ▶	GO to **C12**.
C12	CHECK CLUTCH AIR GAP		
	• Check air gap between clutch hub and pulley. Air gap must be within specified limits. • **Is air gap within limits?**	Yes ▶	REPLACE clutch field coil.
		No ▶	RESET air gap. GO to **C11**.
C13	CHECK CLUTCH SIGNAL AT IRCM		
	• Check for a minimum of 11 volts at Pin 21 of IRCM (clutch input signal) with pressure switch jumped. • **Is 11 volts present?**	Yes ▶	GO to **C14**.
		No ▶	CHECK circuit between pressure switch and IRCM for open. SERVICE as necessary.
C14	CHECK A/C CUT-OUT SIGNAL		
	• Remove wire from Pin 22 of IRCM harness connector. Then, start engine and set the ECC system at MAX/A/C. • **Does clutch energize?**	Yes ▶	The Powertrain Control Module (PCM) 12A650 is causing IRCM to interrupt compressor circuit. Following are possible causes. ▶ Throttle Position Sensor—Sending W.O.T. signal to PCM. Disconnect electrical connector to remove sensor from circuit. Clutch will engage if sensor is sending W.O.T. cut-out signal. ▶ Hot Engine Coolant—Sensor sending hot coolant signal to PCM. Disconnect electrical connector from sensor. Clutch will engage if sensor is sending hot coolant signal to PCM. ▶ A/C Senses Circuit to PCM Open—If circuit is open, PCM will not receive signal from pressure switch to turn A/C clutch ON.
		No ▶	REPLACE IRCM.

COMPRESSOR CLUTCH CIRCUIT DIAGNOSIS—1993 CROWN VICTORIA, GRAND MARQUIS AND TOWN CAR

	TEST STEP	RESULT ▶	ACTION TO TAKE
G1	CHECK SYSTEM OPERATION		
	• Start engine. • Turn A/C ON. • Check battery voltage 12.5 volts or more • Turn blower switch to HI. • **Does compressor clutch engage after 5 second delay?**	Yes ▶ No ▶	Circuit functioning properly. GO to **G2**.
G2	BY-PASS PRESSURE SWITCH		
	• Disconnect electrical connector from pressure switch on accumulator. • Jumper harness connector pins. • Engine must be running and A/C turned to ON position. • **Does clutch engage?**	Yes ▶ No ▶	GO to **G3**. GO to **G4**.
G3	CHECK REFRIGERANT SYSTEM PRESSURES		
	• **Connect gauge set to service ports and observe pressure. Reading should be above 50 psi.** • **Is pressure above 50 psi?**	Yes ▶ No ▶	REPLACE clutch cycling pressure switch. GO to **G1**. CHECK refrigerant system for leaks. SERVICE leak-test and charge system as required. GO to **G1**.
G4	CHECK VOLTAGE AT PRESSURE SWITCH		
	• Check for battery voltage at pressure switch electrical connector Circuit 348 (LG/P, Crown Victoria, Grand Marquis), Circuit 883 (PK/LB, Town Car) to ground. • **Is there battery voltage?**	Yes ▶ No ▶	GO to **G8**. GO to **G5**.
G5	CHECK A/C CONTROL SWITCH		
	• Check for battery voltage at the function selector switch—Pin 4. • **Is there battery voltage?**	Yes ▶ No ▶	SERVICE wiring as necessary. GO to **G1**. GO to **G6**.
G6	CHECK CONTROL SUPPLY VOLTAGE		
	• Check for battery voltage at function selector switch—Pin 2. • **Is there battery voltage?**	Yes ▶ No ▶	REPLACE function selector switch. GO to **G7**.
G7	CHECK FUSE		
	• Check for voltage at Circuit 298 (P/O, Crown Victoria, Grand Marquis), Circuit 640 (Town Car). • Ignition switch must be in the RUN position. • **Is there battery voltage?**	Yes ▶ No ▶ Voltage less than 10 volts ▶	SERVICE wiring between control assembly and fuse panel. GO to **M1**. CHECK fuse. If blown CHECK clutch diode circuit for short. SERVICE as required. GO to **G1**. CHECK charging system operation.
G8	CHECK CLUTCH CIRCUITS		
	• Check for voltage across harness connector at clutch field coil. • A minimum of 10 volts is required. • **Is there a minimum of 10 volts?**	Yes ▶ No ▶	GO to **G10**. GO to **G9**.
G9	CHECK CLUTCH VOLTAGE		
	• Check for voltage at clutch harness connector between Circuit 347 (BK/Y) and ground. • A minimum of 10 volts is required. • **Is there a minimum of 10 volts?**	Yes ▶ No ▶	GO to **G12**. GO to **G13**.

COMPRESSOR CLUTCH CIRCUIT DIAGNOSIS—1993 CROWN VICTORIA, GRAND MARQUIS AND TOWN CAR—CONT'D

	TEST STEP	RESULT ▶	ACTION TO TAKE
G10	JUMP FIELD COIL		
	• Disconnect field coil and jump battery voltage and ground to clutch field coil. • **Does clutch engage?**	Yes ▶ No ▶	CLEAN coil electrical terminals and RETEST system. GO to **G11**.
G11	CHECK CLUTCH AIR GAP		
	• Check air gap between clutch hub and pulley. Air gap must be within specified limits. • **Is air gap within specifications?**	Yes ▶ No ▶	REPLACE clutch field coil. RESET air gap. GO to **G10**.
G12	CHECK CLUTCH GROUND		
	• Check the Circuit 57 (BK) at clutch harness connector for continuity to ground. • Must have continuity with minimum resistance. • **Is there continuity?**	Yes ▶ No ▶	CHECK ground connection. CLEAN as required. GO to **G1**. SERVICE circuit and/or ground connection.
G13	CHECK VOLTAGE AT A/C CUT-OUT RELAY		
	• Check for voltage at the A/C cut-out relay Circuit 883 (PK/LB, Crown Victoria/Grand Marquis, 198 (T/Y) Town Car) to ground. • **Is there voltage?**	No ▶ Yes ▶	SERVICE open circuit between A/C relay and pressure switch. GO to **G14**.
G14	CHECK A/C CUT-OUT RELAY		
	• Disconnect connector from relay. • Jumper across the connector Circuit 883 (PK/LB, Crown Victoria/Grand Marquis, 198 (T/Y) Town Car) to Circuit 347 (BK/Y). • With engine running and A/C on, check for clutch engagement. • **Does clutch engage?**	Yes ▶ No ▶	GO to **G15**. CHECK for shorted diode or wire. SERVICE as required. GO to **G1**.
G15	CHECK A/C CUT-OUT RELAY OPERATION		
	• With engine running and A/C on, reconnect harness connector to A/C cut-out relay and check to see if relay energizes. The clutch circuit will open if the relay energizes. • **Does relay energize?**	No ▶ Yes ▶	REPLACE A/C cut-out relay. The Powertrain Control Module (PCM) is causing relay to energize and interrupt compressor circuit. Any of the following can be the cause. ▶ Throttle Position Sensor—Sending W.O.T. signal to PCM. Disconnect electrical connector to remove sensor from circuit. Clutch will engage if sensor is sending W.O.T. cut-out signal. ▶ Hot Engine Coolant—Sensor sending hot coolant signal to PCM. Disconnect electrical connector from sensor. Clutch will engage if sensor is sending hot coolant signal to PCM. ▶ A/C On Circuit to PCM Open—If circuit is open, PCM will not receive signal from pressure switch to turn A/C clutch on.

NORMAL REFRIGERANT SYSTEM PRESSURE/TEMPERATURE RELATIONSHIPS—MUSTANG, THUNDERBIRD, COUGAR AND MARK VIII

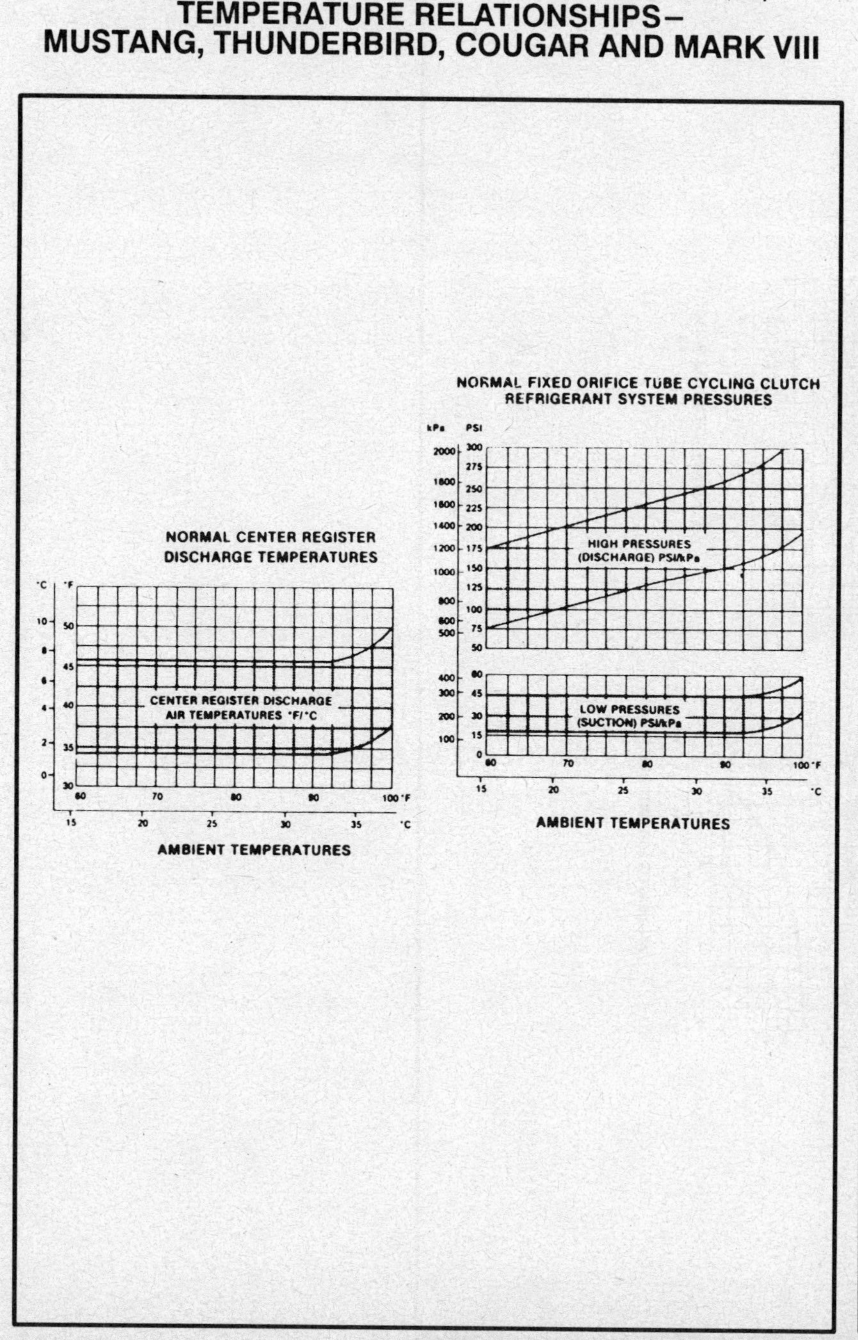

NORMAL REFRIGERANT SYSTEM PRESSURE/TEMPERATURE RELATIONSHIPS—CROWN VICTORIA, GRAND MARQUIS AND TOWN CAR

NORMAL CENTER REGISTER DISCHARGE TEMPERATURES

CENTER REGISTER DISCHARGE AIR TEMPERATURES °F/°C

AMBIENT TEMPERATURES

NORMAL FIXED ORIFICE TUBE CYCLING CLUTCH REFRIGERANT SYSTEM PRESSURES

HIGH PRESSURES (DISCHARGE) PSI/kPa

LOW PRESSURES (SUCTION) PSI/kPa

AMBIENT TEMPERATURES

NORMAL CLUTCH CYCLE RATES AND TIMES—MUSTANG, THUNDERBIRD, COUGAR AND MARK VIII

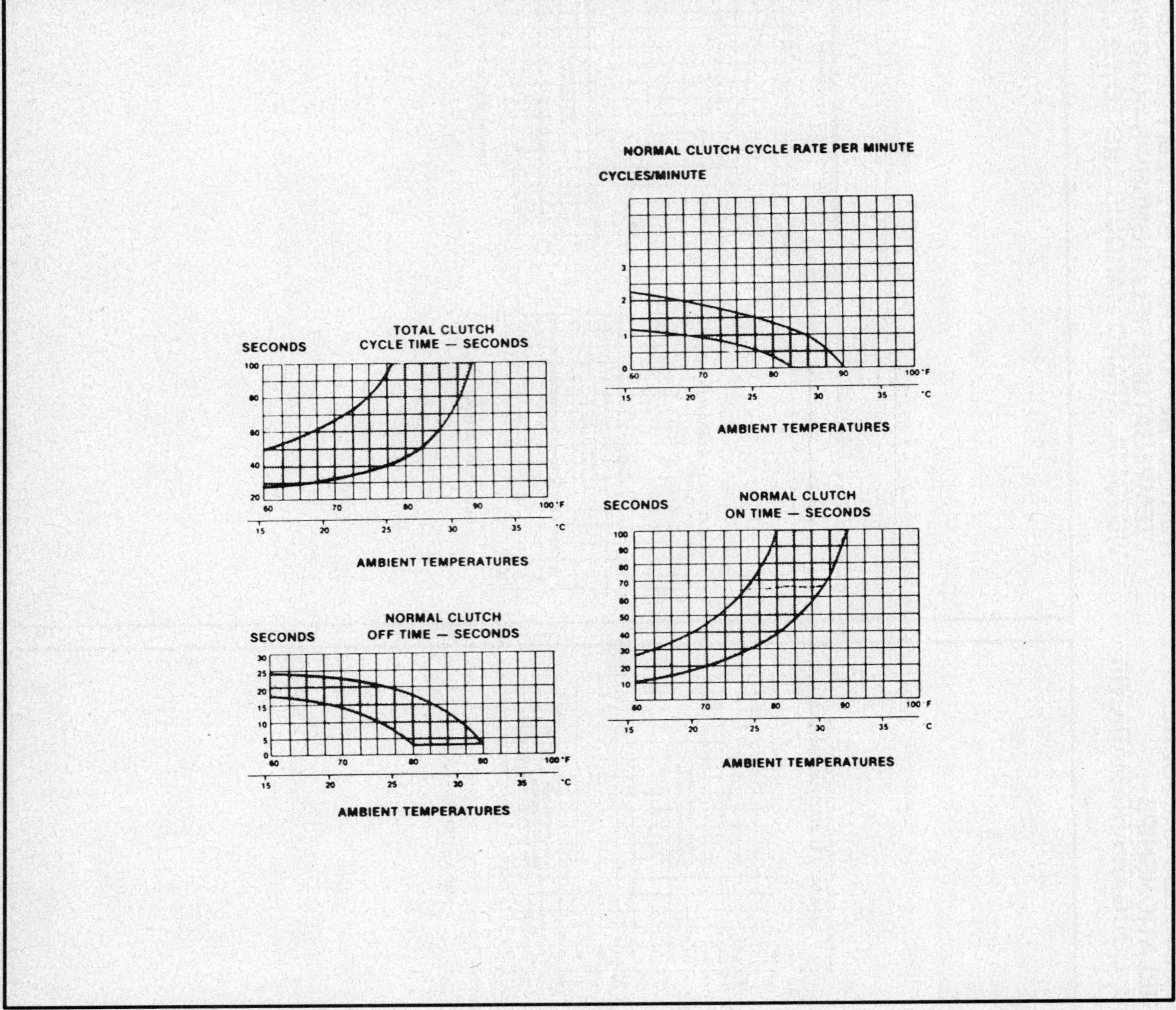

NORMAL CLUTCH CYCLE RATES AND TIMES—CROWN VICTORIA, GRAND MARQUIS AND TOWN CAR

IMPORTANT — TEST REQUIREMENTS

The following test conditions must be established to obtain accurate clutch cycle rate and cycle time readings:

- Run engine at 1500 rpm for 10 minutes.
- Operate A/C system on max A/C (recirculating air).
- Run blower at max speed.
- Stabilize in car temperature @ 70°F to 80°F (21°C to 22°C).

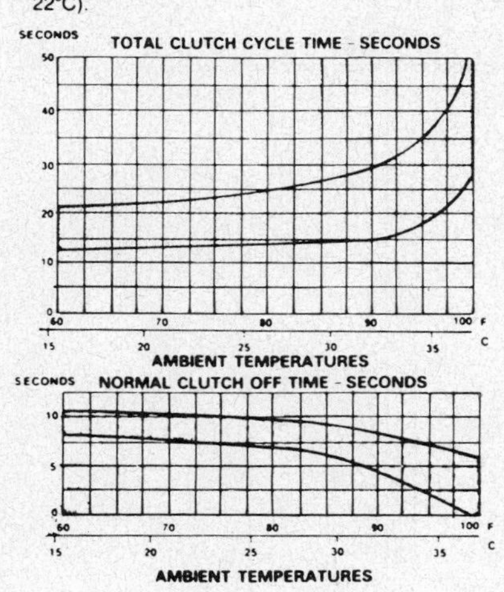

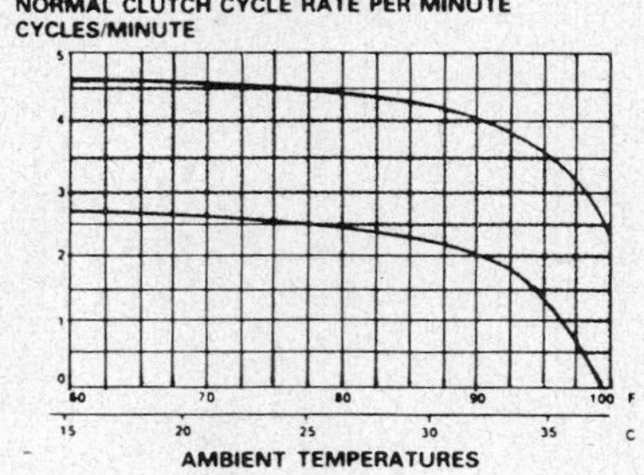

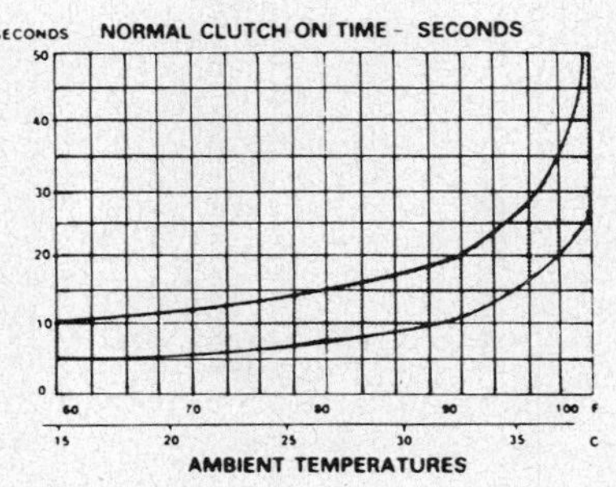

- Heat to heater core
- Refrigerant to evaporator core
- Air distribution for proper location and quantity

The following is divided into 2 parts. The first part contains a general checkout procedure to be used when the fault is not fully defined or more than 1 problem exists. The second part contains a detailed checkout procedure to isolate the fault to a component.

AUTOMATIC TEMPERATURE CONTROL SYSTEM CHECK

NOTE: This test applies specifically to 1993 Crown Victoria and Grand Marquis with non-electronic type Automatic Temperature Control (ATC) System.

1. Engine should be at normal operating temperature and idling above 1200 rpm. In-car temperature should be about 75°F.

2. Check air distribution for proper operation in each mode. Correct any problems before proceeding.
3. Set function lever to **VENT**. Check blower operation in low and high speeds. If okay, move selector to **AUTO**. If blower does not operate properly in all positions, correct inoperative component and proceed.
4. Cycle temperature from **65** to **85** and observe blower speed change and discharge temperature change.
5. Move temperature lever back to **65** and observe blower speed and temperature output.
6. Move function lever to **NORM A/C**. The fresh/recirc door should open and clutch should engage, producing colder air discharge.
7. Move the temperature lever to **72**. Blower should reduce to low or medium low speed and discharge air temperature should rise accordingly.

1993 Town Car

1993 Town Car uses a fully electronic system to operate and control the functions of the climate control system. The basic air conditioning system components are used, but they are supplemented by a series of sensors, switches and electric door actuators to monitor and adjust interior system temperatures and modes to pre-set conditions. Refer to the diagnostic charts and wiring schematics for additional help in diagnosing this system.

ELECTRONIC AUTOMATIC TEMPERATURE CONTROL (EATC) SYSTEM FUNCTIONAL TEST—1993 THUNDERBIRD AND COUGAR

EATC System Functional Test

- The EATC system functional test is designed to find those system failures that the Self Test is unable to test.
- Ensure the engine is cold.
- The in-vehicle temperature should be greater than 10°C (50°F) for proper evaluation of system response.
- Refer to the following charts for testing instructions.

TEST STEP		RESULT	▶	ACTION TO TAKE
A1	TEST 1			
	• Start engine. • Slide blower lever to AUTO.	Control powers up	▶	GO to **A2**.
		Control does not light	▶	REFER to Diagnosis When Self-Test and Functional Test Indicates No Errors Found.
A2	TEST 2			
	• Set control to 75°F and verify that the blower does not come on. (Engine coolant temperature less than 48°C (120°F.)	Blower off	▶	GO to **A3**.
		Blower on	▶	REFER to CELO Inoperative.
A3	TEST 3			
	• Ensure that engine is warm (coolant temperature higher than 48°C (120°F). • Set control at 75 setting.	Blower on	▶	GO to **A4**.
		Blower off	▶	REFER to Blower Speed Controller Diagnosis-No Blower.
A4	TEST 4			
	• Slide blower lever to LO.	Blower goes to low blower	▶	GO to **A5**.
			▶	CHECK battery voltage. If voltage is below 10 volts, REFER to Charging System Diagnosis.
		Blower does not go to low blower	▶	REFER to Blower Speed Controller Diagnosis.
A5	TEST 5			
	• Slide blower lever to HI.	Blower goes to high blower	▶	GO to **A6**.
		Blower does not go to high blower	▶	REFER to Blower Speed Controller Diagnosis.
A6	TEST 6			
	• Press the DEFROST button.	Verify that air is discharged from defroster nozzle with small bleed through the side window demisters. Verify that the outside air / recirc door is in the outside air position.	▶	GO to **A7**.
		Air is not discharged through the defroster or side window demisters.	▶	REFER to Vacuum System Diagnosis.

ELECTRONIC AUTOMATIC TEMPERATURE CONTROL (EATC) SYSTEM FUNCTIONAL TEST—1993 THUNDERBIRD AND COUGAR, CONT'D

TEST STEP		RESULT	▶	ACTION TO TAKE
A7	TEST 7			
	• Press the FLOOR button.	Verify that the air is discharged through the floor ducts.	▶	GO to **A8**.
		Air is not discharged through the floor ducts.	▶	REFER to Vacuum System Diagnosis.
A8	TEST 8			
	• Press the VENT button.	Verify that the air is discharged through the panel ducts.	▶	GO to **A9**.
		Air is not discharged through the panel ducts.	▶	REFER to Vacuum System Diagnosis.
A9	TEST 9			
	• Make sure that the ambient temperature is greater than 40°F. • Press the MAX A/C button.	Verify that the outside air / recirc door is in the recirc position.	▶	GO to **A10**.
		Outside air / recirc door is not in the recirc position.	▶	REFER to Vacuum System Diagnosis.
A10	TEST 10			
	• Press the VENT button.	Verify that the VENT display is lit. Verify that the clutch is off.	▶	GO to **A11**.
		A/C clutch is still on.	▶	REFER to Compressor Clutch Circuit Diagnosis.
A11	TEST 11			
	• Press the MAX / A/C button again.	Verify that the clutch is on.	▶	REFER to Diagnosis When Self-Test And Functional Test Indicate No Errors Found.
		A/C clutch is off.	▶	REFER to Compressor Clutch Circuit Diagnosis.

ELECTRONIC AUTOMATIC TEMPERATURE CONTROL (EATC) SYSTEM (NO CODE) DIAGNOSIS—1993 THUNDERBIRD AND COUGAR

CONDITION	POSSIBLE SOURCE	ACTION
• Cool Discharge Air When System is Set to 90°F and Engine is Warm	• Heater system malfunction. • Blend door not in max. heat.	• Refer to heater system operating principles in this Section. • Check position of blend door. • Check coolant level. • Check blend door shaft attachment. • Test per Blend Door Actuator Diagnosis (assume E2, E6 or E7 was displayed in the Self-Test).
• Warm Discharge Air in Auto/60°F	• Clutch circuit malfunction. • Check refrigerant. • Blend door not in max. A/C position. • Outside/Recirc door not in recirc.	• Test clutch circuit per A/C Compressor Clutch Circuit Diagnosis. • Refer to Refrigerant System Service. • Check position of blend door. • Check blend door shaft attachment. • Test per Blend Door Actuator Diagnosis (assume E2, E6 or E7 was displayed in the Self-Test). • Test per vacuum Leak Diagnosis.
• No Blower	• Damaged CELO switch/wiring. • Damaged blower controller. • Damaged control assembly. • Damaged blower motor. • Damaged wiring.	• Test per No Blower Section of Blower Speed Controller.
• High Blower Only	• Damaged control assembly. • Damaged blower controller. • Damaged wiring.	• Test per High Blower Only Section of Blower Speed Controller.
• Clutch is On in Off Mode	• Damaged control assembly. • Damaged wiring or interface components.	• Test according to A/C Compressor Clutch Circuit Diagnosis.
• Control Assembly Digits Do Not Light Up Blower Off	• Fuse. • Ignition Circuit 298 open. • Ignition Circuit 797 open. • Ground Circuit 57 open. • Damaged control assembly.	• Replace fuse. • Check Circuit 298. • Check Circuit 797. • Check Circuit 57. • Change control assembly.
• Cold Air is Delivered During Heating When Engine is Cold	• Damaged wiring. • Damaged or inoperative engine temperature switch.	• Place system at 85°F/Auto Blower. With ignition off, (ignition must be off when grounding Circuit 244 for valid results) ground Circuit 244 at engine temp. switch. Start vehicle. If blower is off, replace cold engine lockout (CELO). If blower is on, check wiring. If OK, replace control assembly. • Replace engine temperature switch.
• Temperature Set Point Does Not Repeat After Turning Off Ignition	• Circuit 797 not connected to control assembly. • Damaged or inoperative control assembly.	• Remove control assembly connector. With ignition off, check for 12 volts at Pin 14 (Driver's side connector VA). • If no voltage, check fuse/wiring. If voltage, replace control assembly.

ELECTRONIC AUTOMATIC TEMPERATURE CONTROL (EATC) SYSTEM (NO CODE) DIAGNOSIS—1993 THUNDERBIRD AND COUGAR, CONT'D

CONDITION	POSSIBLE SOURCE	ACTION
• Control Assembly Temperature Display Will Not Switch From Fahrenheit To Centigrade When the E/M Trip Computer Button is Pushed	• Damaged or inoperative wiring tripminder or control assembly.	**CAUTION: Accidental shorting of the wrong pin could destroy the control assembly.** • Short Pin 8 of connector VA (Circuit 506) to ground. Turn on ignition. If the display does not switch from F to C, Circuit 506 is open at the control assembly and the control assembly is damaged. Otherwise check the wiring and the tripminder.
• System Does Not Control Temperature	• Sensor hose not connected to aspirator or sensor. • Aspirator not secured to evaporator case. • Sensor seal(s) missing or not installed properly. • Aspirator or sensor hose blocked with foreign material or kinked. • Damaged aspirator hose.	• Inspect and service. • Inspect and service. • Inspect and service. • Inspect and service. • Inspect and service.
• EATC Control Assembly Turns On and Off Erratically. No Control of System	• Damaged charging system. EATC will not function with too low or too high battery voltage.	• **Check battery voltage. If battery voltage is less than 10 volts or greater than 16 volts, check charging system. Do not replace EATC control assembly.**

ELECTRONIC AUTOMATIC TEMPERATURE CONTROL (EATC) IN–CAR SENSOR DIAGNOSIS–1993 THUNDERBIRD AND COUGAR

CONDITION	POSSIBLE SOURCE	ACTION
• Self-Test Error Code E3 or E8	• Sensor open or shorted.	• Disconnect wire harness connector at sensor. Measure resistance across sensor terminals and compare with Sensor Resistance Table below.
	• Wire harness open or shorted.	• Disconnect battery cables. Disconnect wire harness connector from sensor and disconnect both connectors from control assembly. • Check for continuity and for possible shorting between the two wires (Pin 19 and Pin 24 of control assembly connector). Service if necessary. Reconnect wire harness and battery cables.

APPROXIMATE TEMPERATURE	SENSOR RESISTANCE ACCEPTABLE RANGE
10°C to 20°C (50°F to 68°F)	37K to 58K ohms
20°C to 30°C (68°F to 86°F)	24K to 37K ohms
30°C to 40°C (86°F to 104°F)	16K to 24K ohms

ELECTRONIC AUTOMATIC TEMPERATURE CONTROL (EATC) AMBIENT SENSOR DIAGNOSIS–1993 THUNDERBIRD AND COUGAR

CONDITION	POSSIBLE SOURCE	ACTION
• Self-Test Error Code E4 or E9	• Sensor open or shorted.	• Disconnect battery cables. Disconnect the wire harness connector at sensor. Measure resistance across sensor terminal and compare with Sensor Resistance Table in In-Car Temperature Sensor Diagnosis Chart. • If resistance is out of specifications shown in Sensor Resistance Table, replace sensor. If sensor is OK, check sensor wire harness. Reconnect battery cables. NOTE: Install sensor and electrical connections before battery is reconnected.
	• Sensor wire harness open or shorted.	• Disconnect battery cables. Disconnect wire harness connector from sensor and disconnect both connectors from the control assembly. • Inspect for crimped terminals. • Check for continuity and for possible shorting between the two wires (Pins 1 and 24 of control assembly connector). Service if necessary. Reconnect wire harness and battery cables.

ELECTRONIC AUTOMATIC TEMPERATURE CONTROL (EATC) SUNLOAD SENSOR DIAGNOSIS–1993 THUNDERBIRD AND COUGAR

CONDITION	POSSIBLE SOURCE	ACTION
• Self-Test Error Code E5	• Sensor shorted.	• Disconnect battery cables. Disconnect wire harness connector at sensor and disconnect both connectors from control assembly. NOTE: Check the sensor for a short using an ohmmeter. Since the sensor is a Photodiode, there should be some unspecified resistance across the terminals dependent upon the available light in the area. The only test that should be made is for a short circuit (zero resistance). If resistance is zero ohms, replace the sensor. Check for continuity and for possible shorting between the two wires (Pin 12 and Pin 15 of control assembly connector). Repeat if necessary. Reconnect battery cables.

ELECTRONIC AUTOMATIC TEMPERATURE CONTROL (EATC) BLOWER CIRCUIT DIAGNOSIS–1993 THUNDERBIRD AND COUGAR

	TEST STEP	RESULT ▶	ACTION TO TAKE
B1	CHECK BLOWER AT 90°F		
	• Verify that in-vehicle (actual) temperature is less than 85°F. Push VENT button and set control to 90°F. • **Is blower on?**	Yes ▶ No ▶	GO to **B2**. GO to **B3**.
B2	BYPASS CELO SWITCH		
	• Disconnect cold engine lockout (CELO) switch and change temperature setting to 85°F. • **Is blower on?**	Yes ▶ No ▶	REPLACE CELO switch. SERVICE short to ground in CELO circuit.
B3	CHECK IGNITION CIRCUIT		
	NOTE: Unless otherwise noted, leave all electrical connectors in place when checking voltages. • Push the NORM A/C button. Connect a voltmeter between the blower motor Pin 2 and ground.	0 volts ▶ 10 or more volts ▶	SERVICE open fuse or open wire in ignition circuit. GO to **B4**.
B4	CHECK BLOWER MOTOR		
	• Move blower lever to mid-position and connect a voltmeter between Blower Speed Controller (BSC) Pins 4 and 5. • **Is voltage greater than 7 volts?**	No ▶ Yes ▶	REPLACE blower motor. GO to **B5**.
B5	CHECK BSC		
	• Move blower lever to LO and connect voltmeter between BSC Pins 2 and 5.	Voltage is 1 volt or more ▶ Voltage is less than 0.5 volts ▶	REPLACE blower speed controller. GO to **B6**.
B6	CHECK CIRCUIT 246 FOR OPEN		
	• Disconnect blower speed controller connector and measure voltage between Pins 2 and 5 at BSC wiring.	Voltage is 1 volt or more ▶ Voltage is less than 0.5 volts ▶	REPLACE blower speed controller GO to **B7**.
B7	CHECK CIRCUIT 246 FOR SHORT TO GROUND		
	• Connect voltmeter between control assembly Pins 18 and 11 (ground).	Voltage is 1 volt or more ▶ Voltage is less than 0.5 volts ▶	Check circuit 246 between control Pin 18 and BSC Pin 2. GO to **B8**.
B8	CHECK CIRCUIT 246 FOR SHORT		
	• Check circuit 246 for shorts to ground. • **Is circuit grounded?**	Yes ▶ No ▶	SERVICE short to ground in Circuit 246. REPLACE control assembly.

ELECTRONIC AUTOMATIC TEMPERATURE CONTROL (EATC) BLOWER SPEED CONTROLLER DIAGNOSIS–1993 THUNDERBIRD AND COUGAR

	TEST STEP	RESULT	▶	ACTION TO TAKE
C1	CHECK CIRCUIT 515 FOR SHORT TO GROUND			
	• Disconnect the blower speed controller (BSC). • **Is blower on?**	Yes	▶	SERVICE short to ground in Circuit 515 between blower motor Pin 1 and BSC Pin 4.
		No	▶	GO to **C2.**
C2	CHECK CIRCUIT 246			
	• Leave BSC disconnected and check voltage between BSC Pin 2 and Pin 5.	Yes	▶	REPLACE control assembly.
	• **Is voltage 1 volt or more?**	No	▶	GO to **C3.**
C3	CHECK CIRCUIT 57			
	• Leave BSC disconnected and check voltage between BSC Pin 3 and ground.	Yes	▶	REPLACE control assembly.
	• **Is voltage 7 volts or more?**	No	▶	REPLACE BSC.

ELECTRONIC AUTOMATIC TEMPERATURE CONTROL (EATC) COLD ENGINE BLOWER LOCK–OUT (CELO) DIAGNOSIS–THUNDERBIRD AND COUGAR

	TEST STEP	RESULT	▶	ACTION TO TAKE
D1	VERIFY OPERATION			
	• Engine coolant temperature must be less than (110°F) and actual passenger compartment temperature must be less than (85°F). Push the VENT button. Set control to 85°F, AUTO blower mode.	Yes	▶	GO to **D2.**
	• **Is blower on?**	No	▶	CELO OK.
D2	CHECK CIRCUIT 244 FOR OPEN			
	• Turn off ignition. Disconnect CELO wire from switch and short wire to ground. Turn ignition to RUN position.	Yes	▶	SERVICE open in circuit 244 between control assembly and CELO.
	• **Is blower on?**	No	▶	REPLACE CELO switch.

ELECTRONIC AUTOMATIC TEMPERATURE CONTROL (EATC) BLEND DOOR ACTUATOR DIAGNOSIS–1993 THUNDERBIRD AND COUGAR

	TEST STEP	RESULT	▶	ACTION TO TAKE
E1	CHECK ERROR CODES			
	• Check error code(s) identified in the digital display window.	E2, E6, or E7	▶	GO to **E2.**
		Any other number	▶	REFER to error code key.
E2	CHECK ACTUATOR OPERATION			
	• Disconnect the electrical connectors from the control assembly and drive the blend door actuator as follows: Apply +12 volts to Pin 21. Ground Pin 25 of the control assembly connector. The blend door should be driven to full cool. Reverse the leads. The blend door should be driven to full heat.	Yes	▶	GO to **E3.**
	• **Does actuator drive in both directions?**	No	▶	GO to **E5.**
E3	REPEAT SELF-TEST			
	• Connect control assembly and enter self-test diagnostics as outlined.	88°F°C	▶	Blend door actuator OK.
		E2, E6, or E7	▶	GO to **E4.**
E4	CHECK ACTUATOR RESISTANCE			
	• Disconnect control assembly connectors. Measure the resistances between the pins outlined below: Pin 9 (776) to Pin 10 (243): 4.5-5.5K ohms Pin 9 (776) to Pin 4 (351): 0.3-5.5K ohms Pin 4 (351) to Pin 10 (243): 0.3-5.5K ohms	Yes	▶	REPLACE control assembly and WAIT about 30 seconds for the control to calibrate. System OK.
	• **Are resistances in range?**	No	▶	GO to **E5.**
E5	CHECK ACTUATOR WIRING CONNECTOR			
	• Check vehicle wiring harness and connector continuity as shown below: Blend door actuator connector is accessible through the glove compartment.	Continuity good	▶	GO to **E6.**
		No continuity in one or more circuits	▶	GO to **E7.**

Circuit #	Control Pin	Blend Door Pin
351	4	1
776	9	5
243	10	6
249	21	7
250	25	8

CL7414-A

	TEST STEP	RESULT	▶	ACTION TO TAKE
E6	REPLACE BLEND DOOR ACTUATOR			
	• Change blend door actuator. Enter self-test as outlined.	88°F°C	▶	Blend door actuator OK.
		P2, P6, or P7	▶	DEPRESS the COOL button until 88°F°C appears. System OK.
		E2, E6, or E7	▶	GO to **E1.**
E7	SERVICE WIRE HARNESS			
	• Service wiring harness. Connect control assembly and wait about 30 seconds for the system to calibrate.	No error codes	▶	System OK.
		E2, E6, or E7	▶	GO to **E1.**

DIAGNOSIS AND TESTING

SEMI AUTOMATIC TEMPERATURE CONTROL (SATC) DIAGNOSTIC TROUBLE CODE DIRECTORY – 1994 THUNDERBIRD AND COUGAR

Diagnostic Trouble Code	Description	Action
• 01 (Displayed During Diagnostic Procedures)	• Damaged control assembly.	• Go to Pinpoint Test A.
• 02 (Displayed During Diagnostic Procedures) •	• A / C air temperature control door cannot reach desired position. • A / C electronic door actuator motor wiring damaged.	• Go to Pinpoint Test B.
• 03 (Displayed During Diagnostic Procedures)	• Automatic temperature control sensor open.	• Go to Pinpoint Test A.
• 04 (Displayed During Diagnostic Procedures)	• A / C ambient air temperature sensor and bracket	• Go to Pinpoint Test G.
• 05 (Displayed During Diagnostic Procedures)	• A / C sunload sensor short.	• Go to Pinpoint Test H.

DIAGNOSIS AND TESTING (CONTINUED)

SEMI AUTOMATIC TEMPERATURE CONTROL (SATC) SYMPTOM (NO CODE) DIAGNOSIS – 1994 THUNDERBIRD AND COUGAR

CONDITION	POSSIBLE SOURCE	ACTION
• SATC System Inoperative, Intermittent / Improper Tighten Operation	• Circuitry open / shorted. • Damaged automatic temperature control module. • Charging system damaged. • Damaged aspirator hose or elbow.	• Go to Pinpoint Test A.
• Inoperative, Intermittent or Improper Operation	• Circuitry open / shorted. • Damaged A / C blend door actuator / motor. • Damaged EATC module.	• Go to Pinpoint Test B.
• A / C Blower Motor Speed Control Not Operating Correctly	• Circuitry open / shorted. • Damaged A / C blower motor. • Damaged A / C blower motor speed control.	• Go to Pinpoint Test C.
• Temperature Control Lockout Valve and Switch Not Operating Correctly	• Damaged temperature control lockout valve and switch. • Damaged EATC module.	• Go to Pinpoint Test D.
• Temperature Control Lockout Valve and Switch Inoperative	• Damaged temperature control lockout valve and switch. • Damaged EATC module.	• Go to Pinpoint Test D.
• Automatic Temperature Control Solenoid and Manifold Inoperative	• Damaged automatic temperature control solenoid and manifold. • Damaged EATC module. • Circuitry open / shorted.	• Go to Pinpoint Test E.
• Cool Discharge Air When System Is Set to AUTOMATIC and 90°F	• Damaged EATC module.	• Go to Pinpoint Test B.
• Warm Discharge Air In AUTOMATIC and 60°F	• A / C clutch malfunction. • Low refrigerant. • Damaged EATC module.	• Go to Pinpoint Test F.
• A / C Ambient Air Temperature Sensor and Bracket Inoperative	• Damaged A / C ambient air temperature sensor and bracket. • Circuitry open / shorted.	• Go to Pinpoint Test G.
• A / C Sunload Sensor Inoperative	• Damaged A / C sunload sensor. • Circuitry open / shorted.	• Go to Pinpoint Test H.
• Control Assembly / VFD Does Not Light Up—A / C Blower Motor OFF	• Circuitry open / shorted. • Damaged EATC module.	• Go to Pinpoint Test I.
• Cold Air Delivered During Heating When Engine Is Cold	• Damaged automatic temperature control solenoid and manifold. • Damaged EATC module.	• Go to Pinpoint Test J.
• System Does Not Control Temperature	• Circuitry open / shorted. • Damaged EATC module. • Damaged aspirator hose or elbow.	• Go to Pinpoint Test A.
• Control Assembly Turns On and OFF Erratically—No Control of System	• Damaged EATC module. • Charging system damaged.	• Go to Pinpoint Test A.
• Temperature Display Won't Switch Between Celsius and Fahrenheit	• Circuitry open / shorted. • Damaged EATC module.	• Go to Pinpoint Test K.
• Temperature Set Point Does Not Repeat After Turning Ignition Switch OFF	• Blown fuse. • Circuitry open / shorted. • Damaged EATC module.	• Go to Pinpoint Test L.

DIAGNOSIS AND TESTING (CONTINUED)

Pinpoint Tests

PINPOINT TEST A: SATC SYSTEM INOPERATIVE, INTERMITTENT OR IMPROPER OPERATION

	TEST STEP	RESULT	ACTION TO TAKE
A1	CHECK POWER SUPPLY TO SATC MODULE		
	• Partially remove SATC module as outlined. • Turn ignition switch to the RUN position. • Turn SATC control to ON position. • Using a test lamp connected to a known good ground, check Circuit 298 (P / O) at Pin 11 of 13-pin connector and Circuit 276 (BR) at Pin 13 of other connector. • **Did test lamp illuminate?**	Yes ▶ No ▶	GO to **A2.** SERVICE Circuit 298 (P / O) for open circuit. RESTORE vehicle. RETEST system.
A2	CHECK SYSTEM GROUND		
	• Using an ohmmeter connected to a known good ground, connect second lead of Circuit 57 (BK) at Pin 24 of 13-pin connector. • Measure resistance. • **Is resistance 5 ohms or less?**	Yes ▶ No ▶	GO to **A3.** SERVICE Circuit 57 (BK) for open. RESTORE vehicle. RETEST system.
A3	CHECK SATC CONTROL MODULE		
	• Start engine. • Press any A / C or heater button. • **Did A / C or heater actuate?**	Yes ▶ No ▶	GO to **A4.** REPLACE SATC module. RESTORE vehicle. RETEST system.
A4	CHECK ASPIRATOR INSTALLATION		
	• Gain access to aspirator, hose / elbow assembly as outlined. • Check for proper installation of aspirator, hose / elbow. • **Is aspirator installed properly and hose connected?**	Yes ▶ No ▶	GO to **A5.** SERVICE aspirator, hose / elbow as necessary. RESTORE vehicle. RETEST system.
A5	CHECK AUTOMATIC TEMPERATURE CONTROL SENSOR OUTPUT AT SATC MODULE		
	• Turn engine off. Leave ignition switch in RUN position. • Disconnect automatic temperature control sensor. • Using a voltmeter, check Circuit 790 (W / O) at Pin 17 of 13-pin connector for voltage. • **Is voltage present?**	Yes ▶ No ▶	GO to **A6.** REPLACE SATC module. RESTORE vehicle. RETEST system.
A6	CHECK AUTOMATIC TEMPERATURE CONTROL CIRCUIT 790 (W / O)		
	• Turn ignition switch OFF. • Using an ohmmeter, check Circuit 790 (W / O) from SATC module to automatic temperature control sensor connector. • **Is there continuity?**	Yes ▶ No ▶	GO to **A7.** SERVICE Circuit 790 (W / O) for open. RESTORE vehicle. RETEST system.
A7	CHECK AUTOMATIC TEMPERATURE CONTROL SENSOR RETURN CIRCUIT		
	• Using an ohmmeter, check Circuit 470 (PK / BK) for continuity from SATC module to aspirator connector. • **Is there continuity?**	Yes ▶ No ▶	REPLACE automatic temperature control sensor. RESTORE vehicle. RETEST system. SERVICE Circuit 470 (PK / BK) for open. RESTORE vehicle. RETEST system.

DIAGNOSIS AND TESTING (CONTINUED)

PINPOINT TEST B: A/C ELECTRONIC DOOR ACTUATOR MOTOR INOPERATIVE, INTERMITTENT OR IMPROPER OPERATION

<table>
<tr><th colspan="2">TEST STEP</th><th>RESULT ▶</th><th>ACTION TO TAKE</th></tr>
<tr><td>B1</td><td>CHECK FOR SUPPLY TO MOTOR</td><td rowspan="2">Yes ▶
No ▶</td><td rowspan="2">GO to B3.
GO to B2.</td></tr>
<tr><td colspan="2">• Gain access to A/C electronic door actuator motor as outlined.
• Turn ignition switch to RUN position.
• Using a voltmeter, check Circuit 249 (DB/LG) for voltage at motor connector.
• Is voltage present?</td></tr>
<tr><td>B2</td><td>CHECK CIRCUIT 249 (DB/LG)</td><td rowspan="2">Yes ▶
No ▶</td><td rowspan="2">GO to B3.
SERVICE Circuit 249 (DB/LG) for open. RESTORE vehicle. RETEST system.</td></tr>
<tr><td colspan="2">• Turn ignition switch OFF.
• Disconnect A/C blend door actuator.
• Partially remove automatic temperature control sensor.
• Using an ohmmeter, check Circuit 249 (DG/LG) for continuity from automatic temperature control sensor to actuator motor.
• Measure resistance.
• Is resistance 5 ohms or less?</td></tr>
<tr><td>B3</td><td>CHECK CIRCUIT 250 (O)</td><td rowspan="2">Yes ▶
No ▶</td><td rowspan="2">GO to B4.
SERVICE Circuit 250 (O) for open. RESTORE vehicle. RETEST system.</td></tr>
<tr><td colspan="2">• Using ohmmeter, check Circuit 250 (O) for continuity from module to actuator motor.
• Measure resistance.
• Is resistance 5 ohms or less?</td></tr>
<tr><td>B4</td><td>CHECK BLEND DOOR ACTUATOR FEEDBACK CIRCUITS FOR CONTINUITY FROM ACTUATOR TO A/C BLEND DOOR ACTUATOR MOTOR</td><td rowspan="2">Yes ▶
No ▶</td><td rowspan="2">GO to B5.
SERVICE suspect circuit for open. RESTORE vehicle. RETEST system.</td></tr>
<tr><td colspan="2"><table>
<tr><th>Pin Number</th><th>Circuit</th><th>Circuit Function</th></tr>
<tr><td>26</td><td>243 (LG/O)</td><td>Actuator Feedback Potentiometer +</td></tr>
<tr><td>5</td><td>351 (BR/W)</td><td>Actuator Feedback Potentiometer Wiper</td></tr>
<tr><td>6</td><td>776 (O/BK)</td><td>Actuator Feedback Potentiometer -</td></tr>
</table>
• Is resistance 5 ohms or less?</td></tr>
<tr><td>B5</td><td>CHECK A/C BLEND DOOR ACTUATOR MOTOR</td><td rowspan="2">Yes ▶
No ▶</td><td rowspan="2">REPLACE automatic temperature control sensor. RESTORE vehicle. RETEST system.
REPLACE A/C blend door actuator motor. RESTORE vehicle. RETEST system.</td></tr>
<tr><td colspan="2">• Reconnect blend door motor, start engine.
• Push any A/C or heater button.
• Push any other function and listen carefully for blend door operation.
• Did blend door motor run?</td></tr>
</table>

DIAGNOSIS AND TESTING (CONTINUED)

PINPOINT TEST C: A/C BLOWER MOTOR SPEED CONTROL NOT OPERATING CORRECTLY

TEST STEP		RESULT ▶	ACTION TO TAKE
C1	CHECK BLOWER MOTOR SUPPLY VOLTAGE		
	• Gain access to the blower motor control connector. • Turn ignition switch to the ON position. • Using a voltmeter, check voltage at Circuit 687 (GY/Y) at motor connector. • **Is voltage 10 volts or more?**	Yes ▶ No ▶	GO to **C4.** GO to **C2.**
C2	CHECK CIRCUIT 687 (GY/Y) FOR SHORT		
	• Remove blower Fuse 30A at primary junction block. • Using an ohmmeter connected to a known good ground, connect second lead to Circuit 687 (GY/Y) at A/C blower motor. • Measure resistance. • **Is resistance 5 ohms or less?**	Yes ▶ No ▶	SERVICE Circuit 687 (GY/Y) for short. REPLACE fuse. RESTORE vehicle. RETEST system. GO to **C3.**
C3	CHECK CIRCUIT 687 (GY/Y) FOR OPEN		
	• Disconnect A/C blower motor control. Connect a jumper wire to Circuit 687 (GY/Y) at blower motor control connector. Connect other end to a known good ground. • Using an ohmmeter connected to a known good ground, connect second lead to Circuit 687 (GY/Y). • Measure resistance. • **Is resistance 5 ohms or less?**	Yes ▶ No ▶	GO to **C4.** SERVICE Circuit 687 (GY/Y) for open. RESTORE vehicle. RETEST system.
C4	CHECK BLOWER MOTOR SPEED CONTROL GROUND		
	• Gain access to A/C blower motor speed control as outlined. • Using an ohmmeter connected to a known good ground, connect second lead to Circuit 57 (BK) at A/C blower motor speed control connector, J1-2. • Measure resistance. • **Is resistance 5 ohms or less?**	Yes ▶ No ▶	GO to **C5.** SERVICE Circuit 57 (BK) for open. RESTORE vehicle. RETEST system.
C5	CHECK BLOWER MOTOR		
	• **Reconnect A/C blower motor and blower Fuse 30A.** • **Move heater blower motor switch to mid-position and connect a voltmeter between Circuits 515 (O/R) and 57 (BK).** • **Push the A/C button.** • **Measure voltage.** • **Is voltage greater than 7 volts?**	Yes ▶ No ▶	GO to **C6.** REPLACE A/C blower motor. RESTORE vehicle. RETEST system.
C6	CHECK CIRCUIT 246 (P)		
	• **Leave voltmeter connected. Disconnect A/C blower motor speed control.** • **Measure voltage of Circuit 246 (P).** • **Is voltage greater than 1 volt?**	Yes ▶ No ▶	REPLACE A/C blower motor speed control. RESTORE vehicle. RETEST system. GO to **C7.**
C7	CHECK CIRCUIT 246 (P) FOR OPEN		
	• **Connect voltmeter to Circuit 246 (P) at SATC module Pin 23 and Circuit 57 (BK) Pin 24 at SATC module.** • **Measure voltage.** • **Is voltage greater that 1 volt?**	Yes ▶ No ▶	SERVICE Circuit 246 (P) for open. RESTORE vehicle. RETEST system. GO to **C8.**
C8	CHECK CIRCUIT 246 (P) FOR SHORT		
	• **Using an ohmmeter connected to a known good ground, connect second lead to Circuit 246 (P) at SATC module Pin 23.** • **Measure resistance.** • **Is resistance 5 ohms or less?**	Yes ▶ No ▶	SERVICE Circuit 246 (P) for short. RESTORE vehicle. RETEST system. REPLACE SATC control module. RESTORE vehicle. RETEST system.

DIAGNOSIS AND TESTING (CONTINUED)

PINPOINT TEST D: TEMPERATURE CONTROL LOCKOUT VALVE AND SWITCH NOT OPERATING CORRECTLY

TEST STEP		RESULT ▶	ACTION TO TAKE
D1	CHECK LOCKOUT VALVE AND SWITCH OPERATION		
	• Engine coolant temperature must be cold and inside vehicle temperature must be less than 29°C (85°F). • Heater blower motor switch must be AUTO position. • Turn ignition switch to RUN position. • Set control to 85°F and push the vent button. • **Did heater blower turn on?**	Yes ▶ No ▶	GO to **D2.** Temperature control lockout valve and switch OK. RETEST system.
D2	CHECK CIRCUIT 244 (Y/W)		
	• Turn ignition switch OFF. • Disconnect temperature control lockout valve and switch as outlined. • Using a jumper wire connected to a known good ground, connect other end to Circuit 244 (Y/W) at switch connector. • Turn ignition switch to the RUN position. • **Did blower motor run?**	Yes ▶ No ▶	SERVICE Circuit 244 (Y/W) for open. RESTORE vehicle. RETEST system. REPLACE temperature lockout valve and switch. RESTORE vehicle. RETEST system.

PINPOINT TEST E: ELECTRO VACUUM SOLENOID INOPERATIVE

TEST STEP		RESULT ▶	ACTION TO TAKE
E1	CHECK ELECTRO VACUUM SOLENOID SUPPLY		
	• Start engine. • Push NORM A/C button. • Gain access to the automatic temperature control solenoid and manifold as outlined. • Using a test lamp connected to a known good ground, check Circuit 599 (PK/LG) for voltage. • **Did test lamp illuminate?**	Yes ▶ No ▶	GO to **E3.** GO to **E2.**
E2	CHECK CIRCUIT 599 (PK/LG)		
	• Turn engine off, ignition switch to the ON position. • Partially remove SATC module as outlined. • Using test lamp, check Circuit 599 (PK/LG) for voltage at SATC module Pin 14. • **Did test illuminate?**	Yes ▶ No ▶	SERVICE Circuit 599 (PK/LG) for open. RESTORE vehicle. RETEST system. REPLACE SATC module. RESTORE vehicle. RETEST system.
E3	CHECK ELECTRO VACUUM SOLENOID GROUND		
	• Using an ohmmeter connected to a known good ground, connect second lead to Circuit 57 (BK) at automatic temperature control solenoid and manifold. • Measure resistance. • **Is resistance 5 ohms or less?**	Yes ▶ No ▶	GO to **E4.** SERVICE Circuit 57 (BK) for open. RESTORE vehicle. RETEST system.
E4	CHECK VACUUM SUPPLY TO SOLENOID		
	• Start engine. • Disconnect black vacuum hose at solenoid. • Check for vacuum. • **Is vacuum present?**	Yes ▶ No ▶	GO to **E5.** SERVICE black vacuum hose for damage. RESTORE vehicle. RETEST system.
E5	CHECK WHITE VACUUM HOSE		
	• Reconnect black vacuum hose. • Push NORM A/C button. • Disconnect white vacuum hose at electro vacuum solenoid. • Check for vacuum. • **Is vacuum present?**	Yes ▶ No ▶	REPLACE outside recirculate door vacuum motor. RESTORE vehicle. RETEST system. REPLACE automatic temperature control solenoid and manifold. RESTORE vehicle. RETEST system.

DIAGNOSIS AND TESTING (CONTINUED)

PINPOINT TEST F: WARM DISCHARGE AIR IN AUTOMATIC AND 60°F

TEST STEP		RESULT	▶ ACTION TO TAKE
F1	CHECK A/C CLUTCH OPERATION		
	• Start engine. • Push MAX A/C button, set temperature to coldest setting. • **Is A/C system operating properly?**	Yes No	▶ GO to **F2.** ▶ REPLACE A/C Clutch.
F2	CHECK A/C ELECTRONIC DOOR ACTUATOR MOTOR OPERATION		
	• Push DEF/FLR button. • **Did air circulation switch to defrost?**	Yes No	▶ GO to Pinpoint Test E. ▶ GO to Pinpoint Test B.

PINPOINT TEST G: A/C AMBIENT AIR TEMPERATURE SENSOR INOPERATIVE

TEST STEP		RESULT	▶ ACTION TO TAKE
G1	CHECK CIRCUIT 788 (R/O) AT A/C AMBIENT AIR TEMPERATURE SENSOR		
	• Turn ignition switch to the RUN position. • Turn SATC module to NORM A/C position. • Partially remove SATC module as outlined. • Gain access to the A/C ambient air temperature sensor and bracket as outlined. Disconnect A/C ambient air temperature sensor and bracket. • Using voltmeter, check Circuit 788 (R/O) for voltage at sensor connector. • **Is voltage 10 volts or more?**	Yes No	▶ GO to **G4.** ▶ GO to **G2.**
G2	CHECK CIRCUIT 788 (R/O) AT SATC MODULE		
	• Using voltmeter, check Circuit 788 (R/O) at SATC module Pin 1 for voltage. • **Is voltage 10 volts or more?**	Yes No	▶ GO to **G3.** ▶ REPLACE SATC module. RESTORE vehicle. RETEST system.
G3	CHECK CIRCUIT 788 (R/O) FOR OPEN		
	• Turn ignition switch to the OFF position. • Using a jumper connected to a known good ground, connect other end to Circuit 788 (R/O) at sensor connector. • Using an ohmmeter connected to a known good ground, connect second lead to Circuit 788 (R/O) at SATC module connector Pin 1. • Measure resistance. • **Is resistance 5 ohms or less?**	Yes No	▶ GO to **G4.** ▶ SERVICE Circuit 788 (R/O) for open. RESTORE vehicle. RETEST system.
G4	CHECK CIRCUIT 470 (PK/BK)		
	• Connect jumper to Circuit 470 (PK/BK) at sensor connector. • Using an ohmmeter connected to a known good ground, connect second lead to Circuit 470 (PK/BK) at module connector Pin 22. • Measure resistance. • **Is resistance 5 ohms or less?**	Yes No	▶ REPLACE A/C ambient air temperature sensor and bracket. RESTORE vehicle. RETEST system. ▶ SERVICE Circuit 470 (PK/BK) for open. RESTORE vehicle. RETEST system.

DIAGNOSIS AND TESTING (CONTINUED)

PINPOINT TEST H: A/C SUNLOAD SENSOR INOPERATIVE

TEST STEP		RESULT ▶	ACTION TO TAKE
H1	CHECK CIRCUIT 468 (BR) AT SENSOR CONNECTOR		
	• Turn ignition switch to the RUN position. • Turn SATC module to NORM A/C position. • Partially remove SATC module as outlined. • Gain access to the A/C sunload sensor as outlined. Disconnect A/C sunload sensor. • Using voltmeter, check Circuit 468 (BR) for voltage at A/C sunload sensor connector. • **Is voltage 10 volts or more?**	Yes ▶ No ▶	GO to **H4.** GO to **H2.**
H2	CHECK CIRCUIT 468 (BR) AT SATC MODULE		
	• Using voltmeter, check Circuit 468 (BR) at SATC module Pin 16 for voltage. • **Is voltage 10 volts or more?**	Yes ▶ No ▶	GO to **H3.** REPLACE SATC module. RESTORE vehicle. RETEST system.
H3	CHECK CIRCUIT 468 (BR) FOR OPEN		
	• Turn ignition switch to the OFF position. • Using a jumper connected to a known good ground, connect other end to Circuit 468 (BR) at sensor connector. • Using an ohmmeter connected to a known good ground, connect second lead to Circuit 468 (BR) at SATC module connector Pin 16. • Measure resistance. • **Is resistance 5 ohms or less?**	Yes ▶ No ▶	GO to **H4.** SERVICE Circuit 468 (BR) for open. RESTORE vehicle. RETEST system.
H4	CHECK CIRCUIT 476 (BR/Y)		
	• Connect jumper to Circuit 476 (BR/Y) at sensor connector. • Using an ohmmeter connected to a known good ground, connect second lead to Circuit 476 (BR/Y) at module connector Pin 13. • Measure resistance. • **Is resistance 5 ohms or less?**	Yes ▶ No ▶	REPLACE A/C ambient air temperature sensor and bracket. RESTORE vehicle. RETEST system. SERVICE Circuit 476 (BR/Y) for open. RESTORE vehicle. RETEST system.

PINPOINT TEST I: CONTROL ASSEMBLY/VFD DOES NOT LIGHT UP—HEATER BLOWER MOTOR OFF

TEST STEP		RESULT ▶	ACTION TO TAKE
I1	CHECK ILLUMINATION SUPPLY TO SATC MODULE		
	• Turn headlamp switch to the PARK LAMP or HEADLAMP position. • Rotate headlamp dimmer sensor control to full-on without turning the dome lamp on. • Partially remove SATC module as outlined. • Using a test lamp, check Circuit 19 (LB/R) for voltage. • **Did test lamp illuminate?**	Yes ▶ No ▶	GO to **I2.** SERVICE Circuit 19 (LB/R) for open.
I2	CHECK SATC SYSTEM GROUND		
	• Using an ohmmeter connected to a known good ground, connect second lead to Circuit 57 (BK), Pin 24 at SATC module connector. • Measure resistance. • **Is resistance 5 ohms or less?**	Yes ▶	REPLACE SATC control module. RESTORE vehicle. RETEST system.

DIAGNOSIS AND TESTING (CONTINUED)

PINPOINT TEST J: COLD AIR DELIVERED DURING HEATING WHEN ENGINE IS COLD

TEST STEP		RESULT ▶	ACTION TO TAKE
J1	CHECK CIRCUIT 244 (Y/W)		
	• Disconnect temperature control lockout valve and switch. • Turn ignition switch to the OFF position. • Using a jumper wire connected to known good ground, connect other end to Circuit 244 (Y/W). • Start engine and observe if A/C blower motor is running. • **Is blower motor running?**	Yes ▶ No ▶	GO to **J2**. REPLACE temperature control lockout valve and switch. RESTORE vehicle. RETEST system.
J2	CHECK CIRCUIT 244 (Y/W) FOR OPEN		
	• Turn ignition switch to the OFF position. • Leave jumper wire connected. • Partially remove SATC module as outlined. • Using an ohmmeter connected to a known good ground, connect second lead to Circuit 244 (Y/W) at SATC connector. • Measure resistance. • **Is resistance 5 ohms or less?**	Yes ▶ No ▶	REPLACE SATC module. RESTORE vehicle. RETEST system. SERVICE Circuit 244 (Y/W) for open. RESTORE vehicle. RETEST system.

PINPOINT TEST K: TEMPERATURE DISPLAY WON'T SWITCH BETWEEN CELSIUS AND FAHRENHEIT

TEST STEP		RESULT ▶	ACTION TO TAKE
K1	CHECK CIRCUIT 506(R) FOR OPEN		
	CAUTION: Accidental shorting of the wrong pin could destroy the control assembly. • With ignition switch in the OFF position, partially remove SATC module as outlined. • Using a jumper wire connected to a known good ground, connect other end to Circuit 506 (R), Pin 20 at module connector. • Turn ignition switch to the RUN position. • **Did display change?**	Yes ▶ No ▶	GO to **K2**. SERVICE Circuit 506 (R) for open. REPLACE damaged SATC module. RESTORE vehicle. RETEST system.
K2	CHECK CIRCUIT 506 (R) FOR SHORT		
	CAUTION: Accidental shorting of the wrong pin could destroy the control assembly. • Leave jumper connected. • Using an ohmmeter connected to a known good ground, connect other end to Circuit 506 (R) at SATC module connector Pin 20. • Measure resistance. • **Is resistance 5 ohms or less?**	Yes ▶ No ▶	SERVICE Circuit 506 (R) for short. RESTORE vehicle. RETEST system. REPLACE damaged SATC module. RESTORE vehicle. RETEST system.

PINPOINT TEST L: TEMPERATURE SET POINT DOES NOT REPEAT AFTER TURNING IGNITION SWITCH OFF

TEST STEP		RESULT ▶	ACTION TO TAKE
L1	CHECK MEMORY SUPPLY TO SATC MODULE		
	• With ignition switch in the OFF position, partially remove SATC control module as outlined. • Using a voltmeter, check Circuit 797 (LG/P) for voltage at SATC module Pin 12. • **Is battery voltage present?**	Yes ▶ No ▶	REPLACE SATC module. RESTORE vehicle. RETEST system. GO to **L2**.
L2	CHECK CIRCUIT 797 (LG/P) SUPPLY		
	• Remove memory Fuse (5A) at power distribution box. • Using an ohmmeter, check Circuit 797 (LG/P) from SATC module connector Pin 12 to output side of memory fuse (5A) cavity for continuity. • **Is resistance 5 ohms or less?**	Yes ▶ No ▶	REPLACE SATC module. RESTORE vehicle. RETEST system. SERVICE Circuit 797 (LG/P) for open. RESTORE vehicle. RETEST system.

DIAGNOSIS AND TESTING (CONTINUED)

SEMI AUTOMATIC TEMPERATURE CONTROL (SATC) DIAGNOSTIC TROUBLE CODES – 1995 THUNDERBIRD AND COUGAR

TROUBLE CODES	DETECTED CONDITION	ACTION
24	Fault in blend door calibration during self test	Refer to Temperature Blend Door Actuator Diagnosis (Pinpoint Test A)
25	Intermittent fault in blend door calibration	Refer to Temperature Blend Door Actuator Diagnosis (Pinpoint Test A)
30	Self test indicates in-car sensor shorted	Refer to In-Car Temperature Sensor Diagnosis (Pinpoint Test M)
31	Self test indicates in-car sensor open	Refer to In-Car Temperature Sensor Diagnosis (Pinpoint Test M)
40	Self test indicates ambient temperature sensor shorted	Refer to Ambient Temperature Sensor Diagnosis (Pinpoint Test J)
41	Self test indicates ambient temperature sensor open	Refer to Ambient Temperature Sensor Diagnosis (Pinpoint Test J)
42	Ambient temperature sensor intermittent short	Refer to Ambient Temperature Sensor Diagnosis (Pinpoint Test J)
43	Ambient temperature sensor intermittent open	Refer to Ambient Temperature Sensor Diagnosis (Pinpoint Test J)
50	Self test indicates sunload sensor short	Refer to Sunload Sensor Diagnosis (Pinpoint Test K)
53	Sunload sensor intermittent short	Refer to Sunload Sensor Diagnosis (Pinpoint Test K)

SEMI AUTOMATIC TEMPERATURE CONTROL (SATC) SYMPTOM (NO CODE) DIAGNOSIS – 1995 THUNDERBIRD AND COUGAR

CONDITION	POSSIBLE SOURCE	ACTION
• SATC System Inoperative, Intermittent or Improper Operation	• Circuitry open / shorted. • Damaged input sensor(s) / erratic input signals. • Charging system damaged. • Damaged automatic temperature control sensor hose and elbow.	• GO to Pinpoint Test A.
• A / C Electronic Door Actuator Motor Inoperative, Intermittent or Improper Operation	• Circuitry open / shorted. • Damaged A / C electronic door actuator motor. • Damaged SATC module.	• GO to Pinpoint Test B.
• A / C Blower Motor Does Not Run	• Circuitry open / shorted. • Damaged blower motor. • Damaged A / C blower motor speed control.	• GO to Pinpoint Test C.
• A / C Blower Motor Runs Continuously in High Speed	• Damaged A / C blower motor speed control. • Damaged SATC module.	• GO to Pinpoint Test D.
• A / C Blower Motor Runs Erratically or at One Speed Only	• Damaged A / C blower motor speed control. • Damaged SATC module.	• GO to Pinpoint Test E.
• Temperature Control Lockout Valve and Switch Not Operating Correctly	• Damaged temperature control lockout valve and switch. • Damaged SATC module.	• GO to Pinpoint Test A, then REFER to Pinpoint Test F.
• Electro-Vacuum Solenoid Inoperative	• Damaged electro-vacuum solenoid. • Damaged SATC module. • Circuitry open / shorted.	• GO to Pinpoint Test F, then REFER to Pinpoint Test G.
• Cool Discharge Air When System Is Set to AUTOMATIC and 90°F	• Damaged SATC module. • Temperature blend door not on MAX heat position.	• GO to Pinpoint Test A, then REFER to Pinpoint Tests M and J. • GO to Pinpoint Test A, then REFER to Pinpoint Test B.

DIAGNOSIS AND TESTING (CONTINUED)

SATC AIR CONDITIONING SYSTEM (Continued)

CONDITION	POSSIBLE SOURCE	ACTION
• Warm Discharge Air In AUTOMATIC and 60°F	• A/C clutch malfunction. • Low refrigerant. • Damaged SATC module. • Temperature blend door not in MAX A/C position.	• GO to Pinpoint Test A, then REFER to Pinpoint Test H. • GO to Pinpoint Test A, then REFER to Pinpoint Test B.
• A/C Ambient Air Temperature Sensor Inoperative	• Damaged A/C ambient air temperature sensor. • Circuitry open/shorted.	• GO to Pinpoint Test A, then REFER to Pinpoint Test J.
• A/C Sunload Sensor Inoperative	• Damaged A/C sunload sensor. • Circuitry open/shorted.	• GO to Pinpoint Test A, then REFER to Pinpoint Test K.
• Control Assembly/VFD Does Not Light Up—Heater Blower Motor OFF	• Circuitry open/shorted. • Damaged SATC module.	• GO to Pinpoint Test A, then REFER to Pinpoint Test L.
• Cold Air Delivered During Heating When Engine is Cold	• Damaged temperature control lockout valve and switch. • Damaged SATC module.	• GO to Pinpoint Test A, then REFER to Pinpoint Test F.
• System Does Not Control Temperature	• Circuitry open/shorted. • Damaged SATC module. • Damaged automatic temperature control sensor hose and elbow.	• GO to Pinpoint Test A, then REFER to Pinpoint Tests M and J.
• Control Assembly Turns On and OFF Erratically—No Control of System	• Damaged SATC module. • Charging system damaged.	• GO to Pinpoint Test A.
• In-car Temperature Sensor Inoperative	• Damaged automatic temperature control sensor. • Damaged SATC module.	• GO to Pinpoint Test M.
• Temperature Set Point Does Not Repeat After Turning Ignition Switch OFF	• Blown fuse. • Circuitry open/shorted. • Damaged EATC module.	• GO to Pinpoint Test A, then REFER to Pinpoint Test N.

Pinpoint Tests

PINPOINT TEST A: SATC SYSTEM INOPERATIVE, INTERMITTENT OR IMPROPER OPERATION

TEST STEP		RESULT ▶	ACTION TO TAKE
A1	PERFORM SYSTEM SELF TEST		
	• Enter system self test. • **Are error codes displayed?**	Yes ▶ No ▶	REFER to Diagnostic Trouble Code Chart. GO to **A2**.
A2	CHECK SYSTEM OPERATION		
	• Check VFD to determine if system has power. • **Does VFD illuminate and show selected temperature?**	Yes ▶ No ▶	GO to **A8**. GO to **A3**.
A3	CHECK SYSTEM POWER SUPPLY		
	• Partially remove SATC control assembly from instrument panel as outlined. Turn ignition switch to RUN and select any operating position on SATC control. • Using a test lamp connected to a known good ground, check Circuit 298 (P/O) at Pin 11 of control assembly left connector and Pin 4 of function selector switch connector for power. Wiggle the wire to check for an intermittent condition during this test. • **Does test lamp illuminate continuously?**	Yes ▶ No ▶	GO to **A4**. GO to **A5**.

DIAGNOSIS AND TESTING (CONTINUED)

PINPOINT TEST A: SATC SYSTEM INOPERATIVE, INTERMITTENT OR IMPROPER OPERATION (Continued)

	TEST STEP	RESULT	▶ ACTION TO TAKE
A4	CHECK GROUND CIRCUIT		
	• Check continuity of ground circuit with an ohmmeter from Pin 24 (BLACK wire in control left connector) to a known good ground. Wiggle the wire during this test to check for an intermittent condition. • **Is resistance five ohms or less without fluctuation?**	Yes No	▶ GO to A7. ▶ SERVICE Circuit 57 (BK) for open or bad connection causing high resistance. CHECK system for proper operation.
A5	CHECK FUSE		
	• Check 5 amp fuse supplying power at Circuit 298 (P/O). • **Is fuse good?**	Yes No	▶ CHECK Circuit 298 (P/O) for an open circuit. REPAIR as necessary and CHECK system operation. ▶ CHECK Circuit 298 (P/O) for short to ground. REPAIR as necessary, INSTALL new fuse and CHECK system operation.
A6	CHECK FUNCTION SELECTOR SWITCH OPERATION		
	• Perform a continuity check on the A/C damper door switch. • **Does the function selector switch test OK?**	Yes No	▶ CHECK Circuit 276 (BR) for an open. REPAIR as necessary and CHECK system operation. ▶ REPLACE the A/C damper door switch and CHECK system operation.
A7	CHECK FUNCTION SELECTOR SWITCH CONTINUITY		
	• With SATC control assembly removed as in Step A3, turn ignition switch to RUN and the A/C damper door switch to any operating position. • Using a test lamp connected to a known good ground, check Circuit 276 (BR) at Pin 13 of control assembly left connector for power. • **Does test lamp illuminate?**	Yes No	▶ GO to **A8.** ▶ GO to **A6.**
A8	CHECK ASPIRATOR HOSE		
	• Check automatic temperature control sensor hose and elbow to determine if the hose is connected to the automatic temperature control sensor and to the A/C evaporator housing. • **Are the automatic temperature control sensor hose and elbow connected as described?**	Yes No	▶ GO to **A9.** ▶ CONNECT automatic temperature control sensor hose and elbow and CHECK system operation.
A9	CHECK BLOWER MOTOR OPERATION		
	• Install SATC control assembly. Turn ignition switch to RUN and move blower control knob to AUTO position. Select 90°F at the SATC control and check blower motor operation. • **Does blower motor go to high speed?**	Yes No	▶ GO to **A10.** ▶ PERFORM Blower Speed Controller Diagnosis. REFER to Pinpoint Test C.
A10	CHECK BLOWER SPEED CONTROLLER OPERATION		
	• Lower set temperature from 90°F to 60°F in one degree increments and observe blower motor speed changes. • **Does blower motor speed decrease to low speed and then increase to high speed at 60°F?**	Yes No	▶ GO to **A11.** ▶ PERFORM Blower Speed Controller Diagnosis. REFER to Pinpoint Test C.
A11	CHECK A/C CLUTCH		
	• Start engine and select MAX A/C. • **Does A/C clutch engage?**	Yes No	▶ GO to **A1.** ▶ GO to Pinpoint Test H.

DIAGNOSIS AND TESTING (CONTINUED)

PINPOINT TEST B: A/C ELECTRONIC DOOR ACTUATOR MOTOR INOPERATIVE, INTERMITTENT OR IMPROPER OPERATION

	TEST STEP	RESULT	►	ACTION TO TAKE
B1	CHECK FOR CODE			
	NOTE: Letters in parentheses indicate (wire color, circuit no.). See wiring schematics and wiring harness connector end views for circuit identification. • Go to Inspection and Verification in this section and check for SATC error codes. • **Does code "24" display?**	Yes No	► ►	GO to **B2.** GO to Pinpoint Test A.
B2	CHECK ACTUATOR DRIVE			
	• Disconnect both connectors from EATC control head and drive actuator in both directions using any 9-12 volt battery. • Connect battery jumper wires to the following pins: a. Pin 21(+) 249 (DB/LG) and Pin 22 (-) 250 (O). This drives the actuator CW - max cooling. b. Pin 21 (-) 249 (DB/LG) and Pin 22 (+) 250 (O). This drives the actuator CCW - max heating. • **Does actuator drive in both directions?**	Yes No	► ►	GO to **B3.** GO to **B6.**
B3	RETEST SATC SYSTEM			
	• Reconnect control assembly and perform Pinpoint Test A. • **Is test successful?**	Yes No	► ►	Test complete. RESTORE vehicle. GO to **B4.**
B4	MEASURE ACTUATOR RESISTANCE			
	• Using the technique outlined in Step B2, set actuator to full CCW travel (max heat) applying power for 15-20 seconds. • Using any digital or dial type volt-ohmmeter, measure resistance at ATC control module connector as follows: a. Pin 26 (243 (LG/O)) to Pin 6 (776 (O/BK)) 4,500-6,000 ohms b. Pin 5 (351 (BR/W)) to Pin 6 (776 (O/BK)) 250-1,500 ohms c. Pin 5 (351 (BR/W)) to Pin 26 (243 (LG/O)) 3,500-6,000 ohms • **Are all resistance measurements within the acceptable range?**	Yes No	► ►	GO to **B5.** GO to **B6.**
B5	CHECK SATC OPERATION			
	• Change control head and perform SATC Pinpoint Test A. • **Is test successful?**	Yes No	► ►	Test complete. RESTORE vehicle. GO to **B1.**

DIAGNOSIS AND TESTING (CONTINUED)

PINPOINT TEST B: A/C ELECTRONIC DOOR ACTUATOR MOTOR INOPERATIVE, INTERMITTENT OR IMPROPER OPERATION (Continued)

TEST STEP		RESULT	▶ ACTION TO TAKE
B6	CHECK CONTINUITY BETWEEN SATC AND A/C ELECTRONIC DOOR ACTUATOR MOTOR		
	• Check vehicle wiring harness and connector continuity as shown below. Disconnect connectors from both control assembly and blend door actuator. Blend door actuator connector is accessible through the glove compartment.	Yes No	▶ GO to **B7**. ▶ GO to **B8**.
	(see pin table below) • Reconnect all three connectors at end of this test. • **Is there continuity?**		
B7	CHECK SATC PERFORMANCE		
	• Change A/C electronic door actuator motor and perform SATC Pinpoint Test A. • **Is test successful?**	Yes No	▶ Test complete. RESTORE vehicle. ▶ GO to **B1**.
B8	VERIFY SATC SYSTEM OPERATION		
	• Service/replace wiring harness, connect and perform SATC Pinpoint Test A. • **Is test successful?**	Yes No	▶ Test complete. RESTORE vehicle. ▶ GO to**B1**.

Pin Number	Circuit	Circuit Function
1	351 (BR/W)	Feedback Pot. (Wiper)
2	—	Not Used
3	—	Not Used
4	—	Not Used
5	776 (O/BK)	Feedback Pot. (B+)
6	243 (LG/O)	Feedback Pot. (B-)
7	250 (O)	Motor CW
8	249 (DB/LG)	Motor CW B+

PINPOINT TEST C: A/C BLOWER MOTOR DOES NOT RUN

TEST STEP		RESULT	▶ ACTION TO TAKE
C1	CHECK FUSE		
	• Check in-line fuse to determine if it is good. • **Is fuse good?**	Yes No	▶ GO to **C4**. ▶ GO to **C2**.

DIAGNOSIS AND TESTING (CONTINUED)

PINPOINT TEST C: A/C BLOWER MOTOR DOES NOT RUN (Continued)

	TEST STEP	RESULT ▶	ACTION TO TAKE
C2	CHECK CIRCUIT		
	• Turn key OFF. Disconnect three pin connector (C1) from A/C blower motor speed control. Replace fuse and turn key to RUN. Measure voltage across Pins 1 and 2 of connector C1. • **Is voltage greater than 9 volts?**	Yes ▶ No ▶	GO to **C3.** CHECK Circuit 57 (BK), Circuit 181 (BR/O) and Circuit 687 (GY/Y) between ignition switch and A/C blower motor speed control for shorts and/or an open circuit. Make repairs as required.

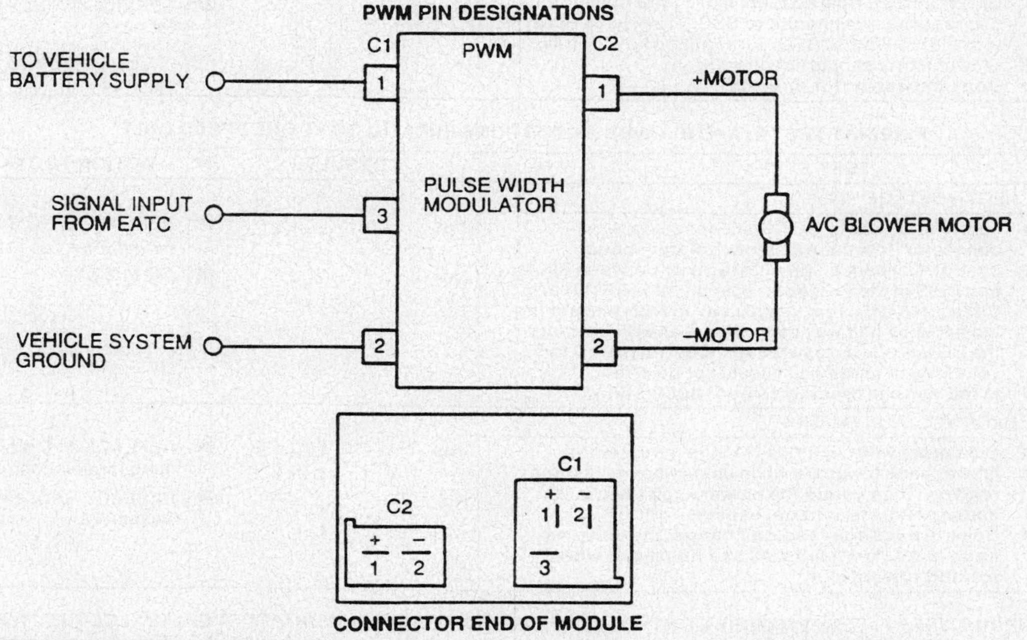

PWM PIN DESIGNATIONS

TO VEHICLE BATTERY SUPPLY — C1 1
SIGNAL INPUT FROM EATC — C1 3
VEHICLE SYSTEM GROUND — C1 2
PWM — PULSE WIDTH MODULATOR
C2 1 — +MOTOR
C2 2 — –MOTOR
A/C BLOWER MOTOR

C2: + 1, – 2
C1: + 1, – 2, 3

CONNECTOR END OF MODULE

	TEST STEP	RESULT ▶	ACTION TO TAKE
C3	CHECK BLOWER SPEED CONTROLLER		
	• Turn key OFF. Connect three pin connector (C1) to A/C blower motor speed control. Turn key to RUN and rotate blower knob to HI. • **Does fuse blow?**	Yes ▶ No ▶	CHECK Circuit 515 (O/R) for short. If OK, then REPLACE the A/C blower motor speed control. GO to **C4.**
C4	CHECK WIRING		
	• Turn key OFF. Remove speed signal wire (Circuit 246 (P) from blower speed controller harness connector. Turn key to RUN with SATC system ON. • **Does blower motor run at high speed?**	Yes ▶ No ▶	GO to **C5.** GO to **C6.**
C5	CHECK WIRING FOR OPEN CIRCUIT		
	• Check Circuit 246 (P) for an open circuit. Wiggle wire while testing. • **Is wire OK?**	Yes ▶ No ▶	REPLACE SATC Control Assembly. REPAIR as necessary.
C6	CHECK VOLTAGE		
	• With Circuit 246 (P) still disconnected, turn key to RUN and set control blower knob to HI. Check voltage across blower speed controller harness connector C2. • **Is voltage greater than 0.5 volt?**	Yes ▶ No ▶	CHECK blower motor. REPLACE if required. REPLACE A/C blower motor speed control.

DIAGNOSIS AND TESTING (CONTINUED)

PINPOINT TEST D: A/C BLOWER MOTOR RUNS CONTINUOUSLY IN HIGH SPEED

TEST STEP		RESULT	► ACTION TO TAKE
D1	CHECK BLOWER OPERATION		
	• Turn key OFF. Disconnect the harness connector from the left rear of the SATC Control Assembly. Ground Pin 23 of the connector (Circuit 246 (P)). Then, turn ignition key to RUN. Blower motor should not operate. • **Does blower motor operate?**	Yes No	► GO to **D2.** ► REPLACE the SATC Control Assembly.
D2	CHECK BLOWER SPEED CONTROLLER		
	• Turn ignition key to OFF. Reconnect harness connector to SATC Control Assembly. Disconnect Circuit 246 (P) from BSC Pin 3 of 3-wire connector and reconnect connector to BSC. Then, jump Pin 2 (ground) to Pin 3 of BSC. Turn ignition key to RUN. Blower motor should not operate. • **Does blower motor operate?**	Yes No	► REPLACE A/C blower motor speed control. ► SERVICE Circuit 246 (P) for open.

PINPOINT TEST E: A/C BLOWER MOTOR RUNS ERRATIC OR AT ONE SPEED ONLY

TEST STEP		RESULT	► ACTION TO TAKE
E1	CHECK VOLTAGE		
	• Turn ignition key to OFF. Disconnect the 3-pin connector from the A/C blower motor speed control. Connect a 10K ohm resistor between Pin 1 and Pin 3 of the connector (Circuit 181 (BR/O) to Circuit 246 (P)). Turn ignition key to RUN and set the blower knob half way between LO and HI. Measure the DC voltage across the resistor (range is 0 to 5 volts). Voltage reading should not be erratic. • **Is the voltage reading erratic (fluctuating)?**	Yes No	► REPLACE SATC Control Assembly. ► GO to **E2.**
E2	CHECK VOLTAGE CHANGE		
	• Continuing with conditions in Step 1, rotate the blower knob toward HI while observing the voltage reading. Then, rotate the blower knob toward LO and observe the voltage reading. • **Does the voltage reading change, increase as knob is rotated toward HI and decrease when rotated toward LO?**	Yes No	► REPLACE A/C blower motor speed control. ► REPLACE SATC Control Assembly.

PINPOINT TEST F: TEMPERATURE CONTROL LOCKOUT VALVE AND SWITCH NOT OPERATING CORRECTLY

TEST STEP		RESULT	► ACTION TO TAKE
F1	CHECK LOCKOUT VALVE AND SWITCH OPERATION		
	• Engine coolant temperature must be cold and inside vehicle temperature must be less than 29°C (85°F). • Heater blower motor switch must be in AUTO position. • Turn ignition switch to RUN position. • Set control to 85°F and select VENT or FLOOR. • **Did blower motor turn on?**	Yes No	► GO to **F2.** ► Temperature control lockout valve and switch OK. RETEST system.
F2	CHECK CIRCUIT 244 (Y/W)		
	• Turn ignition switch OFF. • Disconnect temperature control lockout valve and switch as outlined. • Using a jumper wire connected to a known good ground, connect other end to Circuit 244 (Y/W) at switch connector. • Turn ignition switch to the RUN position and blower motor should not run. • **Did blower motor run?**	Yes No	► GO to **F3.** ► REPLACE temperature control lockout valve and switch. RESTORE vehicle. RETEST system.

DIAGNOSIS AND TESTING (CONTINUED)

PINPOINT TEST F: TEMPERATURE CONTROL LOCKOUT VALVE AND SWITCH NOT OPERATING CORRECTLY (Continued)

TEST STEP		RESULT ▶	ACTION TO TAKE
F3	CHECK CIRCUIT 244 (Y/W)		
	• Disconnect A/C control assembly connector and check for continuity between Pin 19 Circuit 244 (Y/W) and switch connector. • **Is there continuity?**	Yes ▶ No ▶	REPLACE SATC control assembly. SERVICE Circuit 244 (Y/W) for open and RETEST.

PINPOINT TEST G: ELECTRO VACUUM SOLENOID INOPERATIVE

TEST STEP		RESULT ▶	ACTION TO TAKE
G1	CHECK AIR DOOR SOLENOID ELECTRICAL CIRCUIT		
	• Engine temperature must be below 45°C (113°F). • SATC is set at VENT or FLOOR. • Blower switch in AUTO. • SATC temperature set point between 18°C and 29°C (65°F and 85°F). • Ignition switch in the run position. • Check Circuit 298 (P/O) for battery voltage at the electro vacuum solenoid. Wiggle the wire during this test to check for an intermittent condition. • **Is there battery voltage available at solenoid without fluctuation or interruption?**	Yes ▶ No ▶	GO to **G2.** CHECK Circuit 298 (P/O) joint connector 1 to electro vacuum solenoid for open. SERVICE as necessary and RECHECK system.
G2	CHECK SOLENOID GROUND CIRCUIT		
	• Start engine and ground Circuit 599 (PK/LG) at electro vacuum solenoid. • **Does Air inlet door go to recirc position?**	Yes ▶ No ▶	GO to **G3**. GO to **G4**.
G3	CHECK CIRCUIT 599 (PK/LG)		
	• With engine running ground Circuit 599 (PK/LG) at Pin 14 of SATC module. • **Does air inlet door go to recirc position?**	Yes ▶ No ▶	REPLACE SATC module. RESTORE vehicle. RETEST system. SERVICE Circuit 599 (PK/LG) for open. RESTORE vehicle. RETEST system.
G4	CHECK VACUUM SUPPLY TO SOLENOID		
	• Disconnect black vacuum hose at solenoid. • Check for vacuum. • **Is vacuum present?**	Yes ▶ No ▶	GO to **G5.** SERVICE black vacuum hose for damage. RESTORE vehicle. RETEST system.
G5	CHECK WHITE VACUUM HOSE		
	• Reconnect black vacuum hose. • Ground Circuit 599 (PK/LG) at electro vacuum solenoid. • Disconnect white vacuum hose at electro vacuum solenoid. • **Is vacuum present?**	Yes ▶ No ▶	CHECK white vacuum hose for damage. If OK, REPLACE air inlet door vacuum control motor. RESTORE vehicle. RETEST system. REPLACE electro vacuum solenoid. RESTORE vehicle. RETEST system.

DIAGNOSIS AND TESTING (CONTINUED)

PINPOINT TEST H: WARM DISCHARGE AIR IN AUTOMATIC AND 60°F

TEST STEP		RESULT ▶	ACTION TO TAKE
H1	CHECK A/C SYSTEM OPERATION		
	• Start engine. • Select MAX A/C, set temperature to coldest setting. • **Is A/C system operating properly?**	Yes ▶ No ▶	GO to **H2.** GO to **H3.**
H2	CHECK A/C CLUTCH OPERATION		
	NOTE: The ambient temperature must be above approximately 10°C (50°F) for A/C compressor operation. • Start engine. • Turn A/C ON. • Check battery voltage. • Turn heater blower motor switch to HI. • **Does A/C clutch engage after five second delay?**	Yes ▶ No ▶	Circuit functioning properly. RESTORE vehicle. REPLACE A/C Clutch.

PINPOINT TEST J: A/C AMBIENT AIR TEMPERATURE SENSOR INOPERATIVE

TEST STEP		RESULT ▶	ACTION TO TAKE
J1	CHECK CIRCUIT 788 (R/O) AT A/C AMBIENT AIR TEMPERATURE SENSOR		
	• Turn ignition switch to the RUN position. • Turn SATC module to A/C position. • Partially remove SATC module as outlined. • Gain access to the A/C ambient air temperature sensor and bracket as outlined. Disconnect A/C ambient air temperature sensor and bracket. • Using voltmeter, check Circuit 788 (R/O) for voltage at sensor connector. • **Is voltage 10 volts or more?**	Yes ▶ No ▶	GO to **J4.** GO to **J2.**
J2	CHECK CIRCUIT 788 (R/O) AT EATC MODULE		
	• Using voltmeter, check Circuit 788 (R/O) at SATC module Pin 1 for voltage. • **Is voltage 10 volts or more?**	Yes ▶ No ▶	GO to **J3.** REPLACE SATC module. RESTORE vehicle. RETEST system.
J3	CHECK CIRCUIT 788 (R/O) FOR OPEN		
	• Turn ignition switch to the OFF position. • Using a jumper connected to a known good ground, connect other end to Circuit 788 (R/O) at sensor connector. • Using an ohmmeter connected to a known good ground, connect second lead to Circuit 788 (R/O) at SATC module connector Pin 1. • Measure resistance. • **Is resistance 5 ohms or less?**	Yes ▶ No ▶	GO to **J4.** SERVICE Circuit 788 (R/O) for open. RESTORE vehicle. RETEST system.
J4	CHECK CIRCUIT 470 (PK/BK)		
	• Connect jumper to Circuit 470 (PK/BK) at sensor connector. • Using an ohmmeter connected to a known good ground, connect second lead to Circuit 470 (PK/BK) at module connector Pin 2. • Measure resistance. • **Is resistance 5 ohms or less?**	Yes ▶ No ▶	GO to **J5.** SERVICE Circuit 470 (PK/BK) for open. RESTORE vehicle. RETEST system.

DIAGNOSIS AND TESTING (CONTINUED)

PINPOINT TEST J: A/C AMBIENT AIR TEMPERATURE SENSOR INOPERATIVE (Continued)

TEST STEP		RESULT ▶	ACTION TO TAKE
J5			
	• Disconnect battery cables. (This is necessary to reset outside temperature display memory.) • Measure resistance across sensor terminals and compare with Sensor Resistance Table.	Yes ▶ No ▶	REPLACE SATC assembly. RETEST system. REPLACE A/C ambient air temperature sensor and bracket. RETEST system.

SENSOR RESISTANCE TABLE

APPROXIMATE TEMPERATURE	SENSOR RESISTANCE ACCEPTABLE RANGE
10°C to 20°C (50°F to 68°F)	37K to 58K ohms
20°C to 30°C (68°F to 86°F)	24K to 37K ohms
30°C to 40°C (86°F to 104°F)	16K to 24K ohms

• **Is resistance in specifications?**

PINPOINT TEST K: A/C SUNLOAD SENSOR INOPERATIVE

TEST STEP		RESULT ▶	ACTION TO TAKE
K1	CHECK CIRCUIT 468 (BR) AT SENSOR CONNECTOR		
	• Turn ignition switch to the RUN position. • Turn SATC module to A/C position. • Partially remove SATC module as outlined. • Gain access to the A/C sunload sensor as outlined. Disconnect A/C sunload sensor. • Using voltmeter, check Circuit 468 (BR) for voltage at A/C sunload sensor connector. • **Is voltage 10 volts or more?**	Yes ▶ No ▶	GO to **K4.** GO to **K2.**
K2	CHECK CIRCUIT 468 (BR) AT SATC MODULE		
	• Using voltmeter, check Circuit 468 (BR) at SATC module Pin 16 for voltage. • **Is voltage 10 volts or more?**	Yes ▶ No ▶	GO to **K3.** REPLACE SATC module. RESTORE vehicle. RETEST system.
K3	CHECK CIRCUIT 468 (BR) FOR OPEN		
	• Turn ignition switch to the OFF position. • Using a jumper connected to a known good ground, connect other end to Circuit 468 (BR) at sensor connector. • Using an ohmmeter connected to a known good ground, connect second lead to Circuit 468 (BR) at SATC module connector Pin 16. • Measure resistance. • **Is resistance 5 ohms or less?**	Yes ▶ No ▶	GO to **K4.** SERVICE Circuit 468 (BR) for open. RESTORE vehicle. RETEST system.
K4	CHECK CIRCUIT 476 (BR/Y) RESISTANCE		
	• Connect jumper to Circuit 476 (BR/Y) at sensor connector. • Using an ohmmeter connected to a known good ground, connect second lead to Circuit 476 (BR/Y) at module connector Pin 3. • Measure resistance. • **Is resistance 5 ohms or less?**	Yes ▶ No ▶	GO to **K5.** SERVICE Circuit 476 (BR/Y) for open. RESTORE vehicle. RETEST system.
K5	CHECK SENSOR FOR SHORT		
	• Check the A/C sunload sensor for a short using an ohmmeter. Since the A/C sunload sensor is a Photodiode, there should be some unspecified resistance across the terminals dependent upon the available light in the area. The only test that should be made is for a short circuit (zero resistance). • **Is there zero resistance?**	Yes ▶ No ▶	REPLACE A/C sunload sensor. RETEST system. REPLACE SATC assembly. RETEST system.

DIAGNOSIS AND TESTING (CONTINUED)

PINPOINT TEST L: CONTROL ASSEMBLY / VFD DOES NOT LIGHT UP—HEATER BLOWER MOTOR OFF

TEST STEP		RESULT	►	ACTION TO TAKE
L1	CHECK ILLUMINATION SUPPLY TO SATC MODULE			
	• Turn headlamp switch to the PARK LAMP or HEADLAMP position. • Rotate headlamp dimmer sensor control to full-on without turning the dome lamp on. • Partially remove SATC module as outlined. • Using a test lamp, check Circuit 276 (BR) for voltage. • **Did test lamp illuminate?**	Yes No	► ►	GO to **L2.** SERVICE Circuit 276 (BR) for open circuit. RESTORE vehicle. RETEST system.
L2	CHECK SATC SYSTEM GROUND			
	• Using an ohmmeter connected to a known good ground, connect second lead to Circuit 57 (BK), Pin 24 at SATC module connector. • Measure resistance. • **Is resistance 5 ohms or less?**	Yes No	► ►	REPLACE SATC control module. RESTORE vehicle. RETEST system. SERVICE Circuit 57 (BK) for open circuit. RESTORE vehicle. RETEST system.

PINPOINT TEST M: IN-CAR TEMPERATURE SENSOR INOPERATIVE

TEST STEP		RESULT	►	ACTION TO TAKE
M1	CHECK IN-CAR SENSOR OUTPUT AT SATC MODULE			
	NOTE: Verify aspirator tube routing, condition and connection before proceeding. • Turn ignition switch to the RUN position. • Disconnect automatic temperature control sensor. • Using a voltmeter check Pin 17 Circuit 790 (W / O) at SATC assembly for voltage. • **Is voltage present?**	Yes No	► ►	GO to **M2.** REPLACE SATC assembly. RESTORE vehicle. RETEST system.
M2	CHECK CIRCUIT 790 (W / O)			
	• Turn ignition switch off. • Disconnect SATC assembly right connector. • Using an ohmmeter check Circuit 790 (W / O) from SATC assembly to automatic temperature control sensor. • **Is there continuity?**	Yes No	► ►	GO to **M3.** SERVICE Circuit 790 (W / O). RESTORE vehicle. RETEST system.
M3	CHECK IN-CAR SENSOR RETURN CIRCUIT			
	• Using an ohmmeter check Circuit 470 (PK / BK) for continuity from SATC assembly to automatic temperature control sensor. • **Is there continuity?**	Yes No	► ►	GO to **M4.** SERVICE Circuit 470 (PK / BK). RESTORE vehicle. RETEST system.
M4	CHECK IN-CAR SENSOR			
	• Using an ohmmeter measure resistance across sensor terminal and compare with Sensor Resistance Table. (see Sensor Resistance Table below) • **Is resistance within specification?**	Yes No	► ►	REPLACE SATC assembly. RETEST system. REPLACE automatic temperature control sensor. RETEST system.

SENSOR RESISTANCE TABLE

APPROXIMATE TEMPERATURE	SENSOR RESISTANCE ACCEPTABLE RANGE
10°C to 20°C (50°F to 68°F)	37K to 58K ohms
20°C to 30°C (68°F to 86°F)	24K to 37K ohms
30°C to 40°C (86°F to 104°F)	16K to 24K ohms

DIAGNOSIS AND TESTING (CONTINUED)

PINPOINT TEST N: TEMPERATURE SET POINT DOES NOT REPEAT AFTER TURNING IGNITION SWITCH OFF

	TEST STEP	RESULT ▶	ACTION TO TAKE
N1	CHECK MEMORY SUPPLY TO SATC CONTROL ASSEMBLY		
	• With ignition switch in the OFF position, partially remove SATC control assembly as outlined. • Using a voltmeter, check Circuit 797 (LG/P) for voltage at SATC module Pin 12. • **Is battery voltage present?**	Yes ▶	REPLACE SATC control assembly. RESTORE vehicle. RETEST system.
		No ▶	GO to **N2**.
N2	CHECK CIRCUIT 797 (LG/P) SUPPLY		
	• Remove memory Fuse (5A) at power distribution box. • Using an ohmmeter, check Circuit 797 (LG/P) from SATC module connector Pin 12 to output side of memory fuse (5A) cavity for continuity. • **Is resistance 5 ohms or less?**	Yes ▶	CHECK electrical connectors at SATC control assembly, fuse panel, and fuse. REPLACE and/or REPAIR as necessary.
		No ▶	SERVICE Circuit 797 (LG/P) for open. RESTORE vehicle. RETEST system.

AUTOMATIC TEMPERATURE CONTROL (ATC) SYSTEM BLOWER WILL NOT RUN DIAGNOSIS—CROWN VICTORIA AND GRAND MARQUIS

	TEST STEP	RESULT	▶	ACTION TO TAKE
B1	VOLTAGE CHECK			
	• Disconnect blower speed controller (BSC) connector. Start engine, set control to MAX A/C and blower on HIGH. Measure voltage between Pins 4 and 5 of blower speed controller. Should show battery voltage.	Yes	▶	CHECK fuse, blower motor 181 and 261 circuits Crown Victoria/Grand Marquis, 371 Circuit on Town Car.
	• **Is voltage less than 10 volts?**	No	▶	GO to **B2.**
B2	VOLTAGE CHECK			
	• Reconnect BSC connector and disconnect blower motor from harness. Check for voltage across harness connector (261 (O/BK) and 181 (BR/O) wires on Crown Victoria/Grand Marquis, 371 (P/W) on Lincoln Town Car) with blower on HIGH.	10 volts or more	▶	REPLACE blower motor.
		Zero volts	▶	GO to **B3.**
B3	VOLTAGE CHECK			
	• Disconnect BSC connector and check voltage between Pins 3 and 5 or BSC. Should be 10 or more volts with blower on HIGH.	Yes	▶	REPLACE BSC.
	• **Is voltage 10 volts or greater?**	No	▶	GO to **B4.**
B4	VOLTAGE CHECK			
	• Reconnect BSC connector. With engine running and controls set to MAX A/C and blower on HIGH, check voltage between ATC module Pin 5 and ground. Should be 10 or more volts.	Yes	▶	SERVICE 754 (LG/W) Circuit between ATC module and BSC.
	• **Is voltage 10 volts or greater?**	No	▶	GO to **B5.**
B5	VOLTAGE CHECK			
	• With ignition switch in run and control set for MAX A/C, check for battery voltage to ground at Pins 3 and 6 of the ATC function selector switch.	Battery voltage at both pins	▶	REPLACE ATC module.
		Battery voltage at Pin 3 only	▶	REPLACE function selector switch.
		No voltage at either pin	▶	GO to **B6.**
B6				
	• With ignition switch in RUN and function control at MAX A/C, check for battery voltage to ground Pins 1 and 2 of function selector switch.	Battery voltage at both pins	▶	REPLACE function selector switch.
		No voltage at either pin	▶	GO to **B7.**
		No voltage at one pin	▶	CHECK circuit between splice S-217 and function selector switch.
B7	CHECK FUSE			
	• Check fuse F-5 in fuse panel for continuity. • **Is fuse functional?**	Yes	▶	CHECK circuit between fuse panel and function selector for open.
		No	▶	SERVICE circuit and REPLACE fuse. Check system for correct operation.

AUTOMATIC TEMPERATURE CONTROL (ATC) SYSTEM BLOWER ALWAYS IN HIGH DIAGNOSIS—CROWN VICTORIA AND GRAND MARQUIS

	TEST STEP	RESULT	▶	ACTION TO TAKE
C1	CHECK VOLTAGE			
	• Disconnect the blower speed controller (BSC) connector. Start engine, set control to MAX A/C and blower at low speed. Check voltage between Pins 2 and 5 of the blower speed controller connector, while changing the blower speed switch settings. Should be between one and two volts for all settings except HI blower. Zero volts at HI blower.	1-2 volts except in HI	▶	GO to **C2.**
		Zero volts all switch settings	▶	GO to **C3.**
		Voltage above 2 volts all switch settings	▶	REPLACE ATC control module.
C2	CHECK VOLTAGE			
	• Check voltage between Pins 3 and 5 of blower speed controller with blower in any speed except HI. Should be zero volts.	Zero volts	▶	REPLACE BSC.
		Voltage above 10 volts	▶	REPLACE ATC control module.
C3	CHECK VOLTAGE			
	• Connect harness connector to BSC. With engine running, set to MAX A/C and blower set for medium speed, check voltage at Pin 6 of ATC control module.	1-2 volts	▶	SERVICE 752 (Y/R) Wire between ATC module and BSC.
		Zero volts	▶	REPLACE ATC module.

AUTOMATIC TEMPERATURE CONTROL (ATC) SYSTEM NO BLOWER IN LOW OR MEDIUM DIAGNOSIS—CROWN VICTORIA AND GRAND MARQUIS

TEST STEP		RESULT ▶	ACTION TO TAKE
D1	VOLTAGE CHECK		
	• Disconnect the blower speed controller (BSC) connector. Start engine, set control to MAX A / C and blower at low speed. Check voltage between Pins 2 and 5 of BSC, should be between one and two volts.	1-2 volts ▶ Zero volts ▶	REPLACE BSC. GO to **D2**.
D2	VOLTAGE CHECK		
	• Reconnect BSC connector . With engine running and control set at MAX A / C and blower at low speed, check voltage between Pin 6 of ATC module and ground. Should be one to two volts.	1-2 volts ▶ Zero volts ▶	SERVICE 752 (Y / R) Wire between ATC module and BSC. REPLACE ATC module.

AUTOMATIC TEMPERATURE CONTROL (ATC) SYSTEM NO HIGH BLOWER DIAGNOSIS—CROWN VICTORIA AND GRAND MARQUIS

TEST STEP		RESULT ▶	ACTION TO TAKE
E1	VOLTAGE CHECK		
	• Disconnect BSC connector. Start engine, set control at MAX A / C and blower on HIGH. Check voltage between BSC Pins 3 and 5. Should be 10 or more volts. • **Is voltage 10 volts or greater?**	Yes ▶ No ▶	REPLACE BSC. GO to **E2**.
E2	VOLTAGE CHECK		
	• Reconnect BSC connector. With engine running, control set at MAX A / C and blower HIGH, check for voltage between Pin 5 of the ATC control module and ground. Should be 10 or more volts, when blower switch is on HIGH. • **Is voltage 10 volts or greater?**	Yes ▶ No ▶	SERVICE 754 (LG / W) Wire between ATC control module and BSC. REPLACE ATC control module.

AUTOMATIC TEMPERATURE CONTROL (ATC) SYSTEM TEMPERATURE QUICK TEST— THUNDERBIRD AND COUGAR

TEST STEP	RESULT ▶	ACTION TO TAKE
F1 STEP 1		
• Operate system.	No blower operation	▶ VERIFY that blower motor leads are connected at blower motor. ▶ VERIFY that four fuses are good (two in underhood power distribution box and two under dash panel). ▶ VERIFY that blower motor works. ▶ VERIFY power wiring continuity between fuse panel and ATC control assembly. ▶ If fuses are good, blower motor is functional and there is continuity between fuse panel and ATC control assembly. REPLACE electro-vacuum switch on control assembly.
	Mode selections incorrect or erratic	▶ CHECK for pinched or poorly connected vacuum lines. ▶ REPLACE electro-vacuum switch on control assembly.
	No blower operation in AUTO, or from LO to HI	▶ Make sure that blower motor and VBC have a good electrical connection. ▶ CHECK 30 amp fuse (underhood power distribution box and under dash panel). ▶ If above are good, suspect either a wiring short or a damaged ATC control module.
F2 STEP 2		
• Operate system. • Select different blower speeds.	Blower stays at maximum speed in all settings	▶ REFER to variable blower speed control functional test. ▶ VERIFY wiring continuity between VBC and the ATC control module. ▶ If above checks OK, REPLACE the ATC control module.

AUTOMATIC TEMPERATURE CONTROL (ATC) SYSTEM TEMPERATURE QUICK TEST— THUNDERBIRD AND COUGAR, CONT'D

TEST STEP	RESULT ▶	ACTION TO TAKE
F3 STEP 2 (Continued)		
• Operate system. • Select different blower speeds.	With blower switch in AUTO, discharge temperature will not change with change in temperature lever position.	▶ VERIFY that blend door actuator electrical connection is good and that wiring continuity exists between blend door actuator and ATC control module.
	Blower speed does change with temperature lever change	▶ REFER to blend door actuator functional test.
F4 STEP 2 (Continued)		
• Operate system. • Select different blower speeds.	With blower switch in AUTO, discharge temperature remains at full heat no matter what position temperature lever is in.	▶ VERIFY that aspirator hose is connected at dash panel and to in-vehicle temperature sensor. ▶ VERIFY that in-vehicle temperature sensor electrical connection is connected and that electrical continuity exists between sensor and ATC control module.
	Blower at maximum speed	▶ If above checks out OK, VERIFY ambient temperature sensor electrical connection is connected and that electrical continuity exists between sensor and ATC control module.
F5 STEP 2 (Continued)		
• Operate system. • Select different blower speeds.	With blower switch in AUTO, blower speed does not change when temperature lever is slowly moved from 65°F to 85°F. Discharge temperature does change	▶ VERIFY that in-vehicle temperature sensor electrical connection is good and that wiring continuity exists between sensor and ATC control module.

AUTOMATIC TEMPERATURE CONTROL (ATC) SYSTEM TEMPERATURE QUICK TEST—THUNDERBIRD AND COUGAR, CONT'D

	TEST STEP	RESULT ▶	ACTION TO TAKE
F6	STEP 3 • Operate system. • Set temperature selector lever between 72°F and 78°F NOTE: With ambient temperature approximately 24°C (75°F) blower speed should be lower when temperature lever is set between 72°F and 78°F and higher when not in this range.	Blower speed oscillates rapidly or constantly changes ▶	VERIFY that ambient temperature sensor electrical connection is good and that wiring continuity exists between sensor and ATC control module. ▶ REFER to variable blower controller functional test.
F7	STEP 4 • Change blower speed setting.	Blower speed does not change ▶	REFER to variable blower controller functional test. ▶ If above checks OK, REPLACE the ATC control module.
		System operates correctly, but does not "seem" to reach maximum heat or cool ▶	CHECK for loose or intermittent wire connection to ATC control module Pin 11 (Circuit 244 (Y/W)) or Pin 10 (Circuit 54 (LG/Y)). ▶ DISCONNECT vehicle battery for two minutes and allow system to re-calibrate.
F8	STEP 5 • Set select lever to floor. NOTE: Engine coolant temperature must be above 43°C (110°F).	No blower in floor position ▶	REFER to thermal blower lockout switch functional test. ▶ VERIFY that Circuits 244 (Y/W) and 470 (PK/BK) going to thermal blower lockout have a good connection. ▶ CHECK for low coolant level.
F9	STEP 6 • Set select lever to floor. NOTE: Engine coolant temperature must be above 43°C (110°F).	Blower on at all times (no cold engine lockout) ▶	REFER to thermal blower lockout switch functional test.
F10	STEP 7 • Set blower switch to OFF.	Blower does not stop running ▶	CHECK for short in 14401 harness. ▶ REPLACE electro-vacuum selector valve.
F11	STEP 8 • Operate system.	Alternates between long periods of heat and long periods of cool ▶	VERIFY that aspirator hose is connected at dash panel and to in-vehicle sensor. ▶ CHECK aspirator tube for blockages.

AUTOMATIC TEMPERATURE CONTROL SYSTEM BLEND DOOR ACTUATOR TEST—THUNDERBIRD AND COUGAR

	TEST STEP	RESULT ▶	ACTION TO TAKE
G1	CHECK BLEND DOOR ACTUATOR • Disconnect electrical connector from rear of ATC control module and drive actuator in both directions using any 9-12 volt battery. • The following pins can be jumped to use vehicle battery. The ignition switch must be in RUN position: —Pin 4 (456 W/LG) (+), to Pin 3 (455 (GY/R) (-). This drives actuator CW—Maximum cooling. —Pin 4 (456 W/LG) (-), to Pin 3 (455 (GY/R) (+). This drives actuator CCW—maximum heating. • **Does actuator drive in both directions?**	Yes ▶ No ▶	GO to **G2**. REPLACE blend door actuator.
G2	MEASURE ACTUATOR RESISTANCE • Using technique outlined in previous maximum heating step, set actuator to full CCW travel (power 15-20 seconds). • Using any digital or dial type volt-ohmmeter, measure resistance at ATC control module connector as follows: —Pin 7 (660, Y/LG) to Pin 13 (359, BK/W)—4,500-6,000 ohms —Pin 14 (773, DG/O) to Pin 13 (359, BK/W)—250-1,500 ohms. —Pin 14 (773, DG/O) to Pin 7 (660, Y/LG)—3,500-6,000 ohms. • **Are all resistances within range?**	Yes ▶ No ▶	GO to **G3**. REPLACE blend door actuator.
G3	CHECK VEHICLE WIRING • Check vehicle wiring harness and connector continuity as shown below. Disconnect connectors from both ATC control module and blend door actuator. Use any digital or dial type volt-ohmmeter. • **Is there continuity?**	No ▶ Yes ▶	SERVICE/REPLACE wiring harness. REPLACE ATC control module.

ATC MODULE CONNECTOR	ACTUATOR CONNECTOR
Pin 4 (456, W/LG) to	Pin 7
Pin 3 (455, GY/R) to	Pin 8
Pin 7 (660, Y/LG) to	Pin 5
Pin 13 (359, BK/W) to	Pin 6
Pin 14 (733, DG/O) to	Pin 1

ELECTRONIC AUTOMATIC TEMPERATURE CONTROL (EATC) SYSTEM PANEL DISPLAY ERROR CODE KEY CHART—1993 TOWN CAR

Error Code	Detected Condition	Troubleshooting/Repair Procedure
01	Replace Control Assembly	
02	Blend Door Problem	• Refer to Blend Door Actuator Diagnosis
03	In-Vehicle Temp Sensor Open or Short	• Refer to In-Vehicle Temp Sensor Diagnosis
04	Ambient Temp Sensor Open or Short	• Refer to Ambient Temp Sensor Diagnosis
05	Sunload Sensor Short	• Refer to Sunload Sensor Diagnosis
888	Testing Complete—No Test Failure (All Segments On)	• Refer to EATC System Functional Check

ELECTRONIC AUTOMATIC TEMPERATURE CONTROL (EATC) SYSTEM FUNCTIONAL TEST—1993 TOWN CAR

TEST STEP	RESULT	ACTION TO TAKE
1		
• Turn ignition switch to the RUN position. • Press the AUTOMATIC button. • Set control at 90°F setting. • **Does control display 90°F Auto?**	Yes ▶ No ▶	GO to **2**. REFER to Diagnosis When Self-Test And Functional Test Indicate No Errors Found.
2		
• Verify that the blower does not come on. (Engine coolant temp. is less than 120°F). • **Does blower operate?**	Yes ▶ No ▶	REFER to CELO Inoperative. GO to **3**.
3		
• Ensure that engine is warm (coolant temp. is greater than 120°F). • Set control at 75 setting. • **Does blower operate?**	Yes ▶ No ▶	GO to **4**. REFER to Blower Speed Controller Diagnosis-No Blower.
4		
• Rotate blower thumbwheel fully down. • **Does blower go to low blower speed?**	Yes ▶ No ▶	GO to **5**. REFER to Blower Speed Controller Diagnosis.
5		
• Rotate blower thumbwheel fully up. • **Does blower go to high blower speed?**	Yes ▶ No ▶	GO to **6**. REFER to Blower Speed Controller Diagnosis.
6		
• Press the DEFROST button. • Verify that air is discharged from defroster nozzle with small bleed through the side window demistors. • Verify that the outside recirc door is in the outside air position. • **Are these conditions met?**	Yes ▶ No ▶	GO to **7**. REFER to Vacuum System Diagnosis.
7		
• Press the FLOOR button. • Verify that the air is discharged through the floor ducts. • **Is this condition met?**	Yes ▶ No ▶	GO to **8**. REFER to Vacuum System Diagnosis.
8		
• Press the VENT button. • Verify that the air is discharged through the panel registers. • **Is this condition met?**	Yes ▶ No ▶	GO to **9**. REFER to Vacuum System Diagnosis.
9		
• Make sure that the ambient temperature is greater than 40°F. • Press the MAX A/C button. • Verify that the outside recirc door is in the recirc position. • **Is this condition met?**	Yes ▶ No ▶	GO to **10**. REFER to Vacuum System Diagnosis.
10		
• Press the VENT button. • Verify that the VENT display is lit. • Verify that the clutch is off. • **Are these conditions met?**	Yes ▶ No ▶	GO to **11**. REFER to Clutch Does Not Disengage When In OFF Diagnosis.
11		
• Press the MAX A/C button again. • Verify that the MAX A/C display is lit and that the clutch is on. • **Are these conditions met?**	Yes ▶ No ▶	GO to **12**. REFER to No Clutch Operation Diagnosis.
12		
• Press the AUTOMATIC button.	Verify that the AUTO or function and fan VFDs are lit. ▶	REFER to Diagnosis When Self-Test And Functional Test Indicate No Errors Found.

ELECTRONIC AUTOMATIC TEMPERATURE CONTROL (EATC) SYSTEM DIAGNOSIS WHEN SELF-TEST INDICATES NO ERRORS FOUND—1993 TOWN CAR

CONDITION	POSSIBLE SOURCE	ACTION
• Cool Discharge Air When System is Set to AUTOMATIC and 90°F	• Heater system malfunction. • Blend door not in max. heat.	• Check coolant level. • Refer to heater system operating principles (check engine thermostat). • Check position of blend door. • Check blend door shaft attachment. • Test per Blend Door Actuator Diagnosis (assume 2 was displayed in the Self-Test).
• Warm Discharge Air in Auto / 60°F	• Clutch circuit malfunction. • Check refrigerant. • Blend door not in MAX. A/C position. • Outside / Recirc door not in recirc.	• Test clutch circuit per "No Clutch Operation" Diagnosis. • Check Refrigerant System Pressures. • Check position of blend door. • Check blend door shaft attachment. • Test per "Blend Door Actuator" Diagnosis (assume 2 was displayed in the Self-Test). • Test per "Vacuum Leak" Diagnosis.
• Cool Air in 85°F Max. Heat in 90°F	• Sensor shorted.	• TROUBLESHOOT according to Sensor Diagnosis.
• Heat in 65°F Max. Cool in 60°F	• Sensor open.	• TROUBLESHOOT according to Sensor Diagnosis.
• No Blower	• Damaged CELO switch / wiring. • Damaged blower speed controller. • Damage HI blower relay. • Damaged control assembly. • Damaged blower motor. • Damaged wiring.	• Test per "No Blower" Section of Blower Speed Controller.
• High Blower Only	• Damaged control assembly. • Damaged blower controller. • Damaged wiring.	• Test per "High Blower Only" Section of Blower Speed Controller.
• Clutch is Engaged When System is Off	• Damaged control assembly. • Damaged wiring or interface components.	• Test according to "Clutch Does Not Disengage When in OFF". A/C Compressor Clutch Circuit Diagnosis.
• Control Assembly Digits and VFD Do Not Light Up, Blower Off	• Fuse. • Ignition Circuit 298 open. • Ignition Circuit 797 open. • Ground Circuit 57A open. • Damaged control assembly.	• Replace fuse. • Check Circuit 298. • Check Circuit 797. • Check Circuit 57A. • Replace control assembly.
• Cold Air is Delivered During Heating When Engine is Cold	• Damaged wiring. • Damaged or inoperative engine temperature switch.	• Place system at 90°F / Auto. With ignition off, ignition must be off when grounding Circuit 244 (for valid results) ground Circuit 244 at engine temp. switch. Start engine. If blower is off, replace cold engine lockout (CELO). If blower is on, check wiring. If OK, replace control assembly. • Replace engine temperature switch.

ELECTRONIC AUTOMATIC TEMPERATURE CONTROL (EATC) SYSTEM DIAGNOSIS WHEN SELF-TEST INDICATES NO ERRORS FOUND—1993 TOWN CAR—CONT'D

CONDITION	POSSIBLE SOURCE	ACTION
• Control Assembly Temperature Display Will Not Switch From Fahrenheit To Celsius grade When the E/M Trip Computer Button is Pushed	• Damaged or inoperative wiring tripminder or control assembly.	**CAUTION: Accidental shorting of the wrong pin could destroy the control assembly.** • Short Pin 20 of connector VA (Circuit 506) to ground. Turn on ignition. If the display does not switch from F to C, Circuit 506 is open at the control assembly and the control assembly is damaged. Otherwise check the wiring and the tripminder.
• System Does Not Control Temperature	• Sensor hose not connected to aspirator or sensor. • Aspirator not secured to evaporator case. • Sensor seal(s) missing or not installed properly. • Aspirator or sensor hose blocked with foreign material or kinked. • Damaged aspirator hose.	• Inspect and service. • Inspect and service. • Inspect and service. • Inspect and service. • Inspect and service.
• EATC Control Assembly Turns On and Off Erratically. No Control of System	• Damaged charging system. EATC will not function with too low or too high battery voltage.	• Check battery voltage. If battery voltage is less than 10 volts or greater than 16 volts, refer to charging system diagnosis, Do not replace EATC control assembly.

ELECTRONIC AUTOMATIC TEMPERATURE CONTROL (EATC) SYSTEM BLEND DOOR FUNCTIONAL TEST–1993 TOWN CAR

TEST STEP	RESULT	▶	ACTION TO TAKE
1 CHECK BLEND DOOR ACTUATOR			
• Disconnect electrical connector from rear of EATC control module and drive actuator in both directions using an 9-12 volt battery. • The following pins can be jumper to use vehicle battery. The ignition switch must be in RUN position. a. Pin 4 () and Pin 3 (-). This drives actuator CW—maximum cooling. b. Pin 4 (-) and Pin (+). This drives actautor CCW—maximum heating. • **Does actuator drive both dlections?**	Yes No	▶ ▶	GO to **2.** REPLACE blend door actuator.
2 MEASURE ACTUATOR RESISTANCE			
• Using technique outlined in Step b. above, set actautor to full CCW travel (power 15-20 seconds). • Using any digital or dial type volt-ohmmeter, measure resistance at EATC control module connector as follows: a. Pin 7 to Pin 13— 4,500-6,000 ohms b. Pin 14 to Pin 13— 3,500-6,000 ohms c. Pin 14 to Pin 7— 250-1,500 ohms • **Are all resistance measurements within the acceptable range?**	Yes No	▶ ▶	GO to **4.** REPLACE blend door actuator.
3 CHECK VEHICLE WIRING			
• Check vehicle wiring harness and connector continuity as shown below. Disconnect connectors from both EATC control module and blend door actuator. Use any digital or dial type volt-ohmmeter. (see connector table below) • **Is continuity good?**	No Yes	▶ ▶	SERVICE/REPLACE wiring harness. REPLACE EATC control module.

EATC Module Connector		Actuator Connector
Pin 4	to	Pin 7
Pin 3	to	Pin 8
Pin 7	to	Pin 5
Pin 13	to	Pin 6
Pin 14	to	Pin 1

ELECTRONIC AUTOMATIC TEMPERATURE CONTROL (EATC) SYSTEM NO BLOWER DIAGNOSIS–1993 TOWN CAR

TEST STEP	RESULT	▶	ACTION TO TAKE
1 VOLTAGE CHECK			
• Disconnect blower speed controller (BSC) connector. Start engine, set control to MAX A/C and blower on HIGH. Measure voltage between Pins 4 and 5 of blower speed controller. Should show battery voltage. • **Is there at least 10 volts.**	No Yes	▶ ▶	GO to **2.** CHECK and SERVICE as necessary fuse, blower motor 181 and 261 or 371 circuits.
2 VOLTAGE CHECK			
• Reconnect BSC connector and siconnect blower motor from harness. Check for voltage across harness connector (261 O/BK or 371 PK/W and 181 BR/O) with blower on HIGH. • **Is there at least 10 volts?**	Yes No	▶ ▶	REPLACE blower motor. GO to **3.**
3 VOLTAGE CHECK			
• Disconnect BSC connector and check voltage between Pins 3 and 5 of BSC. Should be 10 or more volts with blower oh HIGH. • **Is there at least 10 volts?**	Yes No	▶ ▶	REPLACE BSC. GO to **4.**
4 VOLTAGE CHECK			
• Reconnect BSC connector. With engine running and controls set to MAX A/C and blower on HIGH, check voltage between EATC module Pin 5 and ground. Should be 10 or more volts. • **Is there at least 10 volts?**	Yes No	▶ ▶	SERVICE circuit between EATC module Pin 5 and BSC Pin 3. GO to **5.**
5 VOLTAGE CHECK			
• With ignition switch in run and control set for MAX A/C, check for battery voltage to ground at Pins 3 and 6 of the EATC module. • **Is there voltage at one or both pins?**	Yes No	▶ ▶	REPLACE EATC module. GO to **6.**
6 VOLTAGE CHECK			
• With ignition switch in RUN and function selector switch at MAX A/C, check for battery voltage to ground at Pins 1 and 2 of EATC module. • **Is there voltage at both pins?**	Yes No	▶ ▶ ▶	REPLACE EATC module. GO to **7.** ChHECK circuit between Pins 1 and 2 of EATC module.
7 CHECK FUSE			
• Check fuse F-8 in fuse panel for continuity. • **Is the fuse blown?**	No Yes	▶ ▶	SERVICE circuit and REPLACE fuse. CHECK system for proper operation. CHECK circuit between fuse panel and EATC module for open.

ELECTRONIC AUTOMATIC TEMPERATURE CONTROL (EATC) SYSTEM BLOWER ALWAYS IN HIGH DIAGNOSIS–1993 TOWN CAR

	TEST STEP	RESULT ▶	ACTION TO TAKE
1	CHECK VOLTAGE		
	• Disconnect the blower speed controller (BSC) connector. Start engine, set control to MAX A/C and blower at low speed. Check voltage betwen Pins 2 and 5 of the blower speed controller connector, while changing the blower speed settings. Should be between 1 and 2 volts for all settings except HI blower. Zero volts at HI blower. • **What is the voltage measurement?**	1 to 2 volts except in HI ▶ 0 volts all switch settings ▶ oltage above 2V all switch settings ▶	GO to **2.** GO to **3.** REPLACE EATC module.
2	CHECK VOLTAGE		
	• Check voltage between Pins 3 and 5 of blower speed controller connector with blower in any speed except HI. Should be zero volts. • **Does voltage measure zero?**	Yes ▶ No ▶	REPLACE BSC. REPLACE EATC module.
3	CHECK VOLTAGE		
	• Connect harness connector to BSC. With engine running, set to MAX A/C and blower set for medium speed, check voltage at Pin 6 of EATC module. • **What is the voltage measurement?**	1 to 2 volts ▶ Zero volts ▶	SERVICE wire between EATC module and BSC. REPLACE EATC module.

ELECTRONIC AUTOMATIC TEMPERATURE CONTROL (EATC) SYSTEM NO HIGH BLOWER DIAGNOSIS–1993 TOWN CAR

	TEST STEP	RESULT ▶	ACTION TO TAKE
1	VOLTAGE CHECK		
	• Disconnect BSC connector Start engine, set control at MAX A/C and blower on HIGH. Check voltage between BSC Pins 3 and 5. Should be 10 or more volts. • **Is the voltage measurement 10 or more volts?**	Yes ▶ No ▶	REPLACE BSC. GO to **2.**
2	VOLTAGE CHECK		
	• Reconnect BSC connector. With engine running, control set at MAX A/C and blower on HIGH, check for voltage between Pin 5 of the EATC control module and ground. Should be 10V or more when blower switch is on HIGH. • **Is the voltage measurement 10 or more volts?**	Yes ▶ No ▶	SERVICE circuit between EATC module and BSC. REPLACE EATC module.

ELECTRONIC AUTOMATIC TEMPERATURE CONTROL (EATC) SYSTEM NO LOW OR MEDIUM BLOWER DIAGNOSIS–1993 TOWN CAR

	TEST STEP	RESULT ▶	ACTION TO TAKE
1	VOLTAGE CHECK		
	• Disconnect the blowr speed controller (BSC) connector. Start engine, set control to MAX A/C and blower at low speed. Check voltage between Pins 2 and 5 of BSC. Should be between 1 and 2 volts. • **What is the voltage measurement?**	1 to 2 volts ▶ Zero volts ▶	REPLACE BSC. GO to **2.**
2	VOLTAGE CHECK		
	• Reconnect BSC connector. With engine running and control set at MAX A/C and blower at low speed, check voltage between Pin 6 of EATC module and ground. Should be 1 to 2 volts. • **What is the voltage measurement?**	1 to 2 volts ▶ Zero volts ▶	SERVICE circuit between EATC moduel and BSC. REPLACE EATC module.

ELECTRONIC AUTOMATIC TEMPERATURE CONTROL (EATC) SYSTEM IN– CAR TEMPERATURE SENSOR DIAGNOSIS–1993 TOWN CAR

CONDITION	POSSIBLE SOURCE	ACTION
• Diagnostic-Test Error Code 03 (Warm air discharge at 65°F or cool air discharge at 85°F).	1. Sensor open or shorted.	• Disconnect wire harness connector at sensor. Measure resistance across sensor terminals and compare with Sensor Resistance Table below. • If resistance is out of specifications shown in the table, replace the sensor. If sensor is OK, GO to Step 2.
	2. Wire harness open or shorted.	• Disconnect battery cables. Disconnect wire harness connector from sensor and disconnect both connectors from control assembly. • Check for continuity and for possible shorting between the two wires (Pin 2 and Pin 17 of control assembly connector). Service if necessary. Reconnect wire harness and battery cables.

HELECTRONIC AUTOMATIC TEMPERATURE CONTROL (EATC) SYSTEM AMBIENT TEMPERATURE SENSOR DIAGNOSIS—1993 TOWN CAR

APPROXIMATE TEMPERATURE	SENSOR RESISTANCE ACCEPTABLE RANGE
10°C to 20°C (50°F to 68°F)	37K to 58K ohms
20°C to 30°C (68°F to 86°F)	24K to 37K ohms
30°C to 40°C (86°F to 104°F)	16K to 24K ohms

EATC—AMBIENT TEMPERATURE SENSOR DIAGNOSIS

CONDITION	POSSIBLE SOURCE	ACTION
• Self-Diagnostics Error Code 04 and Outside Temperature Display is Reading—40°F or 140°F (Warm Air Discharge when set at 65°F or Cool Air Discharge when set at 85°F)	1. Sensor open or shorted.	• Disconnect battery cables (this is necessary to reset outside temperature display memory). Disconnect the wire harness connector ar sensor. Measure resistance across sensor terminal and compare with Sensor Resistance Table in In-Vehicle Temperature Sensor Diagnosis Chart. • If resistance is out of specifications shown in Sensor Resistance Table, replace sensor. If sensor is OK, GO to Step 2. Reconnect battery cables. NOTE: Install sensor and electrical connections before battery is reconnected.
• Intermittent Heating and Cooling. Outside Temperature Display Sometimes Inaccurate	2. Sensor wire harness open or shorted.	• Disconnect battery cables. Disconnect wire harness connector from sensor and disconnect both connectors from the control assembly. • Inspect for crimped terminals. • Check for continuity and for possible shorting between the two wire (Pins 1 and 2). Service if necessary. Reconnect wire harness and battery cables.

ELECTRONIC AUTOMATIC TEMPERATURE CONTROL (EATC) SYSTEM NO CLUTCH OPERATION DIAGNOSIS—1993 TOWN CAR

TEST STEP	RESULT	▶	ACTION TO TAKE
1			
• Jump LB/BK and LG/P wires Pin 26 and Pin 25 of driver side connector VA.	Clutch engages	▶	REPLACE control assembly.
	Clutch does not engage	▶	REFER to A/C "Clutch Circuit Diagnosis".
	15A fuse blows.	▶	Clutch or wiring is shorted. CHECK diode in wiring harness across clutch in particular. SERVICE short, then test to see if control assembly will turn clutch off and on. If not, REPLACE control assembly.

ELECTRONIC AUTOMATIC TEMPERATURE CONTROL (EATC) SYSTEM SUNLOAD SENSOR DIAGNOSIS—1993 TOWN CAR

CONDITION	POSSIBLE SOURCE	ACTION
• Self-Diagnostics Error Code 05	1. Sensor shorted.	• Disconnect battery cables. Disconnect wire harness connector at sensor and disconnect both connectors from control assembly. NOTE: Check the sensor for a short using an ohmmeter. Since the sensor is a Photodiode, there should be some unspecified resistance across the terminals dependent upon the available light in the area. The only test that should be made is for a short circuit (zero resistance). If resistance is zero ohms, replace the sensor. Check for continuity and for possible shorting between the two wires (Pin 3 and Pin 16). Repeat if necessary. Reconnect battery cables.

ELECTRONIC AUTOMATIC TEMPERATURE CONTROL (EATC) SYSTEM CLUTCH DOES NOT DISENGAGE IN "OFF" POSITION DIAGNOSIS—1993 TOWN CAR

TEST STEP	RESULT	▶	ACTION TO TAKE
1			
• Disconnect connector VA (driver's side) from control assembly. • **Does clutch disengage?**	Yes	▶	REPLACE control assembly.
	No	▶	CHECK for damaged wiring, damaged integrated relay control module of Powertrain Control Module (PCM) or shorted pressure switch.

DIAGNOSIS AND TESTING (CONTINUED)

ELECTRONIC AUTOMATIC TEMPERATURE CONTROL ((EATC) MODULE ERROR CODES – 1994 CROWN VICTORIA, GRAND MARQUIS AND TOWN CAR

CONDITION	POSSIBLE SOURCE	ACTION
• EATC System Concern	• EATC control module damaged or inoperative. • A/C air temperature control door damaged or inoperative. • Sensor damaged or inoperative.	• Perform the following Diagnostics procedures and On-Board Diagnostics to register codes, then return to Symptom Chart for instructions.
01 (Code displayed during diagnostic procedures)	• Damaged control assembly.	• Replace EATC Control Assembly.
02 (Code displayed during diagnostic procedures)	• A/C air temperature control door damaged or inoperative.	• Refer to A/C Electronic Door Actuator Motor Diagnosis.
03 (Code displayed during diagnostic procedures)	• Automatic temperature control sensor open or short.	• Refer to Automatic Temperature Control Sensor Diagnosis
04 (Code displayed during diagnostic procedures)	• A/C ambient air temperature sensor and bracket open or short.	• Refer to A/C Ambient Air Temperature Sensor Diagnosis
05 (Code displayed during diagnostic procedures)	• A/C sunload sensor short.	• Refer to A/C Sunload Sensor Diagnosis
888 (Code displayed during diagnostic procedures)	• Temperature control lockout valve and switch inoperative. • Vaccum System inoperative. • A/C clutch inoperative or damaged.	• Refer to Pinpoint Test A

DIAGNOSIS AND TESTING (CONTINUED)

ELECTRONIC AUTOMATIC TEMPERATURE CONTROL ((EATC) SYMPTOM (NO CODE) DIAGNOSIS – 1994 CROWN VICTORIA, GRAND MARQUIS AND TOWN CAR

CONDITION	POSSIBLE SOURCE	ACTION
• Cool Discharge Air When System is Set to AUTOMATIC and 90°F (32°C)	• Heater system malfunction.	• Check coolant level. • Check engine thermostat.
	• A/C air temperature control door not in max. heat position.	• Check position of A/C air temperature control door. • Check A/C air temperature control door shaft attachment. • Test per A/C Electronic Door Actuator Motor Diagnosis (assume DTC 02 was displayed in the On-Board Diagnostic).

DIAGNOSIS AND TESTING (CONTINUED)

EATC DIAGNOSIS WHEN ON-BOARD DIAGNOSTIC INDICATES NO ERRORS FOUND (Continued)

CONDITION	POSSIBLE SOURCE	ACTION
• Warm Discharge Air in AUTOMATIC and 60°F (16°C)	• A/C clutch circuit malfunction. • Check refrigerant. • A/C air temperature control door not in MAX A/C position.	• Test A/C clutch circuit per "EATC— No A/C Clutch Operation Diagnosis." • Check Refrigerant System Pressures. • Check position of A/C air temperature control door. • Check A/C air temperature control door shaft attachment. • Test per "EATC—A/C Electronic Door Actuator Motor Functional Diagnosis." (Assume 02 was displayed in the On-Board Diagnostic.) • Test per "Vacuum Leak" Diagnosis.
• Cool Air in 85°F (29°C) Max. Heat in 90°F (32°C)	• Sensor shorted.	• Troubleshoot according to Sensor Diagnosis.
• Heat in 65°F (18°C) Max. Cool in 60°F (16°C)	• Sensor open.	• Troubleshoot according to Sensor Diagnosis.
• No A/C Blower Motor Operation	• Damaged temperature control lockout valve and switch wiring. • Damaged A/C blower motor speed control. • Damage HI blower relay. • Damaged control assembly. • Damaged A/C blower motor. • Damaged wiring.	• Test per "No Heater Blower Motor Operation" Section of A/C Blower Motor Speed Control.
• High A/C Blower Motor Operation Only	• Damaged control assembly. • Damaged A/C blower motor speed control. • Damaged wiring.	• Test per "High Heater Blower Motor Only" Section of A/C Blower Motor Speed Control.
• A/C Clutch is Engaged When System is Off	• Damaged control assembly. • Damaged wiring or interface components.	• Test according to EATC "A/C Clutch Does Not Disengage When In OFF Position." A/C Clutch Circuit Diagnosis.
• Control Assembly Digits and VFD Do Not Light Up, A/C Blower Motor Off	• Fuse. • Ignition Circuit 298 open. • Ignition Circuit 797 open. • Ground Circuit 57A open. • Damaged control assembly.	• Replace fuse. • Check Circuit 298. • Check Circuit 797. • Check Circuit 57A. • Replace control assembly.

DIAGNOSIS AND TESTING (CONTINUED)

EATC DIAGNOSIS WHEN ON-BOARD DIAGNOSTIC INDICATES NO ERRORS FOUND (Continued)

CONDITION	POSSIBLE SOURCE	ACTION
• Cold Air is Delivered During Heating When Engine is Cold	• Damaged wiring.	• Place system at 90°F / AUTOMATIC with ignition switch OFF. (Ignition switch must be OFF when grounding Circuit 244 for valid results). Ground Circuit 244 at temperature control lockout valve and switch. Start engine. If A / C blower motor is off, replace temperature control lockout valve and switch. If A / C blower motor is on, check wiring. If OK, replace control assembly.
	• Damaged or inoperative temperature control lockout valve and switch.	• Replace temperature control lockout valve and switch.
• Control Assembly Temperature Display Will Not Switch From Fahrenheit To Celsius When the E / M Trip Computer Button is Pushed	• Inoperative CCA switch module or control assembly.	**CAUTION: Accidental shorting of the wrong pin could destroy the control assembly.** • Short Pin 20 of connector VA (Circuit 506) to ground. Turn ignition switch ON. If the display does not switch from F to C, Circuit 506 is open at the control assembly and the control assembly is damaged. Otherwise check the wiring and the tripminder.
• System Does Not Control Temperature	• Automatic temperature control sensor hose and elbow not connected to aspirator or automatic temperature control sensor.	• Inspect and service.
	• Aspirator not secured to A / C evaporator housing.	• Inspect and service.
	• Automatic temperature control sensor seal(s) missing or not installed properly.	• Inspect and service.
	• Aspirator or automatic temperature control sensor hose and elbow blocked with foreign material or kinked.	• Inspect and service.
	• Damaged aspirator hose.	• Inspect and service.
• EATC Control Assembly Turns On and Off Erratically. No Control of System	• Damaged charging system. EATC will not function with too low or too high battery voltage.	• Check battery voltage. If battery voltage is less than 10 volts or greater than 16 volts. Do not replace EATC control assembly.

DIAGNOSIS AND TESTING (CONTINUED)

AUTOMATIC TEMPERATURE CONTROL SENSOR DIAGNOSIS

CONDITION	POSSIBLE SOURCE	ACTION
• On-Board Diagnostic DTC 03 (Warm Air Discharge at 65°F (18°C) or Cool Air Discharge at 85°F (29°C) **Sensor Resistance Table** Approximate Temperature — Sensor Resistance Acceptance Range: 50°F to 68°F (10°C to 20°C) — 37K to 58K ohms 68°F to 86°F (20°C to 30°C) — 24K to 37K ohms 86°F to 104°F (30°C to 40°C) — 16K to 24K ohms	• Automatic temperature control sensor open or shorted.	• Disconnect wire harness connector at automatic temperature control sensor. Measure resistance across automatic temperature control sensor terminals and compare with specifications in the following automatic temperature control sensor. Resistance Table. If resistance is out of specifications, replace automatic temperature control sensor. If automatic temperature control sensor is OK, proceed to "Wire harness open or shorted".
• On-Board Diagnostic DTC 03 (Warm Air Discharge at 65°F (18°C) or Cool Air Discharge at 85°F (29°C) **Sensor Resistance Table** Approximate Temperature — Sensor Resistance Acceptance Range: 50°F to 68°F (10°C to 20°C) — 37K to 58K ohms 68°F to 86°F (20°C to 30°C) — 24K to 37K ohms 86°F to 104°F (30°C to 40°C) — 16K to 24K ohms	• Wire harness open or shorted.	• Disconnect battery cables. Disconnect wire harness connector from automatic temperature control sensor and disconnect both connectors from EATC control assembly. Check for continuity and for possible shorting between the two wires (Pin 2 and Pin 17). Service as necessary. Reconnect wire harness and battery cables.

DIAGNOSIS AND TESTING (CONTINUED)

A/C AMBIENT AIR TEMPERATURE SENSOR DIAGNOSIS

CONDITION	POSSIBLE SOURCE	ACTION
• On-Board Diagnostics DTC 04 and Outside Temperature Display is Reading -40°F (-40°C) or 140°F (60°C) (Warm Air Discharge at 65°F (18°C) or Cool Air Discharge at 86°F (30°C) **Sensor Resistance Table** (see below)	• A/C ambient air temperature sensor and bracket open or shorted.	• Disconnect battery cables (necessary to reset outside temperature display memory). Disconnect wire harness connector at A/C ambient air temperature sensor and bracket. Measure resistance across A/C ambient air temperature sensor and bracket terminal and compare with automatic temperature control sensor Resistance Table. If resistance is out of specifications, replace A/C ambient air temperature sensor and bracket. If A/C ambient air temperature sensor and bracket is OK, proceed to "A/C ambient air temperature sensor and bracket wire harness open or shorted". Reconnect battery cables. NOTE: Install A/C ambient air temperature sensor and bracket and electrical connections before battery is reconnected.
• Intermittent Heating and Cooling. Outside Temperature Display sometimes inaccurate	• A/C ambient air temperature sensor and bracket wire harness open or shorted.	• Disconnect battery cables. Disconnect wire harness connector from A/C ambient air temperature sensor and bracket and disconnect both connectors from the EATC control assembly. Check for continuity and for possible shorting between two wires (Pin 1 and Pin 2). Service as necessary. Reconnect wire harness and battery cables.

Sensor Resistance Table

Approximate Temperature	Sensor Resistance Acceptance Range
50°F to 68°F (10°C to 20°C)	37K to 58K ohms
68°F to 86°F (20°C to 30°C)	24K to 37K ohms
86°F to 104°F (30°C to 40°C)	16K to 24K ohms

DIAGNOSIS AND TESTING (CONTINUED)

A/C SUNLOAD SENSOR DIAGNOSIS

CONDITION	POSSIBLE SOURCE	ACTION
• On-Board Diagnostics DTC 05	• A/C sunload sensor shorted.	• Disconnect battery cables. Disconnect wire harness connector at A/C sunload sensor and disconnect both connectors from EATC control assembly. NOTE: Check A/C sunload sensor for a short using an ohmmeter. The A/C sunload sensor is a photodiode so there should be some unspecified resistance across the terminals depending on the light available in the area. The only test that should be made is for a short circuit (zero resistance). If resistance is zero ohms, replace the A/C sunload sensor. • Check for continuity and for possible shorting between two wires (Pin 3 and Pin 16). Repeat if necessary. Reconnect battery cables.

DIAGNOSIS AND TESTING (CONTINUED)

Pinpoint Tests

PINPOINT TEST A: EATC SYSTEM INOPERATIVE, INTERMITTENT OR IMPROPER OPERATION

	TEST STEP	RESULT ▶	ACTION TO TAKE
A1	CHECK CONTROL DISPLAY		
	• Ensure engine is cold. • The In-vehicle temperature should be greater than 10°C (50°F). • Turn ignition switch to the RUN position. • Press the AUTOMATIC button. • Set control at 90°F (32°C) setting. • **Does control display 90°F (32°C) Auto?**	Yes ▶ No ▶	GO to **A2.** REFER to Diagnosis When On-Board Diagnostic and Functional Test Indicate No Errors Found.
A2	CHECK A/C BLOWER MOTOR OPERATION		
	• Verify that the A/C blower motor does not come on. (Engine coolant temp. is less than 120°F (48°C). • **Does A/C blower motor operate?**	Yes ▶ No ▶	REFER to Temperature Control Lockout Valve and Switch Test. GO to **A3.**
A3	CHECK A/C BLOWER MOTOR OPERATION WITH THE WHEEL FULLY UP		
	• Ensure that engine is warm (coolant temp. is greater than 120°F (48°C). • Set control at 75 setting. • **Does A/C blower motor operate?**	Yes ▶ No ▶	GO to **A4.** REFER to A/C Blower Motor Speed Control Diagnosis-Heater Blower Motor Does Not Run At Any Speed.
A4	CHECK A/C BLOWER MOTOR SPEED WITH THUMBWHEEL FULLY DOWN		
	• Rotate blower thumbwheel fully down. • **Does A/C blower motor go to low speed?**	Yes ▶ No ▶	GO to **A5.** REFER to A/C Blower Motor Speed Control Diagnosis-No MEDIUM or LOW Heater Blower Motor Speeds.
A5	CHECK A/C BLOWER MOTOR SPEED WITH THUMBWHEEL FULLY UP		
	• Rotate blower thumbwheel fully up. • **Does A/C blower motor go to high speed?**	Yes ▶ No ▶	GO to **A6.** REFER to A/C Blower Motor Speed Control Diagnosis-No HIGH Heater Blower Motor Speed.
A6	CHECK DEFROSTER AND DEMISTER AIR FLOW		
	• Press the DEFROST button. • Verify that air is discharged from windshield defroster hose nozzles with small bleed through the side A/C side window demister and hoses. • Verify that the heater and A/C air inlet duct door is in the outside air position. • **Are these conditions met?**	Yes ▶ No ▶	GO to **A7.** REFER to Vacuum System Diagnosis.
A7	CHECK AIR FLOW FROM FLOOR DUCT		
	• Press the FLOOR button. • Verify that the air is discharged through the heater outlet floor ducts. • **Is this condition met?**	Yes ▶ No ▶	GO to **A8.** REFER to Vacuum System Diagnosis.

DIAGNOSIS AND TESTING (CONTINUED)

PINPOINT TEST A: EATC SYSTEM INOPERATIVE, INTERMITTENT OR IMPROPER OPERATION (Continued)

TEST STEP		RESULT ▶	ACTION TO TAKE
A8	CHECK AIR FLOW FROM PANEL REGISTERS		
	• Press the VENT button. • Verify that the air is discharged through the panel A/C registers. • **Is this condition met?**	Yes ▶ No ▶	GO to **A9.** REFER to Vacuum System Diagnosis.
A9	CHECK THAT INLET DUCT DOOR IS IN RECIRC POSITION		
	• Make sure that the ambient temperature is greater than 40°F. • Press the MAX A/C button. • Verify that the heater and A/C air inlet duct door is in the recirc position. • **Is this condition met?**	Yes ▶ No ▶	GO to **A10.** REFER to Vacuum System Diagnosis.
A10	CHECK VENT DISPLAY AND A/C CLUTCH		
	• Press the VENT button. • Verify that the VENT display is lit. • Verify that the A/C clutch is off. • **Are these conditions met?**	Yes ▶ No ▶	GO to **A11.** REFER to A/C Clutch Does Not Disengage When In OFF Diagnosis.
A11	CHECK MAX A/C DISPLAY AND A/C CLUTCH		
	• Press the MAX A/C button again. • Verify that the MAX A/C display is lit and that the A/C clutch is on. • **Are these conditions met?**	Yes ▶ No ▶	GO to **A12.** REFER to No A/C Clutch Operation Diagnosis.
A12	CHECK VFDS		
	• Press AUTOMATIC button. • AUTOMATIC or function and fan VFDs should light. • **Do they light?**	Yes ▶ No ▶	Test complete. REFER to Diagnosis When Self-Test and Functional Test Indicate No Errors Found.

DIAGNOSIS AND TESTING (CONTINUED)

ELECTRONIC AUTOMATIC TEMPERATURE CONTROL ((EATC) MODULE ERROR CODES – 1995 CROWN VICTORIA, GRAND MARQUIS AND TOWN CAR

ERROR CODE	DETECTED CONDITION	ACTION
024	Fault in blend door calibration during self test	GO to Pinpoint Test B
025	Intermittent fault in blend door calibration	GO to Pinpoint Test B
030	Self test indicates automatic temperature control sensor shorted	GO to Pinpoint Test P
031	Self test indicates automatic temperature control sensor open	GO to Pinpoint Test P
040	Self test indicates ambient sensor short	GO to Pinpoint Test J
041	Self test indicates ambient sensor open	GO to Pinpoint Test J
042	Ambient sensor intermittent short	GO to Pinpoint Test J
043	Ambient sensor intermittent open	GO to Pinpoint Test J
050	Self test indicates sunload sensor short	GO to Pinpoint Test K
052	Sunload Sensor intermittent short	GO to Pinpoint Test K
115	Intermittent engine coolant temperature signal	GO to Pinpoint Test G or Pinpoint Test H
125	Intermittent vehicle speed signal	GO to Pinpoint Test G or Pinpoint Test H

DIAGNOSIS AND TESTING (CONTINUED)

ELECTRONIC AUTOMATIC TEMPERATURE CONTROL ((EATC) SYMPTOM (NO CODE) DIAGNOSIS – 1995 CROWN VICTORIA, GRAND MARQUIS AND TOWN CAR

CONDITION	POSSIBLE SOURCE	ACTION
• EATC System Inoperative, Intermittent or Improper Operation	• Damaged or inoperative charging system. • Circuitry open / shorted. • Damaged input sensor(s) / erratic input signal(s). • Charging system damaged. • Damaged automatic temperature control sensor hose and elbow.	• GO to Pinpoint Test A.
• A / C Electronic Door Actuator Motor Inoperative, Intermittent or Improper Operation	• Circuitry open / shorted. • Damaged A / C electronic door actuator motor. • Damaged EATC module.	• GO to Pinpoint Test B.
• EATC Heater Blower Motor Does Not Run	• Circuitry open / shorted. • Damaged blower motor. • Damaged A / C blower motor speed control.	• GO to Pinpoint Test C.
• EATC Heater Blower Motor Operates in High in All Blower Wheel Positions	• Damaged A / C blower motor speed control. • Damaged EATC module.	• GO to Pinpoint Test D.
• EATC Heater Blower Motor Does Not Operate at Lower Speeds	• Damaged A / C blower motor speed control. • Damaged EATC module.	• GO to Pinpoint Test E.
• EATC Heater Blower Motor Does Not Operate at High Speed	• Damaged A / C blower motor speed control • Damaged EATC module.	• GO to Pinpoint Test F.
• Intermittent Vehicle Module Data Link Signal—Diagnostic Error Code 115 or 125	• Damaged vehicle speed sensor. • Damaged engine coolant temperature sensor.	• GO to Pinpoint Test G.
• Intermittent Vehicle Module Data Link Signal—Diagnostic Error Codes 115 and 125 Simultaneously	• Damaged powertrain components. • Circuitry open / shorted.	• GO to Pinpoint Test H.
• Warm Discharge Air In AUTOMATIC and 60°F	• A / C clutch malfunction. • Low refrigerant. • Damaged EATC module. • A / C air temperature control door not in max A / C position.	• GO to Pinpoint Test A.
• A / C Ambient Air Temperature Sensor Inoperative	• Damaged A / C ambient air temperature sensor and bracket. • Circuitry open / shorted.	• GO to Pinpoint Test J.
• A / C Sunload Sensor Inoperative	• Damaged A / C sunload sensor. • Circuitry open / shorted.	• GO to Pinpoint Test K.
• Control Assembly / VFD Does Not Light Up—Heater Blower Motor OFF	• Circuitry open / shorted. • Damaged EATC module.	• GO to Pinpoint Test L.
• Cold Engine Blower Control Diagnosis—No Diagnostic Error Code	• Damaged module data link wiring and / or inoperative engine coolant temperature sensor. • Damaged EATC control assembly.	• GO to Pinpoint Test M.
• Temperature Display Won't Switch Between Celsius and Fahrenheit	• Circuitry open / shorted. • Damaged EATC module.	• GO to Pinpoint Test N.

DIAGNOSIS AND TESTING (CONTINUED)

EATC SYSTEM (Continued)

CONDITION	POSSIBLE SOURCE	ACTION
• System Does Not Control Temperature	• Circuitry open / shorted. • Damaged EATC module. • Damaged automatic temperature control sensor hose and elbow. • In-car sensor seals missing or damaged.	• GO to Pinpoint Test P.
• Control Assembly Turns On and OFF Erratically—No Control of System	• Damaged EATC module. • Charging system damaged.	• GO to Pinpoint Test A, then GO to Pinpoint Test P.
• Temperature Set Point Does Not Repeat After Turning Ignition Switch OFF	• Blown fuse. • Circuitry open / shorted. • Damaged EATC module.	• GO to Pinpoint Test Q.

Pinpoint Tests

PINPOINT TEST A: EATC SYSTEM INOPERATIVE, INTERMITTENT OR IMPROPER OPERATION

TEST STEP		RESULT ▶	ACTION TO TAKE
A1	PERFORM EATC SELF TEST		
	• Turn EATC System ON. Press the OFF and FLOOR buttons simultaneously and then press the AUTOMATIC button within two seconds. The test may take as long as 30 seconds. A pulse tracer will circle around the center of the VFD window during the test. When the self test is completed, error codes will be displayed in the VFD window to list faults found during the self test. Error codes will also be given for intermittent faults encountered during system operation. Record these error codes. • **Were error codes other than 888 displayed in the VFD window?**	Yes ▶ No ▶	REFER to Inspection and Verification for Diagnostic Error Codes to find the "Detected Condition." PERFORM the necessary diagnosis and make repairs. GO to **A2**.
A2	CHECK BLOWER MANUAL OVERRIDE LOW SPEED OPERATION		
	• Rotate the blower thumbwheel down to the stop. • **Does the blower motor go to low speed?**	Yes ▶ No ▶	GO to **A3**. REFER to Pinpoint Test E.
A3	CHECK BLOWER MANUAL OVERRIDE HIGH SPEED OPERATION		
	• Rotate the blower thumbwheel up to the stop. • **Does the blower motor go to high speed?**	Yes ▶ No ▶	GO to **A4**. REFER to Pinpoint Test F.
A4	VERIFY DEFROST OVERRIDE OPERATION		
	• Press the Defrost button and check system discharge airflow. Airflow should be from the demister nozzle and duct and the A / C side window demister and hose. Also check to be sure the heater and A / C air inlet duct door is in the outside position. • **Are these two conditions met?**	Yes ▶ No ▶	GO to **A5**. REFER to "Vacuum Leak Diagnosis"
A5	VERIFY FLOOR OVERRIDE OPERATION		
	• Press the FLOOR button and check system discharge airflow. Discharge airflow should be from the heater outlet floor duct. • **Is airflow discharged from the heater outlet floor duct?**	Yes ▶ No ▶	GO to **A6**. REFER to "Vacuum Leak Diagnosis"
A6	VERIFY VENT OVERRIDE OPERATION		
	• Press the VENT button and check system discharge airflow. Airflow should be from the A / C registers. • **Is this condition met?**	Yes ▶ No ▶	GO to **A7**. REFER to "Vacuum Leak Diagnosis"

DIAGNOSIS AND TESTING (CONTINUED)

PINPOINT TEST A: EATC SYSTEM INOPERATIVE, INTERMITTENT OR IMPROPER OPERATION (Continued)

TEST STEP		RESULT ▶	ACTION TO TAKE
A7	VERIFY MAX A / C OVERRIDE OPERATION		
	• With the ambient temperature above 5°C (40°F), press the MAX A / C button. Check that the heater and A / C air inlet duct door is in the recirc. air position (closed to outside air). • **Is the outside-recirc door closed to outside air?**	Yes ▶ No ▶	GO to **A8.** REFER to "Vacuum Leak Diagnosis"
A8	VERIFY A / C CLUTCH DOES NOT ENGAGE IN VENT		
	• Press the VENT button. VENT should be displayed and the A / C clutch should not engage. • **Are these two conditions met?**	Yes ▶ No ▶	GO to **A9.**
A9	VERIFY MAX A / C OPERATION		
	• Press the MAX A / C button again. MAX A / C should be displayed and the A / C clutch should engage for A / C compressor operation. • **Are these two conditions met?**	Yes ▶ No ▶	GO to **A10.**
A10	VERIFY AUTOMATIC OPERATION		
	• Press the AUTOMATIC button. The selected temperature and AUTOMATIC should be shown in the VFD display window. • **Is the VFD correct and complete?**	Yes ▶ No ▶	GO to **A11** if equipped with optional steering wheel remote control buttons. Test complete on vehicles without remote control buttons. RESTORE vehicle. REFER to "EATC Self Test" in Pinpoint Test Step A1 and "Diagnostic Error Codes" in Inspection and Verification.
A11	VERIFY STEERING WHEEL TEMP BUTTON OPERATION		
	• Operate the steering wheel remote control TEMP button to verify that the set temperature increases when the " ʌ " (increase) side of the button is pushed and decreases when the "v" (lower) side of the button is depressed. • **Does the TEMP switch increase and decrease the set temperature as described?**	Yes ▶ No ▶	GO to **A12**. SERVICE Temp Switch.
A12	VERIFY STEERING WHEEL FAN SWITCH OPERATION		
	• Operate the steering wheel remote control FAN button to verify that the blower speed increases when FAN " ʌ " (increase) is depressed and that the blower speed decreases when FAN "v" (lower) is depressed. • **Does the FAN button increase and decrease the blower motor speed as described?**	Yes ▶ No ▶	Test complete. RESTORE vehicle. SERVICE FAN Button.

DIAGNOSIS AND TESTING (CONTINUED)

PINPOINT TEST B: A/C ELECTRONIC DOOR ACTUATOR MOTOR INOPERATIVE, INTERMITTENT OR IMPROPER OPERATION

TEST STEP		RESULT	▶ ACTION TO TAKE
B1	CHECK CODES		
	NOTE: Letters in parentheses indicate (wire color, circuit number). GO to EATC wiring diagram and connector pin diagrams. • Perform Self Test and check error codes. • **Is error code 020 or 021 displayed?**	Yes No	▶ GO to **B2**. ▶ REVIEW Error Code Chart if other error codes are displayed. If no Error Codes, PERFORM Pinpoint Test A.
B2	CHECK ACTUATOR DRIVE		
	• Disconnect both electrical connectors from rear of EATC control assembly. Operate the A/C electronic door actuator motor in both directions using any 12-volt battery. The following pins can be jumped to use the vehicle battery. Make sure the ignition switch is in the RUN position. All pins are located in the C1 (LH) harness connector. • Trial 1: Pin 24 (BK, 57) to Pin 22 (P, 246). • Trial 2: Pin 24 (BK, 57) to Pin 21 (BR/LG, 245). • **Does the A/C electronic door actuator motor drive in both directions?**	Yes No	▶ GO to **B3**. ▶ GO to **B6**.
B3	PERFORM EATC FUNCTIONAL TEST		
	• Reconnect wire harness connectors and perform EATC Functional Test to check system operation. • **Is test successful?**	Yes No	▶ System OK. RESTORE vehicle. ▶ GO to **B4**.
B4	CHECK RESISTANCES		
	• Drive the blend door actuator to the full CCW position (MAX heat). • Disconnect both harness connectors from rear of EATC Control Assembly. Measure resistance between the pins shown below at the control assembly C2 (RH) harness connector. • Pin 15 (R/LG, 436) to Pin 6 (R/W, 438) - 5000-7000 ohms • Pin 5 (Y/LG, 437) to Pin 6 (R/W, 438) - 3500-6000 ohms • Pin 5 (Y/LG, 437) to Pin 15 (R/LG, 436) - 250-1500 ohms • **Are all resistances within value given?**	Yes No	▶ GO to **B5**. ▶ GO to **B6**.
B5	RETEST EATC SYSTEM		
	• Reconnect harness connectors and perform EATC Self Test, Pinpoint Test Step A1. • **Is test successful?**	Yes No	▶ System OK. RESTORE vehicle. ▶ GO to **B1**.
B6	CHECK CONTINUITY		
	• Check vehicle wiring harness and connector continuity as shown below. Disconnect both harness connectors from rear of control assembly and the A/C electronic door actuator motor. The actuator connector is accessible through the glove compartment.	Yes No	▶ REPLACE A/C electronic door actuator motor. GO to **B7**. ▶ GO to **B8**.

Control Assembly Connector		Temperature Blend Door Actuator
C2		
Pin 5 (Y/LG, 437)	to	Pin 3 (Y/LG, 437)
Pin 6 (R/W, 438)	to	Pin 2 (R/W, 438)
Pin 15 (R/LG, 436)	to	Pin 4 (R/LG, 436-Town Car) (LG/O, 436-Crown Victoria, Grand Marquis)
C1		
Pin 21 (BR/LG, 245)	to	Pin 1 (BR/LG)
Pin 22 (P, 246)	to	Pin 5 (P, 246)
Pin 24 (BK, 57)	to	Pin 6 (BK, 57)

• Reconnect all three harness connectors at end of this test.
• **Is there continuity on all six wires?**

DIAGNOSIS AND TESTING (CONTINUED)

PINPOINT TEST B: A/C ELECTRONIC DOOR ACTUATOR MOTOR INOPERATIVE, INTERMITTENT OR IMPROPER OPERATION (Continued)

	TEST STEP	RESULT	ACTION TO TAKE
B7	RETEST AFTER CHANGING BLEND DOOR ACTUATOR		
	• After replacing A/C electronic door actuator motor, perform Pinpoint Test Step A1. • **Is test successful?**	Yes ▶ No ▶	Test complete. GO to **B1**.
B8	RETEST AFTER SERVICING WIRING HARNESS		
	• Service/replace wiring harness. Reconnect and perform Pinpoint Test Step **A1**. • **Is test successful?**	Yes ▶ No ▶	Test complete. GO to **B1**.

PINPOINT TEST C: EATC HEATER BLOWER MOTOR DOES NOT RUN

	TEST STEP	RESULT	ACTION TO TAKE
C1	CHECK BLOWER MOTOR OPERATION		
	• Start engine and select MAX A/C. • **Does blower motor operate?**	Yes ▶ No ▶	PERFORM Pinpoint Test Step **A1**. GO to **C2.**
C2	CHECK VOLTAGE BETWEEN PINS 4 AND 5		
	• Disconnect the harness connector from the A/C blower motor speed control. • Start engine and set A/C control to MAX A/C. Measure voltage between Pins 4 and 5 of blower motor speed control harness connector. Should have battery voltage. • **Is voltage less than 10 volts?**	Yes ▶ No ▶	CHECK Fuse 9, and blower motor Circuits 181 (BR/O) and 515 (O/R). SERVICE as required. GO to **C3.**
C3	VOLTAGE CHECK TO A/C BLOWER MOTOR		
	• Reconnect harness to A/C blower motor speed control. Disconnect blower motor from harness. Check for voltage across harness connector Circuits 515 (O/R) and 181 (BR/O) with blower motor on HI. • **Is voltage measurement 10 volts or more?**	Yes ▶ No ▶	REPLACE blower motor. GO to **C4.**
C4	VOLTAGE CHECK BETWEEN PINS 3 AND 5		
	• Disconnect harness connector from A/C blower motor speed control. Check voltage between Pins 3 and 5 of harness connector. Voltage reading should be 10 or more volts with blower motor on HI. • **Is voltage 10 volts or greater?**	Yes ▶ No ▶	REPLACE A/C blower motor speed control. GO to **C5**.
C5	VOLTAGE CHECK AT EATC		
	• Reconnect A/C blower motor speed control connector. With engine running and control set for MAX A/C and HI blower, check voltage at EATC control assembly Pin 9 and ground. Voltage should be 10 or more volts. • **Is voltage 10 volts or greater?**	Yes ▶ No ▶	SERVICE Circuit776 (O/BK) for Town Car or Circuit 758 (LG/W) for Crown Victoria, Grand Marquis between control assembly (Pin 9) and A/C blower motor speed controller (Pin 3) for open. RESTORE vehicle. RETEST system. REPLACE EATC control assembly. RESTORE vehicle. RETEST system.

DIAGNOSIS AND TESTING (CONTINUED)

PINPOINT TEST D: EATC HEATER BLOWER MOTOR OPERATES IN HIGH IN ALL BLOWER WHEEL POSITIONS

TEST STEP		RESULT	►	ACTION TO TAKE
D1	CHECK BLOWER MOTOR MEDIUM SPEED OPERATION			
	• Start engine, select MAX A/C and position the blower thumbwheel midway between HI and LO. The blower motor should operate at approximately medium speed. • **Is the A/C blower motor speed reduced from high speed?**	Yes	►	PERFORM Pinpoint Test A.
		No	►	GO to **D2.**
D2	CHECK VOLTAGE AT BLOWER SPEED CONTROLLER			
	• Disconnect the harness connector from the A/C blower motor speed control. Start engine, set control at MAX A/C and blower thumbwheel at LO. • Check for voltage between Pins 2 and 5 of the harness connector while rotating the blower motor thumbwheel. The voltage reading should be between 1 and 2 volts for all thumbwheel settings except HI; should have zero volts at HI. • **Is voltage measurement between 1 and 2 volts except in HI?**	Yes	►	GO to **D5.**
		No	►	GO to **D3.**
D3	REVERIFY VOLTAGE IN D2			
	• Verify the voltage measurement in Step D2. • **Is the voltage measurement above 2 volts in all thumbwheel settings?**	Yes	►	REPLACE EATC control assembly. RESTORE vehicle. RETEST system.
		No	►	GO to **D4.**
D4	ZERO VOLTAGE CHECK			
	• Refer to voltage measurement taken in Step D2. • **Is the voltage measurement zero volts for all thumbwheel positions?**	Yes	►	GO to **D6.**
		No	►	RETEST and GO to **D1.**
D5	VOLTAGE CHECK AT ANY POSITION EXCEPT HI			
	• Check voltage between Pins 3 and 5 of A/C blower motor speed control with the blower speed thumbwheel at any position except HI. Should be zero volts. • **Is the voltage measurement zero?**	Yes	►	REPLACE the A/C blower motor speed control. RESTORE vehicle. RETEST system.
		No	►	REPLACE the EATC control assembly. RESTORE vehicle. RETEST system.
D6	VOLTAGE CHECK AT EATC PIN 7			
	• Reconnect harness connector to A/C blower motor speed control. With the engine running, select MAX A/C and set the blower thumbwheel for a medium speed. Check the voltage at Pin 7 of the EATC control assembly. • **Is the voltage measurement between 1 and 2 volts?**	Yes	►	**SERVICE Circuit 756 (R/PK) for Town Car or Circuit 752 (Y/R) for Crown Victoria, Grand Marquis between EATC control assembly Pin 7 and the A/C blower motor speed controller Pin 2. RESTORE vehicle. RETEST system.**
		No	►	GO to **D7.**
D7	VERIFY ZERO VOLTAGE			
	• Verify the voltage measurement taken in Step D6. • **Is the voltage measurement zero volts?**	Yes	►	REPLACE EATC control assembly. RESTORE vehicle. RETEST system.
		No	►	RETEST voltage. GO to **D1.**

DIAGNOSIS AND TESTING (CONTINUED)

PINPOINT TEST E: EATC HEATER BLOWER MOTOR DOES NOT OPERATE AT LOWER SPEEDS

	TEST STEP	RESULT ▶	ACTION TO TAKE
E1	CHECK BLOWER MOTOR LO SPEED OPERATION		
	• Start engine, select MAX A/C and position the blower thumbwheel to LO. The blower motor should operate at low speed. • Slowly rotate the blower thumbwheel to HI. The A/C blower motor speed should increase until high blower speed is obtained. • **Does the A/C blower speed increase to high speed?**	Yes ▶ No ▶	PERFORM Pinpoint Test Step **A1**. GO to **E2.**
E2	CHECK VOLTAGE BETWEEN BLOWER MOTOR SPEED CONTROL PINS 2 AND 5		
	• Turn ignition switch to off. • Disconnect the harness connector from the A/C blower motor speed control. Start engine, select MAX A/C and rotate the blower thumbwheel to LO. Check voltage between Pins 2 and 5 of the blower motor speed controller harness connector. Voltage reading should be between 1 and 2 volts. • **Is the voltage measurement between 1 and 2 volts?**	Yes ▶ No ▶	REPLACE the A/C blower motor speed control. RESTORE vehicle. RETEST system. GO to **E3.**
E3	VERIFY VOLTAGE MEASUREMENT		
	• Verify the voltage reading obtained in Step E2. • **Does the voltage measure zero volts?**	Yes ▶ No ▶	GO to **E4.** RETEST. GO to **E1.**
E4	VOLTAGE CHECK AT EATC PIN 7		
	• Reconnect harness connector to A/C blower motor speed control. Start engine, select MAX A/C and rotate the blower thumbwheel to LO. • Check voltage between Pin 7 of EATC control assembly and ground. Should indicate 1 to 2 volts. • **Is the voltage measurement between 1 and 2 volts?**	Yes ▶ No ▶	SERVICE Circuit 756 (R/PK) for Town Car or Circuit 752 (Y/R) for Crown Victoria, Grand Marquis between Pin 7 of EATC control assembly and Pin 2 of A/C blower motor speed controller for open. RESTORE vehicle. RETEST system. GO to **E5.**
E5	ZERO VOLTAGE CHECK AT PIN 7		
	• Verify the voltage recorded in Step E4. • **Does the voltage between Pin 7 and ground measure zero volts?**	Yes ▶ No ▶	REPLACE the EATC control assembly. RESTORE vehicle. RETEST system. RETEST. GO to **E1.**

DIAGNOSIS AND TESTING (CONTINUED)

PINPOINT TEST F: EATC HEATER BLOWER MOTOR DOES NOT OPERATE AT HIGH SPEED

TEST STEP		RESULT ▶	ACTION TO TAKE
F1	CHECK BLOWER MOTOR HI SPEED OPERATION		
	• Start engine, select MAX A/C and position the blower thumbwheel to a position midway between LO and HI. Verify that the blower motor operates. Then, rotate the blower thumbwheel to HI and check to see if the blower speed responds to the thumbwheel movement. • **Does the blower speed increase with movement of the thumbwheel toward HI?**	Yes ▶ No ▶	PERFORM Pinpoint Test A. GO to **F2.**
F2	CHECK FOR 10 VOLTS OR MORE		
	• With ignition switch OFF, disconnect the harness connector from the A/C blower motor speed control. • Start engine, select MAX A/C and rotate the blower thumbwheel to HI. Check voltage between Pins 3 and 5 of disconnected harness connector. Voltage reading should be 10 or more volts. • **Is voltage 10 volts or more?**	Yes ▶ No ▶	REPLACE A/C blower motor speed control. RESTORE vehicle. RETEST system. GO to **F3.**
F3	VOLTAGE CHECK AT PIN 9 OF EATC		
	• Reconnect harness connector to A/C blower motor speed control. • Start engine, select MAX A/C and rotate blower thumbwheel to HI. Measure voltage between Pin 9 of the EATC control assembly and ground. Must indicate 10 or more volts when the blower thumbwheel is rotated to the stop at HI. • **Is voltage 10 volts or greater?**	Yes ▶ No ▶	SERVICE Circuit 758 (P/W) for Town Car or Circuit 754 (LG/W) for Crown Victoria, Grand Marquis between Pin 9 of EATC control assembly and Pin 3 of A/C blower motor speed controller. RESTORE vehicle. RETEST system. REPLACE EATC control assembly. RESTORE vehicle. RETEST system.

PINPOINT TEST G: INTERMITTENT VEHICLE MODULE DATA LINK SIGNAL—DIAGNOSTIC ERROR CODE 115 OR 125

TEST STEP		RESULT ▶	ACTION TO TAKE
G1	CHECK POWERTRAIN CONTROL MODULE DIAGNOSTICS		
	• Perform Diagnostic Routines for Powertrain Control Module. • **Do the PCM diagnostics indicate a malfunction of a powertrain component or signal?**	Yes ▶ No ▶	SERVICE as directed and again PERFORM Pinpoint Test Step A1. PERFORM a continuity test on the module data link circuits while wiggling the wires (Circuits 914 (T/O) wire and 915 (PK/LB) wire). SERVICE as necessary.

DIAGNOSIS AND TESTING (CONTINUED)

PINPOINT TEST H: INTERMITTENT VEHICLE MODULE DATA LINK SIGNAL—DIAGNOSTIC ERROR CODES 115 AND 125 SIMULTANEOUSLY

TEST STEP		RESULT ▶	ACTION TO TAKE
H1	CHECK POWERTRAIN CONTROL MODULE (PCM) DIAGNOSTICS		
	• Perform Diagnostic Routines for Powertrain Control Module. Refer to Powertrain Control / Emissions Diagnosis Manual[2]. • **Are all the powertrain components functioning properly?**	Yes ▶ No ▶	GO to **H2.** SERVICE or REPLACE as indicated.
H2	CHECK CONTINUITY OF VEHICLE DATA LINK WIRES		
	• Check Circuits 914 (T/O) and 915 (PK/LB) for an open circuit between the EATC control module and the powertrain control module. • **Are either or both circuits open?**	Yes ▶ No ▶	SERVICE as necessary. GO to **H1.** GO to **H3.**
H3	CHECK CIRCUITS FOR AN INTERMITTENT OPEN		
	• Check Circuits 914 (T/O) and 915 (PK/LB) for an intermittent open circuit by wiggling each wire at each connector while checking for continuity. • **Does an intermittent open condition exist?**	Yes ▶ No ▶	SERVICE as necessary. GO to **H1.** CHECK each harness electrical connector for a tight connection; then PERFORM Pinpoint Test A.

PINPOINT TEST J: A/C AMBIENT AIR TEMPERATURE SENSOR INOPERATIVE

TEST STEP		RESULT ▶	ACTION TO TAKE
J1	PERFORM EATC SELF DIAGNOSTICS TEST		
	• Turn the ignition switch to RUN. • Press OFF and FLOOR buttons simultaneously and then press AUTOMATIC button within two seconds. • Self test may run as long as 30 seconds. • After self test, record all error codes and any temperature display readings. • Press the blue (cooler) button to exit self test. • **Are error codes 040, 041, 042 or 043 displayed and is temperature display reading - 40°F (-40°C) or 128°F?**	Yes ▶ No ▶	GO to **J2.** GO to **J3.**
J2	CHECK SENSOR RESISTANCE		
	NOTE: An open sensor will cause the outside temperature display to read -40°F or -40°C. A shorted sensor will cause the outside temperature display to read 128°F. • Disconnect the battery ground cable from the battery (this will reset the outside temperature display memory). • Disconnect the A/C ambient air temperature sensor and bracket. • Using a DVOM, measure the resistance across the two sensor terminals and compare the reading with the following sensor resistance table: (see sensor resistance table below) • **Are resistance values within the specified limits?**	Yes ▶ No ▶	GO to **J3.** REPLACE A/C ambient air temperature sensor and bracket. RESTORE vehicle. RETEST system.

Approximate Temperature	Sensor Resistance Acceptance Range
50°F (10°C) to 68°F (20°C)	37K to 58K ohms
68°F (20°C) to 86°F (30°C)	24K to 37K ohms
86°F (30°C) to 104°F (40°C)	16K to 24K ohms

DIAGNOSIS AND TESTING (CONTINUED)

PINPOINT TEST J: A/C AMBIENT AIR TEMPERATURE SENSOR INOPERATIVE (Continued)

	TEST STEP	RESULT ▶	ACTION TO TAKE
J3	CHECK CIRCUIT 767 (LB/O) AT A/C AMBIENT AIR TEMPERATURE SENSOR		
	• Turn ignition switch to the RUN position. • Turn EATC module to NORM A/C position. • Disconnect A/C ambient air temperature sensor and bracket. • Using voltmeter, check Circuit 767 (LB/O) for voltage at sensor connector. • **Is voltage 10 volts or more?**	Yes ▶ No ▶	GO to **J6**. GO to **J4**.
J4	CHECK CIRCUIT 767 (LB/O) AT EATC MODULE		
	• Using voltmeter, check Circuit 767 (LB/O) at EATC module Pin 1 for voltage. • **Is voltage 10 volts or more?**	Yes ▶ No ▶	GO to **J5**. REPLACE EATC module. RESTORE vehicle. RETEST system.
J5	CHECK CIRCUIT 767 (LB/O) FOR OPEN		
	• Turn ignition switch to the OFF position. • Using a jumper connected to a known good ground, connect other end to Circuit 767 (LB/O) at sensor connector. • Using an ohmmeter connected to a known good ground, connect second lead to Circuit 767 (LB/O) at EATC module connector Pin 1. • Measure resistance. • **Is resistance 5 ohms or less?**	Yes ▶ No ▶	GO to **J6**. SERVICE Circuit 767 (LB/O) for open. RESTORE vehicle. RETEST system.
J6	CHECK CIRCUIT 359 (GY/R)		
	• Connect jumper to Circuit 359 (GY/R) at sensor connector. • Using an ohmmeter connected to a known good ground, connect second lead to Circuit 359 (GY/R) at module connector Pin 2. • Measure resistance. • **Is resistance 5 ohms or less?**	Yes ▶ No ▶	REPLACE A/C ambient air temperature sensor and bracket. RESTORE vehicle. RETEST system. SERVICE Circuit 359 (GY/R) for open. RESTORE vehicle. RETEST system.

PINPOINT TEST K: A/C SUNLOAD SENSOR INOPERATIVE

	TEST STEP	RESULT ▶	ACTION TO TAKE
K1	PERFORM EATC SELF DIAGNOSTICS TEST		
	• Turn the ignition switch to RUN. • Press OFF and FLOOR buttons simultaneously and then press AUTOMATIC button within two seconds. • Self test may run as long as 30 seconds. • After self test, record all error codes. • Press the blue (cooler) button to exit self test. • **Is error code 050, sunload sensor shorted, displayed?**	Yes ▶ No ▶	GO to **K3**. GO to **K2**.
K2	CHECK FOR INTERMITTENT SHORT CIRCUIT		
	• **Upon completion of self test in H1, was error code 052 displayed?**	Yes ▶ No ▶	GO to **K6**. GO to **K4**.

DIAGNOSIS AND TESTING (CONTINUED)

PINPOINT TEST K: A/C SUNLOAD SENSOR INOPERATIVE (Continued)

TEST STEP		RESULT	ACTION TO TAKE
K3	CHECK SUNLOAD SENSOR RESISTANCE		
	• Disconnect battery ground cable. • Disconnect sunload sensor wire harness connector. • Using a DVOM, check the resistance across the two sensor connectors. NOTE: The A/C sunload sensor is a photovoltaic cell and should have some unspecified resistance across the terminals depending on the light available to the sensor. The only test that can be performed without specialized equipment is for a short. If the resistance across the sensor terminals is zero ohms, the sensor is shorted and should be replaced. • **Is there zero resistance?**	Yes ▶ No ▶	REPLACE shorted A/C sunload sensor. RESTORE vehicle. GO to **K1**. GO to **K4**.
K4	CHECK CIRCUIT 468 (BR) AT SENSOR CONNECTOR		
	• Turn ignition switch to the RUN position. • Turn EATC module to NORM A/C position. • Partially remove EATC module as outlined. • Gain access to the A/C sunload sensor as outlined. Disconnect A/C sunload sensor. • Using voltmeter, check Circuit 468 (BR) for voltage at A/C sunload sensor connector. • **Is voltage 10 volts or more?**	Yes ▶ No ▶	GO to **K7**. GO to **K5**.
K5	CHECK CIRCUIT 468 (BR) AT EATC MODULE		
	• Using voltmeter, check Circuit 468 (BR) at EATC module Pin 16 for voltage. • **Is voltage 10 volts or more?**	Yes ▶ No ▶	GO to **K6**. REPLACE EATC module. RESTORE vehicle. RETEST system.
K6	CHECK CIRCUIT 468 (BR) FOR OPEN		
	• Turn ignition switch to the OFF position. • Using a jumper connected to a known good ground, connect other end to Circuit 468 (BR) at sensor connector. • Using an ohmmeter connected to a known good ground, connect second lead to Circuit 468 (BR) at EATC module connector Pin 16. • Measure resistance. NOTE: An open circuit in the wire harness will appear to the EATC control assembly as no sun. • **Is resistance 5 ohms or less?**	Yes ▶ No ▶	GO to **K7**. SERVICE Circuit 468 (BR) for open. RESTORE vehicle. RETEST system.
K7	CHECK CIRCUIT 476 (BR/Y) RESISTANCE		
	• Connect jumper to Circuit 476 (BR/Y) at sensor connector. • Using an ohmmeter connected to a known good ground, connect second lead to Circuit 476 (BR/Y) at module connector Pin 3. • Measure resistance. NOTE: An open circuit in the wire harness will appear to the EATC control assembly as no sun. • **Is resistance 5 ohms or less?**	Yes ▶ No ▶	REPLACE A/C sunload sensor. RESTORE vehicle. RETEST system. SERVICE Circuit 476 (BR/Y) for open. RESTORE vehicle. RETEST system.

DIAGNOSIS AND TESTING (CONTINUED)

PINPOINT TEST L: CONTROL ASSEMBLY / VFD DOES NOT LIGHT UP—HEATER BLOWER MOTOR OFF

TEST STEP		RESULT ▶	ACTION TO TAKE
L1	CHECK ILLUMINATION SUPPLY TO EATC MODULE		
	• Turn headlamp switch to the PARK LAMP or HEADLAMP position. • Rotate headlamp dimmer sensor control to full-on without turning the dome lamp on. • Partially remove EATC module as outlined. • Using a test lamp, check Circuit 19 (LB / R) for voltage. • **Did test lamp illuminate?**	Yes ▶ No ▶	GO to **L2.** SERVICE Circuit 19 (LB / R) for open circuit. RESTORE vehicle. RETEST system.
L2	CHECK EATC SYSTEM GROUND		
	• Using an ohmmeter connected to a known good ground, connect second lead to Circuit 57 (BK), Pin 24 at EATC module connector. • Measure resistance. • **Is resistance 5 ohms or less?**	Yes ▶ No ▶	REPLACE EATC control module. RESTORE vehicle. RETEST system. SERVICE Circuit 57 (BK) for open circuit. RESTORE vehicle. RETEST system.

PINPOINT TEST M: COLD ENGINE BLOWER CONTROL DIAGNOSIS—NO DIAGNOSTIC ERROR CODE

TEST STEP		RESULT ▶	ACTION TO TAKE
M1	CHECK COLD ENGINE BLOWER MOTOR OPERATION		
	• With engine coolant below 49°C (120°F) (cold engine) and control set at "32°C (90°F) AUTOMATIC," check for heater blower motor operation. Blower motor should operate at low blower for 3 1/2 minutes or until engine coolant temperature reaches 49°C (120°F), whichever occurs first. • **Does blower motor operate at low speed with engine coolant temperature below 49°C (120°F) and before 3 1/2 minutes have elapsed since engine start-up?**	Yes ▶ No ▶	GO to **M2.** GO to **M4.**
M2	CHECK WARM ENGINE BLOWER MOTOR OPERATION		
	• Allow engine to operate until blower motor speed increases from low blower. Check amount of time required for blower motor speed to increase. • **Does blower motor speed increase before 3 1/2 minutes have elapsed?**	Yes ▶ No ▶	Cold engine lock out functioning properly. PERFORM Pinpoint Test Step **A1**. GO to **M3.**
M3	PERFORM EATC SELF DIAGNOSTICS		
	• Press OFF and FLOOR buttons simultaneously and then press AUTOMATIC button within two seconds. Self test may run as long as 30 seconds. After self test, error codes will be displayed. Record all error codes and press the blue (Cooler) button. • **Was error code 115 displayed?**	Yes ▶ No ▶	GO to **M5.** GO to **M4.**
M4	CHECK BLOWER MOTOR OPERATION		
	• Select NORM A / C, turn ignition key to RUN and rotate blower thumbwheel to HI. • **Does blower motor operate?**	Yes ▶ No ▶	REPLACE EATC control assembly. RESTORE vehicle. RETEST system. SERVICE blower motor.
M5	CHECK ENGINE COOLANT LEVEL		
	• Check engine coolant level. • **Is engine coolant level low?**	Yes ▶ No ▶	ADD recommended coolant mixture to bring coolant to specified level. RETEST system for proper operation. GO to **M6.**

DIAGNOSIS AND TESTING (CONTINUED)

PINPOINT TEST M: COLD ENGINE BLOWER CONTROL DIAGNOSIS—NO DIAGNOSTIC ERROR CODE (Continued)

	TEST STEP	RESULT ▶	ACTION TO TAKE
M6	CHECK ENGINE COOLANT TEMPERATURE SIGNAL		
	• Perform powertrain control module diagnostics to check for correct operation of engine coolant temperature sensor. • **Do PCM diagnostics indicate an engine coolant temperature sensor fault?**	Yes ▶ No ▶	SERVICE as necessary. GO to **M1.** GO to **M7.**
M7	CHECK CELO SIGNAL CIRCUITS FOR OPEN WIRE		
	• Check Wire Circuits 914 (T/O) and 915 (PK) for an open circuit between the EATC control assembly and the powertrain control module. • **Are either or both circuits open?**	Yes ▶ No ▶	SERVICE as necessary. GO to **M1.** GO to **M8.**
M8	CHECK CELO CIRCUITS FOR AN INTERMITTENT OPEN		
	• Wiggle each wire (T/O) and (PK/LB) at each connector to check for an intermittent open. • **Does an intermittent open condition exist?**	Yes ▶ No ▶	SERVICE as necessary. GO TO **M1.** REPLACE EATC control assembly. RESTORE vehicle. RETEST system.

PINPOINT TEST N: TEMPERATURE DISPLAY WON'T SWITCH BETWEEN CELSIUS AND FAHRENHEIT

	TEST STEP	RESULT ▶	ACTION TO TAKE
N1	CHECK EATC °F TO °C DISPLAY		
	• With EATC system on, depress MAX A/C and defrost buttons simultaneously for at least 3/4 of a second. • **Did display switch from °F to °C?**	Yes ▶ No ▶	GO to **N2.** REPLACE EATC control assembly. RESTORE vehicle. RETEST system.
N2	CHECK CIRCUIT 506 (R) FOR OPEN		
	CAUTION: Accidental shorting of the wrong pin could destroy the control assembly. • With ignition switch in the OFF position, partially remove EATC module as outlined. • Using a jumper wire connected to a known good ground, connect other end to Circuit 506 (R), Pin 20 at module connector. • Turn ignition switch to the RUN position. • **Did display change?**	Yes ▶ No ▶	GO to **N3.** SERVICE Circuit 506 (R) for open. REPLACE damaged EATC module. RESTORE vehicle. RETEST system.
N3	CHECK CIRCUIT 506 (R) FOR SHORT		
	CAUTION: Accidental shorting of the wrong pin could destroy the control assembly. • Leave jumper connected. • Using an ohmmeter connected to a known good ground, connect other end to Circuit 506 (R) at EATC module connector Pin 20. • Measure resistance. • **Is resistance 5 ohms or less?**	Yes ▶ No ▶	SERVICE Circuit 506 (R) for short. RESTORE vehicle. RETEST system. REPLACE damaged EATC module. RESTORE vehicle. RETEST system.

PINPOINT TEST P: SYSTEM DOES NOT CONTROL TEMPERATURE

	TEST STEP	RESULT ▶	ACTION TO TAKE
P1	PERFORM EATC SELF TEST		
	• Turn the ignition switch to RUN. • Press OFF and FLOOR buttons simultaneously and then press AUTOMATIC button within two seconds. • Self test may run as long as 30 seconds. • After self test, record all error codes and any temperature display readings. • Press the blue (Cooler) button to exit self test. • **Is error code 030, 031, 032, or 033 displayed?**	Yes ▶ No ▶	GO to **P2.** GO to **P3.**

DIAGNOSIS AND TESTING (CONTINUED)

PINPOINT TEST P: SYSTEM DOES NOT CONTROL TEMPERATURE (Continued)

	TEST STEP	RESULT ▶	ACTION TO TAKE
P2	CHECK SENSOR RESISTANCE		
	NOTE: An open sensor will cause the warm air discharge at 65°F (18°C) setting. A shorted sensor will cause cool discharge air at 85°F (29°C) setting. • Disconnect the A/C ambient air temperature sensor. • Using a DVOM, measure the resistance across the sensor terminals and compare the readings with the following sensor resistance table: (see table below) • **Are resistance values within the specified limits?**	Yes ▶ No ▶	GO to **P3**. REPLACE A/C ambient air temperature sensor and bracket. RESTORE vehicle. RETEST system.
P3	CHECK ASPIRATOR INSTALLATION		
	• Gain access to automatic temperature control sensor hose and elbow as outlined. • Check for proper installation of automatic temperature control sensor hose and elbow. • **Is aspirator installed properly and hose connected?**	Yes ▶ No ▶	GO to **P4**. SERVICE automatic temperature control sensor hose and elbow as necessary. RESTORE vehicle. RETEST system.
P4	CHECK AUTOMATIC TEMPERATURE CONTROL SENSOR OUTPUT AT EATC MODULE		
	• Turn engine off. Leave ignition switch in RUN position. • Disconnect automatic temperature control sensor. • Using a voltmeter, check Circuit 790 (W/O) at Pin 17 of connector C1 for voltage. • **Is voltage present?**	Yes ▶ No ▶	GO to **P5**. REPLACE EATC module. RESTORE vehicle. RETEST system.
P5	CHECK AUTOMATIC TEMPERATURE CONTROL CIRCUIT 790 (W/O)		
	• Turn ignition switch OFF. • Using an ohmmeter, check Circuit 790 (W/O) from EATC module to automatic temperature control sensor connector. • **Is there continuity?**	Yes ▶ No ▶	GO to **P6**. SERVICE Circuit 790 (W/O) for open. RESTORE vehicle. RETEST system.
P6	CHECK AUTOMATIC TEMPERATURE CONTROL SENSOR RETURN CIRCUIT		
	• Using an ohmmeter, check Circuit 470 (PK/BK) for continuity from EATC module to aspirator connector. • **Is there continuity?**	Yes ▶ No ▶	REPLACE automatic temperature control sensor. RESTORE vehicle. RETEST system. SERVICE Circuit 470 (PK/BK) for open. RESTORE vehicle. RETEST system.

Approximate Temperature	Sensor Resistance Acceptance Range
50°F (10°C) to 68°F (20°C)	37K to 58K ohms
68°F (20°C) to 86°F (30°C)	24K to 37K ohms
86°F (30°C) to 104°F (40°C)	16K to 24K ohms

PINPOINT TEST Q: TEMPERATURE SET POINT DOES NOT REPEAT AFTER TURNING IGNITION SWITCH OFF

	TEST STEP	RESULT ▶	ACTION TO TAKE
Q1	CHECK MEMORY SUPPLY TO EATC MODULE		
	• With ignition switch in the OFF position, partially remove EATC control module as outlined. • Using a voltmeter, check Circuit 797 (LG/P) on Town Car or Circuti 54 (LG/Y) on Crown Victoria, Grand Marquis for voltage at EATC module Pin 12. • **Is battery voltage present?**	Yes ▶ No ▶	REPLACE EATC module. RESTORE vehicle. RETEST system. GO to **Q2**.

DIAGNOSIS AND TESTING (CONTINUED)

PINPOINT TEST Q: TEMPERATURE SET POINT DOES NOT REPEAT AFTER TURNING IGNITION SWITCH OFF (Continued)

TEST STEP		RESULT	►	ACTION TO TAKE
Q2	CHECK CIRCUIT 797 (LG/P) SUPPLY			
	• Remove memory fuse (5A) at power distribution box. • Using an ohmmeter, check Circuit 797 (LG/P) on Town Car or Circuit 54 (LG/Y) on Crown Victoria, Grand Marquis from EATC module connector Pin 12 to output side of memory fuse (5A) cavity for continuity. • **Is resistance 5 ohms or less?**	Yes	►	REPLACE EATC module. RESTORE vehicle. RETEST system.
		No	►	SERVICE Circuit 797 (LG/P) on Town Car or Circuit 54 (LG/Y) for Crown Victoria for open. RESTORE vehicle. RETEST system.

WIRING SCHEMATICS

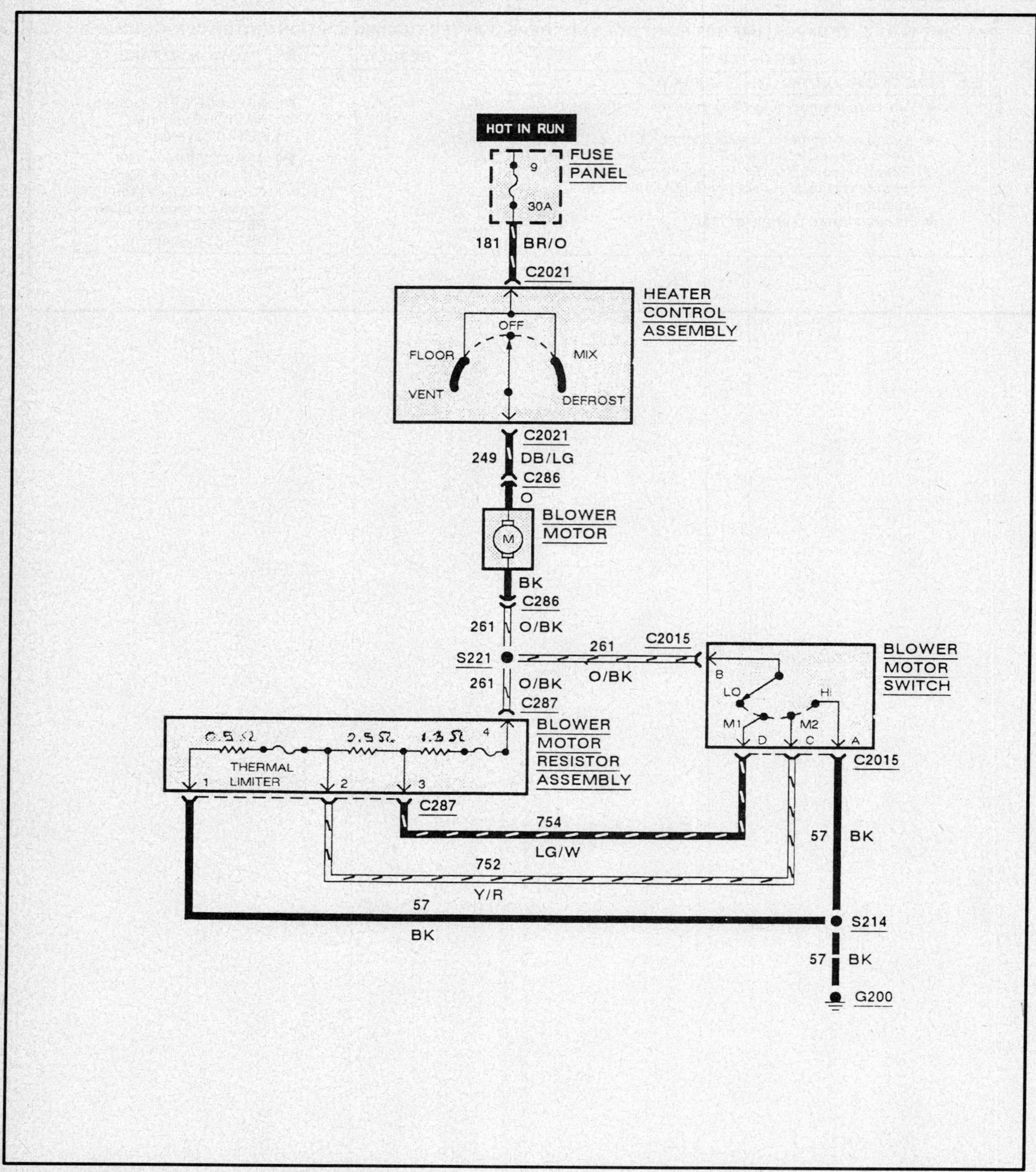

Heater system wiring schematic—Mustang

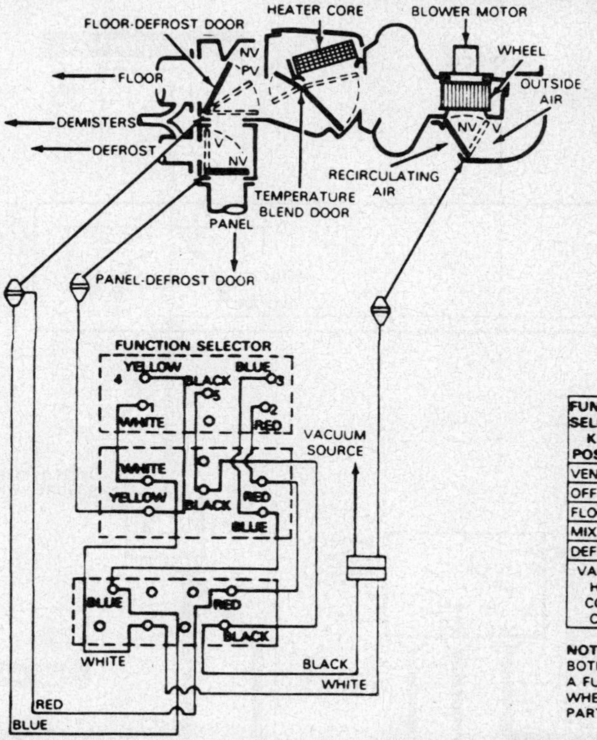

NOTE: DOOR POSITIONS SHOWN REFLECT A FUNCTION SELECTOR KNOB SETTING IN THE OFF POSITION

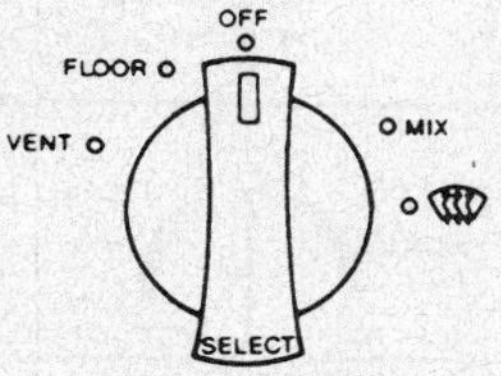

FUNCTION SELECTOR KNOB

FUNCTION SELECTOR KNOB POSITION	OUTSIDE RECIRC AIR DOOR	FLOOR-DEFROST DOOR	PANEL-DEFROST DOOR	BLOWER MOTOR
VENT	NV	NV	V	ON
OFF	V	V	V	OFF
FLOOR	NV	V	NV	ON
MIX	NV	PV	NV	ON
DEFROST	NV	NV	NV	ON
VACUUM HOSE COLOR CODE	WHITE	RED / BLUE	YELLOW	–

NOTE: WHEN VACUUM IS APPLIED TO BOTH FLOOR-DEFROST VACUUM LINES (RED/BLUE), A FULL VACUUM CONDITION EXISTS. WHEN APPLIED TO BLUE LINE ONLY, PARTIAL VACUUM EXISTS.

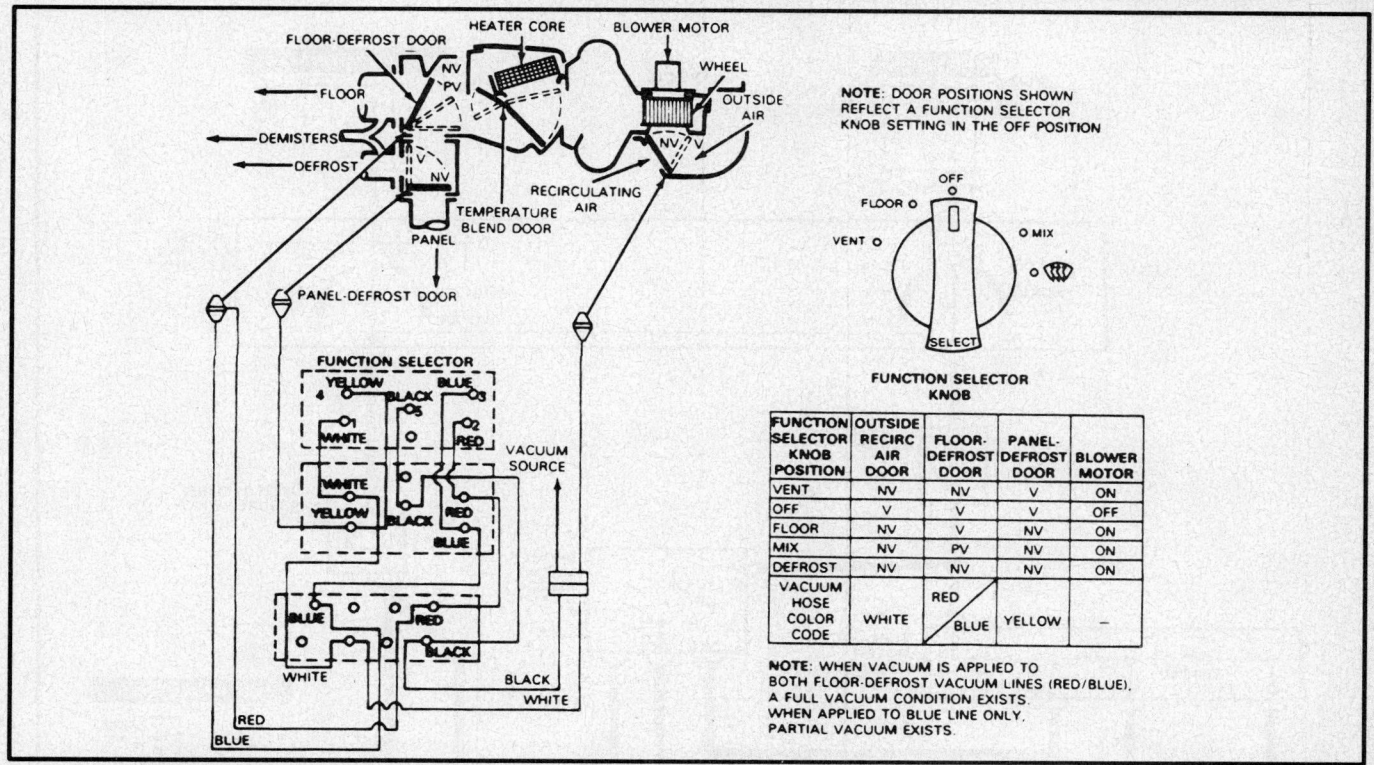

Heater system vacuum schematic and selector test—Mustang

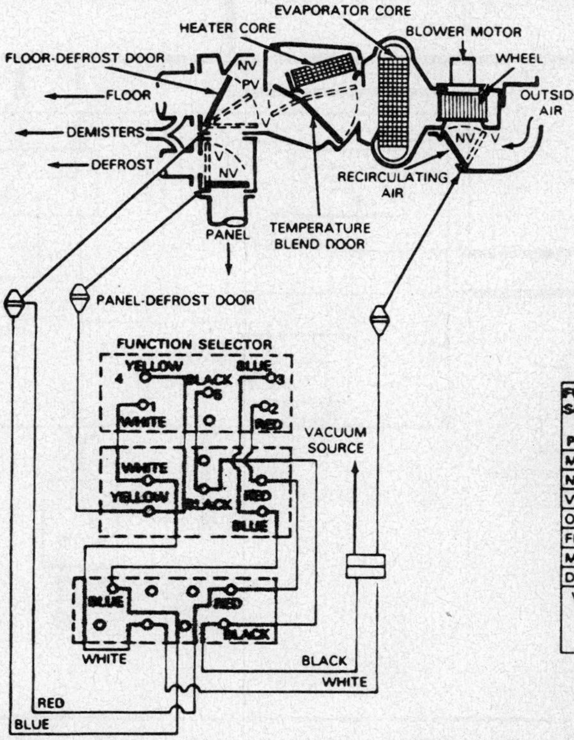

NOTE: DOOR POSITIONS SHOWN REFLECT A FUNCTION SELECTOR KNOB SETTING IN THE MAX A/C POSITION

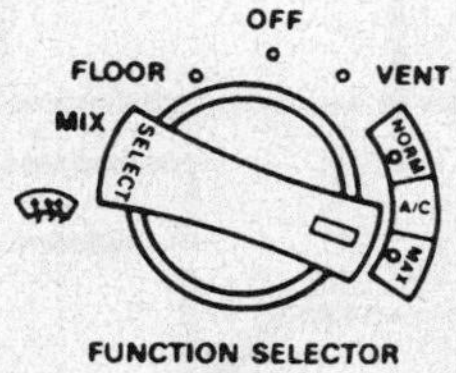

FUNCTION SELECTOR KNOB

FUNCTION SELECTOR KNOB POSITION	OUTSIDE RECIRC AIR DOOR	FLOOR-DEFROST DOOR	PANEL-DEFROST DOOR	BLOWER MOTOR
MAX A/C	V	NV	V	ON
NORM A/C	NV	NV	V	ON
VENT	NV	NV	V	ON
OFF	V	V	V	OFF
FLOOR	NV	V	NV	ON
MIX	NV	PV	NV	ON
DEFROST	NV	NV	NV	ON
VACUUM HOSE COLOR CODE	WHITE	RED / BLUE	YELLOW	–

NOTE: WHEN VACUUM IS APPLIED TO BOTH FLOOR-DEFROST VACUUM LINES (RED/BLUE) A FULL VACUUM CONDITION EXISTS. WHEN APPLIED TO BLUE LINE ONLY, PARTIAL VACUUM EXISTS.

Air conditioning system vacuum schematic and selector test—Mustang

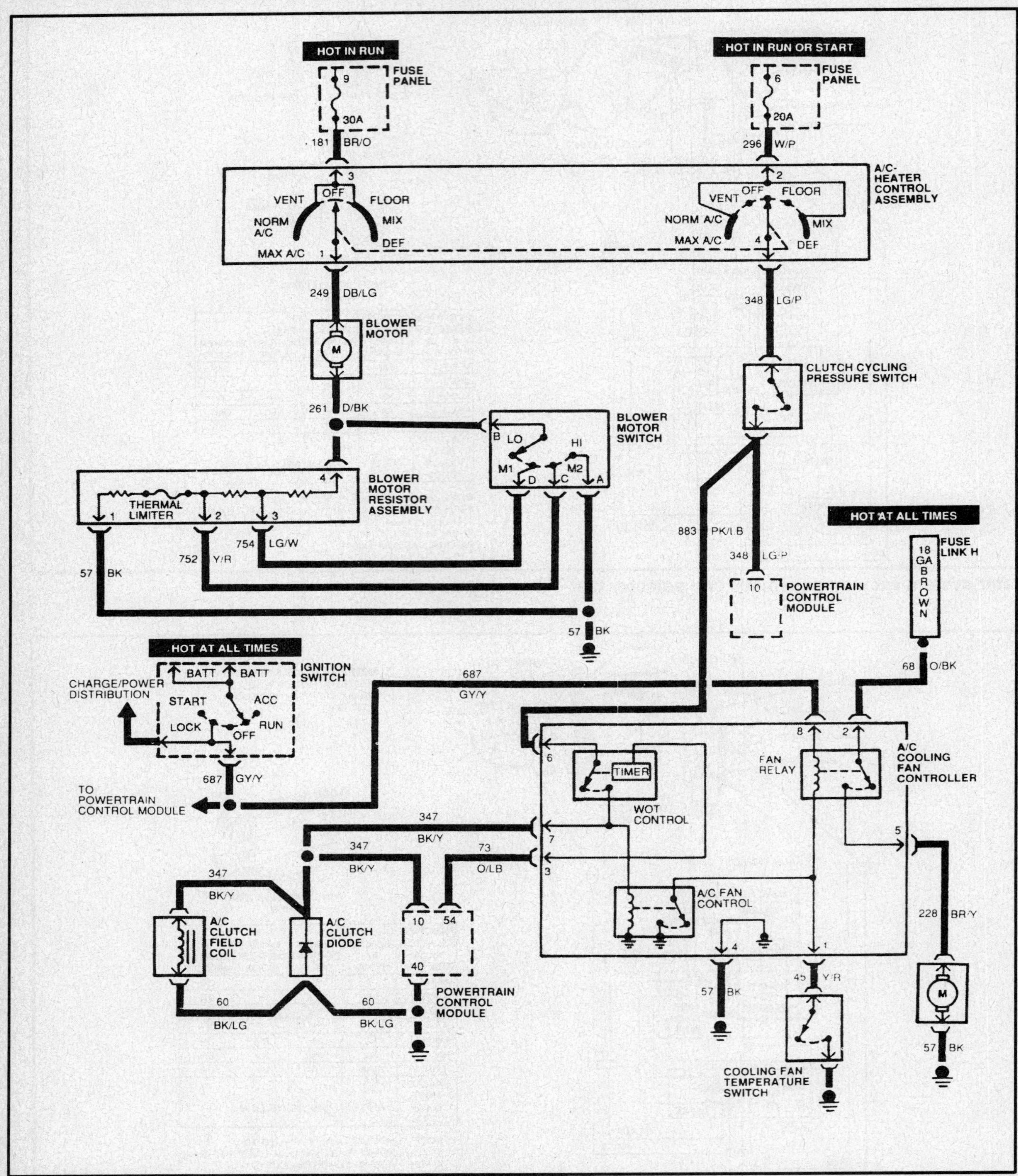

Air conditioning system wiring schematic—Mustang with 2.3L engine

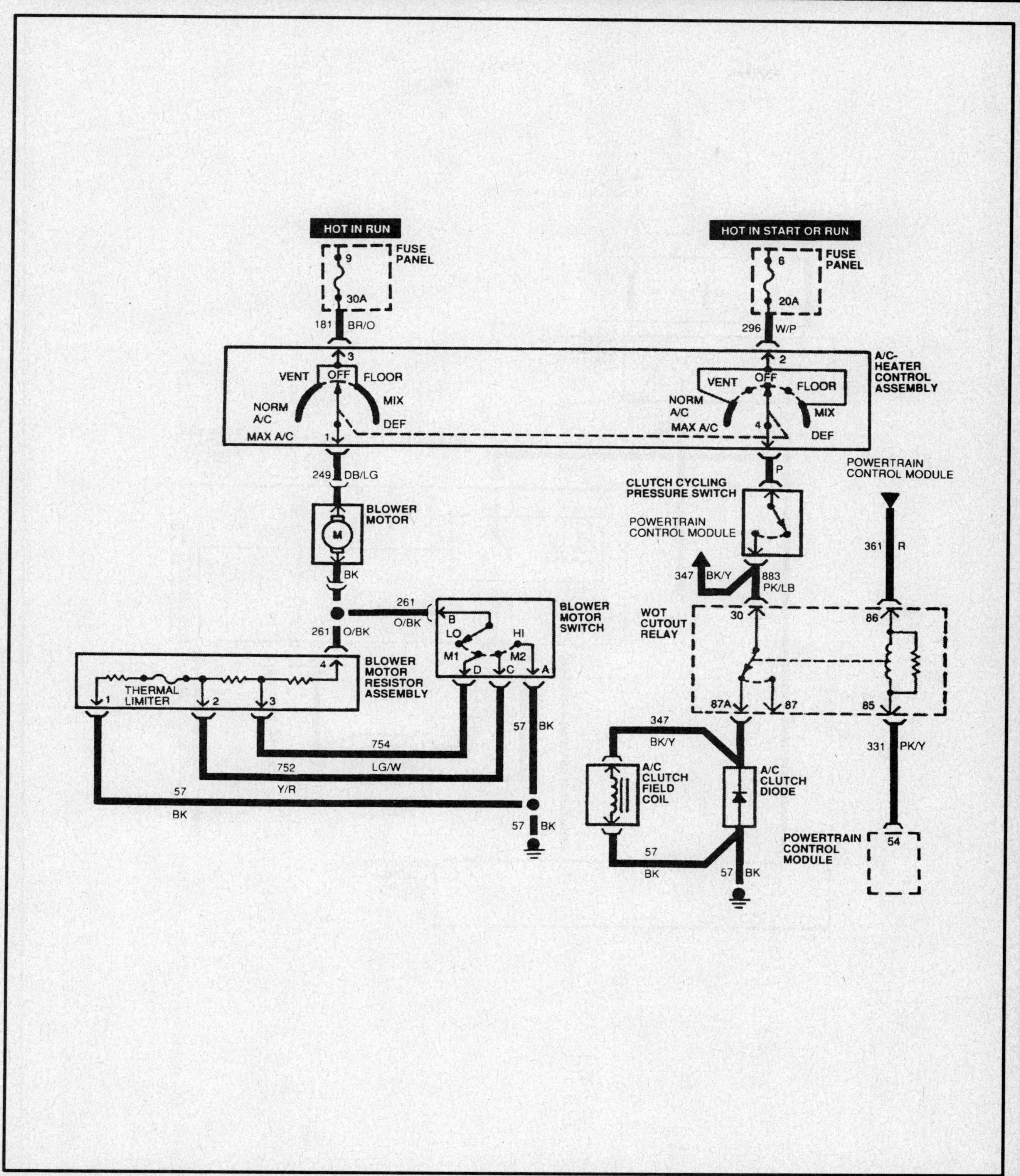

Manual air conditioning/heating system wiring schematic—Mustang with 3.8L or 5.0L engine

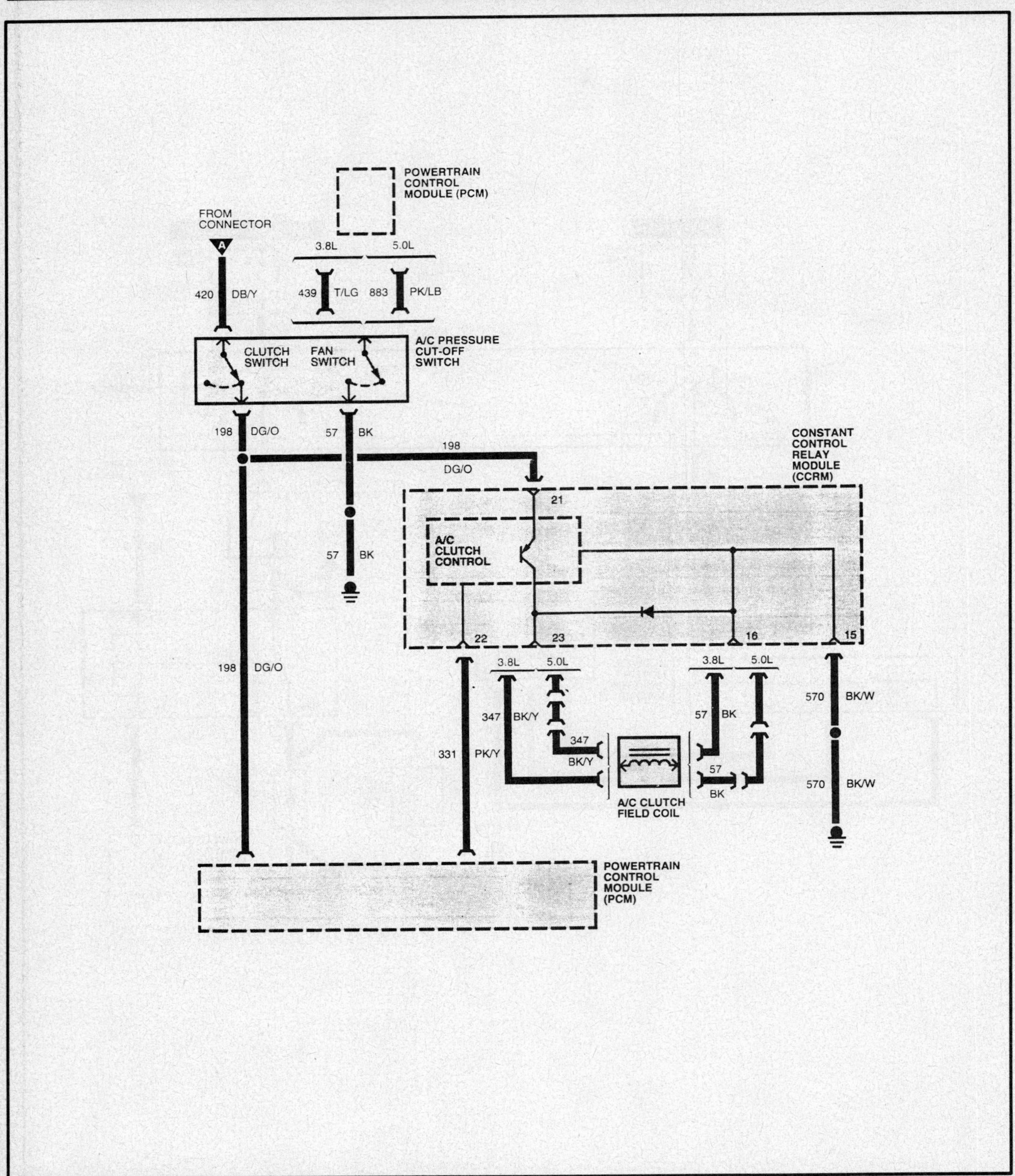

Manual air conditioning/heating system wiring schematic—Mustang with 3.8L or 5.0L engine, Cont'd

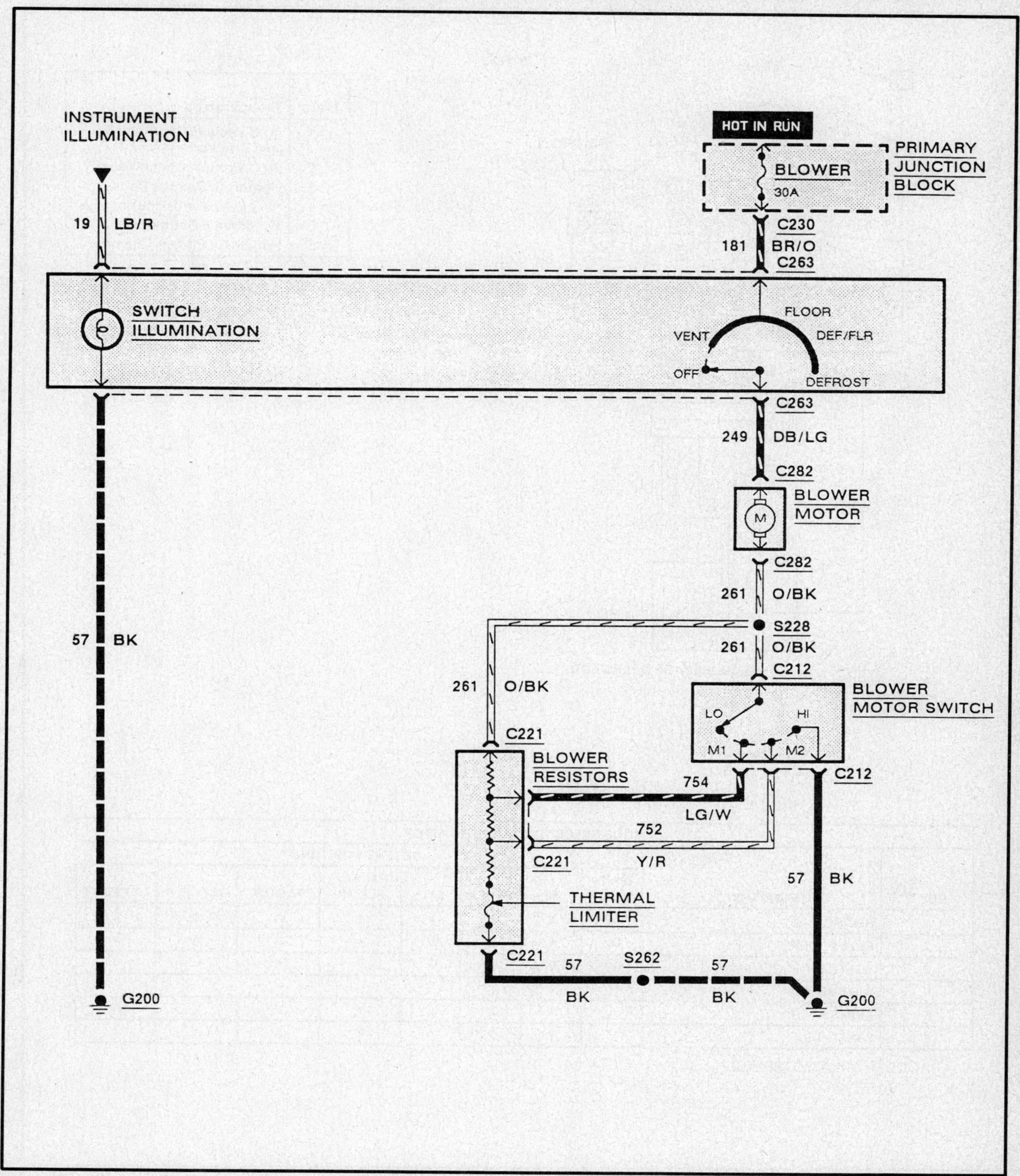

Heater system wiring schematic—1993 Thunderbird and Cougar

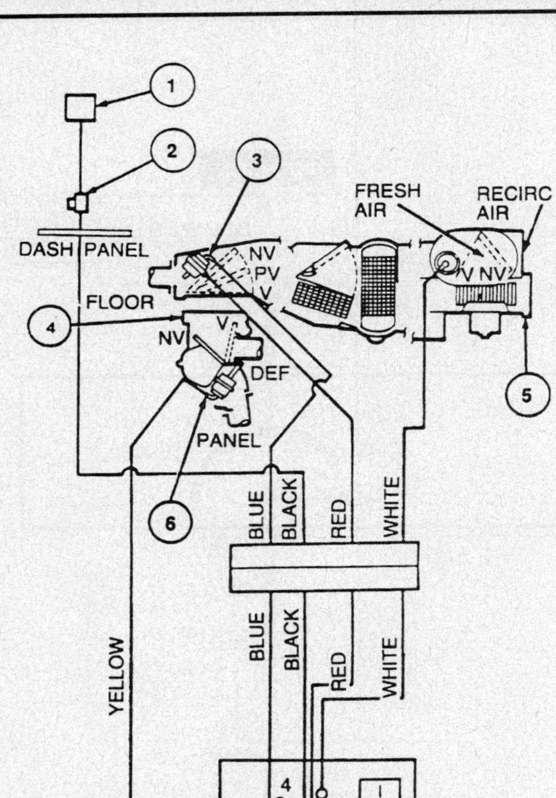

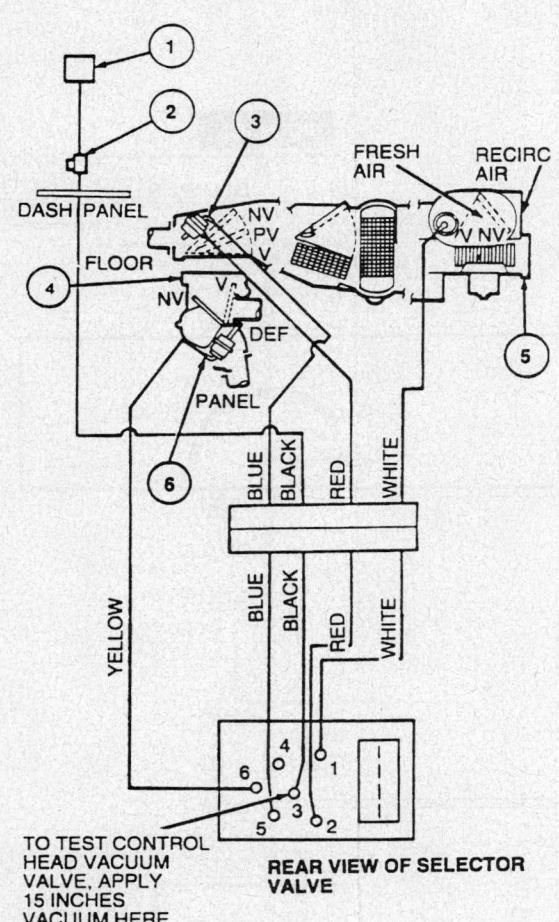

Item	Description
1	A/C Vacuum Reservoir Tank and Bracket
2	A/C Vacuum Check Valve
3	Heater Air Damper Door
4	A/C Evaporator Housing
5	Windshield Defroster Door
6	Heater Air Plenum Chamber

MODE SELECTOR VACUUM SWITCH									
		DETENT POSITION							
PORT	FUNCTION	MAX/A/C	AC	PANEL	OFF	PANEL/FLOOR	FLOOR	DEF/FLR	DEFROST
1	RECIRC-F/A	V	A	A	V	A	A	A	A
2	FULL FLOOR	A	A	A	V	A	V	A	A
3	SOURCE	V	V	V	V	V	V	V	V
4	(NOT USED)					—			
5	DEF/FLOOR	A	A	A	V	V	V	V	A
6	PANEL/DEF	V	V	V	A	V	A	A	A

V = VACUUM, A = ATMOSPHERE

Vacuum schematic and selector test—Thunderbird and Cougar with manual A/C system

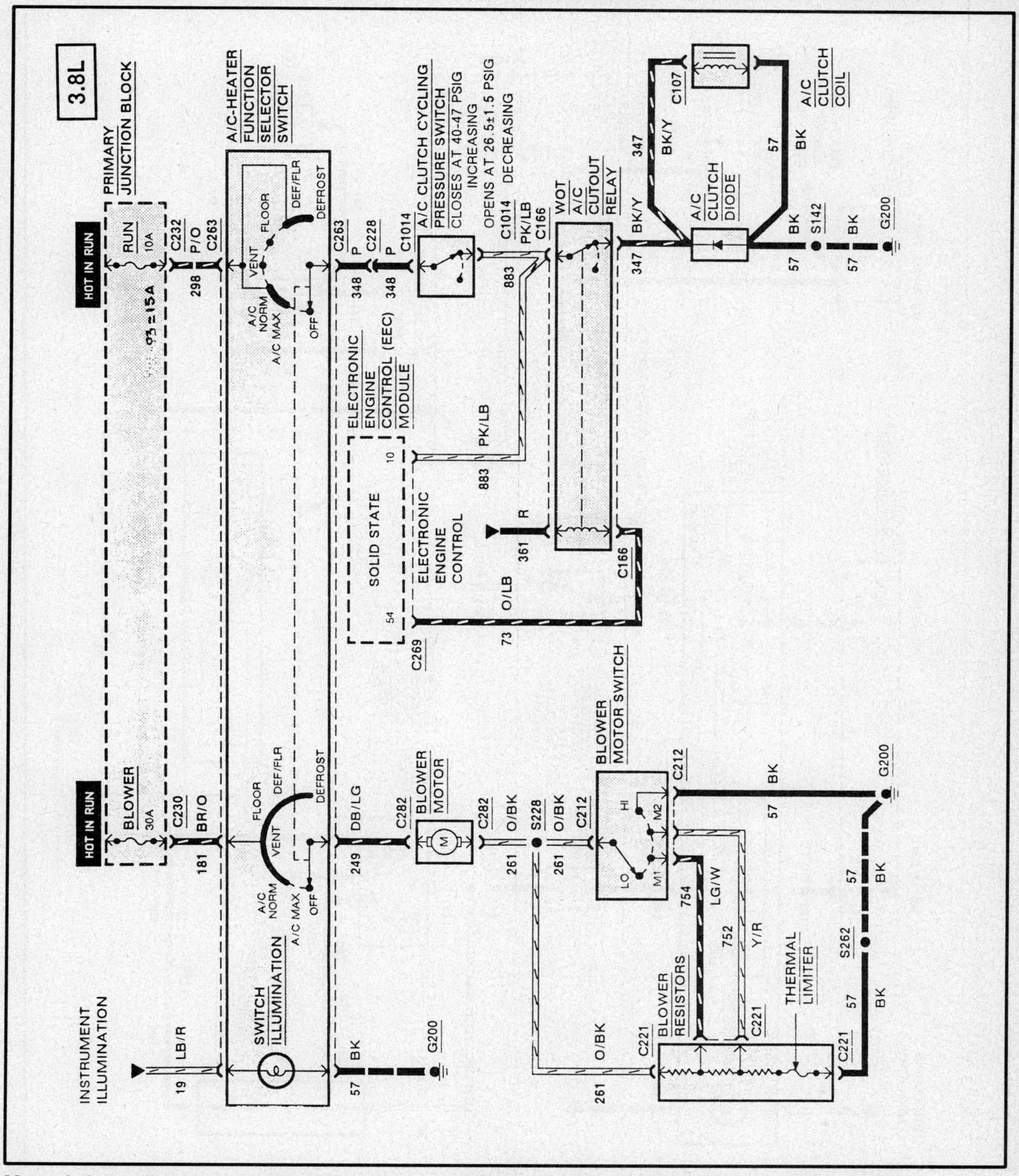

Manual air conditioning system wiring schematic—1993 Thunderbird and Cougar with 3.8L engine

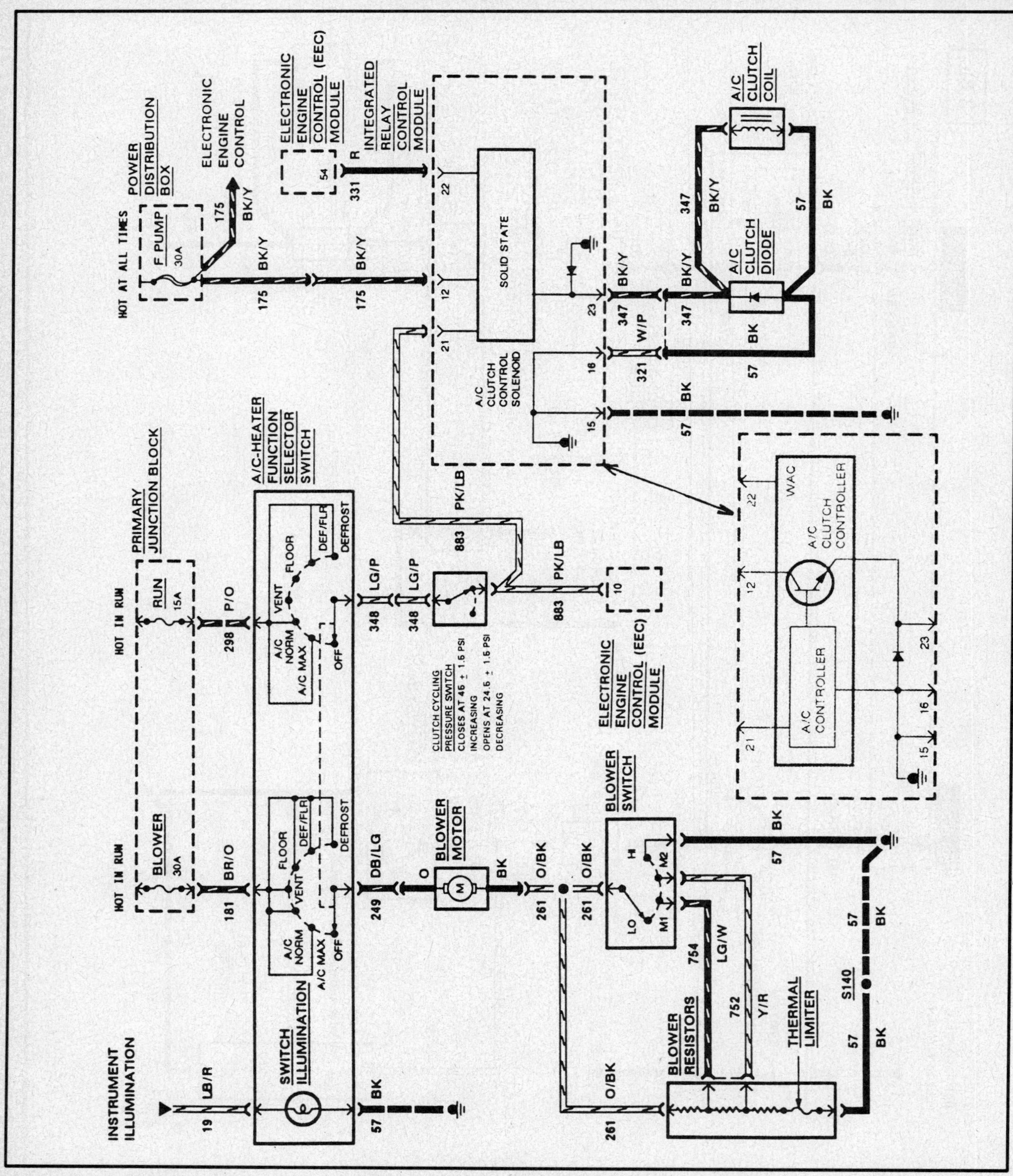

Manual air conditioning system wiring schematic—1993 Thunderbird with 3.8L SC engine

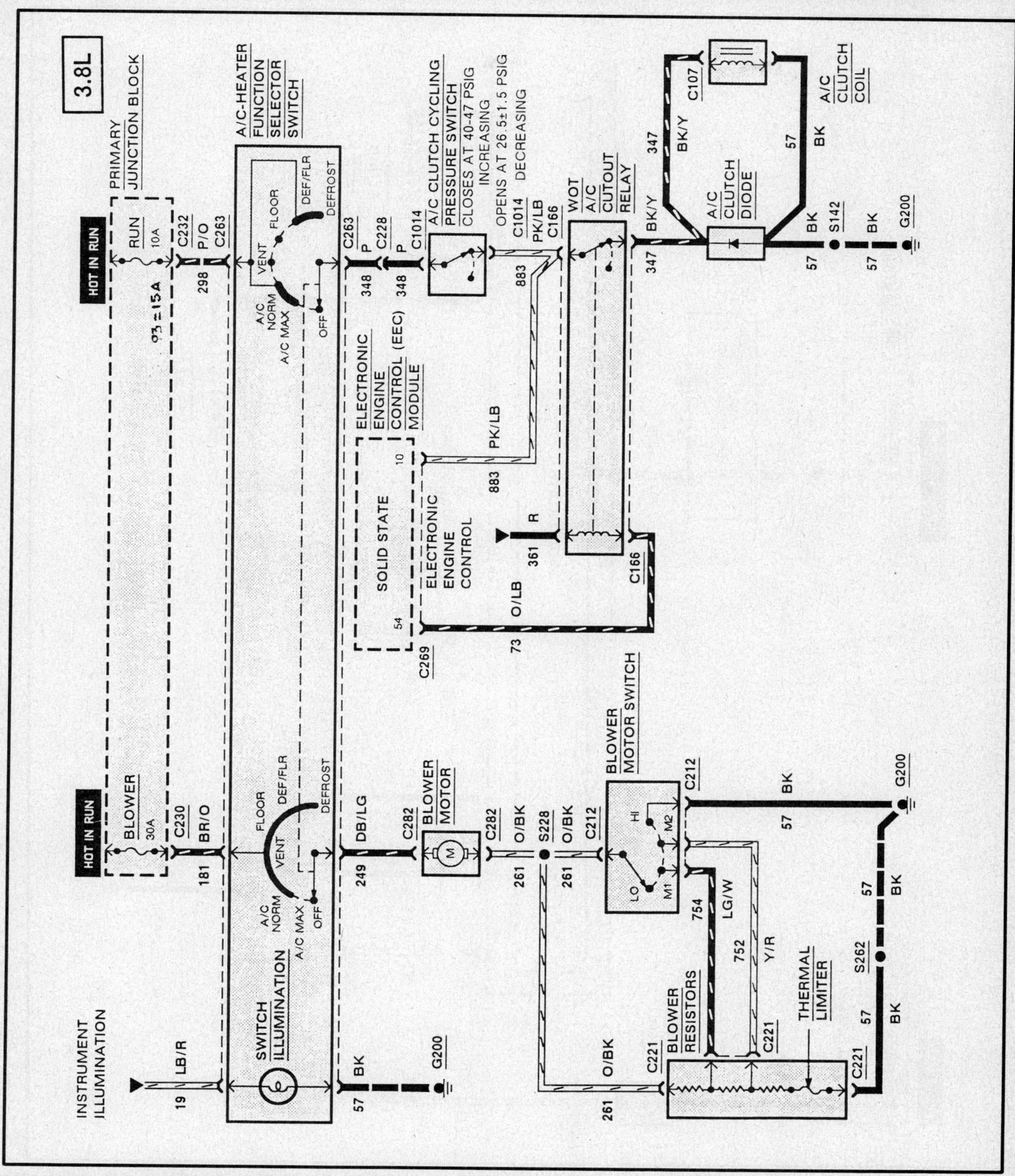

Manual air conditioning system wiring schematic—1993 Thunderbird and Cougar with 5.0L engine

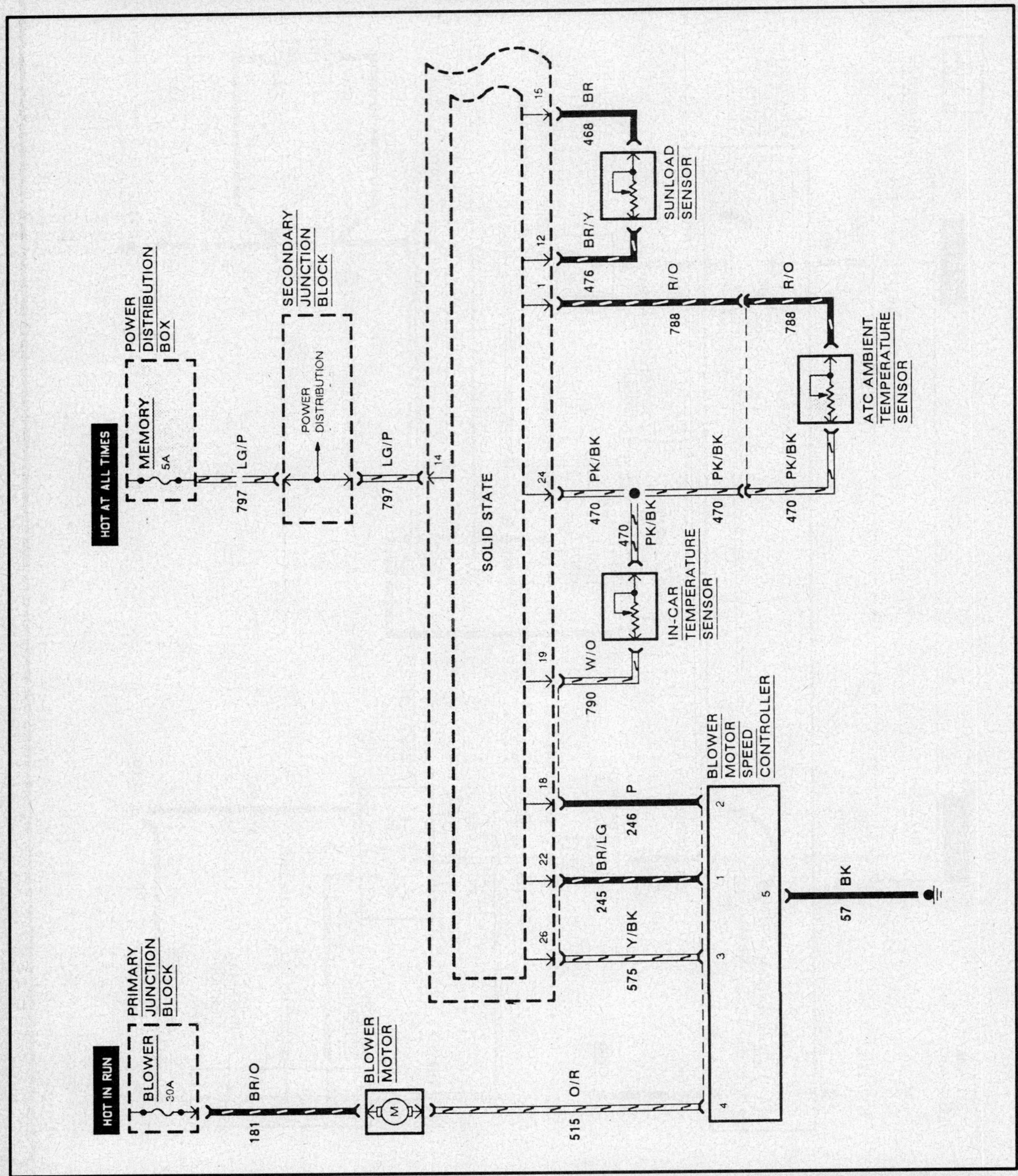

Electronic Automatic Temperature Control (EATC) system wiring schematic—1993 Thunderbird and Cougar

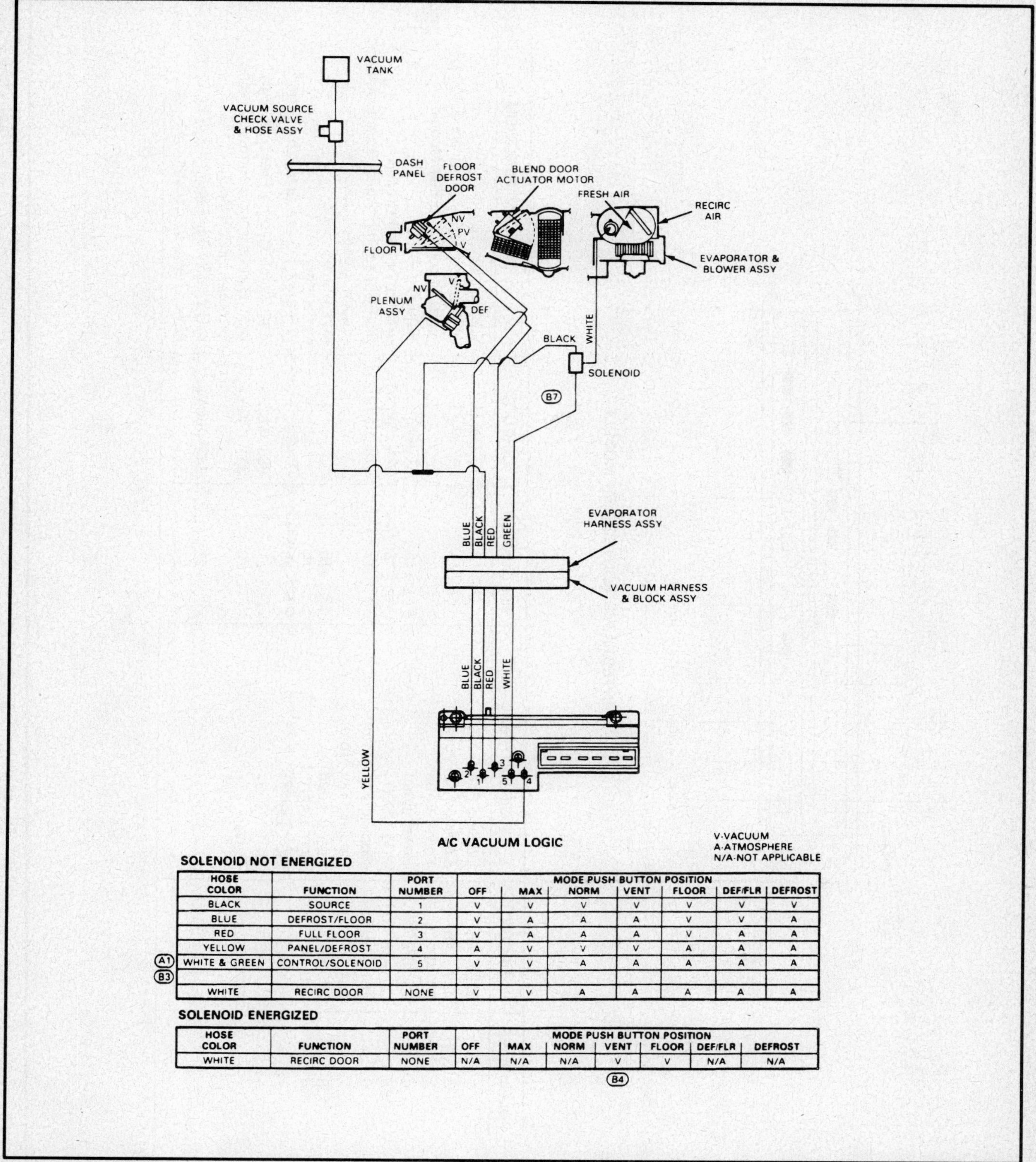

A/C VACUUM LOGIC

V-VACUUM
A-ATMOSPHERE
N/A-NOT APPLICABLE

SOLENOID NOT ENERGIZED

	HOSE COLOR	FUNCTION	PORT NUMBER	OFF	MAX	NORM	VENT	FLOOR	DEF/FLR	DEFROST
	BLACK	SOURCE	1	V	V	V	V	V	V	V
	BLUE	DEFROST/FLOOR	2	V	A	A	A	V	V	A
	RED	FULL FLOOR	3	V	A	A	A	V	A	A
	YELLOW	PANEL/DEFROST	4	A	V	V	V	A	A	A
A1	WHITE & GREEN	CONTROL/SOLENOID	5	V	V	A	A	A	A	A
B3										
	WHITE	RECIRC DOOR	NONE	V	V	A	A	A	A	A

(MODE PUSH BUTTON POSITION: OFF, MAX, NORM, VENT, FLOOR, DEF/FLR, DEFROST)

SOLENOID ENERGIZED

HOSE COLOR	FUNCTION	PORT NUMBER	OFF	MAX	NORM	VENT	FLOOR	DEF/FLR	DEFROST
WHITE	RECIRC DOOR	NONE	N/A	N/A	N/A	V	V	N/A	N/A

(MODE PUSH BUTTON POSITION: OFF, MAX, NORM, VENT, FLOOR, DEF/FLR, DEFROST)

B4

Electronic Automatic Temperature Control (EATC) vacuum schematic and functional tests—Thunderbird and Cougar

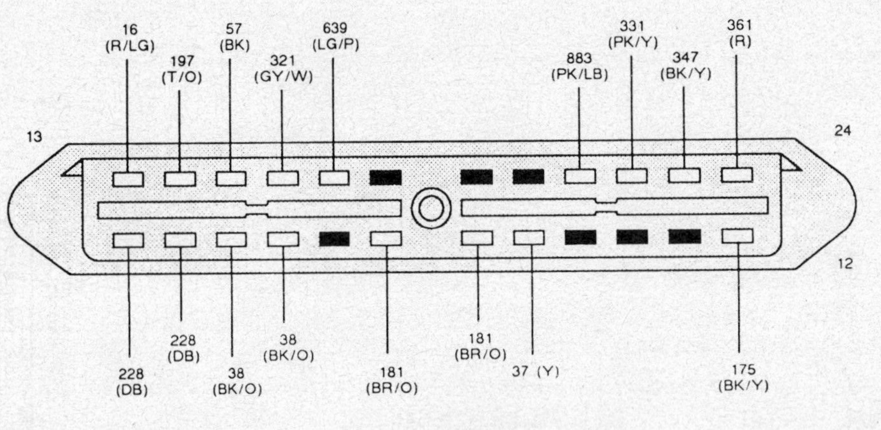

C138
INTEGRATED CONTROLLER MODULE

PIN NUMBER	CIRCUIT	CIRCUIT FUNCTION	PIN NUMBER	CIRCUIT	CIRCUIT FUNCTION
1	228 (DB)	Cooling Fan Motor	13	16 (R/LG)	Start or Run Power
2	228 (DB)	Cooling Fan Motor	14	197 (T/O)	Low Speed Fan Signal from Electronic Engine Control (EEC) Module
3	38 (BK/O)	Power Feed	15	57 (BK)	Ground
4	38 (BK/O)	Power Feed	16	321 (GY/W)	A/C Clutch Coil Ground
5	—	NOT USED	17	639 (LG/P)	High Speed Fan Signal from Electronic Engine Control (EEC) Module
6	181 (BR/O)	Cooling Fan Motor	18	—	NOT USED
7	181 (BR/O)	Cooling Fan Motor	19	—	NOT USED
8	37 (Y)	Power Feed	20	—	NOT USED
9	—	NOT USED	21	883 (PK/LB)	A/C Clutch Cycling Pressure Switch
10	—	NOT USED	22	331 (PK/Y)	WOT Cutout from Electronic Engine Control (EEC) Module
11	—	NOT USED	23	347 (BK/Y)	A/C Clutch Coil Feed
12	175 (BK/Y)	Power	24	361 (R)	Power Relay to EEC Module

Integrated controller module (ICRM) pin identification—1993 Thunderbird and Cougar with EATC

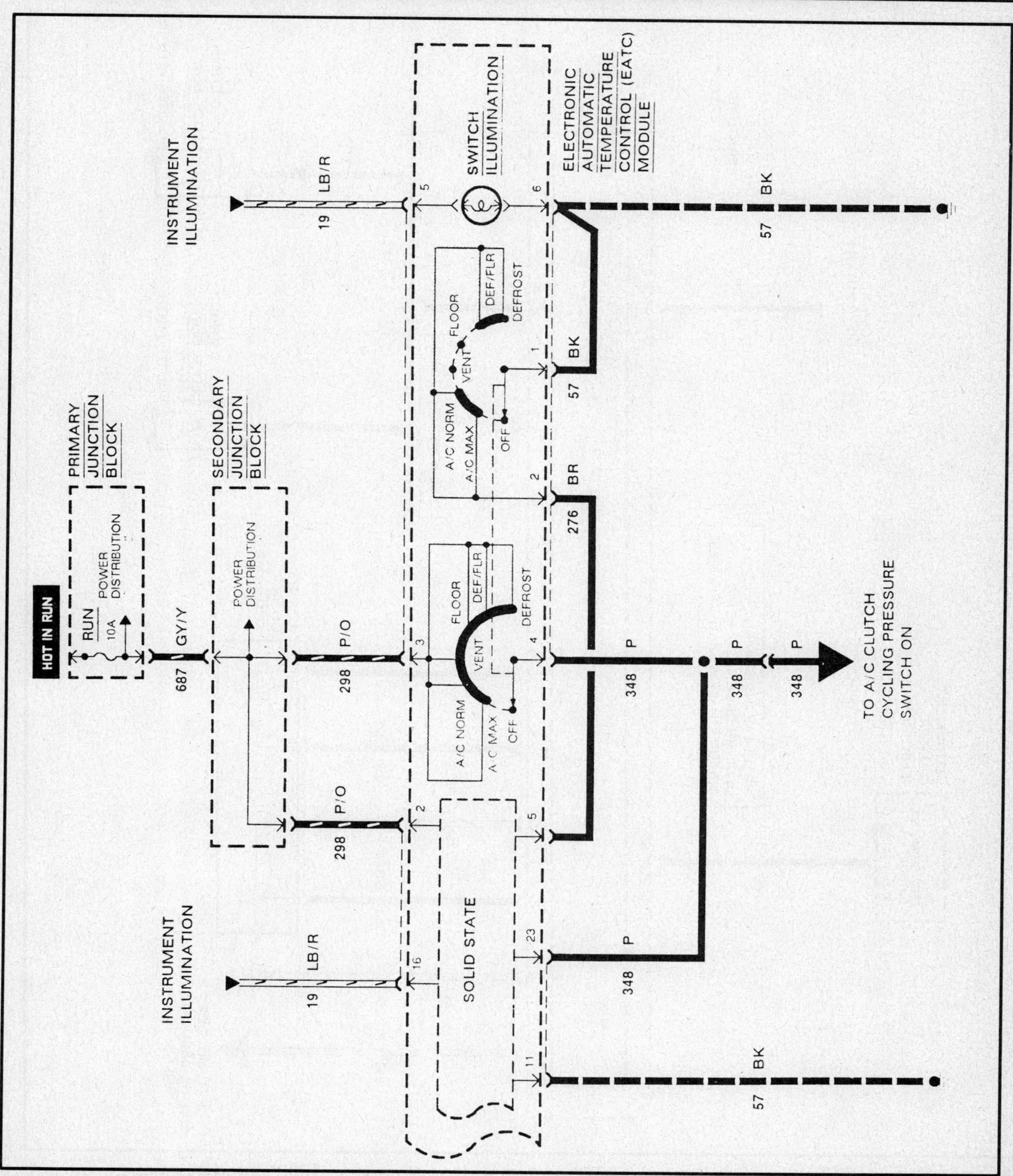

Electronic Automatic Temperature Control (EATC) system wiring schematic—1993 Thunderbird and Cougar

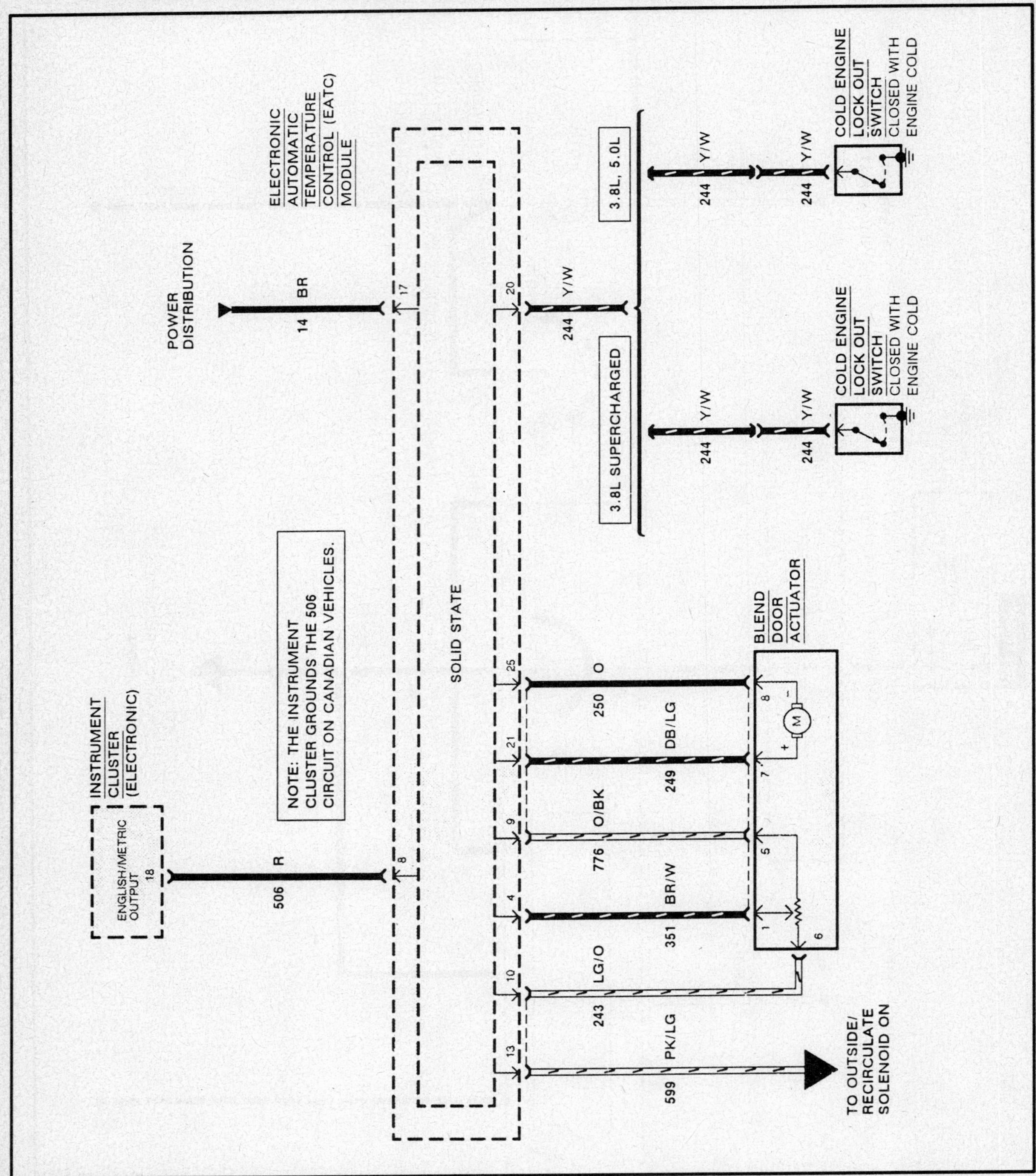

Electronic Automatic Temperature Control (EATC) system wiring schematic—1993 Thunderbird and Cougar–Cont.

CIRCUIT NO	WIRE COLOR	DESCRIPTION
14	BROWN	V-PARKLAMP
19	LIGHT BLUE/RED STRIPE	V-LAMP
57	BLACK	CONTROLLER GROUND
57	BLACK	OTHER GROUNDS
181	BROWN/ORANGE STRIPE	BLOWER VOLTAGE
243	LIGHT GREEN/ORANGE STRIPE	FEEDBACK POT
244	YELLOW/WHITE STRIPE	COLD ENGINE LOCK-OUT SIGNAL
245	BROWN/LIGHT GREEN STRIPE	BLOWER CONTROLLER FEEDBACK
246	PURPLE	BLOWER CONTROL SIGNAL
249	DARK BLUE/LT GREEN STRIPE	MOTOR DRIVE-CW
250	ORANGE	MOTOR DRIVE-CCW
276	BROWN	ON/OFF
298	PURPLE/ORANGE STRIPE	V-IGNITION

CIRCUIT NO	WIRE COLOR	DESCRIPTION
348	PURPLE	A/C CLUTCH FEED
351	BROWN/WHITE STRIPE	FEEDBACK POT WIPER
468	BROWN	SUNLOAD SENSOR
470	PINK/BLACK STRIPE	IN-CAR/AMBIENT SENSOR RETURN
476	BROWN/YELLOW STRIPE	SUNLOAD SENSOR
506	RED	ENGLISH METRIC
515	ORANGE/RED STRIPE	BLOWER SINK
575	YELLOW/BLACK STRIPE	RELAY SIGNAL
599	PINK/LIGHT GREEN STRIPE	SOLENOID DRIVER
776	ORANGE/BLACK STRIPE	FEEDBACK POT
788	RED/ORANGE STRIPE	AMBIENT SENSOR
790	WHITE/ORANGE STRIPE	IN-CAR SENSOR
797	LIGHT GREEN/PURPLE STRIPE	V-BATTERY (MEMORY)

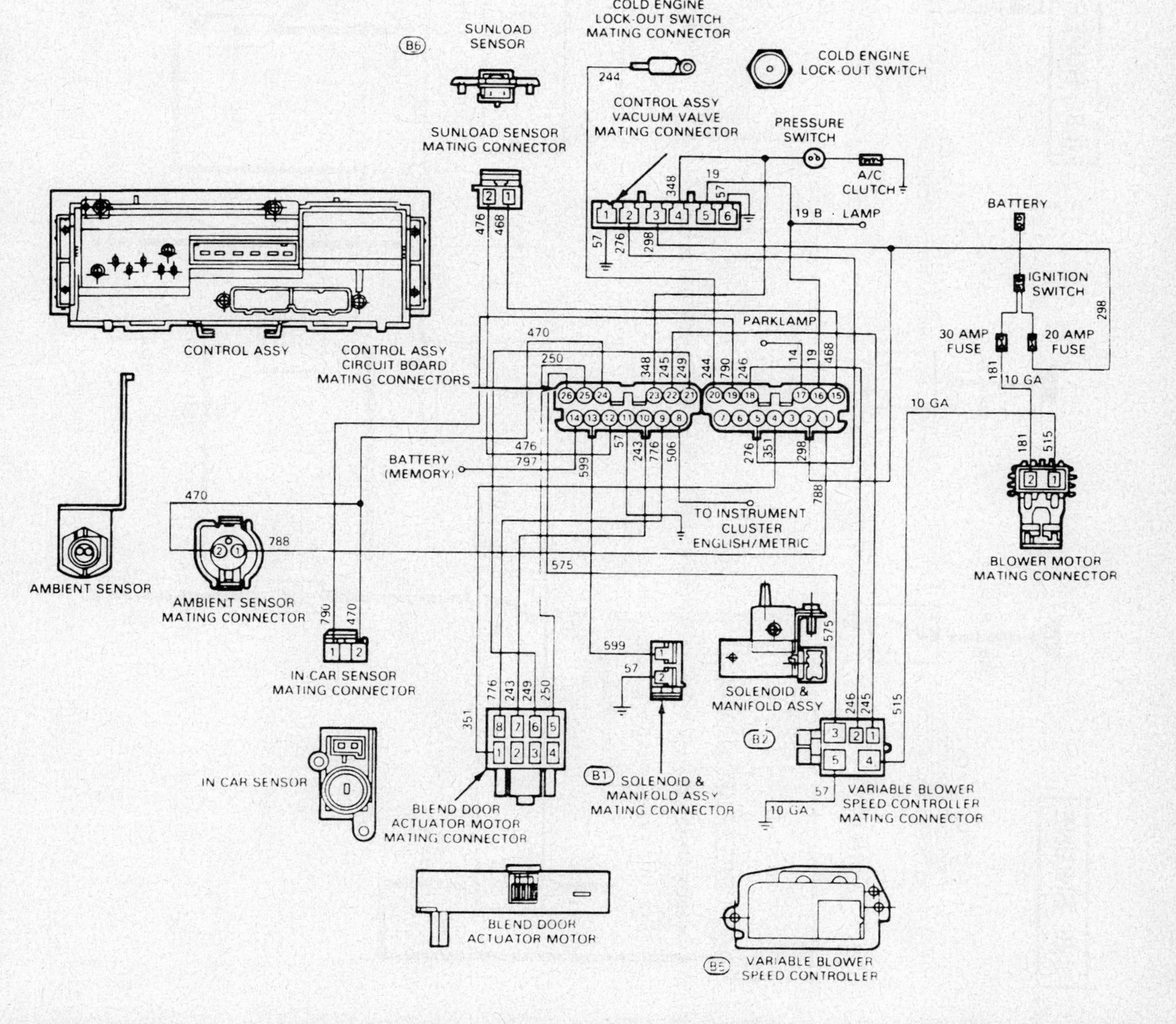

Electronic Automatic Temperature Control (EATC) system showing connector and circuit identification—1993 Thunderbird and Cougar

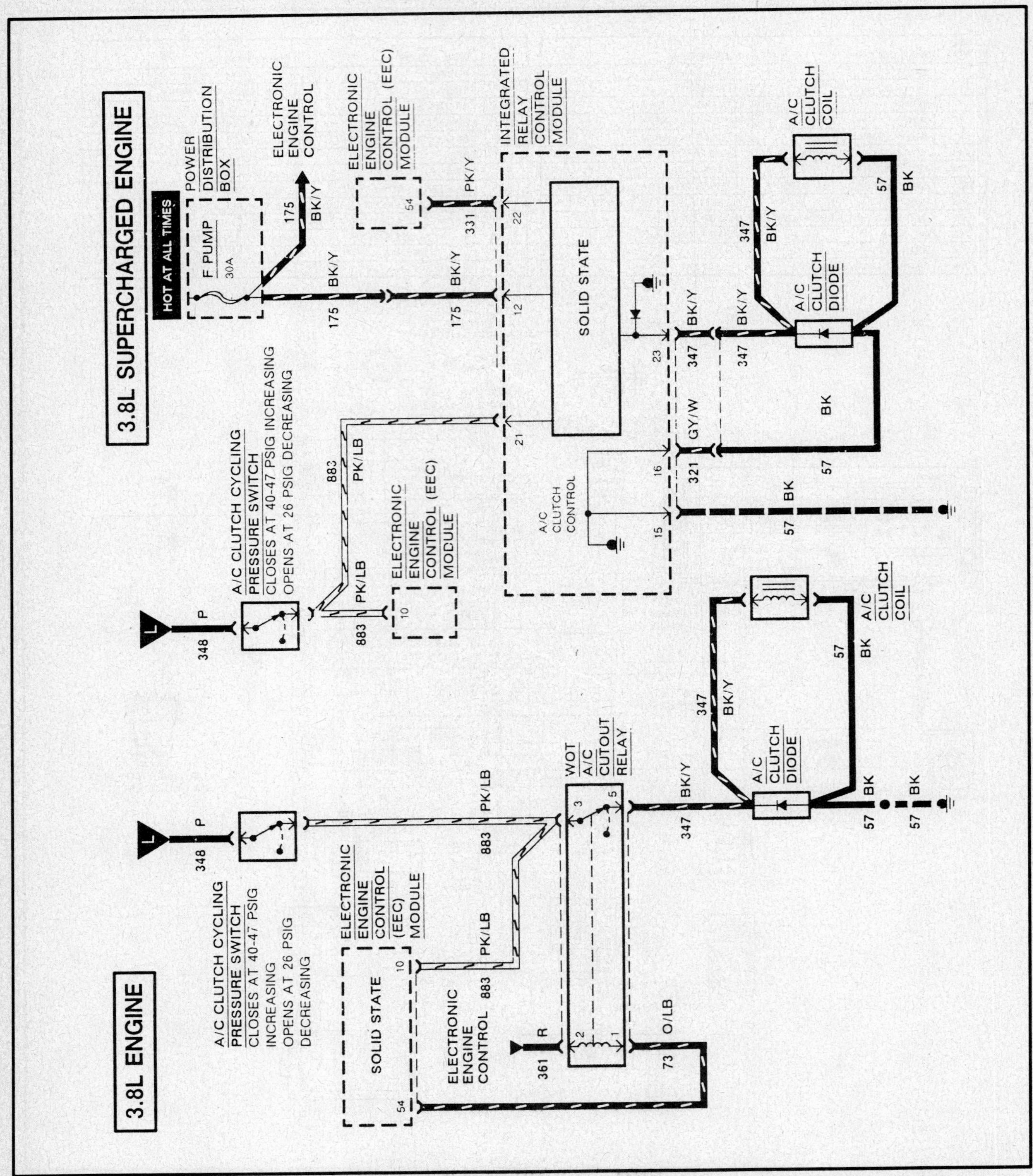

Electronic Automatic Temperature Control (EATC) compressor control system wiring schematic—1993 Thunderbird and Cougar with 3.8L and 3.8L SC engines

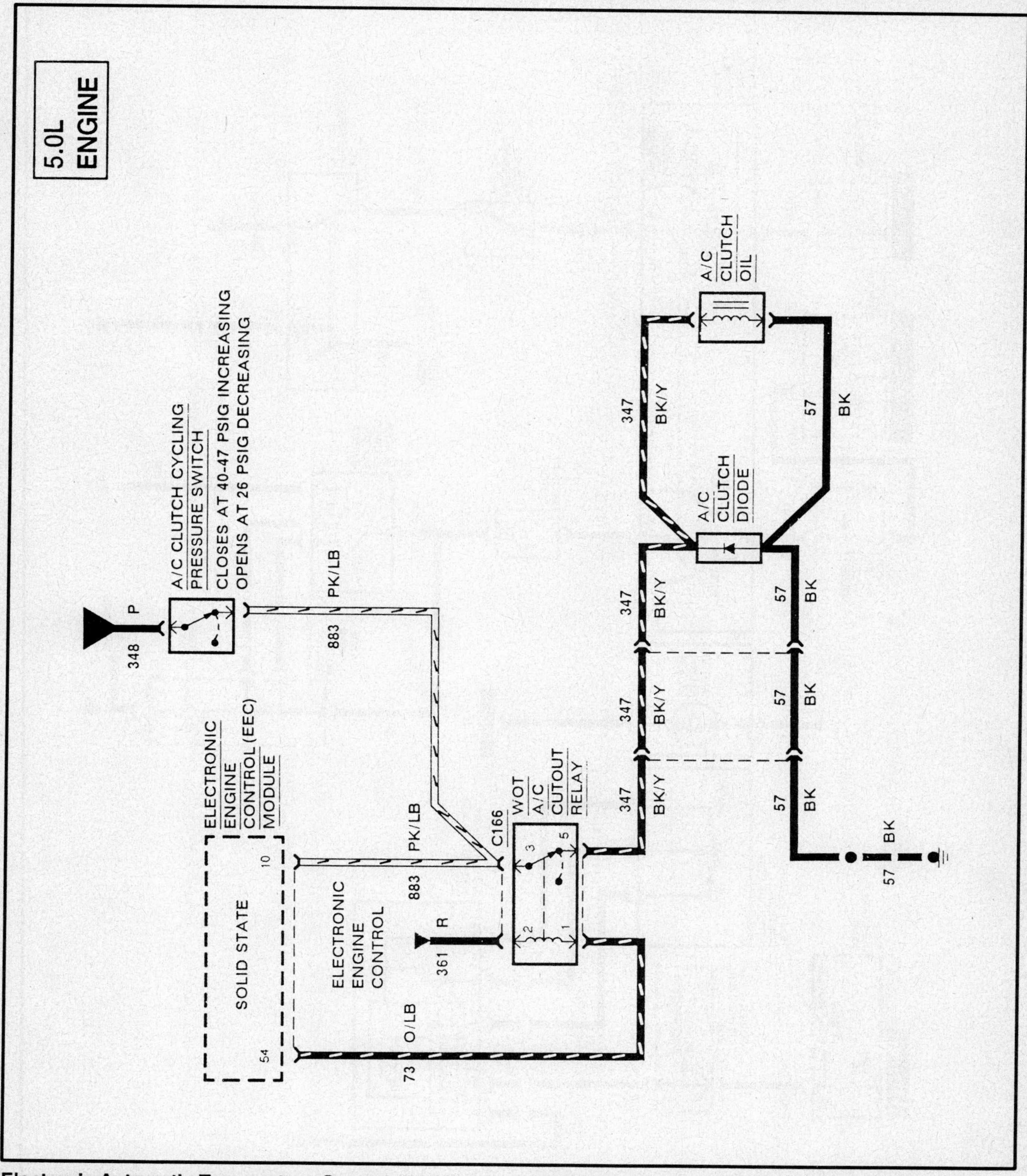

Electronic Automatic Temperature Control (EATC) compressor control system wiring schematic—Thunderbird and Cougar with 5.0L engine

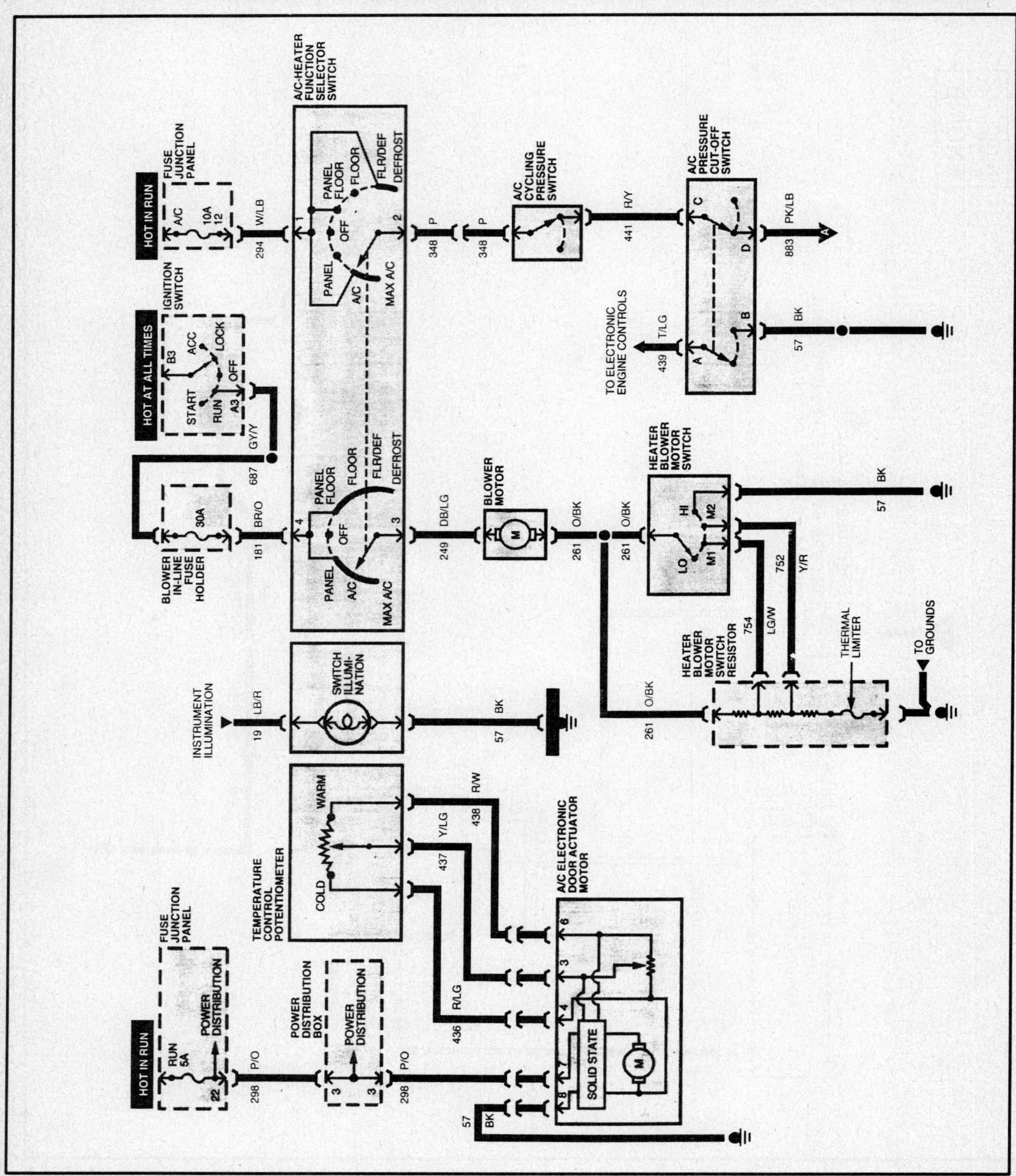

Manual air conditioning system wiring schematic—1994–95 Thunderbird and Cougar

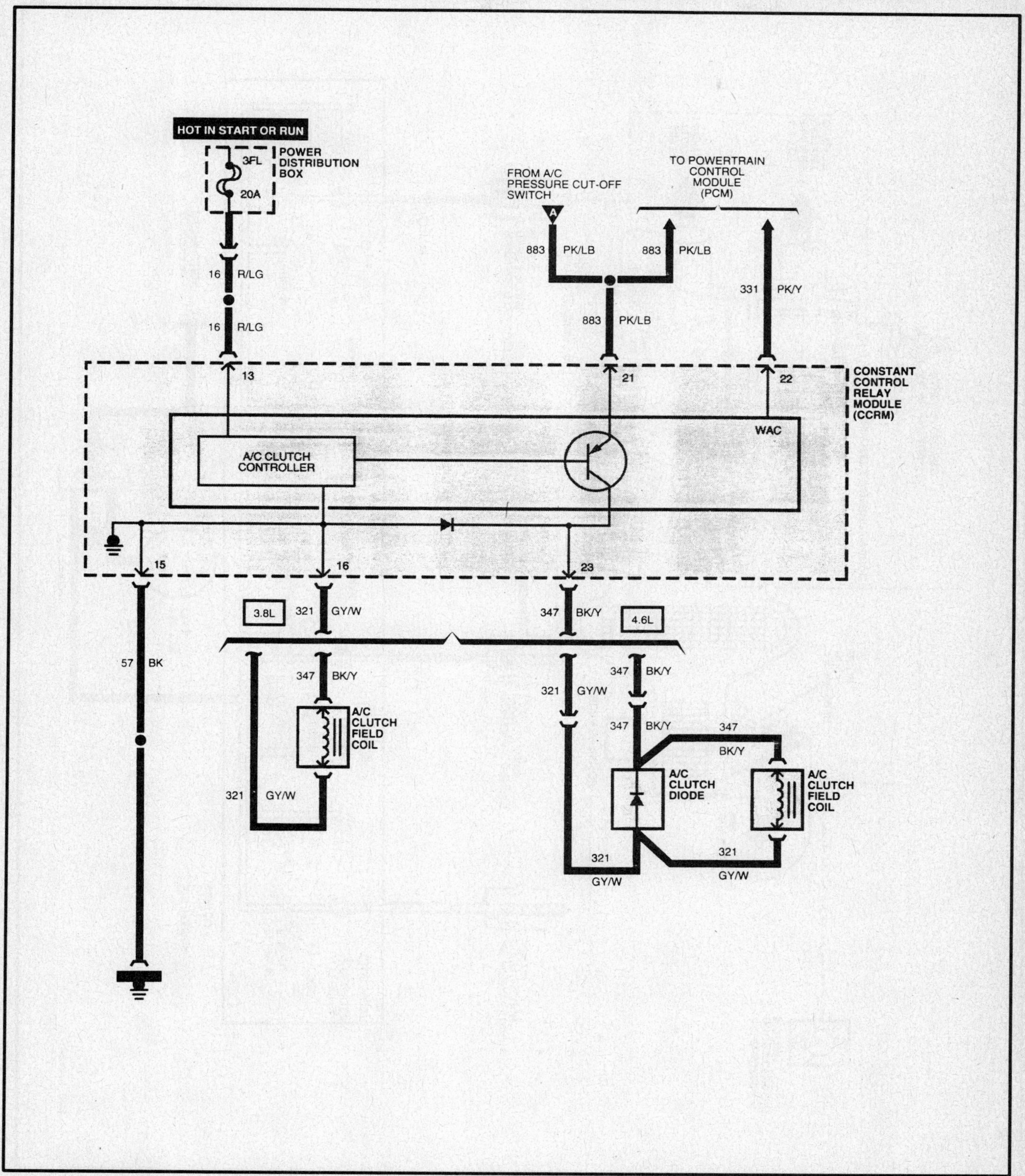

Manual air conditioning system wiring schematic—1994–95 Thunderbird and Cougar, Cont'd

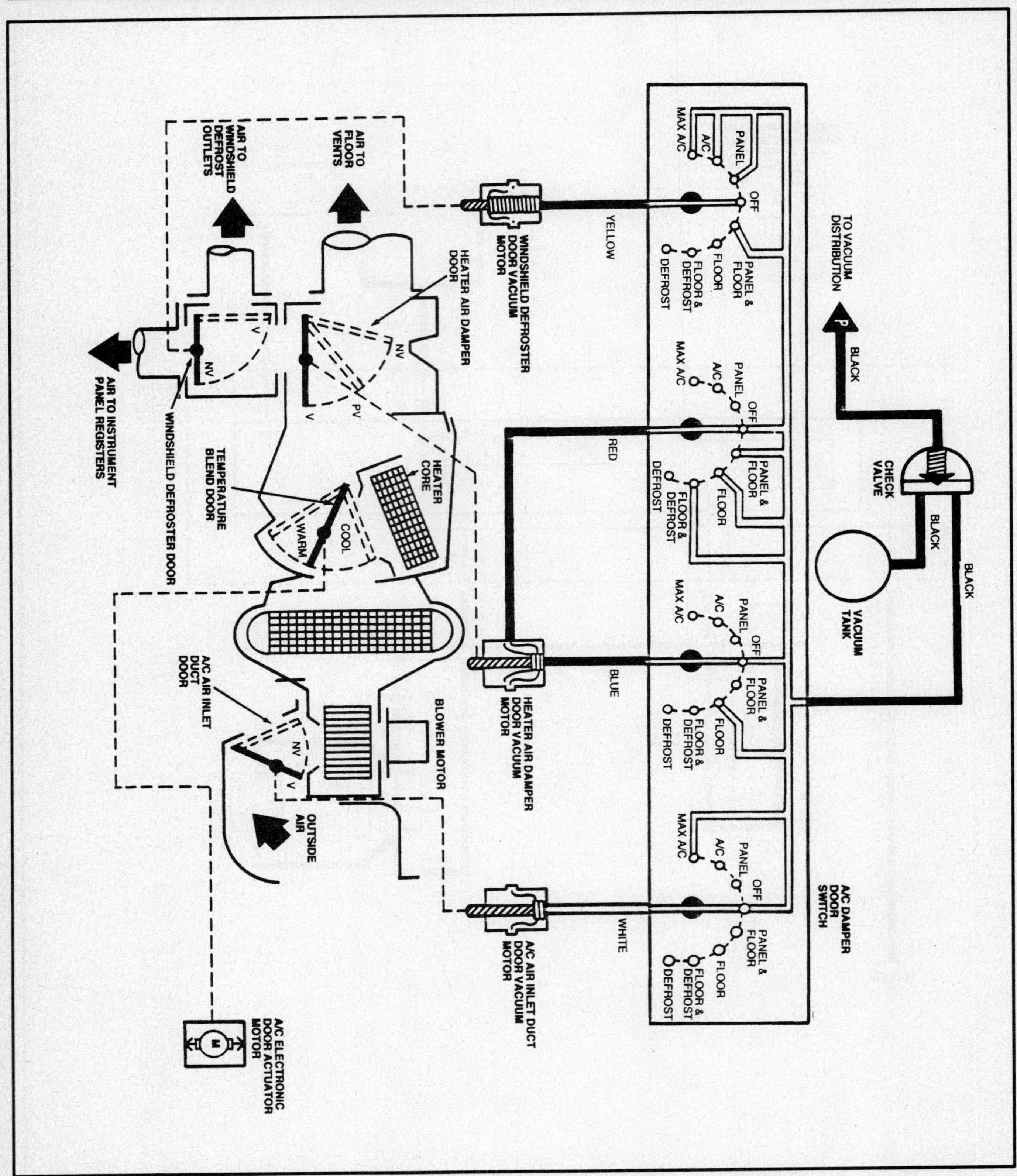

Manual air conditioning system vacuum diagram—1994–95 Thunderbird and Cougar

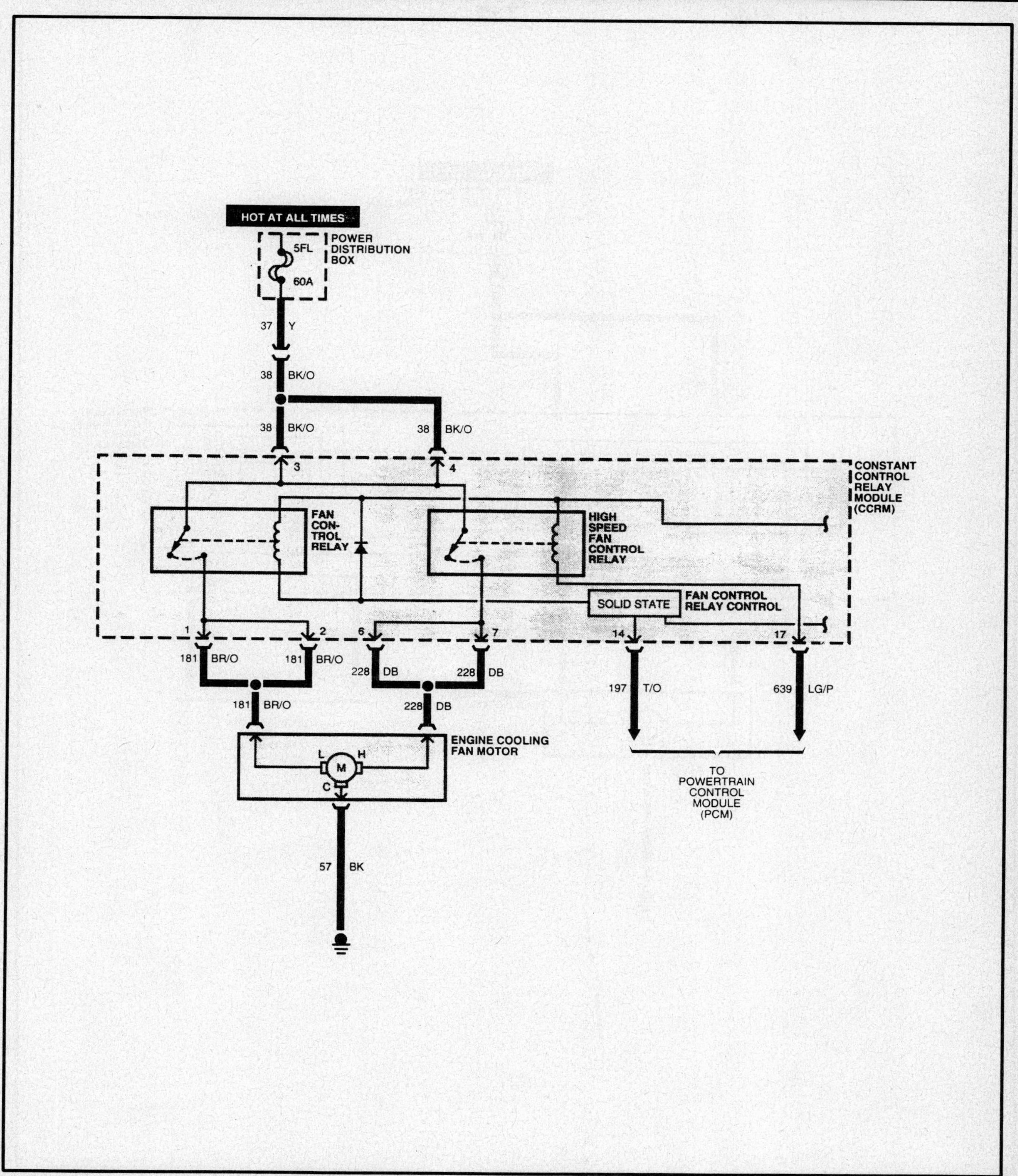

Cooling fan wiring schematic—1994–95 Thunderbird and Cougar 3.8L and 4.6L engines

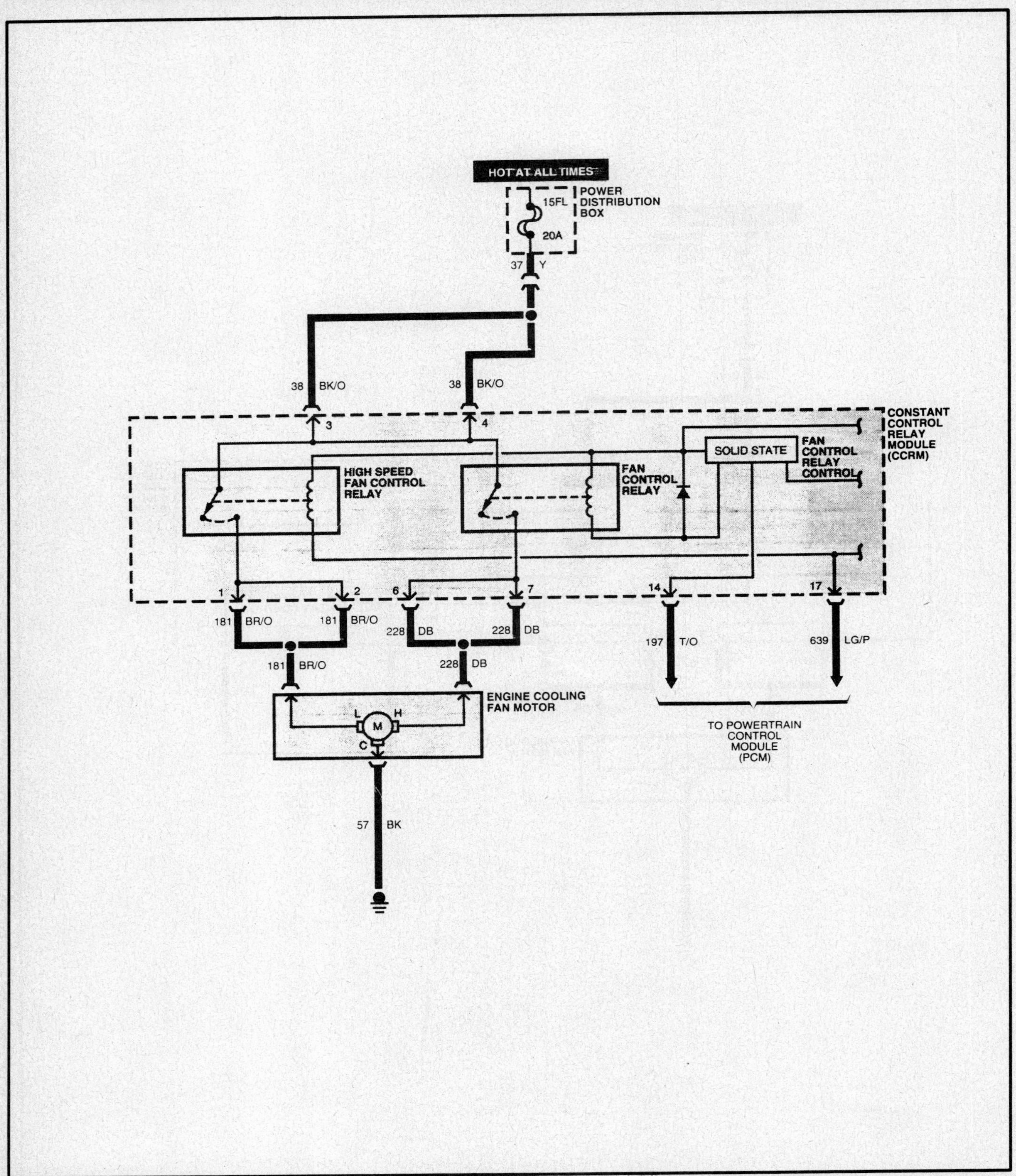

Cooling fan wiring schematic—1994–95 Thunderbird 3.8L SC engine

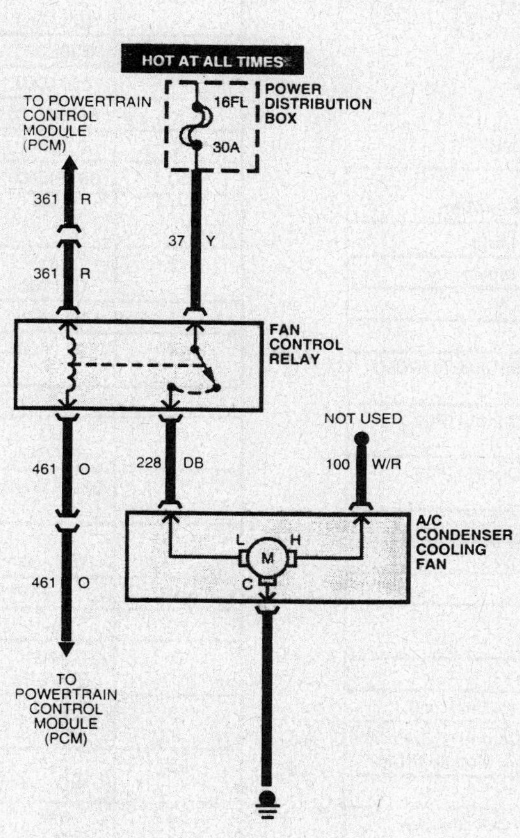

Auxiliary cooling fan wiring schematic—1994–95 Thunderbird 3.8L SC engine

Connector End Views

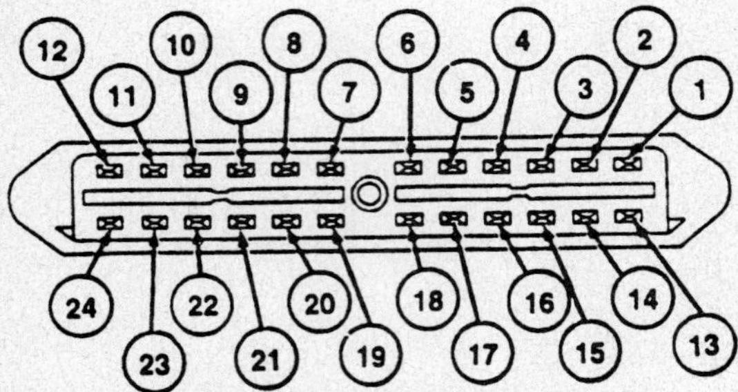

CONSTANT CONTROL RELAY MODULE CONNECTOR

3.8L BASE AND 4.6L ENGINE

Pin Number	Circuit	Circuit Function
1	228 (DB)	Fan Control (FC) Motor
2	228 (DB)	Fan Control (FC) Motor
3	38 (BK/O)	B+
4	38 (BK/O)	B+
5	787 (PK/BK)	Powertrain Control Module (PCM)
6	181 (BR/O)	High Speed Fan Control (FC) Motor
7	181 (BR/O)	High Speed Fan Control (FC) Motor
8	37 (Y)	B+
9	—	Not Used
10	37 (Y)	B+
11	175 (BK/Y)	B+
12	361 (R)	Vehicle Power
13	16 (R/LG)	Power (Hot in START or RUN)
14	197 (T/O)	Low Speed Fan Control (FC) From Powertrain Control Module (PCM)
15	57 (B/K)	Ground
16	321 (GY/W)	A/C Clutch Field Coil Ground
17	639 (LG/P)	High Speed Fan Control (FC) from PCM
18	926 (LB/O)	Powertrain Control Module (PCM)
19	—	Not Used
20	—	Not Used
21	883 (PK/LB)	A/C Cycling Switch
22	331 (PK/Y)	A/C Cutout from Powertrain Control Module (PCM)
23	347 (BK/Y)	A/C Clutch Field Coil Feed
24	361 (R)	Vehicle Power

3.8L SC ENGINE

Pin Number	Circuit	Circuit Function
1	181 (BR/O)	High Speed Fan Control (FC) Motor
2	181 (BR/O)	High Speed Fan Control (FC) Motor
3	38 (BK/O)	B+
4	38 (BK/O)	B+
5	787 (PK/BK)	Powertrain Control Module (PCM)
6	228 (DB)	Fan Control (FC) Motor
7	228 (DB)	Fan Control (FC) Motor
8	38 (BK/O)	B+
9	57 (BK)	Ground
10	38 (BK/O)	B+
11	175 (BK/Y)	B+ Relay Feed
12	181 (BR/O)	High Speed Fan Control (FC) Motor
13	361 (R)	Vehicle Power
14	197 (T/O)	Low Speed Fan Control (FC) from Powertrain Control Module (PCM)
15	57 (BK)	Ground
16	321 (GY/W)	A/C Clutch Field Coil Ground
17	639 (LG/P)	High Speed Fan Control (FC) from Powertrain Control Module (PCM)
18	926 (LB/O)	Powertrain Control Module (PCM) to Fuel Pump Relay Control
19	—	Not Used
20	—	Not Used
21	883 (PK/LB)	A/C Cycling Switch
22	331 (PK/Y)	A/C Cutout from Powertrain Control Module (PCM)
23	347 (BK/Y)	A/C Clutch Field Coil Feed
24	181 (BR/O)	High Speed Fan Control (FC) Motor

Constant control relay module connector pin identification—1994–95 Thunderbird and Cougar

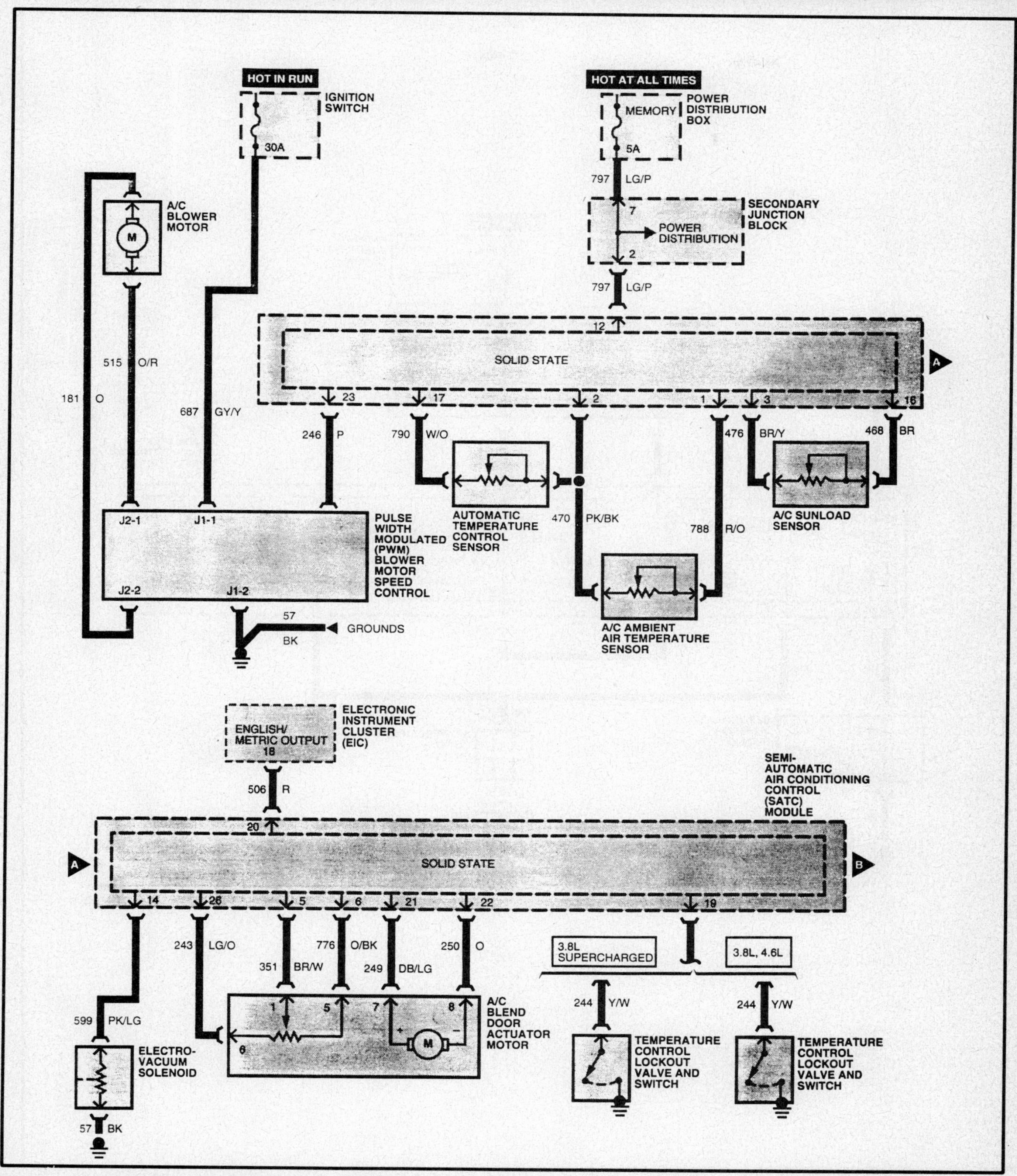

Semi Automatic Temperature Control (SATC) wiring schematic—1994 Thunderbird and Cougar

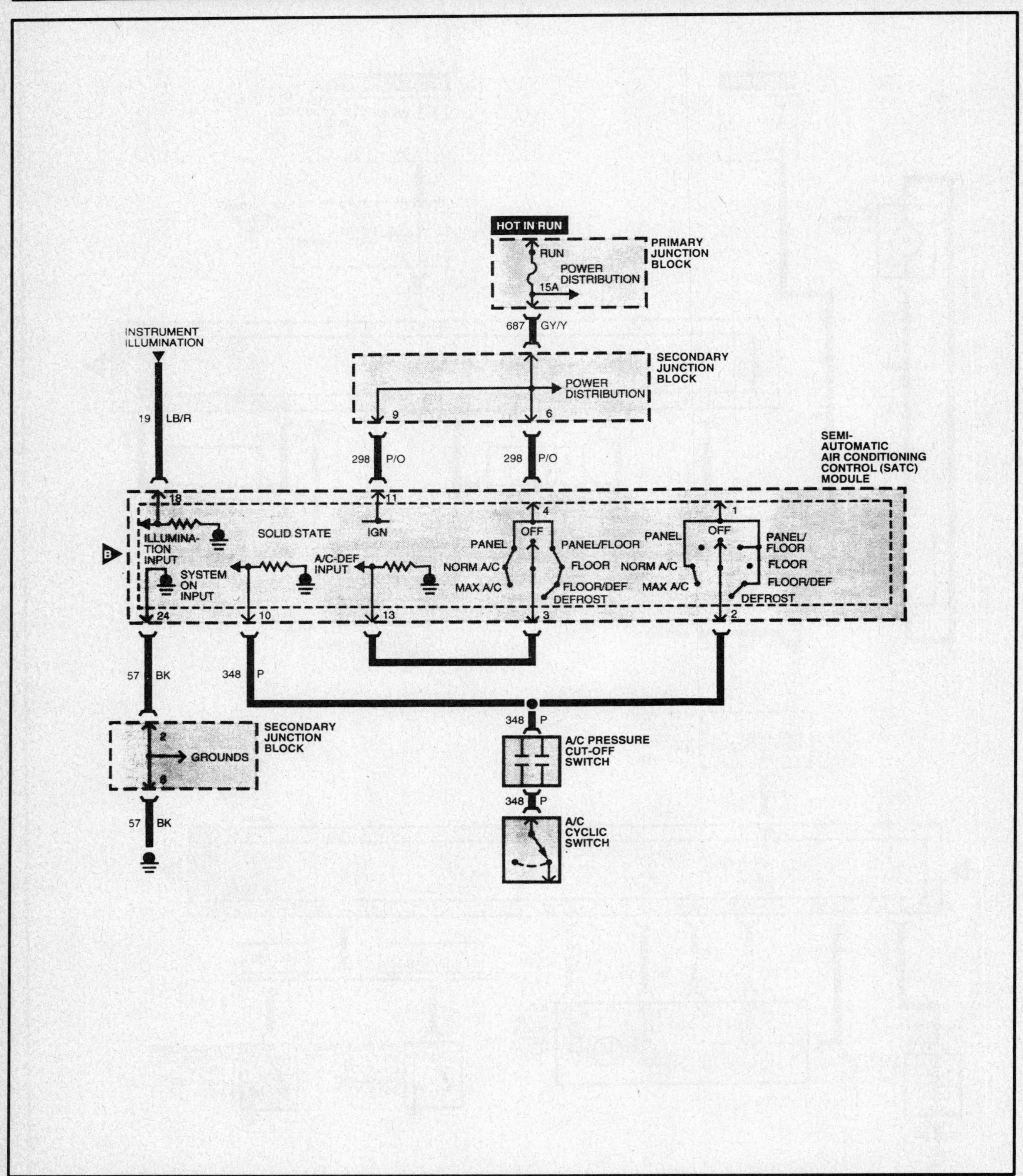

Semi Automatic Temperature Control (SATC) wiring schematic—1994 Thunderbird and Cougar, Cont'd

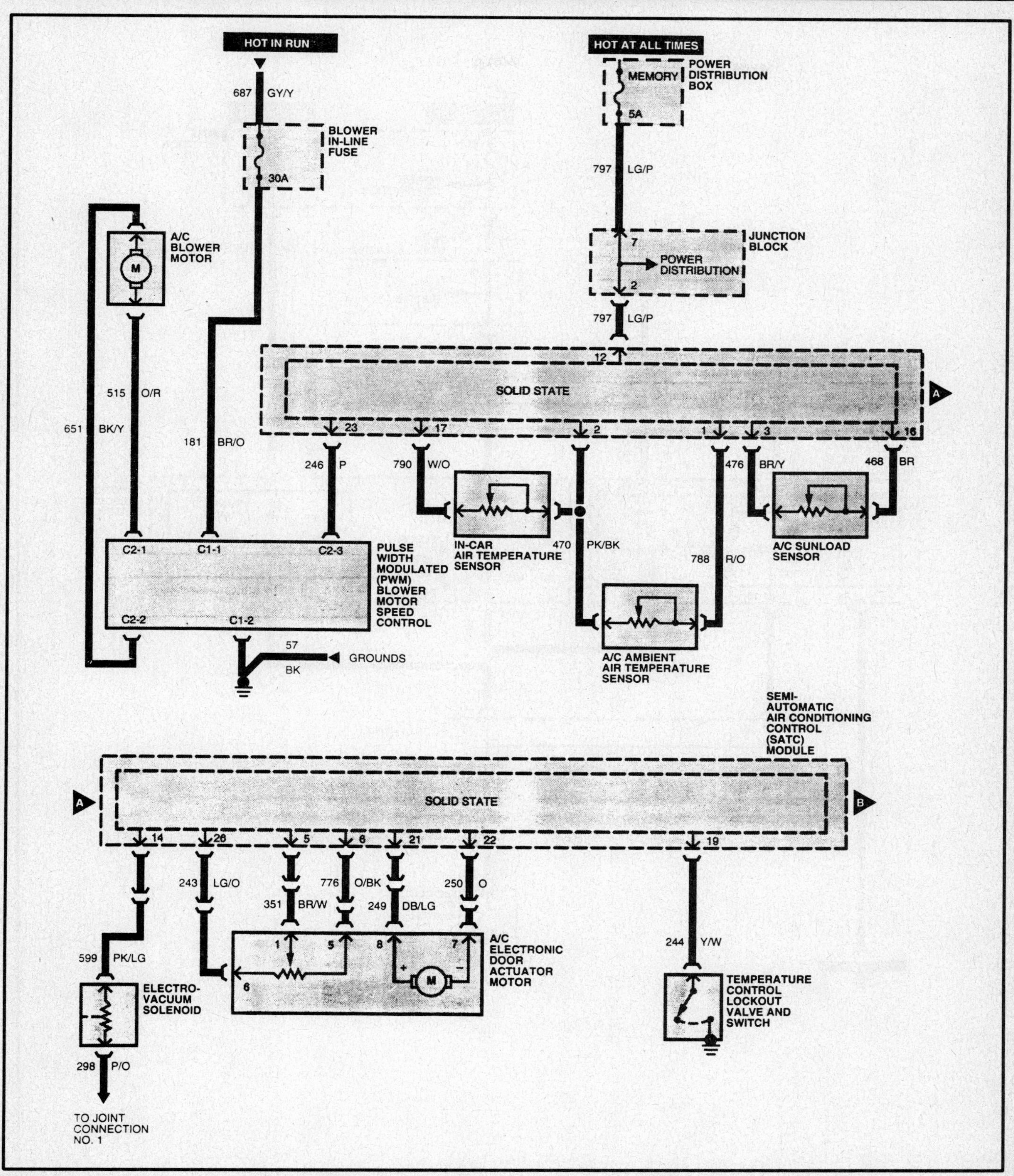

Semi Automatic Temperature Control (SATC) wiring schematic—1995 Thunderbird and Cougar

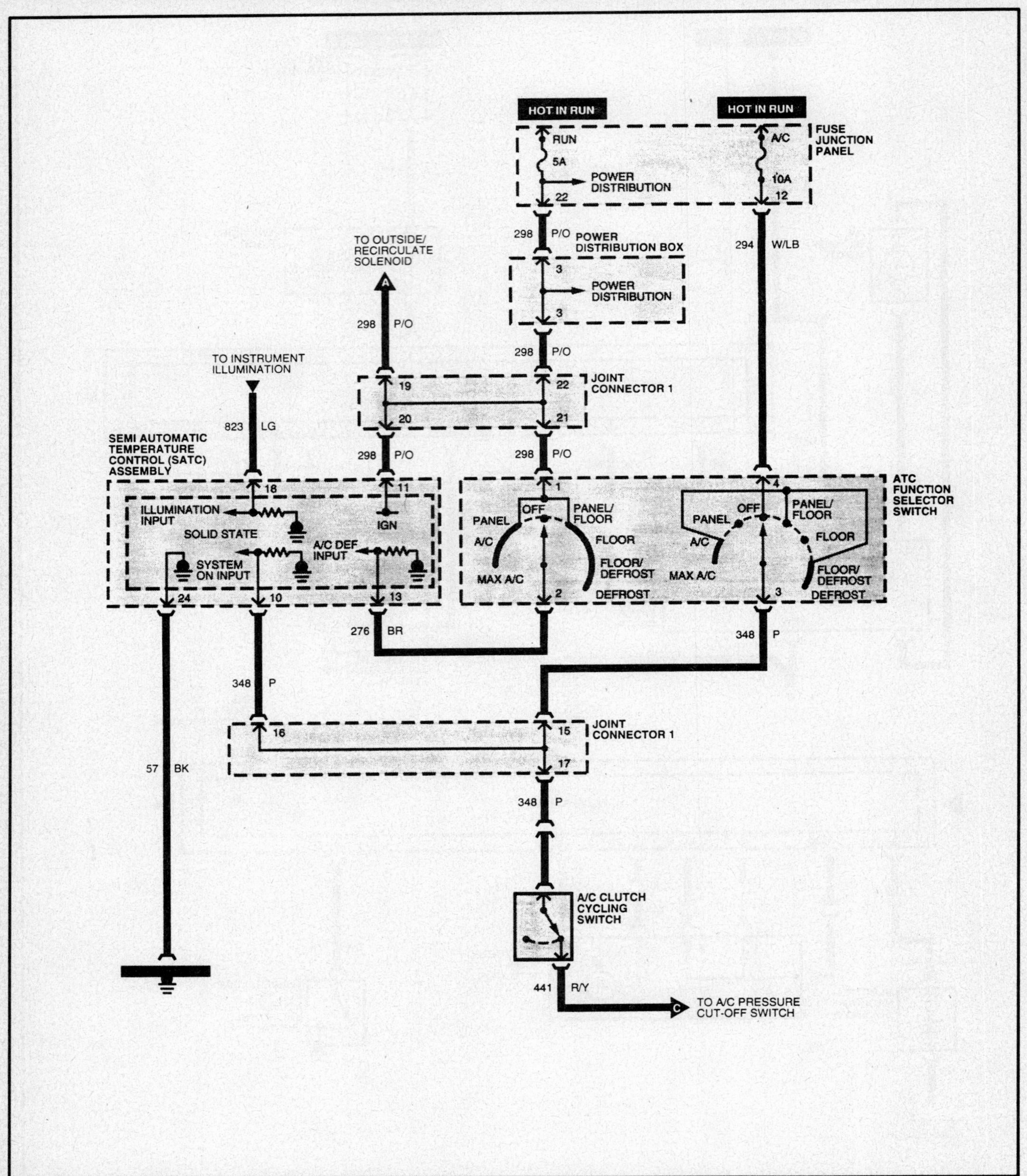

Semi Automatic Temperature Control (SATC) wiring schematic—1995 Thunderbird and Cougar, Cont'd

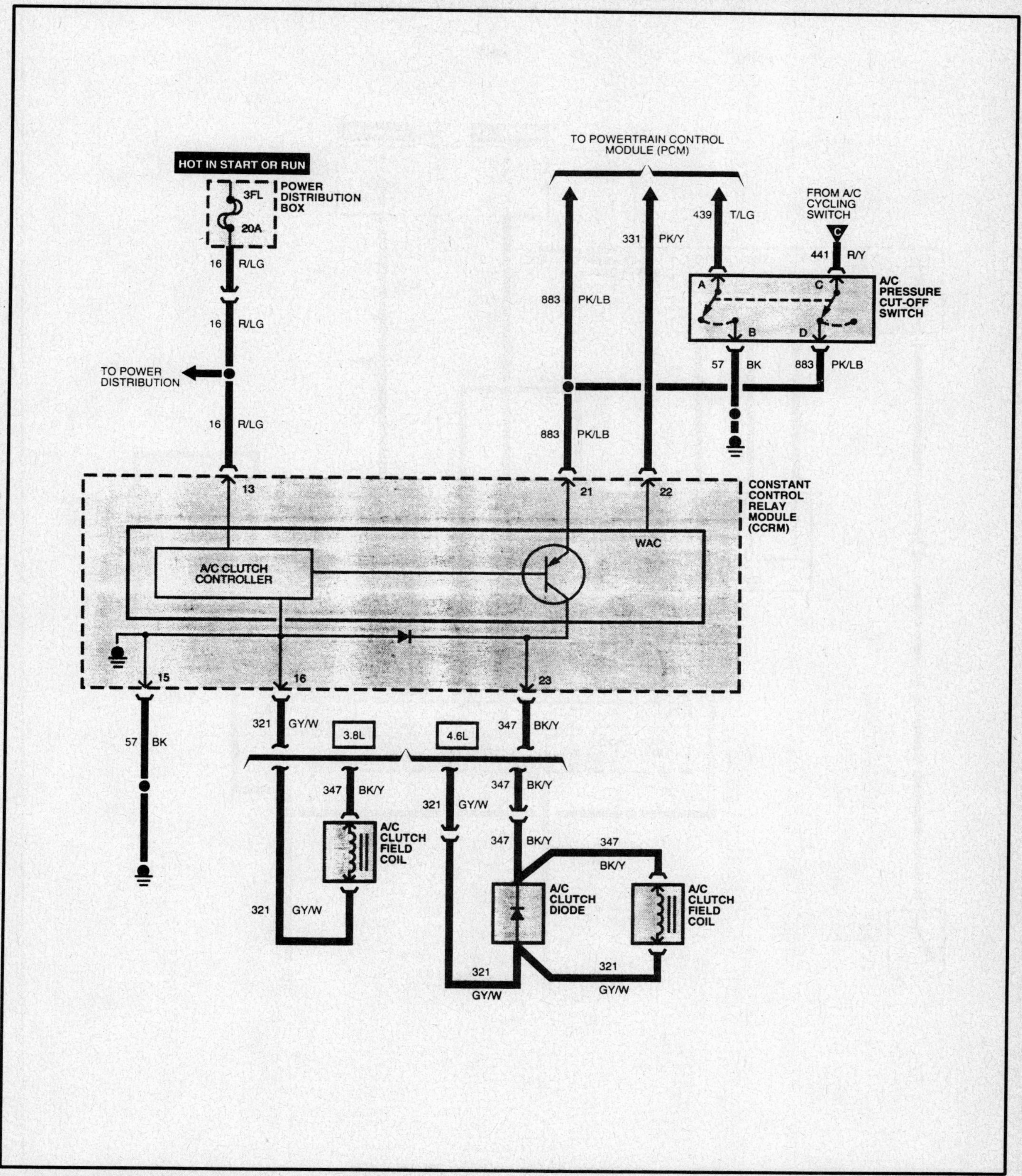

Semi Automatic Temperature Control (SATC) wiring schematic—1995 Thunderbird and Cougar, Cont'd

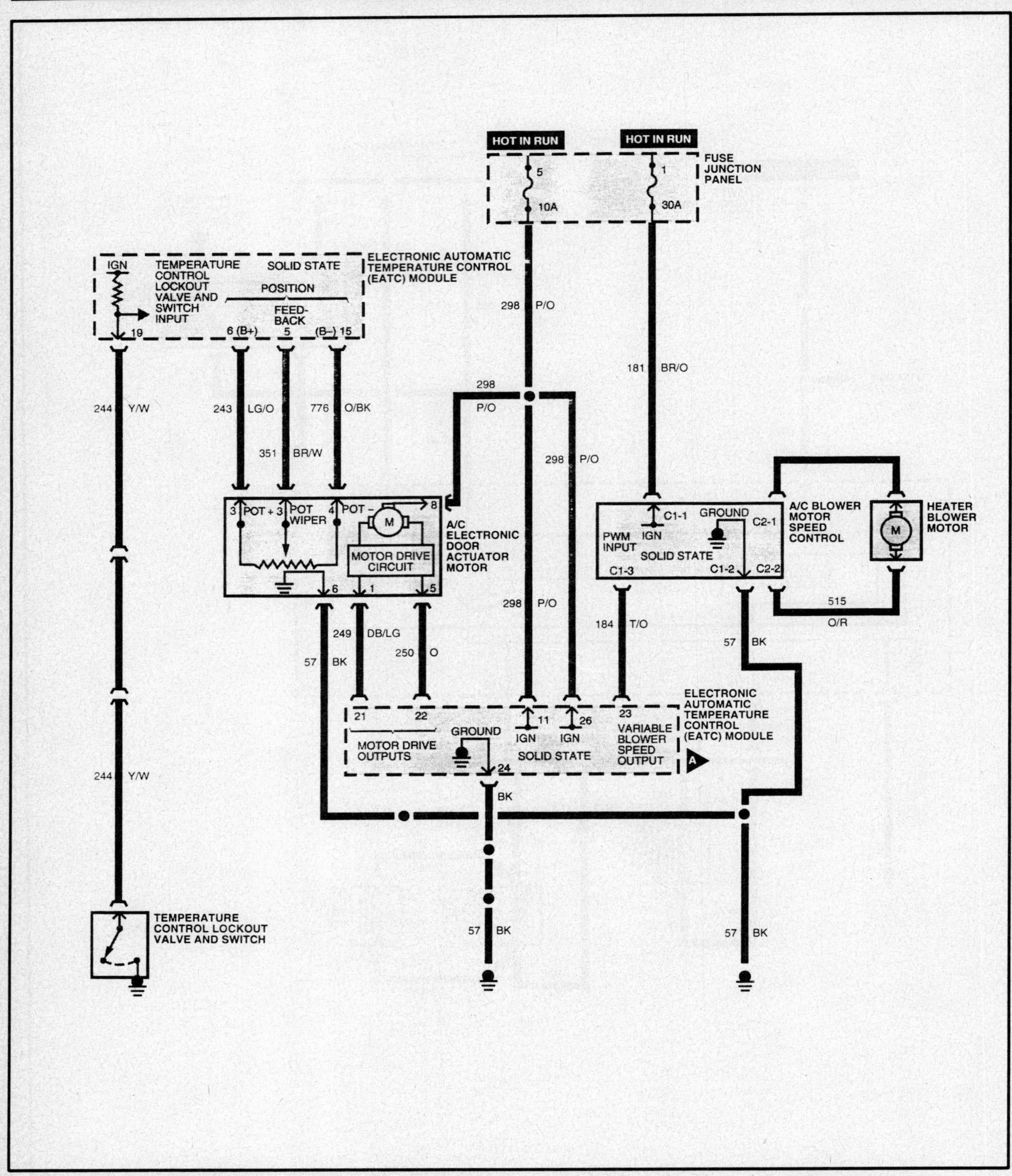

Electronic Automatic Temperature Control (EATC) system wiring schematic—1994–95 Mark VIII

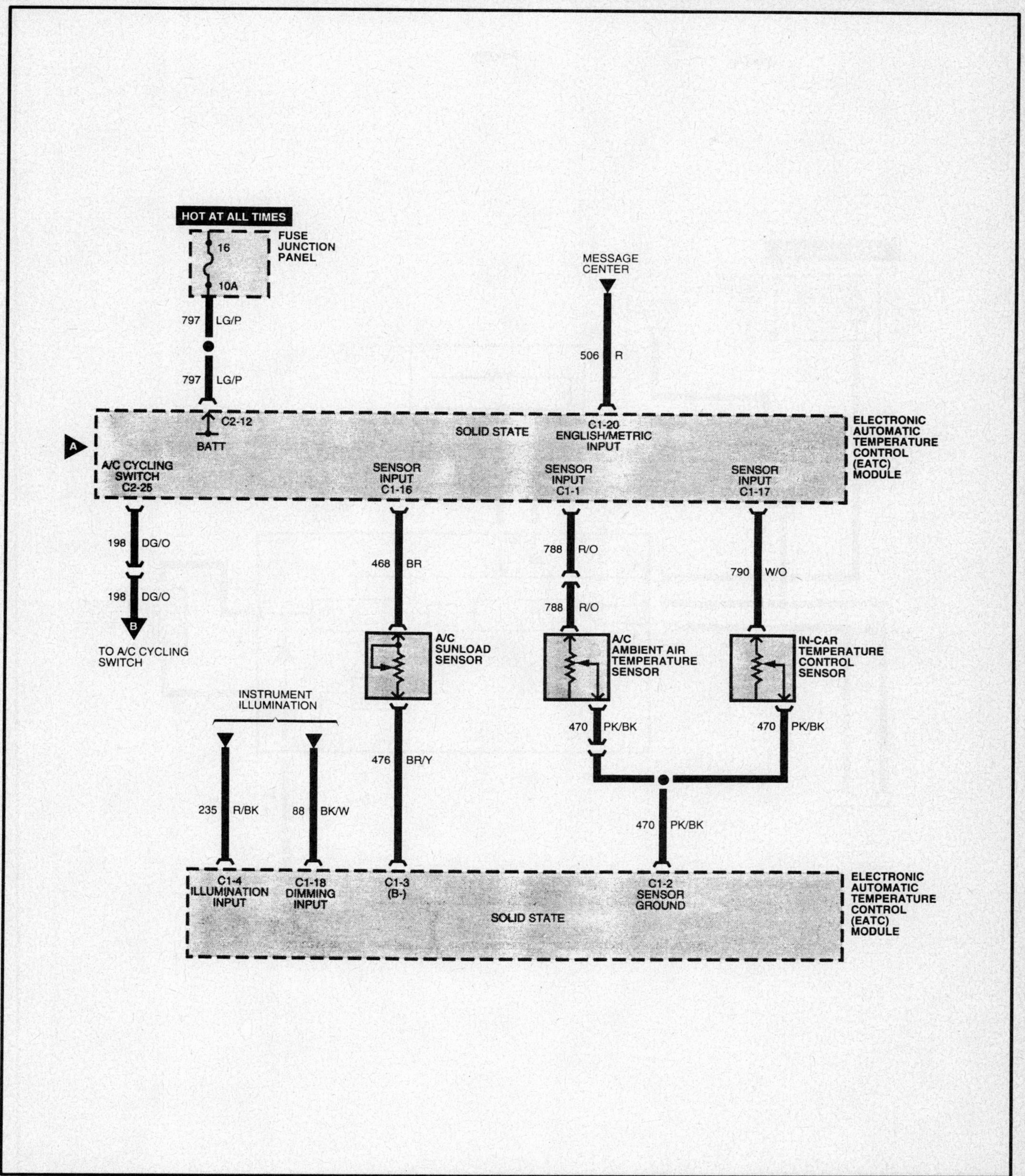

Electronic Automatic Temperature Control (EATC) system wiring schematic—1994–95 Mark VIII, Cont'd

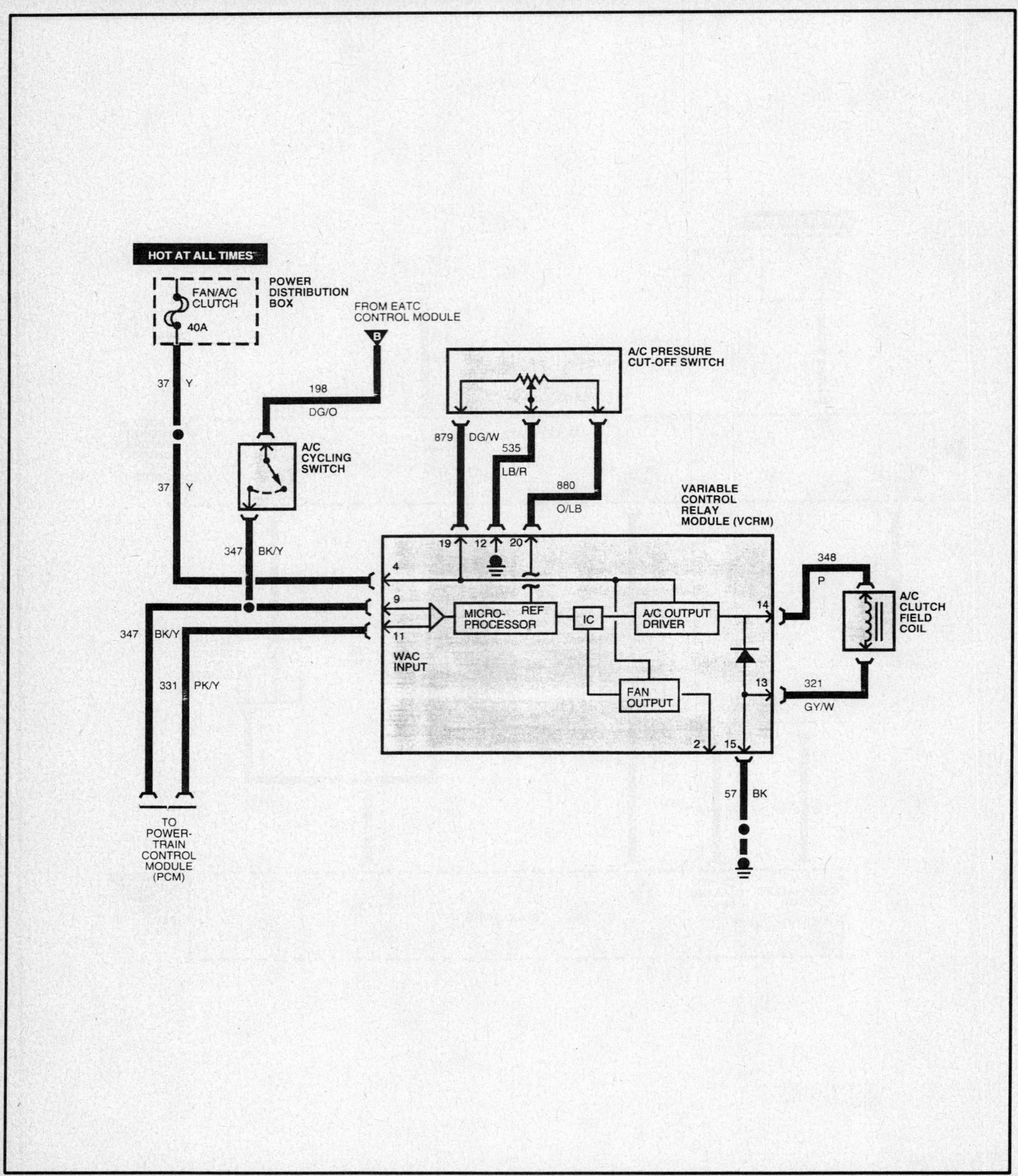

Electronic Automatic Temperature Control (EATC) system wiring schematic—1994–95 Mark VIII, Cont'd

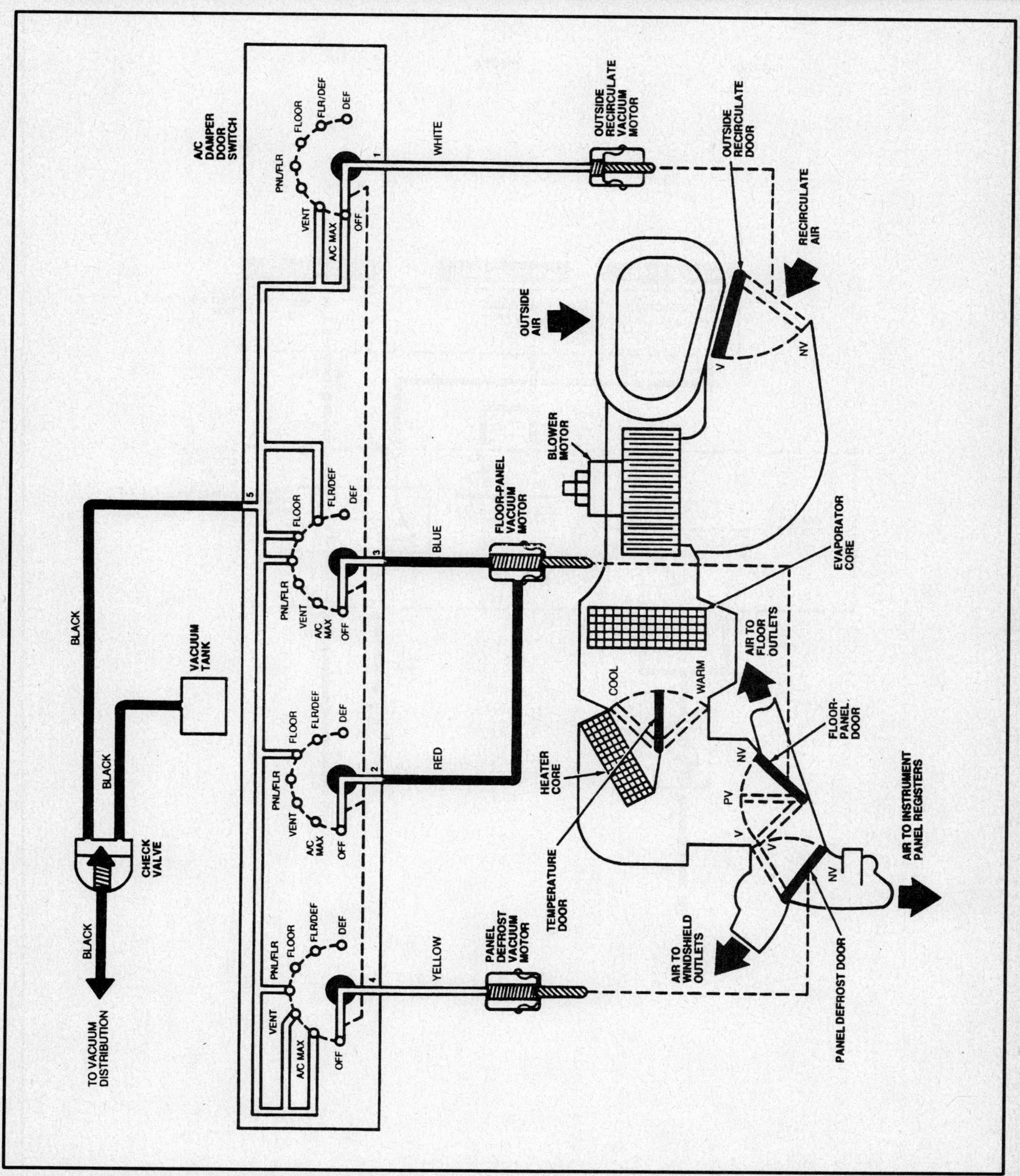

Electronic Automatic Temperature Control (EATC) system vacuum diagram—1994–95 Mark VIII

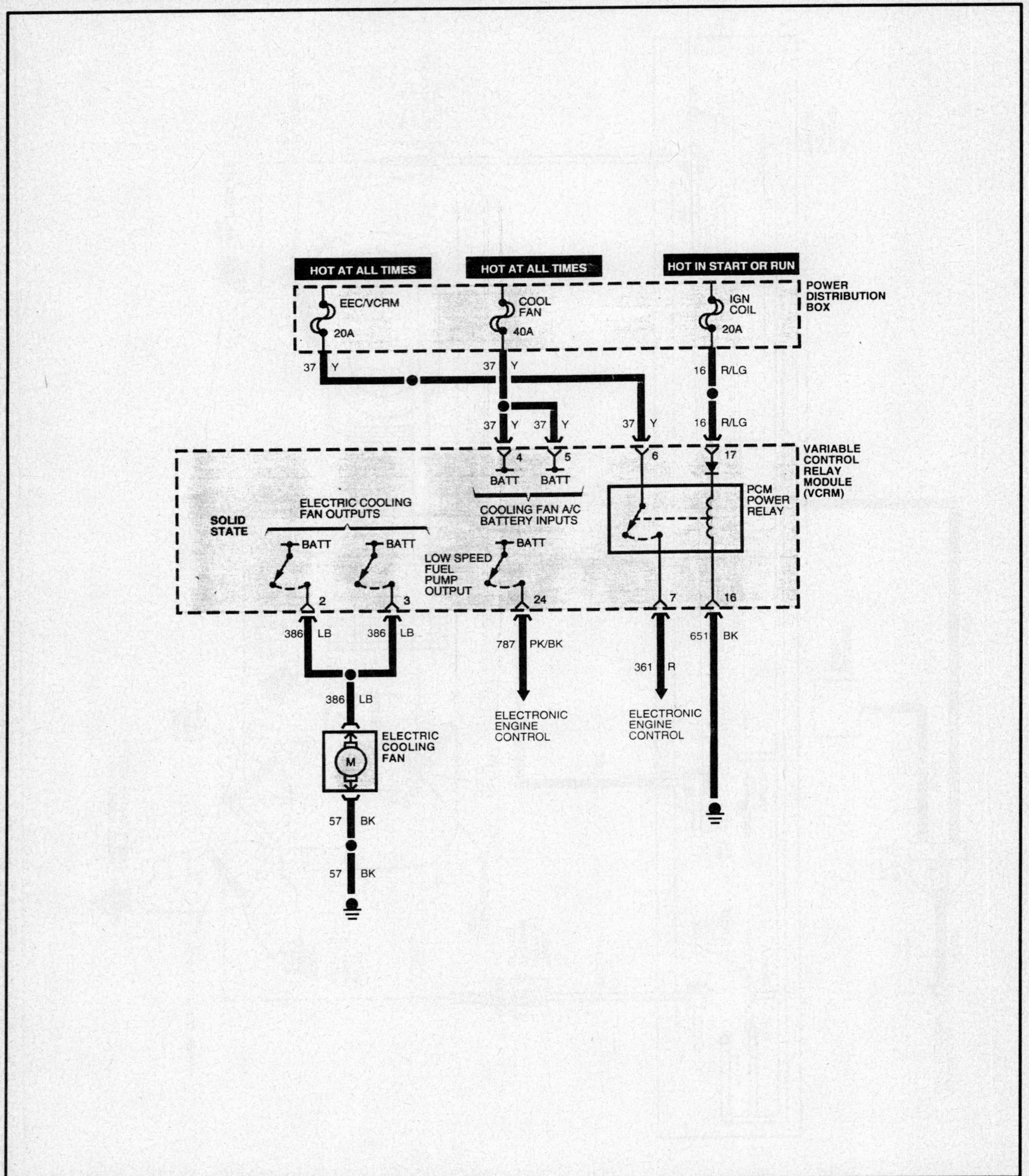

Cooling Fan wiring schematic—1994–95 Mark VIII

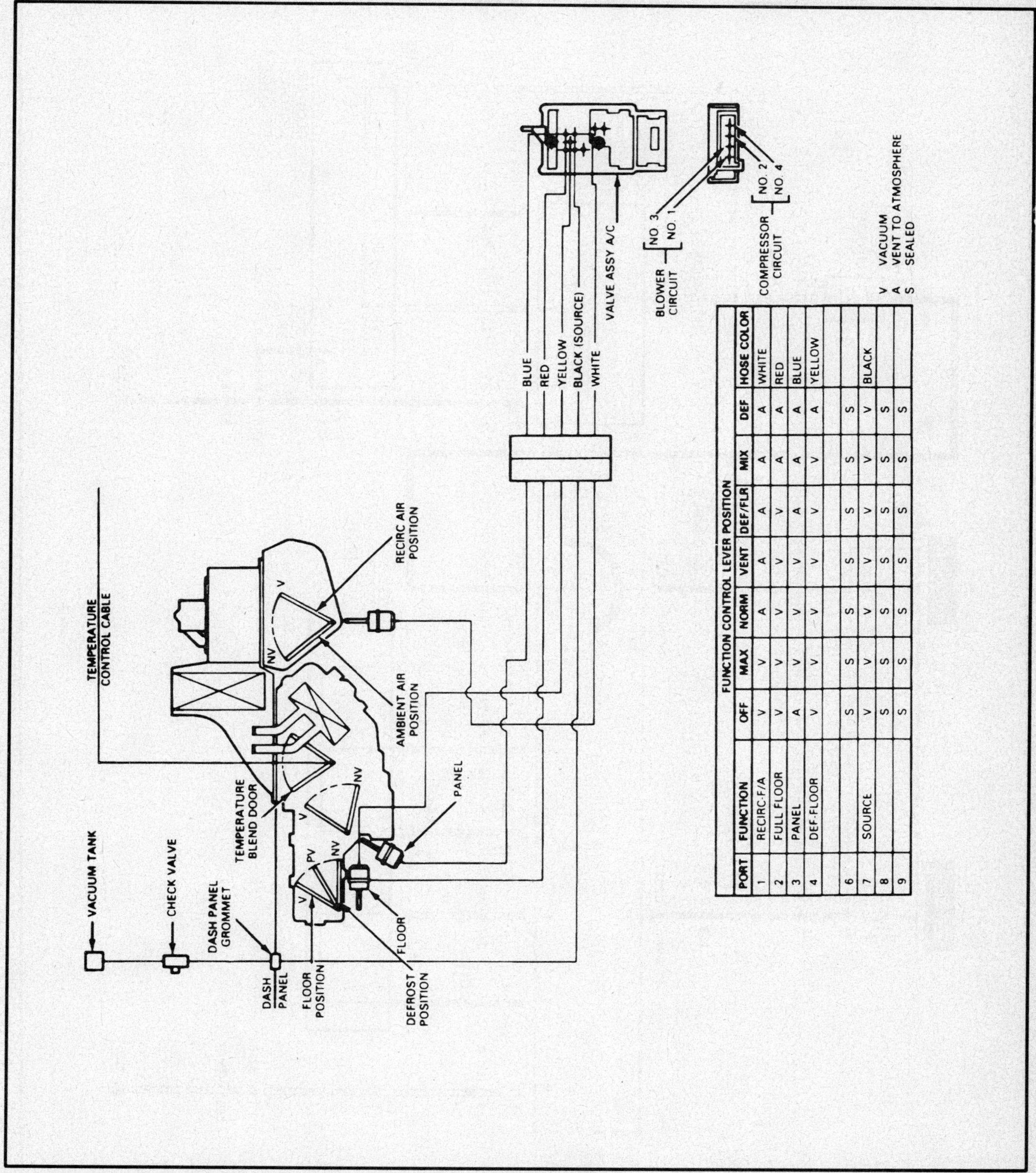

PORT	FUNCTION	FUNCTION CONTROL LEVER POSITION							HOSE COLOR
		OFF	MAX	NORM	VENT	DEF/FLR	MIX	DEF	
1	RECIRC-F/A	V	V	A	A	A	A	A	WHITE
2	FULL FLOOR	V	V	V	V	V	A	A	RED
3	PANEL	A	V	V	V	A	A	A	BLUE
4	DEF-FLOOR	V	V	V	V	V	V	A	YELLOW
6		S	S	S	S	S	S	S	
7	SOURCE	V	V	V	V	V	V	V	BLACK
8		S	S	S	S	S	S	S	
9		S	S	S	S	S	S	S	

Manual air conditioning system vacuum schematic and functional test chart—Crown Victoria and Grand Marquis

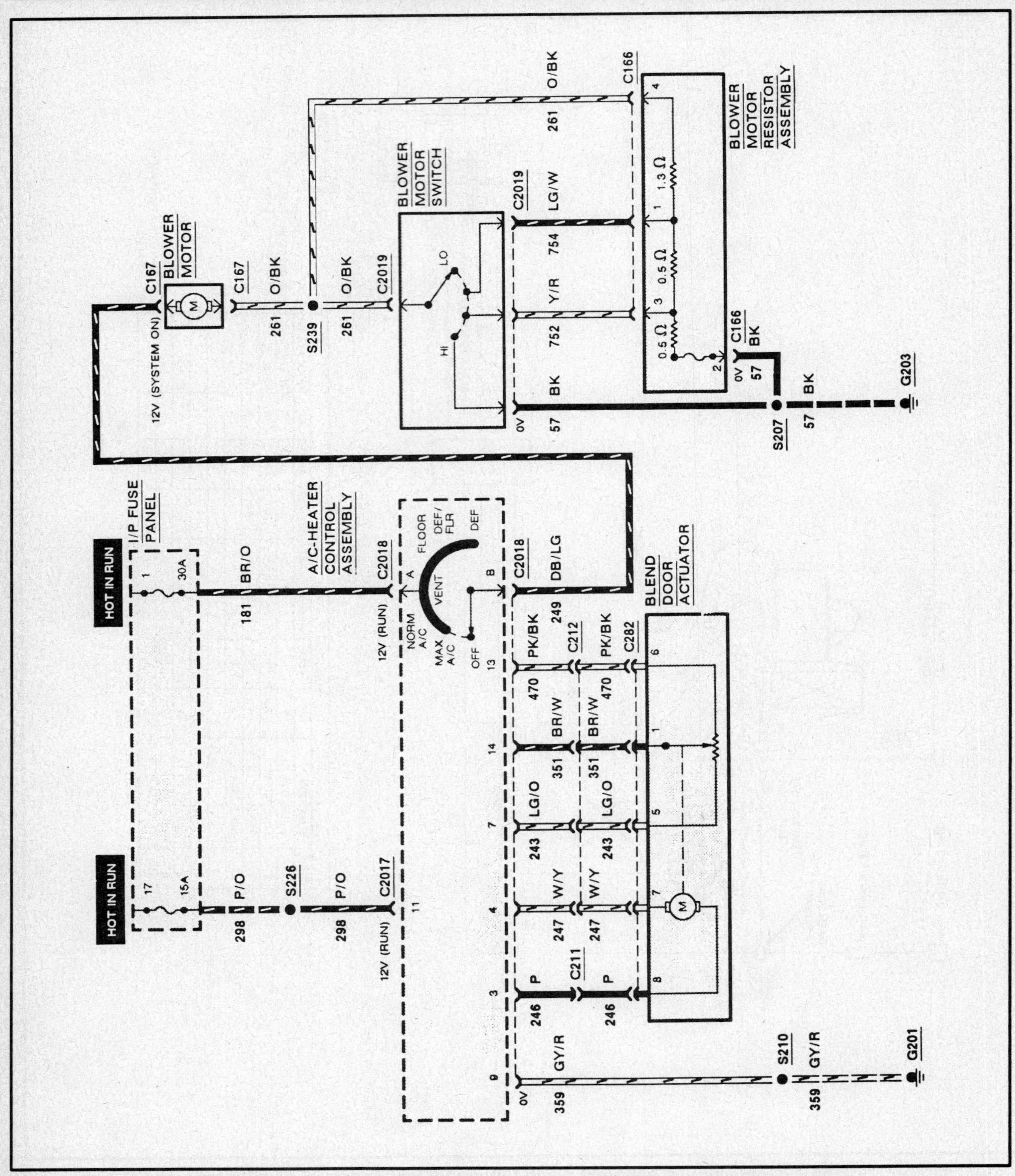

Manual air conditioning system wiring schematic—1993 Crown Victoria and Grand Marquis

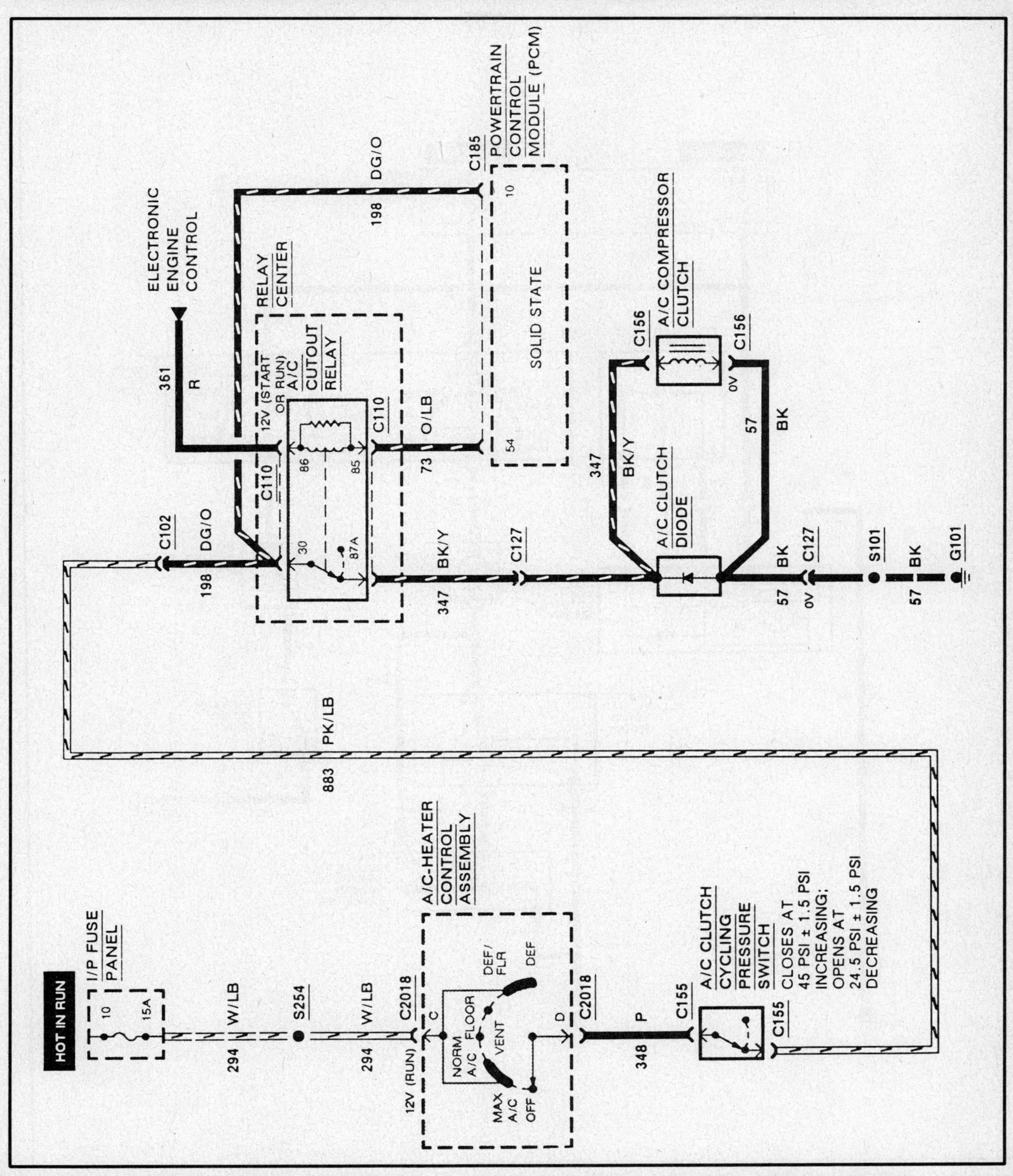

Manual air conditioning system wiring schematic—1993 Crown Victoria and Grand Marquis, Cont'd

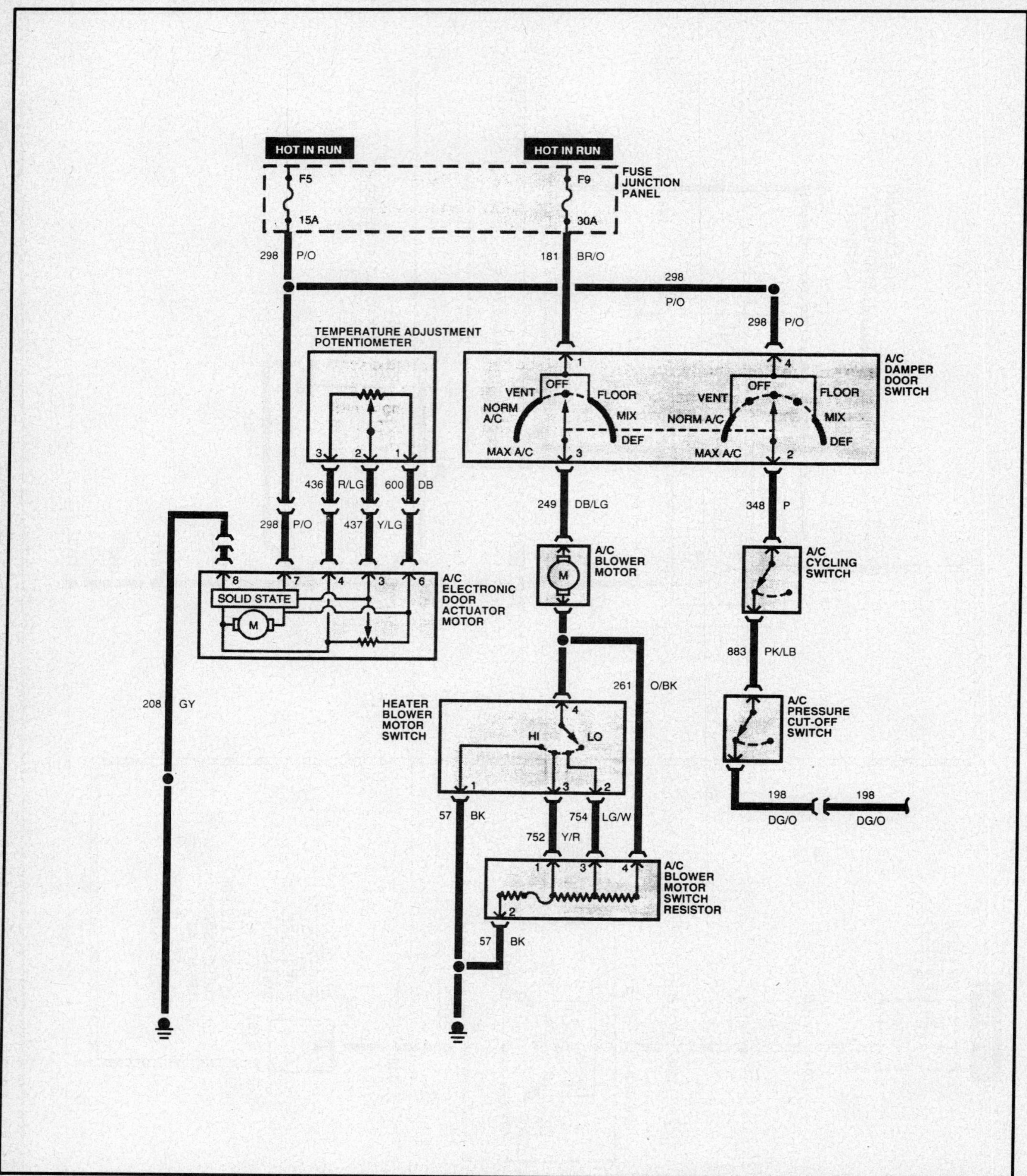

Manual air conditioning system wiring schematic—1994–95 Crown Victoria and Grand Marquis

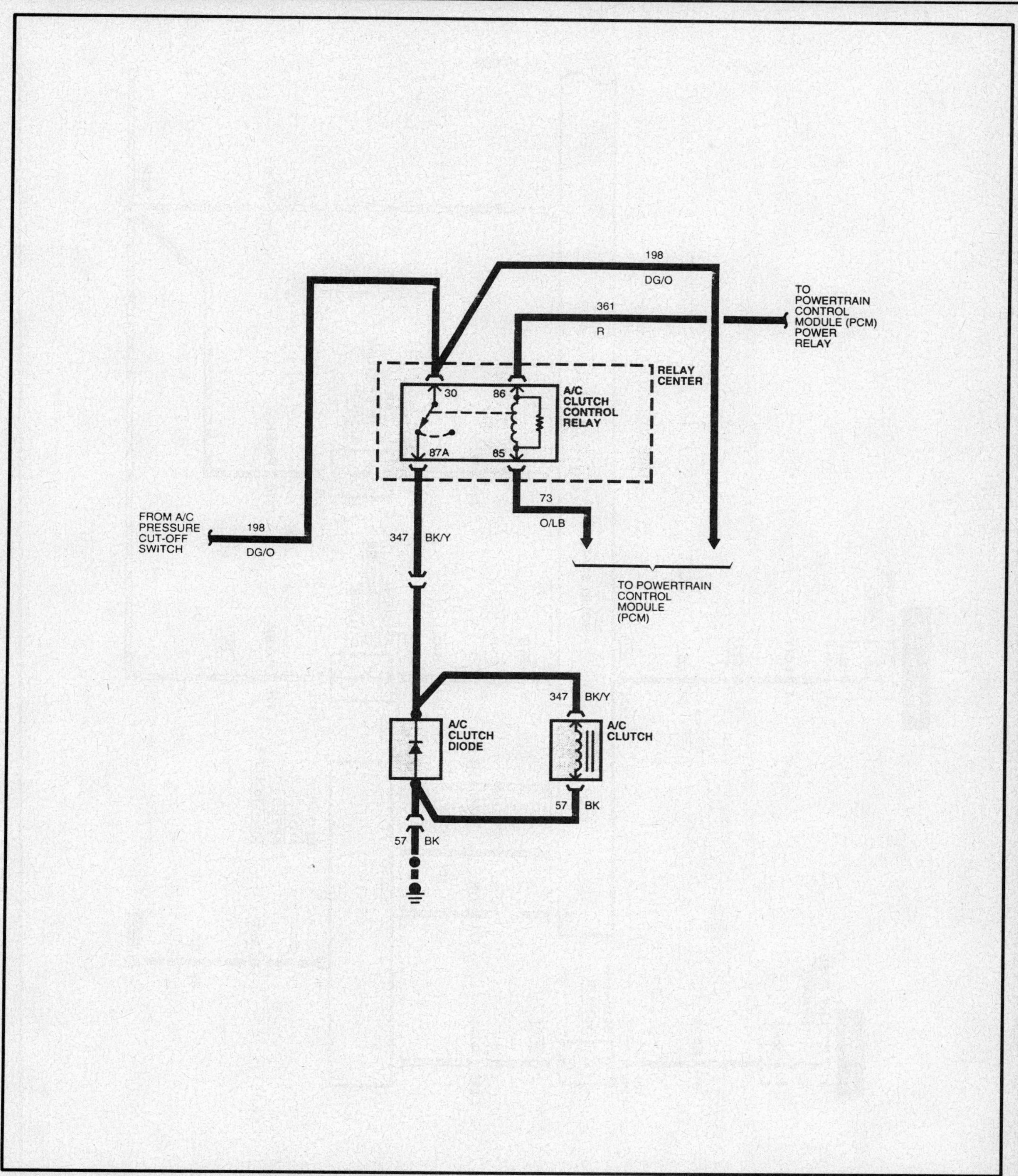

Manual air conditioning system wiring schematic—1994–95 Crown Victoria and Grand Marquis, Cont'd

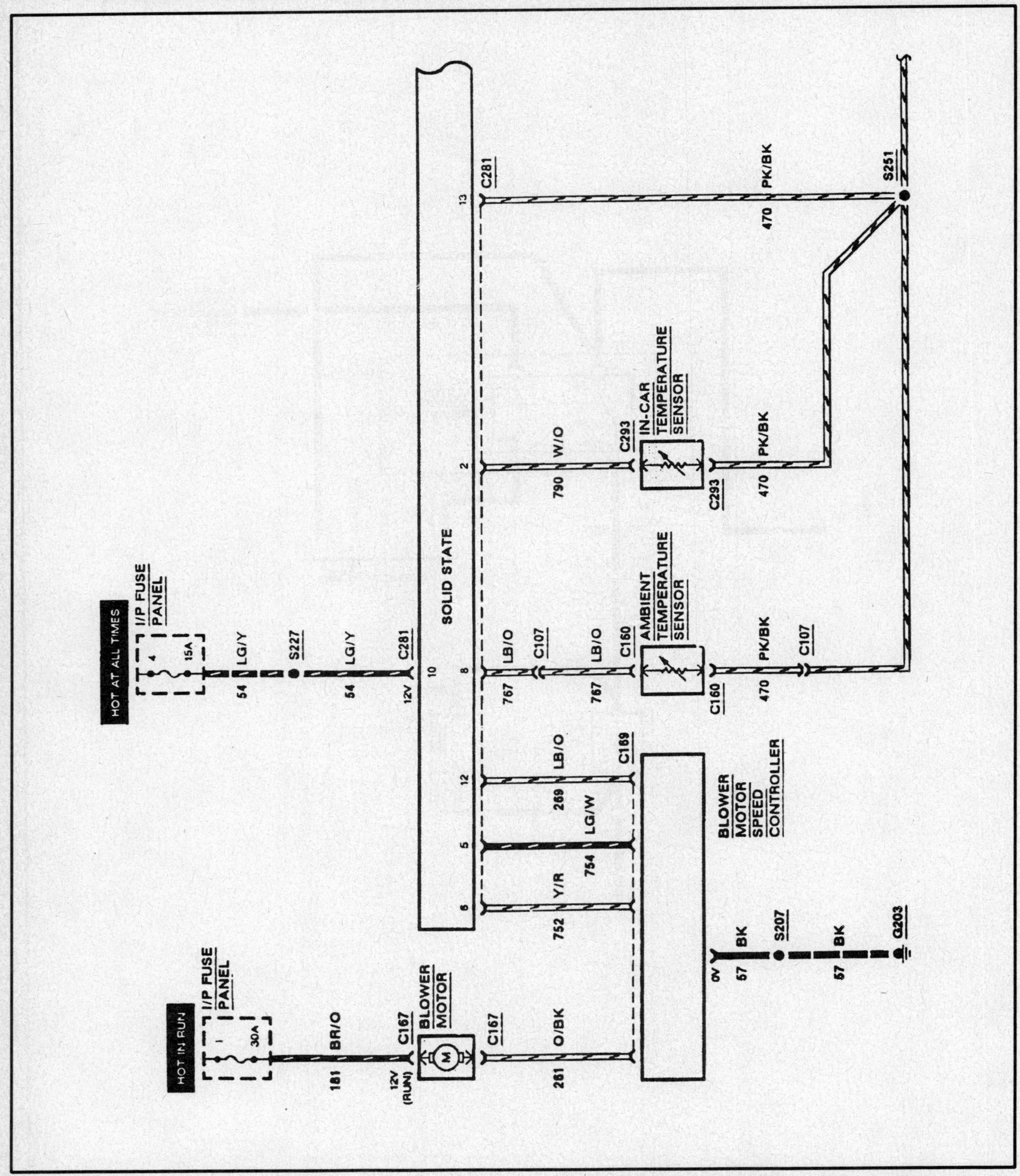

Automatic Temperature Control (ATC) system wiring schematic—1993 Crown Victoria and Grand Marquis

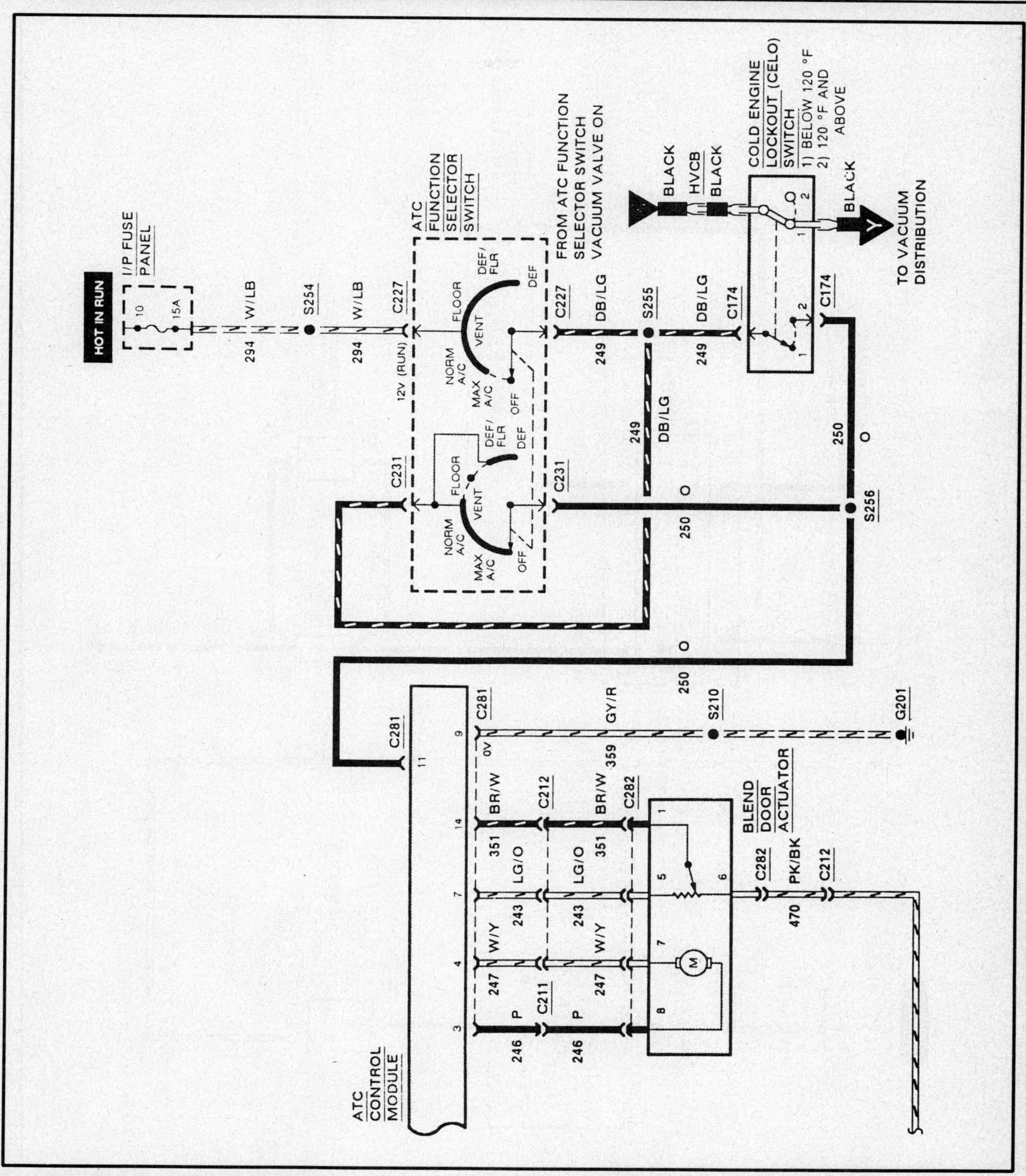

Automatic Temperature Control (ATC) system wiring schematic—1993 Crown Victoria and Grand Marquis, Cont'd

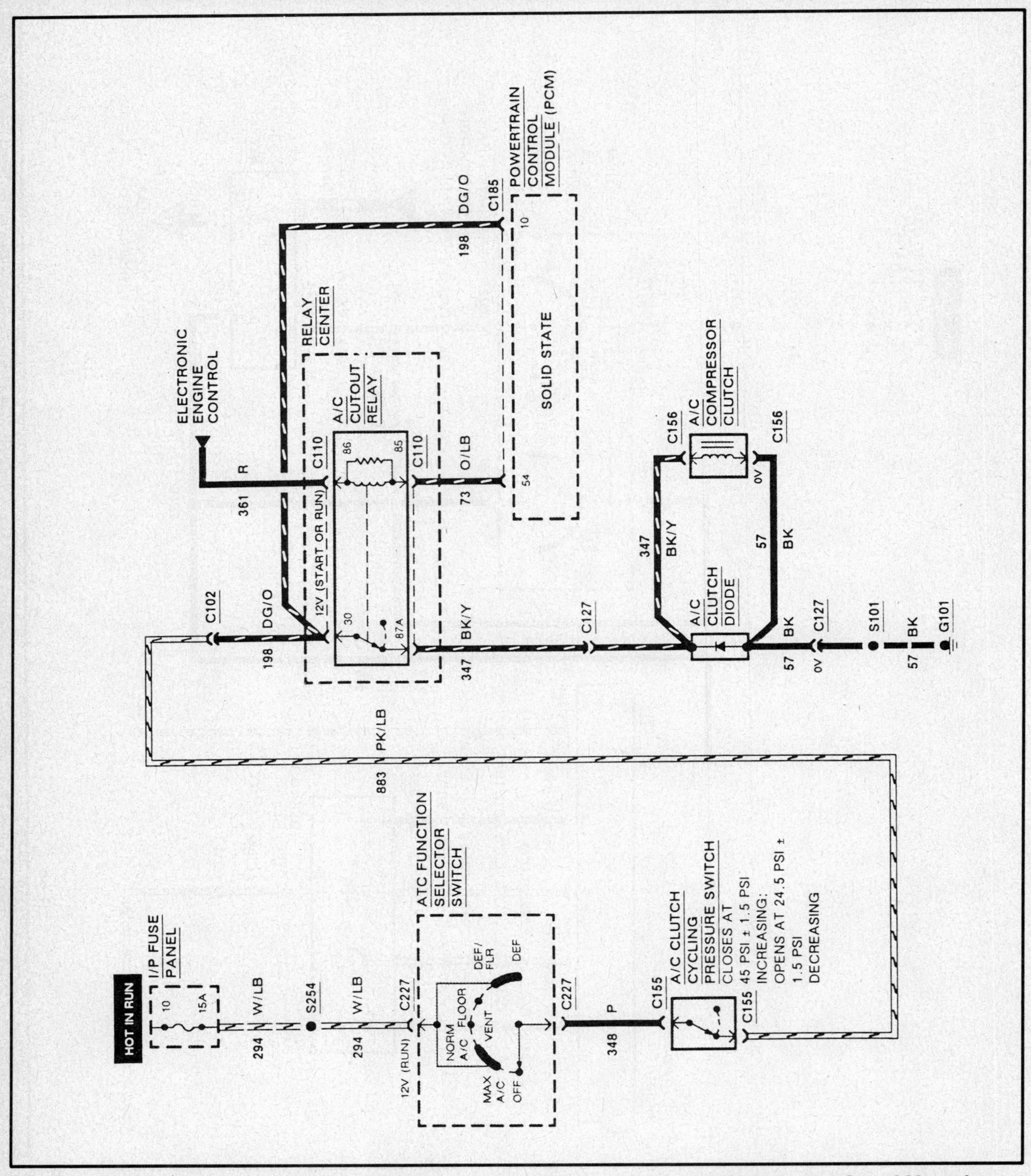

Automatic Temperature Control (ATC) system wiring schematic—1993 Crown Victoria and Grand Marquis, Cont'd

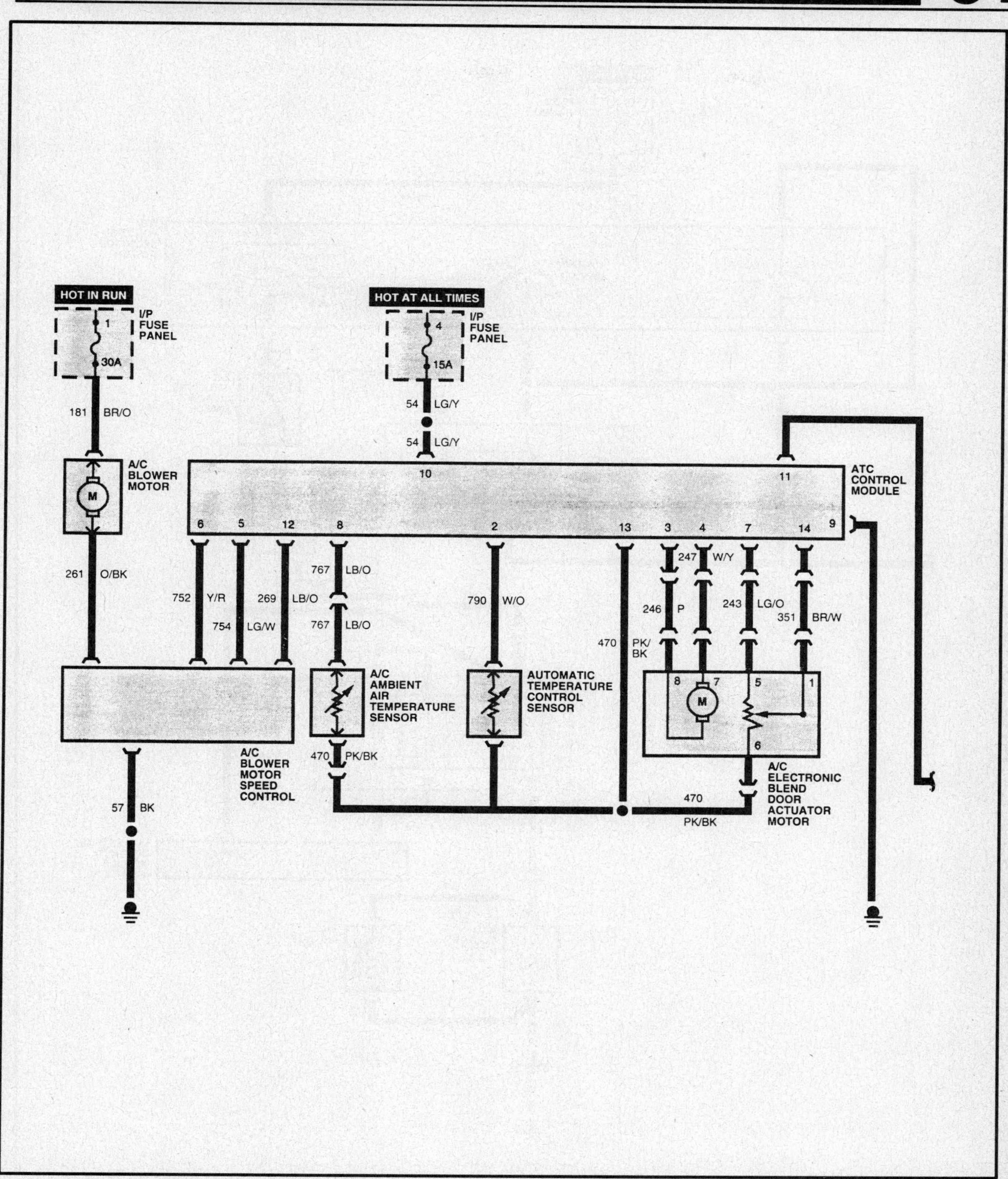

Automatic Temperature Control (ATC) wiring schematic—1994 Crown Victoria and Grand Marquis

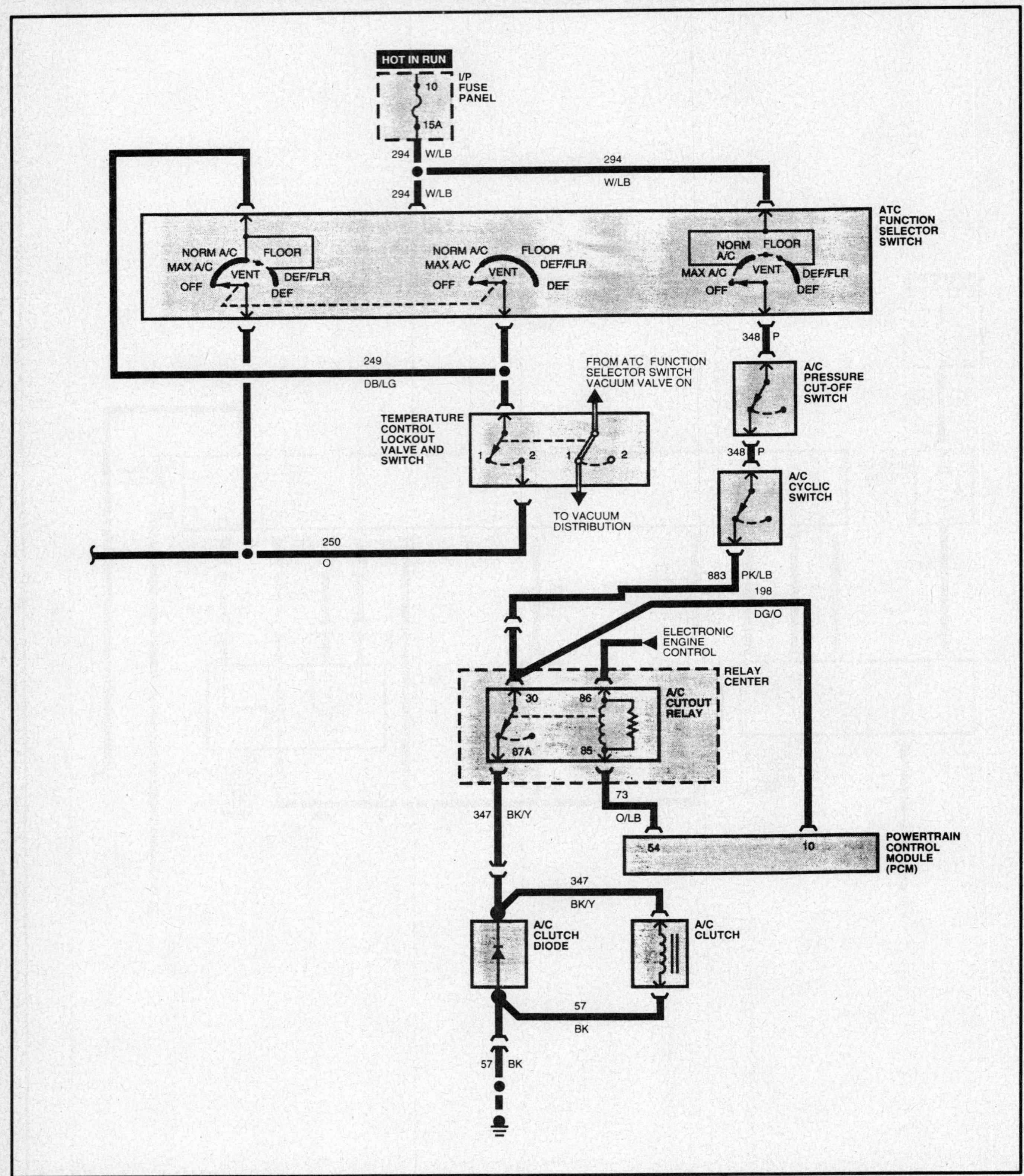

Automatic Temperature Control (ATC) wiring schematic—1994 Crown Victoria and Grand Marquis

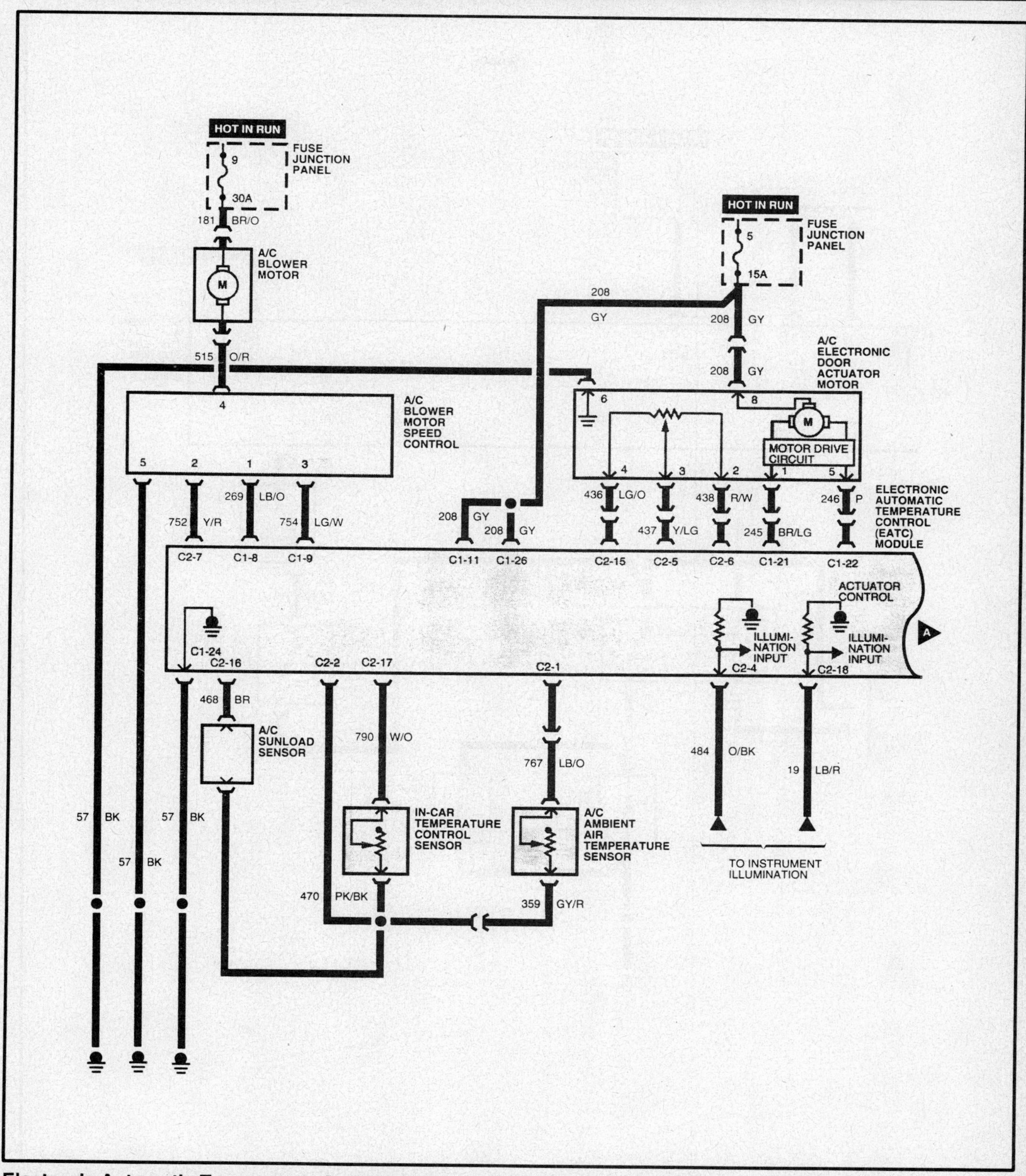

Electronic Automatic Temperature Control (EATC) wiring schematic—1995 Crown Victoria and Grand Marquis

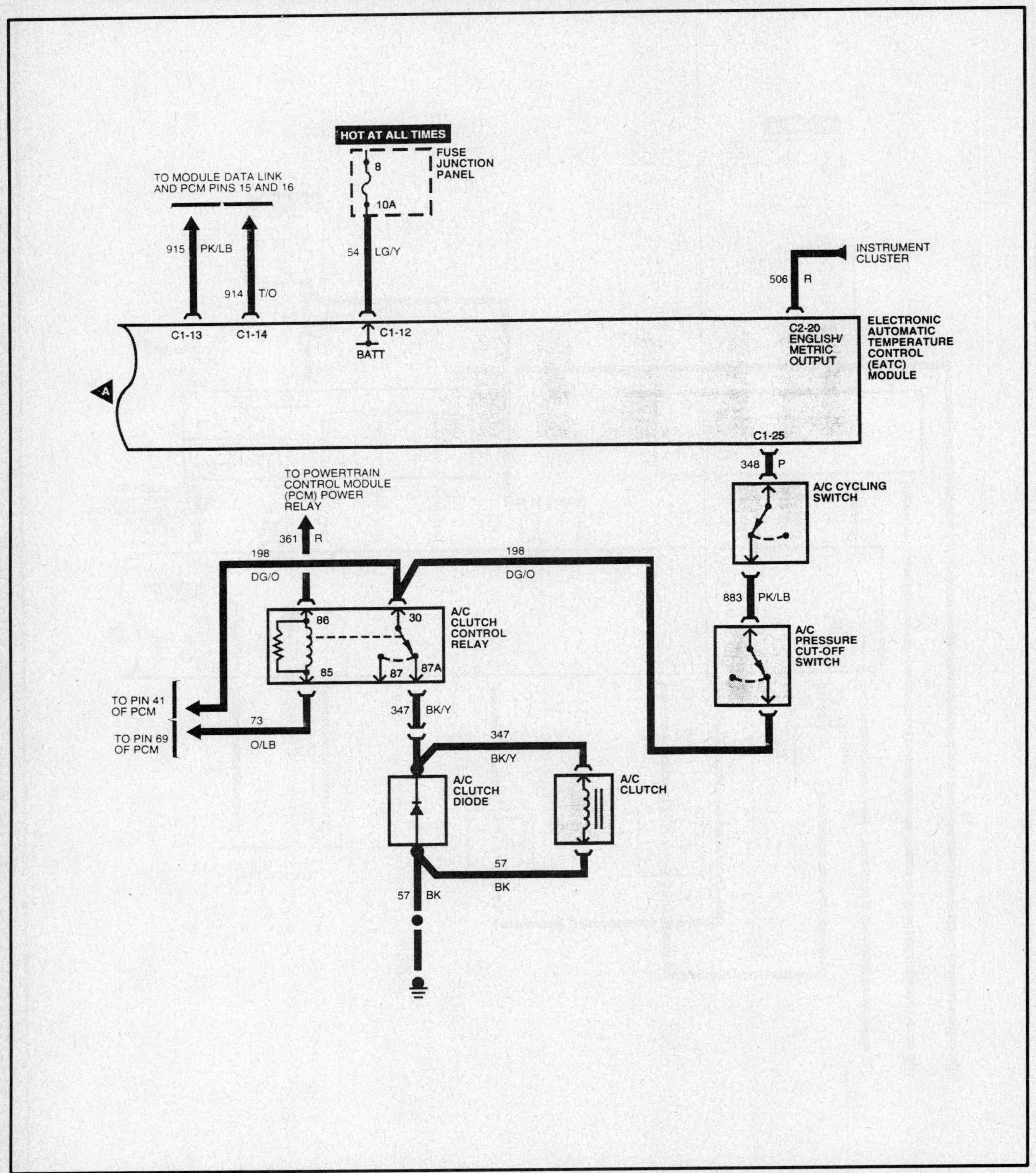

Electronic Automatic Temperature Control (EATC) wiring schematic—1995 Crown Victoria and Grand Marquis, Cont'd

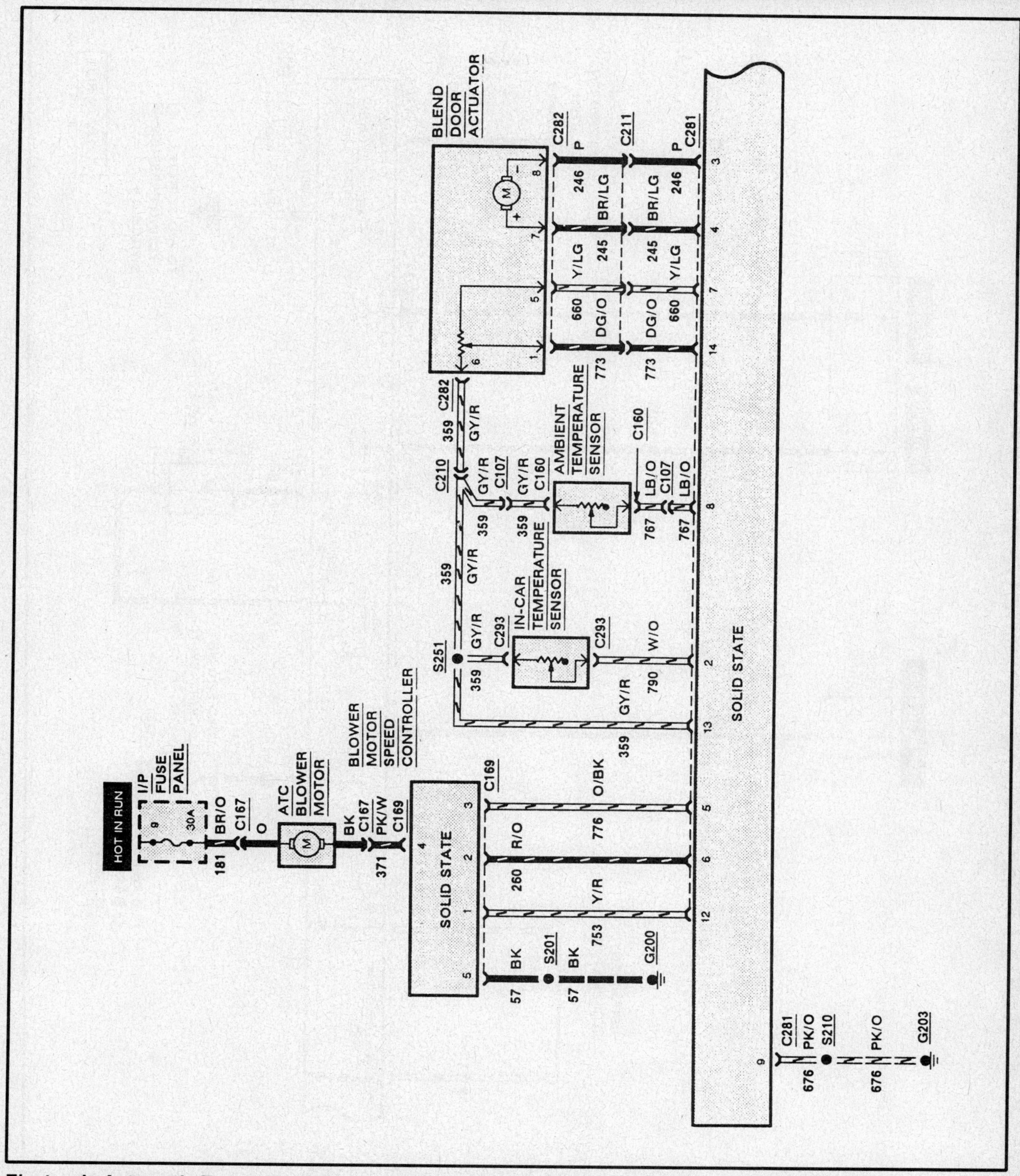

Electronic Automatic Temperature Control (EATC) system wiring schematic—1993–94 Town Car

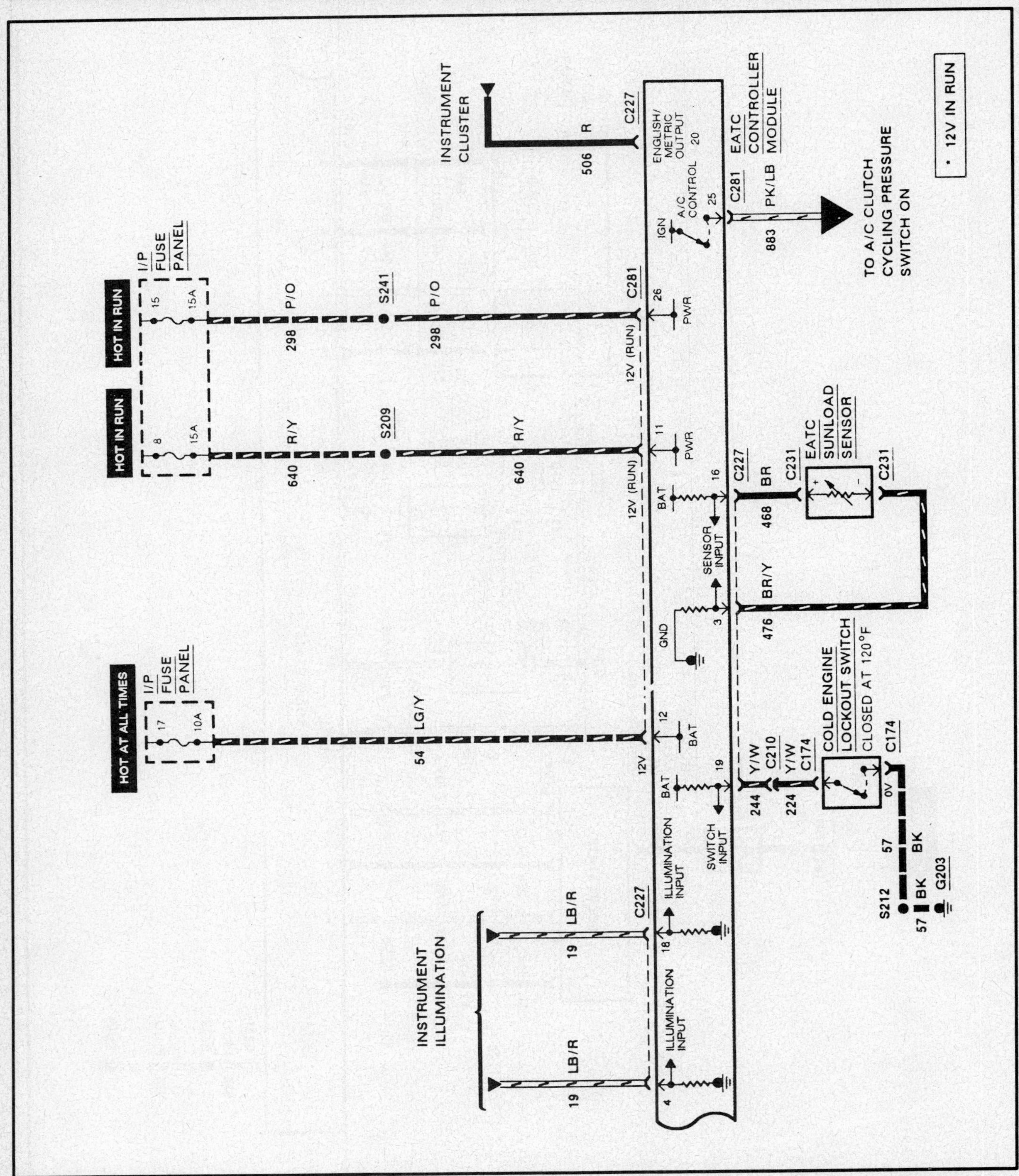

Electronic Automatic Temperature Control (EATC) system wiring schematic—1993–94 Town Car, Cont'd

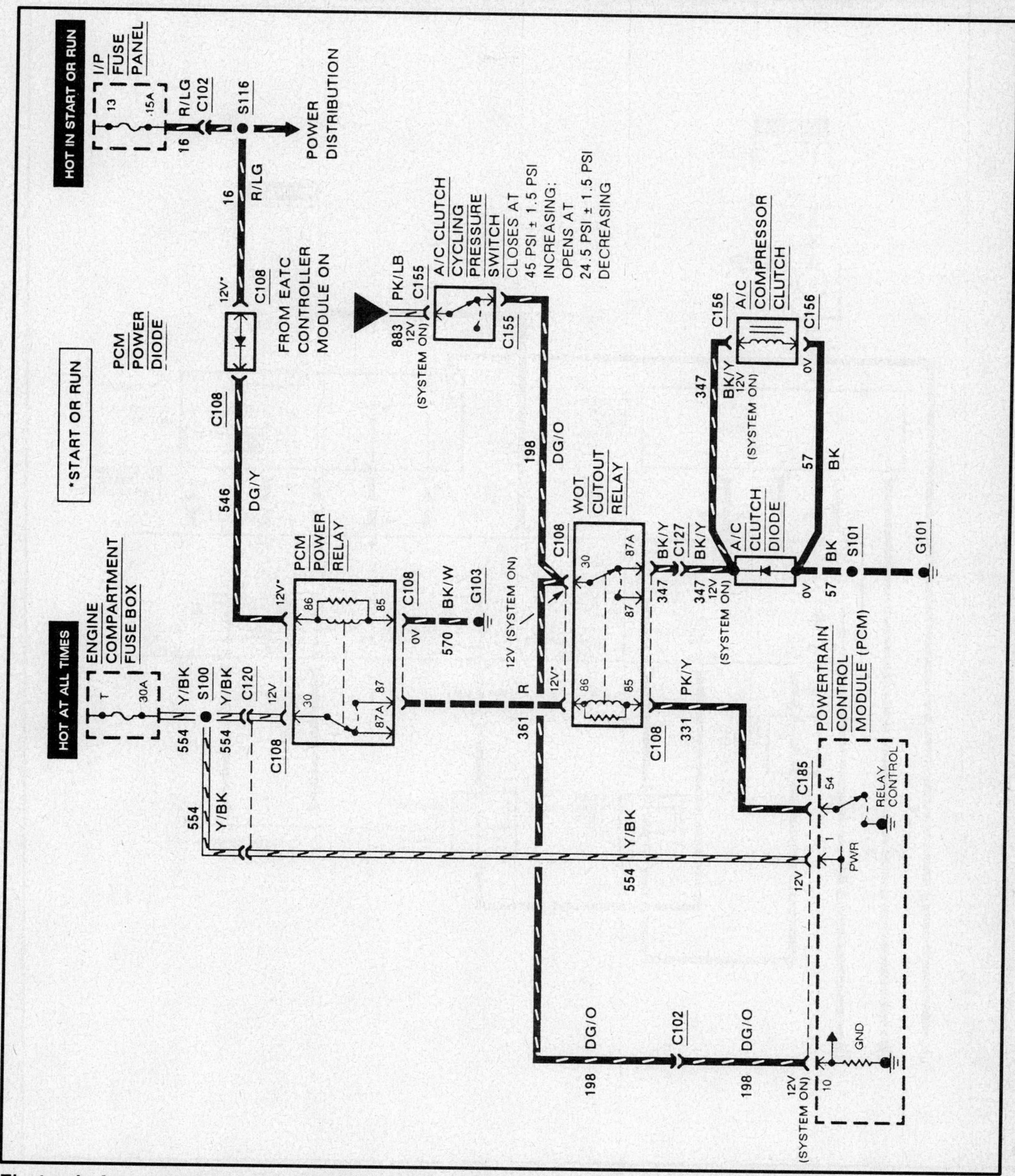

Electronic Automatic Temperature Control (EATC) system wiring schematic—1993–94 Town Car, Cont'd

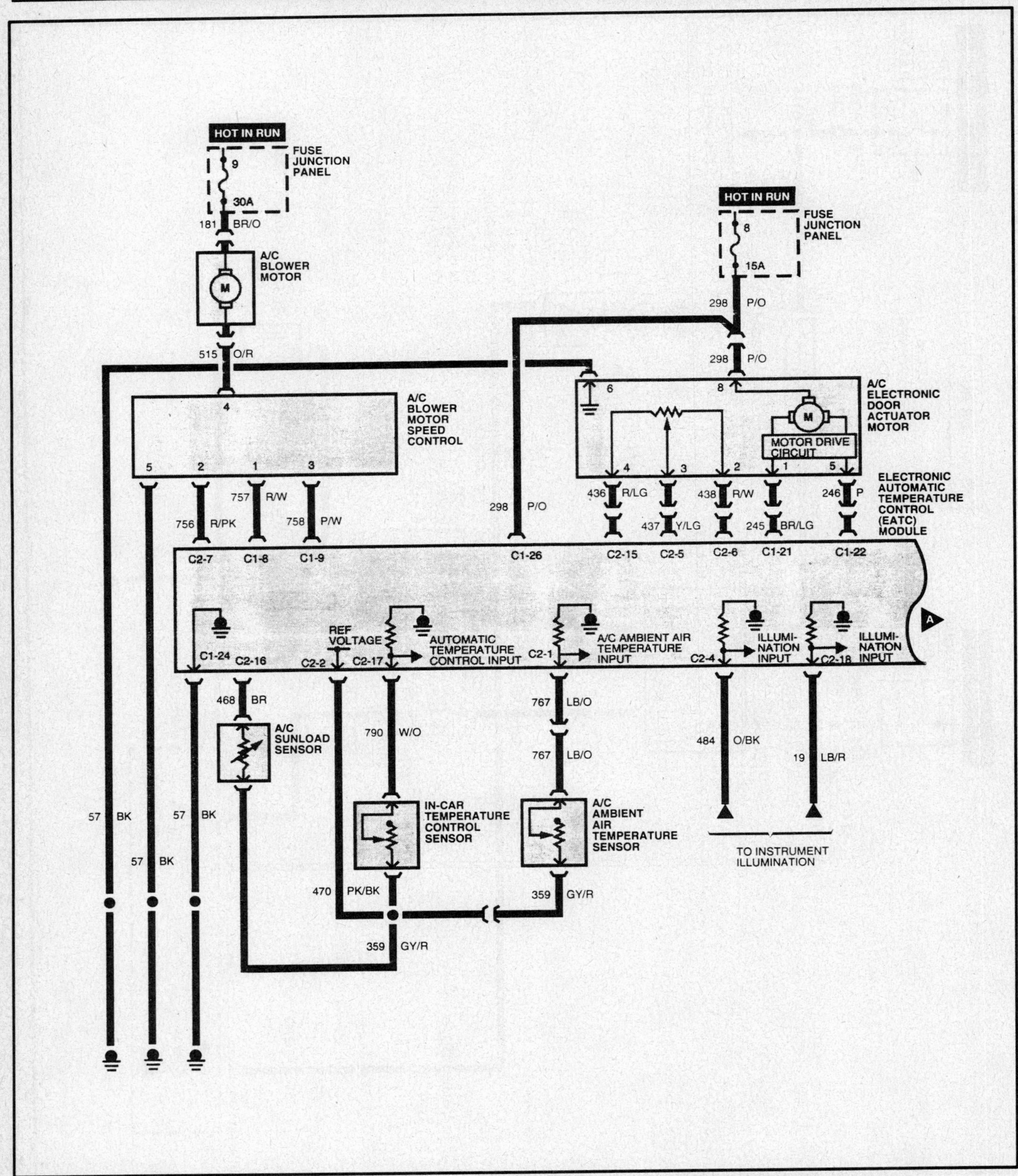

Electronic Automatic Temperature Control (EATC) system wiring schematic—1995 Town Car

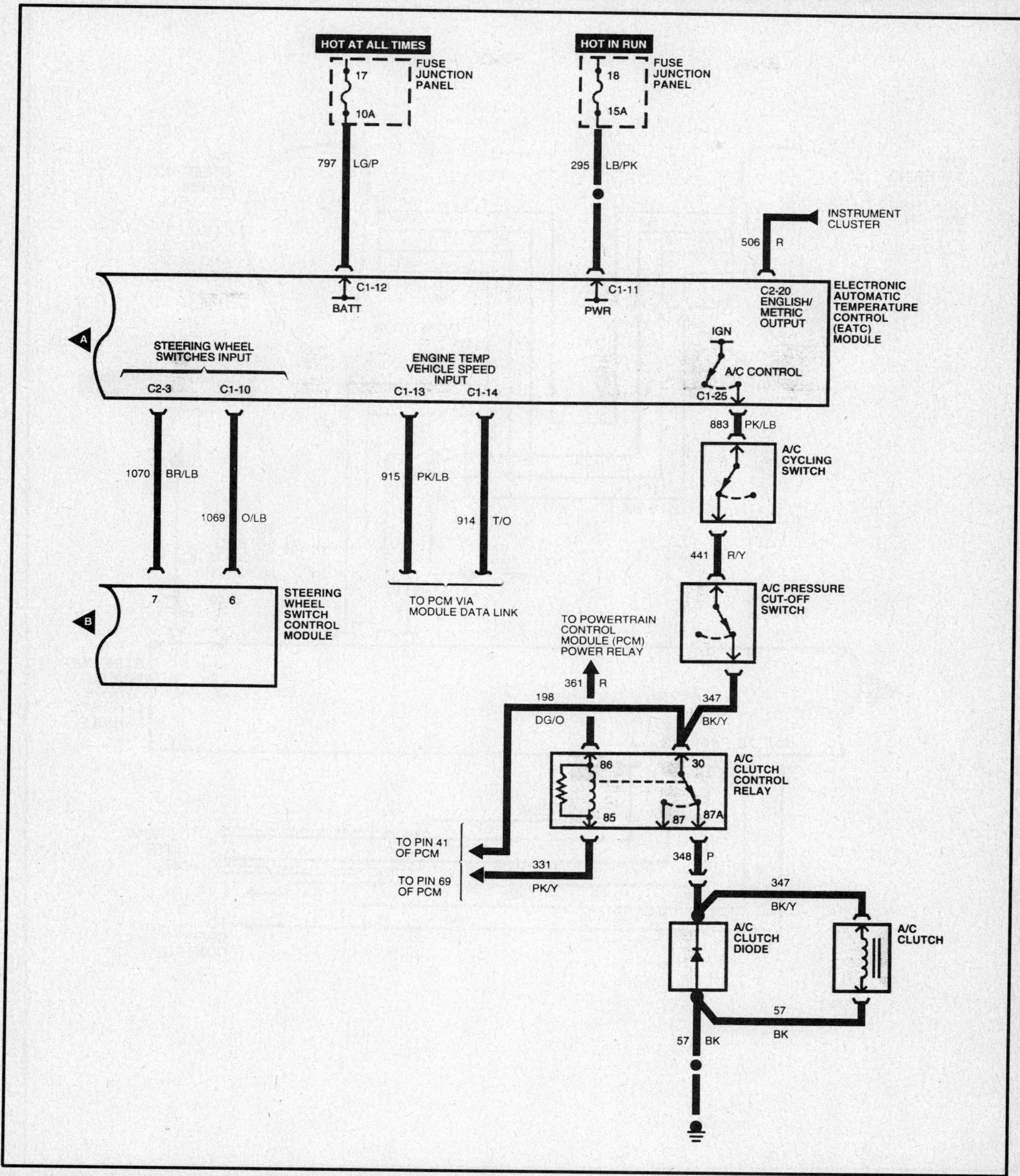

Electronic Automatic Temperature Control (EATC) system wiring schematic—1995 Town Car, Cont'd

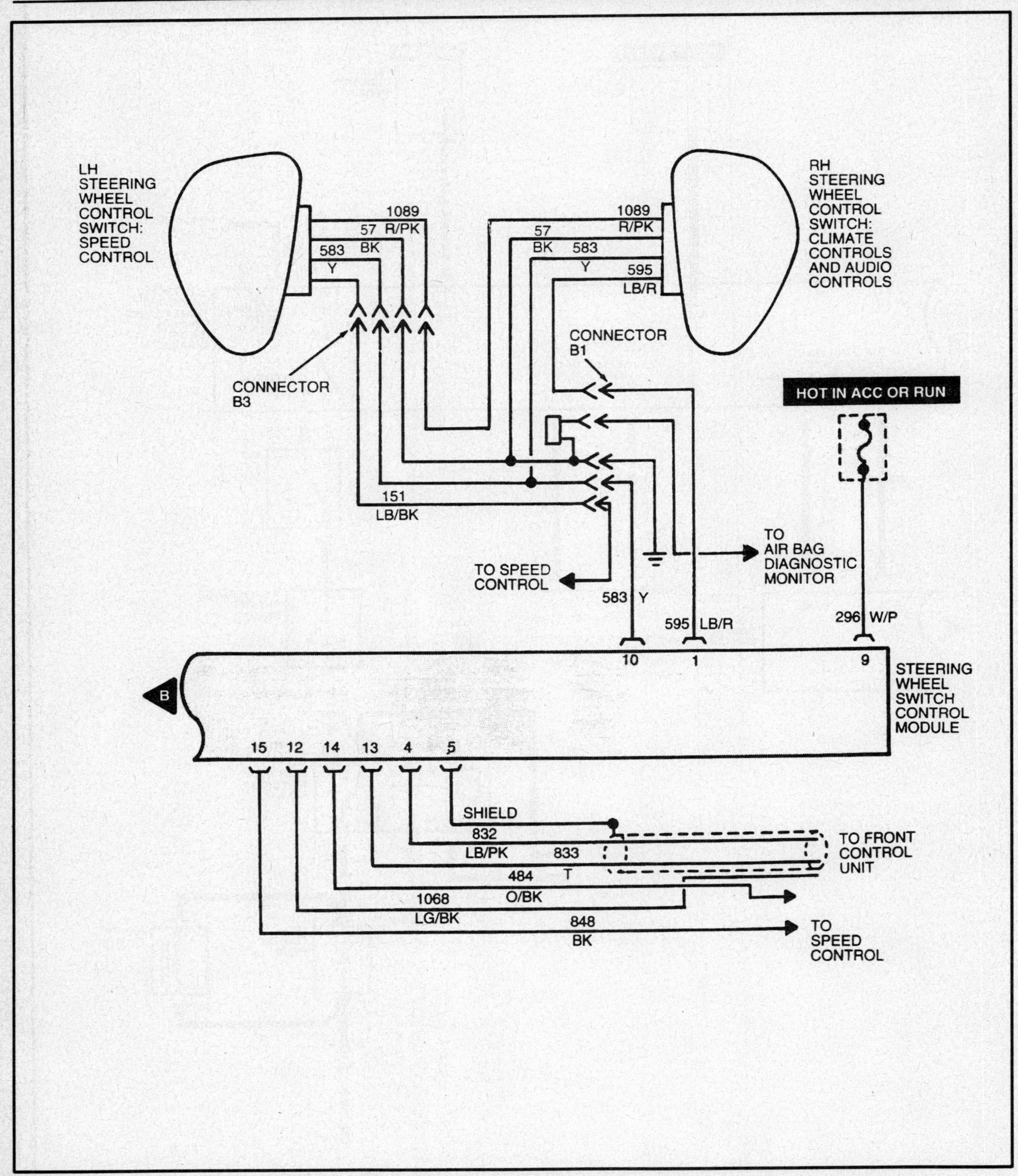

Electronic Automatic Temperature Control (EATC) system wiring schematic—1995 Town Car, Cont'd

7 FORD MOTOR COMPANY 7

AEROSTAR • BRONCO • E-SERIES • EXPLORER • F-SERIES • RANGER • VILLAGER • WINDSTAR

SPECIFICATIONS

ENGINE IDENTIFICATION

Year	Model	Engine Displacement Liters (cc)	Engine Series (ID/VIN)	Fuel System	No. of Cylinders	Engine Type
1993	Aerostar	2.3 (2295)	A	EFI	4	OHV
	Explorer	2.3 (2295)	A	EFI	4	OHV
	Ranger	2.3 (2295)	A	EFI	4	OHV
	Villager	3.0 (2971)	P	SEFI	6	OHV
	Aerostar	3.0 (2971)	U	EFI	6	OHV
	Explorer	3.0 (2971)	U	EFI	6	OHV
	Ranger	3.0 (2971)	U	EFI	6	OHV
	Aerostar	4.0 (4001)	X	EFI	6	OHV
	Explorer	4.0 (4001)	X	EFI	6	OHV
	Ranger	4.0 (4001)	X	EFI	6	OHV
	Bronco	4.9 (4918)	Y	EFI	6	OHV
	E-Series	4.9 (4918)	Y	EFI	6	OHV
	F-Series	4.9 (4918)	Y	EFI	6	OHV
	Bronco	5.0 (4943)	N	EFI	8	OHV
	E-Series	5.0 (4943)	N	EFI	8	OHV
	F-Series	5.0 (4943)	N	EFI	8	OHV
	E-Series	5.8 (5767)	H or R	MFI	8	OHV
	F-Series	5.8 (5767)	H or R	MFI	8	OHV
	E-Series	7.3 (7271)	M or C	Diesel	8	Diesel
	F-Series	7.3 (7271)	M or C	Diesel	8	Diesel
	Bronco	7.5 (7537)	G	EFI	8	OHV
	E-Series	7.5 (7537)	G	EFI	8	OHV
	F-Series	7.5 (7537)	G	EFI	8	OHV
1994	Aerostar	2.3 (2295)	A	EFI	4	OHV
	Explorer	2.3 (2295)	A	EFI	4	OHV
	Ranger	2.3 (2295)	A	EFI	4	OHV
	Aerostar	3.0 (2971)	U	EFI	6	OHV
	Explorer	3.0 (2971)	U	EFI	6	OHV
	Ranger	3.0 (2971)	U	EFI	6	OHV
	Aerostar	4.0 (4001)	X	EFI	6	OHV
	Explorer	4.0 (4001)	X	EFI	6	OHV
	Ranger	4.0 (4001)	X	EFI	6	OHV
	Bronco	4.9 (4918)	Y	MFI	6	OHV
	E-Series	4.9 (4918)	Y	MFI	6	OHV
	F-Series	4.9 (4918)	Y	MFI	6	OHV
	Bronco	5.0 (4943)	N	MFI	8	OHV
	E-Series	5.0 (4943)	N	MFI	8	OHV
	F-Series	5.0 (4943)	N	MFI	8	OHV
	E-Series	5.8 (5767)	H or R	MFI	8	OHV
	F-Series	5.8 (5767)	H or R	MFI	8	OHV

ENGINE IDENTIFICATION

Year	Model	Engine Displacement Liters (cc)	Engine Series (ID/VIN)	Fuel System	No. of Cylinders	Engine Type
1994	Bronco	7.3 (7271)	M	Diesel	8	Diesel
	E-Series	7.3 (7271)	M	Diesel	8	Diesel
	F-Series	7.3 (7271)	M	Diesel	8	Diesel
	Bronco	7.5 (7537)	G	MFI	8	OHV
	E-Series	7.5 (7537)	G	MFI	8	OHV
	F-Series	7.5 (7537)	G	MFI	8	OHV
1995	Aerostar	2.3 (2295)	A	EFI	4	OHV
	Explorer	2.3 (2295)	A	EFI	4	OHV
	Ranger	2.3 (2295)	A	EFI	4	OHV
	Aerostar	3.0 (2971)	U	EFI	6	OHV
	Explorer	3.0 (2971)	U	EFI	6	OHV
	Ranger	3.0 (2971)	U	EFI	6	OHV
	Aerostar	4.0 (4001)	X	EFI	6	OHV
	Explorer	4.0 (4001)	X	EFI	6	OHV
	Ranger	4.0 (4001)	X	EFI	6	OHV
	Bronco	4.9 (4918)	Y	EFI	6	OHV
	E-Series	4.9 (4918)	Y	EFI	6	OHV
	F-Series	4.9 (4918)	Y	EFI	6	OHV
	Bronco	5.0 (4943)	N	MFI	8	OHV
	E-Series	5.0 (4943)	N	MFI	8	OHV
	F-Series	5.0 (4943)	N	MFI	8	OHV
	E-Series	5.8 (5767)	H or R	MFI	8	OHV
	F-Series	5.8 (5767)	H or R	MFI	8	OHV
	Bronco	7.3 (7271)	M	Diesel	8	Diesel
	E-Series	7.3 (7271)	M	Diesel	8	Diesel
	F-Series	7.3 (7271)	M	Diesel	8	Diesel
	Bronco	7.5 (7537)	G	MFI	8	OHV
	E-Series	7.5 (7537)	G	MFI	8	OHV
	F-Series	7.5 (7537)	G	MFI	8	OHV
	Villager	3.0 (2972)	P	SEFI	6	OHV
	E-Series	7.3 (7271)	F	DI Turbo	8	Diesel
	Windstar	3.0 (2971)	U	MFI	6	OHV
	Windstar	3.8 (3798)	U	SEFI	6	OHV

OHV–Overhead Valves
EFI–Electronic Fuel Injection
SEFI–Sequential Electronic Fuel Injection
MFI–Multiport Fuel Injection
DI Turbo–Direct Injection Turbo

REFRIGERANT CAPACITIES

Year	Model	Refrigerant (oz.)	Oil (fl. oz.)	Compressor Type
1993	Aerostar	46 ④	7 ①	FX-15
	Explorer	32	7	FX-15
	Ranger	32	7	FX-15
	Villager	36 ⑤	7 ⑥	FX-15
	Bronco	44	7	FX-15
	F-Series (exc. diesel)	44	7	FX-15
	Econoline	55 ③	10	FS-6
	F-Series (diesel)	55 ③	10	FS-6
1994	Aerostar	46 ④	7 ①	FS-10
	Explorer	26	7	FS-10
	Ranger	22	7	FS-10
	Villager	32 ②	7 ①	FS-10
	Bronco	33	7	FS-10
	F-Series (exc. diesel)	33	7	FX-15
	E-Series	48 ⑧	7 ①	FS-10
	F-Series (diesel)	33	7	FS-10
1995	Aerostar	24	9	FS-10
	Explorer	26 ⑨	9	FS-10
	Ranger	22	9	FS-10
	Bronco	33	7	FX-15
	F-Series	33	7	FX-15
	E-Series with 7.5L and 7.3L (diesel)	55 ③	7 ①	FS-10
	E-Series with 4.9L, 5.0L and 5.8L	44 ⑧	7 ⑥	FS-10
	Villager	32 ②	7 ⑥	FS-10
	Windstar	44 ⑤	9 ⑦	FS-10

① 10 oz. with auxiliary system
② 52 oz. with auxiliary system
③ 71 oz. with auxiliary system
④ 61 oz. with auxiliary system
⑤ 56 oz. with auxiliary system
⑥ 10 oz. with auxiliary system
⑦ 13 oz. with auxiliary system
⑧ 64 oz. with auxiliary system
⑨ 40 oz. with auxiliary system

AIR CONDITIONING BELT TENSION

Year	Model	Engine Liters (cc)	Belt Type	Specifications ① New (lbs.)	Specifications ① Used (lbs.)
1993	Ranger	2.3 (2295)	Poly-V	150–190 ②	140–160 ②
	Villager	3.0 (2971)	Poly-V	150–170	105–145
	Aerostar	3.0 (2971)	Poly-V	150–190 ②	140–160 ②
	Ranger	3.0 (2971)	Poly-V	150–190 ②	140–160 ②

AIR CONDITIONING BELT TENSION

Year	Model	Engine Liters (cc)	Belt Type	Specifications ①	
				New (lbs.)	Used (lbs.)
1993	Aerostar	4.0 (4001)	Poly-V	②	②
	Explorer	4.0 (4001)	Poly-V	②	②
	Ranger	4.0 (4001)	Poly-V	②	②
	Bronco	4.9 (4918)	Poly-V	②	②
	E-Series	4.9 (4918)	Poly-V	②	②
	F-Series	4.9 (4918)	Poly-V	②	②
	Bronco	5.0 (4943)	Poly-V	②	②
	E-Series	5.0 (4943)	Poly-V	②	②
	F-Series	5.0 (4943)	Poly-V	②	②
	Bronco	5.8 (5767)	Poly-V	②	②
	E-Series	5.8 (5767)	Poly-V	②	②
	F-Series	5.8 (5767)	Poly-V	②	②
	E-Series	7.3 (7271)	V-Belt	140–180	95–115
	F-Series	7.3 (7271)	V-Belt	140–180	95–115
	E-Series	7.5 (7537)	Poly-V	②	②
	F-Series	7.5 (7537)	Poly-V	②	②
1994	Ranger	2.3 (2295)	Poly-V	160–190 ②	140–160 ②
	Villager	3.0 (2971)	Poly-V	150–170	125–145
	Aerostar	3.0 (2971)	Poly-V	140–190 ②	140–160 ②
	Ranger	3.0 (2971)	Poly-V	160–190 ②	140–160 ②
	Aerostar	4.0 (4001)	Poly-V	②	②
	Explorer	4.0 (4001)	Poly-V	②	②
	Ranger	4.0 (4001)	Poly-V	②	②
	Bronco	4.9 (4918)	Poly-V	②	②
	E-Series	4.9 (4918)	Poly-V	②	②
	F-Series	4.9 (4918)	Poly-V	②	②
	Bronco	5.0 (4943)	Poly-V	②	②
	E-Series	5.0 (4943)	Poly-V	②	②
	F-Series	5.0 (4943)	Poly-V	②	②
	Bronco	5.8 (5767)	Poly-V	②	②
	E-Series	5.8 (5767)	Poly-V	②	②
	F-Series	5.8 (5767)	Poly-V	②	②
	E-Series	7.3 (7271)	V-Belt	140–180	95–115
	F-Series	7.3 (7271)	V-Belt	140–180	95–115
	E-Series	7.5 (7537)	Poly-V	②	②
	F-Series	7.5 (7537)	Poly-V	②	②
1995	Ranger	2.3 (2295)	Poly-V	150–190 ②	140–160 ②
	Aerostar	3.0 (2971)	Poly-V	150–190 ②	140–160 ②
	Ranger	3.0 (2971)	Poly-V	150–190 ②	140–160 ②
	Aerostar	4.0 (4001)	Poly-V	②	②
	Explorer	4.0 (4001)	Poly-V	②	②
	Ranger	4.0 (4001)	Poly-V	②	②
	Bronco	4.9 (4918)	Poly-V	②	②

AIR CONDITIONING BELT TENSION

Year	Model	Engine Liters (cc)	Belt Type	Specifications ①	
				New (lbs.)	Used (lbs.)
1995	E-Series	4.9 (4918)	Poly-V	②	②
	F-Series	4.9 (4918)	Poly-V	②	②
	Bronco	5.0 (4943)	Poly-V	②	②
	E-Series	5.0 (4943)	Poly-V	②	②
	F-Series	5.0 (4943)	Poly-V	②	②
	Bronco	5.8 (5767)	Poly-V	②	②
	E-Series	5.8 (5767)	Poly-V	②	②
	F-Series	5.8 (5767)	Poly-V	②	②
	E-Series	7.3 (7271)	V-Belt	140–180	95–115
	F-Series	7.3 (7271)	V-Belt	140–180	95–115
	E-Series	7.5 (7537)	Poly-V	②	②
	F-Series	7.5 (7537)	Poly-V	②	②
	Villager	3.0 (2972)	Poly-V	150–170	125–145
	Windstar	3.0 (2972)	Poly-V	150–190	140–160
	Windstar	3.8 (3798)	Poly-V	160–190	130–160

① Readings are tension in pounds, using suitable belt tension gauge; check at mid-point between compressor and crankshaft pulley.

② If equipped with automatic tension; no adjustment required. Where readings are given, they are standard to judge whether belt needs replacement if tightening adjustor bolt does not bring tension into limits.

SYSTEM DESCRIPTION

General Information

The air conditioning system used on Ford trucks is the fixed orifice tube-cycling clutch type. The system components consist of the compressor, magnetic clutch, condenser, evaporator, suction accumulator/drier and the necessary connecting refrigerant lines. The fixed orifice tube assembly is the restriction between the high and low pressure liquid refrigerant and meters the flow of liquid refrigerant into the evaporator core. Evaporator temperature is controlled by sensing the pressure within the evaporator with the clutch cycling pressure switch. The pressure switch controls compressor operation as necessary to maintain the evaporator pressure within specified limits.

All models, except Villager, use a combination of vacuum and cable connections to operate the system air doors, controlling function and temperature. Villager uses a complete electric system, with wiring connections from the control panel to the electrical door actuators.

Aerostar, Econoline Vans, Villager, and Windstar can be optionally equipped with a rear auxiliary system. In addition to the components listed above, vehicles equipped with the rear auxiliary system will also be equipped with an additional evaporator as well as the necessary connecting refrigerant lines.

NOTE: The rear auxiliary air conditioning system on Econoline Vans, Villager, and Windstar are equipped with an expansion valve while the Aerostar uses a fixed orifice tube to regulate the flow of refrigerant into the evaporator.

Service Valve Location

The air conditioning system has a high pressure (discharge) and a low pressure (suction) gauge port valve. These are Schrader valves which provide access to both the high and low pressure sides of the system for service hoses and a manifold gauge set or recycling/charging station so system pressures can be read. The high pressure gauge port valve is located on the compressor discharge manifold (Aerostar) or on the discharge line (except Aerostar). The low pressure gauge port valve is located on the suction accumulator/drier inlet line (exc. Econoline) or on the low pressure suction line near the cowl (Econoline).

An adapter set of fittings may be required to connect a charging station hoses to the service ports.

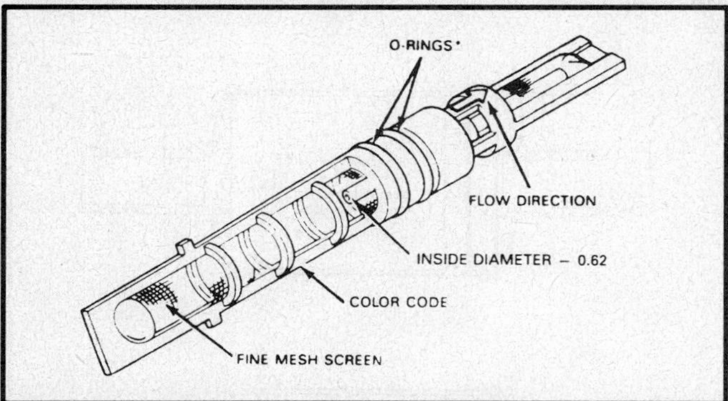

Internal view of fixed orifice tube—typical all models

System Discharging

The manufacturer recommends only the use of a refrigerant recovery, recycling, evacuation and recharging station to meet the demands of environmental concerns. Use only equipment meeting SAE standards J1991 for this purpose. Always follow the equipment manufacturer's instructions for using this equipment. The use of refrigerant recovery systems and recycling stations makes possible the recovery and reuse of refrigerant after contaminants and moisture have been removed. The reuse of refrigerant will minimize the discharge of ozone depleting chlorofluorocarbons into the atmosphere.

System Flushing

Except 1994–95 Villager

A refrigerant system can become badly contaminated for a number of reasons:

- The compressor may have failed due to damage or wear.
- The compressor may have been run for some time with a severe leak or an opening in the system.
- The system may have been damaged by a collision and left open for some time.
- The system may not have been cleaned properly after a previous failure.
- The system may have been operated for a time with water or moisture in it.

A badly contaminated system contains water, carbon and other decomposition products. When this condition exists, the system must be flushed with a special flushing agent using equipment designed specially for this purpose.

Some refrigerants are better suited to flushing than others. Neither Refrigerant-12 (R-12) nor Refrigerant-114 (R-114) is suitable for flushing a system because of low vaporization (boiling) points: –21.6°F (–29.8°C) for R-12 and 38.4°F (3.5°C) for R-114. Both refrigerants would be difficult to use and would not do a sufficient job because of the tendency to vaporize rather than remain in a liquid state, especially in high ambient temperatures.

Refrigerant-11 (R-11) and Refrigerant-113 (R-113) are much better suited for use with special flushing equipment. Both have rather high vaporization points: 74.7°F (23.7°C) for R-11 and 117.6°F (47.5°C) for R-113. Both refrigerants also have low closed container pressures. This reduces the danger of an accidental system discharge due to a ruptured hose or fitting. R-113 will do the best job and is recommended as a flushing refrigerant. Both R-11 and R-113 require a propellant or pump type flushing equipment due to their low closed container pressures. R-12 can be used as a propellant with either flushing refrigerant. R-11 is available in pressurized containers. Although not recommended for regular use, it may become necessary to use R-11 if special flushing equipment is not available. R-11 is more toxic than other refrigerants and should be handled with extra care.

1994–95 Villager

CAUTION

Follow all refrigerant system safety and service precautions.

NOTE: When A/C compressor replacement is caused by internal A/C compressor failure, the A/C system will become contaminated. To remove contamination from the A/C system, it is necessary to replace the suction accumulator/drier and the A/C evaporator core orifice, and to follow the following filtering procedure. If equipped with auxiliary A/C, the auxiliary A/C evaporator filter must also be replaced.

Two A/C service kits have been released to provide the necessary equipment and information to perform the A/C system filtering procedure. Filter kits with the service part number suffix "A" are to be used on vehicles that have a nylon lined evaporator to compressor suction line between the suction accumulator/drier and the A/C compressor. Filter kits with the service part number suffix "B" are for vehicles with rubber lined hose.

1. To determine that the A/C compressor has failed and must be replaced, remove the A/C evaporator core orifice and liquid line, if necessary. Look for a dirty A/C evaporator core orifice and/or a liquid line containing black refrigerant oil and particles.
2. Remove the damaged A/C compressor and drain the oil into a calibrated container. Record the amount.
3. The proper amount of refrigerant oil must be added to the new A/C compressor before it can be installed. Drain the oil from the new A/C compressor.

NOTE: It will be necessary to transfer the A/C clutch from the old A/C compressor to the new A/C compressor.

4. Add clean refrigerant oil to the new A/C compressor in the same amount that was removed from the old unit, plus an additional 1 oz. (30 ml) of new refrigerant oil.
5. Install the new A/C compressor. Be sure the A/C compressor mounting bolts are tightened to the proper specification. Check the tension of the drive belt.
6. Determine the type of evaporator to compressor suction line with which you are working. To do this, cut the hose into 2 pieces (make the cut closer to the A/C compressor than the suction accumulator/drier) and measure the hose wall thickness. Rubber lined hose has a wall thickness of 1/4 inch (6mm) and nylon lined hose has a wall thickness of 1/8 inch (3mm).
7. Obtain the proper service kit for the vehicle being serviced. Filter kits with the service part number suffix "A" are to be used on vehicles with a nylon lined evaporator to compressor suction line. Filter kits with the service part number suffix "B" are for vehicles with a rubber lined evaporator to compressor suction line. The label on the filter shows with which hose it is to be used.
8. Remove a length of evaporator to compressor suction line to accommodate the evaporator to compressor suction line filter and install the filter using the hose clamps provided with the kit. Be sure the filter is correctly oriented for refrigerant system flow. Check the label on the filter. On the filter for nylon lined hose, install O-ring seals (two on each filter tube, being sure they are properly seated in the grooves on the tube). Tighten the hose clamps securely.

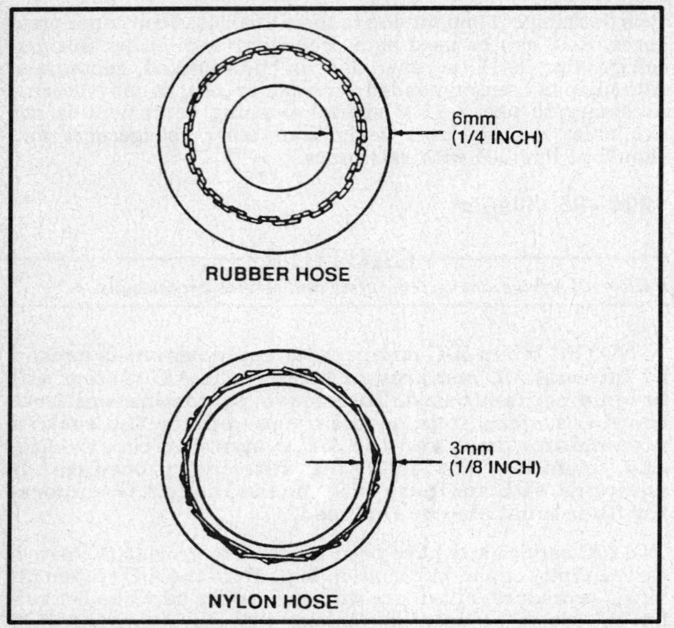

Suction line hose

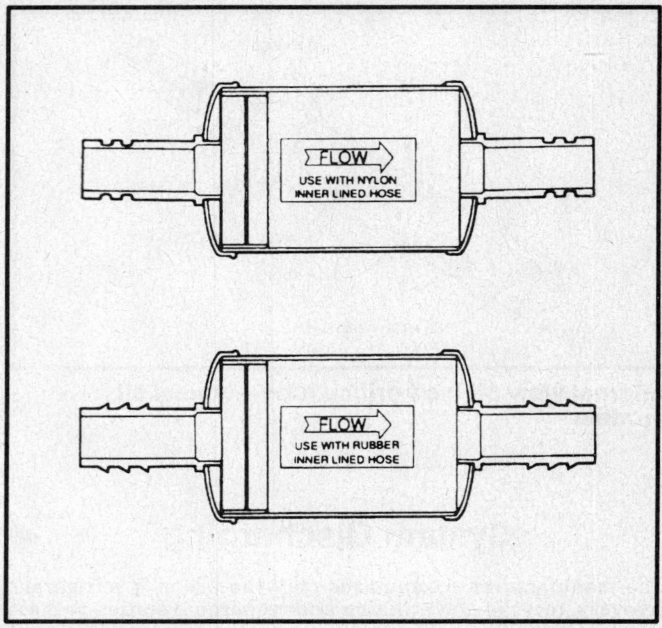

Suction line filter

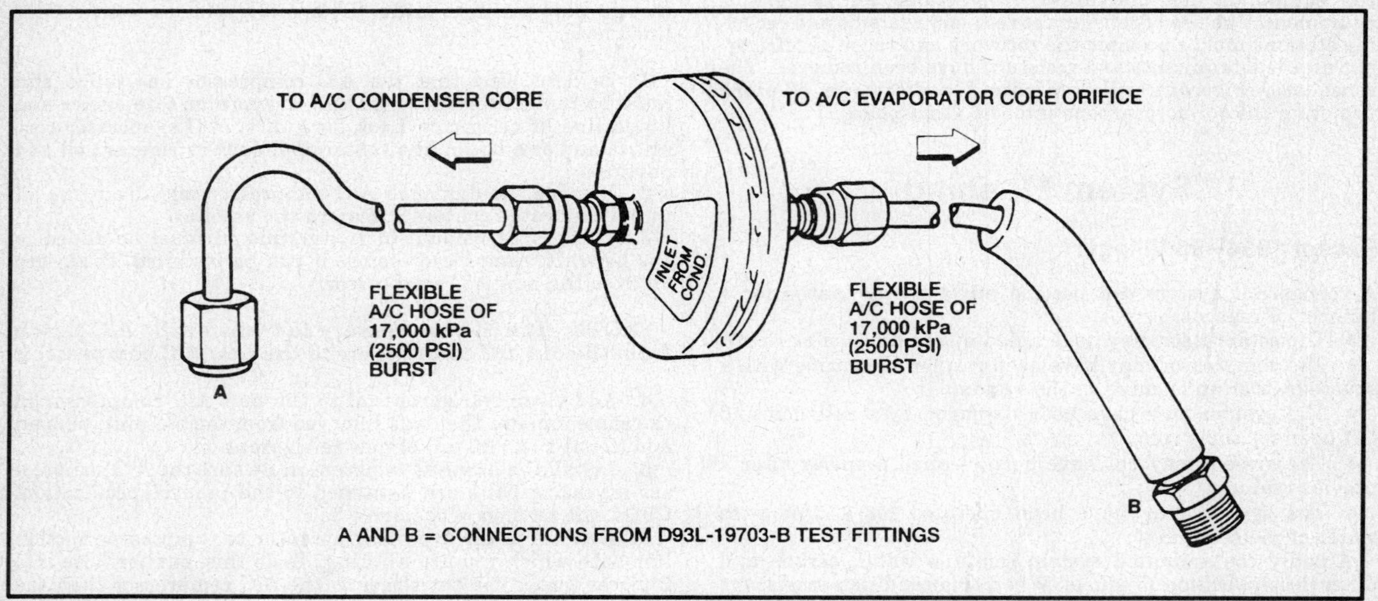

Pancake filter

9. Install a new A/C evaporator core orifice.
10. Install a pancake filter in the condenser to evaporator tube between the A/C condenser core and the A/C evaporator core orifice. Be sure the filter inlet is toward the A/C condenser core. Connections can be made using Test Adapter Set D93L-19703-B or equivalent and flexible refrigerant hose of 2500 psi (17,000 kPa) burst rating. Individual fittings are also available.
11. Evacuate, charge, and leak test the system.
12. Check all refrigerant system hoses, lines and the positioning of the newly installed filters to be sure they do not interfere with other engine compartment components. If necessary, use tie straps to make adjustments.
13. Provide adequate air flow to the front of the vehicle (with a fan, if necessary) and turn the A/C switch **ON**. Set the blower motor switch operation on **HIGH** and the temperature control at **FULL COOL**. Start the engine and let at idle briefly. Make sure the A/C system is operating properly.
14. Gradually bring the engine speed up to 1200 rpm by running it at lower rpms for short periods (first at 800 rpm, then at 1000 rpm). Set the engine at 1200 rpm and run it for an hour with the A/C system operating.
15. Stop the engine.
16. Allow the engine to cool sufficiently to remove the fittings, flexible hoses, and pancake filter from the condenser to evaporator tube. It will be necessary to discharge the system first.
17. Discard the pancake filter. It can be used one time only.
18. Reconnect the condenser to evaporator tube into the system.

19. Evacuate, charge, and leak test the system. Make any necessary adjustments.
20. Check the operation of the system in all models.

System Evacuating

1. Follow the equipment manufacturer's instructions for evacuating the system.
2. Evacuate the system until the low pressure gauge reads at least 25 in. Hg (84kPA) of vacuum. Continue to operate vacuum pump for at least 15 more minutes. If any part of the system has been replaced prior to this operation, continue the pump for an additional 20–30 minutes.
3. When pumping is complete, close the service gauge valves on the air conditioning station and turn OFF the vacuum pump. Watch the low side gauge to be sure vacuum holds for at least 5 minutes with no leak down.
4. If vacuum has held, continue with charging the system. If vacuum bled down, a leak is present and must be found and repaired before continuing. Check all hose, line and component fittings, hose and line conditions, and also the Schrader valves for leaks. After repairs, repeat system evacuating procedure.

System Charging

NOTE: Manufacturer recommends using only a charging cylinder or charging station and recommends against using small cans of refrigerant to recharge the system. Proper amounts of refrigerant are critical to proper system operation and it is difficult to accurately control the charge being introduced into the system.

1. With charging station still attached after evacuating the system follow equipment manufacturer's instructions for recharging, noting the appropriate capacity of the system.
2. Open the station's low side for 1994–95 Villager. Open the high side valve to allow refrigerant to enter the system or as instructed by equipment manufacturer.
3. When no more refrigerant is being drawn into the system, for 1994–95 Villager, close the high side valve before starting engine, start the engine and move the function selector lever to the **NORM/A/C** position on Aerostar and Windstar, the **VENT/HEAT/A/C** position on Bronco II, Explorer and Ranger or the **MAX A/C** position on Bronco, E Series and F Series. Move the blower switch to **HI** to draw the remaining refrigerant into the system. Continue to add refrigerant to the system until the specified weight of refrigerant is in the system. Then close the charging station valves.
4. Operate the system until pressures stabilize to verify normal operation and system pressures.
5. In high ambient temperatures, it may be necessary to operate a high volume fan positioned to blow air through the radiator and condenser to aid in cooling the engine and prevent excessive refrigerant system pressures.
6. When charging is completed and system operating pressures are normal, disconnect the charging station from the vehicle. Install the protective caps on the service gauge port valves.

SYSTEM COMPONENTS

Radiator

REMOVAL AND INSTALLATION

Aerostar, Explorer and Ranger

1. Disconnect the negative battery cable.
2. Drain the cooling system by removing the radiator cap and attaching a 3/8 in. I.D. hose to the drain nipple, located at the lower rear corner of the radiator tank. Then, open the drain and allow the coolant to flow through the hose into a suitable container.
3. Remove the rubber overflow tube from the radiator and store it aside.
4. Remove the shroud's 2 upper attaching screws. Lift the shroud out of the lower retaining clips and drape it on the fan.
5. Loosen the upper and lower hose clamps at the radiator and remove the hoses from the radiator connectors.
6. If equipped with an automatic transmission, disconnect the 2 transmission cooling lines from the oil cooler fittings on the radiator. The intermediate flare fittings should remain installed. Disconnect the transmission cooler tube support bracket from the bottom flange of the radiator by removing the screw.
7. Remove the 2 radiator upper attaching screws. Tilt the radiator back approximately 1 in. and lift directly upward, clear radiator support and the cooling fan.
8. If either hose is to be replaced, loosen the clamp at the engine end and slip the hose off the connections with a twisting motion.
9. Remove the radiator lower support rubber insulators.

To install:

10. Position the radiator lower support rubber insulators onto the lower support.
11. If either hose has been replaced, position the hose on the engine with the index arrow in line with the mark on the fitting at the engine.
12. Position the radiator into the engine compartment to the radiator support, being careful to clear the fan. Make sure the mounting pins on the bottoms of both tanks are inserted into the holes in the lower support rubber insulators and that the radiator is firmly seated on the insulators. Attach the overflow hose to the uppermost nipple on the filler neck.
13. Install the upper attaching bolts to attach the radiator to the radiator support. Tighten to 12–20 ft. lbs. (17–27 Nm).
14. If equipped with an automatic transmission, perform the following procedure:
    - Loosely connect the 2 transmission cooling lines to the radiator oil cooler fittings.
    - Connect the transmission cooler tube support bracket to the bottom flange of the radiator with the attaching screw.
    - Attach the cooler tubes onto the plastic clip on the tube support bracket.
    - Tighten the cooler tube nuts attaching the cooler tube to the radiator connectors. Tighten the tube nuts to 12–18 ft. lbs. (16–24 Nm).
15. Attach the radiator upper hose to the radiator. Position the hose on the radiator connector so the stripe on the hose is at the 12 o'clock position. Slide the compression clamp into it's installed position.
16. Position the lower hose to the radiator with the stripe on the hose at the 6 o'clock position. Slide the compression clamp into it's installed position.
17. Position the shroud in the lower retainer clips and attach the top of the shroud to the radiator with 2 screw and washer assemblies. Attach the overflow hose is attached to the uppermost nipple on the filler neck.

18. Close the radiator draincock and fill the cooling system.
19. Connect the negative battery cable. Operate the engine for 15 minutes and check for leaks. Recheck the coolant level.

Bronco, E-Series and F-Series

1. Disconnect the negative battery cable.
2. Drain the cooling system by removing the radiator cap and opening the draincock located at the lower rear corner of the radiator tank. To prevent coolant loss, slip a hose on the draincock and drain the coolant into a clean container.
3. Remove the rubber overflow tube from the coolant recovery bottle and detach it from the shroud, if necessary.
4. Remove the shroud's 2 or 4 attaching bolts, lift the shroud back and drape it on the fan.
5. Loosen the upper and lower hose clamps at the radiator and remove the hoses from the radiator connectors.
6. If equipped with an automatic transmission, disconnect the 2 automatic transmission oil cooling lines from the radiator fittings.
7. If equipped with the E4OD automatic transmission, disconnect the heated water bypass hose, located directly below the overflow nipple (F-Series gasoline engines), on the radiator lower tank (E-Series) or on the radiator filler neck (F-Series diesel engines).
8. Remove the 2 or 4 radiator attaching bolts. Tilt the radiator back approximately 1 in. and lift directly upward, clear of the radiator support.
9. If either hose is to be replaced, loosen the clamp at the engine end and slip the hose off the connection with a twisting motion.
10. On Bronco and F-Series equipped with gasoline engines, remove the radiator lower support rubber pads.

To install:

11. On Bronco and F-Series equipped with gasoline engines, position the radiator lower support pads to the lower frame.
12. If either hose has been replaced, install on the engine and tighten the clamps to 20–30 inch lbs. (2.25–3.38 Nm).
13. Position the radiator into the engine compartment to the radiator support, being careful to clear the fan. On E-Series and 7.3L diesel equipped vehicles, install the 4 mounting bolts and tighten to 10–15 ft. lbs. (14–20 Nm). On Bronco and F-Series equipped with gasoline engines, install the 2 upper radiator attaching bolts and tighten to 8–11 ft. lbs. (11–14 Nm).
14. If equipped with an automatic transmission, connect the oil cooling lines to the radiator connectors.
15. Attach the upper and lower radiator hoses and clamps.
16. If equipped with the E4OD automatic transmission, attach the heated water bypass hose.
17. On E-Series and 7.3L diesel equipped vehicles, position the shroud to the radiator and attach with 4 bolts. Tighten the bolts to 4–6 ft. lbs. (5.4–8 Nm). On Bronco and F-Series equipped with gasoline engines, position the shroud on the lower retainer clips and attach the top of the shroud to the radiator with 2 washer and screw assemblies. Tighten to 4–6 ft. lbs. (5.5–8 Nm).
18. Attach the rubber overflow tube from the coolant recovery bottle to the radiator, if applicable.
19. Close the draincock and fill the cooling system with a 50/50 mixture of antifreeze and water.
20. Connect the negative battery cable. Operate the engine for 15 minutes and check for leaks. Check the coolant level and bring it up to within 1-1/2 in. of the radiator filler neck.

Villager

1. Disconnect the negative battery cable. Properly drain the cooling system.
2. Disconnect the cooling fan wiring harness clamp (located near the coolant reservoir), then use a prybar to pry apart the 2 cooling fan electrical connectors.
3. Disconnect the radiator overflow tube. Remove the coolant reservoir.
4. Remove the center engine compartment fuse panel bolt and move the panel aside.
5. Disconnect the upper radiator hose from the radiator.
6. Remove the 2 cooling fan and shroud assembly nuts and bolts, the remove the fan harness strap from the bottom of the shroud and lift the fan assembly out, noting the lower mounting slots.
7. Disconnect and plug the transaxle oil cooler lines. Remove the lower radiator hose from the radiator.
8. Remove the 2 radiator support bracket bolts and brackets, and lift the radiator out of the vehicle.

To install:

9. Position the radiator to its mounting and reconnect the oil cooler lines and the lower radiator hose.
10. Slide the cooling fan into the lower mounting slots and secure it with the upper bolts and nuts. Reconnect the fan harness strap to the shroud.
11. Install the upper radiator support brackets, using only original length bolts. Torque to 34–48 ft. lbs.
12. Connect the upper radiator hose.
13. Connect the cooling fan electrical connector and reinstall the clamp.
14. Reposition the fuse panel and secure it with the bolt.
15. Install the coolant reservoir, overflow tube and clamp.
16. Reconnect the negative battery cable. Refill the cooling system with the proper mixture of water and coolant. Start engine and operate to normal temperatures, checking for leaks and proper system operation.

Windstar

1. Disconnect the negative battery cable.
2. Remove the radiator cap and drain the radiator into a drain tray.
3. Disengage grille opening panel pushpins.
4. Disconnect the cooling fan motor wiring connectors.
5. Position the wiring harness out of the way and remove the cooling fan assembly.
6. Disconnect the overflow hose, upper radiator hose and lower radiator hose.

CAUTION

Do not unscrew fittings on radiator. Disconnect and plug transmission lines from radiator.

7. Remove the headlamp mounting clips. If possible, remove the clips with snapring pliers as prying them will cause them to break off.
8. Remove the turn signal lamp retaining nut and position the headlamp and turn the signal lamp out of the way.
9. Remove the grille opening panel bracket screws (4 per side). Do not bend the grille reinforcements.
10. Remove the 2 radiator grille opening panel brackets.
11. Remove the hood latch support retaining screws and pull the support forward.
12. Remove the radiator mounting screws.
13. Remove the 3 reinforcement retaining screws on each side of the grille opening and remove the radiator grille opening panel reinforcement from vehicle.
14. Remove the top condenser-to-radiator mounting screws.
15. Lift up the A/C condenser core while pushing down on the radiator to disengage clips on bottom.
16. Remove the radiator from vehicle.

To install:

17. Install the radiator in place.
18. Put the A/C condenser core back into place.
19. Install the top condenser-to-radiator mounting screws.
20. Install the radiator grille opening panel reinforcement and screws.
21. Install the radiator mounting screws and tighten.

22. Reposition the hood latch support and install the hood latch support retaining screws.
23. Install the radiator grille opening panel brackets and tighten the screws. Do not bend the grille reinforcements.
24. Position the turn signal and head lamp assembly.
25. Install the turn signal lamp retaining bolt and headlamp mounting clip.
26. Connect the transmission cooling lines to the radiator.
27. Connect the overflow hose and lower radiator hose and upper radiator hose.
28. Position the cooling fan and shroud assembly and install the mounting screws.
29. Connect the cooling fan motor wiring connectors.
30. Install the pushpins.
31. Fill and bleed the engine cooling system.
32. Connect the negative battery cable.

COOLING SYSTEM BLEEDING

When the entire cooling system is drained, the following procedure should be used to remove air from the cooling system and ensure a complete fill.

1. Close the radiator draincock and install the cylinder block drain plug(s), if removed.
2. Fill the cooling system with a 50/50 mixture of anti-freeze and water. Disconnect the heater outlet hose at the water pump to bleed trapped air in the system. When the coolant begins to escape, reconnect the hose.
3. Fill with coolant until level is at or slightly below the radiator cap seal in the filler neck.
4. Slide the heater temperature and mode selection levers to the **MAXIMUM HEAT** position.
5. Start the engine and allow to operate at fast idle for approximately 3–4 minutes.
6. With the engine shut **OFF**, wrap the radiator cap with a thick cloth, carefully remove the cap and add coolant as needed.

Condenser

REMOVAL AND INSTALLATION

Aerostar

NOTE: Whenever the condenser is replaced, it will be necessary to replace the suction accumulator/drier.

1. Disconnect the negative battery cable.
2. Discharge the refrigerant from the air conditioning system.
3. Disconnect the compressor discharge line and the liquid line from the condenser at the spring-lock couplings using the spring-lock coupling disconnect procedure. Cap the openings to prevent the entry of dirt and moisture.
4. Tilt the top of the radiator rearward after removing the upper radiator bolts, being careful not to damage the cooling fan and/or radiator.
5. Remove the 2 bolts attaching the 2 condenser upper mounting brackets to the rear side of the radiator support. Lift the condenser from the vehicle.

To install:

NOTE: Add 1 oz. (30ml) of clean refrigerant oil to a replacement condenser to maintain the correct total system oil charge.

6. Check the condenser to make sure there is a rubber isolator on each of the lower mounting studs. Replace if worn or missing.
7. Position the condenser to the vehicle with the lower studs in the lower mount holes and with the upper brackets on the rear face of the upper radiator support.
8. Install the 2 bolts attaching the 2 condenser support mounting brackets to the rear side of the radiator support.
9. Move the radiator into the correct installed position and install the 2 upper retaining bolts.
10. Connect the discharge and liquid lines to the condenser using the spring-lock coupling connection procedure.
11. Connect the negative battery cable. Leak test, evacuate and charge the system. Observe all safety precautions.
12. Check the system for proper operation.

Explorer and Ranger

NOTE: Whenever the condenser is replaced, it will be necessary to replace the suction accumulator/drier.

1. Disconnect the negative battery cable.
2. Discharge the refrigerant from the air conditioning system according to the proper procedure.
3. Disconnect the compressor discharge line and the liquid line from the condenser at the spring-lock couplings using the spring-lock coupling disconnect procedure. Cap the openings to prevent the entry of dirt and moisture.
4. Working under the vehicle, remove the 2 nuts attaching the 2 lower mounting studs.
5. On 1993–94 Explorer, it is necessary to gain access to the condenser seals located on the rear surface of the radiator support on the upper corners of the condenser and vertical side seals insulating the condenser from the radiator. Remove the radiator grille as follows:
   - Remove the 5 plastic retainers located across the top of the grille.
   - Remove the 2 screws attaching the grille to the headlight assemblies.
   - Use a flat-bladed tool to depress the spring tabs (accessible through the lower outboard openings and support.
6. Tilt the top of the radiator rearward, after removing the upper radiator brackets, being careful not to damage the cooling fan and/or the radiator.
7. Remove the 2 bolts attaching the 2 condenser upper mounting brackets to the rear side of the radiator support and lift the condenser from the vehicle.

To install:

NOTE: Add 1 oz. (30ml) of clean refrigerant oil to a replacement condenser to maintain the correct total system oil charge.

8. Assemble the 2 "J" nuts and studs to the bottom of the condenser to be installed.
9. Position the condenser to the vehicle with the lower studs and upper brackets on the rear face of the radiator support.
10. Install the 2 bolts attaching the 2 condenser upper mounting brackets to the rear side of the radiator support. Working under the vehicle, fasten the 2 nuts to the lower studs.
11. Replace condenser to radiator seals on 1993 Explorer as needed.
12. Move the radiator into the correct installed position and install the 2 upper retaining brackets.
13. Connect the discharge and liquid lines to the condenser using the spring-lock coupling connection procedure.
14. Connect the negative battery cable. Leak test, evacuate and charge the system. Observe all safety precautions.
15. Check the system for proper operation.

Bronco and F Series

NOTE: Whenever the condenser is replaced, it will be necessary to replace the suction accumulator/drier.

1. Disconnect the negative battery cable.

2. Discharge the refrigerant from the air conditioning system according to the proper procedure.
3. Disconnect the compressor discharge and liquid lines from the condenser. Cap the lines and condenser openings to prevent the entrance of dirt and moisture.
4. Partially drain the radiator and disconnect the upper hose from the radiator.
5. Working under the vehicle, remove the 2 screws attaching the 2 condenser lower mounting brackets to the front radiator support.
6. Remove the bolts from the radiator upper retaining brackets and tilt the radiator rearward.
7. Tilt the radiator rearward and remove the 2 screws attaching the 2 condenser upper mounting brackets to the rear side of the radiator support. Lift the condenser from the vehicle.

To install:

NOTE: Add 1 oz. (30ml) of clean refrigerant oil to a replacement condenser to maintain the correct total system oil charge.

8. Position the condenser to the vehicle with the lower mounting brackets on the front side of the radiator support and the upper brackets on the rear side.
9. Install the 4 screws attaching the 4 mounting brackets to the radiator support. Tighten the screws to 10–14 ft. lbs. (13.6–19 Nm).
10. Move the radiator into the correct installed position and install the bolts to the upper retaining brackets.
11. Connect the radiator upper hose to the radiator and fill the cooling system to the proper level.
12. Using new O-rings lubricated with clean refrigerant oil, connect the compressor discharge and liquid lines to the condenser. Tighten the connections to 15–20 ft. lbs. (21–27 Nm).
13. Connect the negative battery cable. Leak test, evacuate and charge the system. Observe all safety precautions.
14. Check the system for proper operation.

E-Series

NOTE: Whenever the condenser is replaced, it will be necessary to replace the suction accumulator/drier.

1. Disconnect the negative battery cable.
2. Discharge the refrigerant from the air conditioning system.
3. Disconnect the compressor discharge line and liquid line from the condenser using the spring-lock coupling disconnect procedure. Cap the refrigerant lines and condenser openings to prevent entry of excessive moisture and dirt.
4. On 1993 E-Series, remove the 2 screws retaining the hood latch to the radiator support and position the hood latch aside.
5. On 1993 E-Series, remove the 9 screws retaining the top edge of the radiator grille to the radiator support.
6. On 1993 E-Series, remove the screw retaining the center area of the grille to the grille center support and the screw retaining the grille center support to the radiator support.
7. Working under the vehicle, reposition the splash shield and remove the 2 condenser lower retaining nuts.
8. Remove the 2 bolts retaining the top of the condenser to the radiator upper support.
9. Remove the 4 bolts retaining each end of the radiator upper support to the radiator side supports.
10. Carefully pull the top edge of the grille forward and remove the radiator upper support.
11. Lift the condenser from the vehicle.
12. Remove both seals from the A/C condenser core.

To install:

NOTE: Add 1 oz. (30ml) of clean refrigerant oil to a replacement condenser to maintain the correct total system oil charge.

13. Install the old seals to the new A/C condenser core.
14. Position the condenser to the vehicle and install 2 condenser lower retaining nuts.
15. Position the radiator upper support to the vehicle using care not to damage the radiator grille.
16. Install the 4 bolts retaining each end of the radiator upper supports to the side supports.
17. Install the 2 bolts retaining the top end of the condenser to the radiator upper support.
18. On 1993 E-Series, install the screw retaining the grille center support to the radiator support.
19. On 1993 E-Series, install the 9 screws retaining the top edge of the grille.
20. On 1993 E-Series, install the screw retaining the center area of the grille to the grille center support.
21. Connect the compressor discharge and liquid lines to the condenser using the spring-lock coupling connection procedure.
22. On 1993 E-Series, install and adjust the hood latch.
23. Connect the negative battery cable. Leak test, evacuate and charge the system. Observe all safety precautions.
24. Check the system for proper operation.

Villager

1. Disconnect negative battery cable. Properly discharge the air conditioning system.
2. Drain the cooling system and remove the radiator assembly.
3. Using proper spring lock coupling tool, disconnect the condenser inlet and outlet lines.
4. Remove the condenser inlet line hold-down bracket, remove the 2 condenser retaining bolts, and remove the condenser from the vehicle.

To install:

5. If installing a new condenser, add 1.0–1.7 fl. oz. of new refrigerant oil to the new condenser.
6. Position the condenser and install the 2 retaining bolts and the inlet line bracket.
7. Reconnect the inlet and outlet lines at the respective spring lock couplings, using new O-rings coated with clean refrigerant oil.
8. Install the radiator and refill the cooling system.
9. Evacuate and recharge the air conditioning system. Leak test and make a full performance test of the system.

Windstar

NOTE: Whenever an A/C condenser core is replaced, it is also necessary to replace the suction accumulator/drier.

1. Disconnect the negative battery cable.
2. Discharge A/C refrigerant from the air conditioner system.
3. Remove the push pins retaining the upper grille air deflector and the upper grille air deflector.
4. Disconnect the RH and LH turn signal lamp and headlamp electrical wiring connectors.
5. Remove the RH and LH turn signal lamp assembly retaining nuts and remove the turn signal lamp assemblies.
6. Remove the headlamp retaining clips and remove the headlamp assemblies.
7. Remove the grille opening reinforcement retaining bolts and the reinforcement bracket.
8. Remove the radiator center support and position it out of the way.
9. Remove the front underhood panel.

10. Disconnect the front lamp electrical wiring harness and position it out of the way.
11. Disconnect the cooling fan electrical wiring harness.
12. Remove the electrical wiring harness from cooling fan shroud.
13. Remove the six radiator upper support retaining bolts.
14. Remove the two bolts retaining radiator to radiator upper support.
15. Disconnect the A/C condenser core inlet and the outlet hoses using a Spring Lock Coupling Disconnect.
16. Remove the 2 bolts retaining the A/C condenser cores to the radiator.
17. Remove the bolt retaining compressor manifold and remove the manifold. Plug the compressor manifold and the compressor ports immediately.
18. Remove the A/C condenser core by lifting it up and out.

NOTE: Refrigerant oil should be added to any A/C refrigerant component which requires replacement.

19. Installation is the reverse of the removal procedure.

CAUTION

Make sure correct O-ring seals are installed on A/C fittings.

Compressor

REMOVAL AND INSTALLATION

Except 7.3L DI Turbo Diesel

NOTE: The suction accumulator/drier and the fixed orifice tube should also be replaced whenever the compressor is replaced.

1. Disconnect the negative battery cable.
2. Discharge the refrigerant from the air conditioning system.
3. Windstar, disconnect power steering cooler lines from the power steering pump and the power steering line retaining bolt from A/C compressor.
4. Disconnect the wire connector from the clutch field coil connector.
5. Loosen and remove the drive belt from the compressor pulley. It may be necessary to loosen the tensioner bolt and/or tensioner pulley to loosen the drive belt.
6. Disconnect the refrigerant lines from the compressor or remove the refrigerant line manifold and position manifold with lines out of the way. Plug the refrigerant lines and compressor ports to prevent the entrance of dirt and moisture.
7. Remove the mounting bolts and the necessary mounting brackets and remove the compressor.

NOTE: On some applications the upper compressor bolts may be too long to extract completely. Loosen them until compressor is free and remove bolts from compressor after it is out of the vehicle.

To install:

NOTE: Prior to installing a new service replacement compressor, drain the refrigerant oil from the removed compressor into a calibrated container. Then, drain the refrigerant oil from the new compressor into a clean calibrated container. If the amount of oil drained from the removed compressor was between 3–5 oz. (90–148ml), pour the same amount of clean refrigerant oil into the new compressor. If the amount of oil that was removed from the old compressor is greater than 5 oz. (148ml), pour 5 oz. (148ml) of clean refrigerant oil into the new compressor. If the amount of oil that was removed from the old compressor is less than 3 oz. (90ml), pour 3 oz. (90ml) of clean refrigerant oil into the new compressor. This will maintain the total system oil charge within the specified limits.

When the A/C compressor replacement is caused by internal A/C compressor failure, the A/C system will become contaminated. To remove the contamination from the A/C system, it is necessary to replace the suction accumulator/drier and the A/C evaporator core orifice and to follow the following filtering procedure. If equipped with auxiliary A/C, the auxiliary A/C evaporator filter must also be replaced.

8. If a new compressor is being installed, transfer the necessary components.
9. Install the compressor and any mounting brackets that were removed. Partially install mounting bolts to compressor before positioning it in the vehicle as needed. Tighten to 33–44 ft. lbs. (45–60 Nm).
10. Install the power steering cooling lines and the power steering line retaining bolt.
11. Connect the refrigerant lines. Use new O-rings lubricated with clean refrigerant oil.
12. Install the compressor drive belt and adjust the tension, as necessary.
13. Connect the clutch wires to the clutch field coil.
14. Connect the negative battery cable. Leak test, evacuate and charge the system. Observe all safety precautions.
15. Check the system for proper operation.

7.3L DI Turbo Diesel

1. Disconnect the negative battery cable.
2. Discharge the refrigerant system from the air conditioning system.
3. Disconnect the electrical connector from the A/C cyclic switch on the side of suction accumulator.
4. Remove the A/C cyclic switch from the accumulator.
5. Remove the rocker arm cover, right-hand side.
6. Remove the foil insulator from the A/C evaporator case.
7. Disconnect the accumulator-to-compressor suction line from the suction accumulator. Use a backup wrench to loosen the fitting. Cap the accumulator-to-compressor suction line to prevent entry of dirt and excess moisture.
8. Using a Spring Lock Coupling Disconnect Tool, disconnect the condenser-to-evaporator tube from the A/C evaporator core. Cap the condenser to evaporator tube to prevent entry of dirt and excess moisture.
9. Disconnect the evaporator outlet from the suction accumulator inlet.
10. Loosen the band screw of the top accumulator bracket.
11. In the passenger compartment, remove 1 screw attaching the plenum chamber and evaporator assembly.
12. Remove one nut retaining the MAP sensor bracket to the upper left corner of the A/C evaporator case (if applicable).
13. Remove the spring clip holding the MAP sensor to the housing. Put the MAP sensor aside.
14. Remove 1 nut retaining the upper left corner of A/C evaporator case-to-dash panel.
15. Remove the 2 screws attaching the top accumulator bracket to the evaporator case and remove the bracket.
16. Remove the 2 screws attaching the accumulator to the evaporator case and remove the accumulator.
17. Remove the 4 remaining screws attaching the evaporator case cover to the A/C evaporator case.
18. Remove the left A/C evaporator case cover from the A/C evaporator case.
19. Remove the A/C evaporator core from the A/C evaporator case.
20. Remove the evaporator tube support clamp from the evaporator tube.

To install:

NOTE: If installing a new accumulator/drier, add 2 oz. of new refrigerant oil to the accumulator/drier.

21. Install the evaporator tube support clamp to the evaporator tube.
22. Install the A/C evaporator core to the A/C evaporator case.
23. Install the left A/C evaporator case cover to the A/C evaporator case.
24. Install the 4 screws attaching the evaporator case cover to the A/C evaporator case.
25. Install the 2 screws attaching the accumulator to the evaporator case.
26. Place the evaporator case bracket on the evaporator case. Install the 2 screws.
27. Install 1 nut to the upper left corner of the A/C evaporator case attaching it to the dash panel.
28. Install the spring clip to hold to MAP sensor to the housing.
29. Install 1 nut to secure the MAP sensor bracket to the upper left corner of the A/C evaporator case (if applicable).
30. In the passenger compartment, install 1 screw to attach the plenum chamber to the evaporator assembly.
31. Install the band screw to the top of the accumulator bracket.
32. Install the evaporator outlet to the suction accumulator inlet.
33. Install the condenser to the evaporator tube from the A/C evaporator core.
34. Connect the accumulator-to-compressor suction line to the suction accumulator. Use a backup wrench to tighten the fitting.
35. Staple the A/C evaporator case insulator to the plastic housing in 14 places using 6.4 max staples. Be careful not to puncture the vacuum tank when stapling.
36. Install the rocket arm cover, right-hand side.
37. Install the A/C cyclic switch on the accumulator.
38. Connect the electrical connector from the A/C cyclic switch on the side of the suction accumulator.
39. Recharge the refrigerant system following the recommended service procedures. Observe all safety precautions.

Accumulator/Drier

REMOVAL AND INSTALLATION

The accumulator/drier should be replaced under the following conditions:

- The accumulator/drier is restricted, plugged or perforated.
- The system has been left open for more than 24 hours.
- There is evidence of moisture in the system: internal corrosion of metal lines or the refrigerant oil is thick and dark.
- A component such as a condenser, evaporator, refrigerant line or a seized compressor is replaced. Flush the system and replace the orifice tube when replacing a seized or damaged compressor.
- There is more than 5 oz. of compressor oil in the accumulator/drier, indicating that the bleed hole is clogged. Be sure to check this before a compressor is replaced for lack of performance or seizure.

NOTE: The accumulator/drier must be replaced whenever a condenser, evaporator core, refrigerant line, seized compressor or damage to some other major component requires opening of the refrigerant system in order to service the difficulty.

Do not replace the accumulator/drier every time if the following conditions exist:

- There is a loss of refrigerant charge.
- A component, except as described above, is changed.
- A dent is found in the outer shell of the accumulator/drier.

1. Disconnect the negative battery cable.
2. Discharge the refrigerant from the air conditioning system.
3. Disconnect the electrical connector from the pressure switch. Remove the pressure switch by unscrewing it from the accumulator/drier.
4. On Villager, if equipped with auxiliary rear A/C system, remove the rear A/C line hold-down bracket nut.
5. Remove foil insulator from evaporator the case, (if applicable).
6. Disconnect the suction hose from the accumulator/drier. On Explorer, Ranger, Villager and Windstar, use the spring-lock coupling disconnect procedure. On E-Series, remove the vacuum reservoir and the suction line from the evaporator tube. On Aerostar, remove the 2 mounting bands holding the accumulator/drier and remove the clamp around the inlet tube. On E-Series remove the 2 or 3 mounting screws retaining the bracket for the accumulator/drier. On Bronco, F-Series and E-Series, use 2 wrenches to prevent component damage. Cap the openings to prevent the entrance of dirt and moisture.
7. Loosen the fitting connecting the accumulator/drier to the evaporator core. Use 2 wrenches to prevent component damage.
8. On Explorer and Ranger, remove the lower forward screw holding the flanges of the case and bracket together and the screw holding the evaporator inlet tube to the accumulator bracket. Disconnect the accumulator/drier from the evaporator core and remove the bracket from the accumulator/drier.
9. On Bronco and F-Series, remove the 2 screws attaching the accumulator/drier strap to the evaporator case and clip to the evaporator inlet tube.
10. On Villager, remove 3 mounting bolts and remove the accumulator/drier from its bracket.

To install:

NOTE: If installing a new accumulator/drier, add 2 oz. of new refrigerant oil to the accumulator/drier.

11. On Explorer and Ranger, perform the following procedure:
    - Position the bracket on the replacement accumulator/drier loosely.
    - Using a new O-ring lubricated with clean refrigerant oil, connect the accumulator/drier to the evaporator core tube while aligning the bracket to the slot between the case flanges.
    - Tighten the accumulator/drier to the evaporator core fitting to 26–31 ft. lbs. (32–42 Nm) using a backup wrench. Install the lower forward screw which retains the bracket between the case flanges. Tighten the bracket on the accumulator and reinstall the clip that holds the evaporator inlet tube to the accumulator bracket.
    - Connect the suction hose to the accumulator/drier using the spring-lock coupling connection procedure.
12. On Bronco, F-Series and E-Series, perform the following procedure:
    - Using a new O-ring lubricated with clean refrigerant oil, connect the accumulator/drier to the evaporator core tube. Tighten the connection finger-tight.
    - Position the strap on the accumulator/drier to the evaporator case and clip to the evaporator core inlet tube. Align the strap and clip with the mounting bracket and install the 2 attaching screws. Loosen the connection of the accumulator/drier to the evaporator core if it is necessary to re-position the accumulator/drier to install the strap attaching screws.

- Tighten the accumulator/drier-to-evaporator core fitting to 26–31 ft. lbs. (32–42 Nm) using a backup wrench.

13. On Villager, position the accumulator/drier in its mounting bracket and install 3 mounting bolts securely.
14. On Aerostar, install the 2 mounting bands around the accumulator/drier and install the clamp around the inlet line. Tighten the screws to 15 inch lbs. (1.7 Nm). Reinstall vacuum reservoir, if removed. Connect the suction line(s) to the accumulator/drier using the spring-lock coupling procedure.
15. Install a new O-ring lubricated with clean refrigerant oil on the pressure switch nipple of the accumulator/drier. If equipped with an auxiliary rear A/C system, install the rear A/C line hold-down bracket. Install the pressure switch. Tighten the switch to 5–10 ft. lbs. (7–13 Nm) if the switch has a metal base and hand tighten only if the switch has a plastic base.
16. Connect the electrical connector to the pressure switch and connect the negative battery cable.

NOTE: On models with Electronic Engine Control (EEC), once battery cable is disconnected and reconnected, abnormal driveability symptoms may occur on restart and early driving. The computer PROM must relearn driveability conditions. Vehicle will have to be driven 10 miles or more for this to occur.

17. Leak test, evacuate and charge the system. Observe all safety precautions.
18. Check the system for proper operation.

Fixed Orifice Tube

REMOVAL AND INSTALLATION

Except Villager

1. Disconnect the negative battery cable.
2. Discharge the refrigerant from the air conditioning system according to the proper procedure.
3. Disconnect the liquid line from the evaporator core. Cap the liquid line to prevent the entry of dirt and excessive moisture.
4. Squirt a small amount of clean refrigerant oil into the evaporator core inlet tube to lubricate the tube and orifice O-rings during removal of the fixed orifice tube from the evaporator core tube.
5. Engage fixed orifice tube installer T83–19990–A or equivalent, with the 2 tangs on the fixed orifice tube.

NOTE: Do not attempt to remove the fixed orifice tube with pliers or by twisting the tube. To do so will break the fixed orifice tube body in the evaporator core tube. Use only the recommended tool.

6. Hold the T-handle of the tool to keep it from turning and run the nut on the tool down against the evaporator core tube until the orifice is pulled from the tube.
7. If the fixed orifice tube breaks in the evaporator core tube, it must be removed from the tube with broken orifice tube extractor T83L–19990–B or equivalent.
8. To remove a broken orifice tube, insert the screw end of the extractor into the evaporator core tube and thread the screw end of the tool into the brass tube in the center of the fixed orifice tube. Then, pull the fixed orifice tube from the evaporator core tube.
9. If only the brass center tube is removed during Step 8, insert the screw end of the tool into the evaporator core tube and screw the end of the tool into the fixed orifice tube body. Then, pull the fixed orifice tube body from the evaporator core tube.

To install:

10. Lubricate the O-rings on the fixed orifice tube body liberally with clean refrigerant oil.
11. Place the fixed orifice tube in the fixed orifice tube remover/replacer T83L–19990–A or equivalent, and insert the fixed orifice tube into the evaporator core tube until the orifice is seated at the top.
12. Remove the tool from the fixed orifice tube.
13. Connect the liquid line to the evaporator core using the spring-lock coupling connection procedure.
14. Leak test, evacuate and charge the system. Observe all safety precautions.
15. Check the system for proper operation.

Villager

1. Disconnect the negative battery cable. Properly discharge the A/C system.
2. Partially drain the cooling system so the coolant level is below the thermostat. Remove the upper radiator hose to gain access to the condenser-to-evaporator line.
3. Using Spring Lock tool T84L-19623-B, or equivalent, disconnect the condenser-to-evaporator line at the condenser outlet coupling. Cap all openings to minimize contamination.
4. Use the Spring Lock tool disconnect the condenser-to-evaporator line at the evaporator inlet line coupling near the bulkhead.
5. Remove the hold-down bracket for the A/C line and remove the line (with the fixed orifice tube) from the vehicle.

NOTE: The fixed orifice tube can only be replaced by replacing the condenser-to-evaporator line assembly.

To install:

6. Position the new condenser-to-evaporator line in the vehicle and install the hold-down bracket.
7. Connect the spring lock coupling at the bulkhead and then attach the line at the condenser, also using the spring lock coupling tool.
8. Install the upper radiator hose. Refill the cooling system.
9. Evacuate and recharge the A/C system. Perform a system operation check.

Windstar

1. Disconnect the negative battery cable.
2. Recover the A/C refrigerant system.
3. Remove the cowl top vent panel.
4. Remove the vacuum hoses from the vacuum reservoir mounted on the A/C air inlet duct.
5. Remove the A/C air inlet duct.
6. Locate the condenser to evaporator tube assembly.
7. Disconnect the spring lock couplings at the A/C evaporator core, and the suction/accumulator drier.
8. Remove the condenser-to-evaporator tube from vehicle.
9. Remove the A/C evaporator core orifice from the condenser to evaporator tube.

To install:

10. Installation is the reverse of the removal procedure.

Blower Motor

REMOVAL AND INSTALLATION

Aerostar, Explorer and Ranger

WITHOUT AIR CONDITIONING

1. Disconnect the negative battery cable.
2. Remove the air cleaner or air inlet duct, as necessary.
3. On Aerostar, remove the 2 screws attaching the vacuum reservoir to the blower assembly and remove the reservoir.
4. Disconnect the wire harness connector from the blower motor by pinching the connector while pulling it off the motor.

5. Disconnect the blower motor cooling tube at the blower motor.
6. Remove the 3 screws attaching the blower motor and wheel to the heater blower assembly.
7. Holding the cooling tube aside, pull the blower motor and wheel from the heater blower assembly and remove it from the vehicle.
8. Remove the blower wheel push-nut or clamp from the motor shaft and pull the blower wheel from the motor shaft.

To install:

9. Install the blower wheel on the blower motor shaft.
10. Install the hub clamp or push-nut.
11. Holding the cooling tube aside, position the blower motor and wheel on the heater blower assembly and install the 3 attaching screws.
12. Connect the blower motor cooling tube and the wire harness connector.
13. On Aerostar, install the vacuum reservoir on the hoses with the 2 screws.
14. Install the air cleaner or air inlet duct, as necessary.
15. Connect the negative battery cable and check the system for proper operation.

NOTE: On models with Electronic Engine Control (EEC), once battery cable is disconnected and reconnected, abnormal driveability symptoms may occur on restart and early driving. The computer PROM must relearn driveability conditions. Vehicle will have to be driven 10 miles or more for this to occur.

AIR CONDITIONING

1. Disconnect the negative battery cable.
2. On Explorer and Ranger, remove the solenoid box cover retaining bolts and the solenoid box cover, if equipped.
3. In the engine compartment, disconnect the wire harness from the motor by pushing down on the tab while pulling the connection off at the motor.
4. Remove the air cleaner or air inlet duct, as necessary.
5. On Aerostar, remove the 2 screws holding the vacuum reservoir to the blower housing. Also, remove the pressure switch from the accumulator/drier.
6. Disconnect the blower motor cooling tube from the blower motor.
7. Remove the 3 or 4 blower motor mounting plate attaching screws and remove the motor and wheel assembly from the evaporator assembly blower motor housing.
8. Remove the blower motor hub clamp from the motor shaft and pull the blower wheel from the shaft.

To install:

9. Install the blower motor wheel on the blower motor shaft and install a new hub clamp.
10. Install a new motor mounting seal on the blower housing before installing the blower motor.
11. Position the blower motor and wheel assembly in the blower housing and install the 3 attaching screws.
12. Connect the blower motor cooling tube.
13. On Aerostar, install the pressure switch on the accumulator/drier and also reattach the vacuum reservoir to the side of the blower housing.
14. Connect the electrical wire harness hardshell connector to the blower motor by pushing into place.
15. On Explorer and Ranger, position the solenoid box cover, if equipped, into place and install the 3 retaining screws.
16. Install the air cleaner or air inlet duct, as necessary.
17. Connect the negative battery cable and check the blower motor in all speeds for proper operation.

Bronco and F-Series

1. Disconnect the negative battery cable.
2. If equipped, remove the emission module forward of the blower motor.
3. Disconnect the blower motor wiring connector.
4. Disconnect the blower motor cooling tube at the blower motor.
5. Remove the screws attaching the blower motor and wheel to the heater blower assembly.
6. Holding the cooling tube aside, pull the blower motor and wheel from the heater blower assembly and remove it from the vehicle.
7. Remove the hub clamp and remove the blower wheel from the blower motor shaft.

To install:

8. Install the blower wheel onto the blower motor shaft. Install the hub clamp.
9. Holding the cooling tube aside, position the blower motor and wheel in the heater blower assembly and install the attaching screws.
10. Connect the blower motor cooling tube and the wire harness connector.
11. If equipped, install the emission module forward of the blower motor.
12. Connect the negative battery cable and check the blower motor for proper operation.

E-Series

1. Disconnect blower motor wiring connector.
2. Remove 4 screws retaining blower motor mounting plate to the heater/evaporator case. Remove the blower motor and wheel from the case.
3. If equipped with A/C, note the flat spot on the motor mounting plate to the accumulator/drier, which provides clearance for removal and installation.
4. Installation is reverse of the removal procedure.

Villager

1. Disconnect the negative battery cable.
2. Remove 1 plastic rivet and 4 right hand instrument panel trim screws and remove the right hand instrument panel trim.
3. Disconnect the electrical lead from the blower motor. Remove the air vent tube.
4. Remove 3 blower motor screws and remove the blower motor from the housing.
5. Installation is the reverse of the removal procedure.

Windstar

Removal and Installation

1. Disconnect the negative battery cable.
2. Open the glove box door. Push inward on the sides and open it completely positioning it out of the way for clearance.
3. Disconnect the heater blower motor electrical connector.
4. Remove the 4 blower motor assembly retaining screws.
5. Remove the blower motor assembly.
6. Carefully remove the heater blower wheel retaining pushnut from the blower motor shaft.
7. Remove the blower motor.
8. Three insert nuts are used to secure the motor to the housing and can be serviced if necessary. Tighten the screws to 18 inch lbs. (2 Nm).
9. Installation is the reverse of the removal procedure.

Blower Motor Resistor

REMOVAL AND INSTALLATION

1. Disconnect the negative battery cable.
2. On Villager, remove the right hand instrument panel trim (1 plastic rivet and 4 screws).
3. Disconnect the wire connector from the resistor assembly.
4. Remove the 2 screws attaching the resistor assembly to the blower or evaporator case and remove the resistor.

5. Installation is the reverse of the removal procedure. Apply a bead of sealer around the edge of the board before reinstallation, if needed. Check the blower motor for proper operation in all blower speeds.

Heater Core

REMOVAL AND INSTALLATION

Aerostar, Explorer and Ranger

1. If engine temperature is not cold, allow it to cool, then loosen radiator cap to first stop (using a thick rag to cover cap) and allow any pressure to bleed from system. Retighten radiator cap.
2. Disconnect the heater hoses from the heater core tubes. Plug the hoses to prevent loss of coolant.
3. In the passenger compartment, remove the screws attaching the heater core access cover to the plenum assembly. Remove the access cover.
4. Pull the heater core rearward and down, removing it from the plenum assembly.

To install:

5. Position the heater core and seal in the plenum assembly.
6. Install the heater core access cover to the plenum assembly and secure it with the screws.
7. Connect the heater hoses to the heater core tubes.
8. Fill the cooling system to the proper level. Check the system for proper operation and coolant leaks.

Bronco, E-Series and F-Series

1. Allow the engine to cool. Using safety precautions, cover the radiator cap with a thick cloth and loosen to the first stop to release system pressure. Retighten cap.
2. Disconnect the heater hoses from the heater core in the engine compartment. Plug ends of hoses.
3. On E-Series, remove the lower trim panel from the underside of the instrument panel.
4. On Bronco and F-Series, remove the glove compartment and the "RABS" module on the F-Series.
5. From inside the passenger compartment, remove the screws (7 for 1993-94, 6 for 1995) from the heater core cover and remove the cover. On Bronco and F-Series, disconnect the vacuum source but leave the vacuum harness attached to the cover.
6. Remove the heater core and seal.

To install:

7. Position the heater core and seal into the heater case or plenum.
8. Position the heater core cover and install the attaching screws.
9. On E-Series, install the modesty panel and the retaining clips or screws. On Bronco and F-Series, Connect the vacuum harness to it's source connection and install the glove compartment.
10. Connect the heater hoses to the heater core.
11. Fill the cooling system to the proper level.
12. Connect the negative battery cable and check the system for proper operation and coolant leaks.

Villager

1. Disconnect the negative battery cable. Properly drain the cooling system and disconnect and plug the heater hoses from the core tubes at the bulkhead.

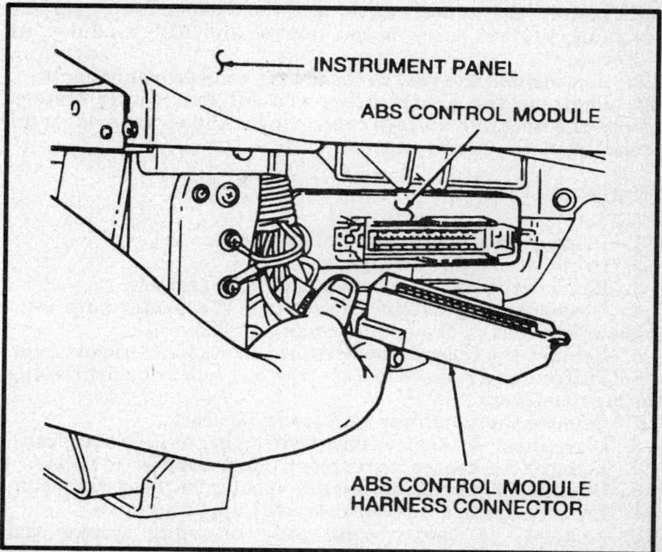

Removing ABS control module–Villager

2. Remove the storage bin, then remove both side covers by the bin and the footlamp, if equipped.
3. Remove the control console bezel (1 screw in center), then remove the ashtray assembly.
4. Remove the climate control console screws, pull the console rearward and detach the electrical connectors. Also remove the 4 radio assembly screws and take the radio out of the vehicle.
5. Remove the floor duct and the right and left knee reinforcement plates. Now remove the ABS control module.
6. The speed control module, keyless entry module if equipped and passive restraint (air bag) module are all located behind the center console and can now be removed after detaching respective connectors and removing retaining nuts or screws.

WARNING: Control modules are very sensitive to static electricity and can be damaged if exposed to static or stray electrical impulses.

7. Remove the center air duct.
8. Remove the 2 ground wire bolts. Remove the U-bracket and the 2 console brackets.
9. Remove the glove box and lamp.
10. Remove the accelerator pedal and pedal stop.
11. Remove the floor air duct.
12. Remove the temperature blend air door actuator and mode door actuator by removing the attaching bracket bolts and detaching the electrical connections.
13. Remove the center distribution duct.
14. Remove the 4 evaporator/blower assembly screws, then the 4 heater assembly screws and remove the heater assembly.
15. Remove the heater pipe plate from the assembly.
16. Remove the heater core retainer, disengage the shut-off valve control rod and remove the heater core from the assembly.

To install:

17. Reassembly heater core to case, install the retainer and pipe plate.
18. Position the heater assembly in the vehicle and attach the 4 retaining screws.
19. Reinstall the center distribution duct, then both blend air and mode door actuators. Install the floor air duct.
20. Install the accelerator stop and pedal.
21. Install the glove box and lamp, then reinstall the center console and U-brackets.

22. Install the center air duct, then install the passive restraint, keyless entry, speed control and ABS modules, as removed.
23. Reassemble the rest of the center console components.
24. Reattach the heater hoses and fill the cooling system. Attach the negative battery cable. Check the entire system for proper operation and leaks.

Windstar

1. Disconnect the negative battery cable.
2. Drain the engine coolant system.
3. Remove the cowl top vent panel for clearance.
4. Disconnect the heater hoses from the heater core inlet and outlet tubes in the engine compartment.
5. Remove the cassette box/center instrument support trim.
6. Pull out and remove the ashtray cup holder by depressing the service lever.
7. Remove the floor/rear seat lower air duct.
8. Disconnect the keyless entry wiring harness (if equipped).
9. Remove the center instrument panel support brackets.
10. Disconnect the climate control vacuum harness connector.
11. Remove the heater floor/rear seat upper air duct.
12. Remove the heater core cover retaining screws and remove the heater core cover.
13. Remove the heater core.
14. Remove the seal from the heater core tubes and discard.
15. Installation is the reverse of the removal procedure.

NOTE: Always use new dash seals when installing heater core.

Evaporator

REMOVAL AND INSTALLATION

Aerostar

1. Disconnect the negative battery cable.
2. Discharge the refrigerant from the air conditioning system.
3. Remove the air cleaner and air inlet duct.
4. Disconnect the electrical connectors from the blower motor, blower motor resistor and pressure switch.
5. Disconnect the liquid line from the inlet tube and the suction line from the accumulator/drier, using the spring-lock coupling disconnect procedure. Cap all open refrigerant lines to prevent the entry of dirt and moisture.
6. Disconnect the vacuum harness check valve from the engine source line and disconnect the vacuum line from the vacuum motor.
7. Remove the 2 mounting bands holding the accumulator/drier to the evaporator core and the clamp from around the evaporator inlet tube.
8. Disconnect the accumulator/drier from the evaporator core outlet tube using the spring-lock coupling disconnect procedure. Remove the accumulator/drier. Cap all open refrigerant connections to prevent the entry of dirt and moisture.
9. Remove the 11 screws holding the evaporator case blower housing to the evaporator case assembly. Remove the evaporator case blower housing from the vehicle.
10. Remove the evaporator core from the vehicle.

To install:

NOTE: Add 3 oz. (90ml) of clean refrigerant oil to a new replacement evaporator core to maintain the total system oil charge.

11. Position the evaporator core into the installed evaporator case half.
12. Position the evaporator case blower housing to the evaporator case and install with the 11 screws.
13. Connect the accumulator/drier to the evaporator core outlet tube.
14. Install the 2 mounting bands around the accumulator/drier and install the clamp around the inlet line. Tighten the screws to 15 inch lbs. (1.7 Nm).
15. Connect the liquid and suction lines using the spring-lock coupling connection procedure.
16. Connect the electrical connectors to the blower motor, pressure switch and blower motor resistor.
17. Connect the vacuum line to the vacuum motor. Connect the vacuum source line from the engine to the check valve.

NOTE: On models with Electronic Engine Control (EEC), once battery cable is disconnected and reconnected, abnormal driveability symptoms may occur on restart and early driving. The computer PROM must relearn driveability conditions. Vehicle will have to be driven 10 miles or more for this to occur.

18. Connect the negative battery cable. Leak test, evacuate and charge the system. Observe all safety precautions.
19. Check the system for proper operation.

Explorer and Ranger

1. Disconnect the negative battery cable.
2. Discharge the refrigerant from the air conditioning system.
3. Disconnect the electrical connector from the pressure switch located on top of the accumulator/drier. Remove the pressure switch.
4. Disconnect the suction hose from the accumulator/drier using the spring-lock coupling disconnect procedure. Cap the openings to prevent the entrance of dirt and moisture.
5. Disconnect the liquid line from the evaporator core inlet tube using a backup wrench to loosen the fitting. Cap the openings to prevent the entrance of dirt and moisture.
6. Remove the screws holding the evaporator case service cover and vacuum reservoir to the evaporator case assembly.
7. Store the vacuum reservoir in a secure position to avoid vacuum line damage.
8. Remove the 2 dash panel mounting nuts.
9. Remove the evaporator case service cover from the evaporator case assembly.
10. Remove the evaporator core and accumulator/drier assembly from the vehicle.

To install:

NOTE: Add 3 oz. (90ml) of clean refrigerant oil to a new replacement evaporator core to maintain the total system oil charge.

11. Position the evaporator core and accumulator/drier assembly into the evaporator case out-board half.
12. Position the evaporator case service cover into place on the evaporator case assembly.
13. Install the 2 dash panel mounting nuts.
14. Install the screws holding the evaporator service case half to the evaporator case assembly.
15. Place the vacuum reservoir in it's installed position. Attach the reservoir to the case with 2 screws.
16. Connect the liquid line to the evaporator inlet tube using a backup wrench to tighten the fitting. Use a new O-ring lubricated with clean refrigerant oil.
17. Install a new accumulator/drier if evaporator core is replaced. Connect the suction hose to the accumulator/drier.
18. Install the pressure switch on the accumulator/drier and tighten finger-tight.

NOTE: Do not use a wrench to tighten the pressure switch.

19. Connect the electrical connector to the pressure switch.

NOTE: On models with Electronic Engine Control (EEC), once battery cable is disconnected and reconnected, abnormal driveability symptoms may occur on restart and early driving. The computer PROM must relearn driveability conditions. Vehicle will have to be driven 10 miles or more for this to occur.

20. Connect the negative battery cable. Leak test, evacuate and charge the system. Observe all safety precautions.
21. Check the system for proper operation.

Bronco and F-Series

1. Disconnect the negative battery cable.
2. Discharge the refrigerant from the air conditioning system.
3. Disconnect the electrical connector from the pressure switch on the side of the accumulator/drier. Remove the pressure switch.
4. Disconnect the suction hose from the accumulator/drier. Use a backup wrench to loosen the fitting. Cap the openings to prevent the entrance of dirt and moisture.
5. Disconnect the liquid line from the evaporator core using the spring-lock coupling disconnect procedure. Cap the liquid line to prevent the entry of dirt and excessive moisture.
6. On 1994 models, remove 1 screw attaching the plenum chamber and heater/evaporator core.
7. On gasoline engine equipped vehicles, remove the nut retaining the MAP sensor bracket to the upper left corner of the evaporator case. Remove the spring clip holding the MAP sensor to the housing and put the MAP sensor aside.
8. Remove the nut retaining the upper left corner of the evaporator case to the dash panel.
9. Remove the 6 screws attaching the left evaporator cover to the evaporator case. Remove the left evaporator cover.
10. Remove the evaporator core and accumulator from the evaporator case.
11. Remove the support straps from the accumulator and separate the accumulator/drier from the evaporator.

To install:

NOTE: Add 3 oz. (90ml) of clean refrigerant oil to a new replacement evaporator core to maintain the total system oil charge.

12. Transfer the accumulator support straps and spring nuts to the replacement evaporator core.
13. Install the evaporator core in the evaporator case.
14. Position the evaporator cover to the evaporator case and install the 6 attaching screws.
15. Install the nut to retain the upper left corner of the case to the dash panel.
16. Install the spring clip to the rib on the evaporator case and push into position.
17. Install the nut to retain the upper left corner of the MAP sensor bracket to the upper left corner of the evaporator case.
18. In the passenger compartment, install the screw to attach the lower edge of the plenum and bottom of the evaporator case to the dash panel.
19. Remove the cap from the evaporator core liquid line connection and install a new fixed orifice tube in the evaporator core tube.
20. Using a new O-ring lubricated with clean refrigerant oil, connect the liquid line to the evaporator core.
21. Using a new O-ring lubricated with clean refrigerant oil, connect the accumulator/drier (install a new accumulator/drier if evaporator core was replaced) to the evaporator core.
22. Install the accumulator support straps. Tighten the accumulator-to-evaporator core fitting to 15–20 ft. lbs. (21–27 Nm). Use a backup wrench to prevent component damage.
23. Using a new O-ring lubricated with clean refrigerant oil, connect the suction hose to the accumulator/drier. Use a backup wrench to prevent component damage.
24. Using a new O-ring lubricated with clean refrigerant oil, install the pressure switch on the accumulator nipple. Connect the electrical connector to the pressure switch.
25. Leak test, evacuate and charge the system. Observe all safety precautions.
26. Check the system for proper operation.

E-Series

1. Disconnect the battery cables and remove the battery (remove the auxiliary battery, if equipped).
2. Discharge the refrigerant from the air conditioning system.
3. Disconnect electrical and vacuum hoses from MAP sensor.
4. Disconnect the suction line from the accumulator/drier and the liquid line from the evaporator core.
5. Remove the screw that attaches the condenser to evaporator tube to the A/C evaporator case and disconnect the condenser to evaporator tube from the inlet.
6. Remove the evaporator support bracket (1 bolt at fender apron and 2 screws on the case).
7. Disconnect the accumulator from the evaporator case.
8. Remove the screws from the evaporator cover and remove the cover.
9. Remove the evaporator core and seal assembly by pulling back the retaining tab in the housing.

To install:

NOTE: Add 3 oz. (90ml) of clean refrigerant oil to a new replacement evaporator core to maintain the total system oil charge.

10. Position the evaporator core and seal assembly on the evaporator assembly.
11. Install the evaporator support bracket.
12. Reconnect the MAP sensor connector and the connectors to the resistor and pressure switch.
13. Install the screws that attach the evaporator cover to the A/C evaporator case.
14. Connect the heater hoses to the heater core and fill the cooling system to the proper level.
15. Install the battery and connect the battery cables.
16. Leak test, evacuate and charge the system. Observe all safety precautions.
17. Check the system for proper operation.

E-Series with Auxiliary A/C System

1. Disconnect the battery cables and remove the battery (remove the auxiliary battery, if equipped).
2. Discharge the refrigerant from the air conditioning system.
3. Remove the third, fourth and fifth bench seats (if equipped).
4. Remove the left center bolster trim panel, left lower front trim panel, left rear lower and upper trim panels (if equipped).
5. Remove the 6 mounting screws and remove the heater core cover.
6. Clamp off the heater water hoses that connect to the heater core to prevent coolant from spilling when the heater core is removed.
7. Loosen the clamps that secure the heater water hoses to the heater core and disconnect the heater core from the heater water hoses.
8. Remove the heater core.
9. Remove the heater core case seal from the heater core.

To install:

10. Install the heater core case seal onto the heater core.
11. Connect the heater core to the heater water hoses, making sure to install the inlet and outlet heater water hoses in their proper positions.

12. Tighten the inlet and outlet clamps.
13. Unclamp the heater core.
14. Place the heater core and seal into the auxiliary heater and air conditioner assembly.
15. Install the heater core cover and 6 mounting screws.
16. Fill the cooling system to specification and check for leaks.
17. Install the left lower and upper trim panels, left lower front trim panel and the left center bolster trim panel (if equipped).
18. Install the third, fourth and fifth bench seats (if equipped).

Villager

1. Properly discharge and recover the refrigerant. Disconnect the negative battery cable.
2. Using the spring lock removal tool, disconnect the evaporator inlet and outlet lines. Plug all openings to minimize contamination.
3. Remove the plastic rivet and 4 right side instrument panel trim screws. Remove the trim panel.
4. Remove the heater duct to the right side of the instrument panel.
5. Disconnect the wiring at the blower motor, resistor and blower door actuator.
6. Remove 5 evaporator/blower assembly bolts and remove assembly.
7. Remove 7 evaporator case screws, separate the case halves, and remove the evaporator core.

To install:

8. Reassemble the evaporator core, adding 1.5–2.5 oz. of refrigerant oil to the evaporator core if installing a new unit.
9. Position the evaporator/blower assembly under the instrument panel and secure with 5 retaining bolts.
10. Connect the wiring as removed. Install the right side duct.
11. Install the right hand instrument panel trim.
12. Use the spring lock coupling tool and reconnect the inlet and outlet lines.
13. Connect the negative battery cable and evacuate and recharge the system. Leak test and check all system operations.

NOTE: On models with Electronic Engine Control (EEC), once battery cable is disconnected and reconnected, abnormal driveability symptoms may occur on restart and early driving. The computer PROM must relearn driveability conditions. Vehicle will have to be driven 10 miles or more for this to occur.

Windstar

1. Disconnect the negative battery cable.
2. Remove the cowl top vent panel assembly for clearance.
3. Disconnect the black vacuum source hose from the vacuum reservoir which is mounted on the side of the fresh air inlet duct.
4. Remove the upper screw and 2 lower nuts and remove the fresh air inlet duct.
5. Drain the engine cooling system and disconnect the heater hoses at the heater core in the engine compartment.
6. Recover the refrigerant from the A/C system and disconnect the refrigerant lines at the A/C evaporator core in the engine compartment.
7. Remove the instrument panel assembly.
8. Disconnect the blower motor and A/C electronic door actuator motor electrical harness connectors and resistor connector.
9. Disconnect the vacuum harness connector.
10. Remove the nut and bolt from the support bracket at the left side of the housing assembly.
11. Remove 4 nuts retaining the A/C evaporator housing which are located in the engine compartment.
12. Remove the A/C evaporator housing assembly.

NOTE: If removed, the A/C evaporator housing requires replacement, transfer all components from the original assembly to the new assembly as necessary.

13. Installation is the reverse of the removal procedure.

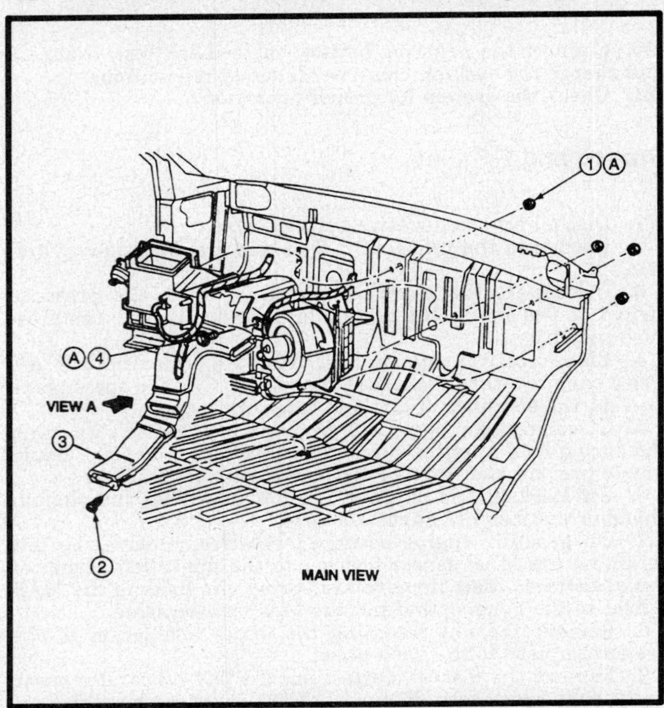

Evaporator housing nut locations—Windstar

Refrigerant Lines

REMOVAL AND INSTALLATION

1. Disconnect the negative battery cable.
2. Discharge the refrigerant from the air conditioning system.
3. Disconnect and remove the refrigerant line. Use a wrench on either side of the fitting or the spring-lock coupling disconnect procedure, as necessary.

To install:

4. Route the new refrigerant line, with the protective caps installed.
5. Connect the new refrigerant line into the system using new O-rings lubricated with clean refrigerant oil. Tighten the connections to 7 ft. lbs. (9 Nm) for a self-sealing coupling and 15–20 ft. lbs. (21–27 Nm) for a non self-sealing coupling, using a backup wrench to prevent component damage, or use the spring-lock coupling connection procedure, if applicable.
6. Connect the negative battery cable. Leak test, evacuate and charge the system. Observe all safety precautions.
7. Check the system for proper operation.

Climate Control Panel

REMOVAL AND INSTALLATION

Aerostar

1. Disconnect the negative battery cable.
2. Remove the instrument panel center console trim.

3. Remove the 3 screws attaching the control assembly to the instrument panel.
4. Pull the control assembly far enough rearward to allow the removal of the electrical connectors. Remove the connectors.
5. Remove the vacuum harness from the function lever selector valve and remove the control vacuum harness.
6. Detach the temperature control cable and remove the control assembly.

To install:

7. Pull the temperature control cable through the opening in the instrument panel.
8. Attach the temperature cable wire to the temperature control lever and snap the cable flag into the control bracket.
9. Connect the vacuum harness to the selector lever.
10. Install the wire harness electrical connectors to the control assembly.
11. Position the control assembly to the instrument panel and install the 3 attaching screws.
12. Install the instrument cluster housing cover or center console trim, as removed.
13. Connect the negative battery cable and check the controls for proper operation.

Explorer (without Automatic Temperature Control) and Ranger

1. Disconnect the negative battery cable.
2. Open the ashtray and remove the 2 screws that hold the ashtray drawer slide to the instrument panel. Remove the ashtray and drawer slide bracket from the instrument panel.
3. Gently pull the finish panel away from the instrument panel and the cluster. The finish panel pops straight back for approximately 1 in., then up to remove. Be careful not to trap the finish panel around the steering column.

NOTE: If equipped with the electronic 4x4 shift-on-the-fly module, disconnect the wire from the rear of the 4x4 transfer switch before trying to remove the finish panel from the instrument panel.

4. Remove the 4 screws attaching the control assembly to the instrument panel.
5. Pull the control through the instrument panel opening enough to allow removal of the electrical connections from the blower switch and control assembly lamp. Remove the 2 hose vacuum harness from the vacuum switch on the side of the control.
6. At the rear of the control, release the temperature and mode cable snap-in flags from the white control bracket.
7. On the bottom side of the control, remove the temperature cable from the control by rotating the cable until the T-pin releases the cable. The temperature cable is black with a blue snap-in flag.
8. Pull enough white cable through the instrument panel opening until the function cable can be held vertical to the control, then remove the control cable from the function (mode) lever. The mode cable is white with a black snap-in flag.
9. Remove the control assembly from the instrument panel.

To install:

10. Pull about 8 in. of the control cables through into the panel opening.
11. Hold the control assembly, facing to the floor, near its position in the instrument panel.
12. Carefully bend and attach the white mode cable to the white plastic lever on the control assembly. Rotate the control assembly back to it's normal position, then snap the black cable flag into the control assembly bracket.
13. On the opposite side of the control assembly, attach the black temperature control cable with the blue plastic snap-in flag to the blue plastic lever on the control. Make sure the end of the cable is seated securely with the T-top pin on the control. Rotate the cable to it's operating position and snap the blue cable flag into the control assembly bracket.
14. Connect the wiring harness to the blower switch and the illumination lamp to it's receptacle. Connect the dual terminal on the vacuum hose to the vacuum switch.
15. Position the control assembly into the instrument panel opening and install the 4 mounting screws.
16. If equipped, reconnect the 4x4 electric shift harness on the rear of the cluster finish panel.
17. Install the cluster finish panel with integral push-pins. Make sure that all pins are fully seated around the rim of the panel.
18. Reinsert the ashtray slide bracket and reconnect the illumination wiring. Reinstall the 2 screws that retain the ashtray retainer bracket and the finish panel.
19. Replace the ashtray and the cigarette lighter.
20. Connect the negative battery cable and check the heater system for proper control assembly operation.

Explorer with Automatic Temperature Control

1. Disconnect the negative battery cable.
2. Remove the cigarette lighter and range selector knob (if applicable).
3. Remove the 2 screws retaining the instrument panel finish panel. Remove the 4 screws retaining the control assembly and pull out the control assembly.
4. Disconnect 2 harness connectors from the control assembly and unbolt the vacuum harness from the control assembly.
5. Remove the control assembly.
6. Installation is the reverse of the removal procedure.

Bronco and F-Series

1. Disconnect the negative battery cable.
2. Remove the trim strip above the control assembly and glove box door. Pull the center finish panel away from the instrument panel to gain access to the 4 screws that attach the control assembly.
3. Remove the 4 screws. Then, pull the control assembly far enough through the opening in the panel to allow disengagement of the electrical connectors for the blower switch and lamp.
4. Disconnect the electrical harness connector from the A/C control assembly.
5. Remove the vacuum harness connector from the notch in the lower edge of the floor distribution duct. Disconnect the vacuum harness from the plenum assembly connector.
6. Carefully detach the temperature control snap-in flange from the underside of the control assembly.
7. Rotate the control assembly 90 degrees and disconnect the temperature control cable from the temperature control tab on the gear rack.
8. Move the control assembly away from the instrument panel.

To install:

9. Pull the temperature control cable into the panel opening for about 8 in.
10. Hold the control assembly against the instrument panel with the face of the control directed toward the roof of the vehicle. Attach the temperature cable to the control lever or gear rack, as removed.
11. Rotate the control assembly to position it into the instrument panel opening. Snap the cable flag into the control bracket. Be sure the flag is firmly seated.
12. Connect the wire harness to the blower switch and control illumination lamp. Attach the vacuum harness to the vacuum selector valve and plenum. Reattach the vacuum harness connector to the notch in the floor duct as removed.
13. Position the control assembly into it's instrument panel opening, noting that the vacuum and electrical harness are properly routed.

14. Install the finish panel and trim strip if removed.
15. Connect the negative battery cable and check the system for proper operation.

NOTE: On models with Electronic Engine Control (EEC), once battery cable is disconnected and reconnected, abnormal driveability symptoms may occur on restart and early driving. The computer PROM must relearn driveability conditions. Vehicle will have to be driven 10 miles or more for this to occur.

E-Series

1. Disconnect the negative battery cable.
2. Remove the trim applique.
3. Remove the screws retaining the control assembly to the mounting bracket.
4. Carefully pull the control assembly from the opening in the mounting bracket.
5. Disconnect the electrical wiring connector from the blower switch, vacuum selector and illumination bulb.
6. Remove the push-on vacuum harness retaining clips from the vacuum selector. Disconnect the vacuum harness from the vacuum selector.
7. Remove the temperature control cable from the control assembly. Disconnect the bullet-type cable retainer from the bracket using needle-nose pliers to compress the retaining ears. Both cable "S" bends are removed from the bottom side of the levers by rotating the cable wire 90 degrees to the lever.

To install:

8. Connect the temperature and function control cables to the control assembly.
9. Connect the vacuum harness to the vacuum selector and retain it with the 2 push-on clips.
10. Connect the electrical wiring connector to the blower switch, vacuum selector valve and illumination bulb wire and socket assembly.
11. Carefully position the control assembly on it's mounting bracket and install the attaching screws.
12. Install the applique and adjust the control cables.
13. Connect the negative battery cable and check the system for proper operation.

Villager

1. Disconnect the negative battery cable.
2. Remove the control console bezel screw from the center of the console bezel. Carefully pull the bezel from the instrument panel.
3. Remove the 4 control panel screws and pull the climate control panel out far enough to reach and disconnect the 5 electrical connectors from the panel. Remove the panel assembly.
4. Installation is the reverse of the removal procedure.

Windstar

1. Disconnect the negative battery cable.
2. Remove the ashtray and cup holder assembly by depressing the service lever and pulling the assembly outward.
3. Remove the 2 trim panel retaining screws and then remove the trim panel.
4. Disconnect the electrical connectors from the finish panel components.
5. Remove the 4 heater and air conditioning control assembly retaining screws.
6. Disconnect the electrical connectors from the control assembly, then remove the control assembly.
7. Installation is the reverse of the removal procedure.

Manual Control Cables

ADJUSTMENT

Aerostar

TEMPERATURE CONTROL CABLE

To check the temperature control cable adjustment, move the temperature control lever back and forth, checking for the sound of the temperature blend door seating against the stop. The temperature control lever should have an equal amount of travel at each end and should not bottom out at either end of the slot. If these conditions are not met, the temperature control cable may not be adjusted properly or may not be connected. To adjust the temperature control cable, proceed as follows:

1. Remove the instrument panel upper finish panel, then remove the auto lamp relay modules from the plenum access hole. Also remove the right speaker.
2. Set the temperature knob to full **WARM** position.
3. Rotate the temperature cam to the full **WARM** position, and, at the same time, open the white bit slot by lifting the tab and adjust the red conduit such that the loop of the cable matches with the cam pin. Insert the loop on the cam pin and release the white bit tab.
4. Turn blower to **HIGH** and rotate the temperature knob, checking for proper cable operation. Readjust if needed.
5. Install the auto lamp relay modules, right speaker and upper finish panel.

Explorer, Ranger, Bronco and F-Series

To check the temperature cable adjustment, move the temperature control lever all the way to the left, then move it all the way to the right. At the extreme ends of lever travel, the door should be heard to firmly seat, indicated by a loud thumping sound, allowing either maximum or no air flow through the heater core.

On Explorer and Ranger, to check the function cable adjustment, check if the lever will reach the detects at far left and right. Also, determine that air flow is correct when function lever is in each mode. If cable adjustment is needed, proceed as follows:

TEMPERATURE CONTROL CABLE

1. Disengage the glove compartment door by squeezing it's sides together. Allow the door to hang free.
2. Working through the glove compartment opening, remove the cable jacket from the metal attaching clip on the top of the plenum by depressing the clip tab and pulling the cable out of the clip.

NOTE: The cable end should remain attached to the door cams.

3. To adjust the temperature control cable, set the temperature lever at **COOL** and hold. With the cable end attached to the temperature door cam, push gently on the cable jacket to seat the blend door. Push until resistance is felt. Reinstall the cable to the clip by pushing the cable jacket into the clip from the top until it snaps in.
4. Operate the system to check temperature cable setting.
5. Install the glove compartment (unless function cable adjustment is needed).
6. Run the system blower on **HIGH** and actuate the levers, checking for proper temperature control.

FUNCTION CONTROL CABLE

1. Set the function (mode) selector lever in **DEFROST** and hold the lever in place. With the cable attached to the function cam, pull on the cam jacket (white) until travel stops. Reinstall the cable to the clip by pushing the cable jacket into the clip until it snaps into place.

2. Install the glove compartment.
3. Run the system blower on **HIGH** and actuate the levers, checking for proper function control.

E-Series

TEMPERATURE CONTROL CABLE

1. Set the temperature control lever on the **COOL** position.
2. Remove the cable from the retaining clip on top of the evaporator-heater case. Leave the cable attached to the yellow crank.
3. Rotate the yellow crank COUNTERCLOCKWISE until the temperature blend door seats.
4. Check again to be sure the temperature lever is in the **COOL** position, then install the cable housing in it's retaining clip by pushing it from the top until it snaps into place.
5. Turn the blower switch to **HI** and move the temperature lever through it's range of travel to check for proper cable adjustment. Readjust, if necessary.

REMOVAL AND INSTALLATION

Aerostar

TEMPERATURE CONTROL CABLE

1. Disconnect the negative battery cable.
2. Remove the instrument panel upper finish panel and the instrument cluster housing assembly.
3. Remove the radio.
4. Working through the opening on the instrument panel top, remove the cable housing from the metal clips on top of the plenum. Disconnect the cable wire end loop from the cam.
5. Remove the control assembly.
6. Remove the cable from the instrument panel.

To install:

7. Install the cable into the instrument panel and connect the cable wire end loop to the cam.
8. Install the control assembly.
9. Adjust the cable.
10. Install the radio.
11. Install the instrument cluster housing assembly and the instrument panel upper finish panel.
12. Connect the negative battery cable and check the system for proper operation.

Explorer and Ranger

TEMPERATURE AND FUNCTION CABLES

1. Disconnect the negative battery cable.
2. Remove the control assembly from the instrument panel.
3. Disengage the glove compartment door by squeezing the sides together and allowing the door to hang free.
4. Working through the glove compartment and/or control opening, remove the temperature and function cable jackets from their clips on top of the plenum by compressing the clip tans and pulling the cables upward.
5. Reach through the glove compartment opening and disconnect the function and temperature cables from their separate cams. The cable ends are secured to the cams under a retention finger.
6. The cables are routed through 2 retainers behind the instrument panel. Remove the cables from these devices. Reaching through the control opening, pull the cables upward out of the wiring shield cut-out. Reaching through the glove box opening, pull the cables out of the plastic retaining clip up inside the instrument panel.
7. Pull the cables out through the control assembly opening.

To install:

8. Working through the glove compartment opening and the control opening in the instrument panel, feed the end of the cables to the cam area. Feed the cables in from the glove compartment opening, making sure the coiled end of the white function cable and the round hole end of the temperature cable go in first.
9. Attach the coiled end of the function cable to its cam, making sure the cable is routed under the cable hold-down on the cam assembly. The pigtail coil may be facing either up or down.
10. Attach the diecast end of the temperature cable to the temperature cam making sure the cable is routed under the cable hold-down feature on the cam assembly.
11. Route the control end of the cable through the instrument panel until the ends stick out of the control opening. It is not necessary to insert the cable into any routing devices previously used. The routing aids are only necessary when the entire instrument panel is removed and reinstalled.

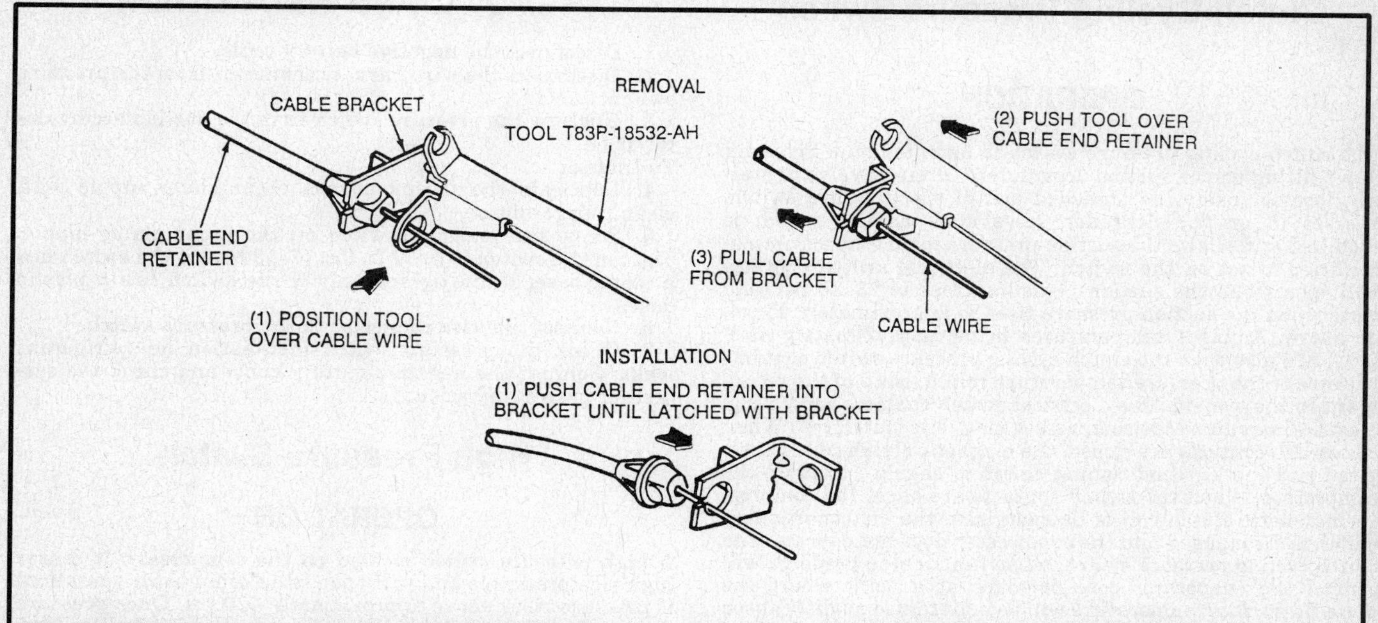
REMOVAL
CABLE BRACKET
TOOL T83P-18532-AH
(2) PUSH TOOL OVER CABLE END RETAINER
CABLE END RETAINER
(3) PULL CABLE FROM BRACKET
(1) POSITION TOOL OVER CABLE WIRE
CABLE WIRE
INSTALLATION
(1) PUSH CABLE END RETAINER INTO BRACKET UNTIL LATCHED WITH BRACKET

Adjusting temperature control cable—E-Series

12. Attach the function and temperature cables to the control. Install the control assembly in the instrument panel.
13. Adjust the cables in their clips on top of the plenum.

NOTE: Make sure the radio antenna cable does not become disengaged from it's mounting and fall into the plenum cam area and cause operating malfunctions.

14. Connect the negative battery cable and make a final check of the system for proper control cable operation.

Bronco and F-Series

TEMPERATURE CONTROL CABLE

1. Disconnect the negative battery cable.
2. Remove the control panel assembly
3. Squeeze the sides of the glove box to free it from the stops and let the door hang down.
4. Remove the screws attaching the ABS module.
5. Through the glove box opening, detach the temperature control cable from the heater core cover, then detach the cable from the cam on top of the plenum.
6. From beneath the lower edge of the instrument panel, pull the cable from its upper retaining tabs (also holding the electrical harness).

To install:

7. Feed the cable to the control attaching point and snap the cable in the upper retaining tabs (along lower edge of instrument panel). The printed part number on the cable should be located in the right hand clip beneath the ashtray.
8. Put the other end of the cable on the cam attachment (loop coil up) and route cable under the hold-down on the cam. Position the cable in the square retaining hole in the heater cover.
9. Attach the cable to the temperature control lever while holding the control assembly close to the opening. Ensure cable does not have kinks or sharp bends.
10. Move the temperature lever to be sure the cable operates properly. Adjust as necessary.
11. Connect the wire and vacuum harness to the control assembly and plenum. Install the control assembly, attach the negative battery cable and check system operation.
12. Install glove box and control panel bezel.

E-Series

TEMPERATURE CONTROL CABLE

1. Disconnect the negative battery cable.
2. Remove the trim and then the control assembly.
3. Carefully pull control assembly rearward and disconnect the electrical connections, then remove the push-on vacuum harness retaining clips and take off the vacuum harness.
4. Disconnect the cable from the control assembly by disconnecting the bullet type retainer. Note that the "S" bend of the cable is remove from the bottom side of the lever by rotating the cable wire 90 degrees to the lever.
5. Remove the cable from the temperature door crank.
6. Remove the temperature control cable through the control panel opening.

To install:

7. Feed the temperature control cable through the control opening.
8. Attach the cable end to the door crank.
9. Attach the other cable end to the control assembly. Position the control assembly and attach the vacuum selector valve and electrical connections.
10. Adjust the temperature control cable. Install the cable housing into it's retaining clip by pushing it from the top until it snaps into place.
11. Connect the negative battery cable and check the system for proper operation.

SENSORS AND SWITCHES

Clutch Cycling Pressure Switch

OPERATION

The clutch cycling pressure switch is mounted on a Schrader valve fitting on the suction accumulator/drier. A valve depressor, located inside the threaded end of the pressure switch, presses in on the Schrader valve stem as the switch is mounted and allows the suction pressure inside the accumulator/drier to act on the switch. The electrical switch contacts will open when the suction pressure drops to 23–26 psi. and close when the suction pressure rises to approximately 45 psi. or above. Ambient temperatures below approximately 45°F (9°C) will also open the clutch cycling pressure switch contacts because of the pressure/temperature relationship of the refrigerant in the system. The electrical switch contacts control the electrical circuit to the compressor magnetic clutch coil. When the switch contacts are closed, the magnetic clutch coil is energized and the air conditioning clutch is engaged to drive the compressor. When the switch contacts are open, the compressor magnetic clutch coil is de-energized, the air conditioning clutch is disengaged and the compressor does not operate. The clutch cycling pressure switch, when functioning properly, will control the evaporator core pressure at a point where the plate/fin surface temperature will be maintained slightly above freezing which prevents evaporator icing and the blockage of airflow.

REMOVAL AND INSTALLATION

1. Disconnect the negative battery cable.
2. Disconnect the wire harness connector from the pressure switch.
3. Unscrew the pressure switch from the suction accumulator/drier.

To install:

4. Lubricate the O-ring on the accumulator nipple with clean refrigerant oil.
5. Screw the pressure switch on the accumulator nipple. Tighten the switch to 5–10 ft. lbs. (7–13 Nm) if the switch has a metal base. Hand tighten only if the switch has a plastic base.
6. Connect the wire connector to the pressure switch.
7. Check the pressure switch installation for refrigerant leaks. Connect the negative battery cable and check the system for proper operation.

High Pressure Switch

OPERATION

A high pressure switch located on the compressor. It senses high side pressures and will open (stop compressor operation) if pressure rises above approximately 420 psi. Once pressure drops below 250 psi the switch will again close and allow compressor to operate normally.

Vacuum Motors

OPERATION

Vacuum motors are used to operate the air directing doors within the plenum. These doors vary the mix of outside and recirculated air, as well as direct the airflow to the floor duct, instrument panel registers or defroster nozzles.

REMOVAL AND INSTALLATION

Aerostar

Vacuum motors are used to operate 3 damper doors: the outside/recirculating air door, the panel/defrost door and the floor/defrost door. Each of these vacuum motors responds to the vacuum selector valve, which is a component of the control assembly.

1. Disconnect the vacuum hose from the vacuum motor.
2. Remove the push pin retaining the vacuum motor arm to the door crank arm.
3. Loosen the 2 motor retaining nuts and lift the motor from the mounting bracket.

To install:

4. Position the vacuum motor to the mounting bracket and the vacuum motor arm to the door crank arm.
5. Tighten the 2 nuts retaining the motor to the mounting bracket.
6. Install the push pin to retain the vacuum motor arm to the door crank arm.
7. Connect the vacuum hose to the vacuum motor and check for proper operation.

Explorer and Ranger

The outside/recirculating air door is the only door which is vacuum controlled on these vehicles.

1. Open the glove compartment and press in the sides of the glove compartment and pull it out allowing it to hang down. The vacuum motor should be visible on the right side of the plenum.
2. Disconnect the vacuum hose from the vacuum motor nipple.
3. Remove the 2 screws attaching the vacuum motor to the plenum.
4. Swing the vacuum motor rearward and disconnect the vacuum motor arm from the shaft on the plenum by sliding the motor arm to the left.

To install:

5. Position the vacuum motor arm so the shaft on the plenum protrudes through the hole in the vacuum motor.
6. Swing the vacuum motor forward and install 2 screws attaching the vacuum motor to the plenum.
7. Connect the vacuum hose to the vacuum motor nipple.
8. Push the sides of the glove compartment and install to the latched position.
9. Start the engine and move the function lever forward in the control assembly to verify that the vacuum motor functions properly.

Bronco and F-Series

Vacuum motors are used to operate 3 damper doors: the outside/recirculating air door, the panel/defrost door and the floor/defrost door. Each of these vacuum motors responds to the vacuum selector valve, which is a component of the control assembly.

OUTSIDE/RECIRCULATING AIR DOOR VACUUM MOTOR

1. Disconnect the negative battery cable.
2. Disconnect the blower motor connector and remove the blower motor.
3. If only the vacuum motor is to be removed, disconnect the 2 screws that attach the motor to the upper surface of the outside door duct and disconnect the 2 vacuum hoses.
4. Pry the motor and arm assembly upward at the arm end to free it from it's mounting peg.

NOTE: A retaining flange that is an integral part of the crank, peg and flange component may partially obstruct the motor arm in it's upward movement along the peg. If this retaining flange should break off when forcing the motor arm upward, a 3/16 in. spring nut must be used to retain the motor arm when the same or a replacement motor is installed.

5. Through the blower motor opening in the case, depress the snap-on door crank while pulling up on the door shaft to release the crank from the door.
6. Remove the door through the blower motor opening.

To install:

7. Insert the door through the blower motor opening. Seat the bottom door pivot first, then swing the top door pivot into place.
8. Hold the door in the full outside air position and snap in the crank.
9. Align the hole in the vacuum motor arm with the peg in the door crank.
10. Slide the arm downward over the peg and along the inner surface of the retaining flange until the arm seats on the base of the flange surface.

NOTE: If the flange has been broken off, then install the 3/16 in. spring nut.

11. Install the blower motor in the housing and connect the blower motor electrical harness.
12. Connect the negative battery cable.

PANEL/DEFROST DOOR VACUUM MOTOR

1. Remove the vacuum hose from the vacuum motor.
2. Remove the 2 screws that attach the motor and bracket assembly to the plenum.
3. Rotate the assembly so the slot in the bracket is parallel with the T-shaped end of the door crank arm. Pull the motor and bracket assembly off the crank arm.

To install:

4. Insert the end of the crank arm into the slot in the motor and bracket assembly. Rotate the assembly into alignment with the bracket attaching holes in the plenum.
5. Install the 2 motor and bracket assembly attaching screws.
6. Install the vacuum hose on the motor.
7. Check the system for proper operation.

FLOOR/DEFROST DOOR VACUUM MOTOR

1. Remove the floor duct as follows:
   - Remove the plastic attaching screw from the bottom side of the plenum.
   - Remove the push nut sleeve from the attaching hole.
   - Disengage the floor duct from the plenum.
2. Disconnect the 2 vacuum hoses from the vacuum motor.
3. Remove the 2 screws that secure the motor and bracket assembly to the plenum.
4. Using a small prybar, depress the tang on the side of the door operating lever and pull the motor arm out of the lever.

To install:

5. Slide the motor arm into the door lever until the locking tang engages.
6. Attach the 2 vacuum hoses.
7. Install the 2 motor and bracket attaching screws.
8. Install the floor duct as follows:
   - Position the duct on the plenum and engage the lugs inside the duct with their mating slots in the plenum. Tilt the duct into place, then push in to secure engagement.

- Start the plastic screw into the push nut sleeve. Then, install through the floor duct flange and into the attaching hole in the plenum. Make sure the attachment is secure.

9. Check the system for proper operation.

E-Series

Vacuum motors are used to operate 3 damper doors: the outside/recirculating air door, the panel/defrost door and the floor/defrost door. Each of these vacuum motors responds to the vacuum selector valve, which is a component of the control assembly.

1. Remove the 2 screws retaining the motor to the plenum case.
2. Carefully lift vacuum motor until its arm is free of the channel retaining the arm to the door crank pin.
3. Disconnect the vacuum hose from the vacuum motor and remove the motor and bracket.

To install:

4. Snap the vacuum motor arm onto the clip or pin as removed.
5. Connect the vacuum hose to the vacuum motor and position the motor and bracket to the plenum case.
6. Install the 2 screws retaining the vacuum motor.
7. If necessary, install a new pushnut to retain the motor arm on the door crank arm.
8. Check the system for proper operation.

Villager

Villager uses electrically operated door actuators to open and close the temperature blend/panel bypass door, the panel/floor/defrost door, and the outside/recirc air door.

OUTSIDE/RECIRC AIR DOOR ACTUATOR

1. Disconnect the negative battery cable.
2. Remove the glove box and lamp. Remove the right side knee reinforcement plates.
3. Remove the right side inner and outer ducts.
4. Remove the 2 Powertrain Control Module (PCM) bracket bolts, remove the PCM and Transaxle Control Module (TCM) and position aside.
5. Remove the 4 door actuator bracket bolts and detach the electrical connector.
6. Remove the actuator assembly, then take off the bracket.
7. Installation is the reverse of the removal procedure.

TEMPERATURE BLEND/PANEL BYPASS DOOR ACTUATOR

1. Disconnect the negative battery cable.
2. Remove the control console bezel, ashtray assembly and storage bin. Remove the right side knee reinforcement plate.
3. Remove the 3 door actuator bracket bolts, detach the electrical connector to the actuator.
4. Remove the actuator assembly, take off 3 screws holding the mounting bracket and separate bracket from actuator.
5. Install by reversing the removal procedure.

1993 Villager

PANEL/FLOOR/DEFROST DOOR ACTUATOR

1. Disconnect the negative battery cable.
2. Working behind the left side of the center console, locate the actuator on the left side of the heater housing and remove 3 door actuator bracket bolts.
3. Detach the electrical connector.
4. Disconnect the door actuator control rod from the actuator and remove the actuator from the heater housing.
5. Remove the 3 screws holding the bracket to the actuator and separate the pieces.
6. Install by reversing the removal procedure.

1994–95 Villager

PANEL/FLOOR/DEFROST DOOR ACTUATOR

1. Disconnect the negative battery cable.
2. Remove the instrument finish panel, ash tray, and cigar lighter.
3. Remove the instrument panel lower center panel, then the RH instrument panel lower reinforcement.
4. Remove the three actuator motor bolts.
5. Disconnect the actuator motor electrical connector then the control rod.
6. Remove the actuator from the heater assembly.
7. Install by reversing the removal procedure.

Windstar

Vacuum motors are used to operate 3 damper doors: the windshield defrost/floor door, panel/floor door and the air inlet/recirculation door. Each of these vacuum motors responds to the vacuum selector valve, which is a component of the control assembly.

WINDSHIELD DEFROST/FLOOR DOOR

1. Disconnect the vacuum hose connectors from the vacuum control motor, then the yellow hose from the side, and the blue hose from the end.
2. Remove the pushpin from the end of the shaft.
3. Remove the 2 mounting screws and remove the vacuum control motor.

NOTE: Make sure the yellow vacuum hose is connected to the side, and the blue vacuum hose is connected to the end of the defrost/floor door vacuum control motor.

4. Installation is the reverse of the removal procedure.

PANEL/FLOOR DOOR

1. Disconnect the vacuum hose connectors, then the red hose from the side and the green hose from the end of the vacuum control motor.
2. Remove the 2 retaining screws from the vacuum control motor.
3. Rotate the vacuum control motor until the shaft is clear of the retainer.
4. Lift shaft off mounting pin and remove vacuum control motor.

NOTE: Make sure the red vacuum hose is connected to the side, and the green vacuum hose is connected to the end of the vacuum control motor assembly.

5. Installation is the reverse of the removal procedure.

AIR INLET/RECIRCULATION DOOR

1. Disconnect the orange vacuum hose.
2. Remove the 2 screws retaining the vacuum control motor.
3. Rotate the vacuum control motor until the shaft is clear of the retainer.
4. Lift the shaft off the mounting pin and remove the vacuum control motor.
5. Installation is the reverse of the removal procedure.

REAR AUXILIARY SYSTEM

Air Conditioning and Heating Assembly

REMOVAL AND INSTALLATION

Windstar

NOTE: The auxiliary heater core and evaporator core are removed from the vehicle with the removal of the air conditioning and heating assembly.

1. Disconnect the the negative battery cable.
2. Properly drain and capture the cooling system coolant.
3. Discharge and recover the refrigerant from the A/C system.
4. Raise and safely support the vehicle.
5. Disconnect the heater water hoses from the auxiliary heater core pipes coming from the front of the vehicle.
6. Drain the auxiliary heater core and the heater water hoses.
7. Disconnect the 2 A/C spring lock couplings.
8. Lower the vehicle.
9. Remove all rear passenger seating.
10. Remove the three push pin retainers from the lower edge of the auxiliary heater and air conditioning service center and remove the cover.
11. Disconnect the heater blower, the blower motor resistor, the blower motor control switch lamp, and the cigar lighter electrical connectors.
12. Disconnect the rear seat remote radio control electrical connector (if equipped).
13. Disconnect the auxiliary heater and the A/C assembly main harness electrical connector. Then disconnect the mode door vacuum control motor vacuum line connector.
14. Remove the 2 LH body side trim panels.
15. Plug all A/C refrigerant lines to prevent dirt or moisture entry.
16. Remove the lower A/C recirculation air duct and the heater extension air ducts.
17. Remove the auxiliary heater and air conditioning assembly.

To install:

18. Position the auxiliary heater and air conditioning assembly in the vehicle and secure it. Connect the two A/C refrigerant couplings.
19. Install the lower air recirculation air duct and the heater extension air ducts and secure them. Then install the 2 LH body side trim panels.
20. Connect the mode door vacuum control motor vacuum line connector.
21. Connect the air conditioning and heating assembly main harness, remote radio control, and cigar lighter electrical connectors.
22. Connect the heater blower, the blower motor resistor, the blower motor control switch lamp, and the cigar lighter electrical connectors.
23. Install the service panel in the LH body side trim panel with the 3 pin retainers.
24. Install the rear passenger seating. Raise the vehicle.
25. Connect the heater water hoses to the heater, then lower the vehicle.
26. Evacuate and charge the A/C system.
27. Connect the negative battery cable.
28. Refill the engine cooling system.

Expansion Valve

REMOVAL AND INSTALLATION

E-Series

1. Remove the evaporator core and seal.
2. Using a back-up wrench on the fittings, remove the liquid jumper line from the expansion valve, then remove the inlet line from the valve. Plug all openings to minimize contamination.
3. Remove the expansion valve from the vehicle.
4. Install a new expansion valve in the reverse procedure.

Windstar

1. Remove the air conditioning and heating assembly.
2. Remove the A/C evaporator core lower access cover screws and remove the cover.
3. Remove the A/C evaporator core from the auxiliary heater and air conditioning assembly.
4. Loosen the 2 rear thermostatic expansion valve pipe fittings and remove the valve from the A/C evaporator core inlet/outlet pipes.
5. Remove the capillary tube retaining clip located on the A/C evaporator core outlet pipe.
6. Installation is the reverse of the removal procedure.

Villager

1. Remove the rear A/C-heater system.
2. Using back-up wrenches, loosen the 4 expansion valve pipe fittings and remove the expansion valve from the evaporator inlet and outlet pipes.
3. Installation is the reverse of the removal procedure.

Fixed Orifice Tube

REMOVAL AND INSTALLATION

Aerostar

1. Disconnect the negative battery cable.
2. Remove the auxiliary service cover.
3. Discharge the refrigerant from the air conditioning system.
4. Disconnect the solenoid valve wiring connector and disconnect the solenoid from the case bracket. Using a backup wrench to prevent damage, disconnect the solenoid valve from the liquid jump line and from the evaporator core. Cap the solenoid to prevent the entrance of dirt and excessive moisture.
5. Squirt a small amount of clean refrigerant oil into the evaporator core inlet tube to lubricate the tube and orifice O-rings during removal of the fixed orifice tube from the evaporator core tube.
6. Engage the fixed orifice tube remover/replacer T83L–19990–A or equivalent, with the 2 tangs on the fixed orifice tube.

NOTE: Do not attempt to remove the fixed orifice tube with pliers or to twist or rotate the orifice tube in the evaporator core tube. To do so will break the fixed orifice tube body in the evaporator core tube. Use only the recommended tool following the recommended service procedures.

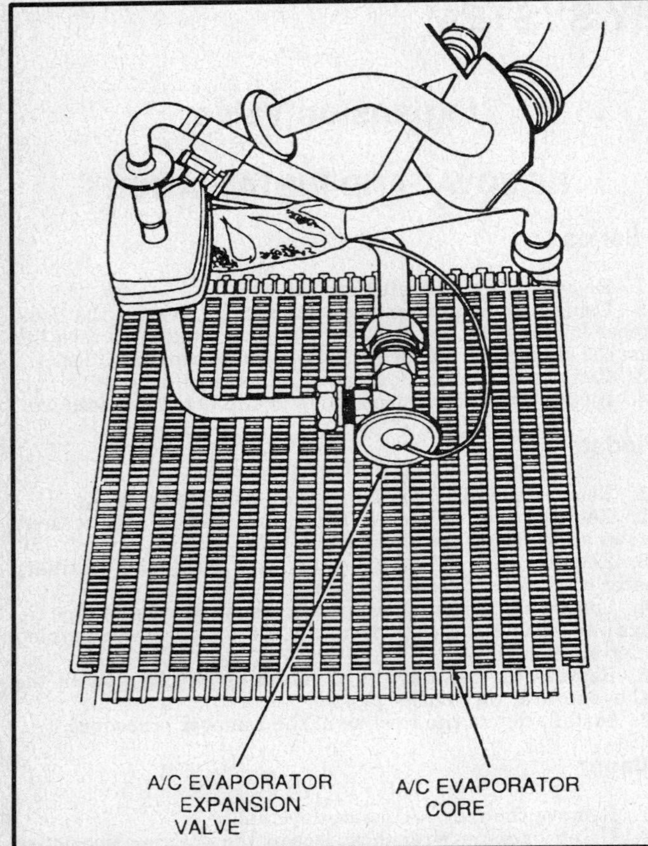

A/C evaporator expansion valve installation—Windstar

7. Hold the T-handle of the tool to keep it from turning and run the nut on the tool down against the evaporator core tube until the orifice is pulled from the tube.
8. If the fixed orifice tube breaks in the evaporator core tube, it must be removed from the tube with the broken orifice tube extractor T83L–19990–B or equivalent.
9. To remove a broken orifice tube, insert the screw end of the broken orifice tube extractor into the evaporator core tube and thread the screw end of the tool into the brass tube in the center of the fixed orifice tube. Then, pull the fixed orifice tube from the evaporator core tube.
10. If only the brass center tube is removed during Step 9, insert the screw end of the broken orifice tube extractor into the evaporator core tube and screw the end of the tool into the fixed orifice tube body. Then, pull the fixed orifice tube body from the evaporator core tube.

To install:

11. Lubricate the O-rings and the fixed orifice tube body liberally with clean refrigerant oil.
12. Place the fixed orifice tube in the fixed orifice tube remover/replacer T83L–19990–A or equivalent, and insert the fixed orifice tube into the evaporator core tube until the orifice is seated at the stop. The orifice tube used in the rear auxiliary system is color coded brown.
13. Remove the tool from the fixed orifice tube.
14. Using a new O-ring lubricated with clean refrigerant oil, connect the solenoid to the evaporator core tube. Tighten the fitting to 15–20 ft. lbs. (21–27 Nm) using a backup wrench.
15. Connect the solenoid electrical connector to the harness and attach to the bracket.
16. Connect the negative battery cable. Leak test, evacuate and charge the system. Observe all safety precautions.
17. Install the service cover.

Blower Motor

REMOVAL AND INSTALLATION

Aerostar

1. Disconnect the negative battery cable.
2. Remove the seat behind the driver and remove the service panel.
3. Remove the 3 screws from the solenoid bracket and disconnect the motor connector.
4. Disconnect the blower motor air cooling tube from the motor.
5. Remove the remaining 2 screws from the motor mounting plate and remove the motor and wheel assembly from the housing.
6. Remove the hub clamp spring from the blower wheel hub and the retainer from the motor shaft. Remove the blower wheel from the motor shaft.
7. Remove the nuts holding the motor to the motor mounting plate.

To install:

8. Install a new motor mounting plate using 2 nuts and tighten to 13–17 inch lbs. (1.5–2.0 Nm).
9. Position the blower wheel on the blower shaft. Being careful to match the flat surfaces exactly, push the wheel down until it stops against the motor. Install a new hub clamp spring on the blower hub.
10. Install a new motor mounting seal on the blower motor flange.
11. Position the blower motor and wheel assembly in the housing and attach with the upper attaching screws.
12. Install the solenoid bracket with the 3 attaching screws.
13. Install the blower motor cooling tube and connect the blower motor connector.
14. Connect the negative battery cable and check the blower motor for proper operation.
15. Install the service cover and passenger seat.

E-Series

1. Disconnect the negative battery cable.
2. Remove the bench seats, as equipped. Remove the left center bolster trim panel, left lower front trim panel, and the left rear lower and upper trim panels if equipped.
3. Disconnect the blower motor resistor connector.
4. Remove the blower motor mounting plate, housing tube, and remove the blower motor.
5. Installation is the reverse of the removal procedure.

Villager

1. Disconnect the negative battery cable.
2. Remove the center seat.
3. Remove the rear auxiliary A/C-heater access panel for the left quarter trim panel.
4. Disconnect the blower motor wire.
5. Remove the 3 blower motor mounting screws and lift the blower assembly from the vehicle.
6. Installation is the reverse of the removal procedure.

Windstar

1. Disconnect the negative battery cable.
2. Remove both the rear passenger seats.
3. Remove the 3 retaining push pins located along the lower edge of the auxiliary A/C assembly trim panel and remove the trim panel.
4. Disconnect the heater blower motor switch and the illumination electrical connectors at trim panel.

5. Disconnect the heater blower motor electrical connector.
6. Remove the ventilation tube from the blower motor and the housing.
7. Remove the 3 screws retaining the blower motor and then the blower motor.
8. Remove the blower wheel retaining pushnut from the heater blower motor shaft then remove the blower wheel.
9. Install by reversing the removal procedure.

Blower Motor Resistor

REMOVAL AND INSTALLATION

1. Disconnect the negative battery cable.
2. Remove the first bench seat, if equipped.
3. Remove the auxiliary heater/air conditioner service cover attaching screws and remove the cover.
4. Disconnect the wire connector from the resistor assembly.
5. Remove the 2 resistor retaining screws and remove the resistor assembly.

To install:

6. Position the resistor to the housing and install the 2 retaining screws.
7. Connect the wire connector to the resistor assembly and connect the negative battery cable.
8. Hold the auxiliary unit cover in place and check the operation of the blower at each blower speed. Do not touch the resistor during or after operation of the blower motor.
9. Install the auxiliary service cover and install the bench seat, if equipped.

Heater Core

REMOVAL AND INSTALLATION

Aerostar

1. Disconnect the negative battery cable. With engine temperature cold and temperature control at FULL HEAT position, back off radiator cap to first detent to relieve system pressure. Retighten cap. This will prevent excess coolant loss when detaching heater hoses.
2. Remove the first seat behind the driver, if equipped.
3. Remove the auxiliary heater/air conditioner cover attaching screws and remove the cover.
4. Remove the auxiliary unit floor duct by removing 1 or 2 attaching screws and rotating the duct gently downward.
5. Remove the remaining 16 screws from the heater assembly cover and remove the cover from the case.
6. Disconnect the heater hoses from the auxiliary heater core by depressing the white tabs while pulling the connectors apart (quick disconnect couplings), then plug the hoses.
7. Slide the heater core and seal assembly out of the housing slot.

To install:

8. Slide the heater core and seal assembly into the housing slot.
9. Connect the heater hoses to the heater core tubes.
10. Fill the cooling system to the proper level and check for coolant leaks.
11. Install the auxiliary heater/air conditioner cover.
12. Install the floor duct.
13. Install the service cover and passenger seat. Reattach the negative battery cable and top off cooling system fluid, if needed.

E-Series

1. Remove the bench seats, as necessary to access the heater system cover.
2. Remove the left center bolster trim panel, the left lower front trim panel, left rear lower and upper trim panels if equipped. Then remove the 6 heater core cover attaching screws.
3. Clamp off if necessary, then remove the heater hoses from the auxiliary heater core and plug the hoses.
4. Slide the heater core and seal assembly out of the housing slot.

To install:

5. Slide the heater core and seal assembly into the housing slot.
6. Remove the plugs from the heater hose and connect the hoses to the heater core tubes.
7. Fill the cooling system to the proper level and check for coolant leaks.
8. Install a new strap to retain the heater core in the case assembly.
9. Install the auxiliary heater and/or air conditioner cover or trim panels, as removed.
10. Install the bench seat, if removed. Tighten the retaining bolts to 25–45 ft. lbs. (34–61 Nm).

Villager

NOTE: The rear heater-A/C assembly on Villager must be removed as a complete unit in order to remove the heater core and/or evaporator core.

1. Properly drain and capture cooling system coolant. Disconnect the negative battery cable and the properly discharge the air conditioning system.
2. Remove the center seats. Remove the 2 left have seat belt lower anchor bolts. Remove the left rear cargo net retainers, if equipped.
3. Remove the lift gate scuff plate, the 3 screws from the left rear quarter trim panel. Gently pry the rear seat remote control if equipped from the trim panel, then disconnect the remote control wiring connector and remove the rear radio control panel. Pull the top of the trim panel away from the body.
4. Disconnect the rear climate control panel wiring, if equipped.
5. Release the left front lap belt guide from the left quarter trim panel and pass the belt through the trim panel. Now remove the trim panel from the vehicle.
6. Remove the upper duct from the assembly (6 screws).
7. Disconnect the blower motor and resistor wiring. Also detach the temperature blend and vent door actuator connectors.
8. Raise and support the vehicle. Use the spring lock coupling tool to disconnect and plug the refrigerant line connections from beneath the vehicle.
9. Disconnect and plug the heater pipes from the heater core.
10. Lower the vehicle, remove the 4 A/C-heater assembly bolts, and remove the assembly from the vehicle. Heater core or evaporator core can be removed from the assembly on the bench.

To install:

11. Reassemble the core(s) to the assembly and install into place with 4 retaining bolts.
12. Raise the vehicle and reconnect the heater pipes and the refrigerant lines.
13. Lower the vehicle. Reconnect all wiring. Install the upper air duct with 6 screws.
14. Reposition the trim panel and pass the lap seat belt through the panel slot.
15. Reconnect the rear climate control panel, install the rear radio and rear remote control.
16. Reinstall the rest of the trim panel and components.
17. Refill the cooling system. Evacuate and recharge the air conditioning system. Reconnect the negative battery cable and check the entire system operation.

Windstar

1. Remove the auxiliary air conditioning and heating assembly.
2. Remove the cover screws and remove the cover from case.
3. Remove the heater core and heater core case seal.
4. Install by reversing the removal procedure.

Evaporator

REMOVAL AND INSTALLATION

Aerostar

1. Disconnect the negative battery cable.
2. Remove the first seat behind the driver, if equipped.
3. Remove the auxiliary air conditioner service cover attaching screws and remove the cover.
4. Discharge the refrigerant from the air conditioning system.
5. Remove the floor duct.
6. Disconnect the suction line from the evaporator core using the spring-lock coupling disconnect procedure. Plug the line to prevent the entrance of dirt and moisture.
7. Disconnect the solenoid bracket from the case.
8. Using backup wrenches, disconnect the evaporator core from the solenoid valve.
9. Remove the auxiliary case cover screws and cover.
10. Remove the resistor block connector and remove the evaporator core.

To install:

NOTE: Add 3 oz. (90ml) of clean refrigerant oil to a new replacement evaporator core to maintain the total system oil charge.

11. Install the evaporator core seal to the tube end of the core.
12. Install a new O-ring lubricated with clean refrigerant oil to the evaporator core inlet line and to the liquid line fitting.
13. Carefully place the core in the case and align the inlet tube with the solenoid. Tighten the connections to 15–20 ft. lbs. (21–27 Nm) using a backup wrench.
14. Install the solenoid bracket to the case assembly.
15. Install the new O-ring on the underbody suction line and lubricate with clean refrigerant oil. Connect to the evaporator core using the spring-lock coupling connection procedure.
16. Wrap the suction line with insulating tape.
17. Reconnect the resistor wiring connector.
18. Install the case cover and the floor duct.
19. Connect the negative battery cable. Leak test, evacuate and charge the system. Observe all safety precautions.
20. Install the service cover and the passenger seat.

E-Series

NOTE: Whenever a refrigerant line, expansion valve or evaporator core in the auxiliary system is replaced, it will be necessary to replace the suction accumulator/drier in the main system.

1. Remove the rear bench seats as needed to access the evaporator assembly.
2. Remove the left center bolster trim panel, left lower front trim panel, left rear lower and upper trim panels if equipped.
3. Disconnect the negative battery cable. Properly discharge the air conditioning system. Properly drain the cooling system.
4. Disconnect and plug the heater hoses from the heater core tubes.
5. Using a back-up wrench, disconnect and cap the liquid line and suction line from evaporator lines.
6. Disconnect the main wiring harness and vacuum line from the heater-A/C assembly.
7. Remove the mounting screw from the vertical duct and push duct up into the headline, then pull duct down and away from its mounting.
8. Remove 2 heater-A/C assembly mounting screws and pull the assembly off the dowel alignment pin. As assembly is lifted out of the vehicle, guide the heater hoses out from the underbody.
9. Remove 4 screws to remove the evaporator cover. Take out the evaporator core and seal.

To install:

NOTE: If installing a new evaporator core, add 2.0 oz. of refrigerant oil during installation.

10. Position the core and seal into the case, making sure to align the evaporator tube seal in the side of the case.
11. Install the evaporator cover. Position the heater-A/C assembly into the vehicle, guiding the heater hose extensions through the lower body, and guiding the assembly onto the alignment dowel pin.
12. Reinstall the vertical duct, taking care of the headliner during installation. Reattach the main wiring harness and vacuum line to the assembly.
13. Reconnect the refrigerant lines and the heater pipes, using back-up wrenches as necessary.
14. Refill the cooling system. Evacuate and recharge the air conditioning system. Attach the negative battery cable and perform a complete system check.
15. Reinstall the trim panels and seats, as removed.

Villager

NOTE: Refer to auxiliary heater core removal procedure, as heater and air conditioning assembly must be removed as a unit before either core can be removed.

Windstar

1. Remove the auxiliary air conditioning and heating assembly.
2. Remove the heater core cover and the heater core.
3. Remove the cover screws and remove the cover from the case.
4. Remove the A/C evaporator core.

To install:

5. Install the A/C evaporator core seal to the tube end of the A/C evaporator core. Install the new O-ring lubricated with clean refrigerant oil to the inlet line and to the condenser-to-evaporator tube O-fitting.
6. Carefully place the A/C evaporator core in the case. Install the new O-ring on the underbody suction line and lubricate with clean refrigerant oil.
7. Wrap the evaporator-to-compressor suction line with insulating tape.
8. Install the case cover and the air conditioning and heating assembly.
9. Leak test, evacuate, and charge the refrigerant system following the recommended service procedures.

Refrigerant Lines

REMOVAL AND INSTALLATION

1. Disconnect the negative battery cable.
2. Discharge the refrigerant from the air conditioning system.
3. Working under the vehicle, as necessary, disconnect and remove the refrigerant line. Use a wrench on either side of the fitting or the spring-lock coupling disconnect procedure, as required.

To install:

4. Route the new refrigerant line, with the protective caps installed.
5. Remove the caps and connect the new refrigerant line into the system using new O-rings lubricated with clean refrig-

erant oil. Tighten the connections using a back-up wrench to prevent component damage, or use the spring-lock coupling connection procedure, if applicable.

6. Connect the negative battery cable. Leak test, evacuate and charge the system. Observe all safety precautions.
7. Check the system for proper operation.

Villager

1. Disconnect the negative battery cable.
2. Properly drain the cooling system and properly discharge the air conditioning system.
3. Raise the vehicle. Chisel off a rivet head from 1 rivet on each of the 4 rear tube hold-down brackets. Remove 2 bolts from each of the hold-down brackets.
4. Detach and plug the rear heater pipes from the main heating system at the engine compartment, then disconnect the heater pipes from the auxiliary heater-A/C assembly.
5. Using the spring coupling disconnect procedure, disconnect the 2 A/C lines at the engine compartment and at the auxiliary A/C assembly.
6. Remove the A/C lines and heater pipes from the vehicle.

To install:

7. Position and join the A/C lines at the auxiliary assembly, then join the spring couplings at the engine compartment. Use the spring lock couplings to finish joining the lines at the rear assembly.
8. Position the heater pipes. Connect the pipes to the main heater system at the engine compartment, then to the auxiliary heater-A/C assembly.
9. Install the 4 hold-down brackets as removed.
10. Lower the vehicle. Evacuate and recharge the system. Refill the cooling system. Reconnect the negative battery cable and check the entire system operation.

SENSORS AND SWITCHES

Solenoid Valve

OPERATION

Aerostar

The solenoid valve used on Aerostar shuts off the flow of refrigerant into the rear evaporator when the rear blower is shut off.

Villager

The coolant control solenoid valve operates on a voltage signal from the battery. The solenoid valve opens to allow a vacuum signal to the coolant control actuator to shut off coolant flow to the rear heater unit with the rear blower OFF. When the rear blower is turned ON, the voltage signal drops to 0 and the vacuum signal is cut-off to the actuator, allowing coolant to flow to the rear heater core. The valve is mounted on the bulkhead behind the intake plenum.

REMOVAL AND INSTALLATION

Aerostar

1. Disconnect the negative battery cable.
2. Remove the first seat behind the driver, if equipped.
3. Remove the auxiliary service cover.
4. Discharge the refrigerant from the air conditioning system.
5. Disconnect the wiring connector from the solenoid and the solenoid from the case bracket.
6. Using a back-up wrench to prevent damage, disconnect the solenoid valve from the liquid jump line and from the evaporator core. Cap the liquid line and core to prevent the entrance of dirt and moisture.
7. Remove the solenoid.

To install:

8. Install new O-rings lubricated with clean refrigerant oil to the liquid jump line and the evaporator core.
9. Install the solenoid to both lines, tightening the connections only finger-tight.
10. Attach the solenoid to the bracket and tighten the screws.
11. Using a back-up wrench, tighten the liquid jump line to the solenoid to 10–15 ft. lbs. (14–20 Nm) and the solenoid to the evaporator core to 15–20 ft. lbs. (21–27 Nm).
12. Connect the solenoid electrical connector to the harness and attach to the bracket.
13. Connect the negative battery cable. Leak test, evacuate and charge the system. Observe all safety precautions.
14. Install the service panel and passenger seat.

Villager

1. Disconnect the negative battery cable.
2. Detach the coolant control solenoid valve connector and disconnect the 2 vacuum lines.
3. Remove the solenoid valve bracket nut and remove the solenoid valve.
4. If removing the actuator, properly drain the cooling system
5. Disconnect the vacuum line at the actuator, remove the actuator retaining nut, disconnect the heater hoses and remove the actuator.
6. Installation is the reverse of the removal procedure.

Vacuum Motor and Actuator

OPERATION

Aerostar

Vacuum is used to control the operation of the function door on the auxiliary unit on Aerostar. It is located in the liquid line of the auxiliary system near the blower assembly. If the front control is in the **HEAT, MIX** or **DEFROST** position, the vacuum motor operated function door in the rear unit will deliver heated air through the floor outlets. If the front control is in the **VENT** position, the door in the rear unit will provide recirculated air which is delivered through the overhead and belt line registers. If the front control is set for air conditioning and there is an air conditioning unit in the rear system, that unit will deliver air conditioning through the overhead and belt line registers. However, if there is no rear air conditioning unit, the rear unit will function as if the front unit were set in the **VENT** position.

Villager

Temperature and airflow are directed by 2 electrically operated door actuators. The temperature blend door actuator controls the airflow as it is diverted through, around or a mix of the heater and evaporator. The system also uses a vent door actuator to control fresh air intake when the heater or A/C system

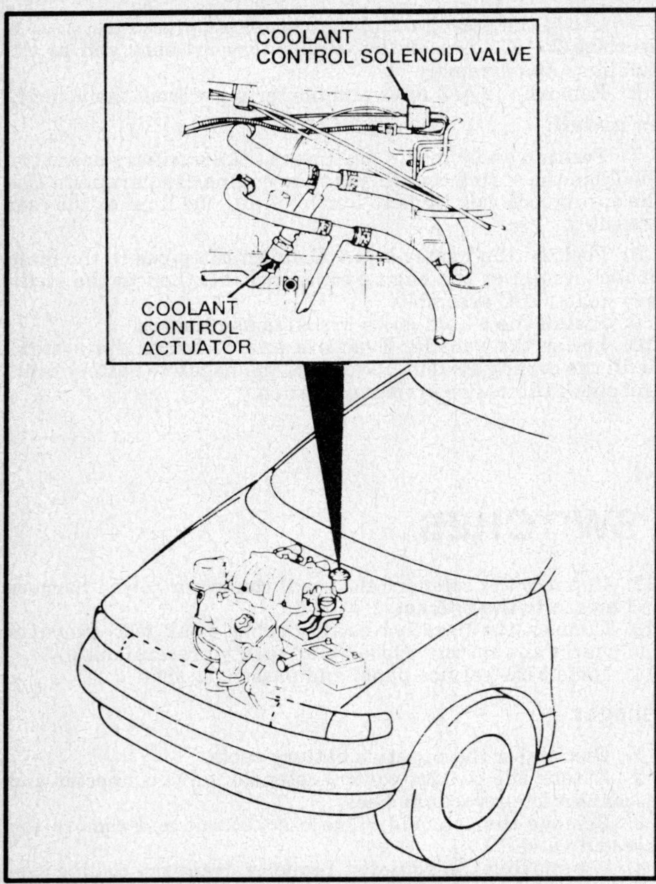

Location of coolant control solenoid and coolant control actuator for auxiliary heater/air conditioning system—Villager

REMOVAL AND INSTALLATION

Aerostar

1. Remove the first seat behind the driver.
2. Remove the auxiliary service panel.
3. Remove the floor duct.
4. Remove the auxiliary cover.
5. Remove the push pin from the crank arm using a suitable tool.
6. Remove the nuts from the studs just above the function door.
7. Disconnect the vacuum line from the vacuum motor and remove the vacuum motor.

To install:

8. Attach the vacuum line to the motor and install the motor on the case. Tighten the nuts to 10–13 inch lbs.
9. Attach the vacuum motor shaft to the mode door crank using the push pin.
10. Install the cover and the floor duct.
11. Install the service cover and passenger seat.

Villager

TEMPERATURE BLEND DOOR ACTUATOR

1. Disconnect the negative battery cable.
2. Remove the left rear quarter trim panel.
3. Disconnect the electrical connector from the temperature blend door actuator.
4. Remove 4 retaining bolts and remove the actuator.
5. Installation is the reverse of the removal procedure.

VENT DOOR ACTUATOR

1. Remove the auxiliary heater-A/C system.
2. Remove the 4 vent door actuator retaining bolts and remove the actuator.
3. Installation is the reverse of the removal procedure.

SYSTEM DIAGNOSIS

BLOWER MOTOR TESTING

Visual Check

Check to see that all blower motor connections are correct including proper ground of the system. Check the resistor connection at the heater case and the heater fuse. Also, check the connection at the rear of the blower switch.

Loose Blower Wheel Test

Place the blower switch in the **HIGH** position. If airflow is not evident but the motor can be heard, the blower wheel may not be secured to the motor shaft. Do not replace the blower motor unless the unit fails the current draw test.

Blower Motor Current Draw Test

EXCEPT AEROSTAR AUXILIARY SYSTEM AND VILLAGER

1. Disconnect the blower motor electrical wire harness.
2. Connect an DVOM (in the AMP position) between the positive terminal on the motor and the corresponding terminal of the wire harness connector. Connect a jumper wire between the ground terminal on the motor and the corresponding terminal of the wire harness connector.
3. Place the temperature control lever in the mid-range position, halfway between **COOL** and **WARM**. Place the function control lever in the **PANEL** or **VENT** position (**MAX** on Aerostar, Explorer and Ranger).
4. With the battery fully charged, start the engine and operate the blower in all speeds. Record the current draw for each blower speed.
5. The current draw for each blower speed should be within the proper limits shown in chart in this article.
6. Disconnect the meter and jumper wire and reconnect the harness connector to the blower motor.
7. Check the blower system for proper operation.

AEROSTAR AUXILIARY SYSTEM

NOTE: Refer to appropriate wiring schematic in this article for auxiliary heater system component test charts.

Blower Motor Voltage Test

EXCEPT AEROSTAR AND E-SERIES AUXILIARY SYSTEM AND VILLAGER

1. On all except E-Series, place the temperature selector lever in the mid-range position, halfway between **COOL** and **WARM.** On E-Series, place the temperature selector lever in the **WARM** position.
2. Place the function control lever in the **PANEL** or the **VENT** position (**MAX** on Aerostar, Explorer and Ranger).
3. Insert the probes of a voltmeter into the connector at the rear of the blower motor and make contact with the wire terminals. With the engine running, measure the voltage drop across the motor.
4. With the engine running and battery voltage approximately 14.2 volts, the voltage reading should be within the specified range.
5. Disconnect the voltmeter from the connector.

AEROSTAR AUXILIARY AIR CONDITIONING SYSTEM

1. Disconnect the harness connector wire from the motor connector near the blower motor.

HEATING SYSTEM DIAGNOSIS

CONDITION	POSSIBLE CAUSE	RESOLUTION
Insufficient, erratic, or no heat or defrost.	Low radiator coolant level due to: Coolant leaks.	Check radiator cap pressure. Replace if below minimum pressure. Fill to specified coolant level. Pressure test for engine cooling system and heater system leaks. Service as required.
	Engine overheating.	Check radiator cap. Replace if below minimum pressure. Remove bugs, leaves, etc. from radiator or condenser fins. Check for: Loose fan belt Sticking thermostat Incorrect ignition timing Water pump impeller damage Restricted cooling system Service as required.
	Loose fan belt.	Replace if cracked or worn and/or adjust belt tension.
	Thermostat.	Check coolant temperature at radiator filler neck. If under 170°F, replace thermostat.
	Plugged or partially plugged heater core.	Clean and backflush engine cooling system and heater core.
	Loose or improperly adjusted control cables.	Adjust to specifications.
	Kinked, clogged, collapsed, soft, swollen, or decomposed engine cooling system or heater system hoses.	Replace damaged hoses and backflush engine cooling system, then heater system, until all particles have been removed.
	Blocked air inlet.	Check cowl air inlet for leaves, foreign material, etc. Remove as required. Check internal blower inlet screen (on vehicles so equipped) for leaves and foreign material.

HEATING SYSTEM DIAGNOSIS, CONT'D

CONDITION	POSSIBLE CAUSE	RESOLUTION
Blower does not operate properly. Check fuse	Blower motor.	Connect a #10 gauge (or larger diameter) jumper wire directly from the positive battery terminal to the positive lead (orange wire) of the blower motor. If the motor runs, the problem must be external to the motor. If the motor will not run, connect a #10 gauge (or larger diameter) jumper wire from the motor black lead to a good ground. If the motor runs, the trouble is in the ground circuit. On vehicles with ground side switching, check the blower resistor, the blower switch and the harness connections. Service as required. If motor still will not run, the motor is inoperative and should be replaced.
	Blower resistor.	Check continuity of resistors for opens or shorts (self-powered test lamp). Service or replace as required.
	Blower wire harness.	Check for proper installation of harness connector terminal connectors. Check wire-to-terminal continuity. Check continuity of wires in harness for shorts, opens, abrasion, etc. Service as required.
	Blower switch(es).	Check blower switch(es) for proper contact. Replace switch(es) as required.
Vacuum motor system	Vacuum leak. Loose or disconnected vacuum hose. Damaged vacuum motor. Misrouted vacuum connections	Repair or repair system components, as required.

BLOWER MOTOR CURRENT DRAW AND VOLTAGE DROP—HEATER ONLY

Switch Position	Aerostar		Explorer/Ranger		Bronco/F Series		E Series	
	Amps	Volts	Amps	Volts	Amps	Volts	Amps	Volts
Off	0	0	0	0	0	0	0	0
Low	3.2	4.1–5.6	3.5–5.5	5	3–5	3–4	4.0	4.0
Medium Low	6.0	6.4–7.9	5.0–7.5	8	6–8	5–7	7.3	6.0
Medium	—	—	—	—	—	—	—	—
Medium High	9.5	8.7–10.2	7.0–9.5	10	10–14	7–10	13.8	9.0
High	13.5	11.3–12.8	9.5–11.5	12	15–22	11–14	23.0	12.8

BLOWER MOTOR CURRENT DRAW AND VOLTAGE DROP—AIR CONDITIONING

Switch Position	Aerostar Amps	Aerostar Volts	Bronco II/ Explorer/Ranger Amps	Bronco II/ Explorer/Ranger Volts	Bronco/ E Series/F Series Amps	Bronco/ E Series/F Series Volts	E Series Auxiliary System Amps	E Series Auxiliary System Volts
Off	0	0	0	0	0	0	0	0
Low	3.6 Max	4.1–5.6	9–11.5	5	6	5	4	4
Medium Low	6.3 Max	6.4–7.9	11.5–14	8	8	7	7.3	6.0
Medium High	9.7 Max	8.7–10.2	14–16.5	10	15	10	13.8	9.0
High	14.1 Max	11.3–12.8	16–18.5	12	25	12.8	23.0	12.8

2. Connect an ammeter between the positive orange wire terminal of the motor connector and the corresponding brown-orange wire terminal. Connect a jumper wire between the 2 negative terminals, the black wire on the blower motor connector and the orange-black connector on the harness connector.
3. Place the temperature control lever in the **MAX HEAT** position and the function control lever in the **HEAT** position.
4. With the battery fully charged, turn the switch **ON** and operate the blower in all blower speeds. Record the current draw for each blower speed.
5. The current draw for each blower speed should be within the specified limits.
6. Disconnect the ammeter and connect the blower motor wire to the harness at the connectors.

E-SERIES AUXILIARY AIR CONDITIONING SYSTEM

1. Separate the blower motor ground wire (black) from the blower motor resistor.
2. Connect the positive lead of an ammeter to the female spade connector on the motor wire and the negative lead to the blower motor resistor.
3. With a fully charged battery, operate the blower in each switch position and record the current draw.
4. The current draw for each switch position should be within the proper limits.
5. Disconnect the ammeter and connect the blower motor ground wire.

Blower Motor Voltage Test

EXCEPT AUXILIARY AIR CONDITIONING SYSTEM

1. On all except E-Series, place the temperature selector lever in the mid-range position, halfway between **COOL** and **WARM**. On E-Series, place the temperature selector lever in the **WARM** position.
2. On Bronco and F-Series, place the function control lever in the **PANEL** position. On Aerostar, Explorer and Ranger, place function control lever in **MAX** position on 1993 models and **VENT** position for 1994–95 models. On E-Series, place the function control lever in the **FLOOR** position.
3. Insert the probes of a voltmeter into the connector at the rear of the blower motor and make contact with the wire terminals. With the engine running, measure the voltage drop across the motor.
4. With the engine running and battery voltage approximately 14.2 volts, the voltage reading should be within the specified range.
5. Disconnect the voltmeter from the connector.

1993 AEROSTAR

1. Set the temperature selector full **HEAT** position.
2. Place the function selector lever in the **MAX A/C** position.
3. Insert the probes of a voltmeter into the wire holes on the motor's connector and make contact with the wire terminals.
4. Measure the voltage drop across the blower motor.
5. With the engine running and battery voltage approximately 14.2 volts, the voltage reading should be within the specified range for each blower switch position.

1994–95 AEROSTAR AND ALL E-SERIES AUXILIARY AIR CONDITIONING SYSTEMS

1. Insert the probes of a DVOM into the wire holes of the blower motor connectors, making contact with the wires.
2. Measure the voltage drop across the motor.
3. With the engine running and battery voltage approximately 14.2 volts, the voltage reading should be within the range specified.

Blower Motor Switch Test

EXCEPT VILLAGER

Check for continuity between the connected terminals indicated on the appropriate schematic. Check the terminal continuity at every lever position. Using a test light, the light should turn on for each connected pair of terminals.

VILLAGER

1. With key **OFF** , remove the front control panel.
2. Disconnect the front blower motor switch connector from the panel and measure the resistance between the wire terminals of the switch as indicated in the accompanying chart.

BLOWER SWITCH CONTINUITY TEST—1993 VILLAGER

Switch Position	Wire Terminals	Resistance (ohms)
1 (low)	All	Greater than 10,000
2 (med.)	Y/BK and BK	Less than 5
	All others	Greater than 10,000
3 (med. high)	Y/BK, LG/R and BK	Less than 5
	All others	Greater than 10,000
4 (high)	LG/R, GN and BK	Less than 5
	All others	Greater than 10,000

1994–95 VILLAGER

Connector Shown from Component Side

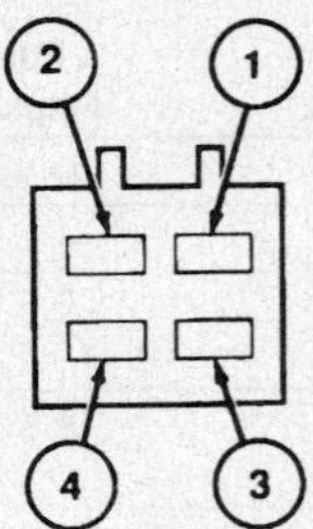

FRONT BLOWER MOTOR SWITCH

Switch Position	Wire Terminals	Resistance (ohms)
1 (LOW)	All	Greater than 10,000
2 (MED.)	3 and 2 All others	Less than 5 Greater than 10,000
3 (MED. HIGH)	3, 4 and 2 All others	Less than 5 Greater than 10,000
4 (HIGH)	4, 1 and 2 All others	Less than 5 Greater than 10,000

HEATER CORE TESTING

Bleeding Air From the Heater Core

NOTE: On Aerostar, the heater core is self purging at an engine rpm of 2000.

Remove the hose at the outlet connection of the heater core; the hose that leads to the water pump. Allow any trapped air to flow out. When a continuous flow of coolant is obtained, connect the hose to the core. Do not overtighten the hose clamps.

Pressure Test

EXCEPT AEROSTAR

1. Drain the cooling system.
2. Disconnect the heater hoses from the heater core tubes.
3. Install a short piece of heater hose, approximately 4 in. long onto each heater core tube.
4. Fill the heater core and hoses with water and install a plug in the end of one hose. In the other hose end, install an adapter suitable to connect with a radiator pressure tester. Secure the hoses to the heater core, plug and adapter with hose clamps.
5. Attach the radiator pressure tester to the adapter. Close the bleed valve at the base of the gauge and pump 30 psi of air pressure into the heater core.
6. Observe the pressure gauge for a minimum of 3 minutes. The pressure should not drop.
7. If the pressure does not drop, no leaks are indicated.
8. If the pressure drops, check the hose connections at the core tubes for leaks. If the hoses do not leak, remove the heater core from the vehicle and bench test the core.

Bench Test

EXCEPT AEROSTAR

1. Drain all coolant from the heater core.
2. Connect the test hoses with the plug and adapter to the core tubes. Tighten the clamps and connect the pressure tester to the adapter.
3. For Windstar apply 15 psi, all others 30 psi of air pressure to the heater core with the radiator pressure tester and submerge the core in water.
4. If a leak is observed, repair or replace the heater core, as necessary.

Air Conditioning System

REFRIGERANT SYSTEM TESTING

Visual Inspection

Obstructed air passages, broken belts, disconnected or broken wires, loose clutch, loose or broken mounting brackets and many refrigerant leaks may be determined by visual inspection.

A refrigerant leak usually appears as an oily residue at the leakage point. The residue soon picks up dust or dirt particles and becomes greasy and dirty.

Most common leaks are caused by damaged or missing O-rings at connecting points.

Leaks may also appear at the schrader valve core. If tightening the valve core does not stop the leak, it should be replaced with a new valve core, 19D701 or equivalent.

Missing service port valve caps can also cause a refrigerant leak. This important primary seal is required to keep dirt out of the system when the service hose is attached. If a cap is missing, thoroughly clean the service port area and install a new cap.

NOTE: Service port valve caps must be installed finger-tight. If tightened with pliers, the sealing surface of the service access gauge port valve may be damaged.

Performance Testing

The best way to diagnose a problem is to note the system pressures, shown by the manifold gauges, and the clutch cycle rate and times. Then, compare the findings with the clutch cycle rate and time charts. Remember when testing:

- System pressures are lower in the suction portion of a cycle and higher in the discharge portion of that cycle.
- A clutch cycle is the time the clutch is engaged plus the time it is disengaged, time ON plus time OFF.
- Clutch cycle times are the lengths of time, in seconds, that the clutch is ON and OFF.

The following procedure is recommended:

1. Connect a manifold gauge set to the system. Purge the air from the red and blue hoses by loosening the hose fittings at the gauge set to allow air to be pushed out by system pressure.

NOTE: The test conditions specified in each chart must be met to obtain accurate test results.

2. Start the engine and turn **ON** the air conditioning as soon as the system is stabilized. Record the high and low pressures, as shown by the manifold gauges. The low pressure should cycle between an approximate 22–45 psi. As the low pressure is dropping, the high pressure should increase. When the clutch disengages, the low side should increase and the high side should decrease.
3. Determine the clutch cycle rate per minute. The clutch ON time plus OFF time is a cycle.
4. Record the clutch OFF time in seconds.
5. Record the clutch ON time in seconds.
6. Record the center register discharge temperature.

7. Determine and record ambient temperatures.
8. Compare test readings with the applicable chart.
9. Plot a vertical line for the recorded ambient temperature from the scale at the bottom of each chart to the top of each chart. Plot a horizontal line for each of the other test readings from the scale at the left side of the appropriate chart.
10. If the point where the 2 lines cross on each of the charts falls within the dark band, the system is operating normally. If the lines cross outside the dark band on one or more of the charts, there is a problem and the specific cause must be determined. This is done with the clutch cycle timing evaluation chart.
11. After servicing and correcting a refrigerant system problem, take additional pressure readings and observe the clutch cycle rate while meeting the conditional requirements to make sure the problem has been corrected.

In many instances, the clutch will not cycle off when temperatures are above 90°F (32°C). This will depend on local conditions and engine/vehicle speed. Also, clutch cycling will normally not occur when the engine is operating at curb idle speed.

If the system contains no refrigerant or is extremely low on refrigerant, the clutch will not engage. A rapid cycling clutch is usually an indication that the system is low on refrigerant.

The following test conditions must be established to obtain accurate pressure readings:

- Run engine at 1500 rpm for 10 minutes.
- Operate the air conditioning system on max air conditioning, recirculating air.
- Run the blower at maximum speed.
- Stabilize in vehicle temperature at 70-80°F (21-27°C).

AIR CONDITIONING TROUBLESHOOTING FLOWCHART

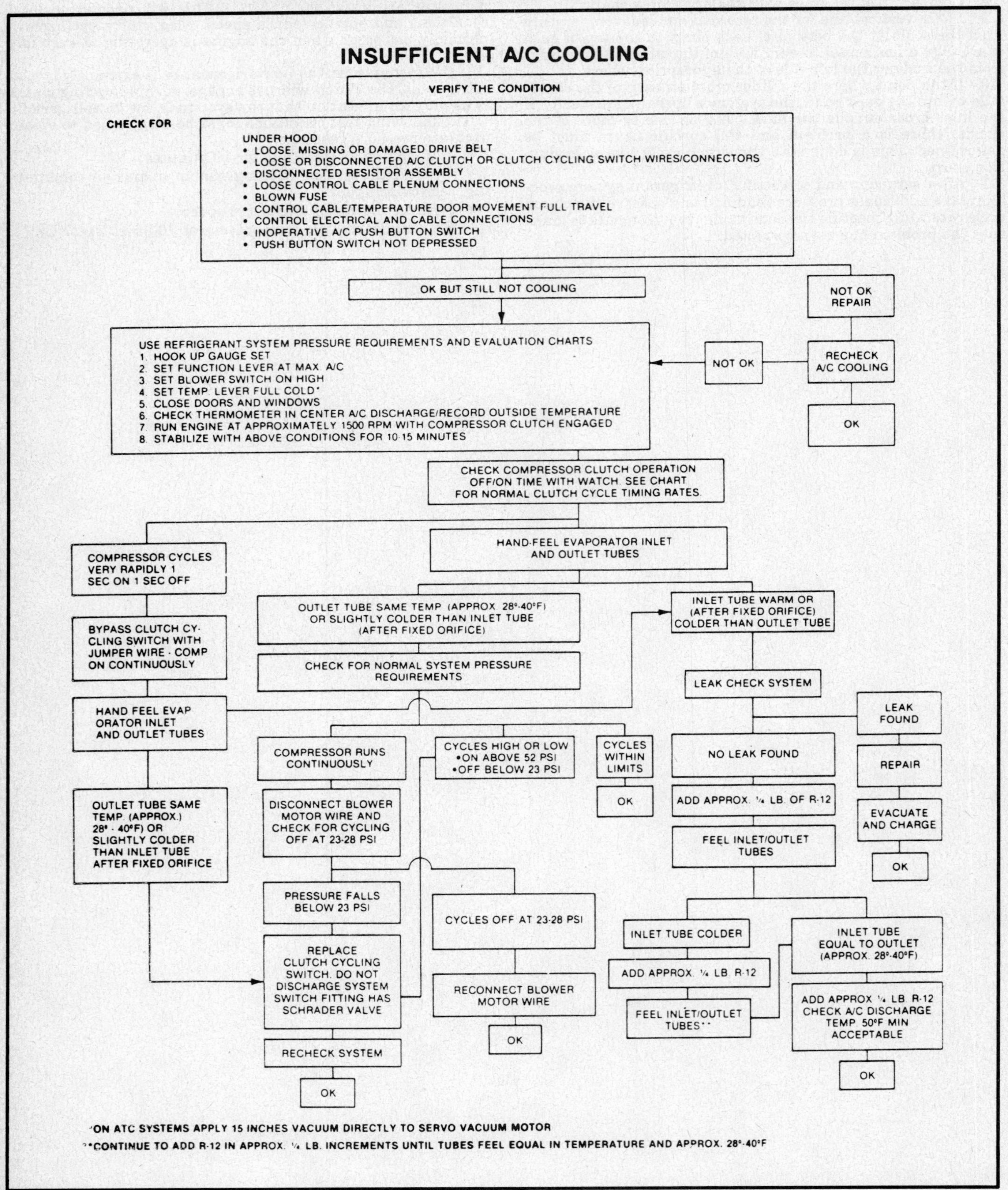

INSUFFICIENT A/C COOLING
VERIFY THE CONDITION
CHECK FOR
UNDER HOOD
• LOOSE, MISSING OR DAMAGED DRIVE BELT
• LOOSE OR DISCONNECTED A/C CLUTCH OR CLUTCH CYCLING SWITCH WIRES/CONNECTORS
• DISCONNECTED RESISTOR ASSEMBLY
• LOOSE CONTROL CABLE PLENUM CONNECTIONS
• BLOWN FUSE
• CONTROL CABLE/TEMPERATURE DOOR MOVEMENT FULL TRAVEL
• CONTROL ELECTRICAL AND CABLE CONNECTIONS
• INOPERATIVE A/C PUSH BUTTON SWITCH
• PUSH BUTTON SWITCH NOT DEPRESSED
OK BUT STILL NOT COOLING
NOT OK REPAIR
USE REFRIGERANT SYSTEM PRESSURE REQUIREMENTS AND EVALUATION CHARTS
1. HOOK UP GAUGE SET
2. SET FUNCTION LEVER AT MAX. A/C
3. SET BLOWER SWITCH ON HIGH
4. SET TEMP. LEVER FULL COLD*
5. CLOSE DOORS AND WINDOWS
6. CHECK THERMOMETER IN CENTER A/C DISCHARGE/RECORD OUTSIDE TEMPERATURE
7. RUN ENGINE AT APPROXIMATELY 1500 RPM WITH COMPRESSOR CLUTCH ENGAGED
8. STABILIZE WITH ABOVE CONDITIONS FOR 10-15 MINUTES
NOT OK
RECHECK A/C COOLING
OK
CHECK COMPRESSOR CLUTCH OPERATION OFF/ON TIME WITH WATCH. SEE CHART FOR NORMAL CLUTCH CYCLE TIMING RATES.
HAND-FEEL EVAPORATOR INLET AND OUTLET TUBES
COMPRESSOR CYCLES VERY RAPIDLY 1 SEC ON 1 SEC OFF
OUTLET TUBE SAME TEMP. (APPROX. 28°-40°F) OR SLIGHTLY COLDER THAN INLET TUBE (AFTER FIXED ORIFICE)
INLET TUBE WARM OR (AFTER FIXED ORIFICE) COLDER THAN OUTLET TUBE
BYPASS CLUTCH CYCLING SWITCH WITH JUMPER WIRE - COMP ON CONTINUOUSLY
CHECK FOR NORMAL SYSTEM PRESSURE REQUIREMENTS
LEAK CHECK SYSTEM
HAND FEEL EVAPORATOR INLET AND OUTLET TUBES
LEAK FOUND
COMPRESSOR RUNS CONTINUOUSLY
CYCLES HIGH OR LOW
•ON ABOVE 52 PSI
•OFF BELOW 23 PSI
CYCLES WITHIN LIMITS
NO LEAK FOUND
REPAIR
OK
ADD APPROX. 1/4 LB. OF R-12
OUTLET TUBE SAME TEMP. (APPROX.) 28° - 40°F) OR SLIGHTLY COLDER THAN INLET TUBE AFTER FIXED ORIFICE
DISCONNECT BLOWER MOTOR WIRE AND CHECK FOR CYCLING OFF AT 23-28 PSI
EVACUATE AND CHARGE
FEEL INLET/OUTLET TUBES
OK
PRESSURE FALLS BELOW 23 PSI
CYCLES OFF AT 23-28 PSI
INLET TUBE COLDER
INLET TUBE EQUAL TO OUTLET (APPROX. 28°-40°F)
REPLACE CLUTCH CYCLING SWITCH. DO NOT DISCHARGE SYSTEM SWITCH FITTING HAS SCHRADER VALVE
ADD APPROX. 1/4 LB. R-12
RECONNECT BLOWER MOTOR WIRE
FEEL INLET/OUTLET TUBES**
ADD APPROX. 1/4 LB. R-12 CHECK A/C DISCHARGE TEMP. 50°F MIN ACCEPTABLE
RECHECK SYSTEM
OK
OK
OK
*ON ATC SYSTEMS APPLY 15 INCHES VACUUM DIRECTLY TO SERVO VACUUM MOTOR
**CONTINUE TO ADD R-12 IN APPROX. 1/4 LB. INCREMENTS UNTIL TUBES FEEL EQUAL IN TEMPERATURE AND APPROX. 28°-40°F

COMPRESSOR CLUTCH CIRCUIT DIAGNOSIS—BRONCO, E-SERIES AND F-SERIES

TEST STEP		RESULT	ACTION TO TAKE
A1	CHECK SYSTEM OPERATION		
	• Turn blower switch On. • Turn ignition switch to Run position. • Compressor clutch should engage.	Clutch operates ▶ Clutch does not operate ▶	System OK. GO to **A2**.
A2	CHECK FOR VOLTAGE		
	• Check for voltage at circuit wire at the clutch cycling pressure switch connector or A C control switch (E-150 — E-350).	Voltage present ▶ No voltage ▶	GO to **A3**. GO to **A9**.
A3	BY-PASS PRESSURE SWITCH		
	• Disconnect connector at clutch cycling pressure switch or control switch (E-150 — E-350). • Jumper connector pins or control switch. • Clutch snould engage.	OK ▶ No OK ~~OK~~ ▶	GO to **A4**. GO to **A5**.
A4	CHECK SYSTEM PRESSURE		
	• Connect manifold gauge set and check system pressure.	Pressure above 55 psi ▶ Pressure below 55 psi (ambient temperature above 50°F) ▶	REPlACE clutch cycling pressure switch. GO to **A1**. CHECK refrigerant system for leaks. REPAIR and CHARGE system as necessary. GO to **A1**.
A5	CHECK VOLTAGE AT CLUTCH		
	• Check for voltage at clutch field coil.	Voltage present ▶ No voltage ▶	GO to **A8**. GO to **A7**.
A6	CHECK CLUTCH GROUND		
	• Jumper ground terminal of clutch field coil to ground. • Clutch should engage.	OK ▶ ~~OK~~ ▶	SERVICE open in ground wire. GO to **A1**. REPLACE clutch field coil. GO to **A1**.
A7	CHECK FUSE		
	• Check Fuse 17 in fuse panel for continuity.	OK ▶ ~~OK~~ ▶	GO to **A8**. CHECK for short. SERVICE as necessary. REPLACE fuse. GO to **A1**.
A8	CHECK A/C CONTROLS		
	• Move Function selector lever to DEFROST position. • Check for voltage at circuit wire at the clutch cycling pressure switch connector.	Voltage present ▶ No voltage ▶	GO to **A10**. GO to **A9**.

COMPRESSOR CLUTCH CIRCUIT DIAGNOSIS—BRONCO, E-SERIES AND F-SERIES, CONT'D

TEST STEP		RESULT	ACTION TO TAKE
A9	CHECK CIRCUIT 294		
	• Remove connector from A/C push-button switch. • Check for voltage at circuit.	Voltage present ▶	GO to **A10**.
		No voltage ▶	CHECK for open in Circuit 294. SERVICE as necessary. GO to **A1**.
A10	CHECK A/C CONTROLS		
	• Check A/C push button switch and Function switch for continuity. **NOTE: A/C push-button switch must be depressed. Function switch must be in DEFROST position.**	Continuity through Function switch only ▶	REPLACE A/C pushbutton switch. GO to **A1**.
		Continuity through A/C pushbutton switch only ▶	REPLACE Function switch. GO to **A1**.
		Continuity through both switches ▶	CHECK for open in circuit between control assembly and clutch cycling pressure switch. SERVICE as necessary. GO to **A1**.

CLUTCH CYCLE TIMING EVALUATION—EXC. AEROSTAR

THESE CONDITIONAL REQUIREMENTS FOR THE FIXED ORIFICE TUBE CYCLING CLUTCH SYSTEM TESTS MUST BE SATISFIED TO OBTAIN ACCURATE PRESSURE READINGS.

- Stabilized in Car Temperatures @ 70°F to 80°F (21°C to 27°C)
- Maximum A/C (Recirculating Air)
- Maximum Blower Speed
- 1500 Engine RPM For 10 Minutes

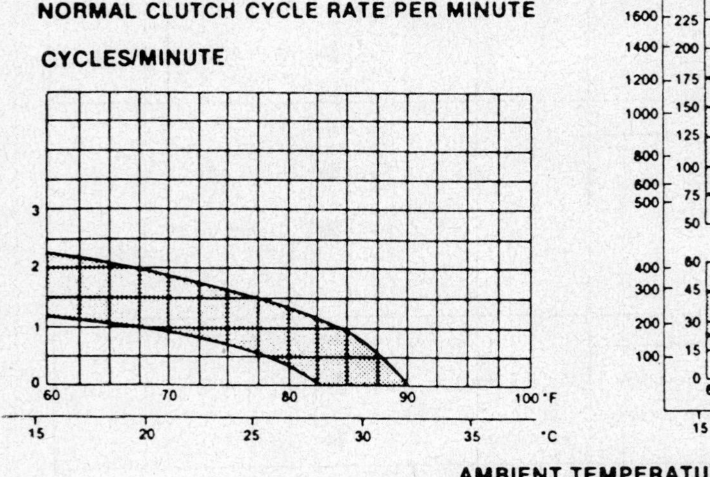

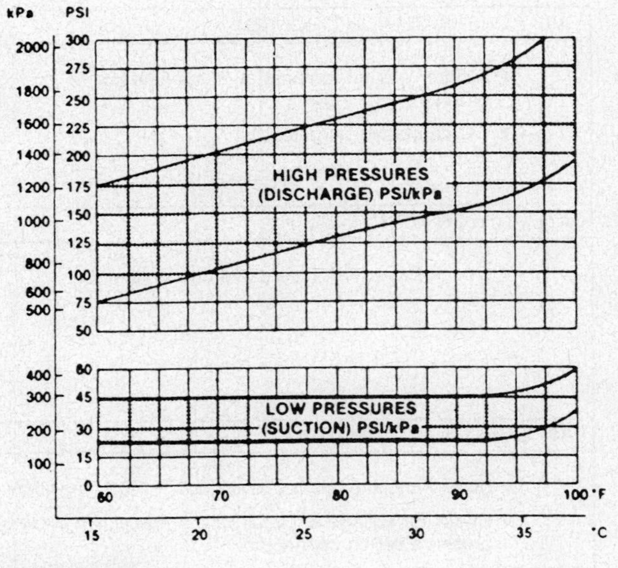

AMBIENT TEMPERATURES

CLUTCH CYCLE TIMING EVALUATION—EXC. AEROSTAR, CONT'D

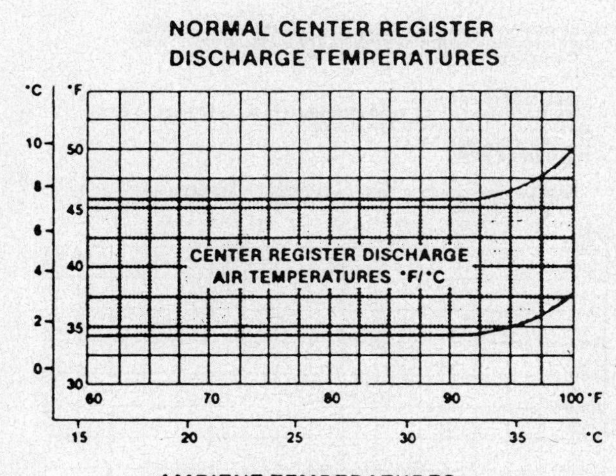

AMBIENT TEMPERATURES

THESE CONDITIONAL REQUIREMENTS FOR THE FIXED ORIFICE TUBE CYCLING CLUTCH SYSTEM TESTS MUST BE SATISFIED TO OBTAIN ACCURATE CLUTCH CYCLE TIMING

- Stabilized in Car Temperatures @ 70°F to 80°F (21°C to 27°C)
- Maximum A/C (Recirculating Air)
- Maximum Blower Speed
- 1500 Engine RPM For 10 Minutes

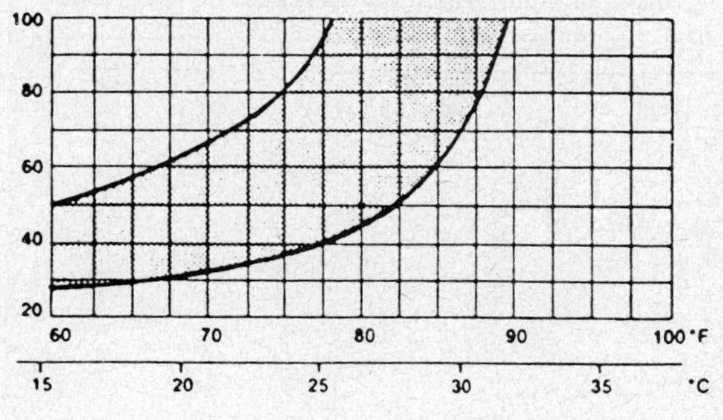

AMBIENT TEMPERATURES

SECONDS

NORMAL CLUTCH
ON TIME — SECONDS

AMBIENT TEMPERATURES

SECONDS

NORMAL CLUTCH
OFF TIME — SECONDS

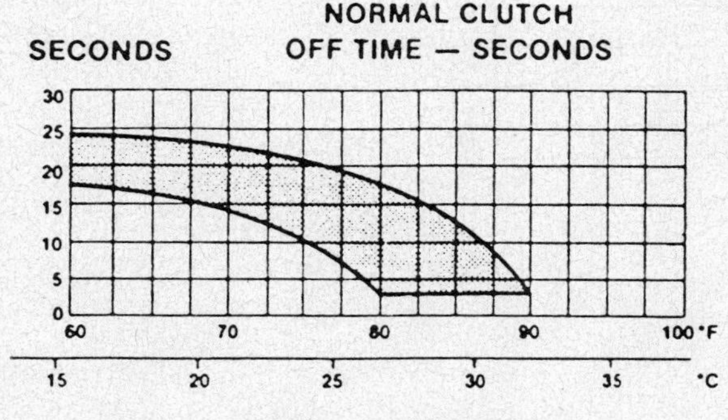

AMBIENT TEMPERATURES

CLUTCH CYCLE TIMING EVALUATION—AEROSTAR

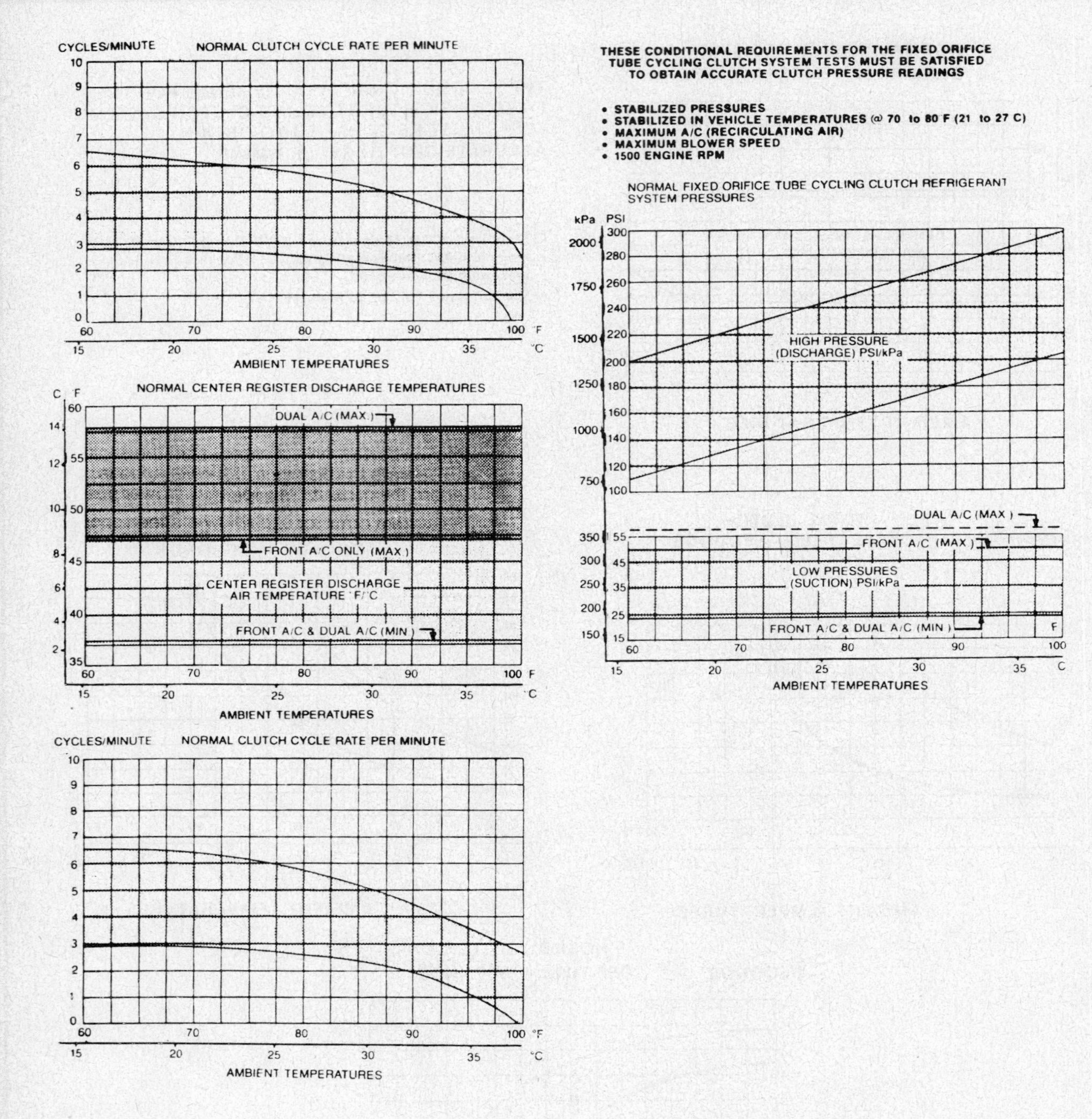
CYCLES/MINUTE
NORMAL CLUTCH CYCLE RATE PER MINUTE
AMBIENT TEMPERATURES
NORMAL CENTER REGISTER DISCHARGE TEMPERATURES
DUAL A/C (MAX.)
FRONT A/C ONLY (MAX.)
CENTER REGISTER DISCHARGE AIR TEMPERATURE °F/°C
FRONT A/C & DUAL A/C (MIN.)
AMBIENT TEMPERATURES
CYCLES/MINUTE
NORMAL CLUTCH CYCLE RATE PER MINUTE
AMBIENT TEMPERATURES
THESE CONDITIONAL REQUIREMENTS FOR THE FIXED ORIFICE TUBE CYCLING CLUTCH SYSTEM TESTS MUST BE SATISFIED TO OBTAIN ACCURATE CLUTCH PRESSURE READINGS
• STABILIZED PRESSURES
• STABILIZED IN VEHICLE TEMPERATURES (@ 70 to 80 F (21 to 27 C)
• MAXIMUM A/C (RECIRCULATING AIR)
• MAXIMUM BLOWER SPEED
• 1500 ENGINE RPM
NORMAL FIXED ORIFICE TUBE CYCLING CLUTCH REFRIGERANT SYSTEM PRESSURES
HIGH PRESSURE (DISCHARGE) PSI/kPa
DUAL A/C (MAX.)
FRONT A/C (MAX.)
LOW PRESSURES (SUCTION) PSI/kPa
FRONT A/C & DUAL A/C (MIN.)
AMBIENT TEMPERATURES

CLUTCH CYCLE TIMING EVALUATION—AEROSTAR, CONT'D

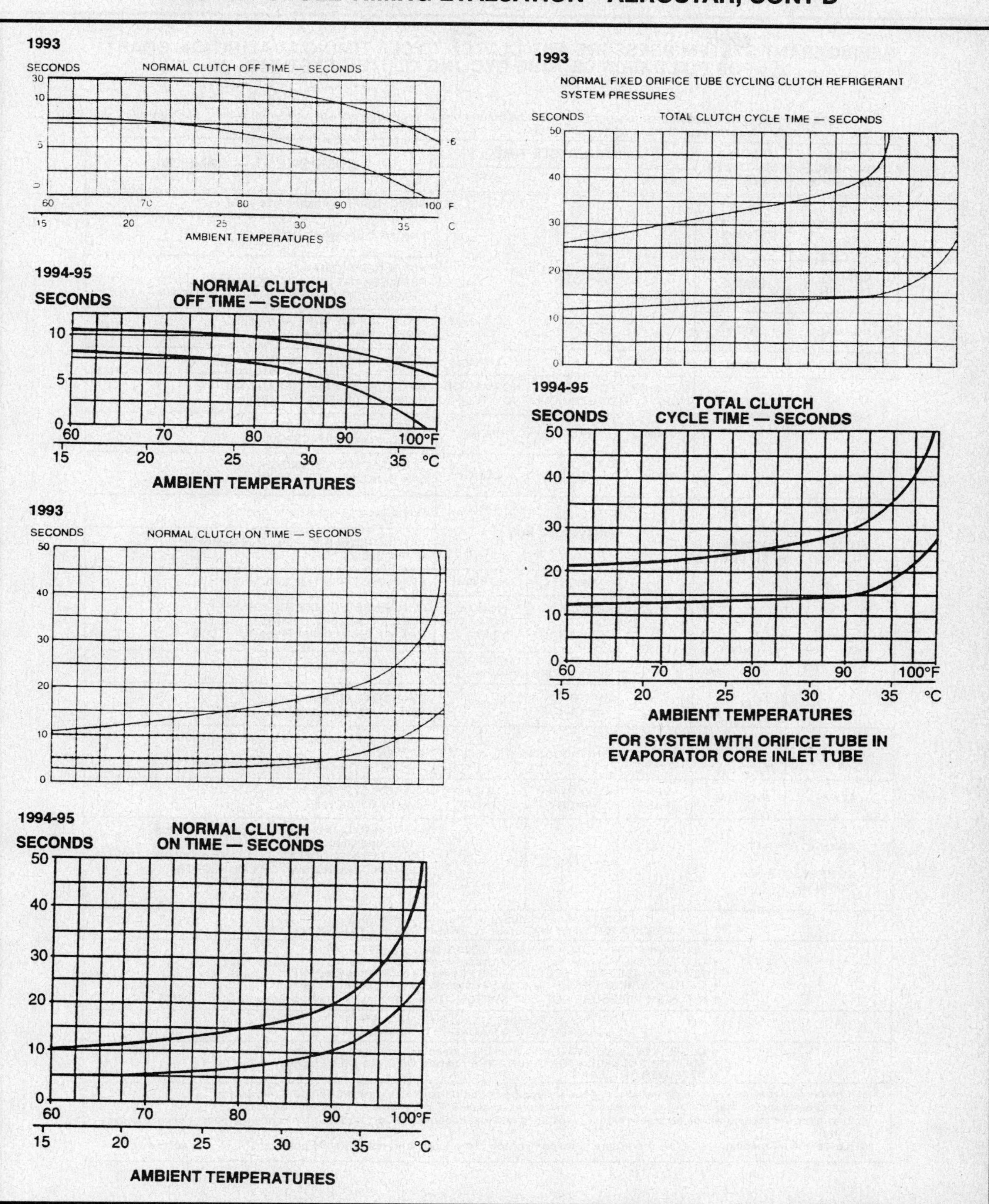
1993
SECONDS
NORMAL CLUTCH OFF TIME — SECONDS
AMBIENT TEMPERATURES
1994-95
SECONDS
NORMAL CLUTCH OFF TIME — SECONDS
AMBIENT TEMPERATURES
1993
SECONDS
NORMAL CLUTCH ON TIME — SECONDS
1994-95
SECONDS
NORMAL CLUTCH ON TIME — SECONDS
AMBIENT TEMPERATURES
1993
NORMAL FIXED ORIFICE TUBE CYCLING CLUTCH REFRIGERANT SYSTEM PRESSURES
SECONDS
TOTAL CLUTCH CYCLE TIME — SECONDS
1994-95
SECONDS
TOTAL CLUTCH CYCLE TIME — SECONDS
AMBIENT TEMPERATURES
FOR SYSTEM WITH ORIFICE TUBE IN EVAPORATOR CORE INLET TUBE

CLUTCH CYCLE TIMING TROUBLESHOOTING

REFRIGERANT SYSTEM PRESSURE AND CLUTCH CYCLE TIMING EVALUATION CHART FOR FIXED ORIFICE TUBE CYCLING CLUTCH SYSTEMS

NOTE: Normal system conditional requirements must be maintained to properly evaluate refrigerant system pressures. Refer to charts applicable to system under test.

HIGH (DISCHARGE) PRESSURE	LOW (SUCTION) PRESSURE	CLUTCH CYCLE TIME			COMPONENT — CAUSES
		RATE	ON	OFF	
HIGH	HIGH	CONTINUOUS RUN			CONDENSER — Inadequate Airflow
HIGH	NORMAL TO HIGH				ENGINE OVERHEATING
NORMAL TO HIGH	NORMAL				AIR IN REFRIGERANT. REFRIGERANT OVERCHARGE (a) HUMIDITY OR AMBIENT TEMP. VERY HIGH (b).
NORMAL	HIGH				FIXED ORIFICE TUBE — Missing. O-Rings Leaking/Missing
NORMAL	HIGH	SLOW	LONG	LONG	CLUTCH CYCLING SWITCH — High Cut-In
NORMAL	NORMAL	SLOW OR NO CYCLE	LONG OR CONTINUOUS	NORMAL OR NO CYCLE	MOISTURE IN REFRIGERANT SYSTEM. EXCESSIVE REFRIGERANT OIL
		FAST	SHORT	SHORT	CLUTCH CYCLING SWITCH — Low Cut-In or High Cut-Out
NORMAL	LOW	SLOW	LONG	LONG	CLUTCH CYCLING SWITCH — Low Cut-Out
NORMAL TO LOW	HIGH	CONTINUOUS RUN			Compressor — Low Performance
NORMAL TO LOW	NORMAL TO HIGH				A/C SUCTION LINE — Partially Restricted or Plugged (c)
NORMAL TO LOW	NORMAL	FAST	SHORT	NORMAL	EVAPORATOR — Low Airflow
			SHORT TO VERY SHORT	NORMAL TO LONG	CONDENSER, FIXED ORIFICE TUBE, OR A/C LIQUID LINE — Partially Restricted or Plugged
			SHORT TO VERY SHORT	SHORT TO VERY SHORT	LOW REFRIGERANT CHARGE
			SHORT TO VERY SHORT	LONG	EVAPORATOR CORE — Partially Restricted or Plugged
NORMAL TO LOW	LOW	CONTINUOUS RUN			A/C SUCTION LINE — Partially Restricted or Plugged. (d) CLUTCH CYCLING SWITCH — Sticking Closed
LOW	NORMAL	VERY FAST	VERY SHORT	VERY SHORT	CLUTCH CYCLING SWITCH — Cycling Range Too Close
ERRATIC OPERATION OR COMPRESSOR NOT RUNNING		—	—	—	CLUTCH CYCLING SWITCH — Dirty Contacts or Sticking Open. POOR CONNECTION AT A/C CLUTCH CONNECTOR OR CLUTCH CYCLING SWITCH CONNECTOR. A/C ELECTRICAL CIRCUIT ERRATIC

ADDITIONAL POSSIBLE CAUSE COMPONENTS ASSOCIATED WITH INADEQUATE COMPRESSOR OPERATION

- COMPRESSOR CLUTCH Slipping • LOOSE DRIVE BELT
- CLUTCH COIL Open — Shorted, or Loose Mounting
- CONTROL ASSEMBLY SWITCH — Dirty Contacts or Sticking Open
- CLUTCH WIRING CIRCUIT — High Resistance, Open or Blown Fuse
- A/C HIGH PRESSURE CUT-OUT SWITCH — Dirty Contacts or Sticking Open (If So Equipped)

ADDITIONAL POSSIBLE CAUSE COMPONENTS ASSOCIATED WITH A DAMAGED COMPRESSOR

- CLUTCH CYCLING SWITCH — Sticking Closed or Compressor Clutch Seized
- SUCTION ACCUMULATOR DRIER — Refrigerant Oil Bleed Hole Plugged
- REFRIGERANT LEAKS

(a) Compressor may make noise on initial run. This is slugging condition caused by excessive liquid refrigerant.
(b) Compressor clutch may not cycle in ambient temperatures above 80°F depending on humidity conditions.
(c) **Low pressure** reading will be **normal to high** if pressure is taken at accumulator and if restriction is downstream of **service access valve**.
(d) **Low pressure** reading will be **low** if pressure is taken near the compressor and restriction is upstream of **service access valve**.

VACUUM SCHEMATICS

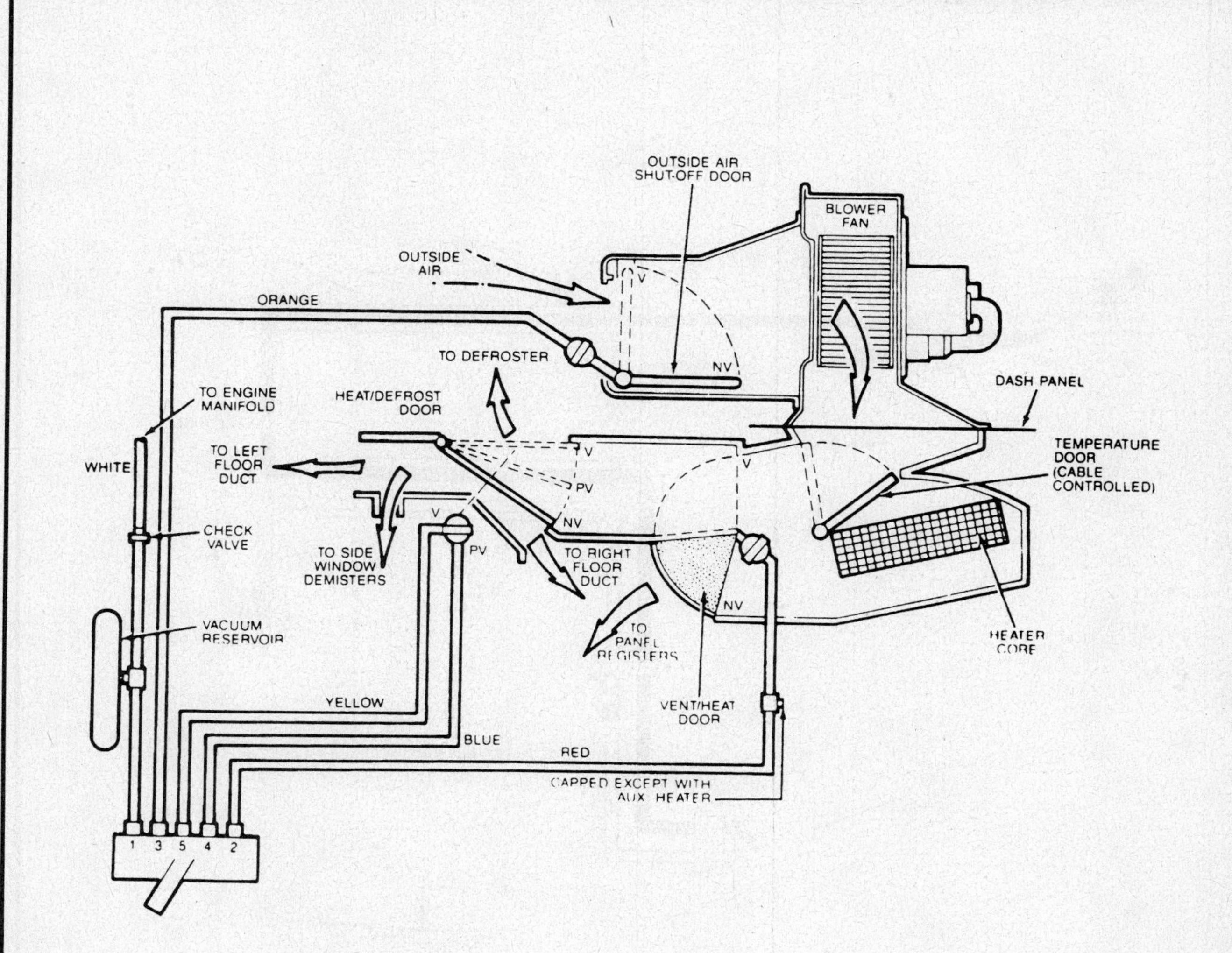

HEATER SYSTEM VACUUM MOTOR TEST CHART

FUNCTION SELECTOR LEVER POSITION	OUTSIDE AIR SHUT-OFF DOOR (port 3)	PARTIAL HEAT/ DEFROST DOOR (port 4)	FULL HEAT/ DEFROST DOOR (port 5)	VENT/HEAT DOOR (port 2)	VACUUM SOURCE (port 1)
OFF	V	NV	NV	NV	V
VENT	NV	NV	NV	V	V
HEAT	NV	V	V	NV	V
MIX	NV	V	NV	NV	V
DEFROST	NV	NV	NV	NV	V
VACUUM HOSE COLOR	ORANGE	BLUE	YELLOW	RED	WHITE

V = VACUUM
NV = NO VACUUM

Vacuum schematic—Aerostar

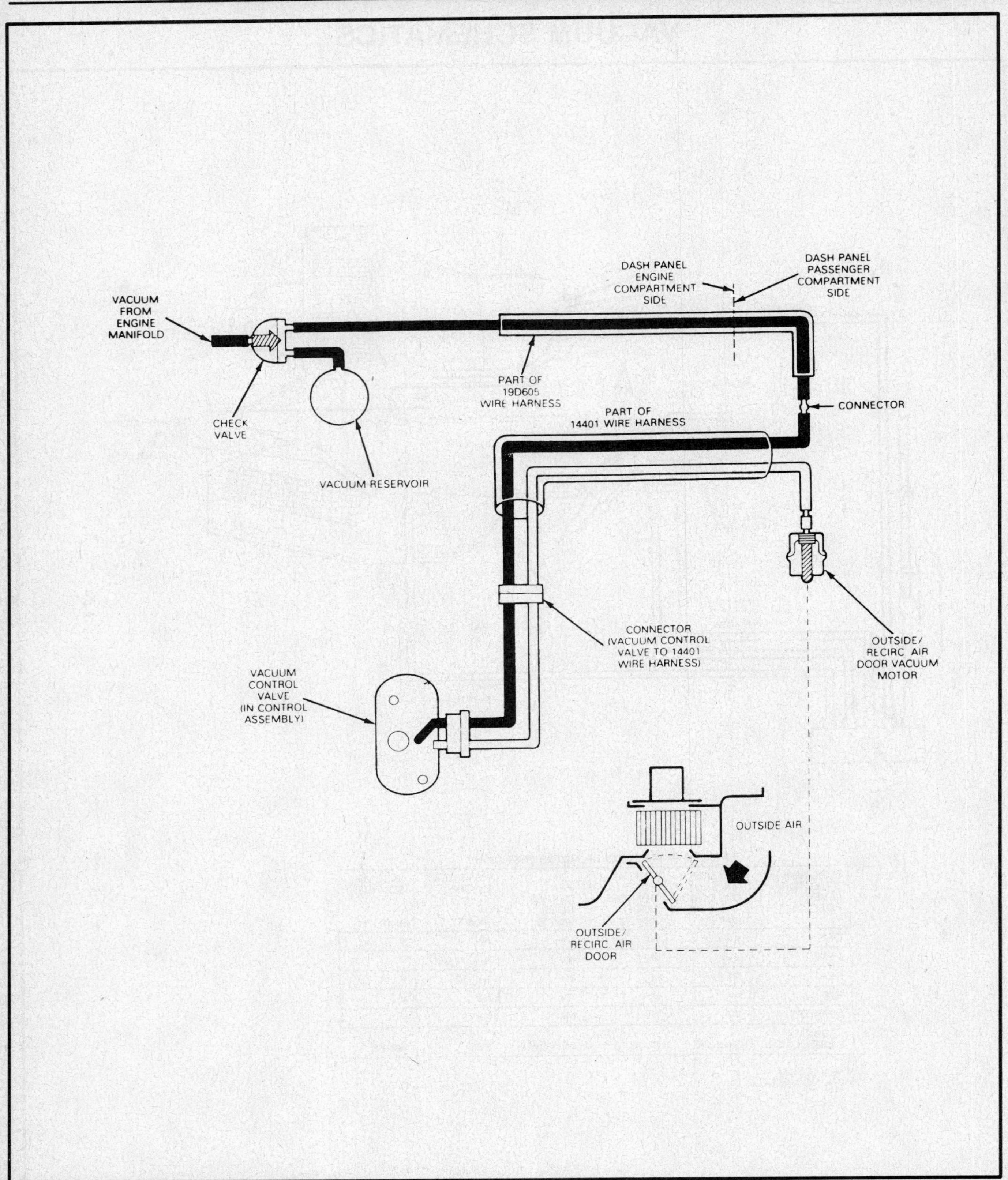

Vacuum schematic—Explorer and Ranger

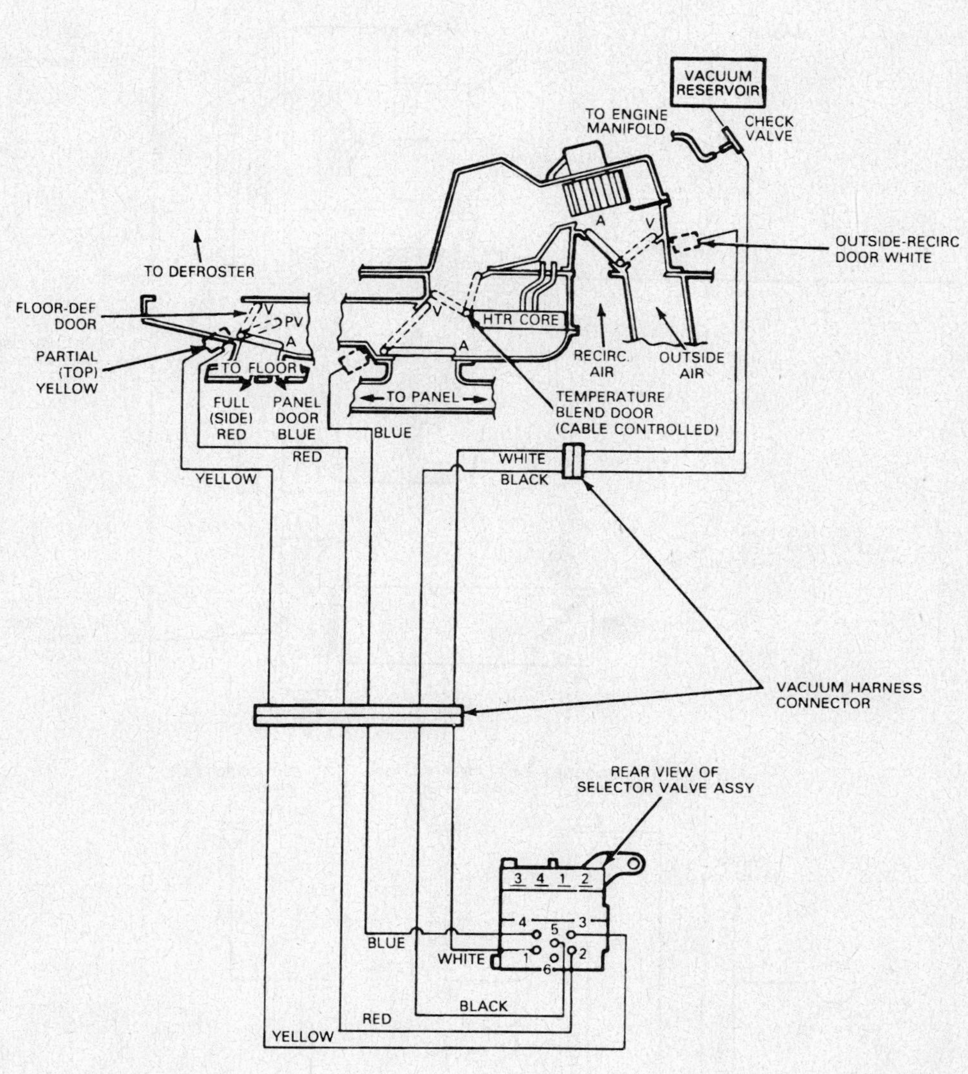

FUNCTION SELECTOR VALVE DETENT POSITIONS

PORT	FUNCTION	VENT	OFF	FLOOR	MIX	DEF
1	RECIRC — O/S	A	V	A	A	A
2	FULL FLOOR	A	V	V	A	A
3	PANEL	V	V	V	V	A
4	MIX	V	V	A	A	A
5	SOURCE	V	V	V	V	V

V = VACUUM
A = ATMOSPHERE

Vacuum schematic—Bronco and F-Series

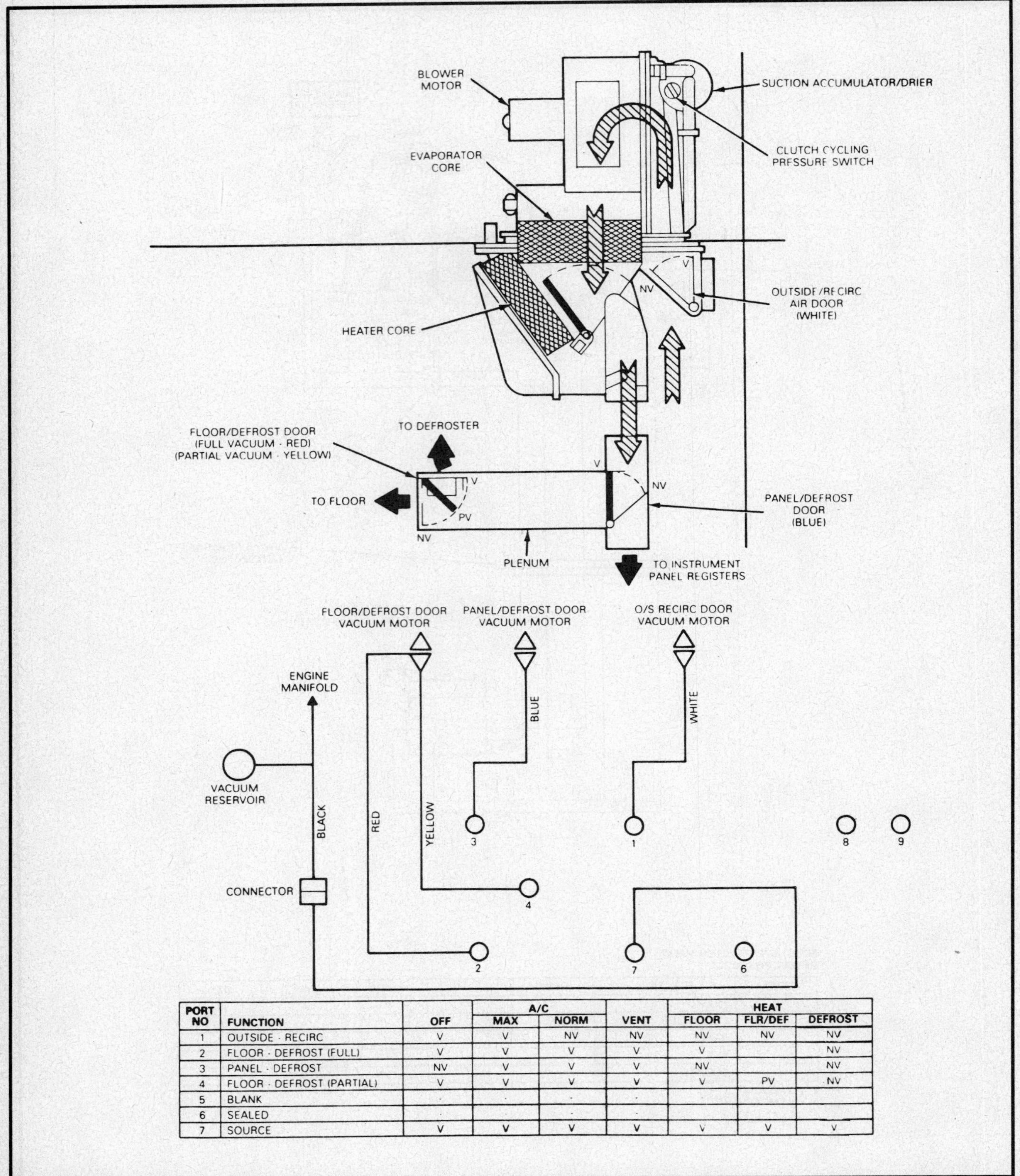

PORT NO	FUNCTION	OFF	A/C		VENT	HEAT		
			MAX	NORM		FLOOR	FLR/DEF	DEFROST
1	OUTSIDE - RECIRC	V	V	NV	NV	NV	NV	NV
2	FLOOR - DEFROST (FULL)	V	V	V	V	V		NV
3	PANEL - DEFROST	NV	V	V	V	NV		NV
4	FLOOR - DEFROST (PARTIAL)	V	V	V	V	V	PV	NV
5	BLANK	-	-	-	-	-		
6	SEALED	-	-	-	-			
7	SOURCE	V	V	V	V	V	V	V

Vacuum schematic—E-Series

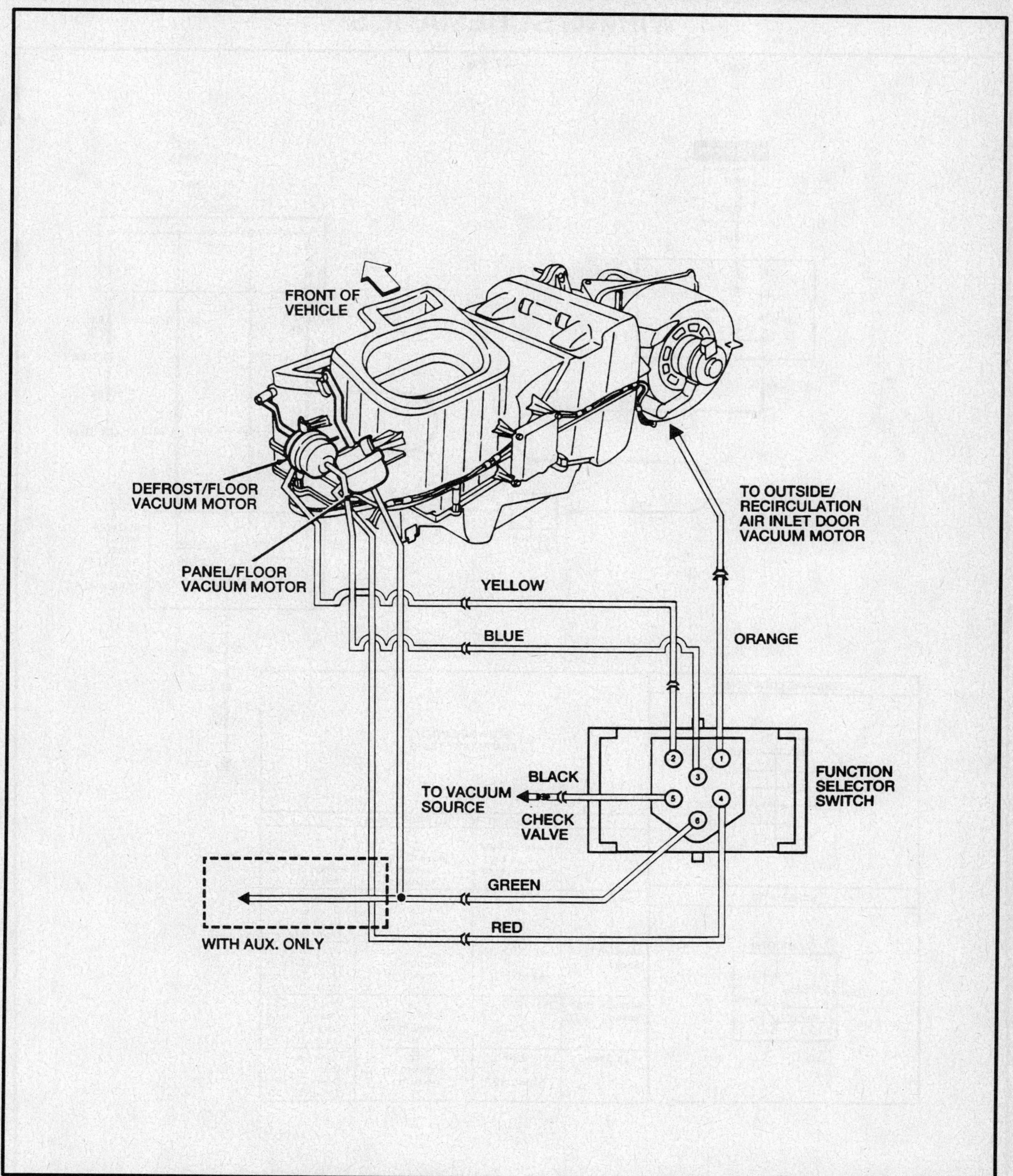

Climate control vacuum schematic—1995 Windstar

WIRING SCHEMATICS

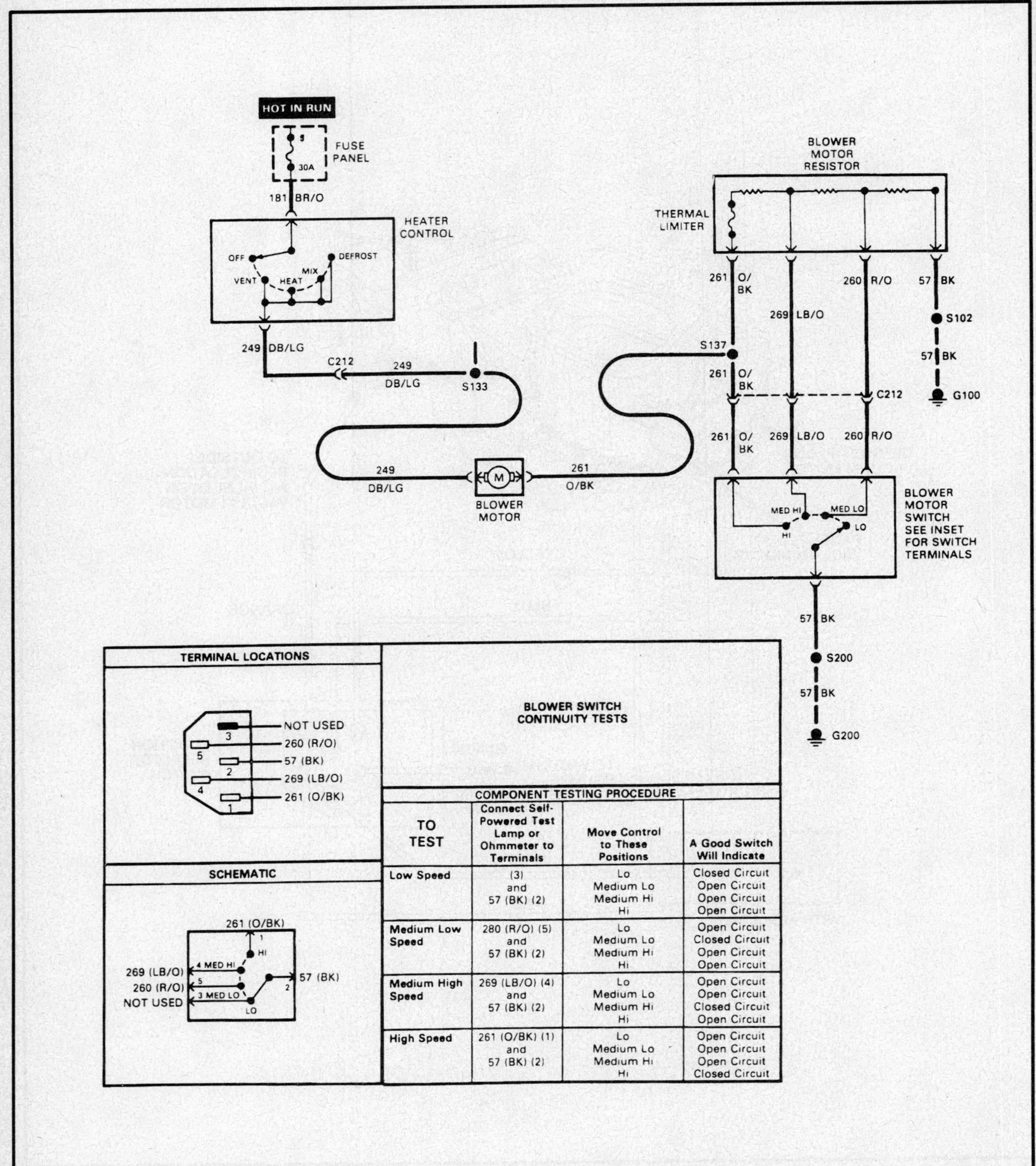

COMPONENT TESTING PROCEDURE

TO TEST	Connect Self-Powered Test Lamp or Ohmmeter to Terminals	Move Control to These Positions	A Good Switch Will Indicate
Low Speed	(3) and 57 (BK) (2)	Lo Medium Lo Medium Hi Hi	Closed Circuit Open Circuit Open Circuit Open Circuit
Medium Low Speed	280 (R/O) (5) and 57 (BK) (2)	Lo Medium Lo Medium Hi Hi	Open Circuit Closed Circuit Open Circuit Open Circuit
Medium High Speed	269 (LB/O) (4) and 57 (BK) (2)	Lo Medium Lo Medium Hi Hi	Open Circuit Open Circuit Closed Circuit Open Circuit
High Speed	261 (O/BK) (1) and 57 (BK) (2)	Lo Medium Lo Medium Hi Hi	Open Circuit Open Circuit Open Circuit Closed Circuit

Heating system electrical schematic—Aerostar

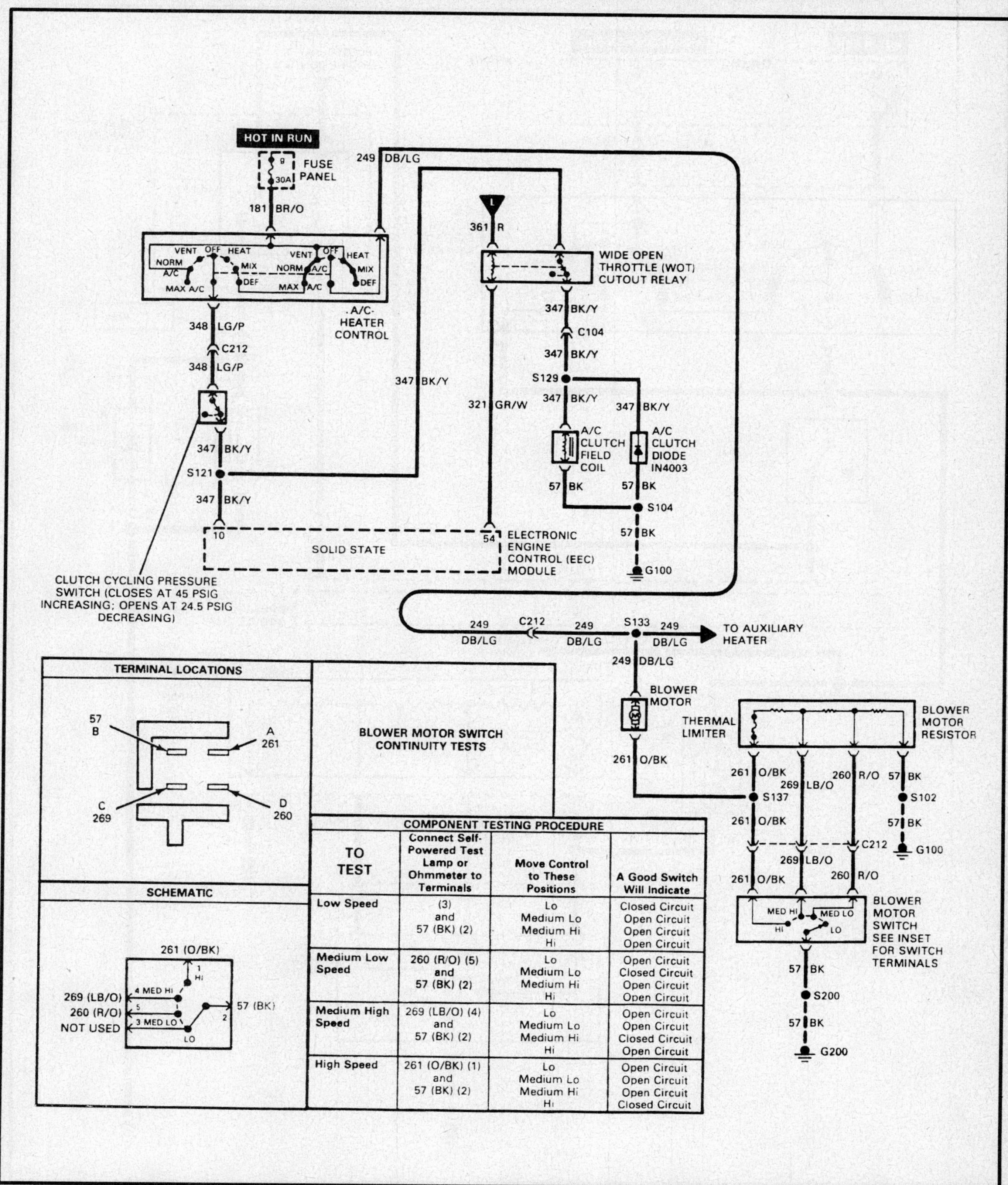

COMPONENT TESTING PROCEDURE

TO TEST	Connect Self-Powered Test Lamp or Ohmmeter to Terminals	Move Control to These Positions	A Good Switch Will Indicate
Low Speed	(3) and 57 (BK) (2)	Lo Medium Lo Medium Hi Hi	Closed Circuit Open Circuit Open Circuit Open Circuit
Medium Low Speed	260 (R/O) (5) and 57 (BK) (2)	Lo Medium Lo Medium Hi Hi	Open Circuit Closed Circuit Open Circuit Open Circuit
Medium High Speed	269 (LB/O) (4) and 57 (BK) (2)	Lo Medium Lo Medium Hi Hi	Open Circuit Open Circuit Closed Circuit Open Circuit
High Speed	261 (O/BK) (1) and 57 (BK) (2)	Lo Medium Lo Medium Hi Hi	Open Circuit Open Circuit Open Circuit Closed Circuit

Heating/air conditioning system electrical schematic—1993 Aerostar

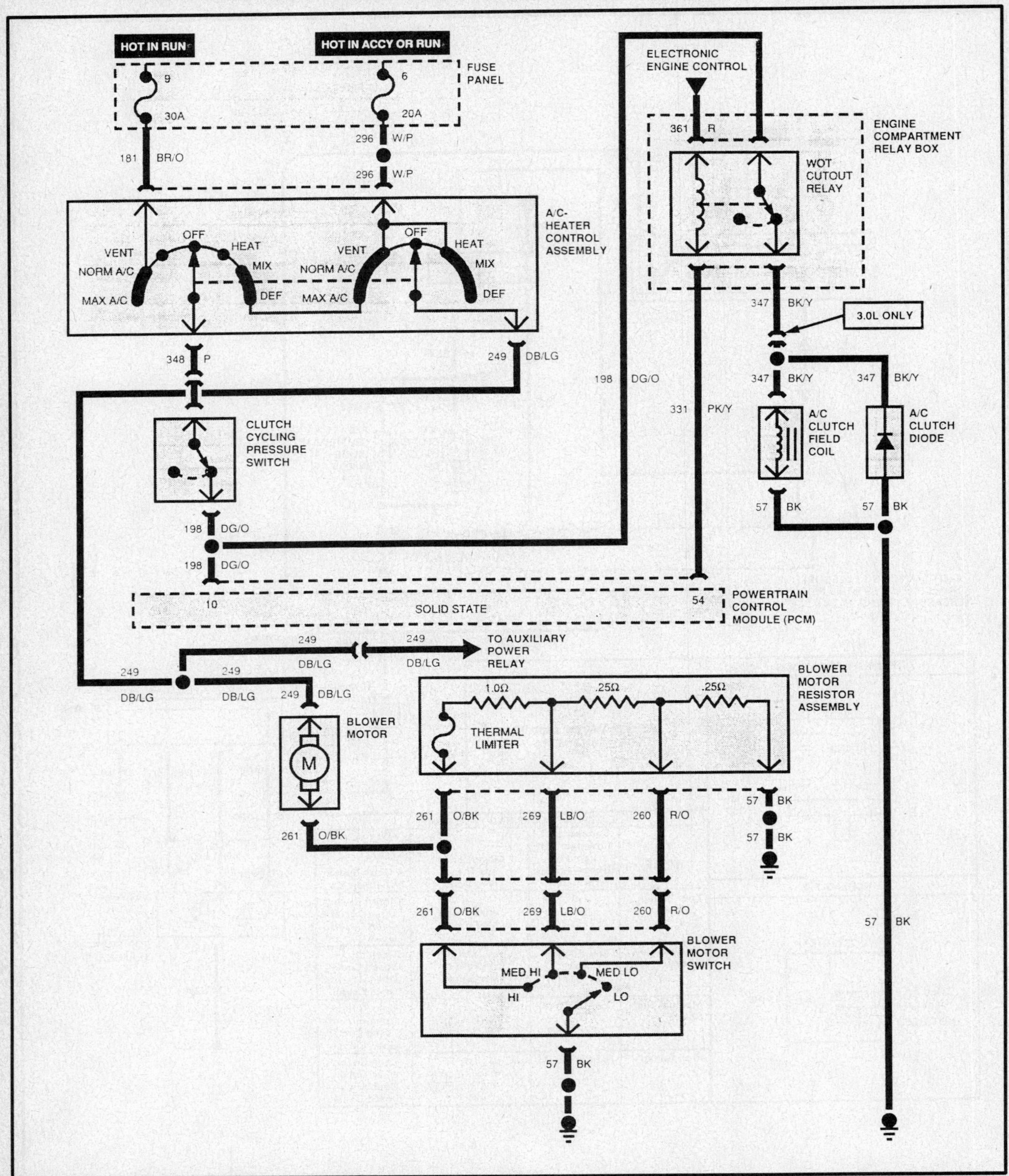

Heating/air conditioning system electrical schematic—1993–94 Aerostar

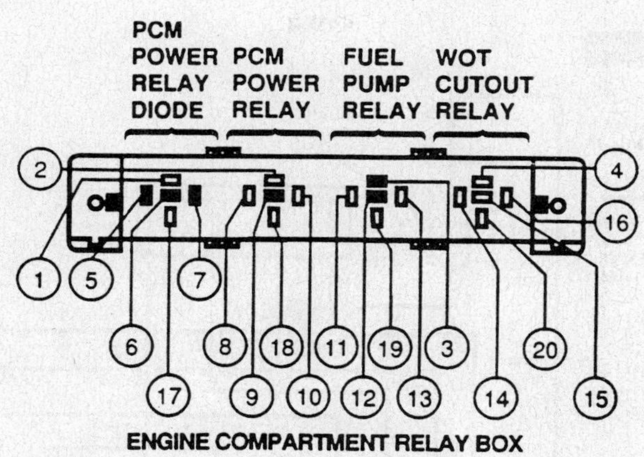

ENGINE COMPARTMENT RELAY BOX

Pin Number	Circuit	Circuit Function
1	454 (R/LG)	Ignition Switch Coil Terminal to Circuit Breaker
2	361 (R)	Power Output from Closed Loop Relay
3	—	Not Used
4	238 (DG/Y)	Fuel Pump Relay to Safety Switch
5	—	Not Used
6	—	Not Used
7	—	Not Used
8	60 (BK/LG)	Constant Voltage Unit to Gauge
9	—	Not Used
10	454 (R/LG)	Ignition Switch Coil Terminal to Circuit Breaker
11	926 (LB/O)	PCM to Fuel Pump Relay Control
12	—	Not Used
13	361 (R)	Power Output from Closed Loop Relay
14	331 (PK/Y)	Wide-Open Throttle A/C Cutout Switch
15	347 (BK/Y)	A/C Cycling Pressure Switch to PCM
16	361 (R)	Power Output from Closed Loop Relay
17	16 (R/LG)	Ignition Switch to Ignition Coil "Battery" Terminal
18	37 (Y)	Battery to Load
19	37 (Y)	Battery to Load
20	198 (DG/O)	A/C Pressure Switch to Control Relay

Heating/air conditioning system electrical schematic—1994–95 Aerostar, Cont'd

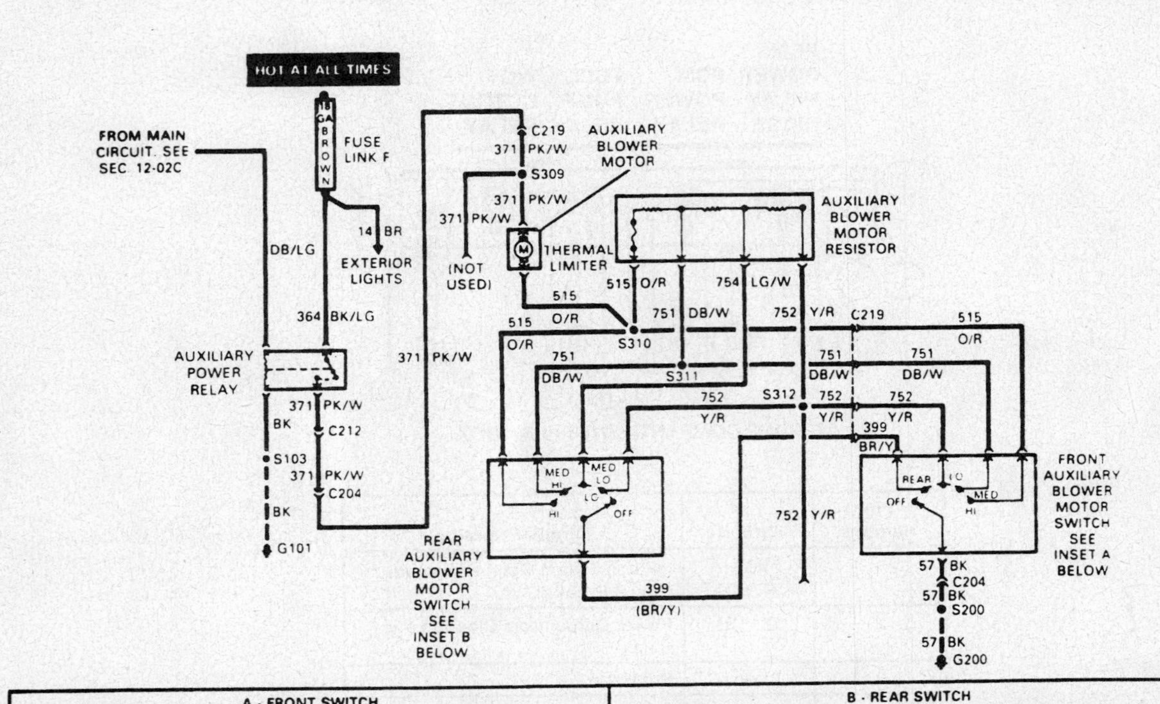

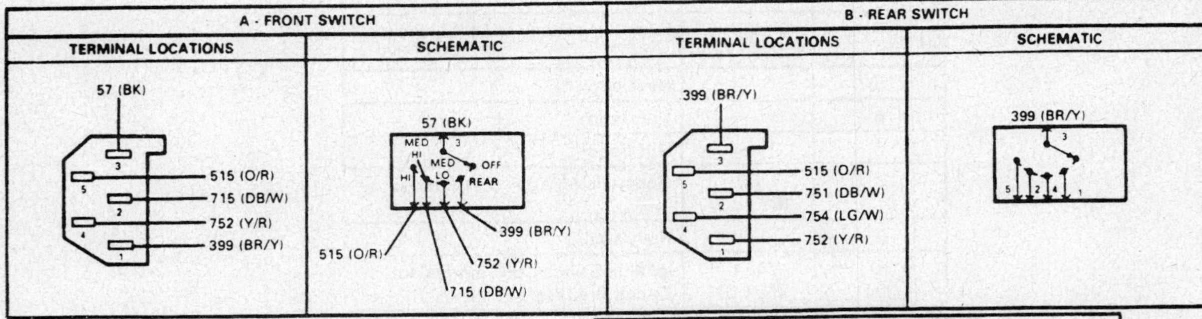

COMPONENT TESTING PROCEDURE

TO TEST	Connect Self-Powered Test Lamp or Ohmmeter to Terminals	Move Control to These Positions	A Good Switch Will Indicate
Rear Select	399 (BR/Y) and 57 (BK) (3)	Off Rear Lo Medium Hi	Open Circuit Closed Circuit Open Circuit Open Circuit Open Circuit
Low Speed	752 (Y/R) (4) and 57 (BK) (3)	Off Rear Lo Medium Hi	Open Circuit Open Circuit Closed Circuit Open Circuit Open Circuit
Medium Speed	715 (DB/W) (2) and 57 (BK) (3)	Off Rear Lo Medium Hi	Open Circuit Open Circuit Open Circuit Closed Circuit Open Circuit
High Speed	515 (O/R) (5) and 57 (BK) (3)	Off Rear Lo Medium Hi	Open Circuit Open Circuit Open Circuit Open Circuit Closed Circuit

COMPONENT TESTING PROCEDURE

TO TEST	Connect Self-Powered Test Lamp or Ohmmeter to Terminals	Move Control to These Positions	A Good Switch Will Indicate
Low Speed	752 (Y/R) (1) and 399 (BR/Y) (3)	Off Lo Medium Lo Medium Hi Hi	Open Circuit Closed Circuit Open Circuit Open Circuit Open Circuit
Medium Low Speed	754 (LG/W) (4) and 399 (BR/Y) (3)	Off Lo Medium Lo Medium Hi Hi	Open Circuit Open Circuit Closed Circuit Open Circuit Open Circuit
Medium High Speed	751 (DB/W) (2) and 399 (BR/Y) (3)	Off Lo Medium Lo Medium Hi Hi	Open Circuit Open Circuit Open Circuit Closed Circuit Open Circuit
High Speed	515 (O/R) (5) and 399 (BR/Y) (3)	Off Lo Medium Lo Medium Hi Hi	Open Circuit Open Circuit Open Circuit Open Circuit Closed Circuit

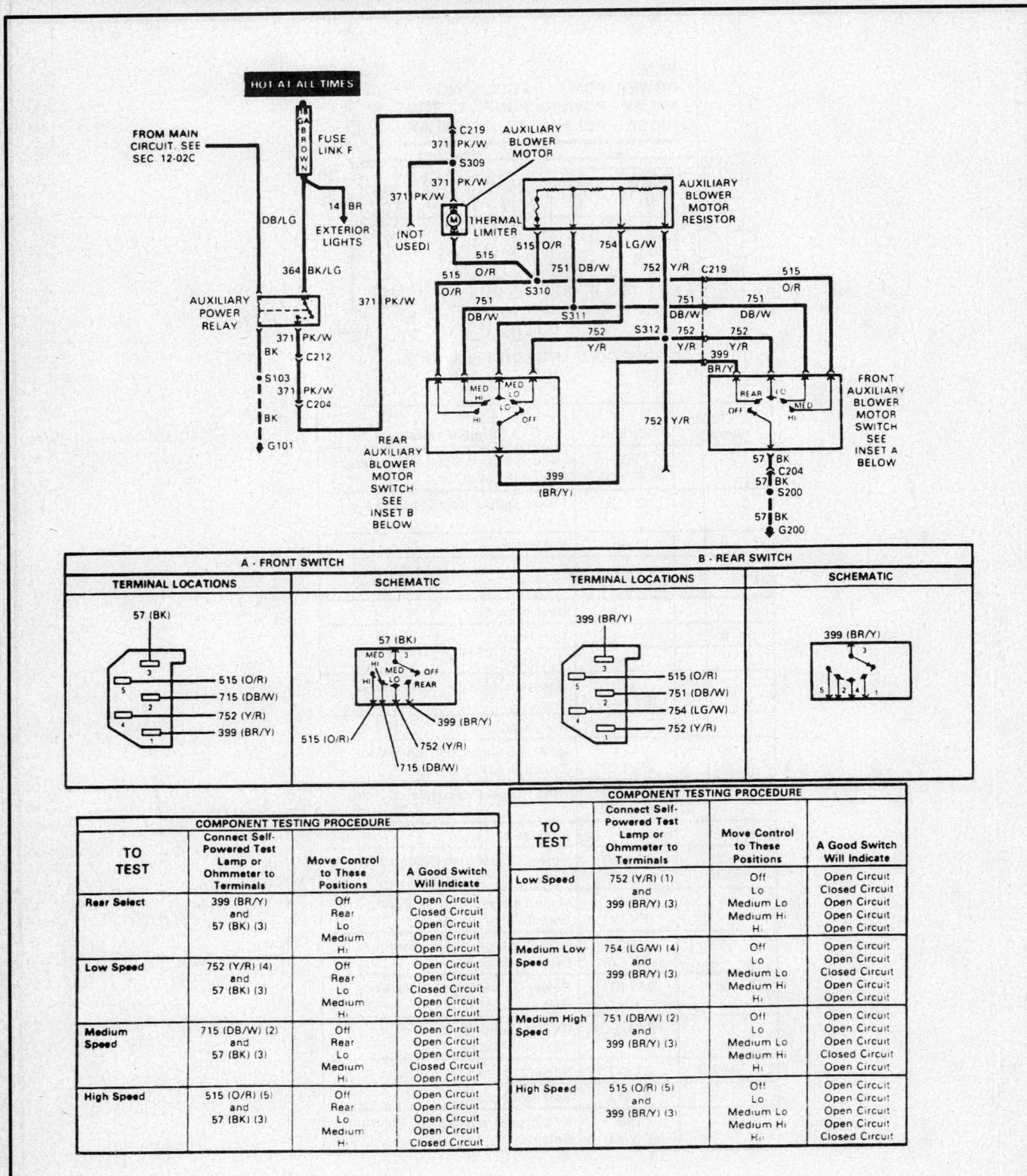

Auxiliary heating system electrical schematic—Aerostar

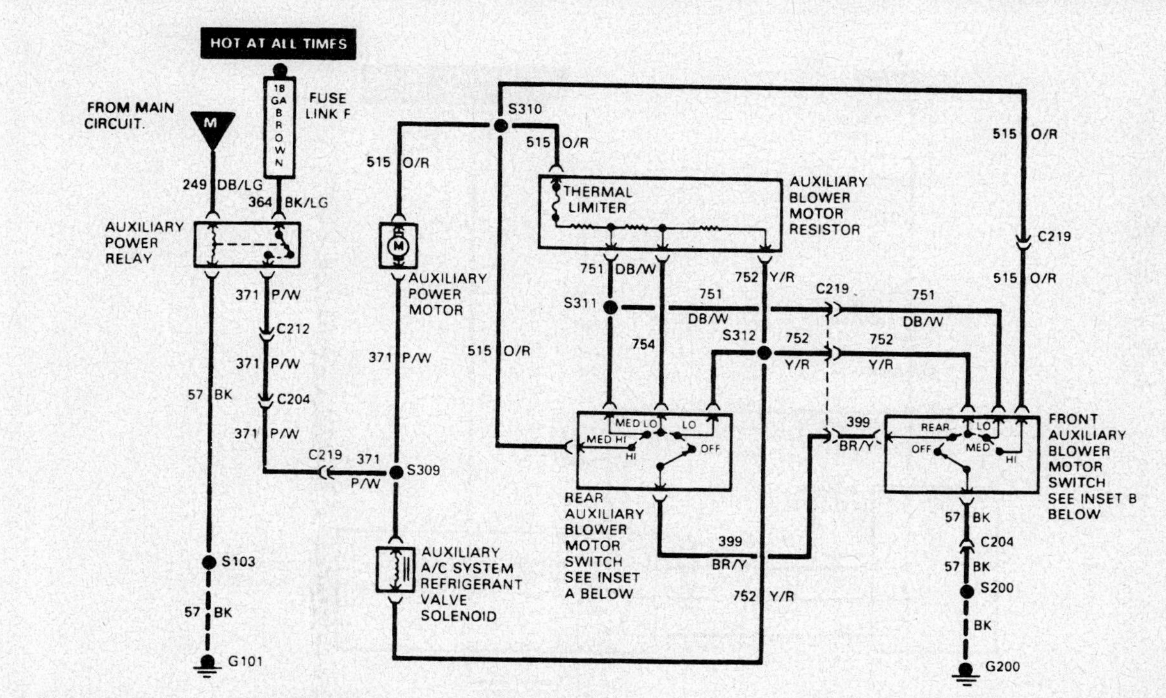

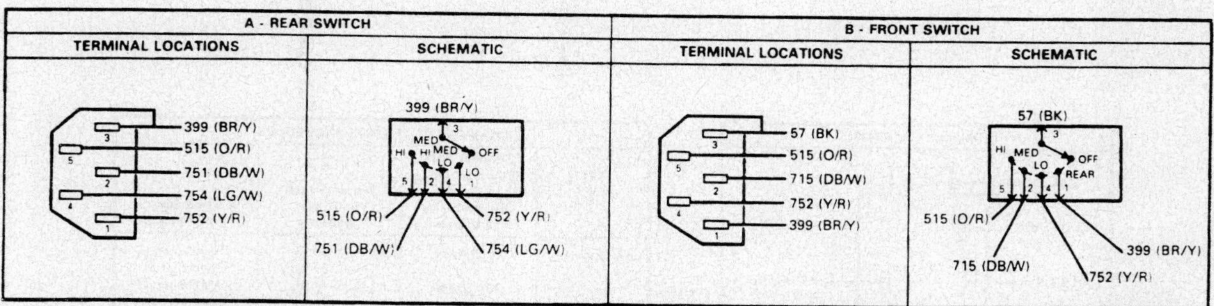

COMPONENT TESTING PROCEDURE

TO TEST	Connect Self Powered Test Lamp or Ohmmeter to Terminals	Move Control to These Positions	A Good Switch Will Indicate
Reset Select	399 (BR/Y) and 57 (BK) (3)	Off Rear Lo Medium Hi	Open Circuit Closed Circuit Open Circuit Open Circuit Open Circuit
Low Speed	752 (Y/R) (4) and 57 (BK) (3)	Off Rear Lo Medium Hi	Open Circuit Open Circuit Closed Circuit Open Circuit Open Circuit
Medium Speed	715 (DB/W) (2) and 57 (BK) (3)	Off Rear Lo Medium Hi	Open Circuit Open Circuit Open Circuit Closed Circuit Open Circuit
High Speed	515 (O/R) (5) and 57 (BK) (3)	Off Rear Lo Medium Hi	Open Circuit Open Circuit Open Circuit Open Circuit Closed Circuit

COMPONENT TESTING PROCEDURE

TO TEST	Connect Self Powered Test Lamp or Ohmmeter to Terminals	Move Control to These Positions	A Good Switch Will Indicate
Low Speed	752 (Y/R) (4) and 399 (BR/Y) (3)	Off Lo Medium Lo Medium Hi Hi	Open Circuit Closed Circuit Open Circuit Open Circuit Open Circuit
Medium Low Speed	754 (LG/W) (4) and 399 (BR/Y) (3)	Off Lo Medium Lo Medium Hi Hi	Open Circuit Open Circuit Closed Circuit Open Circuit Open Circuit
Medium High Speed	751 (DB/W) (2) and 399 (BR/Y) (3)	Off Lo Medium Lo Medium Hi Hi	Open Circuit Open Circuit Open Circuit Closed Circuit Open Circuit
High Speed	515 (O/R) (5) and 399 (BR/Y) (3)	Off Lo Medium Lo Medium Hi Hi	Open Circuit Open Circuit Open Circuit Open Circuit Closed Circuit

Auxiliary heater/air conditioning system electrical schematic—Aerostar

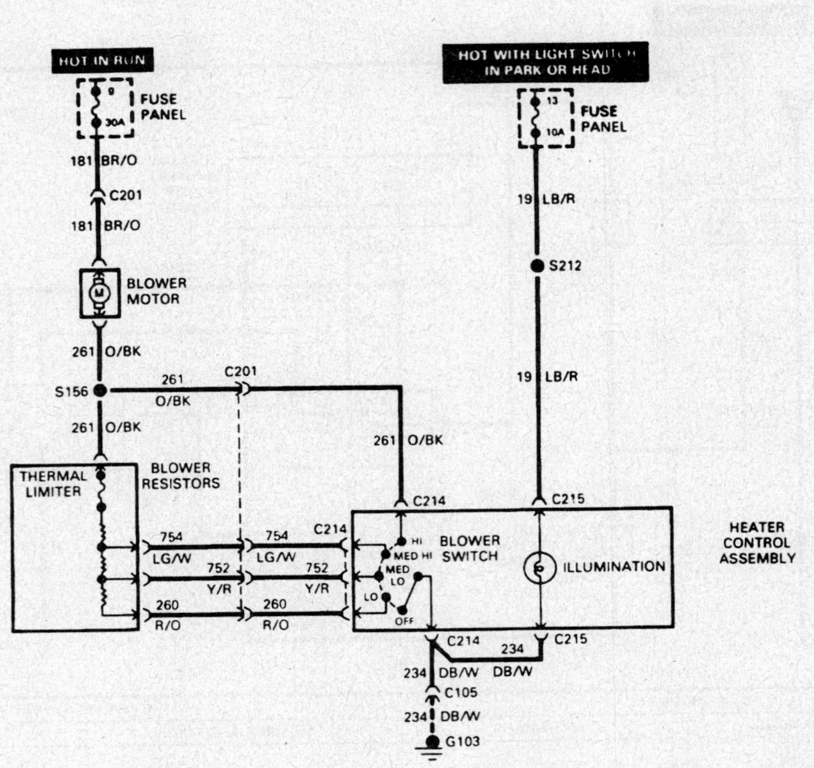

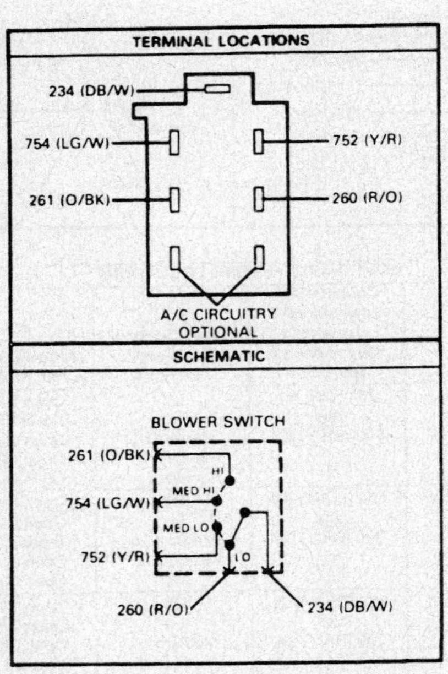

COMPONENT TESTING PROCEDURE

TO TEST	Connect Self-Powered Test Light or Ohmmeter to Terminals	Move Switch to These Positions	A Good Switch Will Indicate
Low Speed	260 R/O and 234 DB/W	Lo Medium Lo Medium Hi Hi	Closed Circuit Open Circuit Open Circuit Open Circuit
Medium Low Speed	752 Y/R and 234 DB/W	Lo Medium Lo Medium Hi Hi	Open Circuit Closed Circuit Open Circuit Open Circuit
Medium Hi Speed	754 LG/W and 234 DB/W	Lo Medium Lo Medium Hi Hi	Open Circuit Open Circuit Closed Circuit Open Circuit
High Speed	261 O/BK and 234 DB/W	Lo Medium Lo Medium Hi Hi	Open Circuit Open Circuit Open Circuit Closed Circuit

WIRE COLOR CODES
BR/O · BROWN/ORANGE
DB/W · DARK BLUE/WHITE
LB/R · LIGHT BLUE/RED
LG/W · LIGHT GREEN/WHITE
O/BK · ORANGE/BLACK
R/O · RED/ORANGE
Y/R · YELLOW/RED

Heating system electrical schematic—Explorer and Ranger

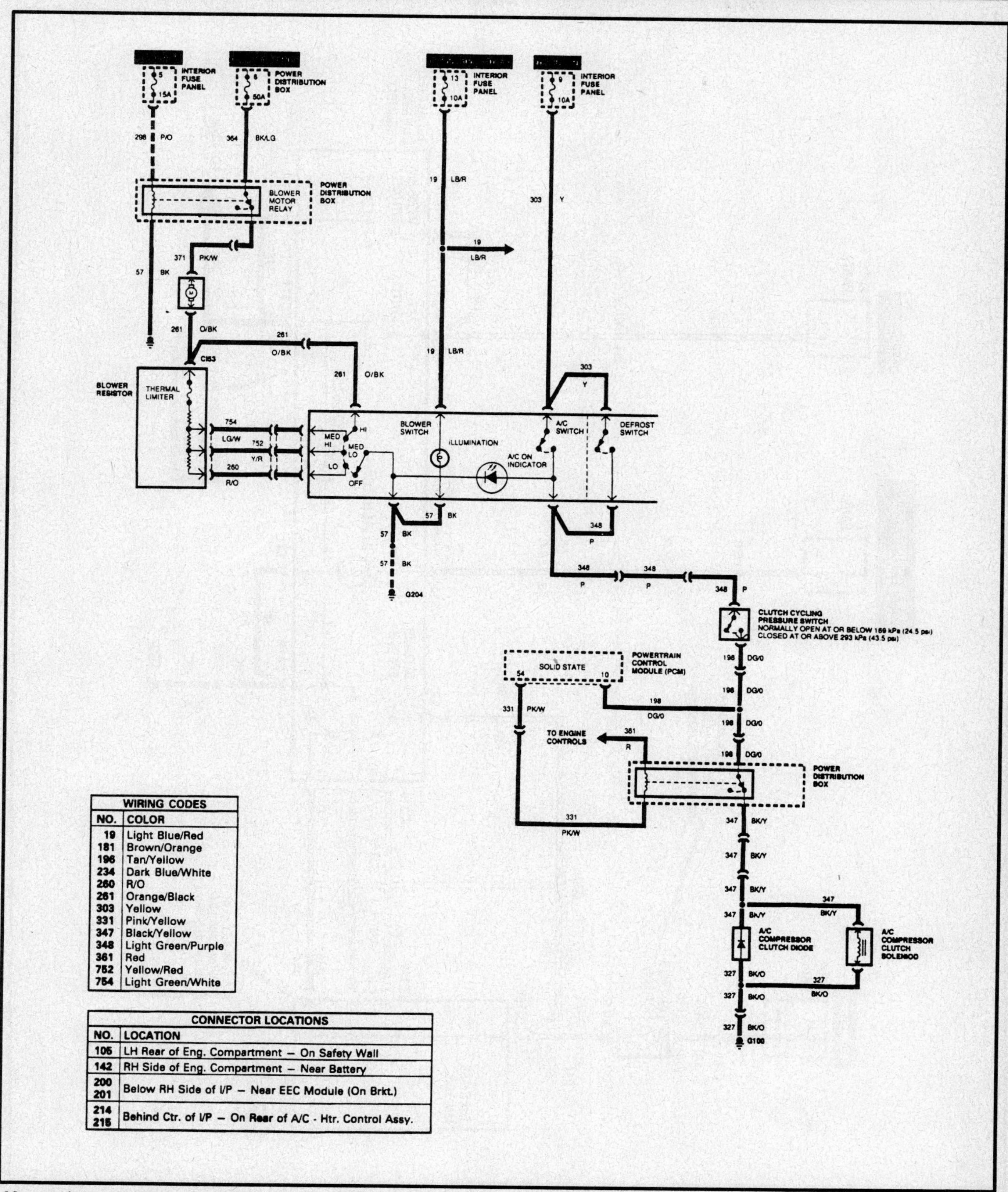

WIRING CODES	
NO.	COLOR
19	Light Blue/Red
181	Brown/Orange
196	Tan/Yellow
234	Dark Blue/White
260	R/O
261	Orange/Black
303	Yellow
331	Pink/Yellow
347	Black/Yellow
348	Light Green/Purple
361	Red
752	Yellow/Red
754	Light Green/White

CONNECTOR LOCATIONS	
NO.	LOCATION
105	LH Rear of Eng. Compartment – On Safety Wall
142	RH Side of Eng. Compartment – Near Battery
200 201	Below RH Side of I/P – Near EEC Module (On Brkt.)
214 215	Behind Ctr. of I/P – On Rear of A/C - Htr. Control Assy.

Heater/air conditioning system electrical schematic—1993 Ranger and Explorer

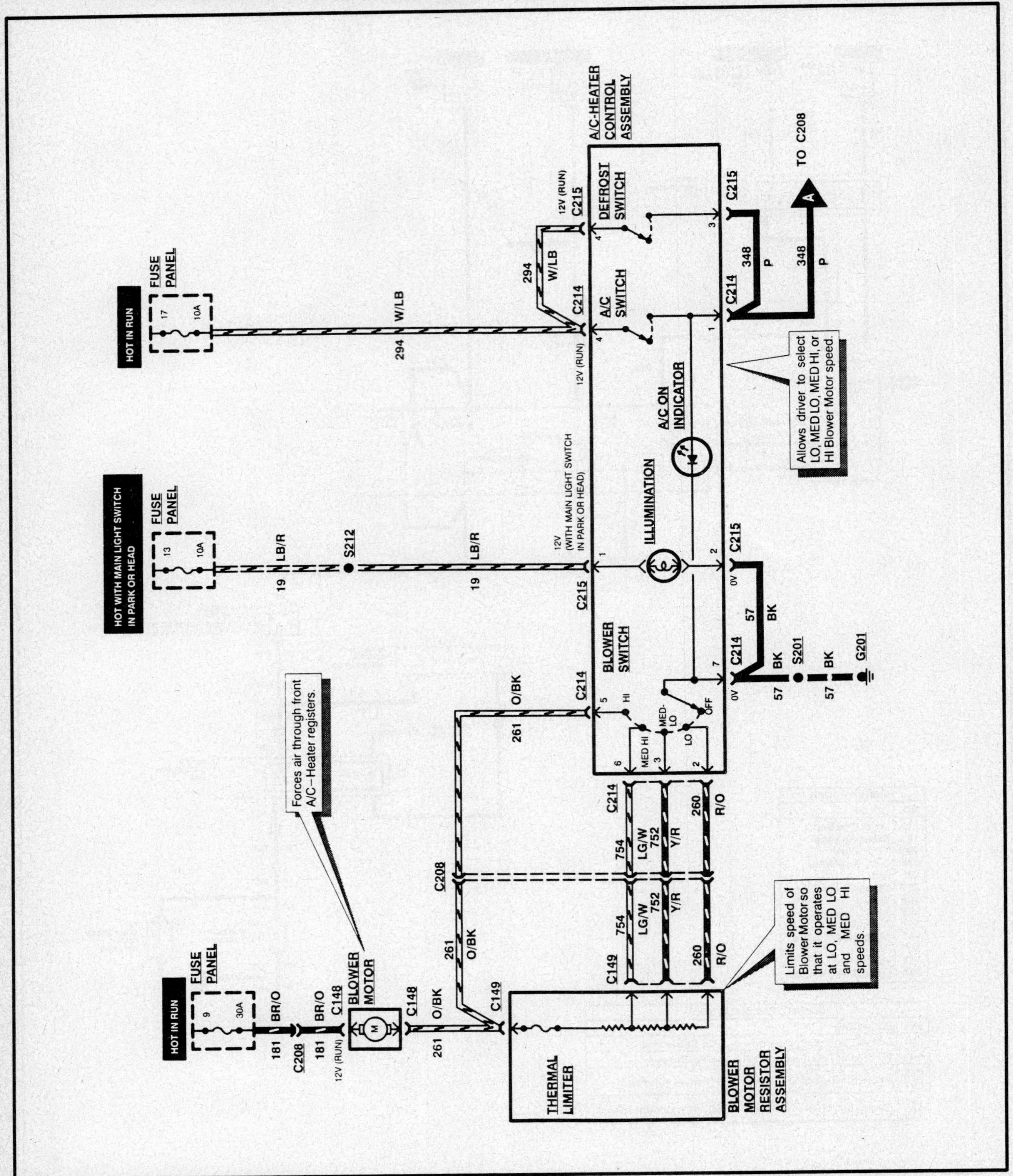

Heater/air conditioning system electrical schematic—1994 Ranger

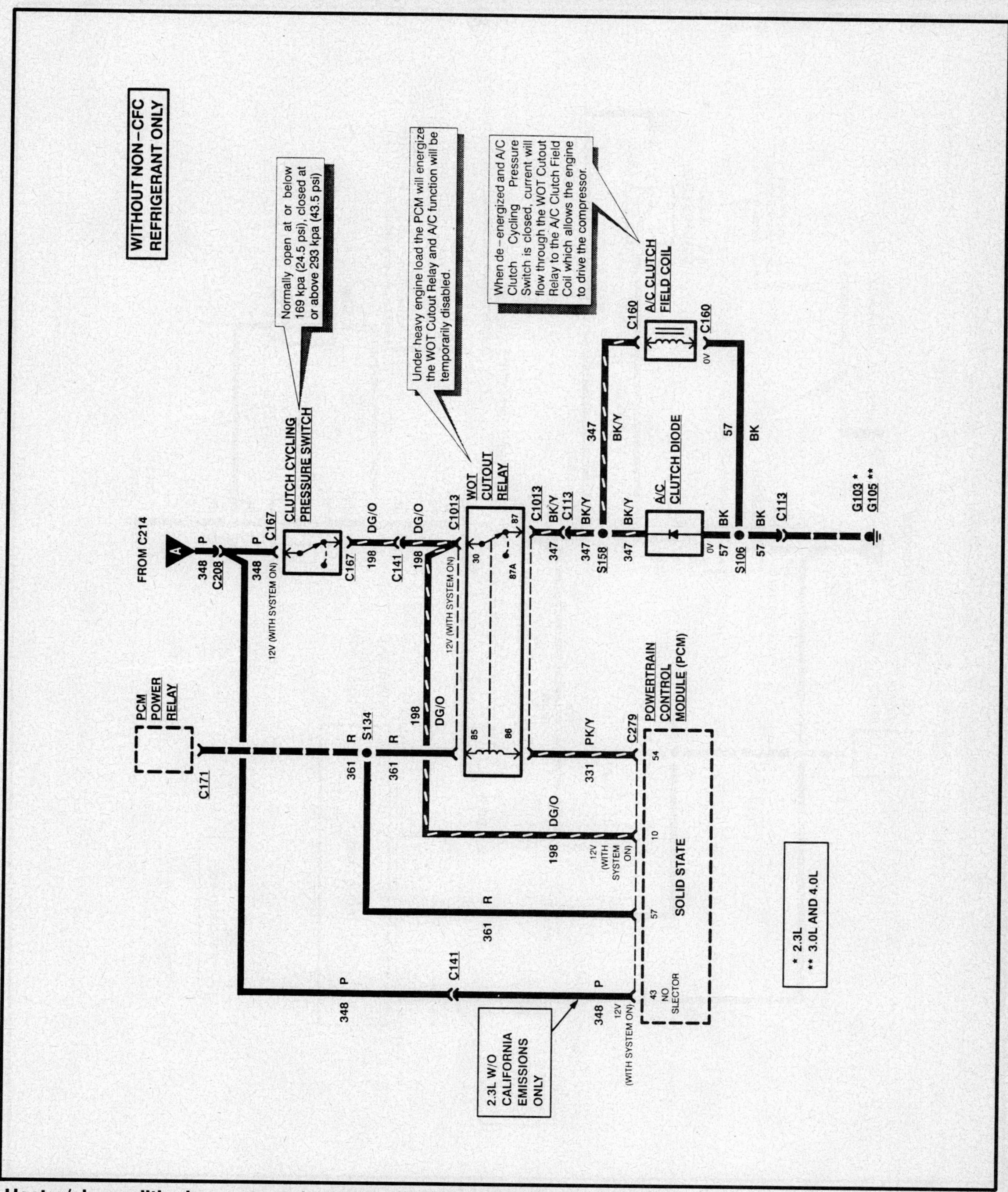
WITHOUT NON-CFC REFRIGERANT ONLY
Normally open at or below 169 kpa (24.5 psi), closed at or above 293 kpa (43.5 psi)
Under heavy engine load the PCM will energize the WOT Cutout Relay and A/C function will be temporarily disabled.
When de-energized and A/C Clutch Cycling Pressure Switch is closed, current will flow through the WOT Cutout Relay to the A/C Clutch Field Coil which allows the engine to drive the compressor.
FROM C214
A
CLUTCH CYCLING PRESSURE SWITCH
WOT CUTOUT RELAY
A/C CLUTCH FIELD COIL
A/C CLUTCH DIODE
PCM POWER RELAY
POWERTRAIN CONTROL MODULE (PCM)
SOLID STATE
2.3L W/O CALIFORNIA EMISSIONS ONLY
* 2.3L
** 3.0L AND 4.0L
G103 *
G105 **
12V (WITH SYSTEM ON)
43 NO SLECTOR

Heater/air conditioning system electrical schematic—1994 Ranger, Cont'd

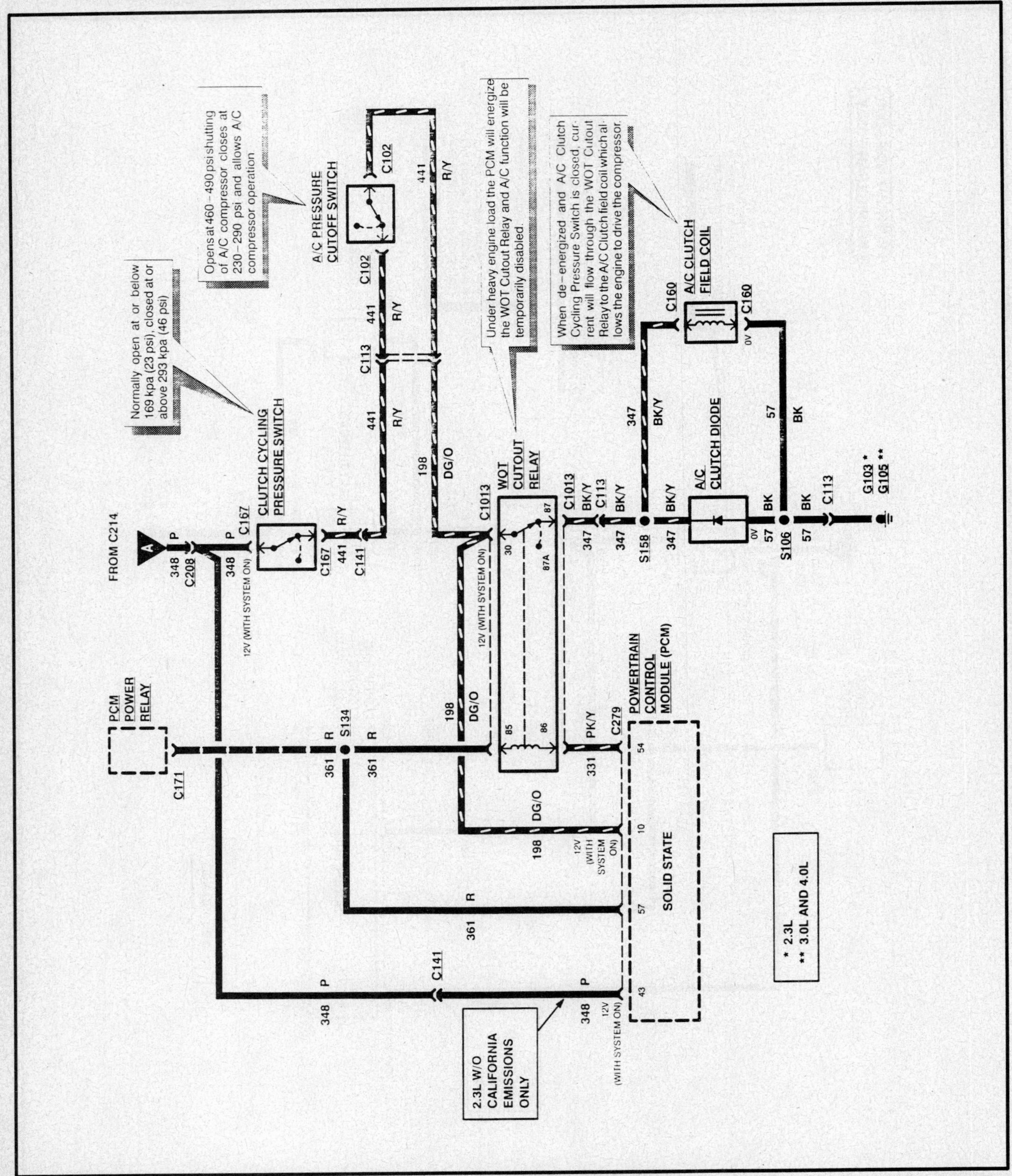
FROM C214
PCM POWER RELAY
C171
CLUTCH CYCLING PRESSURE SWITCH
Normally open at or below 169 kpa (23 psi), closed at or above 293 kpa (46 psi)
A/C PRESSURE CUTOFF SWITCH
Opens at 460 - 490 psi shutting of A/C compressor closes at 230 - 290 psi and allows A/C compressor operation
Under heavy engine load the PCM will energize the WOT Cutout Relay and A/C function will be temporarily disabled.
WOT CUTOUT RELAY
When de-energized and A/C Clutch Cycling Pressure Switch is closed, current will flow through the WOT Cutout Relay to the A/C Clutch field coil which allows the engine to drive the compressor.
A/C CLUTCH FIELD COIL
A/C CLUTCH DIODE
POWERTRAIN CONTROL MODULE (PCM)
SOLID STATE
2.3L W/O CALIFORNIA EMISSIONS ONLY
12V (WITH SYSTEM ON)
G103 *
G105 **
* 2.3L
** 3.0L AND 4.0L

Heater/air conditioning system electrical schematic—1994 Ranger, Cont'd

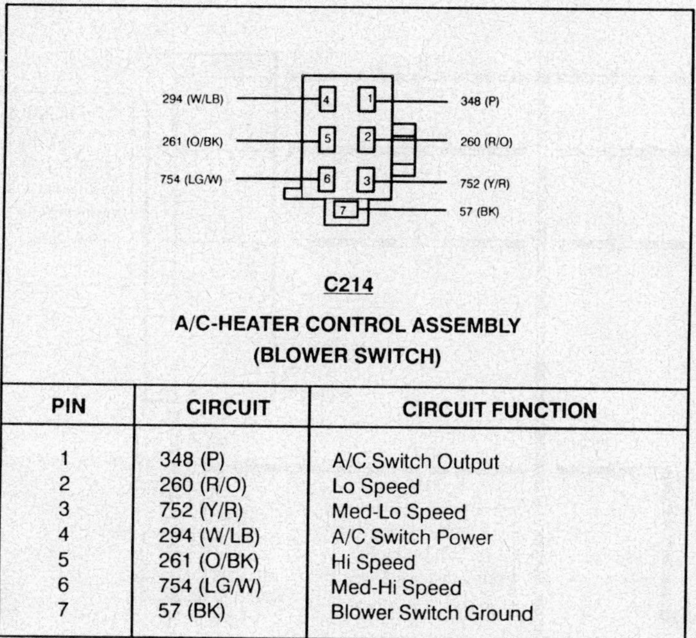

C214

A/C-HEATER CONTROL ASSEMBLY (BLOWER SWITCH)

PIN	CIRCUIT	CIRCUIT FUNCTION
1	348 (P)	A/C Switch Output
2	260 (R/O)	Lo Speed
3	752 (Y/R)	Med-Lo Speed
4	294 (W/LB)	A/C Switch Power
5	261 (O/BK)	Hi Speed
6	754 (LG/W)	Med-Hi Speed
7	57 (BK)	Blower Switch Ground

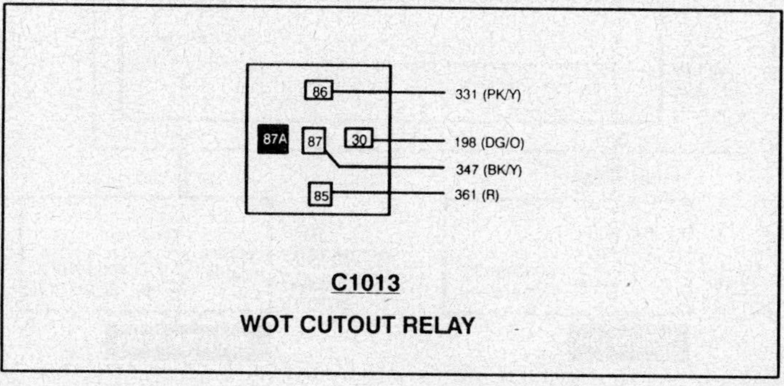

C1013

WOT CUTOUT RELAY

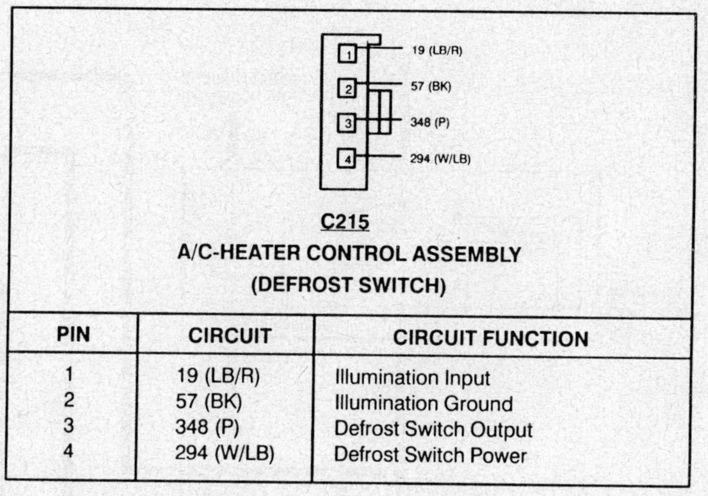

C215

A/C-HEATER CONTROL ASSEMBLY (DEFROST SWITCH)

PIN	CIRCUIT	CIRCUIT FUNCTION
1	19 (LB/R)	Illumination Input
2	57 (BK)	Illumination Ground
3	348 (P)	Defrost Switch Output
4	294 (W/LB)	Defrost Switch Power

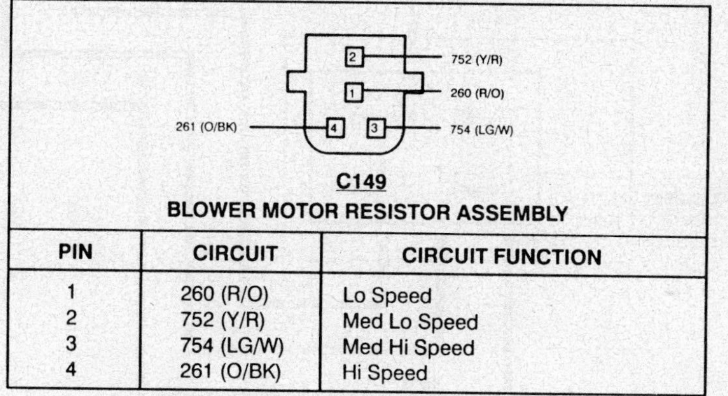

C149

BLOWER MOTOR RESISTOR ASSEMBLY

PIN	CIRCUIT	CIRCUIT FUNCTION
1	260 (R/O)	Lo Speed
2	752 (Y/R)	Med Lo Speed
3	754 (LG/W)	Med Hi Speed
4	261 (O/BK)	Hi Speed

Heater/air conditioning system electrical schematic—1994 Ranger, Cont'd

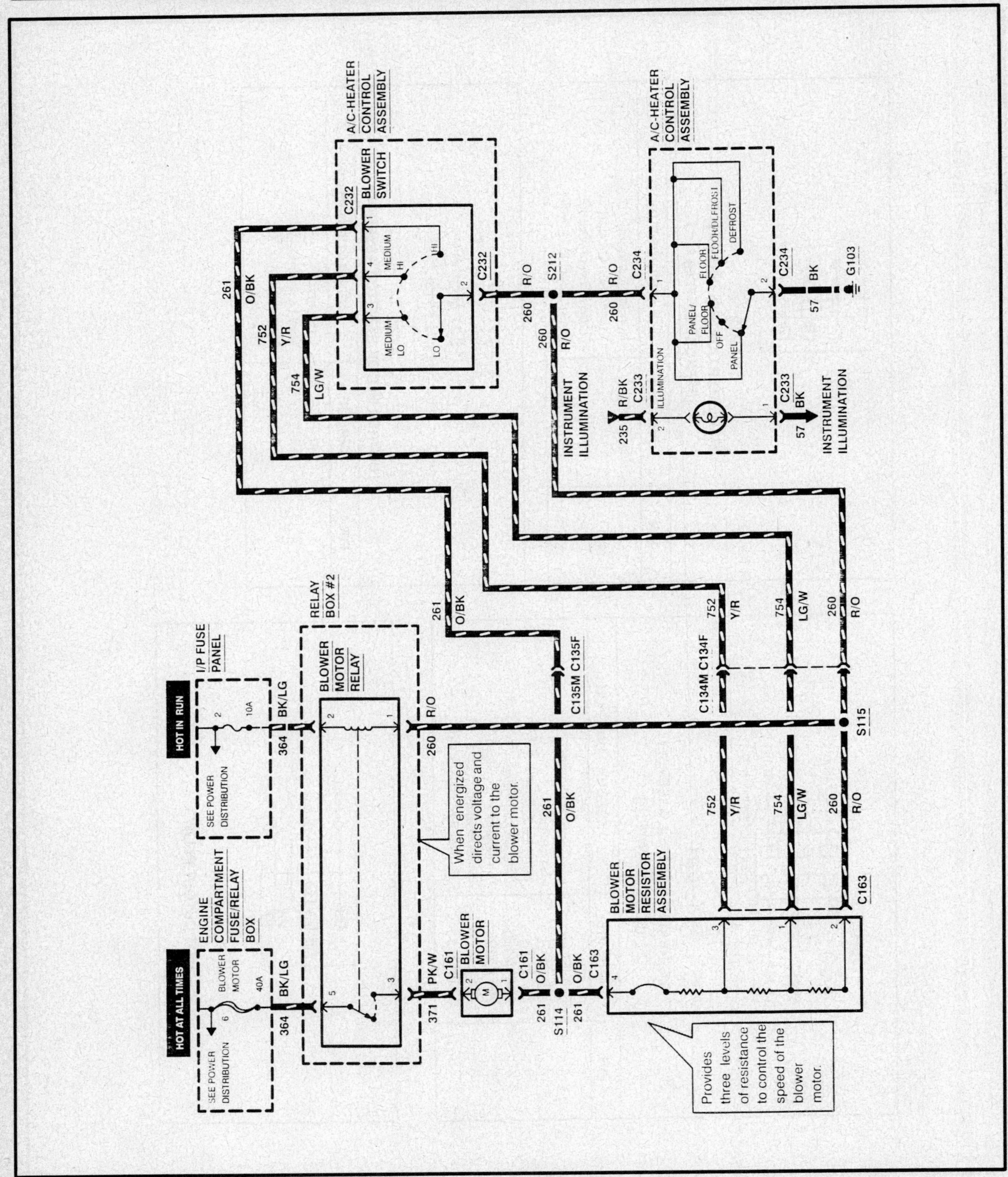

Heater/air conditioning system electrical schematic—1995 Ranger

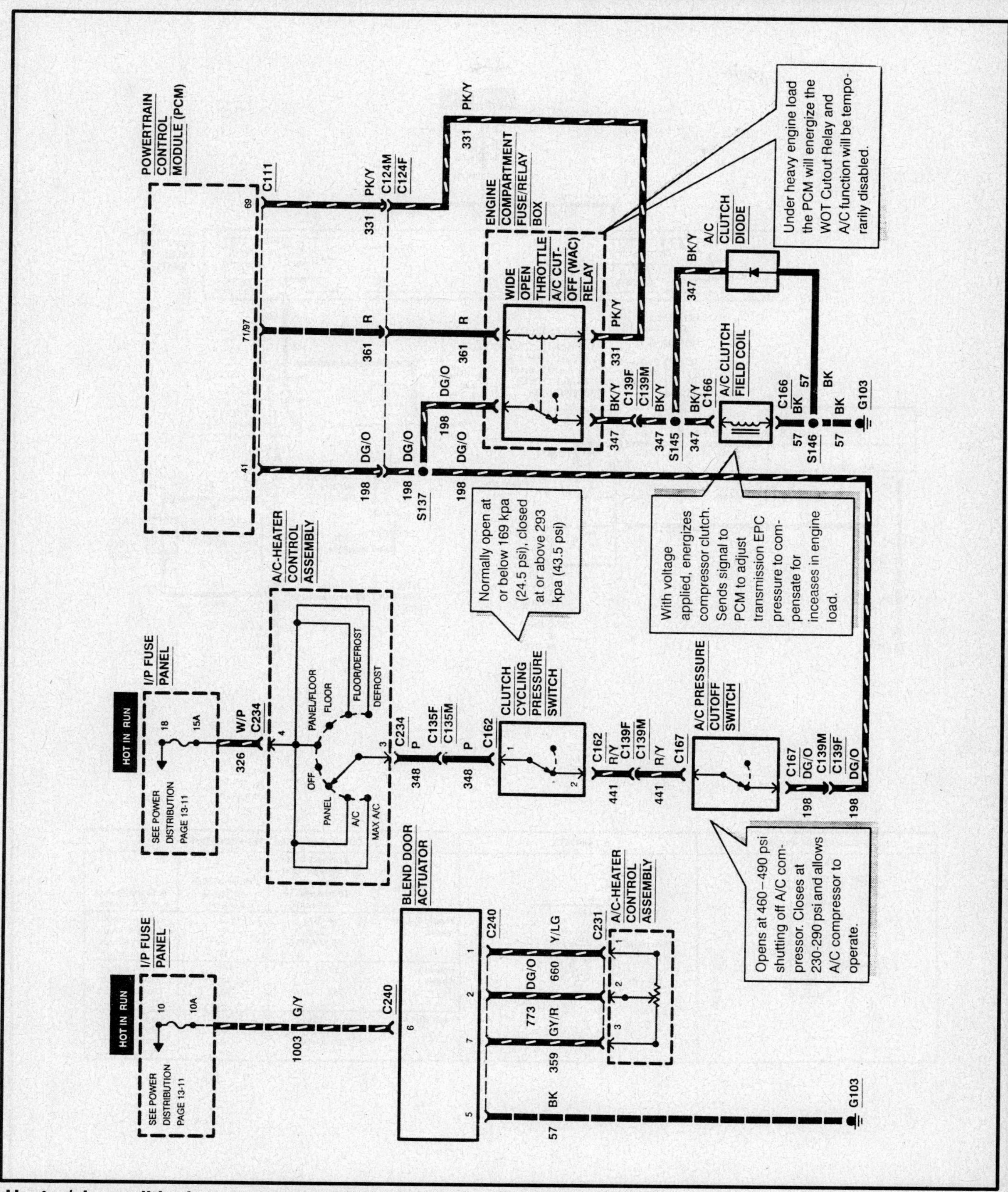

Heater/air conditioning system electrical schematic—1995 Ranger, Cont'd

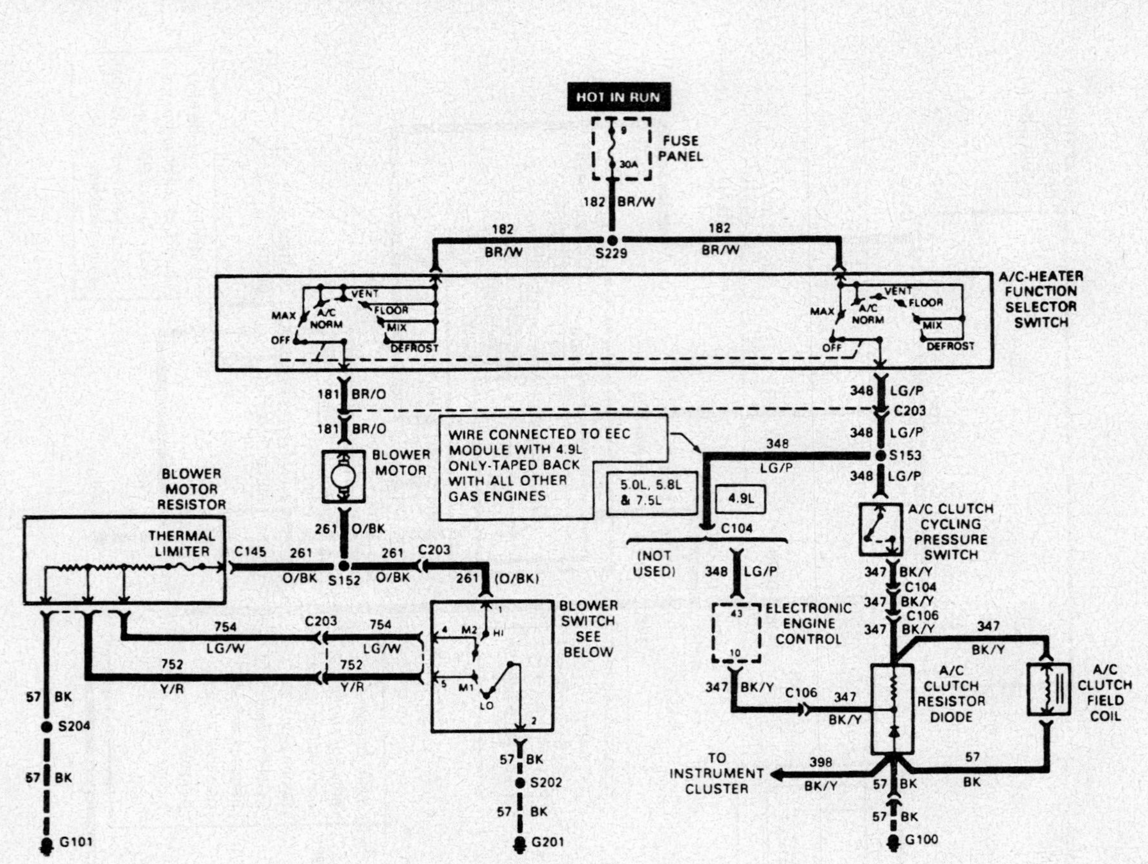

TERMINAL LOCATIONS	SCHEMATIC
261 (O/BK) 754 (LG/W) 57 (BK) 752 (Y/R) 1 2 3 4 5	261 (O/BK) 754 (LG/W) 752 (Y/R) 57 (BK) HI, M2, 4 MED, M1, LO, 5 LO, 2

COMPONENT TESTING PROCEDURE

TO TEST	Connect Self-Powered Test Lamp or Ohmmeter to Terminals	Move Switch to These Positions	A Good Switch Will Indicate
Medium-Low Speed	57 (BK) 2 and 752 (Y/R) 5	Lo M1 M2 Hi	Open circuit Closed circuit Open circuit Open circuit
Medium Speed	57 (BK) 2 and 754 (LG/W)	Lo M1 M2 Hi	Open circuit Open circuit Closed circuit Open circuit
High Speed	57 (BK) 2 and 261 (O/BK) 1	Lo M1 M2 Hi	Open circuit Open circuit Open circuit Closed circuit

Heater/air conditioning system electrical schematic—1993 Bronco and F-Series

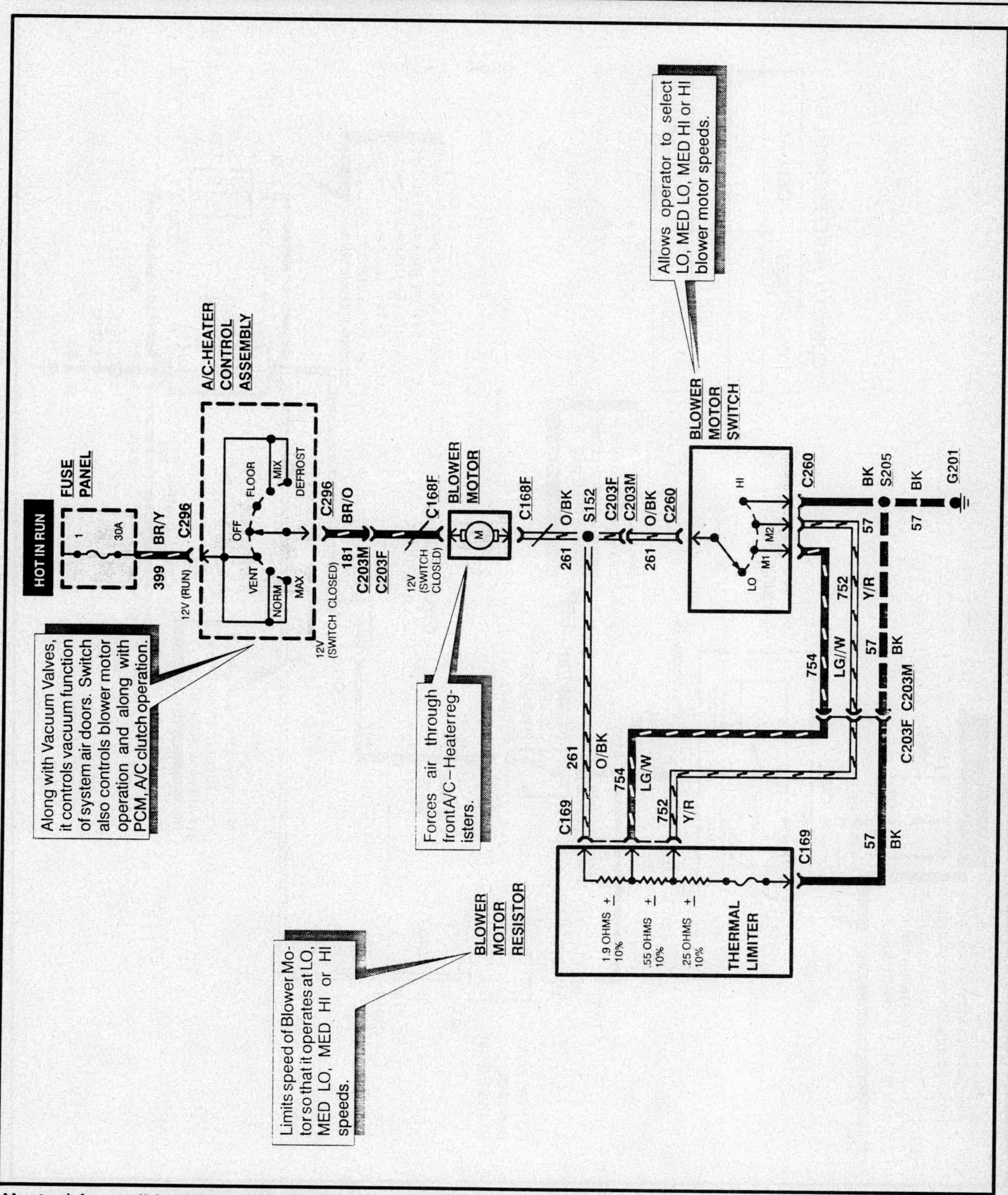

Heater/air conditioning system electrical schematic—1994–95 Bronco and F-Series

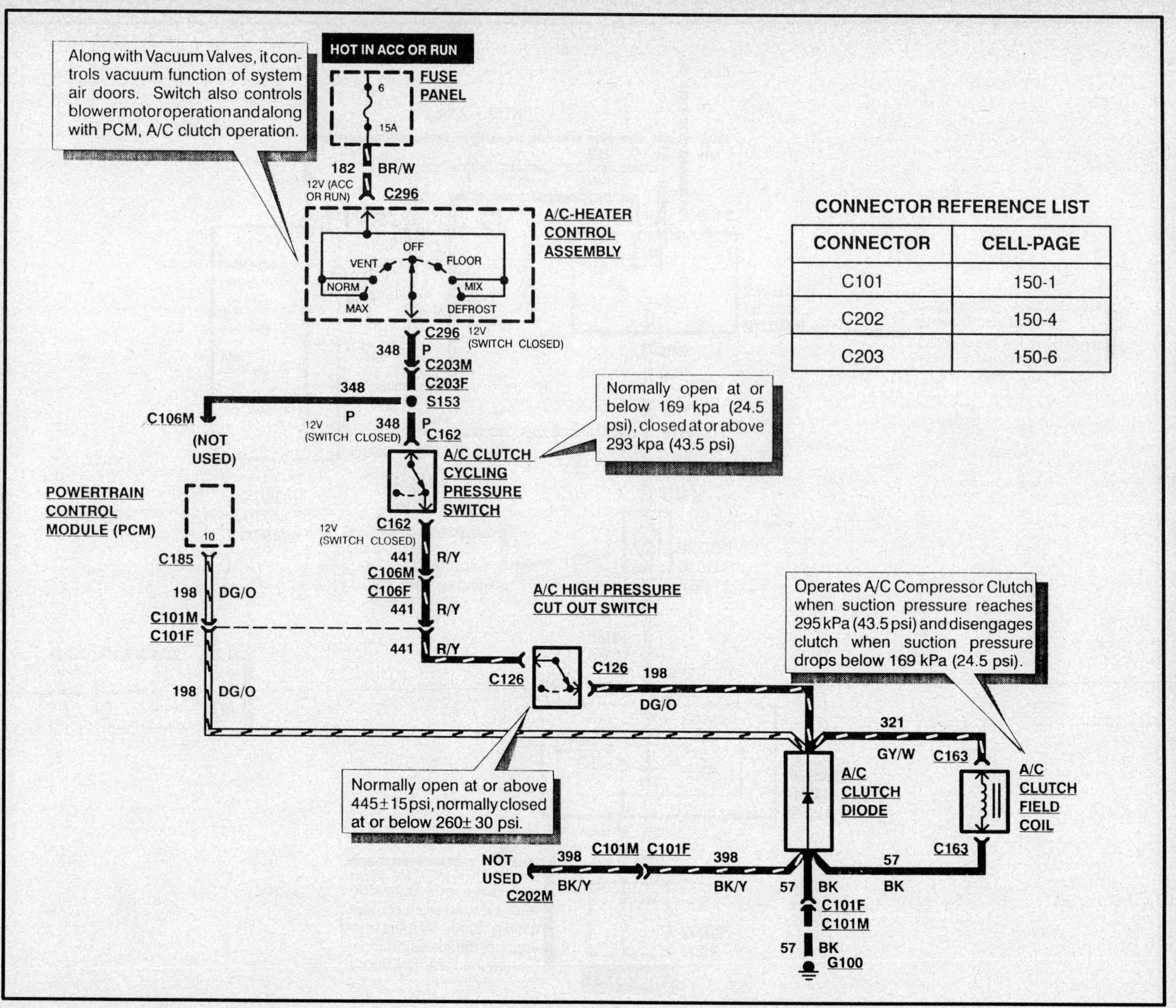

CONNECTOR	CELL-PAGE
C101	150-1
C202	150-4
C203	150-6

Heater/air conditioning system electrical schematic—1994–95 Bronco and F-Series, Cont'd

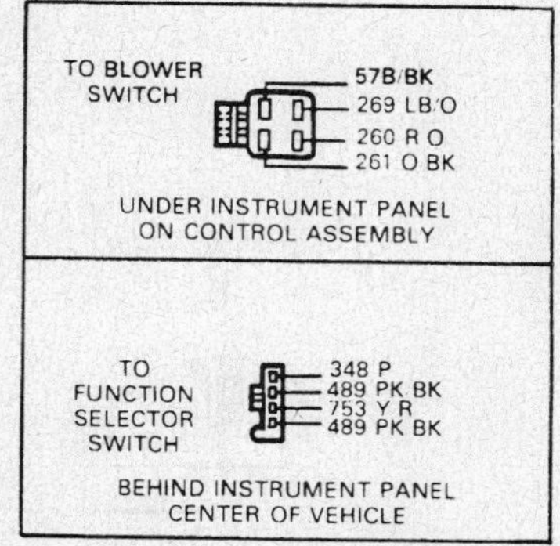
TO BLOWER SWITCH
57B/BK
269 LB/O
260 R O
261 O BK
UNDER INSTRUMENT PANEL ON CONTROL ASSEMBLY
TO FUNCTION SELECTOR SWITCH
348 P
489 PK BK
753 Y R
489 PK BK
BEHIND INSTRUMENT PANEL CENTER OF VEHICLE

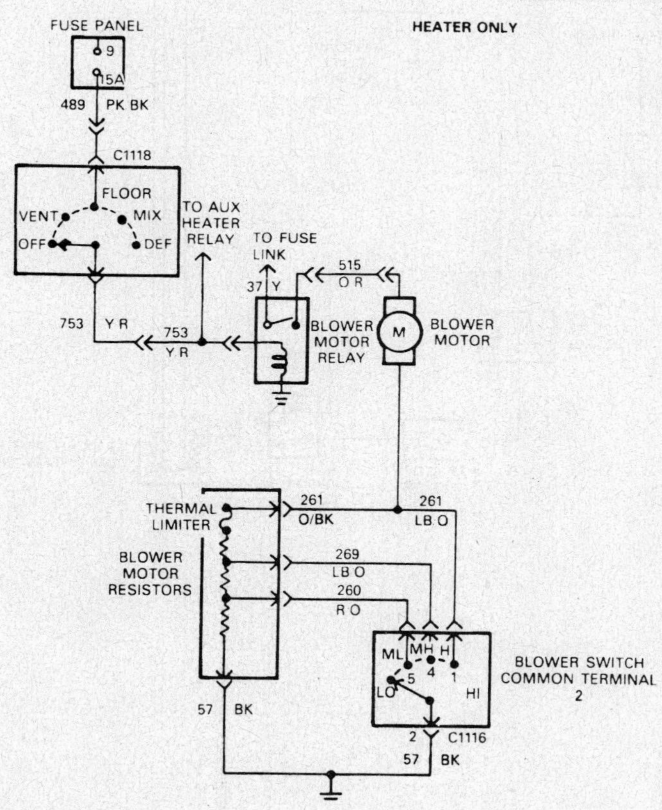
HEATER ONLY
FUSE PANEL
9
15A
489
PK BK
C1118
FLOOR
VENT
MIX
OFF
DEF
TO AUX HEATER RELAY
TO FUSE LINK
37
Y
515
O R
753
Y R
BLOWER MOTOR RELAY
BLOWER MOTOR
M
THERMAL LIMITER
BLOWER MOTOR RESISTORS
261
O/BK
LB O
269
LB O
260
R O
ML
MH
H
5
4
1
LO
HI
BLOWER SWITCH COMMON TERMINAL 2
2
C1116
57
BK

Heating system electrical schematic—E-Series

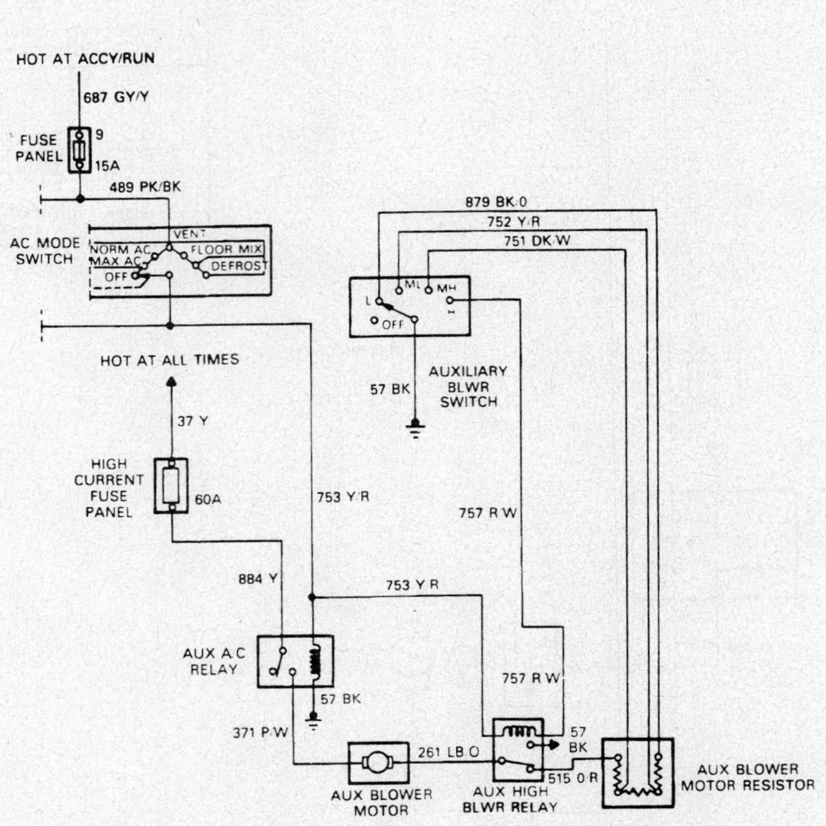

Auxiliary heating system electrical schematic—E-Series

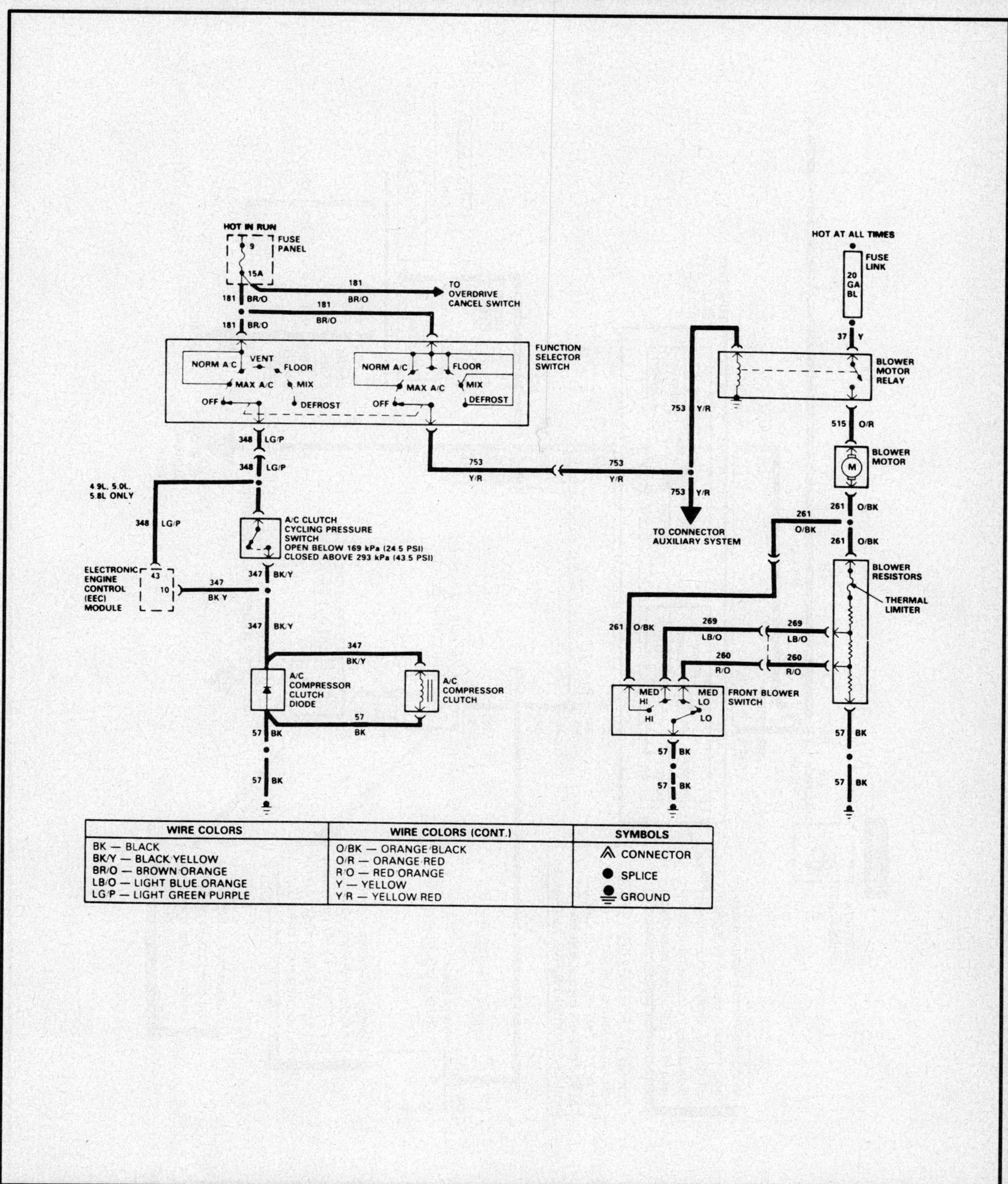

Heater/air conditioning system electrical schematic—1993 E-Series

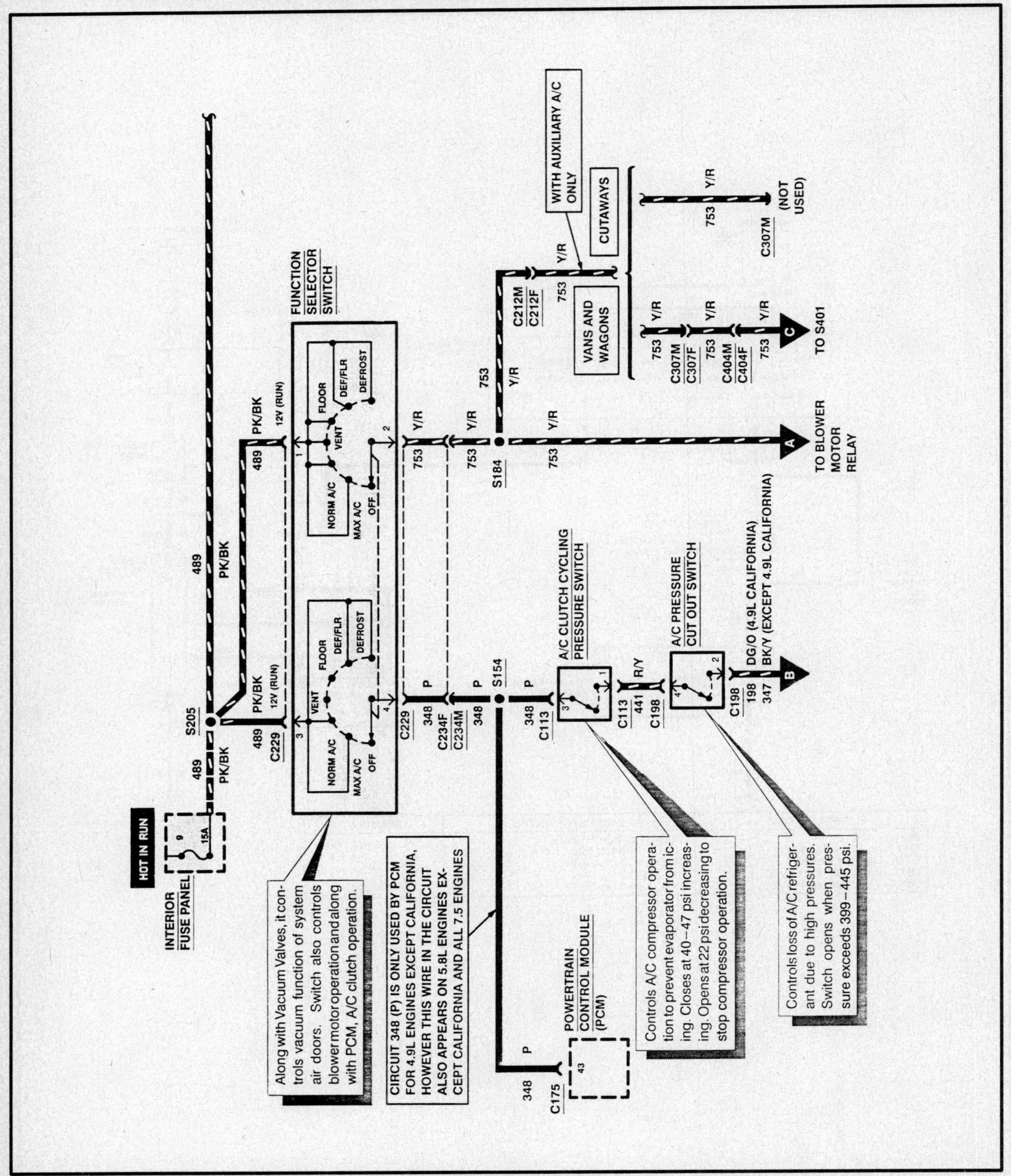

Heater/air conditioning system electrical schematic—1995 E-Series

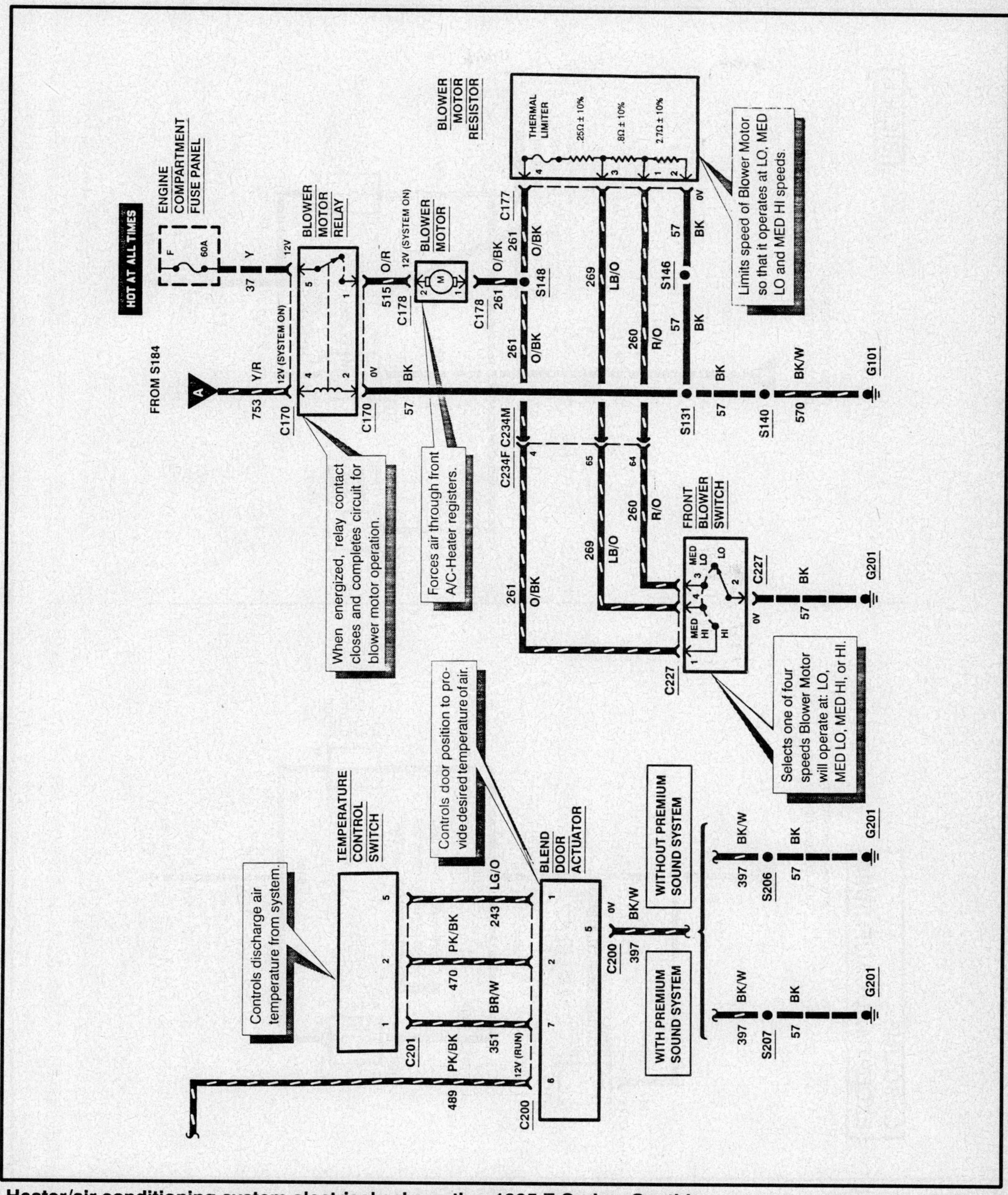

Heater/air conditioning system electrical schematic—1995 E-Series, Cont'd

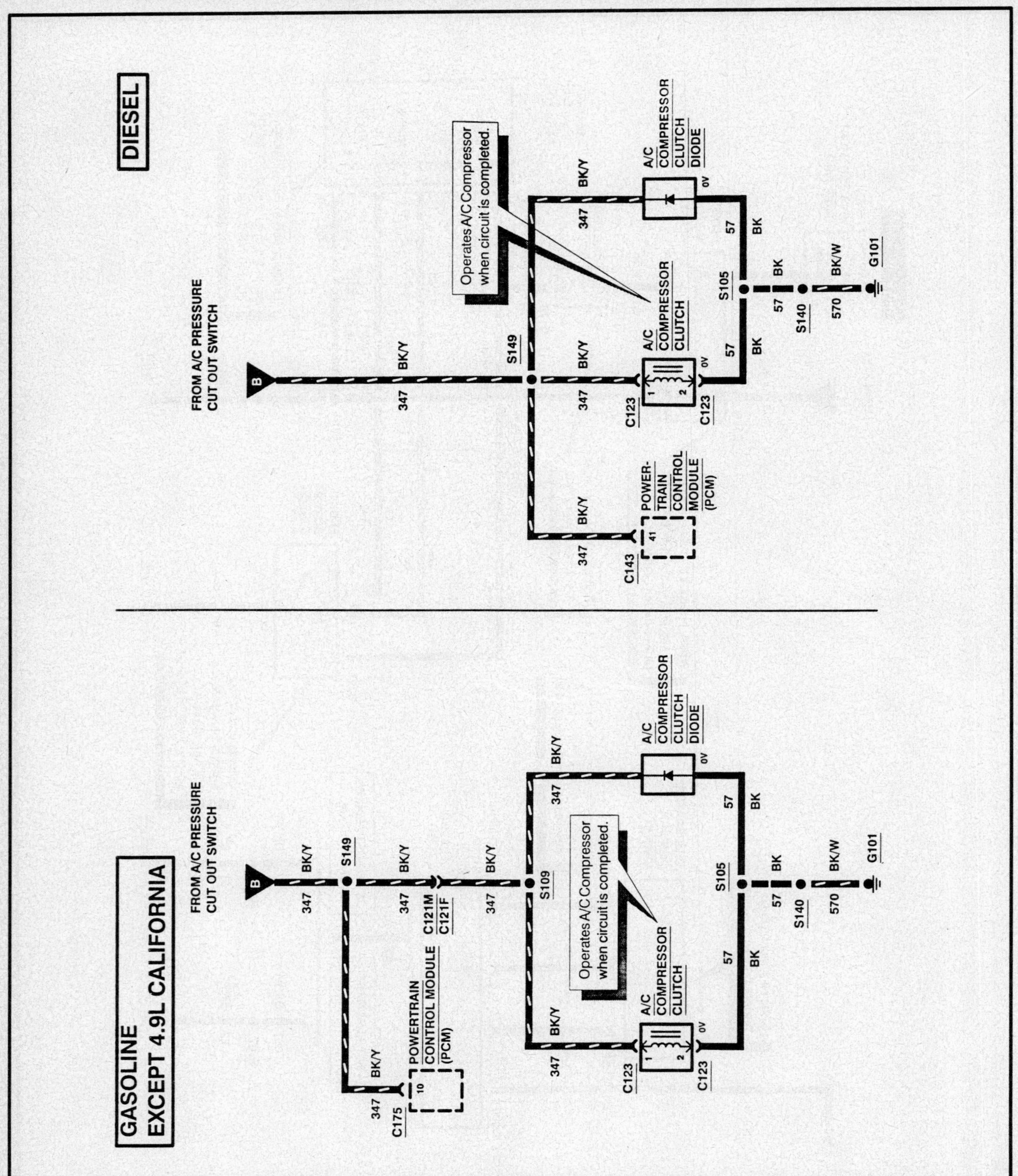

Heater/air conditioning system electrical schematic—1995 E-Series, Cont'd

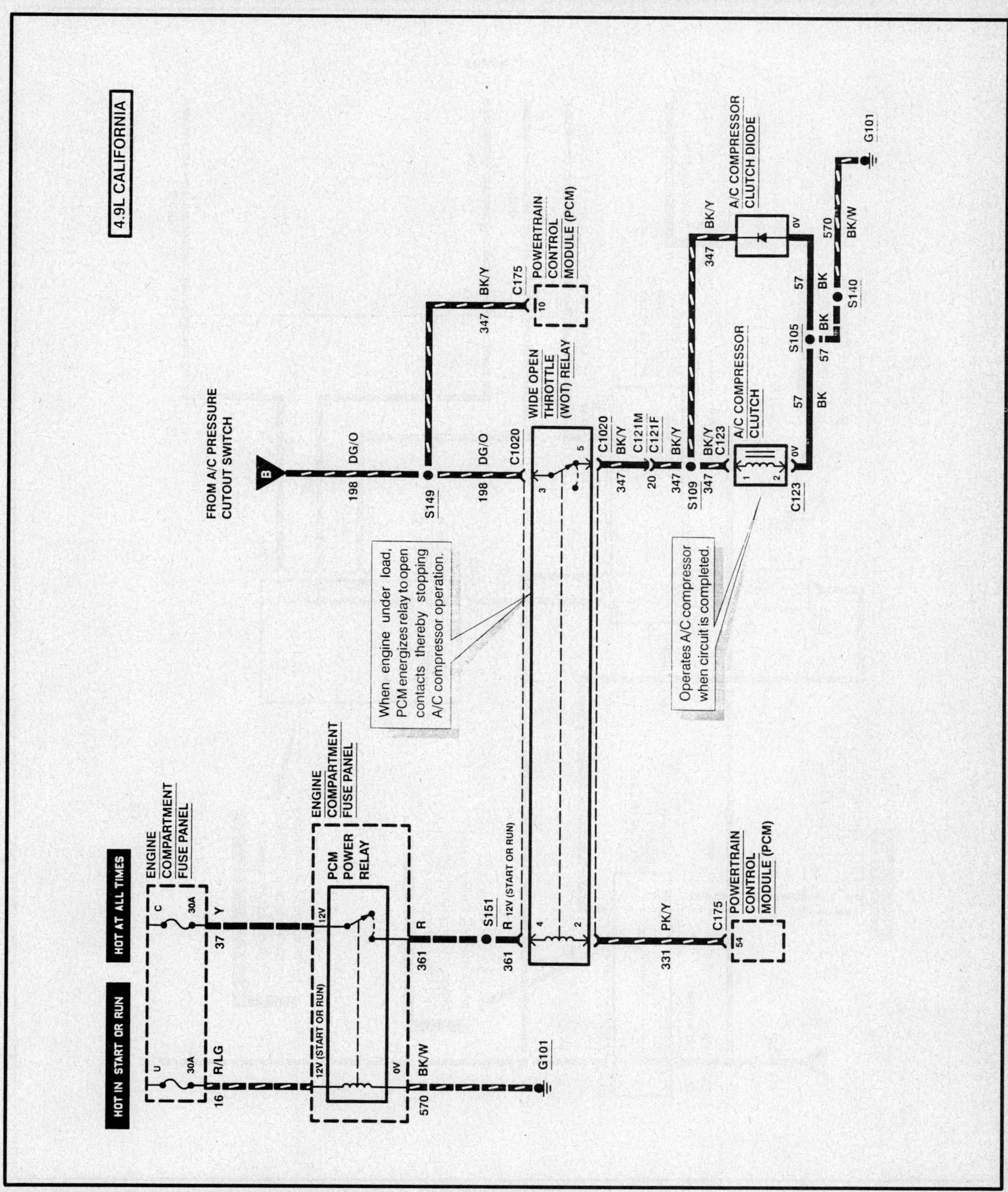

Heater/air conditioning system electrical schematic—1995 E-Series, Cont'd

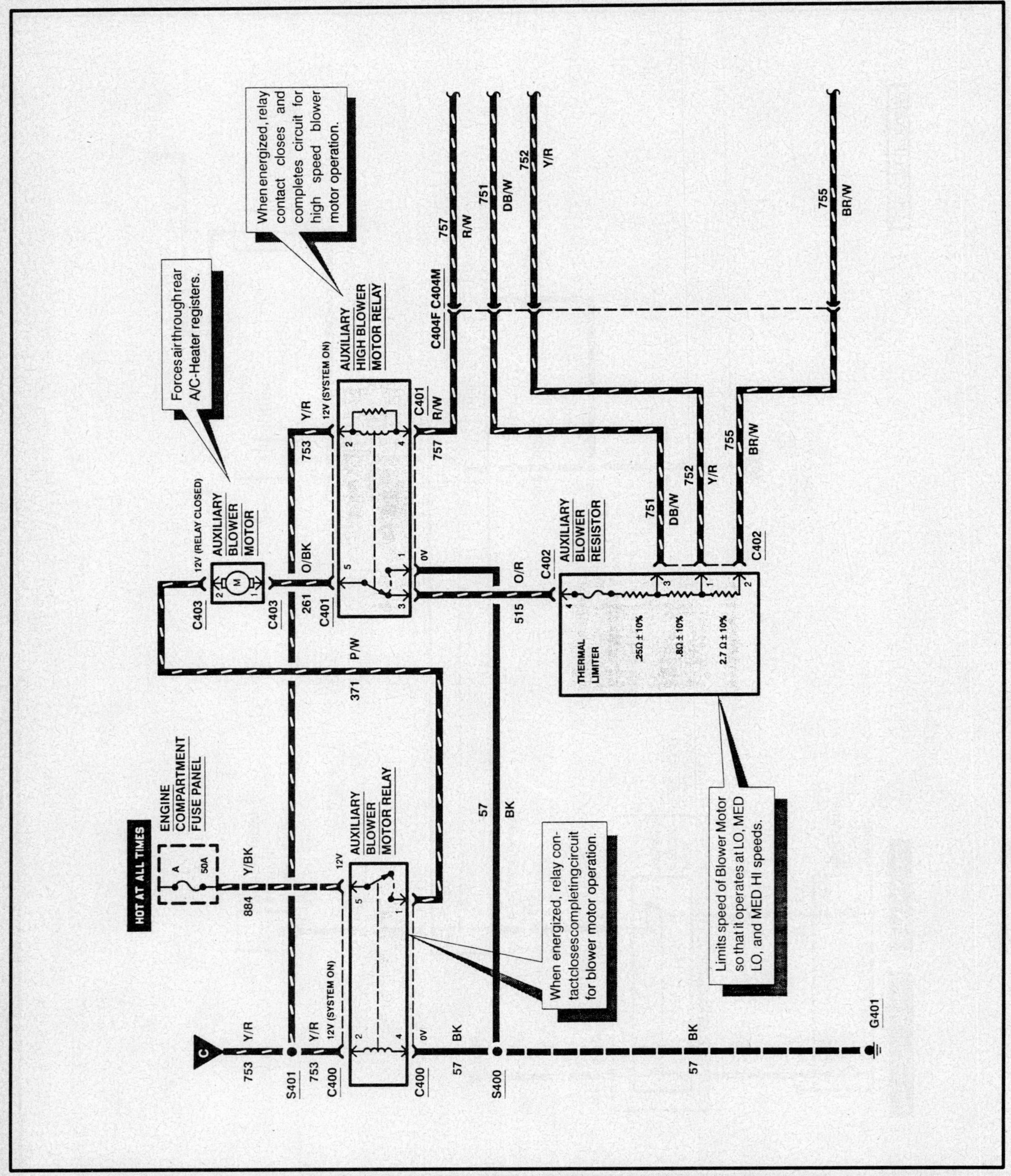

Heater/air conditioning system electrical schematic—1995 E-Series, Cont'd

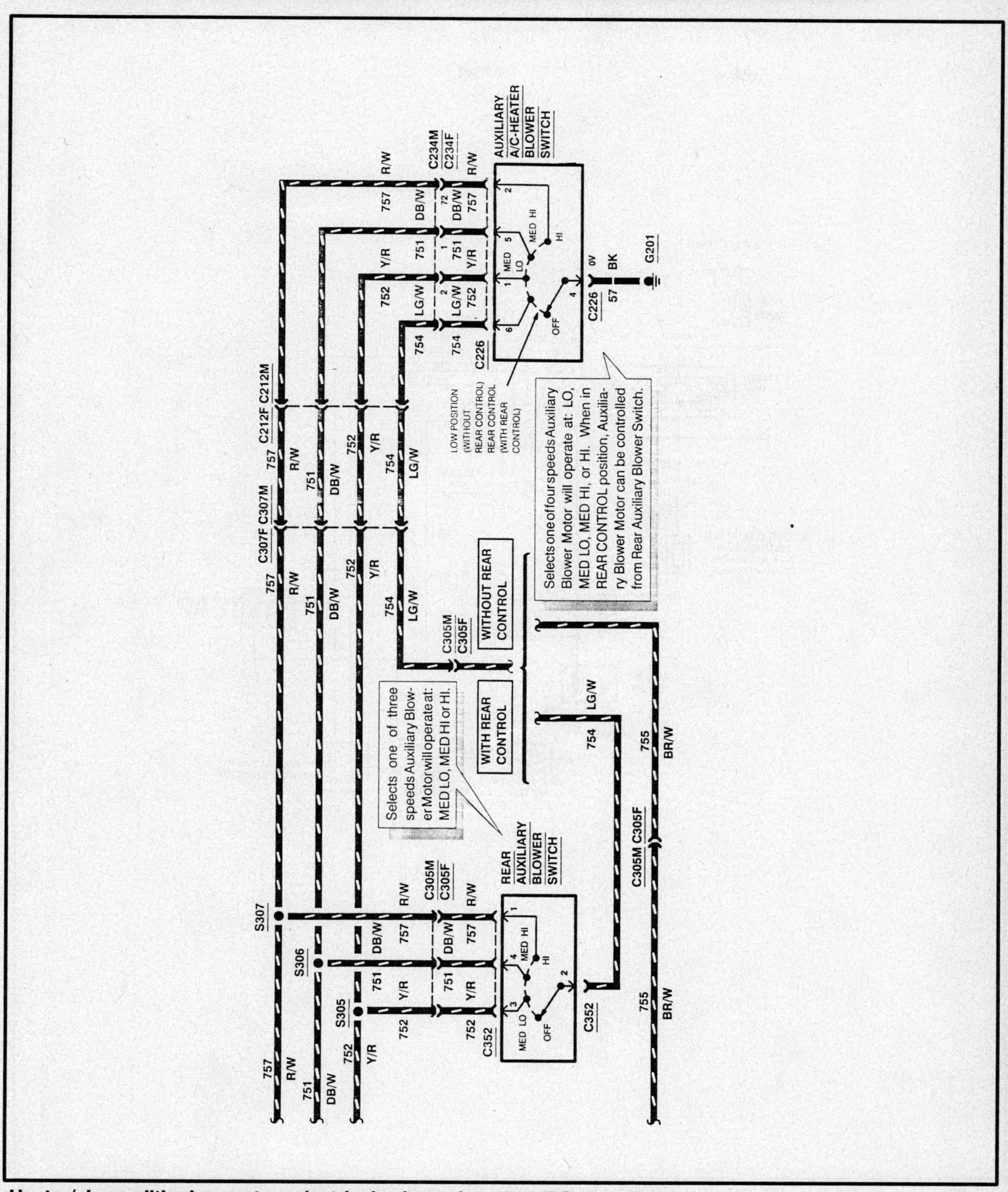

Heater/air conditioning system electrical schematic—1995 E-Series, Cont'd

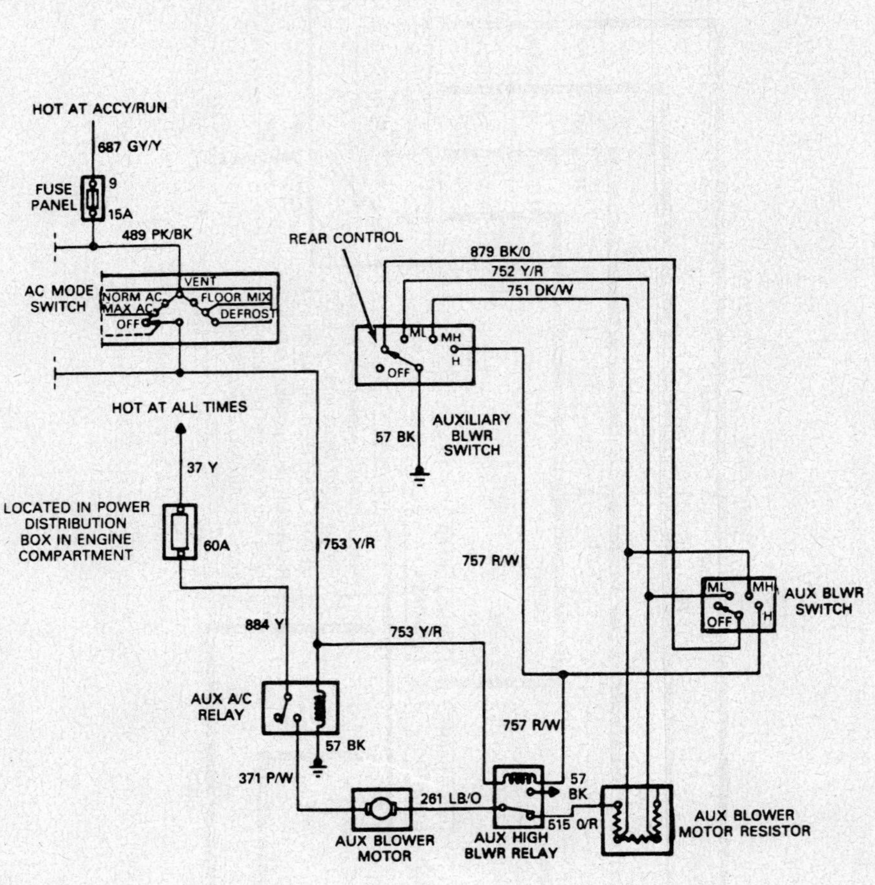

Auxiliary heater/air conditioning system electrical schematic—E-Series (auxiliary system only shown)

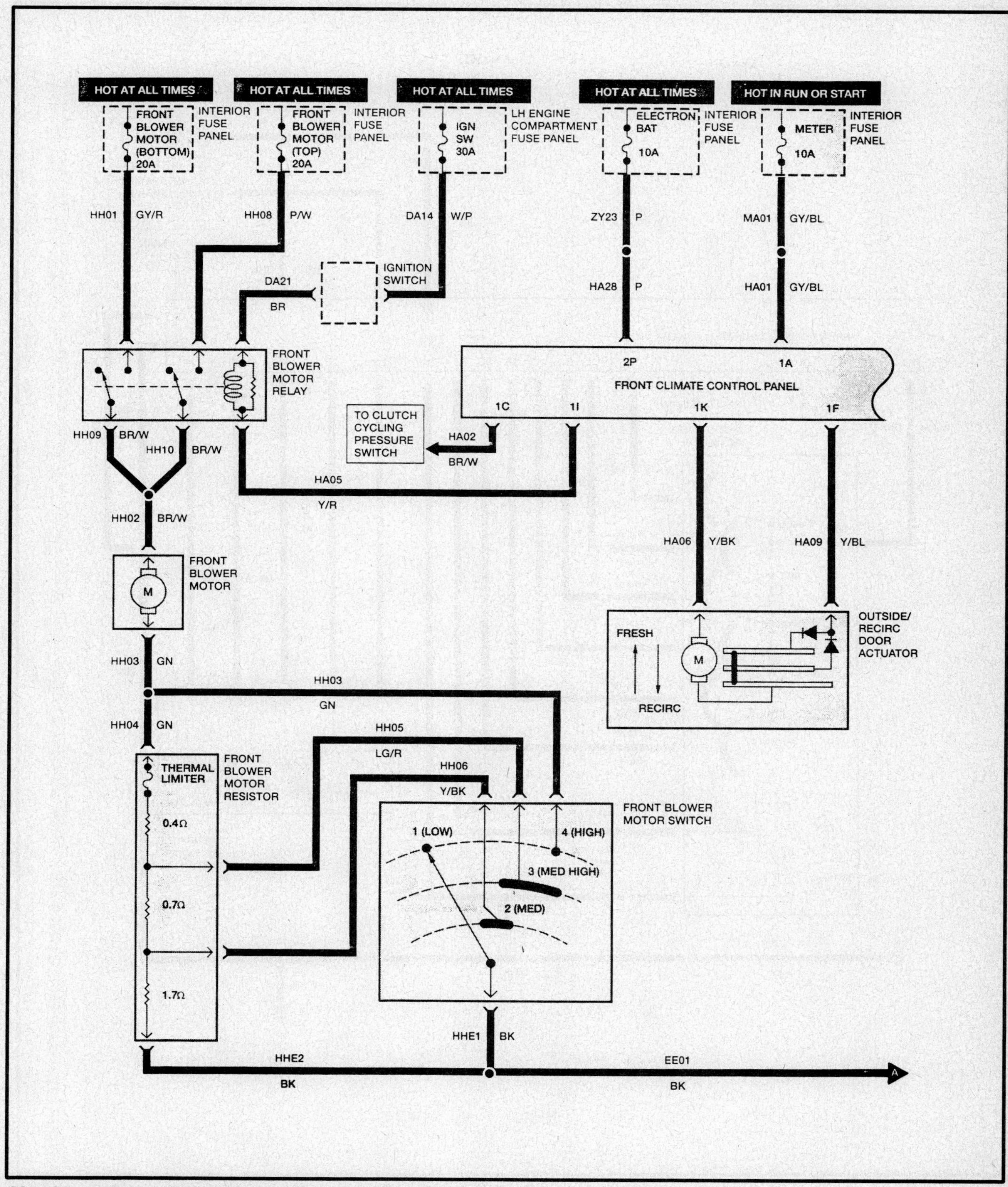

Heating system electrical schematic—1993 Villager

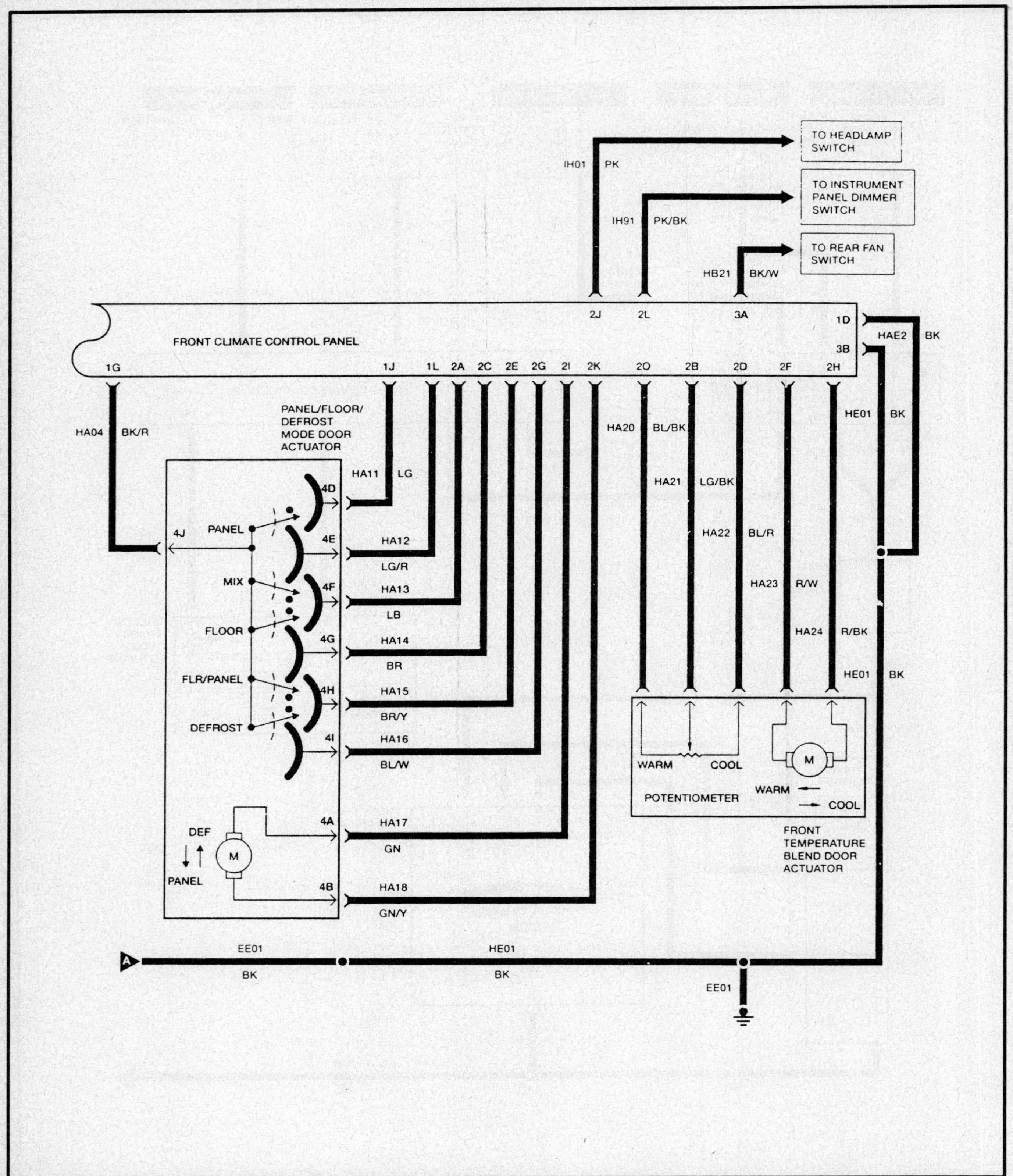

Heating system electrical schematic—1993 Villager, Cont'd

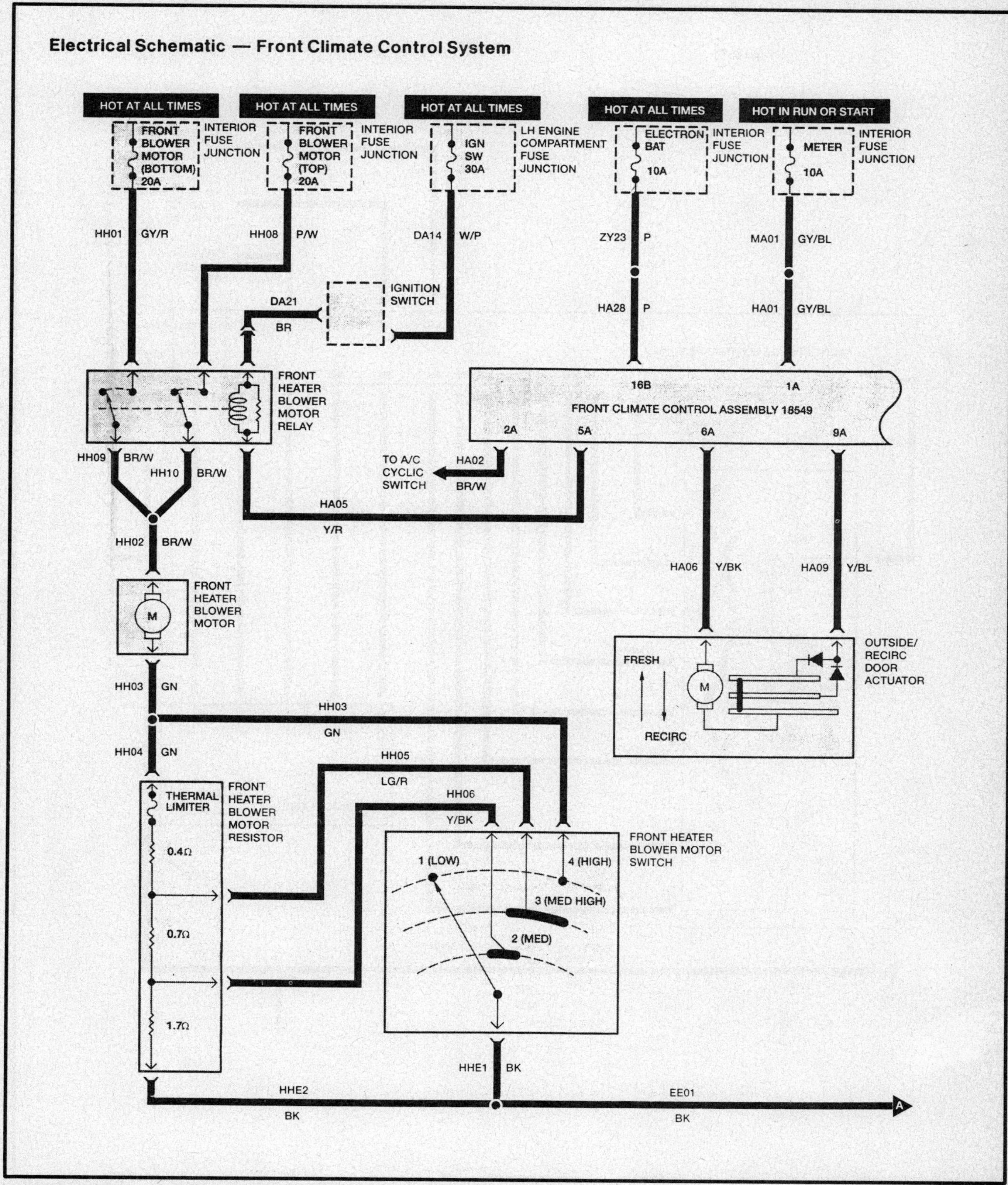

Heating system electrical schematic—1994–95 Villager

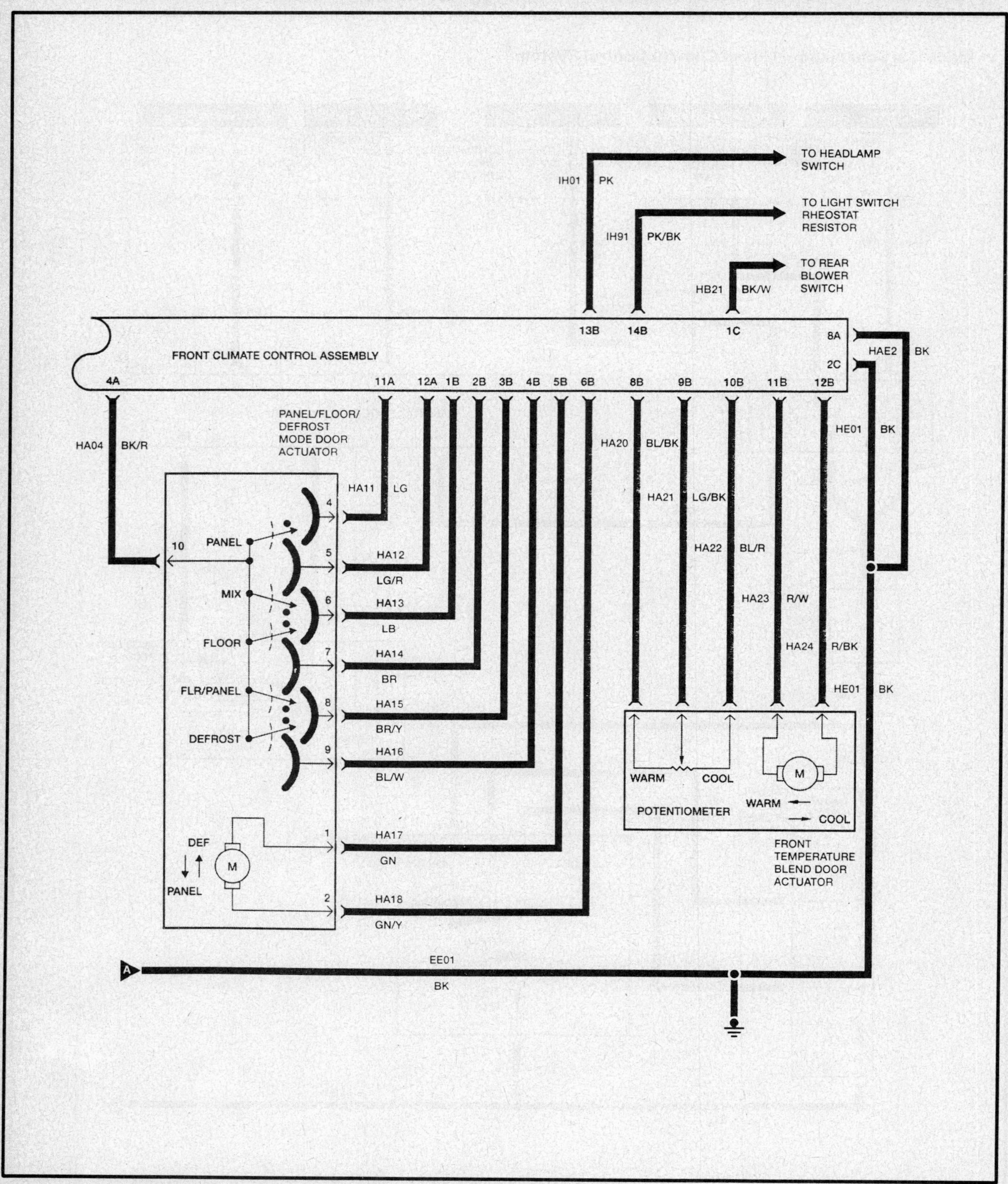

Heating system electrical schematic—1994–95 Villager, Cont'd

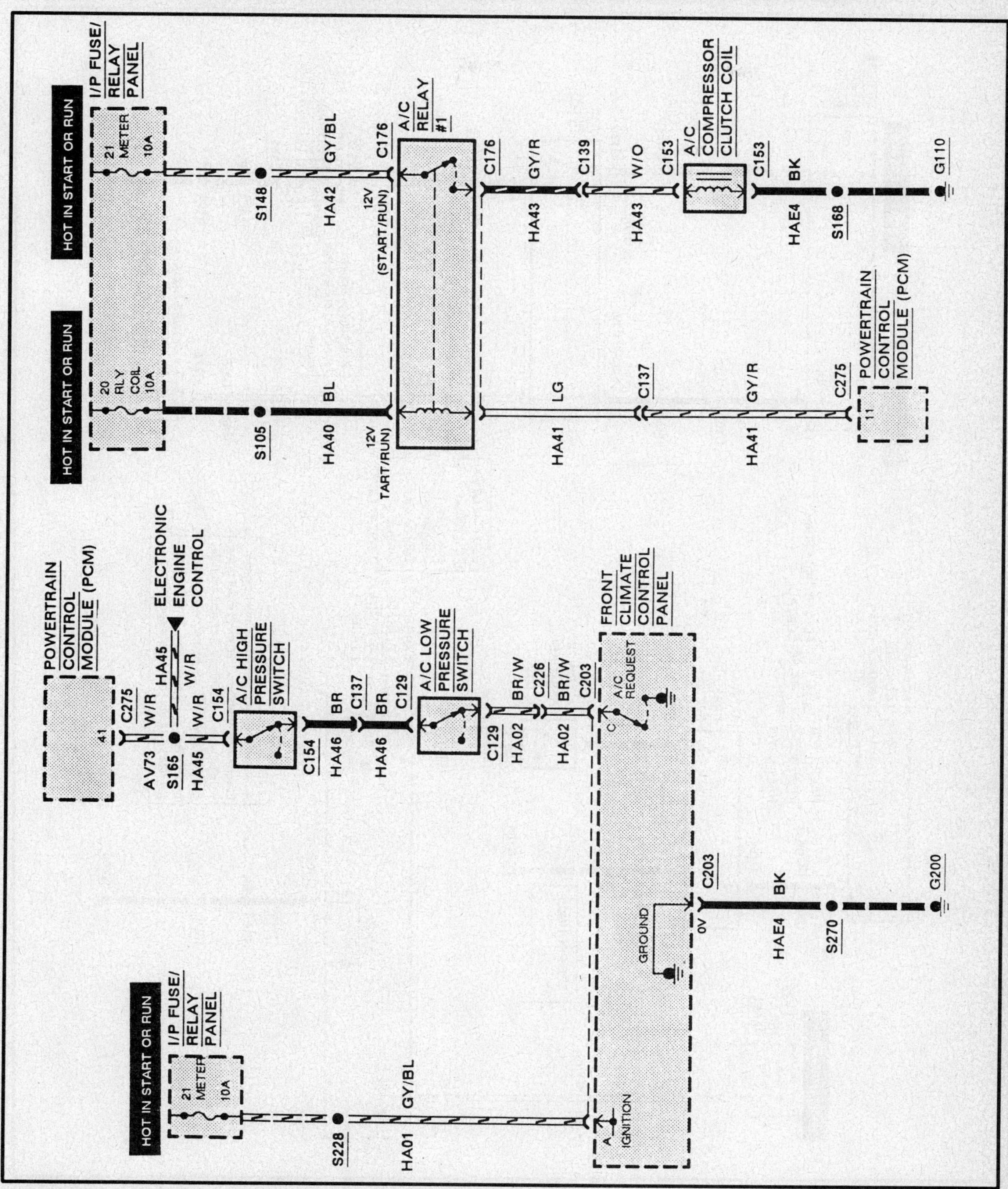

Heater/air conditioning system electrical schematic—1993 Villager

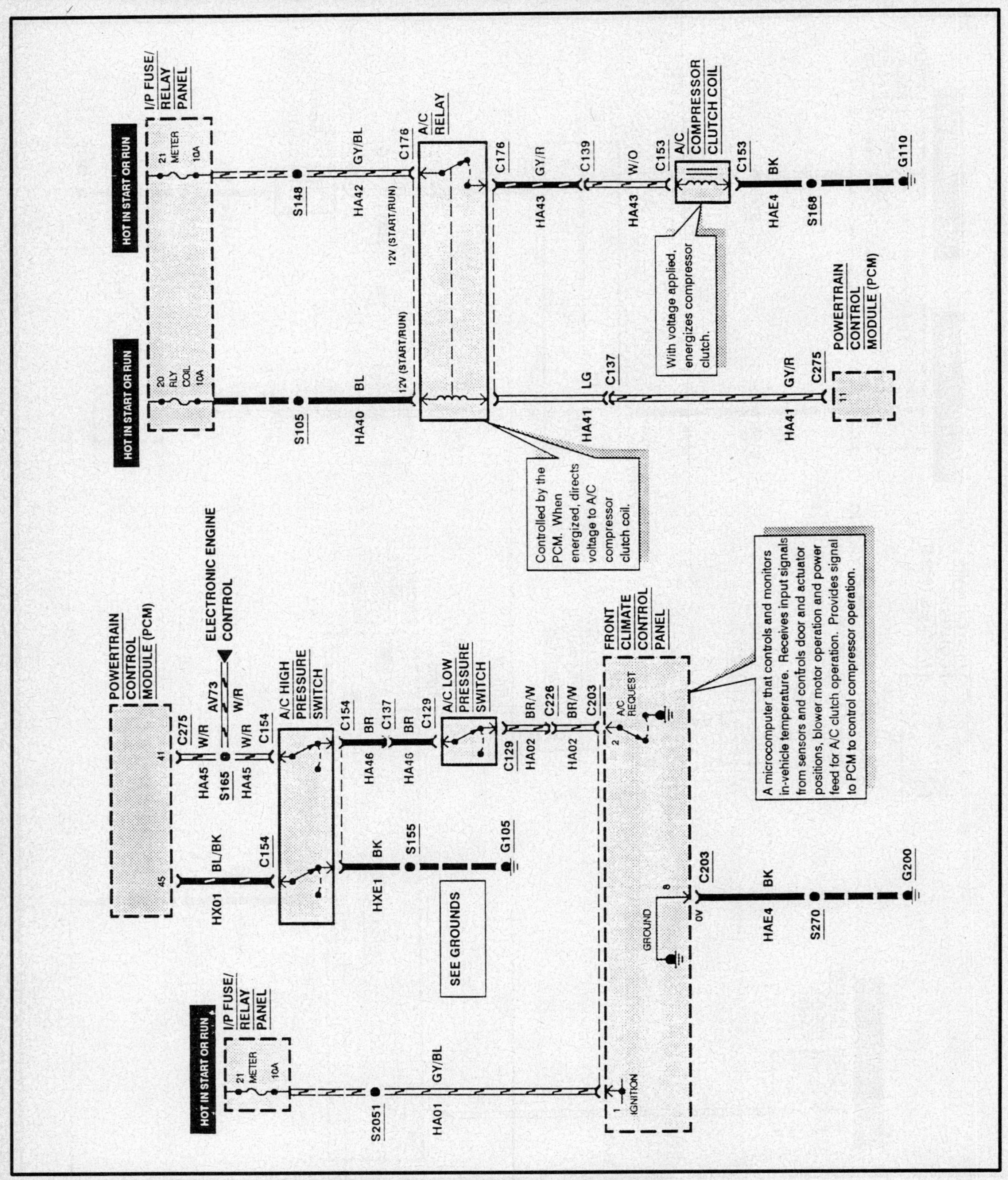

Heater/air conditioning system electrical schematic—1994–95 Villager

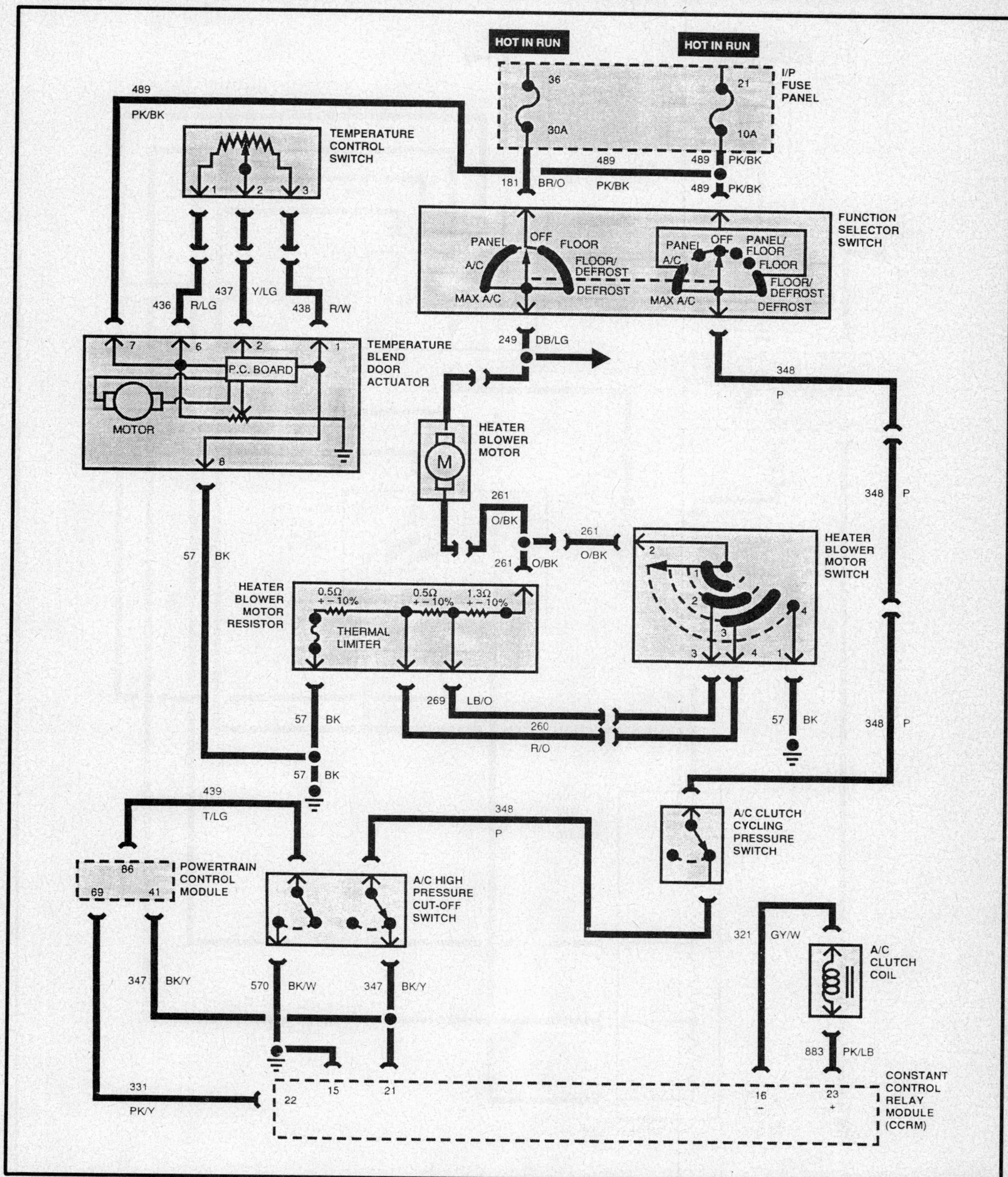

Climate control electrical schematic—1995 Windstar (front climate control system)

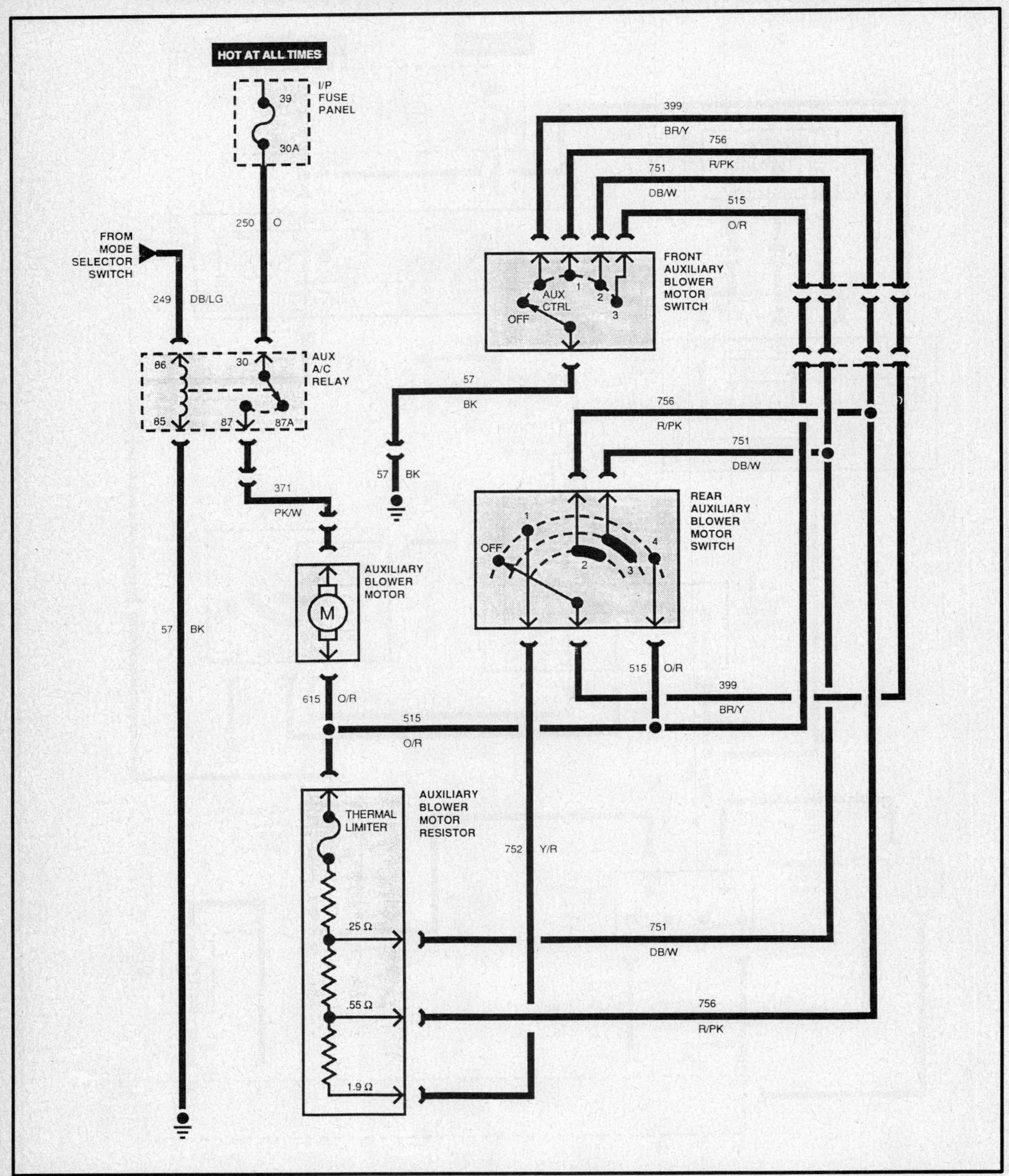

Climate control electrical schematic—1995 Windstar (auxiliary climate control system)

8 GENERAL MOTORS CORPORATION 8

FRONT WHEEL DRIVE VEHICLES

SPECIFICATIONS

ENGINE IDENTIFICATION

Year	Model	Body Code	Engine Displacement Liters (cc)	Engine Series (ID/VIN)	Fuel System	No. of Cylinders	Engine Type
1993	Corsica	L	2.3 (2263)	A	MFI	4	DOHC
	Beretta	L	2.3 (2263)	A	MFI	4	DOHC
	Achieva	N	2.3 (2263)	A	MFI	4	DOHC
	Grand Am	N	2.3 (2263)	A	PFI	4	DOHC
	Sixty Special	CB	4.9 (4920)	B	MFI	8	OHV
	Seville	KS	4.9 (4920)	B	MFI	8	OHV
	Achieva	N	2.3 (2263)	D	MFI	4	DOHC
	Grand Am	N	2.3 (2263)	D	PFI	4	DOHC
	Eldorado	KS	5.0 (5020)	E	TBI	8	OHV
	Seville	KS	5.0 (5020)	E	TBI	8	OHV
	Sixty Special	CB	5.0 (5020)	E	TBI	8	OHV
	Sunbird	J	2.0 (2008)	H	MFI	4	SOHC
	Regal	W	3.8 (3788)	L	PFI	6	OHV
	Riviera	EZ	3.8 (3788)	L	SFI	6	OHV
	Park Avenue	C	3.8 (3788)	L	SFI	6	OHV
	LeSabre	H	3.8 (3788)	L	SFI	6	OHV
	Eighty-Eight Royale	H	3.8 (3788)	L	SFI	6	OHV
	Bonneville	H	3.8 (3788)	L	SFI	6	OHV
	DeVille	C	3.8 (3788)	L	SFI	6	OHV
	Century	A	3.3 (3346)	N	MFI	6	OHV
	Skylark	N	3.3 (3346)	N	MFI	6	OHV
	Achieva	N	3.3 (3346)	N	MFI	6	OHV
	Cutlass Cruiser	A	3.3 (3346)	N	MFI	6	OHV
	Grand Am	N	3.3 (3346)	N	PFI	6	OHV
	Regal	W	3.1 (3149)	T	PFI	6	OHV
	Cavalier	J	3.1 (3149)	T	MFI	6	OHV
	Corsica	L	3.1 (3149)	T	MFI	6	OHV
	Beretta	L	3.1 (3149)	T	MFI	6	OHV
	Lumina	W	3.1 (3149)	T	MFI	6	OHV
	Cutlass Supreme	W	3.1 (3149)	T	MFI	6	OHV
	Grand Prix	W	3.1 (3149)	T	PFI	6	OHV
	Sunbird	J	3.1 (3149)	T	MFI	6	OHV
	Lumina	W	3.4 (3362)	X	PFI	6	OHV
	Grand Prix	W	3.4 (3362)	X	PFI	6	DOHC
	Cutlass Supreme	W	3.4 (3362)	X	MFI	6	OHV
	Ninety-Eight	C	3.8 (3788)	1	SFI	6	OHV
	Skylark	N	2.3 (2263)	3	MFI	4	SOHC
	Achieva	N	2.3 (2263)	3	MFI	4	SOHC
	Grand Am	N	2.3 (2263)	3	PFI	4	SOHC
	Century	A	2.2 (2198)	4	MFI	4	OHV

ENGINE IDENTIFICATION

Year	Model	Body Code	Engine Displacement Liters (cc)	Engine Series (ID/VIN)	Fuel System	No. of Cylinders	Engine Type
1993	Cavalier	J	2.2 (2198)	4	PFI	4	OHV
	Corsica	L	2.2 (2198)	4	MFI	4	OHV
	Beretta	L	2.2 (2198)	4	MFI	4	OHV
	Lumina	W	2.2 (2198)	4	MFI	4	OHV
	Cutlass Ciera	A	2.2 (2198)	4	MFI	4	OHV
	LeMans	T	1.6 (1595)	6	TBI	4	OHV
1994	Grand Am	N	2.3 (2263)	A	MFI	4	DOHC
	Corsica	L	2.3 (2263)	A	PFI	4	DOHC
	Beretta	L	2.3 (2263)	A	PFI	4	DOHC
	Eldorado	EL	4.6 (4562)	Y	MFI	8	OHV
	Seville	KS	4.6 (4562)	Y	MFI	8	OHV
	Bonneville	H	3.8 (3788)	C	SFI	6	OHV
	Cutlass Supreme	W	3.1 (3100)	M	MFI	6	OHV
	Achieva	N	2.3 (2263)	D	MFI	4	DOHC
	Grand Am	N	2.3 (2263)	D	MFI	4	DOHC
	Grand Prix	W	3.4 (3362)	X	SFI	6	OHV
	Achieva	N	2.3 (2263)	A	MFI	4	DOHC
	Eldorado	ET	4.6 (4562)	9	MFI	8	OHV
	Corsica	L	2.2 (2198)	4	MFI	4	OHV
	Beretta	L	2.2 (2198)	4	MFI	4	OHV
	Sunbird	J	2.0 (1988)	H	MFI	4	OHC
	Regal	W	3.8 (3788)	L	PFI	6	OHV
	LeSabre	H	3.8 (3788)	L	SFI	6	OHV
	Park Avenue	C	3.8 (3788)	L	SFI	6	OHV
	Eighty-Eight Royale	H	3.8 (3788)	L	SFI	6	OHV
	Ninety-Eight Regency	C	3.8 (3788)	L	SFI	6	OHV
	Century	A	3.1 (3100)	M	SFI	6	OHV
	Cutlass Ciera	A	3.1 (3100)	M	SFI	6	OHV
	Cutlass Cruiser	A	3.1 (3100)	M	SFI	6	OHV
	Century	A	2.2 (2198)	4	MFI	4	OHV
	Achieva	N	2.3 (2263)	3	MFI	4	SOHC
	Cutlass Ciera	A	2.2 (2198)	4	MFI	4	OHV
	Regal	W	3.1 (3149)	T	PFI	6	OHV
	Lumina	W	3.1 (3149)	T	MFI	6	OHV
	Corsica	L	3.1 (3100)	M	MFI	6	OHV
	Beretta	L	3.1 (3100)	M	MFI	6	OHV
	Cavalier	J	2.2 (2198)	4	MFI	4	OHV
	Cavalier	J	3.1 (3149)	T	MFI	6	OHV
	Grand Prix	W	3.1 (3100)	M	MFI	6	OHV
	Achieva	N	3.1 (3100)	M	SFI	6	OHV
	Sunbird	J	3.1 (3149)	T	TBI	6	OHV

ENGINE IDENTIFICATION

Year	Model	Body Code	Engine Displacement Liters (cc)	Engine Series (ID/VIN)	Fuel System	No. of Cylinders	Engine Type
1994	Grand Am	N	2.3 (2263)	3	MFI	4	SOHC
	Lumina	W	3.4 (3362)	X	SFI	6	OHV
	Cutlass Supreme	W	3.4 (3362)	X	SFI	6	OHV
	Grand Am	N	3.1 (3100)	M	SFI	6	OHV
	Concours	KF	4.6 (4562)	Y	MFI	8	OHV
	DeVille	KD	4.9 (4920)	B	MFI	8	OHV
	Seville	KY	4.6 (4362)	9	MFI	8	OHV
	Eighty-Eight	H	3.8 (3788)	1	SFI	6	OHV
	LeSabre	H	3.8 (3788)	1	SFI	6	OHV
	Ninety-Eight	C	3.8 (3788)	1	SFI	6	OHV
	Park Avenue	C	3.8 (3788)	1	SFI	6	OHV
1995	Grand Am	N	2.3 (2263)	D	MFI	4	DOHC
	Seville	KS	4.9 (4920)	B	MFI	8	DOHC
	Achieva	N	2.3 (2263)	D	MFI	4	DOHC
	Eldorado	KS	5.0 (5020)	E	TBI	8	OHV
	Seville	KS	5.0 (5020)	E	TBI	8	OHV
	Sunfire	J	2.2 (2198)	4	MFI	4	OHV
	Regal	W	3.8 (3788)	L	SFI	6	OHV
	Riviera	G	3.8 (3788)	K	SFI	6	OHV
	Park Avenue	C	3.8 (3788)	L	SFI	6	OHV
	LeSabre	H	3.8 (3788)	L	TPI	6	OHV
	Eighty-Eight Royale	H	3.8 (3788)	L	SFI	6	OHV
	Ninety-Eight	C	3.8 (3788)	L	SFI	6	OHV
	Grand Prix	W	3.8 (3788)	L	SFI	6	OHV
	Bonneville	H	3.8 (3788)	L	SFI	6	OHV
	Century	A	3.1 (3100)	M	SFI	6	OHV
	Skylark	N	3.1 (3100)	M	SFI	6	OHV
	Cutlass Cruiser	A	3.1 (3100)	M	SFI	6	OHV
	Grand Am	N	3.1 (3100)	M	SFI	6	OHV
	Lumina	W	3.8 (3788)	L	SFI	6	OHV
	Century	A	2.2 (2198)	4	MFI	4	OHV
	Cutlass Ciera	A	2.2 (2198)	4	MFI	4	OHV
	Cutlass Ciera	A	3.1 (3100)	M	SFI	6	OHV
	Regal	W	3.1 (3100)	M	MFI	6	OHV
	Cavalier	J	2.3 (2263)	D	MFI	4	DOHC
	Corsica	L	3.1 (3100)	M	MFI	6	OHV
	Beretta	L	3.1 (3100)	M	MFI	6	OHV
	Lumina	W	3.1 (3100)	M	MFI	6	OHV
	Cutlass Supreme	W	3.1 (3100)	M	MFI	6	OHV
	Grand Prix	W	3.1 (3100)	M	MFI	6	OHV
	Sunfire	J	2.3 (2263)	D	MFI	4	DOHC

ENGINE IDENTIFICATION

Year	Model	Body Code	Engine Displacement Liters (cc)	Engine Series (ID/VIN)	Fuel System	No. of Cylinders	Engine Type
1995	Lumina	W	3.4 (3362)	X	SFI	6	OHV
	Cutlass Supreme	W	3.4 (3362)	X	SFI	6	DOHC
	Grand Prix	W	3.4 (3362)	X	SFI	6	OHV
	Park Avenue	C	3.8 (3788)	1	SFI	6	OHV
	Ninety-Eight S'charged	C	3.8 (3788)	1	SFI	6	OHV
	Skylark	N	2.3 (2263)	D	MFI	4	SOHC
	Achieva	N	3.1 (3100)	M	SFI	6	OHV
	Corsica	L	2.2 (2198)	4	MFI	4	OHV
	Beretta	L	2.2 (2198)	4	MFI	4	OHV
	Eldorado	KS	5.7 (5723)	7	TBI	8	OHV
	Seville	KS	5.7 (5723)	7	TBI	8	OHV
	Regal	W	3.4 (3362)	X	SFI	6	OHV
	DeVille	CBN	4.5 (4518)	8	MFI	8	OHV
	Eldorado	KS	4.5 (4518)	8	MFI	8	OHV
	Seville	KS	4.5 (4518)	8	MFI	8	OHV
	Eighty-Eight	H	3.8 (3788)	1	SFI	6	OHV
	Eighty-Eight	H	3.8 (3788)	K	SFI	6	OHV
	LeSabre	H	3.8 (3788)	1	SFI	6	OHV
	LeSabre	H	3.8 (3788)	K	SFI	6	OHV
	Ninety-Eight	C	3.8 (3788)	K	SFI	6	OHV
	Park Avenue	C	3.8 (3788)	K	SFI	6	OHV
	Bonneville	H	3.8 (3788)	1	SFI	6	OHV
	Bonneville	H	3.8 (3788)	K	SFI	6	OHV
	Riviera	G	3.8 (3788)	1	SFI	6	OHV
	Aurora	G	3.8 (3788)	1	SFI	6	OHV
	Aurora	G	4.0 (3992)	C	SFI	8	DOHC
	Monte Carlo	W	3.4 (3362)	X	SFI	6	OHV
	Monte Carlo	W	3.8 (3788)	L	SFI	6	OHV

MFI–Multi-Port Fuel Injection
PFI–Port Fuel Injection
SFI–Sequential Fuel Injection
TBI–Throttle Body Injection
OHV–Overhead Valves
SOHC–Single Overhead Cam
DOHC–Dual Overhead Cam

REFRIGERANT CAPACITIES

Year	Model	Refrigerant (oz.)	Oil (fl. oz.)	Compressor Type
1993	A Body	38	9	V5, HR6-HE
	C Body	38	8	HR-6, HR6-HE
	H Body	38	8	HR-6, HR6-HE
	J Body	36	8	V5
	L Body	42	8	V5

REFRIGERANT CAPACITIES

Year	Model	Refrigerant (oz.)	Oil (fl. oz.)	Compressor Type
1993	N Body	42	8	V5
	T Body	35	8	V5
	W Body	36 ①	9	V5, HR6-HE ①
	EZ Body	38	8	HR6-HE
	CB, CD Body	38.7	8	HR6-HE
	EL, KS Body	NA	8	HR6-HE
1994	A Body	44	8	V5, HR6-HE
	A Body	28	9	V5
	A Body	32	9	V5
	C Body	38.7	8	HR-6, HD6/HR6-HE
	E Body	38	8	HR6-HE
	H Body	38	8	HR-6, HR6-HE
	H Body	38.7	8	HD6/HR6-HE
	J Body	36	8	V5
	L Body	36	8	V5
	N Body	36	8	V5
	T Body	35	8	V5
	W Body	36 ① ②	8	V5, HR-6 ① ②
	EZ Body	38	8	HR6-HE
	CB, CD Body	38.7	8	HR6-HE
	EL, KS Body	NA	8	HR6-HE
	EL, KD, KF, KS, KY Body	32	8	HD6/HR6-HE
	VR, VS Body	NA	8	HR6-HE
1995	A Body	38	9	V5, HR-6, HR6-HE
	A Body	28	9	V5
	A Body	32	9	V5
	C Body	38.7	8	HR-6, HD6/HR6-HE
	E Body	38	8	HR6-HE
	G Body	32	8	HR-6
	H Body	38	8	HR-6, HR6-HE
	H Body	38.7	8	HD6/HR6-HE
	J Body	36	8	V5
	J Body	24	NA	V5
	L Body	42	8	V5
	L Body	36	9	V5
	N Body	42 ④	8 ④	V5
	T Body	35	8	V5
	W Body	36 ① ②	9 ③	V5 ②, HR-6 ①

REFRIGERANT CAPACITIES

Year	Model	Refrigerant (oz.)	Oil (fl. oz.)	Compressor Type
1995	EZ, EC Body	38	8	HR6-HE
	CB, CD Body	38.7	8	HR6-HE
	EL, KS Body	NA	8	HR6-HE

NA–Not available
① Regal with HR-6 compressor uses 44 oz. system refrigerant
② 1994–95 Cutlass Supreme, Grand Prix, Lumina Monte Carlo and Regal with V5 compressor uses 32 oz. system refrigerant
③ 1994–95 Cutlass Supreme, Grand Prix, Lumina and Regal with V5 compressor uses 8 oz. of refrigerant oil
④ 1995 Achieva, Grand Am and Skylark use 36 oz. of refrigerant and 9 oz. of oil

AIR CONDITIONING BELT TENSION

Year	Model	Engine Liters	Belt Type	Specifications	
				New	Used
1993	6	1.6 (1595)	Serpentine	①	①
	H	2.0 (2008)	Serpentine	①	①
	4	2.2 (2198)	Serpentine	50–70 ②	50–70 ②
	A	2.3 (2263)	Serpentine	50 ②	50 ②
	D	2.3 (2263)	Serpentine	50 ②	50 ②
	3	2.3 (2263)	Serpentine	50 ②	50 ②
	T	3.1 (3149)	Serpentine	50–70 ②	50–70 ②
	N	3.3 (3346)	Serpentine	67 ②	②
	X	3.4 (3362)	Serpentine	①	①
	L	3.8 (3788)	Serpentine	50–70 ②	50–70 ②
	1	3.8 (3788)	Serpentine	50–70 ②	50–70 ②
	B	4.9 (4920)	Serpentine	①	①
	E	5.0 (5020)	Serpentine	①	①
1994	6	1.6 (1595)	Serpentine	①	①
	K	2.0 (1988)	Serpentine	①	①
	H	2.0 (1988)	V–Belt	225	112–124
	G/4	2.2 (2198)	Serpentine	63–77 ②	63–77 ②
	4	2.2 (2198)	Serpentine	50–70 ②	50–70 ②
	A	2.3 (2263)	Serpentine	50 ②	50 ②
	D	2.3 (2263)	Serpentine	50 ②	50 ②
	3	2.3 (2263)	Serpentine	50–70 ②	50–70 ②
	R	2.5 (2476)	Serpentine	50–70 ②	50–70 ②
	U	2.5 (2476)	V-Belt	165	90
	M	3.1 (3100)	Serpentine	50–70 ②	50–70 ②
	M	3.1 (3100)	Serpentine	105–125 ②	105–125 ②
	T	3.1 (3149)	Serpentine	50–70 ②	50–70 ②
	N	3.3 (3346)	Serpentine	67 ②	67 ②
	C	3.8 (3788)	Serpentine	①	①
	L/1	3.8 (3788)	Serpentine	50–70 ②	50–70 ②

AIR CONDITIONING BELT TENSION

Year	Model	Engine Liters	Belt Type	Specifications New	Specifications Used
1994	X	3.4 (3362)	Serpentine	①	①
	8	4.5 (4563)	Serpentine	①	①
	B	4.9 (4920)	Serpentine	①	①
	E	5.0 (5020)	Serpentine	①	①
	7	5.7 (5723)	Serpentine	①	①
	Y/9	4.6 (4362)	Serpentine	①	①
	B	4.9 (4920)	Serpentine	①	①
1995	6	1.6 (1595)	Serpentine	1/2–3/4 ③	1/2–3/4 ③
	H	2.0 (2008)	Serpentine	36–44 ②	36–44 ②
	4	2.2 (2198)	Serpentine	67–77 ②	67–70 ②
	4	2.2 (2198)	Serpentine	50–70 ②	50–70 ②
	A	2.3 (2263)	Serpentine	50 ②	50 ②
	D	2.3 (2263)	Serpentine	50 ②	50 ②
	3	2.3 (2263)	Serpentine	50 ②	50 ②
	R	2.5 (2476)	Serpentine	①	①
	M	3.1 (2198)	Serpentine	50–70 ②	50–70 ②
	T	3.1 (3149)	Serpentine	50–70 ②	50–70 ②
	N	3.3 (3346)	Serpentine	67 ②	67 ②
	X	3.4 (3362)	Serpentine	①	①
	L	3.8 (3788)	Serpentine	50–70 ②	50–70 ②
	1	3.8 (3788)	Serpentine	50–70 ②	50–70 ②
	K	3.8 (3788)	Serpentine	50–70 ②	50–70 ②
	C	4.0 (3992)	Serpentine	①	①
	Y or 9	4.6 (4572)	Serpentine	①	①
	B	4.9 (4920)	Serpentine	①	①
	E	5.0 (5020)	Serpentine	①	①

① Equipped with automatic tensioner; no adjustment required.
② Equipped with automatic tensioner; however the specification given (in pounds) is for testing whether the tensioner is maintaining its proper tension (specification given is the average of 3 readings back-to-back).
③ Deflection with thumb pressure applied to belt run between the largest span of the pulleys.

BODY GROUP IDENTIFICATION CHART

Year	Body Group	Manufacturer	Model
1993	A	Buick	Century
		Oldsmobile	Cutlass Ciera
		Oldsmobile	Cutlass Cruiser
		Pontiac	6000
	C	Buick	Park Avenue
		Oldsmobile	Ninety-Eight

BODY GROUP IDENTIFICATION CHART

Year	Body Group	Manufacturer	Model
1993	H	Buick	LeSabre
		Oldsmobile	Eighty-Eight
		Pontiac	Bonneville
	J	Chevrolet	Cavalier
		Pontiac	Sunbird
	L	Chevrolet	Beretta
		Chevrolet	Corsica
	N	Buick	Skylark
		Pontiac	Grand Am
	T	Pontiac	LeMans
	W	Buick	Regal
		Chevrolet	Lumina
		Oldsmobile	Cutlass Supreme
		Pontiac	Grand Prix
	CB	Cadillac	Fleetwood
	CD	Cadillac	DeVille
	EZ	Buick	Riviera
	EL	Cadillac	Eldorado
	KS	Cadillac	Seville
	VR/VS	Cadillac	Allante
1994	A	Buick	Century
		Oldsmobile	Cutlass Ciera
		Oldsmobile	Cutlass Cruiser
	C	Buick	Park Avenue
		Oldsmobile	Ninety-Eight
	E	Oldsmobile	Toronado
	H	Buick	LeSabre
		Oldsmobile	Eighty-Eight
		Pontiac	Bonneville
	J	Chevrolet	Cavalier
		Pontiac	Sunbird
	L	Chevrolet	Beretta
		Chevrolet	Corsica
	N	Oldsmobile	Achieva
		Pontiac	Grand Am
	T	Pontiac	LeMans
	W	Buick	Regal
		Chevrolet	Lumina
		Oldsmobile	Cutlass Supreme
		Pontiac	Grand Prix
	KD/KF	Cadillac	DeVille

BODY GROUP IDENTIFICATION CHART

Year	Body Group	Manufacturer	Model
1994	EC	Buick	Reatta
	EL/ET	Cadillac	Eldorado
	KS/KY	Cadillac	Seville
1995	A	Buick	Century
		Oldsmobile	Cutlass Ciera
		Oldsmobile	Cutlass Cruiser
	C	Buick	Park Avenue
		Oldsmobile	Ninety-Eight
	E	Oldsmobile	Toronado
	G	Buick	Riviera
		Oldsmobile	Aurora
	H	Buick	LeSabre
		Oldsmobile	Eighty-Eight
		Pontiac	Bonneville
	J	Chevrolet	Cavalier
		Pontiac	Sunfire
	L	Chevrolet	Beretta
		Chevrolet	Corsica
	N	Buick	Skylark
		Oldsmobile	Achieva
		Pontiac	Grand Am
	T	Pontiac	LeMans
	W	Buick	Regal
		Chevrolet	Lumina
		Chevrolet	Monte Carlo
		Oldsmobile	Cutlass Supreme
		Pontiac	Grand Prix
	CD	Cadillac	DeVille
	EL	Cadillac	Eldorado
	KS	Cadillac	Seville

SYSTEM DESCRIPTION

General Information

The heater and air conditioning systems are controlled manually or electronically. The systems differ mainly in the way air temperature and the routing of air flow are controlled. The manual system controls air temperature through a cable-actuated lever and air flow through a vacuum switching valve and vacuum actuators. With Electronic Climate Control (ECC) systems, both temperature and air flow are controlled by the BCM through the Climate Control Panel (CCP). Some models (C, H body) are also equipped with dual electronic air conditioning which combines the electronic climate control with an auxiliary system control panel and connections for rear passenger compartment operation.

The heating system provides heating, ventilation and defrosting for the windshield and side windows. The heater core is a heat exchanger supplied with coolant from the engine cooling system. Temperature is controlled by the temperature valve which moves an air door that directs air flow through the heater core for more heat or bypasses the heater core for less heat.

Vacuum actuators control the mode doors which direct air flow to the outlet ducts. The mode selector on the control panel directs engine vacuum to the actuators. The position of the mode doors determines whether air flows from the floor, panel, defrost or panel and defrost ducts (bi-level mode).

There are 3 types of compressors used on front-wheel drive car air conditioning systems. The HR-6, HR6-HE or HD6/HR6-HE compressor, used on Cycling Clutch Orifice Tube (CCOT) systems, is a 6 cylinder axial compressor consisting of 3 double-ended pistons actuated by a swash plate shaft assembly. The compressor cycles ON and OFF according to system demands. The compressor driveshaft is driven by the serpentine belt when the electro-magnetic clutch is engaged.

The V-5 compressor, used on Variable Displacement Orifice Tube (VDOT) and Variable Displacement Thermal Expansion Valve systems, is designed to meet the demands of the air conditioning system without cycling. The compressor employs a variable angle wobble plate controlling the displacement of 5 axially oriented cylinders. Displacement is controlled by a bellows actuated control valve located in the rear head of the compressor. The electro-magnetic compressor clutch connects the compressor shaft to the serpentine drive belt when the coil is energized.

Some models with Electronic Climate Control have built-in self-diagnostic routines to help locate problems. A series of display codes are used for this purpose.

Service Valve Locations

The high-side service valve is normally located in the refrigerant line near the discharge fitting of the compressor.

The low-side service valve is normally located on the accumulator or in the condenser-to-evaporator refrigerant line.

System Discharging

R-12 refrigerant is a chloroflourocarbon which, when released into the atmosphere, can contribute to the depletion of the ozone layer in the upper atmosphere. Ozone filters out harmful radiation from the sun. In order to protect the ozone layer, an approved R-12 Recovery/Recycling machine that meets SAE standards should be employed when discharging the system. Follow the operating instructions provided with the approved equipment exactly to properly discharge the system.

CAUTION

Avoid breathing A/C Refrigerant-R134a and lubricant vapor or mist. Exposure may irritate eyes, nose, and throat. To remove R-134a from the A/C system, use service equipment certified to meet the requirements of SAE. If accidental system discharge occurs, ventilate work area before resuming service. Additional health and safety information may be obtained from refrigerant and lubricant manufacturers.

NOTE: R-134a refrigerant is not compatible with R-12 refrigerant in an A/C system. R-12 in a R-134a system will cause compressor failure, refrigerant oil sludge or poor A/C system performance.

Refrigerant R-134a carries a charge of a special lubricating oil, polyalkaline glycol (PAG) refrigerant oil. GM PAG refrigerant oil will have a slight blue tint. The oil is hydroscopic (absorbs water from the atmosphere) and should be stored in closed containers.

Use only PAG synthetic refrigerant oil for internal circulation through the R-134a A/C system and only mineral base 525 viscosity refrigerant oil on fittings threads and O-rings. If lubricants other than those specified are used, compressor failure and/or fitting seizure is likely to occur.

R-12 and R-134a require separate and non-interchangeable sets of recovery, recycle, and recharge equipment, because the refrigerants and lubricants are not compatible and cannot be mixed even in the smallest amounts. Do not attempt to use one set of equipment for both R-12 and R-134a, as all equipment contains residual amounts of refrigerant and/or lubricant, which will result in contamination, and damage to the recover/recycle equipment. Adaptors to convert from one size fitting to the other must never be used; refrigerant/lubricant contamination will occur and system failure may result.

System Evacuating

If the air conditioning system has been opened to the atmosphere, it should be air and moisture free before being recharged with refrigerant. Moisture and air mixed with refrigerant will raise the compressor head pressure, possibly damage the system's components and will reduce the performance of the system. In addition, air and moisture in the system can lead to internal corrosion of the system components. Moisture will boil at normal room temperature when exposed to a vacuum. To evacuate, or rid the system of air and moisture:

1. Leak test the system and repair any leaks found.
2. Connect an approved charging station, Recovery/Recycling machine or manifold gauge set and vacuum pump to the discharge and suction ports. The red hose is normally connected to the discharge (high pressure) line. The blue hose is connected to the suction (low pressure) line. If using a manifold gauge set, the center (usually yellow) hose is connected to the charging station or Recovery/Recycling machine.
3. Open the discharge and suction ports and start the vacuum pump. If the pump is not able to pull at least 26 in. Hg (27–30 in. Hg. for R-134a system) of vacuum there is a leak that must be repaired before evacuation can occur.
4. Once the system has reached at least 26 in. Hg (27–30 in. Hg. for R-134a system) of vacuum, allow the system to evacuate for at least 10 minutes. The longer the system is evacuated, the more moisture will be removed.
5. Close all valves and turn the pump OFF. If the system loses more than 2 in. Hg of vacuum after 15 minutes, there is a leak that should be repaired.

System Charging

1. Connect an approved charging station, Recovery/Recycling machine or manifold gauge set to the discharge and suction ports. The red hose is normally connected to the discharge (high pressure) line, and the blue hose is connected to the suction (low pressure) line. If using a manifold gauge set, the center (usually yellow) hose is connected to the charging station or Recovery/Recycling machine.
2. Follow the instructions provided with the equipment and charge the system with the specified amount of refrigerant.
3. Perform a leak test.

Supplemental Inflatable Restraint (SIR) System

Before working on or around key instrument panel components which may affect the air bag system, the system must be disabled before service is performed, then enabled once service repairs are completed. This is especially true of removal of key air conditioning system components.

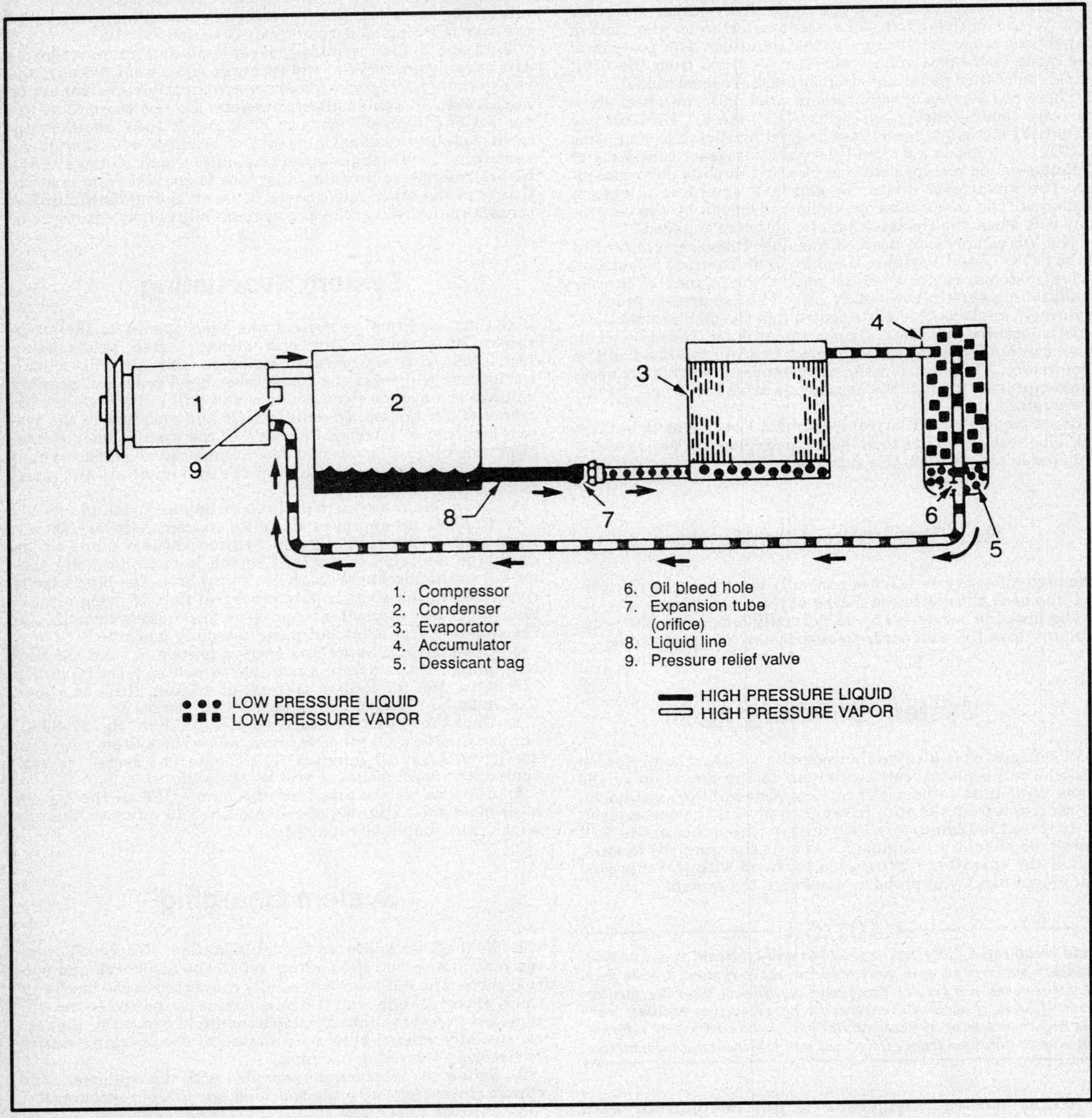

Air conditioning system—typical

DISABLING THE SYSTEM

1. Set the vehicle's front wheels in a straight ahead position.
2. Turn the ignition switch to **LOCK**. Remove the "Air Bag" fuse from the fuse block.
3. Remove the left sound insulator panel from under the instrument panel.
4. If the right sound insulator panel needs to be removed also, detach the electrical components and light bulbs during removal.
5. At the base of the steering column, disconnect the Connector Position Assurance (CPA) and yellow 2-way connector.

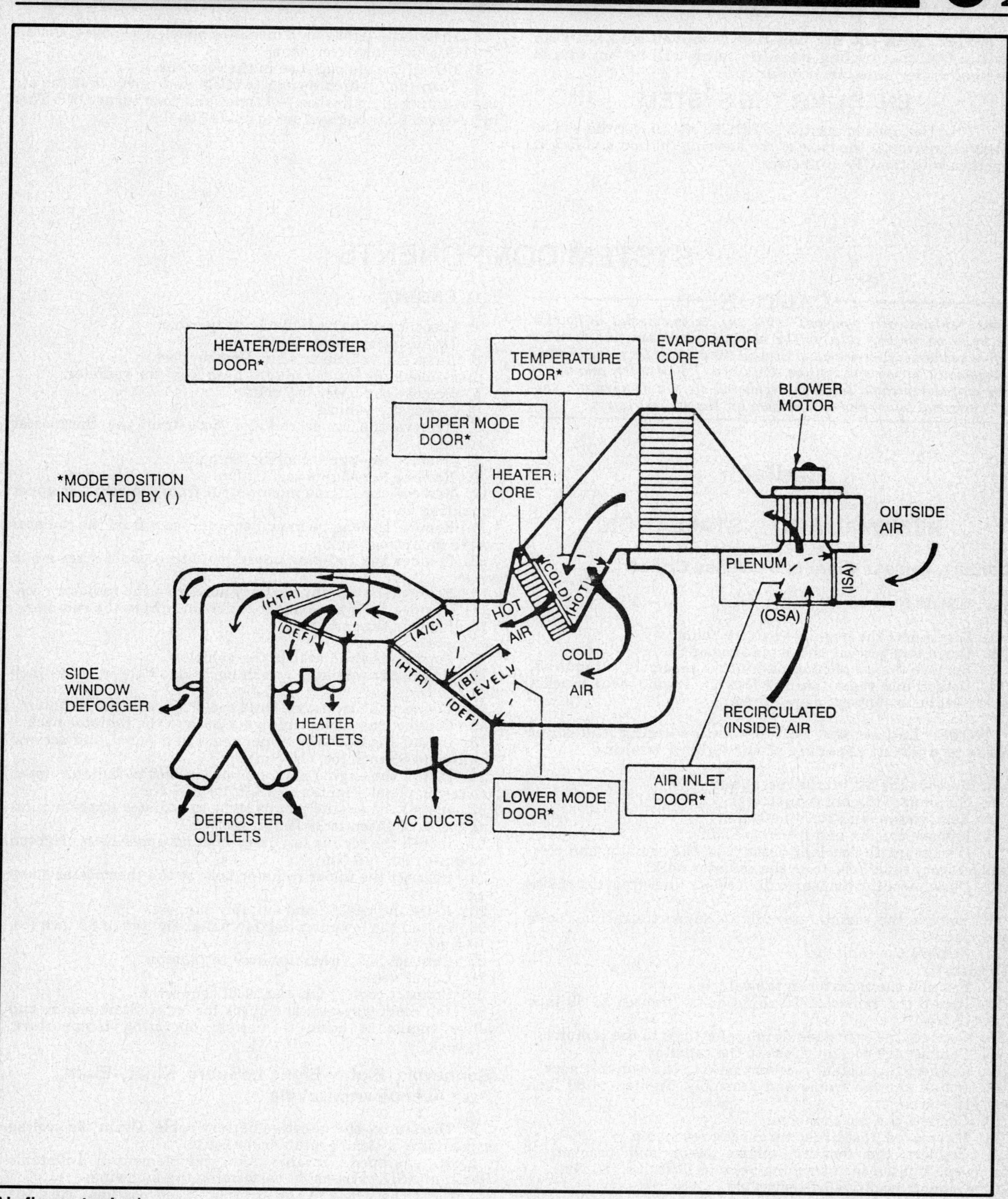
HEATER/DEFROSTER DOOR*
TEMPERATURE DOOR*
EVAPORATOR CORE
BLOWER MOTOR
UPPER MODE DOOR*
*MODE POSITION INDICATED BY ( )
HEATER CORE
OUTSIDE AIR
PLENUM
(ISA)
(OSA)
(HTR)
(DEF)
(A/C)
(COLD)
(HOT)
HOT AIR
(HTR)
(BI-LEVEL)
(DEF)
COLD AIR
SIDE WINDOW DEFOGGER
HEATER OUTLETS
RECIRCULATED (INSIDE) AIR
AIR INLET DOOR*
LOWER MODE DOOR*
DEFROSTER OUTLETS
A/C DUCTS

Air flow—typical

NOTE: With the air bag fuse removed and ignition switch ON, the air bag warning lamp will be on; this is normal under this circumstance.

ENABLING THE SYSTEM

1. Turn the ignition switch to **LOCK**. Reconnect the yellow 2-way connector at the base of the steering column and lock it together with the CPA connector.
2. Install the right sound insulator panel, if removed. Install the left sound insulator panel.
3. Install the air bag fuse in the fuse box.
4. Turn the ignition switch to **RUN** and verify that the air bag warning lamp flashes 7–9 times and then turns OFF. This indicates the air bag system in operational.

SYSTEM COMPONENTS

CAUTION

Some vehicles are equipped with the Supplemental Inflatable Restraint or air bag system. The air bag system must be disabled before performing service on or around the air bag, instrument panel components, wiring and sensors. Failure to follow safety and disabling procedures could result in accidental air bag deployment, possible personal injury and unnecessary air bag system repairs.

Radiator

REMOVAL AND INSTALLATION

Century, Cutlass Ciera and Cutlass Cruiser

2.2L ENGINE

1. Disconnect the negative battery cable.
2. Drain and recover the engine coolant.
3. Remove the air cleaner and intake assembly, if required.
4. Detach and reposition the forward engine strut bracket at the radiator support, as required.

NOTE: Loosen the bolt before swinging the strut aside to prevent shearing of the rubber bushing.

5. Remove the air intake resonator.
6. Disconnect the fan connectors.
7. Remove the fan attaching bolts.
8. Remove the fan and frame assembly.
9. Disconnect the coolant hoses from the radiator and coolant recovery tank hose from the radiator neck.
10. Disconnect the transaxle fluid cooler lines from the radiator.
11. Remove the radiator-to-radiator support attaching bolts and clamps.
12. Remove the radiator.

To install:

13. Position the radiator in the vehicle.
14. Install the radiator attaching bolts. Tighten to 89 inch lbs. (10 Nm).
15. Connect the transaxle fluid cooler lines to the radiator.
16. Connect the coolant hoses to the radiator.
17. Connect the coolant recovery hose to the radiator neck.
18. Install the fan frame and assembly. Tighten to 89 inch lbs. (10 Nm).
19. Connect the fan connector.
20. If removed, install the air intake resonator.
21. Connect the forward engine strut and bracket, if removed. Tighten the attaching bolts to 17 ft. lbs. (23 Nm).
22. Connect negative battery cable.
23. Fill cooling system and check for leaks. Start engine and allow engine to come to normal operating temperature. Recheck for coolant leaks. Allow engine to warm up sufficiently to confirm operation of cooling fan.

3.1L ENGINE

1. Disconnect the negative battery cable.
2. Drain the cooling system.
3. Raise the vehicle and suitably support.
4. Remove the lower radiator hose from the radiator.
5. Remove the lower fan bolts.
6. Lower the vehicle.
7. Remove the upper radiator hose from the thermostat housing.
8. Remove the upper cooling fan bolts.
9. Remove the engine cooling fan.
10. Remove the engine mount strut from the radiator upper mounting panel.
11. Remove the engine mount strut bracket from the radiator upper mounting panel.
12. Remove the radiator upper mounting panel screws and panel.
13. Remove the coolant recovery hose from the radiator neck.
14. Remove the transaxle oil cooler lines from the radiator.
15. Remove the radiator.

To install:

16. Position the radiator in the vehicle.
17. Install the radiator attaching bolts. Tighten to 89 inch lbs. (10 Nm).
18. Connect the transaxle fluid cooler lines to the radiator.
19. Connect the coolant recovery hose to the radiator neck.
20. Install the radiator upper mounting panel and screws. Tighten to 89 inch lbs. (10 Nm).
21. Install the engine mount strut bracket to radiator upper mounting panel. Tighten to 18 ft. lbs. (24 Nm).
22. Install the engine mount strut to radiator upper mounting panel. Tighten to 39 ft. lbs. (53 Nm).
23. Install the cooling fan assembly and upper bolts. Tighten to 89 inch lbs. (10 Nm).
24. Connect the upper radiator hose to the thermostat housing.
25. Raise the vehicle and suitably support.
26. Install the lower cooling fan bolts. Tighten to 89 inch lbs. (10 Nm).
27. Connect lower radiator hose to radiator.
28. Lower vehicle.
29. Connect cooling fan electrical connector.
30. Fill cooling system and check for leaks. Start engine and allow engine to come to normal operating temperature. Recheck.

Bonneville, Eighty-Eight, LeSabre, Ninety-Eight, Park Avenue and DeVille

1. Disconnect the negative battery cable. Drain the cooling system into a clean container for reuse.
2. If equipped, disable the Supplemental Inflatable Restraint (SIR) system by performing the following:
   - Set the wheel in the straight-ahead position. Turn the ignition to **LOCK**.
   - Remove the SIR fuse from the fuse panel.
   - Remove the left side sound insulator.

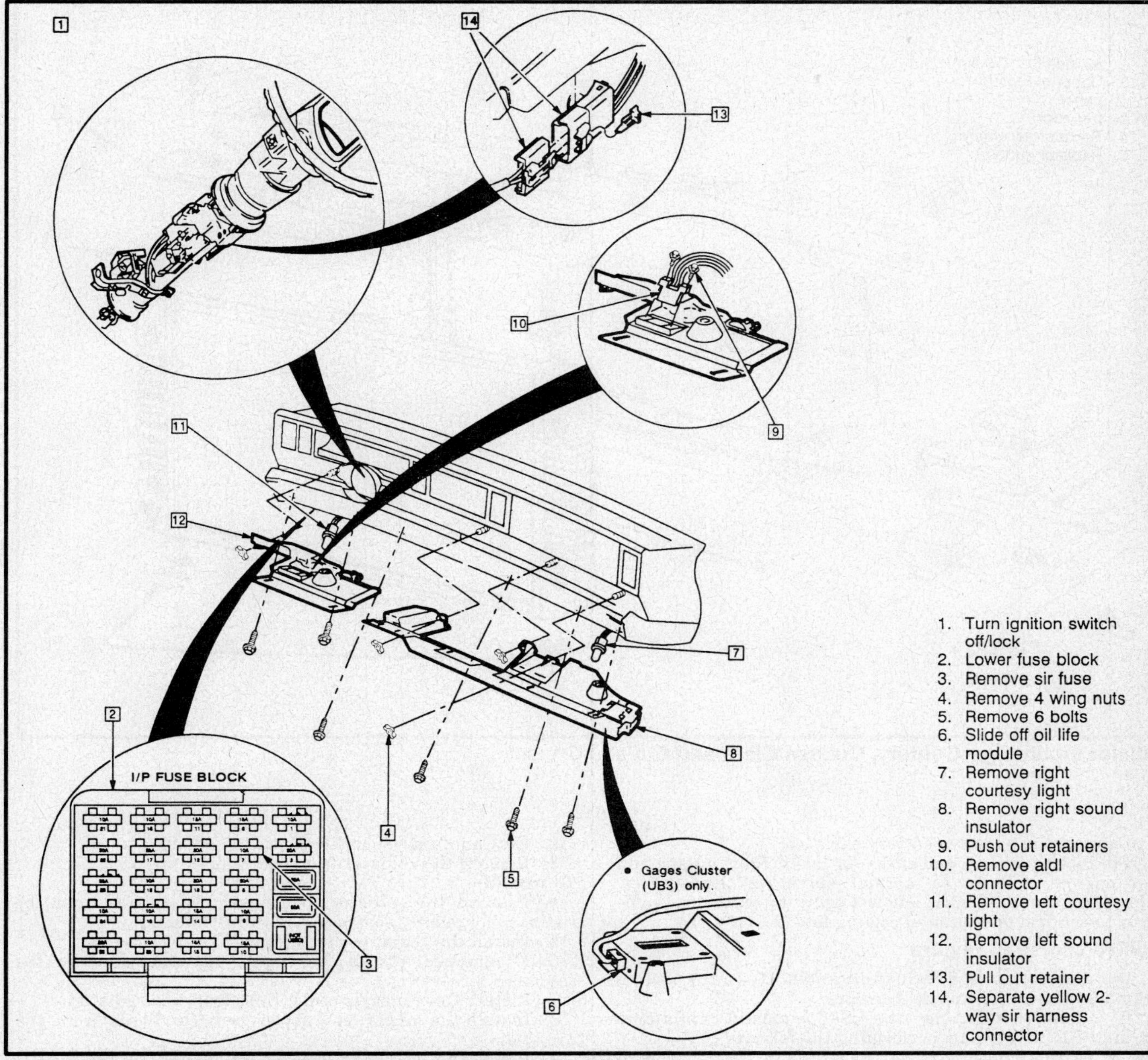
1
14
13
10
9
11
12
7
8
2
I/P FUSE BLOCK
4
5
3
• Gages Cluster (UB3) only.
6
1. Turn ignition switch off/lock
2. Lower fuse block
3. Remove sir fuse
4. Remove 4 wing nuts
5. Remove 6 bolts
6. Slide off oil life module
7. Remove right courtesy light
8. Remove right sound insulator
9. Push out retainers
10. Remove aldl connector
11. Remove left courtesy light
12. Remove left sound insulator
13. Pull out retainer
14. Separate yellow 2-way sir harness connector

Disabling the SIR system—Park Avenue shown; others similar

• Remove the Connector Positive Assurance (CPA) from the yellow 2-way SIR harness connector at the base of the steering column and separate the connector.

3. Remove the upper fan mounting bolts.
4. Remove the upper radiator panel.
5. Disconnect the coolant hoses from the radiator and coolant recovery tank hose from the radiator neck.
6. Disconnect the cooling fan connector.
7. Disconnect the transaxle oil cooler lines from the radiator side tank.
8. Remove the radiator from the vehicle.

To install:

9. Position radiator in the vehicle, locating the bottom of the radiator in the lower mounting pads.
10. Connect the radiator to the radiator support attaching clamp and bolts Tighten to 88 inch lbs. (10 Nm).
11. Connect the transaxle oil cooler lines. Tighten nuts to 20 ft. lbs. (27 Nm).
12. Install the upper radiator panel.
13. Connect the coolant recovery hose to the radiator neck.
14. Install the fan assembly and the fan attaching bolts. Tighten to 84 inch lbs. (10 Nm). On DeVille, install the left and right cooling fans.
15. Connect the cooling fan electrical connector(s).
16. If equipped, enable the Supplemental Inflatable Restraint (SIR) system by performing the following:

• Connect the yellow 2-way SIR connector and insert the Connect Positive Assurance (CPA) at the base of the steering column.

• Install the left side sound insulator.

• Install the SIR fuse in the fuse panel. When ignition is turned to **ON** the warning light should flash 7–9 times as a sign that the system is armed.

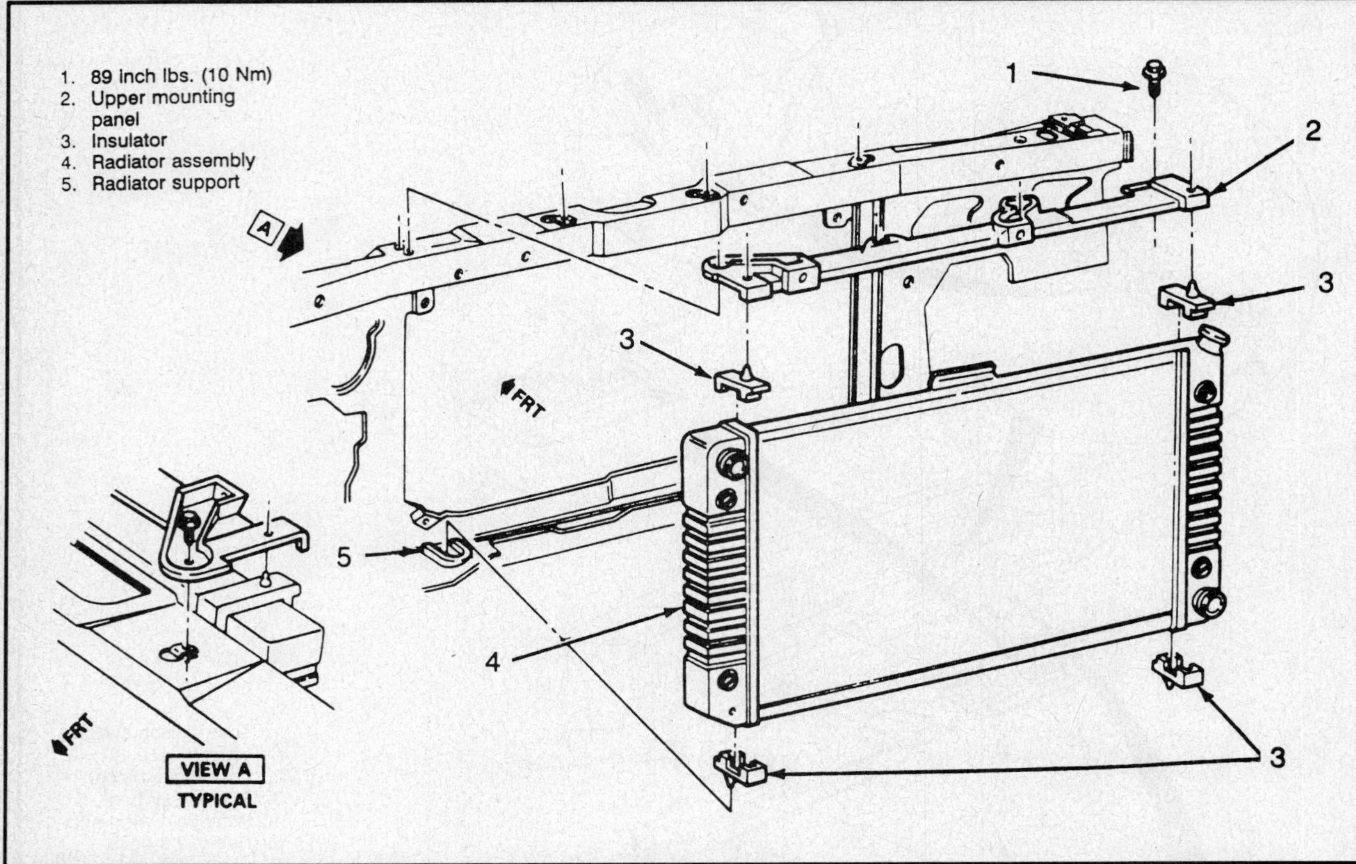

Radiator mounting—Century, Cutlass Ciera and Cutlass Cruiser

17. Connect the negative battery cable.
18. Fill cooling system and check for leaks. Start engine and allow engine to come to normal operating temperature. Recheck for coolant leaks. Allow engine to warm up sufficiently to confirm operation of cooling fan.

Cadillac and 1993 Riviera

1. Disconnect the negative battery cable. Drain the cooling system into a clean container for reuse.
2. If equipped, disable the Supplemental Inflatable Restraint (SIR) system by performing the following:
   - With the wheels straight ahead, turn the ignition to **LOCK**. Remove the SIR fuse from the fuse panel.
   - Remove the left side sound insulator.
   - Remove the Connector Positive Assurance (CPA) from the yellow 2-way SIR harness connector at the base of the steering column and separate the connector.
3. Remove the radiator support cover.
4. Remove the front radiator splash shield, as required.
5. On 1994 Concours, El Dorado and Seville relocate forward discriminating sensor out of the way, remove air cleaner.
6. If equipped, remove the engine-to-radiator torque strut.
7. Remove the cooling fan(s) mounted on the engine side of the radiator on 1994 Deville remove rear cooling fan only.
8. Remove the coolant reservoir hose at the filler neck.
9. Remove the upper and lower radiator hoses from the radiator.
10. Remove the transaxle cooler lines from the radiator.
11. If equipped, remove the engine oil cooler lines from the left side radiator end tank.
12. On Cadillacs, remove radiator top support.
13. Remove the radiator from the vehicle.

To install:

14. Position the radiator in the vehicle. Ensure that the radiator is properly seated in the rubber mounts.
15. Install the radiator support cover.
16. If equipped, install the engine oil cooler lines to the radiator.
17. Install the transaxle cooler lines from the radiator.
18. Install the upper and lower radiator hoses from the radiator.
19. Install the coolant reservoir hose at the filler neck.
20. Install the cooling fan(s) mounted on the engine side of the radiator.
21. If equipped, install the engine-to-radiator torque strut.
22. If removed, install the front radiator splash shield.
23. Install forward discriminating sensor, if removed.
24. Connect the negative battery cable.
25. If equipped, enable the Supplemental Inflatable Restraint (SIR) system by performing the following:
   - Connect the yellow 2-way SIR connector and insert the Connect Positive Assurance (CPA) at the base of the steering column.
   - Install the left side sound insulator.
   - Install the SIR fuse in the fuse panel.
26. Fill cooling system and check for leaks. Start the engine and allow to come to normal operating temperature. Recheck for coolant leaks. Allow the engine to warm up sufficiently to confirm operation of cooling fan.

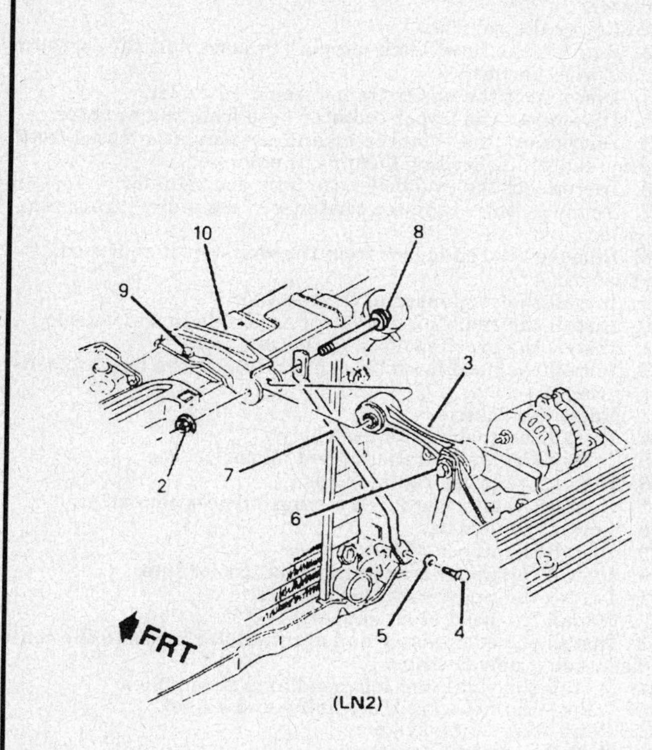

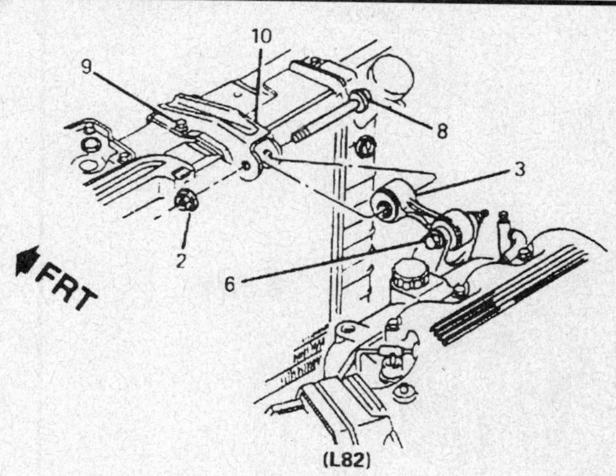

2 NUT, ENGINE MOUNT STRUT
3 STRUT ASSEMBLY, ENGINE MOUNT
4 BOLT/SCREW, ENGINE MOUNT STRUT BRACKET
5 WASHER, ENGINE MOUNT STRUT BRACKET BRACE
6 BOLT/SCREW, ENGINE MOUNT STRUT
7 BRACE, ENGINE MOUNT STRUT BRACKET
8 BOLT/SCREW, ENGINE MOUNT STRUT
9 BOLT/SCREW, ENGINE MOUNT STRUT BRACKET
10 BRACKET, ENGINE MOUNT STRUT

Engine mount strut to radiator assembly—typical

1995 Aurora and Riviera

1. Disconnect the negative battery cable.
2. Raise the vehicle and suitably support.
3. Remove the lower air dam, drain cooling system and install the lower air dam.
4. Lower the vehicle.
5. Remove the upper tie bar.
6. Disconnect the electrical connectors for the cooling fans and remove both left and right cooling fans.
7. Disconnect the electrical connector from the coolant level sensor.
8. Remove the coolant recovery hose from the radiator filler neck.
9. Remove the inlet and outlet radiator hoses from the radiator.
10. Remove the bolts from the condenser.
11. Remove the transaxle cooler lines from the radiator.
12. On 4.0L remove the engine cooler lines from the radiator.
13. Remove the radiator.

To install:

14. Install the radiator in the vehicle, locating bottom of the radiator in the lower mounting pads.
15. Install the transaxle cooler lines to the radiator.
16. Install the engine cooler lines to the radiator.
17. Install the bolts to the condenser, and upper and lower radiator hoses.
18. Install the coolant recovery hose to the radiator filler neck.
19. Connect the electrical connector to the coolant level sensor.
20. Install the left and right cooling fans and install the electrical connectors.
21. Install the upper tie bar assembly.
22. Fill the cooling system and check for leaks.
23. Check and refill the transaxle if needed.

Cavalier and Sunbird

1993–94 MODELS

1. Disconnect the negative battery cable.
2. Drain the cooling system into a clean container for reuse.
3. Disconnect the forward light harness from the frame and unplug the fan connector.
4. Remove the fan attaching bolts.
5. Scribe a line around the hood latch location to aid in reinstallation. Remove the hood latch.
6. Remove the radiator air inlet ducts. Disconnect the coolant hoses from the radiator.
7. If equipped with automatic transaxle, disconnect the transaxle fluid cooler lines from the radiator.
8. If equipped with air conditioning, remove the radiator-to-condenser bolts and the radiator tank to refrigerant line clamp bolt.
9. Remove the radiator-to-radiator support attaching bolts and clamps.
10. Remove the radiator.

To install:

11. Position the radiator in the vehicle, and place the bottom of radiator on lower mounting pads.
12. Install the radiator-to-radiator support attaching bolts and clamps.
13. If equipped with automatic transaxle, connect the transaxle fluid cooler lines from the radiator.
14. If equipped with air conditioning, install the radiator-to-condenser bolts and the radiator tank to refrigerant line clamp bolt.
15. Connect the coolant hoses to the radiator. Install the radiator air ducts.

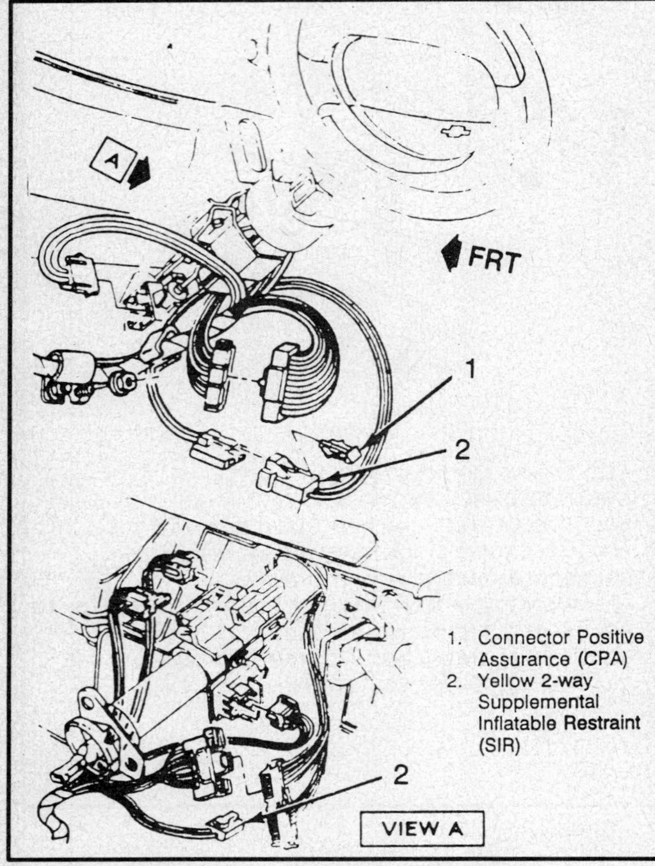

Two-way SIR harness connector—typical

16. Install the hood latch. Observe the scribe mark made during removal.
17. On 1994–95 models, make sure the bottom leg of the frame fits into the rubber grommet (where used) at the lower radiator support. Install the cooling fan attaching bolts.
18. Connect the forward light harness to the frame and connect the fan connector.

NOTE: Be sure to connect the engine ground strap (if used) to the strut brace.

19. Connect the negative battery cable.
20. Fill cooling system and check for leaks. Start the engine and allow to come to normal operating temperature. Recheck for coolant leaks. Allow the engine to warm up sufficiently to confirm operation of cooling fan.

Cavalier and Sunfire

1995 MODELS

1. Disconnect the negative battery cable. Drain the cooling system into a clean container for reuse.
2. Disable the Supplemental Inflatable Restraint (SIN) system.
3. Remove the hood latch from the mounting plate.
4. Remove the right and left headlamp assemblies.
5. Remove the radiator mounts.
6. Raise the vehicle.
7. Disconnect the forward SIR sensor harness.
8. Remove the cooling fan assembly.
9. Disconnect the lower radiator hose from the radiator.
10. Disconnect the lower transmission oil cooler line from radiator.
11. Lower the vehicle.
12. Remove the hood latch support bracket and the forward sensor with harness.
13. Disconnect the upper transmission oil cooler.
14. Disconnect the upper radiator hose from the radiator.
15. Disconnect the compressor and accumulator hoses from the condenser, discarding O-rings, if equipped.
16. Disconnect the overflow hose from the radiator.
17. Remove the radiator/condenser assembly from the vehicle.
18. Remove the condenser from the radiator, if equipped.

To install:

19. Install the condenser to the radiator.
20. Install the radiator/condenser assembly in the vehicle.
21. Install the overflow hose to the radiator.
22. Install the hood latch bracket and route the forward sensor harness.
23. Raise the vehicle.
24. Install the cooling fan assembly.
25. Install the lower transmission oil cooler line.
26. Install the lower radiator hose.
27. Connect the forward SIR sensor harness connector.
28. Lower the vehicle.
29. Install the upper radiator hose.
30. Install the upper transmission oil cooler line.
31. Install the upper radiator mounts.
32. Install the hood latch support.
33. Install the compressor and accumulator hoses to the condenser, using new O-rings.
34. Install the right and left headlamp assemblies.
35. Install the hood latch assembly and adjust.
36. Refill the cooling system.
37. Recharge the A/C system.
38. Enable the SIR.
39. Connect the negative battery cable, and inspect for leaks.

Beretta and Corsica

1. Disconnect the negative battery cable. Drain the cooling system into a clean container for reuse.
2. If equipped, disable the Supplemental Inflatable Restraint (SIR) system by performing the following:
    - With the wheels straight ahead and ignition at **LOCK**, remove the SIR fuse from the fuse panel.
    - Remove the left side sound insulator.
    - Remove the Connector Positive Assurance (CPA) from the yellow 2-way SIR harness connector at the base of the steering column and separate the connector.
3. Remove the air cleaner duct work and air cleaner, as required.
4. Remove the electric cooling fan assembly, remove fan.
5. Remove the coolant recovery reservoir hose from the filler neck.
6. If equipped with an automatic transaxle, disconnect the transaxle fluid cooler lines from the radiator. Cap the lines to prevent the loss of transaxle fluid.
7. Remove the upper radiator hoses.
8. Remove the left and right radiator air baffles, as required.
9. If equipped with Supplemental Inflatable Restraint (SIR), remove the forward discriminating sensor and set aside.
10. Remove the upper radiator support and mount bolts.
11. On GTZ models, remove the upper air baffle.
12. Remove the upper condenser-to-radiator bolts.
13. On 1994–95 models equipped with A/C, remove the condenser line retaining clip, and the condenser-to-radiator bolts.
14. Raise and safely support the vehicle, if required, and remove the splash guard and the lower radiator hose and lower mounting bolts.
15. Remove the radiator.

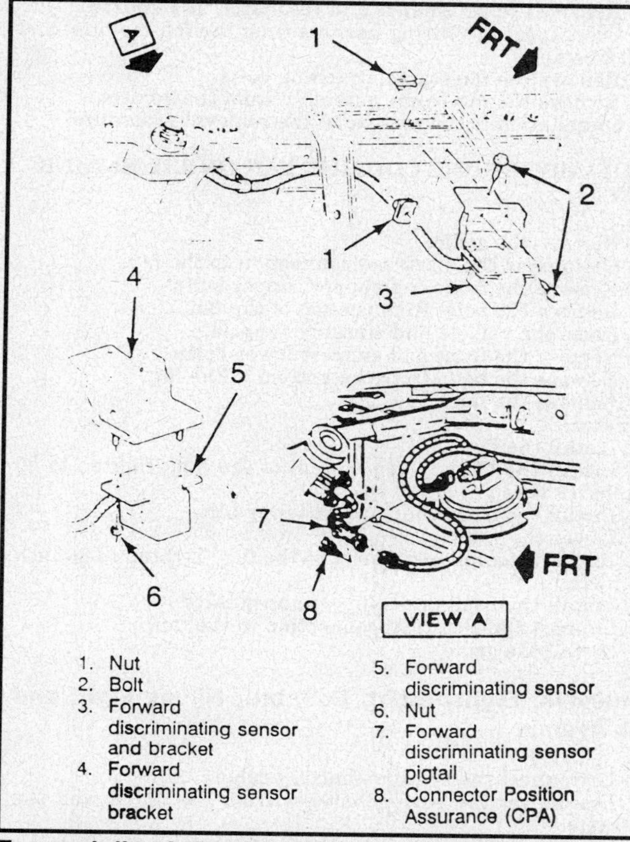

Forward discriminating sensor installation—Beretta and Corsica

To install:

16. Install the radiator.
17. Raise the vehicle, if required, and install the lower mounting bolts and splash guard and the lower radiator hose.
18. Install the upper condenser-to-radiator bolts.
19. On 1994–95 models equipped with A/C, install condenser line retaining clip, and condenser to radiator bolts.
20. Install the upper radiator support and mount bolts.
21. On GTZ models, install the upper radiator air baffle.
22. If equipped with Supplemental Inflatable Restraint (SIR), install the forward discriminating sensor.
23. If removed, install the left and right radiator air baffles.
24. Install the upper and lower radiator hoses.
25. If equipped with an automatic transaxle, connect the transaxle fluid cooler lines to the radiator.
26. Install the coolant recovery reservoir hose to the filler neck.
27. Install the electric cooling fan assembly.
28. If removed, install the air cleaner duct work and air cleaner.
29. Connect the negative battery cable.
30. If equipped, enable the Supplemental Inflatable Restraint (SIR) system by performing the following:
    - Connect the yellow 2-way SIR connector and insert the Connect Positive Assurance (CPA) at the base of the steering column.
    - Install the left side sound insulator.
    - Install the SIR fuse in the fuse panel.
31. Fill cooling system and check for leaks. Start the engine and allow to come to normal operating temperature. Recheck for coolant leaks. Allow the engine to warm up sufficiently to confirm operation of cooling fan.

Achieva, Grand Am and Skylark

1. Disconnect the negative battery cable. Properly drain the cooling system.
2. Remove the air intake duct assembly.
3. Remove the upper transaxle cooler line, the upper radiator hose, and the lower transaxle cooler line.
4. Remove the cooling fan.
5. Remove the splash guard below the lower radiator hose, and remove the lower radiator hose.
6. Remove the condenser refrigerant line retaining clip, condenser-to-radiator bolts, coolant tank hose, radiator bolts and the radiator.
7. Installation is the reverse of the removal procedure.

LeMans

1. Disconnect the negative battery cable.
2. Detach lower radiator hose and drain the engine coolant into a clean container for reuse.
3. Disconnect the upper radiator hose.
4. Disconnect the coolant reservoir hose.
5. Disconnect the cooling fan motor connector, oxygen sensor and temperature sensor.
6. If equipped, remove the transaxle cooler pipes from the radiator. Plug the openings to prevent fluid leakage.
7. Remove the radiator-to-radiator support bolts. Remove the radiator.
8. Remove the radiator fan shroud with motor from the radiator assembly.

To install:

9. Install the fan motor and shroud to the radiator assembly.
10. Install the radiator and attaching bolts.
11. Connect the temperature sensor, oxygen sensor and fan motor connectors.
12. If removed, install the transaxle cooler pipes.
13. Connect the coolant reservoir hose.
14. Connect the lower radiator hose.
15. Fill the cooling system. Bleed air through the upper reservoir hose.
16. Start the engine and allow to come to normal operating temperature. Recheck for coolant leaks. Allow the engine to warm up sufficiently to confirm operation of cooling fan.

Cutlass Supreme, Grand Prix, Lumina, Monte Carlo and Regal

1. Disconnect the negative battery cable.
2. Drain the cooling system into a clean container for reuse.
3. Remove the air cleaner assembly.
4. Remove the engine strut brace bolts from the upper tie bar and rotate the strut(s) and brace(s) rearward. To prevent shearing of the rubber bushing(s), loosen the bolt(s) on the engine strut(s) before swinging the strut(s).
5. Remove the upper radiator mounting panel bolts and clamps.
6. Disconnect the cooling fan electrical connector(s).
7. Remove the upper radiator mounting panel with the cooling fan(s) attached.
8. Disconnect the upper and lower hoses at the radiator.
9. If equipped, disconnect the low coolant sensor electrical connector and remove the sensor.
10. Disconnect and plug all cooler lines from the radiator.
11. Remove the radiator from the vehicle.

To install:

12. Install the radiator in the vehicle. Ensure that the radiator is seated in lower insulator pads.
13. Attach any cooler lines removed.
14. Install the low coolant sensor in the radiator. Connect the sensor electrical connector.
15. Connect the upper and lower radiator hoses.
16. Install the upper radiator mounting panel with the cooling fan(s) attached.
17. Connect the cooling fan electrical connector(s).

18. Install the upper radiator mounting panel bolts and clamps.
19. Swing the engine strut(s) into the proper position.
20. Install the air cleaner assembly.
21. Connect the negative battery cable.
22. Fill cooling system and check for leaks. Start the engine and allow to come to normal operating temperature. Recheck for coolant leaks. Allow the engine to warm up sufficiently to confirm operation of cooling fan.

COOLING SYSTEM BLEEDING

1. Fill the cooling system with the proper ratio of coolant and water.
2. If equipped with an air bleed vent valve on the thermostat housing or by-pass pipe, open the air bleed vent 2–3 turns.
3. Set the heater controls to heat and the temperature controls to the warmest setting.
4. Start the engine and add coolant as necessary to keep the radiator level just below the filler neck.
5. If equipped with an air bleed vent, close the vent when coolant begins to come out of the vent.
6. Set mode control to any position except **MAX** and temperature to **HOT**. Allow the engine to come to normal operating temperature; indicated by the upper radiator hose becoming hot.
7. The air coming out of the heater should be getting hot.
8. Increase idle speed up to 3000 rpm and back to idle about 5 times to expel any trapped air.
9. Check the coolant level in the radiator and coolant reservoir. Install the radiator cap, turning it until the arrows align with the overflow tube.

Cooling Fan

TESTING

1. Check fuse or circuit breaker for power to cooling fan motor.
2. With ambient air temperature above 60°F (16°C), start the engine and set the A/C mode to **MAX**. The fan should come on.
3. With the engine coolant still below normal operating temperature, turn the A/C mode **OFF**. The cooling fan should turn off after a short delay.
4. Remove connector(s) at cooling fan motor(s). Connect jumper wire and apply battery voltage to the positive terminal of the cooling fan motor.
5. Using an ohmmeter, check for continuity in cooling fan motor.

NOTE: Remove the cooling fan connector at the fan motor before performing continuity checks. Perform continuity check of the motor windings only. The cooling fan control circuit is connected electrically to the ECM through the cooling fan relay center. Ohmmeter battery voltage must not be applied to the ECM.

6. Ensure proper continuity of cooling fan motor ground circuit at chassis ground connector.

REMOVAL AND INSTALLATION

Century, Cutlass Ciera and Cutlass Cruiser

WITHOUT AUXILIARY COOLING FAN ON 3.1L ENGINE

1. Disconnect the negative battery cable.
2. Remove the air cleaner and resonator, as required.
3. Disconnect the wiring harness from the fan motor(s) and fan frame(s).
4. Remove the fan frame attaching bolts.
5. Remove the fan frame assembly from the vehicle.
6. Installation is the reverse of the removal procedure.

AUXILIARY ENGINE COOLING FAN ON 3.1L ENGINE ONLY

1. Remove the grille.
2. Disconnect the electrical connection to the fan.
3. Remove the front end support upper bolts.
4. Remove the bolts from the top of the fan.
5. Raise the vehicle and suitably support.
6. Remove the front end support lower bolts.
7. Remove the bolts from the bottom of the fan.
8. Remove the fan.

To install:

9. Install the fan.
10. Install the bolts to the bottom of the fan. Tighten to 80 inch lbs. (9 Nm).
11. Install the front end support lower bolts.
12. Lower the vehicle.
13. Install the remaining bolts to the fan. Tighten to 80 inch lbs. (9 Nm).
14. Install the front end support upper bolts.
15. Connect the electrical connection to the fan.
16. Install the grille.

Bonneville, Eighty-Eight, LeSabre, Ninety-Eight and Park Avenue

1. Disconnect the negative battery cable.
2. Disconnect the wiring harness from the motor and the fan frame.
3. Remove the fan guard and hose support, as required.
4. Remove the fan assembly from the radiator support.

To install:

5. Install the fan assembly to the radiator support.
6. Connect the wiring harness.
7. Connect the negative battery cable.

Aurora, Cadillac and Riviera

FRONT (CONDENSER) COOLING FAN

1. Disconnect the negative battery cable.
2. Disconnect the cooling fan electrical connector.
3. Remove the right headlight bracket (1993 EL/KS and 1994–95 KD/KF body) front finish panel, grille or fan guard, as required.
4. If equipped, remove the radiator support to gain access to the cooling fan.
5. Remove the cooling fan attaching screws.
6. Remove the cooling fan.

To install:

7. Install the cooling fan in the vehicle.
8. If removed, install the radiator support.
9. Install the front finish panel, grille or cowl, as required.
10. Connect the fan electrical connector.
11. Connect the negative battery cable.

REAR (RADIATOR) COOLING FAN

1. Remove the upper engine-to-radiator support torque strut.
2. Detach the fan connector.
3. Remove the oil cooler line bracket from the fan shroud, if equipped.
4. Remove the fan (2 upper and 2 lower bolts).
5. Installation is the reverse of the removal procedure.

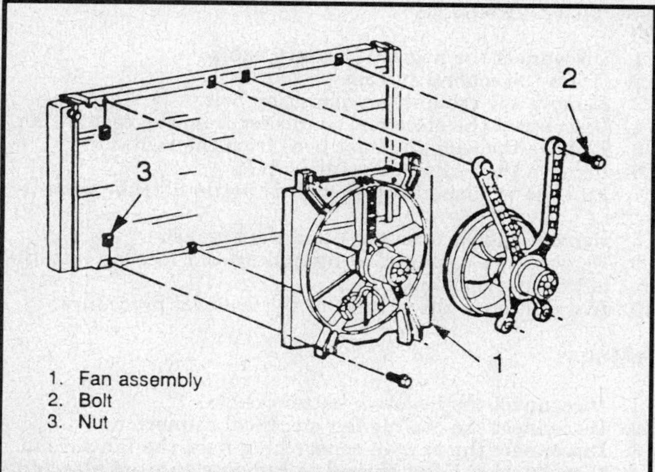

Cooling fan mounting—Bonneville, Eighty-Eight, LeSabre, Ninety-Eight and Park Avenue

LEFT AND RIGHT SIDE (RADIATOR) COOLING FAN

1. Disconnect the negative battery cable.
2. On 1994–95 Concours, El Dorado, and Seville remove the front end beauty panel, the air cleaner, the upper transmission oil cooler line, and relocate the upper radiator hose out of the way.
3. Disconnect the cooling fan electrical connector.
4. Remove the upper or left hand engine-to-radiator torque strut, as required.
5. Remove the cooling fan attaching bolts.
6. Remove the cooling fan.

To install:

7. Install the cooling fan.
8. Install the front end beauty panel, the air cleaner, the upper transmission oil cooler line and the upper radiator hose.
9. If removed, install the upper engine-to-radiator torque strut.
10. Connect the cooling fan electrical connector.
11. Connect the negative battery cable.

Cavalier, 1995 Sunfire and Sunbird

2.0L (VIN H) AND 2.2L (VIN 4) ENGINE

1. Disconnect the negative battery cable.
2. On 1993–94 models, remove the air cleaner duct.
3. Disconnect the wiring harness from the motor and fan frame.
4. Remove the fan assembly from the radiator support.

To install:

5. Install the fan assembly to the radiator support.
6. Connect the wiring harness from the motor and fan frame.
7. Install the air cleaner duct.
8. Connect the negative battery cable.

2.3L (VIN D) ENGINE

1. Disconnect the negative battery cable.
2. Raise the vehicle.
3. Remove the coolant fan mounting bolt.
4. Disconnect the electrical connector from the coolant fan.
5. Remove the coolant fan assembly out through the bottom.

To install:

6. Install the coolant fan assembly in through the bottom.
7. Connect the electrical connector to the coolant fan.
8. Install the coolant fan mounting bolt.
9. Lower the vehicle.
10. Connect the negative battery cable.

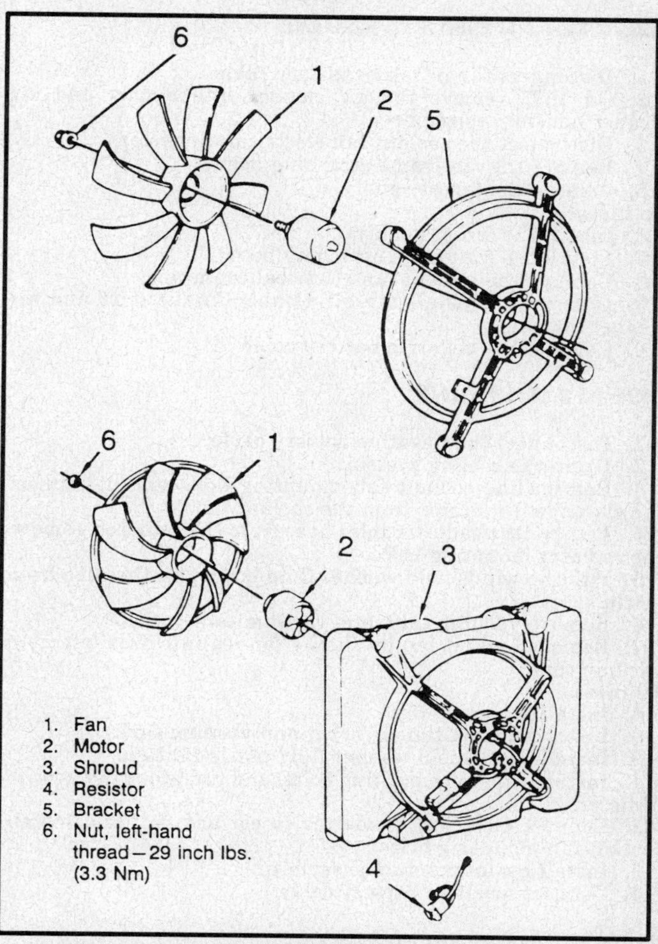

Electric cooling fan—disassembled—typical

3.1L (VIN T) ENGINE

1. Disconnect the negative battery cable.
2. Remove the air cleaner duct and air cleaner.
3. Mark the location of the hood primary latch, then remove it.
4. Drain the engine coolant into a clean container to a level below the radiator inlet (upper) hose.
5. Disconnect the radiator inlet (upper) hose and position aside.
6. If equipped with automatic transaxle, disconnect the transaxle fluid cooler lines at the radiator and position aside.
7. Disconnect the wiring harness connector at the coolant fan. Remove the fan assembly from the radiator support.

To install:

8. Install the fan assembly from the radiator support.
9. Connect the wiring harness connector at the coolant fan.
10. If equipped with automatic transaxle, connect the transaxle fluid cooler lines at the radiator and position aside.
11. Connect the radiator inlet (upper) hose.
12. Install the primary hood latch assembly.
13. Install the air cleaner duct and air cleaner.
14. Connect the negative battery cable.
15. Fill cooling system and check for leaks. Start the engine and allow to come to normal operating temperature. Recheck for coolant leaks. Allow the engine to warm up sufficiently to confirm operation of cooling fan.

Beretta and Corsica

2.2L, 2.3L AND 1993 3.1L ENGINE

1. Disconnect the negative battery cable.
2. On 1993 remove the air cleaner intake duct and air cleaner housing, as required.
3. Disconnect the coolant fan electrical connector.
4. Remove the fan frame attaching bolts.
5. Remove the fan assembly.

To install:

6. Install the fan assembly.
7. Install the fan frame attaching bolts.
8. Connect the coolant fan electrical connector.
9. If removed, install the air cleaner intake duct and air cleaner housing.
10. Connect the negative battery cable.

1994–95 3.1L ENGINE

1. Disconnect the negative battery cable.
2. Drain the cooling system.
3. Remove the coolant fan mounting bolts and disconnect the electrical connector from the coolant fan.
4. Remove the radiator inlet hose from the radiator, remove the radiator mounting bolts.
5. Pull the windshield washer fluid bottle, fill the tube from bottle.
6. Remove vacuum tank and vacuum tank bracket.
7. Remove coolant fan by sliding fan leg into area left from vacuum tank.

To install:

8. Install fan assembly.
9. Install vacuum tank bracket and vacuum tank.
10. Install windshield washer fluid bottle fill tube.
11. Install radiator mounting bolts, and radiator inlet hose to radiator.
12. Connect electrical connector to coolant fan, and install coolant fan mounting bolts.
13. Install air intake duct assembly.
14. Connect negative battery cable.

Achieva, Grand Am and Skylark

1993

1. Disconnect the negative battery cable.
2. Remove the air intake duct assembly.
3. On 3.3L engine, partially drain the cooling system and remove the upper radiator hose.
4. Detach the cooling fan wiring. Remove the fan bolts and remove the fan assembly.
5. Installation is the reverse of the removal procedure.

1994–95 2.3L (VIN A) ENGINE

1. Disconnect the negative battery cable.
2. Disconnect the wiring harness from the motor and the fan frame.
3. Remove the top engine cooling fan bolt.
4. Remove the fan assembly from the radiator support.
5. Installation is the reverse of the removal procedure.

1994–95 2.3L (VIN 3 AND D) ENGINE

1. Disconnect the negative battery cable.
2. Raise the vehicle and support suitably.
3. Remove the bolt from the lower torque axis mount.
4. Remove the fan bolt and disconnect the electrical connector.
5. Rock the engine rearward and remove the fan assembly.
6. Installation is the reverse of the removal procedure.

1994–95 3.1L ENGINE

1. Disconnect the negative battery cable.
2. Drain the cooling system.
3. Remove the coolant fan mounting bolt.
4. Disconnect the electrical connector from the coolant fan.
5. Remove the radiator inlet hose from the radiator.
6. Remove the radiator mounting bolt.
7. Pull the windshield washer fluid bottle fill tube from the bottle.
8. Remove the vacuum tank and the bracket.
9. Remove the coolant fan by sliding the fan leg into the area left from the vacuum tank.
10. Installation is the reverse of the removal procedure.

LeMans

1. Disconnect the negative battery cable.
2. Disconnect the cooling fan electrical connector.
3. Disconnect the oxygen sensor plug from the fan shroud.
4. Disconnect the fan shroud-to-radiator support attaching bolts.
5. Remove the fan motor and shroud assembly.

To install:

6. Install the fan motor and shroud assembly.
7. Install the fan shroud-to-radiator support attaching bolts.
8. Connect the oxygen sensor plug and fan harness to the fan shroud.
9. Connect the negative battery cable.

Cutlass Supreme, Grand Prix, Lumina, Monte Carlo and Regal

1. Disconnect the negative battery cable.
2. Remove the air cleaner assembly.
3. Remove the coolant reservoir, as required.
4. On 1993 models, remove the engine strut brace bolts from the upper tie bar and rotate the strut(s) and brace(s) rearward. In order to prevent shearing of the rubber bushing(s), loosen the bolt(s) on the engine strut(s) before rotating.
5. If equipped, remove the upper radiator panel mounting bolts and clamps.
6. Disconnect the electrical connector(s) from the fan motor(s) and frame(s).
7. Remove the fan frame attaching bolts. Remove the fan assembly or assemblies.

To install:

8. Remove the fan assembly or assemblies.
9. Install the fan frame attaching bolts.
10. Connect the electrical connector(s) to the fan motor(s) and frame(s). Install the upper radiator panel mounting bolts and clamps, if removed.
11. Install the engine strut brace bolts to the upper tie bar.
12. Install the coolant reservoir, as required.
13. Install the air cleaner assembly.
14. Connect the negative battery cable.

Condenser

REMOVAL AND INSTALLATION

CAUTION

Some vehicles are equipped with the Supplemental Inflatable Restraint or air bag system. The air bag system must be disabled before performing service on or around the air bag, instrument panel components, wiring and sensors. Failure to follow safety and disabling procedures could result in accidental air bag deployment, possible personal injury and unnecessary air bag system repairs. Refer to "Supplemental Inflatable Restraint" in this article.

Century, Cutlass Ciera, and Cutlass Cruiser

1993

1. Properly discharge the air conditioning system.
2. On some models it will be necessary to raise and support the vehicle to access the refrigerant lines and to remove the lower support bolts.

NOTE: Use a back-up wrench on the condenser fittings when removing the high-pressure and liquid lines. Cap both refrigerant lines when opening the system to prevent the entry of dirt and moisture and the loss of refrigerant lubricant.

3. Disconnect the high-pressure and liquid lines at the condenser fittings. Discard the O-rings.
4. Remove the grille center support and the lower support bolts, if required.
5. Remove the condenser attaching bolts from the center support.
6. Remove the engine strut bracket and upper radiator support. Lean radiator back.
7. Carefully remove the condenser.

To install:

8. Position the condenser in the vehicle.

NOTE: If replacing the condenser or if the original condenser was flushed during service, add 1 fluid oz. (30 ml) of refrigerant lubricant to the system.

9. Install the upper radiator support, engine strut bracket, center support and lower support bolts, as removed.
10. Install the condenser attaching bolts.
11. Replace the condenser fitting O-rings. Lubricate the O-rings with refrigerant oil.
12. Connect the condenser high-pressure and liquid lines.

NOTE: Use a back-up wrench on the condenser fittings when tightening lines.

13. Evacuate, charge and leak test the system.

1994–95

1. Properly discharge the air conditioning system.
2. Remove the grille center support retaining bolts.
3. Raise the vehicle and suitably support.
4. Remove the center support lower retaining bolts and the support.
5. Remove the left air inlet seal.

NOTE: Use a back-up wrench on the condenser fittings when removing the high-pressure and liquid lines. Cap both refrigerant lines when opening the system to prevent the entry of dirt and moisture and the loss of refrigerant lubricant.

6. Disconnect the inlet and outlet lines from the condenser.
7. Remove the lower condenser mounts and the condenser.

To install:

8. Install the condenser and lower condenser mounts.

NOTE: Use a back-up wrench on the condenser fittings when tightening lines.

9. Connect the inlet and outlet lines to the condenser.
10. Install the left air inlet seal.
11. Install the center support and the lower retaining bolts.
12. Lower the vehicle.
13. Install the grille center support retaining bolts.
14. Evacuate and charge the system.
15. Leak test the system.

Bonneville, Eighty-Eight, LeSabre, Ninety-Eight and Park Avenue

1. Disconnect the negative battery cable. Remove battery hold-down, battery and air cleaner bracket screw, as required.
2. If equipped, disable the Supplemental Inflatable Restraint (SIR) system by performing the following:
   - Set the wheel straight-ahead and turn ignition to **LOCK**. Remove the SIR fuse from the fuse panel.
   - Remove the left side sound insulator.
   - On passenger's side while removing the right insulator panel (if required) detach the electrical connectors and light bulbs.
   - Remove the Connector Positive Assurance (CPA) from the yellow 2-way SIR harness connector at the base of the steering column and separate the connector.
3. Properly discharge the air conditioning system.
4. If equipped, disconnect the auxiliary transaxle cooler lines. On some models, the air cleaner bracket bolt may have to be removed.
5. Remove the upper radiator support panel.
6. On 1993 C Body, remove the coolant overflow tube from the radiator.
7. Disconnect the refrigerant lines at the condenser. Discard the O-rings.

NOTE: Use a back-up wrench on the condenser fittings when removing the high-pressure and liquid lines. Cap both refrigerant lines when opening the system to prevent the entry of dirt and moisture and the loss of refrigerant lubricant.

8. Remove the condenser support bolts and brackets and insulators.
9. Remove the condenser from the vehicle.

To install:

NOTE: If replacing the condenser or if the original condenser was flushed during service, add 1 fluid oz. (30 ml) of refrigerant lubricant to the system.

10. Position the condenser in the vehicle.
11. Install upper insulators and the condenser support bolts.
12. If equipped, connect the auxiliary transaxle cooler lines.
13. Install the upper radiator support.
14. Connect the condenser refrigerant lines.

NOTE: Use a back-up wrench on the condenser fittings when tightening lines.

15. Connect the coolant overflow tube to the radiator.
16. If equipped, enable the Supplemental Inflatable Restraint (SIR) system by performing the following:
   - Connect the yellow 2-way SIR connector and insert the Connect Positive Assurance (CPA) at the base of the steering column.
   - Install the right and left side sound insulator.
   - Install the SIR fuse in the fuse panel.
17. Install the battery and connect the negative battery cable.
18. Evacuate, recharge and leak test the air conditioning system.

Cadillac and 1993 Riviera

1. Disconnect the negative battery cable. Drain the cooling system into a clean container for reuse.
2. If equipped, disable the Supplemental Inflatable Restraint (SIR) system by performing the following:
   - With the front wheels straight ahead, turn the ignition to **LOCK**. Remove the SIR fuse from the fuse panel.
   - Remove the left side sound insulator.
   - Remove the Connector Positive Assurance (CPA) from the yellow 2-way SIR harness connector at the base of the steering column and separate the connector.

3. Properly discharge the air conditioning system.
4. On 1993 DeVille, remove the battery.
5. Remove the upper engine-to-radiator torque strut, as required.
6. Remove the cooling fan(s), the radiator core upper support, as required.
7. Remove the radiator (Riviera and Allante) or the auxiliary transmission cooler lines (1993 DeVille).
8. Disconnect the refrigerant lines at the condenser fittings. Discard the O-rings.

NOTE: Use a back-up wrench on the condenser fittings when tightening lines. Cap the refrigerant lines when opening the system to prevent the entry of dirt and moisture and the loss of refrigerant lubricant.

9. Remove the refrigerant hose bracket, as required.
10. Remove the condenser attaching bolts and upper insulator, if equipped.
11. Remove the condenser.

To install:

NOTE: If replacing the condenser or if the original condenser was flushed during service, add 1 fluid oz. (30 ml) of refrigerant lubricant to the system.

12. Install the condenser in the vehicle. Ensure that the condenser is properly positioned in the mounting insulator.
13. Install the condenser attaching bolts.
14. Install new O-rings on the condenser refrigerant line fittings. Lubricate with refrigerant oil.
15. Connect the refrigerant lines at the condenser fittings. Use a backup wrench on the condenser fittings.
16. If removed, install the refrigerant hose bracket.
17. If removed, install auxiliary transmission cooling lines or the radiator.
18. Install the cooling fan(s).
19. If removed, install the upper engine-to-radiator torque strut.
20. Install the battery (if removed)and connect the negative battery cable.
21. If equipped, enable the Supplemental Inflatable Restraint (SIR) system by performing the following:
    - Connect the yellow 2-way SIR connector and insert the Connect Positive Assurance (CPA) at the base of the steering column.
    - Install the left side sound insulator.
    - Install the SIR fuse in the fuse panel.
22. Evacuate, recharge and leak test the air conditioning system.
23. Fill cooling system and check for leaks. Start the engine and allow to come to normal operating temperature. Recheck for coolant leaks. Allow the engine to warm up sufficiently to confirm operation of cooling fans.

1995 Aurora and Riviera

1. Disconnect the negative battery cable.
2. Properly discharge the air conditioning system.
3. Remove the 10 screws in the upper radiator panel.
4. Remove the condenser-to-radiator screws.
5. Disconnect the condenser inlet and outlet pipes.

NOTE: Use a back-up wrench on the condenser fittings when removing the high-pressure and liquid lines. Cap both refrigerant lines when opening the system to prevent the entry of dirt and moisture and the loss of refrigerant lubricant.

6. Remove the coolant overflow tube from the radiator.
7. Slide the radiator toward the drivers side and remove the condenser.

To install:

NOTE: If replacing the condenser or if the original condenser was flushed during service, add 1 fluid oz. (30 ml) of refrigerant lubricant to the system.

8. Install the condenser into position by sliding the radiator towards drivers side.
9. Install the coolant overflow tube to the radiator.
10. Install the condenser to the radiator screws.
11. Connect the condenser inlet and outlet lines.
12. Install the upper radiator panel and bolts.
13. Evacuate, recharge and leak test the air conditioning system.

Cavalier and 1995 Sunfire

1. Disconnect the negative battery cable.
2. Properly discharge the air conditioning system.
3. On 1993–94 models, remove the right and left headlight trim.
4. On 1995 models perform the following:
    - Remove hood latch from mounting plate.
    - Raise vehicle.
    - Disconnect forward SIR sensor harness.
    - Lower vehicle.
    - Remove right radiator mount.
    - Remove hood latch support bracket and forward sensor with harness.
5. On 1993–94 models, remove the center grille assembly.
6. Remove the right and left headlight housings.
7. Remove the hood bracket and latch assembly.
8. Disconnect the refrigerant lines from the condenser. Discard the O-rings.

NOTE: Use a back-up wrench on the condenser fittings when removing the high-pressure and liquid lines. Cap both refrigerant lines when opening the system to prevent the entry of dirt and moisture and the loss of refrigerant lubricant.

9. On 1993–94 models, remove the condenser air deflector shield.
10. Remove the condenser mounting brackets and the condenser.

To install:

NOTE: If replacing the condenser or if the original condenser was flushed during service, add 1 fluid oz. (30ml) of refrigerant lubricant to the system.

11. Install the condenser in the vehicle and install the brackets.
12. Install the condenser air deflector shield.
13. Install new O-rings on the refrigerant line fittings. Lubricate with refrigerant oil.
14. Connect the refrigerant lines to the condenser.

NOTE: Use a back-up wrench on the condenser fittings when tightening lines.

15. On 1995 models perform the following:
    - Install hood latch support bracket and forward sensor with harness.
    - Install right radiator mount.
    - Raise vehicle.
    - Connect forward SIR sensor harness.
    - Lower vehicle.
16. Install the hood latch and bracket assembly.
17. Install the left and right side headlight housings.
18. On 1993–94 models, install the center grille assembly.
19. On 1993–94 models, install the headlight trim.
20. Connect the negative battery cable.
21. Evacuate, recharge and leak test the air conditioning system.

Sunbird

1. Disconnect the negative battery cable.
2. Properly discharge the air conditioning system.
3. Remove hood latch assembly and cable from latch.
4. If equipped with flip-up headlights:
   - Remove the header filler panels and brackets.
   - Manually open the headlight doors by turning the headlight door actuator knob.
   - Remove the 4 retaining bolts from the headlight door actuators and pull the actuator assemblies forward as far as possible.
5. Remove the front end panel center brace.
6. Disconnect the refrigerant lines at the condenser. Discard the O-rings.

NOTE: Use a back-up wrench on the condenser fittings when removing the high-pressure and liquid lines. Cap both refrigerant lines when opening the system to prevent the entry of dirt and moisture and the loss of refrigerant lubricant.

7. Remove the condenser upper mounting brackets.
8. Remove the condenser.

To install:

NOTE: If replacing the condenser or if the original condenser was flushed during service, add 1 fluid oz. (30ml) of refrigerant lubricant to the system.

9. Install the condenser in the vehicle.
10. Install the condenser upper mounting brackets.
11. Replace the O-rings on the condenser refrigerant lines. Lubricate with refrigerant oil.
12. Connect the high pressure and liquid lines at the condenser.

NOTE: Use a back-up wrench on the condenser fittings when tightening lines.

13. With flip-up headlights:
    - Install the headlight door actuator assemblies and retaining bolts to the headlight mounting panel.
    - Manually close the headlight doors by turning the headlight door actuator knob.
    - Install the header filler panels and brackets.
14. Install the front end panel center brace.
15. Install the cable to latch and hood latch assembly.
16. Evacuate, recharge and leak test the air conditioning system.
17. Connect the negative battery cable.

Beretta and Corsica

1. Disconnect the negative battery cable.
2. If equipped, disable the Supplemental Inflatable Restraint (SIR) system by performing the following:
   - With wheels straight-ahead and ignition at **LOCK**,remove the SIR fuse from the fuse panel.
   - Remove the left side sound insulator.
   - Remove the Connector Positive Assurance (CPA) from the yellow 2-way SIR harness connector at the base of the steering column and separate the connector.
3. Properly discharge the air conditioning system.
4. Remove the radiator upper baffle, as required.
5. Remove the air cleaner assembly.
6. Remove the engine cooling fan.
7. If equipped with SIR, remove the forward discriminating sensor and set aside.

NOTE: Use a back-up wrench on the condenser fittings when removing the high-pressure and liquid lines. Cap the refrigerant lines when opening the system to prevent the entry of dirt and moisture and the loss of refrigerant lubricant.

8. On 1993 models, disconnect the evaporator tube from the condenser. Discard the O-ring.
9. Disconnect the compressor-to-condenser hose from the condenser inlet. Discard the O-ring.
10. On 1994 models, disconnect the R/D tube from condenser outlet.
11. Remove the screws attaching the condenser to the radiator.
12. Remove the bolts and radiator upper mounting brackets.
13. On 1994 models, pull the windshield washer bottle filler neck from the windshield washer bottle.
14. Remove the condenser from the vehicle by tipping the radiator toward the engine.

To install:

NOTE: If replacing the condenser or if the original condenser was flushed during service, add 1 fluid oz. (30ml) of refrigerant lubricant to the system.

15. Install the condenser into position by tipping the radiator toward the engine.
16. On 1994 models, install the filler neck to the windshield washer bottle.
17. Install the radiator upper mounting brackets and bolts.
18. Install the screws attaching the condenser to the radiator.
19. Install new O-rings on the condenser refrigerant line fittings. Lubricate with refrigerant oil.
20. Connect the refrigerant line to the condenser inlet.
21. On 1994 models, install the R/D tube to the condenser outlet.
22. On 1993 models, connect the evaporator tube-to-condenser outlet.

NOTE: Use a back-up wrench on the condenser fittings when tightening lines.

23. Install the forward discriminating sensor.
24. Install the engine cooling fan.
25. Install the air cleaner assembly.
26. If removed, install the upper radiator air baffle.
27. If equipped, enable the Supplemental Inflatable Restraint (SIR) system by performing the following:
    - Connect the yellow 2-way SIR connector and insert the Connect Positive Assurance (CPA) at the base of the steering column.
    - Install the left side sound insulator.
    - Install the SIR fuse in the fuse panel.
28. Evacuate, recharge and leak test the air conditioning system.
29. Connect the negative battery cable.
30. Fill cooling system and check for leaks. Start the engine and allow to come to normal operating temperature. Recheck for coolant leaks. Allow the engine to warm up sufficiently to confirm operation of cooling fan.

Achieva, Grand Am and Skylark

1. Disconnect the negative battery cable. Properly discharge the air conditioning system using recovery equipment.
2. Mark the position of the hood latch and remove the hood latch and the support assembly.
3. Disconnect the refrigerant inlet and outlet lines from the condenser. Immediately cap all openings to minimize contamination. Discard the O-rings.
4. Remove the radiator-to-condenser retaining bolts.
5. Lift the condenser and turn slightly to the left while removing.
6. If installing a replacement condenser, add 1.0 oz. of new refrigerant oil.

7. Installation is the reverse of the removal procedure. Evacuate, recharge and leak test the system.

LeMans

1. Disconnect the negative battery cable.
2. Properly discharge the air conditioning system.
3. Drain the engine coolant into a clean container for reuse.
4. Disconnect the lower coolant hose at the radiator.
5. Disconnect the upper coolant hose at the engine block.
6. If equipped, move the power steering reservoir toward the dash.
7. Remove the radiator.
8. Disconnect the coolant fan wire harness.
9. Disconnect the lower pressure cut-off switch connector.
10. Disconnect the condenser-to-evaporator line at the orifice tube.
11. Disconnect the compressor-to-accumulator hose at the accumulator.
12. Disconnect the condenser-to-compressor hose at the accumulator.

NOTE: Use a back-up wrench on the condenser fittings when removing the high-pressure and liquid lines. Discard the O-rings. Cap the refrigerant lines when opening the system to prevent the entry of dirt and moisture and the loss of refrigerant lubricant.

13. Remove the tube from the retaining clamp.
14. Remove the condenser attaching screws.
15. Remove the condenser.
16. Remove the condenser-to-orifice tube at the condenser.

To install:

NOTE: If replacing the condenser or if the original condenser was flushed during service, add 1 fluid oz. (30ml) of refrigerant lubricant to the system.

17. Install the condenser-to-orifice tube at the condenser.
18. install the condenser.
19. Install the attaching screws.
20. Install the tube to the retaining clamp.
21. Install the new O-rings to the refrigerant lines. Lubricate with refrigerant oil.
22. Connect the condenser-to-compressor hose at the condenser.

NOTE: Use a back-up wrench on the condenser fittings when tightening lines.

23. Connect the compressor-to-accumulator hose at the accumulator.
24. Connect the condenser-to-evaporator line at the orifice tube.
25. Connect the lower pressure cut-off switch connector.
26. Connect the coolant fan wire harness.
27. Install the radiator.
28. If equipped, reposition the power steering reservoir.
29. Connect the upper coolant hose at the engine block.
30. Connect the lower coolant hose at the radiator.
31. Evacuate, recharge and leak test the air conditioning system.
32. Connect the negative battery cable.
33. Fill cooling system and check for leaks. Start the engine and allow to come to normal operating temperature. Recheck for coolant leaks. Allow the engine to warm up sufficiently to confirm operation of cooling fan.

Cutlass Supreme, Grand Prix, Lumina, Monte Carlo and Regal

1993–94 EXCEPT 3.4L (VIN X)

1. Disconnect the negative battery cable.
2. Air cleaner assembly and duct.
3. Properly discharge the air conditioning system.
4. Remove the coolant reservoir, as required.
5. Remove the engine strut brace bolts from the upper tie bar and rotate the strut(s) and brace(s) rearward. In order to prevent shearing of the rubber bushing(s), loosen the bolt(s) on the engine strut(s) before swinging the strut(s).
6. Remove the air intake resonator mounting nut, as required.
7. Using back-up wrenches, disconnect the condenser refrigerant lines. Discard the O-rings. Cap all openings immediately to minimize contamination.
8. Remove the upper radiator mounting panel bolts and clamps, disconnect the electrical connector from fan(s), and remove the upper radiator mounting panel with the cooling fan(s) attached.
9. Tilt the radiator rearward while removing the condenser.

To install:

10. Install the condenser.
11. Install the upper radiator mounting panel with the fan(s) attached.
12. Connect the cooling fan(s) electrical connector(s).
13. Install the upper radiator mounting panel bolts and clamps.
14. Install new O-rings to the condenser refrigerant lines. Lubricate with refrigerant oil.
15. Using back-up wrenches, connect the condenser refrigerant lines.
16. If removed, install the air intake resonator mounting nut.
17. If removed, install the coolant recovery reservoir.
18. Swing the engine strut(s) into position.
19. Install the air cleaner assembly and duct.
20. Evacuate, recharge and leak test the air conditioning system.
21. Connect the negative battery cable.

1993–94 3.4L (VIN X)

1. Remove the radiator as described in this article.
2. Properly discharge the air conditioning system.
3. Using back-up wrenches, disconnect the refrigerant lines from the condenser. Cap all openings immediately. Discard the O-rings.
4. Raise the vehicle and disconnect the lower refrigerant line from the condenser. Cap all openings immediately. Discard the O-rings.
5. Lower the vehicle.
6. Remove the condenser.

To install:

7. Position the condenser. If replacing the condenser, add 1.0 oz. of new refrigerant oil to the unit.
8. Raise the vehicle and connect the lower refrigerant line to the condenser, using new O-rings.
9. Lower the vehicle and attach the upper refrigerant line to the condenser, using new O-rings.
10. Install the radiator.
11. Evacuate, recharge and leak test the system.

1995

1. Disconnect the negative battery cable.
2. Remove the air cleaner and duct assembly.
3. Properly discharge the air conditioning system.
4. Remove the radiator.
5. Remove the air condition lines at the condenser and compressor.

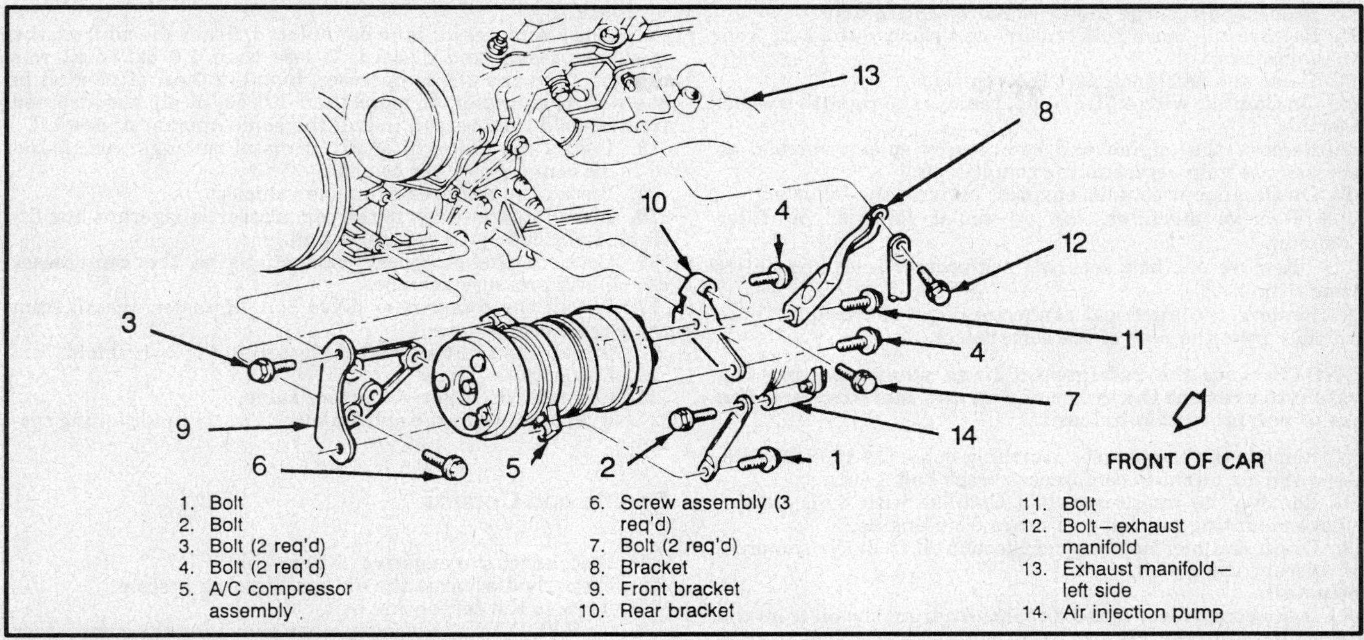

HR-6 compressor mounting—typical

6. Installation is the reverse of the removal procedure.

Compressor

REMOVAL AND INSTALLATION

Century, Cutlass Ciera and Cutlass Cruiser

1. Disconnect the negative battery cable. If necessary for access, remove the air cleaner/air intake system.
2. Disconnect the electrical connectors from the compressor.
3. Properly discharge the air conditioning system.
4. Remove the coupled hose assembly from the rear of the compressor. Discard the O-rings.

NOTE: Cap the refrigerant lines when opening the system to prevent the entry of dirt and moisture and the loss of refrigerant lubricant.

5. Raise and support the vehicle, remove the upper front pivot bolts and remove the splash shield, if required.
6. Release the drive belt tension and remove the belt from the compressor.
7. Remove the compressor attaching bolts. Remove the compressor.
8. Drain and measure the refrigerant oil from the compressor. Discard the old oil.

To install:

9. If the compressor is to be replaced, drain the oil from the new compressor and discard. If less than 1 oz. was drained from the old compressor, add 2 oz. of new oil to the new compressor. If more than 1 oz. was drained from the old compressor, add the same amount to the new compressor.
10. Position the compressor in the vehicle.
11. Install the compressor attaching bolts.
12. Reinstall splash shield and pivot bolts if removed.
13. Install new O-rings to the coupled hose assembly. Lubricate the O-rings with refrigerant oil.
14. Install the coupled hose assembly to the back of the compressor.
15. Install the drive belt. Connect the electrical connectors to the compressor.
16. Evacuate, recharge and leak test the system.
17. Connect negative battery cable.

Bonneville, Eighty-Eight, LeSabre, Ninety-Eight and Park Avenue

1. Disconnect the negative battery cable.
2. Properly discharge the air conditioning system.
3. Release the belt tension and remove the drive belt.
4. Disconnect the compressor electrical connector(s).
5. Remove the compressor pivot bolts.
6. Raise and safely support the vehicle if needed to access the splash shield(s) (compressor or radiator support).
7. Remove the splash shield(s) as required.
8. Remove the compressor adjusting bolts.
9. Remove the coupled hose assembly from the rear of the compressor. Discard the O-rings.

NOTE: Cap the refrigerant lines when opening the system to prevent the entry of dirt and moisture and the loss of refrigerant lubricant.

10. Remove the compressor from the vehicle.
11. Drain and measure the refrigerant oil from the compressor. Discard the old oil.

To install:

12. If the compressor is to be replaced, drain the oil from the new compressor and discard. Add new refrigerant oil equivalent to the amount that was drained from the compressor upon removal if more than 1 oz. If 1 oz. or less was drained, add 2 oz. to new compressor.
13. Position the compressor in the vehicle and install the mounting bolts.
14. Install new O-rings on the coupled hose assembly. Lubricate the O-rings with refrigerant oil.
15. Install the splash shield(s).
16. Lower the vehicle.
17. Install the compressor pivot bolts.
18. Connect the compressor electrical connector(s).
19. Connect the negative battery cable.
20. Evacuate, recharge and leak test the air conditioning system.

Aurora, Cadillac and Riviera

1. Disconnect the negative battery cable.
2. Disconnect the electrical connectors from the compressor.

3. Properly discharge the air conditioning system.
4. Release the drive belt tension and remove the belt from the compressor.
5. Raise and safely support the vehicle.
6. On Cadillac with 4.6L engine, remove the right tire/wheel assembly.
7. Remove the engine and compressor splash shields, as necessary, to gain access to the compressor.
8. On Cadillac with 4.6L engines, perform the following:
- Remove oil filter, the oil cooler lines at oil filter adapter.
- Remove one bolt securing compressor inlet and outlet line fitting.

9. Remove the electrical connector, then the coupled hose assembly from the rear of the compressor.

NOTE: Cap the refrigerant lines when opening the system to prevent the entry of dirt and moisture and the loss of refrigerant lubricant.

10. Remove the compressor attaching bolts. On 1993 DeVille, loosen the air pump-to-compressor brace bolt 1 turn.
11. Remove the compressor. On Cadillac with 4.6L engine, remove mounting bracket and brace from engine.
12. Drain and measure the refrigerant oil from the compressor. Discard the old oil.

To install:

13. If the compressor is to be replaced, drain the oil from the new compressor and discard. Add new refrigerant oil equivalent to the amount that was drained from the compressor upon removal.
14. Position the compressor in the vehicle.
15. Install the compressor attaching bolts.
16. Install new O-rings to the coupled hose assembly. Lubricate the O-rings with refrigerant oil.
17. Install the coupled hose assembly to the back of the compressor.
18. Install the engine and compressor splash shields. On Allante, install the front bumper valance.
19. Install oil filter, the oil cooler lines at oil filter adapter. On Cadillac with 4.6L engine, remove the bolt securing compressor inlet and outlet line fitting.
20. On Cadillac with 4.6L engines, install right tire and wheel assembly.
21. Lower the vehicle.
22. Install the drive belt.
23. Connect the electrical connectors to the compressor.
24. Evacuate, recharge and leak test the system.
25. Connect negative battery cable.

Cavalier, Sunfire and Sunbird

1. Disconnect the negative battery cable.
2. Properly discharge the air conditioning system.
3. Remove the compressor drive belt.
4. Raise and safely support the vehicle.
5. Remove the right side air deflector and splash shield.
6. Disconnect the electrical connections at the compressor switches.
7. Remove the compressor/condenser hose assembly at the rear of the compressor and discard the O-rings.

NOTE: Cap the refrigerant lines when opening the system to prevent the entry of dirt and moisture and the loss of refrigerant lubricant.

8. Remove the compressor attaching bolts.
9. Remove the compressor.
10. Drain and measure the refrigerant oil from the compressor. Discard the old oil.
11. On 1994 Cavalier only, remove the expansion tube. Inspect the tube for contamination or metal cuttings and clean or replace as necessary.

To install:

12. If the compressor is to be replaced, drain the oil from the new compressor and discard. If less than 1.0 oz. of oil was drained from the old compressor, install 2.0 oz. of new oil in the new compressor. If more than 1.0 oz. of oil was drained from the old compressor, install the same amount of new oil.
13. Install the inline filter kit, if metal cuttings were found or if the compressor was seized.
14. Install the compressor in the vehicle.
15. Install new O-rings to the compressor refrigerant line fittings. Lubricate with refrigerant oil.
16. Connect the electrical connections to the compressor clutch and pressure switches.
17. Install the compressor drive belt. If easier, install from the engine compartment.
18. Install the right side air deflector and splash shield.
19. Lower the vehicle.
20. Connect the negative battery cable.
21. Evacuate, recharge and leak test the air conditioning system.

Beretta and Corsica

1. Disconnect the negative battery cable.
2. Properly discharge the air conditioning system.
3. Remove the serpentine belt.
4. On 2.3L (VIN A) vehicles, when removing the compressor for the first time only, perform the following:
- Remove the oil filter (1993 only).
- Remove the stud from the rear of the compressor and discard.

5. Raise and safely support the vehicle.
6. On all except 1993 2.3L, remove the right side lower splash shield.
7. On 1993 2.3L (VIN A), remove the right front tire/wheel assembly and the engine splash shield. Now remove the serpentine belt.
8. Disconnect the compressor electrical connector. Remove the bolt attaching the compressor refrigerant line assembly and disconnect the refrigerant line. Discard the O-rings.

NOTE: Cap the refrigerant lines when opening the system to prevent the entry of dirt and moisture and the loss of refrigerant lubricant.

9. Remove the compressor mounting bolts.
10. Remove the compressor.
11. Drain and measure the refrigerant oil from the compressor. Discard the old oil.

To install:

12. If the compressor is to be replaced, drain the oil from the new compressor and discard. If less than 1.0 oz. of oil was drained from the old compressor, add 2.0 oz. of new oil to the new compressor. If more than 1.0 oz. was drained, add the same amount of new oil to the new compressor.
13. Install the compressor in the vehicle.
14. Install the compressor mounting bolts.
15. Install new O-rings to the compressor refrigerant line fittings. Lubricate with refrigerant oil.
16. Install the bolt attaching the compressor refrigerant line assembly.
17. Connect the compressor electrical connector.
18. Install the right side lower splash shield and wheel/tire assembly as removed..
19. Lower the vehicle.
20. Install the serpentine belt.
21. Evacuate, recharge and leak test the air conditioning system.
22. Connect the negative battery cable.

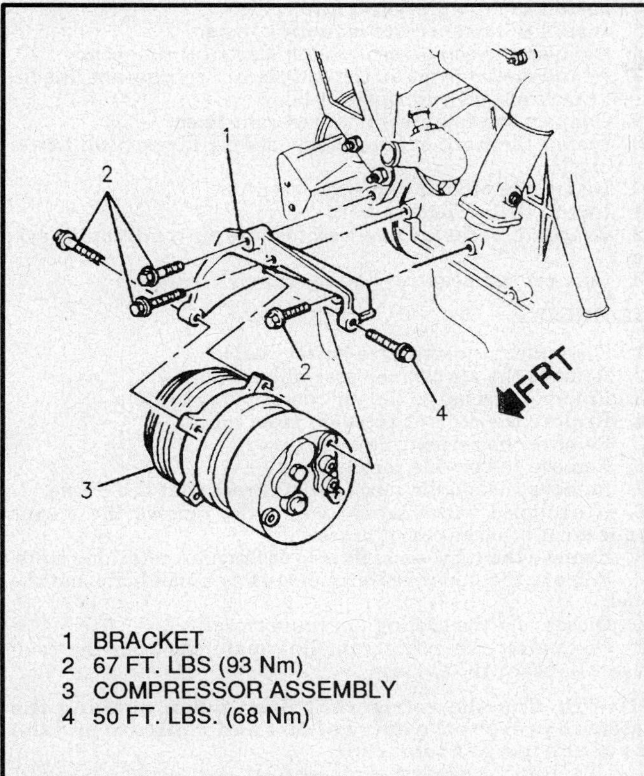

Compressor mounting—2.2L engine

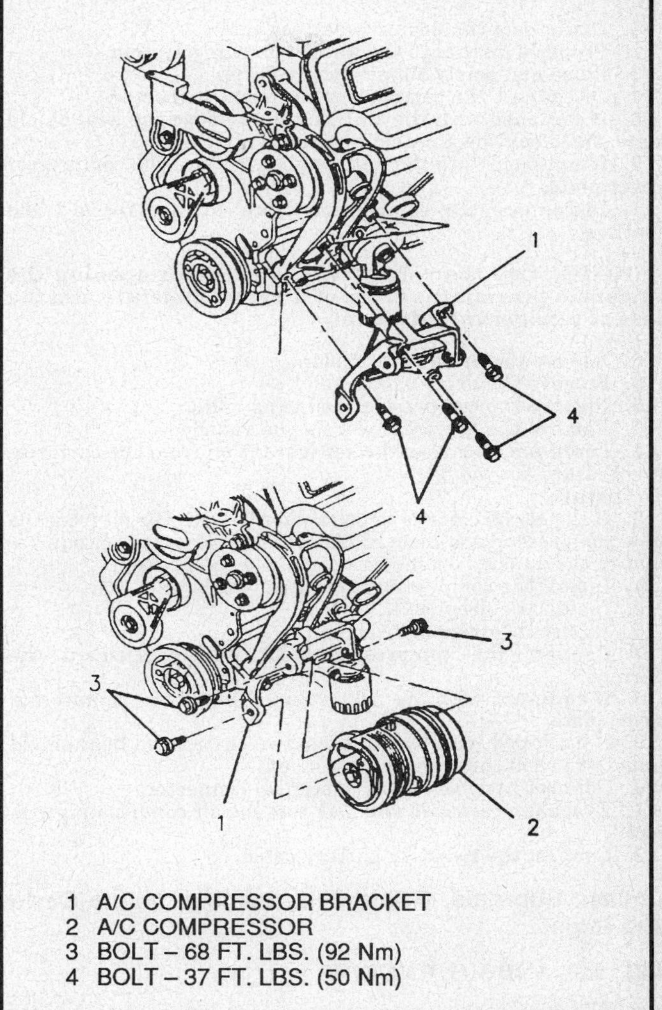

Compressor mounting—3.1L engine

Achieva, Grand Am and Skylark

1. Disconnect the negative battery cable.
2. Properly discharge the air conditioning system.
3. If equipped with the 2.3L engine, when removing the compressor for the first time only, perform the following:
   - Remove the oil filter.
   - Using a 7mm socket, remove the stud in the back of the compressor.
   - Discard the stud.
   - Install the oil filter.

4. If equipped with the 2.0L, 3.1L or 3.3L engine, remove the serpentine belt.
5. Raise and safely support the vehicle.
6. Remove the right side splash shield.
7. If equipped with the 3.3L engine, remove the lower support bracket. Lower the vehicle.
8. If equipped with the 2.3L or 2.5L engine, remove the serpentine belt.
9. Disconnect the compressor electrical connector.
10. Remove the refrigerant line assembly from the back of the compressor. Discard the O-rings.

NOTE: Cap the refrigerant lines when opening the system to prevent the entry of dirt and moisture and the loss of refrigerant lubricant.

11. Remove the compressor attaching bolts.
12. Remove the compressor.
13. Drain and measure the refrigerant oil from the compressor. Discard the old oil.

To install:

14. If the compressor is to be replaced, drain the oil from the new compressor and discard. If less than 1.0 oz. of oil was drained from the old compressor, add 2.0 oz. of new oil to the new compressor. If more than 1.0 oz. of oil was drained from the old compressor, add the same amount to the new compressor.
15. Install the compressor and attaching bolts.
16. Install new O-rings to the compressor refrigerant lines. Lubricate with refrigerant oil.
17. Install the refrigerant line assembly to the back of the compressor.
18. Connect the compressor electrical connector.
19. If equipped with the 2.3L or 2.5L engine, install the serpentine belt.
20. If equipped with the 3.3L engine, raise and safely support the vehicle. Install the lower support bracket.
21. Install the right side splash shield.
22. Lower the vehicle.
23. If equipped with the 2.0L or 3.3L engine, install the serpentine belt.
24. Evacuate, recharge and leak test the air conditioning system.
25. Connect the negative battery cable.

LeMans

1. Disconnect the negative battery cable.
2. Properly discharge the air conditioning system.
3. Raise and safely support the vehicle.
4. Disconnect the compressor electrical connector.
5. If equipped with the 1.6L engine, remove the heat shield nuts, strut bolt, heat shield and strut.
6. If equipped with the 2.0L engine, remove the compressor cover plate.
7. Disconnect the compressor block fitting. Discard the O-rings.

NOTE: Cap the refrigerant lines when opening the system to prevent the entry of dirt and moisture and the loss of refrigerant lubricant.

8. Relieve the drive belt tension.
9. Remove the drive belt.
10. Remove the compressor mounting bolts.
11. Remove the compressor from the vehicle.
12. Drain and measure the refrigerant oil from the compressor. Discard the old oil.

To install:

13. If the compressor is to be replaced, drain the oil from the new compressor and discard. Add new refrigerant oil equivalent to the amount drained from the old compressor.
14. Install the compressor and mounting bolts.
15. Install the drive belt.
16. Adjust the drive belt tension.
17. Connect the compressor block fitting. Discard the O-rings.
18. If equipped with the 2.0L engine, install the compressor cover plate.
19. If equipped with the 1.6L engine, install the heat shield nuts, strut bolt, heat shield and strut.
20. Connect the compressor electrical connector.
21. Evacuate, recharge and leak test the air conditioning system.
22. Connect the negative battery cable.

Cutlass Supreme, Grand Prix, Lumina, Monte Carlo and Regal

2.3L, 2.5L AND 3.1L ENGINES

1. Disconnect the negative battery cable.
2. Properly discharge the air conditioning system.
3. Remove the serpentine belt.
4. On 1994–95 models, remove the air cleaner and duct assembly.
5. Remove the coolant recovery reservoir.
6. On 1994–95 models, raise the vehicle and suitably support. Remove the right engine splash shield.
7. Disconnect the refrigerant hose assembly from the compressor. Discard the O-rings.

NOTE: Cap the refrigerant lines when opening the system to prevent the entry of dirt and moisture and the loss of refrigerant lubricant.

8. Disconnect the compressor clutch electrical connector.
9. Remove the compressor mounting bolts.
10. Remove the compressor. Remove bracket if necessary.
11. Drain and measure the refrigerant oil from the compressor. Discard the old oil.

To install:

12. If the compressor is to be replaced, drain the oil from the new compressor and discard. If less than 1.0 oz. was drained from the old compressor, add 2.0 oz. of new refrigerant oil to the new compressor. If more than 1.0 oz. was drained from the old unit, add new refrigerant oil equivalent to the amount drained from the old compressor.
13. Install the compressor and attaching bolts.
14. Install the compressor in the vehicle.
15. Install the compressor mounting bolts.
16. Connect the compressor clutch electrical connector.
17. Install new O-rings on the compressor refrigerant line fittings. Lubricate with refrigerant oil.
18. Connect the compressor refrigerant lines.
19. Install the right engine splash shield, if removed. Lower the vehicle.
20. Install the coolant recovery reservoir.
21. Install the serpentine belt.
22. Evacuate, recharge and leak test the air conditioning system.
23. Connect the negative battery cable.

3.4L ENGINE

1. Disconnect the negative battery cable.
2. Remove the air cleaner assembly.
3. Properly discharge the air conditioning system.
4. Remove the coolant recovery reservoir.
5. Remove the serpentine belt.
6. Remove the engine torque strut.
7. Remove the engine torque strut bracket at the frame.
8. If equipped with manual transaxle, remove the engine torque strut bracket pencil brace.
9. Remove the right and left side cooling fan retaining bolts.
10. Remove the upper radiator mounting panel bolts and the panel.
11. Disconnect the cooling fan connectors.
12. Disconnect the refrigerant line manifold from the compressor. Discard the O-rings.

NOTE: Cap the refrigerant lines when opening the system to prevent the entry of dirt and moisture and the loss of refrigerant lubricant.

13. Disconnect the compressor electrical connector.
14. Remove the compressor retaining bolts.
15. Remove the compressor from the vehicle.
16. Drain and measure the refrigerant oil from the compressor. Discard the old oil.

To install:

17. If the compressor is to be replaced, drain the oil from the new compressor and discard. Add 2.0 oz. of new refrigerant oil to the new compressor if the amount drained from the old unit was less than 1.0 oz. If more than 1.0 oz., add the same amount as drained from the old compressor.
18. Install the compressor and attaching bolts.
19. Install the compressor in the vehicle.
20. Install the compressor retaining bolts.
21. Connect the compressor electrical connector.
22. Install new O-rings on the compressor refrigerant lines. Lubricate with refrigerant oil.
23. Connect the compressor manifold.
24. Connect the cooling fan connectors.
25. Install the upper radiator mounting panel bolts and the panel.
26. Install the right and left side cooling fan retaining bolts.
27. If equipped with manual transaxle, install the engine torque strut bracket pencil brace.
28. Install the engine torque strut bracket at the frame.
29. Install the engine torque strut.
30. Install the serpentine belt.
31. Install the coolant recovery reservoir.
32. Evacuate, recharge and leak test the air conditioning system.
33. Install the air cleaner assembly.
34. Connect the negative battery cable.

3.8L ENGINE

1. Disconnect the negative battery cable. Properly discharge the air conditioning system.
2. On some models it may require removing the right cooling fan electrical connector and the coolant recovery reservoir and positioning aside.

3. Remove the heat shield, then remove the electrical connectors at the compressor.
4. Raise the vehicle and remove the compressor front upper pivot bolts.
5. Remove the splash shield. Remove the oil cooler pipe retaining bolts.
6. Remove the serpentine belt.
7. Properly disconnect the couple hose assembly from the rear of the compressor.
8. Remove the compressor and bracket (if necessary). Drain and measure the oil from the compressor.

To install:

9. Install the compressor. If a replacement compressor is installed, add drain the oil from the replacement unit. If the amount drained from the old compressor was less than 1.0 oz., add 2.0 oz. to the new unit. If more than 1.0 oz. was drained from the old compressor, add the same amount to the new compressor.
10. Reconnect the refrigerant line connections to the rear of the compressor, using new O-rings.
11. Install the right cooling fan electrical connector and coolant recovery reservoir, if removed.
12. Install the serpentine belt, the oil cooler pipe bolts and the splash shield. Install the front upper pivot bolts.
13. Lower the vehicle. Attach the wiring to the compressor and install the heat shield.
14. Evacuate, recharge and leak test.

Accumulator/Receiver Dehydrator

NOTE: The accumulator should only be replaced if it is damaged and leaking, or if the system has been open (collision damage, removed parts, etc.) for an extended period of time.

REMOVAL AND INSTALLATION

1. Disconnect the negative battery cable.
2. Properly discharge the air conditioning system. On some models the coolant reservoir or air cleaner/air intake assembly removal may be needed for access to the accumulator.
3. If equipped, remove the right rear engine compartment sight shield.
4. On 1994 models with a Receiver Dehydrator (R/D) perform the following:
   - Raise the vehicle.
   - Remove the right front tire/wheel.
   - Partially remove the splash shield.
5. Disconnect the low-pressure lines at the inlet and outlet fittings on the R/D or accumulator.

NOTE: On some models, it is necessary to raise the vehicle to disconnect the refrigerant tube from the accumulator inlet.

Cap the refrigerant lines when opening the system to prevent the entry of dirt and moisture and the loss of refrigerant lubricant.

6. Remove the cruise control stepper motor bracket, and position aside. (if equipped)
7. On 1995 Aurora and Riviera, remove the underhood relay center and passenger side wheel house liner.
8. Disconnect the pressure cycling switch connection as required.
9. Loosen the lower strap bolt and spread the strap. Turn the R/D or accumulator and remove.
10. Drain and measure the oil in the R/D or the accumulator. Discard the old oil.

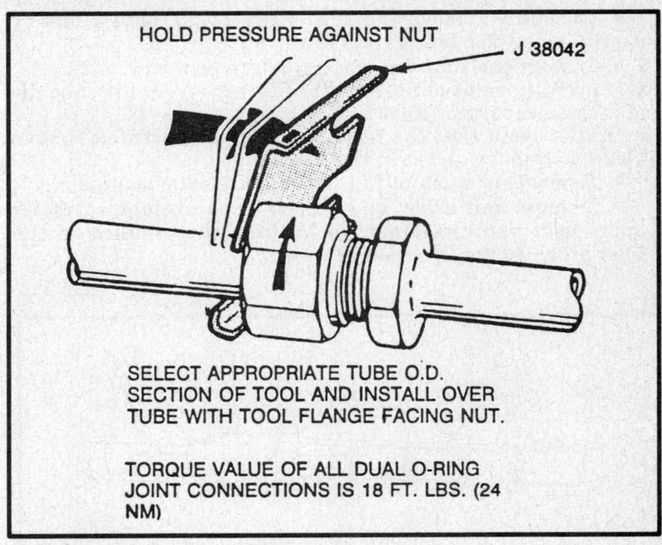

HOLD PRESSURE AGAINST NUT
J 38042
SELECT APPROPRIATE TUBE O.D. SECTION OF TOOL AND INSTALL OVER TUBE WITH TOOL FLANGE FACING NUT.
TORQUE VALUE OF ALL DUAL O-RING JOINT CONNECTIONS IS 18 FT. LBS. (24 NM)

Dual O-ring joint and tool

To install:

11. Add new oil equivalent to the amount drained from the old accumulator. Add an additional 2–3 oz. (60–90 ml) (1 oz. for the R-134a system) (3.5 oz. for the R/D) of oil to compensate for the oil retained by the accumulator desiccant.
12. Position the R/D or accumulator in the securing bracket and tighten the clamp bolt.
13. Install the cruise control stepper motor bracket. (if equipped)
14. Install new O-rings at the inlet and outlet connections on the accumulator. Lubricate the O-rings with refrigerant oil.
15. Connect the low-pressure inlet and outlet lines. Install the air cleaner or sight shield as removed.
16. On 1994 models with an R/D, perform the following:
   - Install the splash shield.
   - Install the tire/wheel.
   - Lower the vehicle.
17. Install the underhood relay center and passenger side wheel house liner.
18. Evacuate, charge and leak test the system.
19. Connect the negative battery cable.

Fixed Orifice Tube

REMOVAL AND INSTALLATION

NOTE: Different designs and colors or orifice tubes may have been used in past production vehicles. When replacing an orifice tube, compare its design to the replacement part for correct orifice tube selection. The different styles of orifice tubes are not interchangeable.

1. Properly discharge the air conditioning system. Remove components (coolant reservoir, etc.) required for access to lines and fittings.
2. Loosen the fitting at the liquid line outlet on the condenser or evaporator inlet pipe and disconnect. Discard the O-ring.
3. Removal of the air cleaner and duct assembly may be required on some models.

NOTE: Use a back-up wrench on the condenser outlet fitting when loosening the lines.

4. Perform the following:
   - Loosen the nut and separate the front evaporator tube from the rear evaporator tube near the compressor to gain access to the expansion tube. Remove A/C line clips, if required.

- Carefully remove the tube with needle-nose pliers or special tool J-26549C, D or 89.
- Inspect the tube for contamination or metal cuttings.

5. Carefully, remove the fixed orifice tube from the tube fitting in the evaporator inlet line.
6. In the event that the restricted or plugged orifice tube is difficult to remove, perform the following:

- Remove as much of the impacted residue as possible.
- Using a hair dryer, epoxy drier or equivalent, carefully apply heat approximately 1/4 in. from the dimples on the inlet pipe. Do not overheat the pipe.

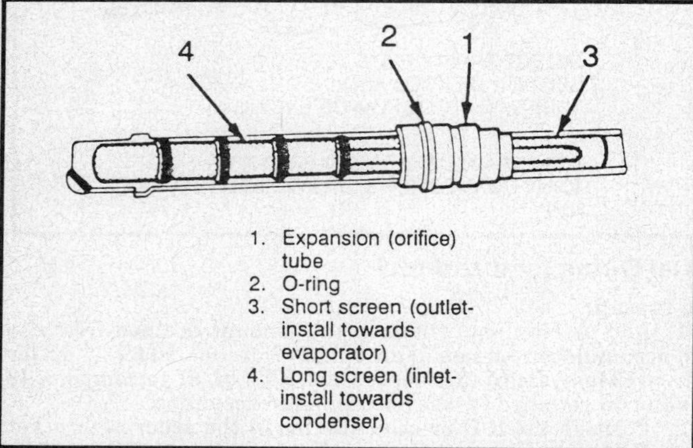

Orifice tube

NOTE: If the system has a pressure switch near the orifice tube, it should be removed prior to heating the pipe to avoid damage to the switch.

- While applying heat, use special tool J 26549-C or equivalent to grip the orifice tube. Use a turning motion along with a push-pull motion to loosen the impacted orifice tube and remove it.

7. Swab the inside of the evaporator inlet pipe with R-11 to remove any remaining residue.

To install:

8. Add 1 oz. of 525 viscosity refrigerant oil to the system.
9. Lubricate the new O-ring and orifice tube with refrigerant oil and insert into the inlet pipe.

NOTE: Ensure that the new orifice tube is inserted in the inlet tube with the smaller screen end first.

10. Connect the evaporator inlet pipe with the condenser outlet fitting. Install air cleaner and duct assembly if removed.

NOTE: Use a back-up wrench on the condenser outlet fitting when tightening the lines.

11. Evacuate, recharge and leak test the system.

Receiver/Drier

REMOVAL AND INSTALLATION

1993 Beretta, Corsica, Achieva, Grand Am and Skylark

1. Disconnect the negative battery cable. Properly discharge the air conditioning system using recovery equipment.
2. Raise the vehicle and remove the right front tire/wheel assembly.
3. Partially remove the splash shield, then disconnect both refrigerant lines from the receiver/drier. Discard the O-rings and cap all openings immediately to minimize contamination.
4. Remove the receiver/drier from the vehicle.
5. If replacing the receiver/drier, add 3.5 oz. of new oil to the replacement unit.
6. Installation is the reverse of the removal procedure. Use new O-rings at all connections. Evacuate, recharge and leak test the system.

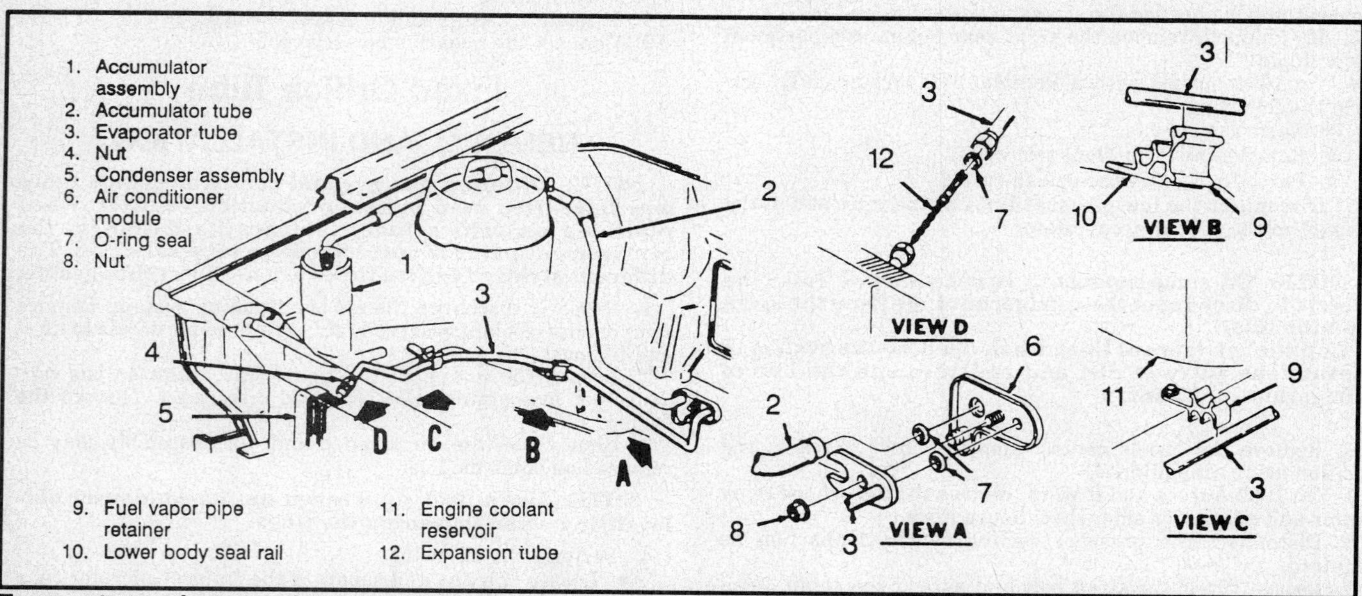

Evaporator and accumulator tube installation—2.0L engine (VIN K)

Thermal Expansion Valve

REMOVAL AND INSTALLATION

1993 Beretta, Corsica, Achieva, Grand Am and Skylark

1. Disconnect the negative battery cable. Disable the SIR system.
2. Properly discharge the air conditioning system using recovery equipment.
3. Remove the right side under dash insulator panel.
4. Remove the electrical junction box at the heater housing.
5. Remove the left side under dash insulator panel and the steering column filler panel.
6. Partially remove the center console, if equipped, and remove the floor duct.

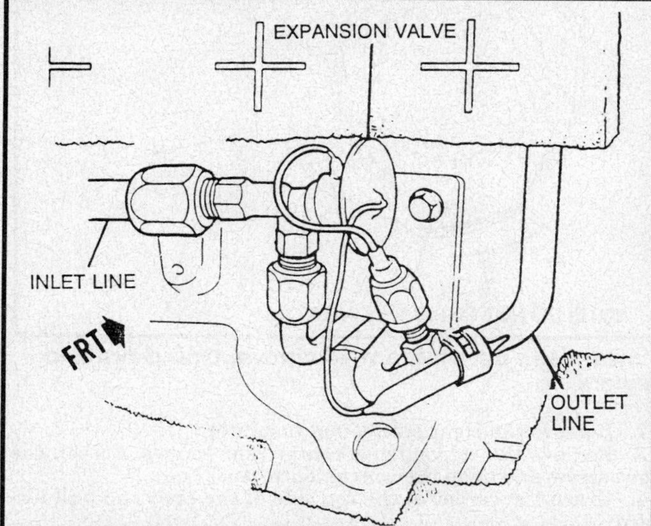

Expansion valve location—Beretta and Corsica

7. Remove the heater core cover, core shroud and straps.

NOTE: The heater core is now suspended by the pipes. Do not put any downward pressure or the pipes will be damaged.

8. Remove the insulation tape, disconnect the fittings and remove the expansion valve.

To install:

9. Install the expansion valve and recover with insulation.
10. Install the heater core straps, shroud and cover.
11. Install the floor ducts, then reattach the center console.
12. Install the instrument panels and electrical junction box as removed.
13. Evacuate, recharge and leak test the system. Enable the SIR system as described in this article.

1994–95 Beretta, Corsica, Achieva, Grand Am and Skylark

1. Disable the SIR.
2. Properly discharge the air condition system.
3. Disconnect the negative battery cable.
4. Remove the right side under dash insulator panel, and electrical junction box at the heater core cover.
5. Remove the left side insulator panel, and steering column filler.
6. Partially remove the shift console, if equipped, to gain access to the floor duct and heater core cover.
7. Remove the floor duct, the heater core cover, the heater core shroud and the straps.

NOTE: The heater core will be suspended by the heater core pipes at this point. Do not apply any downward pressure on the core, otherwise damage may occur to the heater core pipes.

8. Remove the insulation tape from the valve fittings.
9. Remove the thermal expansion valve.

NOTE: Clean all insulation tape from evaporator fittings to insure correct seating/torque of O-rings.

To install:

10. Install the thermal expansion valve (including installation of the new insulation wrap).
11. Install the heater core shroud, straps and heater core cover.

NOTE: The fittings on the Thermal Expansion Valve should be leak checked before finishing re-assembly. This can be done without running vehicle.

- Evacuate and partially recharge the A/C system with 1 lb. (0.48 kg) R-134a.
- Leak test.

12. Install the floor duct, steering column filler, left side insulation panel and electrical junction box to the heater core cover.
13. Install the right side insulation panel and console.
14. Enable the SIR system.
15. Complete charging the system, and leak test.

Blower Motor

REMOVAL AND INSTALLATION

Century, Cutlass Ciera and Cutlass Cruiser

1. Disconnect the negative battery cable.
2. On 3.1L engine, loosen and rotate the alternator away from the blower motor for clearance.
3. On 2.2L engine, remove the air inlet resonator, then detach the strut from the engine and carefully rotate it forward.
4. On models with 3.1L and 3100 engines, perform the following:
   - Drain the cooling system (3.1L engine).
   - Remove the serpentine drive belt.
   - Remove the rear power steering pump bracket (3.1L engine).
   - Detach and plug the heater hose from the coolant pump pipe (3.1L engine).
   - Remove the power steering pump bolts and position it out of the way (3.1L engine).
5. Detach the blower motor electrical connectors. Remove the air vent tube.
6. Remove the blower motor screws and take out the motor assembly.
7. Installation is the reverse of the removal procedure.

Beretta, Corsica, Bonneville, Eighty-Eight, LeSabre, Ninety-Eight, Park Avenue and LeMans

1. Disconnect the negative battery cable. Remove the cross brace bar, if equipped.
2. On 1994–95 Beretta and Corsica with 3.1L, remove the alternator and serpentine belt.
3. Disconnect the electrical connections at the blower motor. Remove the blower motor air tube.

4. Remove the bolts attaching the blower motor to the evaporator case or the heater and A/C module assembly.
5. Remove the blower motor.

NOTE: On some engines it may be necessary to rotate the alternator away in order to completely remove the blower motor.

To install:
6. Position the blower motor in the evaporator case and install the attaching bolts.
7. Connect the electrical connectors at the blower motor.
8. On 1994 Beretta and Corsica with 3.1L, install the alternator and serpentine belt.
9. Install the alternator or cross brace bar, if removed. Connect the negative battery cable.

Aurora, Cadillac and Riviera

1. Disconnect the negative battery cable.
2. Remove the cowl cross-tower brace (2 nuts each).
3. On 1995 Aurora and Riviera, remove the right sound insulator.
4. Remove the relay center bracket and, on 1993 Eldorado and Seville, remove the MAP sensor mounting bracket. Position brackets out of the way with components attached.
5. With utility knife cut rubber insulator at guide lines and remove metal patch plate beneath (1994–95 Cadillacs).
6. Remove the blower motor electrical connector, cooling hose and mounting screws. Remove the blower assembly. On Eldorado and Seville, tilt the motor in the case and detach the fan from the motor.
7. Installation is the reverse of the removal procedure.

Cavalier, Sunfire and Sunbird

1. Disconnect the negative battery cable.
2. Remove right sound insulator (1995 Cavalier and Sunfire).
3. On 3.1L, remove tower-to-tower brace, remove the generator belt and remove or set aside the generator.
4. Detach the electrical connections from the blower motor. Remove the blower motor retaining screws and remove the blower motor.
5. Remove the nut from the blower motor shaft, while holding the blower motor cage (1993 models).
6. Remove the cage from the blower motor shaft (1993 models).

To install:
7. Install the cage to the blower motor shaft (1993 models).
8. Install the nut to the blower motor shaft, while holding the cage (1993 models).
9. Install the blower motor and retaining screw.
10. Connect the blower motor electrical connections at the blower motor.
11. On 3.1L, install the generator, generator belt and brace, as removed.
12. Install right sound insulator (1995 Cavalier and Sunfire).
13. Connect the negative battery cable.

Achieva, Grand Am and Skylark

1. Disconnect the negative battery cable.
2. On 3.3L, remove the power steering pump mounting bolts and set the pump aside without detaching its hoses.
3. On 3.1L engine, remove generator belt and set aside the generator.
4. Remove the electrical connector from the blower. Partially cut the blower case as indicated on the cover (case is 1/8 inch thick–do not cut too deep).
5. Swing the cut out portion of the cover down and remove the blower cooling tube.
6. Remove the blower motor screws and remove the motor.

To install:
7. Position and secure the blower motor in place. Install the cooling tube.
8. Position and install the blower motor cover using retaining clips.
9. Attach the electrical connector. Locate and install the power steering pump mounting bolts (3.3L engine).
10. Attach the battery cable.

Cutlass Supreme, Grand Prix, Lumina, Monte Carlo and Regal

1. Disconnect the negative battery cable.

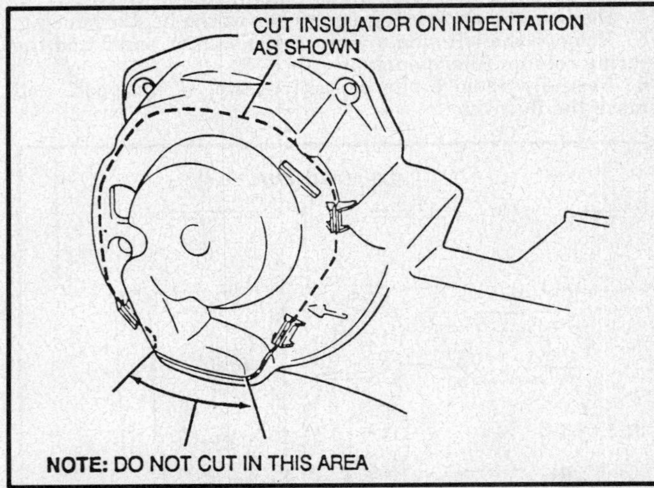
CUT INSULATOR ON INDENTATION AS SHOWN
NOTE: DO NOT CUT IN THIS AREA

Blower case cut diagram—Achieva, Grand Am and Skylark

2. Remove the right side sound insulator.
3. Remove the convenience center rear screws. Loosen the front screw and slide the convenience center out.
4. Grasp the carpet at the top side of the cowl and pull forward.
5. Disconnect the blower motor electrical connection.
6. Disconnect the harness from the clip.
7. Remove the blower motor mounting screws.
8. Remove the blower motor.

To install:
9. Install the blower motor.
10. Connect the harness clip.
11. Connect the blower motor electrical connector.
12. Replace the carpet at the cowl.
13. Place the convenience center into position. Install the front and rear screws.
14. Install the right side lower insulator panel.
15. Connect the negative battery cable.

Blower Motor Resistor/Power Module

REMOVAL AND INSTALLATION

Bonneville, Eighty-Eight, LeSabre, Ninety-Eight and Park Avenue

1. Disconnect the negative battery cable.
2. Remove the rear engine sight shield.
3. Remove the center bolt and positive battery cable from the multi-use relay and fuse bracket.
4. Remove the underhood fuse blocks and relays from the bracket and position aside.
5. Detach the multi-use relay and fuse bracket from the firewall.

6. Disconnect the blower resistor/control module wiring.
7. Remove the blower resistor/control module screws and remove the blower resistor/control module from the blower housing.
8. Installation is the reverse of the removal procedure.

Except Bonneville, Eighty-Eight, LeSabre, Ninety-Eight and Park Avenue

1. Disconnect the negative battery cable.
2. On 1995 Cavalier and Sunfire perform the following:
   - Remove right sound insulator.
   - Remove the blower motor.
   - Cut portion of dash mat to gain access to the rear resistor screw.
3. On DeVille, remove and position aside the multi-use fuse blocks and relays.
4. On 1994–95 Cutlass Supreme, Grand Prix, Lumina, Regal, and Monte Carlo, remove the right lower instrument panel insulator panel.
5. Disconnect the electrical connector at the resistor. Remove the resistor attaching screws.
6. Remove the resistor from the evaporator case or module.

To install:

7. Position the resistor in the evaporator case or module. Install the attaching screws.
8. Connect the electrical connector.
9. On 1995 Cavalier and Sunfire perform the following:
   - Install the blower motor.
   - Install the right sound insulator.
10. On 1994–95 Cutlass Supreme, Grand Prix, Lumina, Monte Carlo and Regal, install the right lower instrument panel insulator panel.
11. Connect the negative battery cable.

Heater Core

REMOVAL AND INSTALLATION

CAUTION

Some vehicles are equipped with the Supplemental Inflatable Restraint or air bag system. The air bag system must be disabled before performing service on or around the air bag, instrument panel components, wiring and sensors. Failure to follow safety and disabling procedures could result in accidental air bag deployment, possible personal injury and unnecessary air bag system repairs. Refer to "Supplemental Inflatable Restraint" in this article.

Century, Cutlass Ciera and Cutlass Cruiser

1. Disconnect the negative battery cable.
2. Drain the cooling system.
3. Disconnect the heater hoses from the heater core inlet and outlet connections in the engine compartment.
4. Blow residual coolant from the heater core using compressed air.
5. Working inside the vehicle, remove the lower instrument panel sound insulator panel (1993 models).
6. Remove the heater floor outlet duct screws or clips and remove the duct (1993 models).
7. Remove the heater core cover by removing the attaching screws and clips.
8. Remove the heater core cover.
9. Remove the heater core retaining straps and remove the heater core.

To install:

10. Position the heater core in the housing and install the retaining straps.
11. Position the heater core cover on the housing and install the attaching screws and clips.
12. Install the floor outlet duct and attaching screws or clips (1993 models).
13. Install the lower instrument panel sound insulator panel (1993 models).
14. Working in the engine compartment, connect the heater core inlet and outlet hoses.
15. Fill the cooling system.
16. Start the engine and check for coolant leaks. Allow the engine to warm up sufficiently to confirm the proper operation of the heater. Recheck for leaks. Top-up coolant.

Bonneville, Eighty-Eight, LeSabre, Ninety-Eight and Park Avenue

1. Disconnect the negative battery cable. Properly drain the cooling system.
2. On 1993 models, if equipped, disable the Supplemental Inflatable Restraint (SIR) system by performing the following:
   - Set wheels straight ahead, turn ignition to **LOCK**. Remove the SIR fuse from the fuse panel.
   - Remove the left side sound insulator. Remove the right sound insulator if needed, detaching electrical components and light bulbs during removal.
   - Remove the Connector Positive Assurance (CPA) from the yellow 2-way SIR harness connector at the base of the steering column and separate the connector.
3. Detach and plug the heater hoses from the core tubes.
4. Remove the A/C programmer (Dual A/C) or the air mix valve actuator (Automatic A/C) or the A/C solenoid switch assembly (Electronic A/C).
5. Remove the heater cover, then remove the heater core.
6. Installation is the reverse of the removal procedure. Enable the SIR system, if applicable. Refill the cooling system.

Aurora, Cadillac and Riviera

1. Disconnect the negative battery cable. Drain the cooling system into a clean container for reuse.
2. If equipped, disable the Supplemental Inflatable Restraint (SIR) system by performing the following:
   - With the wheels straight ahead, turn the ignition to **LOCK**. Remove the SIR fuse from the fuse panel.
   - Remove the left side sound insulator.
   - Remove the Connector Positive Assurance (CPA) from the yellow 2-way SIR harness connector at the base of the steering column and separate the connector.
3. On 1993 Riviera and Cadillacs, remove the console, instrument panel and right side sound insulator panel, as required.
4. On 1995 Aurora and Riviera, remove the right and left sound insulators.
5. Remove the programmer and electrical connectors. Remove the Body Control Module (BCM) electrical connectors. Remove the BCM and mounting bracket (Except 1995 Aurora and Riviera).
6. Remove the Power (engine) Control Module (PCM) electrical connectors. Remove the PCM and mounting bracket.
7. Remove the heater core housing.
8. Disconnect the inlet and outlet hoses from the heater core.
9. Remove the heater core retaining screws.
10. Remove the heater core from the vehicle.

To install:

11. Install the heater core in the vehicle.
12. Connect the inlet and outlet hoses from the heater core.
13. Install the retaining screws.
14. Install the PCM (ECM) and mounting bracket. Install the PCM (ECM) electrical connectors.
15. Install the BCM and mounting bracket. Install the BCM electrical connectors.
16. Install the programmer and electrical connectors.
17. Install the console, instrument panel and right side sound insulator panel.
18. Connect the negative battery cable.

19. If equipped, enable the Supplemental Inflatable Restraint (SIR) system by performing the following:

- Connect the yellow 2-way SIR connector and insert the Connect Positive Assurance (CPA) at the base of the steering column.
- Install the left side sound insulator.
- Install the SIR fuse in the fuse panel. Turn ignition to **ON**. Warning light will flash 7–9 times to signal the system is armed.

20. Fill cooling system and check for leaks. Start the engine and allow to come to normal operating temperature. Recheck for coolant leaks. Allow the engine to warm up sufficiently to confirm operation of cooling fan.

Cavalier, Sunfire and Sunbird

1. Disconnect the negative battery cable.
2. Drain the cooling system into a clean container for reuse.
3. Raise and safely support the vehicle.
4. Remove the drain tube from the heater case. Disconnect the heater hoses from the heater core.
5. Lower the vehicle.
6. Remove the right and left side sound insulators, the steering column trim cover and the heater outlet duct. 1993–94 models.
7. Remove the instrument panel (1995 models).
8. Remove the Diagnostic Energy Reserve Module (DERM) with attaching brackets (1995 models).
9. Carefully remove the heater core cover, pulling it straight to the rear to avoid breaking the drain tube.
10. Loosen the heater core clamps and remove the heater core.

To install:

11. Install the heater core.
12. Install the heater core cover.
13. Install the heater outlet duct, steering column trim cover and the right and left side sound insulators.
14. Install the Diagnostic Energy Reserve Module (DERM) with attaching bracket (1995 models).
15. Install instrument panel (1995 models).
16. Raise and safely support the vehicle.
17. Connect the heater hoses to the heater core.
18. Connect the drain tube to the heater case.
19. Lower the vehicle.
20. Connect the negative battery cable.
21. Fill cooling system and check for leaks. Start the engine and allow to come to normal operating temperature. Recheck for coolant leaks. Allow the engine to warm up sufficiently to confirm operation of cooling fan.

Beretta and Corsica

1. Disconnect the negative battery cable.
2. If equipped, disable the Supplemental Inflatable Restraint (SIR) system by performing the following:
   - Remove the SIR fuse from the fuse panel.
   - Remove the left side sound insulator.
   - Remove the Connector Positive Assurance (CPA) from the yellow 2-way SIR harness connector at the base of the steering column and separate the connector.
3. Remove the center console, both sound insulator panels and the steering column filler trim.
4. Remove the screws and the floor outlet, turning clockwise to release from the rear floor air outlet.
5. Drain the cooling system into a clean container for reuse.
6. Raise and safely support the vehicle.
7. Disconnect the heater hoses from the heater core. Remove the drain tube elbow from the heater core cover.
8. Lower the vehicle.
9. Remove the heater core screw, clamps and the heater core from the vehicle.

To install:

10. Install the heater core screw, clamps and the heater core from the vehicle.
11. Raise and safely support the vehicle.
12. Install the drain tube elbow from the heater core cover.
13. Connect the heater hoses from the heater core.
14. Lower the vehicle.
15. Install the screws and the floor outlet to the rear floor air outlet.
16. Install the center console and/or instrument panel.
17. If equipped, enable the SIR system.
18. Connect the negative battery cable.
19. If equipped, enable the Supplemental Inflatable Restraint (SIR) system by performing the following:
    - Connect the yellow 2-way SIR connector and insert the Connect Positive Assurance (CPA) at the base of the steering column.
    - Install the left side sound insulator.
    - Install the SIR fuse in the fuse panel.
20. Fill cooling system and check for leaks. Start the engine and allow to come to normal operating temperature. Recheck for coolant leaks. Allow the engine to warm up sufficiently to confirm operation of cooling fan.

Achieva, Grand Am and Skylark

1. Disconnect the negative battery cable.
2. Drain the cooling system into a clean container for reuse.
3. Raise and safely support the vehicle.
4. Disconnect the heater hoses at the heater core.
5. Remove the drain tube.
6. Lower the vehicle. Remove the center console (if equipped) and the steering column filler.
7. Remove the right and left sound insulator.
8. Remove the floor air outlet duct and hoses.
9. Remove the heater core cover.
10. Remove the heater core.

To install:

11. Install the heater core.
12. Install the heater core cover.
13. Install the floor air outlet duct and hoses to the duct.
14. Install the right and left sound insulators.
15. If removed, install the steering column filler and the center console.
16. Raise and safely support the vehicle. Install the drain tube.
17. Connect the heater hose to the heater core.
18. Lower the vehicle.
19. Connect the negative battery cable.
20. Fill cooling system and check for leaks. Start the engine and allow to come to normal operating temperature. Recheck for coolant leaks. Allow the engine to warm up sufficiently to confirm operation of cooling fan.

LeMans

WITH AIR CONDITIONING

1. Disconnect the negative battery cable.
2. Drain the engine coolant into a clean container for reuse.
3. If equipped with a manual transaxle, remove the gear shift boot.
4. Remove the package shelf.
5. Remove the front floor console shift plate and front center console.
6. Remove the 2 glove box straps.
7. Remove the hush panel.
8. Remove the 2 retainers, bend the tab and remove outer heater case cover.
9. Remove the heater case cover clips and screws. Remove the heater case cover.
10. Remove the 3 heater core clamps. Remove the heater core.

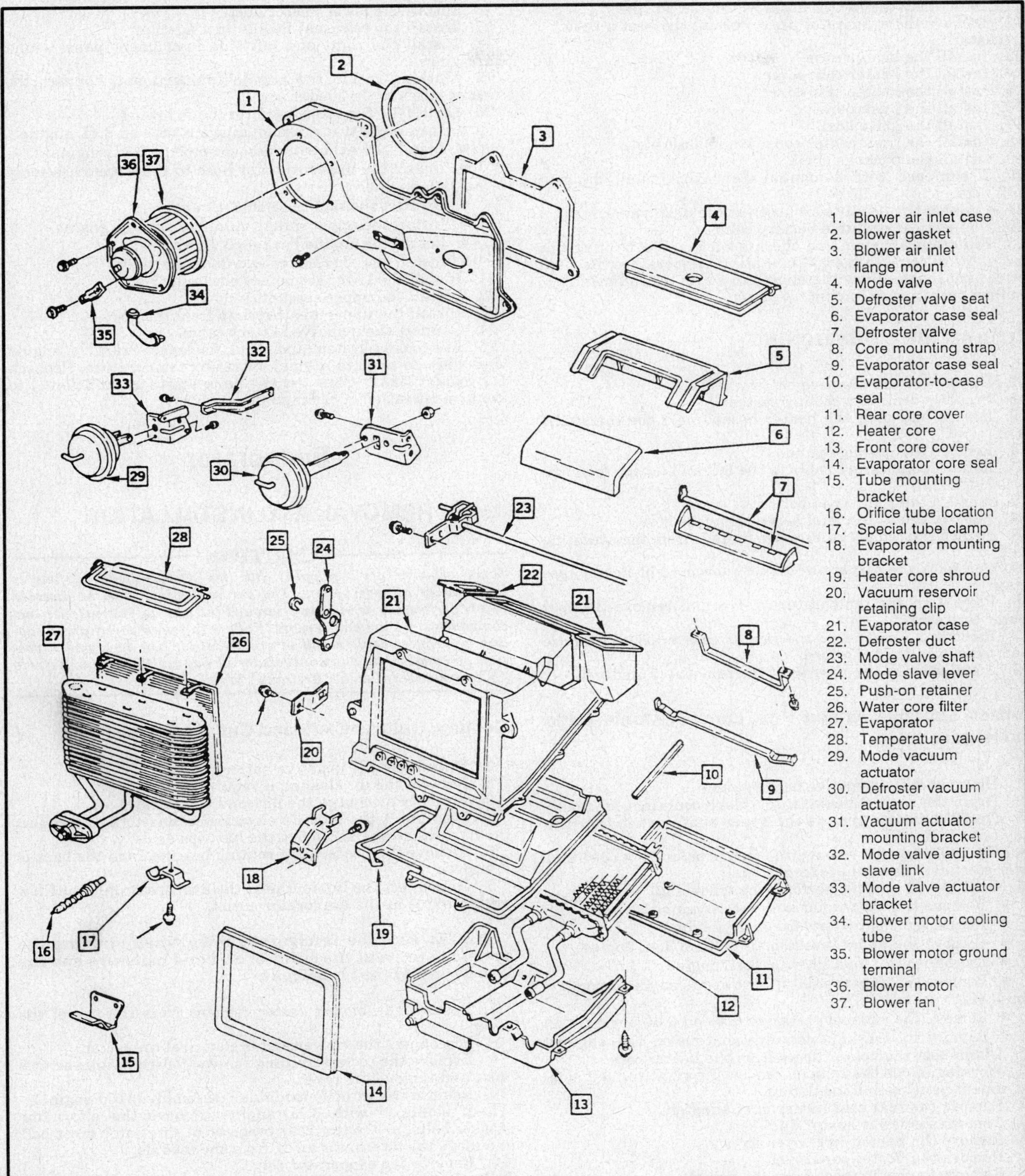
1
2
3
4
5
6
7
8
9
10
11
12
13
14
15
16
17
18
19
20
21
21
22
23
24
25
26
27
28
29
30
31
32
33
34
35
36
37
1. Blower air inlet case
2. Blower gasket
3. Blower air inlet flange mount
4. Mode valve
5. Defroster valve seat
6. Evaporator case seal
7. Defroster valve
8. Core mounting strap
9. Evaporator case seal
10. Evaporator-to-case seal
11. Rear core cover
12. Heater core
13. Front core cover
14. Evaporator core seal
15. Tube mounting bracket
16. Orifice tube location
17. Special tube clamp
18. Evaporator mounting bracket
19. Heater core shroud
20. Vacuum reservoir retaining clip
21. Evaporator case
22. Defroster duct
23. Mode valve shaft
24. Mode slave lever
25. Push-on retainer
26. Water core filter
27. Evaporator
28. Temperature valve
29. Mode vacuum actuator
30. Defroster vacuum actuator
31. Vacuum actuator mounting bracket
32. Mode valve adjusting slave link
33. Mode valve actuator bracket
34. Blower motor cooling tube
35. Blower motor ground terminal
36. Blower motor
37. Blower fan

Heater-evaporator module exploded view—Cavalier and Sunbird

11. Disconnect the heater hoses at the heater core.
12. Remove the evaporator drain hose at the heater case.

To install:

13. Install the heater core.
14. Install the heater core cover.
15. Install the heater case cover.
16. Install the hush panel.
17. Install the glove box.
18. Install the front center console and shift plate.
19. Install the package shelf.
20. If equipped with a manual transaxle, install the gear shift boot.
21. Connect the heater core hoses at the dash panel.
22. Connect the negative battery cable.
23. Fill cooling system and check for leaks. Start the engine and allow to come to normal operating temperature. Recheck for coolant leaks. Allow the engine to warm up sufficiently to confirm operation of cooling fan.

WITHOUT AIR CONDITIONING

1. Disconnect the negative battery cable.
2. Properly drain the cooling system.
3. Detach and plug the heater hoses (mark for reinstallation).
4. Remove the package panel.
5. Rotate temperature cable to the left and detach from the actuating lever.
6. Remove the right knee bolster.
7. Remove the hush panel below the glove box.
8. Detach the temperature valve linkage from the actuating lever.
9. Pull back the carpet and remove lower right heater case screw.
10. Reposition the temperature valve and remove 2 upper heater core screws.
11. Remove 3 screws and the heater case bracket. Remove the heater core from the case.
12. Installation is the reverse of the removal procedure.

Cutlass Supreme, Grand Prix, Lumina, Monte Carlo and Regal

1. Disconnect the negative battery cable.
2. Drain the engine coolant into a clean container for reuse.
3. On 1993 models, remove the upper weatherstrip from the body (except Regal).
4. On 1993 models, remove the upper secondary cowl and lower secondary cowl nut (except Regal).
5. On 1994–95 models, perform the following:
   - Remove the air cleaner and duct assembly.
   - Rotate the engine forward on 3.1L engine.
   - Remove the upper intake mainifold on 3.4L engine.
   - Disconnect the fuel lines on 3.4L engine.
   - Remove the upper radiator hose at the engine assembly on 3.4L.
   - Remove the exhaust crossover pipe on 3.4L engine.
   - Remove the transmission dipstick tube on 3.4L engine.
6. Disconnect the heater hoses from the heater core.
7. Working inside the vehicle, remove the right and left side instrument panel sound insulators.
8. Remove the rear seat heater duct adapter.
9. Remove the lower heater duct.
10. Remove the heater core cover screws.
11. Remove the heater core cover.
12. Remove the heater core from the vehicle.

To install:

13. Install the heater core in the vehicle.
14. Install the heater core cover.
15. Install the heater core cover screws.
16. Install the lower heater duct.
17. Install the rear seat heater duct adapter.
18. Install the right and left side instrument panel sound insulators.
19. Working inside the engine compartment, connect the heater hoses to the heater core.
20. On 1994–95 models, perform the following:
   - Install the transmission dipstick tube on 3.4L engine.
   - Install the exhaust crossover pipe on 3.4L engine.
   - Install the upper radiator hose to the engine assembly on 3.4L engine.
   - Connect the fuel lines on 3.4L engine.
   - Install the upper intake manifold on 3.4L engine.
   - Rotate the engine back on 3.1L engine.
   - Install the air cleaner and duct assembly.
21. Install the lower secondary cowl upper nut.
22. Install the upper secondary cowl.
23. Install the upper weatherstrip from the body.
24. Connect the negative battery cable.
25. Fill cooling system and check for leaks. Start the engine and allow to come to normal operating temperature. Recheck for coolant leaks. Allow the engine to warm up sufficiently to confirm operation of cooling fan.

Evaporator

REMOVAL AND INSTALLATION

CAUTION

Some vehicles are equipped with the Supplemental Inflatable Restraint or air bag system. The air bag system must be disabled before performing service on or around the air bag, instrument panel components, wiring and sensors. Failure to follow safety and disabling procedures could result in accidental air bag deployment, possible personal injury and unnecessary air bag system repairs. Refer to "Supplemental Inflatable Restraint" in this article.

Century, Cutlass Ciera and Cutlass Cruiser

1. Disconnect the negative battery cable.
2. Remove the air cleaner, if required.
3. Properly discharge the air conditioning system.
4. Disconnect the module electrical connectors, disconnect the harness straps and move the harness aside.
5. Remove the heater hose routing bracket from the back of the cover.
6. Disconnect the liquid line at the evaporator inlet and low pressure line at the evaporator outlet.

NOTE: Cap the refrigerant lines when opening the system to prevent the entry of dirt and moisture and the loss of refrigerant lubricant.

7. Remove the blower motor resistor from the top of the cover.
8. Disconnect the blower motor electrical connector.
9. Remove the cover retaining screws (loosen bottom screws only) and remove the cover.
10. Remove the throttle modulator assembly (3100 engine).
11. If equipped with 3.1L engine, remove the alternator bracket bolts, alternator rear brace bolt, alternator pivot bolt and move the alternator away from the module.
12. Remove the evaporator core.

To install:

NOTE: If replacing the evaporator or if the original evaporator was flushed during service, add 2–3 fluid oz. (60–90 ml) of refrigerant lubricant to the system.

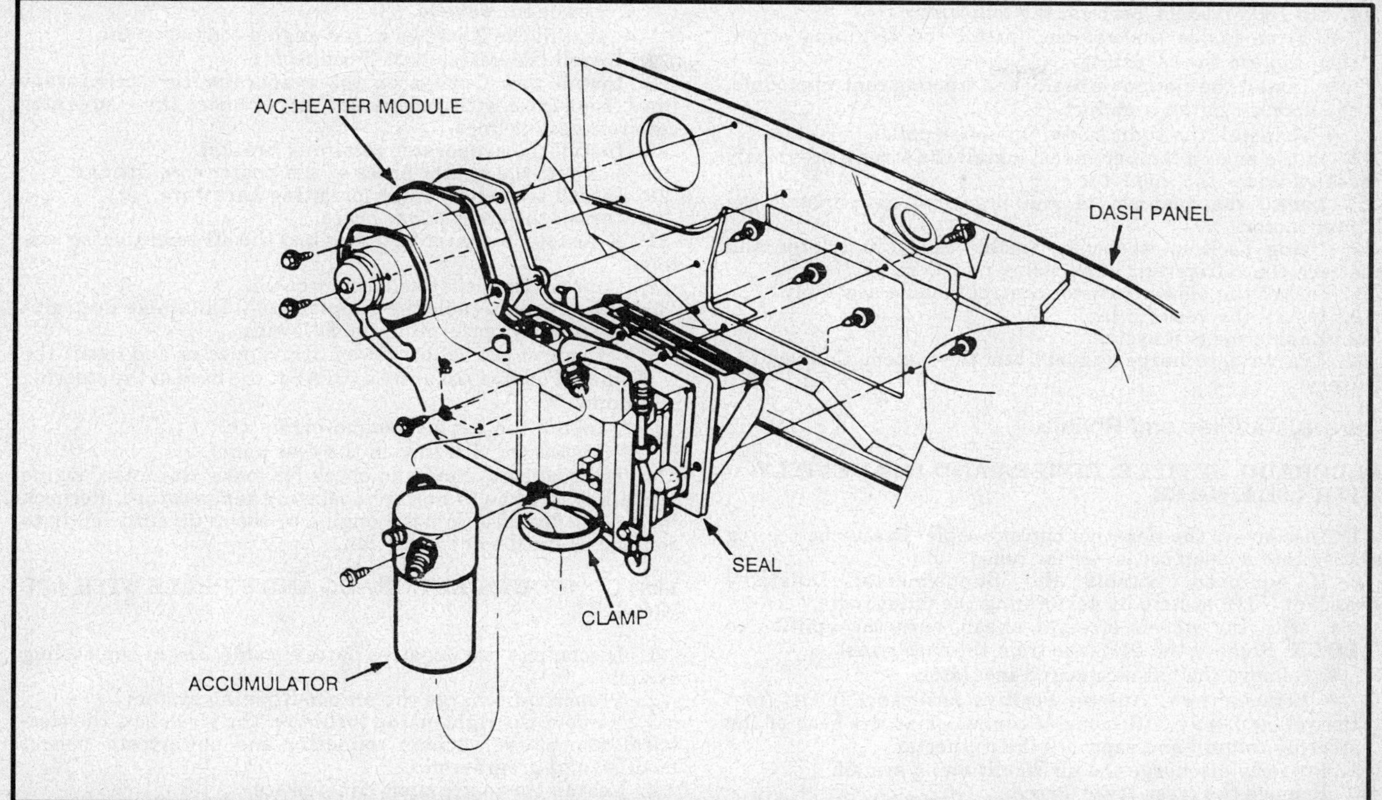

Blower-evaporator module and accumulator—Century and Cutlass Cruiser with 2.5L engine

13. Clean the old gasket material from the cowl.
14. Install the evaporator core in the module.
15. Apply permagum sealer to the case and install the cover using a new gasket.
16. Install the cover attaching screws.
17. Install the throttle modulator assembly (3100 engine).
18. If equipped with 3.1L engine, position the alternator and install the pivot bolts, rear brace bolt and alternator bracket bolts.
19. Connect the blower motor electrical connector.
20. Install the resistor to the top of the cover.
21. Install new O-rings to the liquid and low pressure lines. Lubricate O-rings with refrigerant oil.
22. Connect the liquid line at the evaporator inlet and low pressure line at the evaporator outlet.
23. Install the heater hose routing bracket to the cover.
24. Route the cowl harness in the straps and connect the module electrical connectors.
25. Evacuate, recharge and leak test the system.
26. Connect the negative battery cable.

Bonneville, Eighty-Eight, LeSabre, Ninety-Eight and Park Avenue

1. Disconnect the negative battery cable. Properly discharge the air conditioning system using recovery equipment.
2. If equipped, disable the Supplemental Inflatable Restraint (SIR) system by performing the following:
   - Set wheels straight ahead, turn ignition to **LOCK**. Remove the SIR fuse from the fuse panel.
   - Remove the left side sound insulator. Remove the right sound insulator if needed, detaching electrical components and light bulbs during removal.
   - Remove the Connector Positive Assurance (CPA) from the yellow 2-way SIR harness connector at the base of the steering column and separate the connector.
3. Remove the vacuum tank.
4. Remove the blower control module/blower resistor assembly from the top of the evaporator/blower housing.
5. Remove the accumulator.
6. Remove the liquid line from the evaporator tube. Use backup wrench to separate the connection. Discard the O-ring.

NOTE: Immediately cap all refrigerant system openings to minimize contamination.

7. Remove the blower motor.
8. Remove the brackets from the evaporator housing. Remove the heat shield from the lower side of the housing.
9. Remove the screws and bolts from the housing. Cut along the insulator where indicated, then remove the insulator.
10. Remove the screws located behind the insulator.
11. On 1993 models, perform the following:
   - From inside the vehicle, remove the right sound insulator panel (if not removed previously), detaching electronic components and bulbs.
   - Remove the floor air outlet assembly and floor air duct.
   - Remove the bolt and connector from the electronic brake and traction control module and slide the module out of its bracket.
   - Pull down the carpeting and remove the retaining screw for the evaporator housing.
   - Remove the evaporator housing by pulling from its studs.
12. For all models, remove the evaporator cover and remove the evaporator core.

To install:

13. If the evaporator core is replaced, add 3 oz. of new refrigerant oil. Position the evaporator housing to the firewall.

14. On 1993 models, perform the following:
- From inside the vehicle, install the retaining screw, then replace the carpeting.
- Install the electronic brake and traction control module, the floor air outlet and duct.
- Reinstall the right sound insulator panel.

15. In the engine compartment, install the screws previously revealed under the insulator.
16. Install the heat shield and brackets, then install the blower motor.
17. Using back-up wrenches, install the accumulator and reattach the refrigerant lines, using new O-rings.
18. Install the blower resistor/control module assembly.
19. Install the vacuum tank.
20. Enable the SIR system.
21. Evacuate, recharge and leak test the system. Connect the battery.

Aurora, Cadillac and Riviera

ELDORADO, SEVILLE, RIVIERA AND 1994 DEVILLE WITH 4.9L ENGINE

1. Disconnect the negative battery cable. Drain the cooling system into a clean container for reuse.
2. If equipped, disable the Supplemental Inflatable Restraint (SIR) system by performing the following:
- With the wheels straight ahead, turn the ignition to **LOCK**. Remove the SIR fuse from the fuse panel.
- Remove the left side sound insulator.
- Remove the Connector Positive Assurance (CPA) from the yellow 2-way SIR harness connector at the base of the steering column and separate the connector.

3. Properly discharge the air conditioning system.
4. Remove the cross-tower brace.
5. Remove the relay center mounting hardware and position the relay center aside.
6. Disconnect the heater hoses at the heater core fittings.
7. Remove the evaporator retaining bracket.
8. Remove the evaporator core refrigerant lines. Discard the O-rings. Cap the openings immediately.
9. Remove the heater hose T-connector.
10. Remove the heat shield by performing the following:
- Remove the 2 screws in the engine compartment.
- Raise and safely support the vehicle.
- Remove the 2 housing retaining screws from under the vehicle.

11. Remove the air conditioning module.
12. Lower the vehicle.
13. Remove the power module and blower motor electrical connectors. Remove the power module and blower motor.
14. On 1993–94 Eldorado and 1993 Seville, remove the MAP sensor bracket and diverter valve.
15. Remove the air conditioning module cover screws.
16. Remove the module cover, sound insulator and seal.
17. Remove the evaporator.

To install:

NOTE: If replacing the evaporator or if the original evaporator was flushed during service, add 2–3 fluid oz. (60–90 ml) of refrigerant lubricant to the system.

18. Install the evaporator in the case.
19. Install the module cover, retaining screws, sound insulator and seal.
20. Install the power module and blower motor. Connect the power module and blower motor electrical connectors.
21. On Eldorado and Seville, install the MAP sensor bracket and diverter valve, as required.
22. Raise the vehicle.
23. Install the air conditioning module.
24. Install the heat shield by performing the following:
- Install the 2 screws from under the vehicle.
- Lower the vehicle.
- Install the 2 screws in the engine compartment.

25. Install the heater hose T-connector.
26. Install new O-rings on the evaporator core refrigerant lines. Lubricate with refrigerant oil. Connect the evaporator core refrigerant lines.
27. Install the evaporator retaining bracket.
28. Connect the heater hoses at the heater core fittings.
29. Install the relay center mounting hardware.
30. Install the cross-tower brace.
31. Evacuate, recharge and leak test the air conditioning system.
32. Connect the negative battery cable.
33. If equipped, enable the Supplemental Inflatable Restraint (SIR) system by performing the following:
- Connect the yellow 2-way SIR connector and insert the Connect Positive Assurance (CPA) at the base of the steering column.
- Install the left side sound insulator.
- Install the SIR fuse in the fuse panel.

34. Fill cooling system and check for leaks. Start the engine and allow to come to normal operating temperature. Recheck for coolant leaks. Allow the engine to warm up sufficiently to confirm operation of cooling fan.

1994 CONCOURS, EL DORADO AND SEVILLE WITH 4.6L ENGINE

1. Disconnect the negative battery cable. Drain the cooling system.
2. Properly discharge the air conditioning system.
3. Remove the right sound insulator, the glove box, the electrical connectors, vacuum connector and powertrain control module, and programmer.
4. Loosen the instrument panel brace.
5. Remove the bolt securing the evaporator core housing to the front of the dash (bolt is located above carpet directly behind left side of console).
6. Remove the heater core and cross car brace.
7. Remove the vapor (evaporator/accumulator) line and liquid line from the evaporator.
8. Remove the two bolts securing the harness pass-through to the front of the dash.
9. Disconnect the electrical connectors to the oxygen sensor, blower motor, A/C high and low pressure temperature sensors, A/C fan switch, and A/C low pressure switch.
10. Remove the ignition control module.
11. Remove the coolant bypass hose from the coolant tank.
12. Remove the air filter housing and the PCV valve.
13. Remove the left hand radiator core support and the radiator shroud.
14. Remove the electrical connectors to the transmission selector switch, map sensor, cruise control servo, and release the wiring harness from body.
15. Remove the brake booster hose and the left and right engine struts and the brackets.
16. Remove the upper transmission cooler line and the left and right coolant fans.
17. Remove the discharge line at the condenser, and the suction line from the accumulator.
18. Install the engine support tool.
19. Raise and safely support the vehicle. Remove the left and right front wheels.
20. Remove the fuel line bracket from the transmission.
21. Remove the intermediate shaft pinch bolt from the rack and pinion gear.

CAUTION

Failure to disconnect the intermediate shaft from the rack and pinion stub shaft can result in damage to the steering gear and/or intermediate shaft. This damage can cause loss of steering control which could result in vehicle crash with possible bodily injury.

22. Remove the splash shields for the radiator, the transmission and the left wheel housing.
23. Remove the ABS unit from the cradle bracket.
24. Disconnect the electrical connectors to the P/S pressure switch, vehicle speed sensor, knock sensor and the engine ground wire.
25. Remove the exhaust manifold pipe from the converter.
26. Remove the left and right brake calipers.
27. Remove the left and right vehicle speed sensors from the body.
28. Remove the two rear cradle frame bolts, and loosen the remaining four cradle bolts.
29. Lower the vehicle onto the cradle support stand.
30. Remove the remaining cradle bolts.
31. Remove the struts from the strut towers.
32. Raise the vehicle to lower the powertrain/cradle assembly.
33. Remove the wire harness on the right bank valve cover, and position the harness out of way.
34. Remove the exhaust manifold pipe heat shield.
35. Remove the blower motor.
36. Remove the evaporator core access plate and the liquid line brace.
37. Remove the evaporator core rubber barrier cover (HEBA).
38. Cut the lower portion of the rubber HEBA (evaporator end of case).
39. Remove the evaporator core cover and the evaporator core.

To install:

NOTE: If replacing the evaporator or if the original evaporator was flushed during service, add 3 fluid oz. (60–90ml) of refrigerant lubricant to the system.

40. Install the evaporator core and cover.
41. Install the evaporator core rubber barrier cover and the evaporator core access cover.
42. Install the blower motor.
43. Install the exhaust manifold heat shield.
44. Reposition the loose electrical harness on the right bank valve cover.
45. Lower the vehicle to install the powertrain/cradle assembly.
46. Install the struts to the strut towers, and cradle the support bolts.
47. Install the left and right vehicle speed sensors.
48. Install the left and right brake calipers.
49. Install the exhaust manifold pipe to the converter.
50. Connect the electrical connectors to the P/S pressure switch, vehicle speed sensor, knock sensor, and engine ground wire.
51. Install the ABS unit to the cradle bracket.
52. Install the splash shield for the radiator, the transmission, and the left wheel housing.
53. Install the intermediate shaft pinch bolt to the rack and pinion gear.
54. Install the fuel line bracket to the transmission.
55. Install the left and right front wheels.
56. Lower the vehicle, and remove the engine support tool.
57. Install the discharge line at the condenser, and the suction line to the accumulator.
58. Install the left and right coolant fans.
59. Install the upper transmission cooler line.
60. Install the left and right engine struts and brackets.
61. Install the brake booster hose.
62. Connect the electrical connectors to the transmission selector switch, map sensor, cruise control servo, and wiring harness to the body.
63. Install the left hand radiator core support and the radiator shroud.
64. Install the air filter housing and the PCV valve, and the coolant bypass hose to the coolant tank and ignition control module.
65. Connect the electrical connectors to the oxygen sensor, blower motor, A/C high and low pressure temperature sensors, A/C fan switch, and A/C low pressure switch.
66. Install the two bolts securing the harness pass-through to the front of dash.
67. Install the liquid line from the evaporator and vapor (evaporator/accumulator) line.
68. Install the cross car brace, and the heater core.
69. Connect the electrical connectors, vacuum connector, Powertrain Control Module (PCM), and the programmer.
70. Install the glove box, and the right side sound insulator.
71. Evacuate, recharge and leak test the air conditioning system.
72. Connect the negative battery cable.
73. Fill the cooling system and check for leaks. Start the engine and allow it to come to a normal operating temperature. Recheck for coolant leaks. Allow the engine to warm sufficiently to confirm operation of cooling fan.

1995 AURORA AND RIVIERA

1. Properly discharge the air conditioning system.
2. Disconnect the negative battery cable.
3. Remove the heater and A/C module.
4. Remove the access panel from heater and A/C module.
5. Remove the evaporator retaining straps and the evaporator.

To install:

6. Install the evaporator into the heater and the A/C module.
7. Install the retaining straps with fasteners.
8. Install the access panel to the heater and the A/C module.
9. Install the heater and the A/C module.
10. Connect the negative battery cable.
11. Evacuate, recharge and leak test the air conditioning system.

Cavalier, Sunfire and Sunbird

1. Disconnect the negative battery cable.
2. Properly discharge the air conditioning system.
3. Drain the cooling system into a clean container for reuse.
4. Raise and safely support the vehicle.
5. Disconnect the heater hoses.
6. Disconnect the refrigerant lines at the evaporator core. Discard the O-rings.

NOTE: Cap the refrigerant lines when opening the system to prevent the entry of dirt and moisture and the loss of refrigerant lubricant.

7. Remove the drain tube.
8. Lower the vehicle.
9. Remove the right and left side sound insulators, the steering column trim cover, the heater outlet and the instrument panel compartment as required.
10. Remove the DERM with attaching bracket (1995 models).
11. Remove the heater cover, pulling it straight to the rear in order to avoid breaking the drain tube.
12. Remove the heater core clamps and the heater core.
13. Remove the screws holding the defroster vacuum actuator to the module case. (Except 1995 models).
14. Remove the evaporator cover and the evaporator core.

To install:

NOTE: If replacing the evaporator or if the original evaporator was flushed during service, add 2–3 fluid oz. (60–90 ml) of refrigerant lubricant to the system.

15. Install the evaporator core and cover.
16. Install the screws holding the defroster vacuum actuator to the module case (Except 1995 models).

17. Install the heater core and clamps.
18. Install the heater core cover.
19. Install the instrument panel compartment, heater outlet duct, steering column trim cover and the right and left side sound insulator panels as required.
20. Install the DERM with attaching bracket (1995 models).
21. Raise and safely support the vehicle.
22. Connect the drain tube.
23. Connect the heater hoses and the evaporator lines. Install new O-rings on the evaporator refrigerant line fittings. Lubricate with refrigerant oil.
24. Evacuate, recharge and leak test the air conditioning system. Connect the negative battery cable.
25. Fill cooling system and check for leaks. Start the engine and allow to come to normal operating temperature. Recheck for coolant leaks. Allow the engine to warm up sufficiently to confirm operation of cooling fan.

Beretta and Corsica

1. Disable the SIR system as described in this article.
2. Disconnect the negative battery cable. Properly discharge the air conditioning system with recovery equipment.
3. Raise car from under the vehicle, remove the front exhaust shield.
4. Remove 3 cradle cross brace bolts and swing the cradle aside.
5. Detach the refrigerant lines from the evaporator. Cap all openings immediately and discard the O-rings.
6. Lower the vehicle and remove the right side under-dash insulator panel, and the electrical junction box at the heater housing.
7. Remove the left insulator panel and the steering column filler trim panel.
8. Loosen the center console and remove the floor duct, heater core cover, shroud and straps.

NOTE: The heater core will be suspended by the heater core pipes at this point. Do not apply any downward pressure on the core, otherwise damage may occur to the heater core pipes.

9. Remove the evaporator core.

To install:

10. If replacing the evaporator core, add 3.0 oz. of new oil to the unit during installation.
11. Install the core, the heater core straps, shroud and cover.
12. Install the floor duct and reattach the center console.
13. Install the steering column filler, electrical junction box on the heater housing, and both insulator panels.
14. Raise the vehicle and, using new O-rings, attach the refrigerant lines.
15. Position and attach the cradle cross brace and install the exhaust shield.
16. Lower the vehicle and evacuate, recharge and leak test the system.
17. Connect the negative battery cable. Enable the SIR system.

Achieva, Grand Am and Skylark

1. Disconnect the negative battery cable. Properly discharge the air conditioning system using recovery equipment.
2. Raise the vehicle. Remove the front exhaust shield.
3. Remove 3 bolts from the cradle cross brace and swing it aside.
4. Disconnect the lines from the evaporator. Cap the openings immediately and discard the O-rings. Lower the vehicle.
5. Remove the right side under dash sound insulator panel.
6. Remove the electrical junction box at the heater core cover.
7. Remove the left under dash sound insulator panel and the steering column filler.
8. Loosen the center shift console, if equipped, then remove the floor air duct.
9. Remove the heater core cover and heater core shroud and straps.

NOTE: The heater core will be suspended by the core pipes; do not apply any downward pressure on the core.

10. Remove the evaporator assembly.

To install:

11. Install the evaporator assembly. If evaporator core was replaced, add 3.0 oz. of new refrigerant oil to the core.
12. Install the heater core shroud, straps and cover.
13. Install the floor duct, attach the shift console and install the steering column filler and left insulator panel.
14. Install the electrical junction box and the right side insulator panel.
15. Raise the vehicle and, using new, lubricated O-rings, attach the refrigerant lines.
16. Position the cradle cross brace and install the 3 bolts.
17. Install the exhaust shield and lower the vehicle.
18. Attach the negative battery cable. Evacuate, recharge and leak test the system.

LeMans

1. Disconnect the negative battery cable.
2. Properly discharge the air conditioning system.
3. Drain the engine coolant into a clean container for reuse.
4. Remove the heater core.
5. Disconnect the accumulator-to-evaporator pipe and the orifice tube to the evaporator at the dash panel.
6. Remove the evaporator cover screws and evaporator cover.
7. Remove the evaporator refrigerant lines. Discard the O-rings.

NOTE: Cap the refrigerant lines when opening the system to prevent the entry of dirt and moisture and the loss of refrigerant lubricant.

8. Remove the evaporator brackets.
9. Remove the evaporator.

To install:

NOTE: If replacing the evaporator or if the original evaporator was flushed during service, add 2–3 fluid oz. (60–90 ml) of refrigerant lubricant to the system.

10. Install the evaporator core.
11. Install the pipe clamps.
12. Install the evaporator bracket and screws.
13. Install the evaporator cover.
14. Connect the accumulator-to-evaporator pipe and orifice tube to the evaporator at the dash panel.
15. Install the heater core.
16. Evacuate, recharge and leak test the air conditioning system.
17. Connect the negative battery cable.
18. Fill cooling system and check for leaks. Start the engine and allow to come to normal operating temperature. Recheck for coolant leaks. Allow the engine to warm up sufficiently to confirm operation of cooling fan.

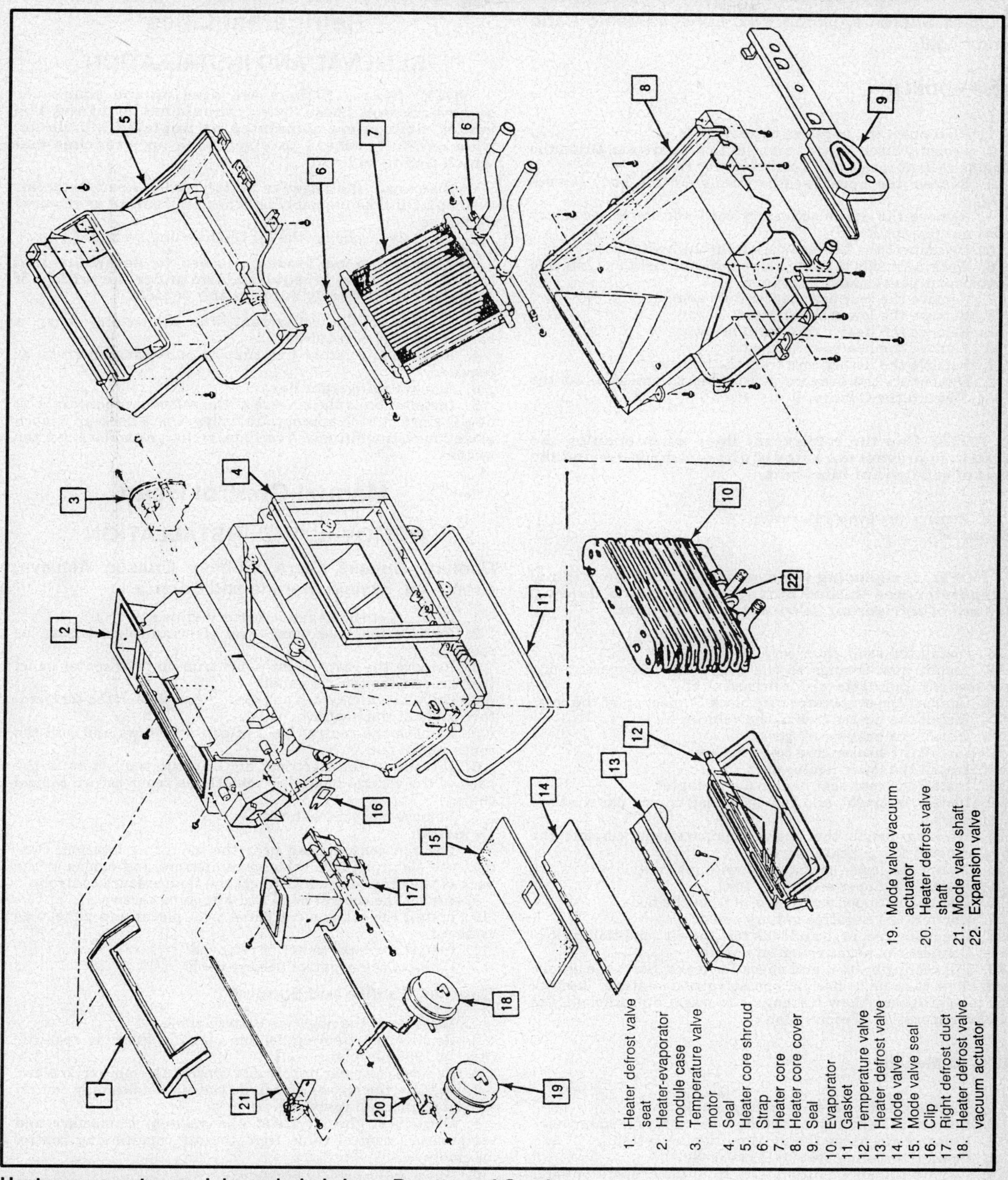

Heater-evaporator module exploded view—Beretta and Corsica

Cutlass Supreme, Grand Prix, Lumina, Monte Carlo and Regal

1993 MODELS

1. Disconnect the negative battery cable.
2. Properly discharge the air conditioning system. Drain the engine coolant into a clean container for reuse.
3. Remove the upper weatherstrip from the body (except Regal).
4. Remove the upper secondary cowl and lower secondary cowl nut (except Regal).
5. Disconnect the heater hoses from the heater core.
6. Working inside the vehicle, remove the right and left side instrument panel sound insulators.
7. Remove the rear seat heater duct adapter.
8. Remove the lower heater duct.
9. Remove the heater core cover screws.
10. Remove the heater core cover.
11. Remove the heater core from the vehicle.
12. Disconnect the evaporator core block connection at the cowl. Discard the O-rings.

NOTE: Cap the refrigerant lines when opening the system to prevent the entry of dirt and moisture and the loss of refrigerant lubricant.

13. Remove the evaporator core.

To install:

NOTE: If replacing the evaporator or if the original evaporator was flushed during service, add 3 fluid oz. (90 ml) of refrigerant lubricant to the system.

14. Install the evaporator core.
15. Install new O-rings to the evaporator refrigerant line connections. Lubricate with refrigerant oil.
16. Connect the evaporator core block connection at the cowl.
17. Install the heater core in the vehicle.
18. Install the heater core cover.
19. Install the heater core cover screws.
20. Install the lower heater duct.
21. Install the rear seat heater duct adapter.
22. Install the right and left side instrument panel sound insulators.
23. Working inside the engine compartment, connect the heater hoses to the heater core.
24. Install the lower secondary cowl upper nut.
25. Install the upper secondary cowl.
26. Install the upper weatherstrip from the body.
27. Connect the negative battery cable.
28. Evacuate, recharge and leak test the air conditioning system. Connect the negative battery cable.
29. Fill cooling system and check for leaks. Start the engine and allow to come to normal operating temperature. Recheck for coolant leaks. Allow the engine to warm up sufficiently to confirm operation of cooling fan.

1994–95 Models

1. Disconnect the negative battery cable.
2. Remove the air cleaner and duct assembly (1995 models).
3. Properly discharge the air conditioning system.
4. Drain the cooling system (1995 models).
5. Remove the air condition lines from the evaporator core.
6. Remove the heater core, evaporator core cover and the evaporator.
7. Installation is the reverse of the removal procedures.

Refrigerant Lines

REMOVAL AND INSTALLATION

NOTE: Brazed fittings are used on the condenser and evaporator. These fittings should not be turned. The brazed fittings are unpainted or unplated aluminum. Note carefully where to place back-up wrenches and which fitting to turn.

1. Disconnect the negative battery cable. Remove the air cleaner/air intake assembly or other components as required for access.
2. Properly discharge the air conditioning system.

NOTE: On some models, access to detaching and installing the lines is required from under the vehicle. If so, raise and properly support the vehicle.

3. Disconnect the refrigerant line connectors, using a backup wrench as required.
4. Remove refrigerant line support or routing brackets, as required.
5. Remove refrigerant line.
6. Installation is the reverse of the removal procedure. Use new O-rings at each appropriate fitting. Use a back-up wrench when connecting fittings. Evacuate, recharge and leak test the system.

Manual Control Head

REMOVAL AND INSTALLATION

Century, Cutlass Ciera, Cutlass Cruiser, Achieva, Grand Am, Skylark, Beretta and Corsica

1. Disconnect the negative battery cable.
2. Remove the hush panel and steering column filler, as required.
3. Remove the instrument panel trim plate or center panel trim around the control panel.
4. On Achieva, Skylark and Grand Am, detach the temperature cable at the heater housing.
5. Remove the control head attaching screws and pull the control head out.
6. Disconnect the electrical and vacuum connectors at the back of the control head. Disconnect the temperature control cable.
7. Remove the control head.

To install:

8. Position control head near the mounting location. Connect the electrical and vacuum connectors and cables to the back of the control head. Connect the temperature control.
9. Install the control head and attaching screws.
10. Install the instrument panel trim plates and panels, as removed.
11. Install the hush panel, if removed.
12. Connect the negative battery cable.

Cavalier, Sunfire and Sunbird

1. Disconnect the negative battery cable.
2. Remove the steering column opening filler, as required (Except 1995 models).
3. Remove the cigar lighter and control assembly trim plate.
4. Remove the screws attaching the air conditioning control assembly and pull rearward.
5. Disconnect the electrical and vacuum connectors and temperature control cable from the air conditioning control assembly.
6. Remove the control assembly.

To install:

7. Connect the electrical and vacuum connections and the temperature control cable to the control assembly.

8. Install the screws attaching the control assembly to the instrument panel.
9. Install the cigar lighter and control assembly trim plate.
10. Install the steering column opening filler (Except 1995 models).
11. Connect the negative battery cable.

LeMans

1. Disconnect the negative battery cable.
2. If equipped with a manual transaxle, remove the gear shift lever boot.
3. Remove the package shelf.
4. Remove the front floor console shift plate and the front center console.
5. Remove the knee bolsters as required.
6. Remove the 2 retainer, bend the tab and remove the cover.
7. Remove the temperature control cable from the actuating lever and the air distributor.
8. Remove the screw underneath the control unit.
9. Disconnect the electrical and vacuum connectors and the control cable.

To install:

10. Install the electrical and vacuum connectors.
11. Attach the control unit with the screw underneath.
12. Connect the temperature control cable to the actuating lever and air distributor.
13. Install the outer heater case cover with the 2 retainers and bend the tab into position.
14. Install the front floor console shift plate and the front center console.
15. Install the package shelf.
16. If equipped with a manual transaxle, install the gear shift lever boot.
17. Connect the negative battery cable.

1994 LeSabre and Park Avenue, 1994–95 Bonneville, Eighty-Eight and Ninety-Eight

1. Remove the instrument panel closeout panel.
2. Disconnect the electrical and vacuum connectors.
3. Remove the heater and A/C control from the closeout.

To install:

4. Install the instrument panel closeout panel.
5. Connect the vacuum and electrical connectors.
6. Install the heater and A/C control to the closeout. (Press into engage clips).

1995 LeSabre and Park Avenue

1. Remove the instrument panel lower trim plates.
2. Remove the air vent deflectors.
3. Remove the instrument panel accessory trim plate screws and the trim plate.
4. Remove the HVAC control assembly screws, and remove the HVAC assembly.
5. Installation is the reverse of the removal procedure.

Cutlass Supreme, Grand Prix, Lumina, Monte Carlo and Regal

1. Disconnect the negative battery cable.
2. Remove the instrument panel trim plate.
3. Loosen the control assembly attaching screws. Pull assembly out.
4. Disconnect cables and electrical connectors, as required.
5. Remove control assembly.

To install:

6. Connect electrical connectors and cables, as required.
7. Install control assembly attaching screws.
8. Install the instrument panel trim plate.
9. Connect the negative battery cable.

1994 Grand Prix

1. Disconnect the negative battery cable.
2. Remove the center console, if equipped.
3. Remove the accessory trim plate.
4. Rotate the control assembly clockwise to the unsnap.
5. Remove the control assembly and the electrical connectors.
6. Installation is reverse of the installation procedure.

Manual Control Cables

ADJUSTMENT

1993 Century, Cutlass Ciera, Cutlass Cruiser, Cavalier and Sunbird

1. Attach the cable to the control assembly.
2. Place the control lever in the **OFF** position.
3. Place the opposite loop of cable on the lever or actuator post.
4. Push the sheath toward the lever until the lever or actuator seats and the lash is out of the cable and control.
5. Tighten the screw to secure the cable.

1994 Cavalier and Sunbird

NOTE: Failure to grip "clip" correctly will damage its ability to hold position on the cable. The temperature control cable must be replaced if "clip" retention fails.

1. Move the temperature control lever toward the **COLD** position.
2. Grip the clip at the module end of the cable while pulling the temperature control lever to the **HOT** position.
3. Move the temperature control lever toward the **HOT** position.
4. Grip at the module end of the cable while pushing the control lever to the **COLD** position.

Century, Cutlass Ciera and Cutlass Cruiser

1994–95 CABLE WITH SLIDING-WITH CLIP

1. Attach the cable to the control assembly.
2. Place the control temperature lever in the **COLD** position.
3. Place the clip of the cable on the heater case temperature door post.
4. Push the control head lever towards **HOT** until the temperature door seats and the spring-back is out of the cable and the control.

Bonneville, Eighty-Eight, LeSabre, Ninety-Eight and Park Avenue

1. Lower the glove compartment to access the control cable turnbuckle.
2. With the temperature control at full **COLD** position, adjust the turnbuckle until the temperature valve just comes to a stop on the left. On LeMans, this adjustment should be done to move the control lever no more than 1.0 inch back from the end of the slot.
3. Move the temperature control to full **HOT** and feel if the valve is held against the right side.
4. If not, repeat adjustment.

Achieva, Grand Am and Skylark

1. With cable installed, move the temperature lever quickly from full **COLD** to full **HOT** positions (some added tension on the lever may be required during initial movement).

2. The cable is now set and should provide equal movement to both ends of its travel and door contact should be heard.
3. On 1993 models, remove the cable end from the actuator and turn the eyelet until the cable end is flush with the end of the eyelet and reinstall. Repeat full adjustment.

REMOVAL AND INSTALLATION

Bonneville, Eighty-Eight, LeSabre, Ninety-Eight, Park Avenue and LeMans and 1993 Century, Cutlass Ciera and Cutlass Cruiser

1. Disconnect the negative battery cable.
2. Remove the control head.
3. Disconnect the cable at the control head and the lever or actuator ends by removing the push-on nuts.
4. Remove any retainers holding the cable. Remove the control cable.
5. Installation is the reverse of the removal procedure.

Century, Cutlass Ciera and Cutlass Cruiser

1994–95 MODELS

1. Remove the control assembly.
2. Remove the lower instrument panel sound insulator.
3. Disconnect the cable at the control assembly end and the temperature door and remove the push-on nuts.
4. Remove the cable.

To install:

5. Position the cable and connect the ends at the temperature door and control assembly. Be sure the retainer clips are seated.
6. Install the push-on nuts.
7. Install the lower instrument panel sound insulator.
8. Install the control assembly.
9. Adjust the cable.

Cavalier and Sunbird

1993–94 MODELS

1. Disconnect the negative battery cable.
2. Remove the right side sound insulator, instrument panel compartment and lower right side of the heater outlet duct.
3. Disconnect the temperature cable at the temperature valve.
4. Steering column trim cover.
5. Remove the right side trim cover.
6. Remove the screws attaching the heater and air conditioner control to the instrument panel.
7. Disconnect the temperature cable from the air conditioner control assembly.

To install:

8. Connect the cable to the air conditioner control assembly.
9. Install the screws attaching the heater and the air conditioner control to the instrument panel.
10. Install the right side trim cover.
11. Install the steering column trim cover.
12. Install the temperature cable at the temperature valve.
13. Install the lower right side of the heater outlet duct, instrument panel compartment and the right side sound insulator.
14. Connect the negative battery cable.

Achieva, Grand Am and Skylark

1. Disconnect the negative battery cable.
2. Remove the right sound insulator and the trim plate for removing the control panel.
3. Remove the control panel and pull it rearward. Detach the control cable from the panel.
4. Detach the cable from the actuator.
5. Installation is the reverse of the removal procedure. Adjust the cable.

Electronic Climate Control Panel

REMOVAL AND INSTALLATION

Bonneville, Eighty-Eight, LeSabre, Ninety-Eight, Park Avenue, Aurora, Riviera and 1993 Cadillac

1. Disconnect the negative battery cable.
2. Remove the instrument panel trim plate(s) to gain access to the electronic control panel:
   - On Park Avenue and LeSabre, remove the lower trim instrument trim panels, air deflectors, glove box, front instrument panel trim.
   - On Eldorado and Seville, remove the knee bolster.
3. Remove the control panel attaching screws.
4. Pull the control panel out far enough to disconnect the electrical connector. Remove control panel.

To install:

5. Connect control panel electrical connector.
6. Install control panel attaching screws.
7. Install the instrument panel trim plate(s).
8. Connect the negative battery cable.

1994–95 Cadillac

1. Disconnect the negative battery cable.
2. Pull fuses A5-IPC (Ign.) and B5-IPC (Batt.) from rear compartment fuse panel and fuse A3-IGN1 from the engine compartment fuse panel.
3. Remove the defroster grille using a small flat-bladed tool, prying upward.
4. Remove the sunload and headlamp auto control sensors from the defroster grille.
5. Remove the 3 screws retaining the upper trim panel through the defroster grille opening.
6. Remove the 4 screws retaining the upper trim panel through the vent openings.
7. Remove the upper trim panel. On the passenger side of vehicle, press down on the forward edge of the trim panel while pulling upward and back on the rear edge of the trim panel (Deville/Concours).
8. Remove the upper trim panel. Pull upward and back on the rear edge of the trim panel (Eldorado/Seville).
9. Disconnect the 2 electrical connectors on top of the instrument cluster.
10. Remove the 4 screws retaining the cluster to the instrument panel.
11. Remove the left sound insulator.
12. Remove the steering column opening filler trim by grasping at the front and rear edges and pulling downward.
13. Remove the 4 bolts retaining the steering column opening bracket and remove the bracket from vehicle.
14. Unclip the shift indicator cable at the steering column.
15. Remove the cluster.
16. Installation is the reverse of the installation procedure.

Cutlass Supreme, 1995 Grand Prix, Lumina, Monte Carlo and Regal

1. Remove the air cleaner, if necessary, to access the battery cables. Disconnect the negative battery cable.
2. Remove the instrument panel trim plate.
3. Remove the retaining screws, pull the control assembly out and detach the electrical connections.
4. Installation is the reverse of the removal procedure.

1994–95 Eighty-Eight and Ninety-Eight

1. Remove the instrument panel close out panel.
2. Disconnect the electrical connection.

3. Remove the heater and A/C control from the close out.
4. Installation is the reverse of the removal procedure.

Passenger Heater and A/C Control

REMOVAL AND INSTALLATION

1994–95 LeSabre, Park Avenue and 1995 Aurora and Riviera

1. Disconnect the negative battery cable.
2. Remove the door panel to gain access to the passenger temperature control.
3. Disconnect the electrical connector.
4. Remove the passenger temperature control.
5. Installation is the reverse of the installation procedure.

1994–95 Eighty-Eight and Ninety-Eight

1. Disconnect the negative battery cable.
2. Remove the door handle insert.
3. Remove the passenger climate control/power window switch plate.
4. Disconnect the electrical connector.
5. Remove the passenger climate control from the switch plate.
6. Installation is the reverse of the removal procedure.

SENSORS AND SWITCHES

Vacuum Actuator

OPERATION

Used on certain heating and air conditioning systems, the vacuum actuators operate the air doors determining the different modes. The actuator consists of a spring loaded diaphragm connected to a lever. When vacuum is applied to the diaphragm, the lever moves the control door to its appropriate position. When the lever on the control panel is moved to another position, vacuum is cut off and the spring returns the actuator lever to its normal position.

TESTING

1. Disconnect the vacuum line from the actuator.
2. Attach a hand-held vacuum pump to the actuator.
3. Apply vacuum to the actuator.
4. The actuator lever should move to its engaged position and remain there while vacuum is applied.
5. When vacuum is released it should move back to its normal position.
6. The lever should operate smoothly and not bind.

REMOVAL AND INSTALLATION

Century, Cutlass Ciera and Cutlass Cruiser

1. Removal of the defroster vacuum actuator requires removal of the instrument panel, defroster nozzle and mode valve housing assembly. Air inlet vacuum actuator requires removal of the wipers, windshield molding and close-out panel. Other actuators are accessible without major component removal.
2. On 1994–95 air inlet vacuum actuator, break the 5 heat stakes by drilling with a 10mm bit (use a drill stop to prevent drilling deeper than 5mm).
3. Remove the vacuum lines and linkage from the actuator.
4. Remove the hardware attaching the actuator.
5. Remove the actuator.

To install:

6. On 1994–95 air inlet vacuum actuator, drill 3.4mm holes, 25mm (1 inch) deep in the center of the 5 heat stakes bosses. Vacuum all drill shavings from inside of valve housing. Use 5 screws and washers to install valve housing top.
7. Install the actuator and attaching hardware.
8. Connect the linkage to the actuator.
9. Connect the vacuum lines to the actuator.
10. Test system to confirm proper functioning of the actuator.

Bonneville, Eighty-Eight, LeSabre, Ninety-Eight and Park Avenue

FRESH-RECIRC, BI-LEVEL, DEFROST VACUUM ACTUATORS

The fresh-recirc, heat-A/C bi-level and defrost vacuum actuators are located on the central air intake housing under the instrument panel. The slave actuator is located under the right side of the instrument panel.

1. Disable the SIR system, if equipped, as defined in this article.
2. On 1993 LeSabre and Park Avenue, removal of the instrument panel will be required to access and remove the vacuum actuators. Removal of the heater-A/C bi-level actuator will also require removal of the air distributor assembly after the instrument panel is removed. 1993 only. Perform the following:
   - Disconnect the negative battery cable.
   - Remove the right sound insulator panel; 1993 only.
   - Remove the right and left reveal inserts on the ends of the defroster grille, then remove the bolts exposed.
   - Remove the upper trim panel by pulling it forward.
   - Remove the information center (3 bolts) from the top of the instrument panel.
   - Remove the lower panel trim plate, the air vent deflectors and the glove compartment.
   - Remove the front instrument panel cluster and control trim panel.
   - Detach the parking brake cable. Remove the lower instrument panel trim and passenger SIR module.
   - Remove the bolts and connectors and remove the instrument panel.
3. Remove the right and left insulator panels. Remove the heater duct, defrost A/C valve and air distribution plenum and assembly, if needed.
4. Remove the vacuum hose, retaining screws, linkage and vacuum actuator.
5. Installation is the reverse of the removal procedure. Enable the SIR system.

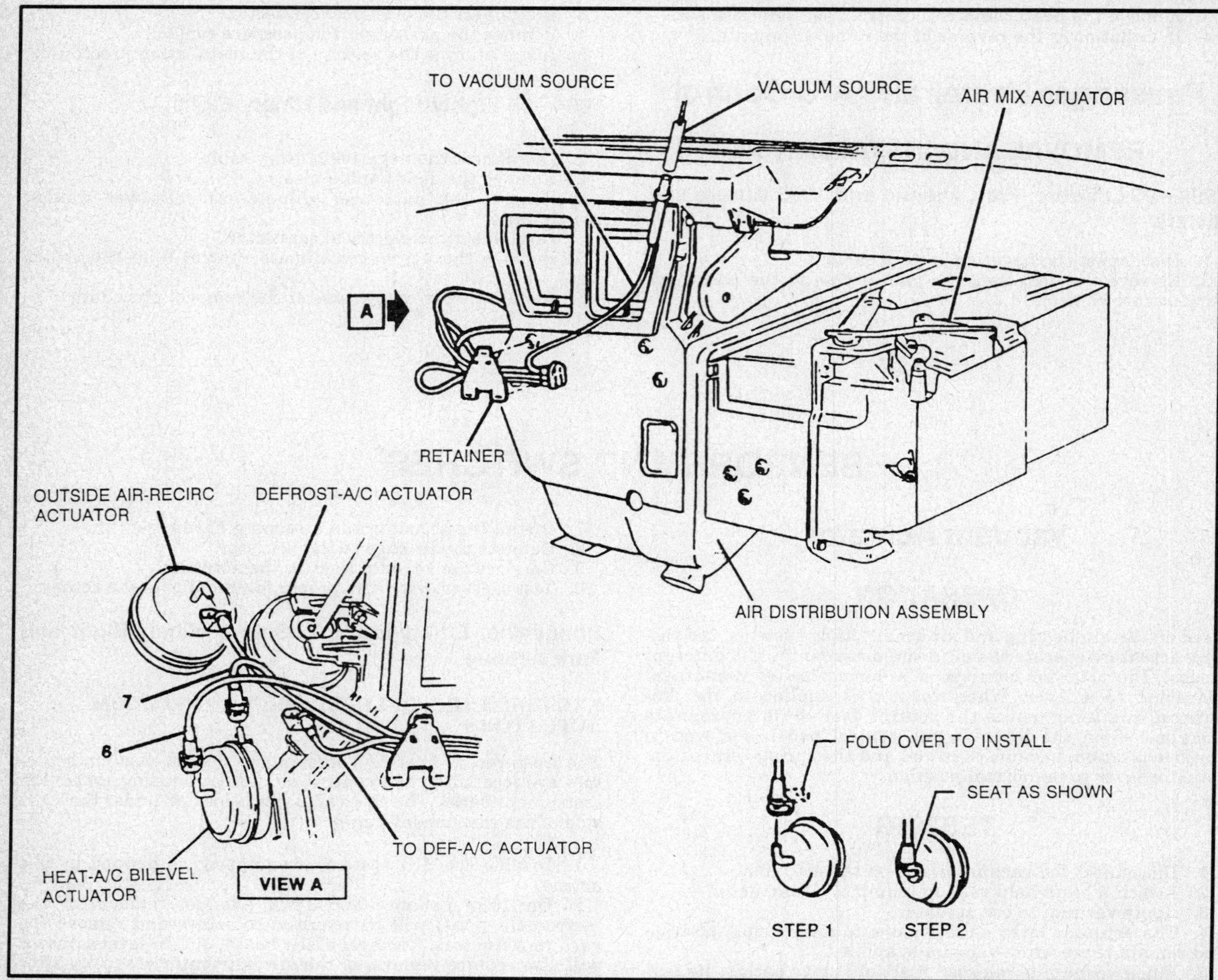

Vacuum actuator locations—Bonneville, Eighty-Eight, LeSabre, Ninety-Eight and Park Avenue shown; others similar

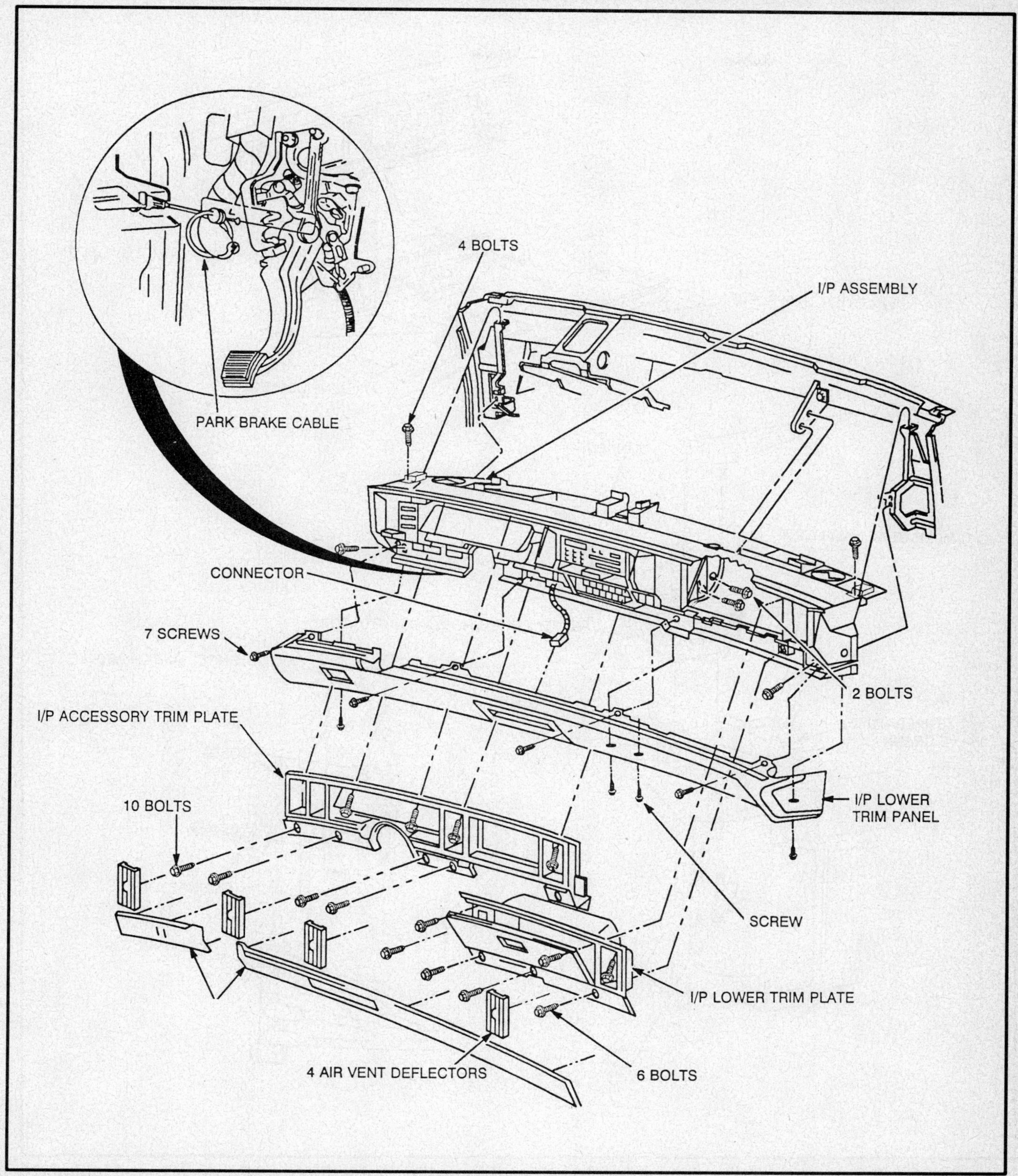

Instrument panel exploded view—Bonneville, Eighty-Eight, LeSabre, Ninety-Eight and Park Avenue

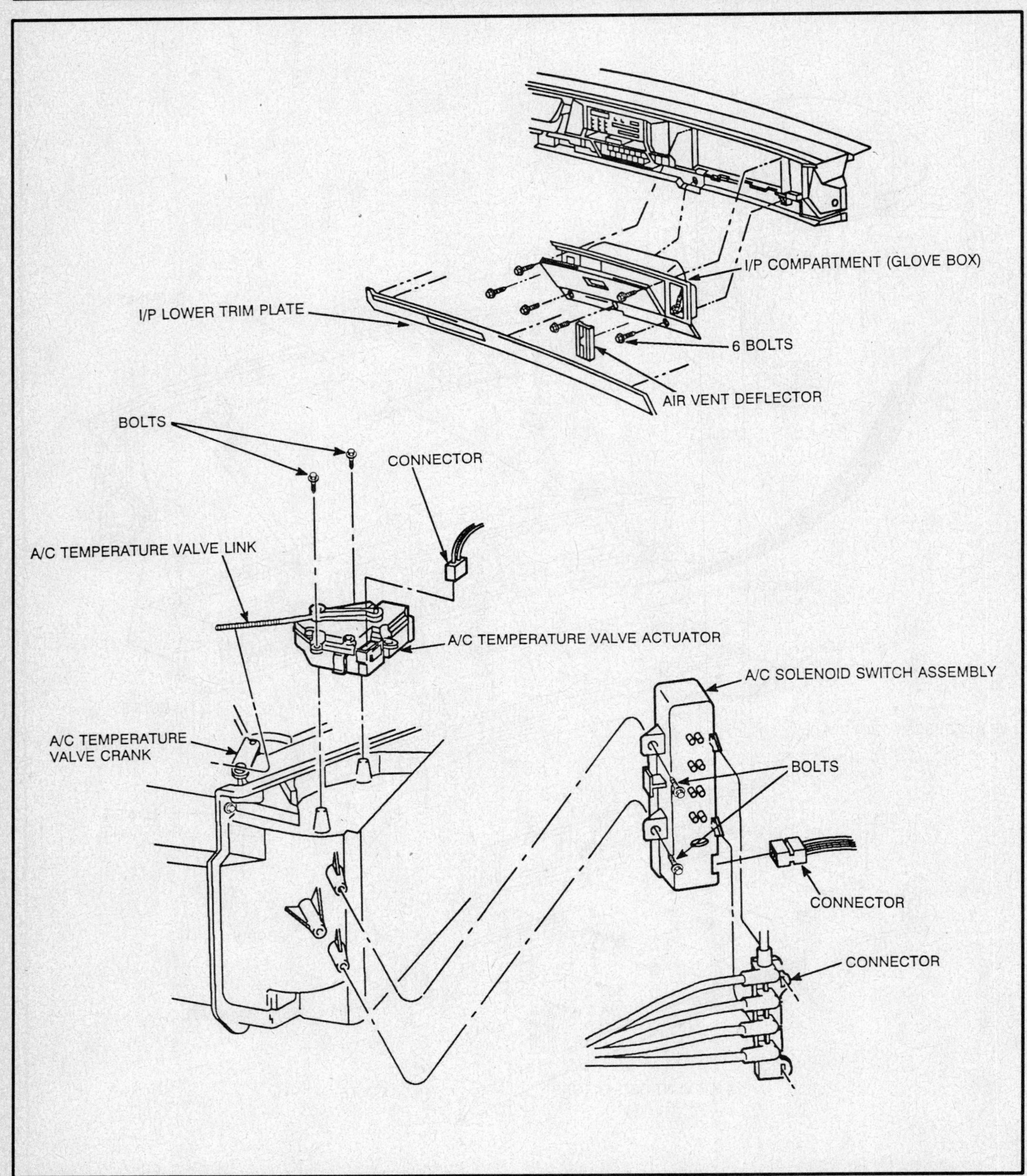

Temperature valve actuator and vacuum solenoid valve—Bonneville, Eighty-Eight, LeSabre, Ninety-Eight and Park Avenue

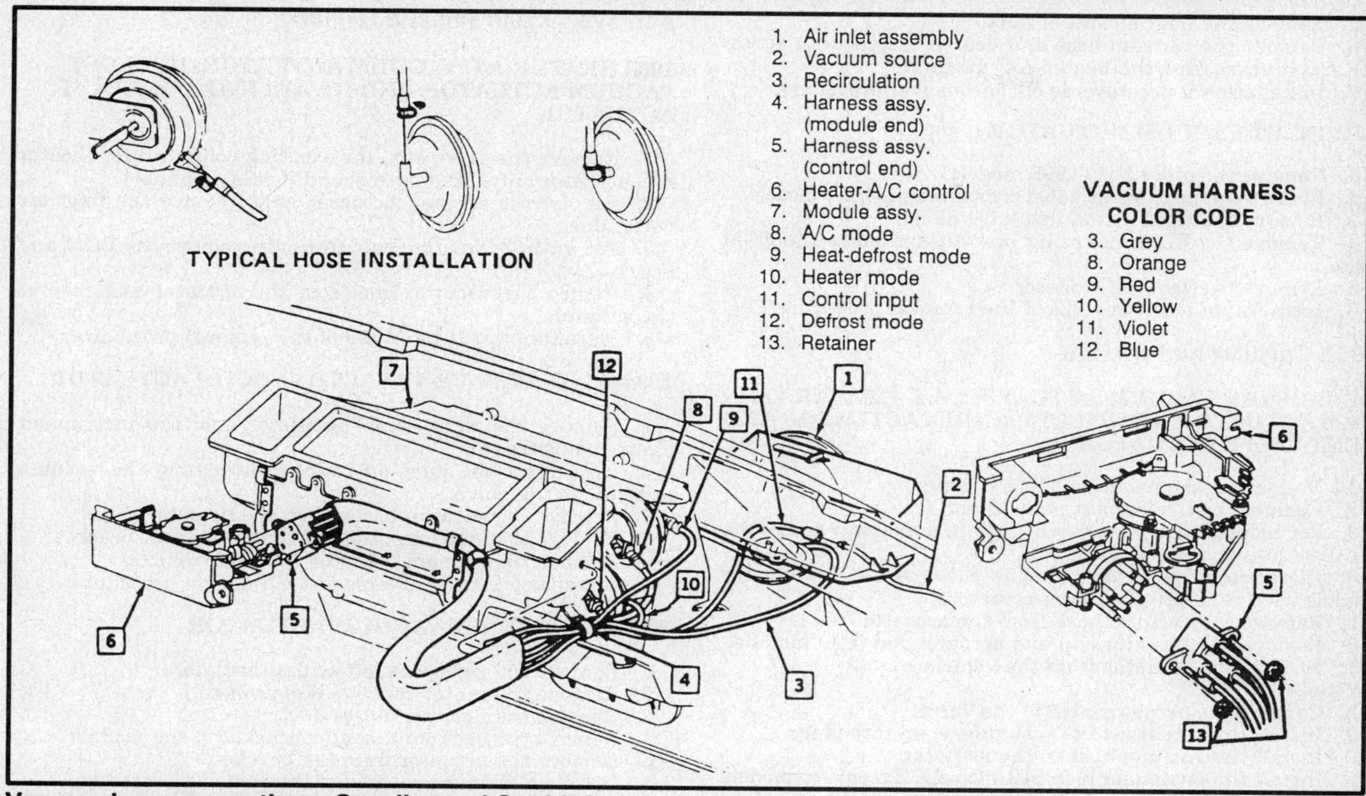

Vacuum harness routing—Cavalier and Sunbird

TEMPERATURE VALVE ACTUATOR AND VACUUM SOLENOID ASSEMBLY

On models with electronic climate control, the temperature valve actuator and vacuum solenoid assembly are located on the right front corner of the air distribution assembly.

1. Disable the SIR system as described in this article.
2. Remove the right sound insulator panel. 1993 only.
3. Remove the instrument panel lower trim plate, the air deflectors and the glove compartment. Swing down glove box on 1994–95 Buick and Oldsmobile.
4. Remove the instrument panel assembly (1994–95 Bonneville).
5. Unsnap the vacuum hose manifold from the solenoid switch assembly. Remove the bolts and take off the solenoid switch assembly.
6. Remove the temperature valve link by prying from the actuator. Remove the bolts, electrical connector, and the temperature valve actuator.
7. Installation is the reverse of the removal procedure.

Cadillac and 1993 Riviera

OUTSIDE AIR VALVE AND/OR DEFROSTER VALVE ACTUATORS

1. Disconnect the negative battery cable.
2. Remove the left sound insulator panel and courtesy lamp.
3. Remove the defrost valve hose (yellow).
4. Remove the 2 actuator screws and remove the actuator.
5. Installation is the reverse of the removal procedure.

UPPER/LOWER MODE VALVE ACTUATORS

1. Disable the SIR system as described in this article.
2. Disconnect the negative battery cable.
3. Remove the instrument panel.
4. Remove the floor air outlet assembly.
5. Detach the windshield defroster vacuum hoses and the defroster air distributor assembly.
6. Remove the vacuum hose from the upper/lower mode valve actuator, remove the 2 nuts and remove the actuator.
7. Installation is the reverse of the removal procedure.

1995 Aurora and Riviera

1. Disconnect the negative battery cable.
2. Disable the SIR system.
3. Remove the sound insulators as required to gain access to the actuators.
4. Remove the knee bolster, and console trim as required.
5. Disconnect the electrical connector from the actuator.
6. Remove the screws retaining the actuator.

To install:

7. Install the actuator and the mounting screws.
8. Connect the electrical connector.
9. Install the knee bolster, and the console trim.
10. Install the sound insulators.
11. Connect the negative battery cable.
12. Enable the SIR system.

NOTE: After the actuator has been replaced, the actuator needs to be recalibrated for proper travel. The ignition must be cycled ON for 3 minutes to allow the programmer and the actuators to recalibrate for proper travel.

1993–94 Cavalier and Sunbird

DEFROSTER VACUUM ACTUATOR AND HEATER-A/C VACUUM ACTUATOR

1. Remove the glove box (1993 models).
2. Remove the instrument panel compartment (1994 models).
3. Remove the steering column filler panel (if removing only the heater-A/C vacuum actuator).
4. Remove the right and left sound insulator panels.

5. Remove the floor air outlet duct.
6. Remove the vacuum hose and detach the vacuum actuator and bracket from the heater-A/C module.
7. Installation is the reverse of the removal procedure.

AIR INLET VACUUM ACTUATOR

1. Remove the glove box (1993 models).
2. Remove the instrument panel compartment (1994 models).
3. Remove the right sound insulator panel.
4. Remove the ECM mounting bracket and move the ECM aside.
5. Remove the vacuum actuator.
6. Installation is the reverse of the removal procedure.

1995 Cavalier and Sunfire

DEFROSTER VACUUM ACTUATOR, A/C-HEATER VACUUM ACTUATOR, AIR INLET VACUUM ACTUATOR AND VENT VALVE ACTUATOR

1. Disconnect the negative battery cable.
2. Remove the instrument panel trim.
3. For models with vent valve vacuum actuator, remove the air distribution duct.
4. Disconnect the passenger side SIR module. Except for models with vent valve vacuum actuators.
5. Remove the vacuum hose from the actuator.
6. Remove the actuator clip and actuator rod from module.
7. Remove the actuator from the vehicle.

To install:

8. Connect the actuator arm to the valve.
9. Install the actuator to the module, snap into place.
10. Install the vacuum hose to the actuator.
11. Install the passenger side SIR module. Except for models with vent valve vacuum actuators.
12. For models with vent valve vacuum actuator, install air distribution duct.
13. Install the instrument panel trim pad.
14. Connect the negative battery cable.

Beretta and Corsica

HEATER/DEFROST OR HEATER/VENT VACUUM ACTUATOR

1. Remove the right sound insulator and the glove compartment. I/P compartment for 1994–95 models.
2. Detach the push-on retainer, remove the hoses from the actuator.
3. Remove the instrument panel support bracket.
4. Remove the vacuum actuator.
5. Installation is the reverse of the removal procedure.

MODE VALVE OR DEFROST VACUUM ACTUATOR

1. Disable the SIR system (1993 models).
2. Disconnect the negative battery cable.
3. Remove the console.
4. Remove the right and left sound insulator (1994–95 models).
5. Detach the push-on retainer and remove the hose from the actuator.
6. Remove the panel support bracket, if needed. Remove the actuator.
7. Installation is the reverse of the removal procedure.

AIR INLET VALVE VACUUM ACTUATOR

1. Disable the SIR system.
2. Remove the right sound insulator panel and then the glove box.
3. Detach the vacuum hose from the actuator, then remove the retaining nuts, disengage the valve arm and remove the actuator.
4. Installation is the reverse of the removal procedure.

Achieva, Grand Am and Skylark

1993 HEATER-A/C VACUUM ACTUATOR, DEFROST VACUUM ACTUATOR AND/OR AIR INLET VACUUM ACTUATOR

1. Remove the glove box, the steering column filler (heater A/C actuator only), and both sound insulator panels.
2. For defrost vacuum actuator only, remove the floor air outlet duct.
3. For air inlet vacuum actuator only, remove the ECM and bracket.
4. Detach the vacuum line from the actuator and remove the actuator.
5. Installation is the reverse of the removal procedure.

1994–95 HEATER/VENT VALVE VACUUM ACTUATOR

1. Remove the right sound insulator, and the instrument panel compartment.
2. Disconnect the push-on retainer attaching the vacuum actuator to the valve.
3. Remove the vacuum hoses from the actuator.
4. Remove the instrument panel center support bracket.
5. Remove the vacuum actuator from the vehicle.
6. Installation is the reverse of the removal procedure.

1994–95 DEFROST VACUUM ACTUATOR

1. Remove the right and left sound insulators.
2. Remove the center console, if equipped.
3. Remove the floor air outlet duct.
4. Remove the vacuum actuator bracket to the module.
5. Remove the actuator from the bracket.
6. Installation is the reverse of the removal procedure.

Cutlass Supreme, Grand Prix, Lumina and Regal

1993–94 MODE VALVE VACUUM ACTUATOR AND AIR INLET VALVE VACUUM ACTUATOR

1. Remove the instrument panel to access the vacuum actuators.
2. Remove the vacuum line.
3. Pinch the arrow heads together and slip the actuator shaft off the valve lever (1994 Cutlass Supreme).
4. Depress the tang of the actuator and slip it off the module bracket. Rotate the actuator to disconnect it from the shaft connections.
5. Installation is the reverse of the removal procedure.

1995 MODE VALVE VACUUM ACTUATOR

1. Remove the windshield side upper garnish moldings.
2. Remove the instrument panel ad cover and sound insulators.
3. Remove the steering column trim panel.
4. Disconnect the parking brake release lever.
5. Remove the lower steering column.
6. Remove the seven bolts holding the instrument panel assembly.
7. Remove the 2 bolts above the steering column.
8. Pull back the instrument panel assembly gently to access the model valve vacuum actuator.
9. Remove the vacuum line.
10. Pinch the arrow heads together and slip the actuator shaft off the valve lever.
11. Depress the tang on the actuator and slip off the bracket on the module.
12. Installation is the reverse of the removal procedure.

1995 AIR INLET VALVE VACUUM ACTUATOR

1. Remove the instrument panel.

2. Remove the vacuum.
3. Depress the tang on the vacuum actuator and slip it off the module bracket.
4. Rotate the actuator to the disconnect actuator shaft from the air inlet valve.
5. Installation is the reverse of the removal procedure.

Temperature Valve Actuator

ADJUSTMENT

Bonneville, Eight-Eight, LeSabre, Ninety-Eight and Park Avenue with Electronic Climate Control

1. Start the engine. Move the temperature lever to full **WARM** position. Allow 15 seconds for the temperature valve actuator crank to move to the full **WARM** position.
2. Gently pull the valve crank toward the actuator until the valve hits the stop.
3. Push the threaded portion of the link into the slot on the plastic pin.

Temperature Valve Motor

REMOVAL AND INSTALLATION

1. Remove the right lower insulator panel.
2. Remove 2 screws holding the convenience center and lower it down.
3. Remove the 2 screws holding the vacuum solenoid and move them aside.
4. Remove 2 screws securing the electric temperature motor and remove the motor.
5. Remove the harness from the motor.
6. Installation is the reverse of the removal procedure.

Programmer Air Mix Valve

ADJUSTMENT

Cadillac and Riviera

1. Remove the right side sound insulator panel and glove box.
2. With the engine ON, set the ECC temperature control to 90°F (32°C). Allow 1-2 minutes for programmer arm to travel to MAXIMUM HEAT position.
3. Unsnap the threaded rod from the plastic retainer on the programmer output arm.
4. Check the air mix valve for free travel (push the valve to maximum A/C position and check for binding).
5. Preload the air mix valve in the maximum heat position by pulling the threaded rod to ensure the valve is sealing. The arm should be in the maximum heat position.
6. Snap the threaded rod back into the plaster retainer.

NOTE: Do this carefully to avoid disturbing the programmer arm or air mix valve position.

7. Set the temperature to 60°F (16°C). Verify that the programmer arm travels to full cooling position.
8. Reinstall the glove box and sound insulator.

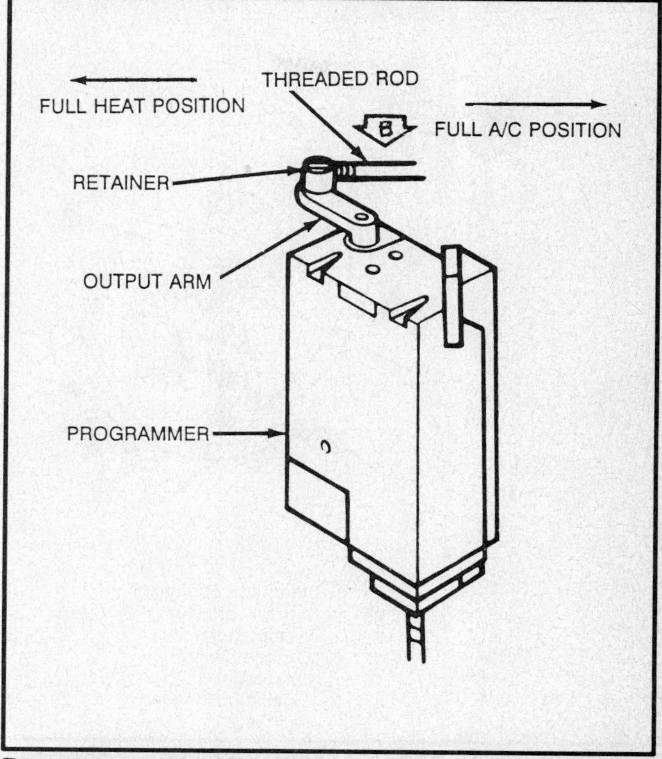

Programmer air mix valve adjustment—Cadillac, and Riviera

High-Side Temperature Sensor

OPERATION

1993 Cadillac

The high-side temperature sensor is located in the high pressure refrigerant line between the condenser and the orifice tube. The BCM monitors refrigerant temperature and determines the pressure based on the pressure-temperature relationship.

1994–95 Cadillac

The high side sensor is located in the high pressure refrigerant liquid line between the condenser and orifice tube. The ACP monitors the refrigerant temperature and transfer that data to the PCM to use in conjunction with the coolant temperature to determine the need for cooling fans, and to prevent the A/C compressor from operating at high discharge pressures.

REMOVAL AND INSTALLATION

1. Disconnect the negative battery cable.
2. Properly discharge the air conditioning system.
3. Disconnect the electrical connector from the sensor.
4. Unscrew and remove the sensor. Discard the O-ring.

To install:

5. Install a new O-ring. Lubricate with refrigerant oil. Install the sensor.
6. Connect electrical connector to the sensor.
7. Connect the negative battery cable.
8. Evacuate, recharge and leak test the air conditioning system.

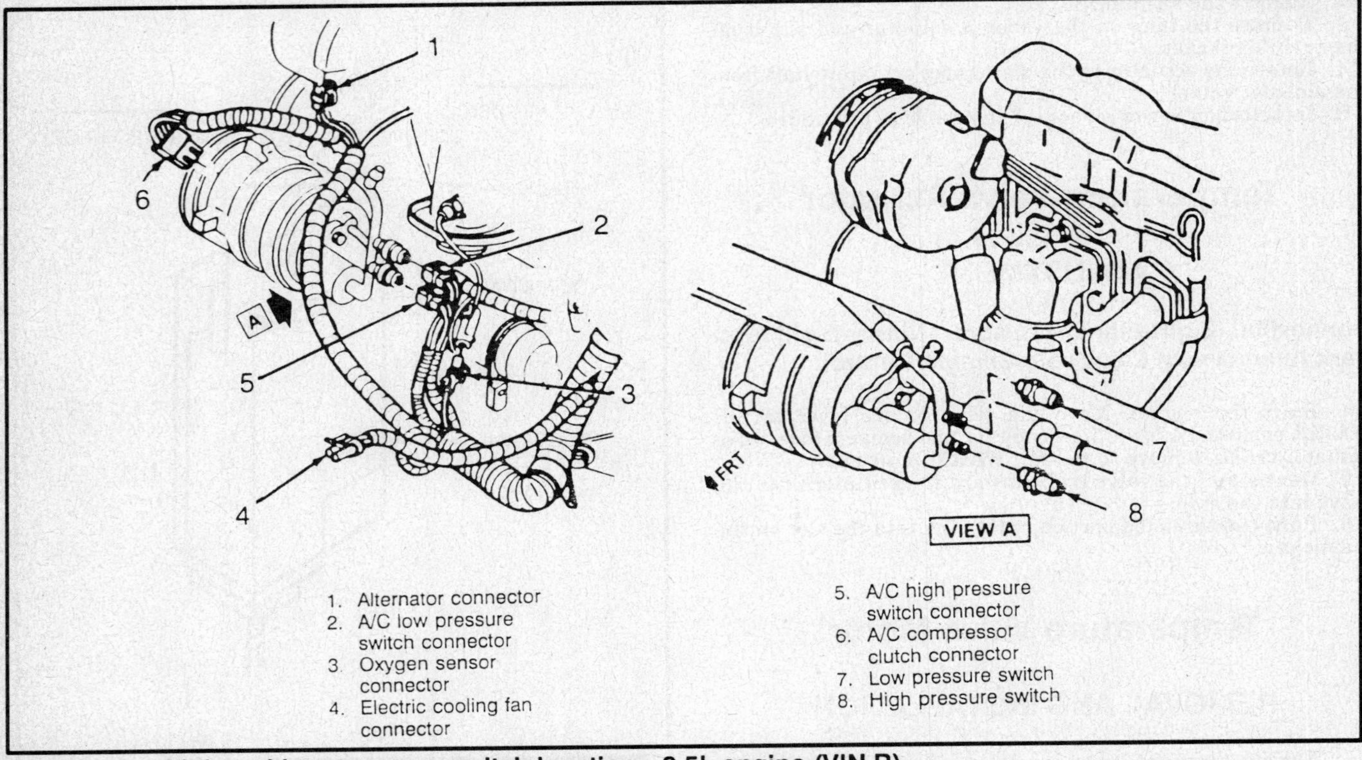

Compressor high and low pressure switch location—2.5L engine (VIN R)

Low-Side Temperature Sensor

OPERATION

1993 Cadillac

The low-side temperature sensor is in the low pressure refrigerant line between the orifice tube and the evaporator. The BCM monitors low-side pressure to determine the maintain system pressure based on the pressure-temperature relationship.

1994–95 Cadillac

The low side sensor is located in the low pressure refrigerant line between the orifice tube and evaporator. The ACP monitors this sensor to determine the low side pressure based on the pressure/temperature relationships of R134a.

REMOVAL AND INSTALLATION

1. Disconnect the negative battery cable.
2. Properly discharge the air conditioning system.
3. Disconnect the electrical connector from the sensor.
4. Unscrew and remove the sensor. Discard the O-ring.

To install:

5. Install a new O-ring. Lubricate with refrigerant oil. Install the sensor.
6. Connect electrical connector to the sensor.
7. Connect the negative battery cable.
8. Evacuate, recharge and leak test the air conditioning system.

High-Pressure Compressor Cut-Off Switch

OPERATION

The function of the switch is to protect the engine from overheating in the event of excessively high compressor head pressure and to deenergize the compressor clutch before the high pressure relief valve discharge pressure is reached. The switch is mounted on the back of the compressor or on the refrigerant hose assembly near the back of the compressor. Servicing a switch mounted on the back of the compressor requires that the system be discharged. Switches mounted on the coupled hose assembly are mounted on Schrader-type valves and do not require discharging the system to be serviced.

REMOVAL AND INSTALLATION

Compressor-Mounted Switch

NOTE: The system must be discharged in order to service the high pressure relief switch mounted to the back of the compressor.

1. Disconnect the negative battery cable.
2. Properly discharge the air conditioning system. Remove the compressor heat shield from under the vehicle.
3. Remove the coupled hose assembly at the rear of the compressor, if required.
4. Disconnect the electrical connector.
5. Remove the switch retaining ring using internal snapring pliers.
6. Remove the switch from the compressor. Discard the O-ring.

To install:

7. Lubricate a new O-ring with refrigerant oil. Insert into the switch cavity.

8. Lubricate the control switch housing with clean refrigerant oil and insert the switch until it bottoms in the cavity.
9. Install the switch retaining snapring with the high point of the curved sides adjacent to the switch housing. Ensure that the retaining ring is properly seated in the switch cavity retaining groove.
10. Connect the electrical connector.
11. Lubricate new coupled hose assembly O-rings with refrigerant oil. Install on the hose assembly fittings.
12. Connect the coupled hose assembly to the compressor. Install the heat shield, if removed.
13. Evacuate, recharge and leak test the system.
14. Connect the negative battery cable.
15. Operate the system to ensure proper operation and leak test the switch.

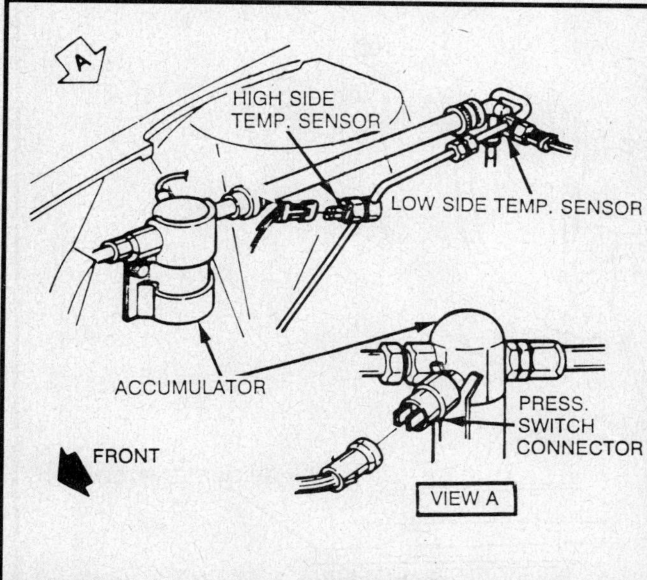

High and low pressure switch locations—DeVille

Refrigerant Line-Mounted Switch

NOTE: The switch is mounted on a Schrader-type valve and does not require that the system be discharged.

1. Disconnect the negative battery cable.
2. Disconnect the electrical connector.
3. Remove the switch from the coupled hose assembly. Discard the O-ring.

To install:

4. Lubricate a new O-ring with refrigerant oil.
5. Install the O-ring on the switch and install the switch.
6. Connect the electrical connector.
7. Connect the negative battery cable.

Low-Pressure Compressor Cut-Off Switch

OPERATION

The function of the switch is to protect the compressor by deenergizing the compressor in the event of a low-charge condition. The switch may be mounted at the back of the compressor or on the coupled hose assembly near the compressor. Servicing the valve requires discharging the system.

REMOVAL AND INSTALLATION

1. Disconnect the negative battery cable.
2. Properly discharge the air conditioning system, if required.
3. Disconnect the electrical connector(s).
4. If the switch is mounted to the rear head of the compressor, remove the coupled hose assembly to gain access to the switch. Remove the switch.
5. If the switch is mounted to the coupled hose assembly, remove the switch from its mounting position.

To install:

6. Install the switch.
7. Lubricate new O-rings with refrigerant oil.
8. If the switch is mounted to the rear head of the compressor, install the switch. Install new O-rings on the coupled hose assembly and install the assembly to the back of the compressor.
9. If the switch is mounted on the coupled hose assembly, install the switch.
10. Connect the electrical connector(s).
11. Evacuate, charge and leak test the system.
12. Connect the negative battery cable.

A/C Pressure Sensor (Transducer)

OPERATION

Achieva, Grand Am, Skylark, Cutlass Supreme, Grand Prix, Lumina and Regal and 1994–95 Cavalier, Sunbird, Sunfire, Century, Cutlass Ciera and Cruiser, Beretta and Corsica

This electronic pressure sensor is mounted in line between the compressor and condenser. As a cutoff device, at pressures that vary depending on model from above 430 psi to 462 psi to below 38 psi to 44 psi, it signals the ECM to cut off compressor operation. It will also boost idle air control when A/C is on during engine idle and it will control the cooling fan operation. The sensor is mounted on a Schrader valve on the high pressure line and therefore does not require system discharging before removal.

REMOVAL AND INSTALLATION

1. Disconnect the negative battery cable.
2. Remove the air cleaner and duct assembly.
3. Detach the electrical connection.
4. Remove the pressure sensor and discard the O-ring.

To install:

5. Install the sensor with a new O-ring.
6. Connect the electrical connector, and install the air cleaner and duct assembly.
7. Connect the negative battery cable.

A/C Coolant Fan Pressure Switch

OPERATION

The A/C Pressure Fan switch is a normally closed switch that monitors high side pressure during A/C operation. When high side pressure reaches 210 psi (1448 kPa) the switch opens signaling the PCM to turn the primary cooling fan to high speed. The switch closes once high side pressure drops to approximately 160 psi (1103 kPa).

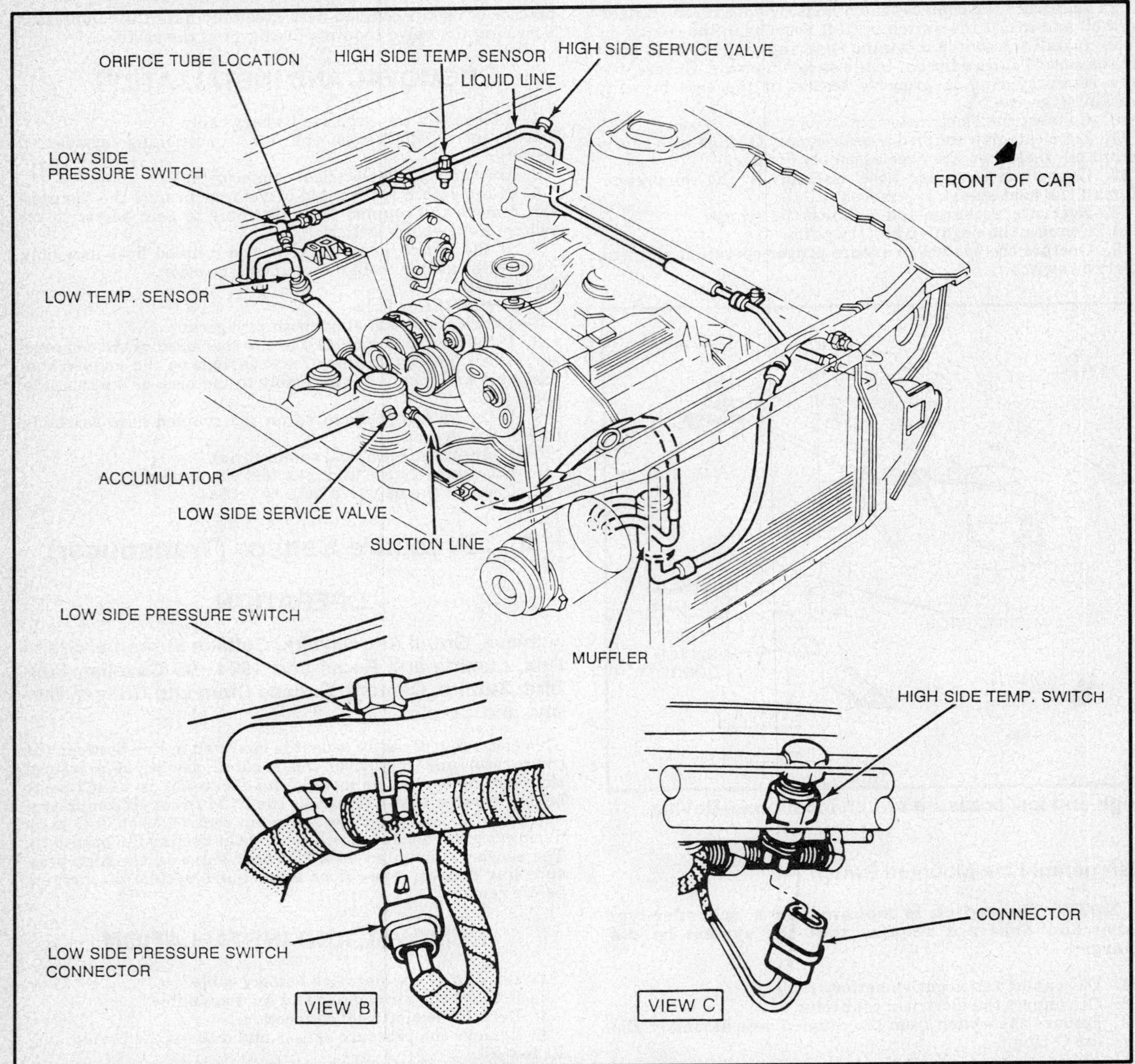

High and low pressure switch locations—Eldorado, Seville and Riviera

The switch is mounted on a Schrader-type valve. It is not necessary to recover the refrigerant from the A/C system to replace this switch.

1995 Aurora and Riviera

1. Disconnect the negative battery cable.
2. Disconnect the electrical connection from the switch.
3. Remove the switch and O-ring seal.

To install:

4. Install the switch using a new O-ring seal.
5. Connect the electrical connection to the switch.
6. Connect the negative battery cable.

Idle Speed Power Steering Pressure Switch

OPERATION

Engine idle speed is maintained by cutting off the compressor when high power steering loads are imposed at idle. The switch is located on the pinion housing portion of the steering rack or on the power steering pressure line. On 1993 A body, only 3.3L engines use this switch.

REMOVAL AND INSTALLATION

1. Disconnect the negative battery cable.
2. On 1994 Cutlass Supreme and Grand Prix, perform the following:
   - Raise the vehicle and suitably support.
   - Remove the left front wheel and tire assembly.
3. Disconnect the electrical connector.
4. Remove the switch.

To install:

5. Install the switch.
6. Connect the electrical connector.
7. Install the left front wheel and tire assembly, if removed. Lower the vehicle.
8. Connect the negative battery cable.
9. Allow the engine to come to normal operating temperature and confirm the proper operation of the switch.

Pressure Cycling Switch

OPERATION

The pressure cycling switch controls the refrigeration cycle by sensing low-side pressure as an indicator of evaporator temperature. The pressure cycling switch is the freeze-protection device in the system and senses refrigerant pressure on the suction side.

REMOVAL AND INSTALLATION

NOTE: The switch is mounted on a Schrader valve on the accumulator. The system need not be discharged to remove the pressure cycling switch.

1. Disconnect the negative battery cable.
2. Remove the rear sight shield, if required.
3. Disconnect the electrical connector.
4. Remove the switch and O-ring seal. Discard the O-ring.

To install:

5. Install a new O-ring. Lubricate with refrigerant oil.
6. Install the switch to the accumulator.
7. Connect the electrical connector.
8. Install the rear sight shield, if removed.
9. Connect the negative battery cable.

In-Vehicle Temperature Sensor

OPERATION

The sensor is located behind the instrument panel, usually near the center. The in-vehicle temperature sensor monitors the temperature inside the passenger compartment. To provide accurate temperature readings, a small amount of air is drawn into the sensor housing, through the aspirator, passing over the thermistor.

REMOVAL AND INSTALLATION

Bonneville, Eighty-Eight, LeSabre, Ninety-Eight and Park Avenue

1. Disconnect the negative battery cable.
2. On Park Avenue and LeSabre, remove the instrument panel lower trim plate, the air vent deflectors and the glove box.
3. Remove the front center instrument panel trim plate.
4. On Eighty-Eight, Ninety-Eight and Bonneville, remove the instrument panel trim plate, tilt it rearward and detach the driver information center keypad and rear defogger switch connector (1993 models).
5. Remove the control panel assembly.
6. Remove the radio, if required.
7. On 1994–95 Eighty-Eight and Ninety-Eight perform the following:
   - Remove the wood grain panel, knee bolster assembly and sensor grille.
   - Remove the sensor from the knee bolster heater and A/C control, (release the retainer clips through grill hole).
8. On 1994–95 Bonneville perform the following:
   - Remove the instrument panel trim plate (snaps out), and the gain control electrical connector (if equipped).
   - Remove the instrument panel cluster trim plate screws, and disconnect the electrical connector from the cigar lighter and remove the screws retaining the head/park lamp switch.
   - Remove the instrument panel cluster trim plate after releasing the head/park lamp switch rod.
9. Separate the aspirator hose from the sensor. Remove the sensor connector and remove the sensor.
10. Installation is the reverse of the removal procedure.

1993 Eldorado, Seville and Riviera

1. Disconnect the negative battery cable.
2. Remove the glove box.
3. Remove the right side-glass defroster hose duct.
4. Detach the electrical connectors from the power control module (PCM) and remove the PCM and bracket.
5. Remove the defroster grille and upper instrument panel pad.
6. Remove the aspirator hose and electrical connector. Remove the in-car temperature sensor.
7. Installation is the reverse of the removal procedure.

1995 Aurora and Riviera

1. Disconnect the negative battery cable.
2. Remove the knee bolster, aspirator tube and electrical connector from the sensor.
3. Remove the in-vehicle temperature sensor from the vehicle.
4. Installation is the reverse of the removal procedure.

1994–95 Cadillac

1. Remove the negative battery cable.
2. Remove the instrument panel top cover.
3. Remove the aspirator hose and the electrical connector.
4. Remove the retaining screw and the inside air temperature sensor.
5. Installation is the reverse of the removal procedure.

Cutlass Supreme, 1995 Lumina, Monte Carlo and Regal

1. Remove the air cleaner if needed to reach the battery. Disconnect the negative battery cable.
2. Remove the glove box.
3. Detach the electrical connector and the aspirator hose at the temperature sensor only.
4. Remove the screws and take out the sensor.
5. Installation is the reverse of the removal procedure.

Outside Temperature Sensor/ Ambient Temperature Sensor

OPERATION

The outside temperature sensor is located behind the front grille and provides an input to the BCM for display upon request on the Climate Control Panel (CCP).

1994–95 Cadillac

This sensor is located in front of the radiator. The sensor data is processed by the ACP and displayed on the CCC.

The ambient temperature sensor is located behind the front grille and is monitored by the HVAC programmer which uses it to display outside air temperature on the control assembly to help determine command signals.

REMOVAL AND INSTALLATION

1. Disconnect the negative battery cable.
2. Remove the grille or cover and air cleaner, if needed.
3. Raise and support the vehicle, if required.
4. Disconnect the electrical connector from the sensor.
5. Remove the attaching screw and the sensor.
6. Installation is the reverse of the removal procedure.

Solar Sensor

OPERATION

Bonneville, Eighty-Eight, LeSabre, Ninety-Eight and Park Avenue

WITH DUAL ZONE ELECTRONIC CLIMATE CONTROL

On models with dual-zone electronic climate control, left and right solar sensors are installed in the upper instrument panel defroster grille where sunlight can reach them. The sensors determine how intense the sunlight is reaching the passenger compartment and provides a signal to the climate control programmer for use in determining system operating modes required to maintain the selected setting.

WITH ELECTRONIC CLIMATE CONTROL

The solar sensor is mounted in the center of the instrument panel under the defroster grilled. It determines sunlight intensity and provides this signal input to the A/C programmer to help adjust operating modes to maintain desired setting.

REMOVAL AND INSTALLATION

Right Solar Sensor

1. Remove the defroster grille by snapping it out, if required.
2. Pull the glove box insert rearward and remove it, if required.
3. Remove the solar sensor from the grille by rotating it. Detach the connector.
4. Installation is the reverse of the removal procedure.

Left Solar Sensor

1. Disconnect the negative battery cable.
2. Disable the Supplemental Inflatable Restraint (SIR) system by performing the following:
   - With wheels straight ahead, turn ignition to **LOCK**. Remove the SIR fuse from the fuse panel.
   - Remove the left side sound insulator.
   - Remove the Connector Positive Assurance (CPA) from the yellow 2-way SIR harness connector at the base of the steering column and separate the connector.
3. On Eighty-Eight and Ninety-Eight, perform the following:
   - Remove the instrument panel cluster trim plate screws and tilt the plate rearward. Detach the keypad and rear defogger switch connectors (1993 models).
   - Remove the radio screws, electrical connector and antenna lead (1993 models). Remove defrost grille (1994–95 models).
   - Detach the wiring from the left solar sensor, turn 1/4 rotation and remove the sensor from the grille.
4. On Park Avenue and LeSabre, perform the following:
   - Remove the lower instrument panel trim pad (1994 models). On 1993 models remove the right sound insulator.
   - Remove the air deflectors and instrument panel trim plate (1994–95 models).
   - Slide the gear selector cable clip off, with gear in "Neutral" (1994–94 models).
   - Remove the screws and instrument panel dimmer switch (1994 models).
   - Remove the instrument cluster retaining bolts, pull the cluster out and detach the connectors (1993–94 models).
   - Remove the left and right reveal covers.
   - Remove the instrument panel upper trim panel screws, and pull the I/P forward.
   - If equipped, remove the left front speaker screws and speaker.
   - Remove the left solar sensor and disconnect the connector.
5. Installation is the reverse of the removal procedure.

Single Solar Sensor

EXCEPT AURORA, CADILLAC AND RIVIERA

1. Remove the cluster trim plate screws and tilt the plate rearward, 1993 only.
2. Remove the driver information center keypad, rear defogger switch and heated windshield switch connectors, as equipped. Remove the trim plate, 1993 only.
3. On 1993 models, remove the radio. Remove defroster grille on 1995 models. Reach through and detach the solar sensor connector.
4. Twist the sensor 1/4 turn to remove.
5. Installation is the reverse of the removal procedure.

AURORA, CADILLAC AND RIVIERA

1. Disable the SIR system as described in this article.
2. Remove the defroster grille end caps, remove the grille and the upper instrument panel trim pad.
3. Remove the solar sensor screw and connector. Remove the sensor.
4. Installation is the reverse of the removal procedure.

SYSTEM DIAGNOSIS

Self-Diagnostics with Electronic Climate Control

OPERATION

1993 DeVille, Eldorado and Seville

Self-diagnostics allow a review of the system when a problem is evident or suspected. By entering the diagnostic phase, the BCM and other on-board computers will display any stored codes indicating problems. BCM codes (including those related to the air conditioning system) are displayed with the prefix **B**. ECM codes start with **E** and SIR system codes start with **R**. This prefix is followed by a 3-digit number and **C** or **H**. The **C** means a current code still in memory since the last diagnostic display, and **H** means a historical code, not present at the last diagnostic display.

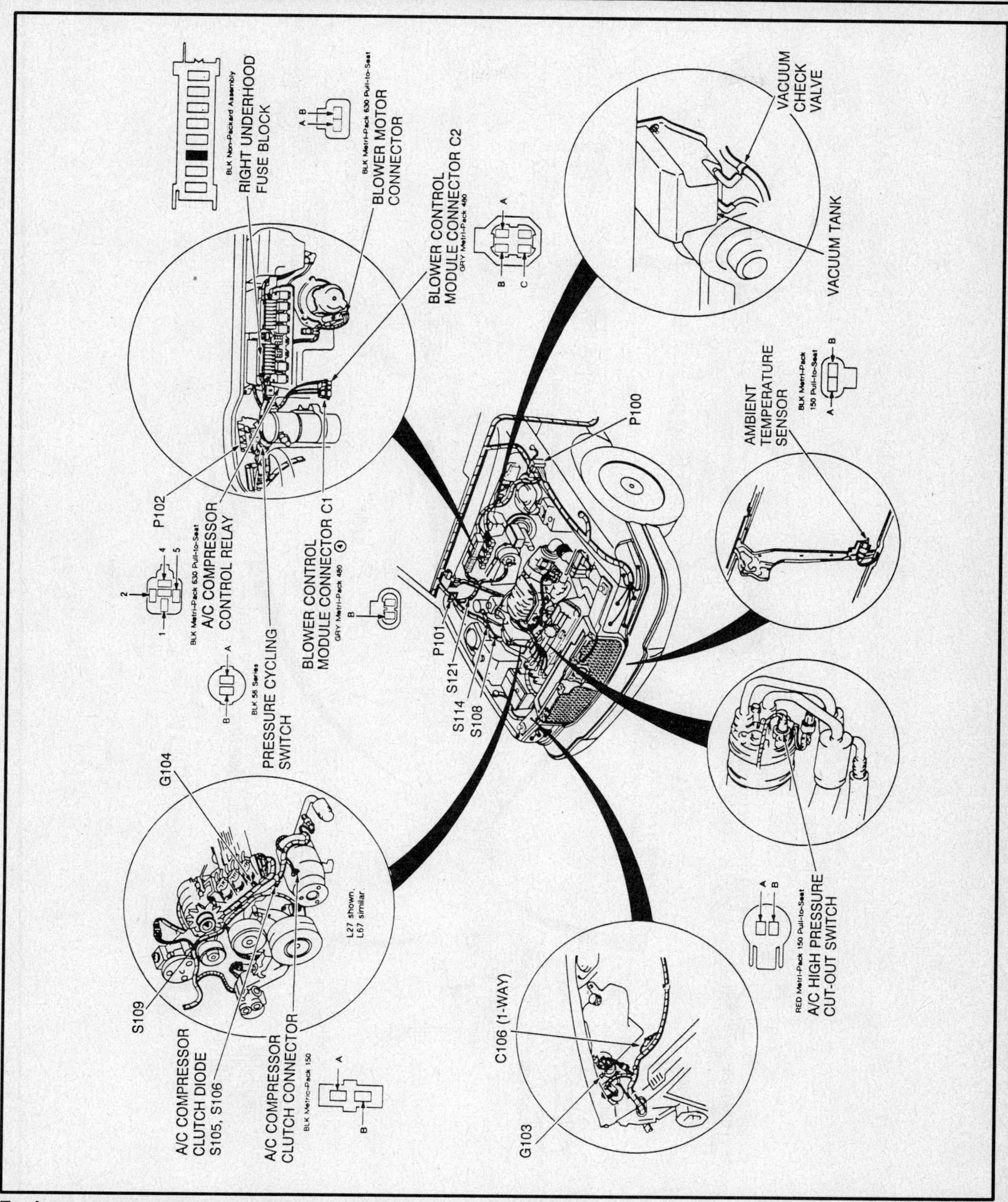

Engine compartment air conditioning system component locations—Bonneville, Eighty-Eight, LeSabre, Ninety-Eight and Park Avenue with dual-zone electronic climate control

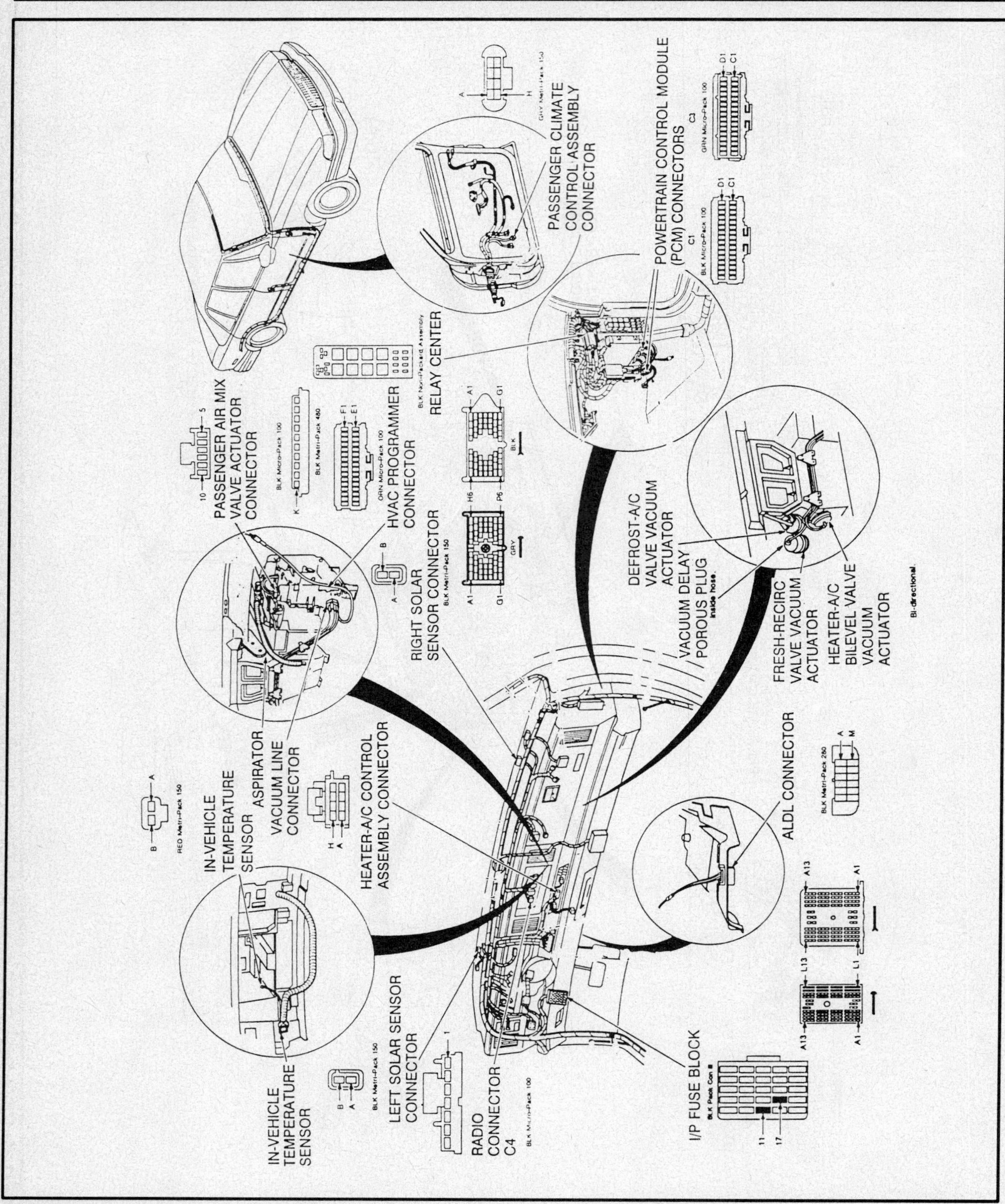

Passenger compartment air conditioning system component locations—Bonneville, Eighty-Eight, LeSabre, Ninety-Eight and Park Avenue with dual-zone electronic climate control

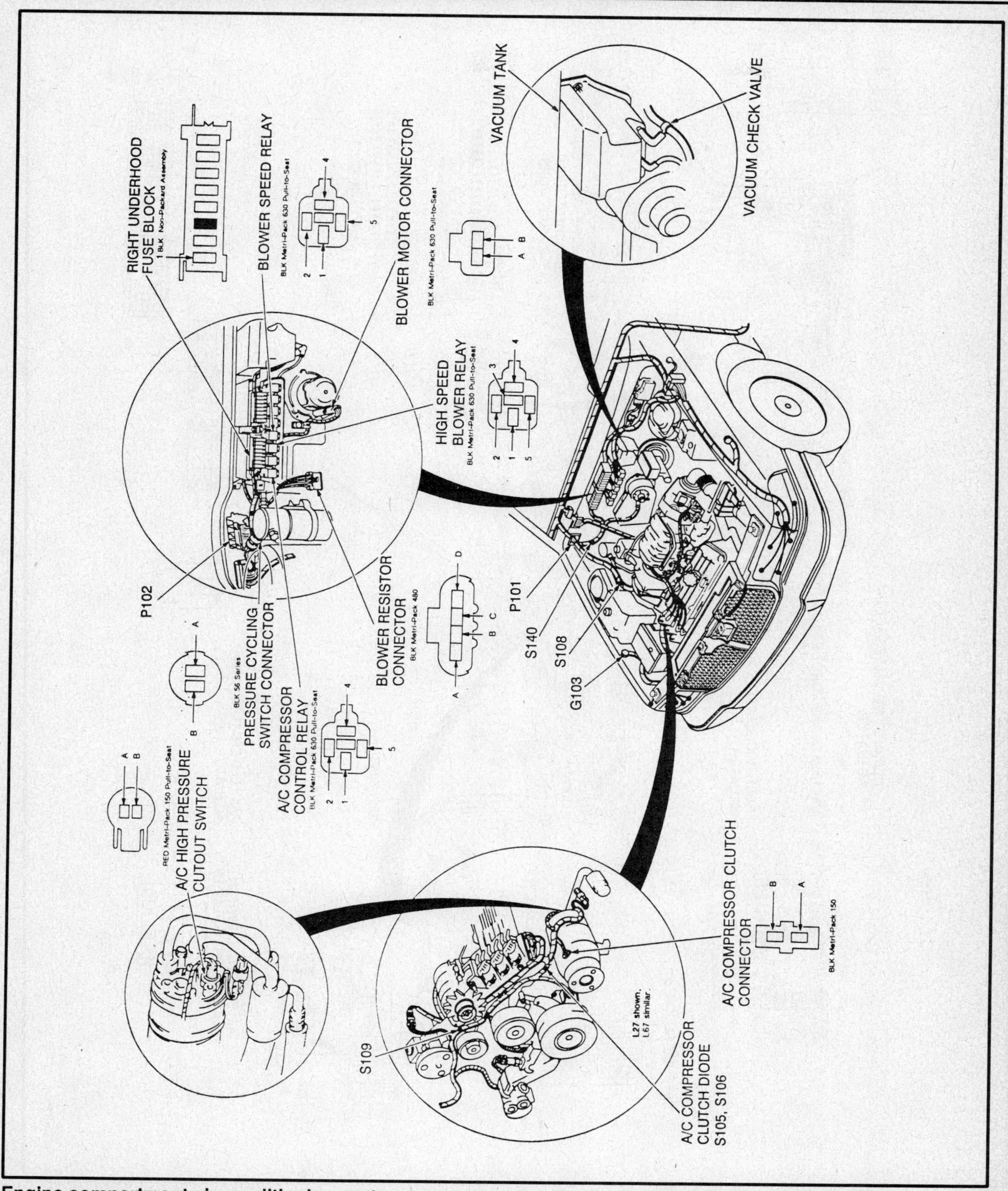

Engine compartment air conditioning system component locations—LeSabre and Park Avenue with electronic climate control

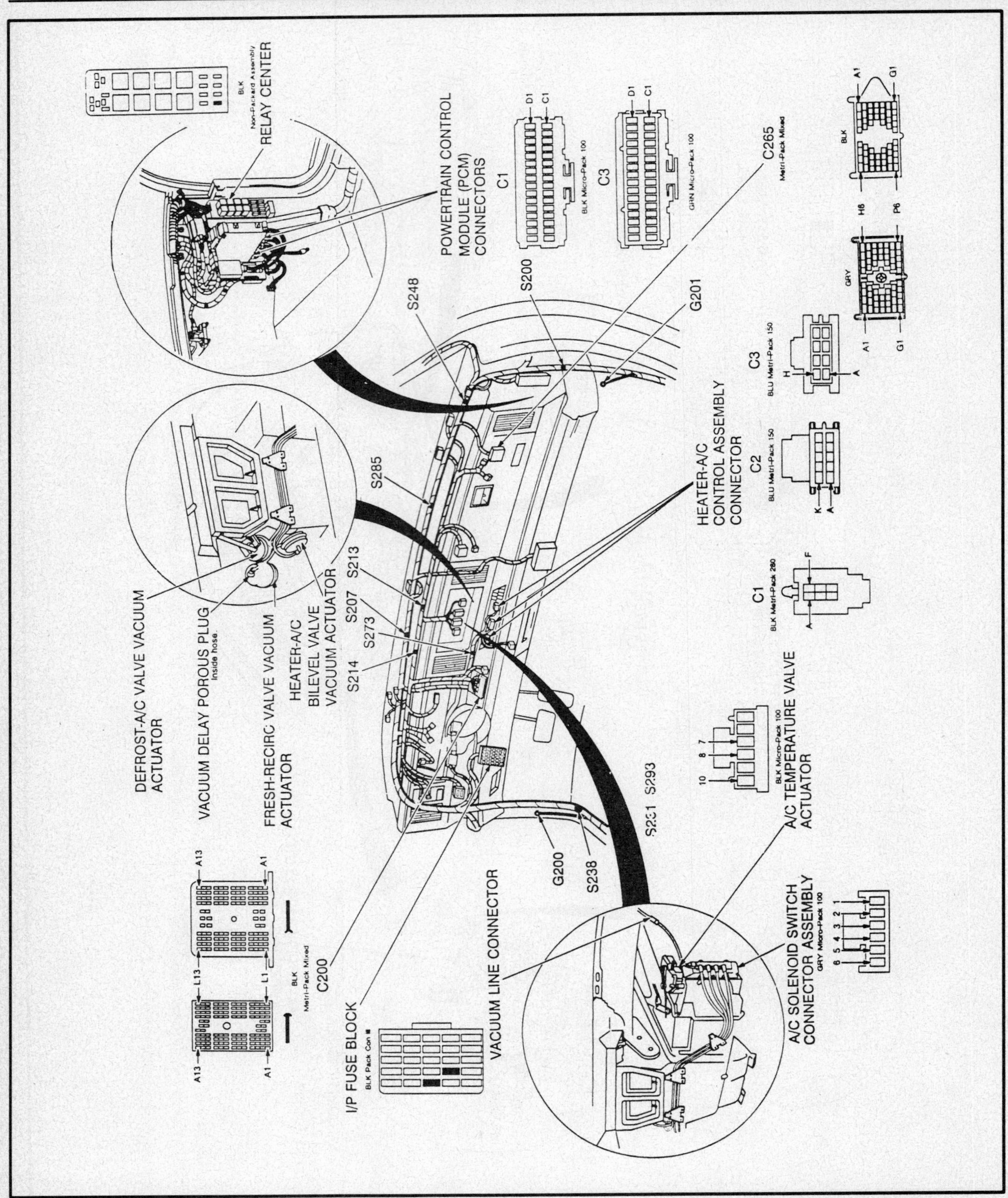

Passenger compartment air conditioning system component locations—LeSabre and Park Avenue with electronic climate control

1994–95 Cadillacs

Self-diagnostics allow a review of the system when a problem is evident or suspected. By entering the diagnostic phase, the IPC and other on board computers will display any stored codes indicating problems. Codes are displayed with the prefix **P** for PCM, **I** for IPC, **A** for ACP, **R** for SIR, **T** for TCS or **S** for RSS. This prefix is followed by a three digit code identifier and the letter **C** or **H** is used to indicate whether the code is current or historical.

1994-95 Cavalier, Sunfire, Century, Cutlass Ciera and Cruiser

Self-diagnostics allow a review of the system on certain control functions. When a malfunction is detected by the ECM/PCM/VCM, a diagnostic trouble code is set and the Malfunction Indicator Lamp (MIL) "Service Engine Soon" is illuminated on some applications.

ENTERING DIAGNOSTICS

NOTE: Do not operate the system in the diagnostic mode without the engine running for more than 1/2 hour. Extended diagnostic periods will deplete the battery and result in false code readings. If longer periods are required, attach a battery charger.

DeVille, Eldorado and Seville

1. Turn the ignition to **ON**.
2. Depress both the **OFF** and **WARMER** buttons at the same time and hold until all display segments light up.

NOTE: A "NO B CODE" message indicates the BCM cannot communicate with that system.

NOTE: If no codes are present for a system, a "NO X CODE" message (with X being the system i.e. E, I, A, R, T , or S) will be displayed. If the communication line to a component is not operating, a "NO X DATA" message will be displayed, indicating that the IPC could not communicate with that system, 1994 Cadillacs.

3. Depressing **OFF** will stop the selection process and return to the beginning of the sequence.
4. Depressing **LO** will display the next available system selection. This can be repeated through the entire sequence as many times as necessary.
5. Depressing **HI** will select the system displayed by the **LO** button for testing.

NOTE: If dashes appear, it means the test selected is not allowed under the current operating conditions.

6. When **CLEAR CODES?** test is selected, it will be followed by **CODES CLEAR** message being displayed for 3 seconds to indicate that all stored trouble codes are cleared from that system's memory. The display will automatically return to the next available test type for the selected system.
7. To get out of diagnostics, depress the **RESET** or **AUTO** button on the instrument panel or turn the ignition switch off. Trouble codes will not be erased when this is done.

TROUBLE CODES

While the diagnostic system can display several systems other than those related to air conditioning, the trouble codes shown in the chart are the only A/C and ECC related trouble codes that will be displayed.

DATA DISPLAY CODES (PARAMETERS)

While in the test selecting mode, data display codes can be used to compare vehicle problems with proper operating characteristics. The data displays (parameters) shown in the chart are only those BCM recorded displays relating to A/C and ECC.

SELF-DIAGNOSIS TROUBLE CODE DISPLAYS
E, VR/VS, EL, KD, KF, KY, KS, CD BODY

Trouble Code Numbers				Description
VR/VS Body	93 EL/KS Body, EZ	94–95 EL/ET, KD/KF, KS/KY Body	CD Body	
B100	A010	A101	F10	Outside temperature sensor circuit
B111	A011	A011	F11	High side temperature sensor
B112	A012	A012	F12	Low side temperature sensor
B113	A013	A013	F13	In-car temperature sensor circuit
B115	A015	A015	F15	Sun sensor circuit
B337	—	—	—	Loss of HVAC programmer data
—	—	A037	—	Loss of IPC programmer data
B440	A040	A040	F40	Air mix door circuit
B441	—	—	—	Cooling fan problems
B446	A046	A046	F46	Low refrigerant charge

SELF-DIAGNOSIS TROUBLE CODE DISPLAYS E, VR/VS, EL, KD, KF, KY, KS, CD BODY

Trouble Code Numbers				Description
VR/VS Body	93 EL/KS Body, EZ	94–95 EL/ET, KD/KF, KS/KY Body	CD Body	
B447	A047	A047	F47	Low refrigerant charge
B448	A048	A048	F48	Low refrigerant pressure
B449	A049	A049	F49	High side temperature too high
B450	A050	A050	—	Coolant temperature too high
—	—	—	F30	Control panel to BCM data circuit
—	—	—	F51	BCM prom error

VR/VS=Allante; EL=Eldorado; EZ=Riviera; KF=Concours
KS/KY=Seville; CD/KD=DeVille

DATA DISPLAY CODES (PARAMETERS) VR/VS, EL, EZ, KD, KF, KY, KS AND CD BODY

Code Numbers				Description ②
VR/VS Body	93 EL/KS Body, EZ	94–95 EL, KD/KF, KS/KY Body	CD Body	
BD20	AD20 ①	AD20 ①	P.2.0	Commanded blower voltage (actual)
BD21	AD21	AD21	P.2.1	Coolant temperature (actual)
BD22	AD22	AD22	P.2.2	Commanded air mix door position (0% = full cold; 100% = full heat)
BD23	AD23	AD23	P.2.3	Actual air mix door position (percent of travel)
BD24	AD24	AD24	P.2.4	Air delivery mode ③
BD25	AD25	AD25	P.2.5	In-car temperature (actual)
BD26	AD26	AD26	P.2.6	Outside air temperature (actual)
BD27	AD27	AD27	P.2.7	High side temperature (at condenser output)
BD28	AD28	AD28	P.2.8	Low side temperature (at evap. inlet)
BD32	AD32	AD32	P.3.2	Sun sensor temperature (actual)
—	—	AD70	—	Rear blower feedback
—	—	AD71	—	Integral control term
—	—	AD98	—	Ignition cycle
—	—	AD99	—	ACP software I.D.

VR/VS=Allante; EL=Eldorado; KF=Concours;
KS/KY=Seville; CD/KD=DeVille;
EZ=Riviera
① AD20 indicates blower speed (0-100%)' others display voltage value.
② All temperatures are displayed in degrees Celsius.
③ 0=Max A/C

1=A/C
2=Bi-level
3=Heater/defroster
4=Heater
5=Off
6=Normal purge
7=Cold purge
8=Front defog

ELECTRONIC CLIMATE CONTROL SELF DIAGNOSTICS— NINETY-EIGHT AND PARK AVENUE

To enter diagnostic mode: (NOTE: Press AUTO at any time to terminate diagnostic mode

- Ignition Switch: RUN
- Press OFF and WARM buttons simultaneously

SEGMENT CHECK (Press OFF)

ECC DIAGNOSTIC TROUBLE CODES (DTCs) AND STATUS LIGHT DISPLAYS (Press OFF)

Press Fan Down → A: Continued on next page

Press OFF ← B: Continued from next page

DIAGNOSTIC CODES	
DTC	DESCRIPTION
00	No codes present.
10 or 110	Ambient Temperature Sensor circuit open or shorted.
13 or 113	In-Vehicle Temperature Sensor circuit open or shorted.
15 or 115	LH Solar Sensor circuit open or shorted.
35 or 135	E & C Data Line failure with Heater And A/C Control Assembly.
38 or 138	Serial Data Line failure with PCM.
40 or 140	Driver Air Mix Motor circuit open or shorted, or not calibrated.
48 or 148	Long term freon loss.
52 or 152	Keep Alive Memory lost; sets with battery disconnected.
66 or 166	Low freon.

NOTE: A number 1 prefix on any diagnostic trouble code indicates a history DTC.

STATUS LIGHT DISPLAYS

- Begins after segment check has been completed.
- Visible at all times during on-board diagnostics use and functions along with ECC Data List and ECC Overrides.

STATUS DISPLAY	INDICATED CONDITION
Snowflake	A/C Compressor Clutch engaged.
First Blower Speed Indicator Bar	Pressure Cycling Switch open.
Second Blower Speed Indicator Bar	Heater-A/C Bi-level Valve Vacuum Actuator employed.
Third Blower Speed Indicator Bar	Defrost-A/C Valve Vacuum Actuator employed.
Fourth Blower Speed Indicator Bar	O/S Air-Recirc Valve Vacuum Actuator employed.

ELECTRONIC CLIMATE CONTROL SELF DIAGNOSTICS— NINETY-EIGHT AND PARK AVENUE, CONT'D

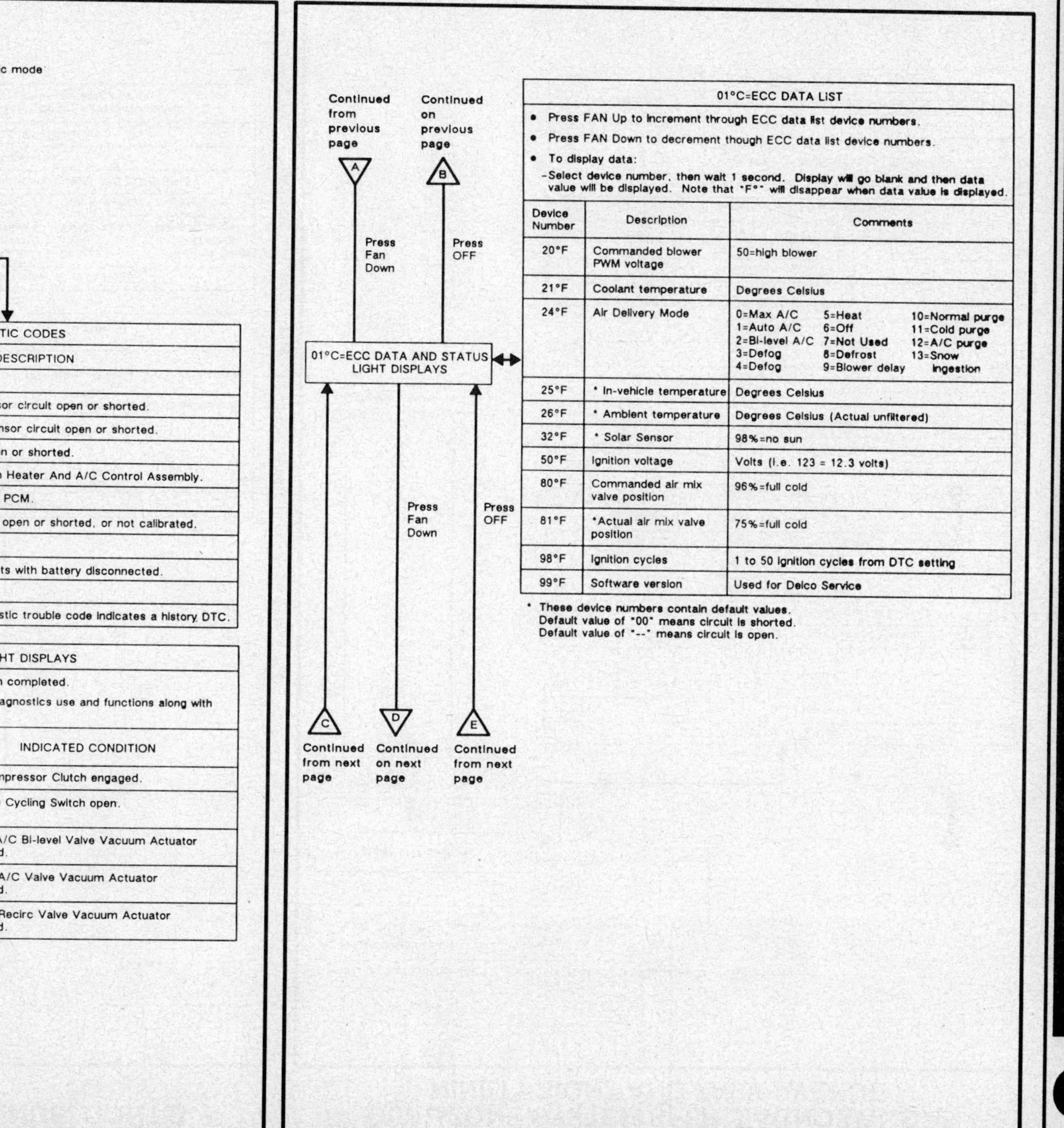

01°C=ECC DATA LIST

- Press FAN Up to increment through ECC data list device numbers.
- Press FAN Down to decrement though ECC data list device numbers.
- To display data:
  - Select device number, then wait 1 second. Display will go blank and then data value will be displayed. Note that "F°" will disappear when data value is displayed.

Device Number	Description	Comments
20°F	Commanded blower PWM voltage	50=high blower
21°F	Coolant temperature	Degrees Celsius
24°F	Air Delivery Mode	0=Max A/C 1=Auto A/C 2=Bi-level A/C 3=Defog 4=Defog; 5=Heat 6=Off 7=Not Used 8=Defrost 9=Blower delay; 10=Normal purge 11=Cold purge 12=A/C purge 13=Snow ingestion
25°F	* In-vehicle temperature	Degrees Celsius
26°F	* Ambient temperature	Degrees Celsius (Actual unfiltered)
32°F	* Solar Sensor	98%=no sun
50°F	Ignition voltage	Volts (i.e. 123 = 12.3 volts)
80°F	Commanded air mix valve position	96%=full cold
81°F	*Actual air mix valve position	75%=full cold
98°F	Ignition cycles	1 to 50 ignition cycles from DTC setting
99°F	Software version	Used for Delco Service

* These device numbers contain default values.
Default value of "00" means circuit is shorted.
Default value of "--" means circuit is open.

ELECTRONIC CLIMATE CONTROL SELF DIAGNOSTICS NINETY-EIGHT AND PARK AVENUE, CONT'D

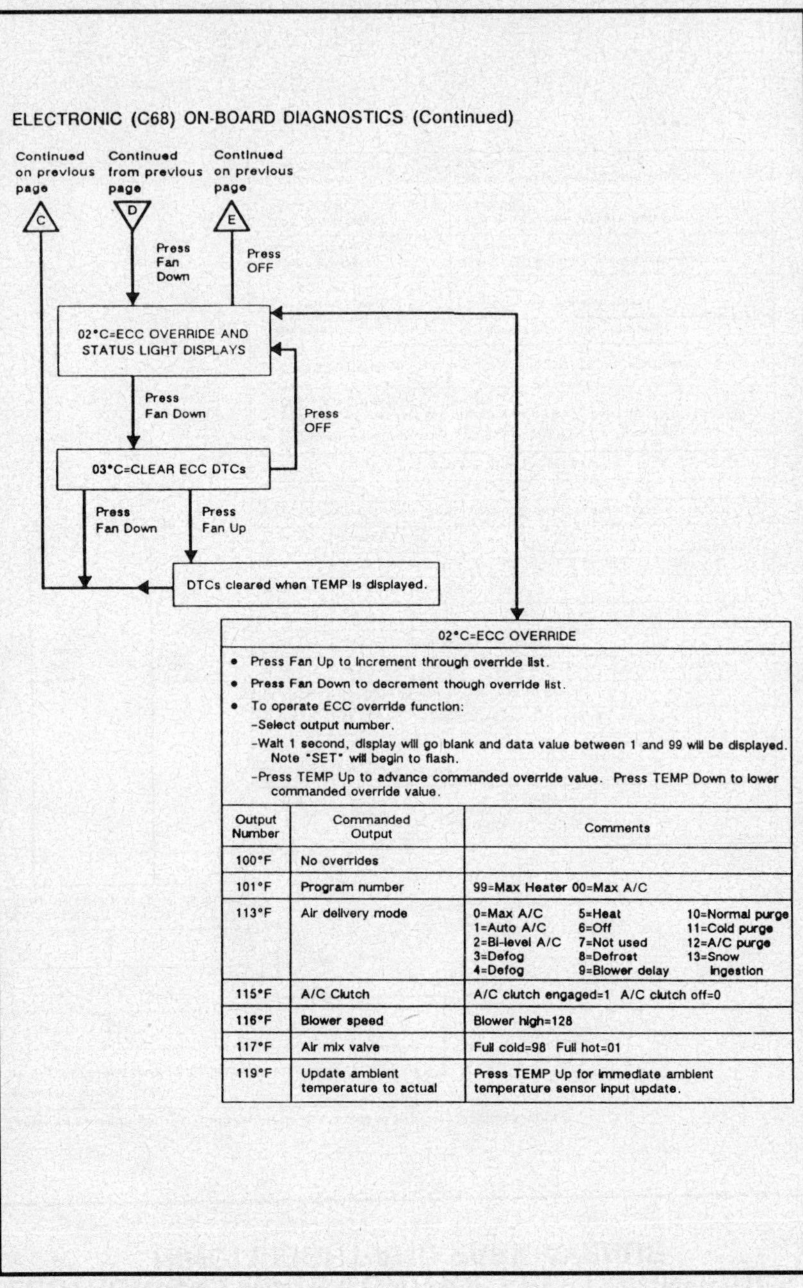

02°C=ECC OVERRIDE

- Press Fan Up to increment through override list.
- Press Fan Down to decrement though override list.
- To operate ECC override function:
  - –Select output number.
  - –Wait 1 second, display will go blank and data value between 1 and 99 will be displayed. Note "SET" will begin to flash.
  - –Press TEMP Up to advance commanded override value. Press TEMP Down to lower commanded override value.

Output Number	Commanded Output	Comments
100°F	No overrides	
101°F	Program number	99=Max Heater 00=Max A/C
113°F	Air delivery mode	0=Max A/C 1=Auto A/C 2=Bi-level A/C 3=Defog 4=Defog 5=Heat 6=Off 7=Not used 8=Defrost 9=Blower delay 10=Normal purge 11=Cold purge 12=A/C purge 13=Snow ingestion
115°F	A/C Clutch	A/C clutch engaged=1 A/C clutch off=0
116°F	Blower speed	Blower high=128
117°F	Air mix valve	Full cold=98 Full hot=01
119°F	Update ambient temperature to actual	Press TEMP Up for immediate ambient temperature sensor input update.

ELECTRONIC CLIMATE CONTROL WITH DUAL-ZONE SYSTEM SELF DIAGNOSTICS—NINETY-EIGHT AND PARK AVENUE

To enter diagnostic mode: (NOTE: Press AUTO at any time to terminate diagnostic mode)

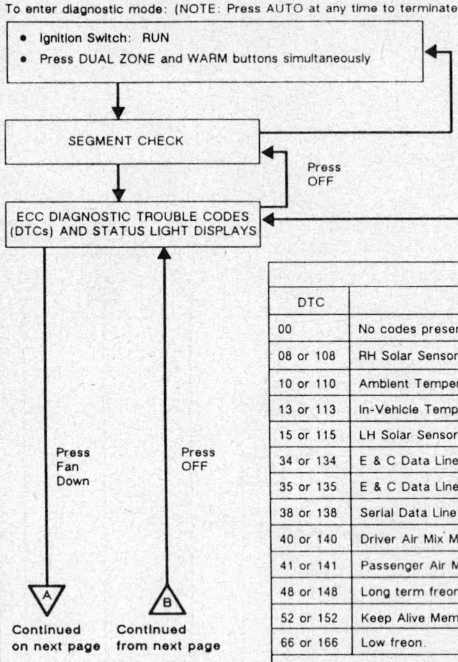

- Ignition Switch: RUN
- Press DUAL ZONE and WARM buttons simultaneously

Press OFF

SEGMENT CHECK

Press OFF

ECC DIAGNOSTIC TROUBLE CODES (DTCs) AND STATUS LIGHT DISPLAYS

Press Fan Down — A — Continued on next page

Press OFF — B — Continued from next page

DIAGNOSTIC CODES

DTC	DESCRIPTION
00	No codes present.
08 or 108	RH Solar Sensor circuit open or shorted.
10 or 110	Ambient Temperature Sensor circuit open or shorted.
13 or 113	In-Vehicle Temperature Sensor circuit open or shorted.
15 or 115	LH Solar Sensor circuit open or shorted.
34 or 134	E & C Data Line failure with Passenger Climate Control Assembly.
35 or 135	E & C Data Line failure with Heater And A/C Control Assembly.
38 or 138	Serial Data Line failure with PCM.
40 or 140	Driver Air Mix Motor circuit open or shorted, or not calibrated.
41 or 141	Passenger Air Mix Motor circuit open or shorted, or not calibrated.
48 or 148	Long term freon loss.
52 or 152	Keep Alive Memory lost; sets with battery disconnected.
66 or 166	Low freon.

NOTE: A number 1 prefix on any diagnostic trouble code indicates a history DTC.

STATUS LIGHT DISPLAYS

- Begins after segment check has been completed.
- Visible at all times during on-board diagnostics use and functions along with ECC Data List and ECC Overrides.

STATUS DISPLAY	INDICATED CONDITION
EXT	A/C Compressor Clutch engaged.
FAN	Pressure Cycling Switch open.
Lower Fan segment bar	Driver and Passenger Defrost-A/C Valves in Heater position.
Upper fan segment bar	Driver and Passenger Mode Valves in A/C position.
No segment bars	Driver and Passenger Mode Valves in Bi-Level position.
AUTO	O/S Air-Recirc. Valve in Recirc. position.

ELECTRONIC CLIMATE CONTROL WITH DUAL-ZONE SYSTEM SELF DIAGNOSTICS—NINETY-EIGHT AND PARK AVENUE, CONT'D

Continued from previous page (A) — Press Fan Down
Continued on previous page (B) — Press OFF

01°C=ECC DATA AND STATUS LIGHT DISPLAYS

Press Fan Down — Continued on next page (D)
Press OFF — Continued from next page (E)
Continued from next page (C)

01°C=ECC DATA LIST

- Press HI to increment through ECC data list device numbers.
- Press LO Down to decrement though ECC data list device numbers.
- To display data:
  - Select device number, then wait 1 second. Display will go blank and then data value will be displayed. Note that "F°" will disappear when data value is displayed.

Device Number	Description	Comments
20°F	Commanded blower PWM voltage	110=high blower
21°F	Coolant temperature	Degrees Celsius
22°F	* Driver Actual air mix valve position	96%=full cold
23°F	*Driver Actual air mix valve position	75%=full cold
24°F	Air Delivery Mode	0=Max A/C 1=Auto A/C 2=Bi-level A/C 3=Defog 4=Defog 5=Heat 6=Off 7=Not Used 8=Defrost 9=Blower delay 10=Normal purge 11=Cold purge 12=A/C purge 13=Snow ingestion
25°F	* In-vehicle temperature	Degrees Celsius
26°F	* Ambient temperature	Degrees Celsius (Actual unfiltered)
32°F	* LH Solar Sensor	98%=no sun
50°F	Ignition voltage	Volts (i.e. 123 = 12.3 volts)
80°F	Passenger commanded air mix valve position	96%=full cold
81°F	* Passenger actual air mix valve position	75%=full cold
83°F	* RH Solar Sensor	98%=no sun
98°F	Ignition cycles	1 to 50 ignition cycles from DTC setting
99°F	Software version	Used for Delco Service

* These device numbers contain default values.
Default value of "00" means circuit is shorted.
Default value of "--" means circuit is open.

ELECTRONIC CLIMATE CONTROL WITH DUAL-ZONE SYSTEM SELF DIAGNOSTICS—NINETY-EIGHT AND PARK AVENUE, CONT'D

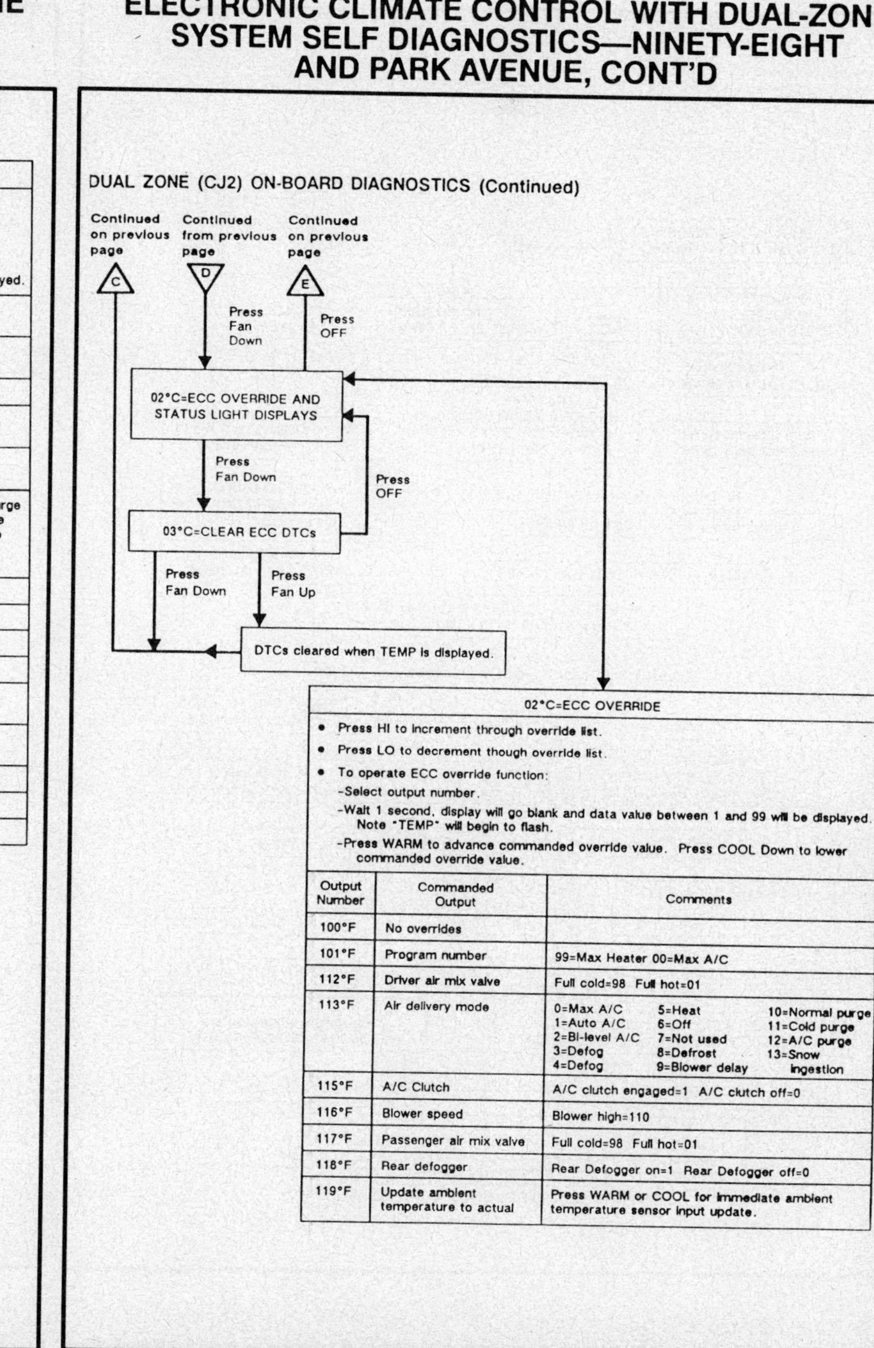

02°C=ECC OVERRIDE

- Press HI to increment through override list.
- Press LO to decrement though override list.
- To operate ECC override function:
  - Select output number.
  - Wait 1 second, display will go blank and data value between 1 and 99 will be displayed. Note "TEMP" will begin to flash.
  - Press WARM to advance commanded override value. Press COOL Down to lower commanded override value.

Output Number	Commanded Output	Comments
100°F	No overrides	
101°F	Program number	99=Max Heater 00=Max A/C
112°F	Driver air mix valve	Full cold=98 Full hot=01
113°F	Air delivery mode	0=Max A/C 1=Auto A/C 2=Bi-level A/C 3=Defog 4=Defog 5=Heat 6=Off 7=Not used 8=Defrost 9=Blower delay 10=Normal purge 11=Cold purge 12=A/C purge 13=Snow ingestion
115°F	A/C Clutch	A/C clutch engaged=1 A/C clutch off=0
116°F	Blower speed	Blower high=110
117°F	Passenger air mix valve	Full cold=98 Full hot=01
118°F	Rear defogger	Rear Defogger on=1 Rear Defogger off=0
119°F	Update ambient temperature to actual	Press WARM or COOL for immediate ambient temperature sensor input update.

CCOT SYSTEM DIAGNOSTIC PROCEDURE

C.C.O.T. SYSTEM AIR CONDITIONING DIAGNOSIS INSUFFICIENT COOLING "CHART A"

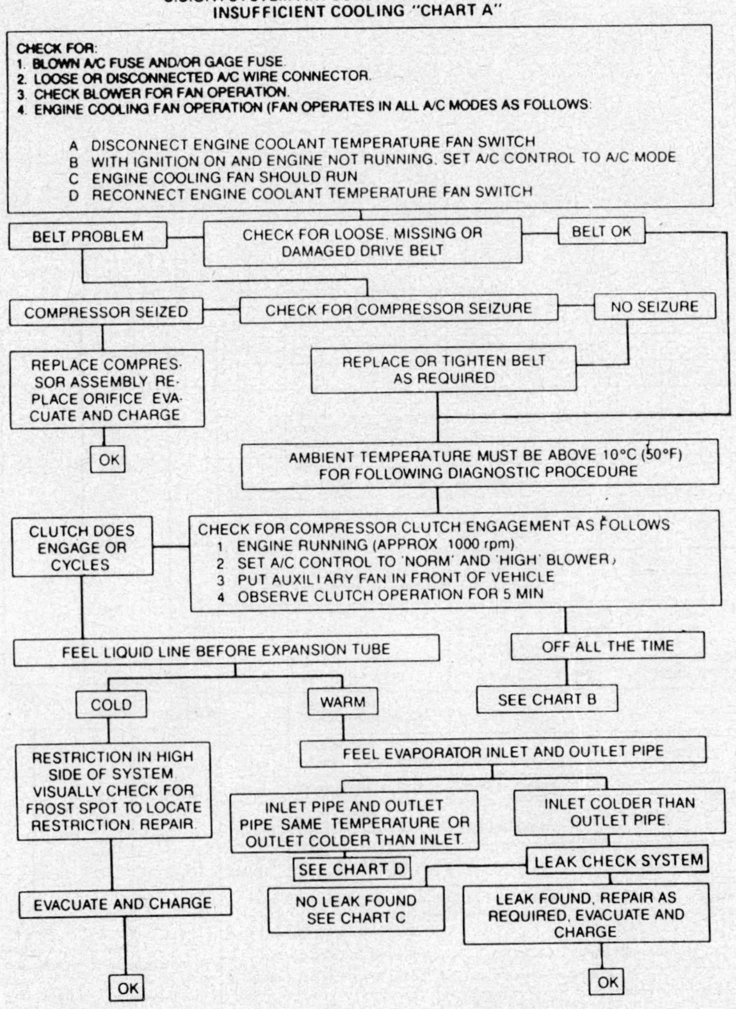

CHECK FOR:
1. BLOWN A/C FUSE AND/OR GAGE FUSE.
2. LOOSE OR DISCONNECTED A/C WIRE CONNECTOR.
3. CHECK BLOWER FOR FAN OPERATION.
4. ENGINE COOLING FAN OPERATION (FAN OPERATES IN ALL A/C MODES AS FOLLOWS:
   - A DISCONNECT ENGINE COOLANT TEMPERATURE FAN SWITCH
   - B WITH IGNITION ON AND ENGINE NOT RUNNING, SET A/C CONTROL TO A/C MODE
   - C ENGINE COOLING FAN SHOULD RUN
   - D RECONNECT ENGINE COOLANT TEMPERATURE FAN SWITCH

CHECK FOR LOOSE, MISSING OR DAMAGED DRIVE BELT

BELT PROBLEM

BELT OK

CHECK FOR COMPRESSOR SEIZURE

COMPRESSOR SEIZED

NO SEIZURE

REPLACE COMPRESSOR ASSEMBLY REPLACE ORIFICE EVACUATE AND CHARGE

OK

REPLACE OR TIGHTEN BELT AS REQUIRED

AMBIENT TEMPERATURE MUST BE ABOVE 10°C (50°F) FOR FOLLOWING DIAGNOSTIC PROCEDURE

CHECK FOR COMPRESSOR CLUTCH ENGAGEMENT AS FOLLOWS
1. ENGINE RUNNING (APPROX 1000 rpm)
2. SET A/C CONTROL TO 'NORM' AND 'HIGH' BLOWER,
3. PUT AUXILIARY FAN IN FRONT OF VEHICLE
4. OBSERVE CLUTCH OPERATION FOR 5 MIN

CLUTCH DOES ENGAGE OR CYCLES

OFF ALL THE TIME

SEE CHART B

FEEL LIQUID LINE BEFORE EXPANSION TUBE

COLD

RESTRICTION IN HIGH SIDE OF SYSTEM. VISUALLY CHECK FOR FROST SPOT TO LOCATE RESTRICTION. REPAIR.

EVACUATE AND CHARGE

OK

WARM

FEEL EVAPORATOR INLET AND OUTLET PIPE

INLET PIPE AND OUTLET PIPE SAME TEMPERATURE OR OUTLET COLDER THAN INLET

SEE CHART D

INLET COLDER THAN OUTLET PIPE

LEAK CHECK SYSTEM

NO LEAK FOUND SEE CHART C

LEAK FOUND, REPAIR AS REQUIRED, EVACUATE AND CHARGE

OK

CCOT SYSTEM DIAGNOSTIC PROCEDURE, CONT'D

C.C.O.T SYSTEM AIR CONDITIONING DIAGNOSIS INSUFFICIENT COOLING "CHART B"

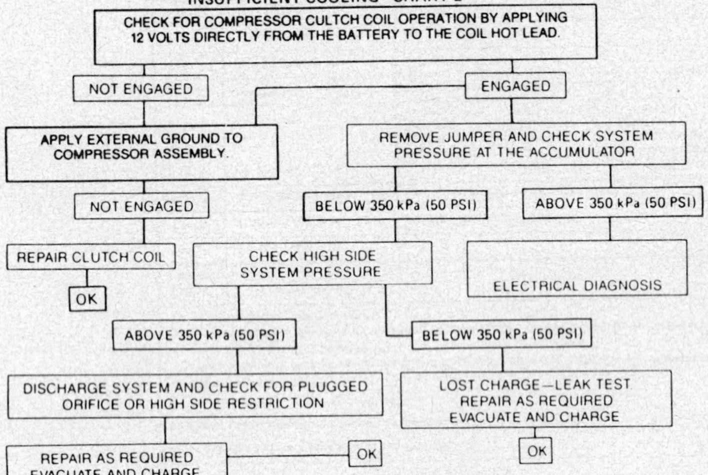

CHECK FOR COMPRESSOR CULTCH COIL OPERATION BY APPLYING 12 VOLTS DIRECTLY FROM THE BATTERY TO THE COIL HOT LEAD.

NOT ENGAGED

APPLY EXTERNAL GROUND TO COMPRESSOR ASSEMBLY.

NOT ENGAGED

REPAIR CLUTCH COIL

OK

ENGAGED

REMOVE JUMPER AND CHECK SYSTEM PRESSURE AT THE ACCUMULATOR

BELOW 350 kPa (50 PSI)

CHECK HIGH SIDE SYSTEM PRESSURE

ABOVE 350 kPa (50 PSI)

DISCHARGE SYSTEM AND CHECK FOR PLUGGED ORIFICE OR HIGH SIDE RESTRICTION

REPAIR AS REQUIRED EVACUATE AND CHARGE

OK

BELOW 350 kPa (50 PSI)

LOST CHARGE—LEAK TEST REPAIR AS REQUIRED EVACUATE AND CHARGE

OK

ABOVE 350 kPa (50 PSI)

ELECTRICAL DIAGNOSIS

C.C.O.T. SYSTEM AIR CONDITIONING DIAGNOSIS INSUFFICIENT COOLING "CHART C"

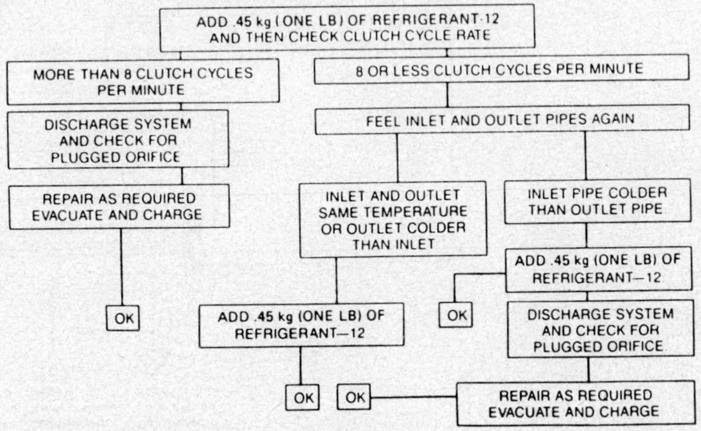

ADD .45 kg (ONE LB) OF REFRIGERANT-12 AND THEN CHECK CLUTCH CYCLE RATE

MORE THAN 8 CLUTCH CYCLES PER MINUTE

DISCHARGE SYSTEM AND CHECK FOR PLUGGED ORIFICE

REPAIR AS REQUIRED EVACUATE AND CHARGE

OK

8 OR LESS CLUTCH CYCLES PER MINUTE

FEEL INLET AND OUTLET PIPES AGAIN

INLET AND OUTLET SAME TEMPERATURE OR OUTLET COLDER THAN INLET

ADD .45 kg (ONE LB) OF REFRIGERANT—12

OK

INLET PIPE COLDER THAN OUTLET PIPE

ADD .45 kg (ONE LB) OF REFRIGERANT—12

OK

DISCHARGE SYSTEM AND CHECK FOR PLUGGED ORIFICE

REPAIR AS REQUIRED EVACUATE AND CHARGE

OK

CCOT SYSTEM DIAGNOSTIC PROCEDURE, CONT'D

C.C.O.T. SYSTEM AIR CONDITIONING DIAGNOSIS INSUFFICIENT COOLING "CHART D"

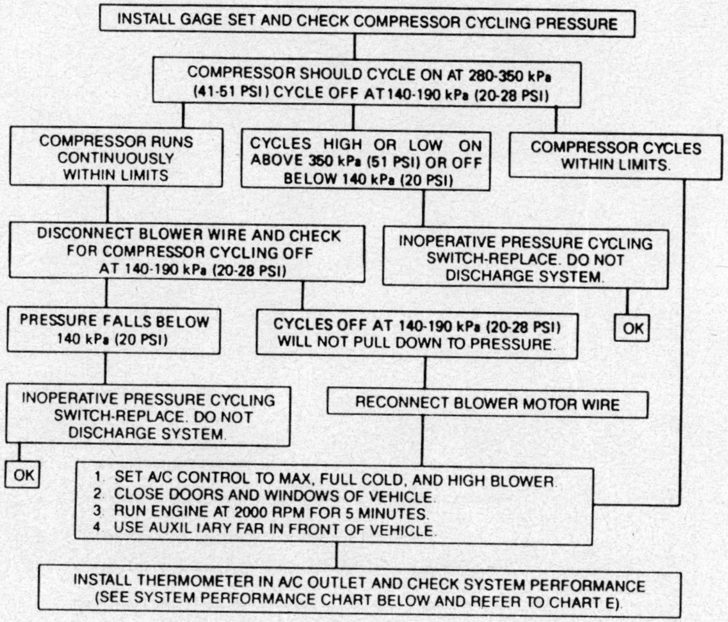

- INSTALL GAGE SET AND CHECK COMPRESSOR CYCLING PRESSURE
- COMPRESSOR SHOULD CYCLE ON AT 280-350 kPa (41-51 PSI) CYCLE OFF AT 140-190 kPa (20-28 PSI)
  - COMPRESSOR RUNS CONTINUOUSLY WITHIN LIMITS
    - DISCONNECT BLOWER WIRE AND CHECK FOR COMPRESSOR CYCLING OFF AT 140-190 kPa (20-28 PSI)
      - PRESSURE FALLS BELOW 140 kPa (20 PSI)
        - INOPERATIVE PRESSURE CYCLING SWITCH-REPLACE. DO NOT DISCHARGE SYSTEM.
          - OK
      - CYCLES OFF AT 140-190 kPa (20-28 PSI) WILL NOT PULL DOWN TO PRESSURE.
        - RECONNECT BLOWER MOTOR WIRE
  - CYCLES HIGH OR LOW ON ABOVE 350 kPa (51 PSI) OR OFF BELOW 140 kPa (20 PSI)
    - INOPERATIVE PRESSURE CYCLING SWITCH-REPLACE. DO NOT DISCHARGE SYSTEM.
      - OK
  - COMPRESSOR CYCLES WITHIN LIMITS.

1. SET A/C CONTROL TO MAX, FULL COLD, AND HIGH BLOWER.
2. CLOSE DOORS AND WINDOWS OF VEHICLE.
3. RUN ENGINE AT 2000 RPM FOR 5 MINUTES.
4. USE AUXIL IARY FAR IN FRONT OF VEHICLE.

INSTALL THERMOMETER IN A/C OUTLET AND CHECK SYSTEM PERFORMANCE (SEE SYSTEM PERFORMANCE CHART BELOW AND REFER TO CHART E).

PERFORMANCE CHART FOR C.C.O.T. SYSTEMS

TEMPERATURE OF AIR ENTERING CONDENSER	°F (°C)	70 (21)	80 (27)	90 (32)	100 (38)
COMPRESSOR OUT PRESSURE	PSI (KPA)	135-170 (950-1200)	165-200 (1150-1400)	200-245 (1400-1700)	245-300 (1700-2050)
ACCUMULATOR PRESSURE	PSI (KPA)	22-28 (150-193)	22-29 (150-200)	26-35 (180-240)	30-40 (205-275)
AVERAGE A/C AIR DISCHARGE	°F (°C)	36-43 (2.2-6.0)	36-43 (2.2-6.0)	36-43 (2.2-6.0)	42-48 (5.5-9.0)

CCOT SYSTEM DIAGNOSTIC PROCEDURE, CONT'D

C.C.O.T. SYSTEM AIR CONDITIONING DIAGNOSIS INSUFFICIENT COOLING "CHART E"

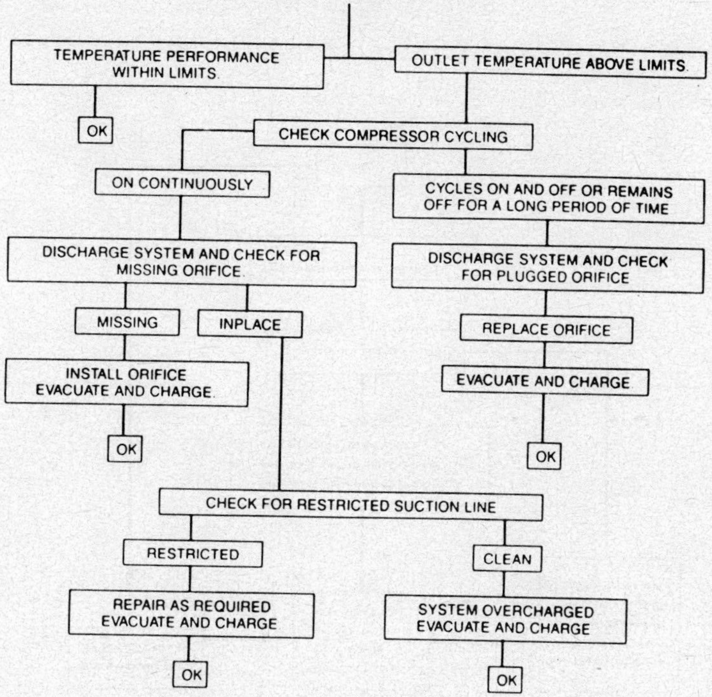

- TEMPERATURE PERFORMANCE WITHIN LIMITS.
  - OK
- OUTLET TEMPERATURE ABOVE LIMITS.
  - CHECK COMPRESSOR CYCLING
    - ON CONTINUOUSLY
      - DISCHARGE SYSTEM AND CHECK FOR MISSING ORIFICE.
        - MISSING
          - INSTALL ORIFICE EVACUATE AND CHARGE.
            - OK
        - INPLACE
          - CHECK FOR RESTRICTED SUCTION LINE
            - RESTRICTED
              - REPAIR AS REQUIRED EVACUATE AND CHARGE
                - OK
            - CLEAN
              - SYSTEM OVERCHARGED EVACUATE AND CHARGE
                - OK
    - CYCLES ON AND OFF OR REMAINS OFF FOR A LONG PERIOD OF TIME
      - DISCHARGE SYSTEM AND CHECK FOR PLUGGED ORIFICE
        - REPLACE ORIFICE
          - EVACUATE AND CHARGE
            - OK

VDOT SYSTEM DIAGNOSTIC PROCEDURE

V-5 SYSTEM AIR CONDITIONING DIAGNOSIS INSUFFICIENT COOLING

STEP 1 – Preliminary Checks

Repair the following as necessary. If outlet air temperature with A/C on is normal after making the following repairs, the system is operating normally.

- A/C fuse
- Clutch coil or rear head switch connections
- Temperature valve. Move temperature valve lever rapidly from cold to hot. Listen for temperature valve hitting at each end. Adjust as necessary.
- A/C blower operation.
- Compressor belt. Check condition and tension of belt. Replace as necessary.
- Engine cooling fan operation. Refer to service manual for diagnosis.
- Condensor. Check for restricted airflow through condensor.
- Compressor clutch operation and condition (overheated or discolored)
- Clutch driver (freewheeling)

VDOT SYSTEM DIAGNOSTIC PROCEDURE, CONT'D

V-5 SYSTEM AIR CONDITIONING DIAGNOSIS INSUFFICIENT COOLING

STEP 2 – Checking Refrigerant Charge

NOTE: Ambient temperature should be above 16°C (60°F) and engine at normal operating temperature.

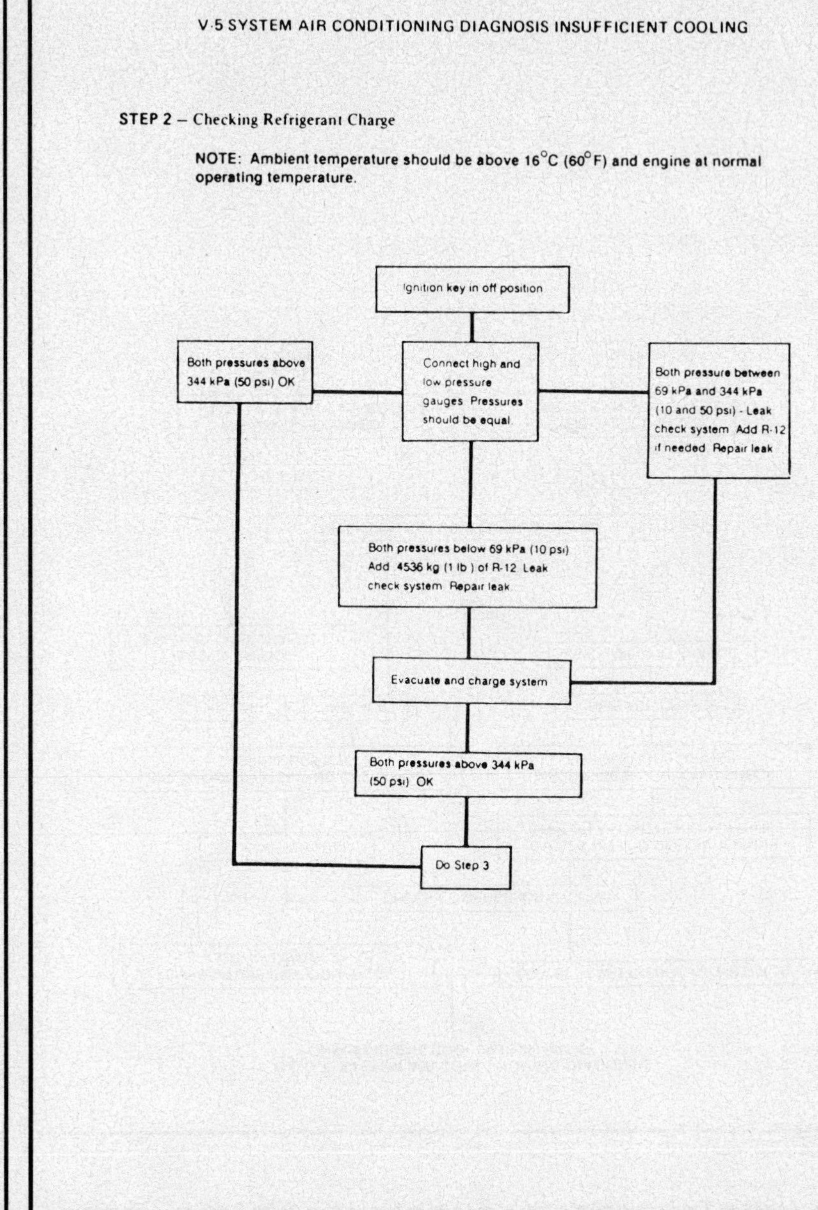

VDOT SYSTEM DIAGNOSTIC PROCEDURE, CONT'D

V-5 SYSTEM AIR CONDITIONING DIAGNOSIS INSUFFICIENT COOLING

STEP 3 – Checking Compressor Clutch Engagement

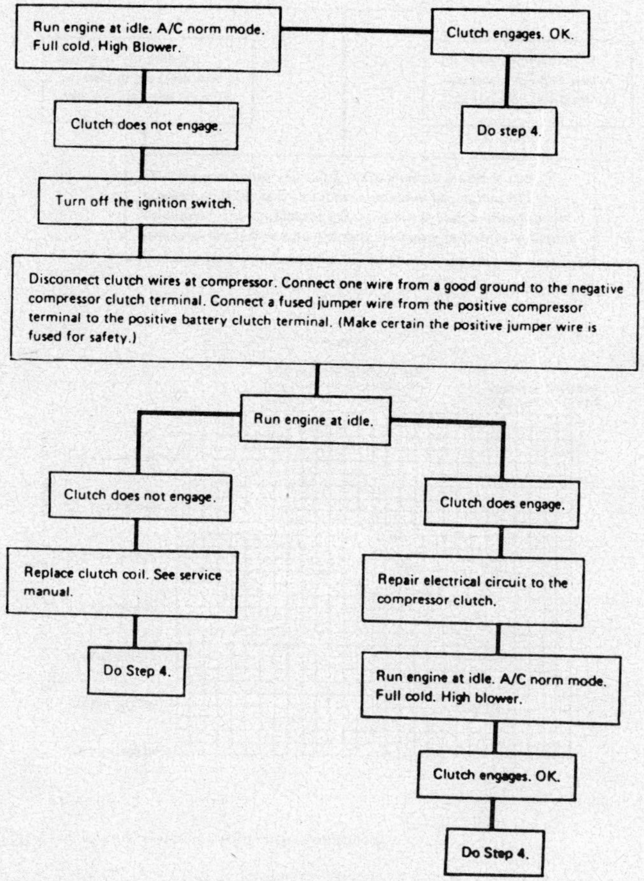

Run engine at idle. A/C norm mode. Full cold. High Blower.

- Clutch engages. OK.
  - Do step 4.
- Clutch does not engage.
  - Turn off the ignition switch.
  - Disconnect clutch wires at compressor. Connect one wire from a good ground to the negative compressor clutch terminal. Connect a fused jumper wire from the positive compressor terminal to the positive battery clutch terminal. (Make certain the positive jumper wire is fused for safety.)
  - Run engine at idle.
    - Clutch does not engage.
      - Replace clutch coil. See service manual.
      - Do Step 4.
    - Clutch does engage.
      - Repair electrical circuit to the compressor clutch.
      - Run engine at idle. A/C norm mode. Full cold. High blower.
      - Clutch engages. OK.
      - Do Step 4.

VDOT SYSTEM DIAGNOSTIC PROCEDURE, CONT'D

V-5 SYSTEM AIR CONDITIONING DIAGNOSIS INSUFFICIENT COOLING

STEP 4 – Checking System Performance

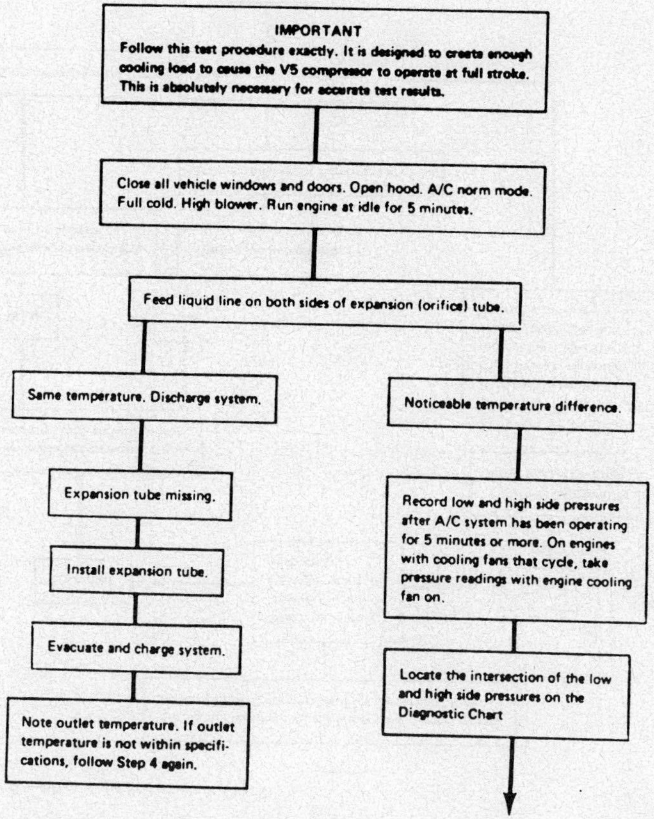

IMPORTANT
Follow this test procedure exactly. It is designed to create enough cooling load to cause the V5 compressor to operate at full stroke. This is absolutely necessary for accurate test results.

Close all vehicle windows and doors. Open hood. A/C norm mode. Full cold. High blower. Run engine at idle for 5 minutes.

Feed liquid line on both sides of expansion (orifice) tube.

- Same temperature. Discharge system.
  - Expansion tube missing.
  - Install expansion tube.
  - Evacuate and charge system.
  - Note outlet temperature. If outlet temperature is not within specifications, follow Step 4 again.
- Noticeable temperature difference.
  - Record low and high side pressures after A/C system has been operating for 5 minutes or more. On engines with cooling fans that cycle, take pressure readings with engine cooling fan on.
  - Locate the intersection of the low and high side pressures on the Diagnostic Chart
  - ↓

VDOT SYSTEM DIAGNOSTIC PROCEDURE, CONT'D

V-5 SYSTEM AIR CONDITIONING DIAGNOSIS INSUFFICIENT COOLING

STEP 4 – Checking System Performance (Continued)

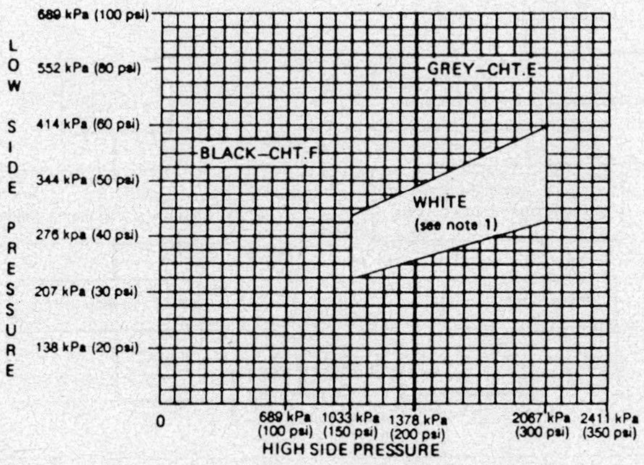

LOW SIDE PRESSURE
689 kPa (100 psi)
552 kPa (80 psi)
414 kPa (60 psi)
344 kPa (50 psi)
276 kpa (40 psi)
207 kPa (30 psi)
138 kPa (20 psi)
0
689 kPa (100 psi)
1033 kPa (150 psi)
1378 kPa (200 psi)
2067 kPa (300 psi)
2411 kPa (350 psi)
HIGH SIDE PRESSURE
GREY–CHT.E
BLACK–CHT.F
WHITE
(see note 1)

(Figure 1)

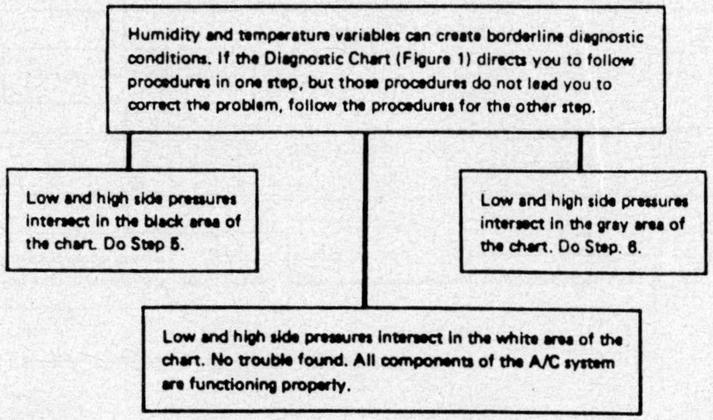

Humidity and temperature variables can create borderline diagnostic conditions. If the Diagnostic Chart (Figure 1) directs you to follow procedures in one step, but those procedures do not lead you to correct the problem, follow the procedures for the other step.
Low and high side pressures intersect in the black area of the chart. Do Step 5.
Low and high side pressures intersect in the gray area of the chart. Do Step. 6.
Low and high side pressures intersect in the white area of the chart. No trouble found. All components of the A/C system are functioning properly.

VDOT SYSTEM DIAGNOSTIC PROCEDURE, CONT'D

V-5 SYSTEM AIR CONDITIONING DIAGNOSIS INSUFFICIENT COOLING

STEP 5 – Black Zone Performance Checks

Engine still running. Vehicle windows and doors closed. Hood open. A/C norm mode. Full Cold. High blower.
Feel liquid line between expansion (orifice) tube and evaporator.
Tube cold.
Tube cool.
Feel liquid line between expansion tube and condensor.
Recover refrigerant check expansion tube.
Warm
Cold
If plugged, remove. Clear lines. Replace expansion tube. If only light debris is present, clean tube with shop air and reuse.
Refrigerant overcharge or air in system.
Restriction in high side.
Recover refrigerant. Remove restriction.
Recover refrigerant.
Evacuate and charge system.
Do Step 4.

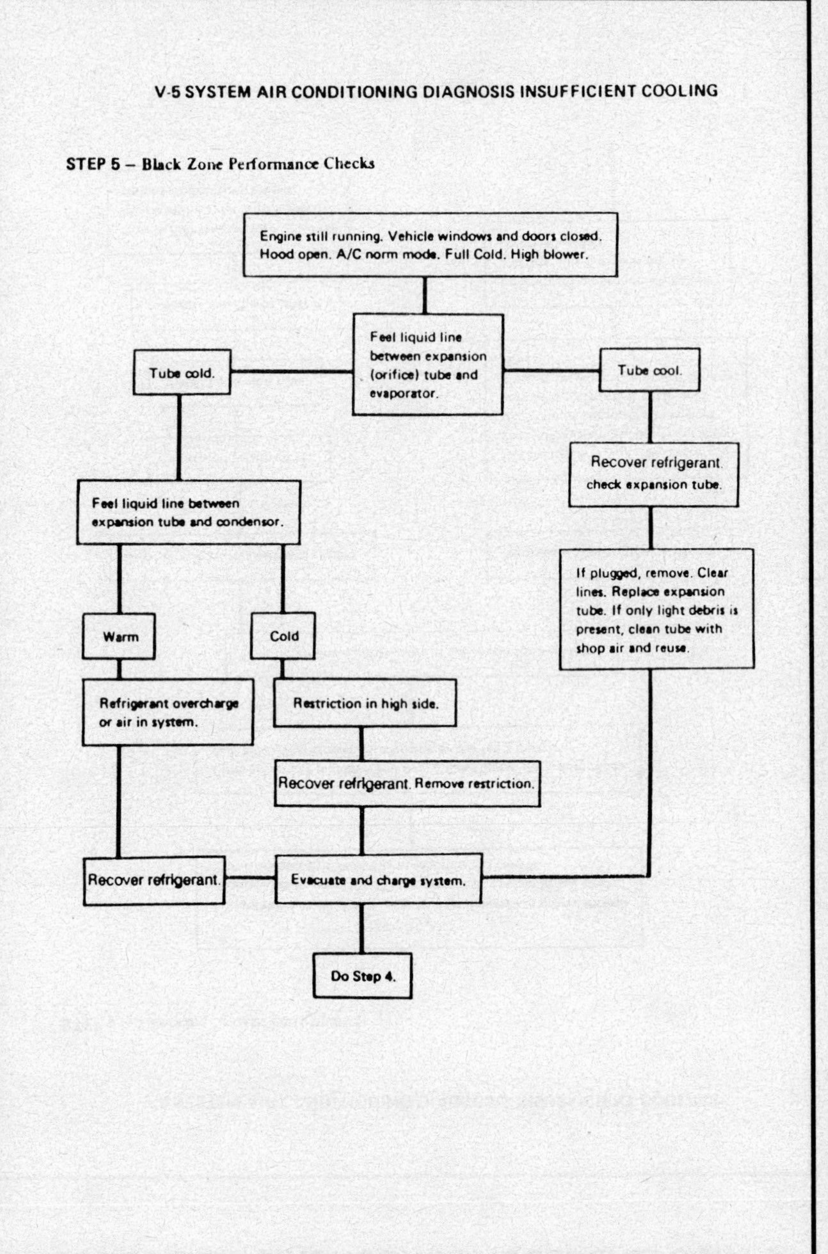

VDOT SYSTEM DIAGNOSTIC PROCEDURE, CONT'D

V-5 SYSTEM AIR CONDITIONING DIAGNOSIS INSUFFICIENT COOLING

STEP 6 – Grey Zone Performance Checks

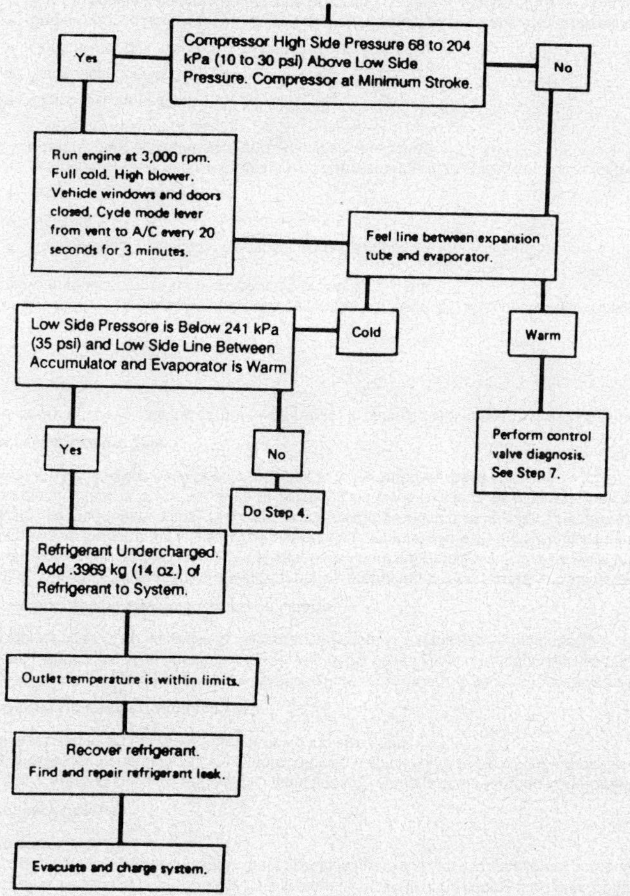

Compressor High Side Pressure 68 to 204 kPa (10 to 30 psi) Above Low Side Pressure. Compressor at Minimum Stroke.

Yes

Run engine at 3,000 rpm. Full cold. High blower. Vehicle windows and doors closed. Cycle mode lever from vent to A/C every 20 seconds for 3 minutes.

Feel line between expansion tube and evaporator.

Cold

Low Side Pressore is Below 241 kPa (35 psi) and Low Side Line Between Accumulator and Evaporator is Warm

Yes

Refrigerant Undercharged. Add .3969 kg (14 oz.) of Refrigerant to System.

Outlet temperature is within limits.

Recover refrigerant. Find and repair refrigerant leak.

Evacuate and charge system.

No

Do Step 4.

Warm

Perform control valve diagnosis. See Step 7.

No

Feel line between expansion tube and evaporator.

VDOT SYSTEM DIAGNOSTIC PROCEDURE, CONT'D

V-5 SYSTEM AIR CONDITIONING DIAGNOSIS INSUFFICIENT COOLING

STEP 7 – Control Valve Diagnosis

IMPORTANT
Follow this test procedure exactly. It is designed to create a low cooling load to cause the V5 compressor to operate at minimum stroke. This is absolutely necessary for accurate test results.

Run engine for 5 minutes at 3,000 rpm. Full cold. Low blower. Vehicle windows and doors closed. Open hood. Max A/C mode.

Low side pressure 172 to 241 kPa (25 to 35 psi)

No

Recover refrigerant.

Replace control valve.

Evacuate and charge system.

Do Step 4.

Yes

Do Step 4.

Low and high side pressures intersect in black color zone.

Recover refrigerant. Replace compressor.

Do Step 4.

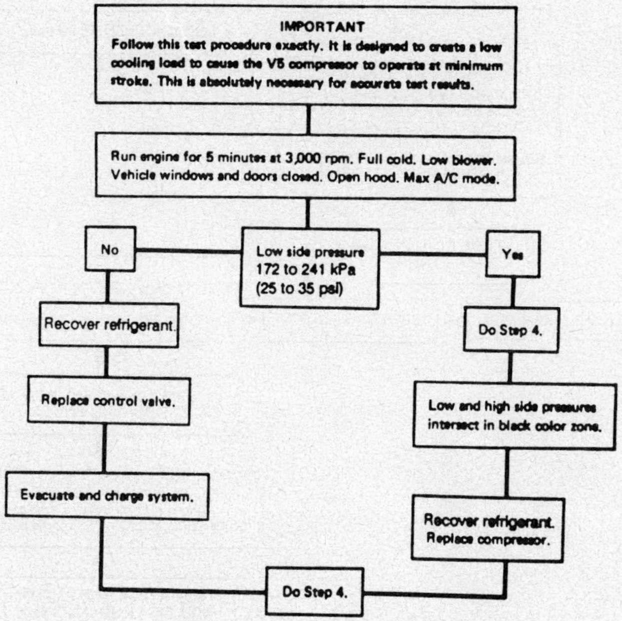

V5/TXV SYSTEM DIAGNOSTICS PROCEDURE

Diagnostic Flow Chart

This chart is the starting point for verifying and diagnosing all air conditioning and HVAC control related complaints. It represents the correct path to follow in response to a customer complaint or condition.

Preliminary Checks

This step covers all physical and visual inspections of interior and underhood components. Many problems can be detected by a thorough inspection. Failure to perform this step could result in wasted time proceeding further down the flow chart.

Vehicle Set Up and Performance Test

To run an air conditioning performance test the vehicle must be set-up according to the service manual instructions. The instructions include ACR_4 installation and controller settings. Improper vehicle set up will result in inaccurate pressure and temperature readings.

General and Specific System Condition Charts

These charts were developed in a wind tunnel by producing known system problems and recording pressures and temperatures at various ambient temperatures. The tests were then validated using the same vehicle set up in a service environment. To find your system problem, compare the performance test readings to the readings on the charts for your ambient temperature. There is some variance in readings between systems of different vehicles; however the target areas have been developed to accommodate these changes.

Compressor Control Test

This is designed to evaluate the compressor's ability to change displacement with varying heat loads.

Step 1 — *Preliminary Checks*

Repair the following as necessary. If discharge temperature with A/C on is normal after making the following repairs, the system is operating properly.

- Connect Tech 1. Check for diagnostic codes, if codes are found refer to service manual
- A/C fuse
- A/C blower operation
- Temperature door. Move temperature door lever rapidly from cold to hot. Listen for temperature door hitting at each end. Adjust as necessary. (Cable operated door only)
- Clutch coil connection
- Transducer connection
- Compressor belt. Replace if damaged or missing
- Engine cooling fan operation (at idle, cooling fan must be on at any A/C mode except 3.1L/V6 engines) cooling fan must be operating in correct direction (drawing outside air through the condenser toward engine)
- Condenser — Check for restricted air flow
- Dealer technical bulletins for updates on A/C system

V5/TXV SYSTEM DIAGNOSTICS PROCEDURE, CONT'D

Step 2 — *Checking Refrigerant Charge/Checking Compressor Clutch Engagement*

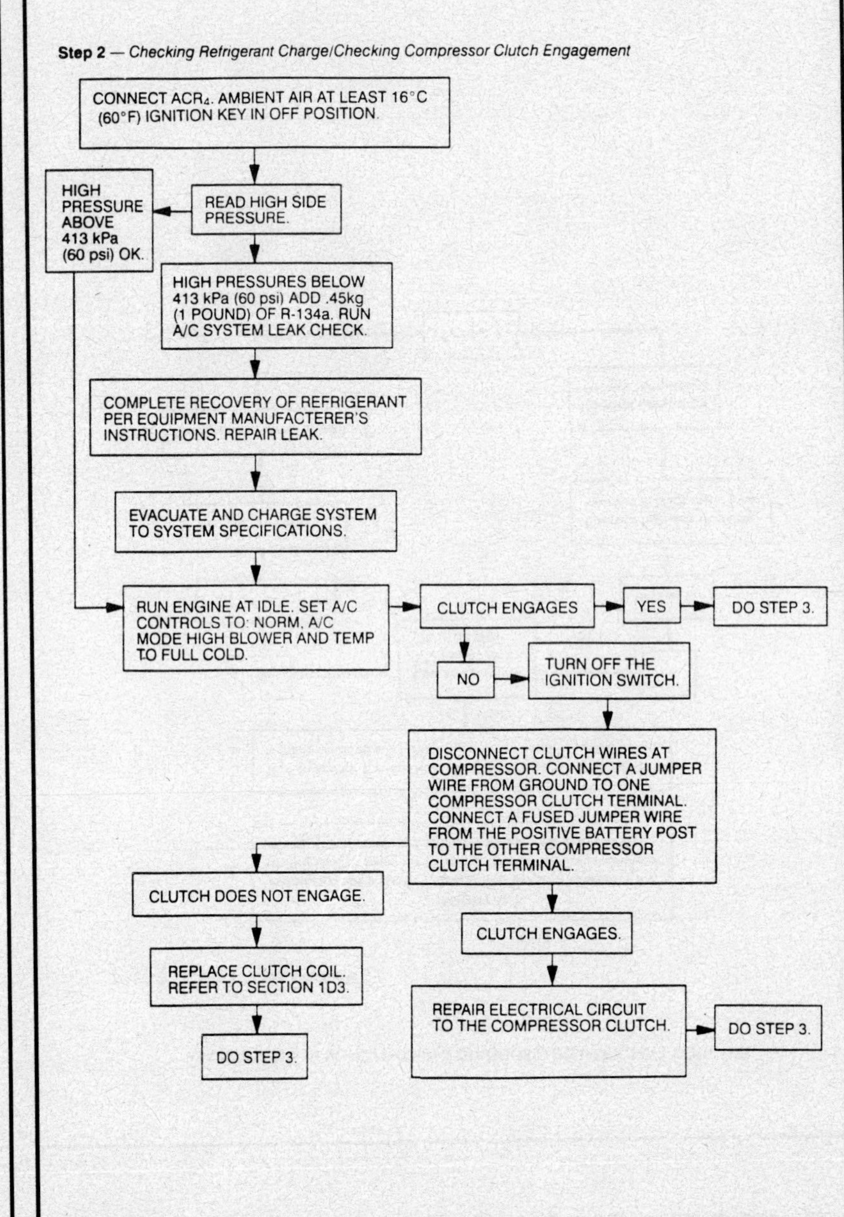

V5/TXV SYSTEM DIAGNOSTICS PROCEDURE, CONT'D

Step 3 — *Noise Considerastions*

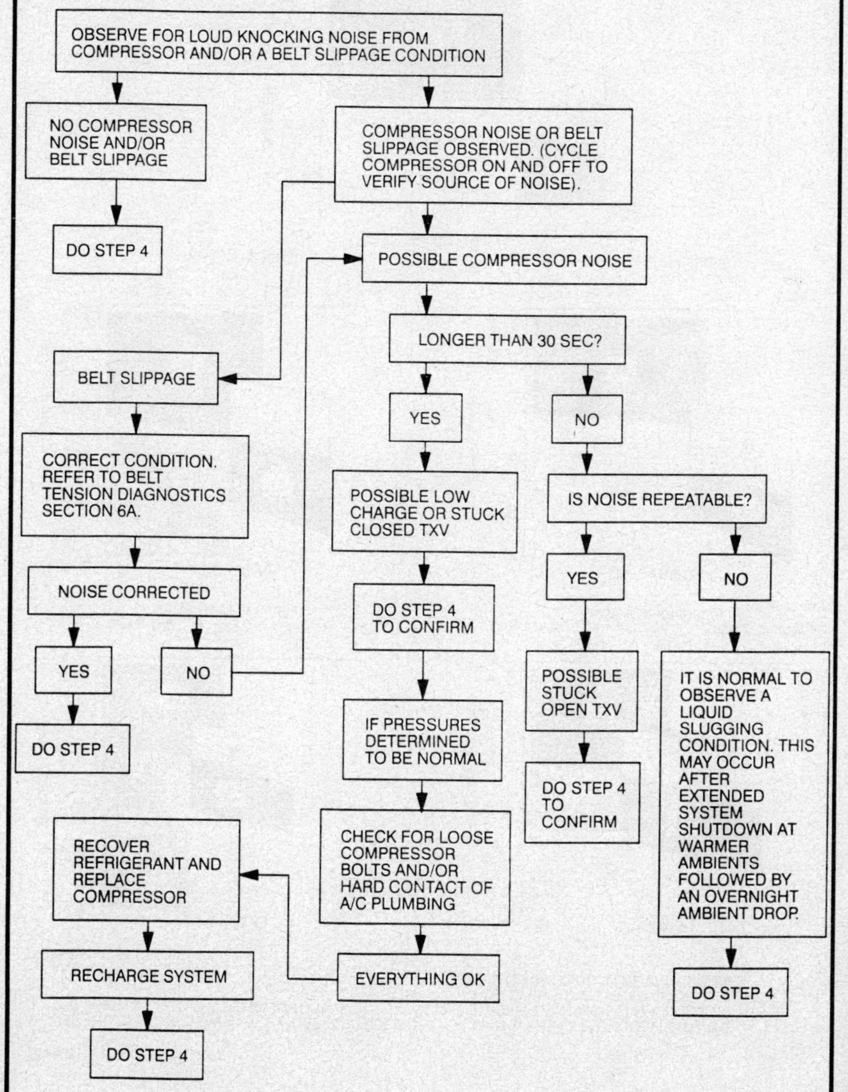

OBSERVE FOR LOUD KNOCKING NOISE FROM COMPRESSOR AND/OR A BELT SLIPPAGE CONDITION

NO COMPRESSOR NOISE AND/OR BELT SLIPPAGE

DO STEP 4

COMPRESSOR NOISE OR BELT SLIPPAGE OBSERVED. (CYCLE COMPRESSOR ON AND OFF TO VERIFY SOURCE OF NOISE).

POSSIBLE COMPRESSOR NOISE

LONGER THAN 30 SEC?

YES

POSSIBLE LOW CHARGE OR STUCK CLOSED TXV

DO STEP 4 TO CONFIRM

IF PRESSURES DETERMINED TO BE NORMAL

CHECK FOR LOOSE COMPRESSOR BOLTS AND/OR HARD CONTACT OF A/C PLUMBING

EVERYTHING OK

NO

IS NOISE REPEATABLE?

YES

POSSIBLE STUCK OPEN TXV

DO STEP 4 TO CONFIRM

NO

IT IS NORMAL TO OBSERVE A LIQUID SLUGGING CONDITION. THIS MAY OCCUR AFTER EXTENDED SYSTEM SHUTDOWN AT WARMER AMBIENTS FOLLOWED BY AN OVERNIGHT AMBIENT DROP.

DO STEP 4

BELT SLIPPAGE

CORRECT CONDITION. REFER TO BELT TENSION DIAGNOSTICS SECTION 6A.

NOISE CORRECTED

YES

DO STEP 4

NO

RECOVER REFRIGERANT AND REPLACE COMPRESSOR

RECHARGE SYSTEM

DO STEP 4

V5/TXV SYSTEM DIAGNOSTICS PROCEDURE, CONT'D

Step 4 — *Checking System Performance*

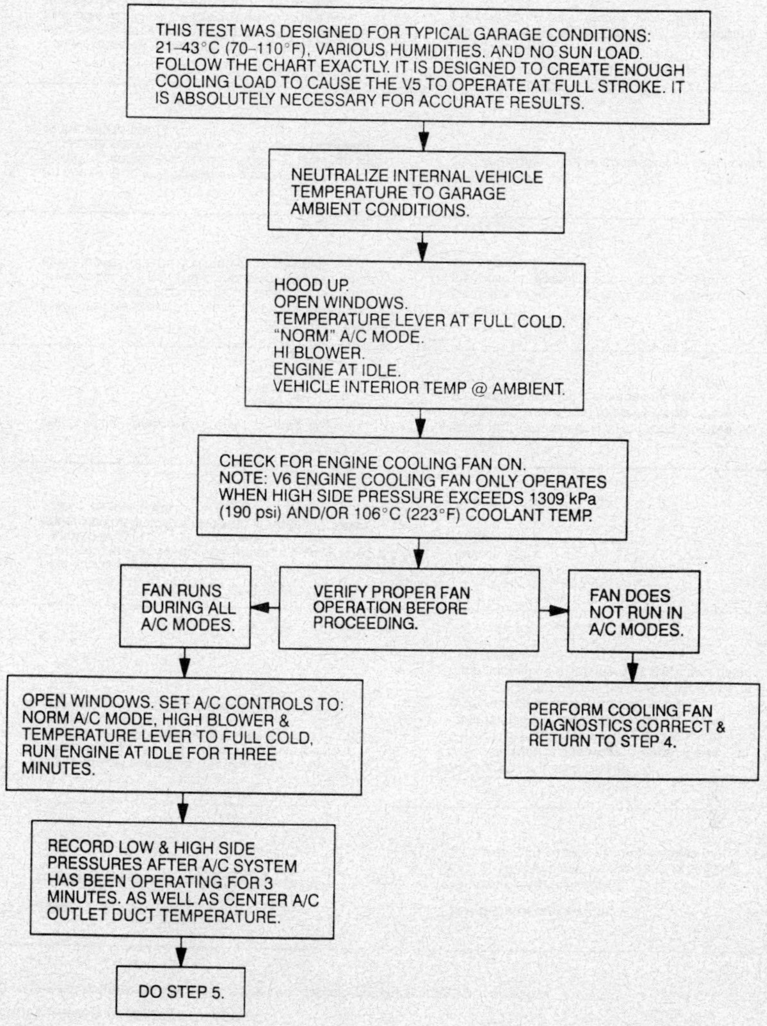

THIS TEST WAS DESIGNED FOR TYPICAL GARAGE CONDITIONS: 21–43°C (70–110°F), VARIOUS HUMIDITIES, AND NO SUN LOAD. FOLLOW THE CHART EXACTLY. IT IS DESIGNED TO CREATE ENOUGH COOLING LOAD TO CAUSE THE V5 TO OPERATE AT FULL STROKE. IT IS ABSOLUTELY NECESSARY FOR ACCURATE RESULTS.

NEUTRALIZE INTERNAL VEHICLE TEMPERATURE TO GARAGE AMBIENT CONDITIONS.

HOOD UP.
OPEN WINDOWS.
TEMPERATURE LEVER AT FULL COLD.
"NORM" A/C MODE.
HI BLOWER.
ENGINE AT IDLE.
VEHICLE INTERIOR TEMP @ AMBIENT.

CHECK FOR ENGINE COOLING FAN ON.
NOTE: V6 ENGINE COOLING FAN ONLY OPERATES WHEN HIGH SIDE PRESSURE EXCEEDS 1309 kPa (190 psi) AND/OR 106°C (223°F) COOLANT TEMP.

VERIFY PROPER FAN OPERATION BEFORE PROCEEDING.

FAN RUNS DURING ALL A/C MODES.

OPEN WINDOWS. SET A/C CONTROLS TO: NORM A/C MODE, HIGH BLOWER & TEMPERATURE LEVER TO FULL COLD. RUN ENGINE AT IDLE FOR THREE MINUTES.

RECORD LOW & HIGH SIDE PRESSURES AFTER A/C SYSTEM HAS BEEN OPERATING FOR 3 MINUTES. AS WELL AS CENTER A/C OUTLET DUCT TEMPERATURE.

DO STEP 5.

FAN DOES NOT RUN IN A/C MODES.

PERFORM COOLING FAN DIAGNOSTICS CORRECT & RETURN TO STEP 4.

V5/TXV SYSTEM DIAGNOSTICS PROCEDURE, CONT'D

Step 5 — *Diagnostic Chart*

1. USE THE CHART BELOW WHICH CORRESPONDS TO THE PRESENT AMBIENT TEMPERATURE.
2. READ THE HIGH SIDE AND LOW SIDE PRESSURES AND NOTE THE LETTER CODED AREA IN WHICH THEY INTERSECT.
3. MATCH THE LETTER CODE WITH THE CORRESPONDING LETTER CODE ON THE FOLLOWING PAGE (STEP 6) AND CONTINUE WITH THE DIAGNOSTIC CODE PROCEDURES.

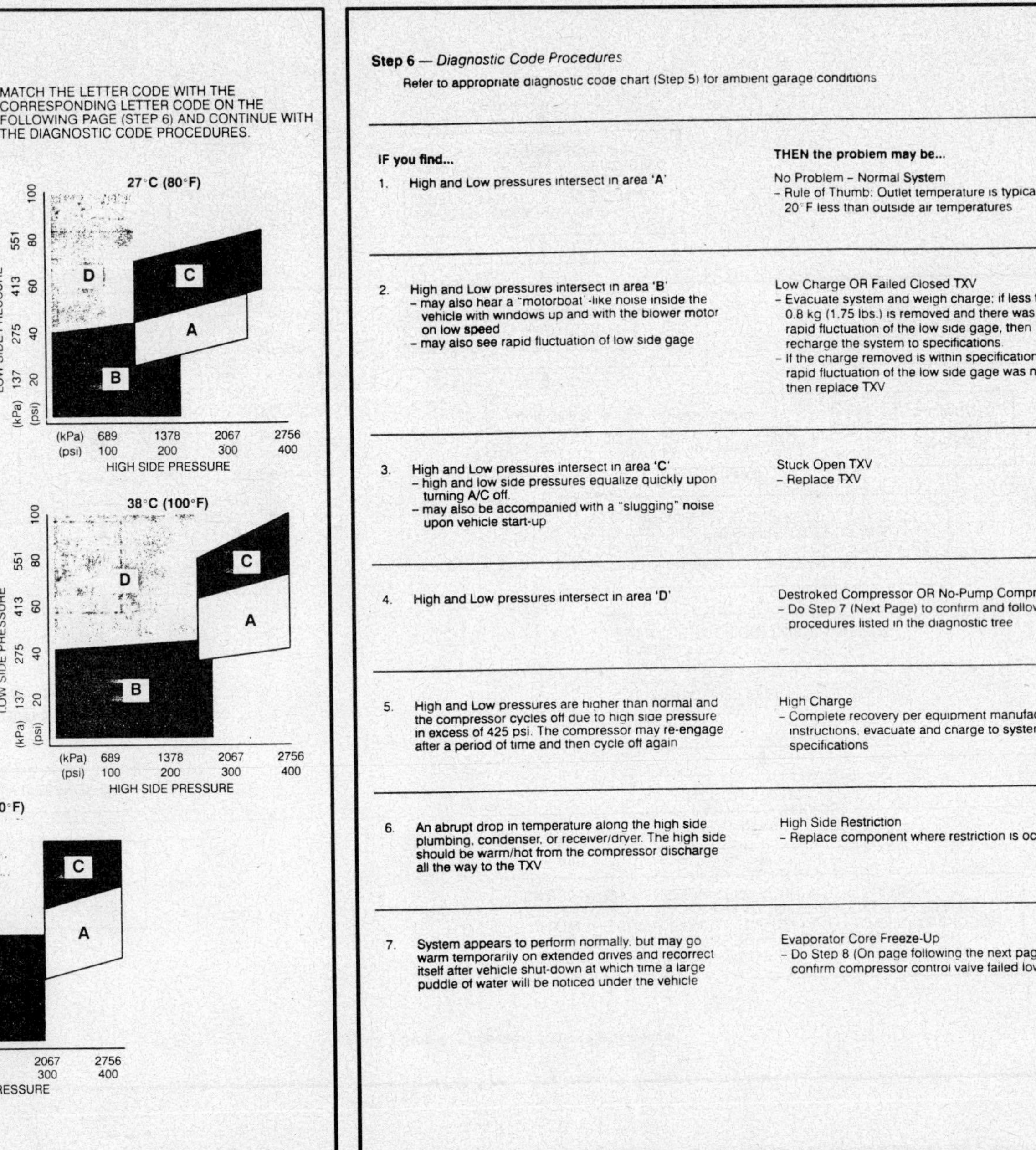

V5/TXV SYSTEM DIAGNOSTICS PROCEDURE, CONT'D

Step 6 — *Diagnostic Code Procedures*

Refer to appropriate diagnostic code chart (Step 5) for ambient garage conditions

IF you find...	THEN the problem may be...
1. High and Low pressures intersect in area 'A'	No Problem – Normal System - Rule of Thumb: Outlet temperature is typically 20°F less than outside air temperatures
2. High and Low pressures intersect in area 'B' - may also hear a "motorboat"-like noise inside the vehicle with windows up and with the blower motor on low speed - may also see rapid fluctuation of low side gage	Low Charge OR Failed Closed TXV - Evacuate system and weigh charge: if less than 0.8 kg (1.75 lbs.) is removed and there was no rapid fluctuation of the low side gage, then recharge the system to specifications. - If the charge removed is within specifications, and rapid fluctuation of the low side gage was noted, then replace TXV
3. High and Low pressures intersect in area 'C' - high and low side pressures equalize quickly upon turning A/C off. - may also be accompanied with a "slugging" noise upon vehicle start-up	Stuck Open TXV - Replace TXV
4. High and Low pressures intersect in area 'D'	Destroked Compressor OR No-Pump Compressor - Do Step 7 (Next Page) to confirm and follow procedures listed in the diagnostic tree
5. High and Low pressures are higher than normal and the compressor cycles off due to high side pressure in excess of 425 psi. The compressor may re-engage after a period of time and then cycle off again	High Charge - Complete recovery per equipment manufacture's instructions, evacuate and charge to system specifications
6. An abrupt drop in temperature along the high side plumbing, condenser, or receiver/dryer. The high side should be warm/hot from the compressor discharge all the way to the TXV	High Side Restriction - Replace component where restriction is occurring
7. System appears to perform normally, but may go warm temporarily on extended drives and recorrect itself after vehicle shut-down at which time a large puddle of water will be noticed under the vehicle	Evaporator Core Freeze-Up - Do Step 8 (On page following the next page) to confirm compressor control valve failed low

V5/TXV SYSTEM DIAGNOSTICS PROCEDURE, CONT'D

Step 7— *Checking For No Stroke Compressor*

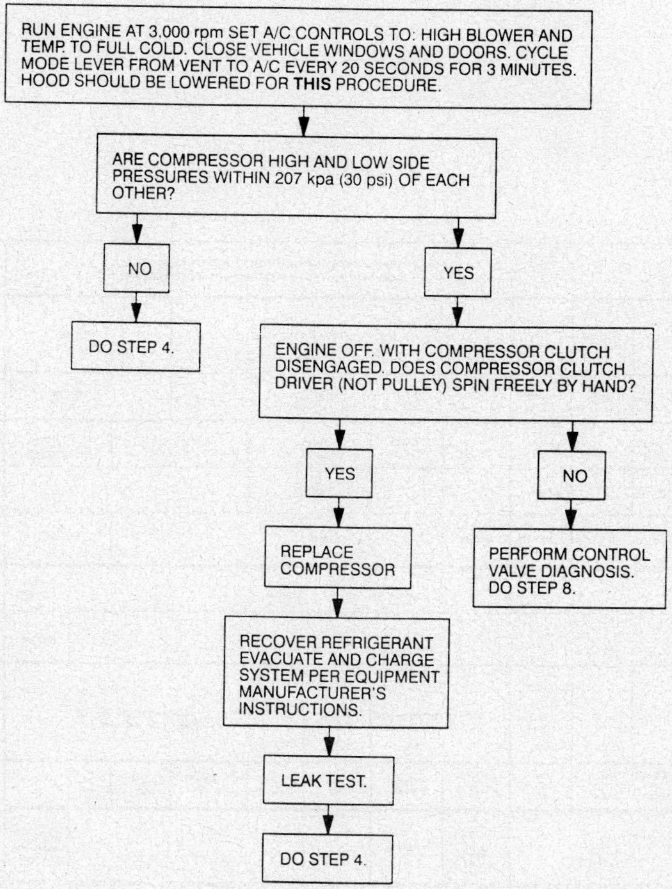

RUN ENGINE AT 3,000 rpm SET A/C CONTROLS TO: HIGH BLOWER AND TEMP. TO FULL COLD. CLOSE VEHICLE WINDOWS AND DOORS. CYCLE MODE LEVER FROM VENT TO A/C EVERY 20 SECONDS FOR 3 MINUTES. HOOD SHOULD BE LOWERED FOR **THIS** PROCEDURE.

ARE COMPRESSOR HIGH AND LOW SIDE PRESSURES WITHIN 207 kpa (30 psi) OF EACH OTHER?

- NO → DO STEP 4.
- YES → ENGINE OFF. WITH COMPRESSOR CLUTCH DISENGAGED. DOES COMPRESSOR CLUTCH DRIVER (NOT PULLEY) SPIN FREELY BY HAND?
  - YES → REPLACE COMPRESSOR → RECOVER REFRIGERANT EVACUATE AND CHARGE SYSTEM PER EQUIPMENT MANUFACTURER'S INSTRUCTIONS. → LEAK TEST. → DO STEP 4.
  - NO → PERFORM CONTROL VALVE DIAGNOSIS. DO STEP 8.

V5/TXV SYSTEM DIAGNOSTICS PROCEDURE, CONT'D

Step 8— *Control Valve Diagnosis*

IMPORTANT

FOLLOW THIS TEST PROCEDURE EXACTLY. IT IS DESIGNED TO CREATE A LOW COOLING LOAD TO CAUSE THE V5 COMPRESSOR TO OPERATE AT LESS THAN FULL STROKE. THIS IS ABSOLUTELY NECESSARY FOR ACCURATE TEST RESULTS.

RUN ENGINE FOR 5 MINUTES AT 2,000 RPM. SET A/C CONTROLS TO: MAX A/C MODE. LOW BLOWER AND TEMP. TO FULL COLD. CLOSE VEHICLE WINDOWS AND DOORS. OPEN HOOD.

IS LOW SIDE PRESSURE BETWEEN 172 AND 310 kPa (25 AND 45 psi)?

- NO → RECOVER REFRIGERANT PER EQUIPMENT MANUFACTURER'S INSTRUCTIONS. → REPLACE CONTROL VALVE → EVACUATE AND CHARGE SYSTEM PER EQUIPMENT MANUFACTURER'S INSTRUCTIONS. → LEAK TEST. → DO STEP 4.
- YES → DO STEP 4.

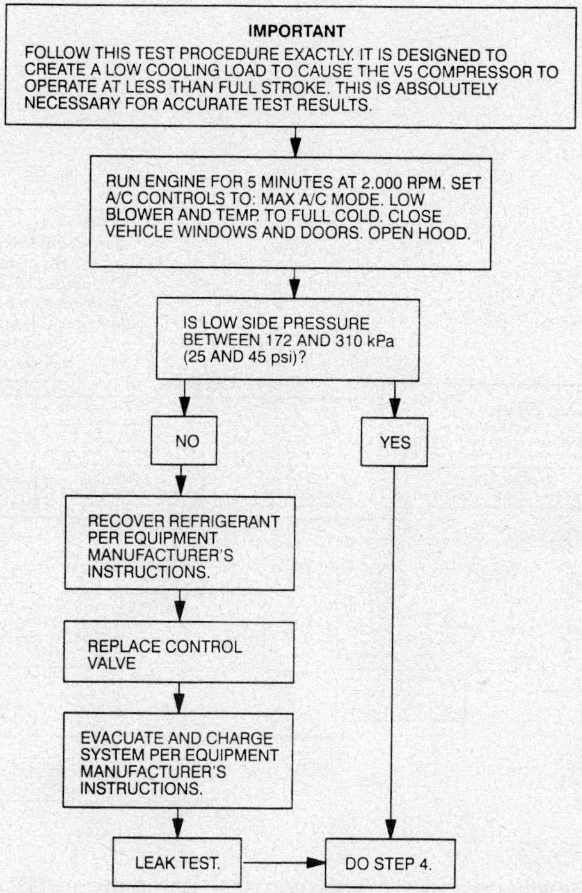

ELECTRONIC CLIMATE CONTROL SYSTEM RESPONSE CHART—1993–94 ELDORADO AND SEVILLE, 1994–95 DEVILLE AND CONCOURS

SYSTEM RESPONSE CHART

AIR DELIVERY MODE (SELECT ACP DATA [AD24] TO SEE MODE NO.)		'AUTO' SELECTED	AUTO OR 'ECON' SELECTED				'OFF' SELECTED	'DEFOG' SELECTED	(defrost symbol) SELECTED	ANY SETTING EXCEPT OFF		
		#0 MAX A/C	#1 A/C	#2 BI-LEVEL	#3 HEATER/ DEFROSTER	#4 HEATER	#5 OFF	#6 DEFOG	#7 FRONT DEFROST	#8 NORMAL PURGE	#9 COLD PURGE	#10 A/C PURGE
AUTO FAN (SELECT ACP DATA AD20 TO SEE COMMANDED BLOWER SPEED		VARIABLE SPEED BASED ON PROGRAM NUMBER					OFF	VARIABLE SPEED BASED ON PROGRAM NUMBER		OFF THEN LO	OFF	5 VOLTS
AIR INLET VALVE	ORANGE HOSE	VACUUM	VENT									
	VALVE POSITION	INSIDE AIR 'RECIRC'	OUTSIDE AIR									
UP-DOWN VALVE	YELLOW HOSE UP (A/C)	VACUUM		VENT					VACUUM	VENT	VACUUM	VENT
	RED HOSE DOWN (HTR)	VENT				VACUUM		VENT		VACUUM	VENT	VACUUM
	VALVE POSITION	AIR DIRECTED UP		AIR DIRECTED UP & DOWN		AIR DIRECTED DOWN		AIR UP & DOWN	AIR UP	AIR DOWN	AIR UP	AIR DOWN
A/C DEF VALVE	BLUE HOSE	VACUUM			VENT					VACUUM	VENT	VACUUM
	VALVE POSITION	AIR DIRECTED TO A/C OUTLETS			AIR DIRECTED DEFROSTER OUTLETS					AIR TO A/C	AIR TO DEFROST	AIR TO A/C
COMPRESSOR		ENABLED EXCEPT IN 'OFF' AND 'ECON' WHEN AMBIENT IS ABOVE 50°F (OR IF HUMID CONDITIONS DETECTED WHEN AMBIENT IS ABOVE 40°F)										

ELECTRONIC CLIMATE CONTROL SYSTEM CHECK —1993 ELDORADO AND SEVILLE

- **IF YOU HAVE NOT REVIEWED THE BASIC INFORMATION ON HOW TO USE THE COMPUTER SELF-DIAGNOSTICS, SEE CONTENTS UNDER 'SELF-DIAGNOSTIC FEATURES'**

- TURN IGNITION 'ON' AND ENTER DIAGNOSTICS
- ARE ANY TROUBLE CODES DISPLAYED?

YES CODES ARE DISPLAYED

- SEE CODES (E0XX) PCM
- SEE CODES (A0XX) ACP
- SEE CODES (I0XX) IPC
- SEE CODES (R0XX) SIR

NO CODES DISPLAYED

- START ENGINE
- SELECT 60 DEGREES AND 'HI' BLOWER
- AMBIENT TEMPERATURE MUST BE ABOVE 50 DEGREES
- DO BLOWER AND COMPRESSOR CLUTCH OPERATE?

BOTH BLOWER AND COMPRESSOR OPERATE

- IF OWNER'S COMPLAINT IS — SEE CHART NUMBER
  - IMPROPER BLOWER SPEED — 3
  - IMPROPER AIR DELIVERY — 4
  - IMPROPER TEMPERATURE CONTROL — 5
  - REAR DEFOG 'ON' CONTINUOUSLY — 6
  - REAR DEFOG INOPERATIVE — 7
  - REAR A/C BLOWER SPEED INCORRECT — 8
  - REAR A/C BLOWER INOPERATIVE — 9
  - REFRIGERATION SYSTEM CHECK — 10

COMPRESSOR DOES NOT OPERATE

SEE CHART 1

BLOWER DOES NOT OPERATE

SEE CHART 2

BOTH BLOWER AND COMPRESSOR DO NOT OPERATE

- CHECK FOR OPEN MAXI FUSE 4 IN RH MAXI FUSE BLOCK
- CHECK CKT 1440 FOR SHORT TO GROUND

CHART 1: ECC SYSTEM NO COMPRESSOR OPERATION —1993 ELDORADO AND SEVILLE

CHART 2: ECC NO BLOWER OPERATION—1993 ELDORADO AND SEVILLE

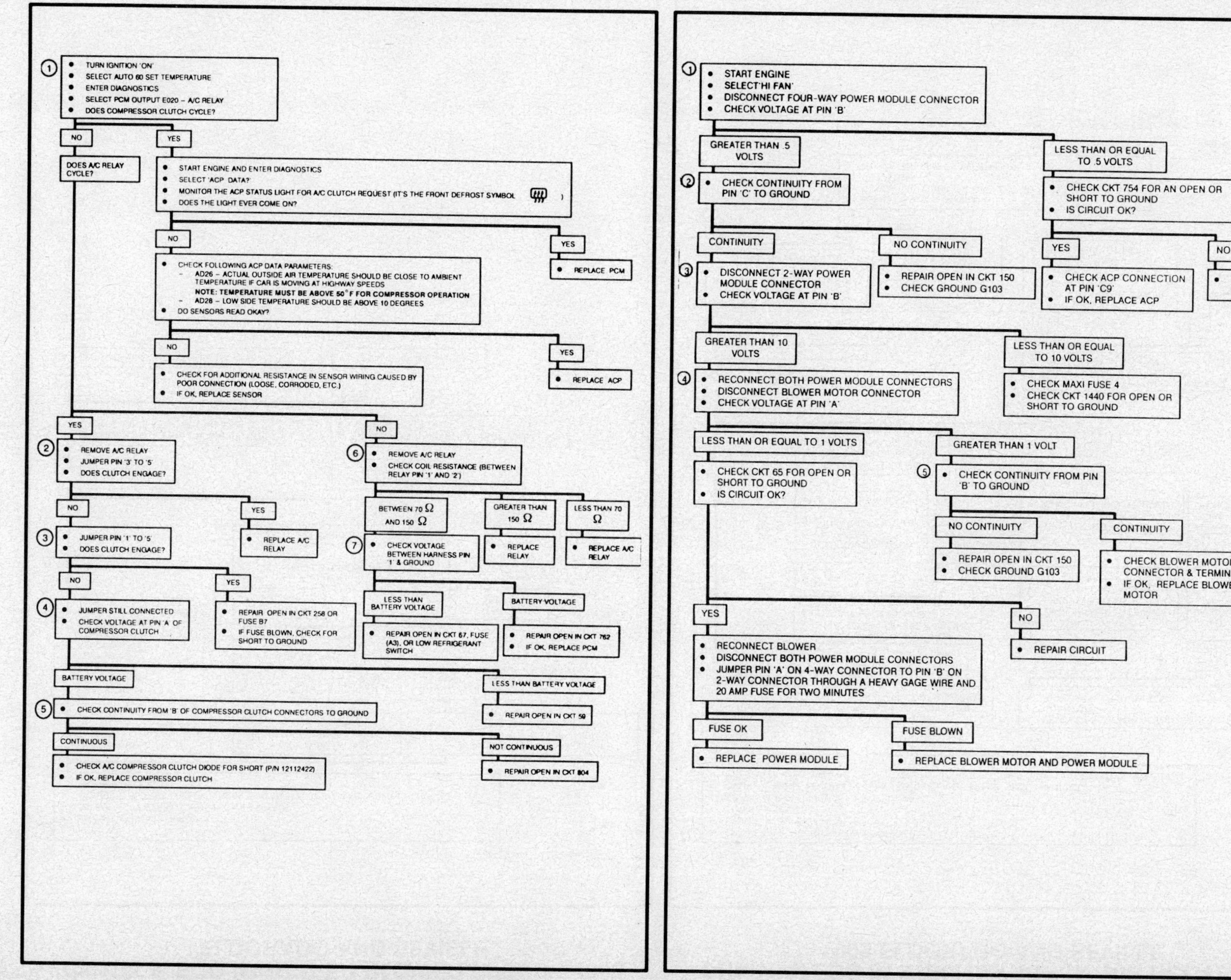

CHART 3: ECC IMPROPER BLOWER SPEED—1993 ELDORADO AND SEVILLE

1
- KEY 'ON'
- ENTER ON-BOARD DIAGNOSTICS
- SELECT ACP OVERRIDE AS16 BLOWER SPEED
- OVERRIDE BLOWER SPEED FROM 99 TO 0 AND NOTE BLOWER SPEED CHANGES, IF ANY, AS NUMBER DECREASES.

NO CHANGE AT ALL IN BLOWER SPEED FROM 99 TO 0

2
- EXIT DIAGNOSTICS
- START ENGINE
- SELECT THE 'LO' BLOWER SETTING
- BACKPROBE ACP CONNECTOR PIN 'C9' AND CHECK VOLTAGE

LESS THAN OR EQUAL 3.0 VOLTS

3
- IS BLOWER MOTOR STILL RUNNING WITH 4-WAY CONNECTOR DISCONNECTED?

YES
- REPAIR SHORT TO VOLTAGE ON CKT 65

NO
- REPLACE POWER MODULE

GREATER THAN 3.0 VOLTS
- CHECK FOR SHORT TO VOLTAGE ON CKT 754
- IF OK, REPLACE ACP

NO CHANGE IN BLOWER SPEED FROM 99 TO ABOUT 30 THEN BLOWER STOPS

4
- EXIT DIAGNOSTICS AND SELECT 'AUTO' MODE WITH 'HIGH' FAN SPEED
- BACKPROBE ACP PIN 'D2' TO GROUND WITH A VOLTMETER

LESS THAN OR EQUAL 2 VOLTS
- CHECK FUSE B11 (BLOWER FEEDBACK)
- REPAIR OPEN OR SHORT TO GROUND IN CKT 65

GREATER THAN 2 VOLTS
- CHECK FOR GOOD CONNECTION AT PIN 'D2'
- IF OK, REPLACE ACP

BLOWER SPEED GRADUALLY AND CONSISTENTLY DECREASES FROM 99 TO ABOUT 30 THEN BLOWER STOPS

GO TO CHART 5 'IMPROPER TEMPERATURE CONTROL

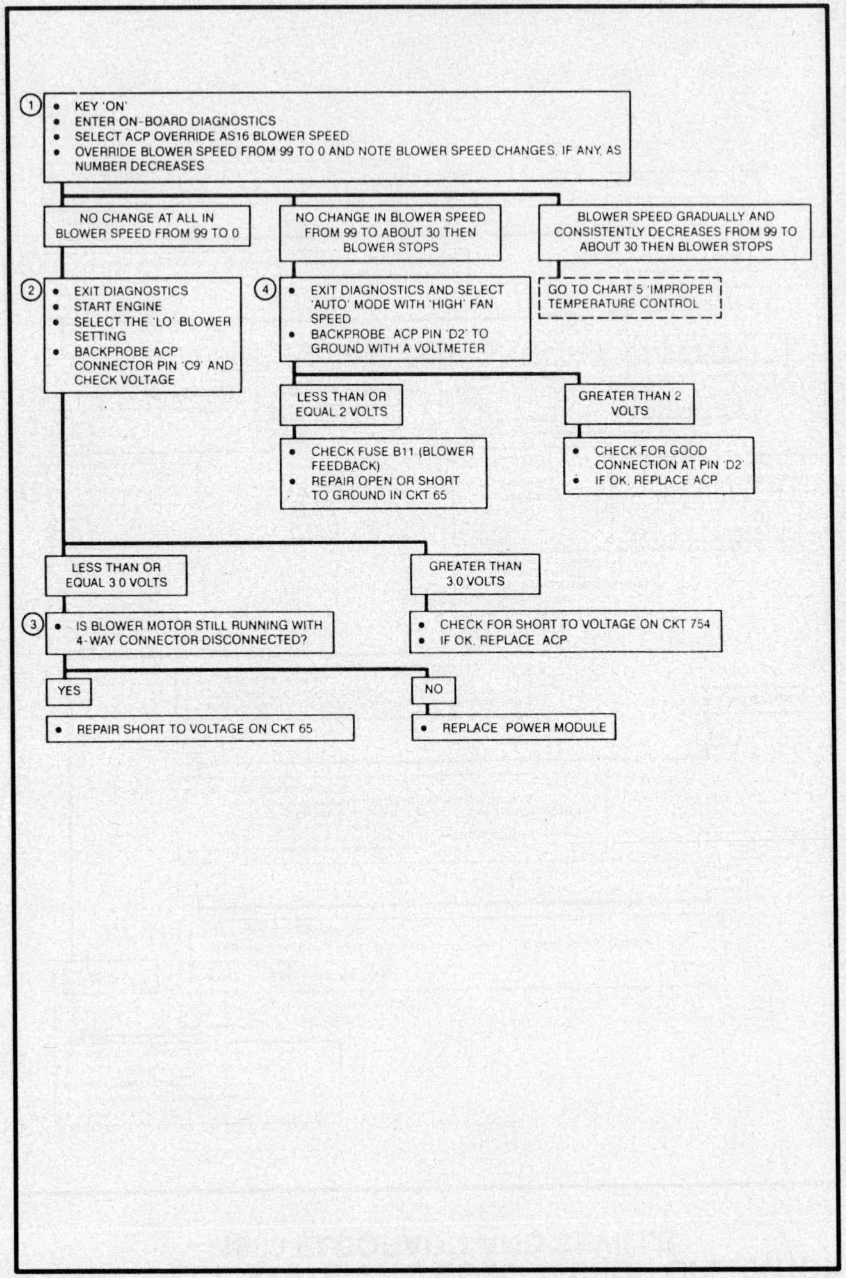

CHART 4: ECC SYSTEM IMPROPER AIR DELIVERY —1993 ELDORADO AND SEVILLE

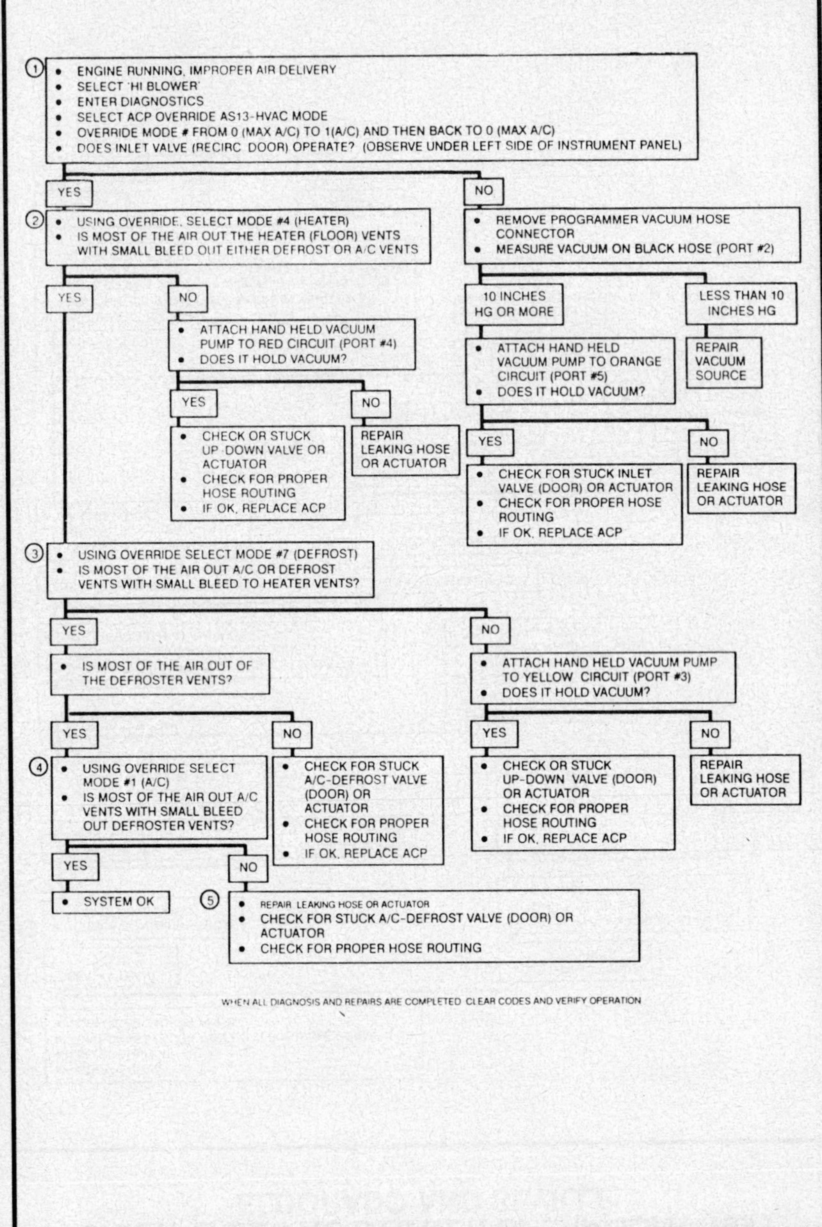

1
ENGINE RUNNING, IMPROPER AIR DELIVERY
SELECT 'HI BLOWER'
ENTER DIAGNOSTICS
SELECT ACP OVERRIDE AS13-HVAC MODE
OVERRIDE MODE # FROM 0 (MAX A/C) TO 1(A/C) AND THEN BACK TO 0 (MAX A/C)
DOES INLET VALVE (RECIRC. DOOR) OPERATE? (OBSERVE UNDER LEFT SIDE OF INSTRUMENT PANEL)
YES
2
USING OVERRIDE, SELECT MODE #4 (HEATER)
IS MOST OF THE AIR OUT THE HEATER (FLOOR) VENTS WITH SMALL BLEED OUT EITHER DEFROST OR A/C VENTS
YES
NO
ATTACH HAND HELD VACUUM PUMP TO RED CIRCUIT (PORT #4)
DOES IT HOLD VACUUM?
YES
CHECK OR STUCK UP-DOWN VALVE OR ACTUATOR
CHECK FOR PROPER HOSE ROUTING
IF OK, REPLACE ACP
NO
REPAIR LEAKING HOSE OR ACTUATOR
NO
REMOVE PROGRAMMER VACUUM HOSE CONNECTOR
MEASURE VACUUM ON BLACK HOSE (PORT #2)
10 INCHES HG OR MORE
ATTACH HAND HELD VACUUM PUMP TO ORANGE CIRCUIT (PORT #5)
DOES IT HOLD VACUUM?
YES
CHECK FOR STUCK INLET VALVE (DOOR) OR ACTUATOR
CHECK FOR PROPER HOSE ROUTING
IF OK, REPLACE ACP
NO
REPAIR LEAKING HOSE OR ACTUATOR
LESS THAN 10 INCHES HG
REPAIR VACUUM SOURCE
3
USING OVERRIDE SELECT MODE #7 (DEFROST)
IS MOST OF THE AIR OUT A/C OR DEFROST VENTS WITH SMALL BLEED TO HEATER VENTS?
YES
IS MOST OF THE AIR OUT OF THE DEFROSTER VENTS?
YES
4
USING OVERRIDE SELECT MODE #1 (A/C)
IS MOST OF THE AIR OUT A/C VENTS WITH SMALL BLEED OUT DEFROSTER VENTS?
YES
SYSTEM OK
NO
5
REPAIR LEAKING HOSE OR ACTUATOR
CHECK FOR STUCK A/C-DEFROST VALVE (DOOR) OR ACTUATOR
CHECK FOR PROPER HOSE ROUTING
NO
CHECK FOR STUCK A/C-DEFROST VALVE (DOOR) OR ACTUATOR
CHECK FOR PROPER HOSE ROUTING
IF OK, REPLACE ACP
NO
ATTACH HAND HELD VACUUM PUMP TO YELLOW CIRCUIT (PORT #3)
DOES IT HOLD VACUUM?
YES
CHECK OR STUCK UP-DOWN VALVE (DOOR) OR ACTUATOR
CHECK FOR PROPER HOSE ROUTING
IF OK, REPLACE ACP
NO
REPAIR LEAKING HOSE OR ACTUATOR
WHEN ALL DIAGNOSIS AND REPAIRS ARE COMPLETED CLEAR CODES AND VERIFY OPERATION

CHART 5: ECC SYSTEM IMPROPER TEMPERATURE CONTROL—1993 ELDORADO AND SEVILLE

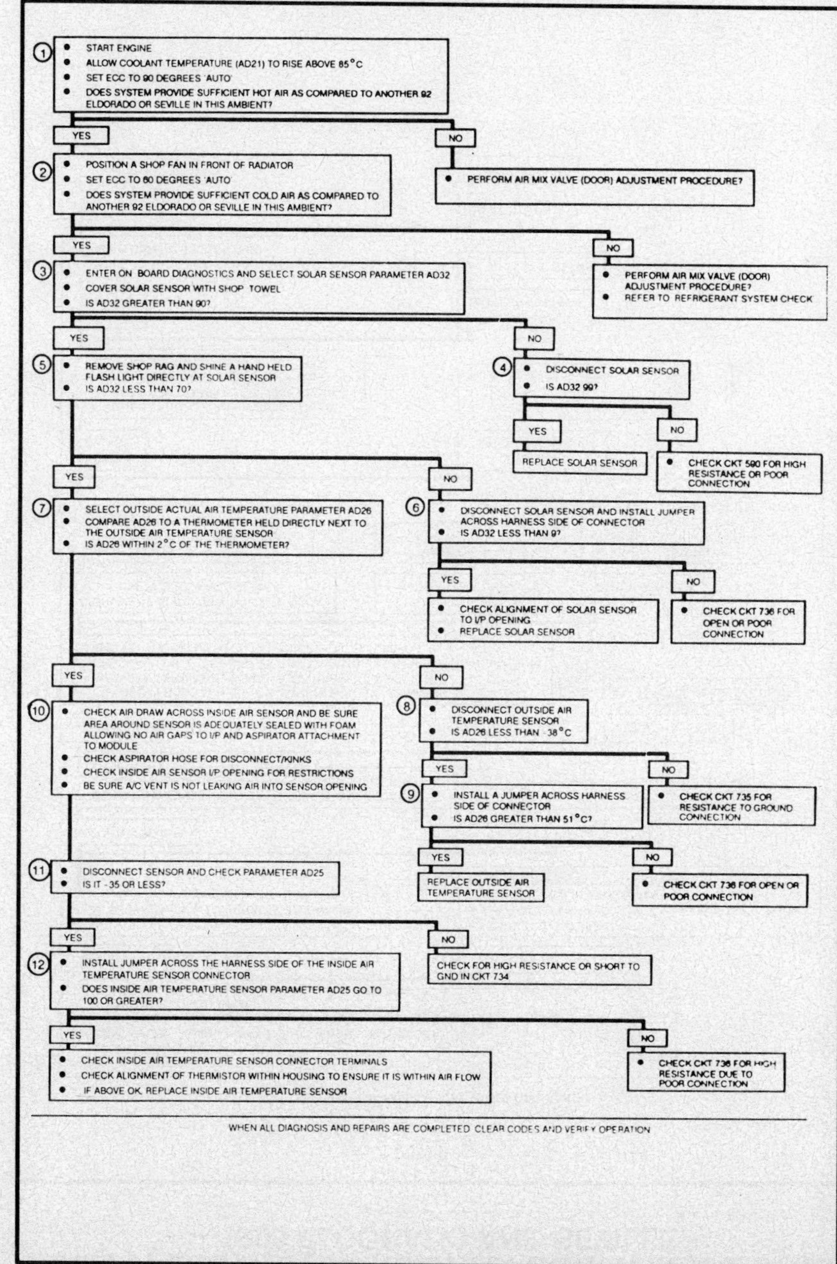
1
START ENGINE
ALLOW COOLANT TEMPERATURE (AD21) TO RISE ABOVE 85°C
SET ECC TO 90 DEGREES 'AUTO'
DOES SYSTEM PROVIDE SUFFICIENT HOT AIR AS COMPARED TO ANOTHER 92 ELDORADO OR SEVILLE IN THIS AMBIENT?
YES
NO
PERFORM AIR MIX VALVE (DOOR) ADJUSTMENT PROCEDURE?
2
POSITION A SHOP FAN IN FRONT OF RADIATOR
SET ECC TO 60 DEGREES 'AUTO'
DOES SYSTEM PROVIDE SUFFICIENT COLD AIR AS COMPARED TO ANOTHER 92 ELDORADO OR SEVILLE IN THIS AMBIENT?
YES
NO
PERFORM AIR MIX VALVE (DOOR) ADJUSTMENT PROCEDURE?
REFER TO REFRIGERANT SYSTEM CHECK
3
ENTER ON BOARD DIAGNOSTICS AND SELECT SOLAR SENSOR PARAMETER AD32
COVER SOLAR SENSOR WITH SHOP TOWEL
IS AD32 GREATER THAN 90?
YES
NO
5
REMOVE SHOP RAG AND SHINE A HAND HELD FLASH LIGHT DIRECTLY AT SOLAR SENSOR
IS AD32 LESS THAN 70?
4
DISCONNECT SOLAR SENSOR
IS AD32 99?
YES
NO
REPLACE SOLAR SENSOR
CHECK CKT 590 FOR HIGH RESISTANCE OR POOR CONNECTION
YES
NO
7
SELECT OUTSIDE ACTUAL AIR TEMPERATURE PARAMETER AD26
COMPARE AD26 TO A THERMOMETER HELD DIRECTLY NEXT TO THE OUTSIDE AIR TEMPERATURE SENSOR
IS AD26 WITHIN 2°C OF THE THERMOMETER?
6
DISCONNECT SOLAR SENSOR AND INSTALL JUMPER ACROSS HARNESS SIDE OF CONNECTOR
IS AD32 LESS THAN 9?
YES
NO
CHECK ALIGNMENT OF SOLAR SENSOR TO I/P OPENING
REPLACE SOLAR SENSOR
CHECK CKT 736 FOR OPEN OR POOR CONNECTION
YES
NO
10
CHECK AIR DRAW ACROSS INSIDE AIR SENSOR AND BE SURE AREA AROUND SENSOR IS ADEQUATELY SEALED WITH FOAM ALLOWING NO AIR GAPS TO I/P AND ASPIRATOR ATTACHMENT TO MODULE
CHECK ASPIRATOR HOSE FOR DISCONNECT/KINKS
CHECK INSIDE AIR SENSOR I/P OPENING FOR RESTRICTIONS
BE SURE A/C VENT IS NOT LEAKING AIR INTO SENSOR OPENING
8
DISCONNECT OUTSIDE AIR TEMPERATURE SENSOR
IS AD26 LESS THAN -38°C
YES
NO
9
INSTALL A JUMPER ACROSS HARNESS SIDE OF CONNECTOR
IS AD26 GREATER THAN 51°C?
CHECK CKT 735 FOR RESISTANCE TO GROUND CONNECTION
YES
NO
REPLACE OUTSIDE AIR TEMPERATURE SENSOR
CHECK CKT 736 FOR OPEN OR POOR CONNECTION
11
DISCONNECT SENSOR AND CHECK PARAMETER AD25
IS IT -35 OR LESS?
YES
NO
12
INSTALL JUMPER ACROSS THE HARNESS SIDE OF THE INSIDE AIR TEMPERATURE SENSOR CONNECTOR
DOES INSIDE AIR TEMPERATURE SENSOR PARAMETER AD25 GO TO 100 OR GREATER?
CHECK FOR HIGH RESISTANCE OR SHORT TO GND IN CKT 734
YES
NO
CHECK INSIDE AIR TEMPERATURE SENSOR CONNECTOR TERMINALS
CHECK ALIGNMENT OF THERMISTOR WITHIN HOUSING TO ENSURE IT IS WITHIN AIR FLOW
IF ABOVE OK, REPLACE INSIDE AIR TEMPERATURE SENSOR
CHECK CKT 736 FOR HIGH RESISTANCE DUE TO POOR CONNECTION
WHEN ALL DIAGNOSIS AND REPAIRS ARE COMPLETED CLEAR CODES AND VERIFY OPERATION

CHART 6: ECC SYSTEM REAR DEFOGGER ON CONTINUOUSLY—1993 ELDORADO AND SEVILLE

- IGNITION 'ON'
- SELECT REAR DEFOG 'OFF'

(1)
- REMOVE REAR DEFOG RELAY (D)
- CHECK VOLTAGE OF POSITIVE FEED BUS OF REAR DEFOGGER GRID LOCATED ON THE DRIVER'S SIDE OF VEHICLE

LESS THAN OR EQUAL TO 0.5 V

(2)
- CHECK RESISTANCE ACROSS THE COIL OF THE RELAY WHILE THE RELAY IS DISCONNECTED (BETWEEN TERMINALS 1 AND 2)

GREATER THAN 70 Ω

(3)
- REINSTALL RELAY
- DISCONNECT ACP CONNECTOR
- CHECK VOLTAGE AT TERMINAL 'D5'

BATTERY VOLTAGE → REPLACE ACP

LESS THAN BATTERY VOLTAGE → REPAIR SHORT TO GROUND ON CKT 291

LESS THAN 70 Ω → REPLACE ACP AND RELAY

GREATER THAN 0.5 V
- CHECK FOR SHORT TO VOLTAGE ON CKT 840 OR 293 OR 676

CHART 7: ECC SYSTEM REAR DEFOGGER INOPERATIVE —1993 ELDORADO AND SEVILLE

CHART 8: ECC SYSTEM REAR A/C BLOWER SPEED INCORRECT—1993 ELDORADO AND SEVILLE

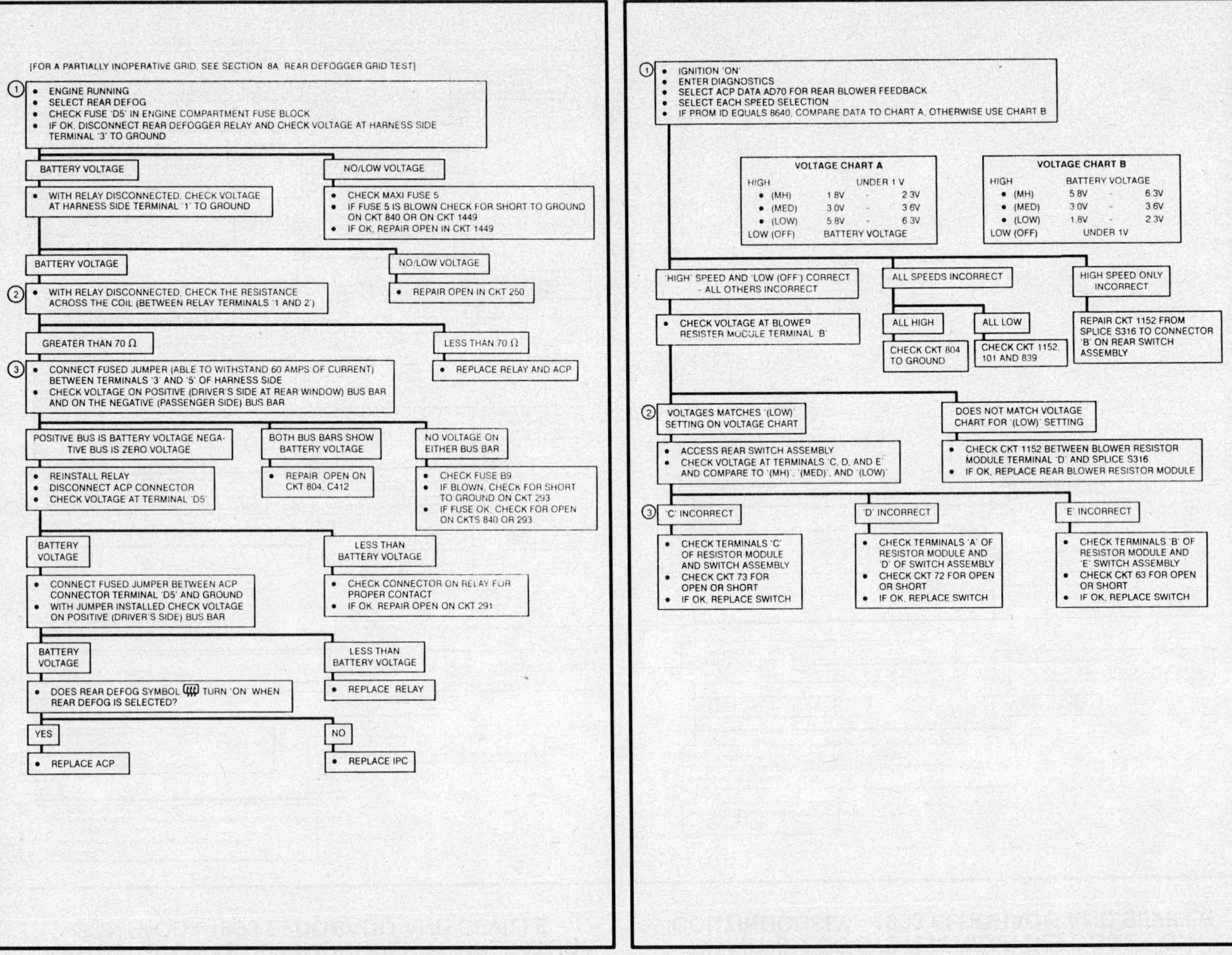

CHART 9: ECC SYSTEM REAR A/C BLOWER INOPERATIVE—1993 ELDORADO AND SEVILLE

CHART 10: ECC REFRIGERANT SYSTEM CHECK —1993 ELDORADO AND SEVILLE

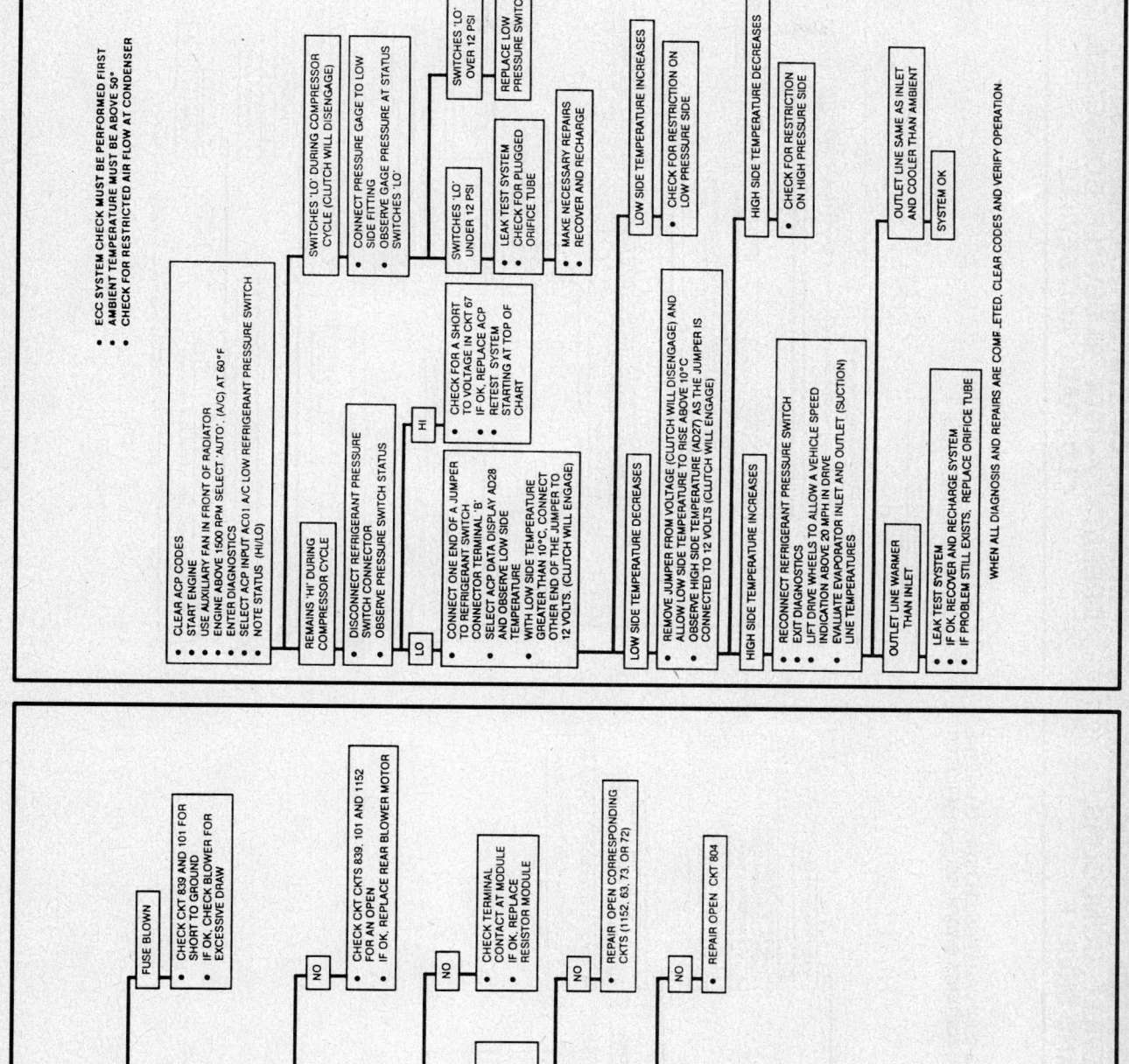

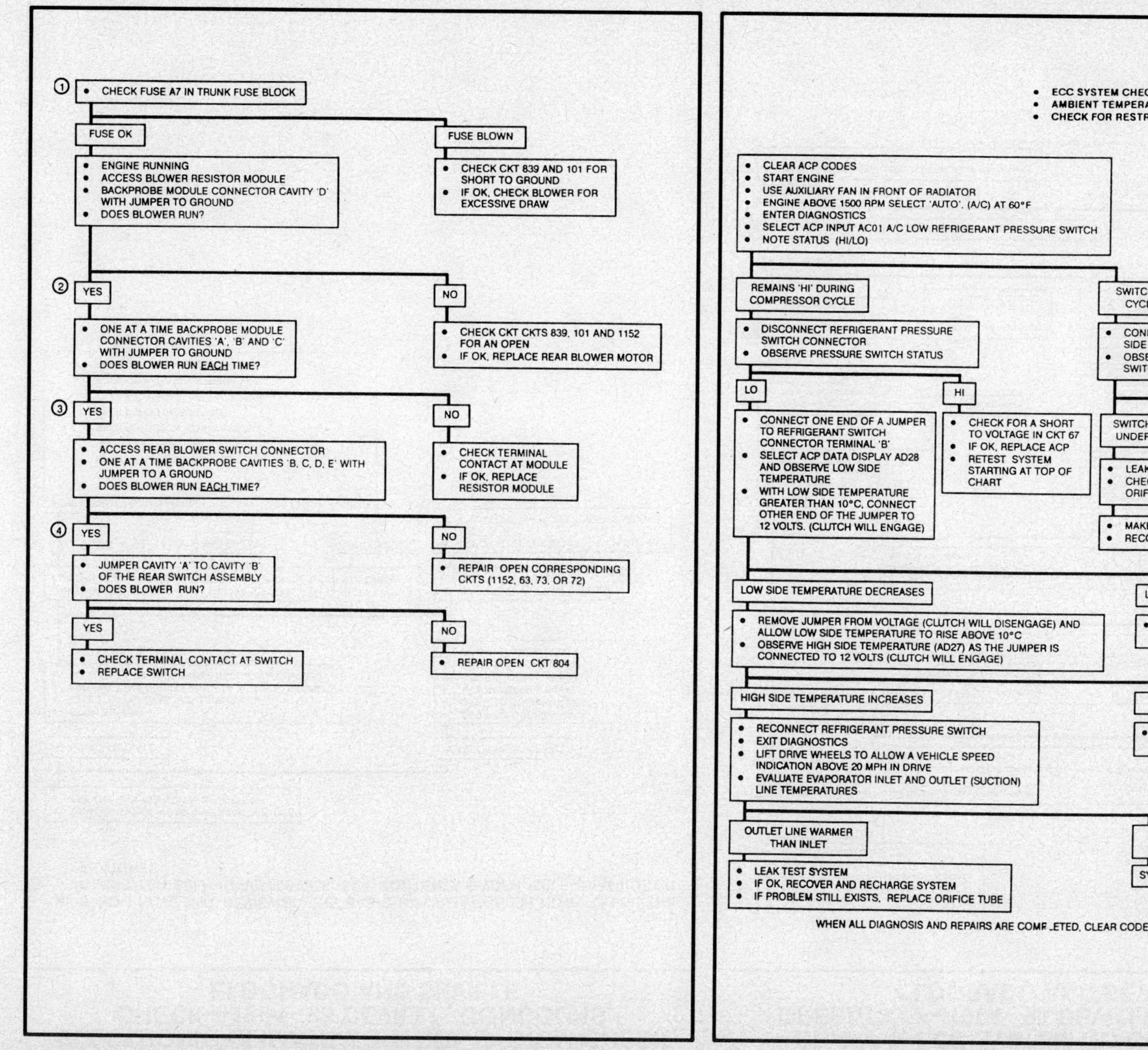

1
• CHECK FUSE A7 IN TRUNK FUSE BLOCK
FUSE OK
• ENGINE RUNNING
• ACCESS BLOWER RESISTOR MODULE
• BACKPROBE MODULE CONNECTOR CAVITY 'D' WITH JUMPER TO GROUND
• DOES BLOWER RUN?
FUSE BLOWN
• CHECK CKT 839 AND 101 FOR SHORT TO GROUND
• IF OK, CHECK BLOWER FOR EXCESSIVE DRAW
2
YES
• ONE AT A TIME BACKPROBE MODULE CONNECTOR CAVITIES 'A', 'B' AND 'C' WITH JUMPER TO GROUND
• DOES BLOWER RUN EACH TIME?
NO
• CHECK CKT CKTS 839, 101 AND 1152 FOR AN OPEN
• IF OK, REPLACE REAR BLOWER MOTOR
3
YES
• ACCESS REAR BLOWER SWITCH CONNECTOR
• ONE AT A TIME BACKPROBE CAVITIES 'B, C, D, E' WITH JUMPER TO A GROUND
• DOES BLOWER RUN EACH TIME?
NO
• CHECK TERMINAL CONTACT AT MODULE
• IF OK, REPLACE RESISTOR MODULE
4
YES
• JUMPER CAVITY 'A' TO CAVITY 'B' OF THE REAR SWITCH ASSEMBLY
• DOES BLOWER RUN?
NO
• REPAIR OPEN CORRESPONDING CKTS (1152, 63, 73, OR 72)
YES
• CHECK TERMINAL CONTACT AT SWITCH
• REPLACE SWITCH
NO
• REPAIR OPEN CKT 804
• ECC SYSTEM CHECK MUST BE PERFORMED FIRST
• AMBIENT TEMPERATURE MUST BE ABOVE 50°
• CHECK FOR RESTRICTED AIR FLOW AT CONDENSER
• CLEAR ACP CODES
• START ENGINE
• USE AUXILIARY FAN IN FRONT OF RADIATOR
• ENGINE ABOVE 1500 RPM SELECT 'AUTO', (A/C) AT 60°F
• ENTER DIAGNOSTICS
• SELECT ACP INPUT AC01 A/C LOW REFRIGERANT PRESSURE SWITCH
• NOTE STATUS (HI/LO)
REMAINS 'HI' DURING COMPRESSOR CYCLE
• DISCONNECT REFRIGERANT PRESSURE SWITCH CONNECTOR
• OBSERVE PRESSURE SWITCH STATUS
LO
• CONNECT ONE END OF A JUMPER TO REFRIGERANT SWITCH CONNECTOR TERMINAL 'B'
• SELECT ACP DATA DISPLAY AD28 AND OBSERVE LOW SIDE TEMPERATURE
• WITH LOW SIDE TEMPERATURE GREATER THAN 10°C, CONNECT OTHER END OF THE JUMPER TO 12 VOLTS. (CLUTCH WILL ENGAGE)
HI
• CHECK FOR A SHORT TO VOLTAGE IN CKT 67
• IF OK, REPLACE ACP
• RETEST SYSTEM STARTING AT TOP OF CHART
SWITCHES 'LO' DURING COMPRESSOR CYCLE (CLUTCH WILL DISENGAGE)
• CONNECT PRESSURE GAGE TO LOW SIDE FITTING
• OBSERVE GAGE PRESSURE AT STATUS SWITCHES 'LO'
SWITCHES 'LO' UNDER 12 PSI
• LEAK TEST SYSTEM
• CHECK FOR PLUGGED ORIFICE TUBE
• MAKE NECESSARY REPAIRS
• RECOVER AND RECHARGE
SWITCHES 'LO' OVER 12 PSI
REPLACE LOW PRESSURE SWITCH
LOW SIDE TEMPERATURE DECREASES
• REMOVE JUMPER FROM VOLTAGE (CLUTCH WILL DISENGAGE) AND ALLOW LOW SIDE TEMPERATURE TO RISE ABOVE 10°C
• OBSERVE HIGH SIDE TEMPERATURE (AD27) AS THE JUMPER IS CONNECTED TO 12 VOLTS (CLUTCH WILL ENGAGE)
LOW SIDE TEMPERATURE INCREASES
• CHECK FOR RESTRICTION ON LOW PRESSURE SIDE
HIGH SIDE TEMPERATURE INCREASES
• RECONNECT REFRIGERANT PRESSURE SWITCH
• EXIT DIAGNOSTICS
• LIFT DRIVE WHEELS TO ALLOW A VEHICLE SPEED INDICATION ABOVE 20 MPH IN DRIVE
• EVALUATE EVAPORATOR INLET AND OUTLET (SUCTION) LINE TEMPERATURES
HIGH SIDE TEMPERATURE DECREASES
• CHECK FOR RESTRICTION ON HIGH PRESSURE SIDE
OUTLET LINE WARMER THAN INLET
• LEAK TEST SYSTEM
• IF OK, RECOVER AND RECHARGE SYSTEM
• IF PROBLEM STILL EXISTS, REPLACE ORIFICE TUBE
OUTLET LINE SAME AS INLET AND COOLER THAN AMBIENT
SYSTEM OK
WHEN ALL DIAGNOSIS AND REPAIRS ARE COMPLETED, CLEAR CODES AND VERIFY OPERATION

ELECTRONIC CLIMATE CONTROL SYSTEM CHECK CHECK—1994–95 DEVILLE, CONCOURS, ELDORADO AND SEVILLE

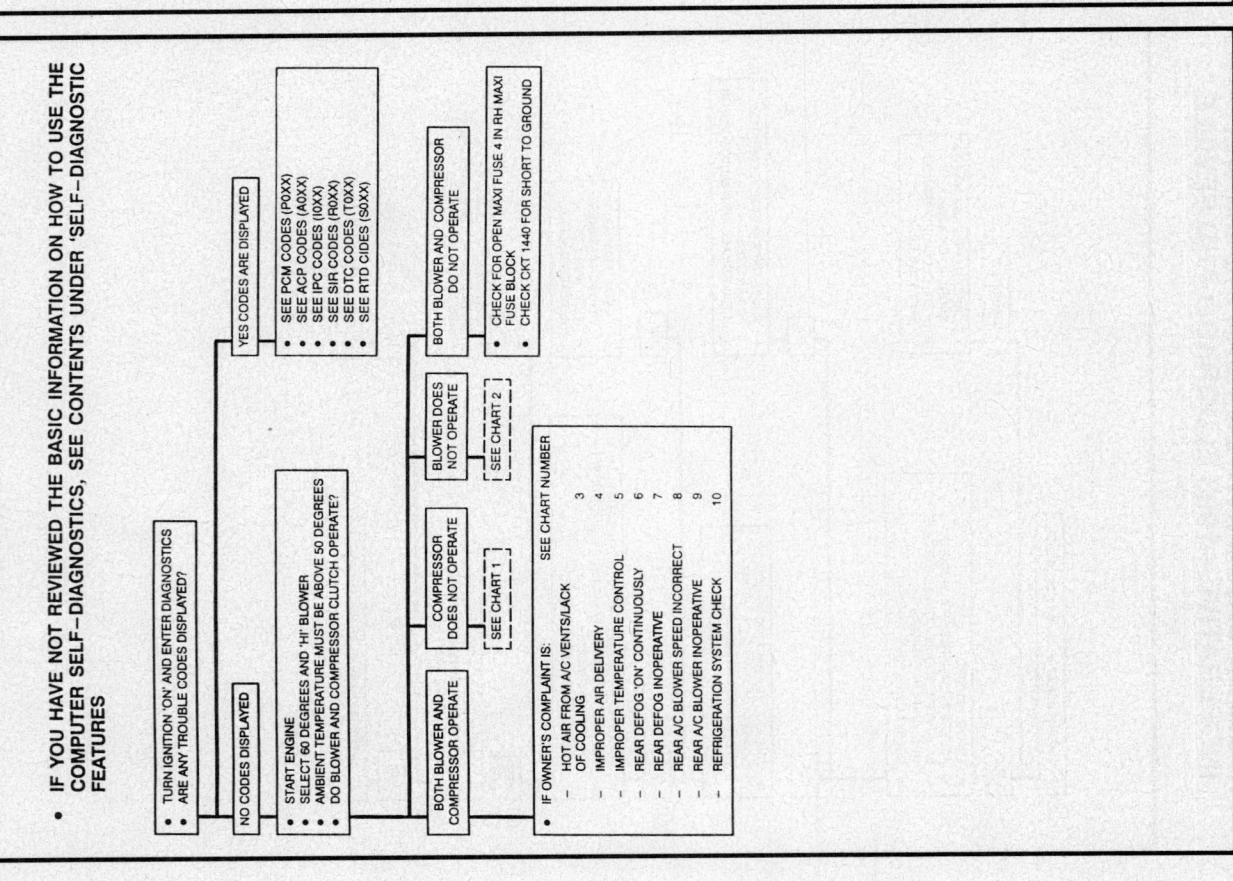

- IF YOU HAVE NOT REVIEWED THE BASIC INFORMATION ON HOW TO USE THE COMPUTER SELF–DIAGNOSTICS, SEE CONTENTS UNDER 'SELF–DIAGNOSTIC FEATURES

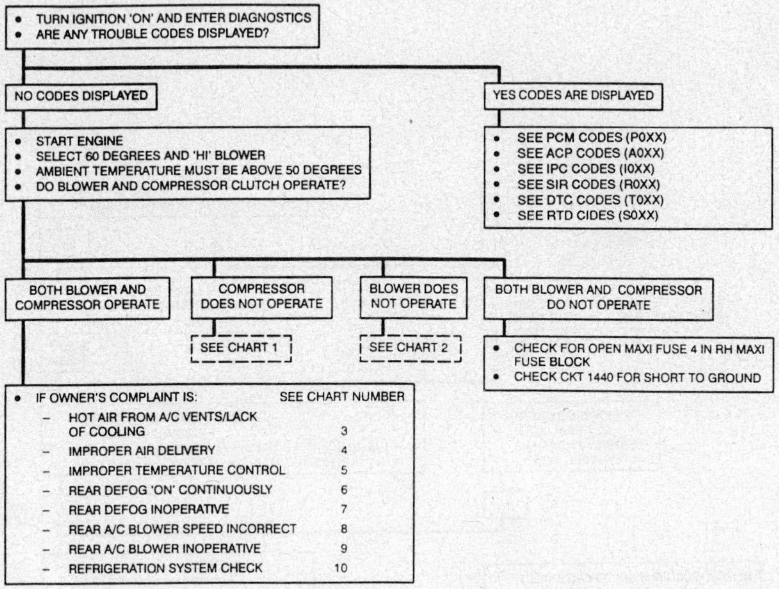

- TURN IGNITION 'ON' AND ENTER DIAGNOSTICS
- ARE ANY TROUBLE CODES DISPLAYED?

NO CODES DISPLAYED

- START ENGINE
- SELECT 60 DEGREES AND 'HI' BLOWER
- AMBIENT TEMPERATURE MUST BE ABOVE 50 DEGREES
- DO BLOWER AND COMPRESSOR CLUTCH OPERATE?

YES CODES ARE DISPLAYED

- SEE PCM CODES (P0XX)
- SEE ACP CODES (A0XX)
- SEE IPC CODES (I0XX)
- SEE SIR CODES (R0XX)
- SEE DTC CODES (T0XX)
- SEE RTD CIDES (S0XX)

BOTH BLOWER AND COMPRESSOR OPERATE

- IF OWNER'S COMPLAINT IS: SEE CHART NUMBER
  - HOT AIR FROM A/C VENTS/LACK OF COOLING 3
  - IMPROPER AIR DELIVERY 4
  - IMPROPER TEMPERATURE CONTROL 5
  - REAR DEFOG 'ON' CONTINUOUSLY 6
  - REAR DEFOG INOPERATIVE 7
  - REAR A/C BLOWER SPEED INCORRECT 8
  - REAR A/C BLOWER INOPERATIVE 9
  - REFRIGERATION SYSTEM CHECK 10

COMPRESSOR DOES NOT OPERATE

SEE CHART 1

BLOWER DOES NOT OPERATE

SEE CHART 2

BOTH BLOWER AND COMPRESSOR DO NOT OPERATE

- CHECK FOR OPEN MAXI FUSE 4 IN RH MAXI FUSE BLOCK
- CHECK CKT 1440 FOR SHORT TO GROUND

CHART 1: ECC SYSTEM NO COMPRESSOR OPERATION—1994–95 DEVILLE, CONSOURS, ELDORADO AND SEVILLE

(1)
- TURN IGNITION 'ON'
- SELECT AUTO 60 SET TEMPERATURE
- ENTER DIAGNOSTICS (SEE SECTION 8D FOR DETAILS)
- SELECT PCM OUTPUT20 – A/C RELAY
- DOES COMPRESSOR CLUTCH CYCLE?

YES

- START ENGINE AND ENTER DIAGNOSTICS
- SELECT 'ACP DATA'
- MONITOR THE ACP STATUS LIGHT FOR A/C CLUTCH REQUEST (IT'S THE FRONT DEFROST SYMBOL
- DOES THE LIGHT EVER COME ON?

YES
- REPLACE PCM

NO
- CHECK FOLLOWING ACP DATA PARAMETERS
  - AD26 – ACTUAL OUTSIDE AIR TEMPERATURE SHOULD BE CLOSE TO AMBIENT TEMPERATURE IF CAR IS MOVING AT HIGHWAY SPEEDS
    NOTE: TEMPERATURE MUST BE ABOVE 40°F FOR COMPRESSOR OPERATION
  - AD28 – LOW SIDE TEMPERATURE SHOULD BE ABOVE 10 DEGREES
- DO SENSORS READ OKAY?

YES
- REPLACE ACP

NO
- CHECK FOR ADDITIONAL RESISTANCE IN SENSOR WIRING CAUSED BY POOR CONNECTION (LOOSE, CORRODED, ETC.)
- IF OK, REPLACE SENSOR

NO

DOES A/C RELAY CYCLE?

YES

(2)
- REMOVE A/C RELAY
- JUMPER PIN '3' TO '5'
- DOES CLUTCH ENGAGE?

YES
- REPLACE A/C RELAY

NO

(3)
- JUMPER PIN '2' TO '5'
- DOES CLUTCH ENGAGE?

YES
- REPAIR OPEN IN CKT 1640 OR FUSE B7
- IF FUSE BLOWN, CHECK FOR SHORT TO GROUND

NO

(4)
- JUMPER STILL CONNECTED
- CHECK VOLTAGE AT PIN 'A' OF COMPRESSOR CLUTCH

LESS THAN BATTERY VOLTAGE
- REPAIR OPEN IN CKT 59

BATTERY VOLTAGE

(5)
- CHECK CONTINUITY FROM 'B' OF COMPRESSOR CLUTCH CONNECTORS TO GROUND

NOT CONTINUOUS
- REPAIR OPEN IN CKT 250

CONTINUOUS
- CHECK A/C COMPRESSOR CLUTCH DIODE FOR SHORT (P/N 12112422)
- IF OK, REPLACE COMPRESSOR CLUTCH

NO

(6)
- REMOVE A/C RELAY
- CHECK COIL RESISTANCE (BETWEEN RELAY PIN '1' AND '2')

GREATER THAN 150 Ω
- REPLACE RELAY

LESS THAN 70 Ω
- REPLACE A/C RELAY

BETWEEN 70 Ω AND 150 Ω

(7)
- CHECK VOLTAGE BETWEEN HARNESS PIN '2' & GROUND

BATTERY VOLTAGE
- REPAIR OPEN IN CKT 782
- IF OK, REPLACE PCM

LESS THAN BATTERY VOLTAGE
- REPAIR OPEN IN CKT 804, CKT 803 OR CKT 39 FUSE (A3), LOW REFRIGERANT SWITCH, HIGH REFRIGERANT PRESSURE SWITCH

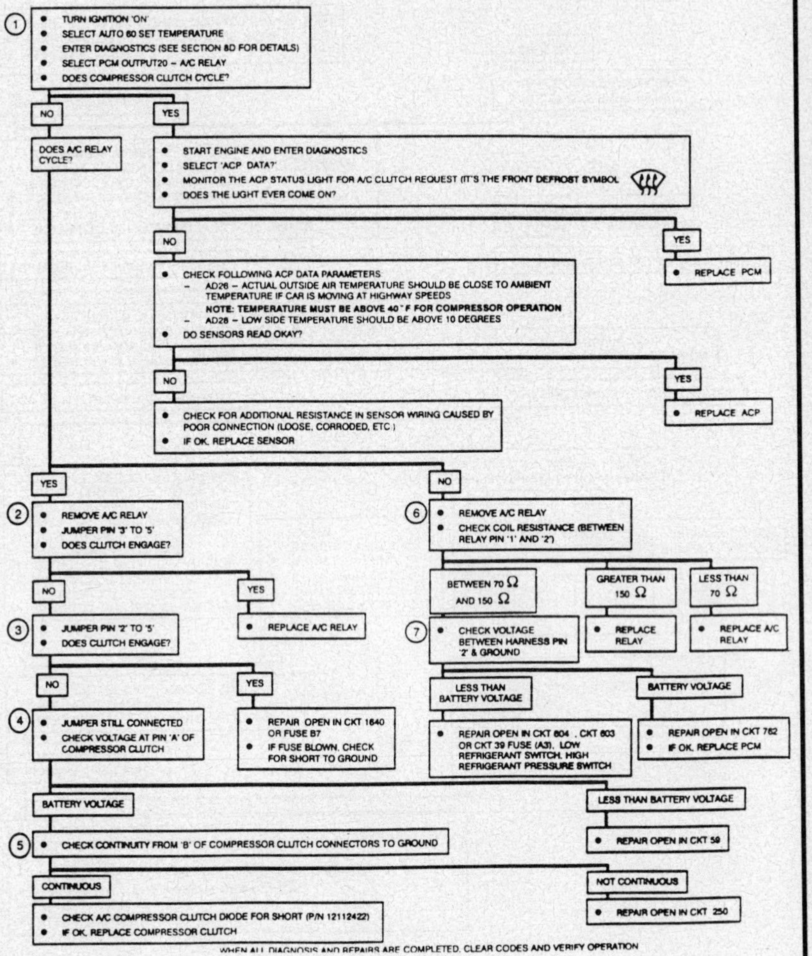

WHEN ALL DIAGNOSIS AND REPAIRS ARE COMPLETED, CLEAR CODES AND VERIFY OPERATION

CHART 2 & 3: ECC NO BLOWER OPERATION—1993 DEVILLE, CONCOURS, ELDORADO AND SEVILLE

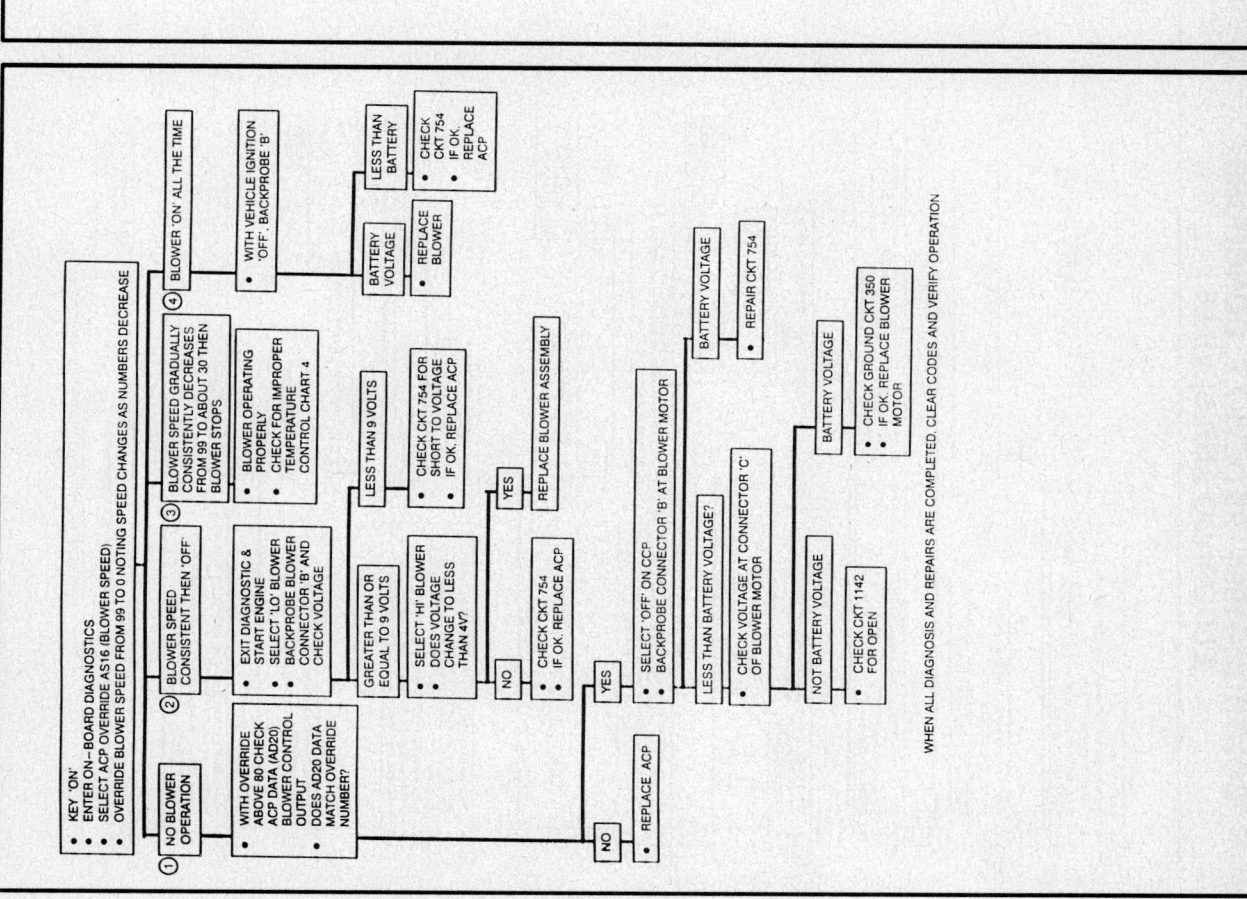

- KEY 'ON'
- ENTER ON–BOARD DIAGNOSTICS
- SELECT ACP OVERRIDE AS16 (BLOWER SPEED)
- OVERRIDE BLOWER SPEED FROM 99 TO 0 NOTING SPEED CHANGES AS NUMBERS DECREASE

(1) NO BLOWER OPERATION

- WITH OVERRIDE ABOVE 80 CHECK ACP DATA (AD20) BLOWER CONTROL OUTPUT
- DOES AD20 DATA MATCH OVERRIDE NUMBER?

NO:
- REPLACE ACP

YES:
- SELECT 'OFF' ON CCP
- BACKPROBE CONNECTOR 'B' AT BLOWER MOTOR

LESS THAN BATTERY VOLTAGE?
- CHECK VOLTAGE AT CONNECTOR 'C' OF BLOWER MOTOR

NOT BATTERY VOLTAGE
- CHECK CKT 1142 FOR OPEN

BATTERY VOLTAGE
- CHECK GROUND CKT 350
- IF OK, REPLACE BLOWER MOTOR

BATTERY VOLTAGE
- REPAIR CKT 754

(2) BLOWER SPEED CONSISTENT THEN 'OFF'

- EXIT DIAGNOSTIC & START ENGINE
- SELECT 'LO' BLOWER
- BACKPROBE BLOWER CONNECTOR 'B' AND CHECK VOLTAGE

GREATER THAN OR EQUAL TO 9 VOLTS
- SELECT 'HI' BLOWER
- DOES VOLTAGE CHANGE TO LESS THAN 4V?

NO:
- CHECK CKT 754
- IF OK, REPLACE ACP

YES:
REPLACE BLOWER ASSEMBLY

LESS THAN 9 VOLTS
- CHECK CKT 754 FOR SHORT TO VOLTAGE
- IF OK, REPLACE ACP

(3) BLOWER SPEED GRADUALLY CONSISTENTLY DECREASES FROM 99 TO ABOUT 30 THEN BLOWER STOPS

- BLOWER OPERATING PROPERLY
- CHECK FOR IMPROPER TEMPERATURE CONTROL CHART 4

(4) BLOWER 'ON' ALL THE TIME

- WITH VEHICLE IGNITION 'OFF', BACKPROBE 'B'

BATTERY VOLTAGE
- REPLACE BLOWER

LESS THAN BATTERY
- CHECK CKT 754
- IF OK, REPLACE ACP

WHEN ALL DIAGNOSIS AND REPAIRS ARE COMPLETED, CLEAR CODES AND VERIFY OPERATION

CHART 4: ECC SYSTEM HOT AIR FROM A/C VENTS, OF COOLING—1994–95 DEVILLE, CONCOURS, ELDORADO AND SEVILLE

- CHECK A/C CAPACITY BY:
  - POSITION A SHOP FAN IN FRONT OF RADIATOR.
  - SET ECC TO 60 DEGREES 'AUTO'.
  - DOES SYSTEM PROVIDE SUFFICIENT COOLING AS COMPARED TO A COMPARABLE VEHICLE IN THIS AMBIENT.
  - IF NO, REFER TO 'REFRIGERANT SYSTEM CHECK' CHART 10.
- DID CONDITION OCCUR FOR OWNER DURING ANY OF THE FOLLOWING CONDITIONS (OR COMBINATION):
  - HIGH AMBIENT.
  - HIGH HUMIDITY.
  - EXTENDED IDLE.
  - SLOW VEHICLE SPEED.
  - TAIL WIND.

THE HIGH SIDE REFRIGERANT PRESSURE SWITCH CAN OPEN UNDER THE ABOVE CONDITIONS THUS DISABLING THE COMPRESSOR WITHOUT SETTING CODES OR ALTERING ECC SETTING AS DESCRIBED UNDER 'HIGH REFRIGERANT PRESSURE SWITCH'. THIS IS TO PREVENT REFRIGERANT DISCHARGE TO THE ATMOSPHERE FROM THE COMPRESSOR PRESSURE RELIEF VALVE. UNDER EXTREME LOADS THIS CAN OCCUR AND IS A NORMAL CONDITION.

CHART 5: ECC SYSTEM IMPROPER TEMPERATURE CONTROL—1994–95 DEVILLE, CONCOURS, ELDORADO AND SEVILLE

(1)
- START ENGINE
- ALLOW COOLANT TEMPERATURE (AD21) TO RISE ABOVE 85°C
- SET ECC TO 90 DEGREES 'AUTO'
- DOES SYSTEM PROVIDE SUFFICIENT HOT AIR AS COMPARED TO A COMPARABLE VEHICLE

NO:
- PERFORM AIR MIX VALVE (DOOR) ADJUSTMENT PROCEDURE?

YES:

(2)
- POSITION A SHOP FAN IN FRONT OF RADIATOR
- SET ECC TO 60 DEGREES 'AUTO'
- DOES SYSTEM PROVIDE SUFFICIENT COLD AIR AS COMPARED TO A COMPARABLE VEHICLE

NO:
- PERFORM AIR MIX VALVE (DOOR) ADJUSTMENT PROCEDURE?
- REFER TO 'REFRIGERANT SYSTEM CHECK', CHART 9

YES:

(3)
- ENTER ON-BOARD DIAGNOSTICS AND SELECT SOLAR SENSOR PARAMETER AD32
- COVER SOLAR SENSOR WITH SHOP TOWEL
- IS AD32 GREATER THAN 90?

NO:

(4)
- DISCONNECT SOLAR SENSOR
- IS AD32 99?

YES: REPLACE SOLAR SENSOR

NO:
- CHECK CKT 590 FOR HIGH RESISTANCE OR POOR CONNECTION

YES:

(5)
- REMOVE SHOP RAG AND SHINE A HAND HELD FLASH LIGHT DIRECTLY AT SOLAR SENSOR
- IS AD32 LESS THAN 70?

NO:

(6)
- DISCONNECT SOLAR SENSOR AND INSTALL JUMPER ACROSS HARNESS SIDE OF CONNECTOR
- IS AD32 LESS THAN 9?

YES:
- CHECK ALIGNMENT OF SOLAR SENSOR TO I/P OPENING
- REPLACE SOLAR SENSOR

NO:
- CHECK CKT 407 FOR OPEN OR POOR CONNECTION

YES:

(7)
- SELECT OUTSIDE ACTUAL AIR TEMPERATURE PARAMETER AD26
- COMPARE AD26 TO A THERMOMETER HELD DIRECTLY NEXT TO THE OUTSIDE AIR TEMPERATURE SENSOR
- IS AD26 WITHIN 2°C OF THE THERMOMETER?

NO:

(8)
- DISCONNECT OUTSIDE AIR TEMPERATURE SENSOR
- IS AD26 LESS THAN −38°C

YES:

(9)
- INSTALL A JUMPER ACROSS HARNESS SIDE OF CONNECTOR
- IS AD26 GREATER THAN 51°C?

YES: REPLACE OUTSIDE AIR TEMPERATURE SENSOR

NO:
- CHECK CKT 407 FOR OPEN OR POOR CONNECTION

NO:
- CHECK CKT 735 FOR RESISTANCE TO GROUND CONNECTION

YES:

(10)
- CHECK AIR DRAW ACROSS INSIDE AIR SENSOR AND BE SURE AREA AROUND SENSOR IS ADEQUATELY SEALED WITH FOAM ALLOWING NO AIR GAPS TO I/P AND ASPIRATOR ATTACHMENT TO MODULE
- CHECK ASPIRATOR HOSE FOR DISCONNECT/KINKS
- CHECK INSIDE AIR SENSOR I/P OPENING FOR RESTRICTIONS
- BE SURE A/C VENT IS NOT LEAKING AIR INTO SENSOR OPENING

(11)
- DISCONNECT SENSOR AND CHECK PARAMETER AD25
- IS IT −35 OR LESS?

NO: CHECK FOR HIGH RESISTANCE OR SHORT TO GND IN CKT 734

YES:

(12)
- INSTALL JUMPER ACROSS THE HARNESS SIDE OF THE INSIDE AIR TEMPERATURE SENSOR CONNECTOR
- DOES INSIDE AIR TEMPERATURE SENSOR PARAMETER AD25 GO TO 100 OR GREATER?

YES:
- CHECK INSIDE AIR TEMPERATURE SENSOR CONNECTOR TERMINALS
- CHECK ALIGNMENT OF THERMISTOR WITHIN HOUSING TO ENSURE IT IS WITHIN AIR FLOW
- IF ABOVE OK, REPLACE INSIDE AIR TEMPERATURE SENSOR

NO:
- CHECK CKT 407 FOR HIGH RESISTANCE DUE TO POOR CONNECTION

WHEN ALL DIAGNOSIS AND REPAIRS ARE COMPLETED, CLEAR CODES AND VERIFY OPERATION

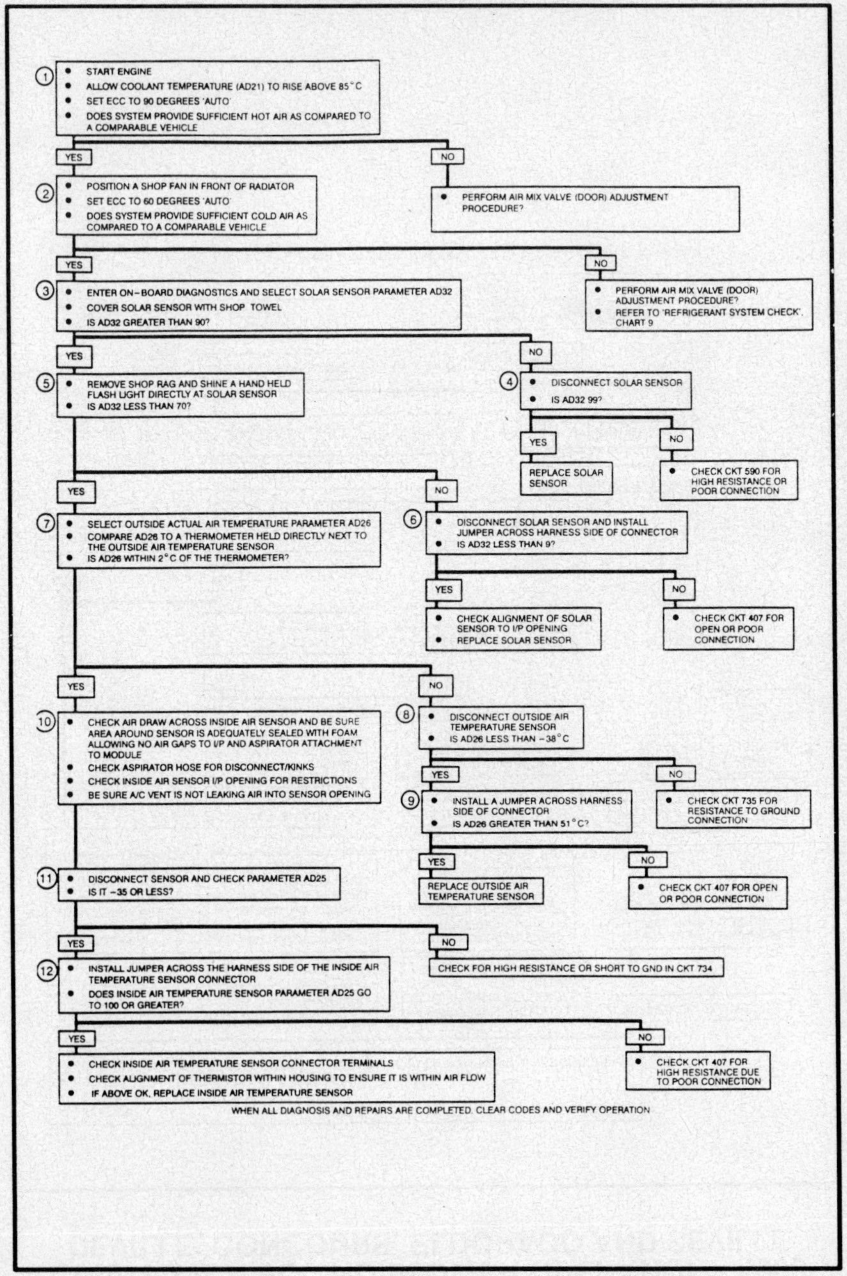

CHART 6: ECC SYSTEM REAR DEFOGGER ON CONTINUOUSLY—1994–95 DEVILLE, CONCOURS, ELDORADO AND SEVILLE

- IGNITION 'ON'
- SELECT REAR DEFOG 'OFF'

(1)
- REMOVE REAR DEFOG RELAY (D)
- CHECK VOLTAGE OF POSITIVE FEED BUSS OF REAR DEFOGGER GRID LOCATED ON THE DRIVER'S SIDE OF VEHICLE

GREATER THAN 0.5 V:
- CHECK FOR SHORT TO VOLTAGE ON CKT 270 OR 267

LESS THAN OR EQUAL TO 0.5 V:

(2)
- CHECK RESISTANCE ACROSS THE COIL OF THE RELAY WHILE THE RELAY IS DISCONNECTED (BETWEEN TERMINALS '1' AND '2')

LESS THAN 70 Ω: REPLACE ACP AND RELAY

GREATER THAN 70 Ω:

(3)
- REINSTALL RELAY
- DISCONNECT ACP CONNECTOR
- CHECK VOLTAGE AT TERMINAL 'D5'

BATTERY VOLTAGE: REPLACE ACP

LESS THAN BATTERY VOLTAGE: REPAIR SHORT TO GROUND ON CKT 193

WHEN ALL DIAGNOSIS AND REPAIRS ARE COMPLETED, CLEAR CODES AND VERIFY OPERATION

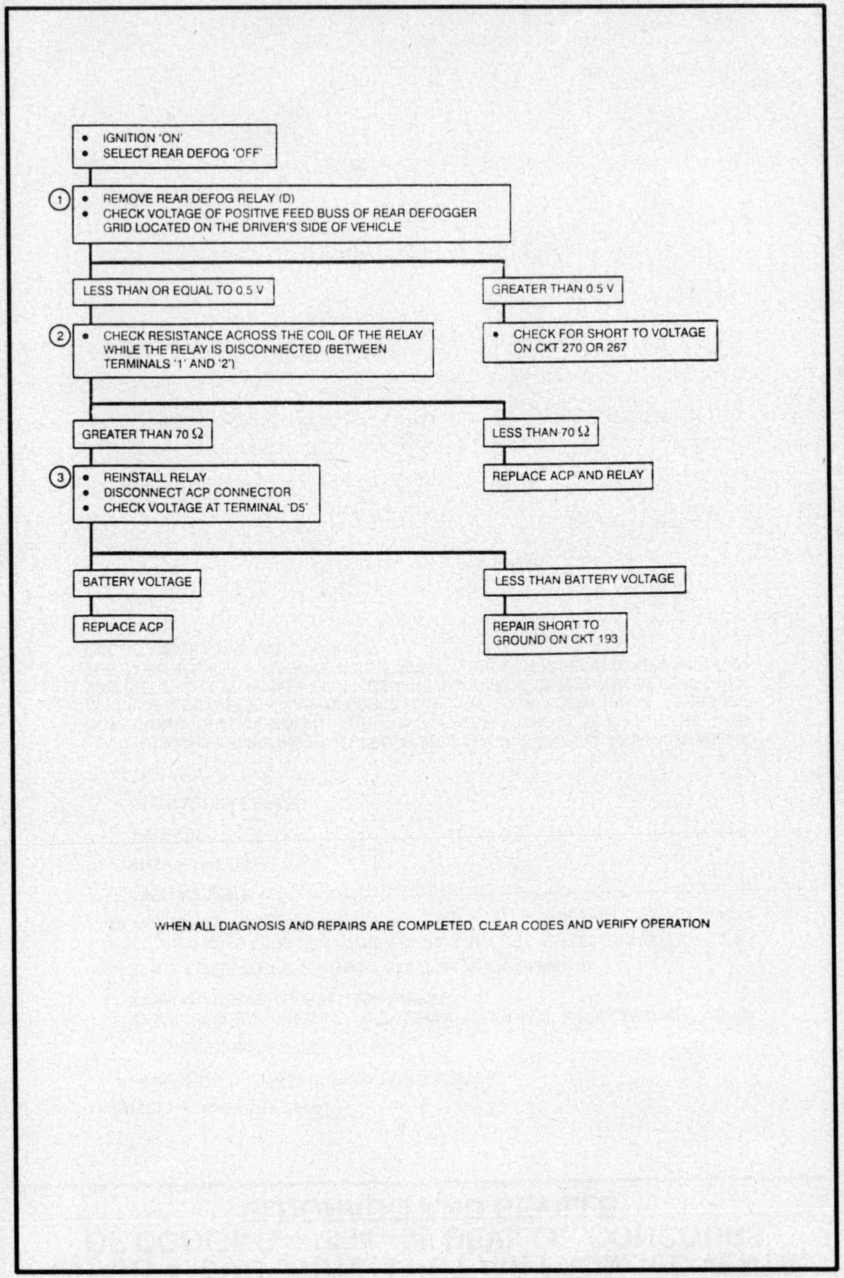

CHART 7: ECC SYSTEM REAR DEFOGGER INOPERATIVE—1994–95 DEVILLE, CONCOURS, ELDORADO AND SEVILLE

[FOR A PARTIALLY INOPERATIVE GRID, SEE SECTION 8A: REAR DEFOGGER GRID TEST]

(1)
- ENGINE RUNNING
- SELECT REAR DEFOG
- CHECK FUSE 'D5' IN ENGINE COMPARTMENT FUSE BLOCK
- IF OK, DISCONNECT REAR DEFOGGER RELAY AND CHECK VOLTAGE AT HARNESS SIDE TERMINAL '3' TO GROUND

BATTERY VOLTAGE
- WITH RELAY DISCONNECTED, CHECK VOLTAGE AT HARNESS SIDE TERMINAL '1' TO GROUND

NO/LOW VOLTAGE
- CHECK MAXI FUSE 5
- IF FUSE 5 IS BLOWN CHECK FOR SHORT TO GROUND ON CKT 293 OR ON CKT 1242
- IF OK, REPAIR OPEN IN CKT 1242

BATTERY VOLTAGE

(2)
- WITH RELAY DISCONNECTED, CHECK THE RESISTANCE ACROSS THE COIL (BETWEEN RELAY TERMINALS '1' AND '2')

NO/LOW VOLTAGE
- REPAIR OPEN IN CKT 241

GREATER THAN 70 Ω

(3)
- CONNECT FUSED JUMPER (ABLE TO WITHSTAND 60 AMPS OF CURRENT) BETWEEN TERMINALS '3' AND '5' OF HARNESS SIDE
- CHECK VOLTAGE ON POSITIVE (DRIVER'S SIDE AT REAR WINDOW) BUSS BAR AND ON THE NEGATIVE (PASSENGER SIDE) BUSS BAR

LESS THAN 70 Ω
- REPLACE RELAY AND ACP

POSITIVE BUSS IS BATTERY VOLTAGE NEGATIVE BUSS IS ZERO VOLTAGE
- REINSTALL RELAY
- DISCONNECT ACP CONNECTOR
- CHECK VOLTAGE AT TERMINAL 'D5'

BOTH BUSS BARS SHOW BATTERY VOLTAGE
- REPAIR OPEN ON CKT 1250, C412

NO VOLTAGE ON EITHER BUSS BAR
- CHECK FUSE B9
- IF BLOWN, CHECK FOR SHORT TO GROUND ON CKT 270
- IF FUSE OK, CHECK FOR OPEN ON CKT 293

BATTERY VOLTAGE
- CONNECT FUSED JUMPER BETWEEN ACP CONNECTOR TERMINAL 'D5' AND GROUND
- WITH JUMPER INSTALLED CHECK VOLTAGE ON POSITIVE (DRIVER'S SIDE) BUSS BAR

LESS THAN 3ATTERY VOLTAGE
- CHECK CONNECTOR ON RELAY FOR PROPER CONTACT
- IF OK, REPAIR OPEN ON CKT 193

BATTERY VOLTAGE
- DOES REAR DEFOG SYMBOL [defog symbol] TURN 'ON' WHEN REAR DEFOG IS SELECTED?

LESS THAN BATTERY VOLTAGE
- REPLACE RELAY

YES
- REPLACE ACP

NO
- REPLACE IPC

WHEN ALL DIAGNOSIS AND REPAIRS ARE COMPLETED, CLEAR CODES AND VERIFY OPERATION

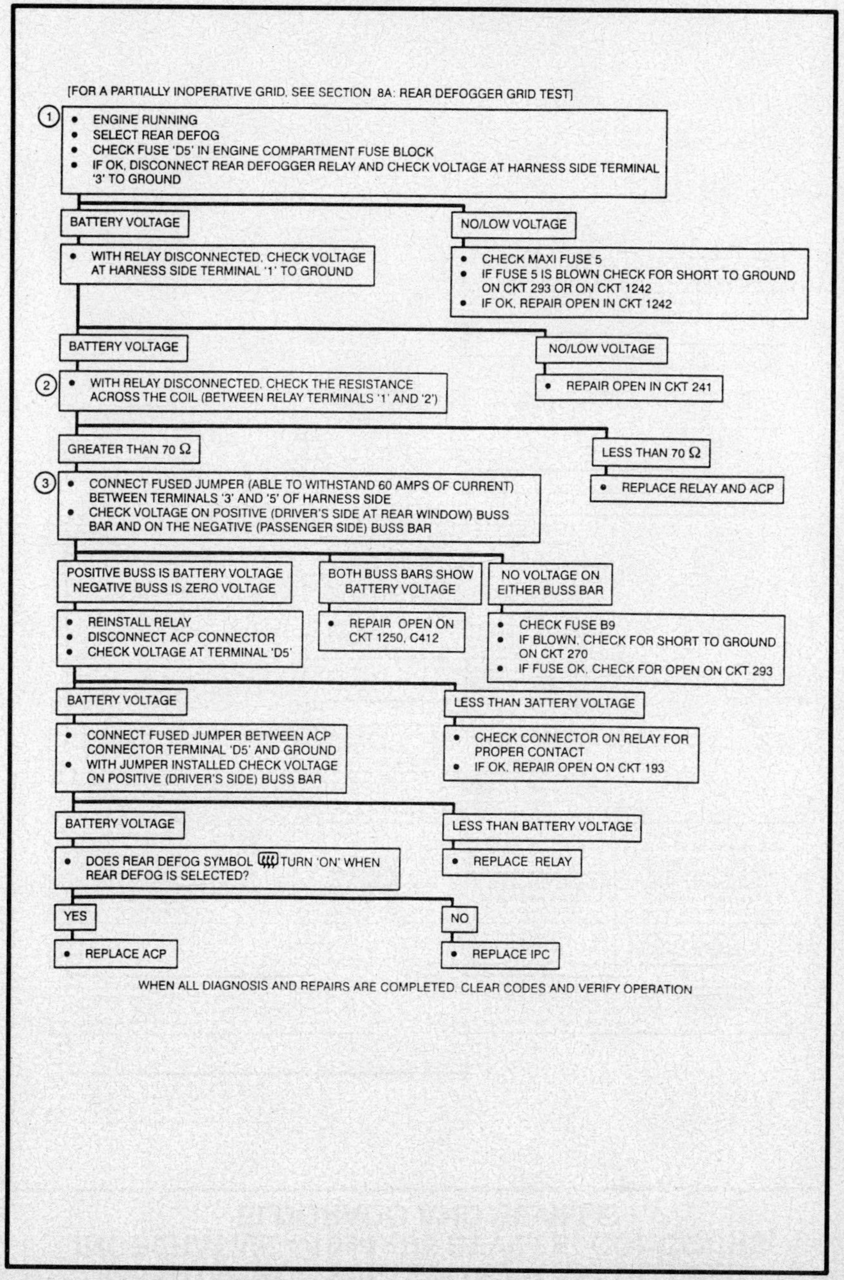

CHART 8: ECC SYSTEM REAR A/C BLOWER SPEED INCORRECT—1994–95 DEVILLE, CONCOURS, ELDORADO AND SEVILLE

(1)
- IGNITION 'ON'
- ENTER DIAGNOSTICS (REFER TO SECTION 8D FOR DETAILS)
- SELECT ACP DATA AD70 FOR REAR BLOWER FEEDBACK
- SELECT EACH SPEED SELECTION
- COMPARE DATA TO CHART

VOLTAGE CHART

HIGH	BATTERY VOLTAGE		
• (MH)	5.8V	–	6.3V
• (MED)	3.0V	–	3.6V
• (LOW)	1.8V	–	2.3V
LOW (OFF)	UNDER 1V		

'HIGH' SPEED AND 'LOW (OFF)' CORRECT – ALL OTHERS INCORRECT
- CHECK VOLTAGE AT BLOWER RESISTER MODULE TERMINAL 'B'

ALL SPEEDS INCORRECT

ALL HIGH
CHECK CKT 804 TO GROUND

ALL LOW
CHECK CKT 52, 1041 AND 65

HIGH SPEED ONLY INCORRECT
REPAIR CKT 52 FROM SPLICE S316 TO CONNECTOR 'B' ON REAR SWITCH ASSEMBLY

(2) VOLTAGES MATCHES '(LOW)' SETTING ON VOLTAGE CHART
- ACCESS REAR SWITCH ASSEMBLY
- CHECK VOLTAGE AT TERMINALS 'C, D, AND E' AND COMPARE TO '(MH)', '(MED)', AND '(LOW)'

DOES NOT MATCH VOLTAGE CHART FOR '(LOW)' SETTING
- CHECK CKT 52 BETWEEN BLOWER RESISTOR MODULE TERMINAL 'D' AND SPLICE S316
- IF OK, REPLACE REAR BLOWER RESISTOR MODULE

(3) 'C' INCORRECT
- CHECK TERMINALS 'C' OF RESISTOR MODULE AND SWITCH ASSEMBLY
- CHECK CKT 73 FOR OPEN OR SHORT
- IF OK, REPLACE SWITCH

'D' INCORRECT
- CHECK TERMINALS 'A' OF RESISTOR MODULE AND 'D' OF SWITCH ASSEMBLY
- CHECK CKT 72 FOR OPEN OR SHORT
- IF OK, REPLACE SWITCH

'E' INCORRECT
- CHECK TERMINALS 'B' OF RESISTOR MODULE AND 'E' SWITCH ASSEMBLY
- CHECK CKT 63 FOR OPEN OR SHORT
- IF OK, REPLACE SWITCH

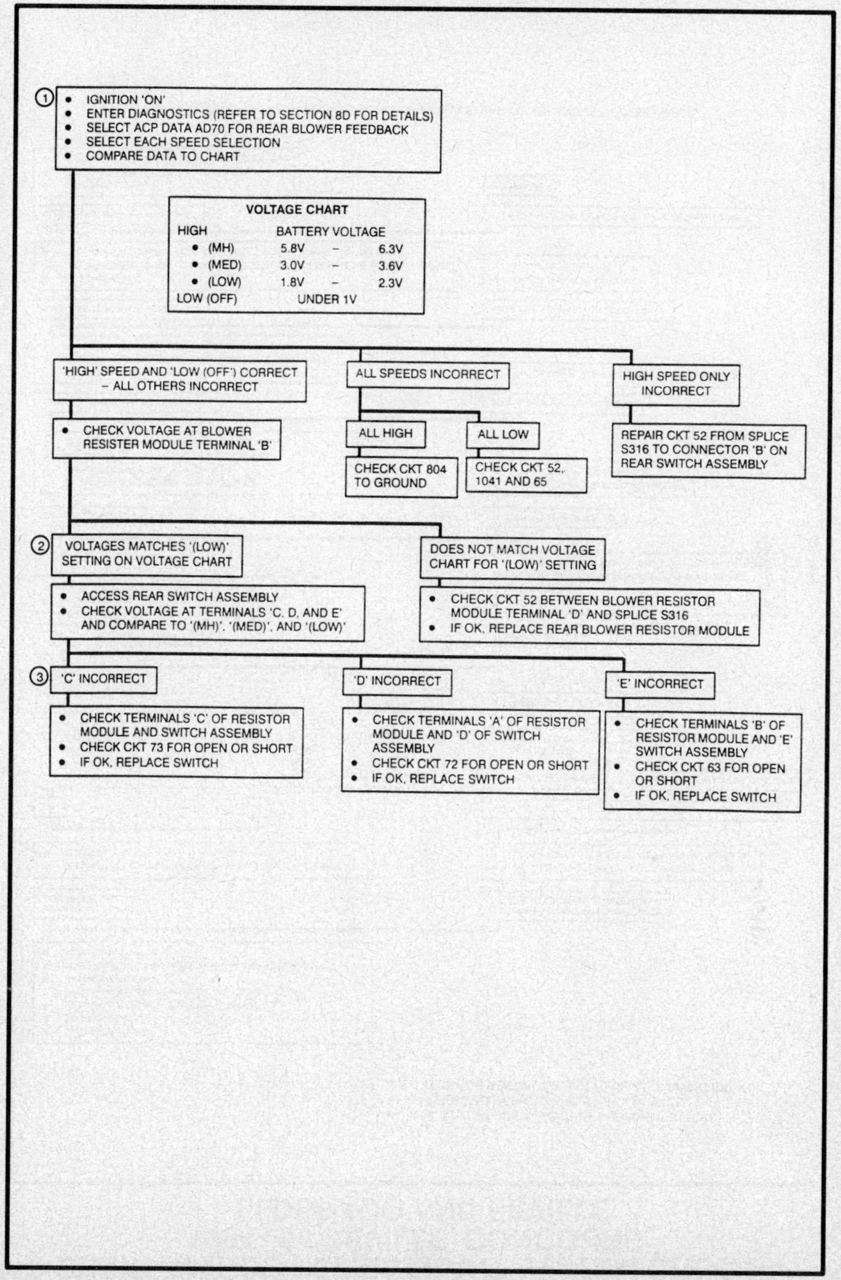

CHART 9: ECC SYSTEM REAR A/C BLOWER INOPERATIVE—1994–95 DEVILLE, CONCOURS, ELDORADO AND SEVILLE

- KEY 'ON'
- WILL BLOWER OPERATE IN ANY SETTING?

NO

(1)
- SET REAR BLOWER SWITCH ON 'HI'
- ENTER ON–BOARD DIAGNOSTICS AND READ PARAMETER AD70
- IS BATTERY VOLTAGE DISPLAYED?

NO
- INSPECT FUSES 'A3' AND 'C9'
- IF 'A3' BLOWN, CHECK CKT 841 FOR SHORT TO GROUND OR FOR RESISTANCE THROUGH BLOWER RELAY (PINS '1' AND '2') LESS THAN 20 OHMS
- IF FUSE 'C9' BLOWN, CHECK FOR SHORT TO GROUND IN CKT'S 1041, 65 AND VERIFY CURRENT DRAW OF BLOWER IS LESS THAN 6 AMPS

- REMOVE BLOWER RELAY 'E'
- CONNECT 10A FUSED JUMPER ACROSS RELAY CONNECTORS 3 AND 5

YES
- REMOVE CONSOLE REAR COVER
- DISCONNECT AND PROVE REAR BLOWER SWITCH CONNECTOR CAVITY 'A' FOR LESS THAN 1 OHM TO GROUND

LESS THAN 1 OHM
- CONNECT TEST LIGHT ACROSS HARNESS TERMINALS 'A' AND 'B'

GREATER THAN 1 OHM
- REPAIR OPEN IN CKT 850

LIGHTS
- CHECK CONNECTOR
- VERIFY TEST LIGHT 'OFF' WITH KEY 'OFF'. IF NOT REPAIR SHORT TO VOLTAGE ON CKT 52
- IF OK, REPLACE SWITCH

NO LIGHT
- REPAIR OPEN IN CKT 52 BETWEEN S316 AND SWITCH

YES

(2)
- REMOVE CONSOLE REAR COVER
- DISCONNECT AND FRONTPROBE REAR BLOWER SWITCH HARNESS CAVITIES 'B, C, D, E', TO GROUND USING 10A FUSED JUMPER

BLOWER RUNS AT CORRECT SPEEDS
- CHECK CONNECTOR TO REAR BLOWER SWITCH IF OK, REPLACE SWITCH

BLOWER DOESN'T RUN AT CORRECT SPEEDS
- VERIFY CONNECTION TO REAR BLOWER RESISTOR MODULE AND WIRING CONTINUITY FROM RESISTOR MODULE TO REAR BLOWER SWITCH
- IF ALL OK, REPLACE RESISTOR MODULE

BLOWER RUNS
- JUMPER RELAY CAVITIES '1' AND '5'
- DOES BLOWER RUN?

YES
- REPAIR OPEN CKT 1250

NO
- REPAIR OPEN CKT 841

BLOWER DOESN'T RUN
- CONNECT TEST LIGHT FROM RELAY CAVITIES '2' AND '3'

LIGHTS
- REINSTALL RELAY
- DISCONNECT BLOWER MOTOR
- CONNECT TEST LIGHT ACROSS BLOWER HARNESS CAVITIES 'A' AND 'B'

NO LIGHT
- REPAIR OPEN IN CKT 65 FROM BLOWER RELAY

LIGHTS
- REPLACE BLOWER MOTOR

NO LIGHT
- CHECK CAVITY '2' FOR GREATER THAN 1 OHM RESISTANCE TO GROUND
- CHECK FOR OPEN CKT 1041

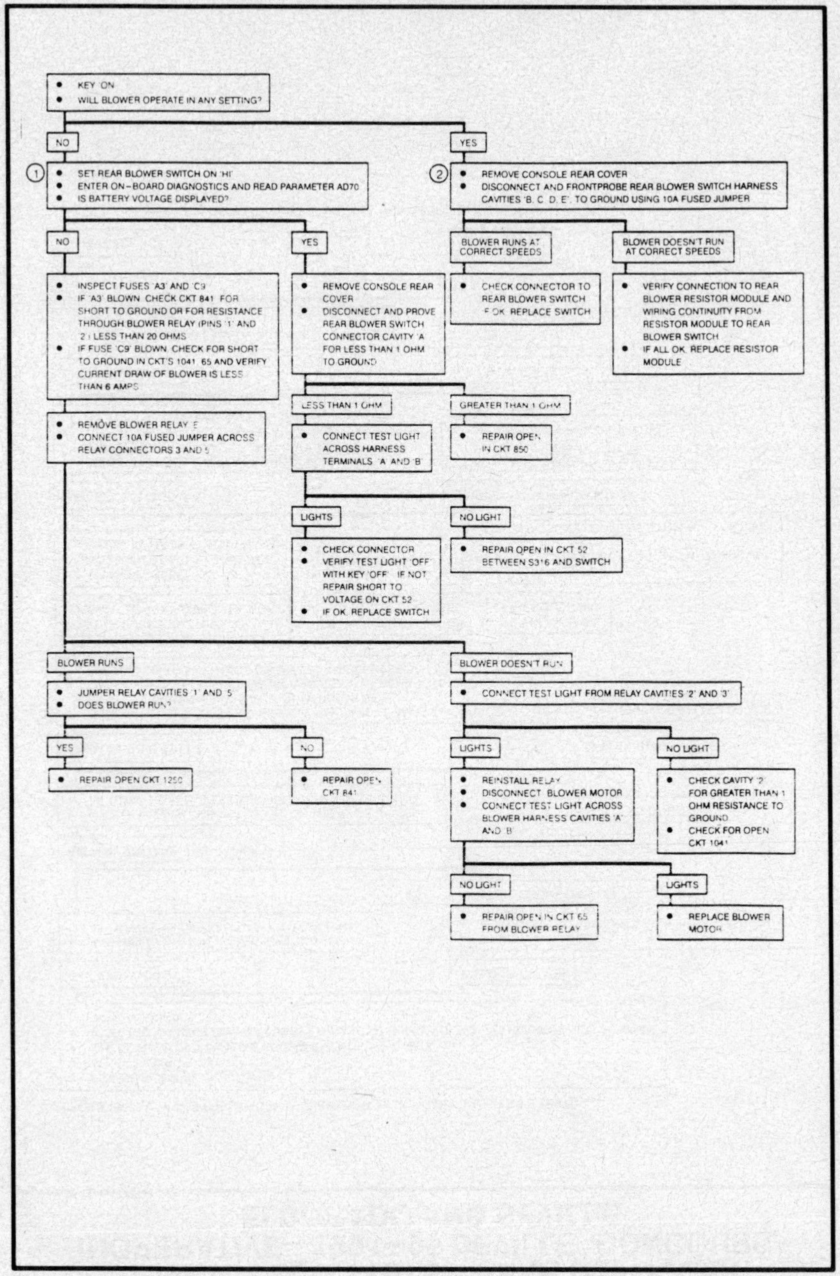

CHART 10: ECC REFRIGERANT SYSTEM CHECK—1994–95 DEVILLE, CONCOURS, ELDORADO AND SEVILLE

- ECC SYSTEM CHECK MUST BE PERFORMED FIRST
- AMBIENT TEMPERATURE MUST BE ABOVE 50°
- CHECK FOR RESTRICTED AIR FLOW AT CONDENSER

- CLEAR ACP CODES
- START ENGINE
- USE AUXILIARY FAN IN FRONT OF RADIATOR
- ENGINE ABOVE 1500 RPM SELECT 'AUTO', (A/C) AT 60°F
- ENTER DIAGNOSTICS
- SELECT ACP INPUT AI01 A/C LOW REFRIGERANT PRESSURE SWITCH
- NOTE STATUS (HI/LO)

REMAINS 'HI' DURING COMPRESSOR CYCLE
- DISCONNECT LOW REFRIGERANT PRESSURE SWITCH CONNECTOR
- OBSERVE LOW PRESSURE SWITCH STATUS ACP AI01

LO
- RECONNECT LOW REFRIGERANT PRESSURE SWITCH
- SELECT ACP INPUT AI03 A/C HIGH PRESSURE SWITCH
- NOTE STATUS (HI/LO)

HI
- CHECK FOR A SHORT TO VOLTAGE IN CKT 603
- IF OK, REPLACE ACP
- RETEST SYSTEM STARTING AT TOP OF CHART

SWITCHES 'LO' DURING COMPRESSOR CYCLE (CLUTCH WILL DISENGAGE)
- CONNECT PRESSURE GAGE TO LOW SIDE FITTING
- OBSERVE GAGE PRESSURE AS STATUS SWITCHES 'LO'

SWITCHES 'LO' UNDER 12 PSI
- LEAK TEST SYSTEM
- CHECK FOR PLUGGED ORIFICE TUBE

- MAKE NECESSARY REPAIRS
- RECOVER AND RECHARGE

SWITCHES 'LO' OVER 12 PSI
- REPLACE LOW PRESSURE SWITCH

SWITCHES 'LO' DURING COMPRESSOR CYCLE (CLUTCH WILL DISENGAGE)
- CONNECT PRESSURE GAGE TO HIGH SIDE FITTING
- OBSERVE GAGE PRESSURE AS STATUS SWITCHES 'LO'

REMAINS 'HI' DURING COMPRESSOR CYCLE
- SELECT ACP DATA DISPLAY AD28 AND OBSERVE LOW SIDE TEMPERATURE
- REMOVE A/C COMPRESSOR CLUTCH RELAY INSTALL JUMPER BETWEEN PINS '3' AND '5' (CLUTCH WILL ENGAGE)

SWITCH 'LO' ABOVE 410 PSI
- CHECK FOR RESTRICTION AT ORIFICE TUBE
- CHECK FOR PROPER FAN OPERATION
- CHECK FOR RESTRICTION WITHIN CONDENSER
- REFER TO 'HIGH REFRIGERANT PRESSURE SWITCH'

SWITCH 'LO' BELOW 410 PSI
- CHECK FOR RESTRICTED CONDENSER
- REPLACE HIGH PRESSURE SWITCH

LOW SIDE TEMPERATURE DECREASES
- REMOVE JUMPER (CLUTCH WILL DISENGAGE)
- OBSERVE HIGH SIDE TEMPERATURE (AD27) AS THE JUMPER IS RECONNECTED (CLUTCH WILL ENGAGE)

LOW SIDE TEMPERATURE INCREASES
- CHECK FOR RESTRICTION ON LOW PRESSURE SIDE

HIGH SIDE TEMPERATURE INCREASES
- EXIT DIAGNOSTICS
- LIFT DRIVE WHEELS TO ALLOW A VEHICLE SPEED INDICATION ABOVE 20 MPH IN DRIVE
- EVALUATE EVAPORATOR INLET AND OUTLET (SUCTION) LINE TEMPERATURES

HIGH SIDE TEMPERATURE DECREASES
- CHECK FOR RESTRICTION ON HIGH PRESSURE SIDE

OUTLET LINE WARMER THAN INLET
- LEAK TEST SYSTEM
- IF OK, RECOVER AND RECHARGE SYSTEM
- IF PROBLEM STILL EXISTS, REPLACE ORIFICE TUBE

OUTLET LINE SAME AS INLET AND COOLER THAN AMBIENT

SYSTEM OK

WHEN ALL DIAGNOSIS AND REPAIRS ARE COMPLETED, CLEAR CODES AND VERIFY OPERATION

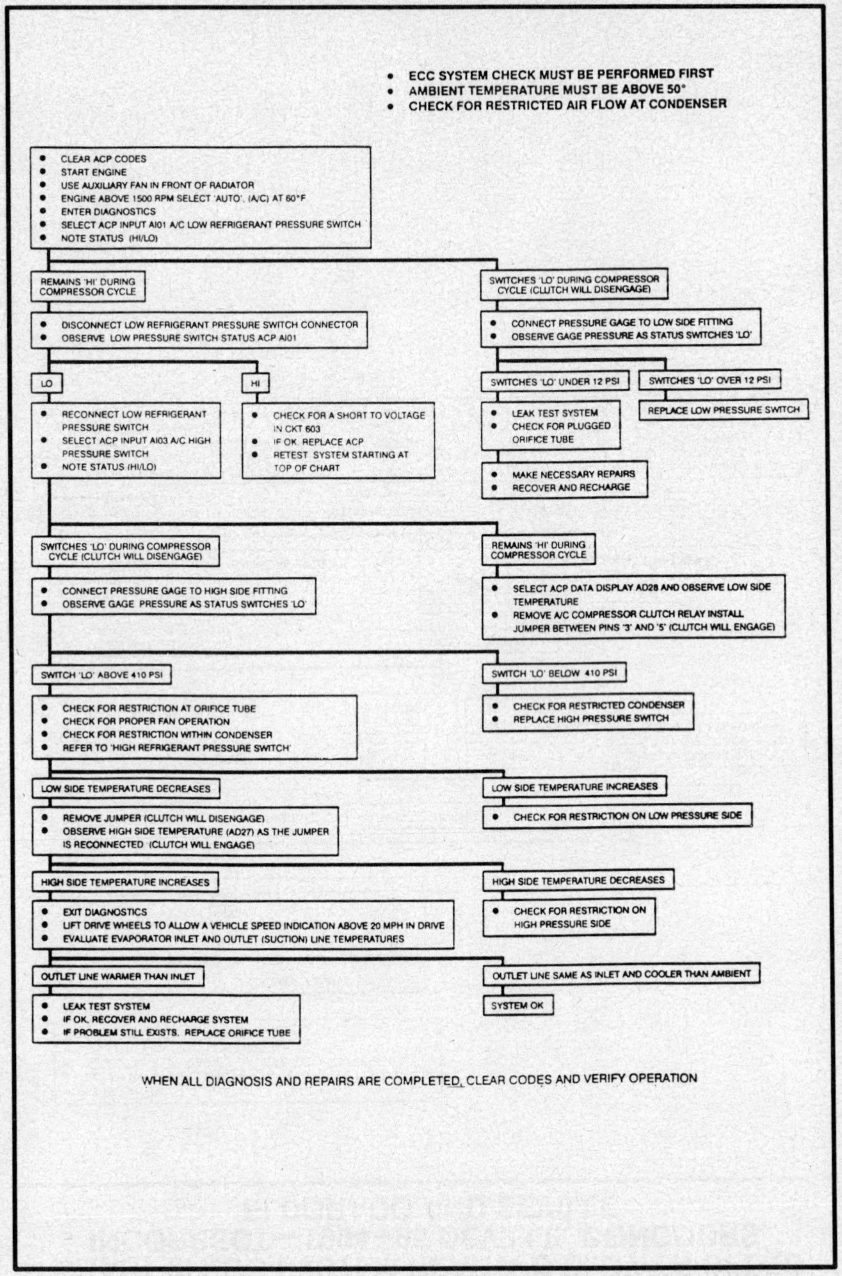

WIRING SCHEMATICS

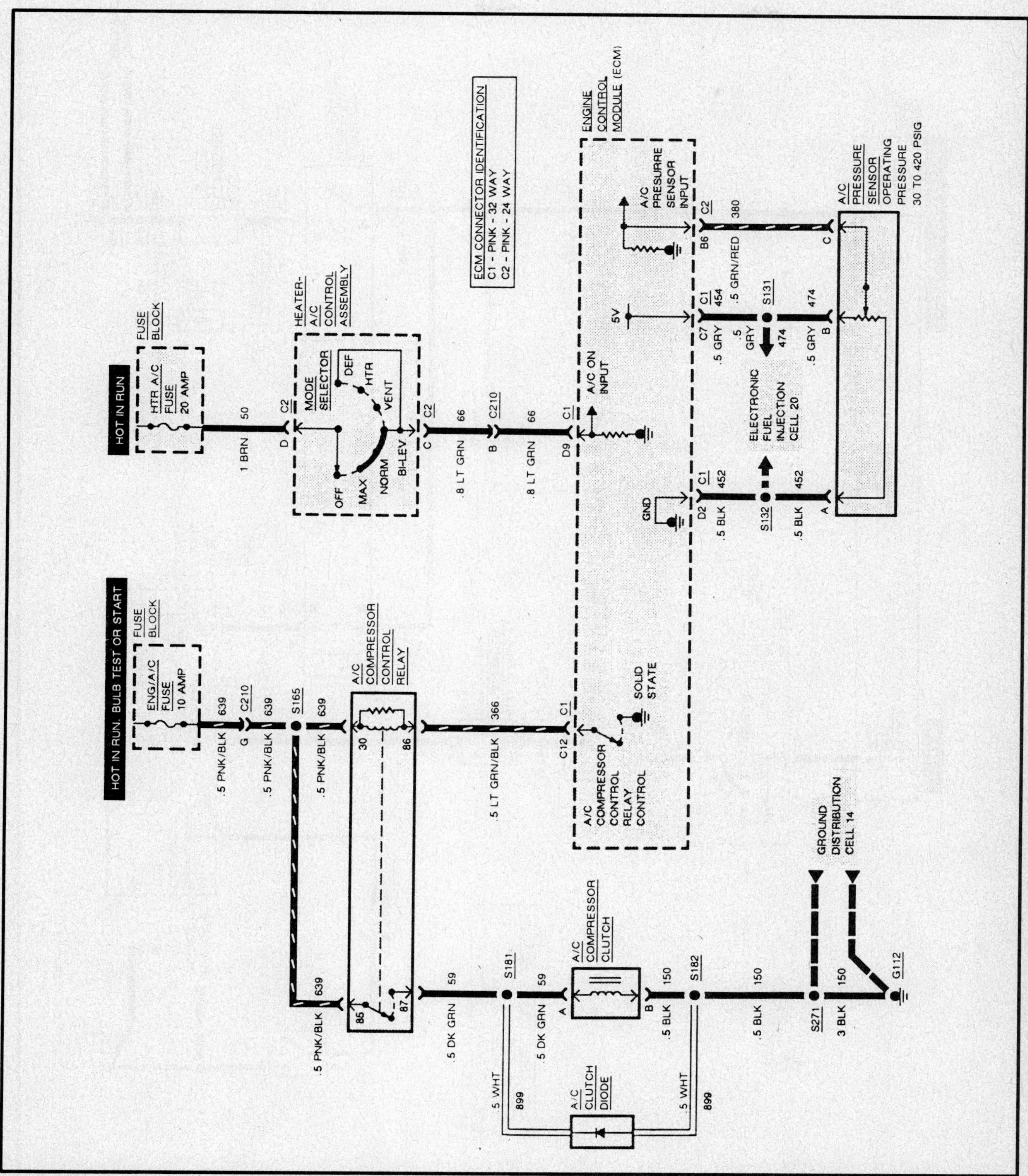

Compressor controls wiring schematic—1993 Century, Cutlass Ciera and Cutlass Cruiser (VIN 4)

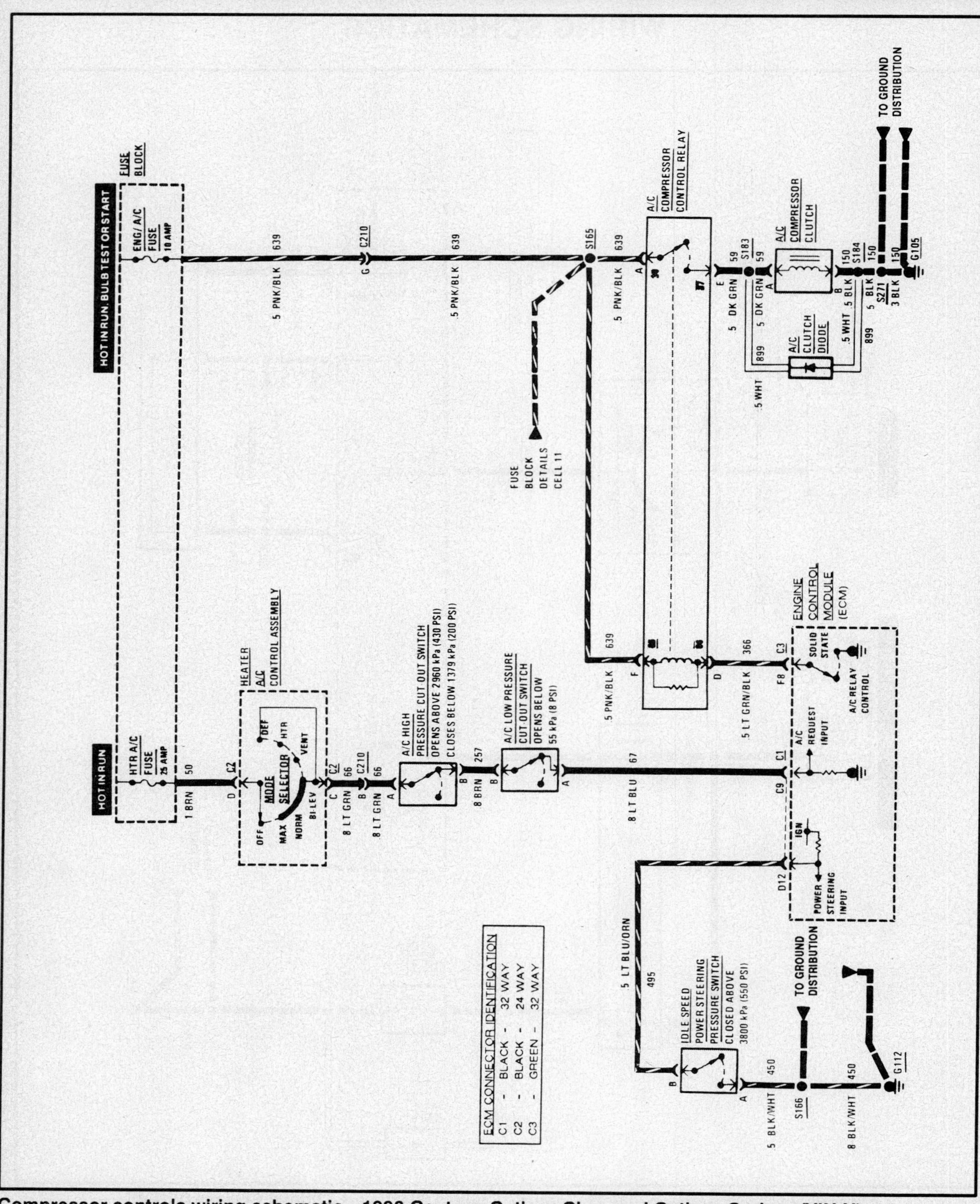

Compressor controls wiring schematic—1993 Century, Cutlass Ciera and Cutlass Cruiser (VIN N)

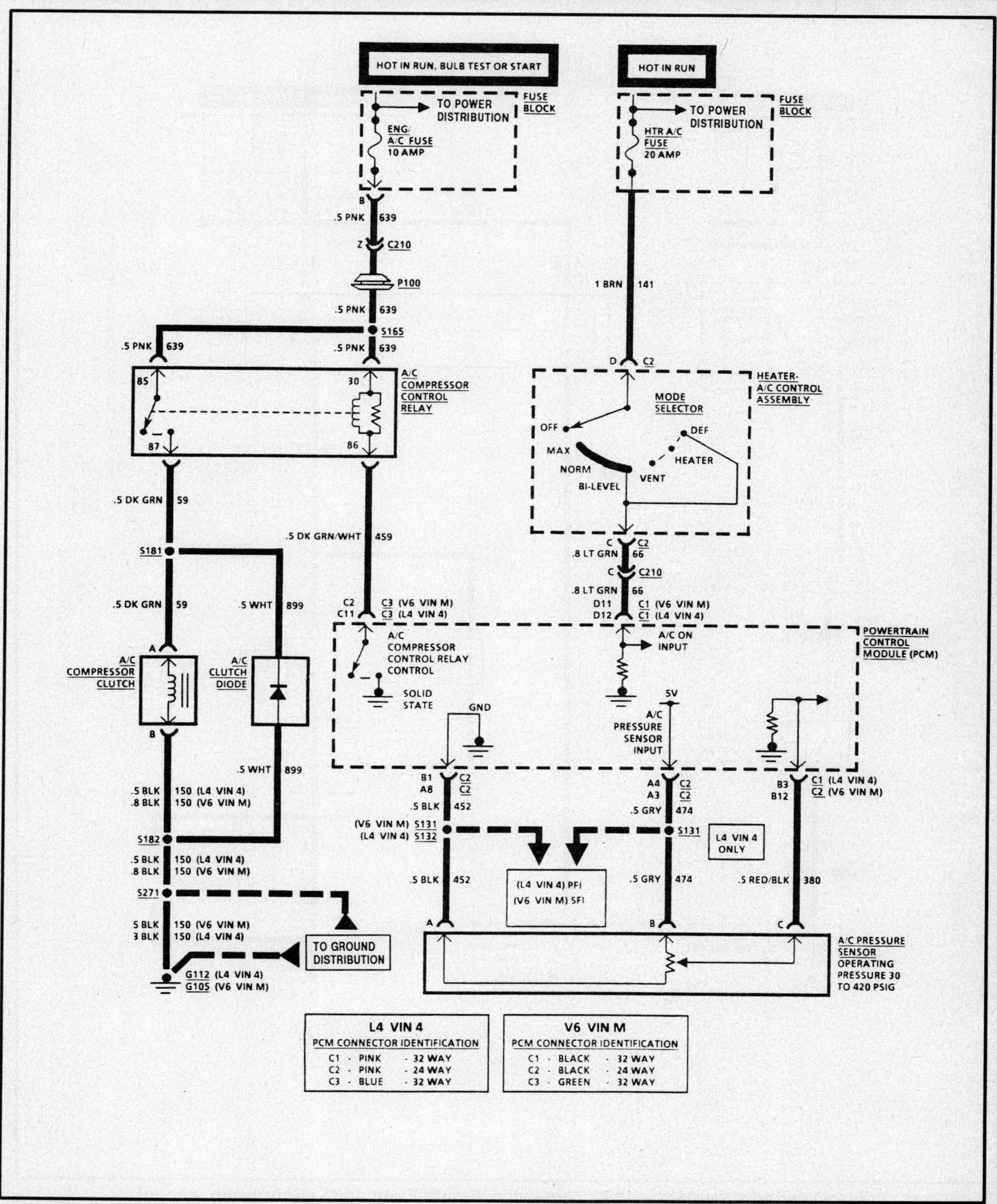

L4 VIN 4

PCM CONNECTOR IDENTIFICATION		
C1	PINK	32 WAY
C2	PINK	24 WAY
C3	BLUE	32 WAY

V6 VIN M

PCM CONNECTOR IDENTIFICATION		
C1	BLACK	32 WAY
C2	BLACK	24 WAY
C3	GREEN	32 WAY

Compressor controls wiring schematic—1994 Century, Cutlass Ciera and Cutlass Cruiser

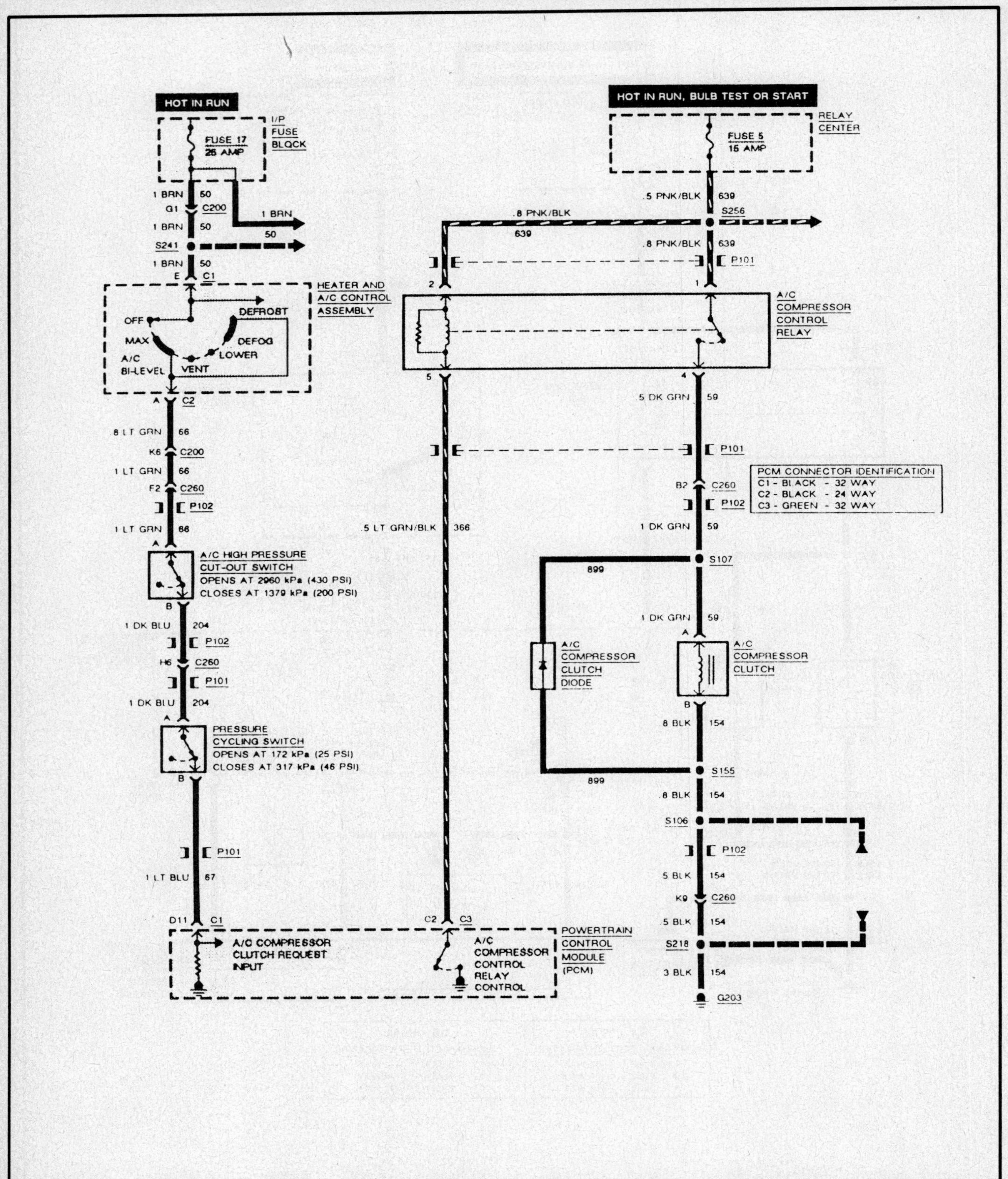

Compressor controls wiring schematic—1993 Bonneville, Eighty-Eight and LeSabre with manual air conditioning

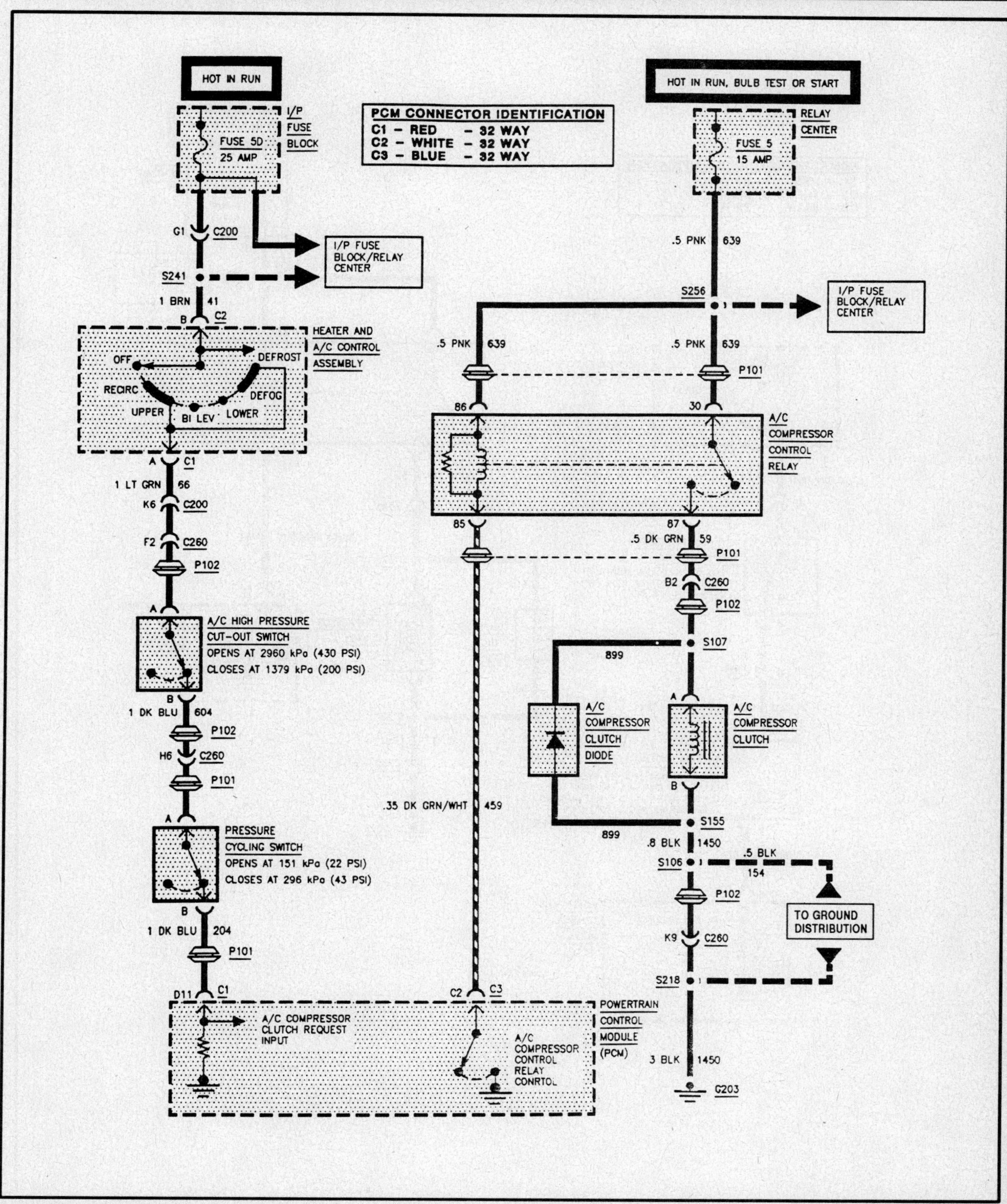

Compressor controls wiring schematic—1994 Eighty-Eight and Ninety-Eight with C61 manual air conditioning

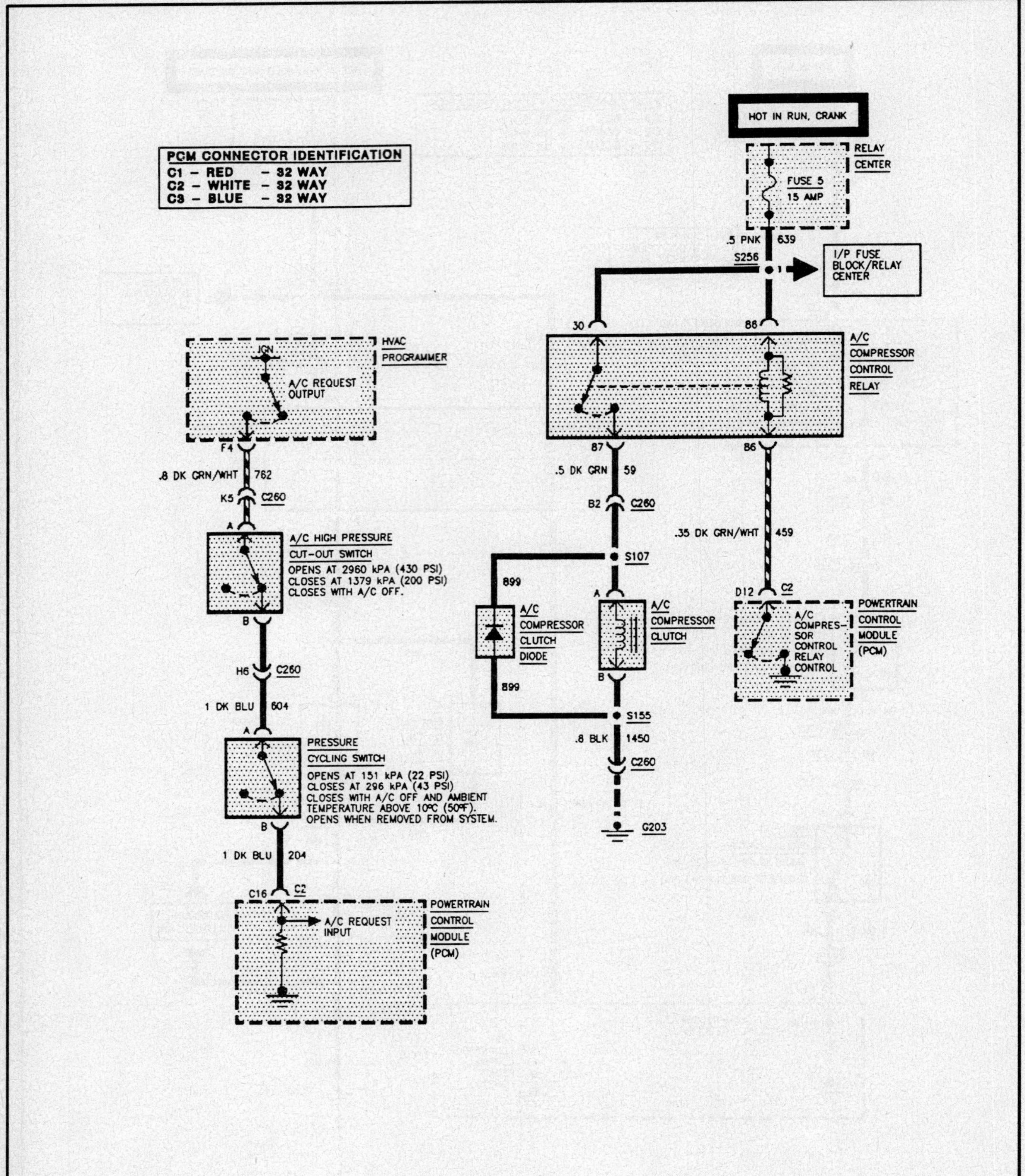

Compressor controls wiring schematic—1994 Eighty-Eight and Ninety-Eight with CJ2 dual zone air conditioning

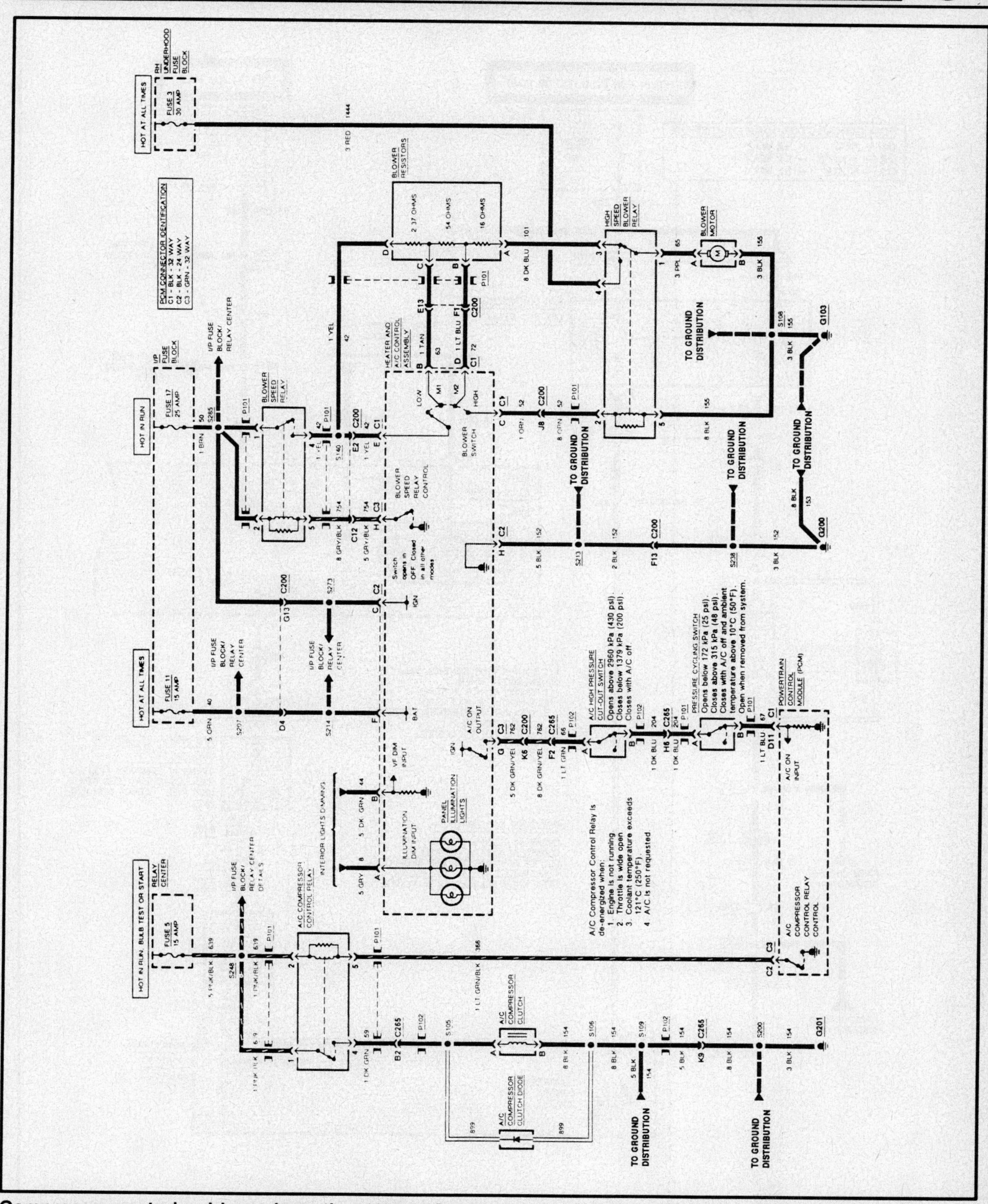

Compressor controls wiring schematic—1993 LeSabre and Park Avenue with C67 electronic climate control

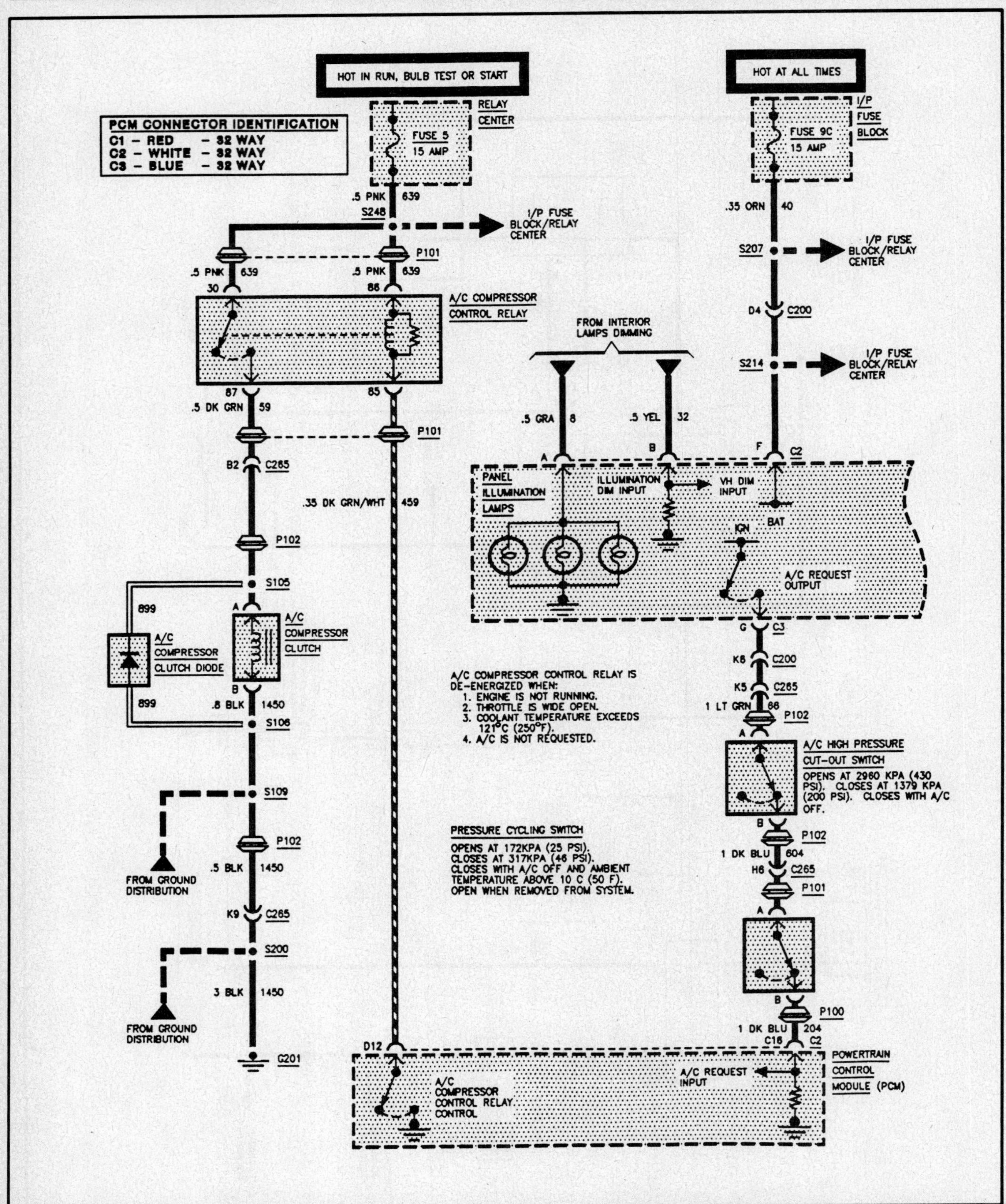

Compressor controls wiring schematic—1994 LeSabre and Park Avenue with C67 electronic air conditioning

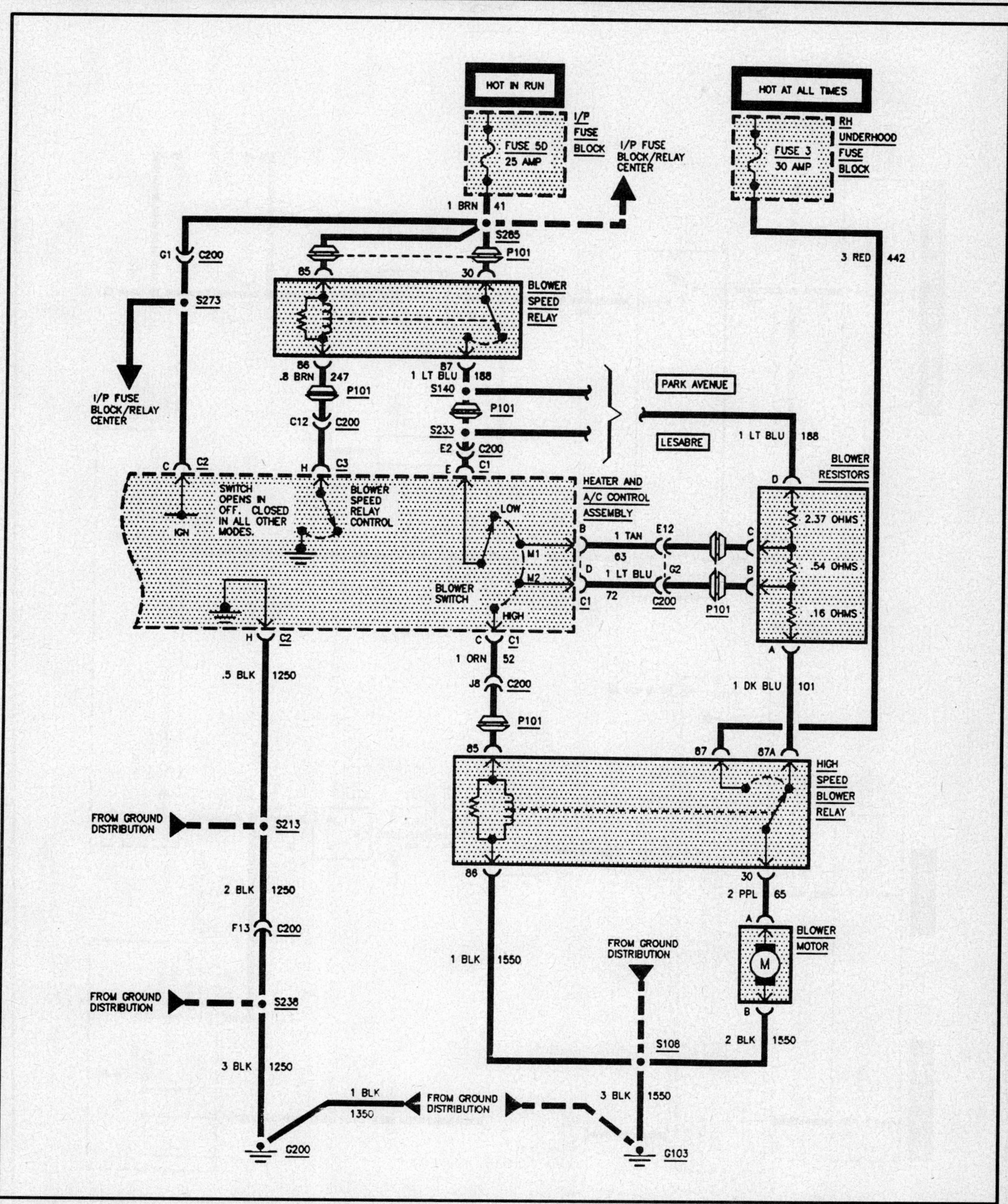

Compressor controls wiring schematic—1994 LeSabre and Park Avenue with C67 electronic air conditioning, cont'd

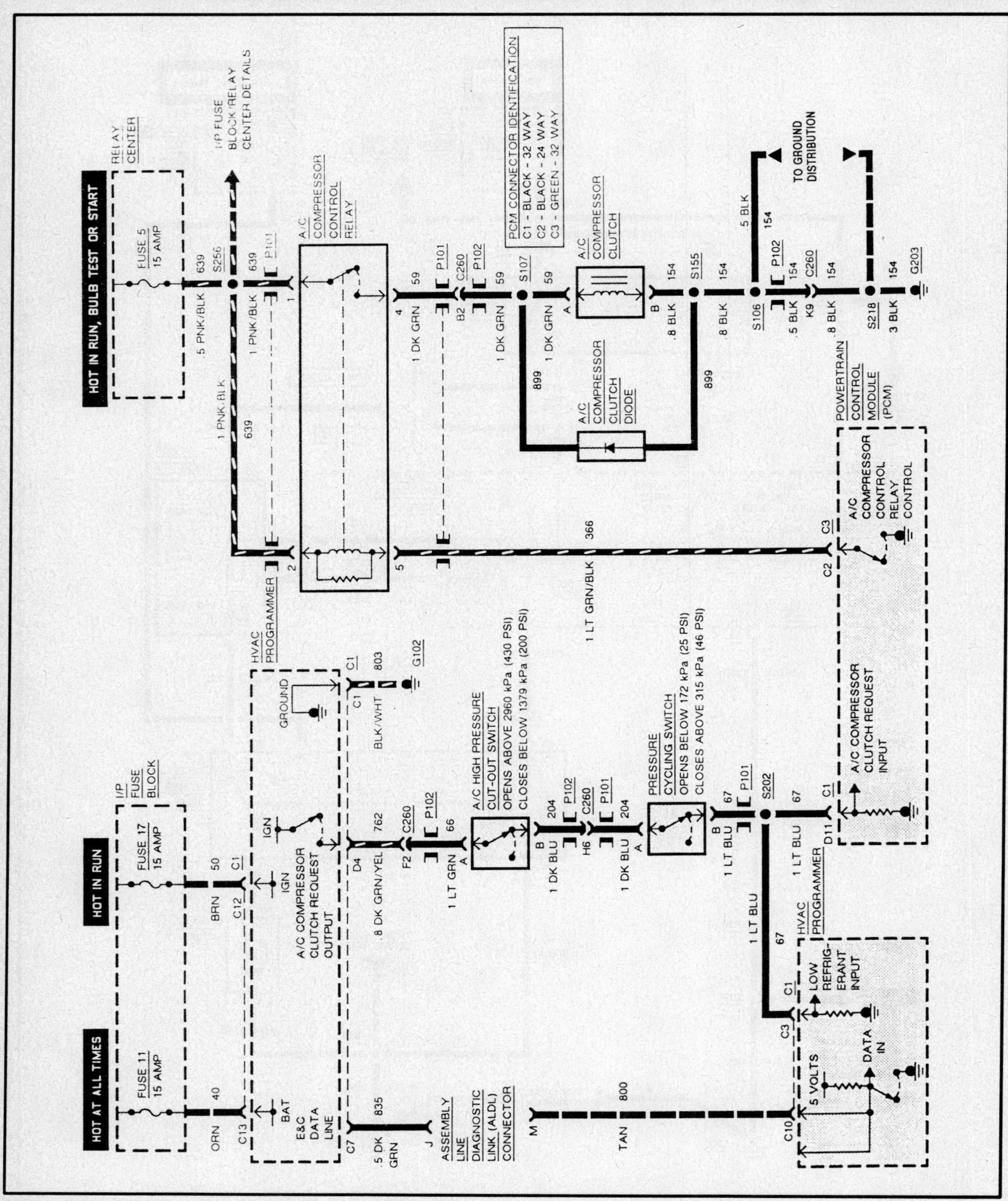

Compressor controls wiring schematic—1994 LeSabre and Park Avenue with C67 electronic air conditioning, cont'd

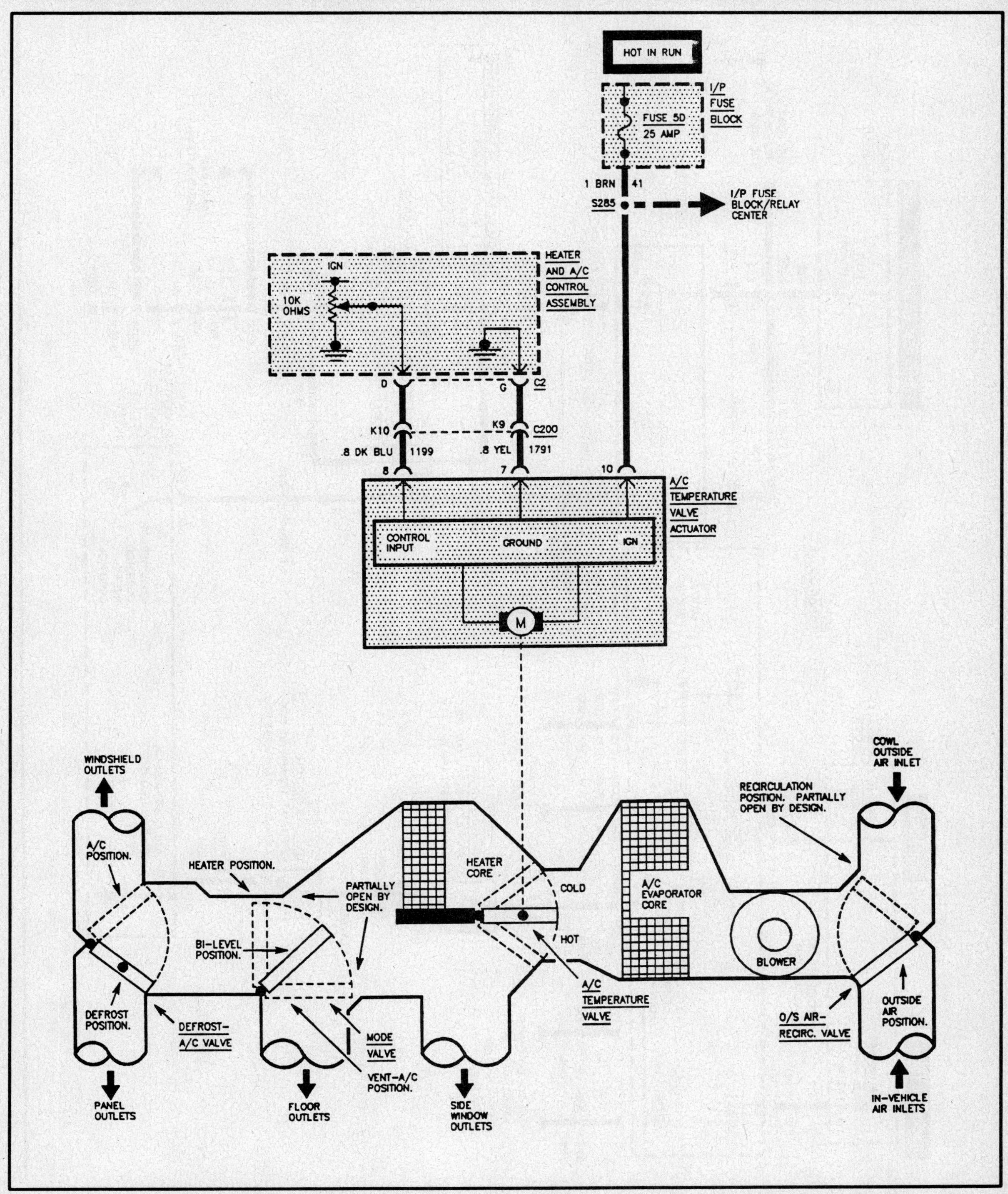

Compressor controls wiring schematic—1993 Bonneville with C68 (self diagnostic) electronic climate control

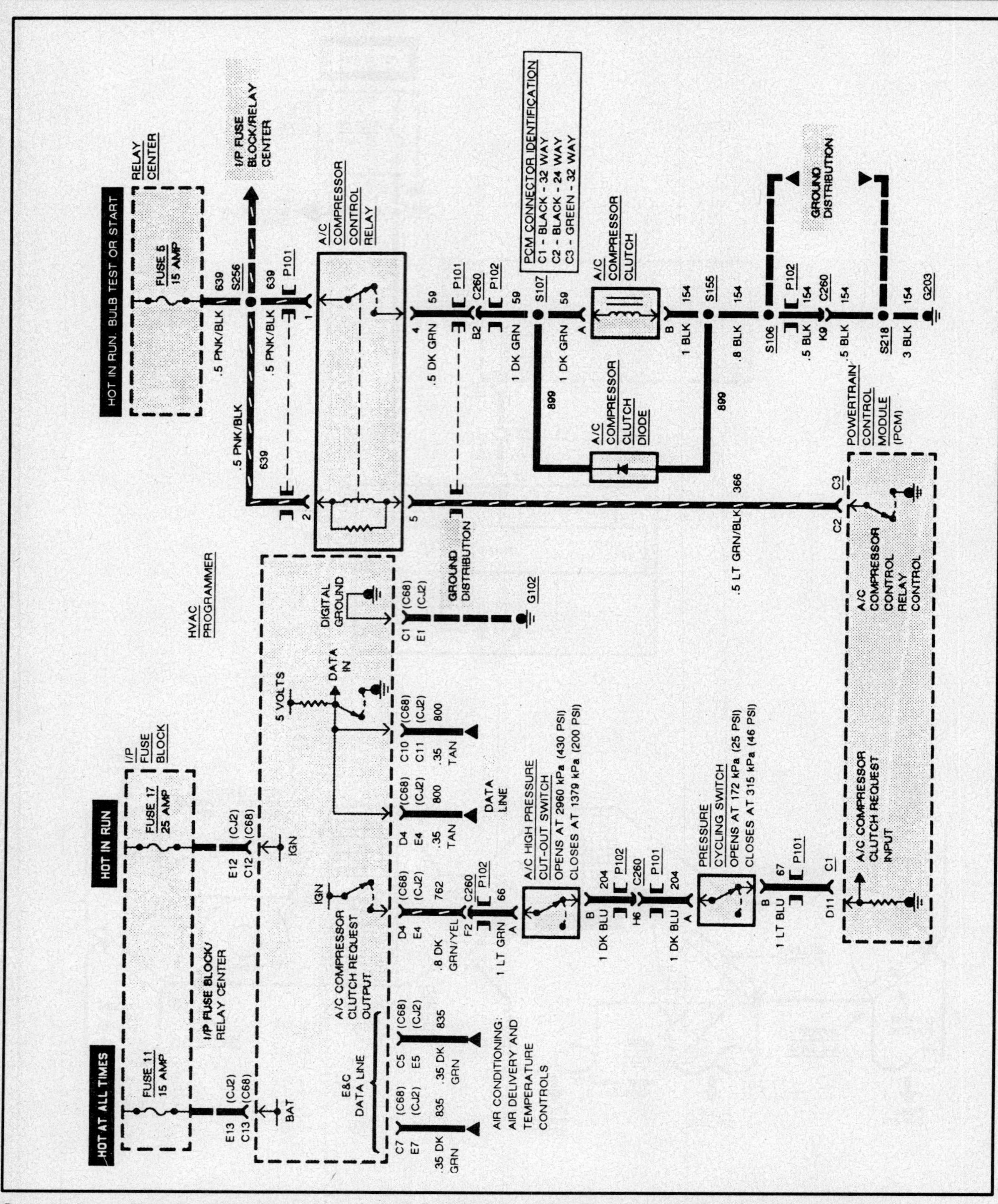

Compressor controls wiring schematic—1993 Eighty-Eight and Ninety-Eight with C68 (self diagnostic) electronic climate control

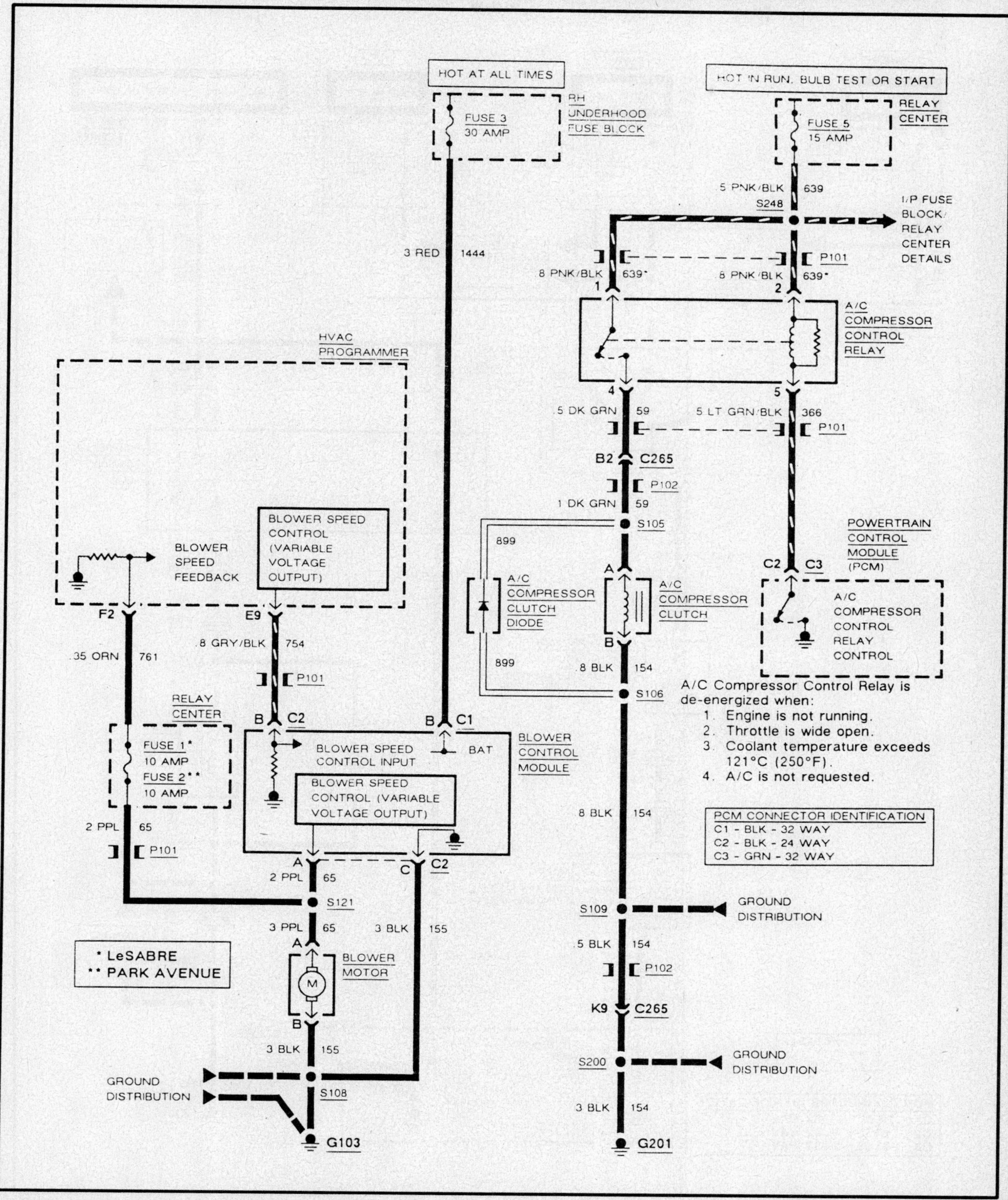

System wiring schematic—1993 LeSabre and Park Avenue with C68 and CJ2 dual-zone electronic climate control

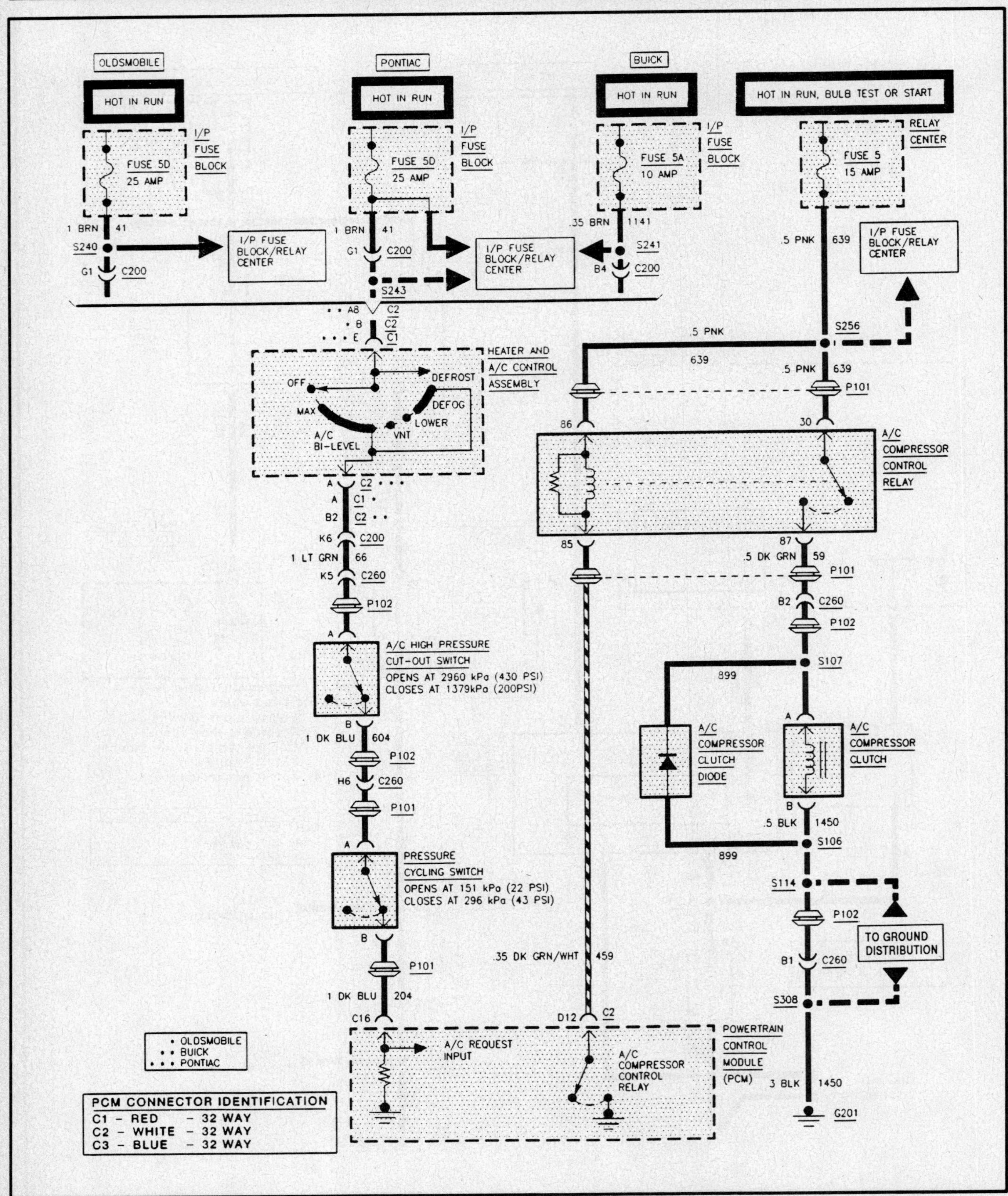

Compressor controls wiring schematic—1995 Bonneville, Eighty-Eight, Ninety-Eight, LeSabre and Park Avenue with C61 manual and C67 electronic air conditioning

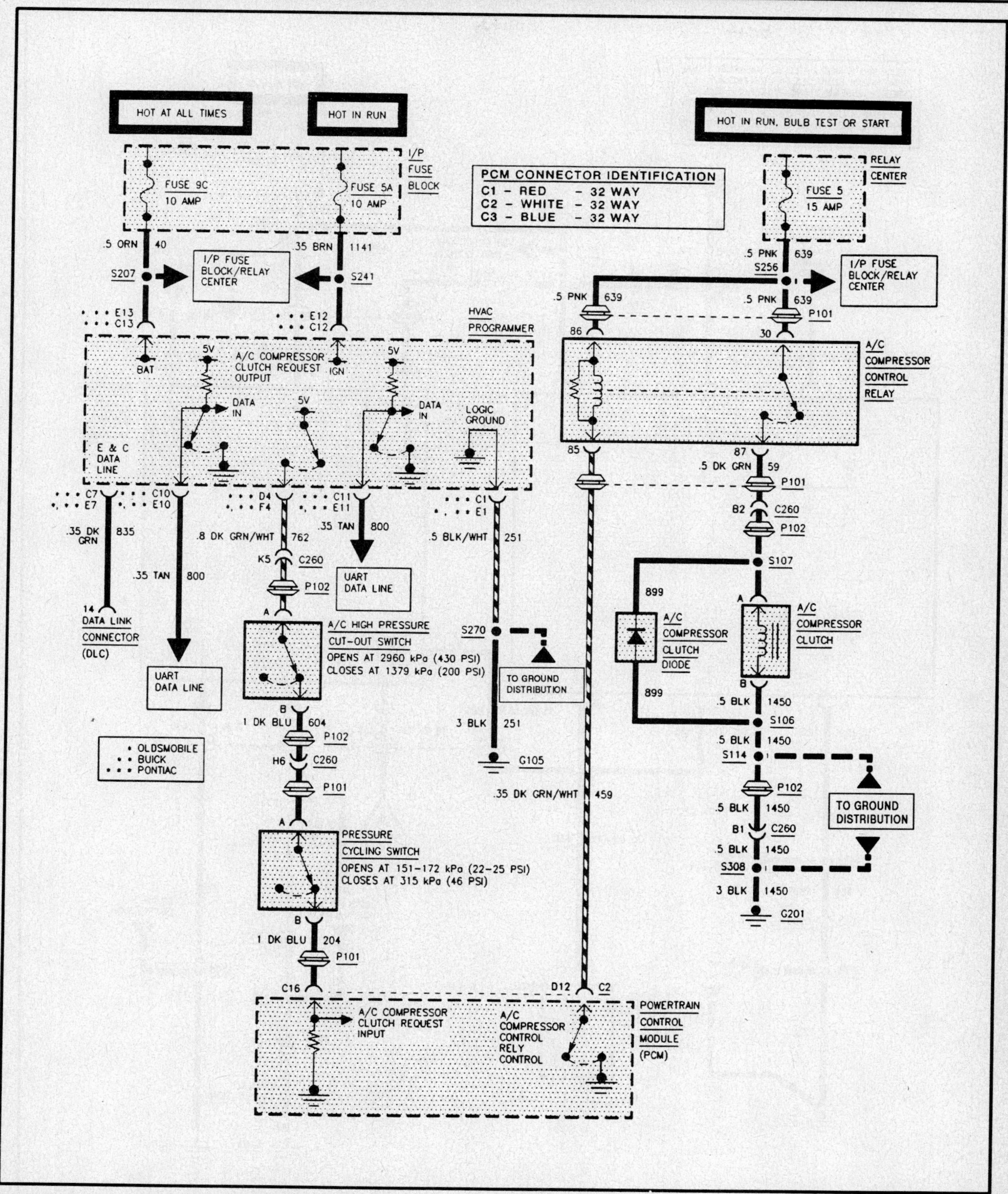

Compressor controls wiring schematic—1995 Bonneville, Eighty-Eight, Ninety-Eight, LeSabre and Park Avenue with C68 manual and CJ2 electronic air conditioning

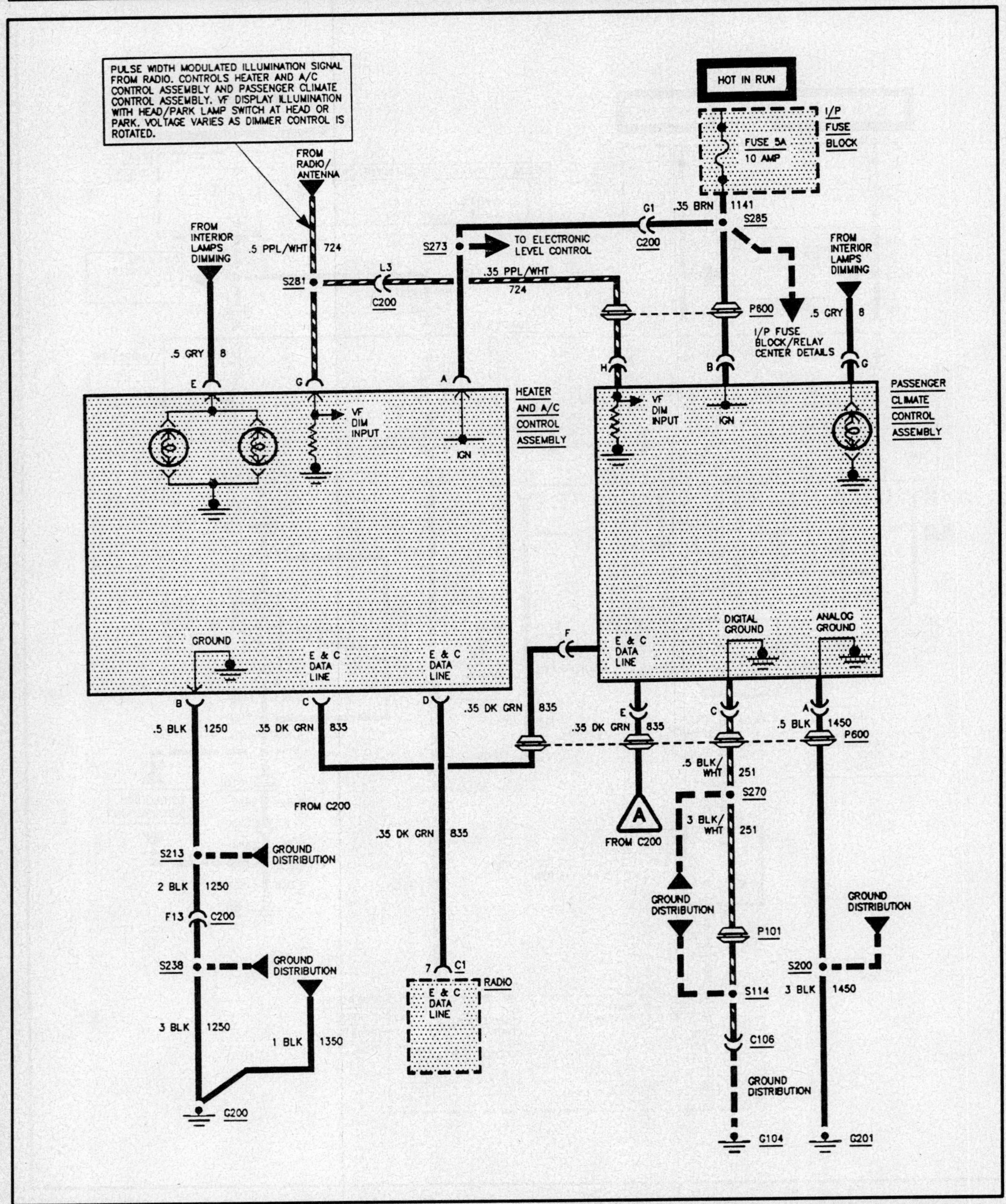

System wiring schematic—1994 LeSabre and Park Avenue with CJ2 dual-zone electronic climate control

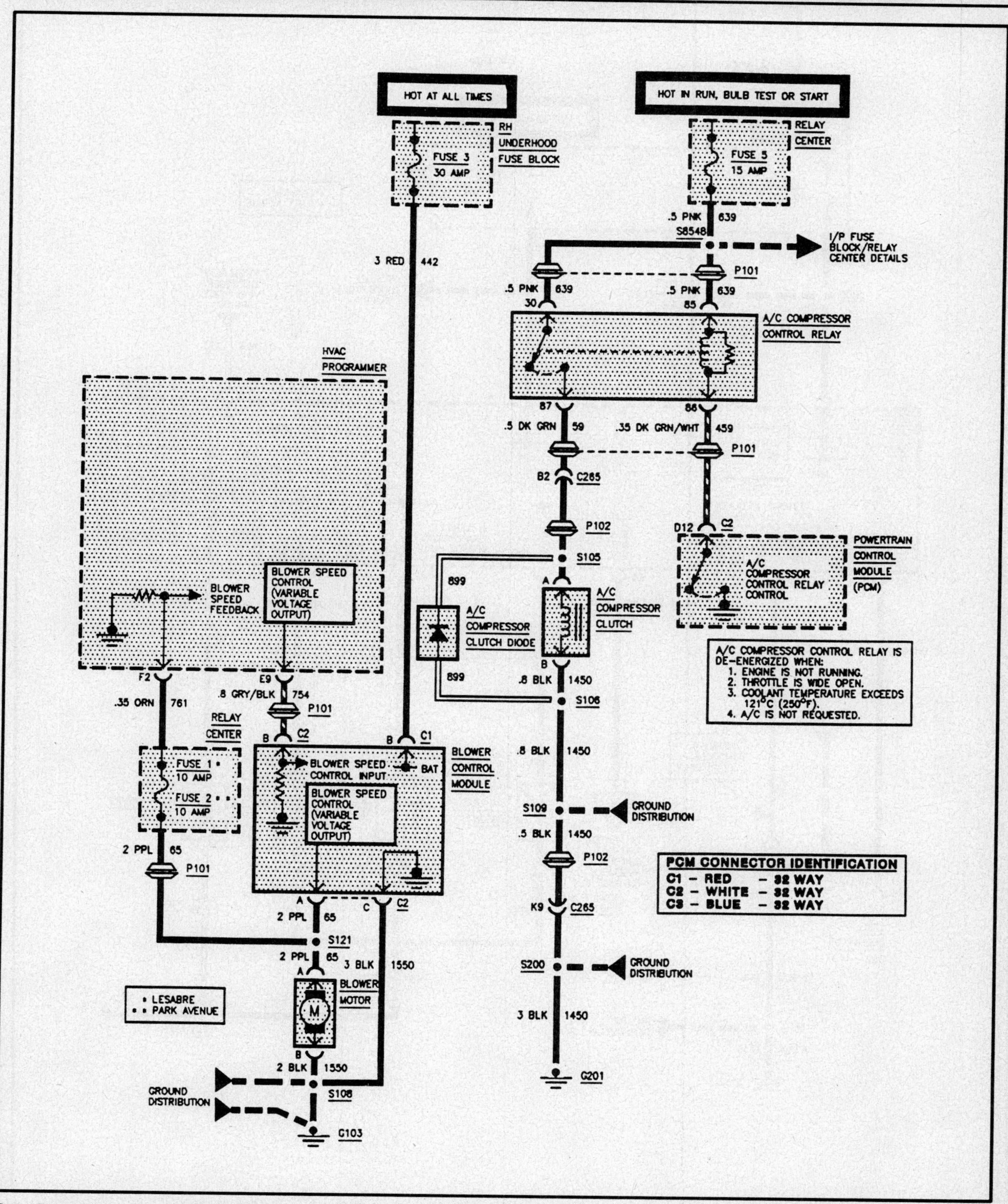

System wiring schematic—1994 LeSabre and Park Avenue with CJ2 dual-zone electronic climate control, Cont'd

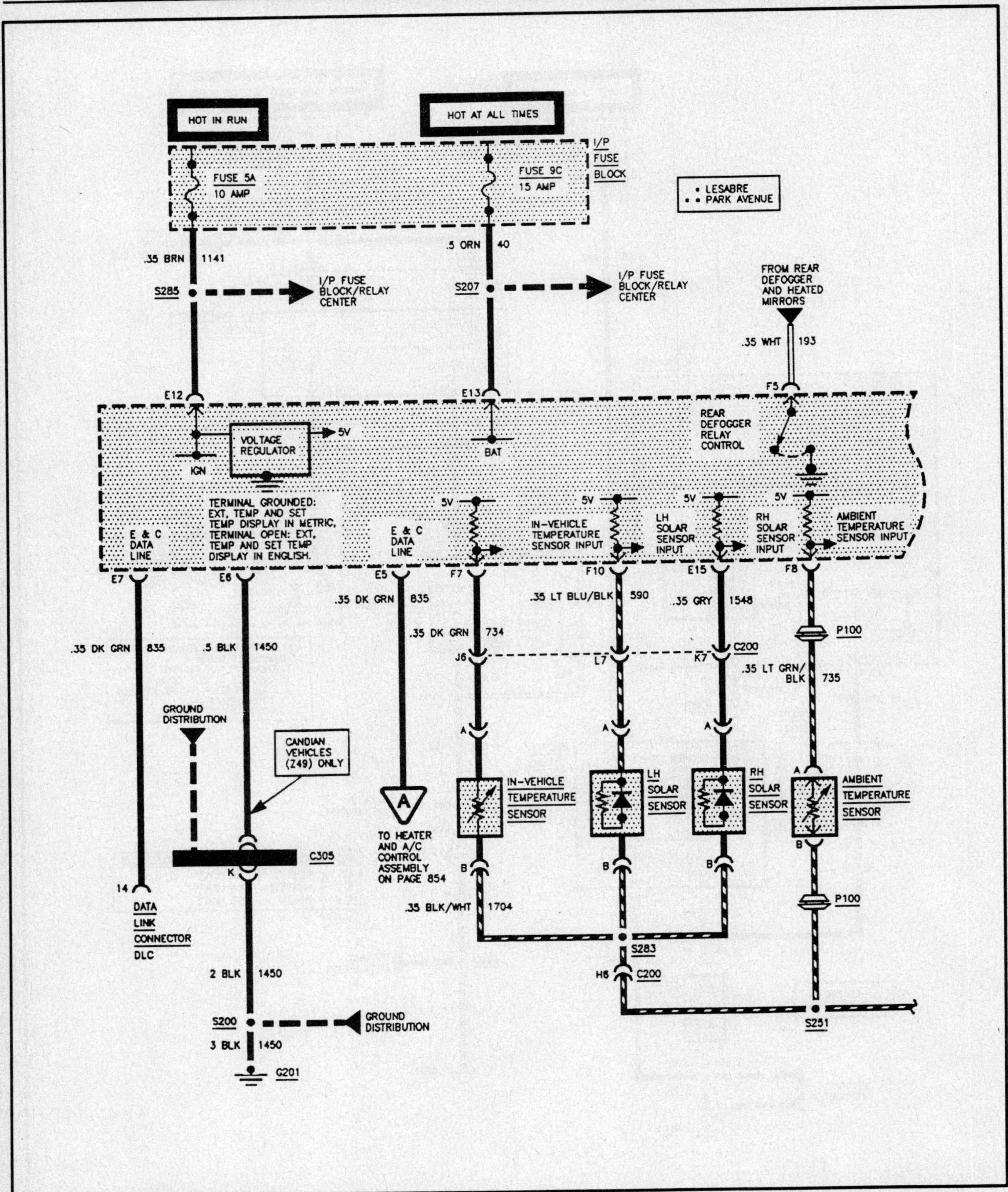

System wiring schematic—1994 LeSabre and Park Avenue with CJ2 dual-zone electronic climate control, Cont'd

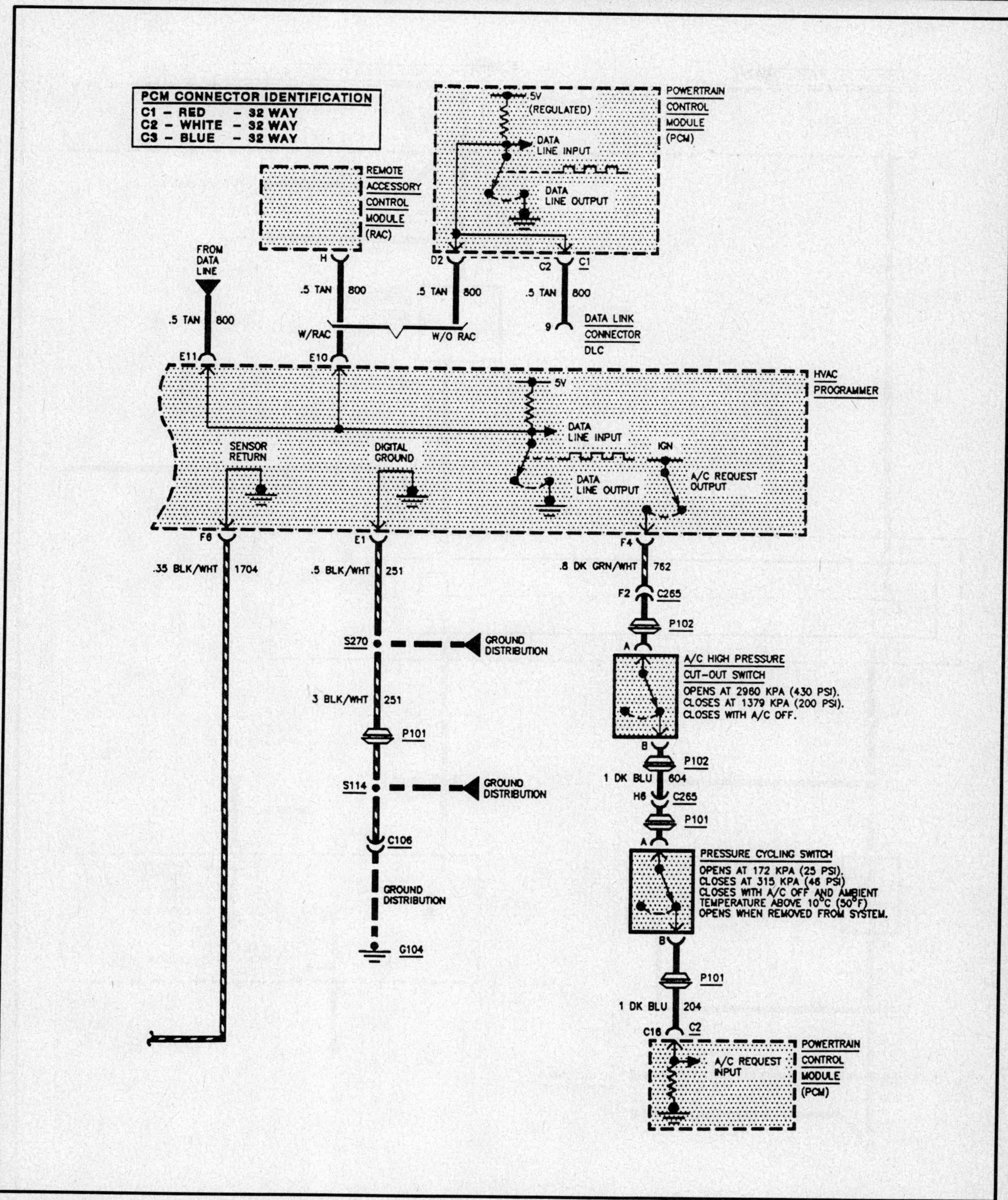

System wiring schematic—1994 LeSabre and Park Avenue with CJ2 dual-zone electronic climate control, Cont'd

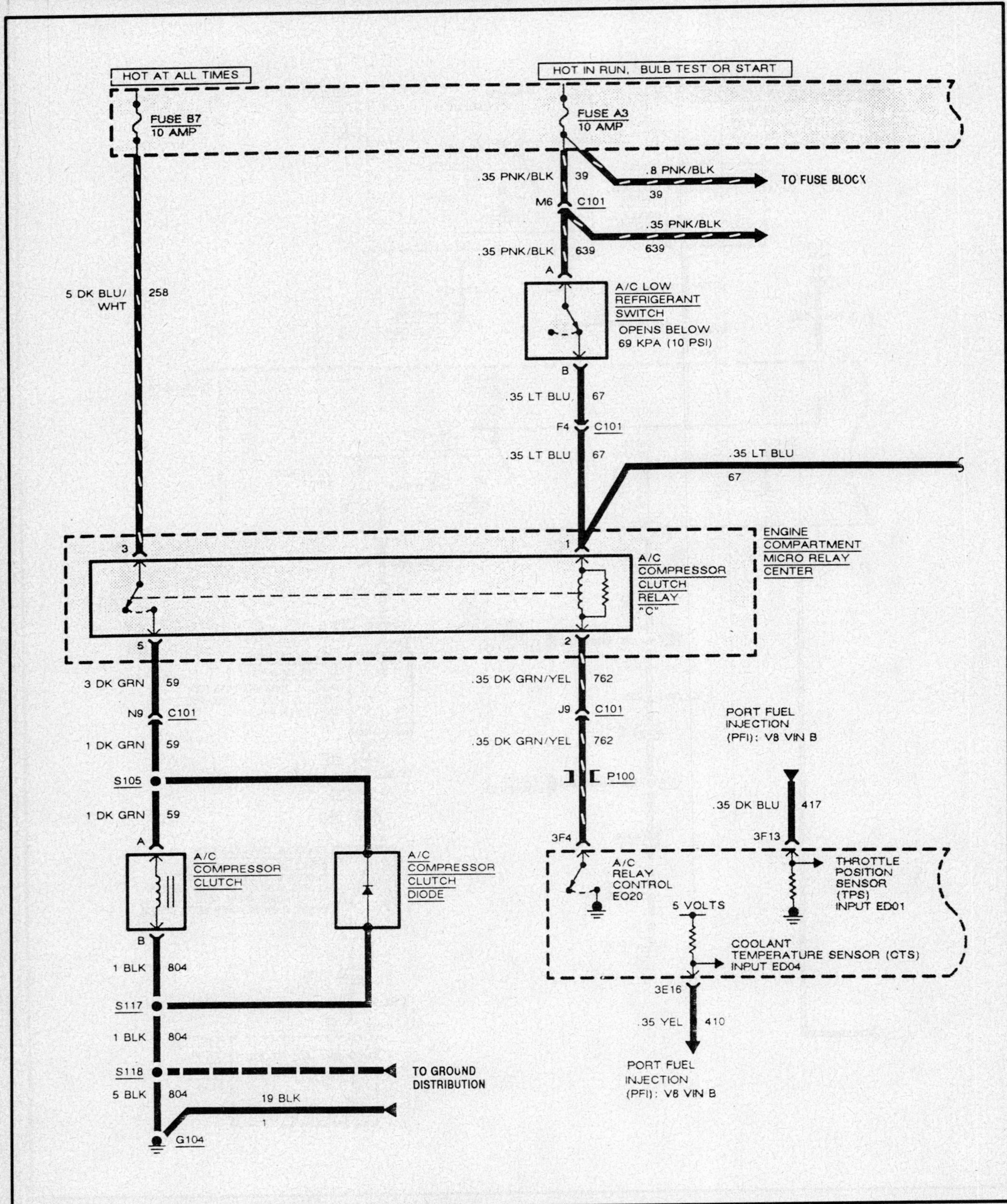

System wiring schematic—1993 Eldorado and Seville

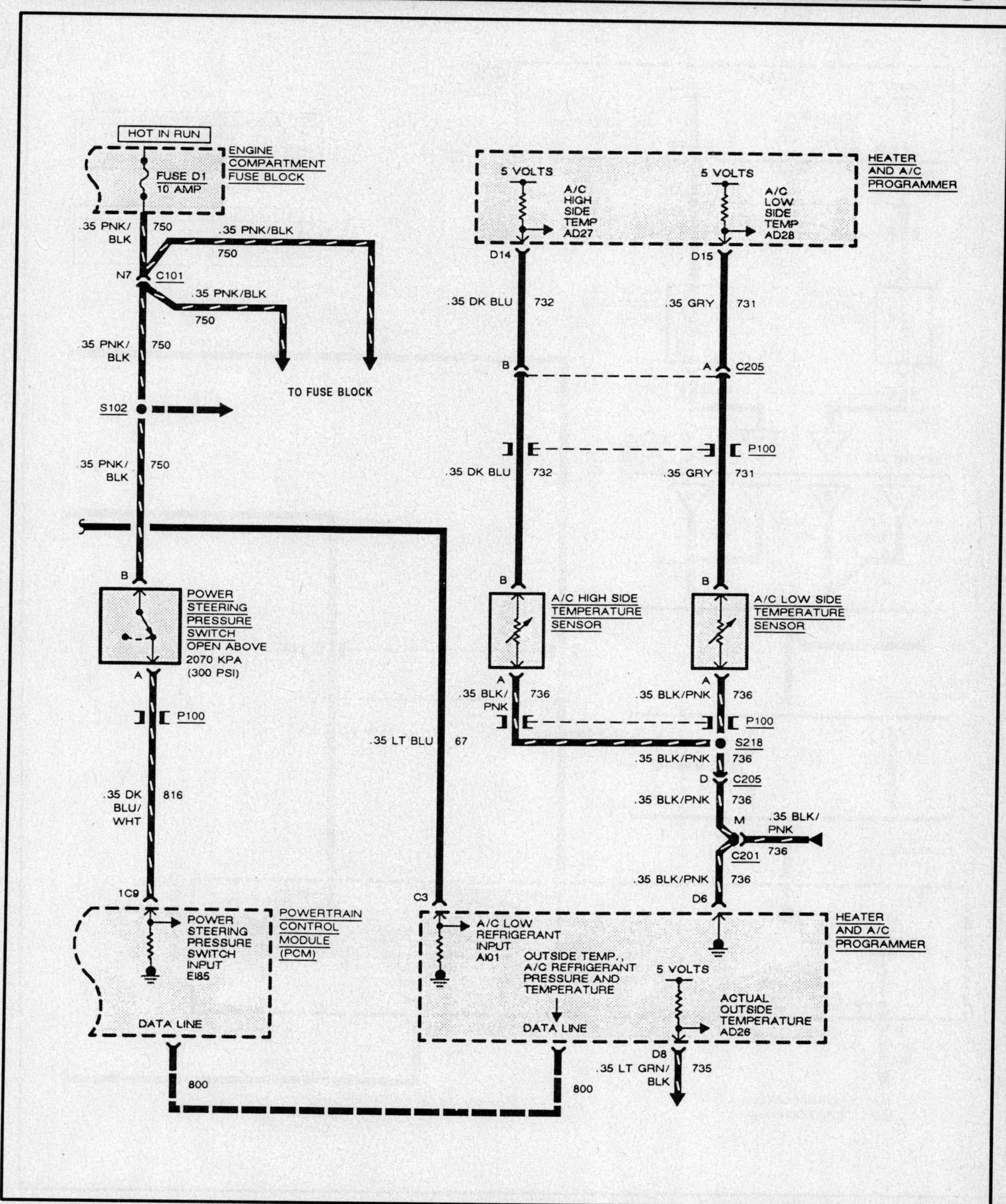

System wiring schematic—1993 Eldorado and Seville, Cont'd

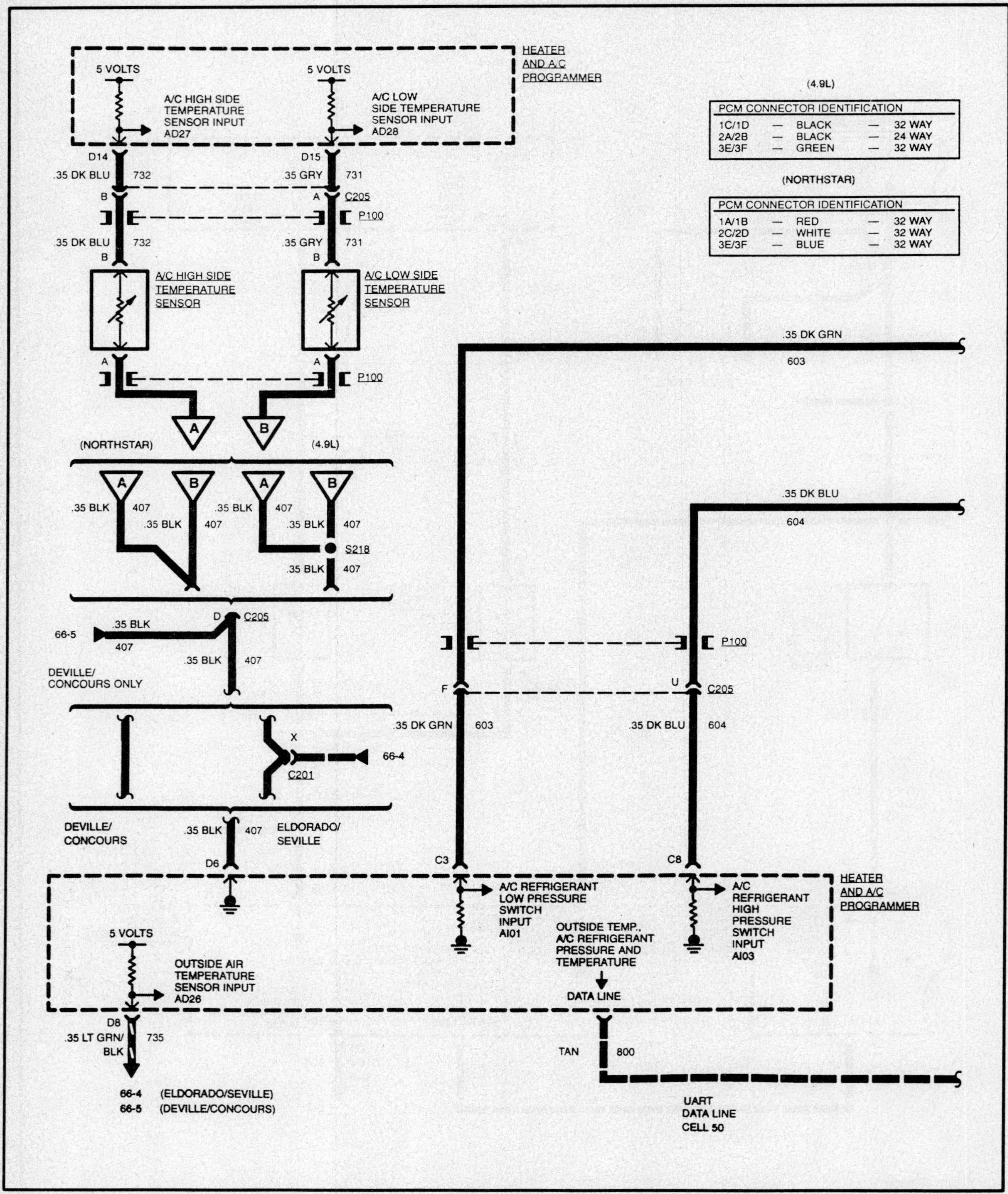

Compressor controls wiring schematic—1994–95 Deville, Concours, Eldorado and Seville with electronic climate control

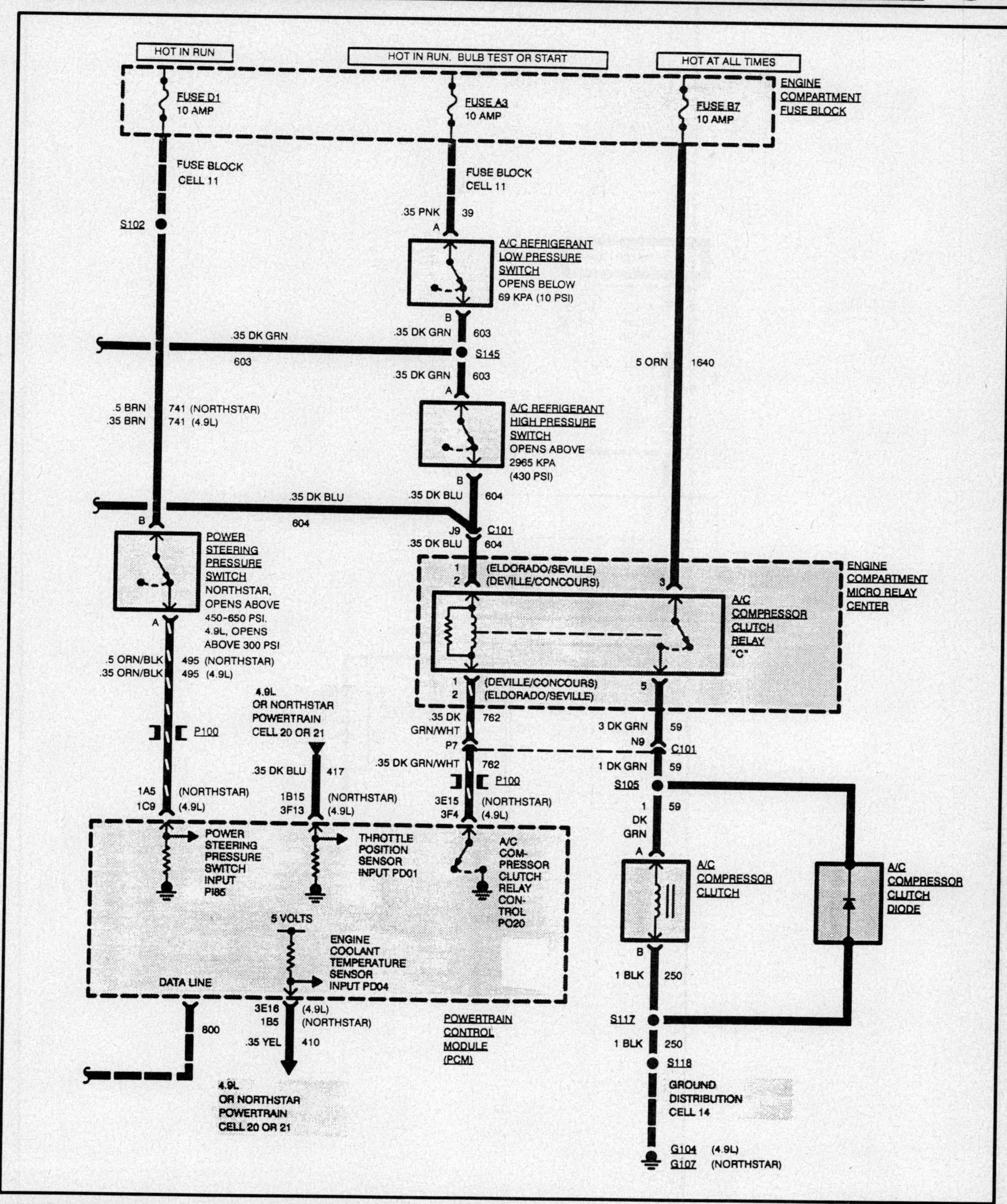

Compressor controls wiring schematic—1994–95 Deville, Concours, Eldorado and Seville with electronic climate control, Cont'd

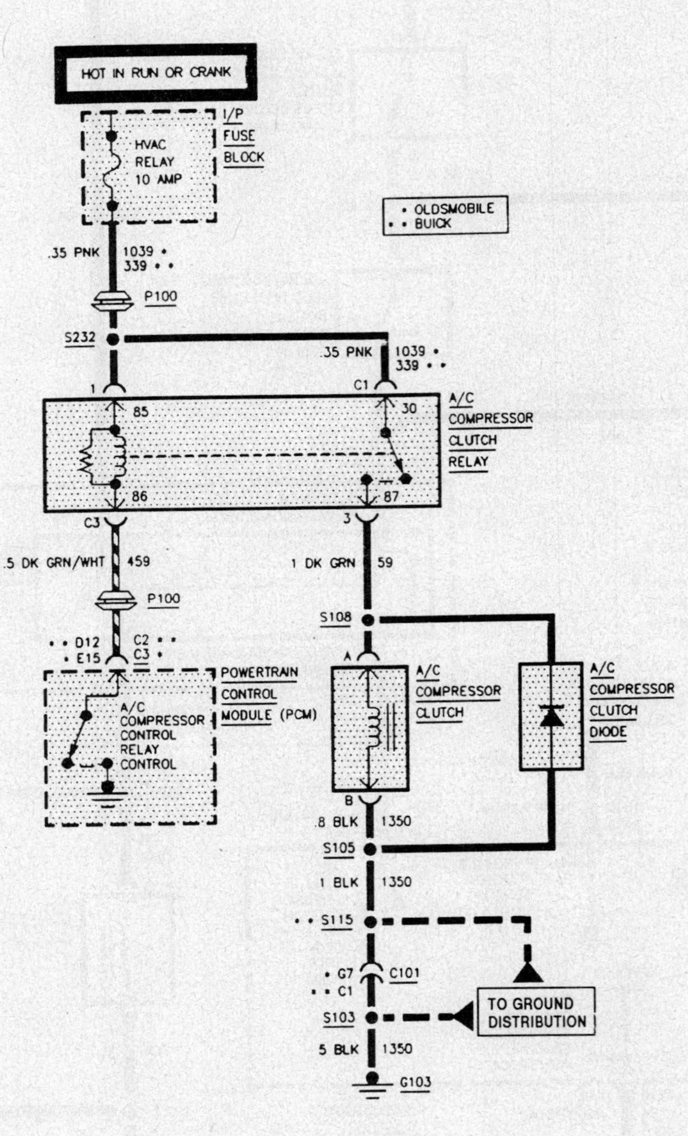

Compressor controls wiring schematic—1995 Aurora and Riviera

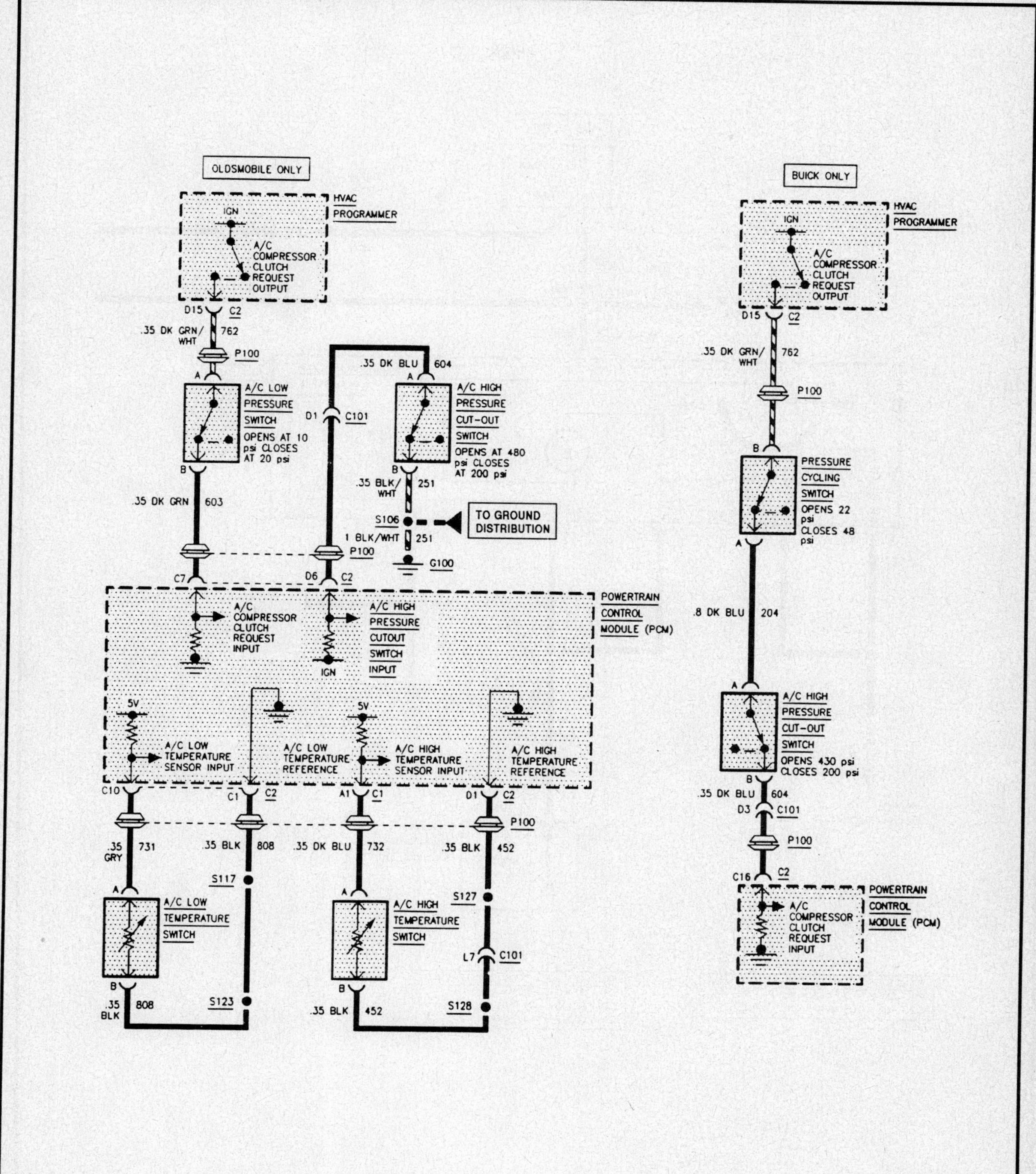

Compressor controls wiring schematic—1995 Aurora and Riviera, Cont'd

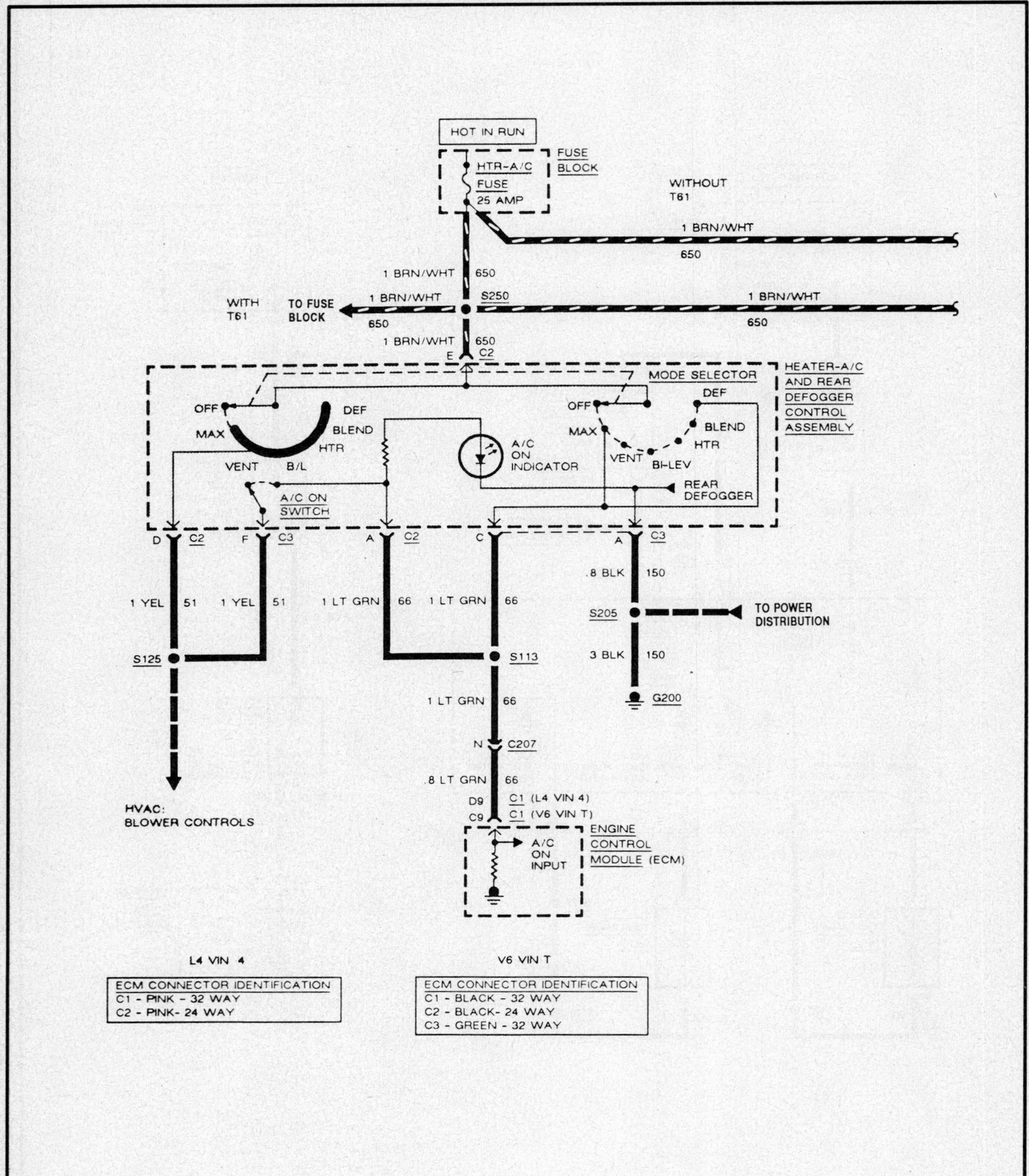

Compressor controls wiring schematic—1993–94 Cavalier

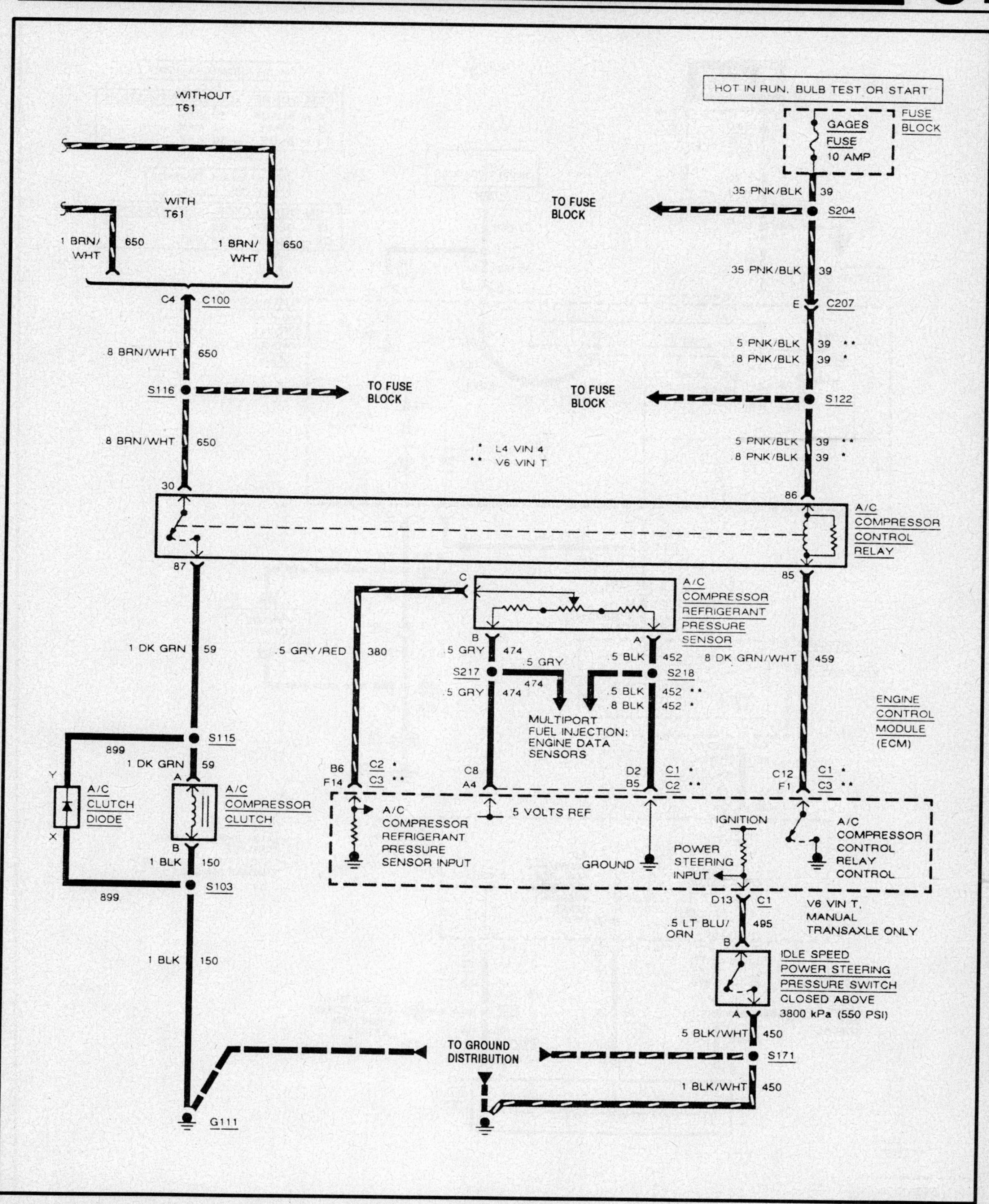

Compressor controls wiring schematic—1993–94 Cavalier, Cont'd

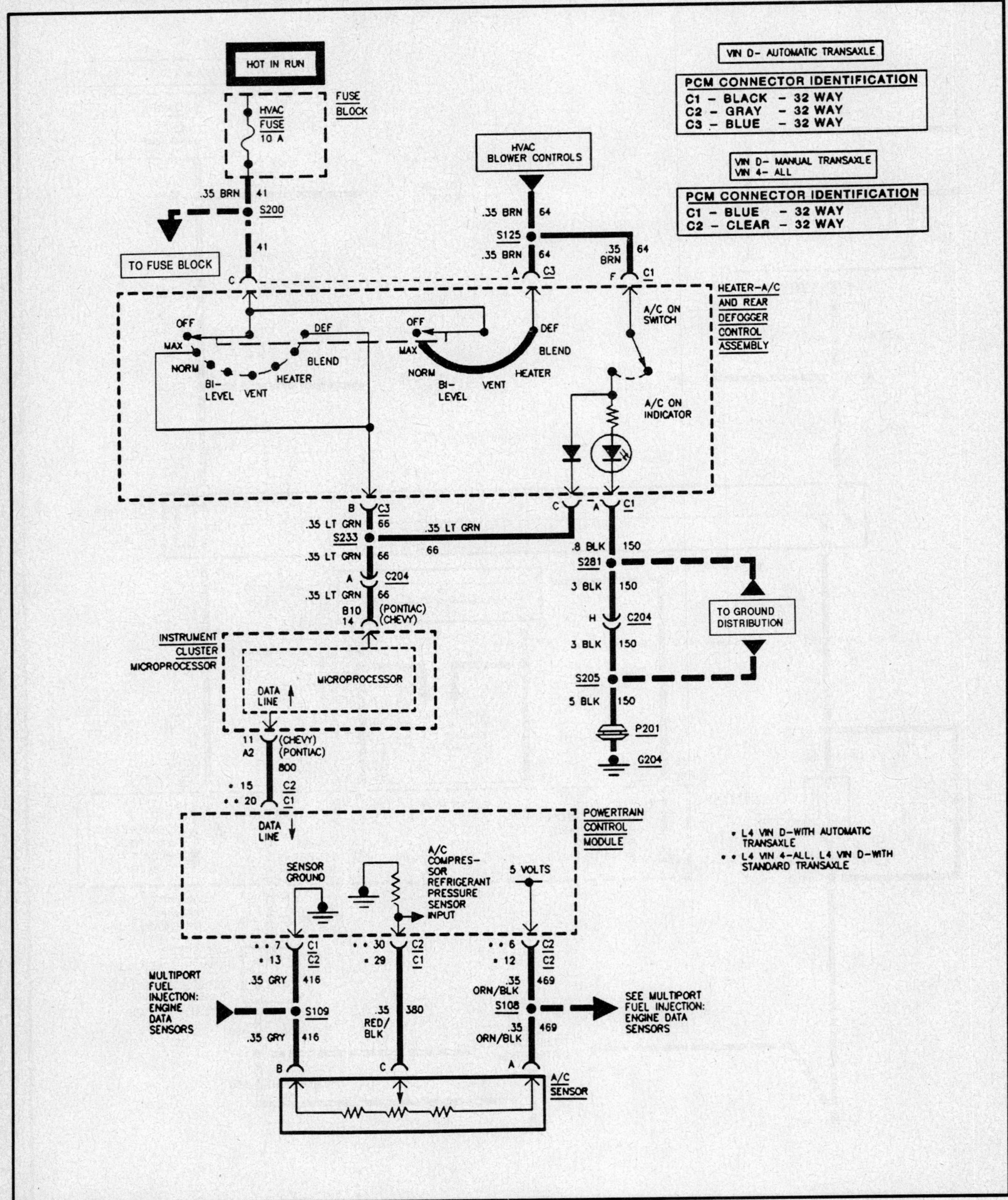

Compressor controls wiring schematic—1995 Cavalier and Sunfire

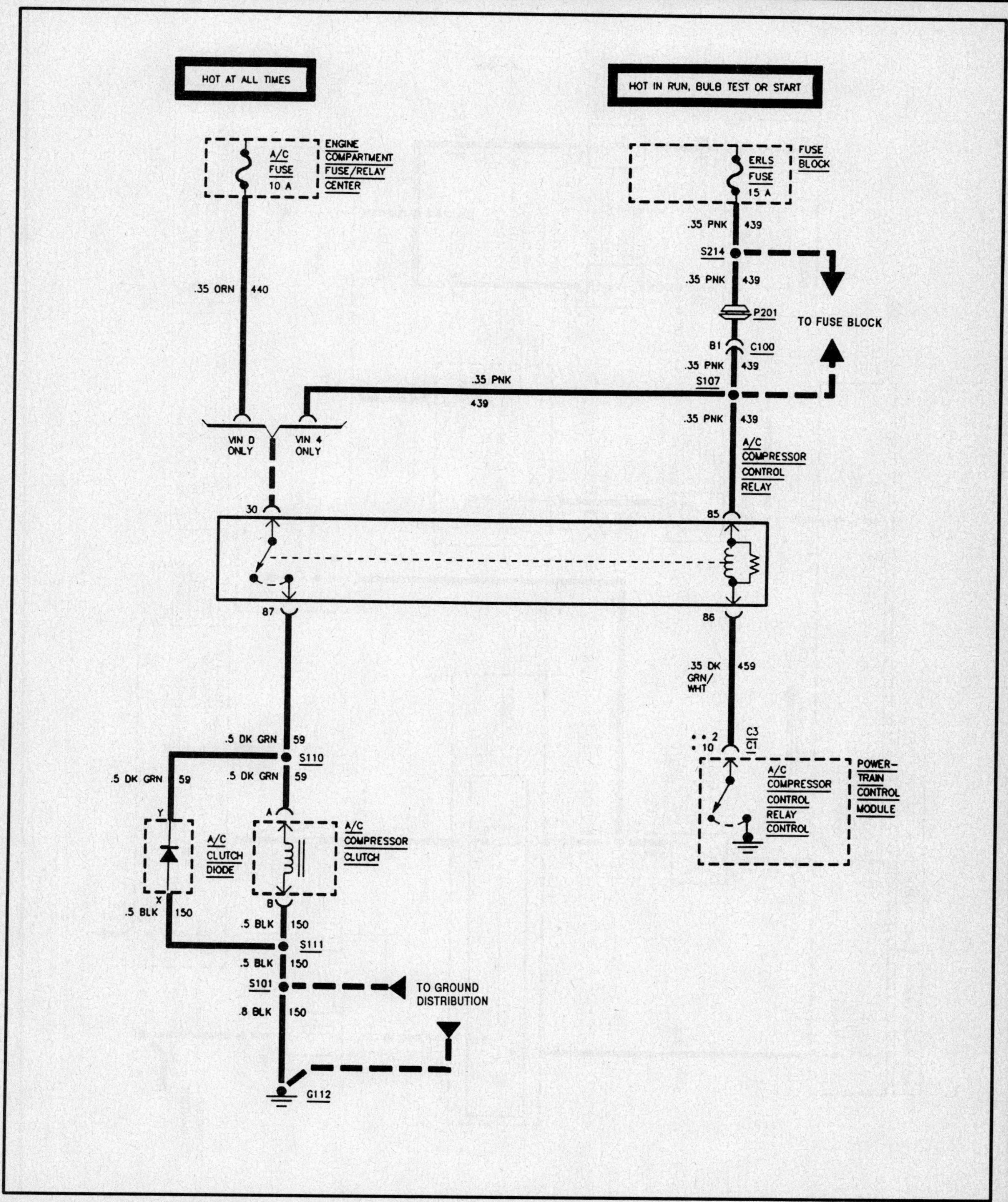

Compressor controls wiring schematic—1995 Cavalier and Sunfire, Cont'd

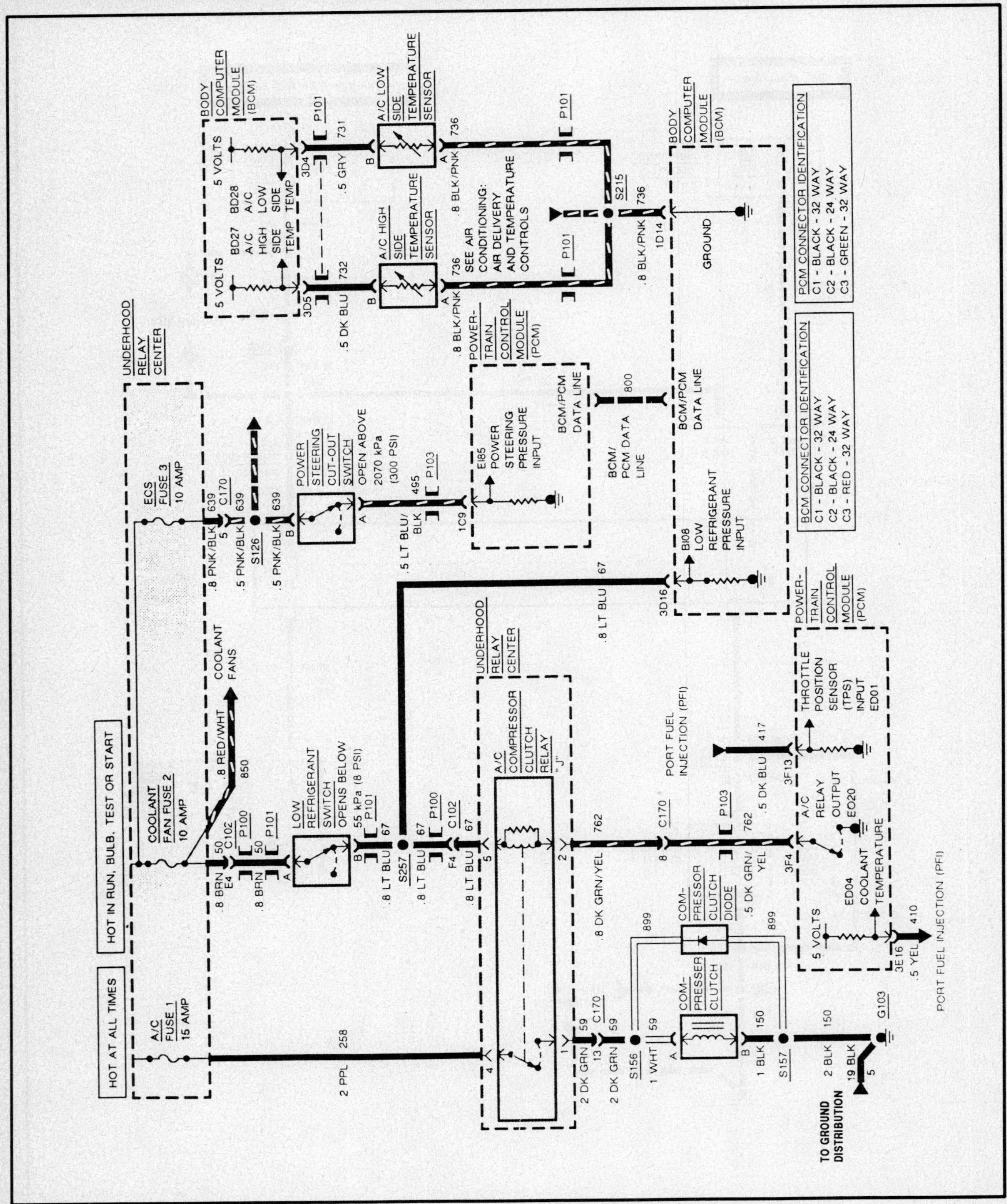

Compressor controls wiring schematic—1993 Sunbird 2.0L (VIN H) and 3.1L (VIN T)

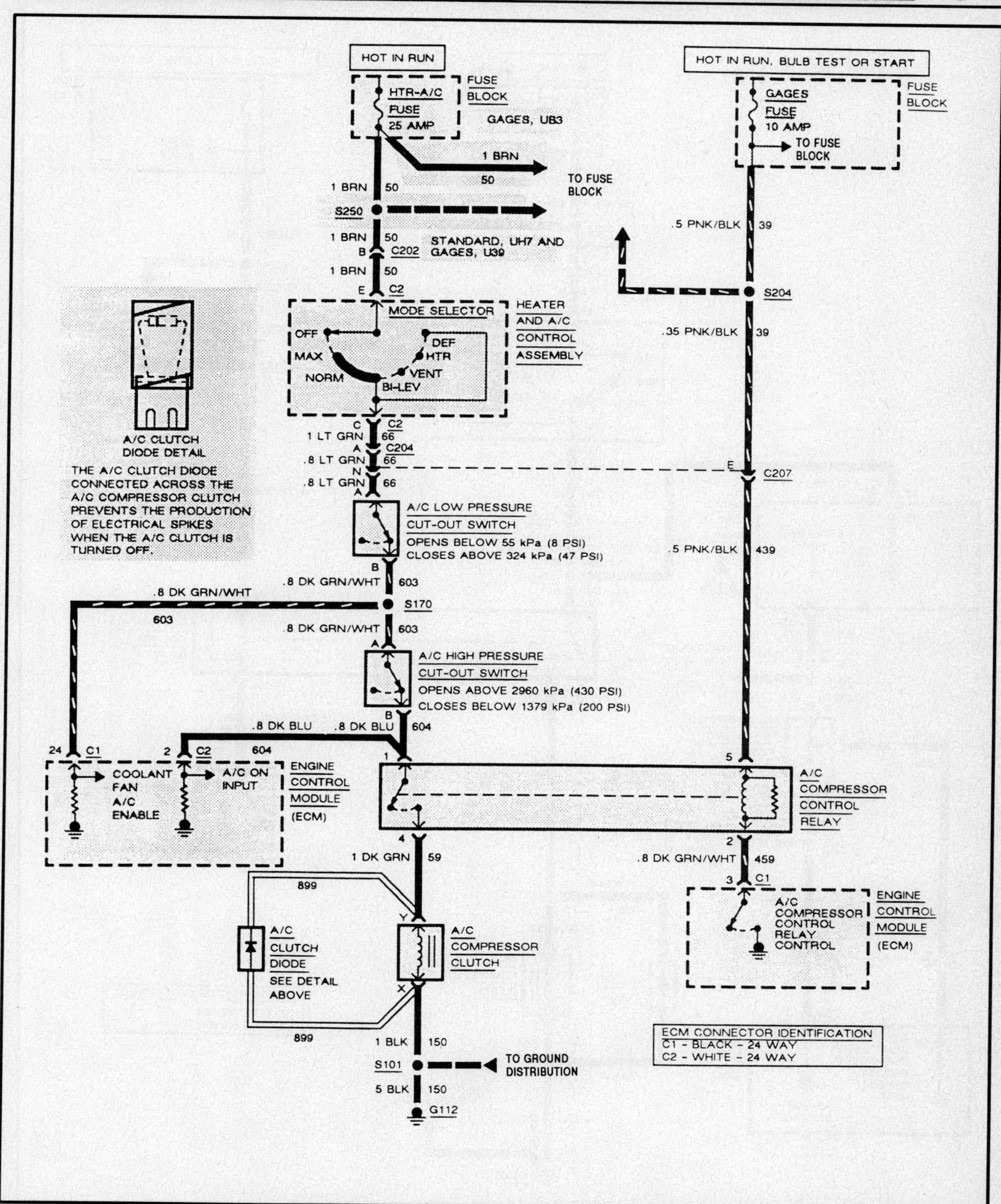

Compressor controls wiring schematic—1993 Sunbird 2.0L (VIN K)

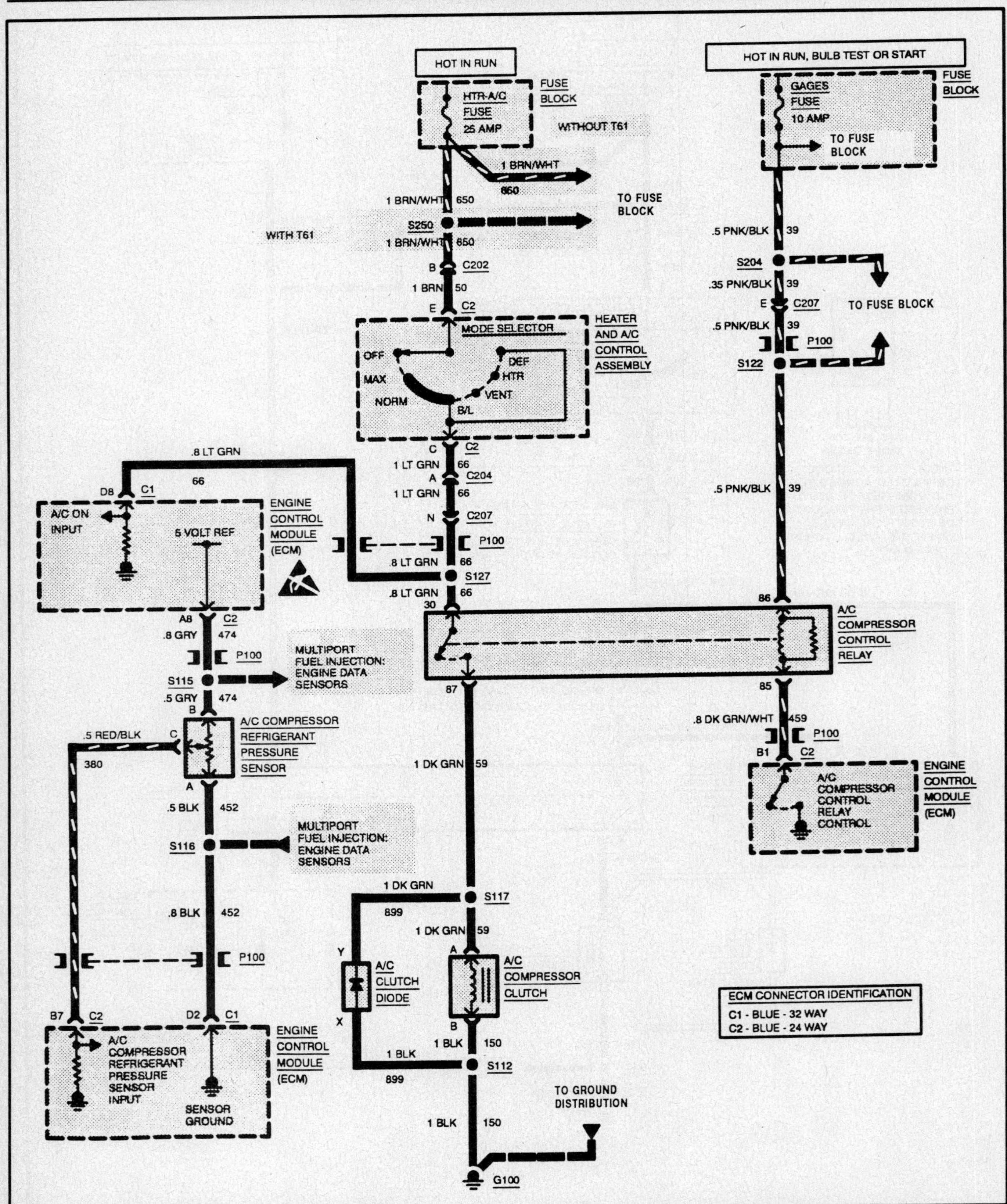

Compressor controls wiring schematic—1994 Sunbird 2.0L (VIN H)

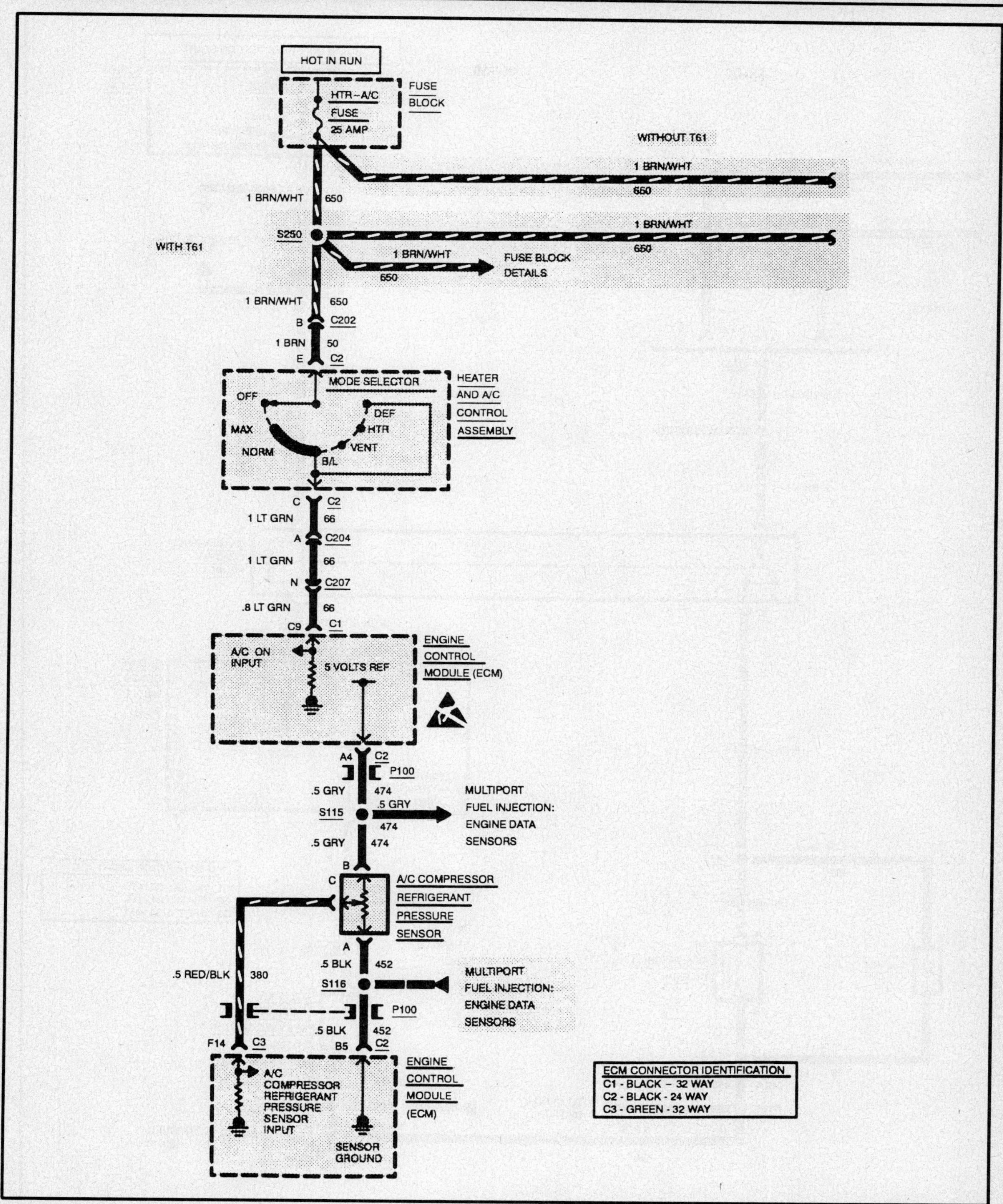

Compressor controls wiring schematic—1994 Sunbird 3.1L (VIN T)

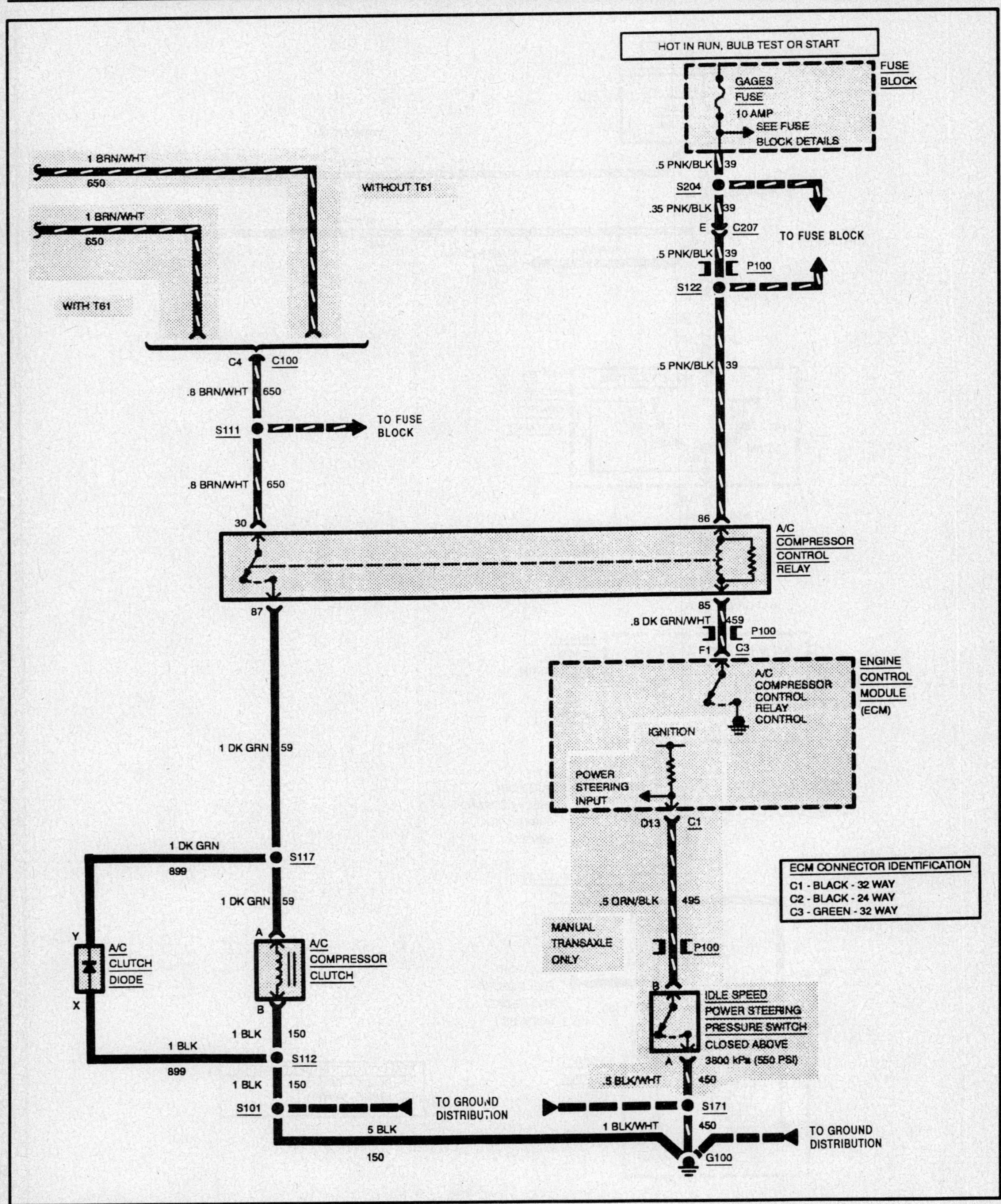

Compressor controls wiring schematic—1994 Sunbird 3.1L (VIN T), Cont'd

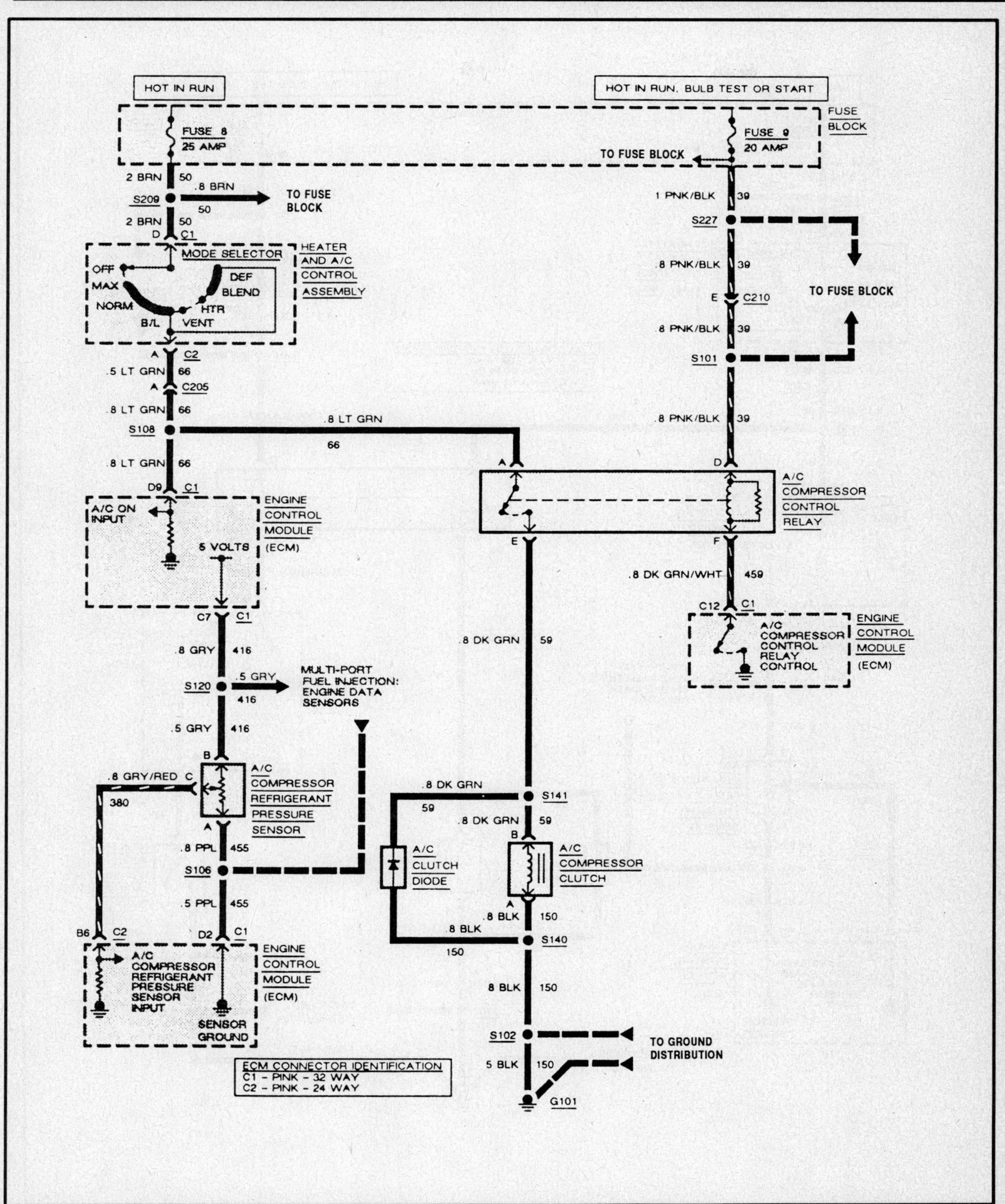

Compressor controls wiring schematic—1993 Beretta and Corsica 2.2L (VIN 4)

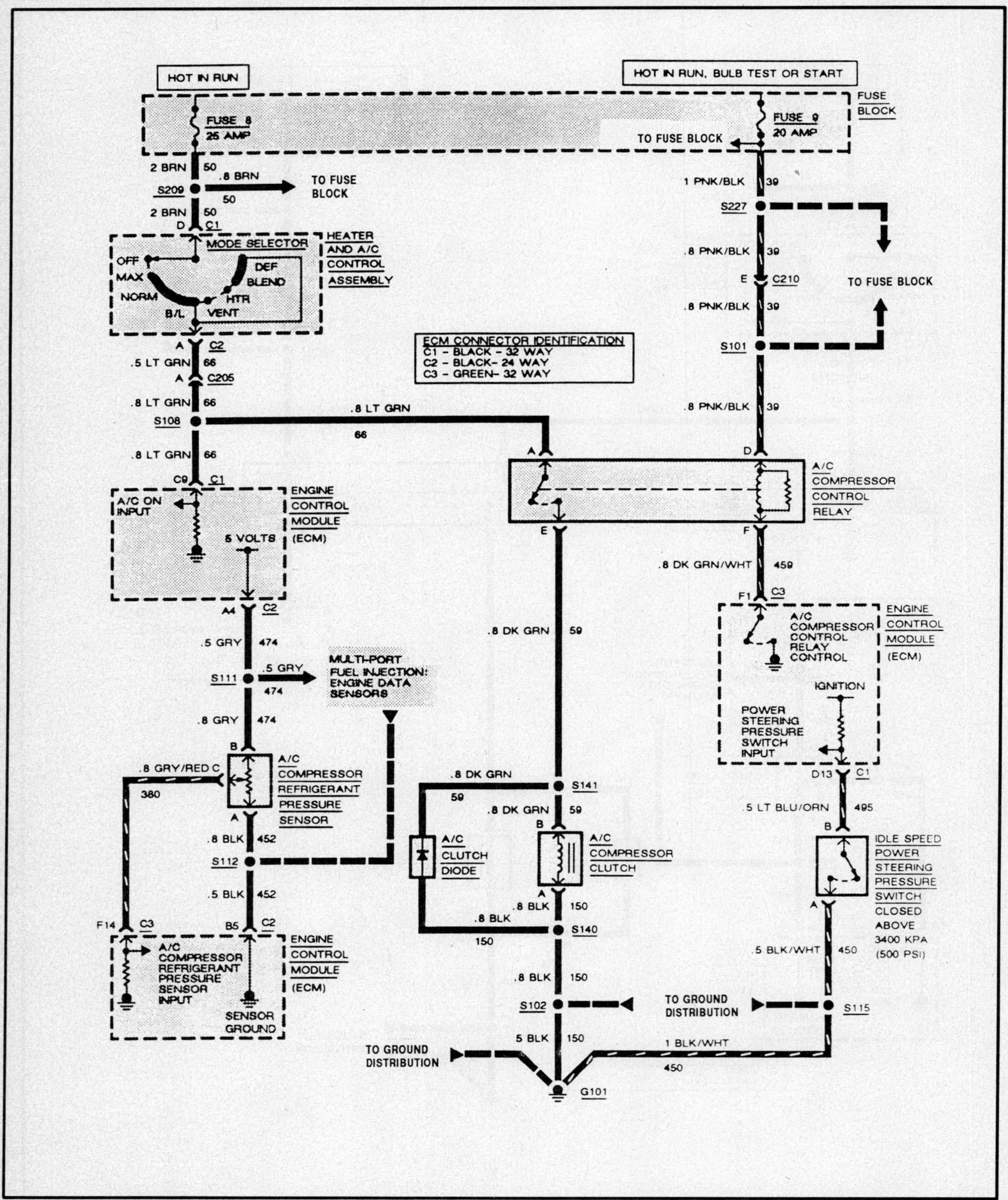

Compressor controls wiring schematic—1993 Beretta and Corsica 2.3L (VIN A) and 3.1L (VIN T)

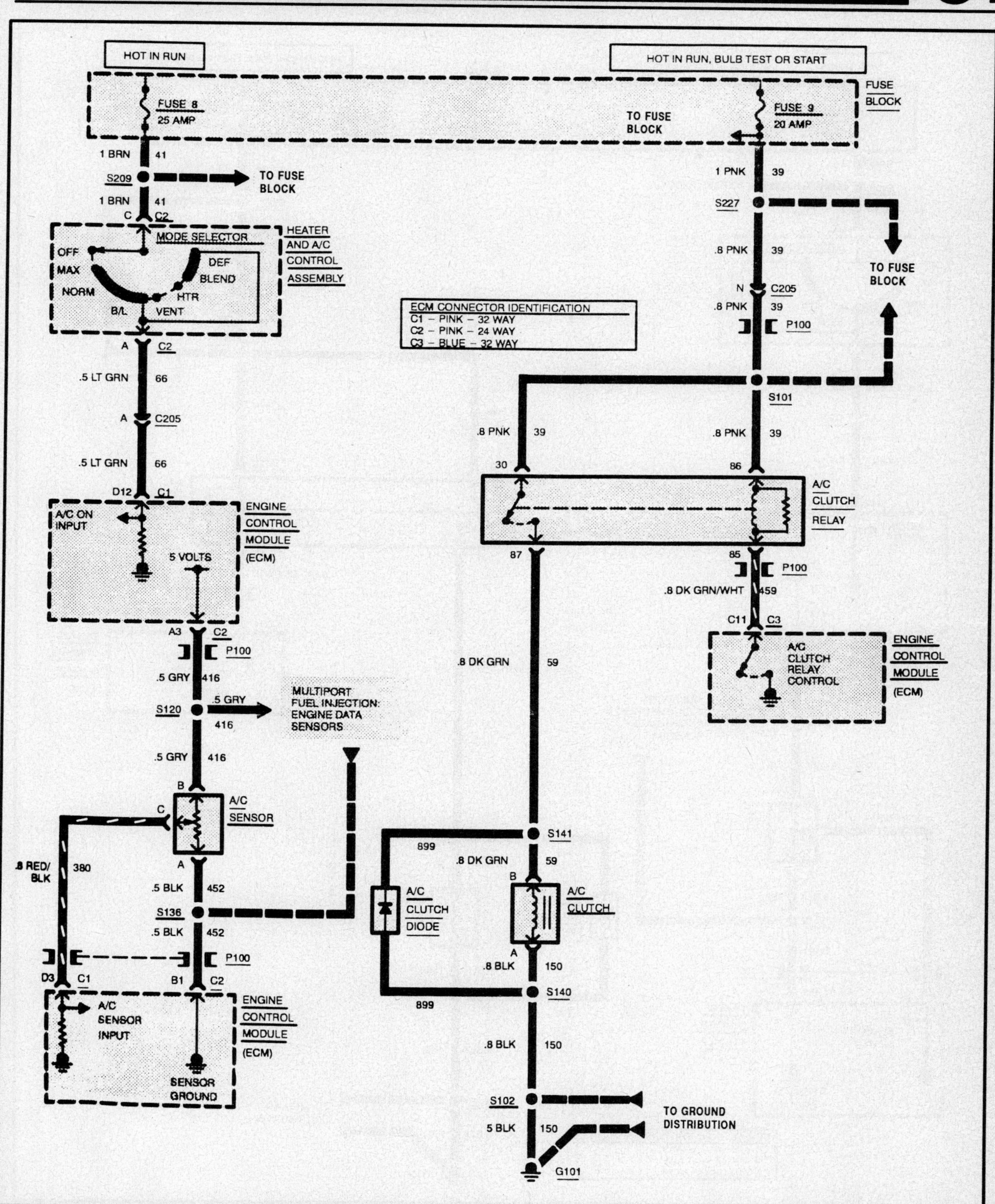

Compressor controls wiring schematic—1994 Beretta and Corsica 2.3L (VIN A)

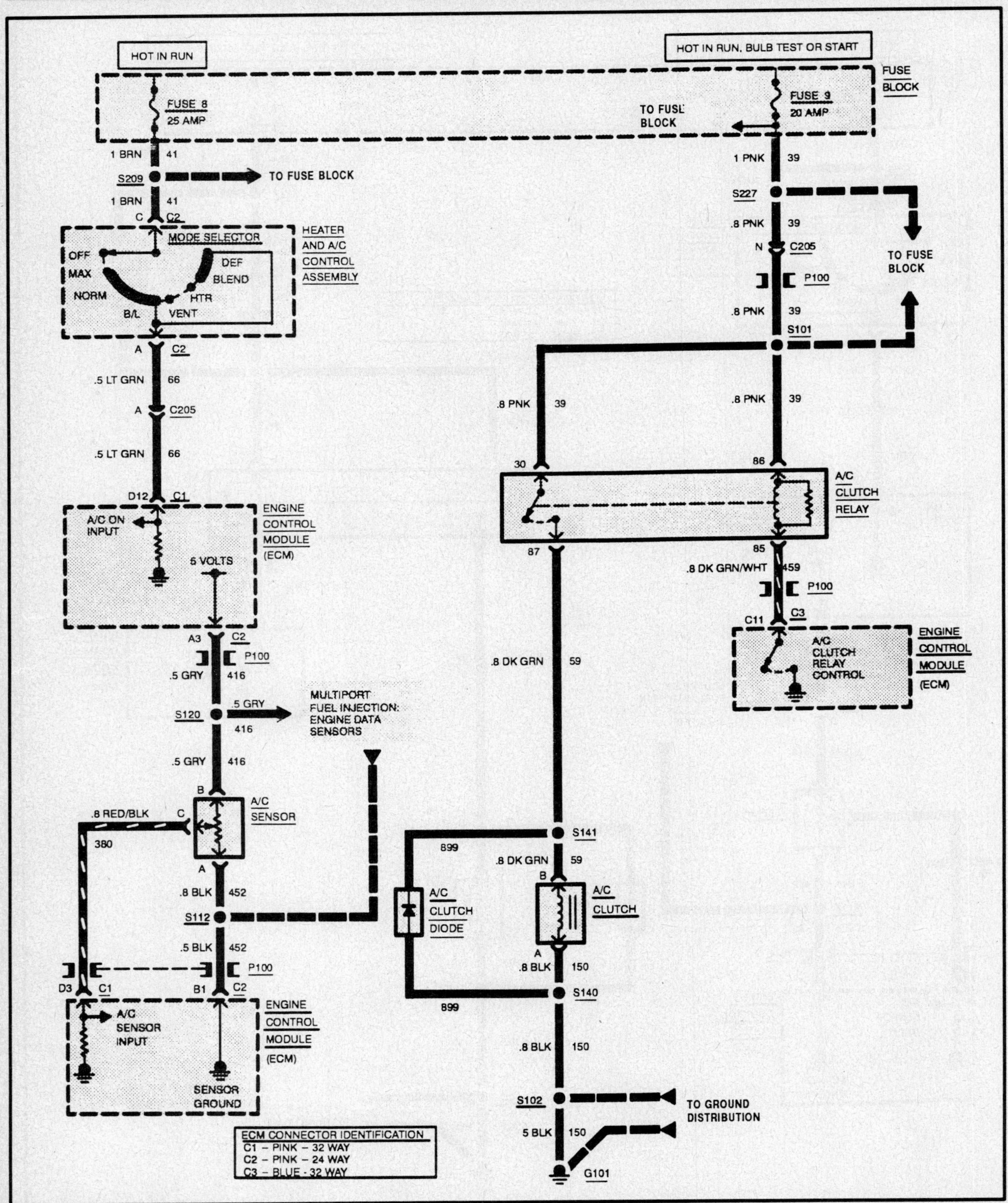

Compressor controls wiring schematic—1994–95 Beretta and Corsica 2.2L (VIN 4)

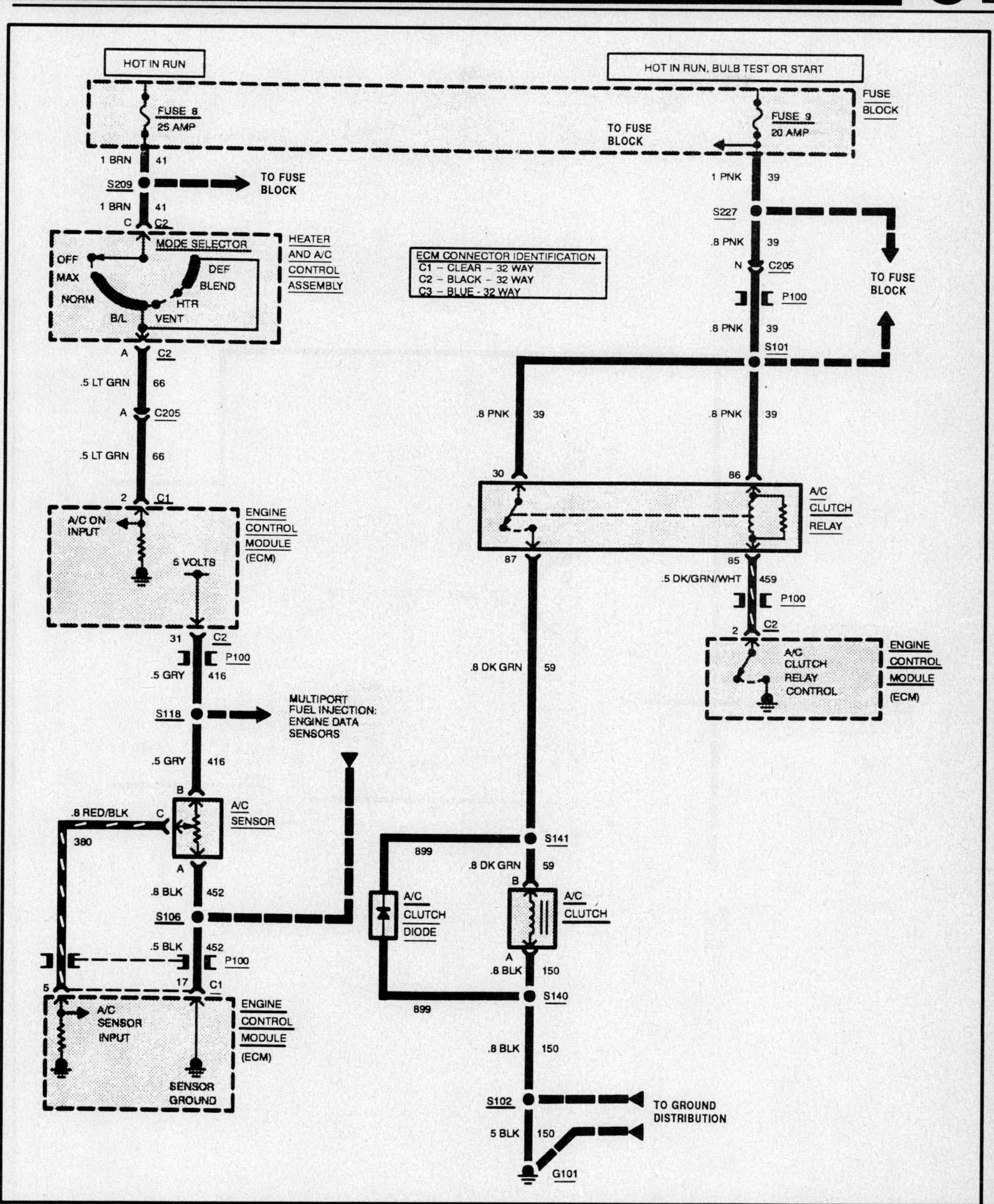

Compressor controls wiring schematic—1994–95 Beretta and Corsica 3.1L (VIN M)

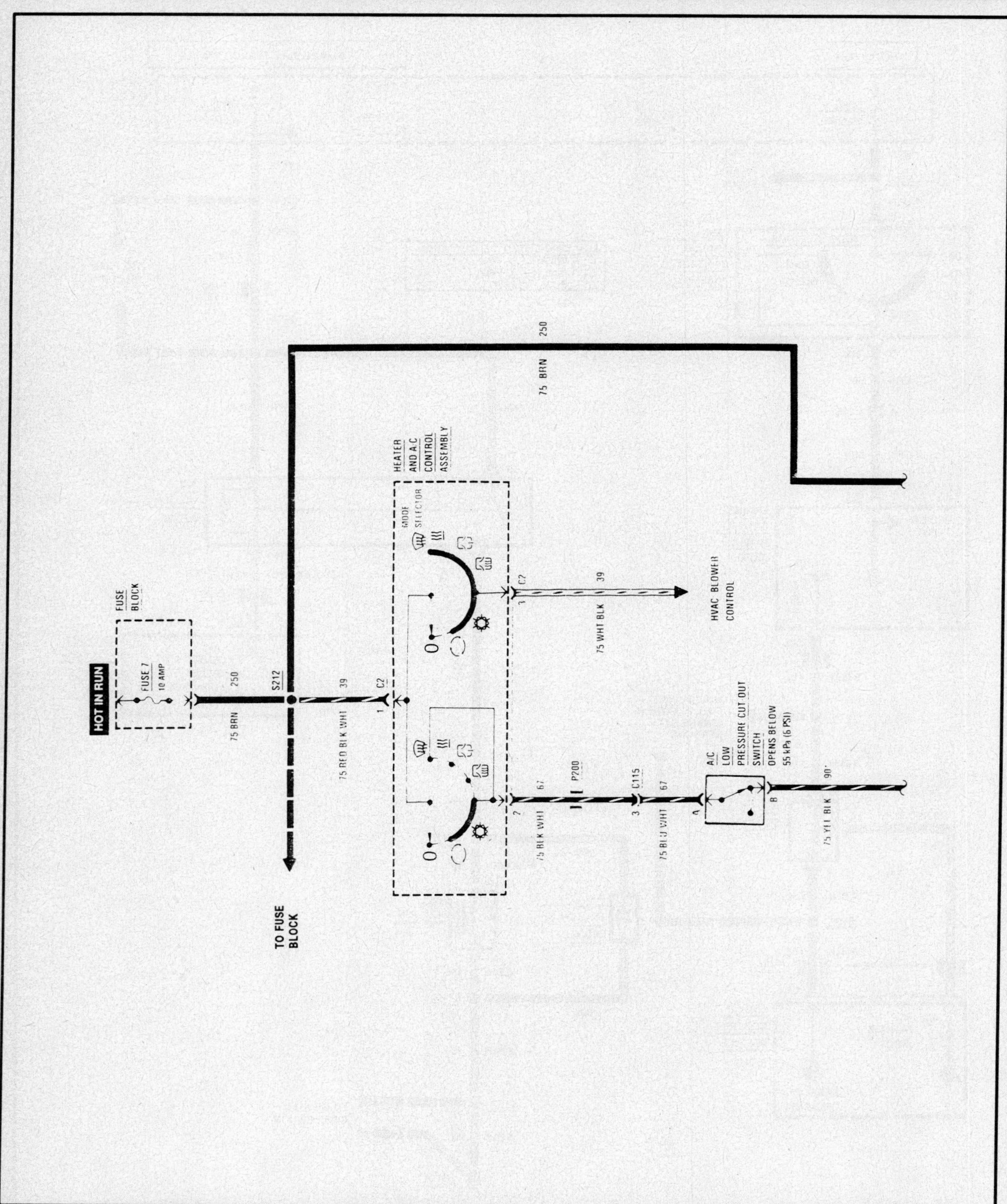

Compressor controls wiring schematic—1993 LeMans

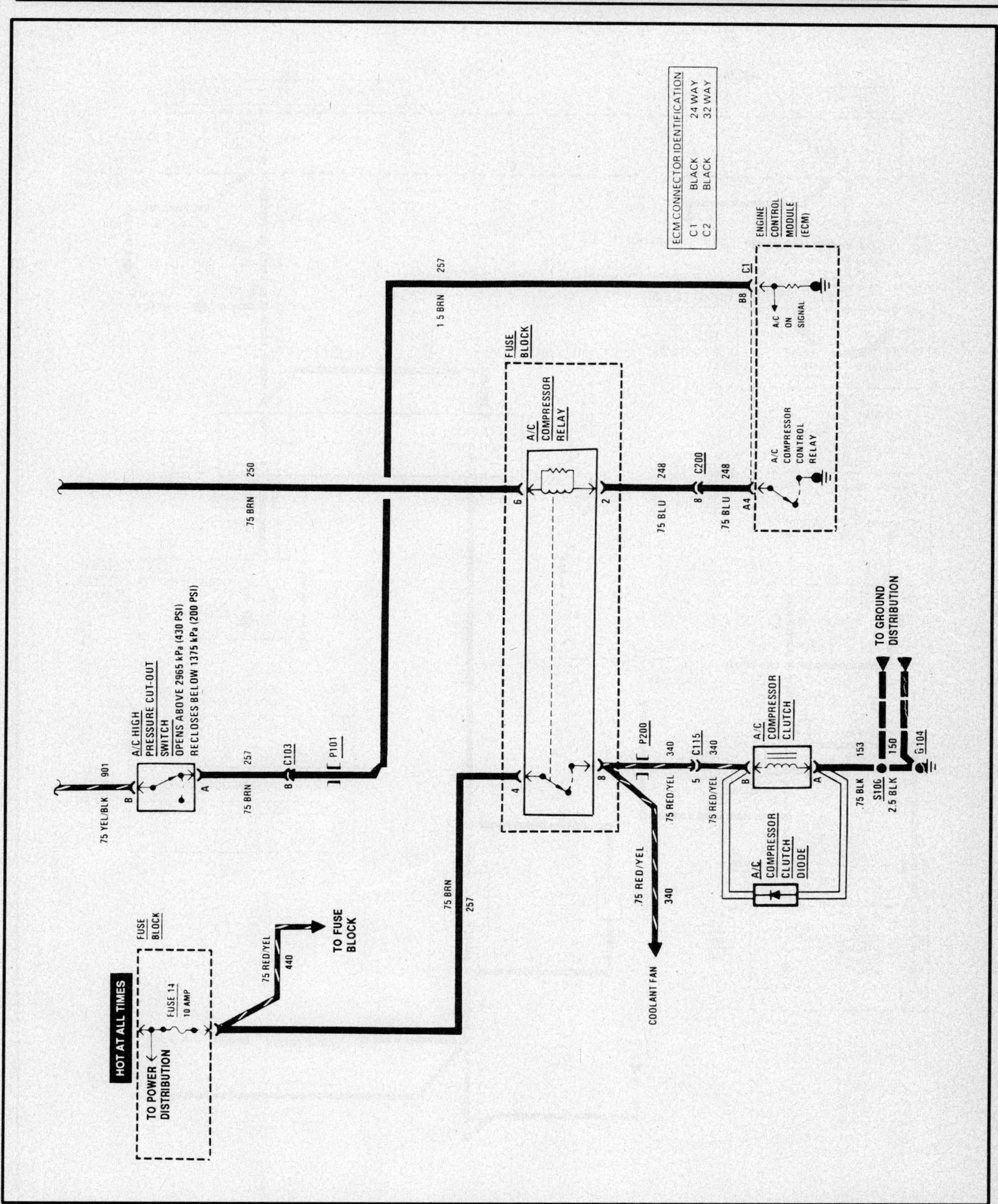

Compressor controls wiring schematic—1993 LeMans, Cont'd

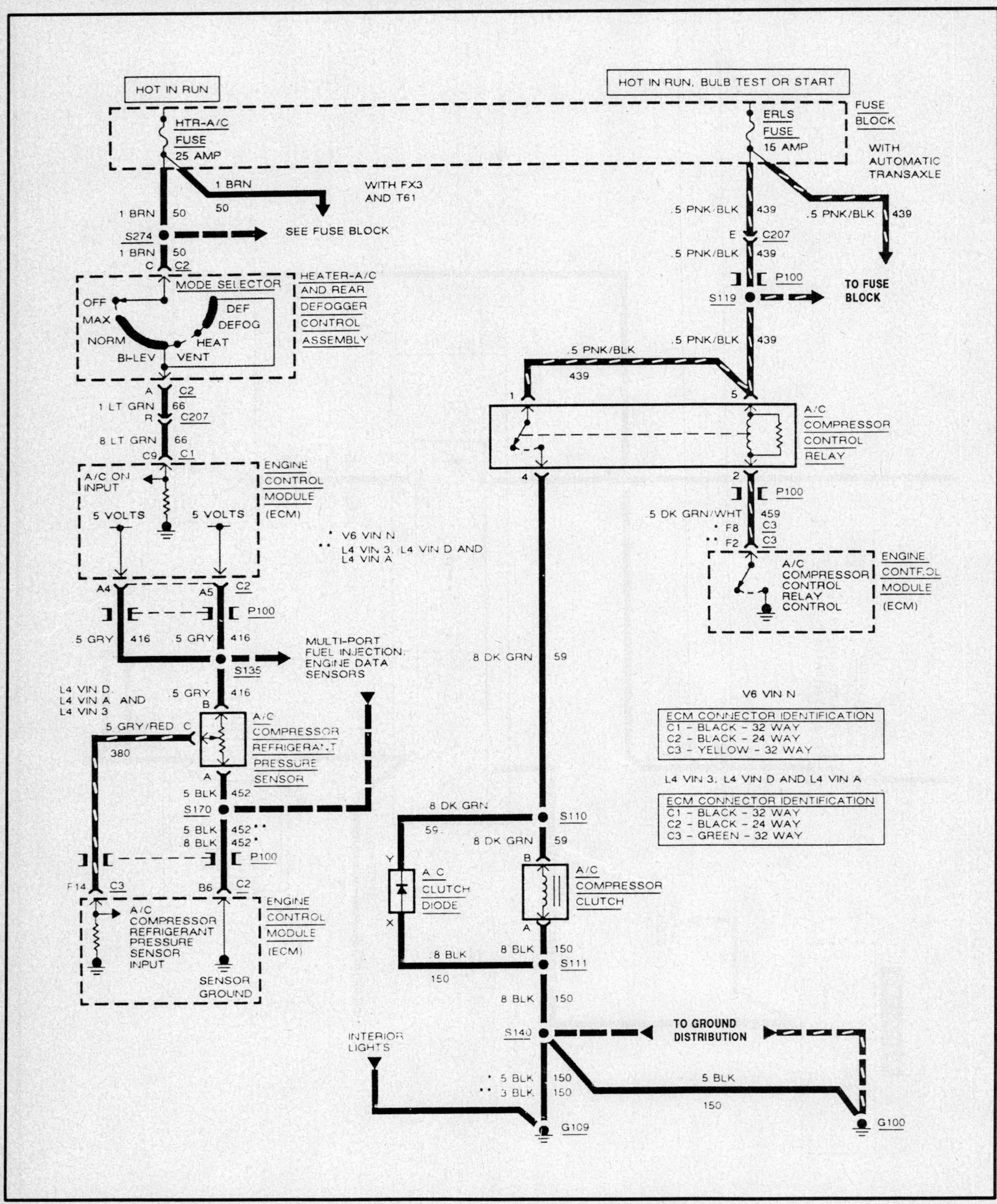

Compressor controls wiring schematic—1993 Achieva, Grand Am and Skylark

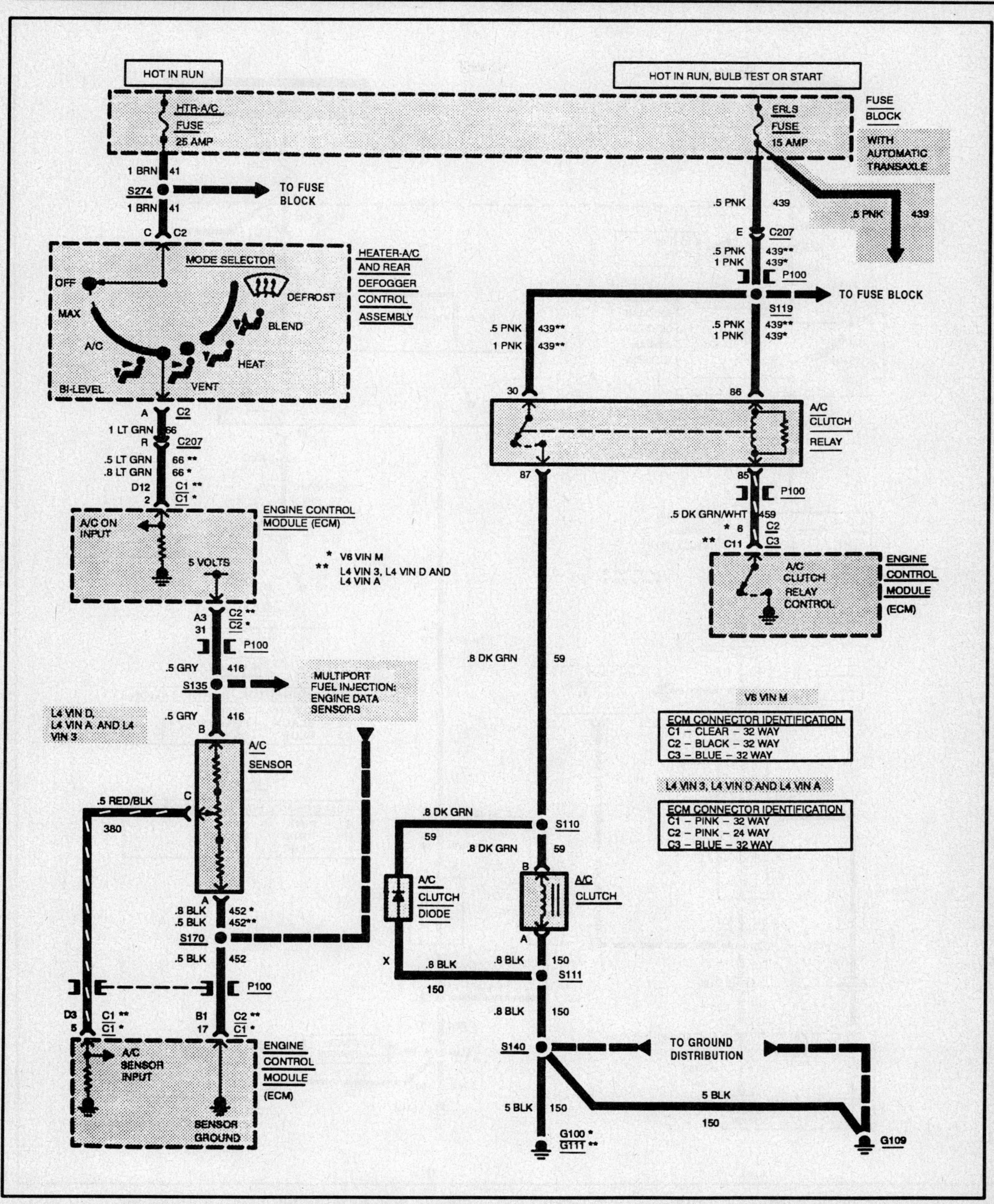

Compressor controls wiring schematic—1994 Grand Am and Achieva with C60 manual air conditioning

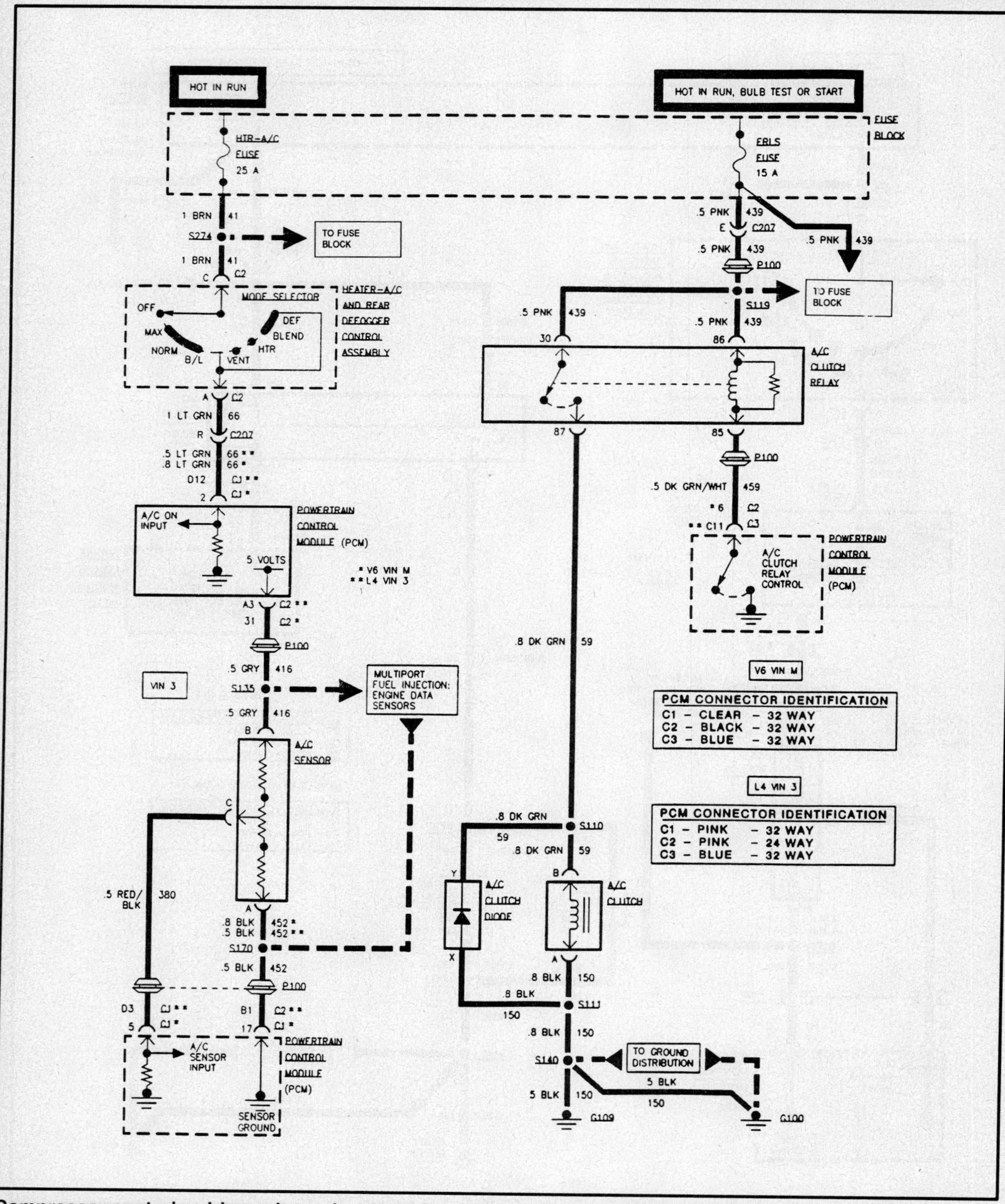

Compressor controls wiring schematic—1995 Grand Am, Achieva and Skylark with C60 manual air conditioning

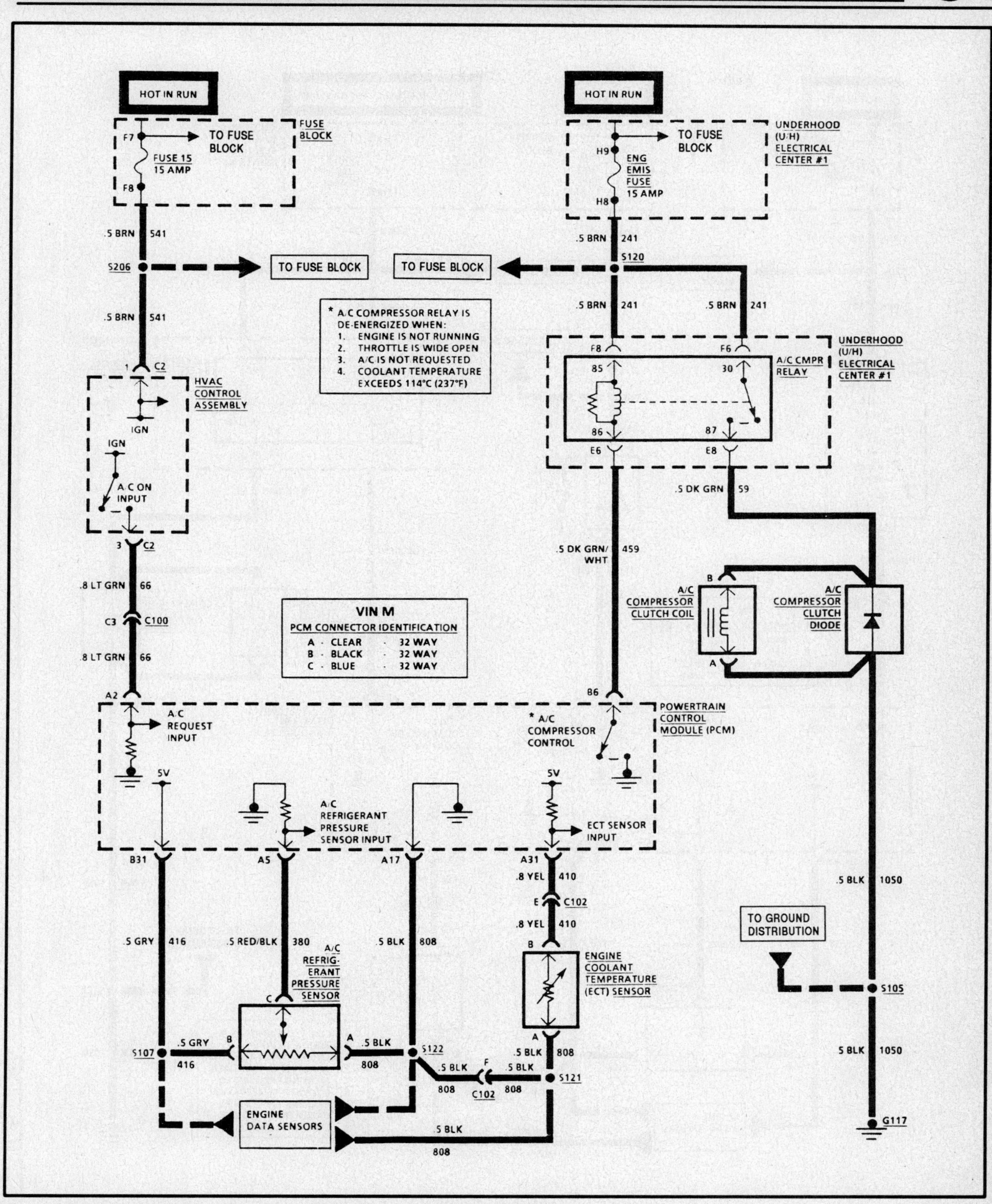

Compressor controls wiring schematic—1994 Grand Prix (VIN M)

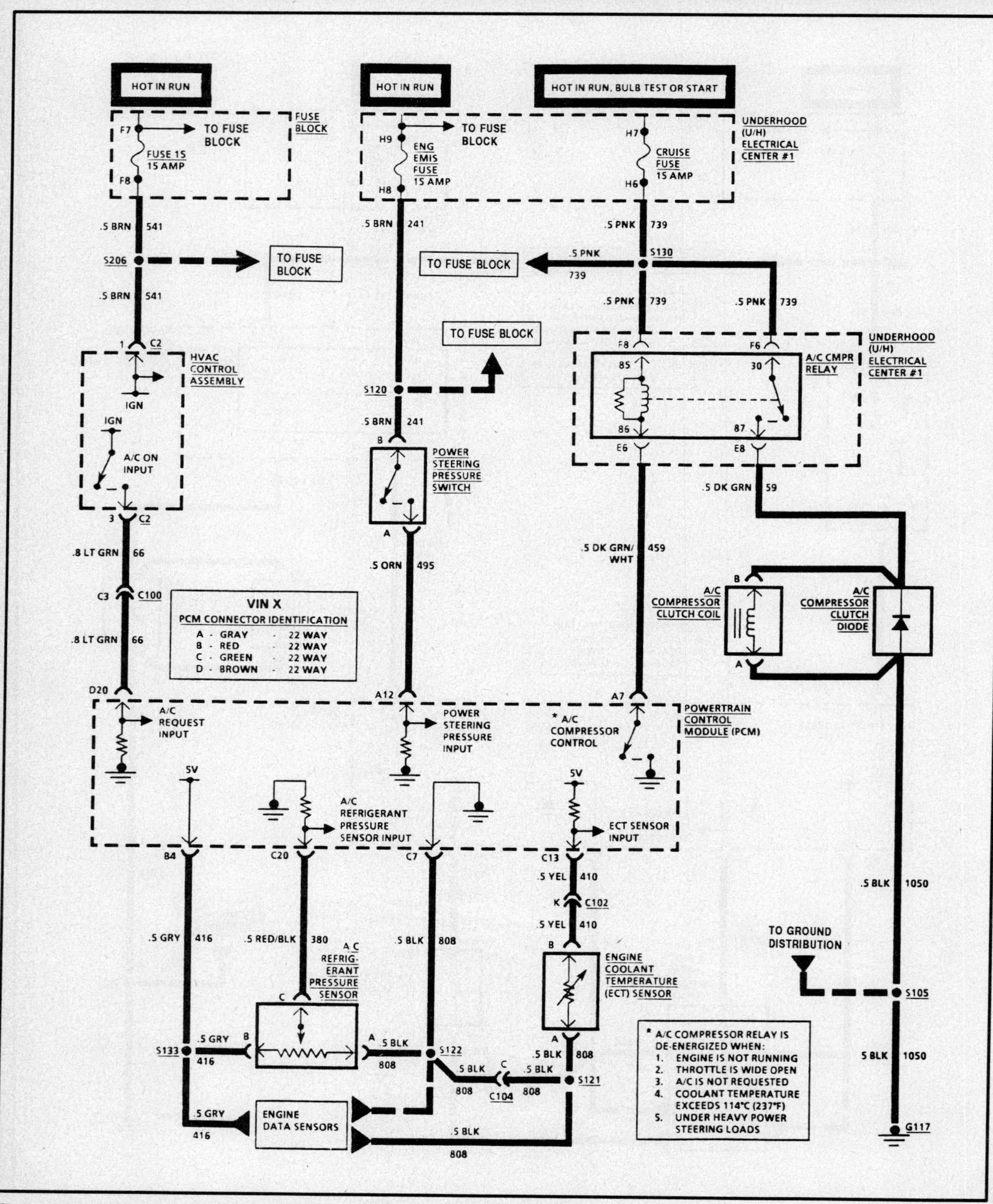

Compressor controls wiring schematic—1994 Grand Prix (VIN X)

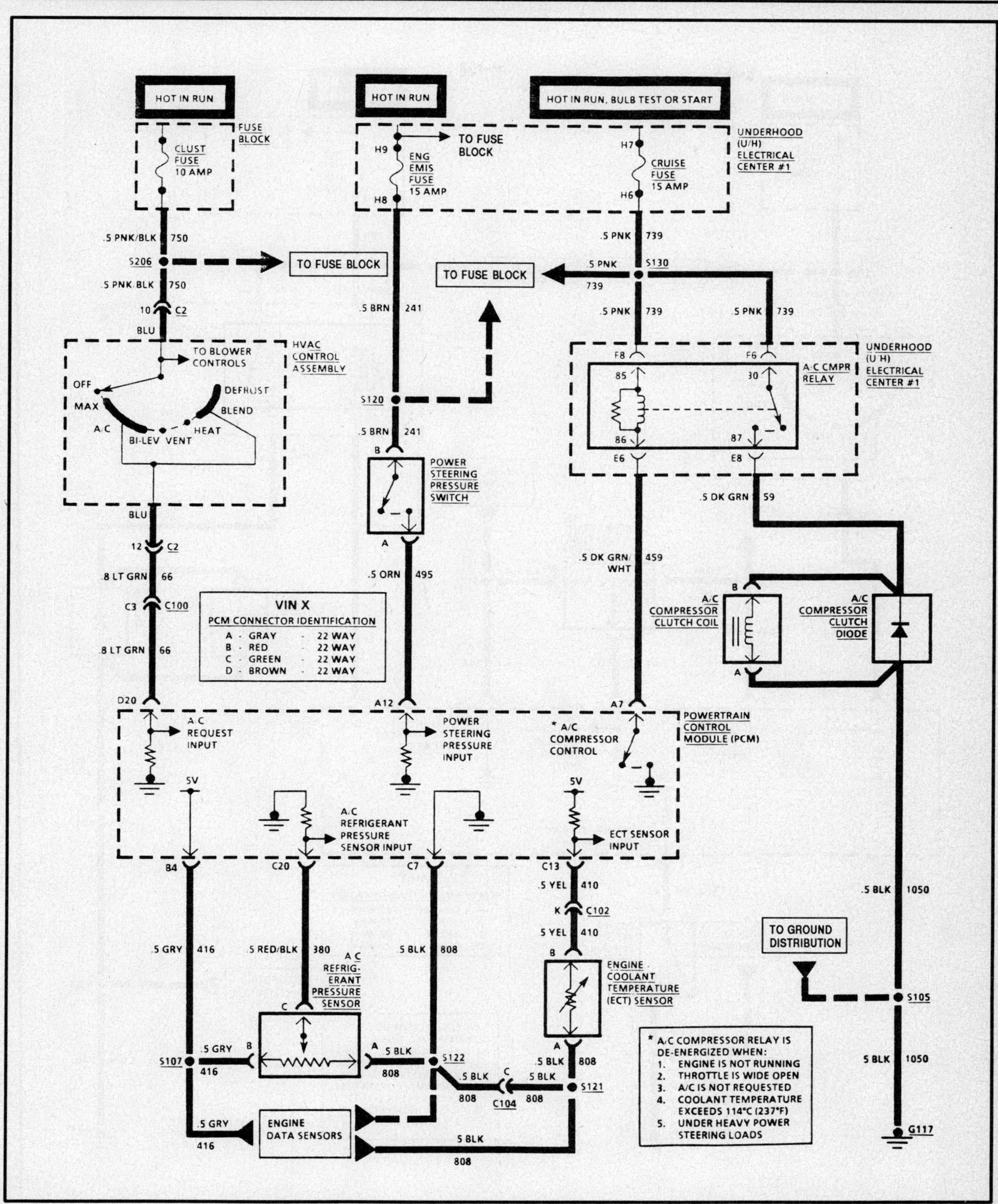

Compressor controls wiring schematic—1994 Lumina (VIN X) C67

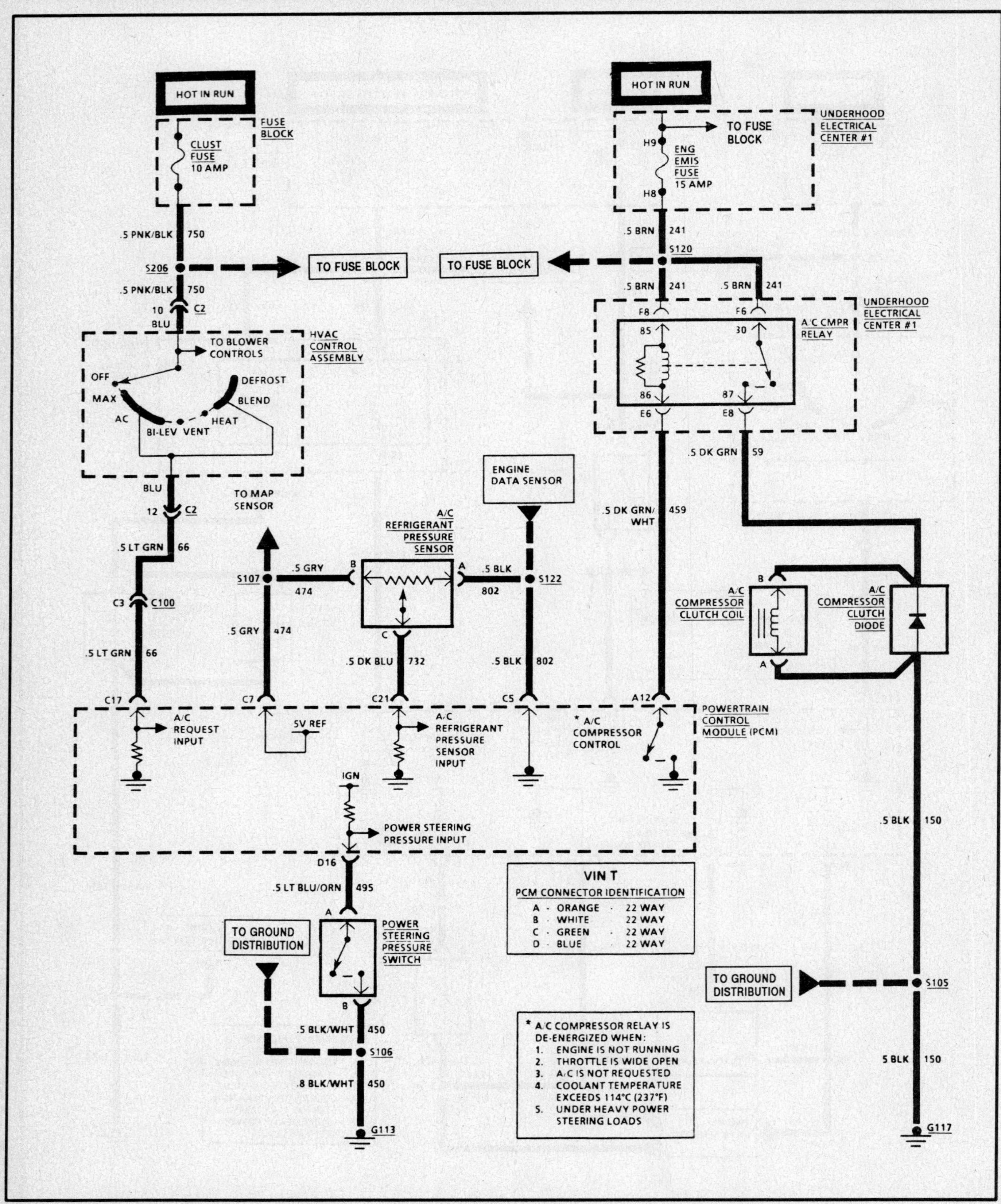

Compressor controls wiring schematic—1994 Lumina (VIN T) C67

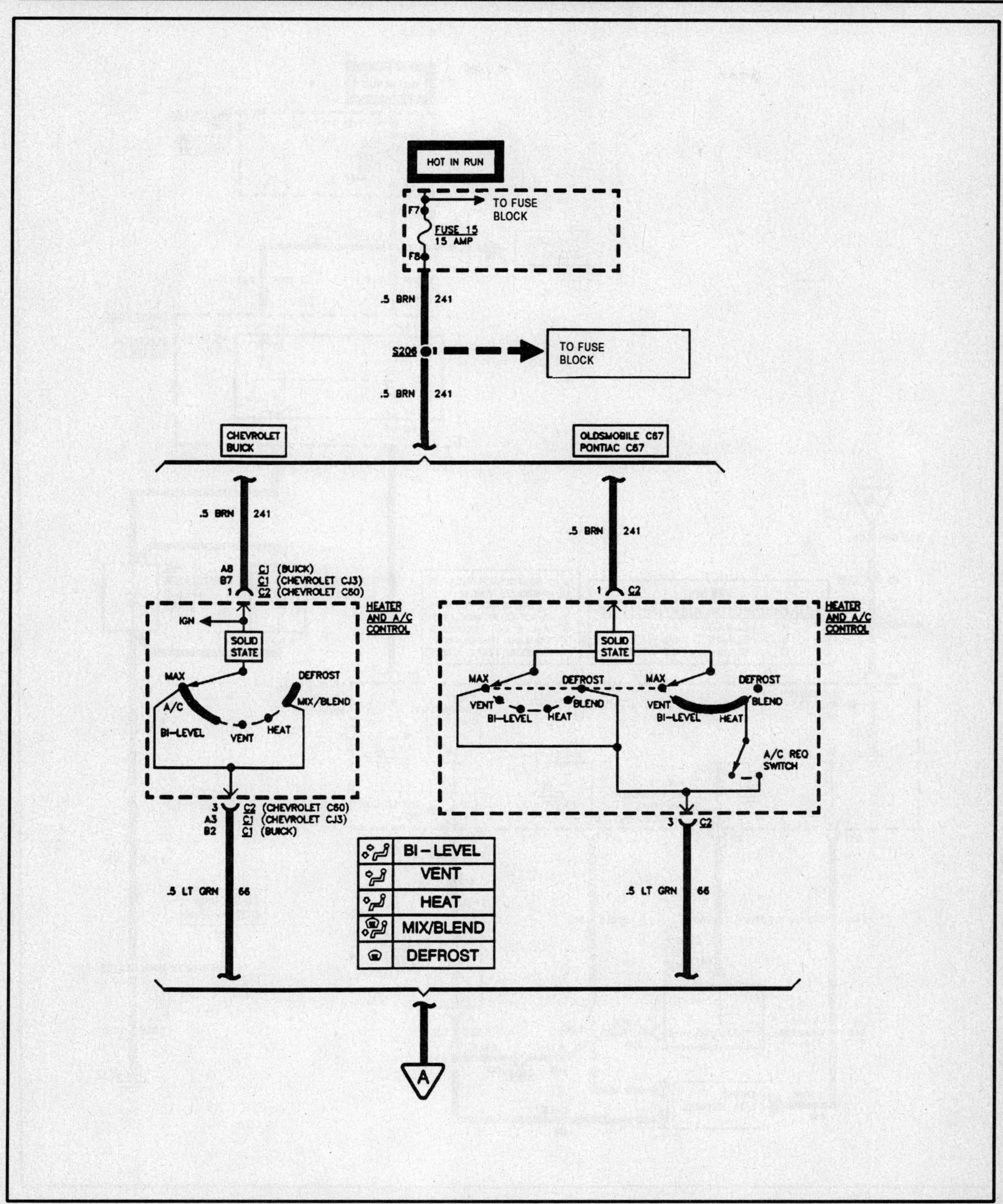

Compressor controls wiring schematic—1995 Cutlass Supreme, Lumina, Monte Carlo, Grand Prix and Regal

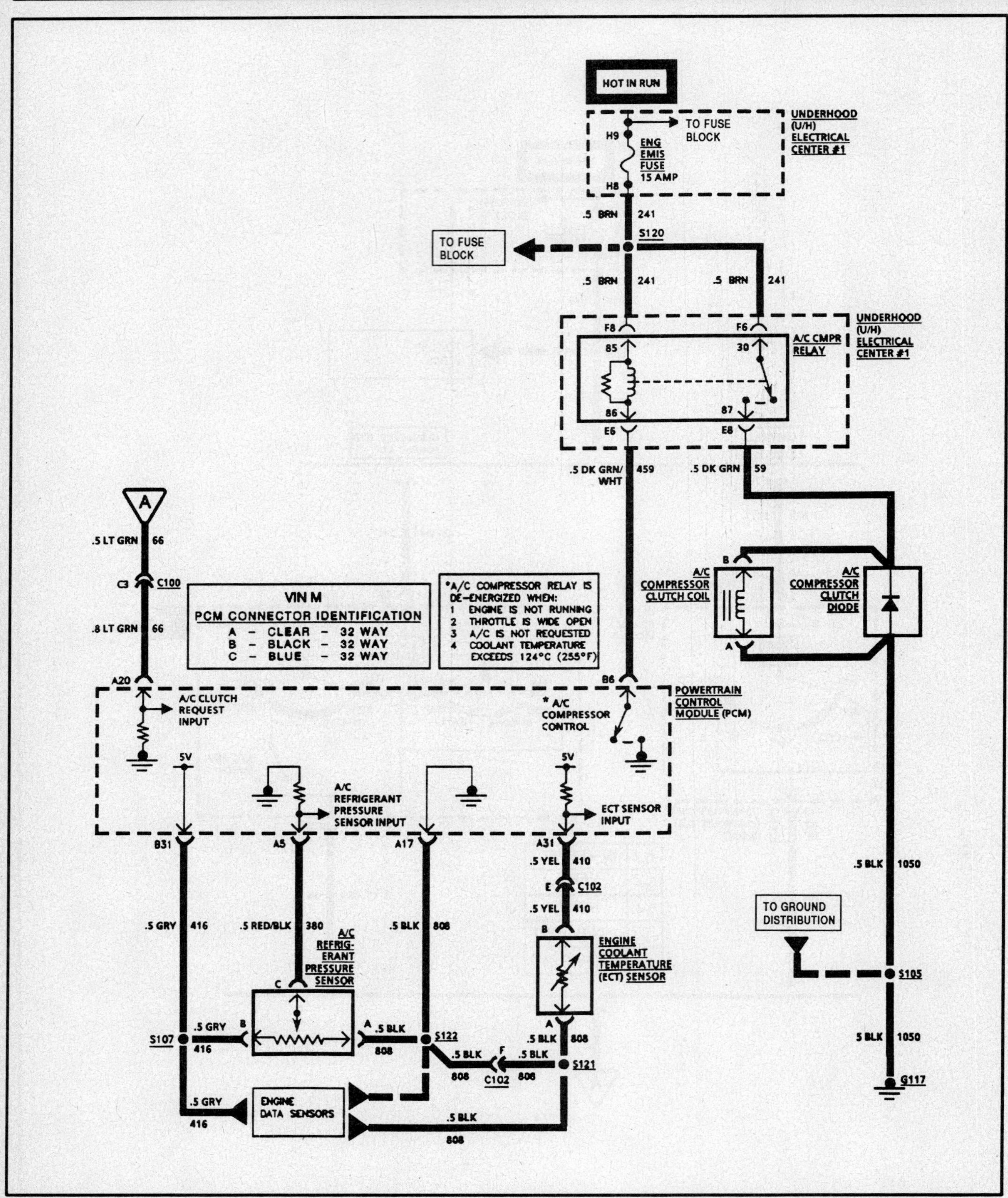

Compressor controls wiring schematic—1995 (VIN M) Cutlass Supreme, Grand Prix, Lumina, Monte Carlo and Regal

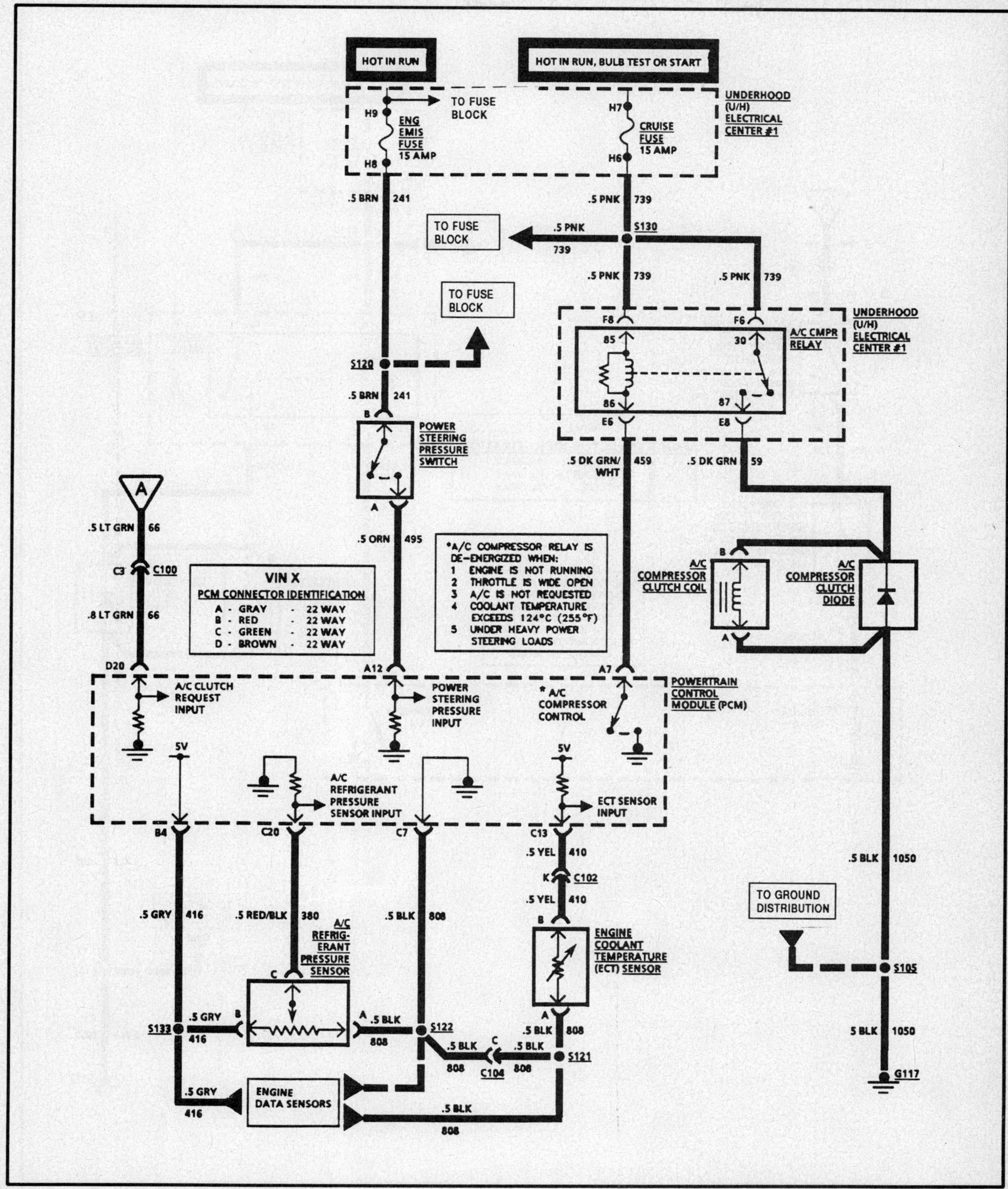

Compressor controls wiring schematic—1995 (VIN X) Cutlass Supreme, Grand Prix, Lumina, Monte Carlo and Regal

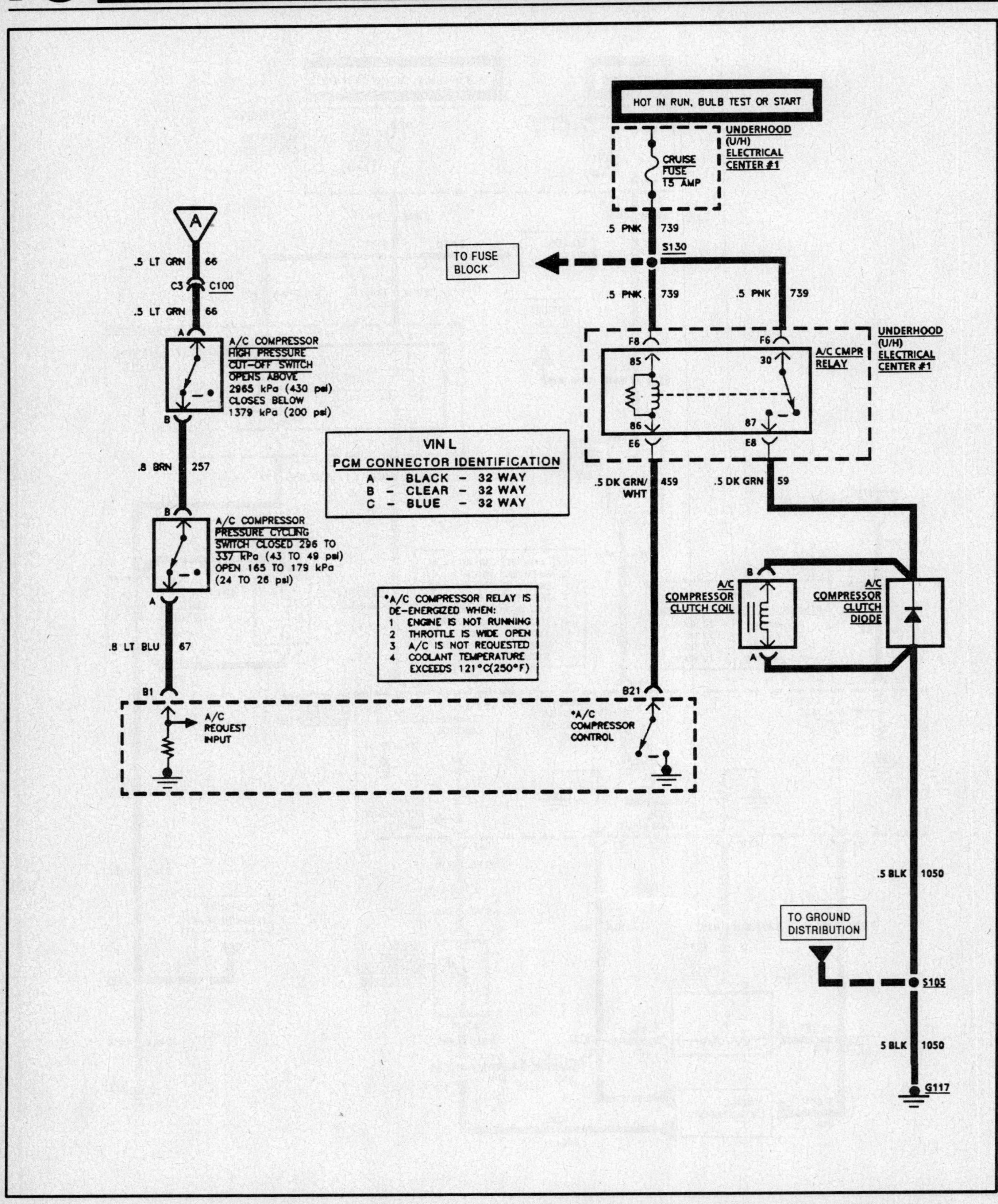

Compressor controls wiring schematic—1995 (VIN L) Cutlass Supreme, Grand Prix, Lumina, Monte Carlo and Regal

9 GENERAL MOTORS CORPORATION 9

CAMARO • CAPRICE • CORVETTE • FIREBIRD • FLEETWOOD • IMPALA SS • ROADMASTER

SPECIFICATIONS

ENGINE IDENTIFICATION

Year	Model	Engine Displacement Liters (cc)	Engine Series (ID/VIN)	Fuel System	No. of Cylinders	Engine Type
1993	Buick Roadmaster	5.7 (5723)	7	TBI	8	OHV
	Cadillac Brougham	5.0 (5020)	7	TBI	8	OHV
	Cadillac Fleetwood Brougham	5.7 (5723)	E	TBI	8	OHV
	Chevrolet Camaro	3.4 (3442)	S	SFI	6	OHV
	Chevrolet Camaro	5.7 (5733)	P	MFI	8	OHV
	Chevrolet Caprice	4.3 (4317)	Z	TBI	8	OHV
	Chevrolet Caprice	5.0 (5020)	E	TBI	8	OHV
	Chevrolet Caprice	5.7 (5723)	7	TBI	8	OHV
	Chevrolet Corvette	5.7 (5723)	P, J ①	TBI	8	OHV
	Pontiac Firebird	3.4 (3413)	S	SFI	6	OHV
	Pontiac Firebird	5.7 (5733)	P	MFI	8	OHV
1994	Buick Roadmaster	5.7 (5733)	P	SFI	8	OHV
	Cadillac Fleetwood	5.7 (5733)	P	SFI	8	OHV
	Chevrolet Camaro	3.4 (3413)	S	SFI	6	OHV
	Chevrolet Camaro	5.7 (5733)	P	MFI	8	OHV
	Chevrolet Caprice	4.3 (4317)	W	SFI	8	OHV
	Chevrolet Caprice	5.7 (5733)	P	SFI	8	OHV
	Chevrolet Corvette	5.7 (5723)	P, J ①	TBI	8	OHV
	Chevrolet Impala SS	4.3 (4723)	W	SFI	8	OHV
	Chevrolet Impala SS	5.7 (5723)	P	SFI	8	OHV
	Pontiac Firebird	3.4 (3413)	S	SFI	6	OHV
	Pontiac Firebird	5.7 (5733)	P	MFI	8	OHV
1995	Buick Roadmaster	5.7 (5723)	P	SFI	8	OHV
	Cadillac Fleetwood	5.7 (5733)	P	SFI	8	OHV
	Chevrolet Camaro	3.8 (3791)	K	SFI	6	OHV
	Chevrolet Camaro	5.7 (5733)	P	SFI	8	OHV
	Chevrolet Caprice	4.3 (4723)	W	SFI	8	OHV
	Chevrolet Caprice	5.7 (5723)	P	SFI	8	OHV
	Chevrolet Corvette	5.7 (5723)	P, J ①	SFI	8	OHV
	Chevrolet Impala SS	4.3 (4723)	W	SFI	8	OHV
	Chevrolet Impala SS	5.7 (5723)	P	SFI	8	OHV
	Pontiac Firebird	3.8 (3791)	K	SFI	6	OHV
	Pontiac Firebird	5.7 (5733)	P	MFI	8	OHV

MFI–Multi-Port Fuel Injection
TBI–Throttle Body Injection
OHV–Overhead Valve
SFI–Sequential Fuel Injection
① VIN J: ZR-1

REFRIGERANT CAPACITIES

Year	Model	Refrigerant (oz.)	Oil (fl. oz.)	Compressor Type
1993	Buick Roadmaster	49.6	6	R–4
	Cadillac Brougham	49.6	6	R–4
	Chevrolet Camaro ②	32.0	8	HD6/HR6–HE
	Chevrolet Caprice	49.6	6	R–4
	Chevrolet Corvette	36.0	8	10PA17 ①, 10PA20
	Pontiac Firebird ②	32.0	8	HD6/HR6–HE
1994	Buick Roadmaster	28.0	8	HD6/HR6–HE
	Cadillac Fleetwood	28.0	8	HD6/HR6–HE
	Chevrolet Camaro	32.0	8	HD6/HR6–HE
	Chevrolet Caprice	28.0	8	HD6/HR6–HE
	Chevrolet Corvette ②	36.0	8	10PA17 ①, 10PA20
	Chevrolet Impala SS	28.0	8	HD6/HR6–HE
	Pontiac Firebird	32.0	8	HD6/HR6–HE
1995	Buick Roadmaster	2.8	8	HD6/HR6–HE
	Cadillac Fleetwood	28.0	8	HD6/HR6–HE
	Chevrolet Camaro	23.0	8	V–5
	Chevrolet Caprice	28.0	8	HD6/HR6–HE
	Chevrolet Corvette ②	36.0	8	10PA17 ①, 10PA20
	Chevrolet Impala SS	28.0	8	HD6/HR6–HE
	Pontiac Firebird	23.0	8	V–5

① 10PA17 used with VIN J engine (ZR–1)
② Use R–134a refrigerant and PAG refrigerant oil. Do not mix, in any amount, with R–12 or R–12 system oil or components.

AIR CONDITIONING BELT TENSION

Year	Model	Engine Liters	Belt Type	Specifications New ①	Specifications Used ①
1993	Buick Roadmaster	5.0	Serpentine	105–127	105–127
	Cadillac Brougham	5.0, 5.7	Serpentine	99–121	99–121
	Chevrolet Camaro	3.4	Serpentine	85–110 ②	85–110 ②
	Chevrolet Camaro	5.7	Serpentine	99–121	99–121
	Chevrolet Caprice	4.3, 5.0, 5.7	Serpentine	105–127	105–127
	Chevrolet Corvette	5.7	Serpentine	③	③
	Pontiac Firebird	3.4	Serpentine	85–110 ②	85–110 ②
	Pontiac Firebird	5.7	Serpentine	99–121	99–121
1994	Buick Roadmaster	5.7	Serpentine	③	③
	Cadillac Fleetwood	5.7	Serpentine	③	③
	Chevrolet Camaro	3.4, 5.7	Serpentine	③	③
	Chevrolet Caprice	4.3, 5.7	Serpentine	③	③
	Chevrolet Corvette	5.7	Serpentine	③	③
	Chevrolet Impala SS	4.3, 5.7	Serpentine	③	③
	Pontiac Firebird	3.4, 5.7	Serpentine	③	③

AIR CONDITIONING BELT TENSION CONT'D

Year	Model	Engine Liters	Belt Type	Specifications	
				New ①	Used ①
1995	Buick Roadmaster	5.7	Serpentine	③	③
	Cadillac Fleetwood	5.7	Serpentine	③	③
	Chevrolet Camaro	3.8, 5.7	Serpentine	③	③
	Chevrolet Caprice	4.3, 5.7	Serpentine	③	③
	Chevrolet Corvette	5.7	Serpentine	③	③
	Chevrolet Impala SS	4.3, 5.7	Serpentine	③	③
	Pontiac Firebird	3.8, 5.7	Serpentine	③	③

① Avg. of 3 readings using gauge J23600–B: run and stop engine 3 times at 30 sec. intervals (normal operating temp.). Spec shown is for guidelines only. If out of spec replace belt or tensioner as needed. No adjustment required.
② Specification given with A/C; if not A/C: 95–140 lbs.
③ No specification given; automatic tensioner, no adjustment required.

SYSTEM DESCRIPTION

General Information

The heater and air conditioning systems are controlled manually or electronically. The systems differ mainly in the way air temperature and the routing of air flow are controlled. The manual system controls air temperature through a cable-actuated lever and air flow through a vacuum switching valve and vacuum actuators. With Electronic Climate Control (ECC) systems, both temperature and air flow are controlled by the Body Control Module (BCM) through the Climate Control Panel (CCP).

The heating system provides heating, ventilation and defrosting for the windshield and side windows. Temperature is controlled by the cable-controlled temperature valve which moves an air door that directs air flow through the heater core for more heat or bypasses the heater core for less heat.

Vacuum actuators control the mode doors which direct air flow to the outlet ducts. The mode selector on the control panel directs engine vacuum to the actuators. The position of the mode doors determines whether air flows from the floor, panel, defrost or panel and defrost ducts (bi-level mode).

The refrigeration system used is designated the Cycling Clutch Orifice Tube (CCOT) except for 1995 the Camaro and Firebird. In this type of system, the compressor cycles ON and OFF by signals from a pressure sensing switch to maintain proper cooling and to prevent evaporator freeze-up. The orifice tube provides a restriction in the high-pressure refrigerant line which meters the flow of refrigerant into the evaporator as a low-pressure liquid.

The 1995 Camaro and Firebird use the Variable Displacement Orifice Tube (VDOT). The air conditioning system has a V5 compressor that can match the automotive air conditioning demand under all conditions without cycling. The basic compressor mechanism is a variable angle wobble–plate with axially oriented cylinders. The control of the compressor displacement is a bellows actuated control valve located in the rear head of the compressor that senses suction pressure. The wobble–plate angle and compressor displacement are controlled by the crankcase–suction pressure differential.

Different types of compressors are used on air conditioning systems. The R-4 compressor, used on 1993 Roadmaster, Caprice and Cadillac Fleetwood, is a fixed displacement refrigerant pump with 4 cylinders arranged radially, extending straight out from the center of the compressor.

The 10PA17 and 10PA20 compressors, used on Corvette, are conventional swash plate compressors with 5 double-ended pistons. The 10PA20 compressor is used on vehicles equipped with the L98 engine and the 10PA17 compressor is used on vehicles equipped with the LT5 engine (ZR1 models).

The HD6/HR6-HE compressor is used on all models except Corvette, 1993 Roadmaster, Fleetwood and Caprice, and 1995 Camaro and Firebird. It is a lightweight, 6-cylinder axial design with 3 double ended pistons. Some differences in mountings may exist based on engine application or equipment. The compressor may have a pressure control switch in the back of the compressor head. These models also use an expansion valve and receiver/drier type system and have a refrigerant pressure sensor in the high side line between the receiver/drier and the expansion valve, and a low pressure cut-off switch in the low side line near the expansion valve.

The 1993 air conditioner systems, except Camaro and Firebird, are charged with R–12 refrigerant. The 1993 Camaro and Firebird and all 1994–95 air conditioning systems are charged with non-CFC R-134a refrigerant and use a special PAG type refrigerant oil. While servicing techniques and handling are similar for both systems, these 2 different refrigerants and their oils are not compatible and must never be mixed in any quantities.

Service Valve Locations

The high-side fitting is normally located in the refrigerant line near the compressor, and the low-side fitting is normally located on the accumulator or in the condenser-to-evaporator refrigerant line. On 1993 Camaro and Firebird, the low side service valve is on the low side line near the compressor and the high side service valve is on the refrigerant line on the outlet side of the condenser.

System Discharging

R-12 refrigerant is a chlorofluorocarbon which, when released into the atmosphere, can contribute to the depletion of the ozone layer in the upper atmosphere. Ozone filters out harmful radiation from the sun. In order to protect the ozone layer, an approved R-12 Recovery/Recycling machine that meets SAE standard J1991 should be employed when discharging the system. Follow the operating instructions provided with the approved equipment exactly to properly discharge the system.

On systems charged with non-CFC R-134a, handling procedures should be much like those for R-12. Never vent this refrigerant to the atmosphere, use proper safety precautions and follow equipment manufacturer's instructions.

System Evacuating

If the air conditioning system has been opened to the atmosphere, it should be air and moisture free before being recharged with refrigerant. Moisture and air mixed with refrigerant will raise the compressor head pressure, resulting in possible damage to the system's components. In addition, air and moisture in the system can lead to internal corrosion of the system components. Moisture will boil at normal room temperature when exposed to a vacuum. To evacuate the R12 system:

1. Leak test the system and repair any leaks found.
2. Connect an approved charging station, Recovery/Recycling machine or manifold gauge set and vacuum pump to the discharge and suction ports. The red hose is normally connected to the discharge (high pressure) line. The blue hose is connected to the suction (low pressure) line. If using a manifold gauge set, the center (usually yellow) hose is connected to the charging station or Recovery/Recycling machine.
3. Open the discharge and suction ports and start the vacuum pump. If the pump is not able to pull at least 26 in. Hg of vacuum there is a leak that must be repaired before evacuation can occur.
4. Once the system has reached at least 26 in. Hg of vacuum, allow the system to evacuate for at least 10 minutes. The longer the system is evacuated, the more moisture will be removed.
5. Close all valves and turn the pump **OFF**. If the system loses more than 2 in. Hg of vacuum after 15 minutes, there is a leak that should be repaired.

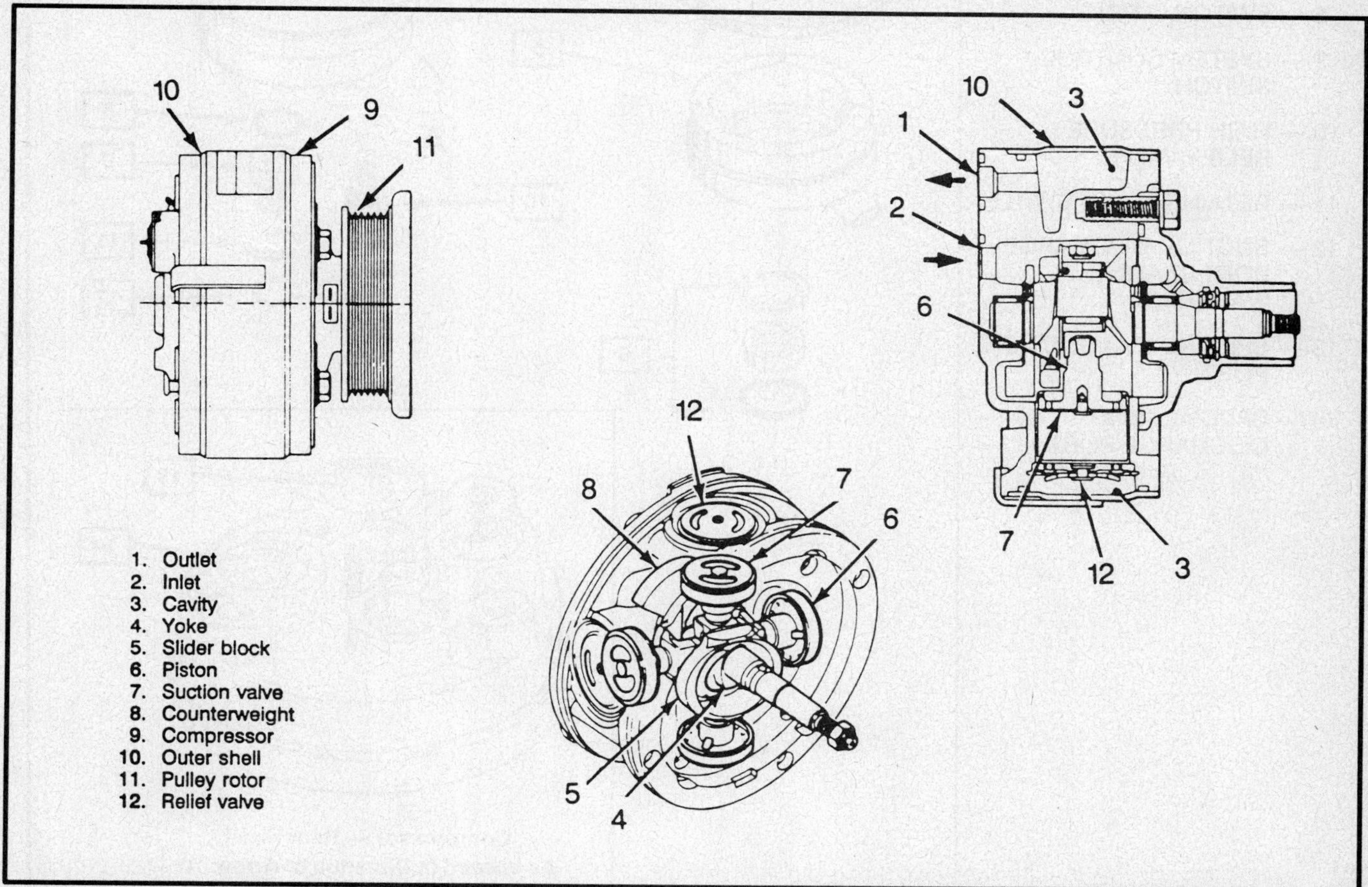

R–4 compressor components

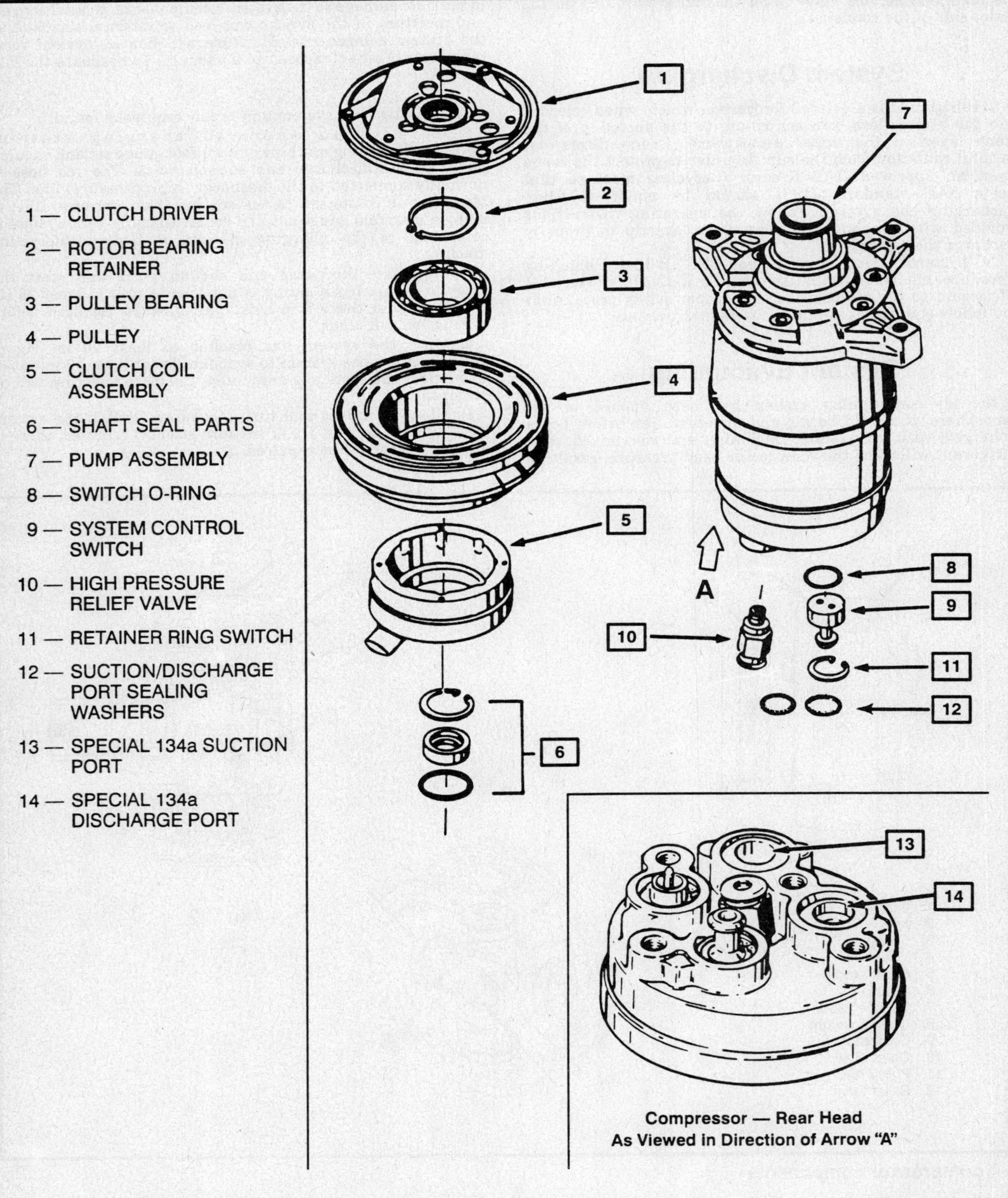
1 — CLUTCH DRIVER
2 — ROTOR BEARING RETAINER
3 — PULLEY BEARING
4 — PULLEY
5 — CLUTCH COIL ASSEMBLY
6 — SHAFT SEAL PARTS
7 — PUMP ASSEMBLY
8 — SWITCH O-RING
9 — SYSTEM CONTROL SWITCH
10 — HIGH PRESSURE RELIEF VALVE
11 — RETAINER RING SWITCH
12 — SUCTION/DISCHARGE PORT SEALING WASHERS
13 — SPECIAL 134a SUCTION PORT
14 — SPECIAL 134a DISCHARGE PORT
1
2
3
4
5
6
7
8
9
10
11
12
A
13
14
Compressor — Rear Head
As Viewed in Direction of Arrow "A"

HD6/HR6–HE compressor components

To evacuate the R–134A system:

1. With the high side and low side hoses connected to the vehicle air conditioning system, open both the high-side (red) and the low-side (blue) valves on the unit control panel.
2. Open both the red **GAS** (vapor) and the blue **LIQUID** valves on the tank.
3. Press **VACUUM** to start the vacuum pump. The display counts down vacuum time to zero to indicate operation time remaining. the display reads **RECYCLE** five seconds after the vacuum pump starts and continues while the process takes place.
4. At approximately the 12-minute mark on the display (pump has run for three minutes), press **HOLD/CONT** key to stop vacuum pump (Figure13).
   a. A "0" vacuum reading indicates a major system leak. Repair leak and restart evacuation procedure.
   b. If a vacuum reading of 91-101 kPa (27-30 inches of Hg) is indicated, close the low-side and high-side valves. Observe the vacuum level for a few minutes as a leak check of the air conditioning system. If vacuum is not maintained, find and repair the air conditioning system leak before continuing.
   c. If a vacuum reading of 91-101 kPa (27-30 inches of Hg) is maintained, open the high-side and low-side valves and press the **HOLD/CONT** key to restart the vacuum pump.
5. When the vacuum sequence has run the programmed time, the display shows **CPL** to indicate that evacuation is complete.

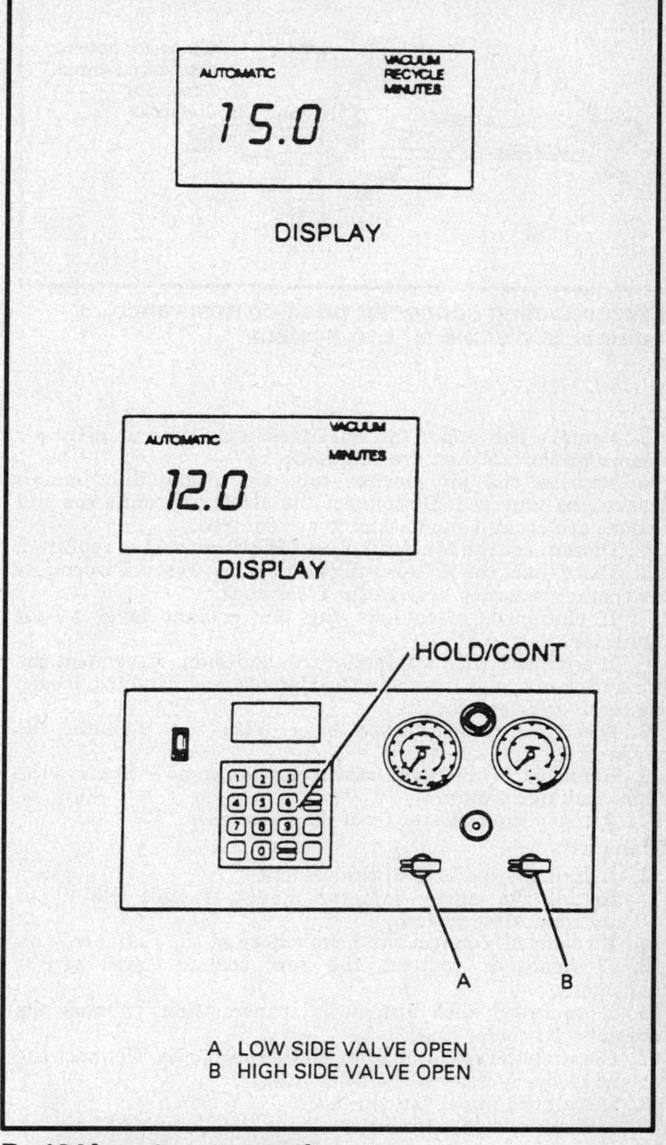

R–134A system evacuation

System Charging

1. Connect an approved charging station, Recovery/Recycling machine or manifold gauge set to the discharge and suction ports. The red hose is normally connected to the discharge (high pressure) line and the blue hose is connected to the suction (low pressure) line. If using a manifold gauge set, the center (usually yellow) hose is connected to the charging station or Recovery/Recycling machine.
2. Follow the instructions provided with the equipment and charge the system with the specified amount of refrigerant.
3. Perform a leak test.

SYSTEM COMPONENTS

Radiator

REMOVAL AND INSTALLATION

CAUTION

Some vehicles are equipped with the Supplemental Inflatable Restraint or air bag system. The air bag system must be disabled before performing service on or around the air bag, instrument panel components, wiring and sensors. Failure to follow safety and disabling procedures could result in accidental air bag deployment, possible personal injury and unnecessary air bag system repairs.

Except Corvette

1. Disconnect battery negative cable. Drain the engine coolant into a clean container for reuse.
2. If equipped, disable the Supplemental Inflatable Restraint (SIR) system by performing the following:
   a. Turn steering to place wheels straight ahead and turn ignition switch to **LOCK**.
   b. Remove the SIR fuse from the fuse panel.
   c. Remove the left side sound insulator.
   d. Remove the connector position assurance retainer and the yellow 2-way SIR harness connector at the base of the steering column.

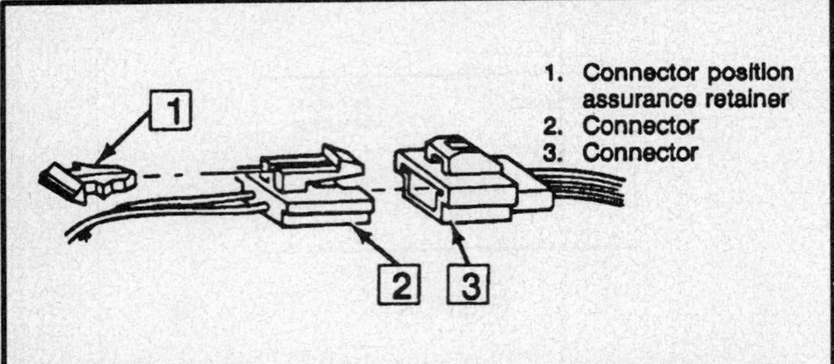

Disconnecting connector position assurance retainer to disable air bag system

3. Remove the upper fan shroud at this time or after air cleaner and/or air duct are removed.
4. Remove the air cleaner top, air intake duct and/or bracket, as required. Disconnect the electrical connector and remove the coolant fan assembly as required.
5. Disconnect the Mass Air Flow (MAF) sensor, as required.
6. Disconnect the radiator inlet and outlet hoses. Disconnect the coolant recovery hose at the filler neck.
7. If equipped, disconnect the low coolant level sensor connector.
8. If equipped with automatic transmission, disconnect the transmission cooler lines. On the Camaro and Firebird, loosen the receiver/drier bracket.
9. Disconnect the heater hose from the radiator, as required.
10. Remove the upper radiator mounting screws. Remove the upper radiator mount.
11. Remove the radiator from the vehicle.

To install:

12. Install the radiator in the vehicle.
13. Install the upper radiator mount. Install the upper radiator mounting screws.
14. If removed, connect the heater hose at the radiator.
15. If removed, connect the low coolant level sensor connector.
16. If equipped with automatic transmission, connect the transmission cooler lines.
17. Connect the radiator inlet and outlet hoses. Connect the coolant recovery hose at the filler neck.
18. Install the upper fan shroud.
19. If disconnected, connect the Mass Air Flow (MAF) sensor.
20. If removed, install the coolant fan assembly.
21. On Cadillac, position the support rods and tighten the anchor bolts, then install the 2 engine compartment support rods to the radiator core support.
22. On Camaro and Firebird, tighten the receiver dehydrator bracket
23. If removed, install the air intake duct.
24. If removed, install the air cleaner top.
25. If equipped, enable the Supplemental Inflatable Restraint (SIR) system by performing the following:
    - Connect the yellow 2-way SIR connector and insert the connector position assurance retainer at the base of the steering column.
    - Install the left side sound insulator.
    - Install the SIR fuse in the fuse panel.
    - Turn ignition to **RUN** and verify that the inflatable restraint indicator flashes 7-9 times and then turns OFF.
26. Connect the negative battery cable.
27. Fill cooling system and check for leaks. Start the engine and allow to come to normal operating temperature. Allow the engine to warm up sufficiently to confirm cooling fan operation. Recheck for leaks. Top-up coolant.

Corvette

1. Disconnect the negative battery cable. Drain the engine coolant into a clean container for reuse.
2. If equipped, disable the Supplemental Inflatable Restraint (SIR) system by performing the following:
    - Remove the SIR fuse from the fuse panel.
    - Remove the left side sound insulator.
    - Remove the Connector Positive Assurance (CPA) from the yellow 2-way SIR harness connector at the base of the steering column and separate the connector.
3. Remove the radiator upper support.
4. Disconnect the upper and lower radiator hoses.
5. If equipped with automatic transmission, disconnect the transmission cooler lines from the radiator.
6. Remove the radiator from the vehicle.

To install:

7. Install the radiator in the vehicle.
8. Install the transmission cooler lines to the radiator, if equipped.
9. Connect the upper and lower radiator hoses.
10. Install the upper radiator support.
11. If equipped, enable the Supplemental Inflatable Restraint (SIR) system by performing the following:
    - Connect the yellow 2-way SIR connector and insert the Connect Positive Assurance (CPA) at the base of the steering column.
    - Install the left side sound insulator.
    - Install the SIR fuse in the fuse panel.
12. Connect the negative battery cable.
13. Fill cooling system and check for leaks. Start the engine and allow to come to normal operating temperature. Allow the engine to warm up sufficiently to confirm cooling fan operation. Recheck for leaks. Top-up coolant.

COOLING SYSTEM BLEEDING

1. Fill the radiator to below the filler neck and the reservoir to **COLD FILL** mark with the proper ratio of anti-freeze (coolant) and water.
2. Set the heater controls to heat and the temperature controls to the warmest setting.
3. With the radiator cap removed, run the engine until normal operating temperature is reached.
4. With the engine at idle, add coolant to the radiator until the level reaches the bottom of the filler neck. Avoid spilling anti-freeze on hot parts of the engine.
5. Install the radiator cap, turning it until the arrows align with the overflow tube.

Cooling Fan

TESTING

1. Check fuse or circuit breaker for power to cooling fan motor.
2. Remove connector(s) at cooling fan motor(s). Connect jumper wire and apply battery voltage to the positive terminal of the cooling fan motor.
3. Using an ohmmeter, check for continuity in cooling fan motor.

NOTE: Remove the cooling fan connector at the fan motor before performing continuity checks. Perform continuity check of the motor windings only. The cooling fan control circuit is connected electrically to the ECM through the cooling fan relay. Ohmmeter battery voltage must not be applied to the ECM.

4. Ensure proper continuity of cooling fan motor ground circuit at chassis ground connector.

REMOVAL AND INSTALLATION

CAUTION

Some vehicles are equipped with the Supplemental Inflatable Restraint or air bag system. The air bag system must be disabled before performing service on or around the air bag, instrument panel components, wiring and sensors. Failure to follow safety and disabling procedures could result in accidental air bag deployment, possible personal injury and unnecessary air bag system repairs.

Camaro and Firebird

1. Disconnect the negative battery cable. If equipped, remove the air cleaner top.
2. If equipped, disable the Supplemental Inflatable Restraint (SIR) system by performing the following:
   - Remove the SIR fuse from the fuse panel.
   - Remove the left side sound insulator.
   - Remove the Connector Positive Assurance (CPA) from the yellow 2-way SIR harness connector at the base of the steering column and separate the connector.
3. Disconnect the wiring harness.
4. Remove the cooling fan-to-radiator support bolts.
5. Remove the cooling fan bracket.
6. Remove the cooling fan assembly.

To install:

7. Install the cooling fan assembly.
8. Install the cooling fan bracket.
9. Install the cooling fan-to-radiator support bolts.
10. Connect the wiring harness.
11. If equipped, install the air cleaner top.
12. If equipped, enable the Supplemental Inflatable Restraint (SIR) system by performing the following:
    - Connect the yellow 2-way SIR connector and insert the Connect Positive Assurance (CPA) at the base of the steering column.
    - Install the left side sound insulator.
    - Install the SIR fuse in the fuse panel.
13. Connect the negative battery cable.

Corvette

PRIMARY (LEFT) COOLING FAN

Except ZR-1

1. Disconnect the negative battery cable. Remove the air intake duct.
2. If equipped, disable the Supplemental Inflatable Restraint (SIR) system by performing the following:
   - Remove the SIR fuse from the fuse panel.
   - Remove the left side sound insulator.
   - Remove the Connector Positive Assurance (CPA) from the yellow 2-way SIR harness connector at the base of the steering column and separate the connector.
3. Disconnect the electrical connector from the fan motor.
4. Remove the screws attaching the fan motor to the fan support.
5. Remove the bolts attaching the fan assembly to the fan shroud.
6. Remove the fan assembly from the vehicle.

To install:

7. Install the fan assembly in the vehicle.
8. Install the bolts attaching the fan assembly to the fan shroud.
9. Install the screws attaching the fan motor to the fan support.
10. Connect the electrical connector from the fan motor.
11. If equipped, enable the Supplemental Inflatable Restraint (SIR) system by performing the following:
    - Connect the yellow 2-way SIR connector and insert the Connect Positive Assurance (CPA) at the base of the steering column.
    - Install the left side sound insulator.
    - Install the SIR fuse in the fuse panel.
12. Connect the negative battery cable.
13. Install the air intake duct.

ZR-1

1. Disconnect the negative battery cable. Remove the surge tank cap. Drain the engine coolant into a clean container for reuse.
2. If equipped, disable the Supplemental Inflatable Restraint (SIR) system by performing the following:
   - Remove the SIR fuse from the fuse panel.
   - Remove the left side sound insulator.
   - Remove the Connector Positive Assurance (CPA) from the yellow 2-way SIR harness connector at the base of the steering column and separate the connector.
3. Remove the air intake duct.
4. Disconnect the coolant hoses from the radiator.
5. Remove the hose and inlet pipe assembly from the vehicle.
6. Disconnect the cooling fan electrical connector.
7. Remove the screws attaching the fan motor to the motor support.
8. Remove the bolt attaching the air conditioner discharge line clamp to the crossmember.
9. Remove the bolts attaching the fan assembly to the fan shroud.
10. Remove the end cap from the power steering pump pulley.
11. Remove the fan assembly from the vehicle.

To install:

12. Install the fan assembly in the vehicle.
13. Install the end cap to the power steering pump pulley.
14. Install the bolts attaching the fan assembly to the fan shroud.
15. Install the bolt attaching the air conditioner discharge line clamp to the crossmember.
16. Install the screws attaching the fan motor to the motor support.
17. Connect the cooling fan electrical connector.
18. Install the hose and inlet pipe assembly to the vehicle.
19. Connect the coolant hoses to the radiator.
20. Install the air intake duct.
21. If equipped, enable the Supplemental Inflatable Restraint (SIR) system by performing the following:
    - Connect the yellow 2-way SIR connector and insert the Connect Positive Assurance (CPA) at the base of the steering column.
    - Install the left side sound insulator.
    - Install the SIR fuse in the fuse panel.
22. Connect the negative battery cable.
23. Fill cooling system and check for leaks. Start the engine and allow to come to normal operating temperature. Allow the engine to warm up sufficiently to confirm cooling fan operation. Recheck for leaks. Top-up coolant.

AUXILIARY (RIGHT) COOLING FAN

Except ZR-1

1. Disconnect the negative battery cable. Remove the upper right bolt attaching the fan assembly to the shroud.
2. If equipped, disable the Supplemental Inflatable Restraint (SIR) system by performing the following:
   - Remove the SIR fuse from the fuse panel.
   - Remove the left side sound insulator.

• Remove the Connector Positive Assurance (CPA) from the yellow 2-way SIR harness connector at the base of the steering column and separate the connector.
3. Raise and safely support the vehicle.
4. Disconnect the electrical connector from the fan motor.
5. Remove the bolts attaching the fan assembly to the fan shroud.
6. Remove the fan assembly from the vehicle.

To install:

7. Install the fan assembly in the vehicle.
8. Install the bolts attaching the fan assembly to the fan shroud.
9. Connect the electrical connector to the fan motor.
10. Lower the vehicle.
11. Install the upper right bolt attaching the fan assembly to the shroud.
12. If equipped, enable the Supplemental Inflatable Restraint (SIR) system by performing the following:
• Connect the yellow 2-way SIR connector and insert the Connect Positive Assurance (CPA) at the base of the steering column.
• Install the left side sound insulator.
• Install the SIR fuse in the fuse panel.
13. Connect the negative battery cable.

ZR-1

1. Disconnect the negative battery cable. Remove the upper right attaching fan assembly to the shroud.
2. If equipped, disable the Supplemental Inflatable Restraint (SIR) system by performing the following:
• Remove the SIR fuse from the fuse panel.
• Remove the left side sound insulator.
• Remove the Connector Positive Assurance (CPA) from the yellow 2-way SIR harness connector at the base of the steering column and separate the connector.
3. Raise and safely support the vehicle.
4. Disconnect the electrical connector from the fan motor.
5. Remove the bolts attaching the fan assembly to the fan shroud.
6. Remove the fan assembly.

To install:

7. Install the fan assembly.
8. Install the bolts attaching the fan assembly to the fan shroud.
9. Connect the electrical connector to a the fan motor.
10. Lower the vehicle.
11. Install the upper right attaching fan assembly to the shroud.
12. If equipped, enable the Supplemental Inflatable Restraint (SIR) system by performing the following:
• Connect the yellow 2-way SIR connector and insert the Connect Positive Assurance (CPA) at the base of the steering column.
• Install the left side sound insulator.
• Install the SIR fuse in the fuse panel.
13. Connect the negative battery cable.

CAPRICE, ROADMASTER, FLEETWOOD AND 1994–95 IMPALA SS

Without heavy-duty cooling

1. Disconnect the negative battery cable.
2. If equipped, disable the Supplement Inflatable Restraint (SIR) system by performing the following:
• Remove the SIR fuse from the fuse panel.
• Remove the left side sound insulator.
• Remove the Connector Positive Assurance (CPA) from the yellow 2-way SIR harness connector at the base of the steering column and separate the connector.
3. Disconnect the electrical connectors from the fan motor.
4. Remove the bolts and screws holding the fan assembly.
5. Remove the fan assembly from the vehicle.

To install:

6. Installation is the reverse of the removal procedure.
7. If equipped, enable the Supplemental Inflatable Restraint (SIR) system by performing the following:
• Connect the yellow 2-way SIR connector and insert the Connect Positive Assurance (CPA) at the base of the steering column.
• Install the left side sound insulator.
• Install the SIR fuse in the fuse panel.
8. Connect the negative battery cable.

With heavy-duty cooling system

1. Disconnect the negative battery cable.
2. If equipped, disable the Supplemental Inflatable Restraint (SIR) system by performing the following:
• Remove the SIR fuse from the fuse panel.
• Remove the left side sound insulator.
• Remove the Connector Positive Assurance (CPA) from the yellow 2-way SIR harness connector at the base of the steering column and separate the connector.
3. Remove the air intake duct and resonator.
4. Disconnect the electrical connector from the fan motor.
5. Remove the bolts and screws holding the upper shroud.
6. Remove the upper shroud.
7. Remove the cooling fan-to-radiator support bolts.
8. Remove the cooling fan assembly.

To install:

9. Installation is the reverse of the removal procedure.
10. If equipped, enable the Supplemental Inflatable Restraint (SIR) system by performing the following:
• Connect the yellow 2-way SIR connector and insert the Connect Positive Assurance (CPA) at the base of the steering column.
• Install the left side sound insulator.
• Install the SIR fuse in the fuse panel.
11. Connect the negative battery cable.

Condenser

REMOVAL AND INSTALLATION

CAUTION

Some vehicles are equipped with the Supplemental Inflatable Restraint or air bag system. The air bag system must be disabled before performing service on or around the air bag, instrument panel components, wiring and sensors. Failure to follow safety and disabling procedures could result in accidental air bag deployment, possible personal injury and unnecessary air bag system repairs.

1993 Cadillac Fleetwood, Caprice, and Roadmaster

1. Disconnect the negative battery cable.
2. Properly discharge the air conditioning system. Drain the engine coolant into a clean container for reuse.
3. If equipped, disable the Supplemental Inflatable Restraint (SIR) system by performing the following:
• Remove the SIR fuse from the fuse panel.
• Remove the left side sound insulator.
• Remove the Connector Positive Assurance (CPA) from the yellow 2-way SIR harness connector at the base of the steering column and separate the connector.
4. Remove the radiator, as described in this article.
5. Disconnect the refrigerant lines at the condenser. Discard the O-rings.

NOTE: Use a backup wrench on the condenser fittings when removing the high-pressure and liquid lines. Cap the refrigerant lines when opening the system to prevent the entry of dirt and moisture and the loss of refrigerant lubricant.

6. Remove the top condenser insulator retainer screws and the insulators.
7. Remove the condenser from the vehicle by gently out of the lower condenser insulators.

To install:

NOTE: If replacing the condenser or if the original condenser was flushed during service, add 1 fluid oz. (30 ml) of refrigerant lubricant to the system.

8. Install the condenser in the vehicle. Ensure that the condenser is seated properly in the lower insulators.
9. Install the upper condenser insulators and retainers.
10. Replace the condenser fitting O-rings. Lubricate the O-rings with refrigerant oil.
11. Install the condenser refrigerant lines.

NOTE: Use a backup wrench on the condenser fittings when tightening lines.

12. Install the radiator.
13. Evacuate, recharge and leak test the air conditioning system.
14. If equipped, enable the Supplemental Inflatable Restraint (SIR) system by performing the following:
   - Connect the yellow 2-way SIR connector and insert the Connect Positive Assurance (CPA) at the base of the steering column.
   - Install the left side sound insulator.
   - Install the SIR fuse in the fuse panel.
15. Connect the negative battery cable.
16. Fill cooling system and check for leaks. Start the engine and allow to come to normal operating temperature. Allow the engine to warm up sufficiently to confirm cooling fan operation. Recheck for leaks. Top-up coolant.

1994-95 Cadillac Fleetwood, Caprice, Impala SS and Roadmaster

1. Disconnect the negative battery cable.
2. Properly discharge the air conditioning system. Drain the engine coolant into a clean container for reuse.
3. If equipped, disable the Supplemental Inflatable Restraint (SIR) system by performing the following:
   - Remove the SIR fuse from the fuse panel.
   - Remove the left side sound insulator.
   - Remove the Connector Positive Assurance (CPA) from the yellow 2-way SIR harness connector at the base of the steering column and separate the connector.
4. Remove the air intake duct and resonators.
5. Remove upper fan shroud and mounting panel as required.
6. Remove the electric engine cooling fans.
7. Disconnect the refrigerant lines at the condenser. Discard the O-rings.

NOTE: Use a backup wrench on the condenser fittings when removing the high-pressure and liquid lines. Cap the refrigerant lines when opening the system to prevent the entry of dirt and moisture and the loss of refrigerant lubricant.

8. Remove the condenser from the vehicle by tilting top of radiator rearward.
9. Remove the upper and lower insulators.
10. Remove the expansion tube from the lower condenser assembly fitting.

To install:

11. Installation is the reverse of the removal procedure.
12. If equipped, enable the Supplemental Inflatable Restraint (SIR) system by performing the following:
   - Connect the yellow 2-way SIR connector and insert the Connector Positive Assurance (CPS) at the base of the steering column.
   - Install the left side sound insulator.
   - Install the SIR fuse in the fuse panel.
13. Connect the negative battery cable.

Camaro and Firebird

1. Disconnect the negative battery cable. Properly discharge the air conditioning system.
2. If equipped, disable the Supplemental Inflatable Restraint (SIR) system by performing the following:
   - Remove the SIR fuse from the fuse panel.
   - Remove the left side sound insulator.
   - Remove the Connector Positive Assurance (CPA) from the yellow 2-way SIR harness connector at the base of the steering column and separate the connector.
3. Remove the air intake duct.
4. Remove the upper radiator shroud.
5. Raise and support the vehicle, drain the cooling system.
6. Remove the electrical cooling fan as required.
7. Remove the thermostat by-pass hose at the water pump as required.
8. Detach the transmission oil cooler pipes at the radiator. Plug the openings.
9. Remove the coolant level sensor connector from the radiator.
10. Remove and plug the air conditioning hose from the condenser.
11. Lower the vehicle and remove the lower radiator hose from the water pump, then remove the upper radiator hose and reservoir hose.
12. Detach and plug the condenser-to-receiver/drier hose.
13. Remove the condenser and radiator as an assembly.
14. To install, reverse the removal procedure. When connecting the high side hose to the condenser, clean the fitting with 525 viscosity refrigerant oil. Use new O-rings.

NOTE: Do not let the oil get into the A/C system while cleaning the fittings.

15. If a new condenser is installed, add 1.0 oz. of new PAG type refrigerant oil to the condenser.
16. Evacuate, recharge and leak test.

Corvette

EXCEPT ZR-1

1. Disconnect the negative battery cable. Properly discharge the air conditioning system and drain the cooling system.
2. If equipped, disable the Supplemental Inflatable Restraint (SIR) system by performing the following:
   - Remove the SIR fuse from the fuse panel.
   - Remove the left side sound insulator.
   - Remove the Connector Positive Assurance (CPA) from the yellow 2-way SIR harness connector at the base of the steering column and separate the connector.
3. Remove the air cleaner, then the radiator upper support for access to fans, shroud and condenser.
4. Remove the fan shroud as follows:
   - Remove both cooling fans.
   - Remove the bolts holding the accumulator bracket to the radiator support.
   - Remove the upper and lower shroud to support screws.

- Remove the bolts retaining impact bar skid plate extension to the drivetrain and front suspension frame. Loosen the extension and place it out of the way.
- Remove the fan shroud.

5. Disconnect the accumulator and compressor refrigerant lines from the condenser. Discard the O-rings.

NOTE: Use a backup wrench on the condenser fittings when removing the high-pressure and liquid lines. Cap the refrigerant lines when opening the system to prevent the entry of dirt and moisture and the loss of refrigerant lubricant.

6. Remove the condenser.

To install:

7. Install the condenser.
8. Replace the condenser fitting O-rings. Lubricate the O-rings with refrigerant oil.
9. Connect the refrigerant lines to the condenser.

NOTE: Use a backup wrench on the condenser fittings when tightening lines.

10. Install the fan shroud.
11. Install the cooling fans.
12. Install the upper radiator support and the air cleaner.
13. Evacuate, recharge and leak test the air conditioning system.
14. If equipped, enable the Supplemental Inflatable Restraint (SIR) system by performing the following:
    - Connect the yellow 2-way SIR connector and insert the
    - Connect Positive Assurance (CPA) at the base of the steering column.
    - Install the left side sound insulator.
    - Install the SIR fuse in the fuse panel.
15. Connect the negative battery cable.

ZR-1

1. Disconnect the negative battery cable. Properly discharge the air conditioning system.
2. If equipped, disable the Supplemental Inflatable Restraint (SIR) system by performing the following:
    - Remove the SIR fuse from the fuse panel.
    - Remove the left side sound insulator.
    - Remove the Connector Positive Assurance (CPA) from the yellow 2-way SIR harness connector at the base of the steering column and separate the connector.
3. Remove the upper radiator support as follows:
    - Drain the cooling system.
    - Remove the air cleaner assembly.
    - Remove the upper air deflector.
    - Detach the cooling fan wiring.
    - Remove the bolts holding the accumulator bracket to the radiator.
    - Remove the upper fan shroud screws, the rubber access plug on top of the radiator, and the radiator bleed hose.
    - Unbolt the upper support from the front side member.
    - Remove the bolt retaining the oil cooler lines to the oil cooler and the seal retainers and seal from the oil cooler and A/C line.
    - Remove the air pump, rear bracket bolt and loosen the front bracket bolt. Remove the air pump intake duct.
    - Remove the upper to lower radiator support screws.
    - Remove the upper radiator support.
4. Disconnect the accumulator and compressor refrigerant lines from the condenser. Discard the O-rings.

NOTE: Use a backup wrench on the condenser fittings when removing the high-pressure and liquid lines. Cap the refrigerant lines when opening the system to prevent the entry of dirt and moisture and the loss of refrigerant lubricant.

5. Remove the condenser and oil cooler assembly from the vehicle.
6. Remove the screws attaching the oil cooler to the condenser.
7. Remove the screws attaching the condenser bracket to the condenser.

To install:

8. Install the screws attaching the condenser bracket to the condenser.
9. Install the screws attaching the oil cooler to the condenser.
10. Install the condenser and oil cooler assembly in the vehicle.
11. Replace the condenser fitting O-rings. Lubricate the O-rings with refrigerant oil.
12. Connect the refrigerant lines to the condenser.

NOTE: Use a backup wrench on the condenser fittings when tightening lines.

13. Install the upper radiator support.
14. Refill the cooling system. Evacuate, recharge and leak test the air conditioning system.
15. If equipped, enable the Supplemental Inflatable Restraint (SIR) system by performing the following:
    - Connect the yellow 2-way SIR connector and insert the Connector Positive Assurance (CPA) at the base of the steering column.
    - Install the left side sound insulator.
    - Install the SIR fuse in the fuse panel.
16. Connect the negative battery cable.

Compressor

REMOVAL AND INSTALLATION

Caprice, Roadmaster and Fleetwood and 1994–95 Impala SS

1. Disconnect the negative battery cable.
2. Properly discharge the air conditioning system.
3. Remove the radiator fan upper shroud and radiator outlet hose and pipe as required.
4. Raise and safely support vehicle as required.
5. Remove the serpentine drive belt and tensioner as required.
6. Disconnect the compressor electrical connectors.
7. Remove the screw and lock washer from the refrigerant line connector block at the rear of the compressor.
8. Disconnect the refrigerant line connector block and remove the O-rings. Plug all openings to minimize contamination.

NOTE: To provide more effective sealing of the refrigerant line connections at the rear of the compressor, new seal washers, when properly installed have an intentional gap between the facing surfaces of the compressor rear head and the connector block.

9. Remove the compressor brace nuts from the braces at the rear of the compressor as required.
10. Remove the compressor mounting bolts.
11. Remove the compressor.
12. Drain and measure the refrigerant oil from the compressor. Discard the old oil.

To install:

13. If the compressor is to be replaced, drain and measure the oil from the new compressor and discard. Add new refrigerant oil equivalent to the amount that was drained from the old compressor upon removal.

14. Position the compressor in the vehicle.
15. Install the compressor mounting bolts.
16. Install the compressor braces and attaching nuts to the rear of the compressor.
17. Replace the compressor fitting O-rings with the same type as were originally installed. Lubricate the O-rings with refrigerant oil.
18. Install the radiator fan upper shroud and radiator outlet hose and pipe if removed.
19. Lower the vehicle, if raised.
20. Install serpentine drive belt and tensioner if removed.
21. Connect the compressor electrical connectors.
22. Evacuate, recharge and leak test the air conditioning
23. Connect the negative battery cable.

Camaro and Firebird

1. Disconnect the negative battery cable. Properly discharge the air conditioning system.
2. Raise and properly support the vehicle.
3. Remove the serpentine belt. On 5.7L LT1 engine only, remove the drive belt tensioner.
4. Remove the hose assembly from the compressor. Immediately cap the openings.
5. Detach the lower transmission oil cooler pipe at the radiator.
6. Detach the electrical connector from the compressor.
7. Remove the compressor bracket-to-engine bolts, then remove the 3 bolts on the compressor flange.
8. Remove the compressor.
9. Drain and measure the oil from the compressor.
10. If installing a new compressor, and the amount of oil drained from the old compressor was less than 1.0 oz., add 2.0 oz. of new PAG type oil to the compressor. If more than 1.0 oz. was drained, add the same amount to the new compressor.
11. Installation is the reverse of the removal procedure.
12. Properly recharge and leak test the system.

Corvette

Except ZR-1

1. Disconnect the negative battery cable.
2. Properly discharge the air conditioning system.
3. Remove the serpentine belt.
4. Disconnect the compressor electrical connector.
5. Disconnect the refrigerant line coupler from the compressor. Discard the O-ring. Cap all openings immediately to minimize contamination.
6. Remove the compressor mounting bolts.
7. Remove the compressor from the vehicle.

To install:

8. If the compressor is to be replaced, drain and measure the oil from the old compressor. Drain and discard the oil from the new compressor. Add new refrigerant oil equivalent to the amount that was drained from the old compressor.
9. Install the fuel feed shield and attaching screws.
10. Position the compressor in the vehicle.
11. Install the compressor mounting bolts.
12. Replace the condenser fitting O-rings. Lubricate the O-rings with refrigerant oil.
13. Connect the refrigerant line coupler at the rear of the compressor.
14. Connect the compressor electrical connectors.
15. Install the serpentine belt.
16. Evacuate, recharge and leak test the air conditioning system.

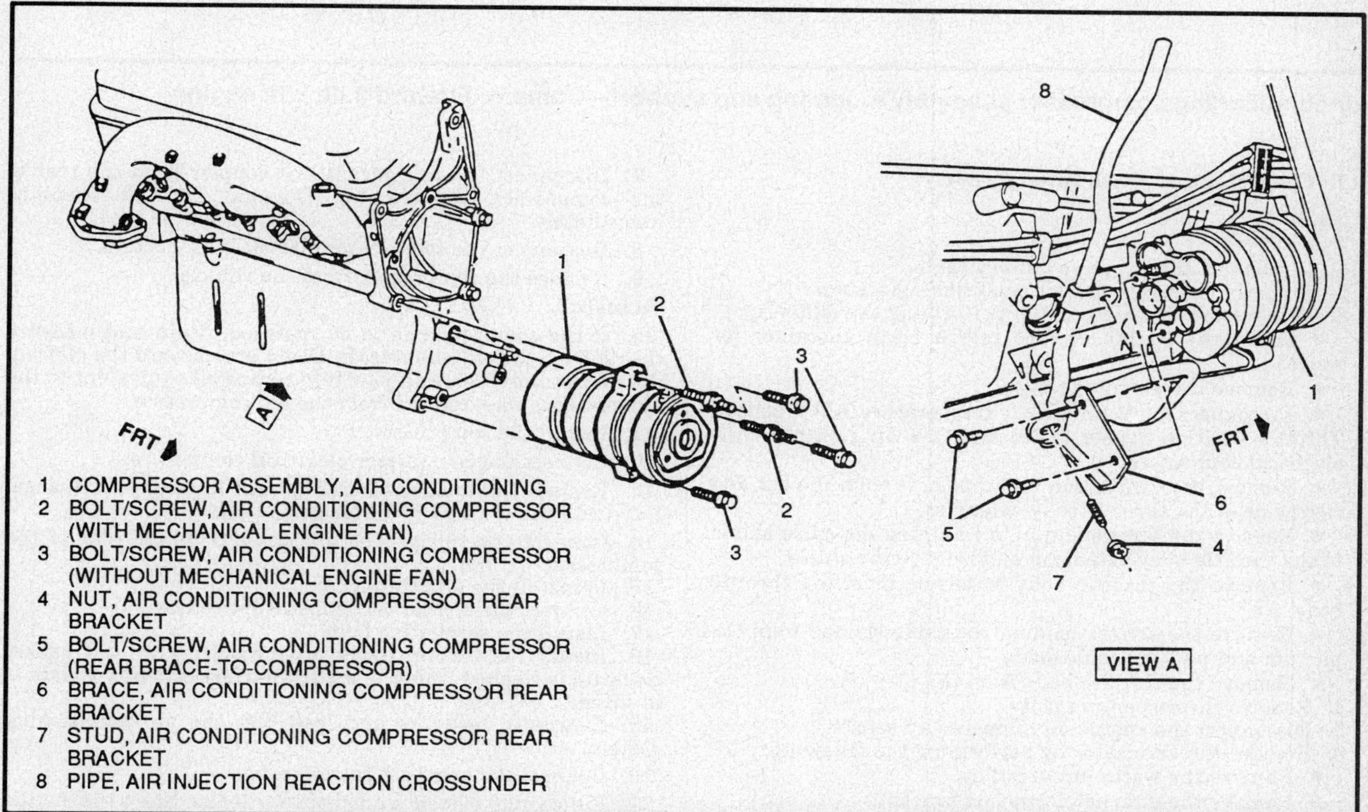

Air conditioning compressor assembly mounting—Fleetwood, Roadmaster, Caprice, 1994–95 Impala SS

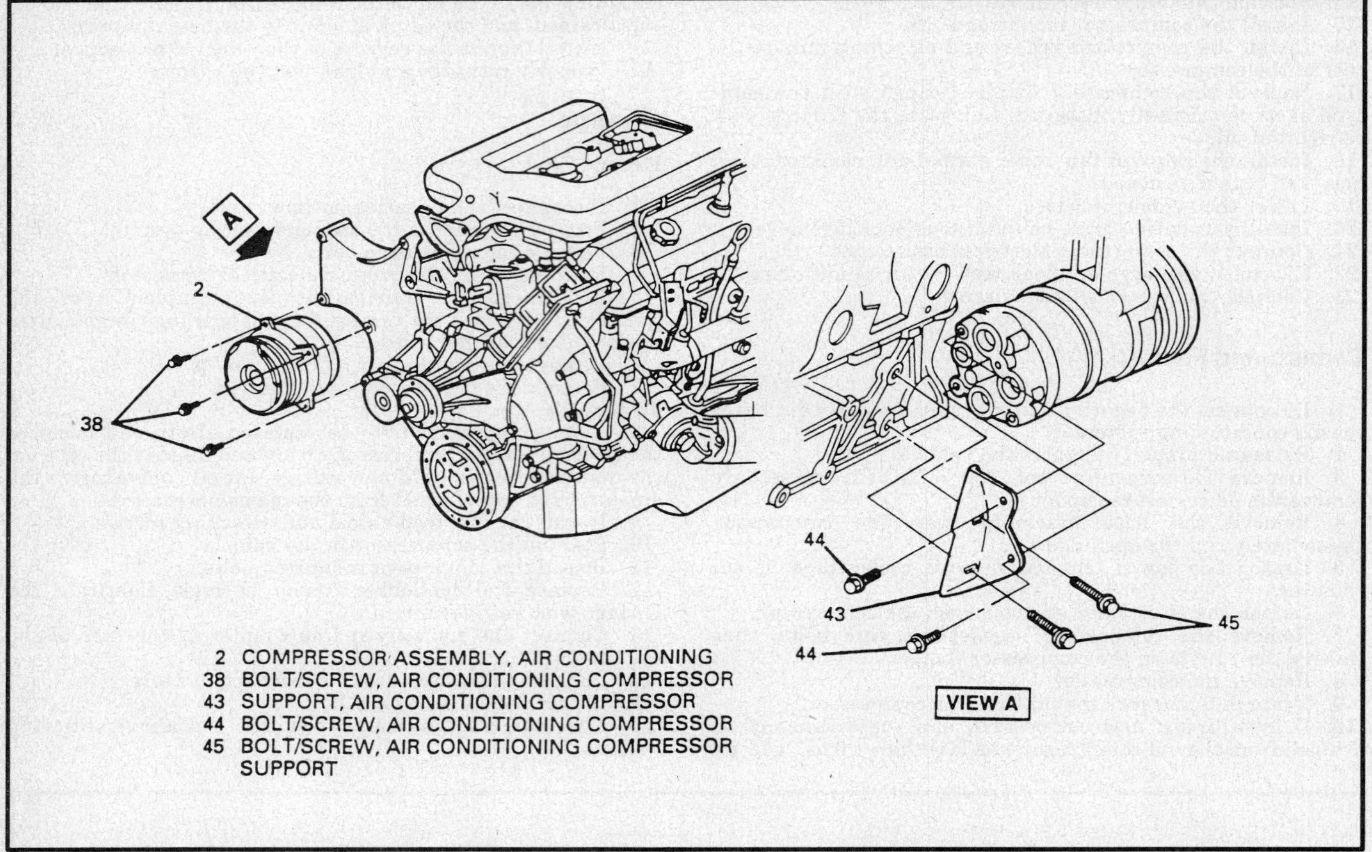

Air conditioning compressor assembly mounting and support—Camaro, Firebird 3.4L L32 engine

17. Connect the negative battery cable.

ZR-1

1. Disconnect the negative battery cable.
2. Properly discharge the air conditioning system.
3. Remove the throttle body by performing the following:
   - Drain the engine coolant into a clean container for reuse.
   - Remove the air intake duct.
   - Disconnect the Manifold Air Temperature (MAT) sensor, Throttle Position Sensor (TPS) and Idle Air Control (IAC) electrical connectors.
   - Remove the ventilation breather hose from the left and right side of the throttle body extension.
   - Remove the screws and nuts retaining the cable shield to the throttle body extension and remove the shield.
   - Remove the throttle body extension from the throttle body.
   - Remove the screws holding the cable clamps from the plenum and pull the cable aside.
   - Remove the throttle body from the plenum.
4. Remove the serpentine belt.
5. Disconnect the engine oil temperature sensor.
6. Remove the alternator by performing the following:
   - Remove the water pump pulley.
   - Remove the alternator support bracket.
   - Remove the alternator lower mounting bolt.
   - Disconnect the alternator electrical connectors.
   - Remove the alternator from the vehicle.
7. Disconnect the refrigerant line coupler from the rear of the compressor. Discard the O-rings. Cap all openings immediately.
8. Disconnect the compressor electrical connectors.
9. Remove the compressor from the vehicle.

To install:

10. If the compressor is to be replaced, drain and measure the oil from the old compressor. Drain and discard the oil from the new compressor. Add new refrigerant oil equivalent to the amount that was drained from the old compressor.
11. Install the compressor.
12. Connect the compressor electrical connectors.
13. Replace the compressor refrigerant line coupler O-rings. Lubricate the O-rings with refrigerant oil.
14. Connect the refrigerant line coupler to the rear of the compressor.
15. Reinstall the alternator.
16. Connect the engine oil temperature sensor.
17. Install the serpentine belt.
18. Install the throttle body after ensuring all old gasket material is cleaned from the mating surface and new gasket is in place.
19. Evacuate, recharge and leak test the air conditioning system.
20. Connect the negative battery cable.
21. Fill cooling system and check for leaks. Start the engine and allow to come to normal operating temperature. Allow the engine to warm up sufficiently to confirm cooling fan operation. Recheck for leaks. Top-up coolant.

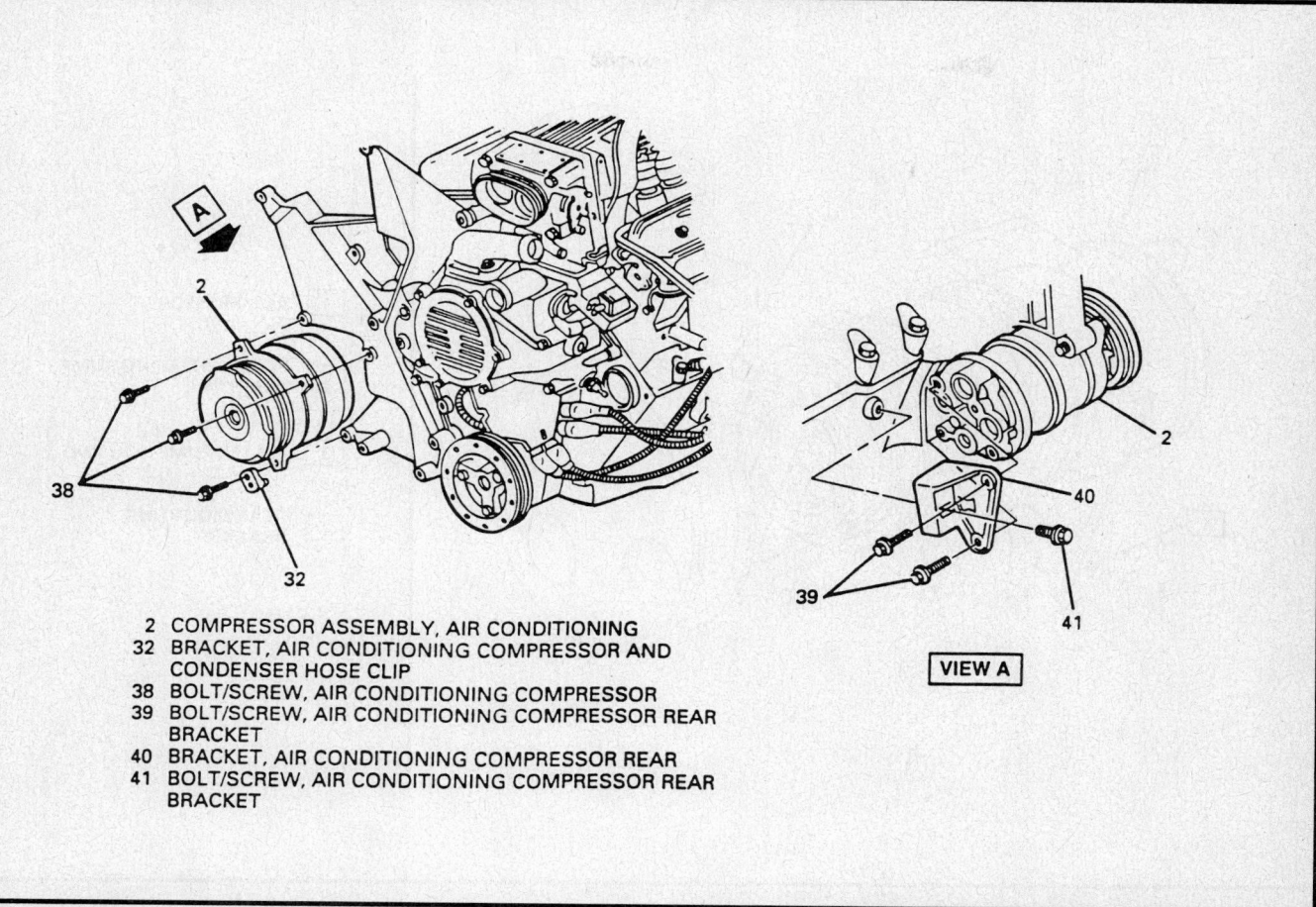

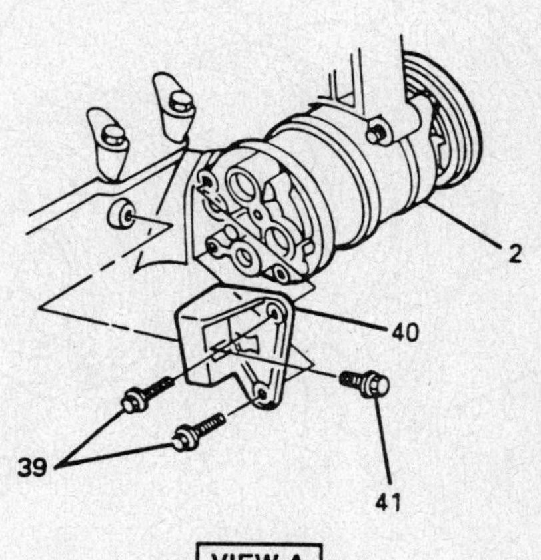

Air conditioning compressor assembly mounting and bracket—Camaro, Firebird 5.7L LT1 engine

Accumulator

REMOVAL AND INSTALLATION

Except 1994 Camaro and Firebird

1. Disconnect the negative battery cable.
2. Properly discharge the air conditioning system.
3. On Corvette, remove the air intake duct.
4. Remove the pressure cycling switch from the accumulator.
5. Disconnect the low-pressure lines at the inlet and outlet fittings on the accumulator. Cap all openings immediately to minimize contamination.
6. Loosen the lower strap bolt and spread the strap. Turn the accumulator and remove, on 1993 models.
7. On 1994–95 models, loosen the bolt/screw enough to remove accumulator assembly from bracket.

To install:

8. Drain and measure the oil from the old accumulator and add equivalent new oil equivalent to the new accumulator, plus an additional 2 oz. (60 ml) of oil to compensate for the oil retained by the accumulator desiccant. On Corvette, add 3.5 oz. total oil to the replacement accumulator.
9. Position the accumulator in the securing bracket and tighten the clamp bolt.
10. Install new O-rings at the inlet and outlet connections on the accumulator. Lubricate the O-rings with refrigerant oil.
11. Connect the low-pressure inlet and outlet lines.
12. Install the cycling pressure switch and air intake if removed.
13. Evacuate, charge and leak test the system.

Receiver/Drier

REMOVAL AND INSTALLATION

1994 Camaro and Firebird

1. Disconnect the negative battery cable. Properly discharge the air conditioning system.
2. Using a back-up wrench, carefully remove the refrigerant lines from the receiver/drier. Immediately cap the openings to minimize further system contamination. Discard the O-rings.

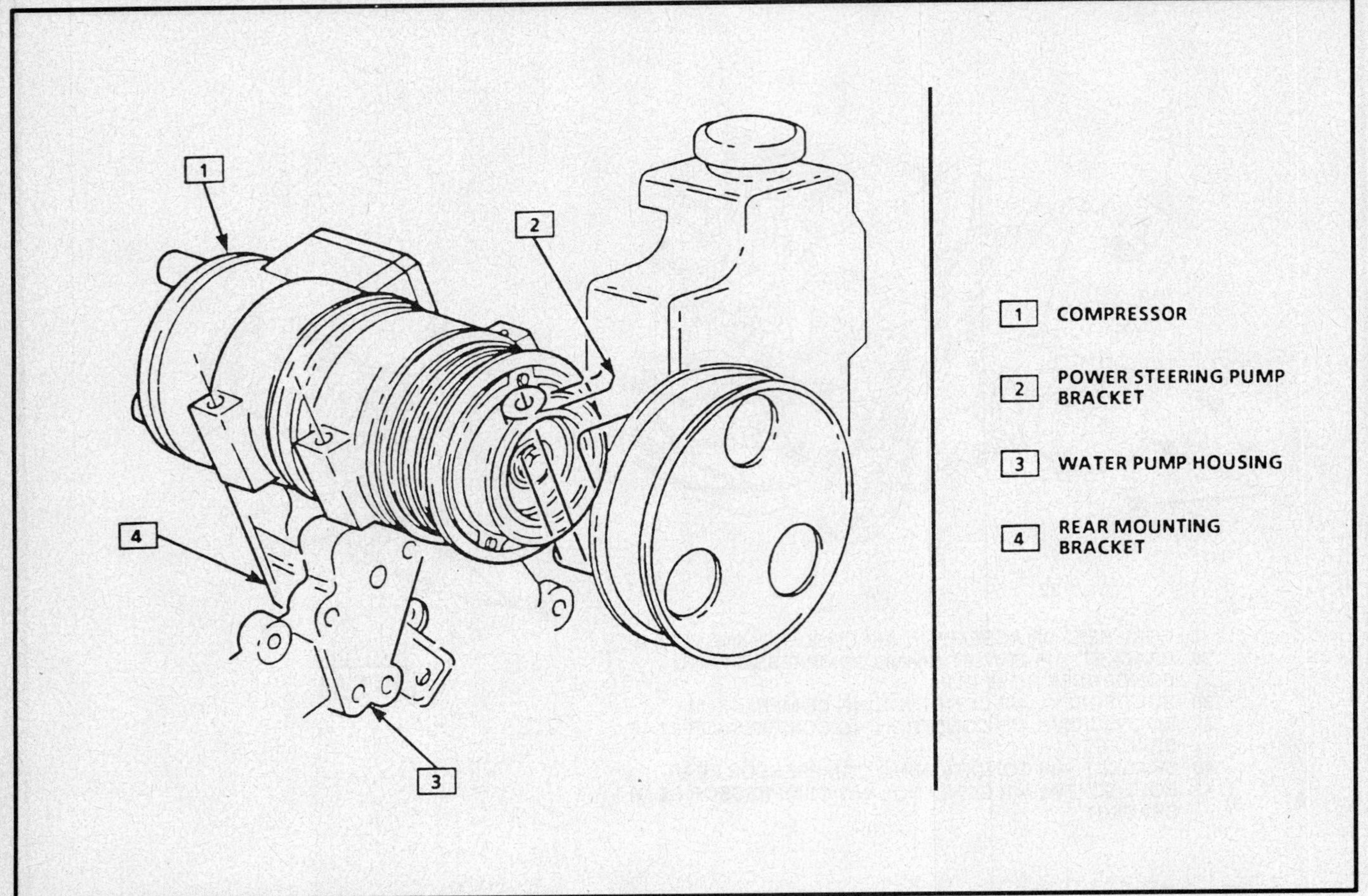

Compressor mounting—Corvette (VIN J)

3. Remove the bracket bolt and screw and remove the receiver/drier.
4. Installation is the reverse of the removal procedure.
5. If installing a new receiver/drier, add 1.0 oz. of new PAG refrigerant oil to the unit.
6. Clean all fittings with 525 viscosity oil (do not let the oil get into the tubes or receiver/drier). Install new O–rings.
7. Evacuate, recharge and leak test.

Expansion Orifice Tube

REMOVAL AND INSTALLATION

NOTE: On Caprice, Fleetwood and Roadmaster, and on 1994–95 Impala SS, the orifice tube is located in the liquid line near the condenser connection. On all other models, the orifice tube is located in the evaporator inlet tube near the liquid line connection.

1. Properly discharge the air conditioning system.
2. Loosen the fitting at the liquid line outlet on the condenser (Caprice, Impala SS, Fleetwood and Roadmaster). On all models, detach the liquid line from the evaporator inlet pipe. Discard the O-rings. Plug all openings (except at location of the orifice tube) to minimize contamination.

NOTE: Use a backup wrench on the fittings when loosening the lines.

3. Carefully, remove the fixed orifice tube from the tube fitting in the evaporator inlet line or from the liquid line at the condenser connection end.
4. In the event that the restricted or plugged orifice tube is difficult to remove, perform the following:
   - Remove as much of the impacted residue as possible.
   - Using a hair dryer, epoxy drier or equivalent, carefully apply heat approximately 1/4 in. from the dimples on the inlet pipe or the liquid line (Caprice, Impala SS, Fleetwood and Roadmaster). Do not overheat the pipe or line.

NOTE: If the system has a pressure switch capillary line near the orifice tube, it should be removed prior to heating the pipe to avoid damage to the switch.

   - While applying heat, use special tool J 26549-D or E (or equivalent) to grip the orifice tube. Use a turning motion along with a push-pull motion to loosen the impacted orifice tube and remove it.
   - Discard the expansion tube if the plastic frame is broken or if the filter screen is torn, damaged or plugged with fine, gritty dirt.
5. Swab the inside of the evaporator inlet pipe or liquid line with solvent to remove any remaining residue.
6. Add 1 oz. of 525 viscosity refrigerant oil to the system.
7. Lubricate the new O-ring and orifice tube with refrigerant oil and insert into the inlet pipe or liquid line, as applicable.

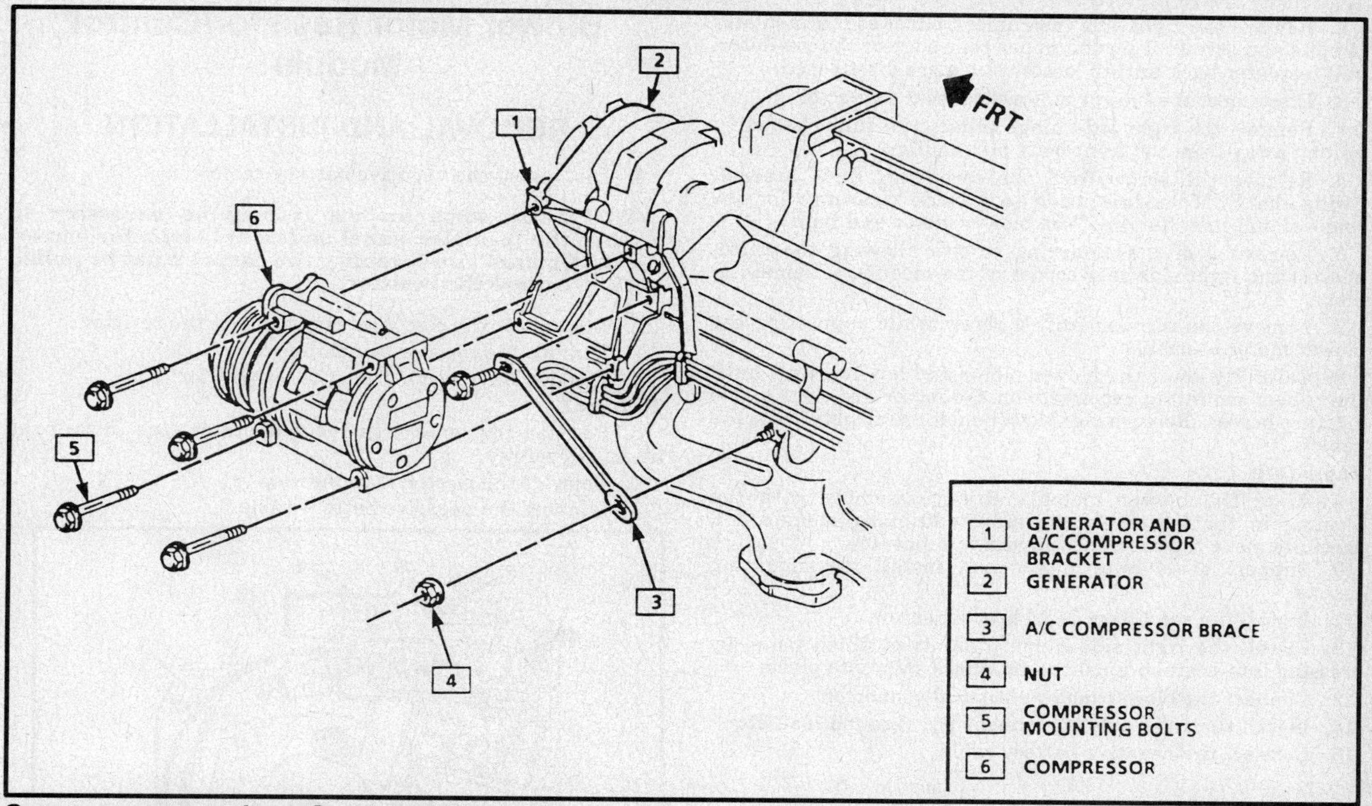

FRT

1 GENERATOR AND A/C COMPRESSOR BRACKET
2 GENERATOR
3 A/C COMPRESSOR BRACE
4 NUT
5 COMPRESSOR MOUNTING BOLTS
6 COMPRESSOR

Compressor mounting—Corvette (VIN P)

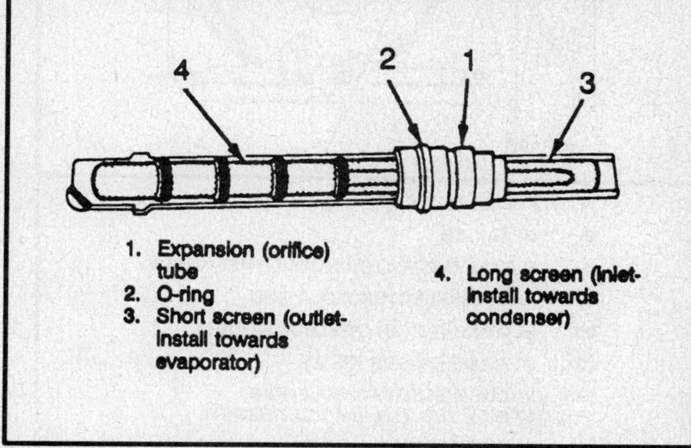

Expansion (orifice) tube

NOTE: Ensure that the new orifice tube is inserted in the inlet tube with the smaller screen end first.

8. Connect the evaporator inlet pipe with the condenser outlet fitting. Reconnect the liquid line at condenser (Caprice, Impala SS, Fleetwood and Roadmaster).

NOTE: Use a backup wrench on the fittings when tightening the lines.

9. Evacuate, recharge and leak test the system.

Expansion Valve

REMOVAL AND INSTALLATION

Camaro and Firebird

1. Disconnect the negative battery cable. Properly discharge the air conditioning system.
2. Detach the electrical connector from the refrigerant pressure sensor.
3. Remove the retaining clamps from the tubes. Using a back-up wrench, disconnect the refrigerant line from the receiver/drier. Immediately cap the openings. Discard the O-ring.
4. Using a back-up wrench, remove the refrigerant lines from the expansion valve. Immediately cap the openings. Discard the O-rings.
5. Remove the bolt from the expansion valve and remove the valve.
6. Installation is the reverse of the removal procedure. Use new O-rings at all fittings.
7. Carefully clean the fittings with 525 viscosity oil (do not let the oil get into the system) before making attachments.
8. Evacuate, recharge and leak test.

Blower Motor

REMOVAL AND INSTALLATION

Caprice, Roadmaster and Fleetwood and 1994–95 Impala SS

1. Disconnect the negative battery cable.

2. Remove the right side instrument panel sound insulator (4 bolts and screws from the upper rear edge of the insulator; pull insulator back until 2 locator studs are disengaged).

3. Disconnect the blower motor electrical connector.

4. Remove the right side hinge pillar trim finish panel by pulling away from the front body hinge pillar.

5. Remove the screw from the secondary ECM bracket. Swing the ECM module aside to provide clearance for the removal and installation of the blower motor and fan.

6. Remove 2 of the mounting screws allowing the third, nearest the right side rear corner of the module, to remain in place.

7. Remove the third mounting screw while supporting the blower motor assembly.

8. Carefully lower the blower motor and fan assembly until the rubber mounting grommets on the motor are clear of the locating bosses. Remove the blower motor assembly from the vehicle.

To install:

9. Align the blower motor and fan assembly with the opening in the bottom of the air conditioning module and carefully move the assembly up and into position.

10. Support the blower motor and install the mounting screws.

11. Install the secondary ECM bracket screw.

12. Install the right side hinge pillar trim finish panel by pressing into position until the retainers snap into place.

13. Connect the blower motor electrical connector.

14. Install the right side instrument panel sound insulator.

15. Connect the negative battery cable.

Camaro and Firebird

1. Set the ignition switch in the LOCK position and remove the key.

2. Remove the right sound insulator panel and side trim to access the blower motor.

3. Remove the retaining screws and remove the blower motor.

4. Installation is the reverse of the removal procedure.

Corvette

1. Disconnect the negative battery cable.

2. Remove the front wheel house rear panel and seal.

3. Disconnect the blower motor electrical connectors.

4. Remove the blower motor cooling tube.

5. Remove the blower motor retaining screws and remove the blower motor and fan assembly.

6. Remove the sealer from the blower motor mounting flange and the mating surface of the upper case.

To install:

7. Apply fresh sealer to the blower motor mounting flange.

8. Install the blower motor and fan assembly. Install the retaining screws.

9. Install the cooling tube.

10. Connect the blower motor electrical connectors.

11. Install the front wheel house rear panel and seal.

12. Connect the negative battery cable.

13. Test the operation of the blower motor to ensure that it functions on all speeds.

Blower Motor Resistor/Control Module

REMOVAL AND INSTALLATION

1. Disconnect the negative battery cable.

NOTE: On some models it may be necessary to remove the insulator panel and/or side trim for access. On the Camaro and Firebird, the carpet must be pulled back to expose the resistor.

2. Disconnect the electrical connector at the resistor.

3. Remove the resistor attaching screws.

4. Remove the resistor from the evaporator case.

To install:

5. Position the resistor in the evaporator case. Install the attaching screws.

6. Connect the electrical connector.

7. Connect the negative battery cable.

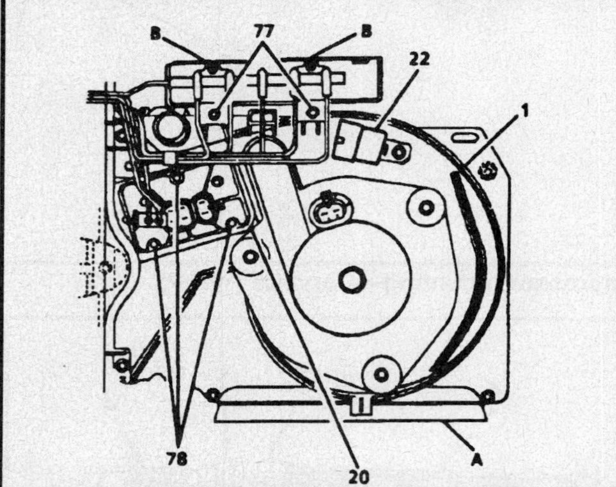

A	FRESH AIR INLET
B	RETAINER
1	H-A/C EVAPORATOR MODULE ASSEMBLY
13	VACUUM/ELECTRIC SOLENOID
20	BLOWER MOTOR CONTROL MODULE
22	REAR DEFOGGER RELAY
77	VACUUM/ELECTRIC SOLENOID, 17 INCH LBS. (1.9 Nm) BOLT/SCREW
78	BLOWER MOTOR CONTROL, 17 INCH LBS. (1.9 Nm) BOLT/SCREW

Control module location for removal—Cadillac Fleetwood and Roadmaster

Heater Core

REMOVAL AND INSTALLATION

Caprice, Roadmaster and Fleetwood and 1994–95 Impala SS

1. Disconnect the negative battery cable. Drain the engine coolant into a clean container for reuse.

2. If equipped, disable the Supplemental Inflatable Restraint (SIR) system by performing the following:
   - Remove the SIR fuse from the fuse panel.
   - Remove the left side sound insulator.
   - Remove the Connector Positive Assurance (CPA) from the yellow 2-way SIR harness connector at the base of the steering column and separate the connector.
3. Remove the screw holding the hot water bypass valve to the cowl panel.
4. Release the heater inlet and outlet pipe quick-disconnect fitting by squeezing both release tabs at the base of the heater core tube and pulling on the pipe to disengage the fitting.
5. Remove the air conditioning module lower case by performing the following, except 1995 models:
   - Remove the right side instrument panel sound insulator.
   - Remove the lower instrument panel reinforcement.
   - Disconnect the 2 vacuum harness connectors at the lower evaporator case and remove from the case. Position the vacuum harnesses aside.
   - Remove the right side hinge pillar trim finish panel by pulling away from the front body hinge pillar.
   - Roll the carpeting back to provide access to the lower forward area of the air conditioning module.
   - Remove the 7 screws attaching the lower evaporator case to the upper air conditioning module.
   - Lower the evaporator case.
6. On 1995 models only, remove the heater core cover.
   - Remove right hand instrument panel insulator and carpet retainer.
   - Remove instrument panel trim plate for Chevrolet or instrument panel lower trim plate for Buick.
   - Remove the instrument panel upper trim pad.
   - Pull right lower corner of instrument panel away from dash and support.
   - Disconnect vacuum harness connectors at heater core cover.
   - Roll floor carpet back for access to forward lower arm of module.
   - Remove heater core cover bolts/screw. Remove heater core cover.
7. Remove the heater core mounting clamp.
8. Remove the heater core and the heater core pipes seal.

To install:

9. Install the heater core by fitting the base of the heater core into the mounting clip at the bottom of the air conditioning module lower case.
10. Install the core pipes seal.
11. On 1995 model only, install heater core cover.
    - Position the heater core cover on the evaporator case and secure it with cover bolts/screw.
    - Replace the floor carpet.
    - Connect the vacuum harness connectors at the heater core cover.
    - Position and secure the right lower corner of the instrument panel.
    - Install the instrument panel trim pad.
    - Install the instrument panel trim plate for Chevrolet or the instrument panel lower trim plate for Buick.
    - Install the right hand instrument panel insulator and carpet retainer.
12. Install the air conditioning module lower case by performing the following, if removed:
    - Place the evaporator case into position.

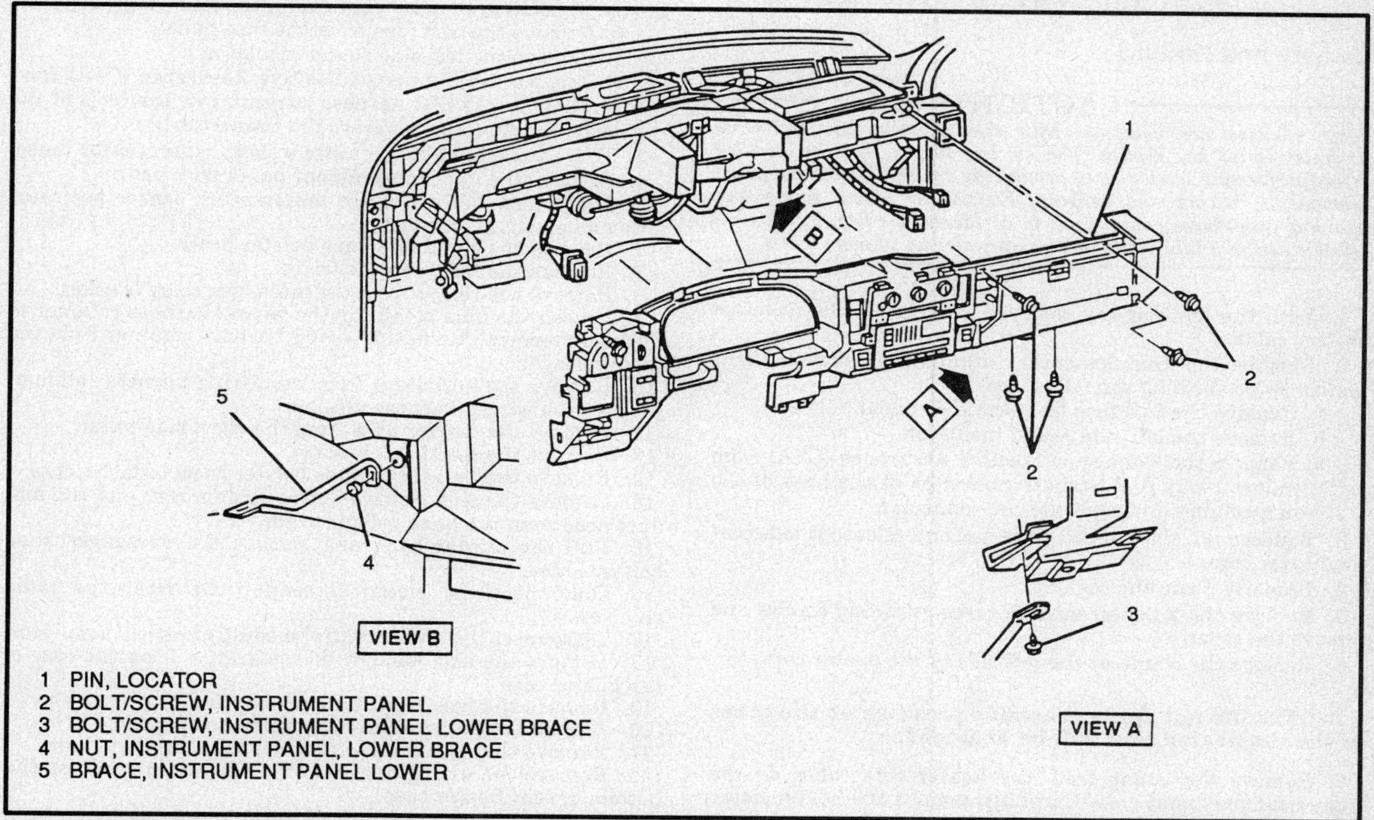

Instrument panel assembly—Caprice, 1994–95 Impala SS

- Install the 7 screws attaching the lower evaporator case to the upper air conditioning module.
- Fit the carpeting back in place under the air conditioning module and against the cowl panel.
- Install the right side hinge pillar trim finish panel.
- Connect the 2 vacuum harness connectors to the lower evaporator case. Ensure that the vacuum lines are routed properly.
- Install the lower instrument panel reinforcement.
- Install the right side instrument panel sound insulator.

13. Connect the heater core inlet and outlet pipe quick-connect fittings.

NOTE: Ensure that the quick-connect orientation tabs are properly aligned before connecting the fittings. Do not rely on an audible click alone to verify proper connection. Test for proper engagement by pushing the fittings together and then pulling back.

14. Connect the negative battery cable.
15. Fill cooling system and check for leaks. Start the engine and allow to come to normal operating temperature. Allow the engine to warm up sufficiently to confirm cooling fan operation. Recheck for leaks. Top-up coolant.
16. If equipped, enable the Supplemental Inflatable Restraint (SIR) system by performing the following:
    - Connect the yellow 2-way SIR connector and insert the connector position assurance retainer at the base of the steering column.
    - Install the left side sound insulator.
    - Install the SIR fuse in the fuse panel.
    - Turn ignition to **RUN** and verify that the inflatable restraint indicator flashes 7-9 times and then turns off.

Camaro and Firebird

CAUTION

Some vehicles are equipped with the Supplemental Inflatable Restraint or air bag system. The air bag system must be disabled before performing service on or around the air bag, instrument panel components, wiring and sensors. Failure to follow safety and disabling procedures could result in accidental air bag deployment, possible personal injury and unnecessary air bag system repairs.

1. With the ignition key removed, disconnect the negative battery cable.
2. Disable the Supplemental Inflatable Restraint (SIR) system by performing the following:
    - Remove the SIR fuse from the fuse panel.
    - Remove the left side sound insulator.
    - Remove the Connector Positive Assurance (CPA) from the yellow 2-way SIR harness connector at the base of the steering column and separate the connector.
3. Squeeze the sides of the glove box and release it to access the heater core.
4. Properly drain the coolant.
5. Remove the 2 heater module cover retaining screws and remove the cover.
6. Remove the clamp at the left side of the heater core.

NOTE: Do not apply excessive pressure on the tubes or the the heater core will be damaged.

7. Remove the clamp from the heater core tubes on the engine compartment side. Carefully remove the heater hoses from the core tubes. Plug the hoses to prevent leakage.
8. Pull the heater core toward the rear of the vehicle to remove it.

To install:

9. Position the heater core into place and then attach the heater hoses to the core tubes. Install the hose clamp.

NOTE: Lubricate the heater tubes with petroleum jelly for best sealing. Be sure seals around the heater pipes remain in place.

10. Install the heater core clamp, then install the heater core module cover.
11. Properly fill the cooling system, then operate the system and check for leaks.
12. Install the glove box assembly.
13. If equipped, enable the Supplemental Inflatable Restraint (SIR) system by performing the following:
    - Connect the yellow 2-way SIR connector and insert the Connector Positive Assurance (CPA) at the base of the steering column.
    - Install the left side sound insulator.
    - Install the SIR fuse in the fuse panel.

Corvette

CAUTION

Some vehicles are equipped with the Supplemental Inflatable Restraint or air bag system. The air bag system must be disabled before performing service on or around the air bag, instrument panel components, wiring and sensors. Failure to follow safety and disabling procedures could result in accidental air bag deployment, possible personal injury and unnecessary air bag system repairs.

1. Disconnect the negative battery cable.
2. If equipped, disable the Supplemental Inflatable Restraint (SIR) system by performing the following:
    - Remove the SIR fuse from the fuse panel.
    - Remove the left side sound insulator.
    - Remove the Connector Positive Assurance (CPA) from the yellow 2-way SIR harness connector at the base of the steering column and separate the connector.
3. Drain the engine coolant into a clean container for reuse.
4. Remove the upper instrument panel trim pad.
5. Disconnect the in-vehicle temperature sensor aspirator hose and electrical connector.
6. Remove the right side knee bolster brace.
7. Remove the floor heat deflector.
8. Remove the relays from the multi-use relay bracket.
9. Loosen the nuts retaining the wiring harness retainer to the radio receiver. Slide the wiring harness retainer from the radio receiver.
10. Remove the harnesses from the wiring harness retainer. Remove the wiring harness retainer.
11. Remove the carrier nuts from the right side pillar.
12. Remove the multi-use bracket.
13. Remove the passenger knee bolster brace attachments.
14. Remove the side window defroster duct rose bud clip and duct hose from the knee bolster brace.
15. Pull the carrier back and remove the passenger knee bolster brace.
16. Disconnect the electrical connections from the radio receiver.
17. Disconnect the cruise control module electrical connector.
18. Remove the side window defroster duct from the rear of the heater case.
19. Remove the fuse block from the carrier.
20. Disconnect the vacuum hose from the actuator.
21. Remove the vacuum line retainer tape on the heater.
22. Remove the wiring harness from the retainer clip on the bottom of rear heater case.
23. Remove the side window defroster duct extension from the heater case.
24. Remove the rear heater case half.

25. Remove the high fill reservoir.
26. Disconnect the heater hoses from the heater core.
27. Remove the heater core from the case.

To install:

28. Install the heater core in the case.
29. Connect the heater hoses to the heater core.
30. Install the high fill reservoir.
31. Install the rear heater case half.
32. Install the side window defroster duct extension to the defroster duct.
33. Connect the harnesses to the retainer clip on the bottom of the rear heater case.
34. Install the vacuum line and tape onto the retainer.
35. Connect the vacuum hose to the actuator.
36. Install the fuse block to the carrier.
37. Install the side window defroster duct to the rear of the heater case.
38. Connect the radio receiver and cruise control module electrical connectors.
39. Install the multi-use relay bracket and knee bolster brace.
40. Install the side window defroster duct hose and rose bud clip to the knee bolster brace.
41. Install the carrier-to-pillar attachments.
42. Install the wiring harness to the harness retainer. Connect the wiring harness retainer to the radio receiver.
43. Install the relays to the multi-use relay bracket.
44. Install the floor heat deflector.
45. Install the right side knee bolster brace.
46. Connect the in-vehicle temperature sensor connectors.
47. Connect the in-vehicle temperature sensor aspirator hose.
48. Install the instrument panel upper trim pad.
49. Connect the negative battery cable.
50. Fill cooling system and check for leaks. Start the engine and allow to come to normal operating temperature. Allow the engine to warm up sufficiently to confirm cooling fan operation. Recheck for leaks. Top-up coolant.
51. If equipped, enable the Supplemental Inflatable Restraint (SIR) system by performing the following:
    - Connect the yellow 2-way SIR connector and insert the Connector Positive Assurance (CPA) at the base of the steering column.
    - Install the left side sound insulator.
    - Install the SIR fuse in the fuse panel.

Evaporator

REMOVAL AND INSTALLATION

Caprice, Roadmaster and Fleetwood and 1994–95 Impala SS

1. Disconnect the negative battery cable. Properly discharge the air conditioning system.
2. If equipped, disable the Supplemental Inflatable Restraint (SIR) system by performing the following:
    - Remove the SIR fuse from the fuse panel.
    - Remove the left side sound insulator.
    - Remove the Connector Positive Assurance (CPA) from the yellow 2-way SIR harness connector at the base of the steering column and separate the connector.
3. Disconnect the refrigerant lines at the evaporator inlet and outlet fittings. Discard the O-rings. Cap all openings immediately to minimize contamination.
4. Remove the air conditioning module lower case by removing the instrument panel sound insulator, the instrument panel lower reinforcement, 2 vacuum harness connectors at the evaporator housing, the right hinge pillar trim finish panel assembly, then the lower case, except 1995 models.
5. On 1995 models only, remove the heater core cover as follows:
    - Remove right-hand instrument panel insulator and carpet retainer.
    - Remove instrument panel trim plate for Chevrolet or instrument panel lower trim plate for Buick.
    - Remove the instrument panel upper trim pad.
    - Pull the right lower corner of instrument panel away from the dash and support.
    - Disconnect the vacuum harness connectors at the heater core cover.
    - Roll the floor carpet back for access to the forward lower area of the module.
    - Remove the heater core cover bolts/screws. Remove the heater core cover.
6. Remove the evaporator mounting bracket.
7. Remove the evaporator by sliding rearward and down.

To install:

8. Ensure that seals are properly positioned on the air conditioning module mounting flanges.
9. Install the evaporator mounting bracket.
10. Install the air conditioning module lower case.
11. On 1995 models only, install the heater core cover. Installation is the reverse of the removal procedure.
12. Add 3 oz. (90 ml) of refrigerant oil to the system.
13. Replace the evaporator fitting O-rings. Lubricate the O-rings with refrigerant oil.
14. Connect the refrigerant lines to the evaporator inlet and outlet fittings.
15. Evacuate, recharge and leak test the air conditioning system.
16. Connect the negative battery cable.
17. If equipped, enable the Supplemental Inflatable Restraint (SIR) system by performing the following:
    - Connect the yellow 2-way SIR connector and insert the Connector Positive Assurance (CPA) at the base of the steering column.
    - Install the left side sound insulator.
    - Install the SIR fuse in the fuse panel.

Camaro and Firebird

1. Be sure the ignition key is removed. Properly discharge the air conditioning system.
2. Properly drain the cooling system.
3. Remove the right side instrument panel insulator panel.
4. Remove the heater hose-to-core tube clamp assembly. Detach and plug the heater hoses from the heater core tubes at the firewall.
5. Remove the glove box assembly.
6. Remove the heater core.
7. Detach the evaporator temperature sensor connector and use needle-nose pliers to pull the evaporator probe straight out. Remove the temperature sensor.
8. Detach the temperature control cable from the heater assembly.
9. Slide the temperature valve (air door) case assembly down to disengage the upper clips, then remove the case assembly.
10. Remove the expansion valve.
11. Using a small saw, remove the perforated section of the heater/evaporator case.
12. Remove the 2 evaporator clamp bolts, slide the evaporator core to the left and remove it through the opening as cut out.

To install:

13. If installing a new evaporator core, transfer the condensate screen to the new core. Position the evaporator core and slide as far to the right as possible until fully seated.

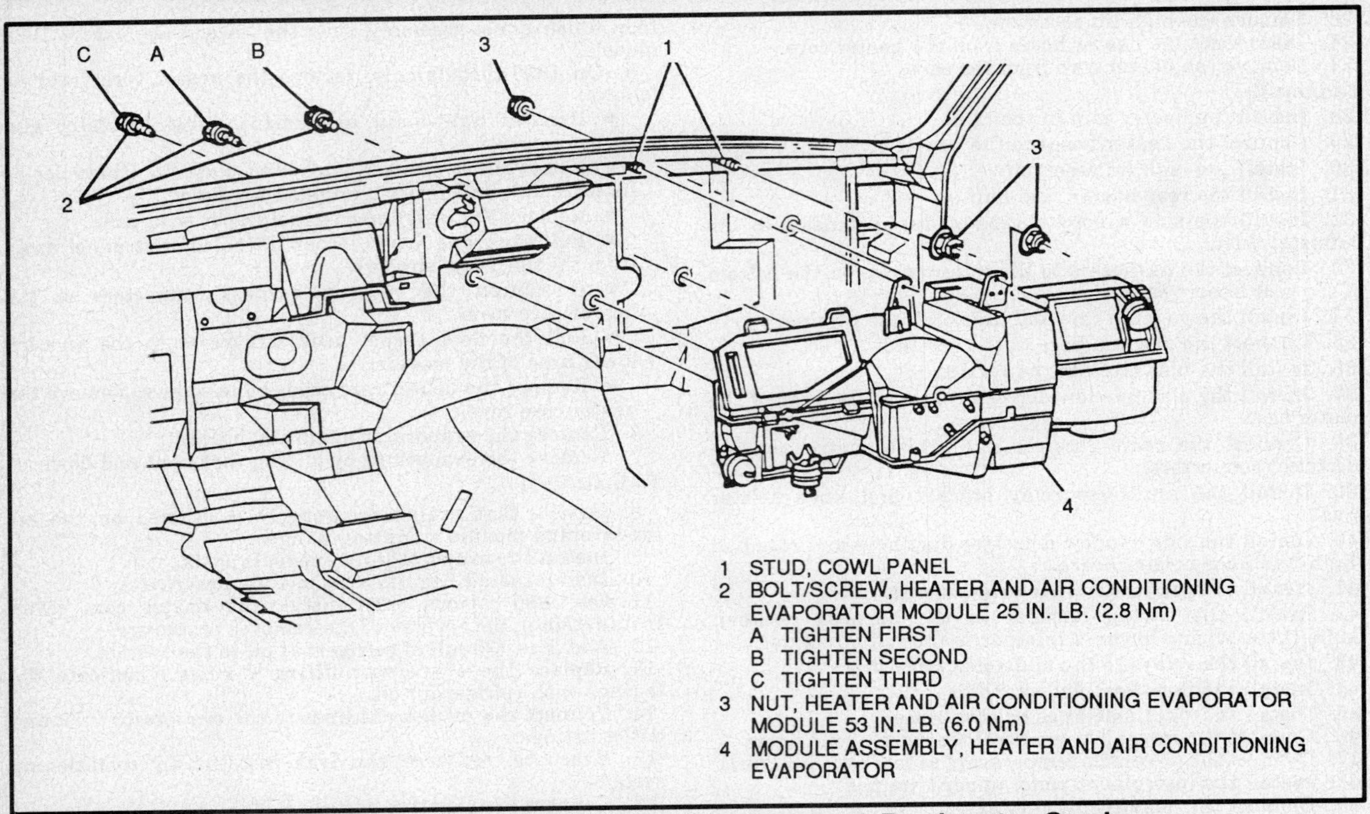

1 STUD, COWL PANEL
2 BOLT/SCREW, HEATER AND AIR CONDITIONING EVAPORATOR MODULE 25 IN. LB. (2.8 Nm)
A TIGHTEN FIRST
B TIGHTEN SECOND
C TIGHTEN THIRD
3 NUT, HEATER AND AIR CONDITIONING EVAPORATOR MODULE 53 IN. LB. (6.0 Nm)
4 MODULE ASSEMBLY, HEATER AND AIR CONDITIONING EVAPORATOR

Heater and air conditioning evaporator module assembly—Fleetwood, Roadmaster, Caprice, 1994–95 Impala SS

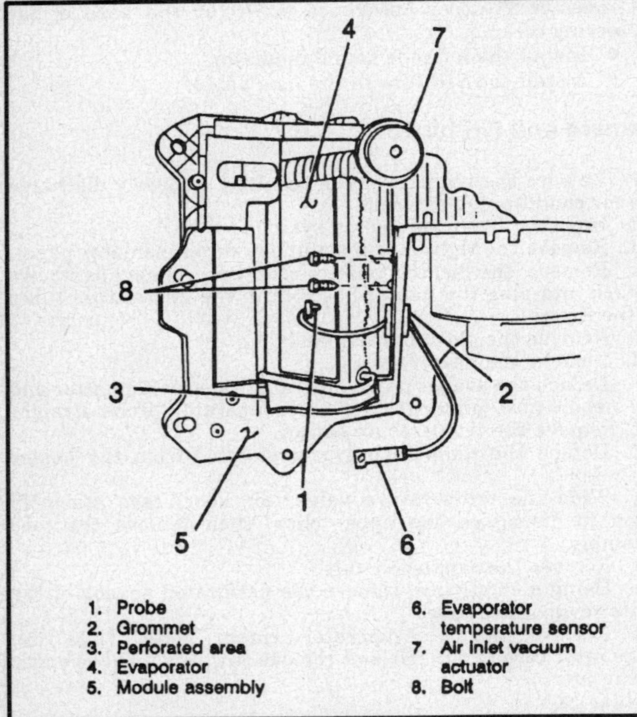

Evaporator temperature sensor assembly—Camaro and Firebird

14. Install the evaporator core clamp.

15. If a new core is installed, add 3.0 oz. of new PAG type refrigerant oil to the unit.

16. Install the expansion valve, using new O-rings at all fittings.

17. Apply non-epoxy sealant (GM 3012078 or equivalent) between the evaporator core and the upper and lower case, just behind the expansion valve to prevent air leaks.

18. Position the perforated section of the case and use an epoxy glue to seal it in place.

19. Install the temperature valve (air door) case, engaging the upper clips and install the retaining bolts.

20. Attach the temperature control cable.

21. Install the heater core.

22. Install the glove box assembly.

23. Attach the heater hoses and clamp assembly to the core tubes.

24. Install the right side instrument panel insulator panel.

25. Fill and bleed the cooling system.

26. Partially charge the A/C system and perform a leak test. If okay, discharge, evacuate, fully charge and test the system.

Corvette

1. Disconnect the negative battery cable. Properly discharge the air conditioning system.

2. If equipped, disable the Supplemental Inflatable Restraint (SIR) system by performing the following:
   - Remove the SIR fuse from the fuse panel.
   - Remove the left side sound insulator.

- Remove the Connector Positive Assurance (CPA) from the yellow 2-way SIR harness connector at the base of the steering column and separate the connector.

3. Drain the engine coolant into a clean container for reuse.
4. Remove the front wheel house rear panel and seal.
5. Disconnect the blower motor electrical connectors.
6. Disconnect the evaporator outlet hose. Cap openings immediately to minimize contamination.
7. Remove the pressure cycling switch.
8. Disconnect the heater hoses.
9. Disconnect the evaporator inlet line and remove the expansion tube. Cap openings immediately to minimize contamination.
10. Remove the suction line bracket from the evaporator case.
11. Remove the right side rear bolt from the upper front fender.
12. Remove the bulkhead bolts and nuts securing the evaporator and blower assembly to the bulkhead.
13. Remove the evaporator case from the vehicle.
14. Split the evaporator case and remove the evaporator core.

To install:

15. Add 3 oz. (90 ml) of refrigerant oil to the system.
16. Position the evaporator core seal between the evaporator case halves.
17. Install the evaporator core in the evaporator case.
18. Install the evaporator case in the vehicle.
19. Install the rear right side bolt to the upper front fender.
20. Install the vapor pipe bracket to the evaporator case.
21. Replace the evaporator fitting O-rings. Lubricate the O-rings with refrigerant oil.
22. Install the orifice tube into the evaporator inlet line. Connect the line.
23. Connect the heater hoses.
24. Install the pressure cycling switch.
25. Connect the blower motor electrical connectors.
26. Install the front panel and seal at the wheel house.
27. Evacuate, recharge and leak test the air conditioning system.
28. Connect the negative battery cable.
29. Fill cooling system and check for leaks. Start the engine and allow to come to normal operating temperature. Allow the engine to warm up sufficiently to confirm cooling fan operation. Recheck for leaks. Top-up coolant.
30. If equipped, enable the Supplemental Inflatable Restraint (SIR) system by performing the following:
    - Connect the yellow 2-way SIR connector and insert the Connector Positive Assurance (CPA) at the base of the steering column.
    - Install the left side sound insulator.
    - Install the SIR fuse in the fuse panel.

Refrigerant Lines

REMOVAL AND INSTALLATION

1. Disconnect the negative battery cable.
2. Properly discharge the air conditioning system.
3. Disconnect the refrigerant line connectors, using a backup wrench as required.
4. Remove refrigerant line support or routing brackets, as required.
5. Remove refrigerant line.

To install:

6. Position new refrigerant line in place, leaving protective caps installed until ready to connect.
7. Install new O-rings on refrigerant line connector fittings. Lubricate with refrigerant oil. Clean all fittings with 525 viscosity refrigerant oil (do not let the oil get into the system).
8. Connect refrigerant line, using a backup wrench, as required.
9. Install refrigerant line support or routing brackets, as required.
10. Evacuate, recharge and leak test the system.
11. Connect the negative battery cable.

Manual Control Head

REMOVAL AND INSTALLATION

Caprice and 1994–95 Impala SS

1. Disconnect the negative battery cable.
2. If equipped, disable the Supplemental Inflatable Restraint (SIR) system by performing the following:
    - Remove the SIR fuse from the fuse panel.
    - Remove the left side sound insulator.
    - Remove the Connector Positive Assurance (CPA) from the yellow 2-way SIR harness connector at the base of the steering column and separate the connector.
3. Remove the steering column opening filler. Loosen the steering column mounting nuts.
4. Remove the trim plates, as required to gain access to the control panel attaching screws. Remove the control assembly attaching screws.
5. Pull the control assembly out of the instrument panel fan enough to disconnect the control cable assembly ends, electrical and vacuum harness connectors.
6. Disconnect the control cables by performing the following:
    - Remove the push nut retainer from the pin for the temperature control cable.
    - Pull the control cable sheath retainer clips from the control assembly and tilt the control assembly to slip the cable ends off the pins of the mode lever.
7. Remove the heater blower switch knob and spring clip and remove the blower switch, as required. Remove the control assembly.

To install:

8. If removed, hold the blower switch in position and install the spring clip. Install the blower switch knob.
9. Place the control assembly in position. Connect the control cables by slipping the end loops over the pins of the mode lever. If equipped, press the retainer clips into the slots in the control assembly.
10. If equipped, connect the control cable and push nut retainer. Press the cable sheath retainer clip into the slot in the control assembly.
11. Connect the vacuum harness and electrical connectors.
12. Install the control assembly and attaching screws.
13. Install the instrument panel trim plate.
14. Tighten the steering column mounting nuts. Install the steering column opening filler.
15. Connect the negative battery cable.
16. If equipped, enable the Supplemental Inflatable Restraint (SIR) system by performing the following:
    - Connect the yellow 2-way SIR connector and insert the Connector Positive Assurance (CPA) at the base of the steering column.
    - Install the left side sound insulator.
    - Install the SIR fuse in the fuse panel.

Camaro and Firebird

1. Disconnect the negative battery cable.
2. If equipped, disable the Supplemental Inflatable Restraint (SIR) system by performing the following:

- Remove the SIR fuse from the fuse panel.
- Remove the left side sound insulator.
- Remove the Connector Positive Assurance (CPA) from the yellow 2-way SIR harness connector at the base of the steering column and separate the connector.

3. On Camaro, remove the upper instrument panel cover panel, then remove the instrument cluster trim plate.
4. On Firebird, remove the control panel assembly trim plate.
5. Remove the control panel assembly retaining screws, pull the control panel out far enough to detach the vacuum, electrical and temperature control cable connections.
6. If necessary, remove the blower switch connector and the vacuum harness connector from the vacuum selector valve.
7. Installation is the reverse of the removal procedure.

Corvette

1. Disconnect the negative battery cable.
2. If equipped, disable the Supplemental Inflatable Restraint (SIR) system by performing the following:
   - Remove the SIR fuse from the fuse panel.
   - Remove the left side sound insulator.
   - Remove the Connector Positive Assurance (CPA) from the yellow 2-way SIR harness connector at the base of the steering column and separate the connector.
3. Remove the instrument panel trim plate. Remove the control panel attaching screws.
4. Slide and rotate control panel out far enough to disconnect the control cables, and electrical and vacuum connectors.
5. Remove control panel.

To install:

6. Place the control panel in position.
7. Connect the control cables, and electrical and vacuum connectors.
8. Install the control panel attaching screws.
9. Install the instrument panel trim plate.
10. Connect the negative battery cable.
11. If equipped, enable the Supplemental Inflatable Restraint (SIR) system by performing the following:
    - Connect the yellow 2-way SIR connector and insert the Connector Positive Assurance (CPA) at the base of the steering column.
    - Install the left side sound insulator.
    - Install the SIR fuse in the fuse panel.

Manual Control Cables

ADJUSTMENT

With the temperature control cable properly connected at each end, and the control panel properly installed, quickly move the control lever twice back and forth the full length of its travel. A distinct click or thump will be heard at each extreme position. This procedure will self-adjust the cable.

REMOVAL AND INSTALLATION

Caprice and 1994–95 Impala SS

TEMPERATURE CONTROL CABLE

1. If equipped, disable the Supplemental Inflatable Restraint (SIR) system by performing the following:
   - Remove the SIR fuse from the fuse panel.
   - Remove the left side sound insulator.
   - Remove the Connector Positive Assurance (CPA) from the yellow 2-way SIR harness connector at the base of the steering column and separate the connector.
2. Disconnect the negative battery cable.
3. Remove the control panel assembly as described in this article.
4. Remove the instrument panel compartment by removing the screws from the compartment lower hinge and latch, and removing the compartment from the upper trim pad.
5. Detach the electrical connector from the lamp switch.
6. Remove the cable clips and take out the temperature control cable.
7. Install in reverse of the removal procedure.
8. Enable the Supplemental Inflatable Restraint (SIR) system after procedure is complete by doing the following:
   - Connect the yellow 2-way SIR connector and insert the Connector Positive Assurance (CPA) at the base of the steering column.
   - Install the left side sound insulator.
   - Install the SIR fuse in the fuse panel.

Camaro and Firebird

TEMPERATURE CONTROL CABLE

1. If equipped, disable the Supplemental Inflatable Restraint (SIR) system by performing the following:
   - Remove the SIR fuse from the fuse panel.
   - Remove the left side sound insulator.
   - Remove the Connector Positive Assurance (CPA) from the yellow 2-way SIR harness connector at the base of the steering column and separate the connector.
2. Disconnect the negative battery cable.
3. Remove the right instrument panel insulator.
4. Detach the temperature control cable from the heater assembly.
5. On Camaro, remove the left side instrument panel (cluster) trim panel.
6. On Firebird, remove the control panel trim plate.
7. Pull the control assembly out far enough to disconnect the temperature control cable.
8. Installation is the reverse of the removal procedure.
9. Enable the Supplemental Inflatable Restraint (SIR) system after procedure is complete by doing the following:
   - Connect the yellow 2-way SIR connector and insert the Connector Positive Assurance (CPA) at the base of the steering column.
   - Install the left side sound insulator.
   - Install the SIR fuse in the fuse panel.

Corvette

TEMPERATURE CONTROL CABLE

1. If equipped, disable the Supplemental Inflatable Restraint (SIR) system by performing the following:
   - Remove the SIR fuse from the fuse panel.
   - Remove the left side sound insulator.
   - Remove the Connector Positive Assurance (CPA) from the yellow 2-way SIR harness connector at the base of the steering column and separate the connector.
2. Disconnect the negative battery cable.
3. Remove the heater and air conditioner control panel.
4. Remove the radio.
5. Remove the instrument panel compartment.
6. Remove the screws and retaining clips securing the cable.
7. Remove the temperature control cable.

To install:

8. Route the temperature control cable to the heater and air conditioner control assembly.
9. Install the retaining clips and screws.

10. Install the right side sound insulator or compartment, as removed.
11. Install the radio.
12. Install the heater and air conditioner control assembly.
13. Connect the negative battery cable.
14. Adjust the temperature control cable.
15. Enable the Supplemental Inflatable Restraint (SIR) system after procedure is complete by doing the following:
    - Connect the yellow 2-way SIR connector and insert the Connector Positive Assurance (CPA) at the base of the steering column.
    - Install the left side sound insulator.
    - Install the SIR fuse in the fuse panel.

Electronic Control Head

REMOVAL AND INSTALLATION

Roadmaster and Fleetwood

1. Disconnect the negative battery cable.
2. If equipped, disable the Supplemental Inflatable Restraint (SIR) system by performing the following:
    - Remove the SIR fuse from the fuse panel.
    - Remove the left side sound insulator.
    - Remove the Connector Positive Assurance (CPA) from the yellow 2-way SIR harness connector at the base of the steering column and separate the connector.
3. Remove the steering column opening filler. Loosen the steering column mounting nuts.
4. Remove the instrument panel trim plate screws. Remove the trim plate by pulling straight away from the instrument panel carrier snapping the trim plate integral retaining clips out of the slots in the instrument panel carrier.
5. Pull the control assembly out of the instrument panel carrier fan enough to reach the electrical connectors. Disconnect the connectors.
6. Remove the control assembly.

To install:

7. Install the control assembly.
8. Connect the electrical connectors.
9. Install the control assembly and retaining screws.
10. Position the instrument panel trim plate to the instrument panel carrier. Press forward along the lower edge of the trim plate to snap the trim plate integral retaining clips into the slots in the instrument panel carrier.
11. Install the instrument panel trim plate screws.
12. Tighten the steering column mounting nuts.
13. Install the steering column opening filler.
14. If equipped, enable the Supplemental Inflatable Restraint (SIR) system by performing the following:
    - Connect the yellow 2-way SIR connector and insert the Connector Positive Assurance (CPA) at the base of the steering column.
    - Install the left side sound insulator.
    - Install the SIR fuse in the fuse panel.
15. Connect the negative battery cable.

Corvette

1. Disconnect the negative battery cable.
2. If equipped, disable the Supplemental Inflatable Restraint (SIR) system by performing the following:
    - Remove the SIR fuse from the fuse panel.
    - Remove the left side sound insulator.
    - Remove the Connector Positive Assurance (CPA) from the yellow 2-way SIR harness connector at the base of the steering column and separate the connector.
3. Remove the instrument panel trim plate. Remove the instrument panel upper trim pad assembly.
4. Remove the control head screws.
5. Remove the control enough to disconnect the electrical connector.

To install:

6. Connect the electrical connector to the back of the control head.
7. Install the control head screws.
8. Install the instrument panel upper trim pad assembly.
9. Install the instrument panel trim plate.
10. If equipped, enable the Supplemental Inflatable Restraint (SIR) system by performing the following:
    - Connect the yellow 2-way SIR connector and insert the Connector Positive Assurance (CPA) at the base of the steering column.
    - Install the left side sound insulator.
    - Install the SIR fuse in the fuse panel.
11. Connect the negative battery cable.

SENSORS AND SWITCHES

Vacuum Actuators

OPERATION

Used on certain heating and air conditioning systems, the vacuum actuators operate the air doors determining the different modes. The actuator consists of a spring loaded diaphragm connected to a lever. When vacuum is applied to the diaphragm, the lever moves the control door to its appropriate position. When the lever on the control panel is moved to another position, vacuum is cut off and the spring returns the actuator lever to its normal position.

TESTING

1. Disconnect the vacuum line from the actuator.
2. Attach a hand-held vacuum pump to the actuator.
3. Apply vacuum to the actuator.
4. The actuator lever should move to its engaged position and remain there while vacuum is applied.
5. When vacuum is released it should move back to its normal position.
6. The lever should operate smoothly and not bind.

REMOVAL AND INSTALLATION

Caprice, Roadmaster and Fleetwood and 1994–95 Impala SS

DEFROSTER VALVE ACTUATOR, AIR INLET ACTUATOR, AND MODE VALVE ACTUATOR

1. If equipped with an air bag system, disconnect the negative battery cable, then perform the following:
    - Remove the SIR fuse from the fuse panel.
    - Remove the left side sound insulator.

- Remove the Connector Positive Assurance (CPA) from the yellow 2-way SIR harness connector at the base of the steering column and separate the connector.

2. To remove the defroster valve actuator, remove the instrument panel steering column opening filler (2 bolts/screws on lower edge, then pull from clips), then follow steps **5** through **9**.
3. To remove the air inlet valve actuator, remove the instrument panel, then follow steps **5** through **9**.
4. To remove the mode valve actuator, remove the instrument panel sound insulator under the right side of the instrument panel, then follow steps **5** through **9**.
5. Detach the vacuum hose at the actuator by sliding the tab of the connector retainer past the L-shaped bend in the vacuum tube while sliding hose off.
6. With a thin-blade tool, disengage the catch locking the actuator to the evaporator module assembly and slide the actuator away to remove it.
7. Unhook the actuator arm from the air door crank.

To install:

8. Installation is the reverse of the removal procedure.

NOTE: Bend the retaining tab of the vacuum hose connector back and hold it while slipping the tab and connector onto the vacuum tube, then pull the tab over the L-bend.

9. To Enable the air bag system, perform the following:
   - Connect the yellow 2-way SIR connector and insert the Connector Positive Assurance (CPA) at the base of the steering column.
   - Install the left side sound insulator.
   - Install the SIR fuse in the fuse panel.
   - Connect the negative battery cable.

Camaro and Firebird

DEFROSTER/HEATER ACTUATOR, BI-LEVEL MODE ACTUATOR, VENT MODE ACTUATOR

1. Disconnect the negative battery cable, then perform the following:
   - Remove the SIR fuse from the fuse panel.
   - Remove the left side sound insulator.
   - Remove the Connector Positive Assurance (CPA) from the yellow 2-way SIR harness connector at the base of the steering column and separate the connector.
2. Remove the instrument panel assembly for access to all the actuators as follows:
   - Remove the sound insulator from under both sides of the instrument panel.
   - Remove the removable top assembly.
   - Remove the window rail trim panel.
   - Remove the knee bolster and deflector.
   - Remove the stoplamp switch.
   - Detach and lower the steering column assembly.
   - Remove the upper instrument panel trim panel assembly.
   - Remove the radio trim plate.
   - Remove the instrument cluster bezel.
   - Remove the instrument cluster assembly by removing the retaining screws and pulling the cluster out to detach to electrical connectors.
   - Remove the radio assembly.
   - Remove the heater-A/C control panel as described in this article.
   - Remove the left side air ducts.
   - Remove the gear shift knob, cover and the center console.
   - Remove the fuse block and the ALDL connector from the instrument panel.
   - Detach the hazard and chime assembly from the convenience center.
   - Remove the instrument panel upper bolts and lower nuts and lower the instrument panel assembly to a suitable location while completing the removal procedure.
   - Remove the rest of the air duct assembly.
   - Remove the audio alarm from the convenience center.
   - Detach all connections and remove the wiring harness from its clips and retainers on the instrument panel assembly.
   - Remove the instrument panel assembly.
3. Locate the vacuum actuator and detach the linkage and retaining screws and remove the actuator.
4. Installation is the reverse of the removal procedure.

Corvette

PLENUM VALVE VACUUM ACTUATOR

1. If equipped with an air bag system, disconnect the negative battery cable, then perform the following:
   - Remove the SIR fuse from the fuse panel.
   - Remove the left side sound insulator.
   - Remove the Connector Positive Assurance (CPA) from the yellow 2-way SIR harness connector at the base of the steering column and separate the connector.
2. Remove the right sound insulator.
3. Detach the electrical connector and threaded rod from the actuator.
4. Remove the vacuum line from the actuator, the 2 retaining screws, and take off the plenum valve vacuum actuator.
5. Installation is the reverse of the removal procedure.

To install:

6. To Enable the air bag system, perform the following:
   - Connect the yellow 2-way SIR connector and insert the Connector Positive Assurance (CPA) at the base of the steering column.
   - Install the left side sound insulator.
   - Install the SIR fuse in the fuse panel.
   - Connect the negative battery cable.

DIVERTER VALVE REAR ACTUATOR

1. If equipped with an air bag system, disconnect the negative battery cable, then perform the following:
   - Remove the SIR fuse from the fuse panel.
   - Remove the left side sound insulator.
   - Remove the Connector Positive Assurance (CPA) from the yellow 2-way SIR harness connector at the base of the steering column and separate the connector.
2. Remove the right sound insulator.
3. Detach the electrical connector and threaded rod from the actuator.
4. Remove the vacuum line from the actuator, the 2 retaining screws, and take off the plenum valve vacuum actuator.

To install:

5. Installation is the reverse of the removal procedure.
6. To Enable the air bag system, perform the following:
   - Connect the yellow 2-way SIR connector and insert the Connector Positive Assurance (CPA) at the base of the steering column.
   - Install the left side sound insulator.
   - Install the SIR fuse in the fuse panel.
   - Connect the negative battery cable.

DEFROSTER VALVE VACUUM ACTUATOR

1. If equipped with an air bag system, disconnect the negative battery cable, then perform the following:
   - Remove the SIR fuse from the fuse panel.

- Remove the left side sound insulator.
- Remove the Connector Positive Assurance (CPA) from the yellow 2-way SIR harness connector at the base of the steering column and separate the connector.

2. Properly drain the cooling system.
3. Remove the instrument panel.
4. Remove the defroster duct from the instrument panel reinforcement.
5. Remove the hood release bracket from the panel reinforcement.
6. Remove the hood reinforcement bolts, nuts and shims.
7. Remove the duct case.
8. Remove the defroster valve vacuum actuator.

To install:

9. Installation is the reverse of the removal procedure.
10. To Enable the air bag system, perform the following:
    - Connect the yellow 2-way SIR connector and insert the Connector Positive Assurance (CPA) at the base of the steering column.
    - Install the left side sound insulator.
    - Install the SIR fuse in the fuse panel.
    - Connect the negative battery cable.

Electric Actuators

OPERATION

Caprice, Roadmaster, Fleetwood and Corvette and 1994–95 Impala SS

TEMPERATURE AIR VALVE ACTUATOR

The temperature air valve is positioned by an electric motor on the rear face of the air conditioning assembly and is driven by an electric motor instead of a temperature control cable as used on manual air conditioning systems. This system also uses the vacuum actuators for all other A/C air door operations.

REMOVAL AND INSTALLATION

Caprice, Roadmaster and Fleetwood and 1994–95 Impala SS

NOTE: Before removing the actuator, any fault codes displayed should be cleared by first pressing the OFF switch on the control panel, and then disconnecting the negative battery cable.

1. If equipped with an air bag system, disconnect the negative battery cable, then perform the following:
    - Remove the SIR fuse from the fuse panel.
    - Remove the left side sound insulator.
    - Remove the Connector Positive Assurance (CPA) from the yellow 2-way SIR harness connector at the base of the steering column and separate the connector.
2. Remove the ashtray.
3. Remove the tilt lever from the steering column, then remove the steering column opening filler plate.
4. Partially lower the steering column by loosening the mounting nuts, then remove the instrument panel full front trim panel by removing 8 screws (pull it straight out to disengage 7 retaining clips).
5. Remove the temperature air valve actuator.

To install:

6. Installation is the reverse of the removal procedure.
7. To Enable the air bag system, perform the following:
    - Connect the yellow 2-way SIR connector and insert the Connector Positive Assurance (CPA) at the base of the steering column.
    - Install the left side sound insulator.
    - Install the SIR fuse in the fuse panel.
    - Connect the negative battery cable.

Corvette

1. If equipped with an air bag system, disconnect the negative battery cable, then perform the following:
    - Remove the SIR fuse from the fuse panel.
    - Remove the left side sound insulator.
    - Remove the Connector Positive Assurance (CPA) from the yellow 2-way SIR harness connector at the base of the steering column and separate the connector.
2. Remove the heater/evaporator case assembly.
3. Remove the temperature door electrical connector and motor from the heater/evaporator case assembly.
4. Installation is the reverse of the removal procedure.

To install:

5. To Enable the air bag system, perform the following:
    - Connect the yellow 2-way SIR connector and insert the Connector Positive Assurance (CPA) at the base of the steering column.
    - Install the left side sound insulator.
    - Install the SIR fuse in the fuse panel.
    - Connect the negative battery cable.

Coolant Temperature Sensor

OPERATION

The coolant temperature sensor provides an engine temperature signal to the ECM. The ECM controls operation of the cooling fans and, in cases of high engine temperature, de-energizes the compressor clutch.

LOCATION

On 3.4L V6 engine – located on the top front of the engine below the intake plenum.

On 4.3L (VIN W) engine – located on the left side of the engine, below manifold.

On 5.0L (VIN E) engine – located on the top left side of the engine or near the thermostat housing.

On 5.0L (VIN F) and 5.7L (VIN 8) engines – located on the left front of the engine.

On 5.7L (VIN 7) engine – located on the left side of the engine, at the front of the intake manifold.

On 5.7L (VIN J) engine – located under the plenum, next to No. 1 cylinder injector.

On 5.7L (VIN P) engine – located on the left side of the engine, below manifold.

REMOVAL AND INSTALLATION

1. Disconnect the negative battery cable.
2. Drain the cooling system into a clean container for reuse.
3. Disconnect the electrical connector from the coolant temperature sensor.
4. Remove the coolant temperature sensor.

To install:

5. Install the coolant temperature sensor.
6. Connect the electrical connector.
7. Fill the cooling system.
8. Connect the negative battery cable.

9. Start the engine and check for leaks.

In-Vehicle Temperature Sensor

OPERATION

On Roadmaster, the in-vehicle temperature sensor is located at the top of the instrument panel carrier, to the right of the radio; on Cadillac Fleetwood, it is located at the top of the instrument panel, just to the right of the radio, and, on Corvette it is in the A/C outlet directly in front of the passenger's seat.

The in-vehicle temperature sensor monitors the temperature inside the passenger compartment. To provide accurate temperature readings, a small amount of air is drawn into the sensor housing, through the aspirator, passing over the thermistor.

REMOVAL AND INSTALLATION

1. Disconnect the negative battery cable.
2. Remove the necessary instrument panel trim pieces.
3. On Roadmaster, remove duct from sensor assembly.
4. Disconnect connector from harness assembly connector.
5. Remove the screws and the sensor.

To install:

6. Install the new sensor.
7. If remove, reconnect duct to sensor assembly
8. Reconnect harness assembly if required.
9. Install the instrument panel trim pieces.
10. Connect the negative battery cable.

Outside Temperature Sensor

OPERATION

The outside temperature sensor is located behind the radiator grille and provides an input to the electronic control programmer to determine the system operation depending upon outside temperature and operator-set condition on the control panel.

REMOVAL AND INSTALLATION

1. Disconnect the negative battery cable.
2. Remove the grille, as required.
3. Disconnect the electrical connector from the sensor.
4. Remove the attaching screw and the sensor.

To install:

5. Install the sensor and attaching screw.
6. Connect the electrical connector to the sensor.
7. Connect the negative battery cable.

High-Pressure Compressor Cut-Off Switch

OPERATION

The function of the switch is to protect the engine from overheating in the event of excessively high compressor head pressure and to de-energize the compressor clutch before the high pressure relief valve discharge pressure is reached. The switch is mounted on the back of the compressor or on the refrigerant hose assembly near the back of the compressor.

REMOVAL AND INSTALLATION

Compressor-Mounted Switch

NOTE: On the Cadillac Fleetwood, the sensor assembly is mounted on a Schrader type valve, so it is not necessary to discharge the refrigerant system. On all others, the system must be discharged in order to service the high pressure relief switch mounted to the back of the compressor.

1. Disconnect the negative battery cable.
2. Properly discharge the air conditioning system.
3. Remove the coupled hose assembly at the rear of the compressor.
4. Disconnect the electrical connector.
5. Remove the switch retaining ring using internal snap-ring pliers.
6. Remove the switch from the compressor. Discard the O-ring.

To install:

7. Lubricate a new O-ring with refrigerant oil. Insert into the switch cavity.
8. Lubricate the control switch housing with clean refrigerant oil and insert the switch until it bottoms in the cavity.
9. Install the switch retaining snap-ring with the high point of the curved sides adjacent to the switch housing. Ensure that the retaining ring is properly seated in the switch cavity retaining groove.
10. Connect the electrical connector.
11. Lubricate new coupled hose assembly O-rings with refrigerant oil. Install on the hose assembly fittings.
12. Connect the coupled hose assembly to the compressor.
13. Evacuate, recharge and leak test the system.
14. Connect the negative battery cable.
15. Operate the system to ensure proper operation and leak test the switch.

Refrigerant Line-Mounted Switch

NOTE: The switch is mounted on a Schrader-type valve and does not require that the system be discharged.

1. Disconnect the negative battery cable.
2. Disconnect the electrical connector.
3. Remove the switch from the coupled hose assembly. Discard the O-ring.

To install:

4. Lubricate a new O-ring with refrigerant oil.
5. Install the O-ring on the switch and install the switch.
6. Connect the electrical connector.
7. Connect the negative battery cable.

Compressor Low Pressure Cut-Off Switch

OPERATION

Camaro and Firebird

This switch is used to prevent continuous compressor operation if the system is low on refrigerant. The cut-off switch is wired inline with the compressor clutch coil circuit. It is the only switch that can override the PCM command to engage the compressor.

REMOVAL AND INSTALLATION

Camaro and Firebird

NOTE: The switch is located on a Schrader type valve; therefore, the system does not need to be discharged for removal.

1. Detach the electrical connector from the switch.
2. Remove the switch assembly and seal. Discard the seal.
3. Installation is the reverse of the removal procedure. Use a new seal.

Pressure Cycling Switch or Evaporator Inlet Temperature Sensor

OPERATION

The pressure cycling switch controls the refrigeration cycle by sensing low-side pressure as an indicator of evaporator temperature. The pressure cycling switch is the freeze-protection device in the system and senses refrigerant pressure on the suction side.

REMOVAL AND INSTALLATION

NOTE: The switch is mounted on a Schrader valve on the accumulator or on the evaporator inlet tube. The system need not be discharged to remove the pressure cycling switch.

1. Disconnect the negative battery cable.
2. Disconnect the electrical connector.
3. Remove the switch and O-ring seal. Discard the O-ring.

To install:

4. Install a new O-ring. Lubricate with refrigerant oil.
5. Install the switch to the accumulator or refrigerant line.
6. Connect the electrical connector.
7. Connect the negative battery cable.

Evaporator Temperature Sensor

OPERATION

Camaro and Firebird

This sensor, with a probe inserted into the evaporator coils, measures evaporator temperature and sends a signal to the PCM. The thermistor in the probe varies resistance according to the temperature. The purpose is to signal the PCM to cease compressor operation and prevent evaporator freeze-up as the temperature drops.

REMOVAL AND INSTALLATION

1. Remove the heater core.
2. Detach the evaporator temperature sensor electrical connector.
3. Use needle-nose pliers and pull the probe straight out from the coils.
4. Remove the sensor assembly and grommet.
5. Installation is the reverse of the removal procedure, except the probe should be inserted in a different location near the original location.

A/C Refrigerant Pressure Sensor

OPERATION

Camaro and Firebird

The pressure sensor is attached to the evaporator inlet line and sensor high side pressures. The pressure signal is sent to the PCM which can activate increased cooling fan operation to assist cooling under high pressure conditions, cut off compressor operation if high side pressure is too high or if ambient temperature is too low.

REMOVAL AND INSTALLATION

NOTE: The sensor is located on a Schrader-type valve; therefore, the system does not have to be discharged for removal.

1. Detach the electrical connector from the sensor.
2. Remove the sensor assembly and the seal.
3. Installation is the reverse of the removal procedure. Use a new seal on the sensor.

SYSTEM DIAGNOSIS

C.C.O.T. SYSTEM AIR CONDITIONING DIAGNOSIS INSUFFICIENT COOLING—CHART A

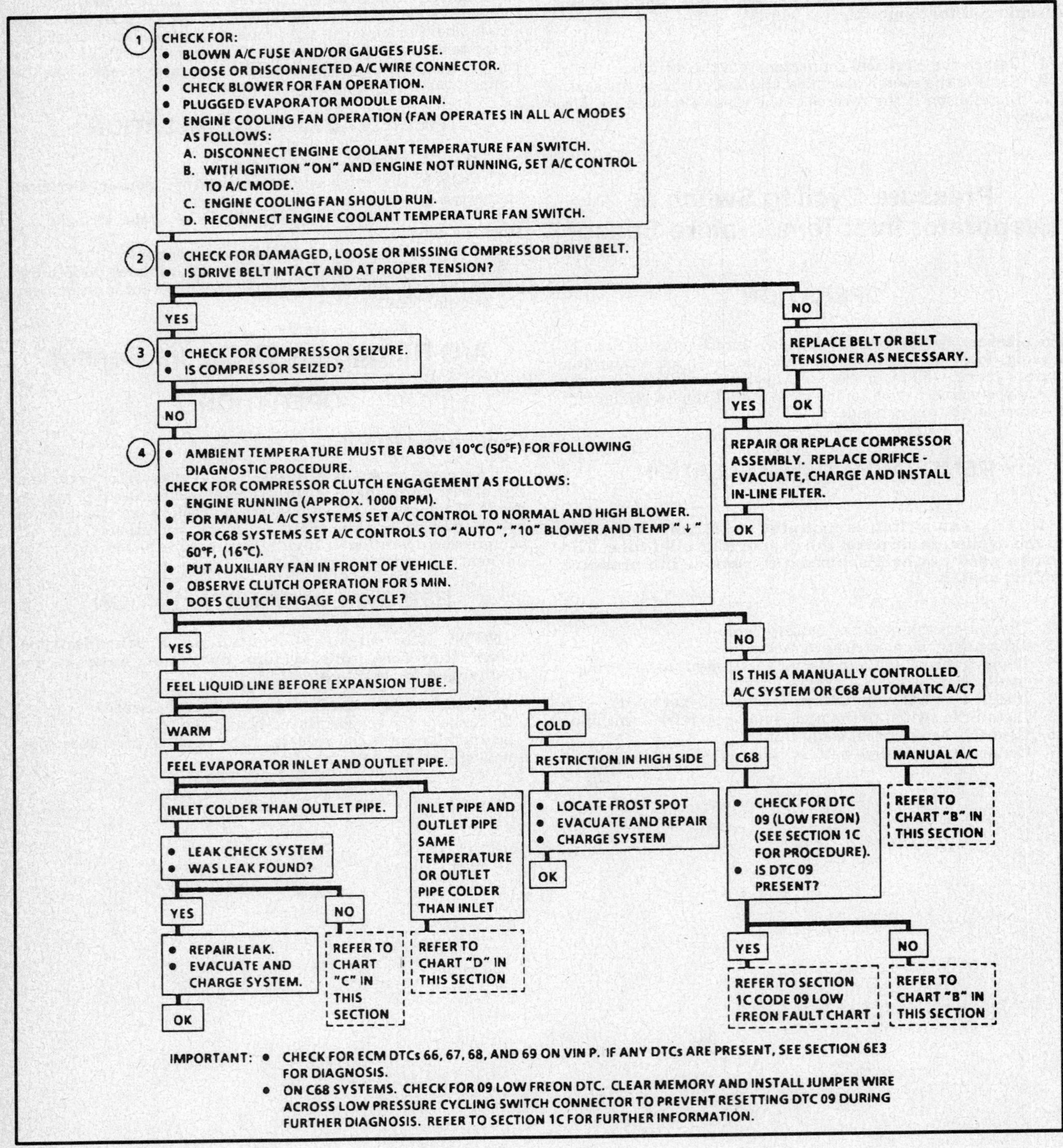
1
CHECK FOR:
• BLOWN A/C FUSE AND/OR GAUGES FUSE.
• LOOSE OR DISCONNECTED A/C WIRE CONNECTOR.
• CHECK BLOWER FOR FAN OPERATION.
• PLUGGED EVAPORATOR MODULE DRAIN.
• ENGINE COOLING FAN OPERATION (FAN OPERATES IN ALL A/C MODES AS FOLLOWS:
A. DISCONNECT ENGINE COOLANT TEMPERATURE FAN SWITCH.
B. WITH IGNITION "ON" AND ENGINE NOT RUNNING, SET A/C CONTROL TO A/C MODE.
C. ENGINE COOLING FAN SHOULD RUN.
D. RECONNECT ENGINE COOLANT TEMPERATURE FAN SWITCH.
2
• CHECK FOR DAMAGED, LOOSE OR MISSING COMPRESSOR DRIVE BELT.
• IS DRIVE BELT INTACT AND AT PROPER TENSION?
YES
NO
REPLACE BELT OR BELT TENSIONER AS NECESSARY.
OK
3
• CHECK FOR COMPRESSOR SEIZURE.
• IS COMPRESSOR SEIZED?
NO
YES
REPAIR OR REPLACE COMPRESSOR ASSEMBLY. REPLACE ORIFICE - EVACUATE, CHARGE AND INSTALL IN-LINE FILTER.
OK
4
• AMBIENT TEMPERATURE MUST BE ABOVE 10°C (50°F) FOR FOLLOWING DIAGNOSTIC PROCEDURE.
CHECK FOR COMPRESSOR CLUTCH ENGAGEMENT AS FOLLOWS:
• ENGINE RUNNING (APPROX. 1000 RPM).
• FOR MANUAL A/C SYSTEMS SET A/C CONTROL TO NORMAL AND HIGH BLOWER.
• FOR C68 SYSTEMS SET A/C CONTROLS TO "AUTO", "10" BLOWER AND TEMP "↓" 60°F, (16°C).
• PUT AUXILIARY FAN IN FRONT OF VEHICLE.
• OBSERVE CLUTCH OPERATION FOR 5 MIN.
• DOES CLUTCH ENGAGE OR CYCLE?
YES
FEEL LIQUID LINE BEFORE EXPANSION TUBE.
WARM
FEEL EVAPORATOR INLET AND OUTLET PIPE.
INLET COLDER THAN OUTLET PIPE.
• LEAK CHECK SYSTEM
• WAS LEAK FOUND?
YES
• REPAIR LEAK.
• EVACUATE AND CHARGE SYSTEM.
OK
NO
REFER TO CHART "C" IN THIS SECTION
INLET PIPE AND OUTLET PIPE SAME TEMPERATURE OR OUTLET PIPE COLDER THAN INLET
REFER TO CHART "D" IN THIS SECTION
COLD
RESTRICTION IN HIGH SIDE
• LOCATE FROST SPOT
• EVACUATE AND REPAIR
• CHARGE SYSTEM
OK
NO
IS THIS A MANUALLY CONTROLLED A/C SYSTEM OR C68 AUTOMATIC A/C?
C68
• CHECK FOR DTC 09 (LOW FREON) (SEE SECTION 1C FOR PROCEDURE).
• IS DTC 09 PRESENT?
YES
REFER TO SECTION 1C CODE 09 LOW FREON FAULT CHART
NO
REFER TO CHART "B" IN THIS SECTION
MANUAL A/C
REFER TO CHART "B" IN THIS SECTION
IMPORTANT: • CHECK FOR ECM DTCs 66, 67, 68, AND 69 ON VIN P. IF ANY DTCs ARE PRESENT, SEE SECTION 6E3 FOR DIAGNOSIS.
• ON C68 SYSTEMS. CHECK FOR 09 LOW FREON DTC. CLEAR MEMORY AND INSTALL JUMPER WIRE ACROSS LOW PRESSURE CYCLING SWITCH CONNECTOR TO PREVENT RESETTING DTC 09 DURING FURTHER DIAGNOSIS. REFER TO SECTION 1C FOR FURTHER INFORMATION.

C.C.O.T. SYSTEM AIR CONDITIONING DIAGNOSIS INSUFFICIENT COOLING—CHART B

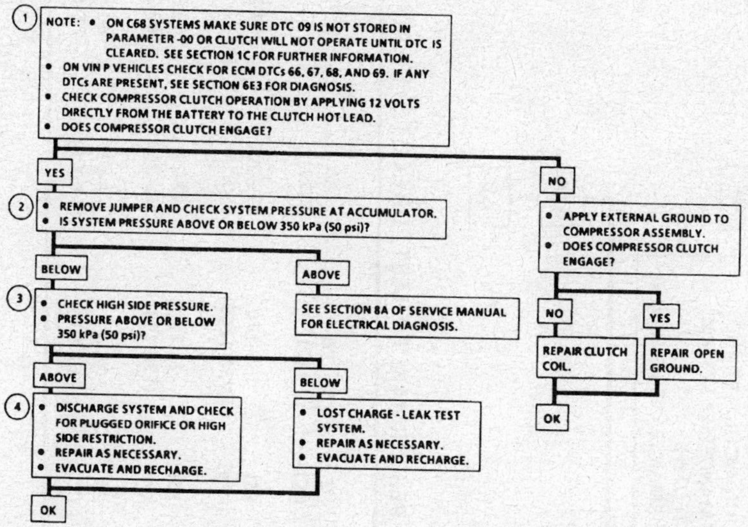

1. NOTE: • ON C68 SYSTEMS MAKE SURE DTC 09 IS NOT STORED IN PARAMETER -00 OR CLUTCH WILL NOT OPERATE UNTIL DTC IS CLEARED. SEE SECTION 1C FOR FURTHER INFORMATION.
   - ON VIN P VEHICLES CHECK FOR ECM DTCs 66, 67, 68, AND 69. IF ANY DTCs ARE PRESENT, SEE SECTION 6E3 FOR DIAGNOSIS.
   - CHECK COMPRESSOR CLUTCH OPERATION BY APPLYING 12 VOLTS DIRECTLY FROM THE BATTERY TO THE CLUTCH HOT LEAD.
   - DOES COMPRESSOR CLUTCH ENGAGE?

YES

2. • REMOVE JUMPER AND CHECK SYSTEM PRESSURE AT ACCUMULATOR.
   - IS SYSTEM PRESSURE ABOVE OR BELOW 350 kPa (50 psi)?

BELOW

3. • CHECK HIGH SIDE PRESSURE.
   - PRESSURE ABOVE OR BELOW 350 kPa (50 psi)?

ABOVE

4. • DISCHARGE SYSTEM AND CHECK FOR PLUGGED ORIFICE OR HIGH SIDE RESTRICTION.
   - REPAIR AS NECESSARY.
   - EVACUATE AND RECHARGE.

BELOW

- LOST CHARGE - LEAK TEST SYSTEM.
- REPAIR AS NECESSARY.
- EVACUATE AND RECHARGE.

OK

ABOVE

SEE SECTION 8A OF SERVICE MANUAL FOR ELECTRICAL DIAGNOSIS.

NO

- APPLY EXTERNAL GROUND TO COMPRESSOR ASSEMBLY.
- DOES COMPRESSOR CLUTCH ENGAGE?

NO — REPAIR CLUTCH COIL.

YES — REPAIR OPEN GROUND.

OK

C.C.O.T. SYSTEM AIR CONDITIONING DIAGNOSIS INSUFFICIENT COOLING—CHART C

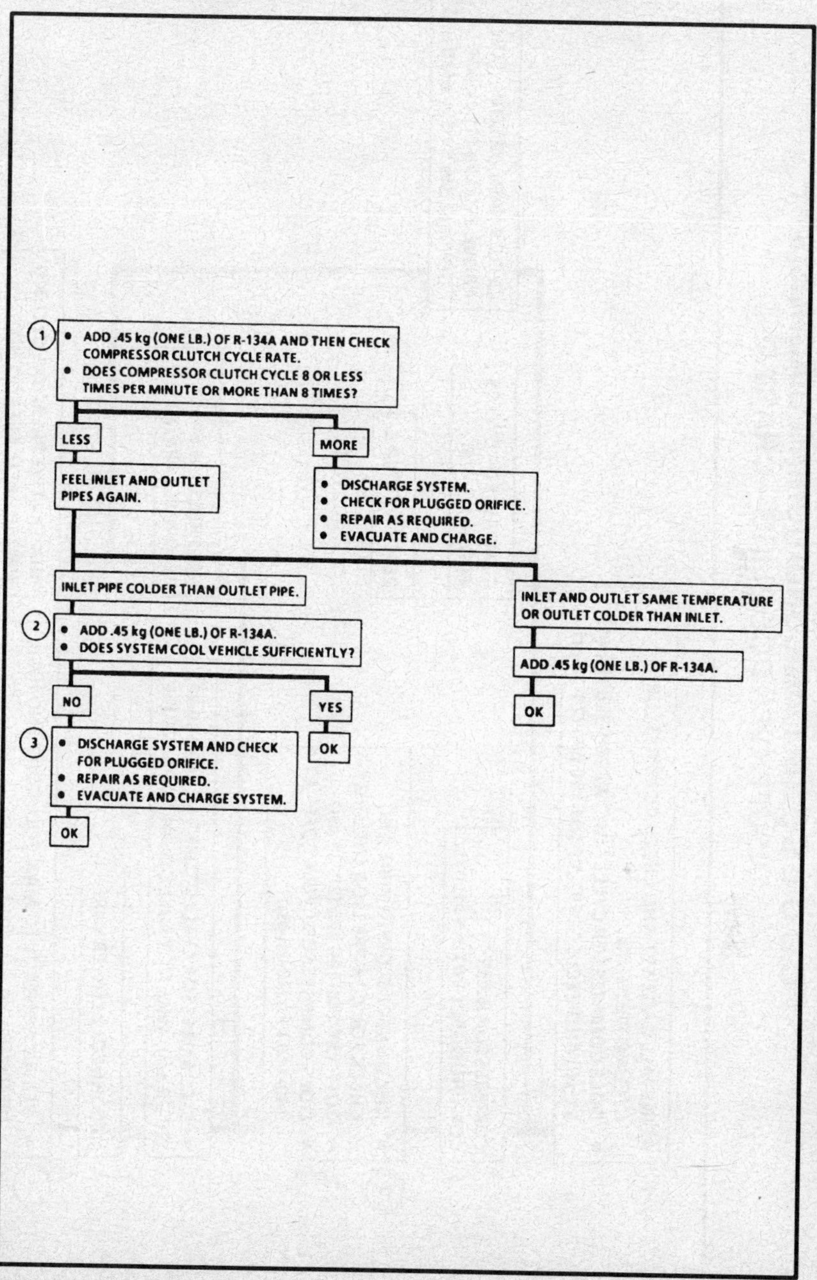

1
• ADD .45 kg (ONE LB.) OF R-134A AND THEN CHECK COMPRESSOR CLUTCH CYCLE RATE.
• DOES COMPRESSOR CLUTCH CYCLE 8 OR LESS TIMES PER MINUTE OR MORE THAN 8 TIMES?
LESS
FEEL INLET AND OUTLET PIPES AGAIN.
MORE
• DISCHARGE SYSTEM.
• CHECK FOR PLUGGED ORIFICE.
• REPAIR AS REQUIRED.
• EVACUATE AND CHARGE.
INLET PIPE COLDER THAN OUTLET PIPE.
2
• ADD .45 kg (ONE LB.) OF R-134A.
• DOES SYSTEM COOL VEHICLE SUFFICIENTLY?
NO
3
• DISCHARGE SYSTEM AND CHECK FOR PLUGGED ORIFICE.
• REPAIR AS REQUIRED.
• EVACUATE AND CHARGE SYSTEM.
OK
YES
OK
INLET AND OUTLET SAME TEMPERATURE OR OUTLET COLDER THAN INLET.
ADD .45 kg (ONE LB.) OF R-134A.
OK

C.C.O.T. SYSTEM AIR CONDITIONING DIAGNOSIS
INSUFFICIENT COOLING—CHART D

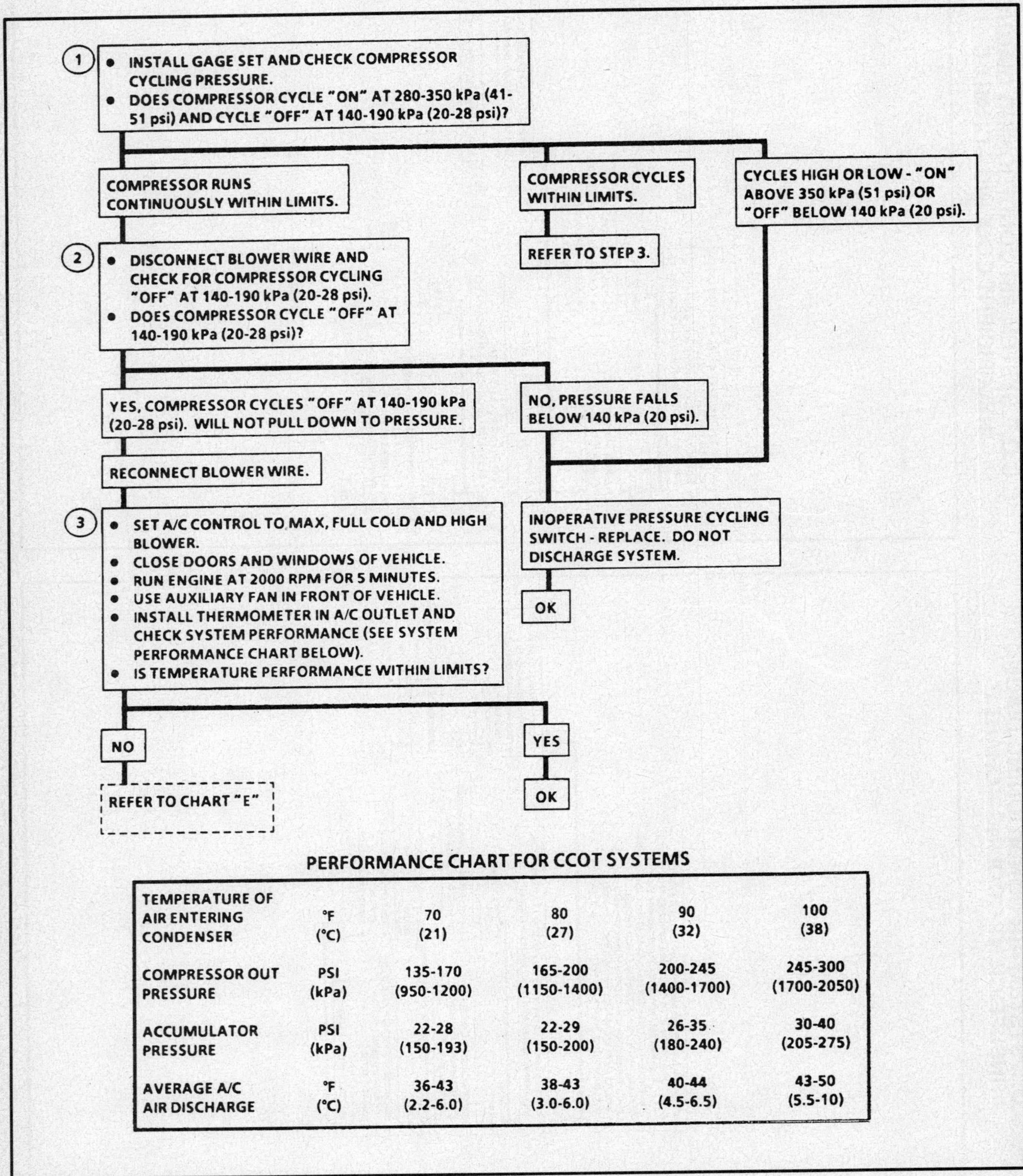
1
• INSTALL GAGE SET AND CHECK COMPRESSOR CYCLING PRESSURE.
• DOES COMPRESSOR CYCLE "ON" AT 280-350 kPa (41-51 psi) AND CYCLE "OFF" AT 140-190 kPa (20-28 psi)?
COMPRESSOR RUNS CONTINUOUSLY WITHIN LIMITS.
COMPRESSOR CYCLES WITHIN LIMITS.
CYCLES HIGH OR LOW - "ON" ABOVE 350 kPa (51 psi) OR "OFF" BELOW 140 kPa (20 psi).
REFER TO STEP 3.
2
• DISCONNECT BLOWER WIRE AND CHECK FOR COMPRESSOR CYCLING "OFF" AT 140-190 kPa (20-28 psi).
• DOES COMPRESSOR CYCLE "OFF" AT 140-190 kPa (20-28 psi)?
YES, COMPRESSOR CYCLES "OFF" AT 140-190 kPa (20-28 psi). WILL NOT PULL DOWN TO PRESSURE.
NO, PRESSURE FALLS BELOW 140 kPa (20 psi).
RECONNECT BLOWER WIRE.
INOPERATIVE PRESSURE CYCLING SWITCH - REPLACE. DO NOT DISCHARGE SYSTEM.
OK
3
• SET A/C CONTROL TO MAX, FULL COLD AND HIGH BLOWER.
• CLOSE DOORS AND WINDOWS OF VEHICLE.
• RUN ENGINE AT 2000 RPM FOR 5 MINUTES.
• USE AUXILIARY FAN IN FRONT OF VEHICLE.
• INSTALL THERMOMETER IN A/C OUTLET AND CHECK SYSTEM PERFORMANCE (SEE SYSTEM PERFORMANCE CHART BELOW).
• IS TEMPERATURE PERFORMANCE WITHIN LIMITS?
NO
YES
REFER TO CHART "E"
OK

PERFORMANCE CHART FOR CCOT SYSTEMS

TEMPERATURE OF AIR ENTERING CONDENSER	°F (°C)	70 (21)	80 (27)	90 (32)	100 (38)
COMPRESSOR OUT PRESSURE	PSI (kPa)	135-170 (950-1200)	165-200 (1150-1400)	200-245 (1400-1700)	245-300 (1700-2050)
ACCUMULATOR PRESSURE	PSI (kPa)	22-28 (150-193)	22-29 (150-200)	26-35 (180-240)	30-40 (205-275)
AVERAGE A/C AIR DISCHARGE	°F (°C)	36-43 (2.2-6.0)	38-43 (3.0-6.0)	40-44 (4.5-6.5)	43-50 (5.5-10)

C.C.O.T. SYSTEM AIR CONDITIONING DIAGNOSIS
INSUFFICIENT COOLING—CHART E

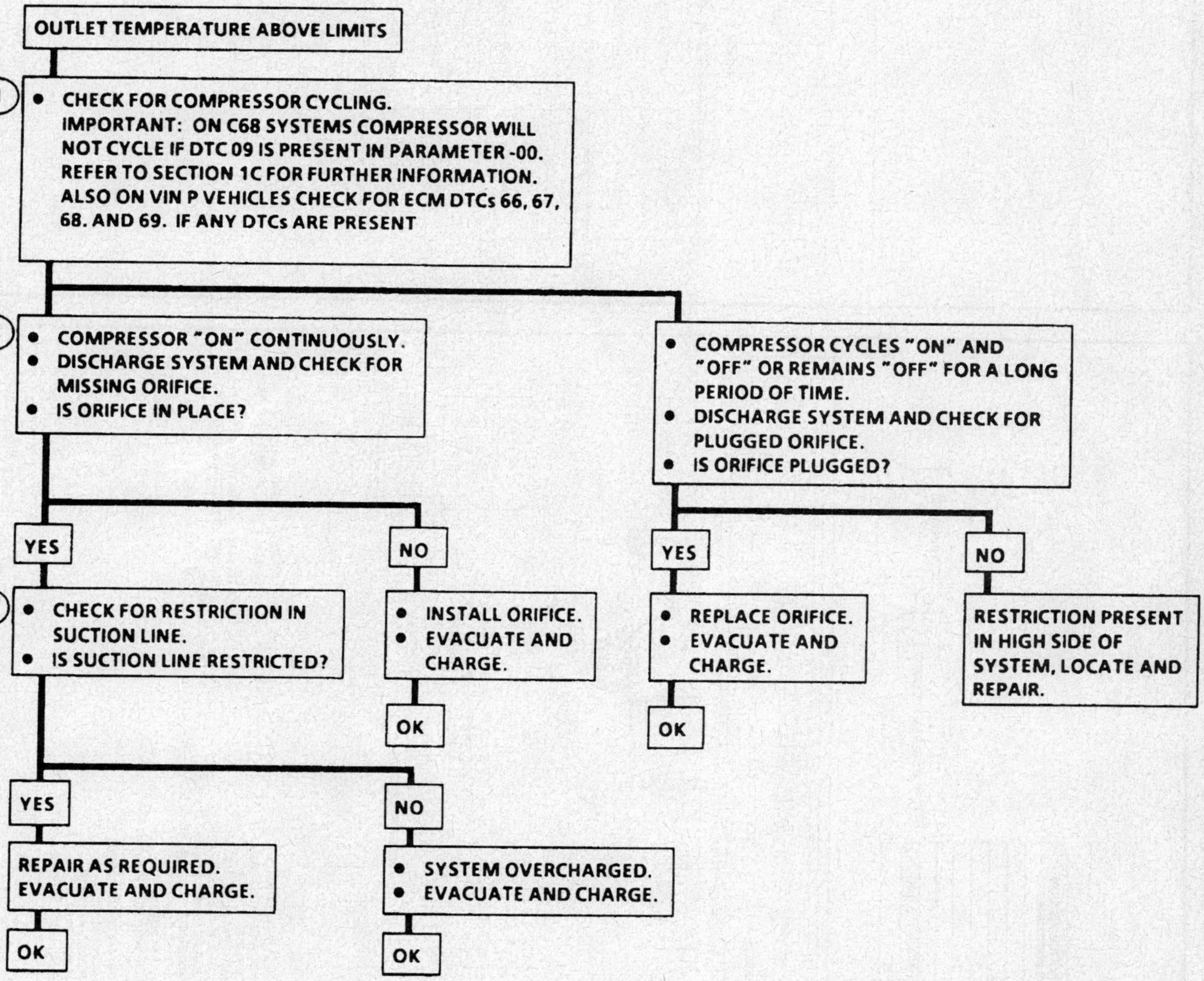

OUTLET TEMPERATURE ABOVE LIMITS

1
- CHECK FOR COMPRESSOR CYCLING.
  IMPORTANT: ON C68 SYSTEMS COMPRESSOR WILL NOT CYCLE IF DTC 09 IS PRESENT IN PARAMETER -00. REFER TO SECTION 1C FOR FURTHER INFORMATION. ALSO ON VIN P VEHICLES CHECK FOR ECM DTCs 66, 67, 68. AND 69. IF ANY DTCs ARE PRESENT

2
- COMPRESSOR "ON" CONTINUOUSLY.
- DISCHARGE SYSTEM AND CHECK FOR MISSING ORIFICE.
- IS ORIFICE IN PLACE?

YES

3
- CHECK FOR RESTRICTION IN SUCTION LINE.
- IS SUCTION LINE RESTRICTED?

YES

REPAIR AS REQUIRED.
EVACUATE AND CHARGE.

OK

NO

- SYSTEM OVERCHARGED.
- EVACUATE AND CHARGE.

OK

NO

- INSTALL ORIFICE.
- EVACUATE AND CHARGE.

OK

- COMPRESSOR CYCLES "ON" AND "OFF" OR REMAINS "OFF" FOR A LONG PERIOD OF TIME.
- DISCHARGE SYSTEM AND CHECK FOR PLUGGED ORIFICE.
- IS ORIFICE PLUGGED?

YES

- REPLACE ORIFICE.
- EVACUATE AND CHARGE.

OK

NO

RESTRICTION PRESENT IN HIGH SIDE OF SYSTEM, LOCATE AND REPAIR.

VACUUM AND AIR DELIVERY CHART CAMARO AND FIREBIRD

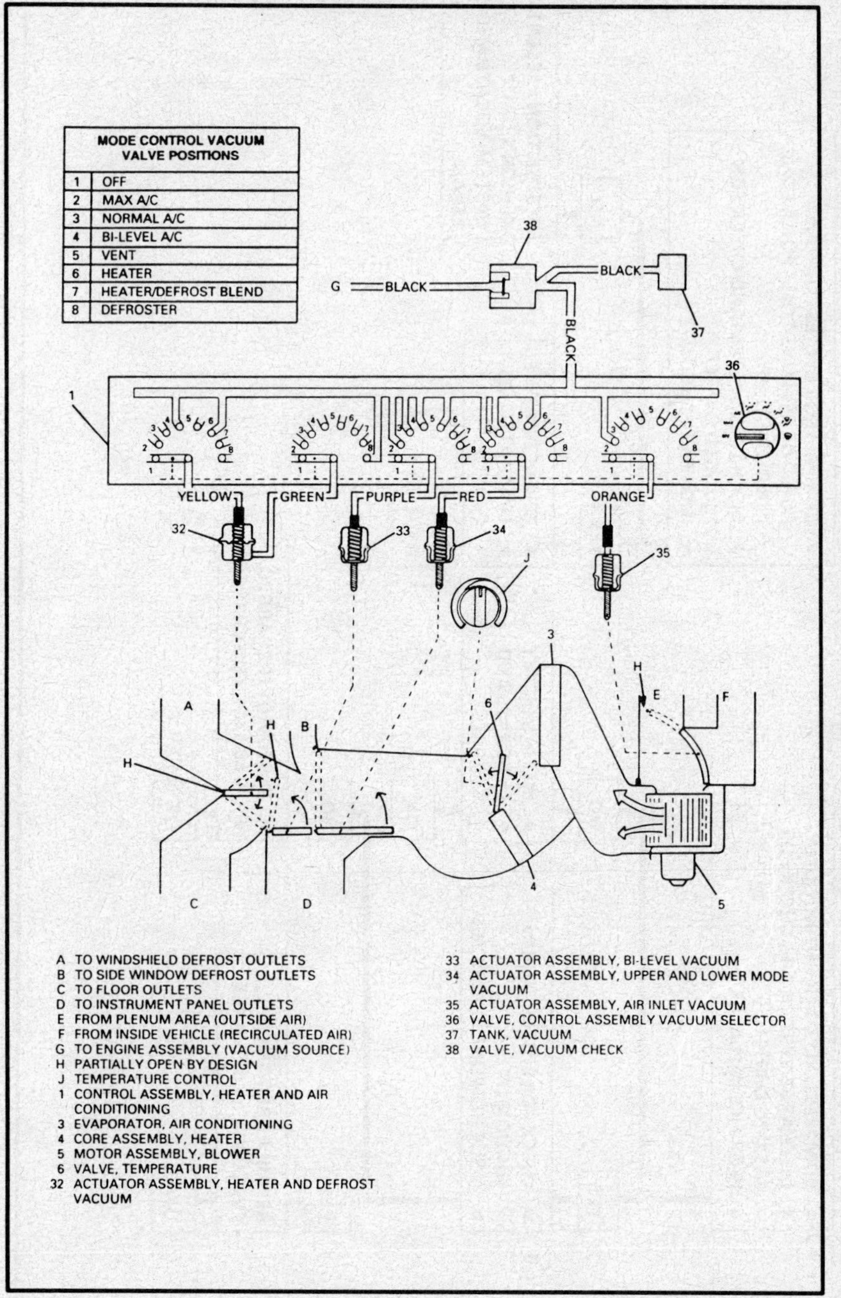

MODE CONTROL VACUUM VALVE POSITIONS	
1	OFF
2	MAX A/C
3	NORMAL A/C
4	BI-LEVEL A/C
5	VENT
6	HEATER
7	HEATER/DEFROST BLEND
8	DEFROSTER

A TO WINDSHIELD DEFROST OUTLETS
B TO SIDE WINDOW DEFROST OUTLETS
C TO FLOOR OUTLETS
D TO INSTRUMENT PANEL OUTLETS
E FROM PLENUM AREA (OUTSIDE AIR)
F FROM INSIDE VEHICLE (RECIRCULATED AIR)
G TO ENGINE ASSEMBLY (VACUUM SOURCE)
H PARTIALLY OPEN BY DESIGN
J TEMPERATURE CONTROL
1 CONTROL ASSEMBLY, HEATER AND AIR CONDITIONING
3 EVAPORATOR, AIR CONDITIONING
4 CORE ASSEMBLY, HEATER
5 MOTOR ASSEMBLY, BLOWER
6 VALVE, TEMPERATURE
32 ACTUATOR ASSEMBLY, HEATER AND DEFROST VACUUM
33 ACTUATOR ASSEMBLY, BI-LEVEL VACUUM
34 ACTUATOR ASSEMBLY, UPPER AND LOWER MODE VACUUM
35 ACTUATOR ASSEMBLY, AIR INLET VACUUM
36 VALVE, CONTROL ASSEMBLY VACUUM SELECTOR
37 TANK, VACUUM
38 VALVE, VACUUM CHECK

A/C PERFORMANCE TEST CHART CAMARO AND FIREBIRD

TEMPERATURE	HUMIDITY	GAGE PRESSURES LOW	GAGE PRESSURES HIGH	CENTER OUTLET TEMP	EVAP ASSEMBLY TEMP DISPLAYED ON TECH 1
21° - 27°C	LESS THAN 50%	110 - 165 kPa (16 - 24 psi)	793-1310 kPa (115 - 190 psi)	3° - 9°C (38° - 48°F)	1° - 6°C (33° - 43°F)
(70° - 80°F)	HIGHER THAN 50%	145 - 200 kPa (21 - 29 psi)	793 - 1379 kPa (115 - 200 psi)	4° - 13°C (40° - 55°F)	2° - 10°C (35° - 50°F)
27° - 33°C	LESS THAN 50%	131 - 207 kPa (19 - 30 psi)	965 - 1482 kPa (140 - 215 psi)	3° - 13°C (38° - 55°F)	1° -10°C (33° - 50°F)
(80° - 90°F)	HIGHER THAN 50%	165 - 269 kPa (24 - 39 psi)	1034 - 1620 kPa (150 - 235 psi)	7° - 18°C (45° - 65°F)	4° - 16°C (40° - 60°F)
33° - 38°C	LESS THAN 40%	172 - 290 kPa (25 - 42 psi)	1138 - 1793 kPa (165 - 260 psi)	7° - 17°C (45° - 63°F)	4° - 14°C (40° - 58°F)
(90° - 100°F)	HIGHER THAN 40%	234 - 296 kPa (34 - 43 psi)	1276 - 1862 kPa (185 - 270 psi)	13° - 20°C (55° - 68°F)	10° - 18°C (50° - 65°F)
38° - 44°C	LESS THAN 20%	255 - 296 kPa (37 - 43 psi)	1448 - 2000 kPa (210 - 290 psi)	12° - 18°C (53° - 64°F)	9° - 16°C (48° - 61°F)
(100° - 110°F)	HIGHER THAN 20%	262 - 352 kPa (38 - 51 psi)	1517 - 2137 kPa (220 - 310 psi)	14° - 21°C (58° - 70°F)	13° - 18°C (55° - 65°F)

A/C SYSTEM DIAGNOSTIC CHART CAMARO AND FIREBIRD

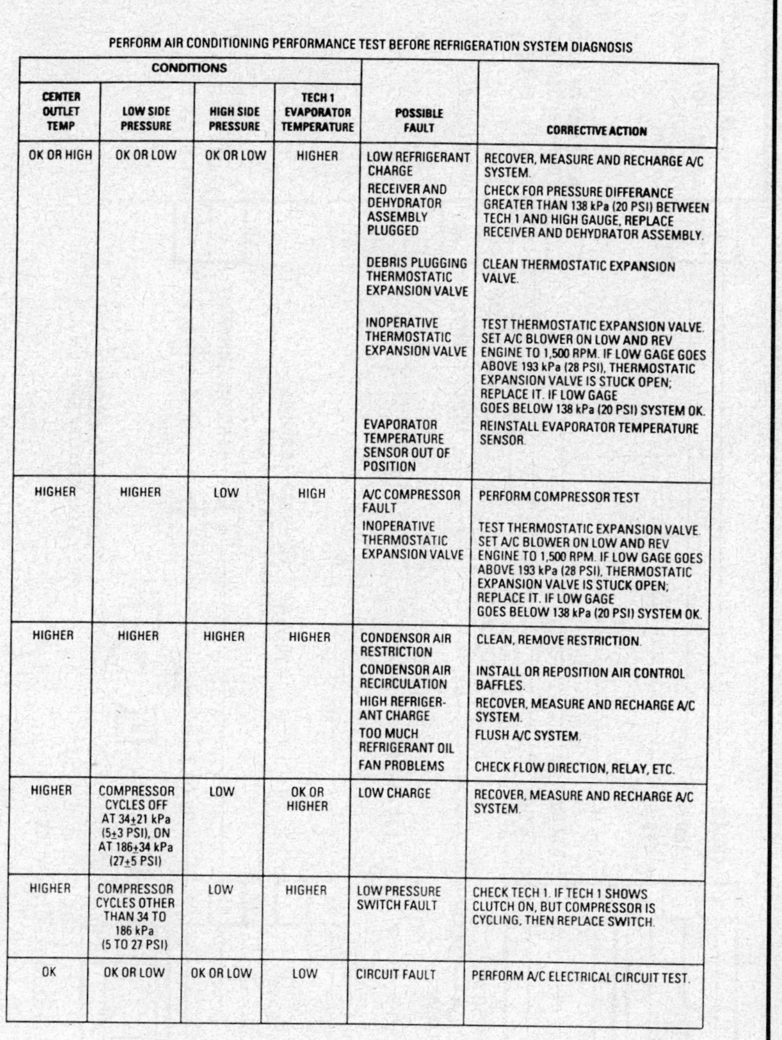

PERFORM AIR CONDITIONING PERFORMANCE TEST BEFORE REFRIGERATION SYSTEM DIAGNOSIS

CONDITIONS					
CENTER OUTLET TEMP	LOW SIDE PRESSURE	HIGH SIDE PRESSURE	TECH 1 EVAPORATOR TEMPERATURE	POSSIBLE FAULT	CORRECTIVE ACTION
OK OR HIGH	OK OR LOW	OK OR LOW	HIGHER	LOW REFRIGERANT CHARGE	RECOVER, MEASURE AND RECHARGE A/C SYSTEM.
				RECEIVER AND DEHYDRATOR ASSEMBLY PLUGGED	CHECK FOR PRESSURE DIFFERANCE GREATER THAN 138 kPa (20 PSI) BETWEEN TECH 1 AND HIGH GAUGE, REPLACE RECEIVER AND DEHYDRATOR ASSEMBLY.
				DEBRIS PLUGGING THERMOSTATIC EXPANSION VALVE	CLEAN THERMOSTATIC EXPANSION VALVE.
				INOPERATIVE THERMOSTATIC EXPANSION VALVE	TEST THERMOSTATIC EXPANSION VALVE. SET A/C BLOWER ON LOW AND REV ENGINE TO 1,500 RPM. IF LOW GAGE GOES ABOVE 193 kPa (28 PSI), THERMOSTATIC EXPANSION VALVE IS STUCK OPEN; REPLACE IT. IF LOW GAGE GOES BELOW 138 kPa (20 PSI) SYSTEM OK.
				EVAPORATOR TEMPERATURE SENSOR OUT OF POSITION	REINSTALL EVAPORATOR TEMPERATURE SENSOR.
HIGHER	HIGHER	LOW	HIGH	A/C COMPRESSOR FAULT	PERFORM COMPRESSOR TEST
				INOPERATIVE THERMOSTATIC EXPANSION VALVE	TEST THERMOSTATIC EXPANSION VALVE. SET A/C BLOWER ON LOW AND REV ENGINE TO 1,500 RPM. IF LOW GAGE GOES ABOVE 193 kPa (28 PSI), THERMOSTATIC EXPANSION VALVE IS STUCK OPEN; REPLACE IT. IF LOW GAGE GOES BELOW 138 kPa (20 PSI) SYSTEM OK.
HIGHER	HIGHER	HIGHER	HIGHER	CONDENSOR AIR RESTRICTION	CLEAN, REMOVE RESTRICTION.
				CONDENSOR AIR RECIRCULATION	INSTALL OR REPOSITION AIR CONTROL BAFFLES.
				HIGH REFRIGERANT CHARGE	RECOVER, MEASURE AND RECHARGE A/C SYSTEM.
				TOO MUCH REFRIGERANT OIL	FLUSH A/C SYSTEM.
				FAN PROBLEMS	CHECK FLOW DIRECTION, RELAY, ETC.
HIGHER	COMPRESSOR CYCLES OFF AT 34±21 kPa (5±3 PSI), ON AT 186±34 kPa (27±5 PSI)	LOW	OK OR HIGHER	LOW CHARGE	RECOVER, MEASURE AND RECHARGE A/C SYSTEM.
HIGHER	COMPRESSOR CYCLES OTHER THAN 34 TO 186 kPa (5 TO 27 PSI)	LOW	HIGHER	LOW PRESSURE SWITCH FAULT	CHECK TECH 1. IF TECH 1 SHOWS CLUTCH ON, BUT COMPRESSOR IS CYCLING, THEN REPLACE SWITCH.
OK	OK OR LOW	OK OR LOW	LOW	CIRCUIT FAULT	PERFORM A/C ELECTRICAL CIRCUIT TEST.

A/C PERFORMANCE READINGS CHART CAMARO AND FIREBIRD

- QUICKLY ROTATE TEMPERATURE KNOB FROM "FULL COLD" TO "FULL HOT" AND BACK TO "FULL COLD". LISTEN FOR TEMPERATURE VALVE TO SEAT IN BOTH "FULL HOT" AND "FULL COLD" POSITION (A "THUD" NOISE SHOULD BE HEARD).
- DOES TEMPERATURE VALVE SEAT IN BOTH POSITIONS?

YES →

- CLOSE DOORS AND WINDOWS.
- SELECT "FULL COLD, MAX A/C" MODE AND "HIGH" BLOWER MOTOR SPEED.
- PLACE VEHICLE IN PARK (AUTOMATIC TRANSMISSION ASSEMBLY) AND SET PARKING BRAKE (MANUAL OR AUTOMATIC TRANSMISSION ASSEMBLY).
- START ENGINE ASSEMBLY.
- DOES COMPRESSOR ENGAGE?

NO → A/C COMPRESSOR CIRCUIT DIAGNOSIS

YES →

- INSTALL TECH 1 WITH 93 POWERTRAIN CARTRIDGE.
- SELECT "FIELD SERVICE" MODE.
- CHECK COOLING FAN OPERATION:
  - V-6 COOLING FAN OPERATING.
  - V-8 BOTH COOLING FANS OPERATING.
- ARE COOLING FAN(S) OPERATING?

NO →

- REPAIR COOLING FAN CIRCUIT.

YES →

- INSTALL J 39183-C (R-134a MANIFOLD GAGE SET) OR J 39500-GM (ACR⁴ SYSTEM) ONTO VEHICLE.
- INSTALL J 6742-03 (PRECISION THERMOMETER) OR EQUIVALENT INTO CENTER INSTRUMENT PANEL OUTLET.
- WITH VEHICLE RUNNING IN "MAX A/C" MODE, "FULL COLD" AND "HIGH" BLOWER MOTOR SPEED FOR 5 MINUTES, RECORD THE FOLLOWING INFORMATION:
  - — A/C SYSTEM HIGH AND LOW SIDE PRESSURE
  - — EVAPORATOR TEMPERATURE
  - — AMBIENT TEMPERATURE AND HUMIDITY
- COMPARE WITH AIR CONDITIONING PERFORMANCE CHART
- IS VEHICLE A/C PERFORMANCE WITHIN SPECIFICATIONS?

NO → REFER TO "REFRIGERATION SYSTEM DIAGNOSIS CHART"

YES → SYSTEM OK

NO (temperature valve does not seat) →

- DISCONNECT TEMPERATURE CABLE AT HEATER AND EVAPORATOR MODULE ASSEMBLY.
- ROTATE TEMPERATURE LEVER FROM "FULL HOT" TO "FULL COLD" WHILE WATCHING CABLE END.
- DOES CABLE END ROTATE WHEN TEMPERATURE LEVER IS ROTATED?

NO → REPAIR OR REPLACE TEMPERATURE CABLE AS NECESSARY.

YES →

- MANUALLY ROTATE TEMPERATURE VALVE BY HAND.
- DOES TEMPERATURE VALVE SEAT IN BOTH "FULL HOT" AND "FULL COLD" POSITION WITH APPROXIMATELY 50 DEGREES OF TRAVEL?

YES → REPLACE TEMPERATURE CABLE.

NO → REPAIR OR REPLACE HEATER AND EVAPORATOR MODULE ASSEMBLY.

Manual Air Conditioning Systems

ON-BOARD DIAGNOSTIC COMPRESSOR CIRCUIT CHECK

1993 Camaro and Firebird

On these models, the ECM can be used for on-board diagnosis of the compressor circuit. The ECM can determine if the compressor is engaged or not through the A/C clutch status line. When voltage is present at the ECM A/C clutch status terminal, an A/C status **ON** will be displayed on the scan tool (Tech 1® or equivalent). Diagnostic Trouble Code (DTC) **67** indicates trouble in the compressor circuit and will set under the following conditions:

1. If the refrigerant pressure does not increase more than 9 psi when the A/C clutch cycles ON.
2. If the refrigerant pressure sensor is fixed at one value or if the pressure sensor ground is open.
3. If the relay power feed (circuit 139) is intermittent the A/C clutch status terminal may not detect voltage when the compressor clutch is ON.
4. If the status line becomes intermittently open or shorted while the compressor is ON, the ECM will be incorrectly detecting the clutch cycling.
5. If the compressor clutch is disconnected or if circuit 59 is open between the splice and the clutch, the clutch will not engage, but the ECM will detect voltage on the status line, indicating the clutch is ON.

NOTE: A DTC 67 will store in the ECM memory but will not turn on the SERVICE ENGINE SOON (malfunction indicator) lamp.

Automatic Climate Control Systems

Cadillac Brougham

ENTERING THE DIAGNOSTIC MODE

1. Turn ignition to **ON**. Depress the **OFF** and **WARMER** buttons and hold both down until all display panel segments illuminate, indicating the beginning of the diagnostic readout.

NOTE: The purpose of illuminating the control head is to check that all segments of the displays are working. Diagnosis should not be attempted unless all segments appear; if not, this could lead to misdiagnosis. If any segment is inoperative, the affected display panel will have to be replaced.

2. After the displays end, any trouble codes stored in the electronic control module (ECM) computer memory will be displayed in numerical sequence.
3. Display of electronic climate control (ECC) trouble codes begins with current codes followed by historical codes (previously recognized, but not current, system errors). Each code will display for 1.6 seconds.
4. The code display will repeat until a button on the climate control panel is depressed. Make note of the codes separately to avoid losing them if they are erased.

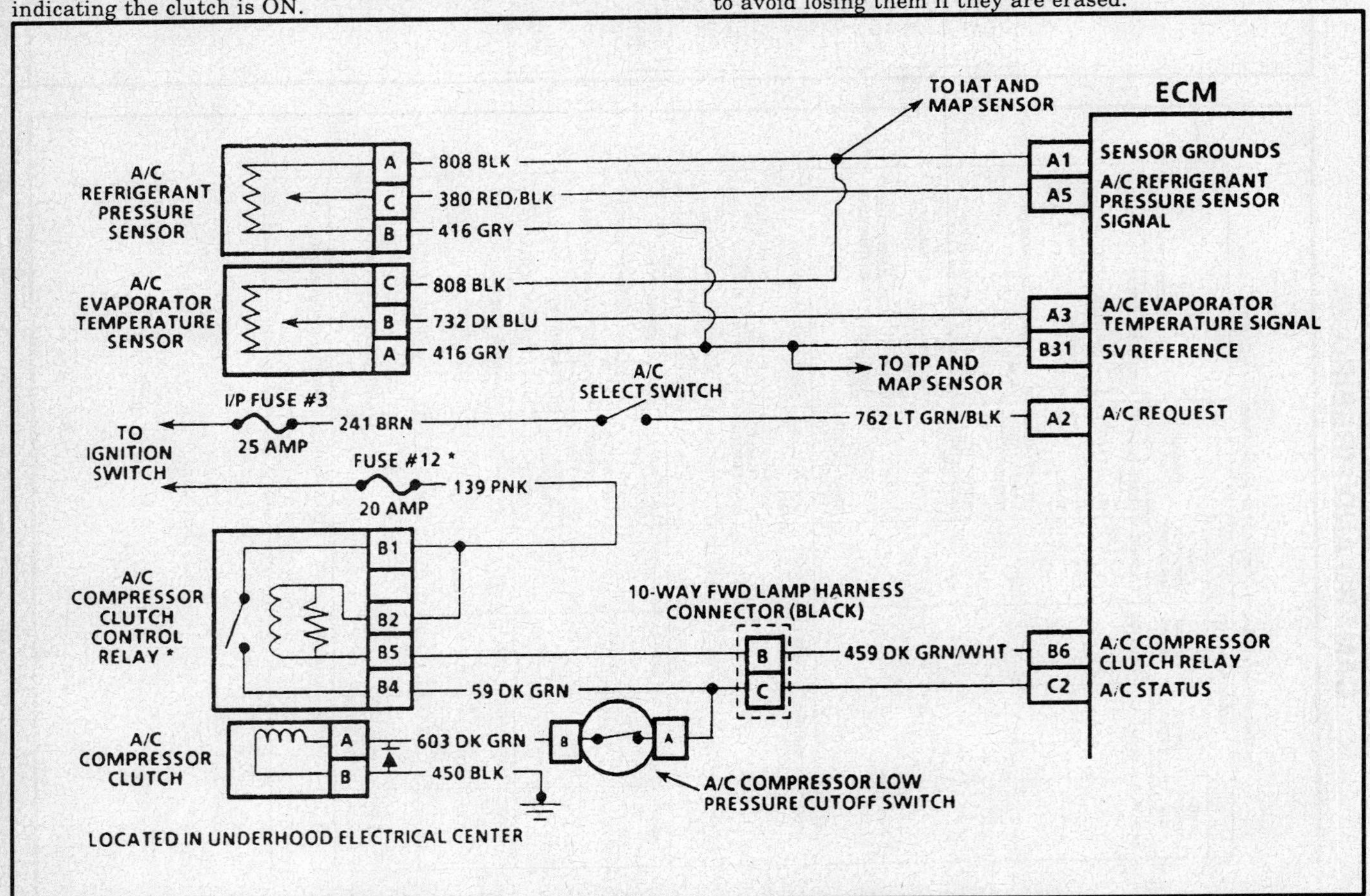

Compressor clutch and ECM circuit for trouble diagnosis—Camaro and Firebird

CLEARING CODES AND EXITING DIAGNOSTIC MODE

1. Trouble codes in the computer memory can be erased by entering the diagnostic mode and then depressing the **OFF** and **LO** buttons simultaneously. Hold until **00** appears.
2. Depress the **AUTO** button or turn the ignition switch **OFF** for 10 seconds to exit the diagnostic mode. The trouble codes will not be erased by only performing this step. The temperature setting will reappear.

Corvette

ENTERING THE DIAGNOSTIC MODE

To enter the diagnostic mode, push and hold the fan UP and fan DOWN arrows at the same time for approximately 5 seconds. The LCD will show **00**. Push the auto fan button and the LCD will show any fault codes stored in the memory.

Roadmaster and Fleetwood

AUTOMATIC CLIMATE CONTROL CHECK

Diagnostic must begin with an automatic climate control check of the system operation. If a fault is detected during normal system operation, the **°F/°C** symbol will flash rapidly and the trouble code can be produced by the control assembly.

1. Before starting the engine, cycle the ignition switch **ON–OFF–ON**. The control panel should light and repeat the last previous mode selection, temperature setting and blower speed.
2. If the display does not light, ignition power may not be reaching the control assembly. Check fuse 6 (20 amp) and fuse 4 (10 amp).
3. If the display changes each time the ignition switch is turned on, circuit 640 (orange wire) from the fuse block may be disconnected.
4. Select **AUTO** and the maximum temperature setting. Start the engine (if engine coolant temperature is low, the blower will not run until engine reaches normal temperature). While engine is cold, temporarily switch to **FAN** to verify that the blower will operate, then return to **AUTO**.
5. With engine running, set **60** on the temperature selection. The blower should run at high speed and air mode should switch to recirculation. Cold air comes from the panel, display will show **UPPER**. Within 45 seconds, discharge air should be at least 20 degrees lower than the outside air temperature.
6. Set temperature to **90** for maximum heating. Air inlet should switch to outside air and blower speed should reduce, and air flow should move to the floor and instrument panel outlets. Then the blower will increase again to high speed and all air should come from the floor. The control panel should display these features.
7. Touch the **DEFROST** indicator button and watch that air flow changes to the appropriate defrost outlets. Within 45 seconds, the temperature from the defroster should be at least 20 degrees warmer than the outside air temperature.
8. Operate the fan button to its various speeds and watch that the display indicates appropriate changes in speeds.
9. Touch the **AUTO** switch to return to automatic control operation.

ENTERING DIAGNOSTIC MODE

With the exception of trouble code **09** (low freon detected), trouble codes will not be stored in the microprocessor.

1. To enter the diagnostic mode, press and hold the **UP** portion of the **TEMP** switch, then also depress the **OFF** switch (command should be entered in about 5 seconds).
2. The display will show any codes that are present:
   00 – No system faults
   01 – Temperature valve actuator circuit open
   02 – Temperature valve actuator circuit short
   03 – Outside air temperature sensor assembly open
   04 – Outside air temperature sensor assembly short
   05 – Inside air temperature sensor assembly open
   06 – Inside air temperature sensor assembly short
   07 – Sun load sensor assembly open
   08 – Sun load sensor assembly short
   09 – Low freon detected
   10 – Universal asynchronous receiver transmitter failed
3. While in the diagnostic mode, other systems or circuits can be checked. Press the **FAN** switch (up or down side) until the desired index number is displayed.

CLEARING CODES/EXITING THE DIAGNOSTIC MODE

1. To clear the trouble codes and reset the self-diagnostic system, press **OFF** button while in the diagnostic mode.
2. To exit the diagnostic mode, press either the **AUTO** button or the **ECON** button.

AUTOMATIC A/C SYSTEM PARAMETERS—ROADMASTER

Index Number	Parameter	Value
02	Inside Air Temperature Sensor	Value should Increase as Temperature Decreases.
03	Outside Air Temperature Sensor	Value should Increase as Temperature Decreases.
04	Sun Load Sensor	Above 200 = Dark; 150 or below = Bright Sun.
05	Engine Temperature	Degrees Celsius (°C).
06	Vehicle Speed	Miles Per Hour.
11	Temperature Air Valve Position Command	0 = Full Cold Position; 225 = Full Hot Position.
12	Temperature Air Valve Position Feedback	Within 3 Points of Temperature Air Valve Position Command Value (Index No. 11).
13	Temperature Air Valve Position — Full Hot	Initial Reading During Calibration should be 180 or Higher.
14	Temperature Air Valve Position — Full Cold	Initial Reading During Calibration should be 50 or Lower.
18	Number of Consecutive Short Compressor Cycles (for Low Freon Detection)	If 10 Short Compressor Cycles are Detected the Compressor will be Disabled.

ECC SYSTEM DIAGNOSIS—ROADMASTER

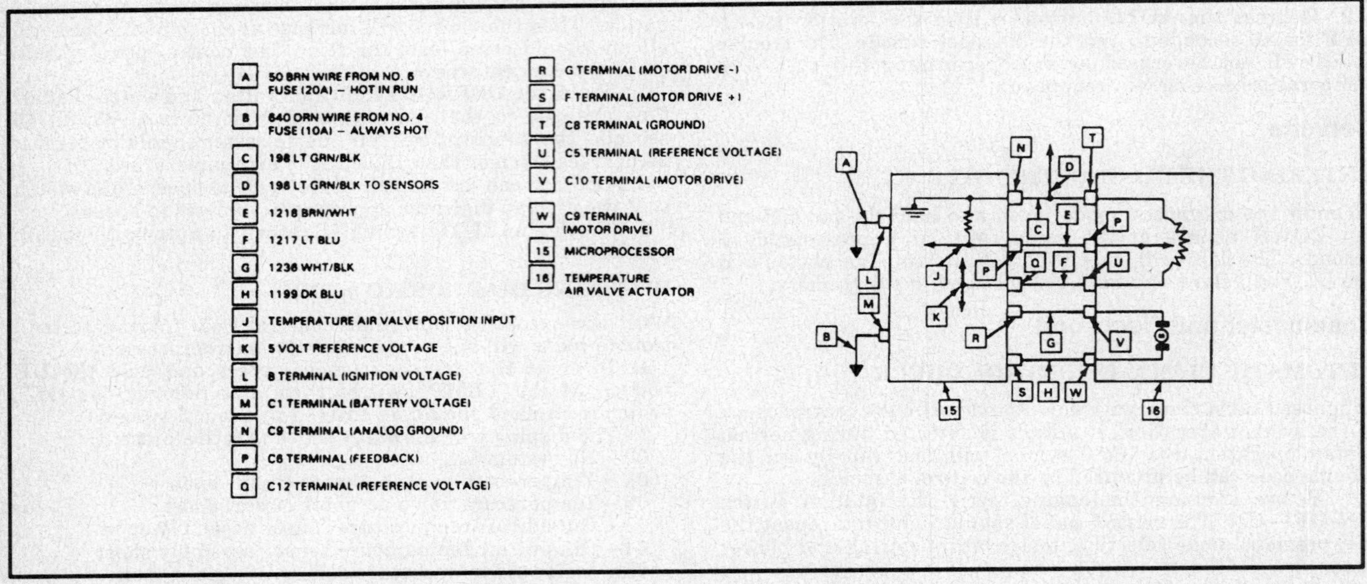

1994–95 DIAGNOSTIC POINTERS AND PARAMETERS—ROADMASTER

Pointer #		Display Range	Default Value
–02	ACAC System (HVAC) Diagnostic Trouble Codes	Indicates trouble codes stored	
		Parameters	–
–05	Program Number	0–255 Parameters	–
–07	Commanded Blower Motor Speed	0–128	–
–14	Vehicle Speed	In mph	25 (mph)
–15	HVAC Learn Mode (Temperature Calibration Offset)	–5° to 5° (F)	00
–18	Sun Load Sensor	0–255	240
–20	Current Temperature Valve Position	0–255	–
–22	Temperature Valve Position (Full Cold)	180–250	180
–23	Temperature Valve Position (Full Hot)	5–60	60
–24	Coolant Temperature	In°C	91°C
–25	Commanded TemperatureValve Position	0–255	128
–27	Air Delivery Mode. Refer to Chart 3, "Improper Air Delivery" for diagnosis.	–	–
–28	Inside Air Temperature Sensor	Value increases as temperature decreases. Refer to CHART 03 and CHART 04 for more information.	128 (75°F)
–31	Outside Air Temperature Sensor	Value increases as temperature decreases. Refer to CHART 01 and CHART 02 for more information.	128 (49°F)
–37	EEPROM revision #	–	–

1994–95 ROADMASTER AND FLEETWOOD OUTSIDE AIR TEMPERATURE SENSOR CIRCUIT (C68) (CIRCUIT OPEN)—CHART 01

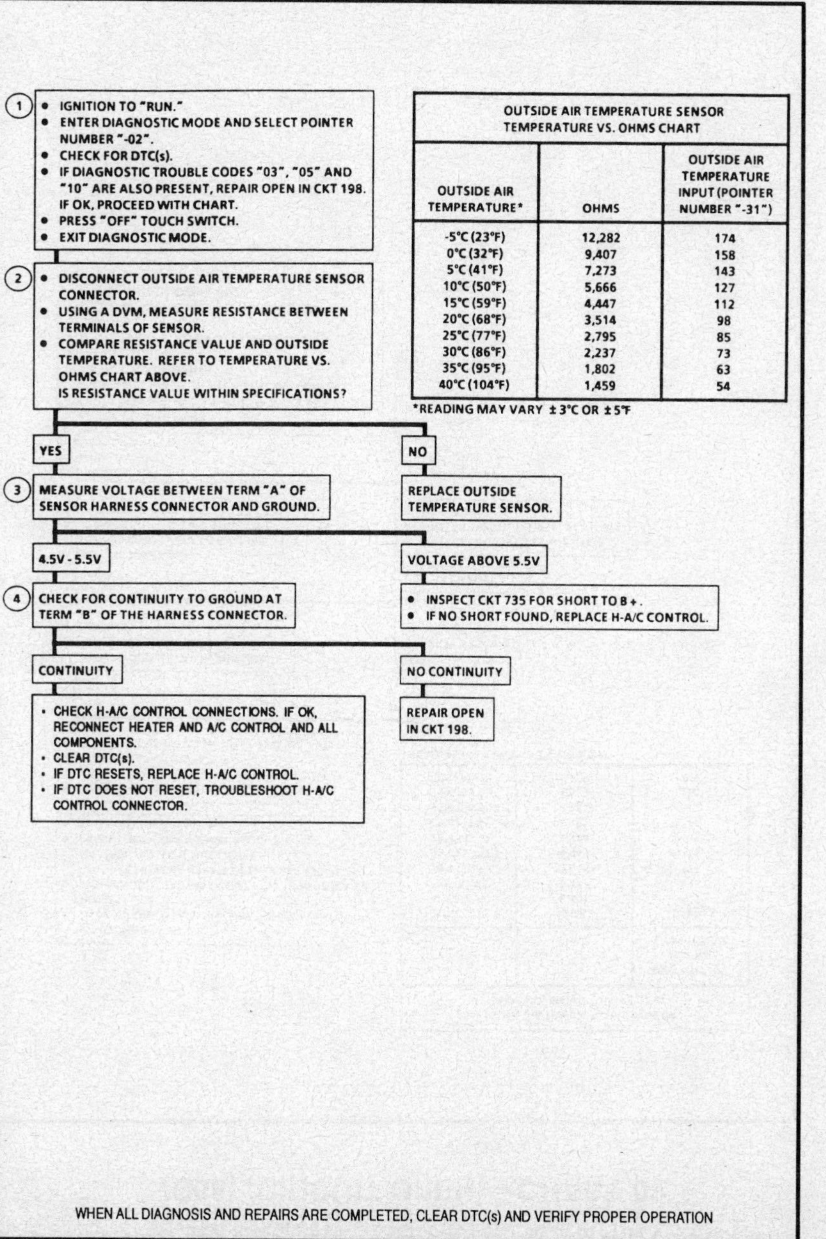

1
• IGNITION TO "RUN."
• ENTER DIAGNOSTIC MODE AND SELECT POINTER NUMBER "-02".
• CHECK FOR DTC(s).
• IF DIAGNOSTIC TROUBLE CODES "03", "05" AND "10" ARE ALSO PRESENT, REPAIR OPEN IN CKT 198. IF OK, PROCEED WITH CHART.
• PRESS "OFF" TOUCH SWITCH.
• EXIT DIAGNOSTIC MODE.
2
• DISCONNECT OUTSIDE AIR TEMPERATURE SENSOR CONNECTOR.
• USING A DVM, MEASURE RESISTANCE BETWEEN TERMINALS OF SENSOR.
• COMPARE RESISTANCE VALUE AND OUTSIDE TEMPERATURE. REFER TO TEMPERATURE VS. OHMS CHART ABOVE.
IS RESISTANCE VALUE WITHIN SPECIFICATIONS?
YES
NO
REPLACE OUTSIDE TEMPERATURE SENSOR.
3
MEASURE VOLTAGE BETWEEN TERM "A" OF SENSOR HARNESS CONNECTOR AND GROUND.
4.5V - 5.5V
VOLTAGE ABOVE 5.5V
• INSPECT CKT 735 FOR SHORT TO B+.
• IF NO SHORT FOUND, REPLACE H-A/C CONTROL.
4
CHECK FOR CONTINUITY TO GROUND AT TERM "B" OF THE HARNESS CONNECTOR.
CONTINUITY
NO CONTINUITY
REPAIR OPEN IN CKT 198.
• CHECK H-A/C CONTROL CONNECTIONS. IF OK, RECONNECT HEATER AND A/C CONTROL AND ALL COMPONENTS.
• CLEAR DTC(s).
• IF DTC RESETS, REPLACE H-A/C CONTROL.
• IF DTC DOES NOT RESET, TROUBLESHOOT H-A/C CONTROL CONNECTOR.
WHEN ALL DIAGNOSIS AND REPAIRS ARE COMPLETED, CLEAR DTC(s) AND VERIFY PROPER OPERATION

OUTSIDE AIR TEMPERATURE SENSOR TEMPERATURE VS. OHMS CHART

OUTSIDE AIR TEMPERATURE*	OHMS	OUTSIDE AIR TEMPERATURE INPUT (POINTER NUMBER "-31")
-5°C (23°F)	12,282	174
0°C (32°F)	9,407	158
5°C (41°F)	7,273	143
10°C (50°F)	5,666	127
15°C (59°F)	4,447	112
20°C (68°F)	3,514	98
25°C (77°F)	2,795	85
30°C (86°F)	2,237	73
35°C (95°F)	1,802	63
40°C (104°F)	1,459	54

*READING MAY VARY ±3°C OR ±5°F

1994–95 ROADMASTER AND FLEETWOOD OUTSIDE AIR TEMPERATURE SENSOR CIRCUIT (c68) (CIRCUIT SHORTED)—CHART 02

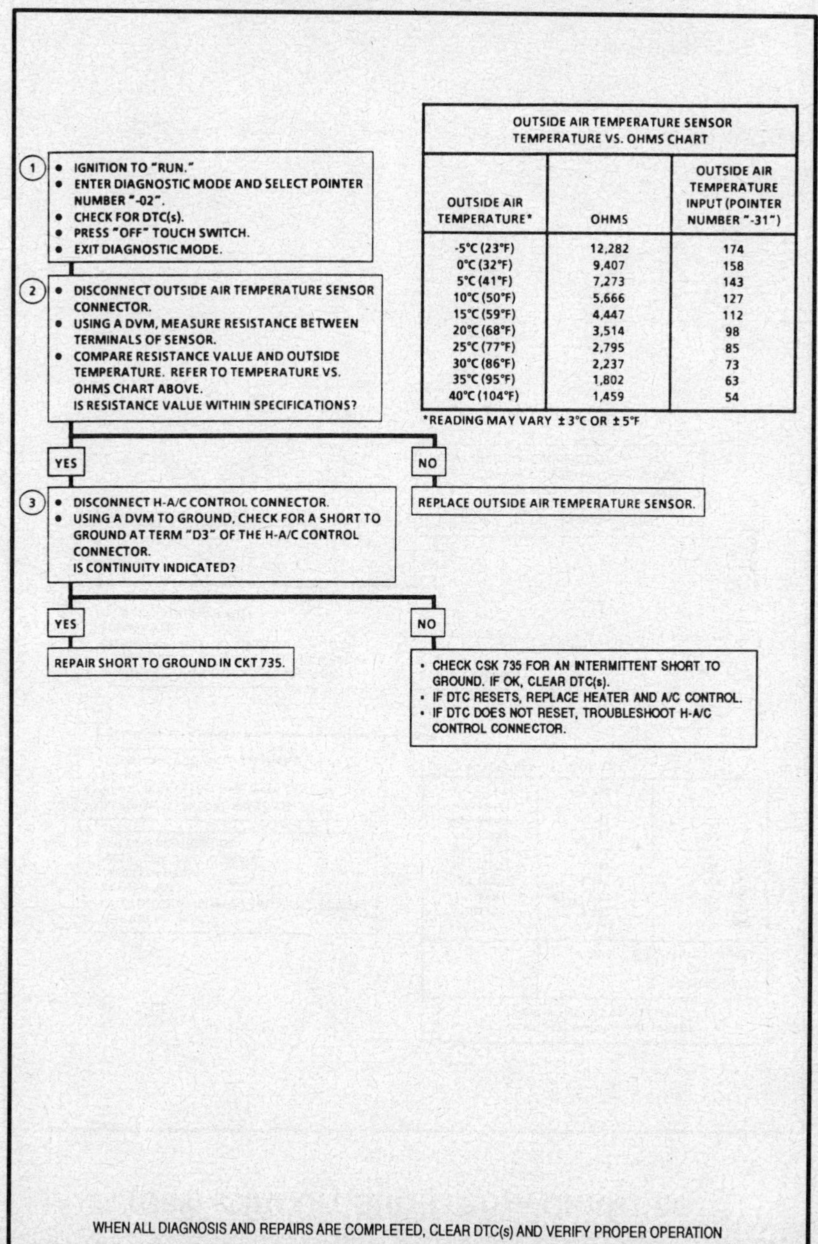

1
• IGNITION TO "RUN."
• ENTER DIAGNOSTIC MODE AND SELECT POINTER NUMBER "-02".
• CHECK FOR DTC(s).
• PRESS "OFF" TOUCH SWITCH.
• EXIT DIAGNOSTIC MODE.
2
• DISCONNECT OUTSIDE AIR TEMPERATURE SENSOR CONNECTOR.
• USING A DVM, MEASURE RESISTANCE BETWEEN TERMINALS OF SENSOR.
• COMPARE RESISTANCE VALUE AND OUTSIDE TEMPERATURE. REFER TO TEMPERATURE VS. OHMS CHART ABOVE.
IS RESISTANCE VALUE WITHIN SPECIFICATIONS?
YES
NO
REPLACE OUTSIDE AIR TEMPERATURE SENSOR.
3
• DISCONNECT H-A/C CONTROL CONNECTOR.
• USING A DVM TO GROUND, CHECK FOR A SHORT TO GROUND AT TERM "D3" OF THE H-A/C CONTROL CONNECTOR.
IS CONTINUITY INDICATED?
YES
NO
REPAIR SHORT TO GROUND IN CKT 735.
• CHECK CSK 735 FOR AN INTERMITTENT SHORT TO GROUND. IF OK, CLEAR DTC(s).
• IF DTC RESETS, REPLACE HEATER AND A/C CONTROL.
• IF DTC DOES NOT RESET, TROUBLESHOOT H-A/C CONTROL CONNECTOR.
WHEN ALL DIAGNOSIS AND REPAIRS ARE COMPLETED, CLEAR DTC(s) AND VERIFY PROPER OPERATION

OUTSIDE AIR TEMPERATURE SENSOR TEMPERATURE VS. OHMS CHART

OUTSIDE AIR TEMPERATURE*	OHMS	OUTSIDE AIR TEMPERATURE INPUT (POINTER NUMBER "-31")
-5°C (23°F)	12,282	174
0°C (32°F)	9,407	158
5°C (41°F)	7,273	143
10°C (50°F)	5,666	127
15°C (59°F)	4,447	112
20°C (68°F)	3,514	98
25°C (77°F)	2,795	85
30°C (86°F)	2,237	73
35°C (95°F)	1,802	63
40°C (104°F)	1,459	54

*READING MAY VARY ±3°C OR ±5°F

1994–95 ROADMASTER AND FLEETWOOD IN-CAR AIR TEMPERATURE SENSOR CIRCUIT (C68) (CIRCUIT OPEN)—CHART 03

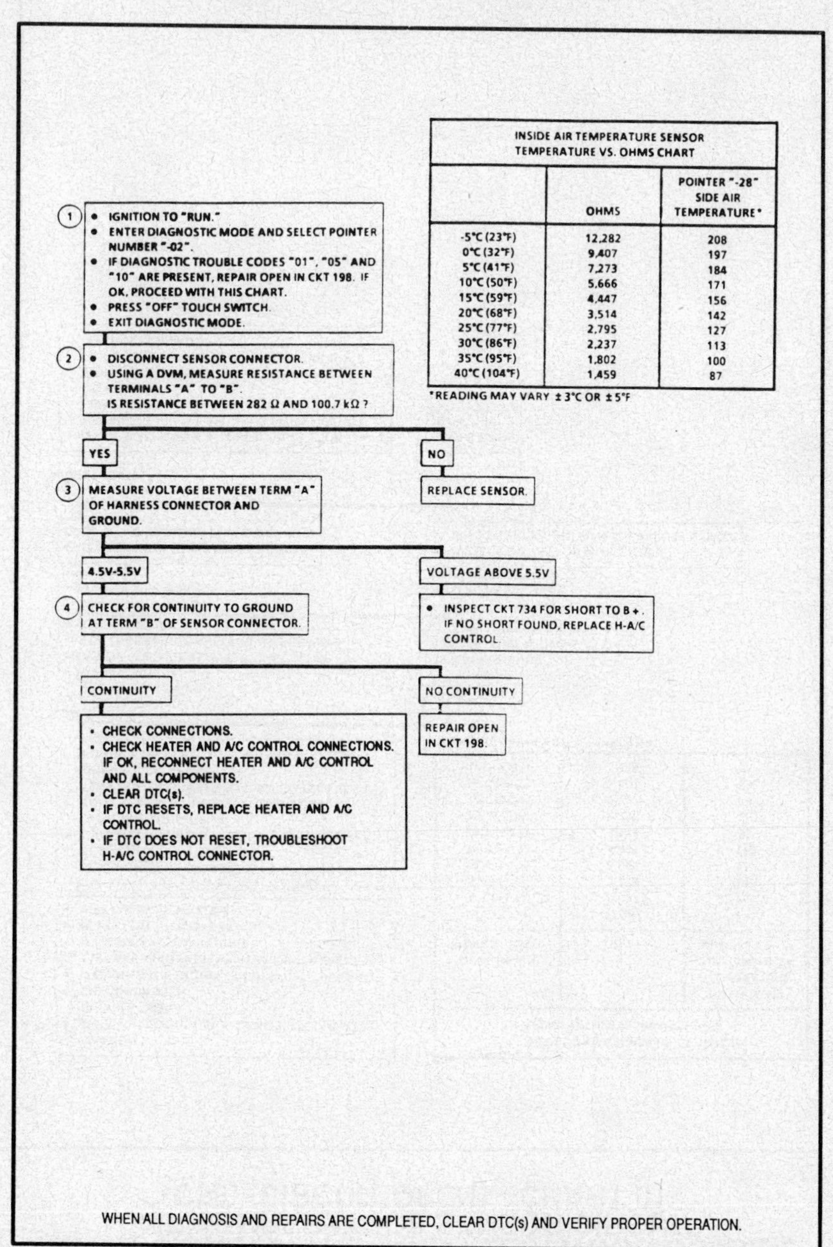
1 • IGNITION TO "RUN."
• ENTER DIAGNOSTIC MODE AND SELECT POINTER NUMBER "-02".
• IF DIAGNOSTIC TROUBLE CODES "01", "05" AND "10" ARE PRESENT, REPAIR OPEN IN CKT 198. IF OK, PROCEED WITH THIS CHART.
• PRESS "OFF" TOUCH SWITCH.
• EXIT DIAGNOSTIC MODE.
2 • DISCONNECT SENSOR CONNECTOR.
• USING A DVM, MEASURE RESISTANCE BETWEEN TERMINALS "A" TO "B".
IS RESISTANCE BETWEEN 282 Ω AND 100.7 kΩ ?
YES
NO
REPLACE SENSOR.
3 MEASURE VOLTAGE BETWEEN TERM "A" OF HARNESS CONNECTOR AND GROUND.
4.5V-5.5V
VOLTAGE ABOVE 5.5V
• INSPECT CKT 734 FOR SHORT TO B+. IF NO SHORT FOUND, REPLACE H-A/C CONTROL.
4 CHECK FOR CONTINUITY TO GROUND AT TERM "B" OF SENSOR CONNECTOR.
CONTINUITY
NO CONTINUITY
REPAIR OPEN IN CKT 198.
• CHECK CONNECTIONS.
• CHECK HEATER AND A/C CONTROL CONNECTIONS. IF OK, RECONNECT HEATER AND A/C CONTROL AND ALL COMPONENTS.
• CLEAR DTC(s).
• IF DTC RESETS, REPLACE HEATER AND A/C CONTROL.
• IF DTC DOES NOT RESET, TROUBLESHOOT H-A/C CONTROL CONNECTOR.
WHEN ALL DIAGNOSIS AND REPAIRS ARE COMPLETED, CLEAR DTC(s) AND VERIFY PROPER OPERATION.

INSIDE AIR TEMPERATURE SENSOR TEMPERATURE VS. OHMS CHART

	OHMS	POINTER "-28" SIDE AIR TEMPERATURE*
-5°C (23°F)	12,282	208
0°C (32°F)	9,407	197
5°C (41°F)	7,273	184
10°C (50°F)	5,666	171
15°C (59°F)	4,447	156
20°C (68°F)	3,514	142
25°C (77°F)	2,795	127
30°C (86°F)	2,237	113
35°C (95°F)	1,802	100
40°C (104°F)	1,459	87

*READING MAY VARY ± 3°C OR ± 5°F

1994–95 ROADMASTER AND FLEETWOOD IN-CAR AIR TEMPERATURE SENSOR CIRCUIT (C68) (CIRCUIT SHORTED)—CHART 04

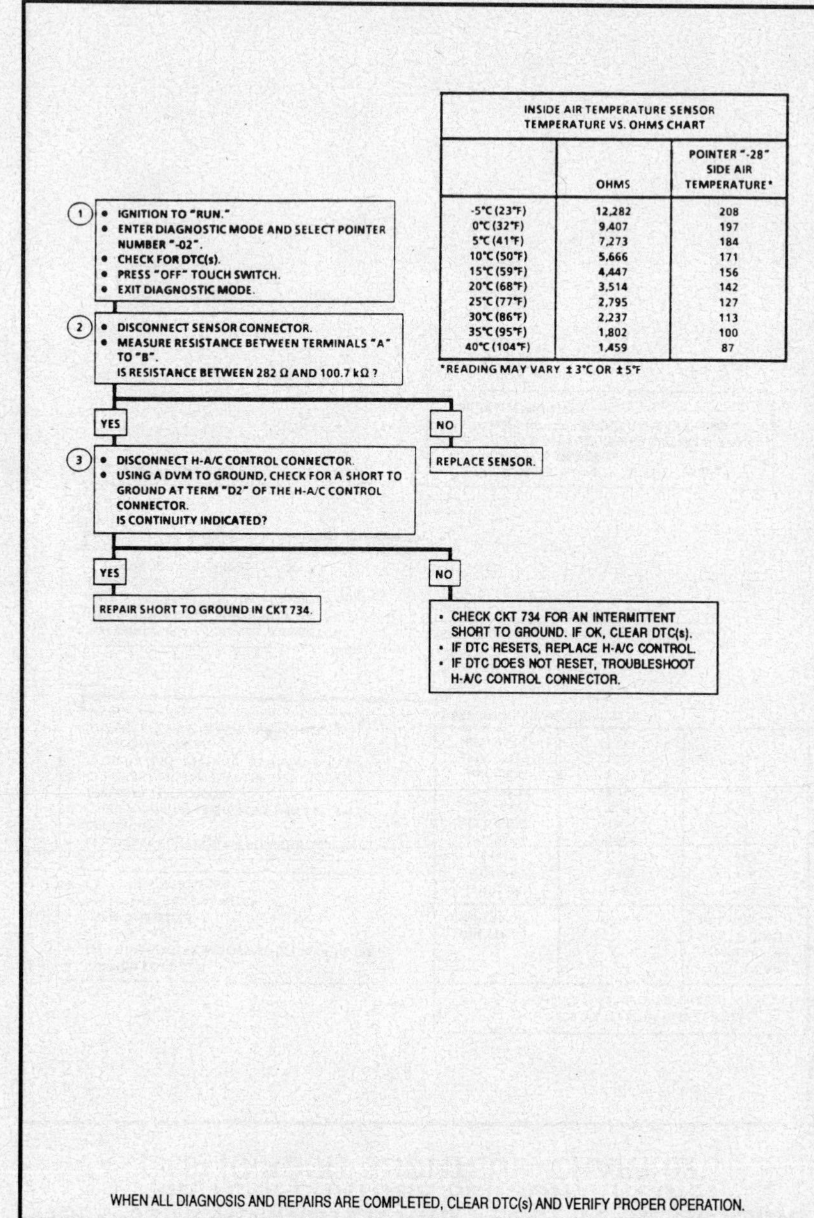
1 • IGNITION TO "RUN."
• ENTER DIAGNOSTIC MODE AND SELECT POINTER NUMBER "-02".
• CHECK FOR DTC(s).
• PRESS "OFF" TOUCH SWITCH.
• EXIT DIAGNOSTIC MODE.
2 • DISCONNECT SENSOR CONNECTOR.
• MEASURE RESISTANCE BETWEEN TERMINALS "A" TO "B".
IS RESISTANCE BETWEEN 282 Ω AND 100.7 kΩ ?
YES
NO
REPLACE SENSOR.
3 • DISCONNECT H-A/C CONTROL CONNECTOR.
• USING A DVM TO GROUND, CHECK FOR A SHORT TO GROUND AT TERM "D2" OF THE H-A/C CONTROL CONNECTOR.
IS CONTINUITY INDICATED?
YES
NO
REPAIR SHORT TO GROUND IN CKT 734.
• CHECK CKT 734 FOR AN INTERMITTENT SHORT TO GROUND. IF OK, CLEAR DTC(s).
• IF DTC RESETS, REPLACE H-A/C CONTROL.
• IF DTC DOES NOT RESET, TROUBLESHOOT H-A/C CONTROL CONNECTOR.
WHEN ALL DIAGNOSIS AND REPAIRS ARE COMPLETED, CLEAR DTC(s) AND VERIFY PROPER OPERATION.

INSIDE AIR TEMPERATURE SENSOR TEMPERATURE VS. OHMS CHART

	OHMS	POINTER "-28" SIDE AIR TEMPERATURE*
-5°C (23°F)	12,282	208
0°C (32°F)	9,407	197
5°C (41°F)	7,273	184
10°C (50°F)	5,666	171
15°C (59°F)	4,447	156
20°C (68°F)	3,514	142
25°C (77°F)	2,795	127
30°C (86°F)	2,237	113
35°C (95°F)	1,802	100
40°C (104°F)	1,459	87

*READING MAY VARY ± 3°C OR ± 5°F

1994–95 ROADMASTER AND FLEETWOOD SUN LOAD SENSOR CIRCUIT (C68) (CIRCUIT OPEN)—CHART 05

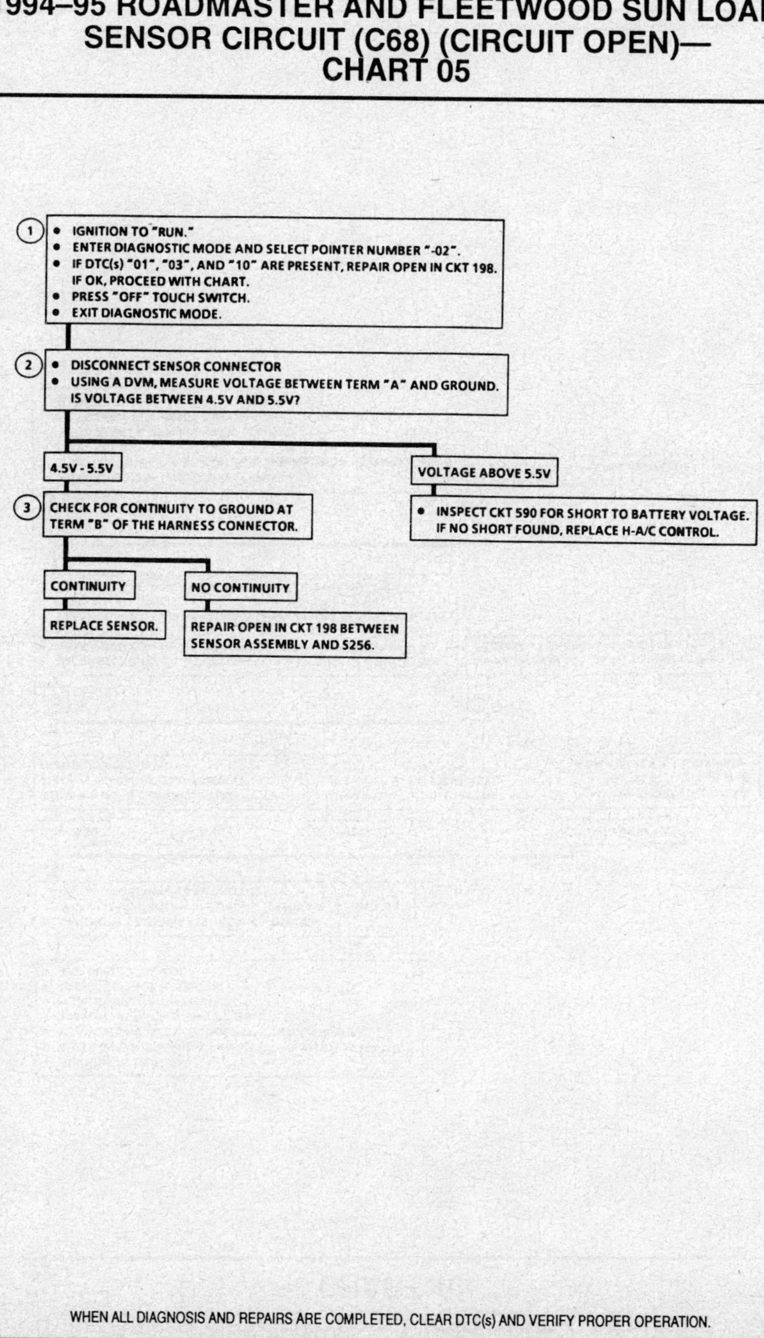
1
• IGNITION TO "RUN."
• ENTER DIAGNOSTIC MODE AND SELECT POINTER NUMBER "-02".
• IF DTC(s) "01", "03", AND "10" ARE PRESENT, REPAIR OPEN IN CKT 198. IF OK, PROCEED WITH CHART.
• PRESS "OFF" TOUCH SWITCH.
• EXIT DIAGNOSTIC MODE.
2
• DISCONNECT SENSOR CONNECTOR
• USING A DVM, MEASURE VOLTAGE BETWEEN TERM "A" AND GROUND. IS VOLTAGE BETWEEN 4.5V AND 5.5V?
4.5V - 5.5V
VOLTAGE ABOVE 5.5V
3
CHECK FOR CONTINUITY TO GROUND AT TERM "B" OF THE HARNESS CONNECTOR.
• INSPECT CKT 590 FOR SHORT TO BATTERY VOLTAGE. IF NO SHORT FOUND, REPLACE H-A/C CONTROL.
CONTINUITY
NO CONTINUITY
REPLACE SENSOR.
REPAIR OPEN IN CKT 198 BETWEEN SENSOR ASSEMBLY AND S256.
WHEN ALL DIAGNOSIS AND REPAIRS ARE COMPLETED, CLEAR DTC(s) AND VERIFY PROPER OPERATION.

1994–95 ROADMASTER AND FLEETWOOD SUN LOAD SENSOR CIRCUIT (C68) (CIRCUIT SHORTED)—CHART 06

1
- IGNITION TO "RUN."
- ENTER DIAGNOSTIC MODE AND SELECT POINTER NUMBER "-02".
- CHECK FOR DTC(s).
- PRESS "OFF" TOUCH SWITCH.
- EXIT DIAGNOSTIC MODE.

2
- DISCONNECT SUN LOAD CONNECTOR.
- DISCONNECT H-A/C CONTROL CONNECTOR.
- USING A DVM TO GROUND, CHECK FOR A SHORT TO GROUND AT TERM "C2" OR THE H-A/C CONTROL CONNECTOR. IS CONTINUITY INDICATED?

YES

REPAIR SHORT TO GROUND IN CKT 590.

NO

- CHECK CKT 590 FOR AN INTERMITTENT SHORT TO GROUND. IF OK, RECONNECT HEATER-A/C CONTROL AND ALL OTHER COMPONENTS.
- IF DTC RESETS, REPLACE HEATER AND A/C CONTROL.
- IF DTC DOES NOT RESET, TROUBLESHOOT H-A/C CONTROL CONNECTOR.

WHEN ALL DIAGNOSIS AND REPAIRS ARE COMPLETED, CLEAR DTC(s) AND VERIFY PROPER OPERATION.

1994–95 ROADMASTER AND FLEETWOOD AIR MIX MOTOR CIRCUIT (C68) (CIRCUIT OPEN)— CHART 10

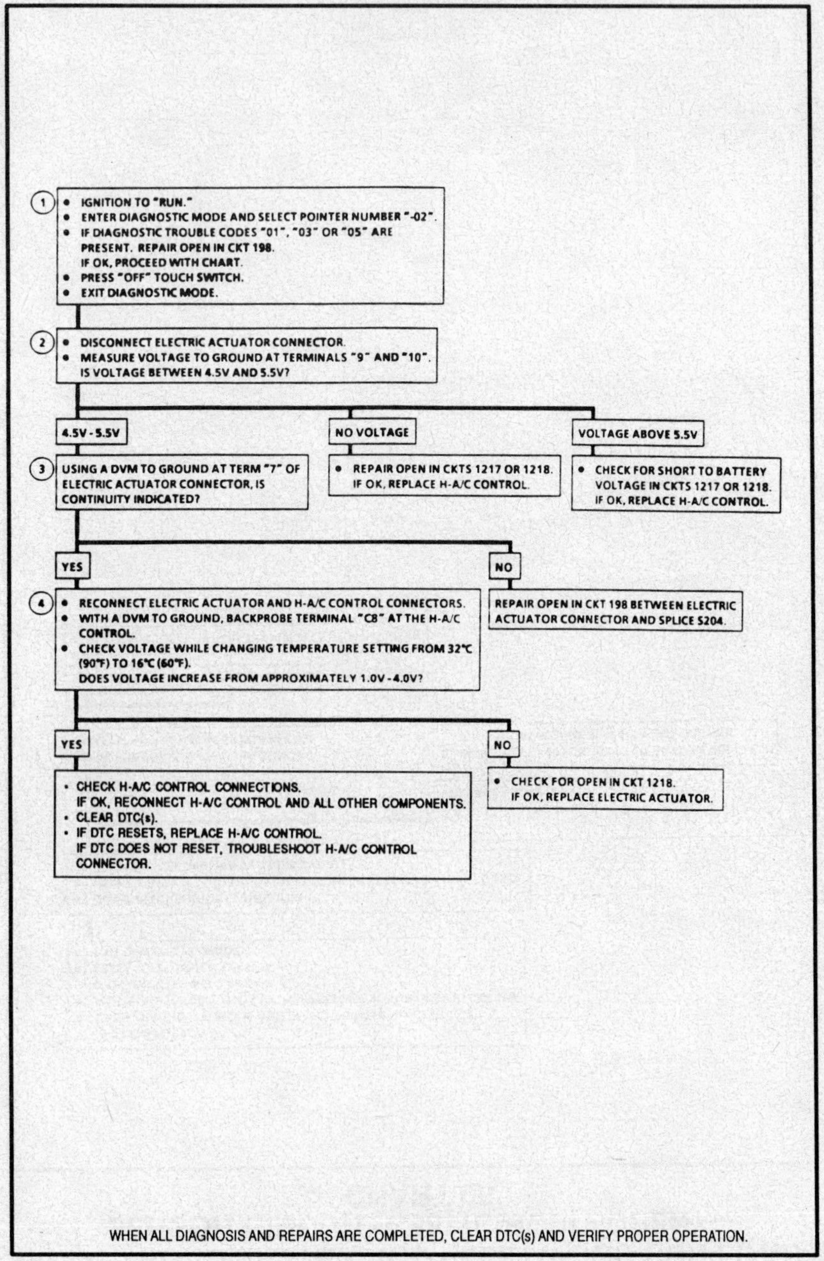

1
• IGNITION TO "RUN."
• ENTER DIAGNOSTIC MODE AND SELECT POINTER NUMBER "-02".
• IF DIAGNOSTIC TROUBLE CODES "01", "03" OR "05" ARE PRESENT. REPAIR OPEN IN CKT 198. IF OK, PROCEED WITH CHART.
• PRESS "OFF" TOUCH SWITCH.
• EXIT DIAGNOSTIC MODE.
2
• DISCONNECT ELECTRIC ACTUATOR CONNECTOR.
• MEASURE VOLTAGE TO GROUND AT TERMINALS "9" AND "10". IS VOLTAGE BETWEEN 4.5V AND 5.5V?
4.5V - 5.5V
NO VOLTAGE
VOLTAGE ABOVE 5.5V
3
USING A DVM TO GROUND AT TERM "7" OF ELECTRIC ACTUATOR CONNECTOR, IS CONTINUITY INDICATED?
• REPAIR OPEN IN CKTS 1217 OR 1218. IF OK, REPLACE H-A/C CONTROL.
• CHECK FOR SHORT TO BATTERY VOLTAGE IN CKTS 1217 OR 1218. IF OK, REPLACE H-A/C CONTROL.
YES
NO
4
• RECONNECT ELECTRIC ACTUATOR AND H-A/C CONTROL CONNECTORS.
• WITH A DVM TO GROUND, BACKPROBE TERMINAL "C8" AT THE H-A/C CONTROL.
• CHECK VOLTAGE WHILE CHANGING TEMPERATURE SETTING FROM 32°C (90°F) TO 16°C (60°F). DOES VOLTAGE INCREASE FROM APPROXIMATELY 1.0V - 4.0V?
REPAIR OPEN IN CKT 198 BETWEEN ELECTRIC ACTUATOR CONNECTOR AND SPLICE S204.
YES
NO
• CHECK H-A/C CONTROL CONNECTIONS. IF OK, RECONNECT H-A/C CONTROL AND ALL OTHER COMPONENTS.
• CLEAR DTC(s).
• IF DTC RESETS, REPLACE H-A/C CONTROL. IF DTC DOES NOT RESET, TROUBLESHOOT H-A/C CONTROL CONNECTOR.
• CHECK FOR OPEN IN CKT 1218. IF OK, REPLACE ELECTRIC ACTUATOR.
WHEN ALL DIAGNOSIS AND REPAIRS ARE COMPLETED, CLEAR DTC(s) AND VERIFY PROPER OPERATION.

1994–95 ROADMASTER AND FLEETWOOD AIR MIX MOTOR CIRCUIT (C68) (CIRCUIT SHORTED)— CHART 11

1
• DISCONNECT H-A/C CONTROL FROM ITS CONNECTOR.
• DISCONNECT ELECTRIC ACTUATOR FROM ITS CONNECTOR.
• USING A DVM TO GROUND, CHECK FOR A SHORT TO GROUND AT ELECTRIC ACTUATOR CONNECTOR TERMINALS "9" AND "10". IS CONTINUITY INDICATED?
NO
YES
2
• RECONNECT H-A/C CONTROL AND ELECTRIC ACTUATOR CONNECTORS.
• WITH A DVM TO GROUND, BACKPROBE TERM "C8" AT THE H-A/C CONTROL.
• CHECK VOLTAGE WHILE CHANGING TEMPERATURE SETTING FROM 32°C (90°F) TO 16°C (60°F). DOES VOLTAGE INCREASE FROM APPROXIMATELY 1.0V - 4.0V?
REPAIR SHORT TO GROUND IN CKTS 1217 AND/OR 1218.
YES
NO
• CHECK H-A/C CONTROL CONNECTIONS. IF OK, CLEAR DTC(s).
• IF DTC RESETS, REPLACE H-A/C CONTROL. IF DTC DOES NOT RESET, TROUBLESHOOT H-A/C CONTROL CONNECTOR.
• CHECK FOR OPEN IN CKT 1218. IF OK, REPLACE ELECTRIC ACTUATOR.
WHEN ALL DIAGNOSIS AND REPAIRS ARE COMPLETED, CLEAR DTC(s) AND VERIFY PROPER OPERATION

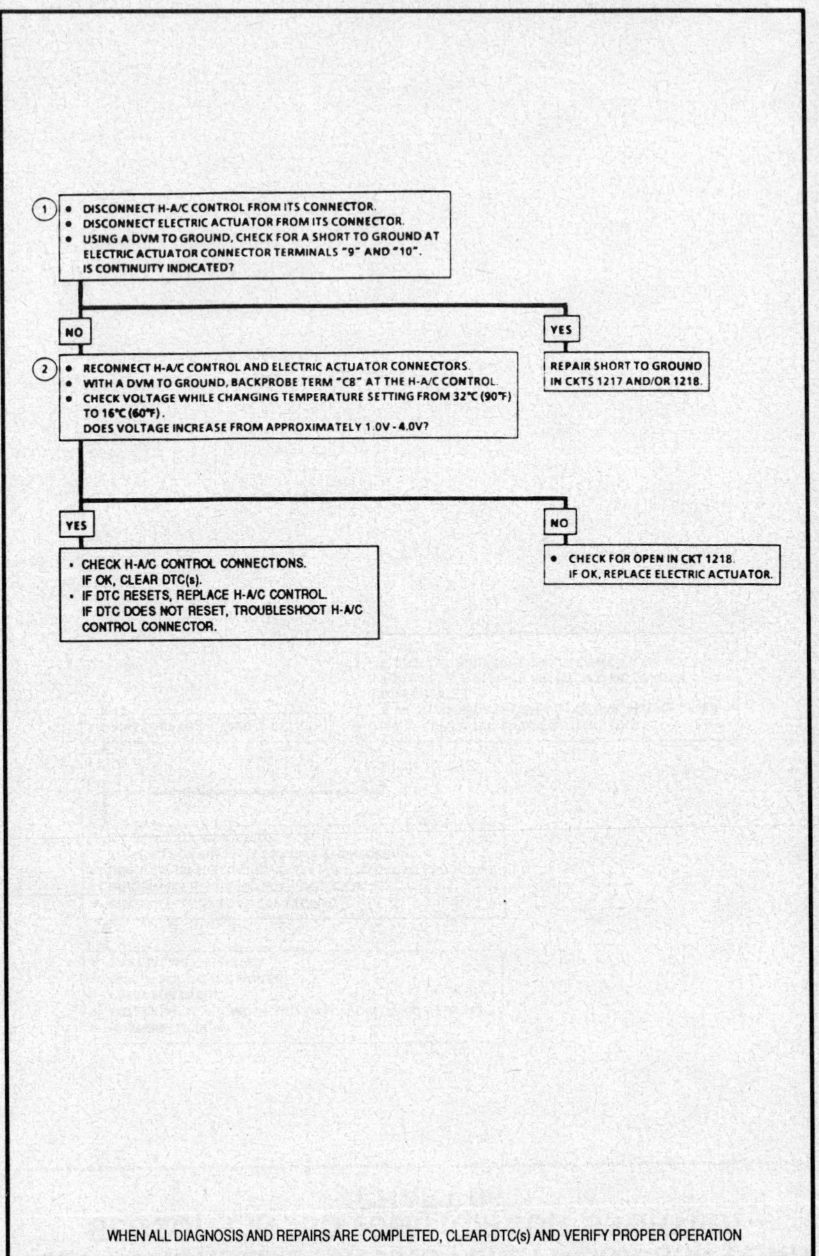

1994–95 ROADMASTER AND FLEETWOOD SERIAL DATA COMMUNICATION (C68) (CIRCUIT SHORTED TO B +, OPEN)—CHART 26

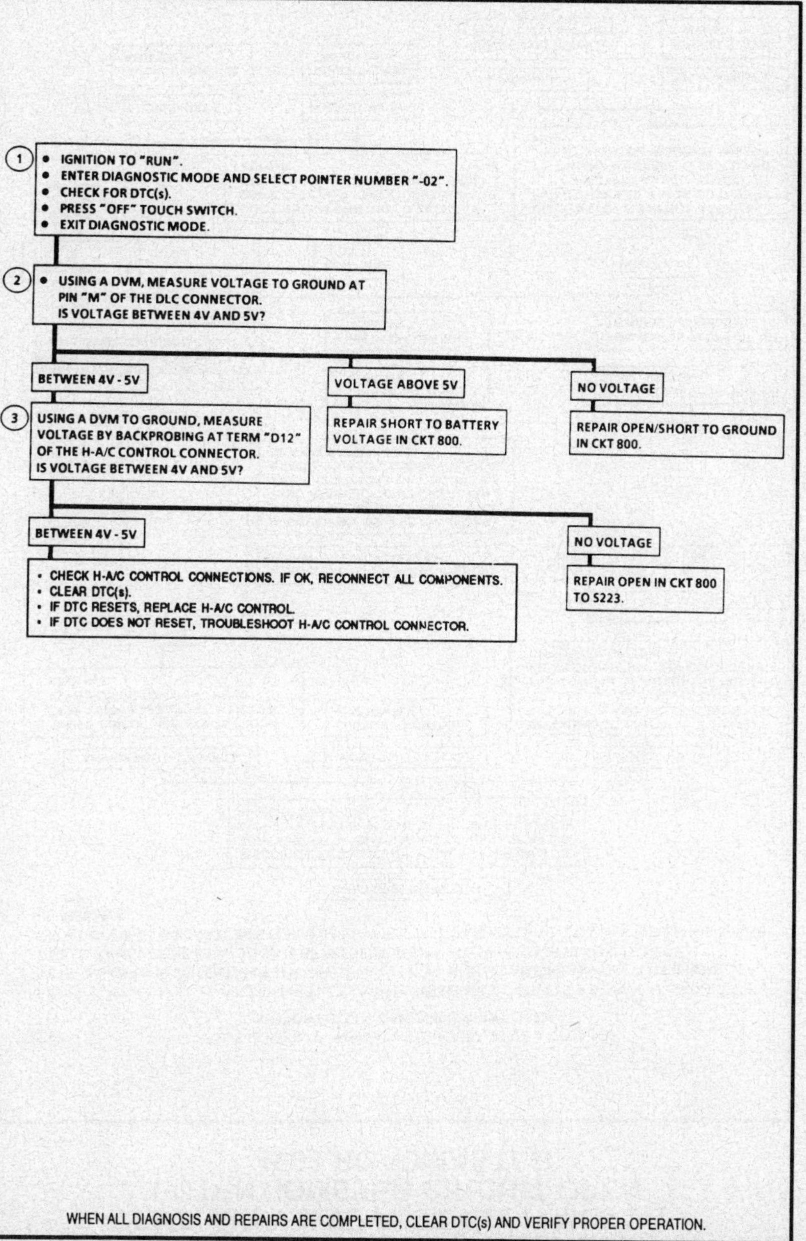

1
• IGNITION TO "RUN".
• ENTER DIAGNOSTIC MODE AND SELECT POINTER NUMBER "-02".
• CHECK FOR DTC(s).
• PRESS "OFF" TOUCH SWITCH.
• EXIT DIAGNOSTIC MODE.
2
• USING A DVM, MEASURE VOLTAGE TO GROUND AT PIN "M" OF THE DLC CONNECTOR. IS VOLTAGE BETWEEN 4V AND 5V?
BETWEEN 4V - 5V
VOLTAGE ABOVE 5V
NO VOLTAGE
3
USING A DVM TO GROUND, MEASURE VOLTAGE BY BACKPROBING AT TERM "D12" OF THE H-A/C CONTROL CONNECTOR. IS VOLTAGE BETWEEN 4V AND 5V?
REPAIR SHORT TO BATTERY VOLTAGE IN CKT 800.
REPAIR OPEN/SHORT TO GROUND IN CKT 800.
BETWEEN 4V - 5V
NO VOLTAGE
• CHECK H-A/C CONTROL CONNECTIONS. IF OK, RECONNECT ALL COMPONENTS.
• CLEAR DTC(s).
• IF DTC RESETS, REPLACE H-A/C CONTROL.
• IF DTC DOES NOT RESET, TROUBLESHOOT H-A/C CONTROL CONNECTOR.
REPAIR OPEN IN CKT 800 TO S223.
WHEN ALL DIAGNOSIS AND REPAIRS ARE COMPLETED, CLEAR DTC(s) AND VERIFY PROPER OPERATION.

1994–95 ROADMASTER AND FLEETWOOD INVALID EEPROM DETECTED (C68)—CHART 27

1

- IGNITION "OFF."
- WAIT 10 SECONDS, REENTER DIAGNOSTICS.
- SELECT POINTER "-02".
- CLEAR HVAC DTCs.
- CHECK FOR DTC 27.

DOES DTC 27 RESET?

YES → REPLACE H-A/C CONTROL.

NO → TROUBLESHOOT H-A/C CONTROL CONNECTOR.

WHEN ALL DIAGNOSIS AND REPAIRS ARE COMPLETED, CLEAR DTC(s) AND VERIFY PROPER OPERATION.

ECC SYSTEM DIAGNOSIS—FAULT CODE 01 TEMP. AIR VALVE ACTUATOR MOTOR POTENTIOMETER CIRCUIT OPEN 1993 ROADMASTER

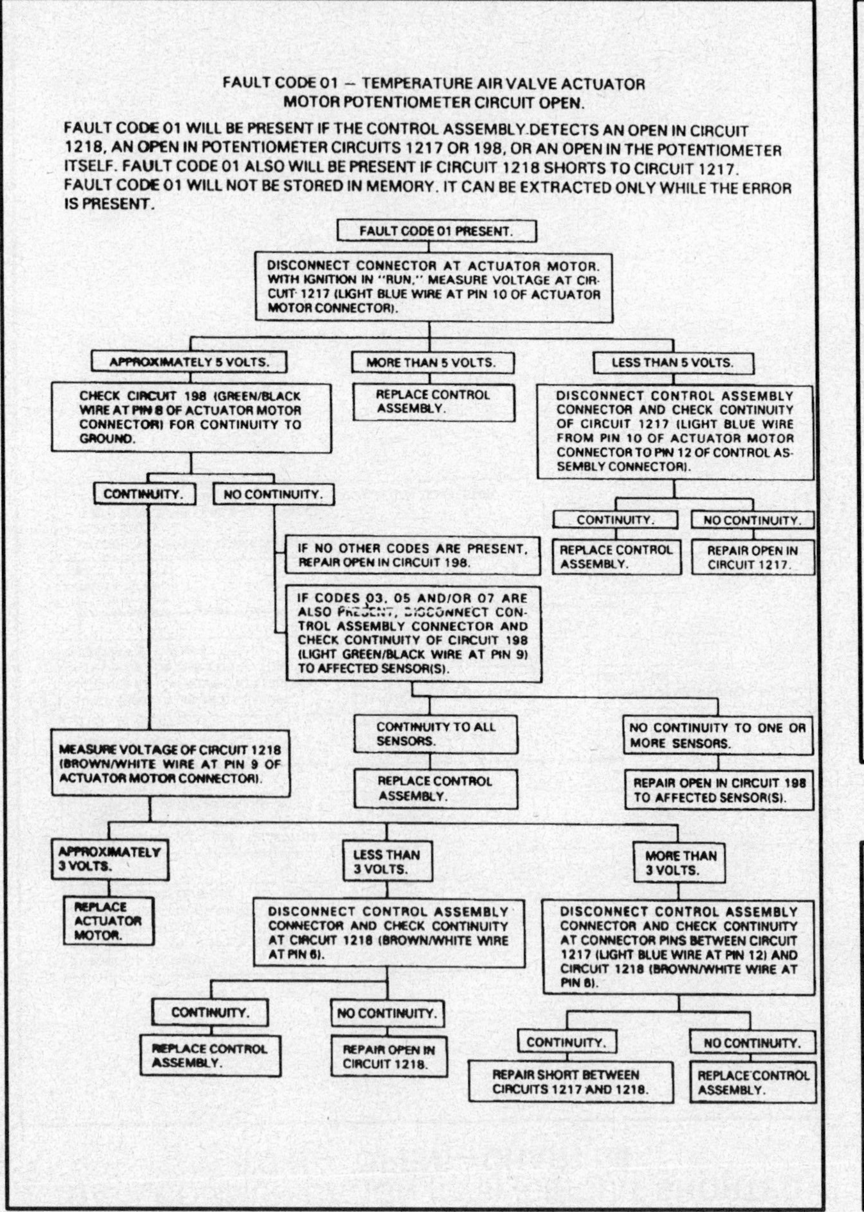

FAULT CODE 01 – TEMPERATURE AIR VALVE ACTUATOR MOTOR POTENTIOMETER CIRCUIT OPEN.
FAULT CODE 01 WILL BE PRESENT IF THE CONTROL ASSEMBLY DETECTS AN OPEN IN CIRCUIT 1218, AN OPEN IN POTENTIOMETER CIRCUITS 1217 OR 198, OR AN OPEN IN THE POTENTIOMETER ITSELF. FAULT CODE 01 ALSO WILL BE PRESENT IF CIRCUIT 1218 SHORTS TO CIRCUIT 1217.
FAULT CODE 01 WILL NOT BE STORED IN MEMORY. IT CAN BE EXTRACTED ONLY WHILE THE ERROR IS PRESENT.
FAULT CODE 01 PRESENT.
DISCONNECT CONNECTOR AT ACTUATOR MOTOR. WITH IGNITION IN "RUN," MEASURE VOLTAGE AT CIRCUIT 1217 (LIGHT BLUE WIRE AT PIN 10 OF ACTUATOR MOTOR CONNECTOR).
APPROXIMATELY 5 VOLTS.
MORE THAN 5 VOLTS.
LESS THAN 5 VOLTS.
CHECK CIRCUIT 198 (GREEN/BLACK WIRE AT PIN 8 OF ACTUATOR MOTOR CONNECTOR) FOR CONTINUITY TO GROUND.
REPLACE CONTROL ASSEMBLY.
DISCONNECT CONTROL ASSEMBLY CONNECTOR AND CHECK CONTINUITY OF CIRCUIT 1217 (LIGHT BLUE WIRE FROM PIN 10 OF ACTUATOR MOTOR CONNECTOR TO PIN 12 OF CONTROL ASSEMBLY CONNECTOR).
CONTINUITY.
NO CONTINUITY.
CONTINUITY.
NO CONTINUITY.
REPLACE CONTROL ASSEMBLY.
REPAIR OPEN IN CIRCUIT 1217.
IF NO OTHER CODES ARE PRESENT, REPAIR OPEN IN CIRCUIT 198.
IF CODES 03, 05 AND/OR 07 ARE ALSO PRESENT, DISCONNECT CONTROL ASSEMBLY CONNECTOR AND CHECK CONTINUITY OF CIRCUIT 198 (LIGHT GREEN/BLACK WIRE AT PIN 9) TO AFFECTED SENSOR(S).
CONTINUITY TO ALL SENSORS.
NO CONTINUITY TO ONE OR MORE SENSORS.
REPLACE CONTROL ASSEMBLY.
REPAIR OPEN IN CIRCUIT 198 TO AFFECTED SENSOR(S).
MEASURE VOLTAGE OF CIRCUIT 1218 (BROWN/WHITE WIRE AT PIN 9 OF ACTUATOR MOTOR CONNECTOR).
APPROXIMATELY 3 VOLTS.
LESS THAN 3 VOLTS.
MORE THAN 3 VOLTS.
REPLACE ACTUATOR MOTOR.
DISCONNECT CONTROL ASSEMBLY CONNECTOR AND CHECK CONTINUITY AT CIRCUIT 1218 (BROWN/WHITE WIRE AT PIN 6).
DISCONNECT CONTROL ASSEMBLY CONNECTOR AND CHECK CONTINUITY AT CONNECTOR PINS BETWEEN CIRCUIT 1217 (LIGHT BLUE WIRE AT PIN 12) AND CIRCUIT 1218 (BROWN/WHITE WIRE AT PIN 6).
CONTINUITY.
NO CONTINUITY.
CONTINUITY.
NO CONTINUITY.
REPLACE CONTROL ASSEMBLY.
REPAIR OPEN IN CIRCUIT 1218.
REPAIR SHORT BETWEEN CIRCUITS 1217 AND 1218.
REPLACE CONTROL ASSEMBLY.

ECC SYSTEM DIAGNOSIS—FAULT CODE 02 TEMP. AIR VALVE ACTUATOR MOTOR POTENTIOMETER CIRCUIT OPEN 1993 ROADMASTER

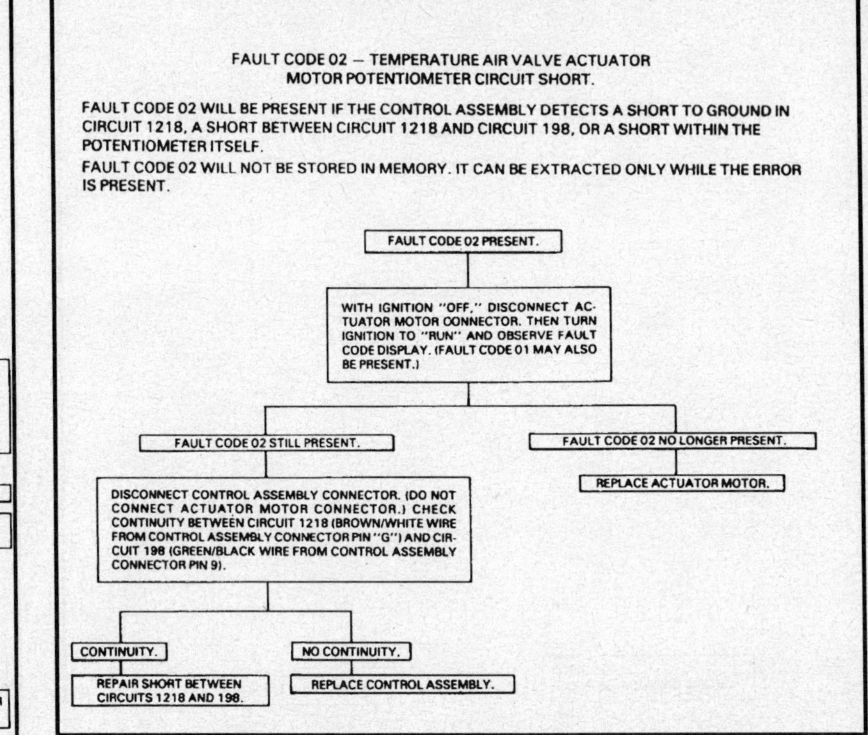

FAULT CODE 02 – TEMPERATURE AIR VALVE ACTUATOR MOTOR POTENTIOMETER CIRCUIT SHORT.
FAULT CODE 02 WILL BE PRESENT IF THE CONTROL ASSEMBLY DETECTS A SHORT TO GROUND IN CIRCUIT 1218, A SHORT BETWEEN CIRCUIT 1218 AND CIRCUIT 198, OR A SHORT WITHIN THE POTENTIOMETER ITSELF.
FAULT CODE 02 WILL NOT BE STORED IN MEMORY. IT CAN BE EXTRACTED ONLY WHILE THE ERROR IS PRESENT.
FAULT CODE 02 PRESENT.
WITH IGNITION "OFF," DISCONNECT ACTUATOR MOTOR CONNECTOR. THEN TURN IGNITION TO "RUN" AND OBSERVE FAULT CODE DISPLAY. (FAULT CODE 01 MAY ALSO BE PRESENT.)
FAULT CODE 02 STILL PRESENT.
FAULT CODE 02 NO LONGER PRESENT.
REPLACE ACTUATOR MOTOR.
DISCONNECT CONTROL ASSEMBLY CONNECTOR. (DO NOT CONNECT ACTUATOR MOTOR CONNECTOR.) CHECK CONTINUITY BETWEEN CIRCUIT 1218 (BROWN/WHITE WIRE FROM CONTROL ASSEMBLY CONNECTOR PIN "G") AND CIRCUIT 198 (GREEN/BLACK WIRE FROM CONTROL ASSEMBLY CONNECTOR PIN 9).
CONTINUITY.
NO CONTINUITY.
REPAIR SHORT BETWEEN CIRCUITS 1218 AND 198.
REPLACE CONTROL ASSEMBLY.

ECC SYSTEM DIAGNOSIS—ROADMASTER

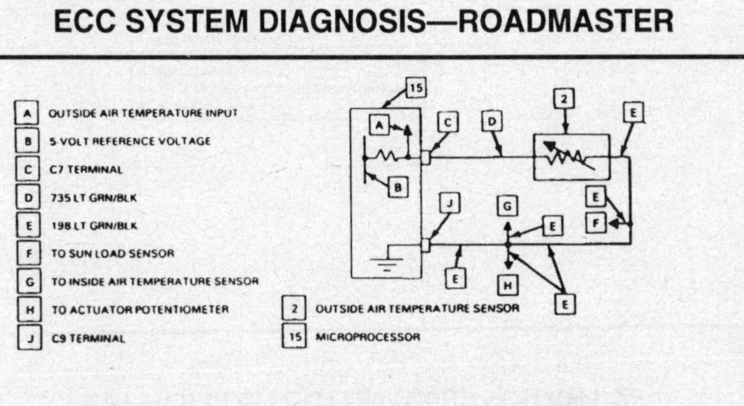

ECC SYSTEM DIAGNOSIS—FAULT CODE 03 OUTSIDE AIR TEMP. SENSOR CIRCUIT OPEN 1993 ROADMASTER

FAULT CODE 03 – OUTSIDE AIR TEMPERATURE SENSOR CIRCUIT OPEN.

FAULT CODE 03 WILL BE PRESENT IF THE CONTROL ASSEMBLY DETECTS AN OPEN IN CIRCUIT 735, AN OPEN WITHIN THE SENSOR OR PIGTAIL, OR AN OPEN IN CIRCUIT 198.

FAULT CODE 03 WILL NOT BE STORED IN MEMORY. IT CAN BE EXTRACTED ONLY WHILE THE ERROR IS PRESENT.

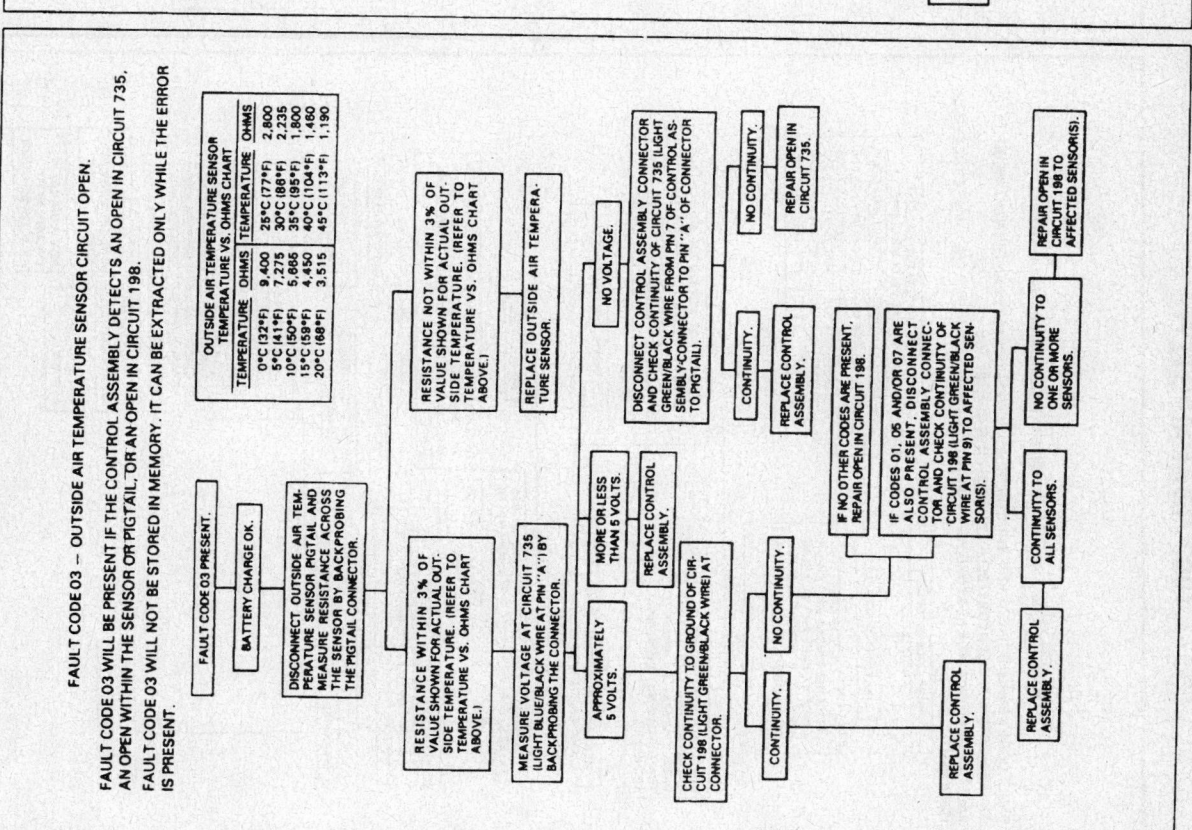

OUTSIDE AIR TEMPERATURE SENSOR TEMPERATURE VS. OHMS CHART

TEMPERATURE	OHMS	TEMPERATURE	OHMS
0°C (32°F)	9,400	25°C (77°F)	2,800
5°C (41°F)	7,275	30°C (86°F)	2,235
10°C (50°F)	5,665	35°C (95°F)	1,800
15°C (59°F)	4,450	40°C (104°F)	1,460
20°C (68°F)	3,515	45°C (113°F)	1,190

FAULT CODE 03 PRESENT.

BATTERY CHARGE OK.

DISCONNECT OUTSIDE AIR TEMPERATURE SENSOR PIGTAIL AND MEASURE RESISTANCE ACROSS THE SENSOR BY BACKPROBING THE PIGTAIL CONNECTOR.

- RESISTANCE NOT WITHIN 3% OF VALUE SHOWN FOR ACTUAL OUTSIDE TEMPERATURE. (REFER TO TEMPERATURE VS. OHMS CHART ABOVE.)
  - REPLACE OUTSIDE AIR TEMPERATURE SENSOR.
- RESISTANCE WITHIN 3% OF VALUE SHOWN FOR ACTUAL OUTSIDE TEMPERATURE. (REFER TO TEMPERATURE VS. OHMS CHART ABOVE.)
  - MEASURE VOLTAGE AT CIRCUIT 735 (LIGHT BLUE/BLACK WIRE AT PIN "A") BY BACKPROBING THE CONNECTOR.
    - MORE OR LESS THAN 5 VOLTS.
      - REPLACE CONTROL ASSEMBLY.
    - NO VOLTAGE.
      - DISCONNECT CONTROL ASSEMBLY CONNECTOR AND CHECK CONTINUITY OF CIRCUIT 735 (LIGHT GREEN/BLACK WIRE FROM PIN 7 OF CONTROL ASSEMBLY CONNECTOR TO PIN "A" OF CONNECTOR TO PIGTAIL).
        - CONTINUITY.
          - REPLACE CONTROL ASSEMBLY.
        - NO CONTINUITY.
          - REPAIR OPEN IN CIRCUIT 735.
    - APPROXIMATELY 5 VOLTS.
      - CHECK CONTINUITY TO GROUND OF CIRCUIT 198 (LIGHT GREEN/BLACK WIRE) AT CONNECTOR.
        - CONTINUITY.
          - REPLACE CONTROL ASSEMBLY.
        - NO CONTINUITY.
          - IF NO OTHER CODES ARE PRESENT, REPAIR OPEN IN CIRCUIT 198.
          - IF CODES 01, 05 AND/OR 07 ARE ALSO PRESENT, DISCONNECT CONTROL ASSEMBLY CONNECTOR AND CHECK CONTINUITY OF CIRCUIT 198 (LIGHT GREEN/BLACK WIRE AT PIN 9) TO AFFECTED SENSOR(S).
            - CONTINUITY TO ALL SENSORS.
              - REPLACE CONTROL ASSEMBLY.
            - NO CONTINUITY TO ONE OR MORE SENSORS.
              - REPAIR OPEN IN CIRCUIT 198 TO AFFECTED SENSOR(S).

ECC SYSTEM DIAGNOSIS—FAULT CODE 04 OUTSIDE AIR TEMP. SENSOR CIRCUIT SHORT 1993 ROADMASTER

FAULT CODE 04 – OUTSIDE AIR TEMPERATURE SENSOR CIRCUIT SHORT.

FAULT CODE 04 WILL BE PRESENT IF THE CONTROL ASSEMBLY DETECTS A SHORT TO GROUND IN CIRCUIT 735, A SHORT BETWEEN THE TWO CIRCUITS WITHIN THE SENSOR PIGTAIL, A SHORT WITHIN THE SENSOR ITSELF, OR CIRCUIT 735 SHORTS TO CIRCUIT 198.

FAULT CODE 04 WILL NOT BE STORED IN MEMORY. IT CAN BE EXTRACTED ONLY WHEN THE ERROR IS PRESENT.

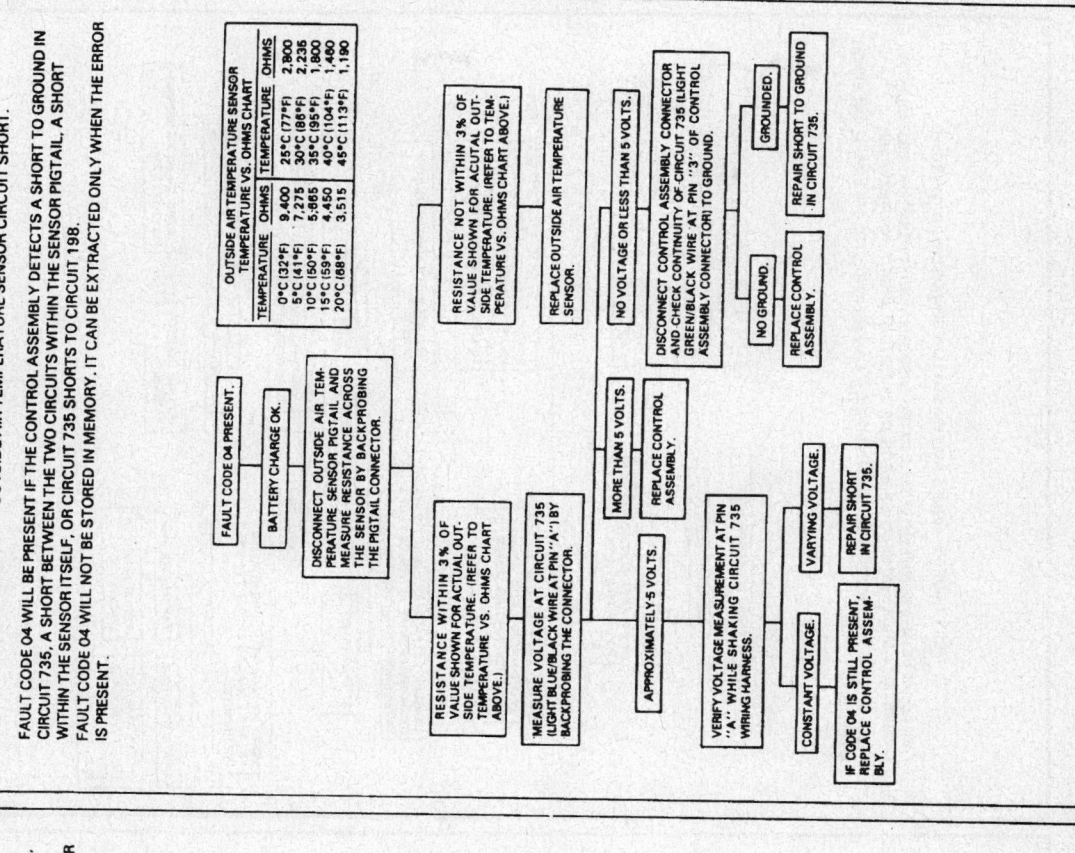

OUTSIDE AIR TEMPERATURE SENSOR TEMPERATURE VS. OHMS CHART

TEMPERATURE	OHMS	TEMPERATURE	OHMS
0°C (32°F)	9,400	25°C (77°F)	2,800
5°C (41°F)	7,275	30°C (86°F)	2,235
10°C (50°F)	5,665	35°C (95°F)	1,800
15°C (59°F)	4,450	40°C (104°F)	1,460
20°C (68°F)	3,515	45°C (113°F)	1,190

FAULT CODE 04 PRESENT.

BATTERY CHARGE OK.

DISCONNECT OUTSIDE AIR TEMPERATURE SENSOR PIGTAIL AND MEASURE RESISTANCE ACROSS THE SENSOR BY BACKPROBING THE PIGTAIL CONNECTOR.

- RESISTANCE NOT WITHIN 3% OF VALUE SHOWN FOR ACUTAL OUTSIDE TEMPERATURE. (REFER TO TEMPERATURE VS. OHMS CHART ABOVE.)
  - REPLACE OUTSIDE AIR TEMPERATURE SENSOR.
- RESISTANCE WITHIN 3% OF VALUE SHOWN FOR ACTUAL OUTSIDE TEMPERATURE. (REFER TO TEMPERATURE VS. OHMS CHART ABOVE.)
  - MEASURE VOLTAGE AT CIRCUIT 735 (LIGHT BLUE/BLACK WIRE AT PIN "A") BY BACKPROBING THE CONNECTOR.
    - APPROXIMATELY 5 VOLTS.
      - VERIFY VOLTAGE MEASUREMENT AT PIN "A" WHILE SHAKING CIRCUIT 735 WIRING HARNESS.
        - CONSTANT VOLTAGE.
          - IF CODE 04 IS STILL PRESENT, REPLACE CONTROL ASSEMBLY.
        - VARYING VOLTAGE.
          - REPAIR SHORT IN CIRCUIT 735.
    - MORE THAN 5 VOLTS.
      - REPLACE CONTROL ASSEMBLY.
    - NO VOLTAGE OR LESS THAN 5 VOLTS.
      - DISCONNECT CONTROL ASSEMBLY CONNECTOR AND CHECK CONTINUITY OF CIRCUIT 735 (LIGHT GREEN/BLACK WIRE AT PIN "3" OF CONTROL ASSEMBLY CONNECTOR) TO GROUND.
        - NO GROUND.
          - REPLACE CONTROL ASSEMBLY.
        - GROUNDED.
          - REPAIR SHORT TO GROUND IN CIRCUIT 735.

ECC SYSTEM DIAGNOSIS—FAULT CODE 05 INSIDE AIR TEMP. SENSOR CIRCUIT OPEN 1993 ROADMASTER

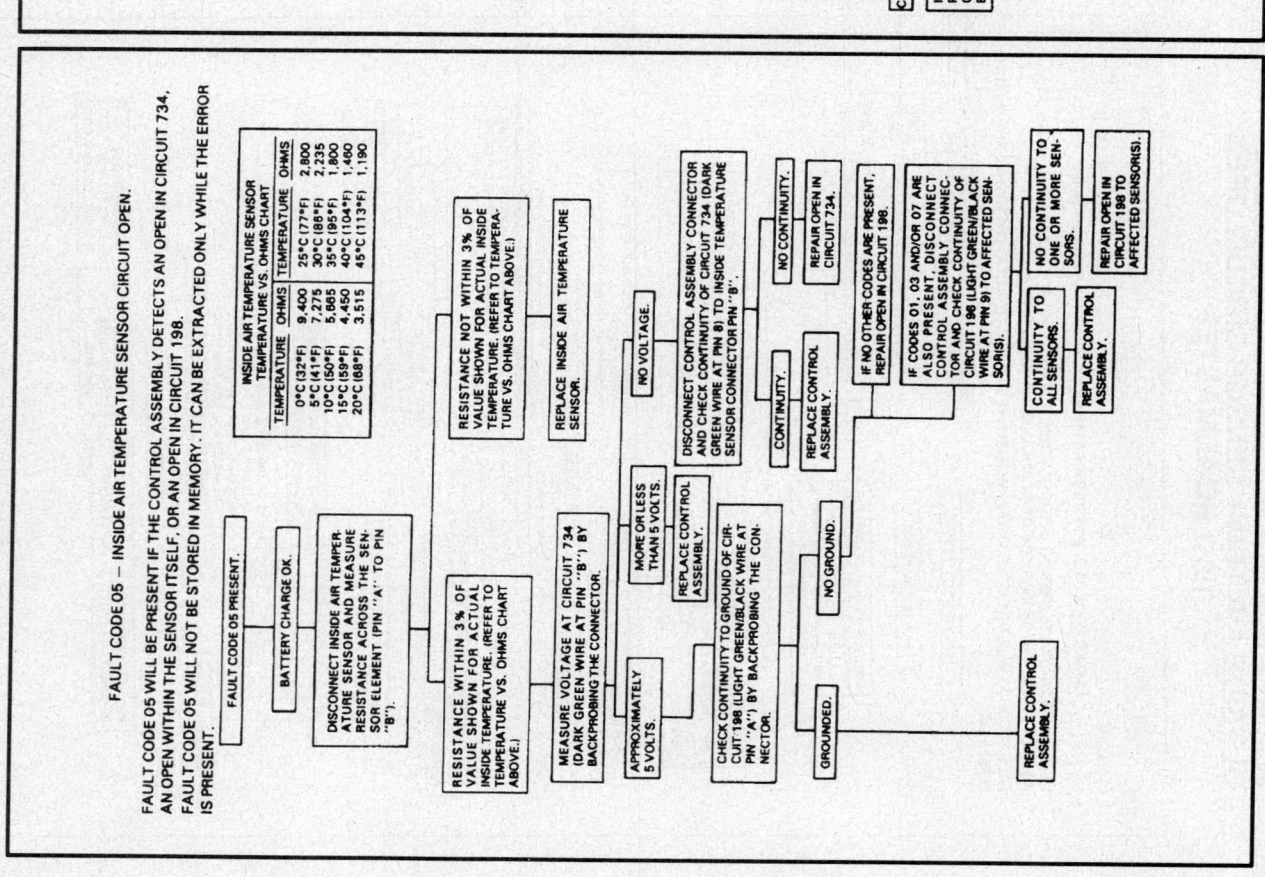

FAULT CODE 05 – INSIDE AIR TEMPERATURE SENSOR CIRCUIT OPEN.

FAULT CODE 05 WILL BE PRESENT IF THE CONTROL ASSEMBLY DETECTS AN OPEN IN CIRCUIT 734, AN OPEN WITHIN THE SENSOR ITSELF, OR AN OPEN IN CIRCUIT 198.

FAULT CODE 05 WILL NOT BE STORED IN MEMORY. IT CAN BE EXTRACTED ONLY WHILE THE ERROR IS PRESENT.

INSIDE AIR TEMPERATURE SENSOR TEMPERATURE VS. OHMS CHART

TEMPERATURE	OHMS	TEMPERATURE	OHMS
0°C (32°F)	9,400	25°C (77°F)	2,800
5°C (41°F)	7,275	30°C (86°F)	2,235
10°C (50°F)	5,665	35°C (95°F)	1,800
15°C (59°F)	4,450	40°C (104°F)	1,460
20°C (68°F)	3,515	45°C (113°F)	1,190

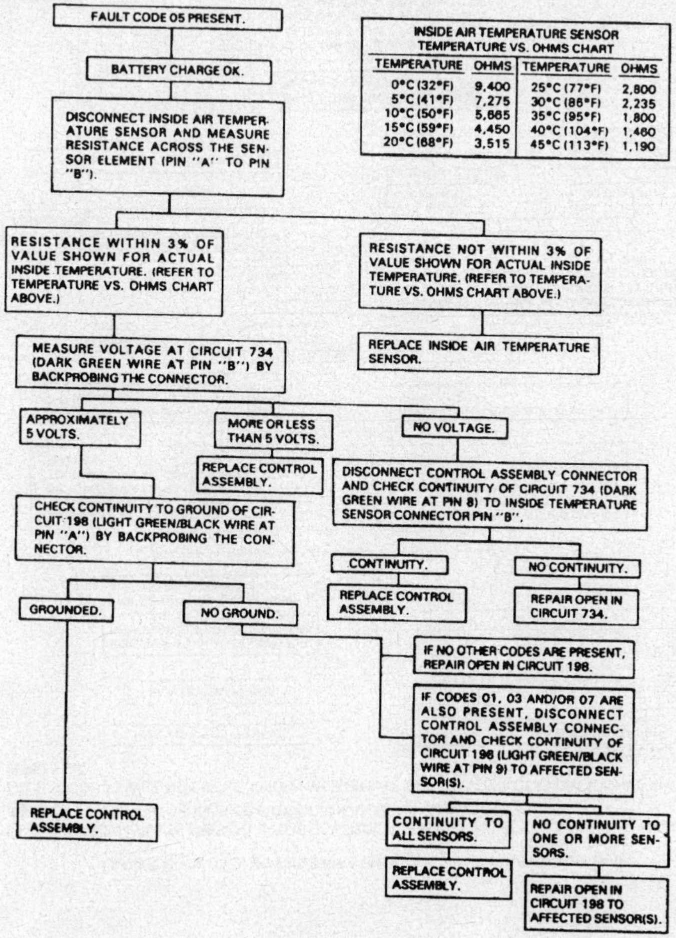

- FAULT CODE 05 PRESENT.
- BATTERY CHARGE OK.
- DISCONNECT INSIDE AIR TEMPERATURE SENSOR AND MEASURE RESISTANCE ACROSS THE SENSOR ELEMENT (PIN "A" TO PIN "B").
- RESISTANCE WITHIN 3% OF VALUE SHOWN FOR ACTUAL INSIDE TEMPERATURE. (REFER TO TEMPERATURE VS. OHMS CHART ABOVE.)
- RESISTANCE NOT WITHIN 3% OF VALUE SHOWN FOR ACTUAL INSIDE TEMPERATURE. (REFER TO TEMPERATURE VS. OHMS CHART ABOVE.)
- REPLACE INSIDE AIR TEMPERATURE SENSOR.
- MEASURE VOLTAGE AT CIRCUIT 734 (DARK GREEN WIRE AT PIN "B") BY BACKPROBING THE CONNECTOR.
- APPROXIMATELY 5 VOLTS.
- MORE OR LESS THAN 5 VOLTS.
- REPLACE CONTROL ASSEMBLY.
- NO VOLTAGE.
- DISCONNECT CONTROL ASSEMBLY CONNECTOR AND CHECK CONTINUITY OF CIRCUIT 734 (DARK GREEN WIRE AT PIN 8) TO INSIDE TEMPERATURE SENSOR CONNECTOR PIN "B".
- CONTINUITY.
- REPLACE CONTROL ASSEMBLY.
- NO CONTINUITY.
- REPAIR OPEN IN CIRCUIT 734.
- CHECK CONTINUITY TO GROUND OF CIRCUIT 198 (LIGHT GREEN/BLACK WIRE AT PIN "A") BY BACKPROBING THE CONNECTOR.
- GROUNDED.
- REPLACE CONTROL ASSEMBLY.
- NO GROUND.
- IF NO OTHER CODES ARE PRESENT, REPAIR OPEN IN CIRCUIT 198.
- IF CODES 01, 03 AND/OR 07 ARE ALSO PRESENT, DISCONNECT CONTROL ASSEMBLY CONNECTOR AND CHECK CONTINUITY OF CIRCUIT 198 (LIGHT GREEN/BLACK WIRE AT PIN 9) TO AFFECTED SENSOR(S).
- CONTINUITY TO ALL SENSORS.
- REPLACE CONTROL ASSEMBLY.
- NO CONTINUITY TO ONE OR MORE SENSORS.
- REPAIR OPEN IN CIRCUIT 198 TO AFFECTED SENSOR(S).

ECC SYSTEM DIAGNOSIS—FAULT CODE 06 INSIDE AIR TEMP. SENSOR CIRCUIT SHORT 1993 ROADMASTER

FAULT CODE 06 – INSIDE AIR TEMPERATURE SENSOR CIRCUIT SHORT.

FAULT CODE 06 WILL BE PRESENT IF THE CONTROL ASSEMBLY DETECTS A SHORT TO GROUND IN CIRCUIT 734, A SHORT WITHIN THE SENSOR, OR CIRCUIT 734 SHORTS TO CIRCUIT 198.

FAULT CODE 06 WILL NOT BE STORED IN MEMORY. IT CAN BE EXTRACTED ONLY WHILE THE ERROR IS PRESENT.

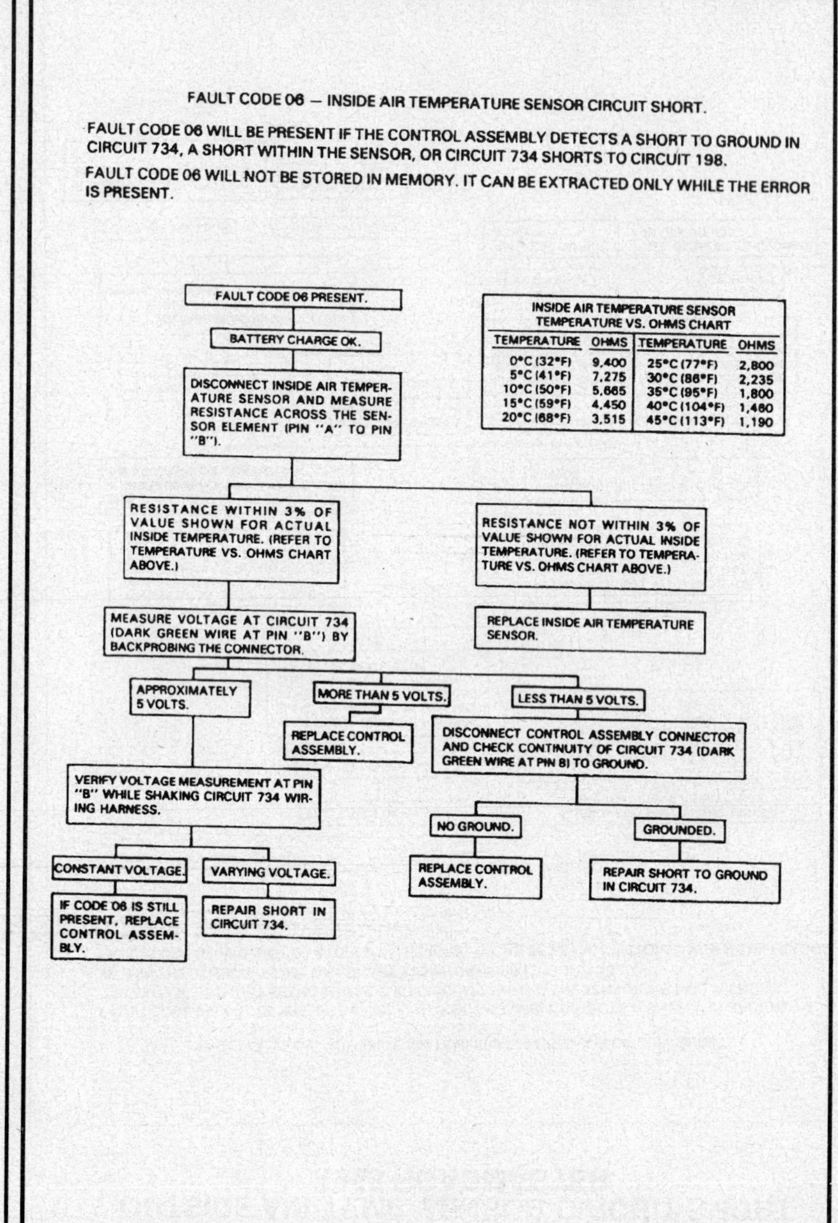

ECC SYSTEM DIAGNOSIS—FAULT CODE 07 SUNLOAD SENSOR CIRCUIT OPEN 1993 ROADMASTER

FAULT CODE 07 – SUN LOAD SENSOR CIRCUIT OPEN.

FAULT CODE 07 WILL BE PRESENT IF THE CONTROL ASSEMBLY DETECTS AN OPEN IN CIRCUIT 590, AN OPEN WITHIN THE SENSOR ITSELF, OR AN OPEN IN CIRCUIT 198.

FAULT CODE 07 WILL NOT BE STORED IN MEMORY. IT CAN BE EXTRACTED ONLY WHILE THE ERROR IS PRESENT.

ECC SYSTEM DIAGNOSIS—FAULT CODE 08 SUNLOAD SENSOR CIRCUIT SHORT 1993 ROADMASTER

FAULT CODE 08 – SUN LOAD SENSOR CIRCUIT SHORT.

FAULT CODE 08 WILL BE PRESENT IF THE CONTROL ASSEMBLY DETECTS A SHORT TO GROUND OR TO CIRCUIT 198 IN CIRCUIT 590, OR A SHORT WITHIN THE SENSOR ITSELF.

FAULT CODE 08 WILL NOT BE STORED IN MEMORY. IT CAN BE EXTRACTED ONLY WHILE THE ERROR IS PRESENT.

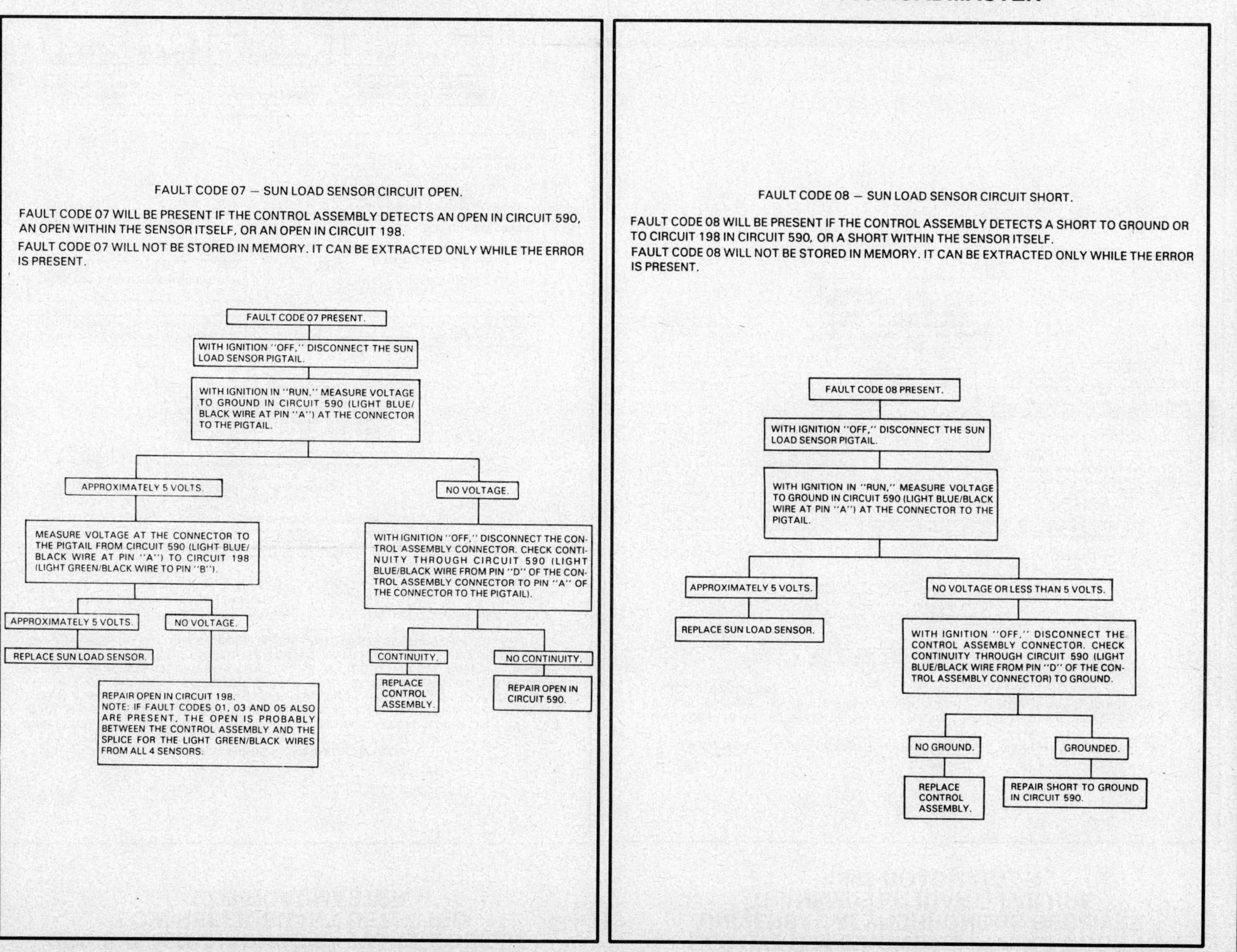

FAULT CODE 07 PRESENT.
WITH IGNITION "OFF," DISCONNECT THE SUN LOAD SENSOR PIGTAIL.
WITH IGNITION IN "RUN," MEASURE VOLTAGE TO GROUND IN CIRCUIT 590 (LIGHT BLUE/BLACK WIRE AT PIN "A") AT THE CONNECTOR TO THE PIGTAIL.
APPROXIMATELY 5 VOLTS.
MEASURE VOLTAGE AT THE CONNECTOR TO THE PIGTAIL FROM CIRCUIT 590 (LIGHT BLUE/BLACK WIRE AT PIN "A") TO CIRCUIT 198 (LIGHT GREEN/BLACK WIRE TO PIN "B").
APPROXIMATELY 5 VOLTS.
REPLACE SUN LOAD SENSOR.
NO VOLTAGE.
REPAIR OPEN IN CIRCUIT 198.
NOTE: IF FAULT CODES 01, 03 AND 05 ALSO ARE PRESENT, THE OPEN IS PROBABLY BETWEEN THE CONTROL ASSEMBLY AND THE SPLICE FOR THE LIGHT GREEN/BLACK WIRES FROM ALL 4 SENSORS.
NO VOLTAGE.
WITH IGNITION "OFF," DISCONNECT THE CONTROL ASSEMBLY CONNECTOR. CHECK CONTINUITY THROUGH CIRCUIT 590 (LIGHT BLUE/BLACK WIRE FROM PIN "D" OF THE CONTROL ASSEMBLY CONNECTOR TO PIN "A" OF THE CONNECTOR TO THE PIGTAIL).
CONTINUITY.
REPLACE CONTROL ASSEMBLY.
NO CONTINUITY.
REPAIR OPEN IN CIRCUIT 590.
FAULT CODE 08 PRESENT.
WITH IGNITION "OFF," DISCONNECT THE SUN LOAD SENSOR PIGTAIL.
WITH IGNITION IN "RUN," MEASURE VOLTAGE TO GROUND IN CIRCUIT 590 (LIGHT BLUE/BLACK WIRE AT PIN "A") AT THE CONNECTOR TO THE PIGTAIL.
APPROXIMATELY 5 VOLTS.
REPLACE SUN LOAD SENSOR.
NO VOLTAGE OR LESS THAN 5 VOLTS.
WITH IGNITION "OFF," DISCONNECT THE CONTROL ASSEMBLY CONNECTOR. CHECK CONTINUITY THROUGH CIRCUIT 590 (LIGHT BLUE/BLACK WIRE FROM PIN "D" OF THE CONTROL ASSEMBLY CONNECTOR) TO GROUND.
NO GROUND.
REPLACE CONTROL ASSEMBLY.
GROUNDED.
REPAIR SHORT TO GROUND IN CIRCUIT 590.

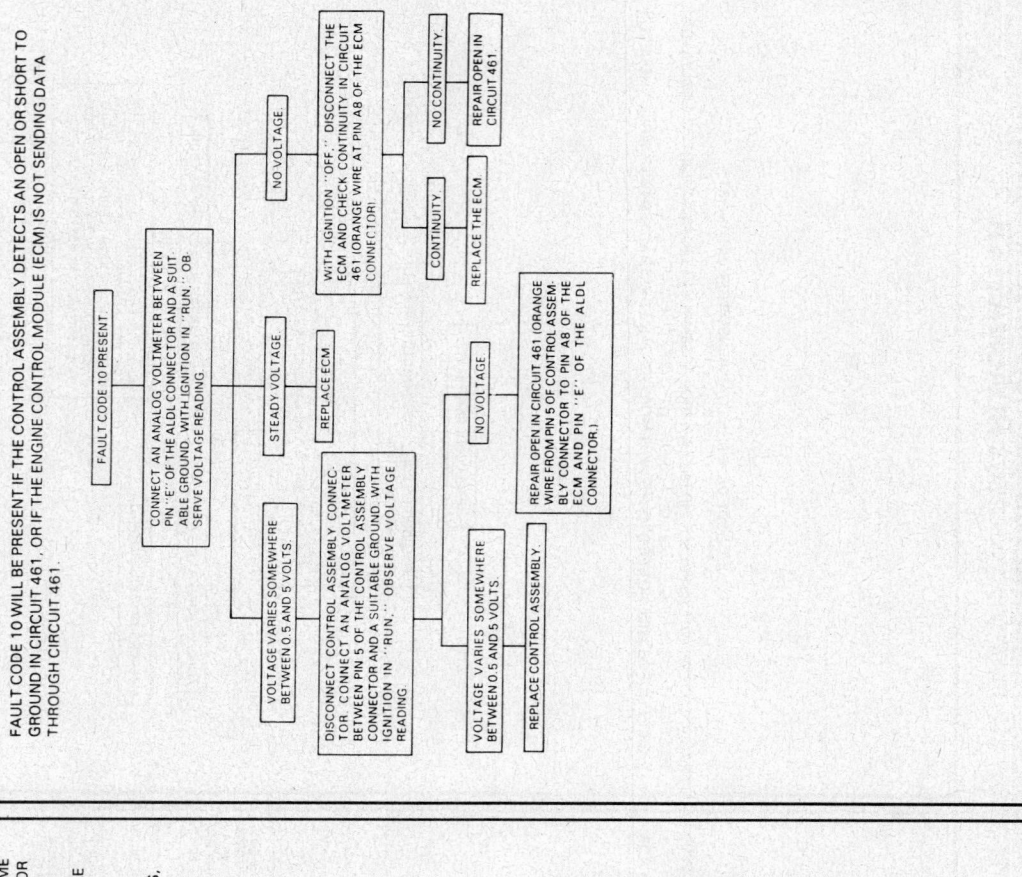

ECC SYSTEM DIAGNOSIS—FAULT CODE 09 LOW REFRIGERANT DETECTED 1993 ROADMASTER

FAULT CODE 09 — LOW FREON DETECTED.

FAULT CODE 09 WILL BE PRESENT IF THE CONTROL ASSEMBLY DETECTS COMPRESSOR "ON" TIME IS TOO SHORT AT SPEEDS ABOVE 5 MPH. THE CONTROL ASSEMBLY MONITORS THE COMPRESSOR CYCLING SWITCH TO DETERMINE COMPRESSOR "ON" TIME THROUGH CIRCUIT 67. EACH TIME COMPRESSOR "ON" TIME IS TOO SHORT, THE CONTROL ASSEMBLY WILL RECORD THIS AS AN EVENT. IF TEN EVENTS ARE DETECTED CONSECUTIVELY, THE CONTROL ASSEMBLY WILL DISABLE THE COMPRESSOR UNTIL THE FAULT IS CLEARED. AS CONTROL ASSEMBLY MONITORS EVENTS, ANY COMPRESSOR "ON" TIME DETECTED WITHIN LIMITS WILL RESET THE EVENT COUNT TO ZERO.

FAULT CODE 09 WILL BE STORED IN MEMORY AND CAN BE CLEARED BY ENTERING DIAGNOSTICS, THEN PRESSING THE "OFF" TOUCH SWITCH.

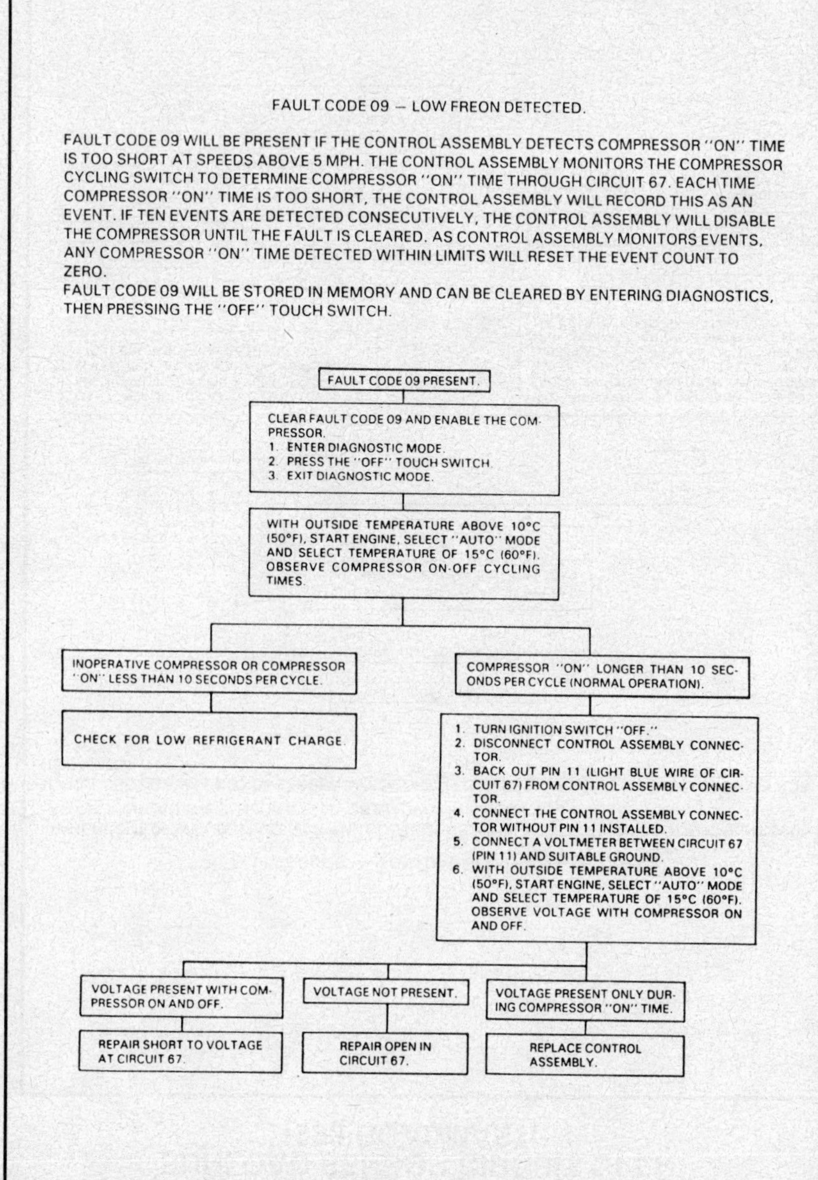

EEC SYSTEM DIAGNOSIS—FAULT CODE 10 UNIVERSAL ASYNCHRONOUS RECEIVER TRANSMITTER (UART) FAILURE 1993 ROADMASTER

FAULT CODE 10 — UNIVERSAL ASYNCHRONOUS RECEIVER TRANSMITTER (UART) FAILURE.

FAULT CODE 10 WILL BE PRESENT IF THE CONTROL ASSEMBLY DETECTS AN OPEN OR SHORT TO GROUND IN CIRCUIT 461, OR IF THE ENGINE CONTROL MODULE (ECM) IS NOT SENDING DATA THROUGH CIRCUIT 461.

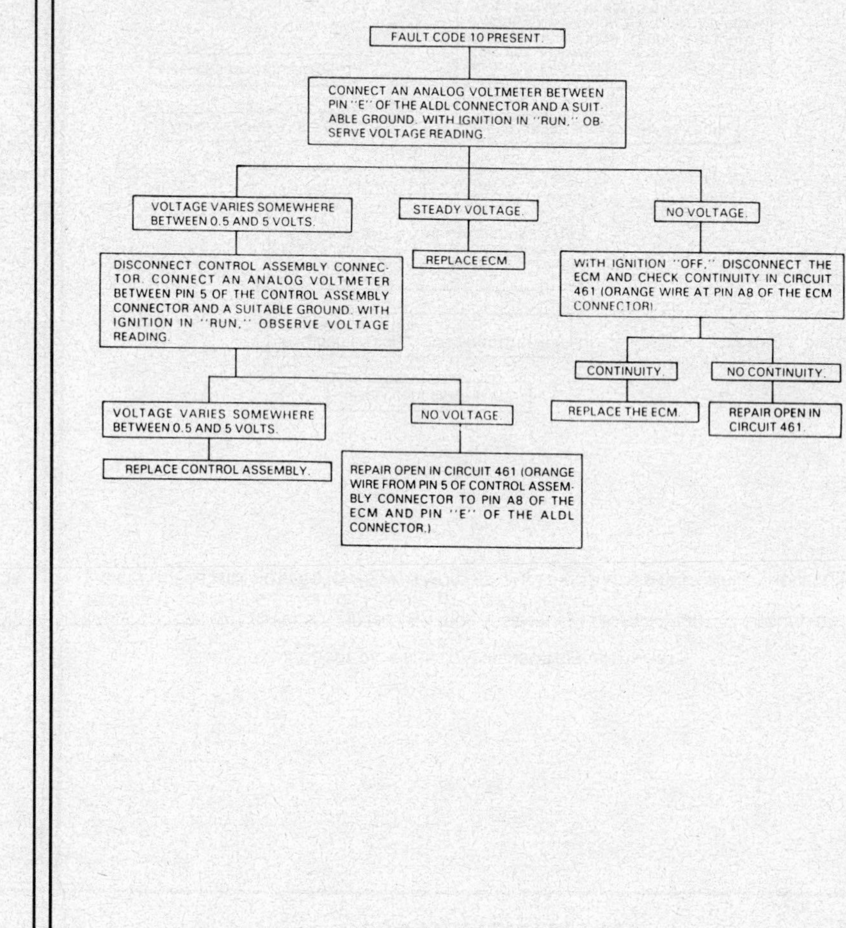

ECC SYSTEM DIAGNOSIS—COMPRESSOR CONTROL AND U.A.R.T. CIRCUITS 1993 ROADMASTER

- A 50 BRN WIRE
- B 59 DK GRN WIRE
- C 66 LT GRN WIRE
- D 67 LT BLU WIRE
- E 459 DK GRN/WHT WIRE
- F 461 ORN WIRE
- G 762 DK GRN/YEL
- H RELAY CONTROL
- J REFRIGERANT PRESSURE INPUT
- K AIR CONDITIONING REQUEST INPUT
- L COMPRESSOR CONTROL
- M SERIAL DATA OUTPUT
- N TO FUSE 6 (20A), IGN 3 CKT
- P TO ALDL
- Q TERMINAL "A"
- R TERMINAL "A8"
- S TERMINAL "B"
- T TERMINAL "B8"
- U TERMINAL "C1"
- V TERMINAL "C2"
- W TERMINAL "C3"
- X TERMINAL "C5"
- Y TERMINAL "C10"
- Z TERMINAL "C11"
- AA 1592 DK BLU WIRE
- 15 MICROPROCESSOR
- 21 CONTROL RELAY
- 22 COMPRESSOR RELAY
- 23 ECM
- 41 COMPRESSOR CLUTCH COIL
- 42 DIODE
- 46 HIGH PRESSURE CUTOFF SWITCH
- 47 PRESSURE CYCLING SWITCH

1994–95 DIAGNOSTIC POINTERS AND PARAMETERS—CADILLAC FLEETWOOD

Pointer #		Display Range	Default Value
–00	PCM System Diagnostic Trouble Codes	–	–
–01	CCM System Diagnostic Trouble Codes	–	–
–02	ACAC System (HVAC) Diagnostic Trouble Codes	Trouble codes stored	–
–03	SIR System Diagnostic Trouble Codes	–	–
–04	ABS/TCS System Diagnostic Trouble Codes	–	–
–05	Program Number	Parameters 0–255 Parameters	– –
–07	Commanded Blower Motor Speed	0–128	–
–14	Vehicle Speed	In mph	25 (mph)
–15	HVAC Learn Mode (Temperature Calibration Offset)	–5° to 5° (F)	–
–18	Sun Load Sensor	0–255	240
–20	Current Temperature Valve Position	0–255	–
–22	Temperature Valve Position (Full Cold)	180–250	180
–23	Temperature Valve Position (Full Hot)	5–60	60
–24	Coolant Temperature	In °C	91°C
–25	Commanded TemperatureValve Position	0–255	128
–27	Air Delivery Mode. Refer to Chart 3, "Improper Air Delivery" for diagnosis.	–	–
–28	Inside Air Temperature Sensor	Value increases as temperature decreases. Refer to CHART 03 and CHART 04 for more information.	128 (75° F) 128 (49° F) –
–31	Outside Air Temperature Sensor	Value increases as temperature decreases. Refer to CHART 01 and CHART 02 for more information.	
–37	EEPROM revision #	–	

ECC SYSTEM DIAGNOSIS—CORVETTE

1 LCD DISPLAY
2 LED MODE INDICATORS
3 AUTO BLOWER/FAN UP/FAN DOWN/DIAGNOSTICS
4A HEATED MIRRORS/REAR DEFROST - COUPES CONVERTIBLE HARDTOP
4B HEATED MIRRORS/ONLY CONVERTIBLE
5 DEFROST/DEFOGGER
6 HEATER
7 VENT
8 BI-LEVEL
9 RECIRCULATION
10 AUTOMATIC (FROM TEMPERATURE SET)
11 DECREASE TEMPERATURE
12 TEMPERATURE SET
13 INCREASE TEMPERATURE

	CONTROL SETTINGS			SYSTEM RESPONSE					
STEP	MODE CONTROL	TEMPERATURE SETTING	FAN SETTING	BLOWER SPEED	HEATER OUTLETS	A/C OUTLETS	DEFROSTER OUTLETS	S.W.D.** OUTLETS	*SEE NOTES
1	OFF	60°F	MANUAL 1	OFF	NO AIRFLOW	NO AIRFLOW	NO AIRFLOW	NO AIRFLOW	
2	AUTO	60°F	MANUAL 1	LOW	NO AIRFLOW	AIRFLOW	NO AIRFLOW	MINIMAL AIRFLOW	
3	AUTO	60°F	MAN 1 TO AUTO	LOW TO HIGH	NO AIRFLOW	AIRFLOW	NO AIRFLOW	MINIMAL AIRFLOW	A
4	RECIRC	60°F	AUTO	HIGH	NO AIRFLOW	AIRFLOW	NO AIRFLOW	MINIMAL AIRFLOW	
5	BI-LEVEL	60°F	AUTO	HIGH	AIRFLOW	AIRFLOW	AIRFLOW	MINIMAL AIRFLOW	
6	VENT	60°F	AUTO	HIGH	NO AIRFLOW	AIRFLOW	NO AIRFLOW	MINIMAL AIRFLOW	B
7	HTR	90°F	AUTO	HIGH	AIRFLOW	NO AIRFLOW	MINIMAL AIRFLOW	AIRFLOW	C
8	DEF	90°F	AUTO	HIGH	MINIMAL AIRFLOW	NO AIRFLOW	AIRFLOW	AIRFLOW	C

** ONLY A SMALL QUANTITY OF AIR WILL BE DISCHARGED AT THESE

COOLING FUNCTIONAL TEST

1 DOOR OR WIDOWS CLOSED
2 TEMPERATURE INDICATORS AT CONDENSER INLET AND RH UPPER COOLING OUTLET
3 CLOSE LH SIDE, CENTER AND LOWER RH COOLING OUTLETS
4 START ENGINE AND RUN AT 2000 RPM
5 SET TEMPERATURE TO 60°F (MAX COOL) BY PRESSING COOL BUTTON
6 AFTER ONE MINUTE THE AIR TEMPERATURE DROP AT THE RH UPPER COOLING OUTLET SHOULD BE AS FOLLOWS

CONDENSER INLET TEMPERATURE (F°)	70	80	90-100
CENTER OUTLET TEMPERATURE DROP (F° MINIMUM)	20	25	30

*NOTES

A NOTICEABLE BLOWER SPEED INCREASE MUST OCCUR FROM MANUAL (1) TO AUTO
B LISTEN FOR REDUCTION OF AIR NOISE DUE TO RECIRCULATION DOOR CLOSING
C CHECK FOR SMALL AMOUNT OF AIR FLOW AT S W D OUTLETS

ECC SYSTEM DIAGNOSTIC PARAMETERS CORVETTE

PARAMETER #	PARAMETER DESCRIPTION	DISPLAY RANGE
0	SYSTEM FAULTS	00 - 10
1	TEMPERATURE SETTING IN DEGREES	60°F - 90°F
2	IN-CAR TEMPERATURE SENSOR	10 = (HOT) - 130 (230) = (COLD)
3	OUTSIDE AMBIENT TEMPERATURE SENSOR	10 = (HOT) - 130 (230) = (COLD)
4	SUN LOAD SENSOR	MAX LIGHT 0 MAX DARK -120 (220)
* 5	IGNITION SYSTEM VOLTAGE	0 = 9 VOLTS -155 (255) = 16 VOLTS
* 6	ENGINE SPEED (RPM ÷ 25)	
* 7	VEHICLE SPEED	
9	SYSTEM MODE (00 = OFF 01 = RECIRCULATION, 02 = A/C 03 = BI-LEVEL, 04 = HEATER 06 = DEFROST, 07 = VENT 10 = MANUAL RECIRCULATION)	AUTO MODE WILL DISPLAY 01THROUGH 04 DEPENDING ON SET TEMPERATURE.
* 10	BLOWER PWM (PULSE WIDTH MODULATION)	0 = 0 VOLTS 128 = 14 VOLTS
* 11	PROGRAM NUMBER	00 = (COLD) - 155 (255) = (HOT)
* 12	MIX NUMBER	-155 (255) = (COLD) 00 = (HOT)
* 16	COOLANT TEMP.	°C
* 17	SOLAR CORRECTION	114 - MAX LIGHT 128 MAX DARK
* 30	STORED FULL HOT VALUE	0 - 50
* 31	TEMPERATURE DOOR TRAVEL RANGE	100 - 200
34	TEMPERATURE DOOR POSITION REQUESTED	00 = FULL HOT -153 (253) = FULL COLD
* 35	COMPRESSOR ON TIME	.1 SECOND INCREMENTS
* 36	NUMBER OF TIMES BELOW CRITICAL TIME	
* 37	SOFTWARE VERSION NUMBER	

* NOT USED FOR SYSTEM DIAGNOSIS

NOTICE: A MINUS (-) SIGN TO THE LEFT OF THE PARAMETER DISPLAY RANGE FIGURE WILL INDICATE AN ADDITIONAL 100 TO THE DISPLAY

EXAMPLE: - 130 = 230

ECC SYSTEM WIRING DIAGNOSIS—CORVETTE

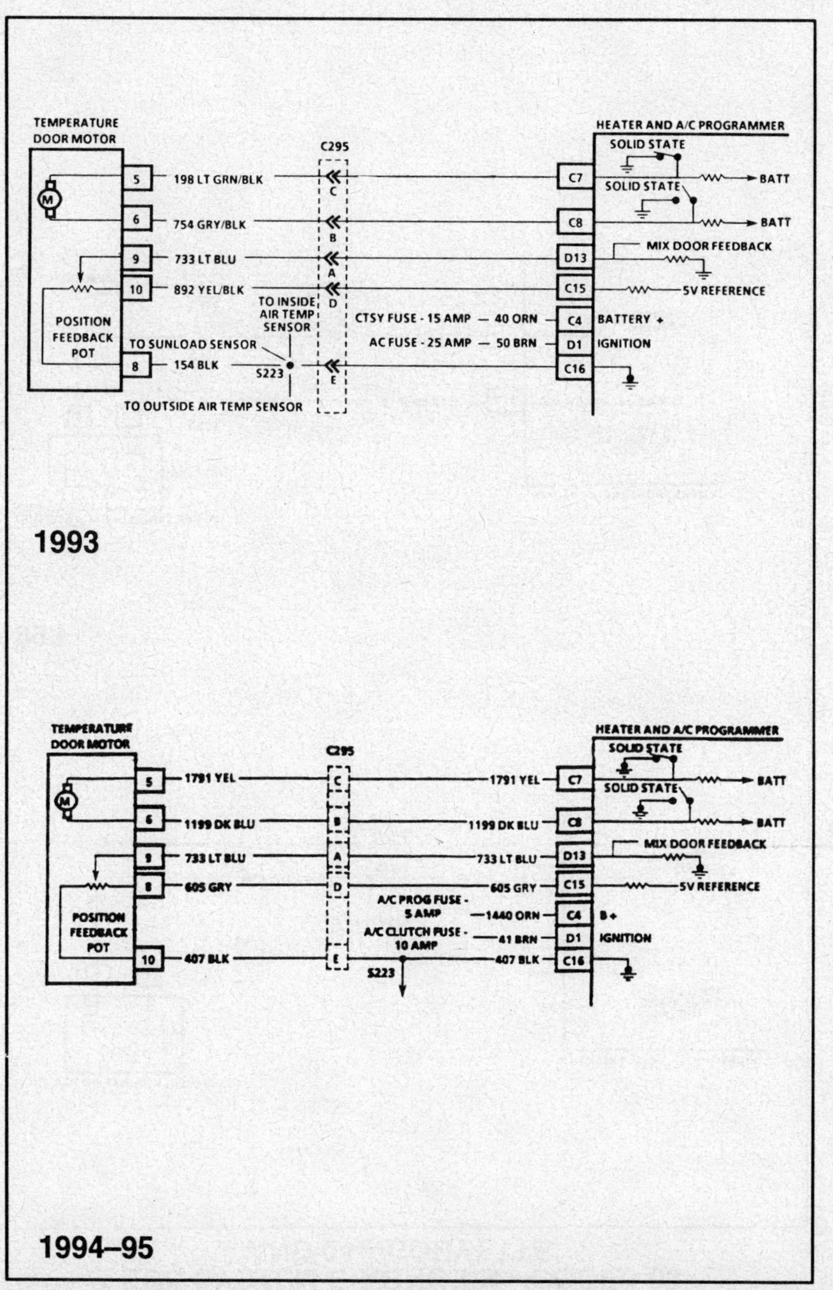

CORVETTE TEMPERATURE DOOR MOTOR CIRCUIT FAULT CHARTS 01 AND 02

1
- IGNITION "OFF."
- REMOVE NEGATIVE BATTERY CABLE, REINSTALL AFTER 1 MINUTE.
- IGNITION "ON."

DOES DTC RESET?

- **NO:** IF DTC DID NOT RESET, SYSTEM OK.
- **YES:** Go to 2.

2
- RUN ENGINE UNTIL REACHING NORMAL OPERATING TEMPERATURE.
- SET TEMPERATURE FULL HOT 33°C (90°F).
- ENTER DIAGNOSTICS PARAMETER 34. PARAMETER 34 SHOULD READ 00.
- SET TEMPERATURE FULL COLD 16°C (60°F).
- ENTER DIAGNOSTICS PARAMETER 34. PARAMETER 34 SHOULD READ -153 (253) COUNTS.

IS PARAMETER 34 WITHIN SPECIFIED RANGE?

- **NO:** REPLACE HVAC PROGRAMMER. → OK
- **YES:** Go to 3.

3
- ENTER DIAGNOSTICS PARAMETER 24. PARAMETER 24 SHOULD READ -153 (253) COUNTS IN FULL COLD.
- SET TEMPERATURE FULL HOT 33°C (90°F).
- ENTER DIAGNOSTICS PARAMETERS 24. PARAMETER 24 SHOULD READ 00.

IS PARAMETER 24 WITHIN SPECIFIED RANGE?

- **YES:** Go to 4.
- **NO:**
  - REMOVE BLOWER POWER MODULE FROM HEATER CASE TO VIEW TEMPERATURE DOOR.
  - CHECK FOR OBSTRUCTIONS.

  ANY OBSTRUCTIONS PRESENT?
  - **YES:** REMOVE OBSTRUCTION AND RE-CHECK DOOR OPERATION.
  - **NO:**
    - SET TEMPERATURE TO 24°C (75°F).
    - USING A SCREWDRIVER, LIGHTLY CHECK TEMPERATURE DOOR FREEPLAY.

    DOES TEMPERATURE DOOR FREEPLAY EXCEED 5 MM (0.2 IN.)?
    - **YES:** SEE "DIAGNOSTIC AIDS" ON FACING PAGE.
    - **NO:** GO TO STEP 5.

4
- REMOVE BLOWER POWER MODULE FROM HEATER CASE TO VIEW TEMPERATURE DOOR.
- KEY "ON."
- HAVE A HELPER SET TEMPERATURE FULL HOT THEN FULL COLD THEN BACK TO FULL HOT. WAIT 1 MINUTE BETWEEN CYCLES.

DOES TEMPERATURE DOOR MOVE TO FULL HOT AND COLD POSITIONS?

- **YES:** Go to 5.
- **NO:** Go to 6.

5
- IGNITION "ON."
- SET TEMPERATURE FULL COLD 16°C (60°F).
- IGNITION "OFF."
- REMOVE LOWER I/P TRIM PANEL R.H. TO GAIN ACCESS TO C295.
- DISCONNECT C295 AND MEASURE TEMPERATURE DOOR MOTOR RESISTANCE USING DVM AT TERMINALS "A" AND "D". FULL COLD RESISTANCE SHOULD BE 1.96K + -500Ω.
- CONNECT C295.
- IGNITION "ON."
- SET TEMPERATURE FULL HOT 33°C (90°F).
- IGNITION "OFF."
- DISCONNECT C295 AND MEASURE TEMPERATURE DOOR MOTOR RESISTANCE AT TERMINALS "A" AND "D". FULL HOT RESISTANCE SHOULD BE 7.7K + -500Ω.

ARE RESISTANCES WITHIN SPECIFIED RANGE?

6
- REMOVE I/P LOWER TRIM PANEL R.H. TO GAIN ACCESS TO C295.
- KEY "ON."
- USING DVM, CHECK FOR APPROX. 8 VOLTS BY BACKPROBING TERMINALS "B" AND "C" AT C295 WHILE ADJUSTING TEMPERATURE FULL HOT TO FULL COLD (WAIT 1 MINUTE BETWEEN CYCLES).

APPROX. 8 VOLTS PRESENT?

ECC SYSTEM DIAGNOSIS—CODES 03 AND 04—CORVETTE

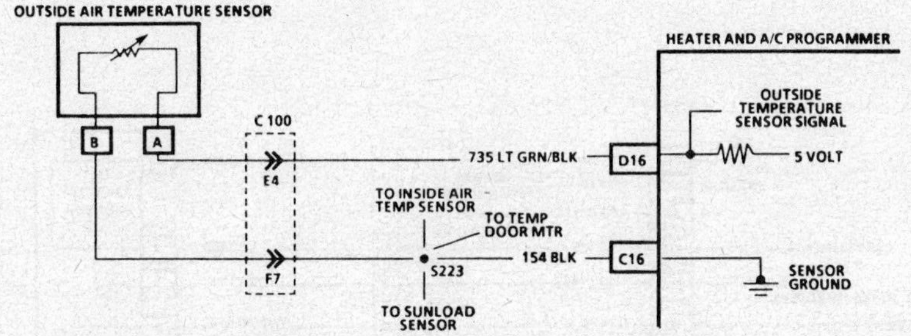

OUTSIDE AIR TEMPERATURE SENSOR
B
A
C 100
E4
F7
735 LT GRN/BLK
154 BLK
TO INSIDE AIR TEMP SENSOR
TO TEMP DOOR MTR
S223
TO SUNLOAD SENSOR
D16
C16
HEATER AND A/C PROGRAMMER
OUTSIDE TEMPERATURE SENSOR SIGNAL
5 VOLT
SENSOR GROUND

1993

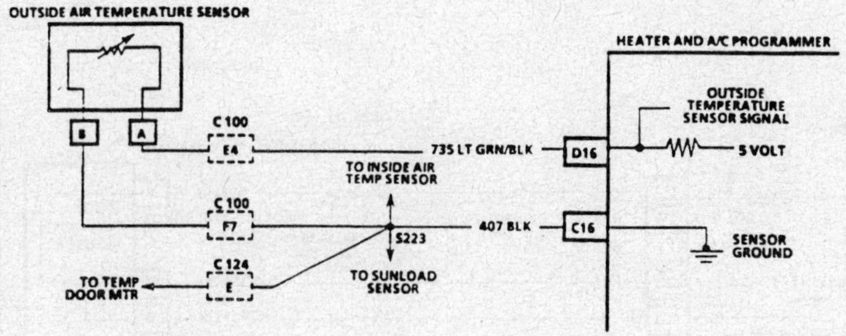

OUTSIDE AIR TEMPERATURE SENSOR
B
A
C 100
E4
C 100
F7
C 124
E
TO TEMP DOOR MTR
735 LT GRN/BLK
407 BLK
TO INSIDE AIR TEMP SENSOR
S223
TO SUNLOAD SENSOR
D16
C16
HEATER AND A/C PROGRAMMER
OUTSIDE TEMPERATURE SENSOR SIGNAL
5 VOLT
SENSOR GROUND

1994–95

ECC SYSTEM DIAGNOSIS—CODES 03 AND 04—CORVETTE, CONT'D

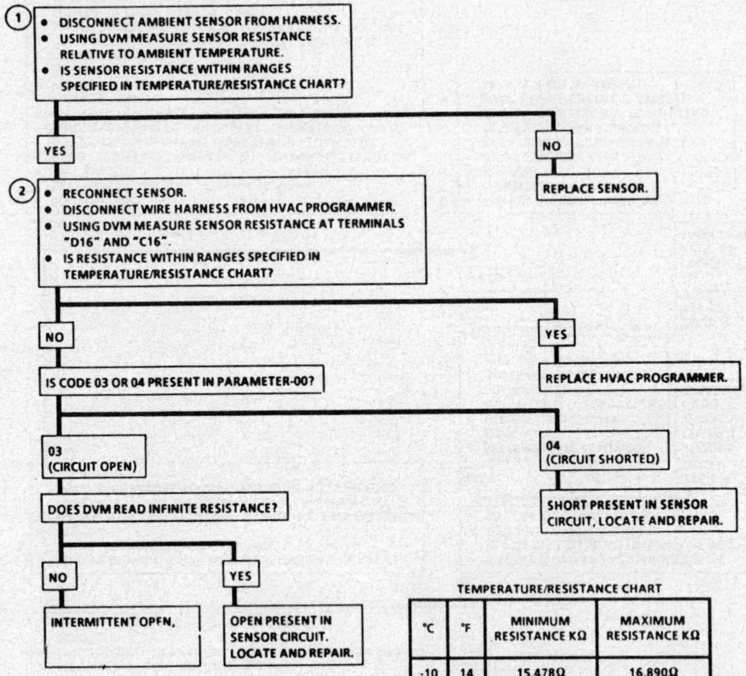

(1)
- DISCONNECT AMBIENT SENSOR FROM HARNESS.
- USING DVM MEASURE SENSOR RESISTANCE RELATIVE TO AMBIENT TEMPERATURE.
- IS SENSOR RESISTANCE WITHIN RANGES SPECIFIED IN TEMPERATURE/RESISTANCE CHART?

NO → REPLACE SENSOR.

YES →

(2)
- RECONNECT SENSOR.
- DISCONNECT WIRE HARNESS FROM HVAC PROGRAMMER.
- USING DVM MEASURE SENSOR RESISTANCE AT TERMINALS "D16" AND "C16".
- IS RESISTANCE WITHIN RANGES SPECIFIED IN TEMPERATURE/RESISTANCE CHART?

YES → REPLACE HVAC PROGRAMMER.

NO → IS CODE 03 OR 04 PRESENT IN PARAMETER-00?

04 (CIRCUIT SHORTED) → SHORT PRESENT IN SENSOR CIRCUIT, LOCATE AND REPAIR.

03 (CIRCUIT OPEN) → DOES DVM READ INFINITE RESISTANCE?

NO → INTERMITTENT OPFN,

YES → OPEN PRESENT IN SENSOR CIRCUIT. LOCATE AND REPAIR.

TEMPERATURE/RESISTANCE CHART

°C	°F	MINIMUM RESISTANCE KΩ	MAXIMUM RESISTANCE KΩ
-10	14	15.478Ω	16.890Ω
-5	23	11.765Ω	12.800Ω
0	32	9.039Ω	9.775Ω
5	41	7.009Ω	7.536Ω
10	50	5.477Ω	5.856Ω
15	59	4.310Ω	4.583Ω
20	68	3.416Ω	3.612Ω
25	77	2.725Ω	2.865Ω
30	86	2.175Ω	2.299Ω
35	95	1.746Ω	1.857Ω
40	104	1.410Ω	1.508Ω
45	113	1.145Ω	1.231Ω
50	122	.935Ω	1.010Ω

ECC SYSTEM DIAGNOSIS – CODES 05 AND 06 CORVETTE

(1)
- DISCONNECT IN-VEHICLE TEMPERATURE SENSOR FROM HARNESS.
- USING DVM MEASURE SENSOR RESISTANCE RELATIVE TO AMBIENT TEMPERATURE.
- IS SENSOR RESISTANCE WITHIN RANGES SPECIFIED IN TEMPERATURE/RESISTANCE CHART?

NO → REPLACE SENSOR.

YES →

(2)
- RECONNECT SENSOR.
- DISCONNECT WIRE HARNESS AT HVAC PROGRAMMER.
- USING DVM MEASURE SENSOR RESISTANCE AT HARNESS TERMINALS "C16" AND "D15".
- IS RESISTANCE WITHIN RANGES SPECIFIED IN TEMPERATURE/RESISTANCE CHART?

YES → REPLACE HVAC PROGRAMMER.

NO → IS CODE 05 OR 06 PRESENT IN PARAMETER-00?

CODE 06 (CIRCUIT SHORTED). → SHORT PRESENT IN SENSOR CIRCUIT, LOCATE AND REPAIR.

CODE 05 (CIRCUIT OPEN). → DOES DVM READ INFINITE RESISTANCE?

YES → OPEN IN SENSOR CIRCUIT. LOCATE AND REPAIR.

NO → INTERMITTENT OPEN

TEMPERATURE/RESISTANCE CHART

°C	°F	MINIMUM RESISTANCE KΩ	MAXIMUM RESISTANCE KΩ
0	32	9.039Ω	9.775Ω
5	41	7.009Ω	7.536Ω
10	50	5.477Ω	5.856Ω
15	59	4.310Ω	4.583Ω
20	68	3.416Ω	3.612Ω
25	77	2.725Ω	2.865Ω
30	86	2.175Ω	2.299Ω
35	95	1.746Ω	1.857Ω
40	104	1.410Ω	1.508Ω
45	113	1.145Ω	1.231Ω
50	122	.935Ω	1.010Ω
55	131	.770Ω	.836Ω

ECC SYSTEM DIAGNOSIS–CODES 07 AND 08 CORVETTE

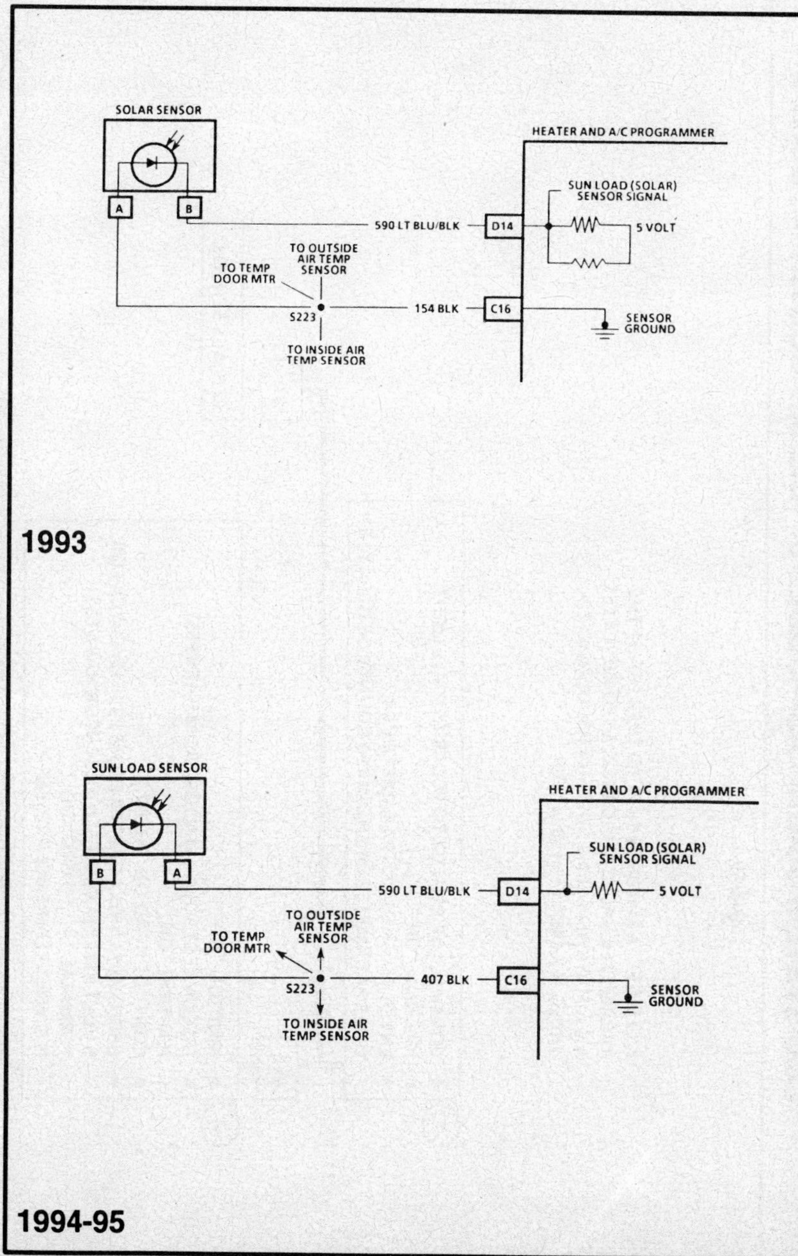

ECC SYSTEM DIAGNOSIS—CODES 07 AND 08–CORVETTE, CONT'D

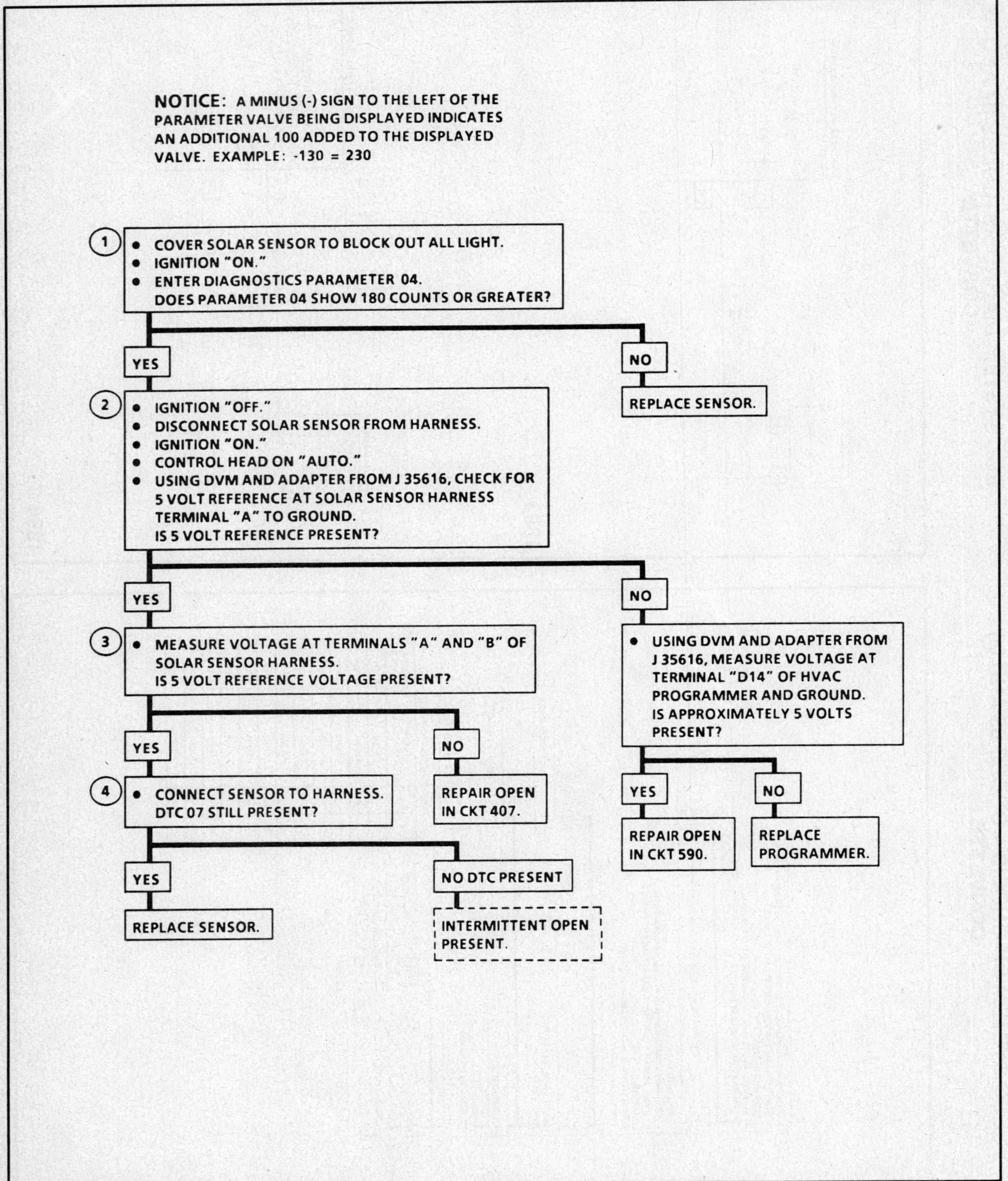

NOTICE: A MINUS (-) SIGN TO THE LEFT OF THE PARAMETER VALVE BEING DISPLAYED INDICATES AN ADDITIONAL 100 ADDED TO THE DISPLAYED VALVE. EXAMPLE: -130 = 230
1
• COVER SOLAR SENSOR TO BLOCK OUT ALL LIGHT.
• IGNITION "ON."
• ENTER DIAGNOSTICS PARAMETER 04.
DOES PARAMETER 04 SHOW 180 COUNTS OR GREATER?
YES
NO
REPLACE SENSOR.
2
• IGNITION "OFF."
• DISCONNECT SOLAR SENSOR FROM HARNESS.
• IGNITION "ON."
• CONTROL HEAD ON "AUTO."
• USING DVM AND ADAPTER FROM J 35616, CHECK FOR 5 VOLT REFERENCE AT SOLAR SENSOR HARNESS TERMINAL "A" TO GROUND.
IS 5 VOLT REFERENCE PRESENT?
YES
NO
3
• MEASURE VOLTAGE AT TERMINALS "A" AND "B" OF SOLAR SENSOR HARNESS.
IS 5 VOLT REFERENCE VOLTAGE PRESENT?
• USING DVM AND ADAPTER FROM J 35616, MEASURE VOLTAGE AT TERMINAL "D14" OF HVAC PROGRAMMER AND GROUND.
IS APPROXIMATELY 5 VOLTS PRESENT?
YES
NO
4
• CONNECT SENSOR TO HARNESS.
DTC 07 STILL PRESENT?
REPAIR OPEN IN CKT 407.
YES
NO
REPAIR OPEN IN CKT 590.
REPLACE PROGRAMMER.
YES
NO DTC PRESENT
REPLACE SENSOR.
INTERMITTENT OPEN PRESENT.

ECC SYSTEM DIAGNOSIS—CODE 09—1993 CORVETTE VIN P

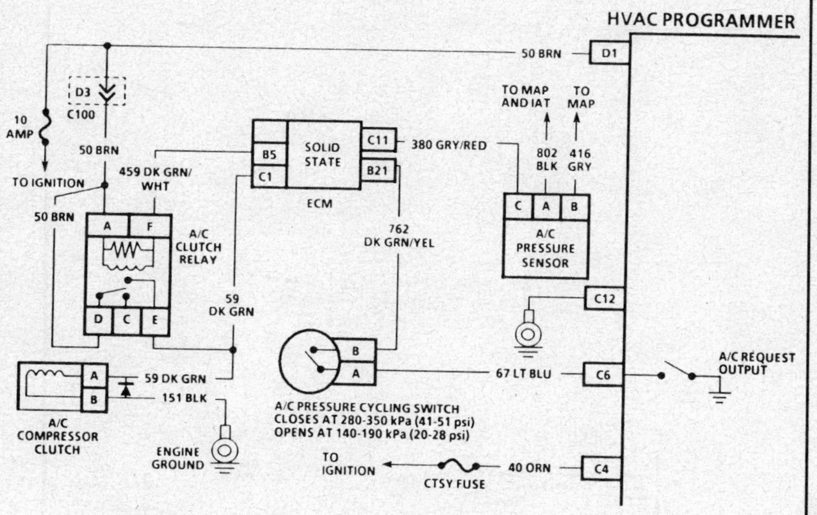

HVAC PROGRAMMER
50 BRN
D1
D3
C100
10 AMP
TO IGNITION
50 BRN
459 DK GRN/WHT
50 BRN
A/C CLUTCH RELAY
A F D C E
B5 C1 SOLID STATE C11 B21
ECM
380 GRY/RED
762 DK GRN/YEL
59 DK GRN
TO MAP AND IAT
TO MAP
802 BLK
416 GRY
C A B
A/C PRESSURE SENSOR
C12
C6
C4
67 LT BLU
A/C REQUEST OUTPUT
59 DK GRN
151 BLK
A/C COMPRESSOR CLUTCH
ENGINE GROUND
A/C PRESSURE CYCLING SWITCH CLOSES AT 280-350 kPa (41-51 psi) OPENS AT 140-190 kPa (20-28 psi)
TO IGNITION
CTSY FUSE
40 ORN

ECC SYSTEM DIAGNOSIS—CODE 09—1993 CORVETTE VIN P, CONT'D

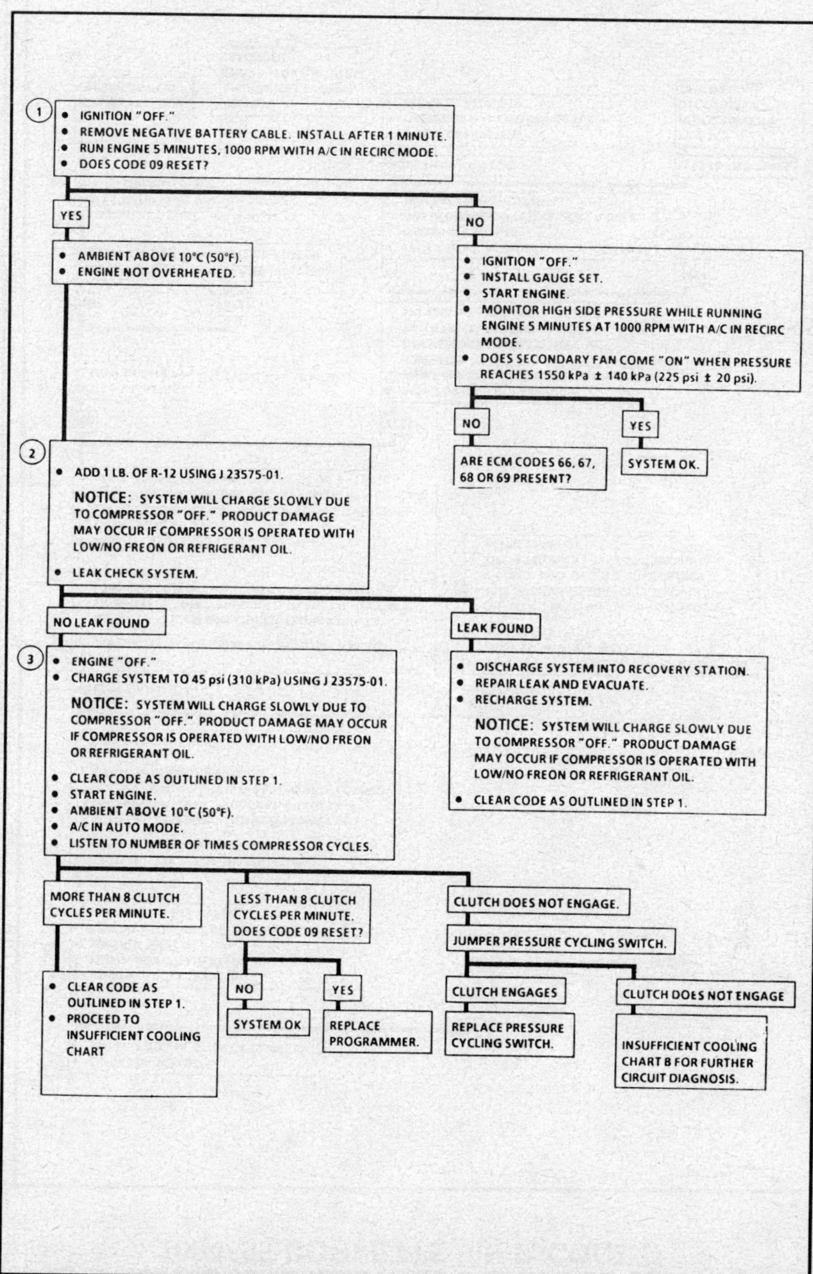

1
• IGNITION "OFF."
• REMOVE NEGATIVE BATTERY CABLE. INSTALL AFTER 1 MINUTE.
• RUN ENGINE 5 MINUTES, 1000 RPM WITH A/C IN RECIRC MODE.
• DOES CODE 09 RESET?
YES
• AMBIENT ABOVE 10°C (50°F).
• ENGINE NOT OVERHEATED.
NO
• IGNITION "OFF."
• INSTALL GAUGE SET.
• START ENGINE.
• MONITOR HIGH SIDE PRESSURE WHILE RUNNING ENGINE 5 MINUTES AT 1000 RPM WITH A/C IN RECIRC MODE.
• DOES SECONDARY FAN COME "ON" WHEN PRESSURE REACHES 1550 kPa ± 140 kPa (225 psi ± 20 psi).
NO
ARE ECM CODES 66, 67, 68 OR 69 PRESENT?
YES
SYSTEM OK.
2
• ADD 1 LB. OF R-12 USING J 23575-01.
NOTICE: SYSTEM WILL CHARGE SLOWLY DUE TO COMPRESSOR "OFF." PRODUCT DAMAGE MAY OCCUR IF COMPRESSOR IS OPERATED WITH LOW/NO FREON OR REFRIGERANT OIL.
• LEAK CHECK SYSTEM.
NO LEAK FOUND
LEAK FOUND
3
• ENGINE "OFF."
• CHARGE SYSTEM TO 45 psi (310 kPa) USING J 23575-01.
NOTICE: SYSTEM WILL CHARGE SLOWLY DUE TO COMPRESSOR "OFF." PRODUCT DAMAGE MAY OCCUR IF COMPRESSOR IS OPERATED WITH LOW/NO FREON OR REFRIGERANT OIL.
• CLEAR CODE AS OUTLINED IN STEP 1.
• START ENGINE.
• AMBIENT ABOVE 10°C (50°F).
• A/C IN AUTO MODE.
• LISTEN TO NUMBER OF TIMES COMPRESSOR CYCLES.
• DISCHARGE SYSTEM INTO RECOVERY STATION.
• REPAIR LEAK AND EVACUATE.
• RECHARGE SYSTEM.
NOTICE: SYSTEM WILL CHARGE SLOWLY DUE TO COMPRESSOR "OFF." PRODUCT DAMAGE MAY OCCUR IF COMPRESSOR IS OPERATED WITH LOW/NO FREON OR REFRIGERANT OIL.
• CLEAR CODE AS OUTLINED IN STEP 1.
MORE THAN 8 CLUTCH CYCLES PER MINUTE.
• CLEAR CODE AS OUTLINED IN STEP 1.
• PROCEED TO INSUFFICIENT COOLING CHART
LESS THAN 8 CLUTCH CYCLES PER MINUTE. DOES CODE 09 RESET?
NO
SYSTEM OK
YES
REPLACE PROGRAMMER.
CLUTCH DOES NOT ENGAGE.
JUMPER PRESSURE CYCLING SWITCH.
CLUTCH ENGAGES
REPLACE PRESSURE CYCLING SWITCH.
CLUTCH DOES NOT ENGAGE
INSUFFICIENT COOLING CHART B FOR FURTHER CIRCUIT DIAGNOSIS.

ECC SYSTEM DIAGNOSIS—CODE 09— 1994–95 CORVETTE VIN P

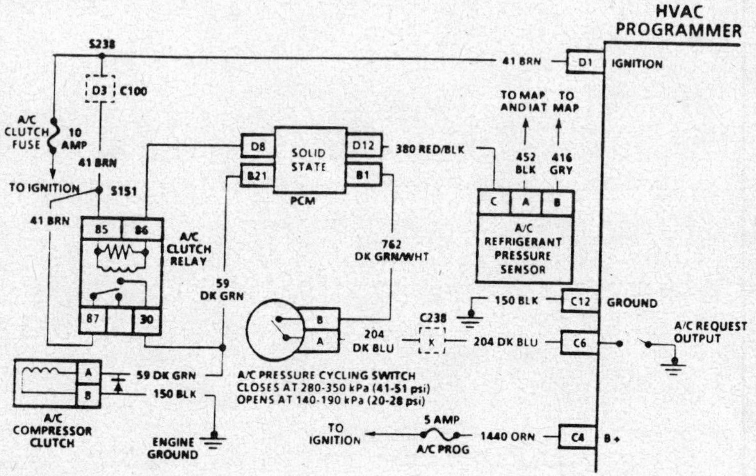

HVAC PROGRAMMER
S238
41 BRN
D1 IGNITION
D3 C100
A/C CLUTCH FUSE 10 AMP
41 BRN
TO IGNITION
S151
41 BRN
TO MAP AND IAT
TO MAP
D8 SOLID STATE D12
B21 PCM B1
380 RED/BLK
452 BLK
416 GRY
C A B
A/C REFRIGERANT PRESSURE SENSOR
85 86
A/C CLUTCH RELAY
87 30
762 DK GRN/WHT
59 DK GRN
150 BLK
C12 GROUND
C238
204 DK BLU
204 DK BLU
C6
A/C REQUEST OUTPUT
B A
A/C PRESSURE CYCLING SWITCH CLOSES AT 280-350 kPa (41-51 psi) OPENS AT 140-190 kPa (20-28 psi)
A B
59 DK GRN
150 BLK
A/C COMPRESSOR CLUTCH
ENGINE GROUND
TO IGNITION
5 AMP A/C PROG
1440 ORN
C4 B+

ECC SYSTEM DIAGNOSIS—CODE 09— 1994–95 CORVETTE VIN P, CONT'D

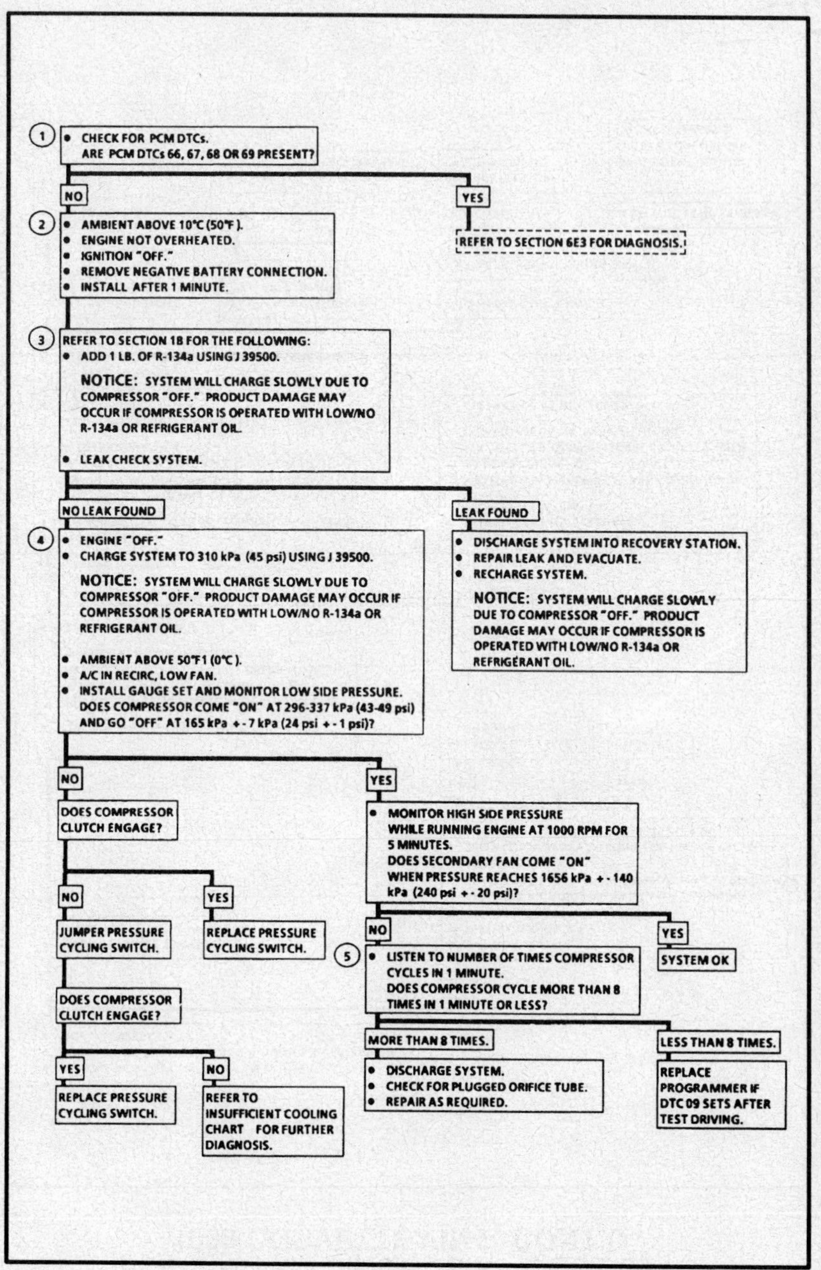

1 • CHECK FOR PCM DTCs. ARE PCM DTCs 66, 67, 68 OR 69 PRESENT?
NO
YES
REFER TO SECTION 6E3 FOR DIAGNOSIS.
2 • AMBIENT ABOVE 10°C (50°F).
• ENGINE NOT OVERHEATED.
• IGNITION "OFF."
• REMOVE NEGATIVE BATTERY CONNECTION.
• INSTALL AFTER 1 MINUTE.
3 REFER TO SECTION 1B FOR THE FOLLOWING:
• ADD 1 LB. OF R-134a USING J 39500.
NOTICE: SYSTEM WILL CHARGE SLOWLY DUE TO COMPRESSOR "OFF." PRODUCT DAMAGE MAY OCCUR IF COMPRESSOR IS OPERATED WITH LOW/NO R-134a OR REFRIGERANT OIL.
• LEAK CHECK SYSTEM.
NO LEAK FOUND
LEAK FOUND
• DISCHARGE SYSTEM INTO RECOVERY STATION.
• REPAIR LEAK AND EVACUATE.
• RECHARGE SYSTEM.
NOTICE: SYSTEM WILL CHARGE SLOWLY DUE TO COMPRESSOR "OFF." PRODUCT DAMAGE MAY OCCUR IF COMPRESSOR IS OPERATED WITH LOW/NO R-134a OR REFRIGERANT OIL.
4 • ENGINE "OFF."
• CHARGE SYSTEM TO 310 kPa (45 psi) USING J 39500.
NOTICE: SYSTEM WILL CHARGE SLOWLY DUE TO COMPRESSOR "OFF." PRODUCT DAMAGE MAY OCCUR IF COMPRESSOR IS OPERATED WITH LOW/NO R-134a OR REFRIGERANT OIL.
• AMBIENT ABOVE 50°F1 (0°C).
• A/C IN RECIRC, LOW FAN.
• INSTALL GAUGE SET AND MONITOR LOW SIDE PRESSURE. DOES COMPRESSOR COME "ON" AT 296-337 kPa (43-49 psi) AND GO "OFF" AT 165 kPa +-7 kPa (24 psi +-1 psi)?
NO
YES
DOES COMPRESSOR CLUTCH ENGAGE?
• MONITOR HIGH SIDE PRESSURE WHILE RUNNING ENGINE AT 1000 RPM FOR 5 MINUTES. DOES SECONDARY FAN COME "ON" WHEN PRESSURE REACHES 1656 kPa +-140 kPa (240 psi +-20 psi)?
NO
YES
JUMPER PRESSURE CYCLING SWITCH.
REPLACE PRESSURE CYCLING SWITCH.
NO
YES
5 • LISTEN TO NUMBER OF TIMES COMPRESSOR CYCLES IN 1 MINUTE. DOES COMPRESSOR CYCLE MORE THAN 8 TIMES IN 1 MINUTE OR LESS?
SYSTEM OK
DOES COMPRESSOR CLUTCH ENGAGE?
MORE THAN 8 TIMES.
LESS THAN 8 TIMES.
YES
NO
• DISCHARGE SYSTEM.
• CHECK FOR PLUGGED ORIFICE TUBE.
• REPAIR AS REQUIRED.
REPLACE PROGRAMMER IF DTC 09 SETS AFTER TEST DRIVING.
REPLACE PRESSURE CYCLING SWITCH.
REFER TO INSUFFICIENT COOLING CHART FOR FURTHER DIAGNOSIS.

ECC SYSTEM DIAGNOSIS—CODE 09—1993 CORVETTE VIN J

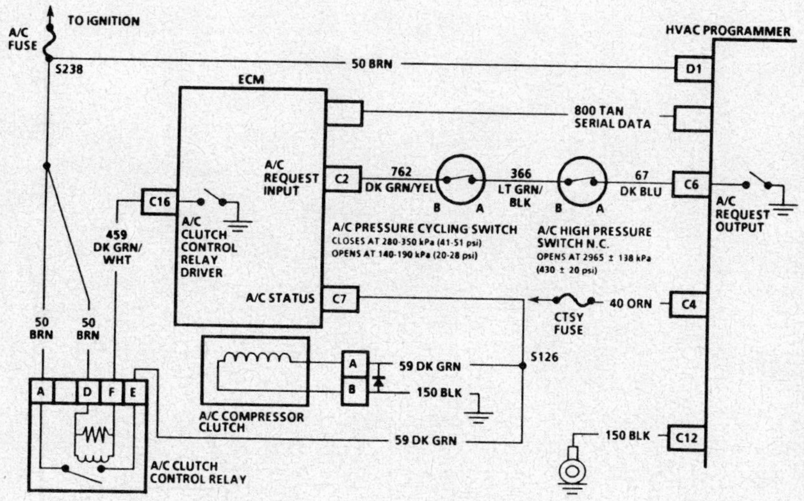

A/C FUSE
TO IGNITION
S238
50 BRN
HVAC PROGRAMMER
D1
ECM
800 TAN SERIAL DATA
A/C REQUEST INPUT
C2
762 DK GRN/YEL
366 LT GRN/BLK
67 DK BLU
C6
A/C REQUEST OUTPUT
C16
A/C CLUTCH CONTROL RELAY DRIVER
459 DK GRN/WHT
A/C PRESSURE CYCLING SWITCH
CLOSES AT 280-350 kPa (41-51 psi)
OPENS AT 140-190 kPa (20-28 psi)
A/C HIGH PRESSURE SWITCH N.C.
OPENS AT 2965 ± 138 kPa (430 ± 20 psi)
A/C STATUS
C7
CTSY FUSE
40 ORN
C4
50 BRN
50 BRN
S126
59 DK GRN
150 BLK
A/C COMPRESSOR CLUTCH
59 DK GRN
150 BLK
C12
A/C CLUTCH CONTROL RELAY

ECC SYSTEM DIAGNOSIS—CODE 09—1993 CORVETTE VIN J, CONT'D

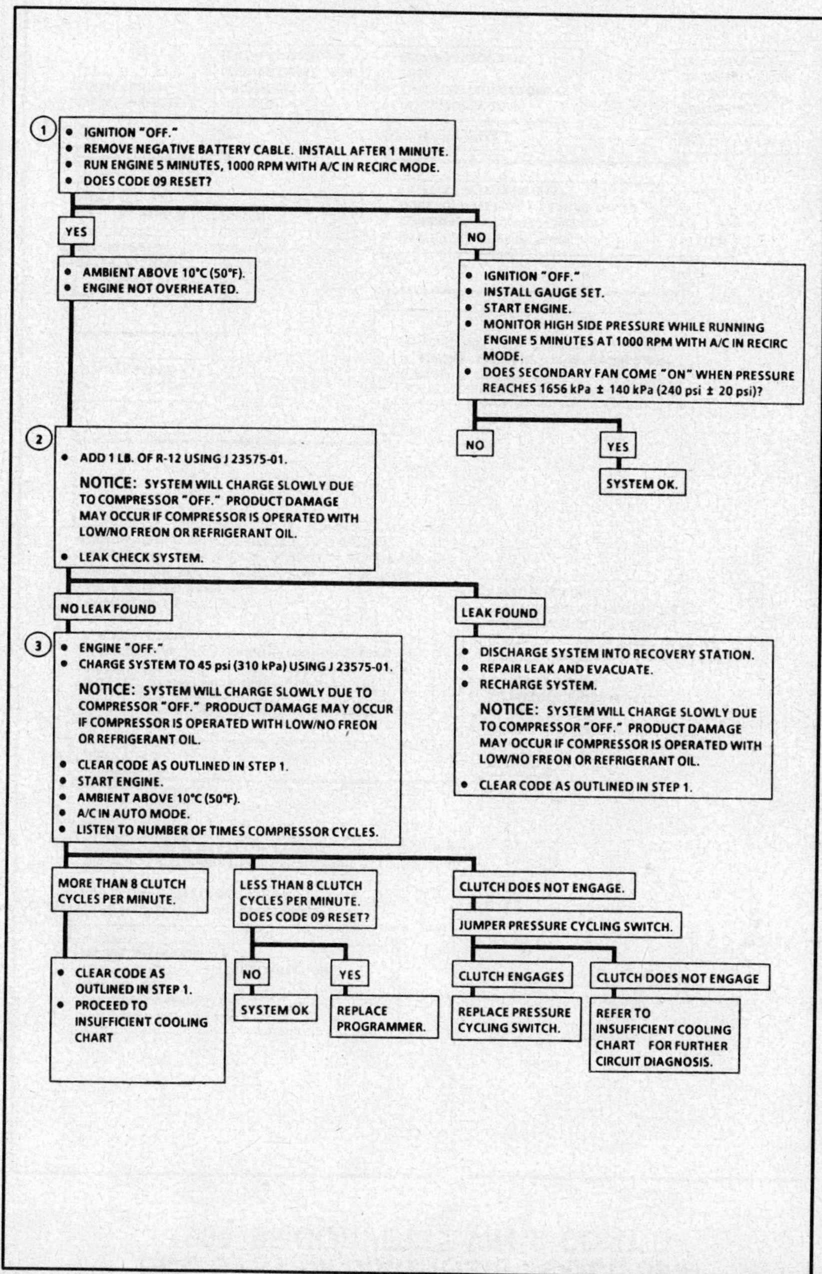
1
• IGNITION "OFF."
• REMOVE NEGATIVE BATTERY CABLE. INSTALL AFTER 1 MINUTE.
• RUN ENGINE 5 MINUTES, 1000 RPM WITH A/C IN RECIRC MODE.
• DOES CODE 09 RESET?
YES
NO
• AMBIENT ABOVE 10°C (50°F).
• ENGINE NOT OVERHEATED.
• IGNITION "OFF."
• INSTALL GAUGE SET.
• START ENGINE.
• MONITOR HIGH SIDE PRESSURE WHILE RUNNING ENGINE 5 MINUTES AT 1000 RPM WITH A/C IN RECIRC MODE.
• DOES SECONDARY FAN COME "ON" WHEN PRESSURE REACHES 1656 kPa ± 140 kPa (240 psi ± 20 psi)?
NO
YES
SYSTEM OK.
2
• ADD 1 LB. OF R-12 USING J 23575-01.
NOTICE: SYSTEM WILL CHARGE SLOWLY DUE TO COMPRESSOR "OFF." PRODUCT DAMAGE MAY OCCUR IF COMPRESSOR IS OPERATED WITH LOW/NO FREON OR REFRIGERANT OIL.
• LEAK CHECK SYSTEM.
NO LEAK FOUND
LEAK FOUND
3
• ENGINE "OFF."
• CHARGE SYSTEM TO 45 psi (310 kPa) USING J 23575-01.
NOTICE: SYSTEM WILL CHARGE SLOWLY DUE TO COMPRESSOR "OFF." PRODUCT DAMAGE MAY OCCUR IF COMPRESSOR IS OPERATED WITH LOW/NO FREON OR REFRIGERANT OIL.
• CLEAR CODE AS OUTLINED IN STEP 1.
• START ENGINE.
• AMBIENT ABOVE 10°C (50°F).
• A/C IN AUTO MODE.
• LISTEN TO NUMBER OF TIMES COMPRESSOR CYCLES.
• DISCHARGE SYSTEM INTO RECOVERY STATION.
• REPAIR LEAK AND EVACUATE.
• RECHARGE SYSTEM.
NOTICE: SYSTEM WILL CHARGE SLOWLY DUE TO COMPRESSOR "OFF." PRODUCT DAMAGE MAY OCCUR IF COMPRESSOR IS OPERATED WITH LOW/NO FREON OR REFRIGERANT OIL.
• CLEAR CODE AS OUTLINED IN STEP 1.
MORE THAN 8 CLUTCH CYCLES PER MINUTE.
LESS THAN 8 CLUTCH CYCLES PER MINUTE. DOES CODE 09 RESET?
CLUTCH DOES NOT ENGAGE.
JUMPER PRESSURE CYCLING SWITCH.
• CLEAR CODE AS OUTLINED IN STEP 1.
• PROCEED TO INSUFFICIENT COOLING CHART
NO
SYSTEM OK
YES
REPLACE PROGRAMMER.
CLUTCH ENGAGES
REPLACE PRESSURE CYCLING SWITCH.
CLUTCH DOES NOT ENGAGE
REFER TO INSUFFICIENT COOLING CHART FOR FURTHER CIRCUIT DIAGNOSIS.

ECC SYSTEM DIAGNOSIS—CODE 09—1994–95 CORVETTE VIN J

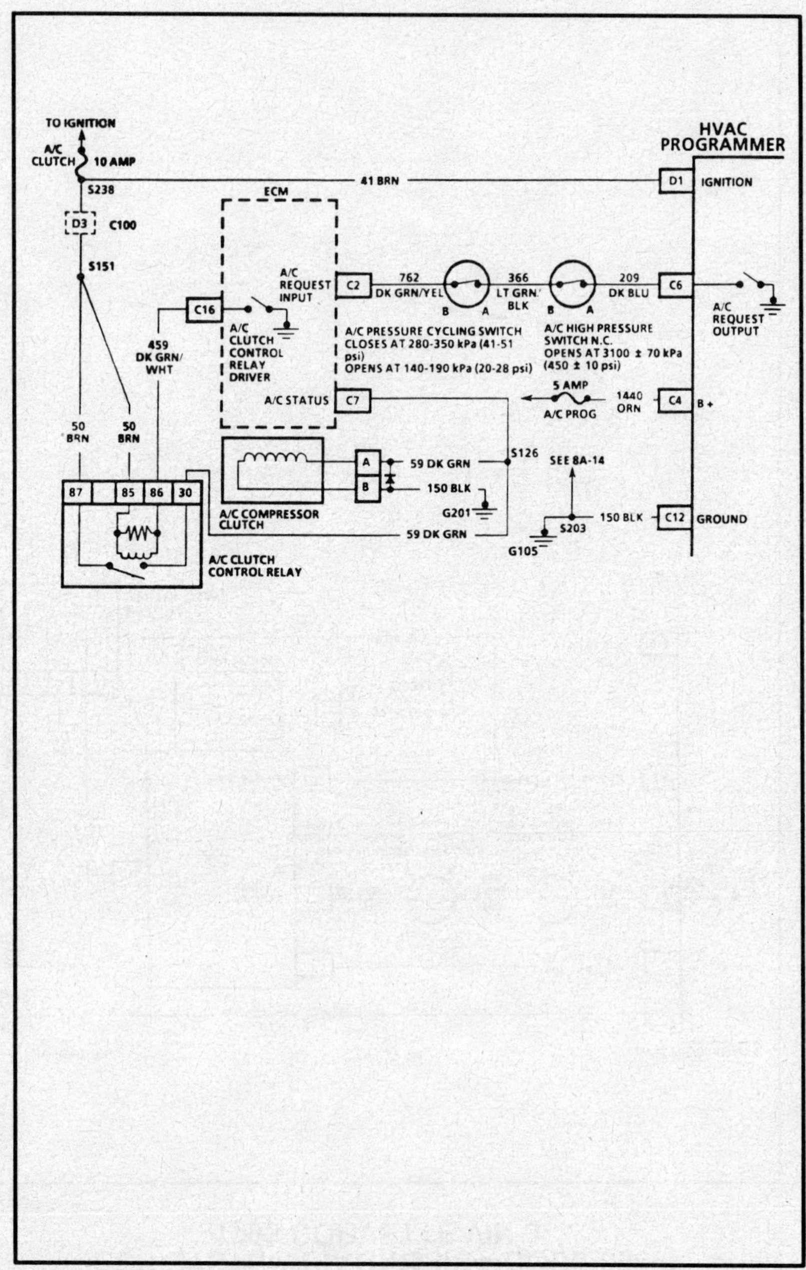
TO IGNITION
A/C CLUTCH
10 AMP
S238
D3
C100
S151
41 BRN
ECM
HVAC PROGRAMMER
D1
IGNITION
A/C REQUEST INPUT
C2
762 DK GRN/YEL
366 LT GRN/BLK
209 DK BLU
C6
A/C REQUEST OUTPUT
C16
A/C CLUTCH CONTROL RELAY DRIVER
459 DK GRN/WHT
A/C PRESSURE CYCLING SWITCH CLOSES AT 280-350 kPa (41-51 psi) OPENS AT 140-190 kPa (20-28 psi)
A/C HIGH PRESSURE SWITCH N.C. OPENS AT 3100 ± 70 kPa (450 ± 10 psi)
A/C STATUS
C7
5 AMP
A/C PROG
1440 ORN
C4
B+
50 BRN
50 BRN
S126
SEE 8A-14
59 DK GRN
150 BLK
G201
150 BLK
C12
GROUND
S203
G105
87
85
86
30
A/C COMPRESSOR CLUTCH
A/C CLUTCH CONTROL RELAY

ECC SYSTEM DIAGNOSIS—CODE 09—1994–95 CORVETTE VIN J, CONT'D

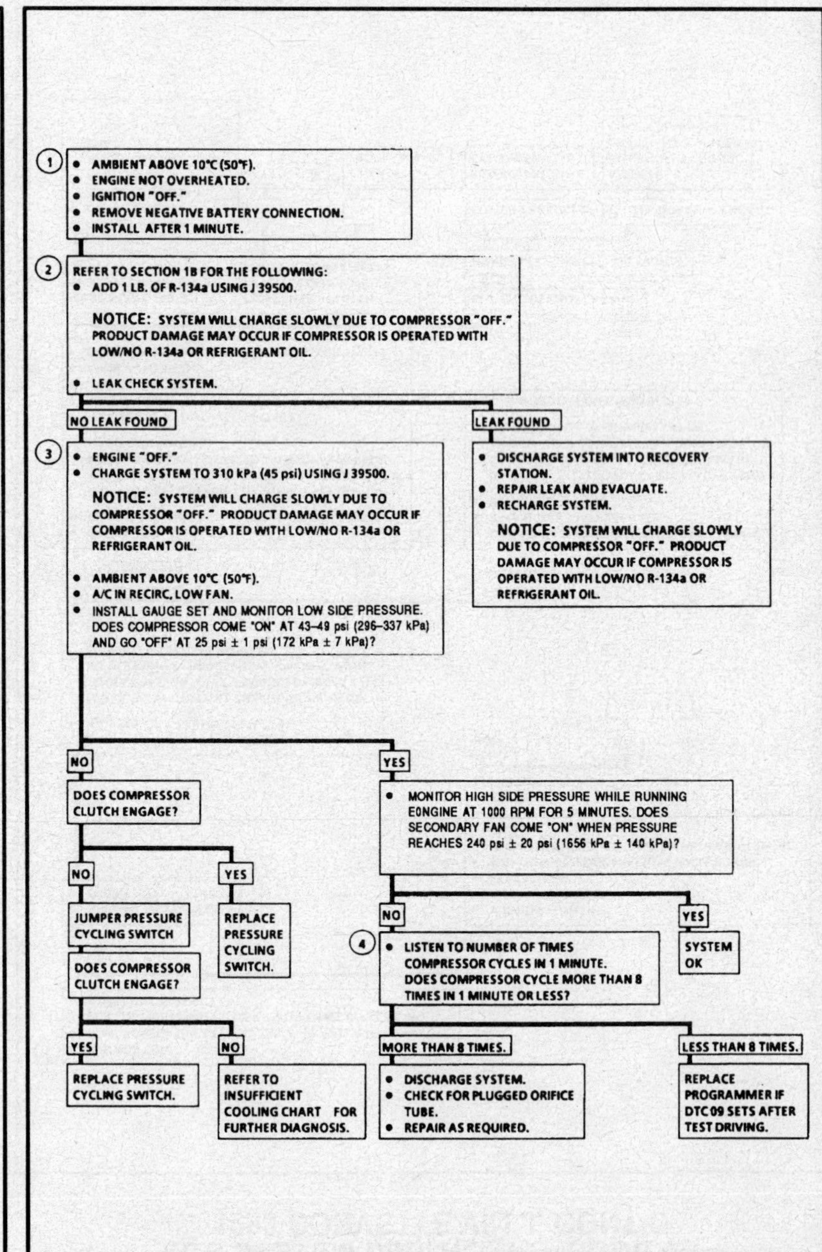
1
• AMBIENT ABOVE 10°C (50°F).
• ENGINE NOT OVERHEATED.
• IGNITION "OFF."
• REMOVE NEGATIVE BATTERY CONNECTION.
• INSTALL AFTER 1 MINUTE.
2
REFER TO SECTION 1B FOR THE FOLLOWING:
• ADD 1 LB. OF R-134a USING J 39500.
NOTICE: SYSTEM WILL CHARGE SLOWLY DUE TO COMPRESSOR "OFF." PRODUCT DAMAGE MAY OCCUR IF COMPRESSOR IS OPERATED WITH LOW/NO R-134a OR REFRIGERANT OIL.
• LEAK CHECK SYSTEM.
NO LEAK FOUND
LEAK FOUND
3
• ENGINE "OFF."
• CHARGE SYSTEM TO 310 kPa (45 psi) USING J 39500.
NOTICE: SYSTEM WILL CHARGE SLOWLY DUE TO COMPRESSOR "OFF." PRODUCT DAMAGE MAY OCCUR IF COMPRESSOR IS OPERATED WITH LOW/NO R-134a OR REFRIGERANT OIL.
• AMBIENT ABOVE 10°C (50°F).
• A/C IN RECIRC, LOW FAN.
• INSTALL GAUGE SET AND MONITOR LOW SIDE PRESSURE. DOES COMPRESSOR COME "ON" AT 43–49 psi (296–337 kPa) AND GO "OFF" AT 25 psi ± 1 psi (172 kPa ± 7 kPa)?
• DISCHARGE SYSTEM INTO RECOVERY STATION.
• REPAIR LEAK AND EVACUATE.
• RECHARGE SYSTEM.
NOTICE: SYSTEM WILL CHARGE SLOWLY DUE TO COMPRESSOR "OFF." PRODUCT DAMAGE MAY OCCUR IF COMPRESSOR IS OPERATED WITH LOW/NO R-134a OR REFRIGERANT OIL.
NO
YES
DOES COMPRESSOR CLUTCH ENGAGE?
• MONITOR HIGH SIDE PRESSURE WHILE RUNNING E0NGINE AT 1000 RPM FOR 5 MINUTES. DOES SECONDARY FAN COME "ON" WHEN PRESSURE REACHES 240 psi ± 20 psi (1656 kPa ± 140 kPa)?
NO
YES
JUMPER PRESSURE CYCLING SWITCH
DOES COMPRESSOR CLUTCH ENGAGE?
REPLACE PRESSURE CYCLING SWITCH.
NO
YES
4
• LISTEN TO NUMBER OF TIMES COMPRESSOR CYCLES IN 1 MINUTE. DOES COMPRESSOR CYCLE MORE THAN 8 TIMES IN 1 MINUTE OR LESS?
SYSTEM OK
YES
NO
REPLACE PRESSURE CYCLING SWITCH.
REFER TO INSUFFICIENT COOLING CHART FOR FURTHER DIAGNOSIS.
MORE THAN 8 TIMES.
LESS THAN 8 TIMES.
• DISCHARGE SYSTEM.
• CHECK FOR PLUGGED ORIFICE TUBE.
• REPAIR AS REQUIRED.
REPLACE PROGRAMMER IF DTC 09 SETS AFTER TEST DRIVING.

WIRING SCHEMATICS

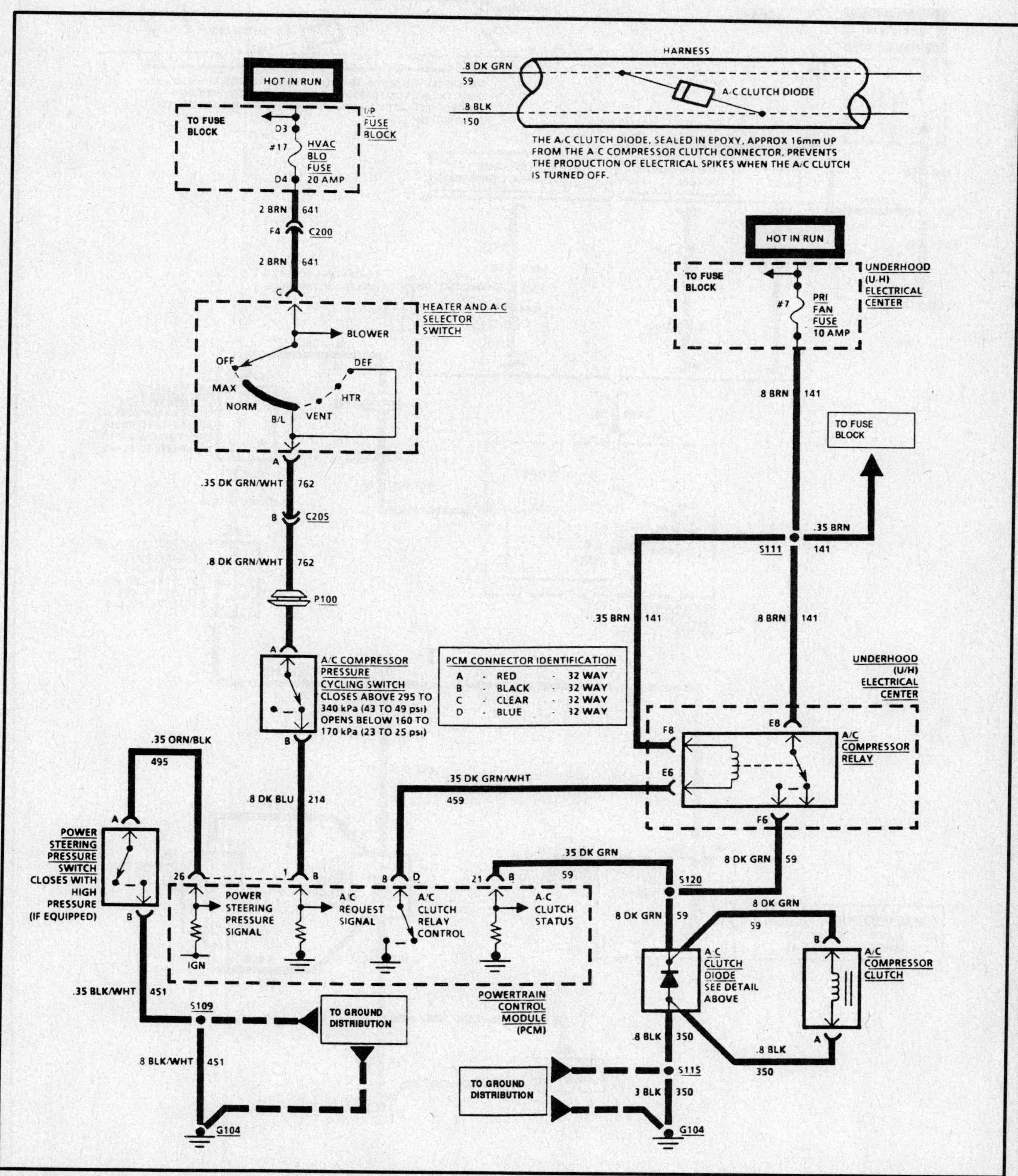

HVAC compressor control manual A/C (C60)—1994–95 Caprice/Impala SS and Roadmaster

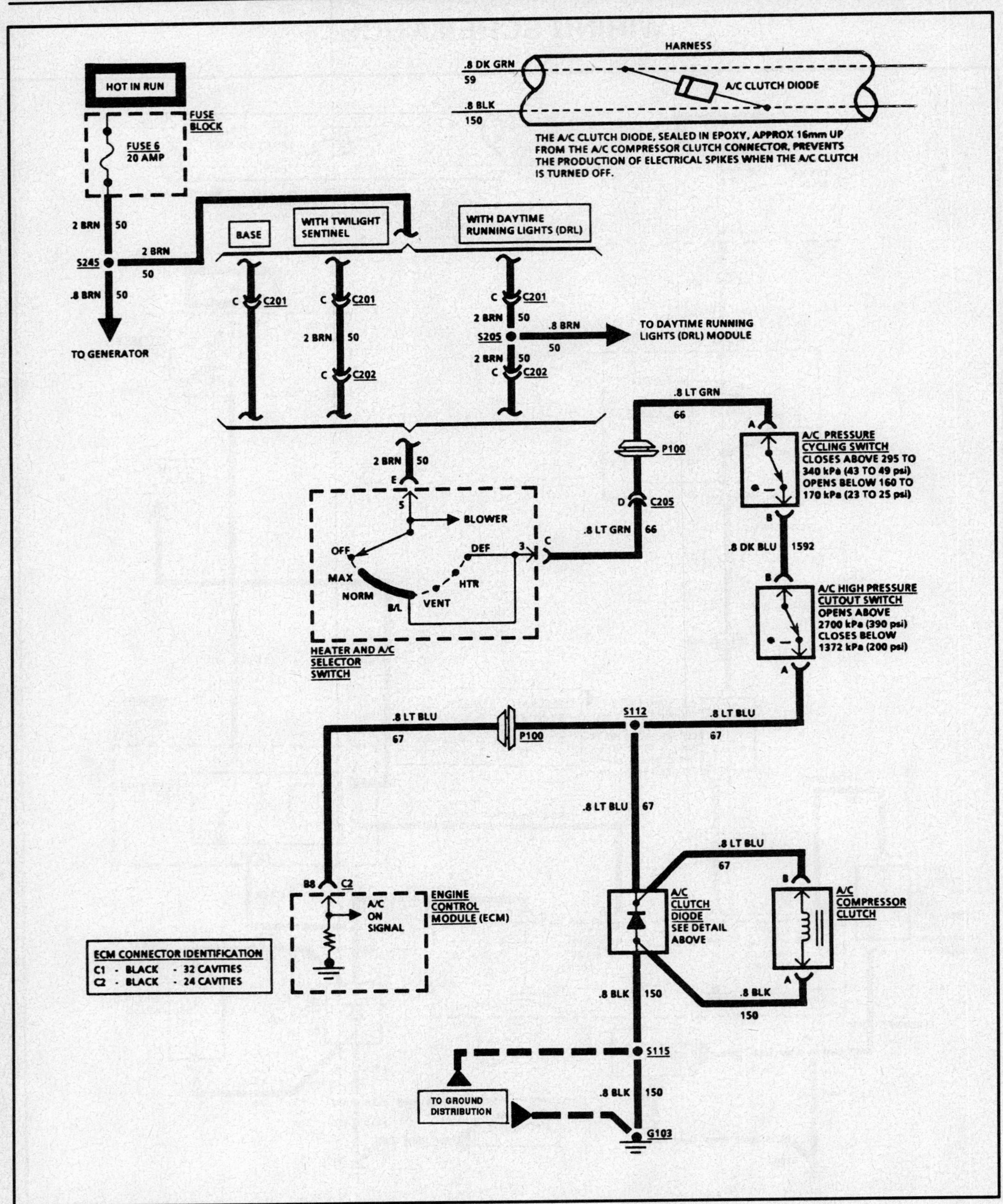

Manual A/C compressor controls schematic—1993 Caprice (VIN Z)

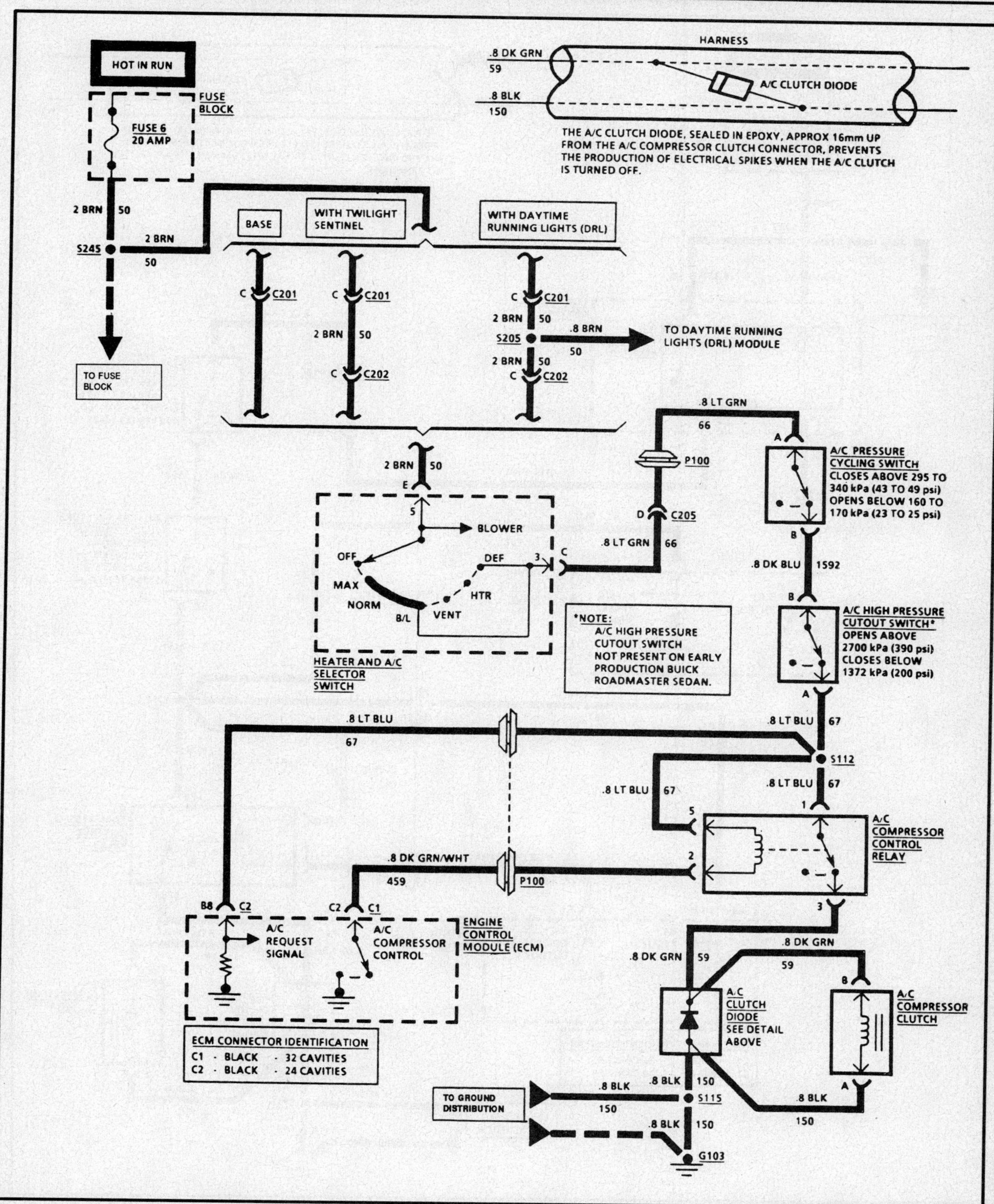

Manual A/C compressor controls schematic—1993 Caprice (VIN E and 7) and 1993 Roadmaster

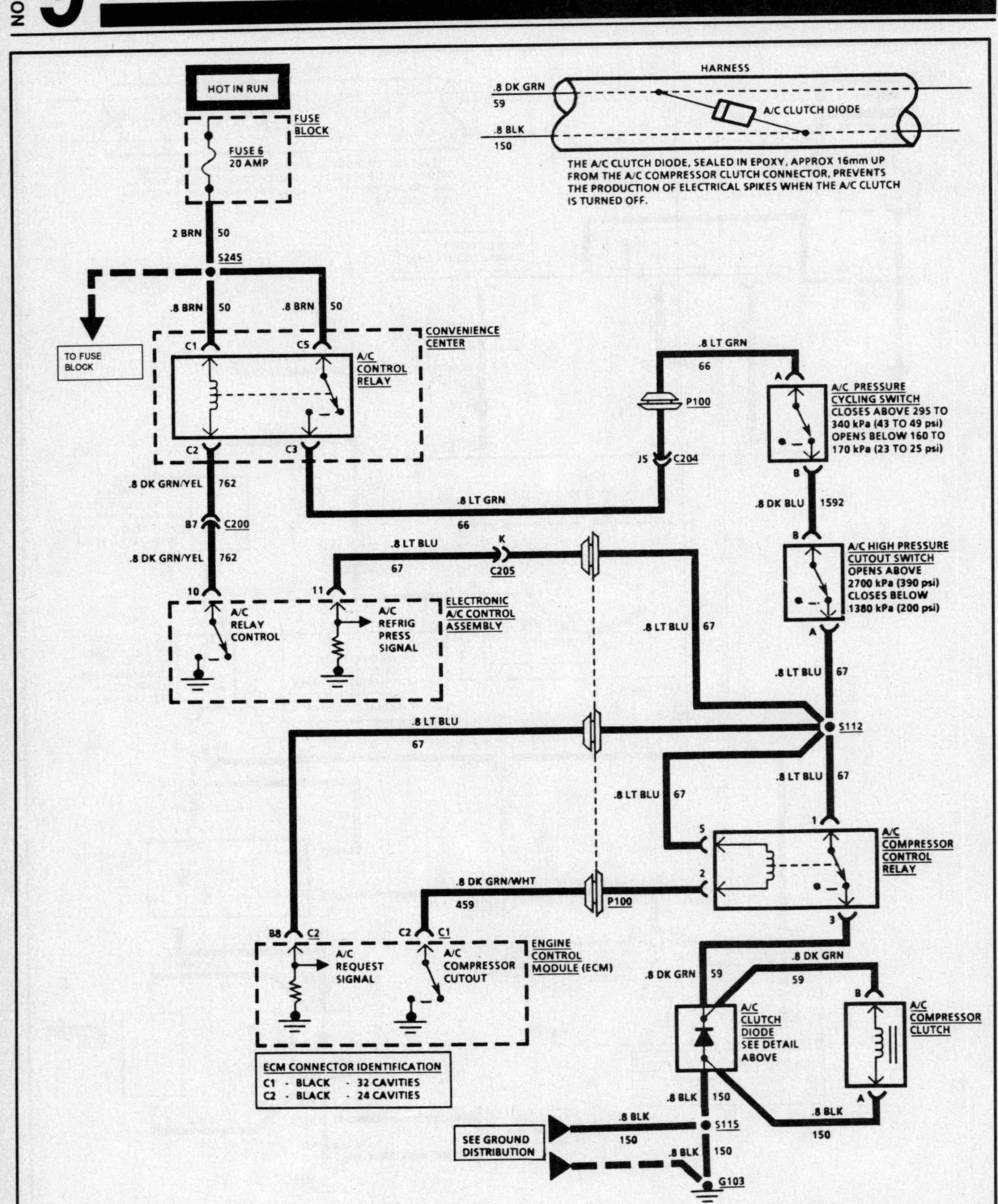

Automatic A/C compressor controls schematic—1993 Roadmaster

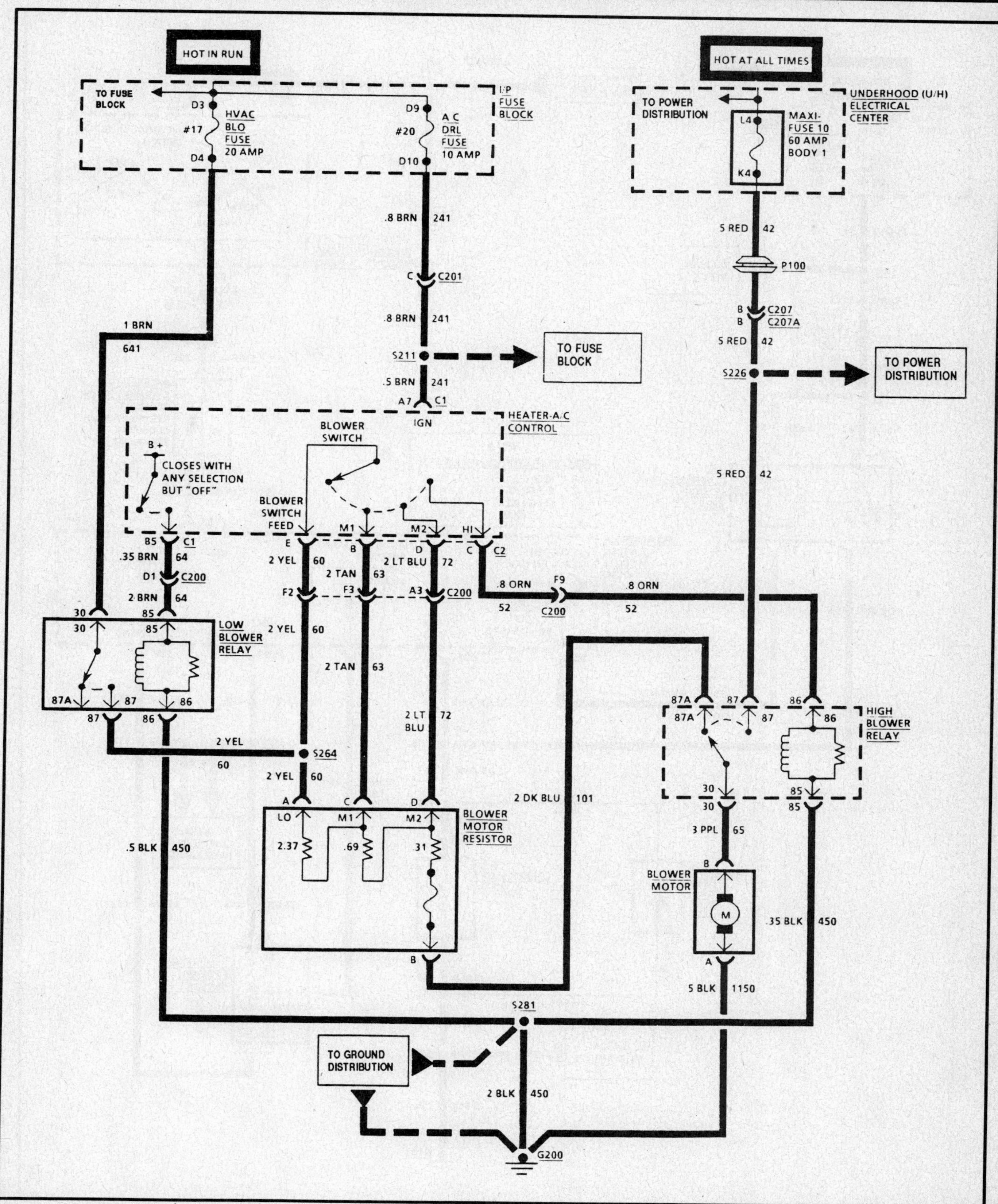

HVAC blower control electronic A/C (C67)—1994–95 Roadmaster

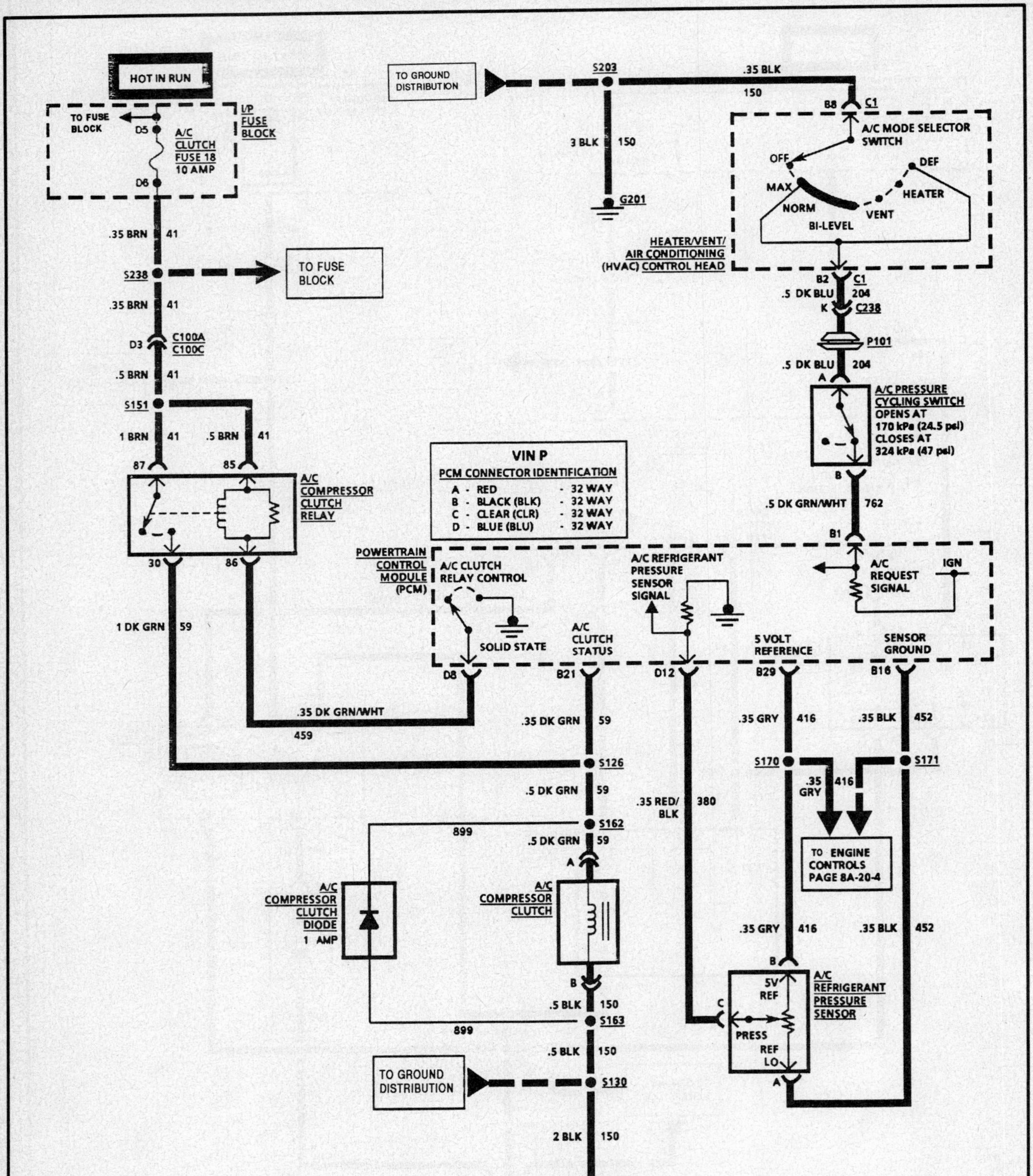

HVAC compressor control C60, manual—1994–95 Corvette

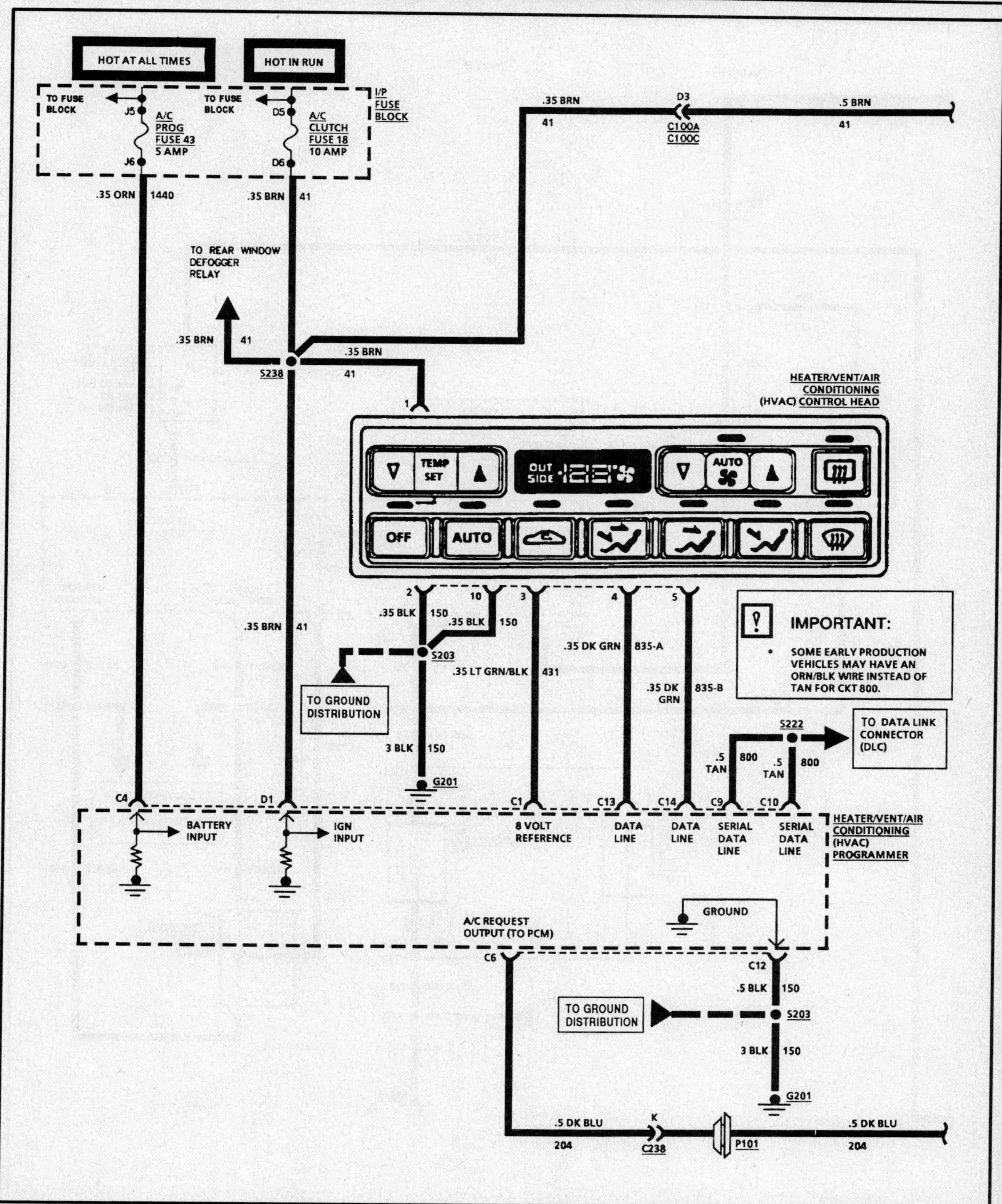

HVAC compressor control C68, electronic (VIN P)—1994–95 Corvette

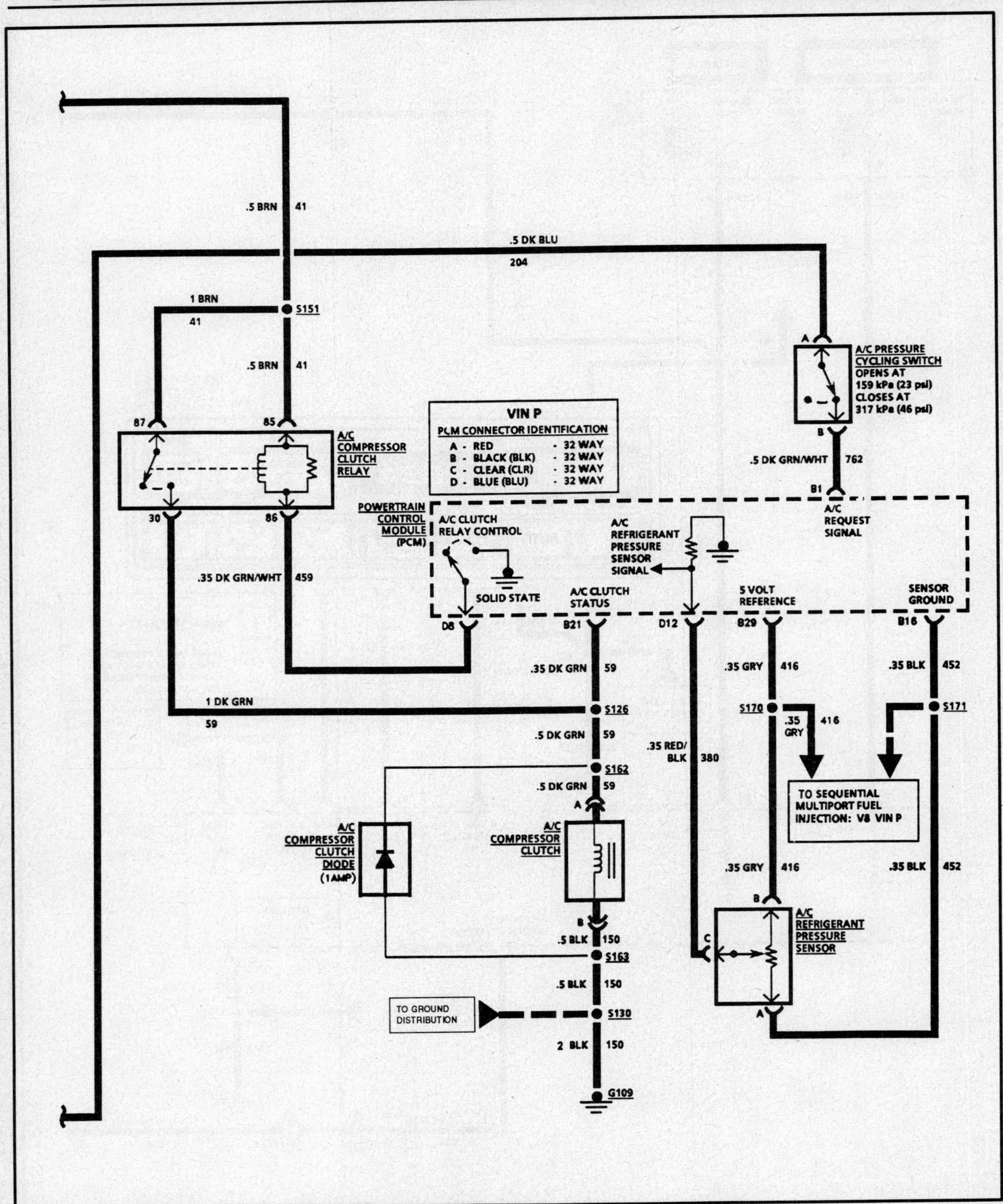

HVAC compressor control C68, electronic (VIN P)—1994–95 Corvette, Cont'd

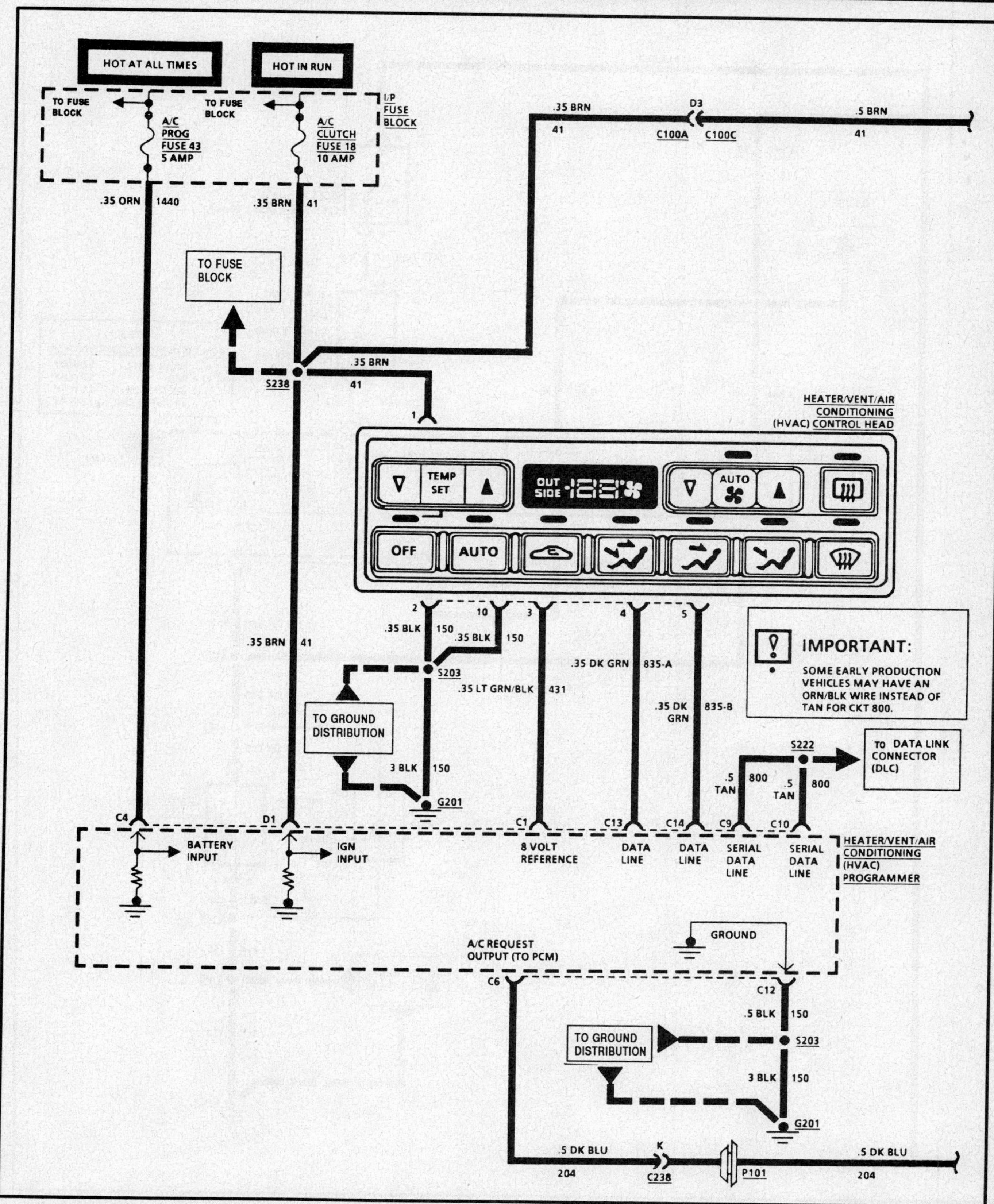

HVAC compressor control C68, electronic (VIN J)—1994–95 Corvette

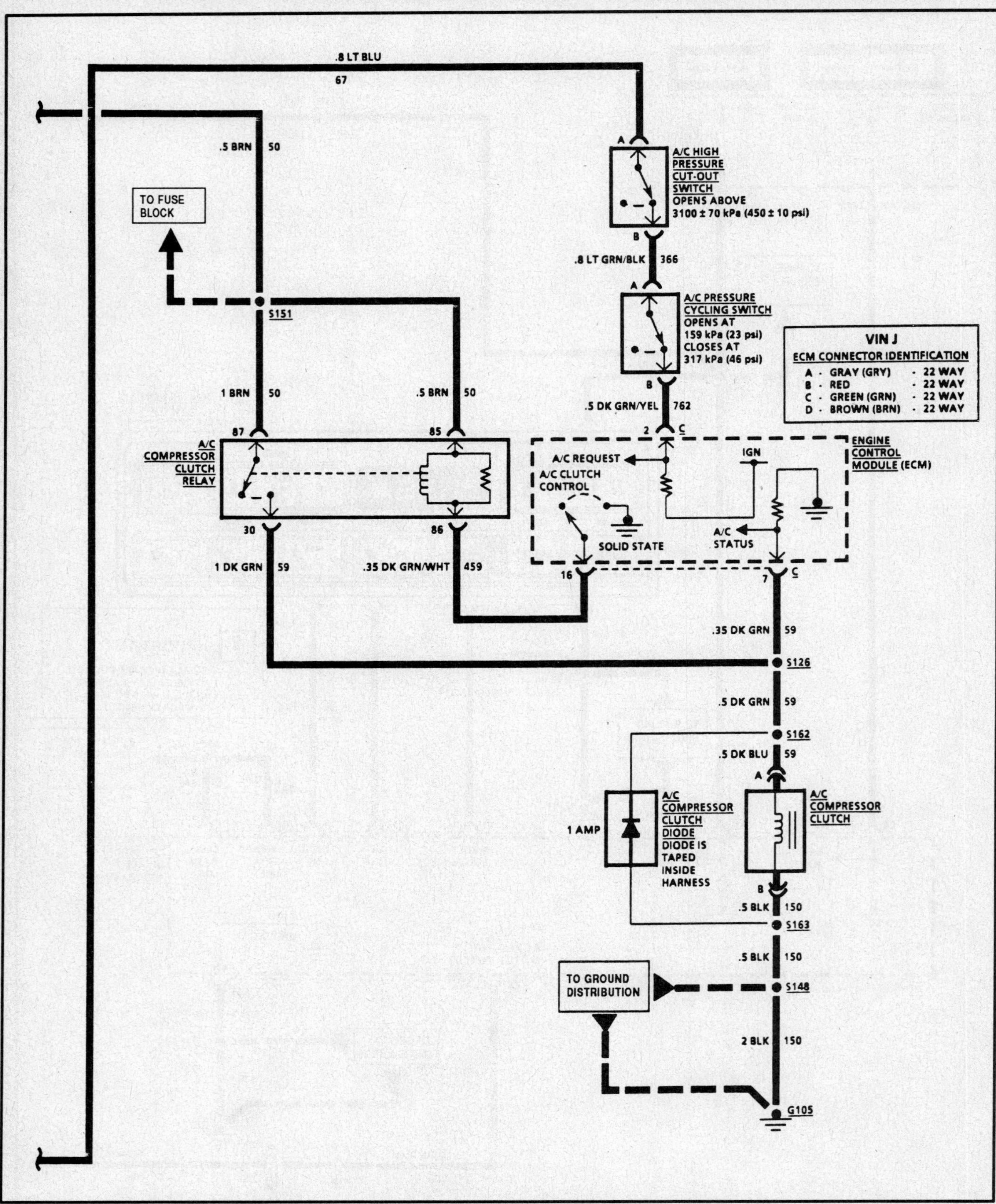

HVAC compressor control C68, electronic (VIN J)—1994–95 Corvette, Cont'd

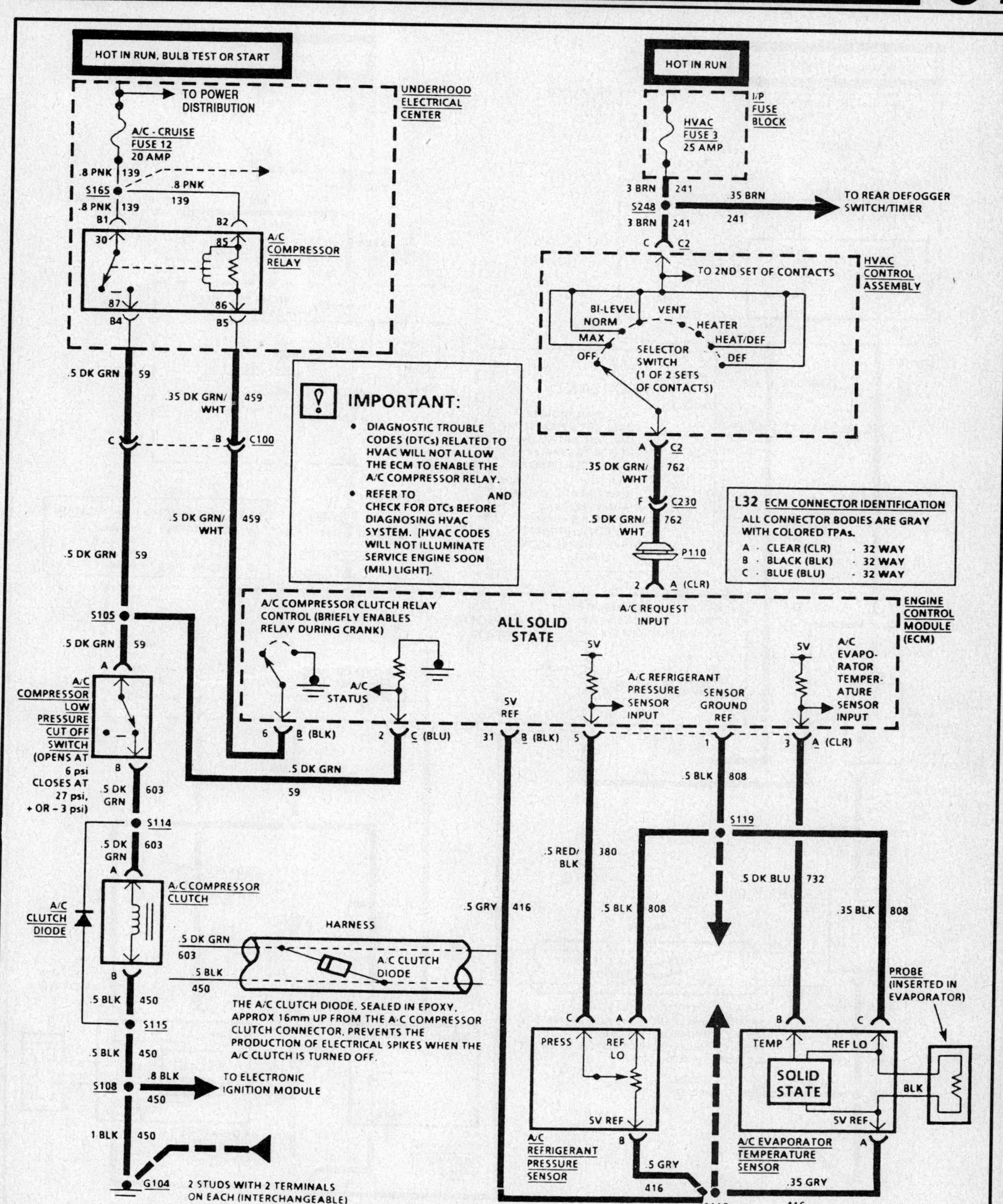

HVAC compressor control wiring schematic—Camaro/Firebird with V6 engine

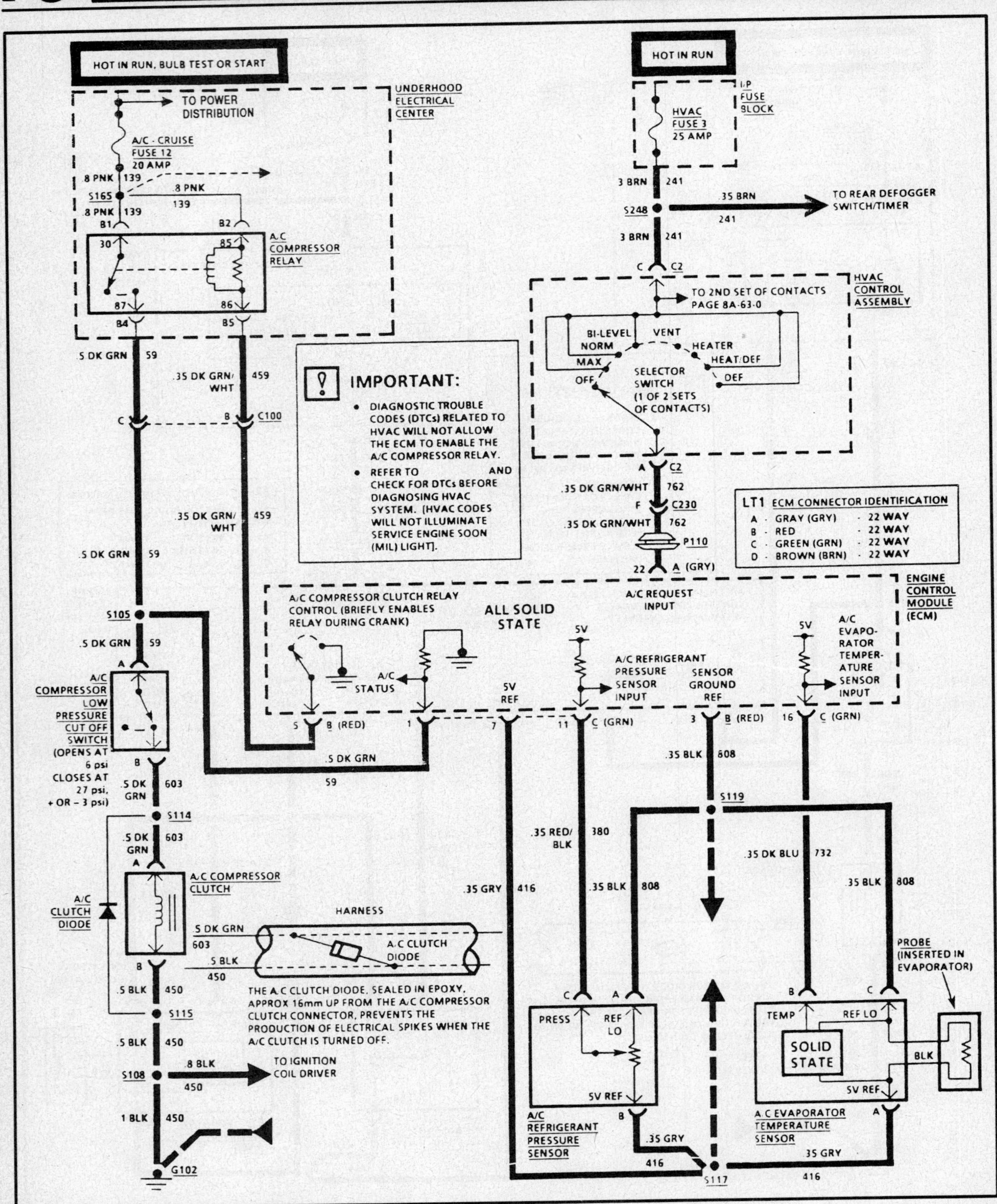

HVAC compressor control wiring schematic—Camaro/Firebird with V8 engine

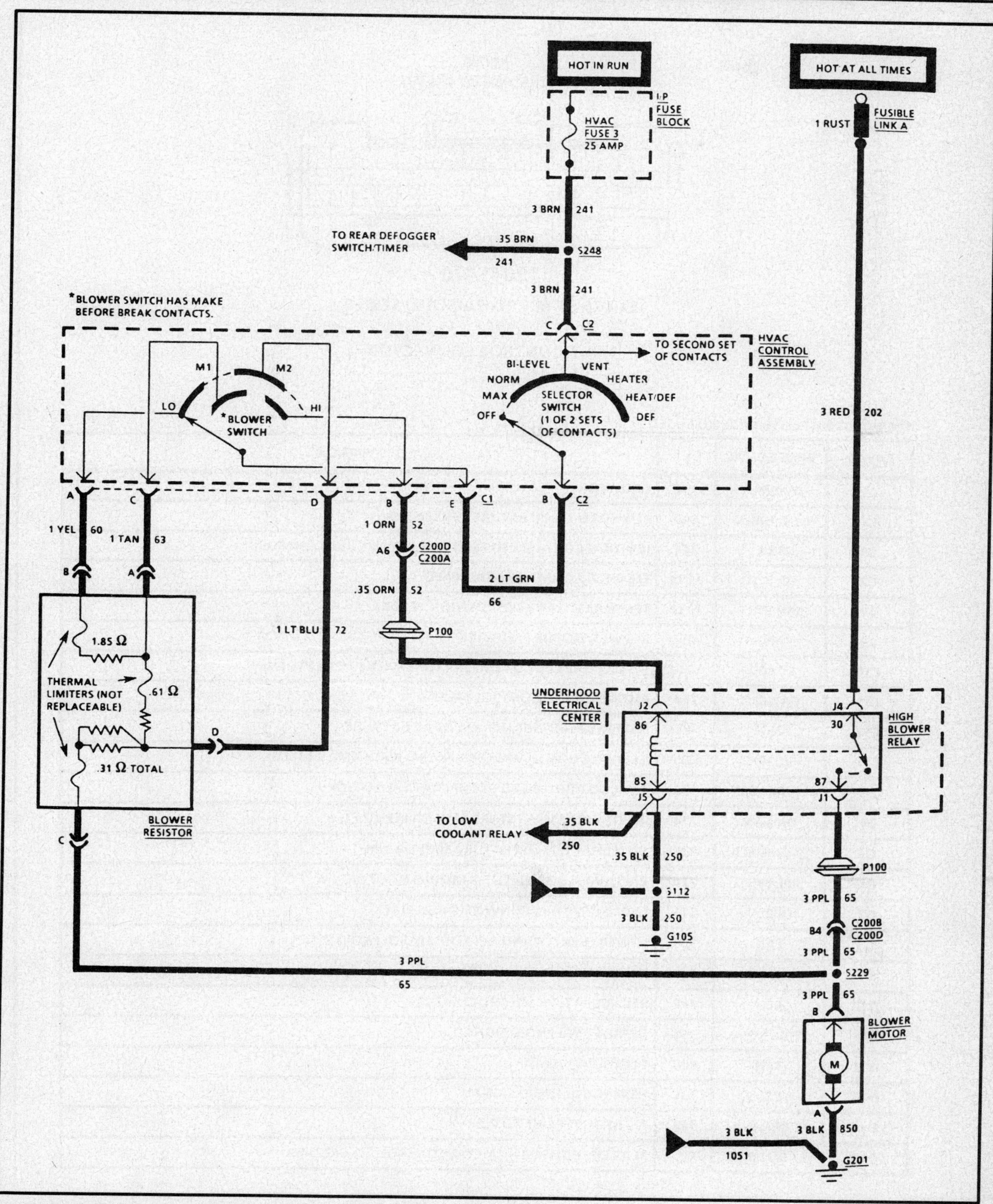

HVAC blower control wiring schematic—(C60) Camaro/Firebird

(WIRE ENTRY VIEW)

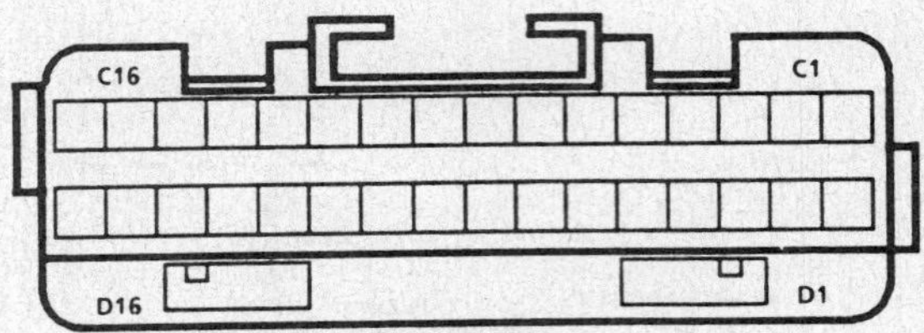

12045470

32-WAY F MICRO-PACK 100 SERIES

NAT

H-A/C CONTROL CONNECTOR

**CAVITIES NOT LISTED ARE NOT USED

CAVITY	WIRE COLOR	CKT	DESCRIPTION
C1	BLK/WHT	351	GROUND
C2	LT BLU/BLK	590	SUN LOAD TEMPERATURE SENSOR INPUT
C5	BRN	241	IGNITION CONTROLLED FEED THRU I/P #25 HVAC IGN FUSE
C7	DK BLU	1199	ELECTRIC ACTUATOR DRIVE FEED
C8	BRN/WHT	1218	TEMPERATURE VALVE POSITION FEEDBACK
C9	PPL	65	BLOWER MOTOR FEEDBACK
C10	LT BLU	1217	+5V REFERENCE TO TEMPERATURE VALVE ACTUATOR
C11	GRY/BLK	754	BLOWER SPEED CONTROL SIGNAL
C12	ORN	40	BATTERY FEED THRU I/P #33 HVAC BAT FUSE
C16	PPL/WHT	1370	ILLUMINATION LAMPS FEED FROM HEADLAMP SWITCH
D1	LT GRN/BLK	198	ANALOG GROUND FOR TEMPERATURE SENSORS
D2	DK GRN	734	INSIDE AIR TEMPERATURE SENSOR INPUT
D3	LT GRN/BLK	735	OUTSIDE AIR TEMPERATURE SENSOR INPUT
D4	PPL/WHT	724	VACUUM FLUORESCENT DIMMING INPUT SIGNAL
D7	LT BLU	811	ENGLISH/METRIC CONVERSION SIGNAL
D8	TAN	363	LOWER (HEATER AND DEFROSTER) SOLENOID SIGNAL
D9	PPL	361	UPPER (A/C) SOLENOID SIGNAL
D10	RED	362	RECIRCULATION SOLENOID SIGNAL
D11	LT GRN/BLK	366	DEFROST SOLENOID SIGNAL
D12	TAN	800	DLC DATA LINK
D13	LT BLU	706	HEATER SOLENOID SIGNAL
D14	DK GRN/WHT	762	A/C REQUEST LINE TO PCM
D15	LT BLU/BLK	71	REAR DEFOGGER RELAY COIL CONTROLLED GROUND

Air conditioning automatic control connector—1994–95 Roadmaster, Fleetwood

10 GENERAL MOTORS CORPORATION 10

C/K SERIES (PICK–UP) • BLAZER/JIMMY • SUBURBAN • G SERIES (VAN) • ASTRO/SAFARI • S/T SERIES • S10 BLAZER/S15 JIMMY/BRAVADA • LUMINA APV • SILHOUETTE • TRANS SPORT

SPECIFICATIONS

ENGINE IDENTIFICATION

Year	Model	Engine Displacement Liters (cc)	Engine Series (ID/VIN)	Fuel System	No. of Cylinders	Engine Type
1993	C/K Series (Pick-Up)	4.3 (4297)	Z	TBI	6	OHV
		5.0 (5002)	H	TBI	8	OHV
		5.7 (5740)	K	TBI	8	OHV
		6.2 (6216)	C, J	DFI	8	Diesel
		6.5 (6511)	F	DFI	8	Diesel
		7.4 (7446)	N	TBI	8	OHV
	Blazer	4.3 (4297)	Z	TBI	6	OHV
		5.0 (5002)	H	TBI	8	OHV
		5.7 (5740)	K	TBI	8	OHV
		6.2 (6216)	C, J	DFI	8	Diesel
		6.5 (6511)	F	DFI	8	Diesel
		7.4 (7446)	N	TBI	8	OHV
	Jimmy	4.3 (4297)	Z	TBI	6	OHV
		5.0 (5002)	H	TBI	8	OHV
		5.7 (5740)	K	TBI	8	OHV
		6.2 (6216)	C, J	DFI	8	Diesel
		6.5 (6511)	F	DFI	8	Diesel
		7.4 (7446)	N	TBI	8	OHV
	Suburban	4.3 (4297)	Z	TBI	6	OHV
		5.0 (5002)	H	TBI	8	OHV
		5.7 (5740)	K	TBI	8	OHV
		6.2 (6216)	C, J	DFI	8	Diesel
		6.5 (6511)	F	DFI	8	Diesel
		7.4 (7446)	N	TBI	8	OHV
	G Series (Van)	4.3 (4297)	Z	TBI	6	OHV
		5.0 (5002)	H	TBI	8	OHV
		5.7 (5740)	K	TBI	8	OHV
		6.2 (6216)	C, J	DFI	8	Diesel
		7.4 (7446)	N	TBI	8	OHV
	S10/S15 Blazer	2.5 (2476)	A	TBI	4	OHV
		2.8 (2837)	R	TBI	6	OHV
		4.3 (4297)	W	CPI	6	OHV
		4.3 (4297)	Z	TBI	6	OHV
	S10/S15 Pick-Up	2.5 (2476)	A	TBI	4	OHV
		2.8 (2837)	R	TBI	6	OHV
		4.3 (4297)	W	CPI	6	OHV
		4.3 (4297)	Z	TBI	6	OHV

ENGINE IDENTIFICATION

Year	Model	Engine Displacement Liters (cc)	Engine Series (ID/VIN)	Fuel System	No. of Cylinders	Engine Type
1993	Astro	4.3 (4297)	W	CPI	6	OHV
		4.3 (4297)	Z	TBI	6	OHV
	Safari	4.3 (4297)	Z	TBI	6	OHV
		4.3 (4297)	Z	TBI	6	OHV
	Lumina APV	3.1 (3149)	D	TBI	6	OHV
		3.8 (3788)	L	PFI	6	OHV
	Silhouette	3.1 (3149)	D	TBI	6	OHV
		3.8 (3788)	L	PFI	6	OHV
	Trans Sport	3.1 (3149)	D	TBI	6	OHV
		3.8 (3788)	L	PFI	6	OHV
	Bravado	4.3 (4297)	W	CPI	6	OHV
1994	C/K Series (Pick-Up)	4.3 (4297)	Z	TBI	6	OHV
		5.0 (5002)	H	TBI	8	OHV
		5.7 (5740)	K	TBI	8	OHV
		6.5 (6511)	P, S, F	DFI	8	Diesel
		7.4 (7446)	N	TBI	8	OHV
	Blazer	4.3 (4297)	Z	TBI	6	OHV
		5.0 (5002)	H	TBI	8	OHV
		5.7 (5740)	K	TBI	8	OHV
		6.5 (6511)	P, S, F	DFI	8	Diesel
		7.4 (7446)	N	TBI	8	OHV
	Suburban	4.3 (4297)	Z	TBI	6	OHV
		5.0 (5002)	H	TBI	8	OHV
		5.7 (5740)	K	TBI	8	OHV
		6.5 (6511)	P, S, F	DFI	8	Diesel
		7.4 (7446)	N	TBI	8	OHV
	G Series (Van)	4.3 (4297)	Z	TBI	6	OHV
		5.0 (5002)	H	TBI	8	OHV
		5.7 (5740)	K	TBI	8	OHV
		6.5 (6511)	P	DFI	8	Diesel
		7.4 (7446)	N	TBI	8	OHV
	S10/S15 Blazer	2.5 (2476)	A	TBI	4	OHV
		2.8 (2837)	R	TBI	6	OHV
		4.3 (4297)	W	CPI	6	OHV
		4.3 (4297)	Z	TBI	6	OHV
	S10/S15 Pick-Up	2.5 (2476)	A	TBI	4	OHV
		2.8 (2837)	R	TBI	6	OHV
		4.3 (4297)	W	CPI	6	OHV
		4.3 (4297)	Z	TBI	6	OHV
	Astro	4.3 (4297)	Z	TBI	6	OHV
		4.3 (4297)	W	CPI	6	OHV

ENGINE IDENTIFICATION

Year	Model	Engine Displacement Liters (cc)	Engine Series (ID/VIN)	Fuel System	No. of Cylinders	Engine Type
1994	Safari	4.3 (4297)	Z	TBI	6	OHV
		4.3 (4297)	W	CPI	6	OHV
	Lumina APV	3.1 (3149)	D	TBI	6	OHV
		3.8 (3788)	L	SFI	6	OHV
	Silhouette	3.1 (3149)	D	TBI	6	OHV
		3.8 (3788)	L	SFI	6	OHV
	Trans Sport	3.1 (3149)	D	TBI	6	OHV
		3.8 (3788)	L	SFI	6	OHV
	Bravada	4.3 (4297)	W	CMFI	6	OHV
1995	C/K Series (Pick-Up)	4.3 (4297)	Z	TBI	6	OHV
		5.0 (5002)	H	TBI	8	OHV
		5.7 (5740)	K	TBI	8	OHV
		6.5 (6511)	P, S, F	DFI	8	Diesel
		7.4 (7446)	N	TBI	8	OHV
	Blazer	4.3 (4297)	Z	TBI	6	OHV
		5.0 (5002)	H	TBI	8	OHV
		5.7 (5740)	K	TBI	8	OHV
		6.5 (6511)	P, S, F	DFI	8	Diesel
		7.4 (7446)	N	TBI	8	OHV
	Suburban	4.3 (4297)	Z	TBI	6	OHV
		5.0 (5002)	H	TBI	8	OHV
		5.7 (5740)	K	TBI	8	OHV
		6.5 (6511)	P, S, F	DFI	8	Diesel
		7.4 (7446)	N	TBI	8	OHV
	G Series (Van)	4.3 (4297)	Z	TBI	6	OHV
		5.0 (5002)	H	TBI	8	OHV
		5.7 (5740)	K	TBI	8	OHV
		6.5 (6511)	P	DFI	8	Diesel
		7.4 (7446)	N	TBI	8	OHV
	S10/S15 Blazer	2.2 (2179)	4	MFI	4	OHV
		4.3 (4297)	W	CPI	6	OHV
		4.3 (4297)	Z	TBI	6	OHV
	S10/S15 Pick-Up	2.2 (2179)	4	MFI	4	OHV
		4.3 (4297)	W	CPI	6	OHV
		4.3 (4297)	Z	TBI	6	OHV
	Astro	4.3 (4297)	W	CPI	6	OHV
	Safari	4.3 (4297)	W	CPI	6	OHV
	Lumina APV	3.1 (3149)	D	TBI	6	OHV
		3.8 (3788)	L	SFI	6	OHV
	Silhouette	3.1 (3149)	D	TBI	6	OHV
		3.8 (3788)	L	SFI	6	OHV

ENGINE IDENTIFICATION

Year	Model	Engine Displacement Liters (cc)	Engine Series (ID/VIN)	Fuel System	No. of Cylinders	Engine Type
1995	Trans Sport	3.1 (3149)	D	TBI	6	OHV
		3800	L	SFI	6	OHV

CMFI–Central Multiport Fuel Injection
CPI–Central Port Injection
DFI–Diesel Fuel Injection
MFI–Multiport Fuel Injection
PFI–Port Fuel Injection
SFI–Sequential Fuel Injection
TBI–Throttle Body Injection
OHV–Overhead Valves

REFRIGERANT CAPACITIES

Year	Model	Refrigerant (oz.)	Oil (fl. oz.)	Compressor Type
1993	C/K Series (Pick-Up)	40	8	HR110T
	Blazer (without aux. A/C)	48	8	HR110T
	Blazer (with aux. A/C)	66	11	HR110T
	Jimmy (without aux. A/C)	48	8	HR110T
	Jimmy (with aux. A/C)	66	11	HR110T
	Suburban (without aux. A/C)	48	8	HR110T
	Suburban (with aux. A/C)	66	11	HR110T
	G Series (exc. diesel, without aux. A/C)	48	8	HR6–HE
	G Series (exc. diesel, with aux. A/C)	68	11	HR6–HE
	G Series (diesel, without aux. A/C)	48	8	A–6
	G Series (diesel with aux. A/C)	68	11	A–6
	S10/S15 Blazer	40	8	HR100T
	S10/S15 Pick-Up	40	8	HR100T
	S10/S15 Blazer	40	8	V–5
	S10/S15 Pick-Up	40	8	V–5
	Astro (without aux. A/C)	48	8	HR6–HE
	Astro (with aux. A/C)	60	10.5	HR6–HE
	Safari (without aux. A/C)	48	8	HR6–HE
	Safari (with aux. A/C)	60	10.5	HR6–HE
	Lumina APV (without aux. A/C)	42	8	V–5 or HR6–HE
	Lumina APV (with aux. A/C)	60	10.5	V–5 or HR6–HE
	Silhouette (without aux. A/C)	42	8	V–5 or HR6–HE
	Silhouette (with aux. A/C)	60	10.5	V–5 or HR6–HE
	Trans Sport (without aux. A/C)	42	8	V–5 or HR6–HE
	Trans Sport (with aux. A/C)	60	10.5	V–5 or HR6–HE
	Bravada	40	8	HR100T/HR110–MD
1994	C/K Series (Pick-Up)	32	8	HR110–MD
	Blazer (without aux. A/C)	36	8	HR110–MD
	Blazer (with aux. A/C)	64	11	HR110–MD
	Suburban (without aux. A/C)	36	8	HR110–MD

REFRIGERANT CAPACITIES

Year	Model	Refrigerant (oz.)	Oil (fl. oz.)	Compressor Type
1994	Suburban (with aux. A/C)	64	11	HR110–MD
	G Series (without aux. A/C)	48	8	HR6–HE
	G Series (with aux. A/C)	68	11	HR6–HE
	S10/S15 Blazer	32	8	HR110–MD
	S10/S15 Pick-Up	32	8	HR110–MD
	S10/S15 Blazer	32	9	V–5
	S10/S15 Pick-Up	32	9	V–5
	Astro (without aux. A/C)	32	8	HR6–HE
	Astro (with aux. A/C)	48	11	HR6–HE
	Safari (without aux. A/C)	32	8	HR6–HE
	Safari (with aux. A/C)	48	11	HR6–HE
	Lumina APV (without aux. A/C)	36	8	V–5 or HR6–HE
	Lumina APV (with aux. A/C)	48	11	V–5 or HR6–HE
	Silhouette (without aux. A/C)	36	8	V–5 or HR6–HE
	Silhouette (with aux. A/C)	48	11	V–5 or HR6–HE
	Trans Sport (without aux. A/C)	36	8	V–5 or HR6–HE
	Trans Sport (with aux. A/C)	48	11	V–5 or HR6–HE
	Bravada	37	8	HR100T
1995	C/K Series (Pick-Up)	32	8	HR110–MD
	Blazer	36	8	HR110–MD
	Suburban (without aux. A/C)	36	8	HR110–MD
	Suburban (with aux. A/C)	64	11	HR110–MD
	G Series (without aux. A/C)	48	8	HR6–HE
	G Series (with aux. A/C)	68	11	HR6–HE
	S10/S15 Blazer	32	8	HR110–MD
	S10/S15 Pick-Up	32	8	HR110–MD
	S10/S15 Blazer	32	9	V–5
	S10/S15 Pick-Up	32	9	V–5
	Astro (without aux. A/C)	32	8	HR6–HE
	Astro (with aux. A/C)	48	11	HR6–HE
	Safari (without aux. A/C)	32	8	HR6–HE
	Safari (with aux. A/C)	48	11	HR6–HE
	Lumina APV (without aux. A/C)	36	8	V–5 or HR6–HE
	Lumina APV (with aux. A/C)	48	11	V–5 or HR6–HE
	Silhouette (without aux. A/C)	36	8	V–5 or HR6–HE
	Silhouette (with aux. A/C)	48	11	V–5 or HR6–HE
	Trans Sport (without aux. A/C)	36	8	V–5 or HR6–HE
	Trans Sport (with aux. A/C)	48	11	V–5 or HR6–HE

AIR CONDITIONING BELT TENSION

Year	Model	Engine Liters	Belt Type	Specifications New	Specifications Used
1993	C/K Series (Pick-Up)	All	Serpentine	①	①
	Blazer	All	Serpentine	①	①
	Jimmy	All	Serpentine	①	①
	Suburban	All	Serpentine	①	①
	G Series (Van)	exc. diesel	Serpentine	①	①
	G Series (Van)	Diesel	V-Belt	169 lbs.	90 lbs.
	S10/S15 Blazer	All	Serpentine	①	①
	S10/S15 Pick-Up	All	Serpentine	①	①
	Astro	4.3L	Serpentine	①	①
	Safari	4.3L	Serpentine	①	①
	Lumina APV	3.1L	Serpentine	①	①
	Silhouette	3.1L	Serpentine	①	①
	Trans Sport	3.1L	Serpentine	①	①
	Lumina APV	3.8L	Serpentine	①	①
	Silhouette	3.8L	Serpentine	①	①
	Trans Sport	3.8L	Serpentine	①	①
	Bravada	4.3L	Serpentine	①	①
1994	C/K Series (Pick-Up)	All	Serpentine	①	①
	Blazer	All	Serpentine	①	①
	Suburban	All	Serpentine	①	①
	G Series (Van)	All	Serpentine	①	①
	S10/S15 Blazer	All	Serpentine	①	①
	S10/S15 Pick-Up	All	Serpentine	①	①
	Astro	4.3L	Serpentine	①	①
	Safari	4.3L	Serpentine	①	①
	Lumina APV	All	Serpentine	①	①
	Silhouette	All	Serpentine	①	①
	Trans Sport	All	Serpentine	①	①
	Bravada	4.3L	Serpentine	①	①
1995	C/K Series (Pick-Up)	All	Serpentine	①	①
	Blazer	All	Serpentine	①	①
	Suburban	All	Serpentine	①	①
	G Series (Van)	All	Serpentine	①	①
	S10/S15 Blazer	All	Serpentine	①	①
	S10/S15 Pick-Up	All	Serpentine	①	①
	Astro	4.3L	Serpentine	①	①
	Safari	4.3L	Serpentine	①	①
	Lumina APV	All	Serpentine	①	①
	Silhouette	All	Serpentine	①	①
	Trans Sport	All	Serpentine	①	①

① Equipped with automatic tensioner; no adjustment required.

SYSTEM DESCRIPTION

General Information

C/K Series

The C and K Series models, which includes full-size Pick-Ups, Blazer, Jimmy and Suburban, use an electronically controlled air conditioning and heating system. These systems use a Cycling Clutch Orifice Tube (CCOT) system and an HR110T compressor to control operations. The compressor relay and high blower relay energize their respective components under key conditions. The Suburban model also uses a rear auxiliary system which has its own rear blower motor, heater core and evaporator; however, the system functions primarily from connections to the front system.

G Series (Vans)

These models use a manually controlled CCOT system with either an HR6-HE or A-6 compressor. Temperature operation is cable controlled from the panel lever, while other air door operations for mode control are vacuum operated. The high pressure cut-off switch prevents system damage in the event of excessive pressures. These models may also be equipped with a rear auxiliary system, with its own rear blower motor, heater core, and evaporator. All other operations are tied to the front system. All models use non-CFC R-134a refrigerant and PAG type refrigerant oil.

S10/S15 Series

These models include the mid-size Pick-Ups, Blazers and Jimmys, also use a manually controlled CCOT system with an HR100T compressor or a Variable Displacement Orifice Tube (VDOT) system with a variable displacement V-5 compressor which operates full time. The V-5 compressor is designed to meet the demands of the system without cycling. The compressor employs a variable angle wobble plate controlling the displacement of 5 axially oriented cylinders. Displacement is controlled by a bellows actuated control valve located in the rear head of the compressor. The electro-magnetic compressor clutch connects the compressor shaft to the serpentine drive belt when the coil is energized. The temperature operation is cable controlled and other air mode operations are vacuum controlled.

Astro and Safari

The manually controlled systems use a CCOT operation with an HR6–HE compressor. The temperature is cable controlled and the mode operations are vacuum controlled. In addition to the clutch cycling pressure switch which prevents evaporator freeze-up, the system also uses a high pressure cut-off switch to prevent damage.

Lumina APV, Silhouette and Trans Sport

All models with 3.1L engine front-only systems use the VDOT system with a V-5 compressor. On models with 3.8L or 3.1L engine with rear auxiliary systems, a CCOT system with an HR6-HE compressor is used. Temperature is electrically controlled while mode doors are vacuum controlled. As noted, some models may use an auxiliary rear system. All systems use non-CFC R-134a refrigerant and PAG type refrigerant oil.

Bravada

Bravada uses a manually controlled system. The CCOT components use an HR100T/HR110-MD compressor. The temperature function is cable controlled by the control panel lever and the mode functions are vacuum operated.

Supplemental Inflatable Restraint (SIR) System

CAUTION

On vehicles equipped with the Supplemental Inflatable Restraint (SIR) system (air bag) it will be necessary to disable the SIR system before performing any other work on or around SIR system components or wiring. Failure to follow proper procedures could result in SIR system deployment, personal injury or unneeded SIR system repairs.

DISABLING THE SIR SYSTEM

1. Turn the steering wheel so that the front wheels point straight ahead.
2. Turn the ignition switch to **LOCK** and remove the key.
3. Remove the **AIR BAG** fuse.
4. On Lumina APV, Silhouette and Trans Sport, remove the left side sound insulator.
5. On C/K Series, G Series, Astro/Safari and S10/S15, remove the steering column filler panel.
6. Remove the Connector Position Assurance (CPA) retainer.
7. Disconnect the yellow 2-way SIR connector at the base of the steering column.

ENABLING THE SIR SYSTEM

1. Turn the ignition switch to **LOCK** and remove the key.
2. Connect the yellow 2-way SIR connector at the base of the steering column and insert the Connector Position Assurance (CPA) retainer.
3. On Lumina APV, Silhouette and Trans Sport, install the left side sound insulator.
4. On C/K Series, G Series, Astro/Safari and S10/S15, install the steering column filler panel.
5. Install the **AIR BAG** fuse.
6. Turn the ignition switch to **RUN** and verify that the **AIR BAG** warning lamp flashes 7 times and turns off.

Service Valve Locations

The high-side fitting is normally located in the refrigerant line near the compressor. The low-side fitting is normally located on the accumulator or in the condenser-to-evaporator refrigerant line.

System Discharging

R-12 refrigerant is a chlorofluorocarbon which, when released into the atmosphere, can contribute to the depletion of the ozone layer in the upper atmosphere. Ozone filters out harmful radiation from the sun. In order to protect the ozone layer, an approved R-12 recovery/recycling machine that meets SAE standards should be employed when discharging the system. Follow the operating instructions provided with the approved equipment exactly to properly discharge the system.

In 1993, some models use non-CFC R-134a refrigerant and PAG type refrigerant oil. These systems must also be discharged using approved recovery/recycling equipment meeting SAE standards. Note that the same equipment used for R-12 systems cannot be used on R-134a systems. This is because these refrigerants are not compatible when mixed in any amounts. Also, special service valve fittings may be found on R-134a systems to prevent inadvertent use of R-12 service equipment.

System Evacuating

NOTE: Determine if system is R-12 or R-134a filled and use appropriate service equipment designed for each system. Follow equipment manufacturer's instructions.

If the air conditioning system has been opened to the atmosphere, it should be air and moisture free before being recharged with refrigerant. Moisture and air mixed with refrigerant will raise the compressor head pressure, possibly damage the system's components and will reduce the performance of the system. In addition, air and moisture in the system can lead to internal corrosion of the system components. Moisture will boil at normal room temperature when exposed to a vacuum. To evacuate or rid the system of air and moisture:

1. Leak test the system and repair any leaks found.
2. Connect an approved charging station, recovery/recycling machine or manifold gauge set and vacuum pump to the discharge and suction ports. The red hose is normally connected to the discharge (high pressure) line. The blue hose is connected to the suction (low pressure) line. If using a manifold gauge set, the center (usually yellow) hose is connected to the charging station or recovery/recycling machine.
3. Open the discharge and suction ports and start the vacuum pump. If the pump is not able to pull at least 26 in. Hg of vacuum there is a leak that must be repaired before evacuation can occur.
4. Once the system has reached at least 26 in. Hg of vacuum, allow the system to evacuate for at least 10 minutes. The longer the system is evacuated, the more moisture will be removed.
5. Close all valves and turn the pump **OFF**. If the system loses more than 2 in. Hg of vacuum after 15 minutes, there is a leak that should be repaired.

System Charging

NOTE: Determine if system is R-12 or R-134a filled and use appropriate service equipment designed for each system. Follow equipment manufacturer's instructions.

1. Connect an approved charging station, recovery/recycling machine or manifold gauge set to the discharge and suction ports. The red hose is normally connected to the discharge (high pressure) line, and the blue hose is connected to the suction (low pressure) line. If using a manifold gauge set, the center (usually yellow) hose is connected to the charging station or recovery/recycling machine.
2. Follow the instructions provided with the equipment and charge the system with the specified amount of refrigerant.
3. Perform a leak test.

SYSTEM COMPONENTS

Radiator

REMOVAL AND INSTALLATION

C/K Series, G Series (exc. Diesel), S10/S15 Series, Astro Safari, Bravada

1. Disconnect the negative battery cable.
2. Drain the engine coolant into a clean container for reuse.
3. Remove the upper fan shroud.
4. On C/K Series and G Series (gasoline engines), remove the lower fan shroud (some additional component removal may be required for access to lower shroud on G Series).
5. Remove the upper insulators.
6. Disconnect the radiator inlet and outlet hoses.
7. If equipped with an automatic transmission, disconnect the transmission fluid cooler lines from the radiator. If equipped, disconnect the engine oil cooler lines.
8. Disconnect the coolant overflow hose from the filler neck.
9. Remove the radiator from the vehicle.
10. Remove the lower insulators, as required.

To install:

11. If removed, install the lower radiator insulators.
12. Install the radiator in the vehicle.
13. If equipped, connect the engine oil cooler lines.
14. If equipped with an automatic transmission, connect the transmission fluid cooler lines to the radiator.
15. Connect the radiator inlet and outlet hoses.
16. Install the upper insulators.
17. Install the lower and upper fan shrouds, as removed.
18. Connect the coolant overflow hose to the filler neck.
19. Connect the negative battery cable.
20. Fill cooling system and check for leaks. Start the engine and allow to come to normal operating temperature. Recheck for leaks. Top-up coolant.

G Series Van With Diesel Engine

1. Disconnect the negative battery cable.
2. Drain the engine coolant into a clean container for reuse.
3. Remove the air intake snorkel.
4. Remove the windshield washer bottle.
5. Disconnect the hood release cable.
6. Remove the upper fan shroud.
7. Disconnect the upper radiator hose from the radiator.
8. Disconnect the transmission cooler lines from the radiator.
9. Disconnect the low coolant sensor electrical connector.
10. Disconnect the overflow hose from the radiator.
11. Raise and safely support the vehicle.
12. Disconnect the lower radiator hose from the radiator.
13. Lower the vehicle.
14. Remove the master cylinder from the brake booster by performing the following:
    - Disconnect the brake lines from the master cylinder.

NOTE: Cover the ends of the brake lines and the brake line fittings on the master cylinder to prevent the entry of dirt and the excess loss of brake fluid.

- Remove the master cylinder mounting nuts.
- Position the combination valve bracket aside.
- Remove the master cylinder from the vehicle.

15. Remove the radiator from the vehicle.

To install:

16. Position the radiator in the vehicle.
17. Install the master cylinder on the brake booster by performing the following:
    - Place the master cylinder in position.
    - Position the combination valve bracket on the mounting studs.
    - Install the mounting nuts.
    - Connect the brake lines to the master cylinder.
    - Properly bleed the brake system.
18. Raise and safely support the vehicle.

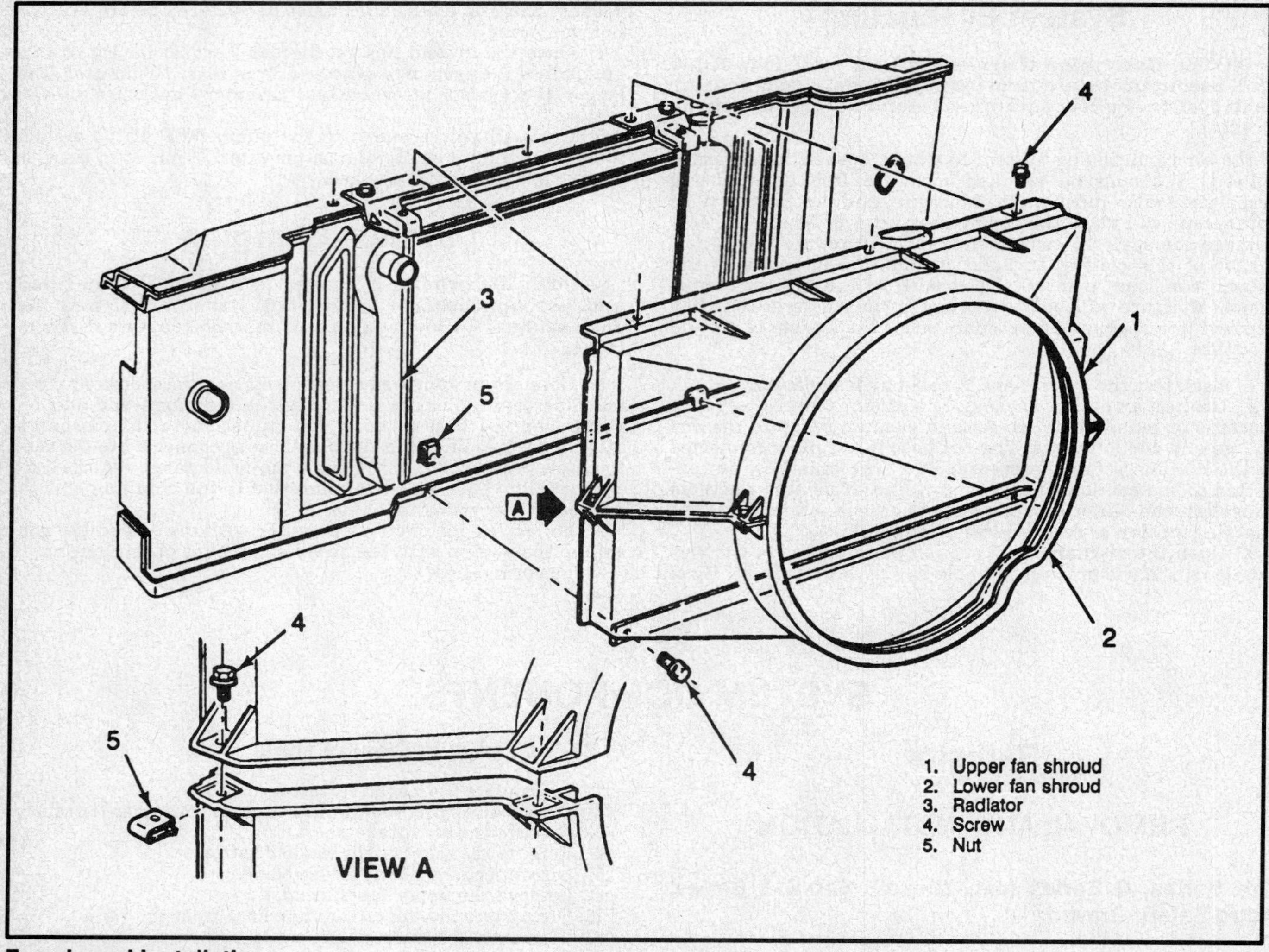

Fan shroud installation

19. Connect the lower radiator hose.
20. Lower the vehicle.
21. Connect the engine oil cooler lines to the radiator.
22. Connect the overflow hose to the radiator.
23. Connect the low coolant sensor electrical connector.
24. Connect the transmission oil cooler lines to the radiator.
25. Connect the upper radiator hose to the radiator.
26. Install the upper fan shroud.
27. Connect the hood release cable.
28. Install the windshield washer bottle.
29. Install the air intake snorkel.
30. Fill cooling system and check for leaks. Start the engine and allow to come to normal operating temperature. Recheck for leaks. Top-up coolant.

Lumina APV, Silhouette and Trans Sport

1. Disconnect the negative battery cable.
2. Drain the engine coolant into a clean container for reuse.
3. Remove the forward engine strut bracket at the radiator and swing the strut rearward.

NOTE: To prevent shearing of the rubber bushing, loosen the bolt before swinging the strut aside.

4. Remove the forward light harness from the fan frame and disconnect the fan connector.
5. Remove the fan attaching bolts. Remove the fan and frame assembly.
6. Remove the hood latch from the radiator support. Scribe the latch location before removal to aid in reinstallation.
7. Disconnect the coolant hoses from the radiator and coolant recovery tank hose from the radiator neck.
8. Disconnect the transaxle fluid cooler lines.
9. Remove the radiator-to-radiator support attaching bolts and clamps.
10. Remove the radiator from the vehicle.

To install:

11. Install the radiator in the vehicle. Ensure that the bottom of the radiator is seated in the lower mounting pads.
12. Install the radiator-to-radiator support attaching clamp and bolts.
13. Connect the transaxle cooler lines.
14. Connect the coolant hoses to the radiator.
15. Connect the coolant recovery hose to the radiator neck.
16. Install the hood latch to the radiator support. Observe the matchmarks made during removal.
17. Install the fan and frame assembly.
18. Connect the fan electrical connector and install the forward light wiring harness to the fan frame.
19. Swing the forward engine strut and brace forward until the brace contacts the radiator support. Install the brace-to-radiator support attaching bolts. Tighten to 37 ft. lbs. (50 Nm).

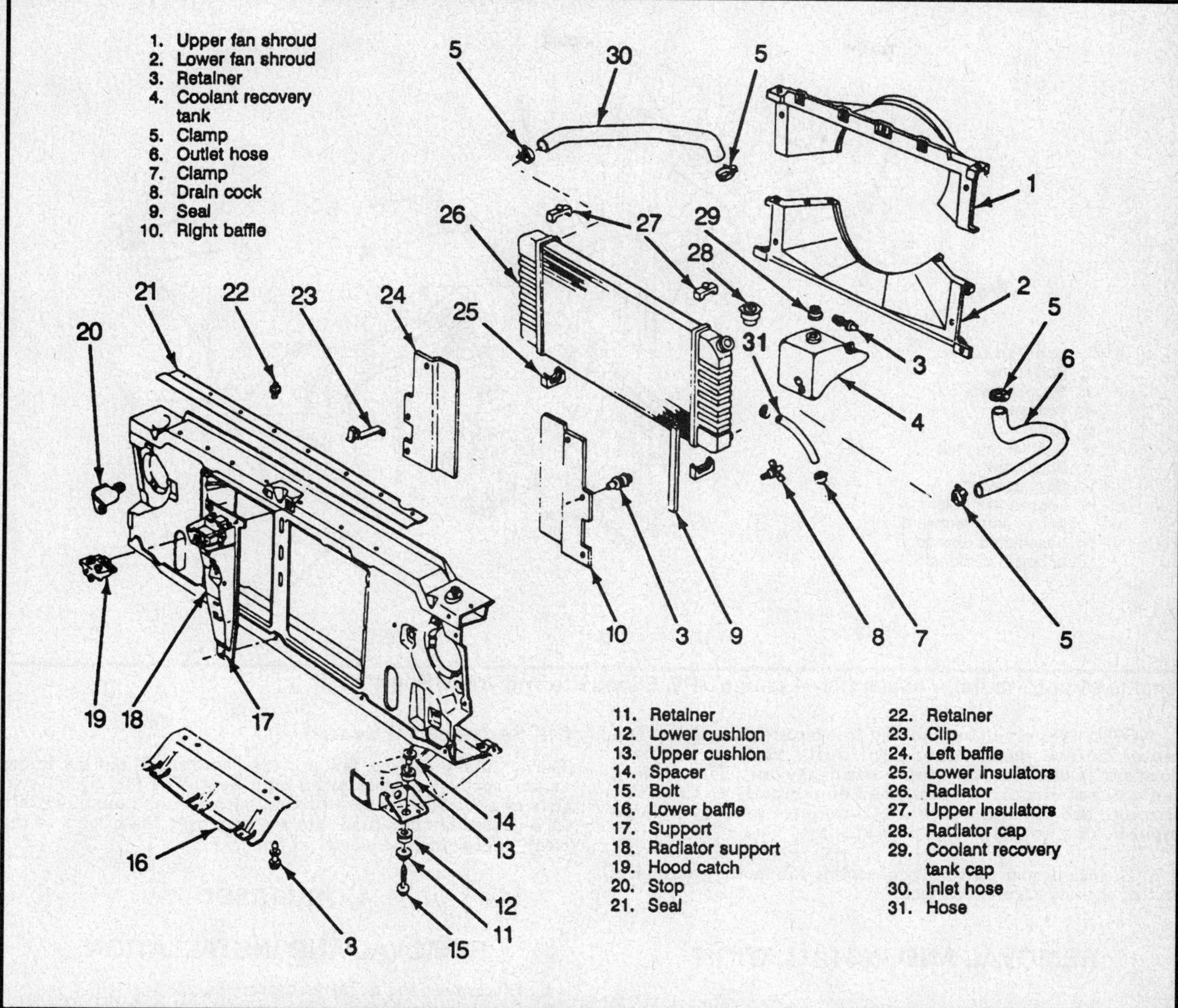

Radiator and related components—S10/S15 Series and Bravada shown

20. Connect the negative battery cable.
21. Fill cooling system and check for leaks. Start the engine and allow to come to normal operating temperature. Allow the engine to warm up sufficiently to confirm operation of the cooling fan. Recheck for leaks. Top-up coolant.

COOLING SYSTEM BLEEDING

1. On Lumina APV, Silhouette and Trans Sport, if engine block drains were removed, be sure they are properly installed.
2. Fill the cooling system with the proper ratio of coolant and water.
3. Set the heater controls to heat and the temperature controls to the warmest setting.
4. Start the engine and add coolant, as necessary, to keep the radiator level just below the filler neck.
5. Allow the engine to come to normal operating temperature; indicated by the upper radiator hose becoming hot.
6. The air coming out of the heater should be getting hot.
7. Check the coolant level in the radiator and coolant reservoir. Install the radiator cap, turning it until the arrows align with the overflow tube.

Electric Cooling Fan

TESTING

Lumina APV, Silhouette and Trans Sport

1. Check fuse or circuit breaker for power to cooling fan motor.
2. Remove connector(s) at cooling fan motor(s). Connect jumper wire and apply battery voltage to the positive terminal of the cooling fan motor.
3. Using an ohmmeter, check for continuity in cooling fan motor.

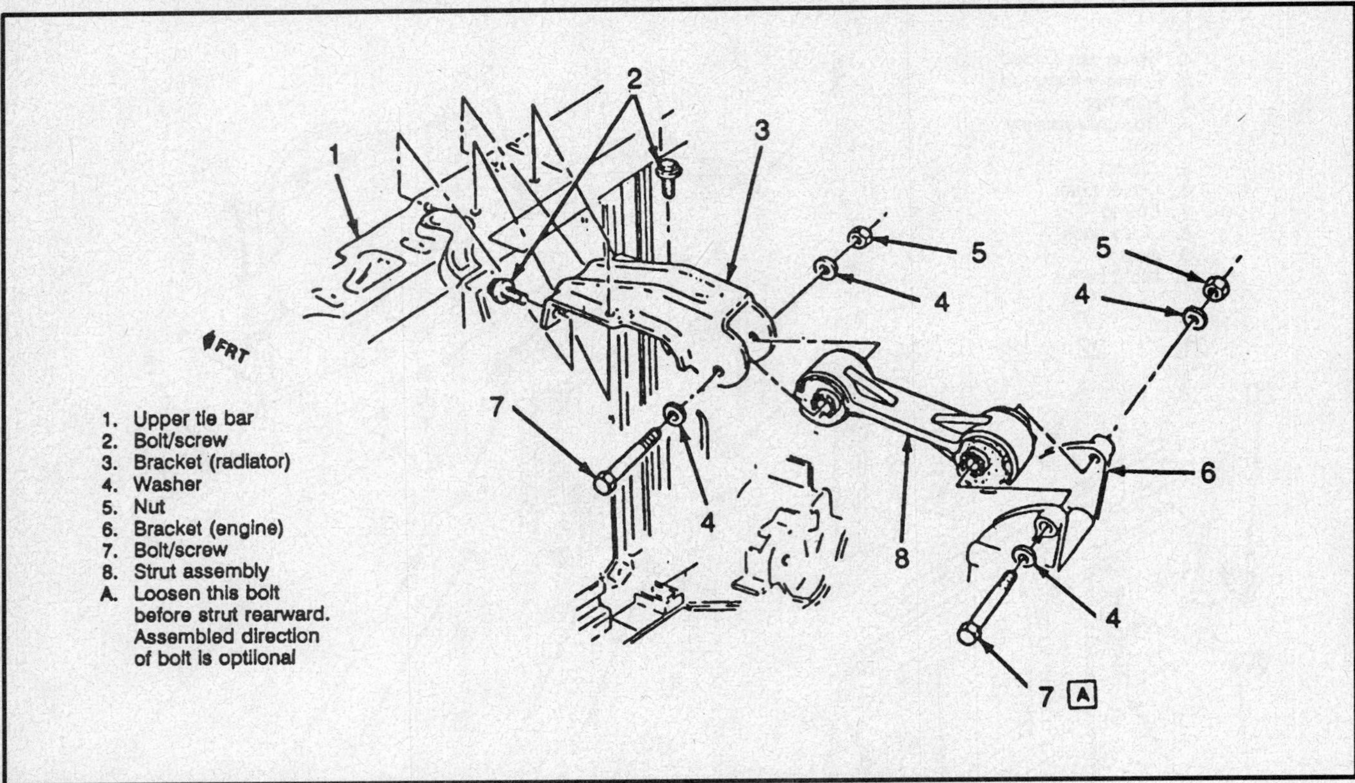

Engine strut-to-radiator assembly—Lumina APV, Silhouette and Trans Sport

NOTE: Remove the cooling fan connector at the fan motor before performing continuity checks. Perform continuity check of the motor windings only. The cooling fan control circuit is connected electrically to the ECM through the cooling fan relay. Ohmmeter battery voltage must not be applied to the ECM.

4. Ensure proper continuity of cooling fan motor ground circuit at chassis ground connector.

REMOVAL AND INSTALLATION

Lumina APV, Silhouette and Trans Sport

1. Disconnect the negative battery cable.
2. Remove the forward engine strut bracket at the radiator and swing the strut rearward.

NOTE: To prevent shearing of the rubber bushing, loosen the bolt before swinging the strut aside.

3. Remove the forward light harness from the fan frame and disconnect the fan connector.
4. Remove the fan attaching bolts and remove the fan and frame assembly.

To install:

5. Install the fan and frame assembly.
6. Connect the fan electrical connector and install the forward light wiring harness to the fan frame.
7. Swing the forward engine strut and brace forward until the brace contacts the radiator support. Install the brace-to-radiator support attaching bolts. Tighten to 37 ft. lbs. (50 Nm).
8. Connect the negative battery cable.

C/K Series and G Series

The auxiliary cooling fan provides additional cooling under engine conditions generating high heat. The fan circuit consists of a coolant temperature sensor, relay and auxiliary fan. At a preset temperature, the sensor closes the circuit to the relay, energizing the electrical fan.

Condenser

REMOVAL AND INSTALLATION

1. Disconnect the negative battery cable.
2. Properly discharge and recover the air conditioning system refrigerant.
3. Perform the following specific procedures:
   - On C/K Series, remove the fan shroud and remove the grille assembly.
   - On G Series Van, remove the grille, hood lock and center hood lock support.
   - On S Series and Bravada, remove the upper fan shroud and the radiator. If equipped, remove the shields at either side of the radiator support.
   - On Astro and Safari, remove the grille and front-end panel. Remove the radiator bar support.
   - On Lumina APV, Silhouette and Trans Sport, remove the center support grille. Remove the upper and lower air deflectors. Remove the upper condenser seal from the front engine compartment panel assembly.
4. Disconnect the condenser inlet and outlet fitting connections. Discard the O-rings. Cap all openings immediately to minimize contamination.

NOTE: Use a backup wrench on the condenser fittings when disconnecting the refrigerant lines.

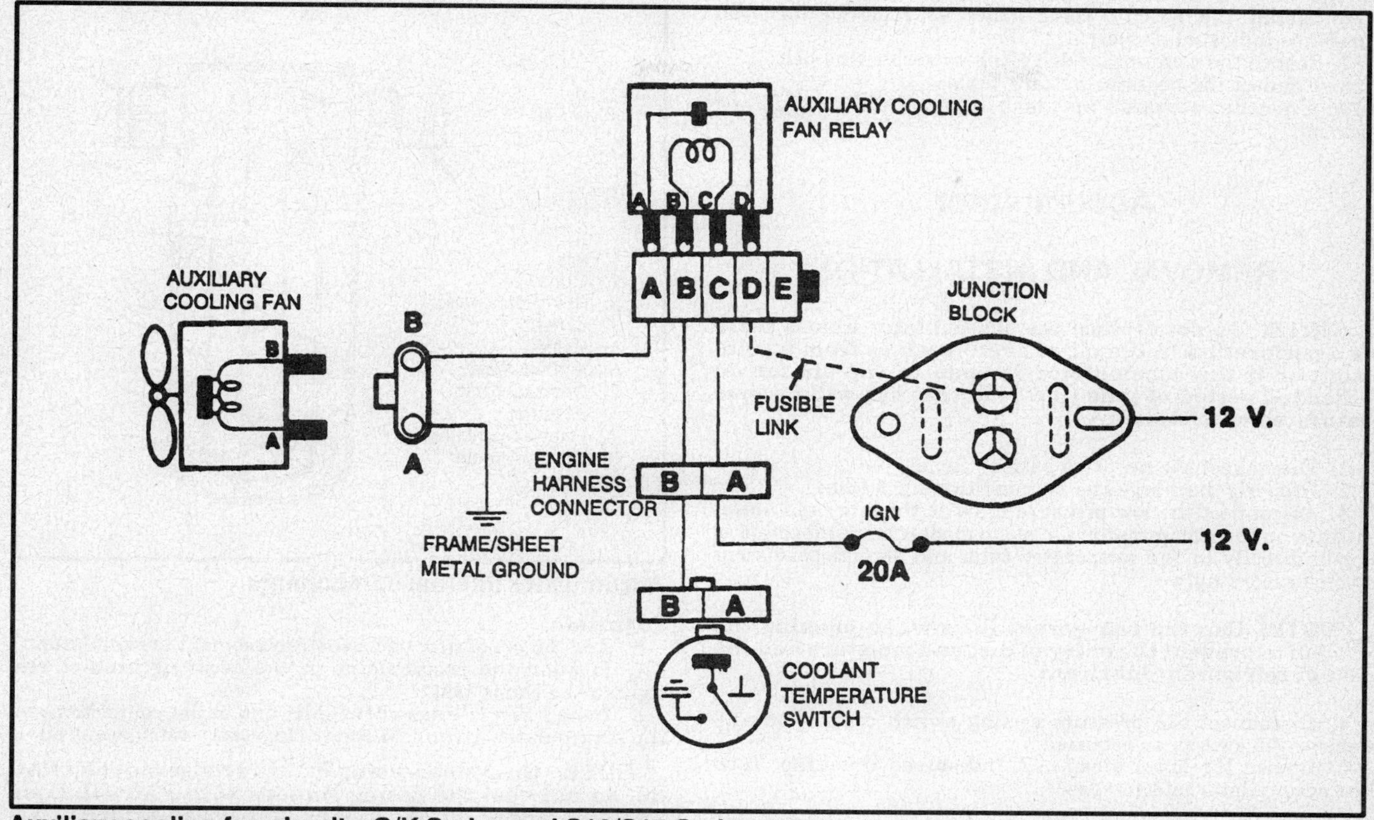

Auxiliary cooling fan circuit—C/K Series and S10/S15 Series

5. Remove the condenser-to-radiator support screws, if needed. Remove the condenser support brackets.
6. Remove the condenser insulators and remove the condenser. On all C and K Series models, remove the condenser from the vehicle by pulling it forward. Bend the left side grille support outboard to gain clearance for the removal of the condenser.
7. Remove the lower condenser insulators, as required.
8. To install, reverse the removal procedure. If using a replacement condenser, add 1 oz. of refrigerant lubricant to the system. Evacuate, recharge and leak test the air conditioning system.

NOTE: On systems using R-134a refrigerant and PAG oil, do not coat the fitting threads with PAG oil. Long term contact of oil on threads may cause future disassembly problems. Use only 525 viscosity mineral oil. Do not wipe threads with a cloth. Coat O-rings with 525 viscosity mineral oil only.

Compressor

REMOVAL AND INSTALLATION

1. Disconnect the negative battery cable.
2. Properly discharge and recover the air conditioning system refrigerant.
3. Remove the compressor drive belt or serpentine belt, except Astro and Safari.
4. Perform the following specific operations:
   - On G Series, remove the engine cover and the air cleaner.
   - On Astro and Safari, remove the engine cover, the air cleaner, the drive belt and the oil filler tube.
   - On Lumina APV, Silhouette and Trans Sport, raise and support the vehicle. Remove the right front wheel and wheel splash shield for access to the compressor mounting bolts.
5. Remove the refrigerant line coupler assembly or refrigerant lines from the compressor. Discard the O-rings. Cap the refrigerant lines when opening the system to prevent the entry of dirt and moisture and the loss of refrigerant lubricant.
6. Disconnect the compressor electrical connector.
7. Remove all nuts and bolts from the compressor and/or compressor brace as needed to remove the compressor.
8. Remove the compressor from the vehicle.
9. Drain and measure the refrigerant oil from the compressor. Discard the old oil.

To install:

10. If the compressor is to be replaced, drain the oil from the new compressor and discard. Add new refrigerant oil equivalent to the amount that was drained from the old compressor upon removal.
11. Install the compressor in the vehicle.
12. Install the mounting nuts, bolts and/or braces, as removed.
13. Connect the compressor electrical connector.
14. Replace the compressor O-rings. Lubricate with refrigerant lubricant.
15. Connect the refrigerant line coupler assembly or refrigerant lines to the compressor. Use new O-rings.

NOTE: On systems using R-134a refrigerant and PAG oil, do not coat the fitting threads with PAG oil. Long term contact of oil on threads may cause future disassembly problems. Use only 525 viscosity mineral oil. Do not wipe threads with a cloth. Coat O-rings with 525 viscosity mineral oil only.

16. Install the specific components as removed for each model as indicated above.
17. Install the compressor drive belt or serpentine belt.
18. Connect the negative battery cable.
19. Evacuate, recharge and leak test the air conditioning system.

Accumulator

REMOVAL AND INSTALLATION

NOTE: Do not replace the accumulator unless there is a perforation in the outer shell (such as from a collision) or if the accumulator is open to the air for an extended period of time (the desiccant bag will become saturated with moisture).

1. Disconnect the negative battery cable.
2. Properly discharge the air conditioning system.
3. Disconnect the low-pressure lines at the inlet and outlet fittings on the accumulator. On some models one connection is made directly to the evaporator tube and should be disconnected accordingly.

NOTE: Cap the refrigerant lines when opening the system to prevent the entry of dirt and moisture and the loss of refrigerant lubricant.

4. Disconnect the pressure cycling switch connection and remove the switch, as required.
5. Loosen the lower strap bolt and spread the strap. Turn the accumulator and remove.

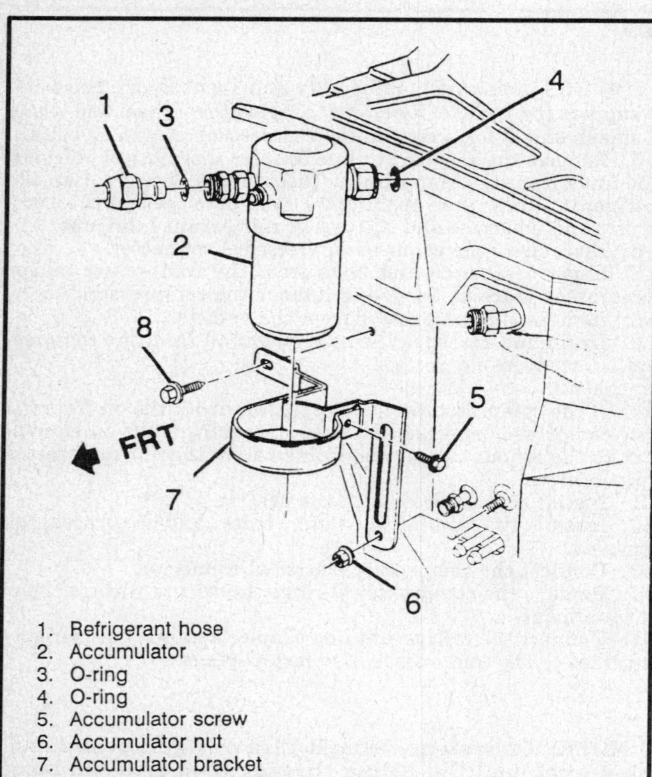

Accumulator removal—C/K Series

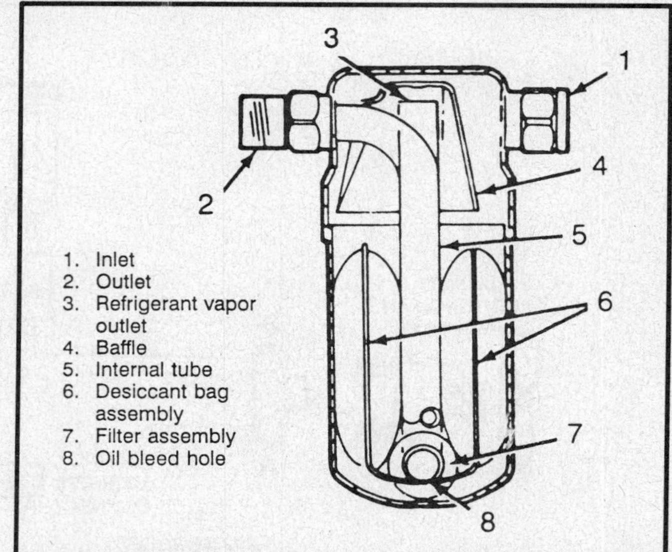

Accumulator internal components

To install:

6. Add 3.5 oz. of new oil to the replacement accumulator.
7. Position the accumulator in the securing bracket and tighten the clamp bolt.
8. Install new O-rings at the inlet and outlet connections on the accumulator. Lubricate the O-rings with refrigerant oil.

NOTE: On systems using R-134a refrigerant and PAG oil, do not coat the fitting threads with PAG oil. Long term contact of oil on threads may cause future disassembly problems. Use only 525 viscosity mineral oil. Do not wipe threads with a cloth. Coat O-rings with 525 viscosity mineral oil only.

9. Connect the low-pressure inlet and outlet lines or attachment to the evaporator tube.
10. Evacuate, charge and leak test the system.
11. Connect the negative battery cable.

Fixed Orifice Tube

REMOVAL AND INSTALLATION

1. Properly discharge the air conditioning system.
2. Loosen the fitting at the liquid line outlet on the condenser and the evaporator inlet pipe and disconnect. Discard the O-ring. Cap openings on condenser and evaporator immediately to minimize contamination.

NOTE: Use a backup wrench on the condenser outlet fitting when loosening the lines.

3. Using removal tool J26549D (or equivalent), carefully remove the fixed orifice tube from the tube fitting in the evaporator inlet line or in the refrigerant line.
4. In the event that the restricted or plugged orifice tube is difficult to remove, perform the following:
   - Remove as much of the impacted residue as possible.
   - Using a hair dryer, epoxy drier or equivalent, carefully apply heat approximately 1/4 in. from the dimples on the inlet pipe. Do not overheat the pipe.

NOTE: If the system has a pressure switch near the orifice tube, it should be removed prior to heating the pipe to avoid damage to the switch.

   - While applying heat, use special tool J 26549-C or equivalent to grip the orifice tube. Use a turning motion along with a push-pull motion to loosen the impacted orifice tube and remove it.

5. Swab the inside of the evaporator inlet pipe with solvent to remove any remaining residue.

To install:

6. Add 1 oz. of 525 viscosity refrigerant oil to the system.

NOTE: On systems using R-134a refrigerant and PAG oil, do not coat the fitting threads with PAG oil. Long term contact of oil on threads may cause future disassembly problems. Use only 525 viscosity mineral oil. Do not wipe threads with a cloth. Coat O-rings with 525 viscosity mineral oil only.

7. Lubricate the new O-ring and orifice tube with refrigerant oil and insert into the inlet pipe.

NOTE: Ensure that the new orifice tube is inserted in the inlet tube with the smaller screen end first.

8. Connect the evaporator inlet pipe with the condenser outlet fitting.

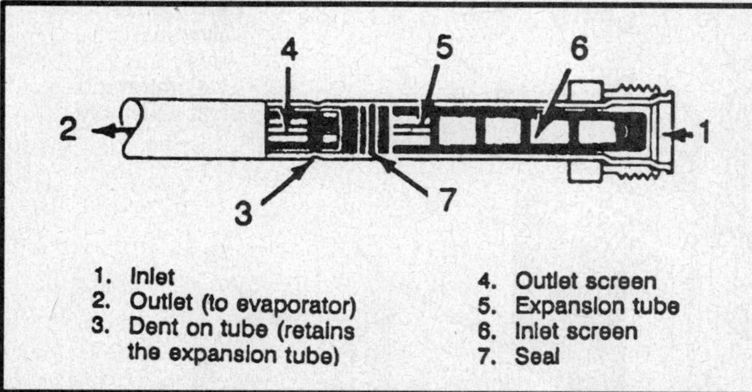

Orifice tube internal components

NOTE: Use a backup wrench on the condenser outlet fitting when tightening the lines.

9. Evacuate, recharge and leak test the system.

Blower Motor

REMOVAL AND INSTALLATION

C/K Series (Pick-Up, Blazer, Jimmy and Suburban)

1. Disconnect the negative battery cable.
2. Remove the instrument panel compartment.
3. Remove the front screw from the right door sill plate. Remove the right side cowl kick panel.
4. Disconnect the electrical connector from the blower motor.
5. Remove the ECM and mounting bracket.
6. If equipped, remove the courtesy light attaching screws and set the light aside.
7. Remove the bolt from the right side dash support.
8. Remove the blower motor cover, cooling tube, and the flange screws.
9. Carefully, remove the blower motor to avoid distorting the fan.
10. Remove the fan, as required.

To install:

11. If removed, install the fan to the blower motor shaft.
12. Carefully, guide the blower motor and blower fan assembly into position.
13. Install the blower motor flange screws, cover and cooling tube.
14. Install the bolt to the right side dash support.
15. If equipped, install the courtesy light and ECM and bracket.
16. Connect the electrical connector to the blower motor.
17. Install the right side cowl kick panel.
18. Install the front screw into the front door sill plate. Install the instrument panel compartment.
19. Connect the negative battery cable.
20. Operate the blower motor to ensure that it functions on all speeds.

G Series Van, S10/S15 Series, Astro, Safari, Bravada

1. Disconnect the negative battery cable.
2. Except S10/S15 Series, disconnect the coolant overflow hose from the coolant recovery bottle. Remove the recovery bottle fasteners. Remove the recovery bottle from the vehicle.
3. On Astro and Safari, disconnect the windshield washer hose and electrical connector. Remove the windshield washer fluid bottle.
4. Disconnect the blower motor wiring harness.
5. Remove the blower motor cooling tube, as required.
6. Remove the 5 motor mounting screws.
7. Remove the motor and fan assembly. Carefully pry on the blower flange to separate the blower flange from the sealer.
8. Remove the blower motor shaft nut.
9. Remove the fan from the motor.

To install:

10. Install the fan to the motor shaft. Ensure that the open end of the fan wheel faces away from the blower motor.
11. Install the nut on the blower motor shaft.
12. Apply a bead of permagum sealer to the mounting flange.
13. Install the blower motor and fan assembly to the case. Install the 5 mounting screws.
14. Connect the blower motor wiring harness.
15. If disconnected, connect the blower motor cooling tube.
16. Install the coolant recovery bottle and windshield washer bottle, if removed.
17. Connect the negative battery cable.
18. Operate the blower motor to ensure that it functions on all speeds.

Lumina APV, Silhouette and Trans Sport

1. Disconnect the negative battery cable.
2. Remove the engine air cleaner.
3. Remove the left side windshield wiper arm link.
4. Disconnect the blower motor electrical connector.
5. Remove the blower motor retaining screws. Remove the blower motor.

To install:

6. Install the blower motor and retaining screws.
7. Connect the blower motor electrical connector.
8. Install the left side windshield wiper arm link.
9. Install the air cleaner.
10. Connect the negative battery cable.
11. Operate the blower motor to ensure that it functions on all speeds.

Blower Motor Resistor

REMOVAL AND INSTALLATION

1. Disconnect the negative battery cable.
2. Disconnect the electrical connector at the resistor.
3. Remove the resistor attaching screws.
4. Remove the resistor from the evaporator case.

To install:

5. Position the resistor in the evaporator case. Install the attaching screws.
6. Connect the electrical connector.
7. Connect the negative battery cable.

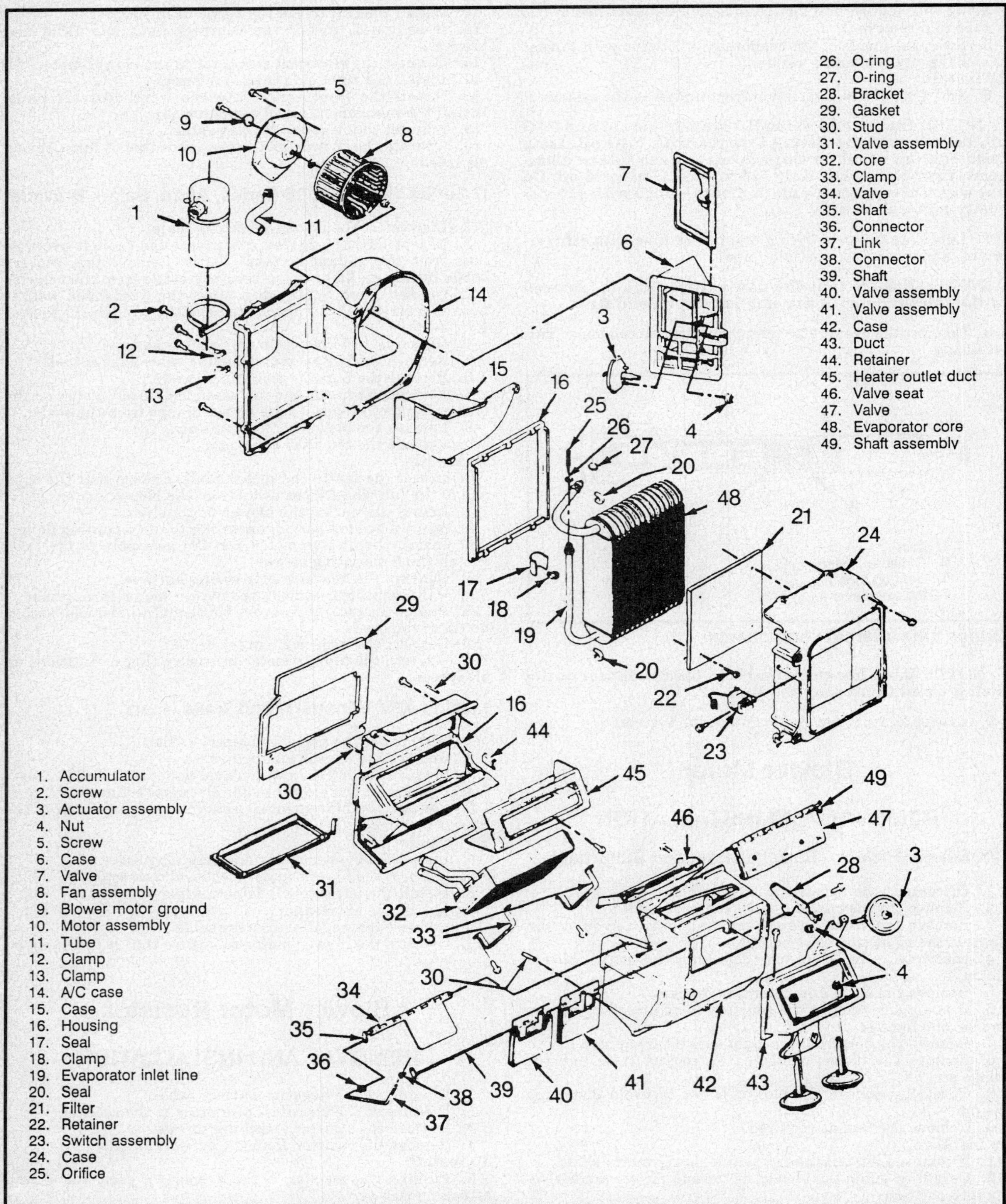

Evaporator and blower motor assembly exploded view — G Series Van

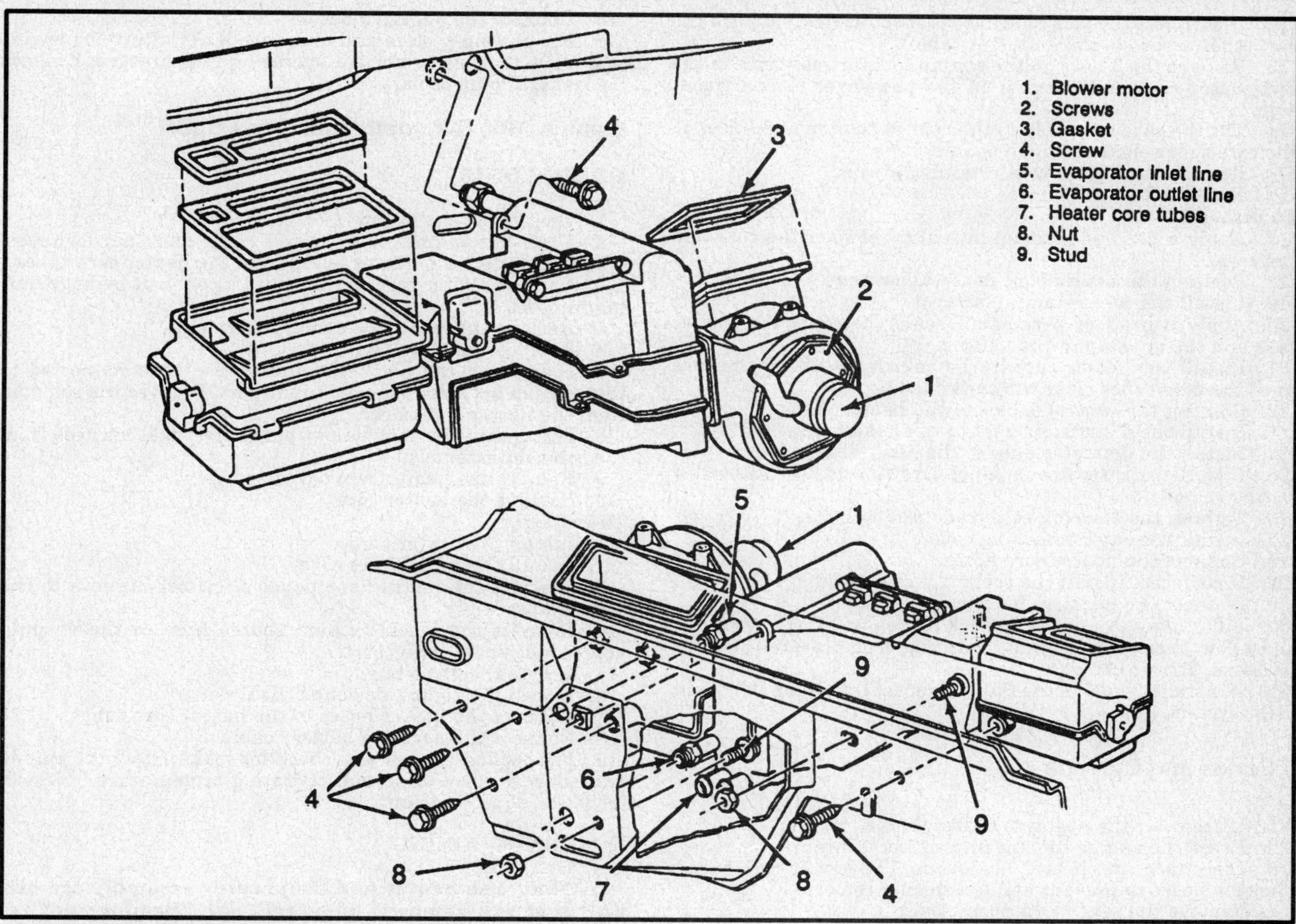

Evaporator/heater core case — C/K series

Heater Core

REMOVAL AND INSTALLATION

C/K Series (Pick-Up, Blazer, Jimmy and Suburban)

1. If installed, disable the Supplemental Inflatable Restraint (SIR) system.
2. Disconnect the negative battery cable. Properly drain the cooling system. Disconnect the heater hoses and remove the coolant reservoir.
3. Remove the instrument panel compartment.
4. Detach the electrical connectors from the blower and heater housing.
5. Remove the center floor air distribution duct and the ECM and mounting tray.
6. Remove the hinge pillar trim panels.
7. Remove the blower motor cover and the blower motor.
8. Remove the steering wheel.
9. Loosen and tilt back the instrument panel.
10. Remove the screws and nuts and remove the heater case from the vehicle.
11. Remove the screws from the heater core cover and lift out the core.
12. Installation is the reverse of the removal procedure. Be sure the heater seals are in place.
13. If installed, enable the Supplemental Inflatable Restraint (SIR) system.

G Series Van

1. If installed, disable the Supplemental Inflatable Restraint (SIR) system.
2. Disconnect the negative battery cable.
3. Drain the engine coolant into a clean container for reuse.
4. Remove the coolant recovery tank, as required.
5. Disconnect the heater hoses from the heater core tubes. Plug the tubes to prevent spillage during removal.
6. Remove the screws that hold the air distributor duct to the distributor case and the air distributor duct to the engine cover.
7. Remove the engine housing cover.
8. Loosen and raise the right side of the instrument panel to aid in removal of the heater case.
9. Lower the steering column.
10. Remove the screws attaching the defroster duct to the distributor case.
11. Remove the distributor to heater case screws.

12. Disconnect the control cables and set aside (fold back the carpet for access to the defroster cable).
13. Remove the 3 nuts on the engine compartment side of the distributor case and 1 screw on the passenger compartment side.
14. Tilt the case assembly to the rear at the top and lift until the core tubes clear the dash openings.
15. Remove the heater core retaining straps.
16. Remove the heater core.

To install:

17. Apply a bead of permagum sealer between the core and the case.
18. Position the heater core in the heater case.
19. Install the core retaining straps.
20. Apply a bead of permagum sealer between the heater case and the opening in the vehicle.
21. Install the heater case in the vehicle by tilting the case until the core tubes clear the cowl opening.
22. Connect the control cables to the heater case.
23. Install the distributor duct to the heater case.
24. Install the defroster duct to the heater case.
25. Install the instrument panel screws that were loosened during removal.
26. Tighten the steering column retaining bolts.
27. Install the engine housing cover.
28. Connect the heater core hoses.
29. If removed, install the coolant recovery tank.
30. Connect the negative battery cable.
31. Fill cooling system and check for leaks. Start the engine and allow to come to normal operating temperature. Recheck for leaks. Top-up coolant.
32. If installed, enable the Supplemental Inflatable Restraint (SIR) system.

S Series and Bravada

1. Disconnect the negative battery cable.
2. Drain the engine coolant into a clean container for reuse.
3. Disconnect the heater hoses from the heater core tubes. Plug the hoses to prevent spillage during removal.
4. Remove the rear heater core cover.
5. Remove the heater core brackets.
6. Remove the heater core.

To install:

7. Install the heater core.
8. Install the heater core brackets.
9. Install the rear heater core cover.
10. Connect the heater hoses to the heater core tubes.
11. Connect the negative battery cable.
12. Fill cooling system and check for leaks. Start the engine and allow to come to normal operating temperature. Recheck for leaks. Top-up coolant.

Astro and Safari

1. Disconnect the negative battery cable.
2. Drain the engine coolant into a clean container for reuse.
3. Disconnect the heater hoses from the heater core tubes.
4. Lower the filler panel from in front of the heater assembly.
5. Remove the lower air distributor duct and the defroster outlet duct.
6. Remove the heater case cover.
7. Remove the heater core and seals.

To install:

8. Install the heater core seals.
9. Install the heater core.
10. Install the heater core case cover.
11. Install the defroster outlet duct.
12. Install the lower air distributor duct.
13. Install the lower panel to the front of the heater assembly.
14. Connect the heater hoses to the heater core tubes.
15. Connect the negative battery cable.
16. Fill cooling system and check for leaks. Start the engine and allow to come to normal operating temperature. Recheck for leaks. Top-up coolant.

Lumina APV, Silhouette and Trans Sport

HEATER ONLY

1. Disconnect the negative battery cable.
2. Drain the engine coolant into a clean container for reuse.
3. Disconnect the heater hoses from the heater core tubes.
4. Cap the heater core tube fittings to prevent leakage during removal.
5. Remove the right side sound insulator.
6. Remove the glove box.
7. Disconnect the black vacuum source hose connected to the vacuum actuator solenoid input port. Remove the solenoid from the heater core cover.
8. Disconnect the instrument panel electrical harness from the solenoid assembly.
9. Remove the heater core cover.
10. Remove the heater core.

To install:

11. Install the heater core.
12. Install the heater core cover.
13. Connect the instrument panel electrical harness to the solenoid assembly.
14. Connect the black vacuum source hose to the vacuum actuator solenoid input port.
15. Install the glove box.
16. Install the right side sound insulator.
17. Connect the heater hoses to the heater core tubes.
18. Connect the negative battery cable.
19. Fill cooling system and check for leaks. Start the engine and allow to come to normal operating temperature. Recheck for leaks. Top-up coolant.

AIR CONDITIONING

NOTE: The heater and evaporator assembly are one unit and are removed together. See "Evaporator" removal information in this article.

Evaporator

REMOVAL AND INSTALLATION

C/K Series (Pick-Up, Blazer, Jimmy and Suburban)

1. If installed, disable the Supplemental Inflatable Restraint (SIR) system.
2. Disconnect the negative battery cable. Properly drain cooling system.
3. Properly discharge the air conditioning system using recovery type equipment.
4. Remove the instrument panel compartment.
5. Detach the electrical connectors on the evaporator housing.
6. Remove the center floor air distribution duct. Remove the ECM and its mounting tray.
7. Remove the hinge pillar trim panels.
8. Remove the blower motor cover and the blower motor.
9. Remove the steering column.
10. Loosen and tilt back the instrument panel assembly.
11. Remove the coolant recovery reservoir. Detach and plug the heater hoses from the tube connections at the firewall.
12. Properly detach the refrigerant line and the accumulator from the firewall connections to the evaporator. Plug all openings to minimize contamination. Discard the O-rings.

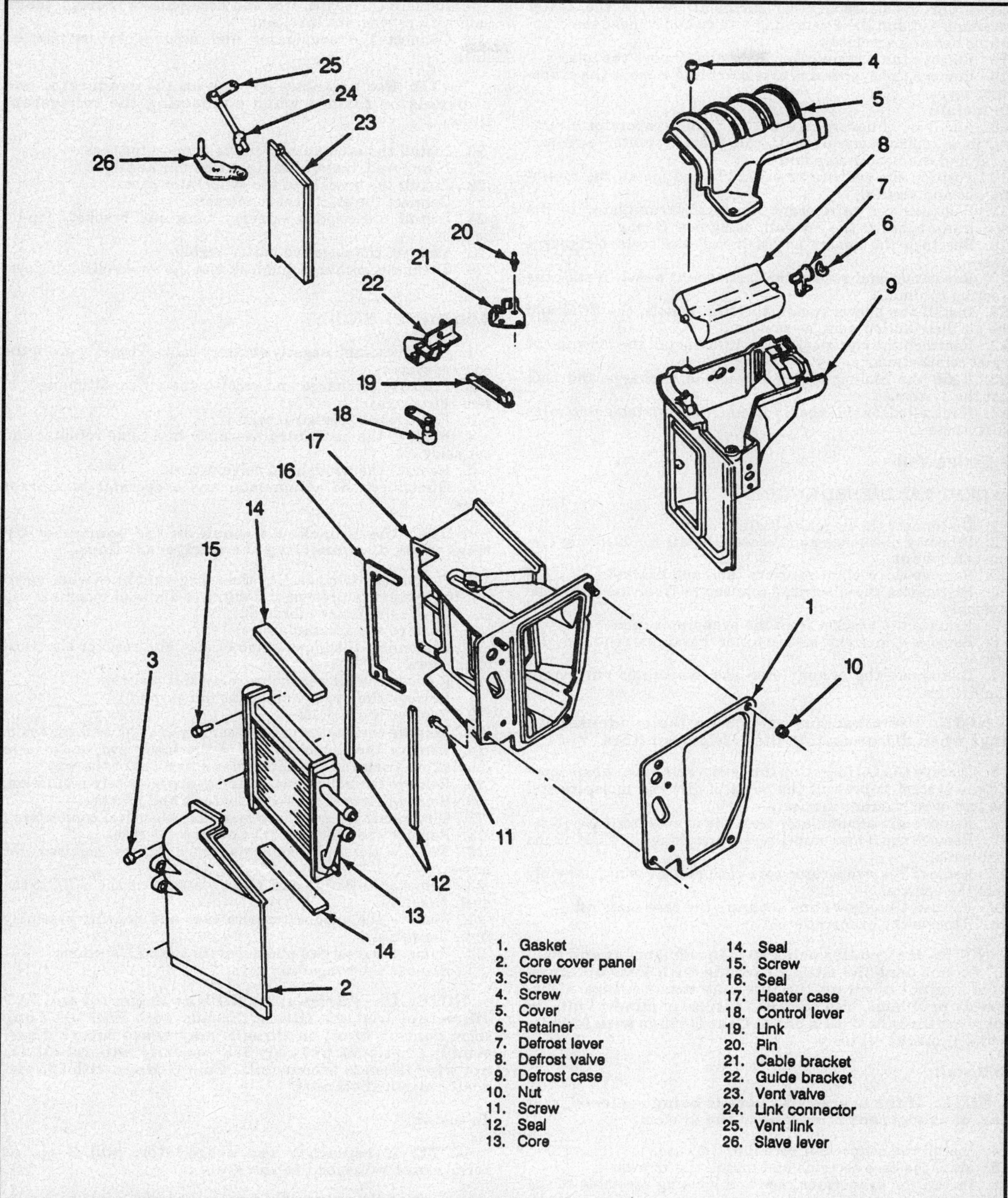

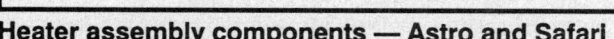

Heater assembly components — Astro and Safari

13. From the passenger compartment, remove the center retaining nut and the 6 retaining screws and remove the evaporator housing assembly.
14. Remove the bottom cover plate and remove the heater
15. Remove the evaporator case cover and remove the evaporator core.

To install:

16. Add 3 oz. of new refrigerant oil to the evaporator if putting in a replacement unit. Install the evaporator core and cover and the heater core and cover.
17. Position the evaporator assembly and install the retaining nut and screws.
18. Reattach the refrigerant line and accumulator to the evaporator tubes at the firewall, using new O-rings.
19. Reattach the heater hoses. Install the coolant recovery reservoir.
20. Reposition and secure the instrument panel. Install the steering column.
21. Install the blower motor, the trim panels, the ECM and the air distribution duct, as removed.
22. Reattach the electrical connectors. Install the instrument panel compartment.
23. Refill the cooling system. Evacuate, recharge and leak test the system.
24. If installed, enable the Supplemental Inflatable Restraint (SIR) system.

G Series Van

EXCEPT 6.2L DIESEL ENGINE

1. Disconnect the negative battery cable.
2. Properly discharge and recover the air conditioning system refrigerant.
3. Remove the coolant recovery tank and bracket.
4. Disconnect the electrical connectors from the core case assembly.
5. Remove the bracket from the evaporator case.
6. Remove the right side marker light, as required, for access.
7. Disconnect the accumulator and evaporator refrigerant line fittings.

NOTE: Use a backup wrench on the condenser fittings when disconnecting the refrigerant lines.

8. Discard the O-rings. Cap the refrigerant lines when opening the system to prevent the entry of dirt and moisture and the loss of refrigerant lubricant.
9. Remove the accumulator from the evaporator case.
10. Remove the 3 nuts and 1 screw attaching the ECM to the dash panel.
11. Remove the evaporator core case and housing assembly from the vehicle.
12. Remove the screws and separate the case sections.
13. Remove the evaporator core.

NOTE: On systems using R-134a refrigerant and PAG oil, do not coat the fitting threads with PAG oil. Long term contact of oil on threads may cause future disassembly problems. Use only 525 viscosity mineral oil. Do not wipe threads with a cloth. Coat O-rings with 525 viscosity mineral oil only.

To install:

NOTE: If the evaporator core is being replaced, add 3 oz. of refrigerant lubricant to the system.

14. Install the evaporator core into the case.
15. Mate the case sections and install the screws.
16. Install the evaporator case and housing assembly to the vehicle.
17. Position the ECM to the dash panel and install the 3 retaining nuts and 1 screw.
18. Replace the evaporator and accumulator O-rings. Lubricate with refrigerant lubricant.
19. Connect the evaporator and accumulator refrigerant lines.

NOTE: Use a backup wrench on the evaporator and accumulator fittings when connecting the refrigerant lines.

20. Install the accumulator to the evaporator case.
21. If removed, install the right side marker light.
22. Install the bracket to the evaporator case.
23. Connect the electrical connectors.
24. Install the coolant recovery tank and bracket. Top-up coolant.
25. Connect the negative battery cable.
26. Evacuate, recharge and leak test the air conditioning system.

6.2L DIESEL ENGINE

1. Disconnect the negative battery cable. Properly drain the cooling system.
2. Properly discharge and recover the air conditioning system refrigerant.
3. Remove the cold air intake.
4. Remove the hood latch assembly and cable retainer and set aside.
5. Remove the windshield solvent tank.
6. Disconnect the accumulator and evaporator refrigerant lines.

NOTE: Use a backup wrench on the condenser fittings when disconnecting the refrigerant lines.

7. Discard the O-rings. Cap the refrigerant lines when opening the system to prevent the entry of dirt and moisture and the loss of refrigerant lubricant.
8. Remove the accumulator.
9. Disconnect the blower motor relay and resistor electrical connectors.
10. Remove the blower motor relay and resistor.
11. Remove the upper half of the fan shroud.
12. Remove the radiator.
13. Remove the heater valve assembly bracket and set aside.
14. Remove the upper screws of the lower evaporator core insulation. Push the insulation down and out of the way.
15. Remove the blower motor and evaporator core insulation.
16. Remove the coolant recovery tank and bracket.
17. Disconnect the core case assembly electrical connectors.
18. Remove the bracket at the evaporator case.
19. Remove the right side marker light, as required, for access.
20. Remove the 3 nuts and 1 screw attaching the ECM to the dash panel.
21. Remove the evaporator core case and housing assembly from the vehicle.
22. Remove the screws and separate the case sections.
23. Remove the evaporator core.

NOTE: On systems using R-134a refrigerant and PAG oil, do not coat the fitting threads with PAG oil. Long term contact of oil on threads may cause future disassembly problems. Use only 525 viscosity mineral oil. Do not wipe threads with a cloth. Coat O-rings with 525 viscosity mineral oil only.

To install:

NOTE: If replacing the evaporator, add 3 oz. of refrigerant lubricant to the system.

24. Position the evaporator core in the case.
25. Mate the case sections and install the retaining screws.
26. Install the core case and housing assembly in the vehicle.

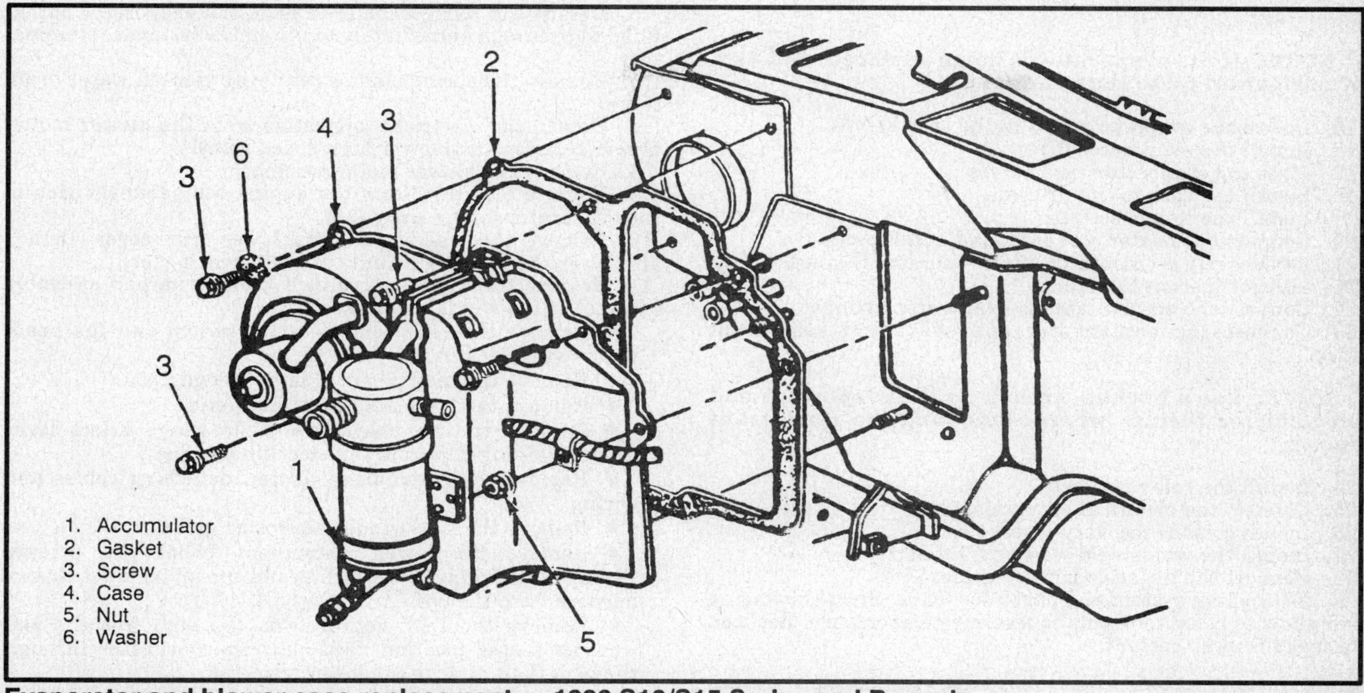

Evaporator and blower case replacement — 1993 S10/S15 Series and Bravada

27. Install the ECM to the dash panel using the 3 nuts and 1 screw.
28. Replace the evaporator inlet line O-rings. Lubricate with refrigerant lubricant.
29. Connect the evaporator inlet line.

NOTE: Use a backup wrench on the evaporator fittings when connecting the refrigerant lines.

30. Install the right side marker light.
31. Install the bracket to the evaporator case.
32. Connect the core case assembly electrical connectors.
33. Install the recovery tank and bracket.
34. Install the blower motor and evaporator core insulation.
35. Raise the lower evaporator insulation into position and install the upper screws.
36. Install the heater valve assembly bracket.
37. Install the radiator.
38. Install the upper half of the fan shroud.
39. Install the blower motor relay and resistor. Connect the blower motor relay and resistor electrical connectors.
40. Install the accumulator.
41. Replace the accumulator O-rings. Lubricate with refrigerant lubricant.
42. Connect the accumulator refrigerant line.

NOTE: Use a backup wrench on the accumulator fittings when connecting the refrigerant lines.

43. Install the windshield solvent tank.
44. Install the hood latch assembly and cable retainer.
45.Install the cold air intake.
45. Connect the negative battery cable. Refill the cooling system.
46. Evacuate, recharge and leak test the air conditioning system.

S10/S15 Series and Bravada

1. Disconnect the negative battery cable. Properly discharge the air conditioning system. Drain the cooling system.
2. Detach and plug the heater hoses from the heater core.
3. Remove the blower resistor with the wiring attached. On Bravada, detach electrical connectors, leaving resistor in place.
4. Detach all other electrical connections from the evaporator housing.
5. Disconnect the refrigerant line from the evaporator tube. Disconnect the discharge hose from the accumulator. Plug all openings to minimize contamination.
6. Remove the retaining screws and nuts from the firewall studs and remove the blower and evaporator assembly.
7. Remove the accumulator.
8. Remove the retaining screws and separate the evaporator case halves. Remove the evaporator core.
9. Installation is the reverse of the removal procedure. Add 3.0 oz. of new refrigerant oil to the evaporator if replacing the core. Evacuate, recharge and leak test the system.

Astro and Safari

1. Disconnect the negative battery cable.
2. Properly discharge and recover the air conditioning system refrigerant.
3. Drain the engine coolant into a clean container for reuse.
4. Remove coolant recovery reservoir.
5. Remove the windshield washer fluid bottle.
6. Disconnect the electrical connectors.
7. Disconnect the heater hoses from the heater core tubes. Cap the heater core tubes to prevent leakage during removal.
8. Disconnect the refrigerant lines from the evaporator and accumulator or disconnect the accumulator from the evaporator tube.

NOTE: Use a backup wrench on the evaporator and accumulator fittings when disconnecting the refrigerant lines.

9. Discard the O-rings. Cap the refrigerant lines when opening the system to prevent the entry of dirt and moisture and the loss of refrigerant lubricant.
10. Remove the relay bracket.
11. Remove the case flange nuts.
12. Remove the blower case. Separate the case halves.
13. Remove the filter.
14. Remove the evaporator core.

To install:

NOTE: If the evaporator is being replaced, add 3 oz. of refrigerant oil to the system.

15. Install the evaporator core in the case halves.
16. Install the evaporator filter.
17. Mate the evaporator case halves.
18. Install the case to the firewall.
19. Install the flange screws.
20. Connect the heater core inlet and outlet pipes.
21. Replace the accumulator and evaporator O-rings. Lubricate with refrigerant lubricant.
22. Connect the accumulator-to-evaporator fittings.
23. Connect the accumulator and evaporator refrigerant lines.

NOTE: Use a backup wrench on the evaporator and accumulator fittings when connecting the refrigerant lines.

24. Install the relay bracket.
25. Connect the electrical connections.
26. Install coolant recovery reservoir.
27. Install the windshield washer fluid bottle.
28. Connect the negative battery cable.
29. Fill cooling system and check for leaks. Start the engine and allow to come to normal operating temperature. Recheck for leaks. Top-up coolant.

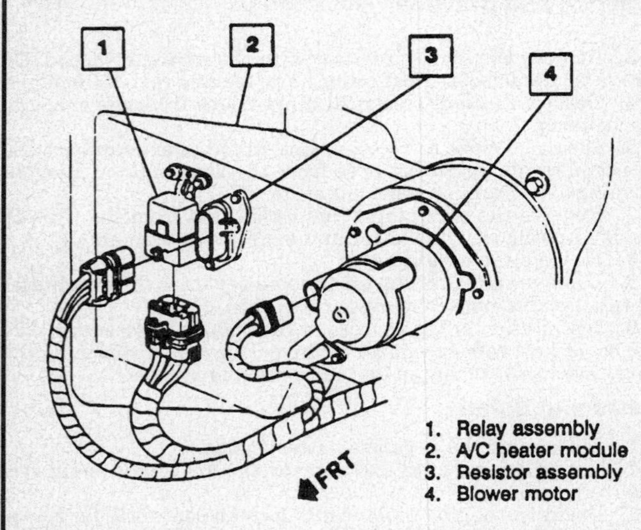

Blower motor, relay and resistor locations—Lumina APV, Silhouette and Trans Sport

30. Evacuate, recharge and leak test the air conditioning system.

Lumina APV, Silhouette and Trans Sport

1. If installed, disable the Supplemental Inflatable Restraint (SIR) system.
2. Disconnect the negative battery cable. Properly discharge the air conditioning system using recovery type equipment.
3. Properly drain the cooling system. Disconnect the heater hoses from the firewall.
4. Blow compressed air through the heater core nipples to remove remaining coolant from the heater and prevent leakage on removal.
5. Detach the refrigerant lines from the evaporator outlet. Plug all openings immediately to minimize system contamination.
6. Remove the spring clamps retaining plenum water drain tubes.
7. Detach the electrical connectors from the blower motor, blower resistor and blower high speed relay.
8. Remove the blower motor assembly.
9. Remove 5 screws from the engine compartment side of the evaporator-heater assembly.
10. Remove the steering column lower trim cover. Detach and lower the steering column to the driver's seat.
11. Remove the upper instrument panel trim pad assembly (nearest to the windshield) as follows:
    - Remove the rear window wiper switch and the headlight switch.
    - Remove the instrument cluster housing.
    - Remove the left sound insulator panel.
    - Remove the automatic transaxle range select lever cable retaining clip from the steering column.
    - Remove the instrument cluster, detaching cables and wiring.
    - Remove the side window defroster grilles.
    - Remove the lower instrument panel pad screws. Remove the switch harness clips and the instrument cluster harness from the pad.
    - Remove the DRL sensor from the pad, free the pad from its seated position, feed electrical harnesses through the pad, then remove the lower trim pad.
    - Remove the defroster vent grilles from the upper trim panel.
    - Remove the screws and take out the upper instrument trim panel.
12. Remove the front seat.
13. Remove the instrument panel harness connector from all components.
14. Remove the right sound insulator panel.
15. Remove the glove box and remaining instrument panel components and trim pieces.
16. Detach the black source vacuum line to the actuator electric solenoid assembly.
17. Remove the heater-A/C retaining screws at the dash panel. Remove the assembly.

To install:

18. Position and secure the heater-A/C assembly to the dash panel. Connect the vacuum hose.
19. Install the instrument panel and glove box in reverse of the removal procedure.
20. Install the front seat.
21. Install the 5 screws for the heater-A/C assembly from the engine compartment side.
22. Reattach the electrical connections. Install the condensation drain tubes.
23. Reconnect the refrigerant lines to the evaporator tubes, using new O-rings.

NOTE: On systems using R-134a refrigerant and PAG oil, do not coat the fitting threads with PAG oil. Long term contact of oil on threads may cause future disassembly problems. Use only 525 viscosity mineral oil. Do not wipe threads with a cloth. Coat O-rings with 525 viscosity mineral oil only.

24. Connect the heater hoses. Refill the cooling system.

NOTE: Add 3.0 oz. of new refrigerant oil if the evaporator core was replaced.

25. Connect the negative battery cable. Evacuate, recharge and leak test the system.
26. If installed, enable the Supplemental Inflatable Restraint (SIR) system.

Refrigerant Lines

REMOVAL AND INSTALLATION

1. Disconnect the negative battery cable.
2. Properly discharge and recover the air conditioning system refrigerant.
3. Disconnect the refrigerant line connectors, using a backup wrench as required.
4. Remove refrigerant line support or routing brackets, as required.
5. Remove refrigerant line.

To install:

6. Position new refrigerant line in place, leaving protective caps installed until ready to connect.

NOTE: On systems using R-134a refrigerant and PAG oil, do not coat the fitting threads with PAG oil. Long term contact of oil on threads may cause future disassembly problems. Use only 525 viscosity mineral oil. Do not wipe threads with a cloth. Coat O-rings with 525 viscosity mineral oil only.

7. Install new O-rings on refrigerant line connector fittings. Lubricate with refrigerant oil.
8. Connect refrigerant line, using a backup wrench, as required.
9. Install refrigerant line support or routing brackets, as required.
10. Evacuate, recharge and leak test the system.
11. Connect the negative battery cable.

Manual Control Head

REMOVAL AND INSTALLATION

1. Disconnect the negative battery cable.
2. Remove the instrument panel bezel or fascia.
3. Remove the control assembly mounting screws.
4. Pull the control assembly out far enough to reach the cables and electrical connectors.
5. Disconnect the control cables.
6. Disconnect the electrical connectors.
7. If equipped, disconnect the vacuum harness.
8. Remove the blower switch, as required.
9. Remove the control assembly.

To install:

10. Install the control assembly.
11. If removed, install the blower switch.
12. If equipped, connect the vacuum harness.
13. Connect the electrical connectors.
14. Connect the control cables.
15. Place the control assembly into position and install the mounting screws.
16. Install the instrument panel bezel or fascia.
17. Connect the negative battery cable.

Manual Control Cables

ADJUSTMENT

S10/S15 Series

1. Remove the retainer from the lever.
2. Remove the cable.
3. Bend the cable to lengthen or shorten.
4. Reattach the cable to the lever and move the control lever in the full range of its travel and listen for the door opening and closing. Readjust the cable, as necessary.
5. Install the retainer.

G Series

1. Remove the glove box.
2. Loosen the cable attaching screws at the defroster duct assembly (make sure the cable is installed in the bracket on the defroster duct assembly).
3. Place the temperature lever in full **HOT** position and hold while tightening the cable attaching screw.
4. Quickly move the temperature lever back and forth to each end of its travel. The adjusting tab should self-adjust and the door should be heard hitting its stops.
5. Install the glove box.

REMOVAL AND INSTALLATION

1. Remove the trim panels or bezels.
2. Remove the control assembly and pull out far enough to disconnect the control cable.
3. Remove the retainer at the actuator lever and remove the cable from the actuator lever.
4. Remove the routing and mounting brackets or loosen enough to slide the cable through.
5. Remove the cable.

To install:

6. Feed the cable through the brackets and into position.
7. Attach the cable at both ends and install the retainers.
8. Check cable adjustment.

Electronic Control Head

REMOVAL AND INSTALLATION

C/K Series (All) with A/C

1. Disconnect the negative battery cable.
2. Remove the instrument panel bezel from around the control panel.
3. Remove the 2 screws, pull the control assembly out and detach the electrical connectors, and remove the control assembly.
4. To install, reverse the removal procedure.

Lumina APV, Silhouette and Trans Sport

1993 MODELS

1. Disconnect the negative battery cable.
2. Remove 2 screws holding the steering column opening filler panel in place. Detach the retaining clips.
3. Open the glove box door. Remove 8 screws retaining the instrument panel lower extension housing and position the housing away from the instrument panel.
4. Remove the courtesy lamp assembly from the housing and position the housing out of the way.
5. Remove 2 screws holding the control panel to the instrument panel. Pull the assembly out and detach the electrical connectors.
6. Installation is the reverse of the removal procedure.

1994–95 MODELS

1. Disconnect the negative battery cable.
2. Remove the instrument panel lower extension housing.
3. Remove the control assembly retaining screws.
4. Pull the control assembly out and away from the instrument panel lower trim pad and detach the wiring harness connectors.
5. Remove the control assembly from the vehicle.
6. Installation is the reverse of the removal procedure.

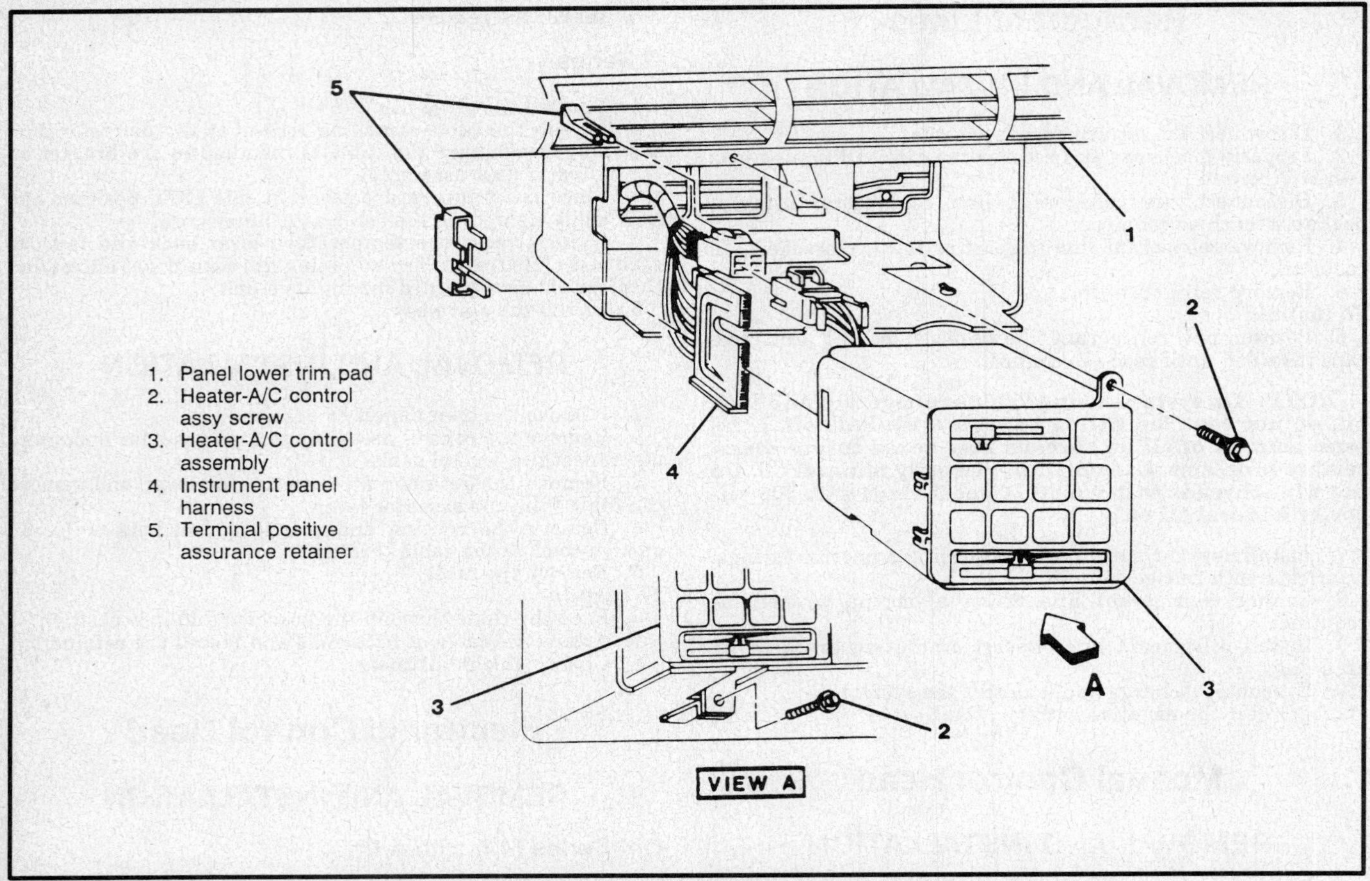

Heater and air conditioner control assembly—Lumina APV, Silhouette and Trans Sport

SENSORS AND SWITCHES

Vacuum Actuators

OPERATION

Used on certain heating and air conditioning systems, the vacuum actuators operate the air doors determining the different modes. The actuator consists of a spring loaded diaphragm connected to a lever. When vacuum is applied to the diaphragm, the lever moves the control door to its appropriate position. When the lever on the control panel is moved to another position, vacuum is cut off and the spring returns the actuator lever to its normal position.

TESTING

1. Disconnect the vacuum line from the actuator.
2. Attach a hand-held vacuum pump to the actuator.
3. Apply vacuum to the actuator.
4. The actuator lever should move to its engaged position and remain there while vacuum is applied.
5. When vacuum is released it should move back to its normal position.
6. The lever should operate smoothly and not bind.

REMOVAL AND INSTALLATION

1. If installed, disable the Supplemental Inflatable Restraint (SIR) system.
2. Disconnect the negative battery cable.
3. On Lumina APV, Silhouette and Trans Sport, remove the right and/or left insulator panel to access the actuators, and for the temperature actuator, removal of the upper trim pad is required.
4. On C/K Series, instrument panel compartment removal is required for access to the temperature/defrost actuator and the mode actuator.
5. On Astro and Safari, remove the engine coolant, heater hoses, engine cover, vacuum connectors, heater core, and heater assembly to access the air inlet valve vacuum actuators; and for the mode valve vacuum actuator, removal of the right floor air outlet is required.
6. On Bravada, remove the windshield wiper arms and cowl vent grille to access the air inlet valve assembly; and for the plenum side vent actuator, re-moval of the front door sill plate and cowl side vent cover is required.
7. On S/T Series, remove the instrument panel to access the temperature valve actuator and the center outlet duct and defroster valve actuator.
8. Remove the vacuum/electrical connectors from the actuator.
9. Disconnect the linkage from the actuator.

10. Remove the hardware attaching the actuator.
11. Remove the actuator.

To install:

12. Install the actuator and attaching hardware.
13. Connect the linkage to the actuator.
14. Connect the vacuum/electrical connectors to the actuator.
15. Test system to confirm proper functioning of the actuator.
16. If installed, enable the Supplemental Inflatable Restraint (SIR) system.

Coolant Temperature Sensor

OPERATION

The coolant temperature sensor provides an engine temperature signal to the ECM. The ECM controls the operation of the electric cooling fans, if equipped, and in cases of high engine temperature, de-energizes the compressor clutch. The coolant temperature sensor is located in the front of the engine, usually mounted on or near the thermostat housing.

REMOVAL AND INSTALLATION

1. Disconnect the negative battery cable.
2. Drain the cooling system into a clean container for reuse.
3. Disconnect the electrical connector from the coolant temperature sensor.
4. Remove the coolant temperature sensor.

To install:

5. Install the coolant temperature sensor.
6. Connect the electrical connector.
7. Fill the cooling system.
8. Connect the negative battery cable.
9. Start the engine and check for leaks.

High-Pressure Compressor Cut-Off Switch

OPERATION

Used on all models, the function of the switch is to protect the compressor in the event of excessively high compressor head pressure and to de-energize the compressor clutch before the high pressure relief valve discharge pressure is reached. The high-pressure switch is mounted on the back of the compressor on a Schrader-type valve and does not require discharging the system to be serviced.

REMOVAL AND INSTALLATION

1. Disconnect the negative battery cable.
2. Disconnect the electrical connector.
3. Remove the switch from the coupled hose assembly. Discard the O-ring.

To install:

4. Lubricate a new O-ring with refrigerant oil.
5. Install the O-ring on the switch and install the switch.
6. Connect the electrical connector.
7. Connect the negative battery cable.

Low-Pressure Compressor Cut-Off Switch

OPERATION

S/T Series, Lumina APV, Silhouette and Trans Sport

The function of the switch is to de-energize the compressor in the event of a low-charge condition. The switch also prevents the compressor from running in excessively cold weather. The switch is mounted at the back of the compressor. Servicing the valve requires discharging the system.

REMOVAL AND INSTALLATION

1. Disconnect the negative battery cable.
2. Properly discharge and recover the air conditioning system refrigerant.
3. Disconnect the electrical connector(s).
4. Remove the switch. Discard the O-ring.

To install:

5. Replace the O-ring. Lubricate the new O-ring with refrigerant oil.
6. Install the switch.
7. Connect the electrical connector(s).
8. Evacuate, charge and leak test the system.
9. Connect the negative battery cable.

Pressure Cycling Switch

OPERATION

The pressure cycling switch controls the refrigeration cycle by sensing low-side pressure as an indicator of evaporator temperature. The pressure cycling switch is the freeze-protection device in the system and senses refrigerant pressure on the suction side. The pressure cycling switch is not used with V-5 compressors since Variable Displacement Orifice Tube (VDOT) system does not cycle.

REMOVAL AND INSTALLATION

NOTE: The switch is mounted on a Schrader valve on the accumulator. The system need not be discharged to remove the pressure cycling switch.

1. Disconnect the negative battery cable.
2. Disconnect the electrical connector.
3. Remove the switch and O-ring seal. Discard the O-ring.

To install:

4. Install a new O-ring. Lubricate with refrigerant oil.
5. Install the switch to the accumulator.
6. Connect the electrical connector.
7. Connect the negative battery cable.

REAR AUXILIARY SYSTEM

Expansion Valve

REMOVAL AND INSTALLATION

G Series Van

1. Disconnect the negative battery cable.
2. Properly discharge and recover the air conditioning system refrigerant.
3. Remove the rear duct work.
4. Disconnect the blower motor harness connector.
5. Disconnect the ground wire.

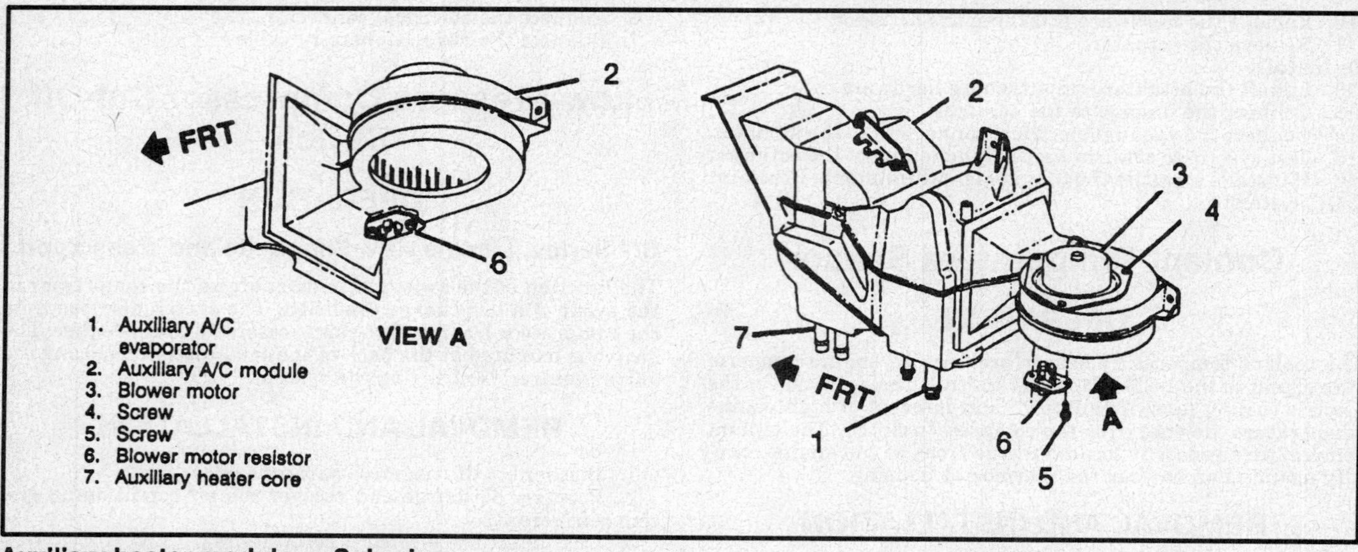

Auxiliary heater module — Suburban

NOTE: Support the lower case and motor assemblies.

6. Remove the lower-to-upper blower and evaporator case screws.
7. Lower the case with the motor assembly.
8. Remove the expansion valve sensing bulb clamps.
9. Disconnect the expansion valve refrigerant lines.

NOTE: Use a backup wrench on the expansion valve fittings when disconnecting the refrigerant lines.

10. Discard the O-rings.

NOTE: Cap the refrigerant lines when opening the system to prevent the entry of dirt and moisture and the loss of refrigerant lubricant.

11. Remove the expansion valve assembly.

To install:

12. Place the expansion valve in position.

NOTE: On systems using R-134a refrigerant and PAG oil, do not coat the fitting threads with PAG oil. Long term contact of oil on threads may cause future disassembly problems. Use only 525 viscosity mineral oil. Do not wipe threads with a cloth. Coat O-rings with 525 viscosity mineral oil only.

13. Replace the expansion valve O-rings. Lubricate with refrigerant lubricant.
14. Connect the expansion valve refrigerant lines.

NOTE: Use a backup wrench on the expansion valve fittings when connecting the refrigerant lines.

15. Attach the expansion valve sensing bulb and install the clamps.
16. Raise the lower case and blower motor assembly. Install the lower case-to-upper case screws.
17. Connect the blower motor electrical connector.
18. Connect the ground wire.
19. Install the rear duct.
20. Connect the negative battery cable.
21. Evacuate, recharge and leak test the air conditioning system.

Lumina APV, Silhouette, Trans Sport

1. Disconnect the negative battery cable.
2. Remove the rear evaporator and blower assembly.
3. Remove the rear heater hoses.
4. Remove the lower outlet sealing plate from the heater core cover. Remove the screws holding the heater core cover in place. Remove the heater core cover.
5. Remove the heater core bracket, pipe strap and heater core from the module.
6. Remove the expansion valve cover. Remove the evaporator core case half screws.
7. Remove the beltline duct sealing gasket. Remove the evaporator core case half.
8. Remove the capillary tube retaining clip, detach the expansion valve fittings and remove the expansion valve.
9. Installation is the reverse of the removal procedure. Refill the cooling system. Evacuate, recharge and leak test the air conditioning system.

NOTE: On systems using R-134a refrigerant and PAG oil, do not coat fitting threads with PAG oil. Long term contact of this oil on threads may cause future disassembly problems. Use only 525 viscosity mineral oil. Do not wipe threads with a cloth. Coat O-rings with 525 viscosity mineral oil only.

Evaporator Tube

REMOVAL AND INSTALLATION

Suburban

1. Disconnect the negative battery cable.
2. Properly discharge and recover the air conditioning system refrigerant.
3. Remove the duct work.
4. Disconnect the evaporator tube refrigerant lines.

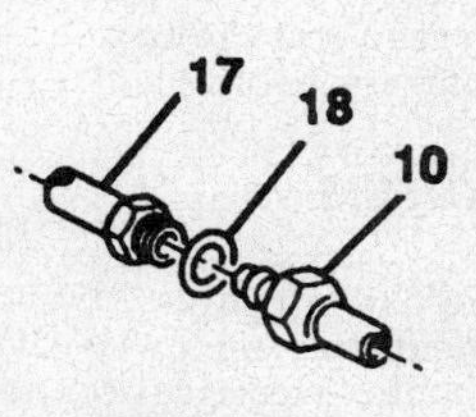

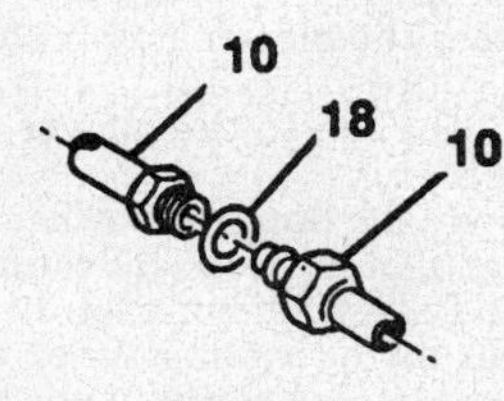

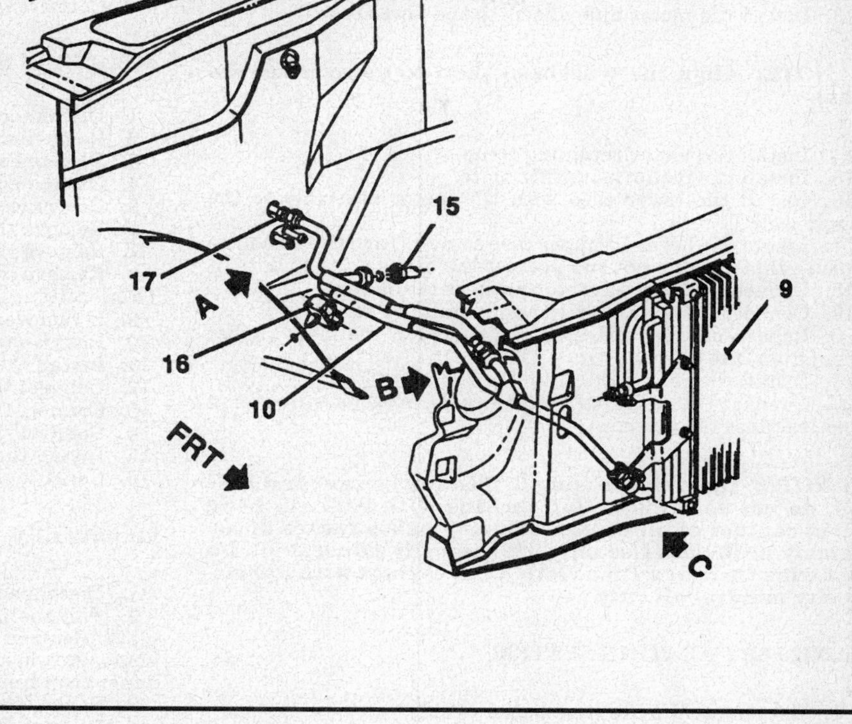

9. CONDENSER, A/C
10. TUBE, A/C EVAPORATOR
15. HOSE, AUX. A/C EVAPORATOR
16. CLIP, A/C EVAPORATOR TUBE
17. EVAPORATOR, A/C
18. O-RING

Auxiliary evaporator tube — Suburban

NOTE: Use a backup wrench on the evaporator tube fittings when disconnecting the refrigerant lines.

5. Discard the O-rings.

NOTE: Cap the refrigerant lines when opening the system to prevent the entry of dirt and moisture and the loss of refrigerant lubricant.

6. Remove the evaporator tube

To install:

7. Place the evaporator tube in position.

NOTE: On systems using R-134a refrigerant and PAG oil, do not coat the fitting threads with PAG oil. Long term contact of oil on threads may cause future disassembly problems. Use only 525 viscosity mineral oil. Do not wipe threads with a cloth. Coat O-rings with 525 viscosity mineral oil only.

8. Replace the evaporator tube O-rings. Lubricate with refrigerant lubricant.
9. Connect the evaporator tube refrigerant lines.

NOTE: Use a backup wrench on the evaporator tube fittings when connecting the refrigerant lines.

10. Install the duct work.
11. Connect the negative battery cable.
12. Evacuate, recharge and leak test the air conditioning system.

Blower Motor

REMOVAL AND INSTALLATION

Suburban

1. Disconnect the negative battery cable.
2. Remove the right rear quarter trim panel cover.
3. Detach the electrical connectors, remove the retaining screws and remove the blower motor assembly.
4. Installation is the reverse of the removal procedure.

G Series Van

AUXILIARY AIR CONDITIONING SYSTEM

1. Disconnect the negative battery cable. Discharge the air conditioning system using recovery type equipment.
2. Remove the rear duct work.
3. Place the refrigerant lines aside. Pull back the foam rubber insulation on the high pressure line before moving.
4. Remove the ground wire screw and disconnect the ground wire.
5. Disconnect the blower motor electrical connector.

NOTE: Support the lower case of the auxiliary air conditioning system.

6. Remove the lower-to-upper evaporator-blower case screws.
7. Lower the case with the motor assembly.
8. Remove the motor mounting plate.
9. Remove the motor retaining strap.
10. Remove the motor and wheels.
11. Remove the wheels from the blower motor shaft, as required.

To install:

12. If removed, install the wheels on the blower motor shaft. Install the tension springs on the wheel hubs.
13. Install the motor and wheels to the lower case.

NOTE: Align the wheels so they do not contact the case.

14. Install the motor retaining strap.
15. Install the motor mounting plate.
16. Install the lower case with the motor assembly to the upper case.
17. Install the lower-to-upper case screws. Turn the wheels to ensure that they do not rub against the case.
18. Connect the blower motor harness connector.
19. Connect the ground wire and install the screw.
20. Reposition the refrigerant hoses. Push the foam rubber insulation into place.
21. Install the rear duct.
22. Connect the negative battery cable. Evacuate, recharge and leak test the system.

NOTE: On systems using R-134a refrigerant and PAG oil, do not coat the fitting threads with PAG oil. Long term contact of oil on threads may cause future disassembly problems. Use only 525 viscosity mineral oil. Do not wipe threads with a cloth. Coat O-rings with 525 viscosity mineral oil only.

AUXILIARY HEATING SYSTEM

1. Disconnect the negative battery cable.
2. Remove the cover. Disconnect the blower motor wiring harness.
3. Remove the blower motor retaining clamp.
4. Remove the fan motor support.
5. Remove the fan assembly from the case.
6. Remove the fan blade retaining nut and fan blade from the motor, as required.

To install:

7. If removed, install the fan blade onto the motor shaft and install the fan blade retaining nut.
8. Install the motor in the case. Apply a bead of sealer to the motor flange.
9. Install the motor support.
10. Install the lower motor retaining clamp.
11. Connect the blower motor wiring harness.
12. Install the cover.
13. Connect the negative battery cable.

Astro and Safari

AUXILIARY AIR CONDITIONING SYSTEM

1. Disconnect the negative battery cable.
2. If equipped, remove the storage box at the left side pillar, near the rear door.
3. Remove the auxiliary air conditioning system evaporator-blower cover.
4. Disconnect the blower motor electrical connections.
5. Remove the cooling tube.
6. Remove the blower motor flange screws.
7. Remove the blower motor.

To install:

8. Install the blower motor.
9. Install the blower motor flange screws.
10. Connect the blower motor electrical connector.
11. Connect the blower motor cooling tube.
12. Install the auxiliary air conditioning system evaporator-blower cover.
13. If equipped, install the rear storage box.
14. Connect the negative battery cable.

AUXILIARY HEATING SYSTEM

1. Disconnect the negative battery cable.
2. Remove the auxiliary heater core-blower cover.
3. Disconnect the blower motor electrical connector.
4. Disconnect the ground terminal connector.
5. Disconnect the blower motor cooling tube.
6. Remove the blower motor flange screws.
7. Remove the blower motor.
8. Remove the fan from the blower motor shaft, as required.

To install:

9. If removed, install the fan to the blower motor shaft.
10. Install the blower motor.
11. Install the blower motor flange screws.
12. Connect the blower motor electrical connector.
13. Connect the ground terminal connector.
14. Connect the blower motor cooling tube.
15. Install the auxiliary heater core-blower cover.
16. Connect the negative battery cable.

Lumina APV, Silhouette and Trans Sport

1. Disconnect negative battery cable.
2. Pull the driver's seat fully forward. Remove the left sill plate. Remove the second row seating, anchor plates by the heater-A/C module, shoulder belt guide bolts and the quarter upper trim finish panel.
3. Remove the rear wheelhouse trim finish panel.
4. Remove the body lock trim finish panel and the screws for the quarter lower/center pillar panel.
5. Remove the rear module fan switch assembly. Remove the quarter lower/center pillar panel.
6. Route the shoulder belt from the center pillar panel. Remove the screws holding the beltline and B-pillar ducts. Remove the beltline duct.
7. Remove the screws holding the auxiliary module. Detach the electrical connector from the blower motor and remove the cooling hose.
8. Remove the motor and fan assembly from the module.
9. Installation is the reverse of the removal procedure.

Blower Motor Resistor

REMOVAL AND INSTALLATION

G Series

The blower resistor for the rear blower is mounted on the front blower-evaporator housing.

1. Disconnect the negative battery cable.
2. Disconnect the electrical connector at the resistor.
3. Remove the resistor attaching screws.
4. Remove the resistor from the evaporator case.

To install:

5. Position the resistor in the evaporator case. Install the attaching screws.
6. Connect the electrical connector.
7. Connect the negative battery cable.

Astro and Safari

1. Disconnect the negative battery cable.
2. Remove the side cover to expose the blower motor assembly.

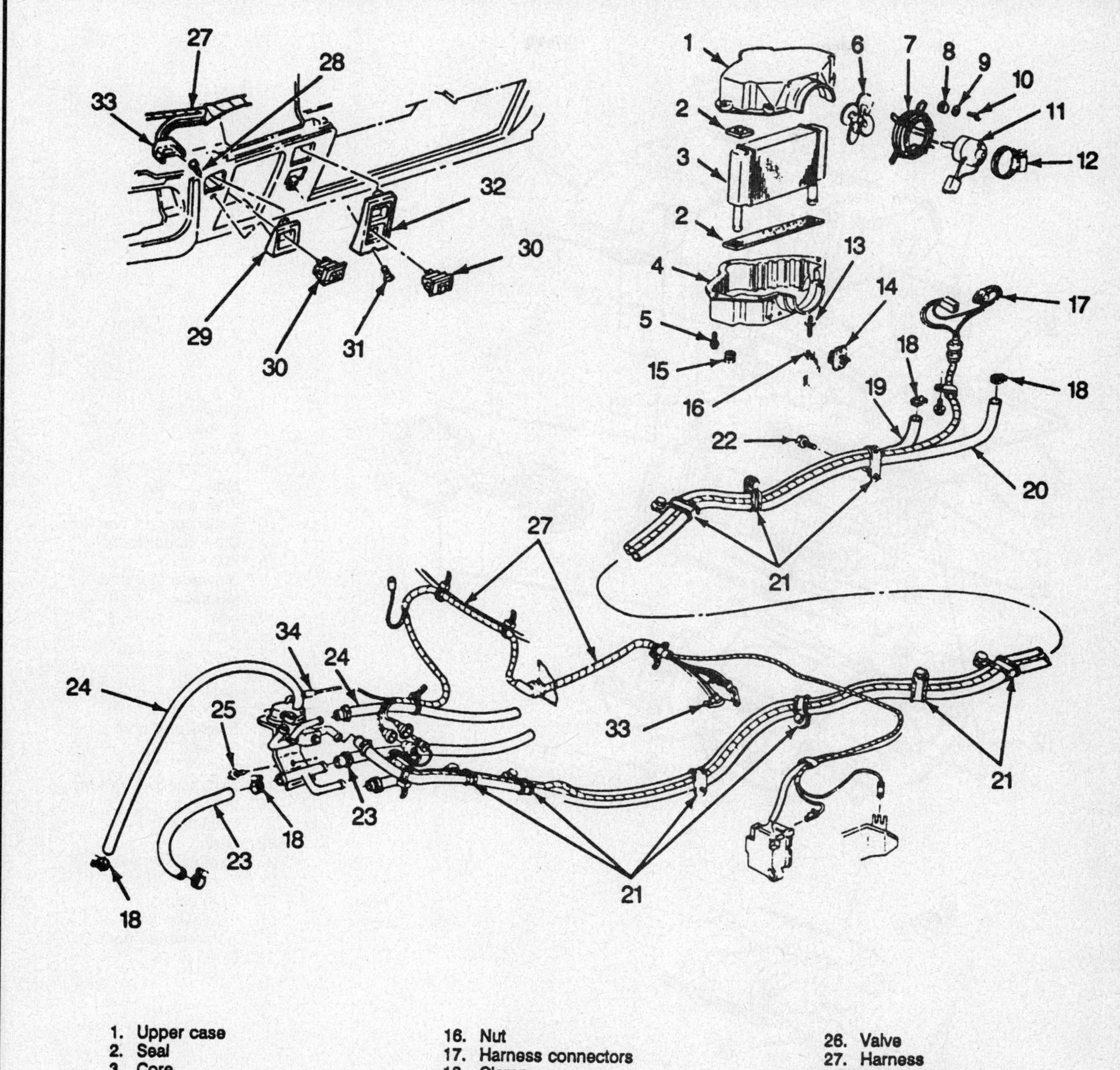

1. Upper case
2. Seal
3. Core
4. Lower case
5. Screw
6. Fan
7. Support
8. Grommet
9. Washer
10. Screw
11. Motor
12. Clamp
13. Stud
14. Resistor
15. Seal
16. Nut
17. Harness connectors
18. Clamp
19. Auxiliary heater inlet rear hose
20. Auxiliary heater outlet rear hose
21. Clip
22. Screw
23. Water heater outlet hose
24. Water heater inlet hose
25. Screw
26. Valve
27. Harness
28. Screw
29. Auxiliary heater switch (single function) bezel
30. Auxiliary heater control switch
31. Screw
32. Auxiliary heater/rear air conditioning control switch (dual function)
33. Connector
34. Vacuum line

Auxiliary heating system — 1993 Suburban

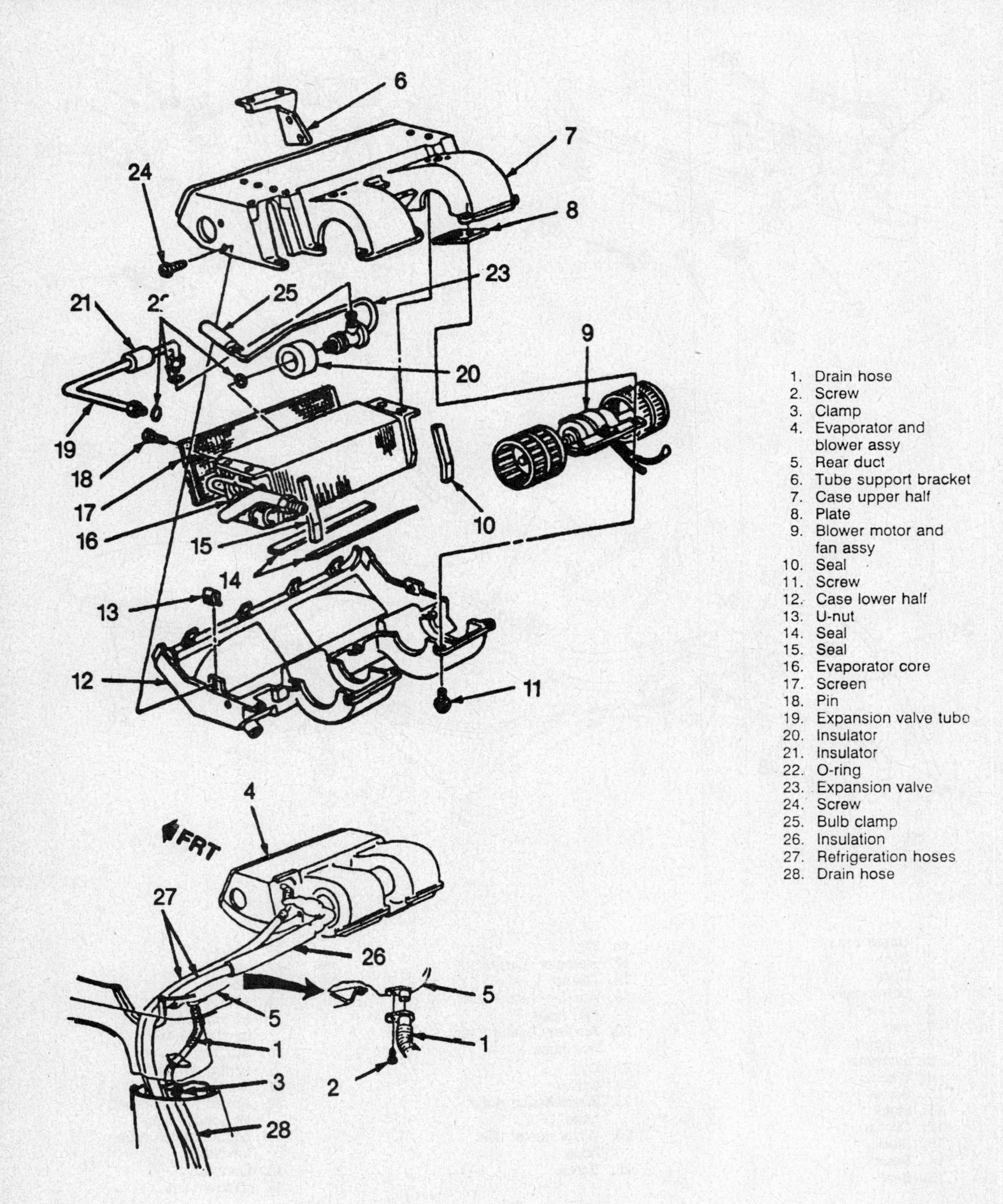

Auxiliary interior roof mounted evaporator and blower — G Series Van

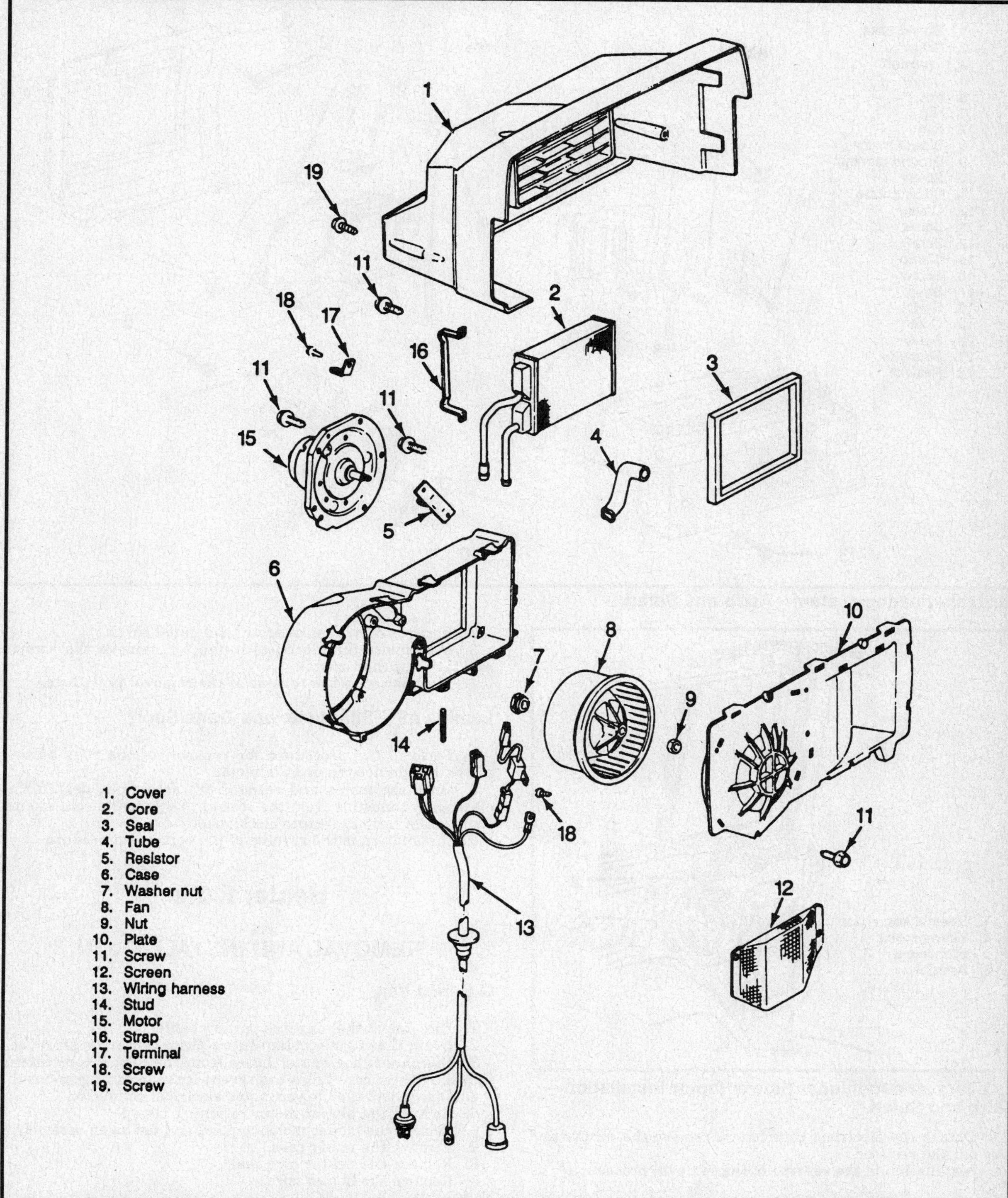

Auxiliary heating system — G Series Van

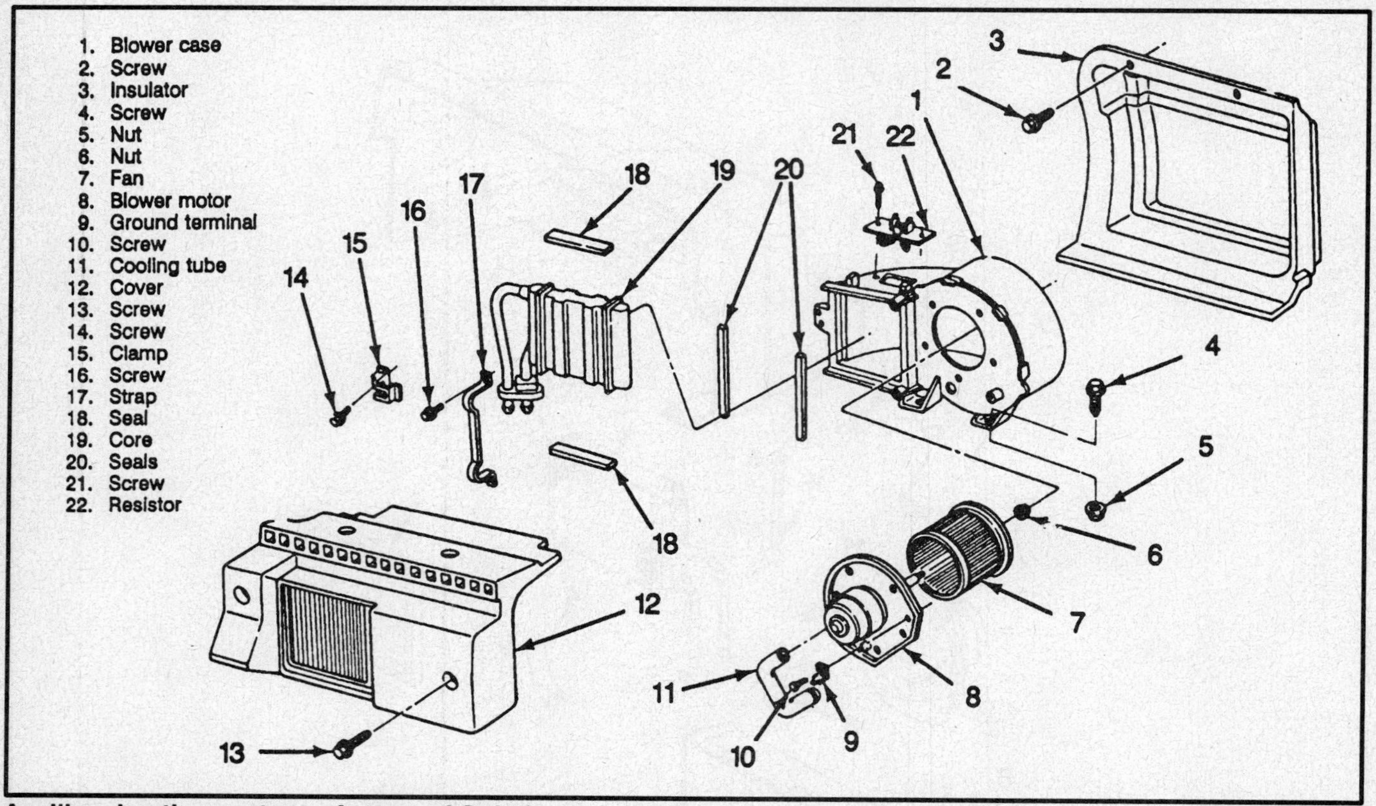

1. Blower case
2. Screw
3. Insulator
4. Screw
5. Nut
6. Nut
7. Fan
8. Blower motor
9. Ground terminal
10. Screw
11. Cooling tube
12. Cover
13. Screw
14. Screw
15. Clamp
16. Screw
17. Strap
18. Seal
19. Core
20. Seals
21. Screw
22. Resistor

Auxiliary heating system—Astro and Safari

1. Resistor connector
2. Blower motor connectors
3. Resistor

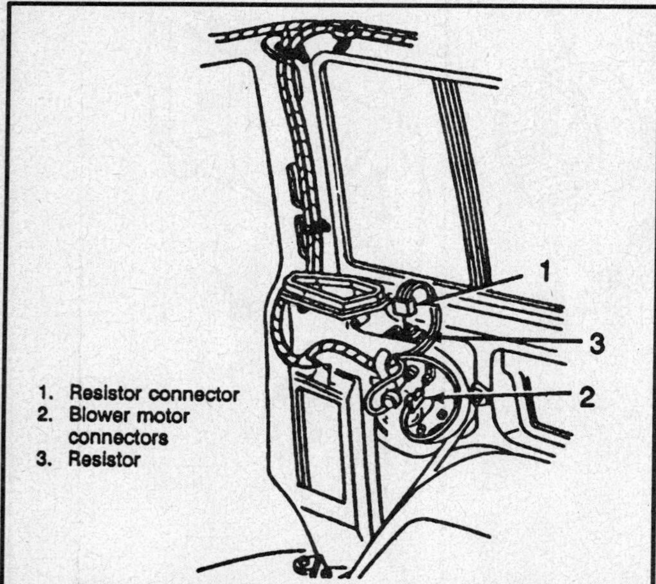

Auxiliary air conditioner blower motor installation—Astro and Safari

3. Detach the electrical connectors, remove the screws and take out the resistor.
4. Installation is the reverse of the removal procedure.

Suburban

1. Disconnect the negative battery cable.
2. Remove right rear quarter trim panel cover.
3. Disconnect the electrical connector, remove the screws and take out the resistor.
4. Installation is the reverse of the removal procedure.

Lumina APV, Silhouette and Trans Sport

1. Perform the procedure for removal of the rear blower motor, but do not remove the motor.
2. Once the motor and resistor are accessible, detach the electrical connection from the resistor, remove the screws and remove the resistor (rotate clockwise).
3. Installation is the reverse of the removal procedure.

Heater Core

REMOVAL AND INSTALLATION

G Series Van

1. Disconnect the negative battery cable.
2. Drain the engine coolant into a clean container for reuse.
3. Disconnect the heater hoses from the heater core tubes. Cap the heater core tubes to prevent leakage during removal.
4. Disconnect the blower motor electrical connector.
5. Remove the blower motor retaining clamp.
6. Remove the blower motor, support and fan as an assembly.
7. Remove the upper case.
8. Remove the heater core seal.
9. Remove the heater core.

To install:

10. Install the heater core.
11. Install the seal.

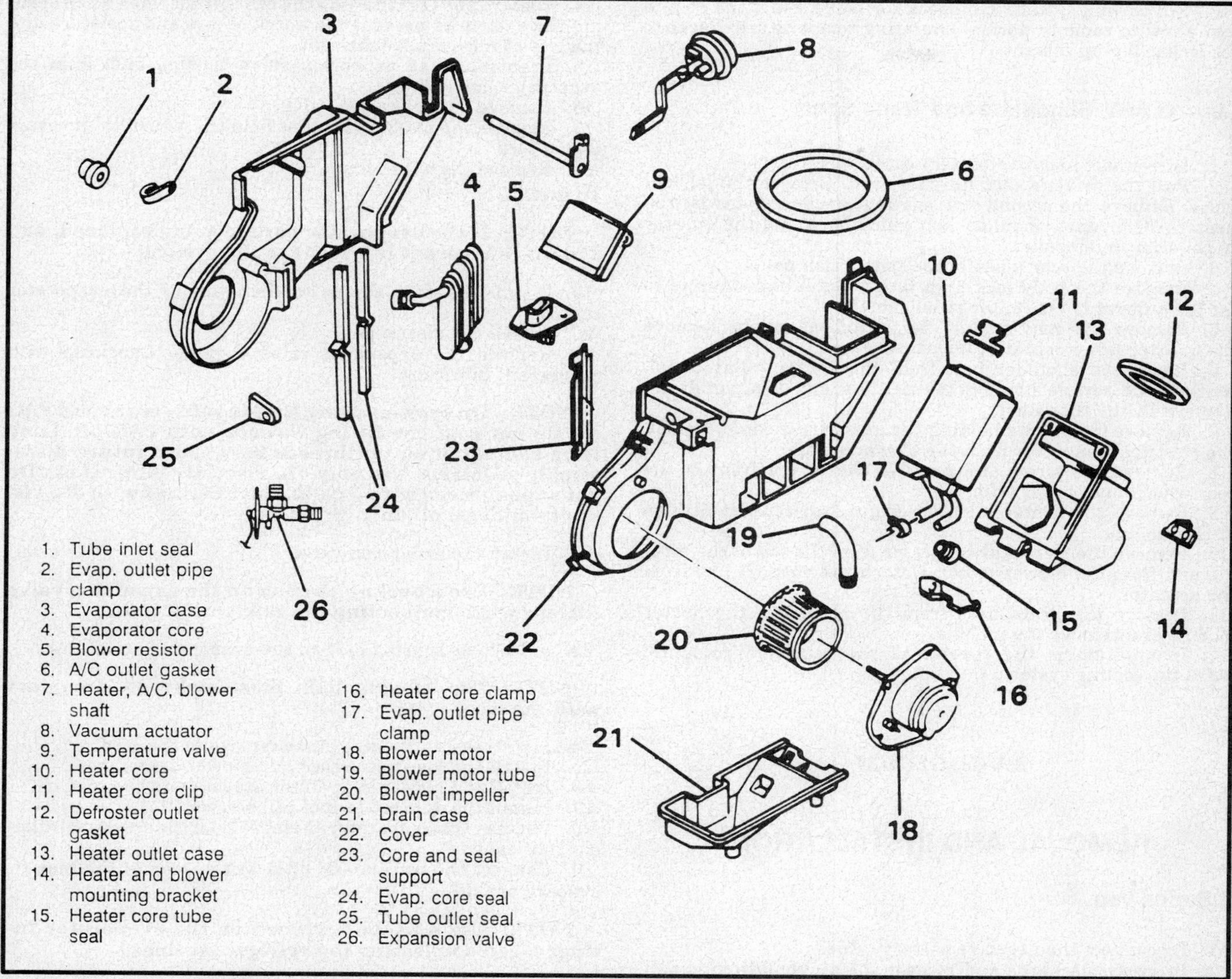

Auxiliary evaporator and blower module exploded view—Lumina APV, Silhouette and Trans Sport

12. Install the upper case.
13. Install the motor, support and fan assembly.
14. Install the blower motor retaining clamp.
15. Connect the blower motor electrical connector.
16. Connect the heater core hoses.
17. Connect the negative battery cable.
18. Fill cooling system and check for leaks. Start the engine and allow to come to normal operating temperature. Recheck for leaks. Top-up coolant.

Suburban

1. Disconnect the negative battery cable. Properly drain the cooling system.
2. Remove the quarter interior trim. Remove the right rear quarter trim panel, and remove the right rear wheelhouse.
3. Remove the auxiliary heater hoses from the core. Detach the electrical connectors.
4. Remove the floor drain valve. Unbolt and remove the heater module (and blower, if needed).
5. Detach the heater case cover and remove the core.
6. Installation is the reverse of the removal procedure.

Astro and Safari

1. Disconnect the negative battery cable.
2. Drain the engine coolant into a clean container for reuse.
3. Disconnect the heater hoses from the auxiliary heater core tubes. Cap the heater core tubes to prevent leakage during removal.
4. Remove the auxiliary heating core-blower cover.
5. Remove the heater core retaining screws.
6. Remove the heater core mounting strap and clamp.
7. Remove the heater core.
8. Remove the seals from the heater core.

To install:

9. Install the seals to the heater core.
10. Install the heater core.
11. Install the mounting strap and clamp.
12. Install the heater core retaining screws.
13. Install the auxiliary heating core-blower cover.
14. Connect the heater hoses to the auxiliary heater core tubes.
15. Connect the negative battery cable.

16. Fill cooling system and check for leaks. Start the engine and allow to come to normal operating temperature. Recheck for leaks. Top-up coolant.

Lumina APV, Silhouette and Trans Sport

1. Disconnect negative battery cable.
2. Pull the driver's seat fully forward. Remove the left sill plate. Remove the second row seating, anchor plates by the heater-A/C module, shoulder belt guide bolts and the quarter upper trim finish panel.
3. Remove the rear wheelhouse trim finish panel.
4. Remove the body lock trim finish panel and the screws for the quarter lower/center pillar panel.
5. Remove the rear module fan switch assembly. Remove the quarter lower/center pillar panel.
6. Route the shoulder belt from the center pillar panel. Remove the screws holding the beltline and B-pillar ducts. Remove the beltline duct.
7. Remove the screws holding the auxiliary module. Detach the electrical connector from the blower switch.
8. Remove the screw and rosebud clip at the front of the rear wheelhouse lower trim.
9. Remove the heater inlet/outlet quick-disconnect fittings at the module.
10. Remove the electrical connector from the top of the module and from the blower motor. Detach the vacuum line from the actuator.
11. Remove the drain hose from the bottom of the heater module and remove the module.
12. Installation is the reverse of the removal procedure. Refill the cooling system.

Evaporator

REMOVAL AND INSTALLATION

G Series Van

1. Disconnect the negative battery cable.
2. Properly discharge and recover the air conditioning system refrigerant.
3. Remove the rear duct work.
4. Disconnect the blower motor harness connector.
5. Disconnect the ground wire.
6. Disconnect the refrigerant lines at the rear of the blower-evaporator assembly.

NOTE: Use a backup wrench on the evaporator fittings when disconnecting the refrigerant lines.

7. Discard the O-rings. Cap the refrigerant lines when opening the system to prevent the entry of dirt and moisture and the loss of refrigerant lubricant.
8. Remove the blower-evaporator support to roof rail screws.
9. Remove the blower and evaporator core from the vehicle.
10. Invert the blower and evaporator core unit and place on a work bench.
11. Remove the lower case assembly.
12. Remove the upper case and supports from the evaporator core.
13. Disconnect the expansion valve refrigerant lines.

NOTE: Use a backup wrench on the expansion valve fittings when disconnecting the refrigerant lines.

14. Discard the O-rings. Cap the refrigerant lines when opening the system to prevent the entry of dirt and moisture and the loss of refrigerant lubricant.
15. Disconnect the expansion valve sensing bulb from the evaporator outlet line.
16. Remove the expansion valve.
17. Remove the plastic pins that hold the screen to the evaporator core.
18. Remove the wire screen.

To install:

NOTE: If the evaporator core is being replaced, add 3 oz. of refrigerant lubricant to the system.

19. Install the wire screen to the front of the evaporator core.
20. Install the plastic pins.
21. Replace the expansion valve O-rings. Lubricate with refrigerant lubricant.

NOTE: On systems using R-134a refrigerant and PAG oil, do not coat the fitting threads with PAG oil. Long term contact of oil on threads may cause future disassembly problems. Use only 525 viscosity mineral oil. Do not wipe threads with a cloth. Coat O-rings with 525 viscosity mineral oil only.

22. Install the expansion valve.

NOTE: Use a backup wrench on the expansion valve fittings when connecting the refrigerant lines.

23. Attach the sensing bulb to the evaporator outlet line.

NOTE: The sensing bulb must make good contact with the line.

24. Install the upper case and supports to the core.
25. Install the lower core case and blower assembly.
26. Install the blower-evaporator assembly to the roof.
27. Install the support-to-roof rail screws.
28. Replace the evaporator O-rings. Lubricate with refrigerant lubricant.
29. Connect the refrigerant lines to the rear of the blower-evaporator unit.

NOTE: Use a backup wrench on the evaporator fittings when connecting the refrigerant lines.

30. Connect the blower motor electrical connector.
31. Connect the ground wire.
32. Install the rear duct work.
33. Connect the negative battery cable.
34. Evacuate, recharge and leak test the air conditioning system.

Suburban

1. Disconnect the negative battery cable. Properly discharge the refrigerant using recovery type equipment. Drain the cooling system.
2. Remove the rear quarter interior trim, the right rear quarter trim panel and the right rear wheelhouse.
3. Remove the rear heater hoses from the auxiliary heater core.
4. Detach the auxiliary refrigerant hoses from the rear evaporator. Plug all openings immediately to minimize contamination.
5. Detach the electrical connectors, remove the evaporator case cover and remove the evaporator core.
6. Installation is the reverse of the removal procedure. Add 3.0 oz. of new refrigerant oil if replacing the evaporator core. Evacuate, recharge and leak test the system. Refill the cooling system.

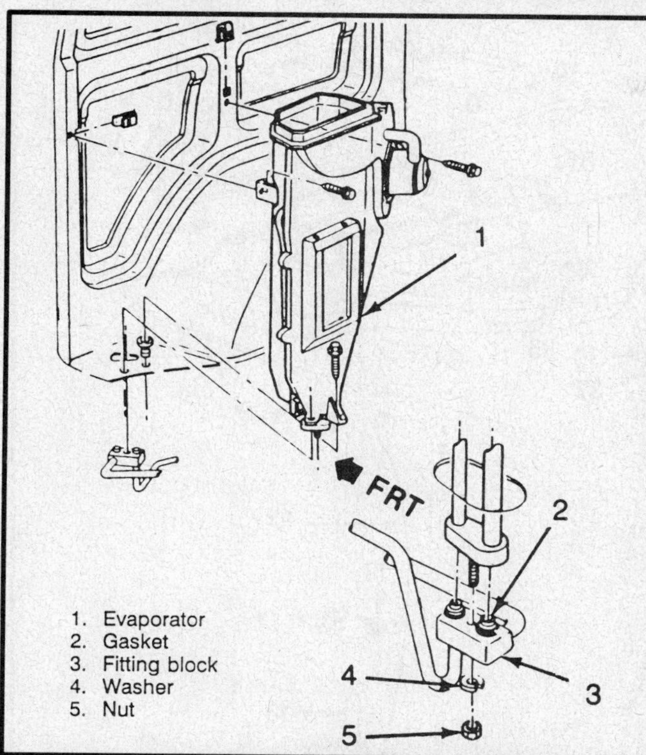

Auxiliary air conditioner evaporator installation—Astro and Safari

Astro and Safari

1. Disconnect the negative battery cable.
2. Properly discharge and recover the air conditioning system refrigerant.
3. If equipped, remove the storage box at the left side pillar, near the rear door.
4. Remove the auxiliary air conditioning system evaporator-blower cover. Remove the rear ducts.
5. Disconnect the electrical connector(s), as required.
6. Disconnect the tube fitting block. Discard the O-rings.

NOTE: Cap the refrigerant lines when opening the system to prevent the entry of dirt and moisture and the loss of refrigerant lubricant.

7. Remove the screws attaching the blower motor and evaporator case assembly. Remove the assembly.
8. Separate the case halves.
9. Remove the evaporator core seal.
10. Remove the evaporator.

To install:

11. Install the evaporator core.
12. Install the evaporator core seal.
13. Reassemble the case halves.
14. Install the blower motor and evaporator case assembly in the vehicle. Install the retaining screws.
15. Replace the tube fitting O-rings. Lubricate with refrigerant lubricant.
16. Connect the tube fitting block. Tighten to 18 ft. lbs. (25 Nm).
17. If disconnected, connect the electrical connector(s). Install the rear ducts.
18. Install the auxiliary air conditioning system evaporator-blower cover.
19. If equipped, install the rear storage box.
20. Connect the negative battery cable.
21. Evacuate, recharge and leak test the air conditioning system.

Lumina APV, Silhouette and Trans Sport

1. Disconnect negative battery cable. Properly discharge the refrigerant system using recovery type equipment. Drain the cooling system.
2. Pull the driver's seat fully forward. Remove the left sill plate. Remove the second row seating, anchor plates by the heater-A/C module, shoulder belt guide bolts and the quarter upper trim finish panel.
3. Remove the rear wheelhouse trim finish panel.
4. Remove the body lock trim finish panel and the screws for the quarter lower/center pillar panel.
5. Remove the rear module fan switch assembly. Remove the quarter lower/center pillar panel.
6. Route the shoulder belt from the center pillar panel. Remove the screws holding the beltline and B-pillar ducts. Remove the beltline duct.
7. Remove the refrigerant line fittings from the rear module.
8. Remove the heater inlet/outlet quick-disconnect fittings at the module.
9. Remove the screws retaining the evaporator module.
10. Remove the electrical connector from the top of the module and from the blower motor. Detach the vacuum line from the actuator.
11. Remove the drain hose from the bottom of the module and remove the module.
12. Installation is the reverse of the removal procedure. Refill the cooling system. Evacuate, recharge and leak test the air conditioning system.

Refrigerant Lines

REMOVAL AND INSTALLATION

1. Disconnect the negative battery cable.
2. Properly discharge and recover the air conditioning system refrigerant.
3. Disconnect the refrigerant line connectors, using a backup wrench as required.
4. Remove refrigerant line support or routing brackets, as required.
5. Remove refrigerant line.

To install:

6. Position new refrigerant line in place, leaving protective caps installed until ready to connect.

NOTE: On systems using R-134a refrigerant and PAG oil, do not coat the fitting threads with PAG oil. Long term contact of oil on threads may cause future disassembly problems. Use only 525 viscosity mineral oil. Do not wipe threads with a cloth. Coat O-rings with 525 viscosity mineral oil only.

7. Install new O-rings on refrigerant line connector fittings. Lubricate with refrigerant oil.
8. Connect refrigerant line, using a backup wrench, as required.
9. Install refrigerant line support or routing brackets, as required.
10. Evacuate, recharge and leak test the system.
11. Connect the negative battery cable.

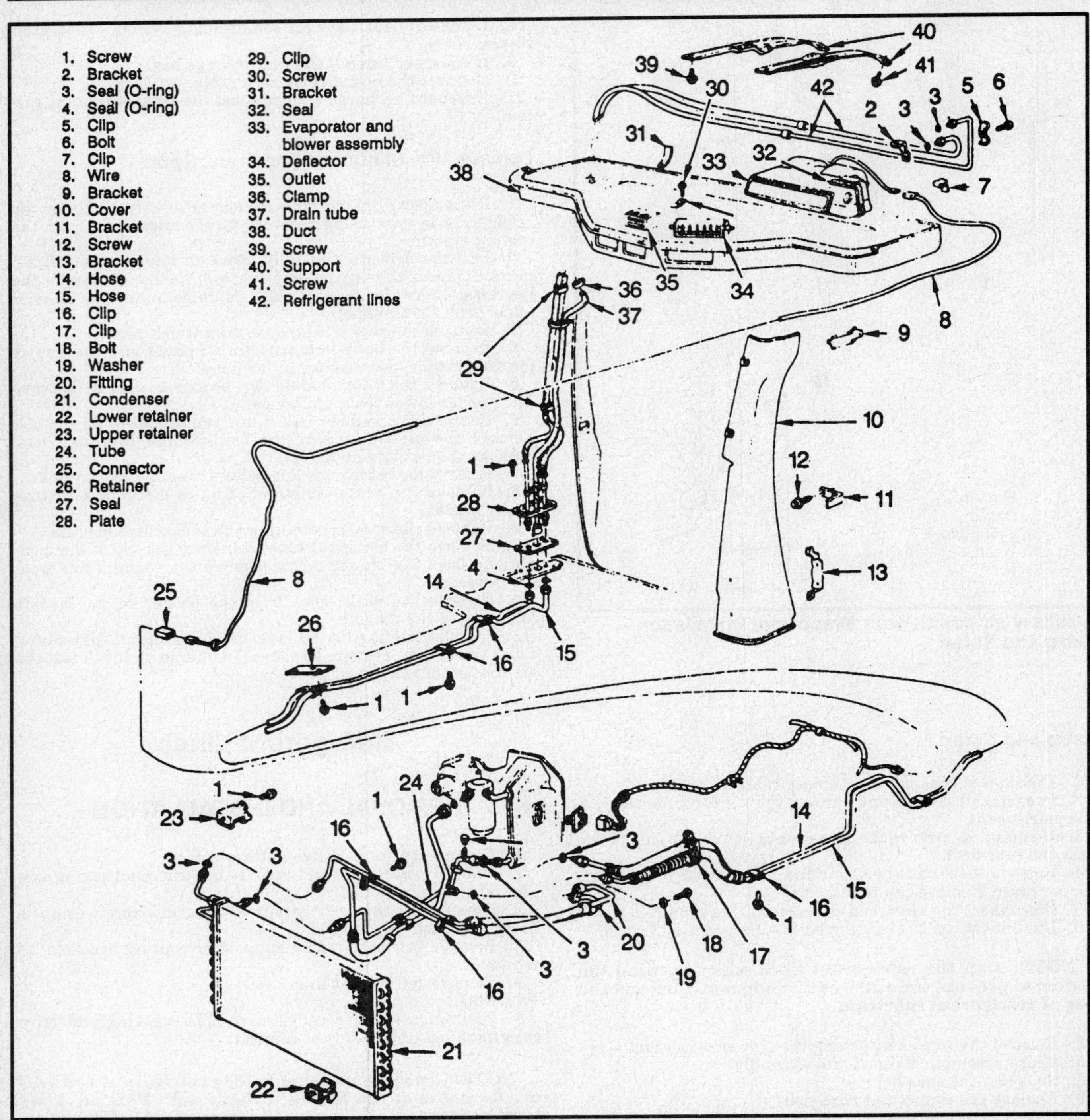

Auxiliary air conditioner refrigerant lines—Suburban

SYSTEM DIAGNOSIS

AUXILIARY FAN DIAGNOSIS—C/K SERIES AND G SERIES VAN

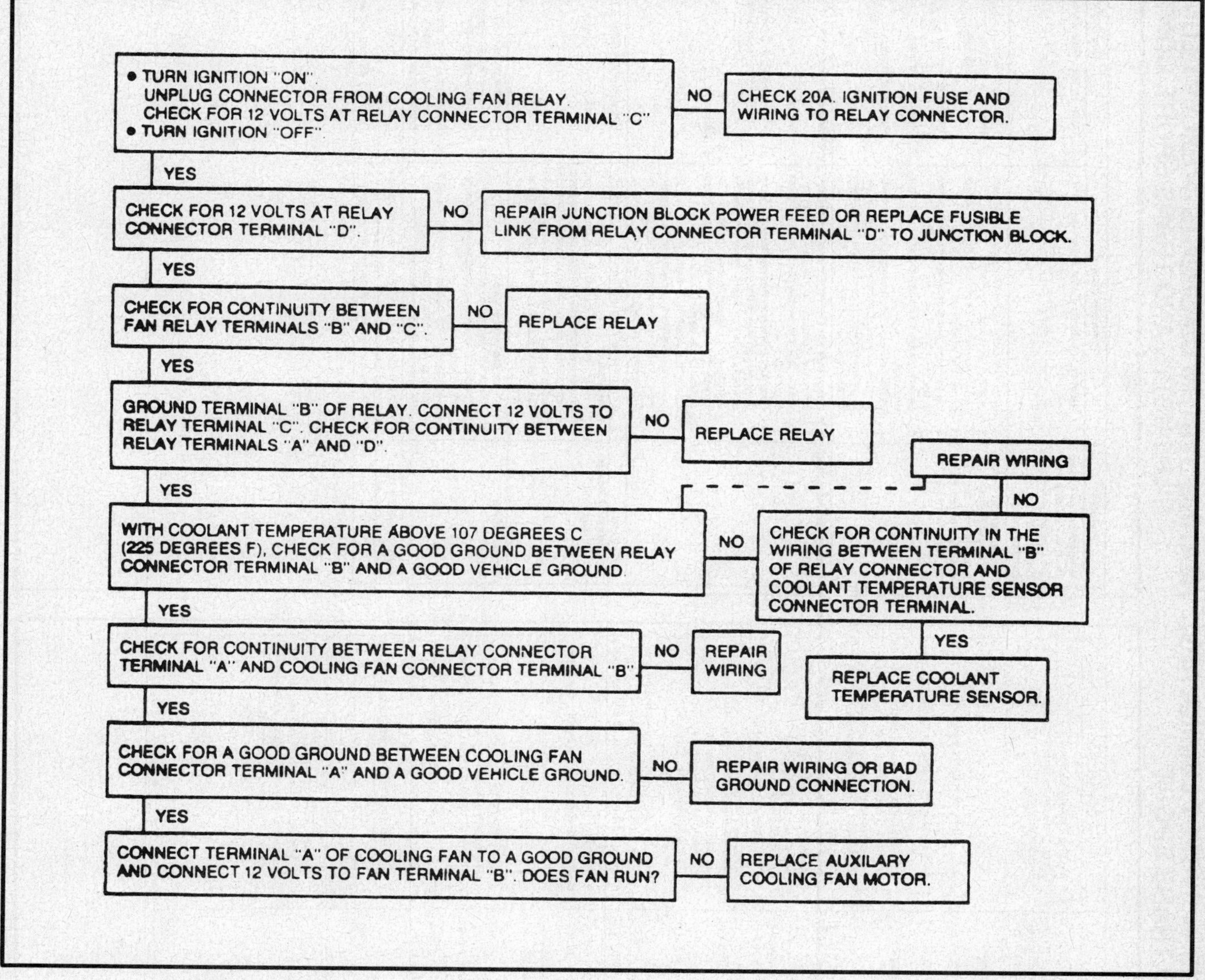

• TURN IGNITION "ON".
UNPLUG CONNECTOR FROM COOLING FAN RELAY.
CHECK FOR 12 VOLTS AT RELAY CONNECTOR TERMINAL "C"
• TURN IGNITION "OFF".
NO
CHECK 20A. IGNITION FUSE AND WIRING TO RELAY CONNECTOR.
YES
CHECK FOR 12 VOLTS AT RELAY CONNECTOR TERMINAL "D".
NO
REPAIR JUNCTION BLOCK POWER FEED OR REPLACE FUSIBLE LINK FROM RELAY CONNECTOR TERMINAL "D" TO JUNCTION BLOCK.
YES
CHECK FOR CONTINUITY BETWEEN FAN RELAY TERMINALS "B" AND "C".
NO
REPLACE RELAY
YES
GROUND TERMINAL "B" OF RELAY. CONNECT 12 VOLTS TO RELAY TERMINAL "C". CHECK FOR CONTINUITY BETWEEN RELAY TERMINALS "A" AND "D".
NO
REPLACE RELAY
YES
WITH COOLANT TEMPERATURE ABOVE 107 DEGREES C (225 DEGREES F), CHECK FOR A GOOD GROUND BETWEEN RELAY CONNECTOR TERMINAL "B" AND A GOOD VEHICLE GROUND.
NO
CHECK FOR CONTINUITY IN THE WIRING BETWEEN TERMINAL "B" OF RELAY CONNECTOR AND COOLANT TEMPERATURE SENSOR CONNECTOR TERMINAL.
NO
REPAIR WIRING
YES
REPLACE COOLANT TEMPERATURE SENSOR.
YES
CHECK FOR CONTINUITY BETWEEN RELAY CONNECTOR TERMINAL "A" AND COOLING FAN CONNECTOR TERMINAL "B".
NO
REPAIR WIRING
YES
CHECK FOR A GOOD GROUND BETWEEN COOLING FAN CONNECTOR TERMINAL "A" AND A GOOD VEHICLE GROUND.
NO
REPAIR WIRING OR BAD GROUND CONNECTION.
YES
CONNECT TERMINAL "A" OF COOLING FAN TO A GOOD GROUND AND CONNECT 12 VOLTS TO FAN TERMINAL "B". DOES FAN RUN?
NO
REPLACE AUXILARY COOLING FAN MOTOR.

HEATING SYSTEM DIAGNOSIS — EXCEPT LUMINA APV, SILHOUETTE AND TRANS SPORT

PROBLEM	POSSIBLE CAUSE	CORRECTION
No Heat	1 Low coolant level 2 Door(s) which control the air flow are not operating correctly (Move the control levers rapidly back and forth Listen for the door to hit the housing If the door is heard hitting the housing, its operation is OK.) a Cable end retaining screws are loose or missing b Broken or unhooked cable ends c Pivot shaft of door is out of its seating d Door blockage 3 Blower motor does not turn a Blown fuse b Poor ground c Faulty lead connection to motor d Faulty blower motor resistor e Faulty fan switch f Shorted or open circuit between switch and resistor, or between resistor and motor 4 No air flow, air intake tube blocked a Blower motor does not work b Plugged ducts c Door(s) which control air flow are not operating correctly 5 Plugged heater core and/or hoses 6 Engine cooling system will not warm up 7 Faulty heater core 8 Faulty pulleys or improper water pump belt tension	1 Fill the cooling system 2 Determine and correct cause of malfunction a Tighten or install screws b Replace the cable or secure with a new push nut c Seat the pivot shaft correctly d Remove the blockage 3 Repair or replace blower motor a Locate and repair the short b Repair the ground c Restore the proper connection d Replace the resistor e Replace the switch f Locate the point of the open or shorted circuit and repair 4 Restore the air flow, clean the screen a See number 3, above b Remove the blockage c See number 2, above 5 Remove the hoses from the engine and water pump Reverse flush 6 Check engine thermostat and radiator cap 7 Replace the core 8 Replace the pulleys or tighten the belts
Poor Removal of Fog or Frost	1 Air control doors are not functioning properly 2 Blower motor does not spin 3 Plugged defroster outlets or ducts 4 Operation of defroster with "AIR" lever in the "BLUE" (cold) position	1 See "NO HEAT" 2 See "NO HEAT" 3 Remove blockage 4 Put "AIR" lever in the "RED" (hot) position
Too Warm in Cab	1 Temperature door not operating correctly 2 Overheated engine 3 Blower motor operating only on high speed (faulty resistor)	1. See "NO HEAT." 2. Perform Cooling System Diagnosis. 3. Replace the blower motor resistor.
Heater Gurgle	1 Low coolant level 2 Plugged heater core and/or hoses	1 Fill the cooling system 2 Disconnect the coolant lines of the heater core at the engine water jacket and water pump Reverse flush

HEATING SYSTEM DIAGNOSIS — EXCEPT LUMINA APV, SILHOUETTE AND TRANS SPORT, CONT'D

Problem	Possible Cause	Correction
Temperature of Heater Air at the Outlets Is Too Low to Heat Up Passenger Compartment	Refer to "Insufficient Heat Diagnosis."	Refer to "Insufficient Heat Diagnosis."
Temperature of Heater Air at the Outlets is Adequate but the Vehicle Will Not Build Up Sufficient Heat	1. Floor side kick pad ventilators partially open. 2. Leaking grommets in dash. 3. Leaking welded seams along the rocker panel and windshield. 4. Leaks through the access holes and screw holes. 5. Leaking rubber molding around the door and windows. 6. Leaks between the sealing edge of blower and the air inlet assembly and cowl, and between the sealing edge of the heater distributor assembly and cowl.	1. Check and adjust. 2. Reseal or replace. 3. Clean and rewash. 4. Reseal or replace. 5. Reseal or replace. 6. Reseal or replace.
Inadequate Defrosting Action	1. Check that the DEFROST lever completely opens the defroster door in the DEF position. 2. Insure that the temperature and air doors open fully. 3. Look for obstructions in the defroster ducts. 4. Check for air leak in the ducting between the defroster outlet on heater assembly and the defroster duct under the instrument panel. 5. Check the position of the bottom of the nozzle to the heater locating tab. 6. Check the position of the defroster nozzle openings relative to instrument panel openings. Mounting tabs provide positive position if properly installed.	1. Adjust if necessary. 2. Adjust. 3. Remove any obstructions. 4. Seal area as necessary. 5. Adjust. 6. Adjust the defroster nozzle openings.
Inadequate Circulation of Heated Air Through the Vehicle	1. Check the heater outlet for correct installation. 2. Inspect the floor carpet to insure that the carpet lies flat under the front seat and does not obstruct air flow. Also inspect around the outlet ducts to insure that the carpet is well fastened to floor to prevent cupping of the air flow.	1. Remove and install. 2. Correct as necessary.
Erratic Heater Operation	1. Check the coolant level. 2. Check for kinked heater hoses. 3. Check the operation of all bowden cables and doors. 4. Sediment in the heater lines and radiator causing the engine thermostat to stick open. 5. Partially plugged heater core.	1. Fill to the proper level. 2. Relieve kinks or replace hoses. 3. Adjust as necessary. 4. Flush the system and clean or replace thermostat as necessary. 5. Backflush core as necessary.
Hard Operating or Broken Controls	1. Check for loose cable tab screws or misadjusted, misrouted or kinked cables. 2. Check for sticking heater system door(s).	1. Correct as required. 2. Lubricate as required using a silicone spray.

INSUFFICIENT HEAT DIAGNOSIS—EXCEPT LUMINA APV, SILHOUETTE AND TRANS SPORT

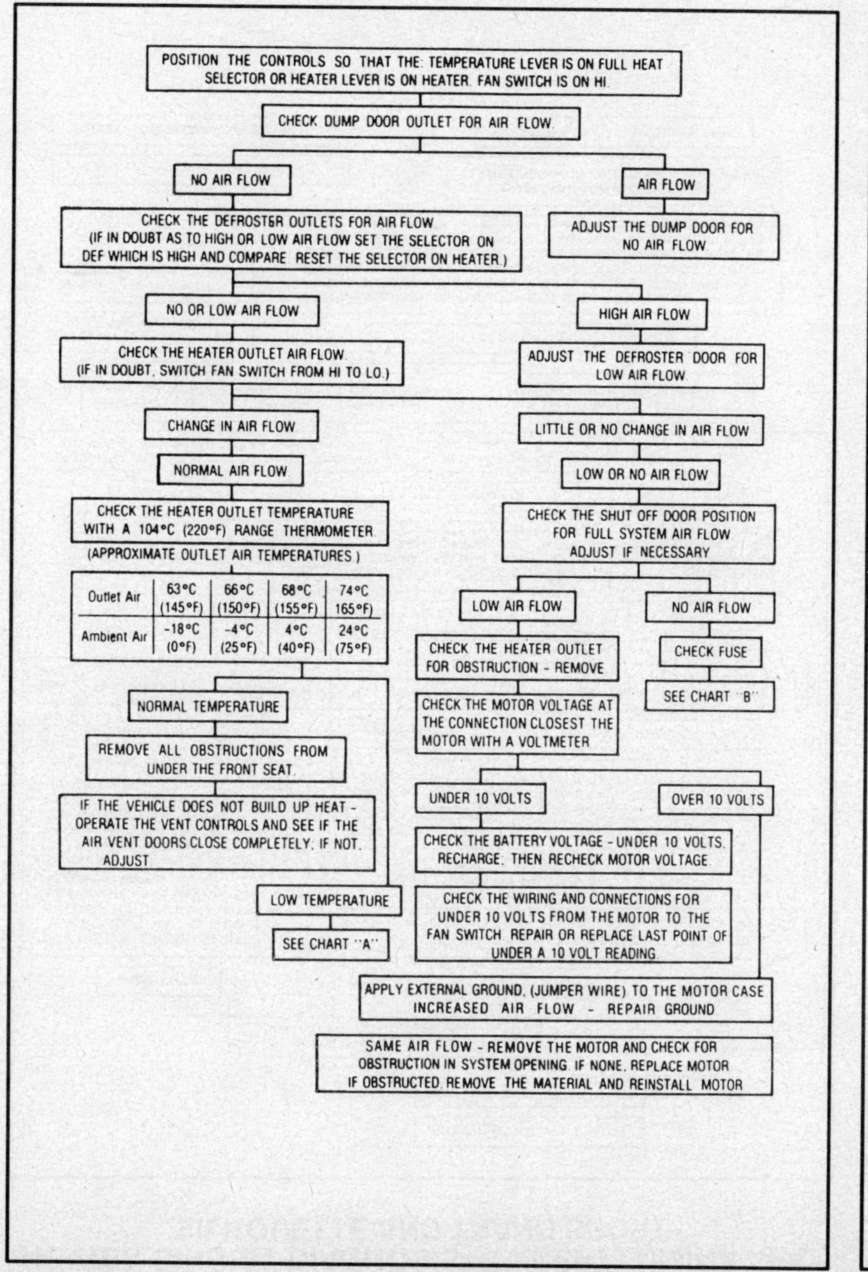
POSITION THE CONTROLS SO THAT THE: TEMPERATURE LEVER IS ON FULL HEAT SELECTOR OR HEATER LEVER IS ON HEATER. FAN SWITCH IS ON HI.
CHECK DUMP DOOR OUTLET FOR AIR FLOW.
NO AIR FLOW
AIR FLOW
CHECK THE DEFROSTER OUTLETS FOR AIR FLOW. (IF IN DOUBT AS TO HIGH OR LOW AIR FLOW SET THE SELECTOR ON DEF WHICH IS HIGH AND COMPARE. RESET THE SELECTOR ON HEATER.)
ADJUST THE DUMP DOOR FOR NO AIR FLOW.
NO OR LOW AIR FLOW
HIGH AIR FLOW
CHECK THE HEATER OUTLET AIR FLOW. (IF IN DOUBT, SWITCH FAN SWITCH FROM HI TO LO.)
ADJUST THE DEFROSTER DOOR FOR LOW AIR FLOW.
CHANGE IN AIR FLOW
LITTLE OR NO CHANGE IN AIR FLOW
NORMAL AIR FLOW
LOW OR NO AIR FLOW
CHECK THE HEATER OUTLET TEMPERATURE WITH A 104°C (220°F) RANGE THERMOMETER.
(APPROXIMATE OUTLET AIR TEMPERATURES.)
Outlet Air 63°C (145°F) 66°C (150°F) 68°C (155°F) 74°C 165°F)
Ambient Air -18°C (0°F) -4°C (25°F) 4°C (40°F) 24°C (75°F)
CHECK THE SHUT OFF DOOR POSITION FOR FULL SYSTEM AIR FLOW. ADJUST IF NECESSARY
LOW AIR FLOW
NO AIR FLOW
CHECK THE HEATER OUTLET FOR OBSTRUCTION - REMOVE.
CHECK FUSE
SEE CHART "B"
NORMAL TEMPERATURE
CHECK THE MOTOR VOLTAGE AT THE CONNECTION CLOSEST THE MOTOR WITH A VOLTMETER
REMOVE ALL OBSTRUCTIONS FROM UNDER THE FRONT SEAT.
IF THE VEHICLE DOES NOT BUILD UP HEAT - OPERATE THE VENT CONTROLS AND SEE IF THE AIR VENT DOORS CLOSE COMPLETELY; IF NOT, ADJUST
UNDER 10 VOLTS
OVER 10 VOLTS
CHECK THE BATTERY VOLTAGE - UNDER 10 VOLTS, RECHARGE; THEN RECHECK MOTOR VOLTAGE.
LOW TEMPERATURE
SEE CHART "A"
CHECK THE WIRING AND CONNECTIONS FOR UNDER 10 VOLTS FROM THE MOTOR TO THE FAN SWITCH. REPAIR OR REPLACE LAST POINT OF UNDER A 10 VOLT READING.
APPLY EXTERNAL GROUND, (JUMPER WIRE) TO THE MOTOR CASE INCREASED AIR FLOW - REPAIR GROUND.
SAME AIR FLOW - REMOVE THE MOTOR AND CHECK FOR OBSTRUCTION IN SYSTEM OPENING. IF NONE, REPLACE MOTOR IF OBSTRUCTED, REMOVE THE MATERIAL AND REINSTALL MOTOR

INSUFFICIENT HEAT DIAGNOSIS—EXCEPT LUMINA APV, SILHOUETTE AND TRANS SPORT, CONT'D

CHART A

CHECK THE SYSTEM TEMPEARTURE AFTER REPAIRING THE ITEM CHECKED TO COMPLETE THE DIAGNOSIS.
CHECK THE COOLANT LEVEL; IF LOW, FILL. LOOK FOR OR FEEL ALL RADIATOR AND HEATER HOSES AND CONNECTIONS FOR LEAKS. REPAIR OR REPLACE. CHECK THE RADIATOR CAP FOR DAMAGE AND REPAIR IF REQUIRED.
CHECK THE HEATER AND RADIATOR HOSES FOR KINKS - STRAIGHTEN AND REPALCE AS NECESSARY.
CHECK THE TEMPERATURE DOOR FOR MAX HEAT POSITION. ADJUST IF NECESSARY.
HEATER CORE
FEEL THE TEMPERATURE OF THE HEATER INLET AND OUTLET HOSES.
WARM INLET AND OUTLET HOSES
CHECK THE ENGINE THERMOSTAT.
HOT INLET AND WARM OUTLET HOSES
CHECK THE PULLEYS, BELT TENSION, ETC. FOR PROPER OPERATION. REPLACE OR SERVICE AS NECESSARY.
REMOVE THE HOSES FROM HEATER CORE. REVERSE FLUSH WITH TAP WATER. IF PLUGGED, REPAIR OR REPLACE.

CHART B

CHECK FUSE
FUSE BLOWN - REPLACE FUSE
AIR FLOW - SYSTEM OKAY
BLOWS FUSE
REMOVE THE POSITIVE LEAD FROM THE MOTOR AND REPLACE THE FUSE.
FUSE REMAINS OK - REMOVE THE MOTOR AND CHECK FOR AN OBSTRUCTION IN THE SYSTEM OPENING. IF NONE REPLACE THE MOTOR. IF OBSTRUCTION, REMOVE THE MATERIAL AND RE-INSTALL THE MOTOR
BLOWS FUSE - CHECK FOR A SHORTED WIRE IN THE BLOWER ELECTRIC CIRCUIT. SEE HEATER CIRCUIT DIAGNOSTIC CHART
FUSE OK
FUSE OK - SEE HEATER CIRCUIT DIAGNOSTIC CHART

HEATER CIRCUIT DIAGNOSIS—EXCEPT LUMINA APV, SILHOUETTE AND TRANS SPORT

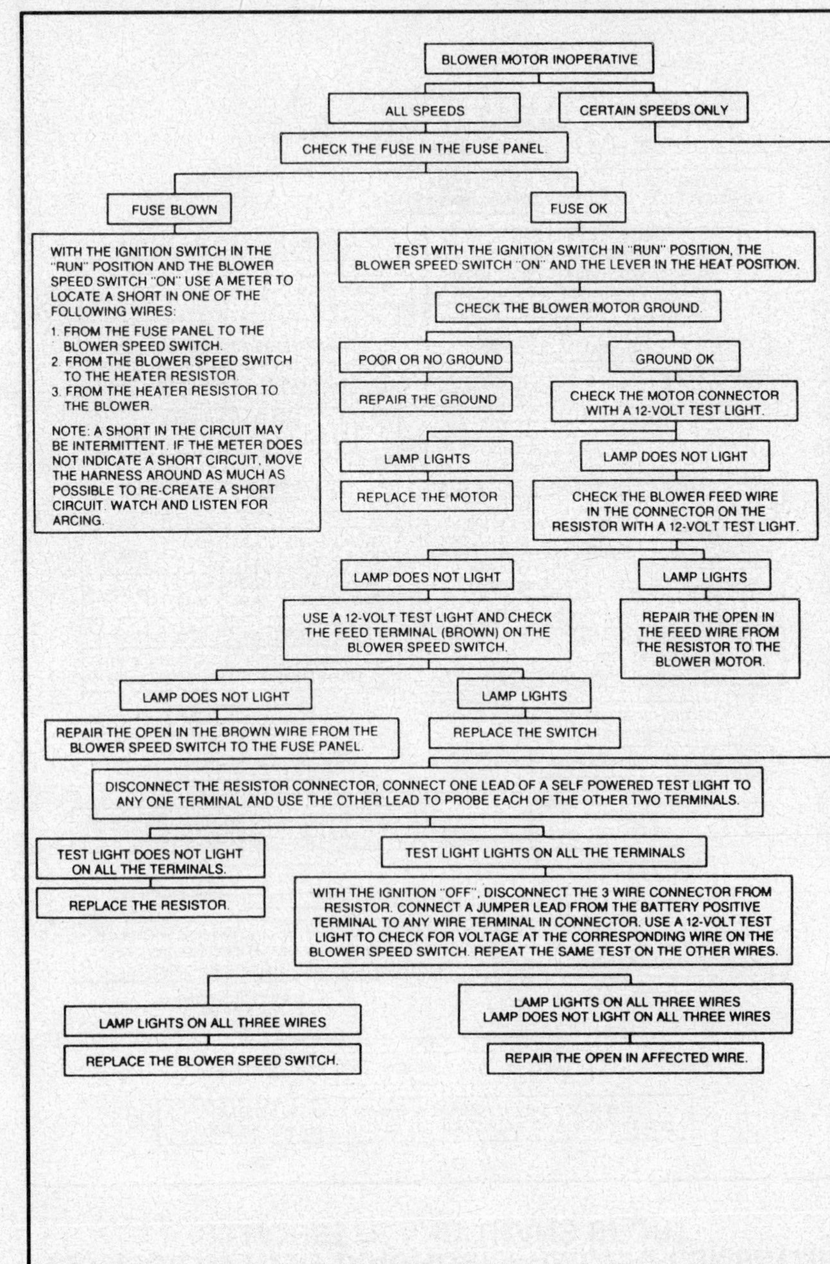

HEATER SYSTEM CONTROL LOGIC—LUMINA APV, SILHOUETTE AND TRANS SPORT

VACUUM HARNESS

VACUUM VALVE CONNECTOR

5 4 3 2 1

VIOLET SOURCE INPUT

RED — FULL HEAT PORT "B"

YELLOW — FULL VENT OR DEFROST PORT "A"

BLUE — DEFROST OR VENT (UPPER MODE)

BROWN — VENT OR HEAT SLAVE

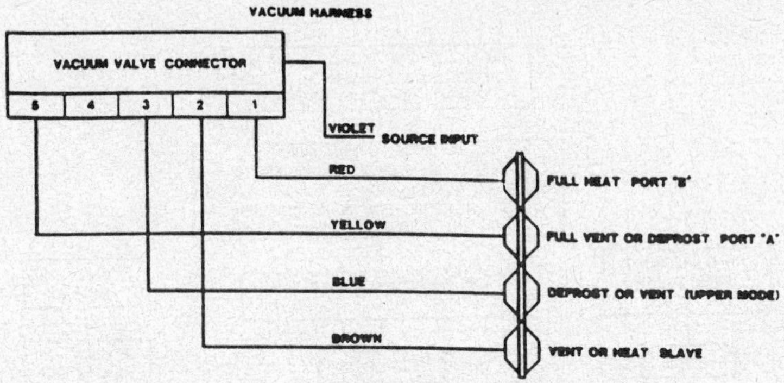

VACUUM VALVE LOGIC - MODE LEVER POSITIONS

PORT	OFF	MAX A/C	NORM A/C	BI LEVEL	VENT	HEATER	DEFROST	DEFOG
LOWER MODE HEATER	VENT	VENT	VENT	VENT	VENT	VAC	VENT	VENT
SLAVE DOOR	VENT	VAC	VAC	VAC	VAC	VENT	VENT	VENT
UPPER MODE DEFROST A/C	VENT	VAC	VAC	VAC	VAC	VENT	VENT	VENT
LOWER MODE A/C DEFROST	VENT	VAC	VAC	VENT	VAC	VENT	VAC	VENT

HEATER SYSTEM DIAGNOSIS—LUMINA APV, SILHOUETTE AND TRANS SPORT

HEATER FUNCTIONAL TEST

STEP	CONTROL SETTINGS						SYSTEM RESPONSE				
	MODE BUTTON	LITE ON	TEMP SETT.	BLOWER FAN SW FRT	BLOWER FAN SW RR	BLOWER SPEED	RR OPT AUX. DUCT	HEATER OUTLETS	A C I P OUTLETS	DEF OUTLETS	SIDE WDO DEF
1	OFF	YES	FULL HOT	HI	OFF	OFF	NO AIR FLOW	NO AIR FLOW	NO AIR FLOW	NO AIR FLOW	NO AIR FLOW
2	DEFR.	YES	FULL HOT	HI	OFF	HI	NO AIR FLOW	AIR FLOW	NO AIR FLOW	HOT AIR FLOW	SOME HOT AIR FLOW
3	MIX	YES	FULL HOT	HI	OFF	HI	SOME AIR FLOW	HOT AIR FLOW	NO AIR FLOW	HOT AIR FLOW	SOME HOT AIR FLOW
4	HEATER	YES	FULL HOT	HI	OFF	HI	AIR FLOW	HOT AIR FLOW	NO AIR FLOW	SOME AIR FLOW	SOME HOT AIR FLOW
5	BI-LEVEL	YES	FULL COLD	HI	OFF	HI	SOME AIR FLOW	AIR FLOW	COOL AIR FLOW	SOME AIR FLOW	SOME AIR FLOW
6	VENT	YES	FULL HOT	HI	OFF	HI	SOME AIR FLOW	NO AIR FLOW	HOT AIR FLOW	NO AIR FLOW	SOME AIR FLOW
7	VENT	YES	FULL COLD	HI	OFF	HI	SOME AIR FLOW	NO AIR FLOW	COOL AIR FLOW	NO AIR FLOW	SOME AIR FLOW
8	VENT	YES	FULL COLD	LOW	OFF	LOW	SOME AIR FLOW	NO AIR FLOW	COOL AIR FLOW	NO AIR FLOW	SOME AIR FLOW
9	HEATER	YES	FULL HOT	LOW	HI	LOW/HI	HOT AIR FLOW	SOME HOT AIR FLOW	NO AIR FLOW	SOME AIR FLOW	SOME AIR FLOW

- TEMPERATURE DOOR ACTUATOR MOTOR SHOULD BE HEARD DURING TEMPERATURE SETTING CHANGES, AND NOTICEABLE BLOWER SPEED INCREASE MUST OCCUR FROM LOW TO MID, TO MID, AND HIGH
- CHECK TEMPERATURE LEVER FOR EFFORT AND TRAVEL (COLD TO HOT) (TEMPERATURE CHANGE SHOULD OCCUR).
- CHECK FOR AIR FLOW AS DEFINED IN SYSTEM RESPONSE.
- ALL I/P OUTLETS MUST BE CHECKED FOR: 1) BARREL ROTATION. 2) VANE OPERATION. 3) BARREL AND VANES MUST HOLD PRESENT POSITION IN HI BLOWER OPERATION.

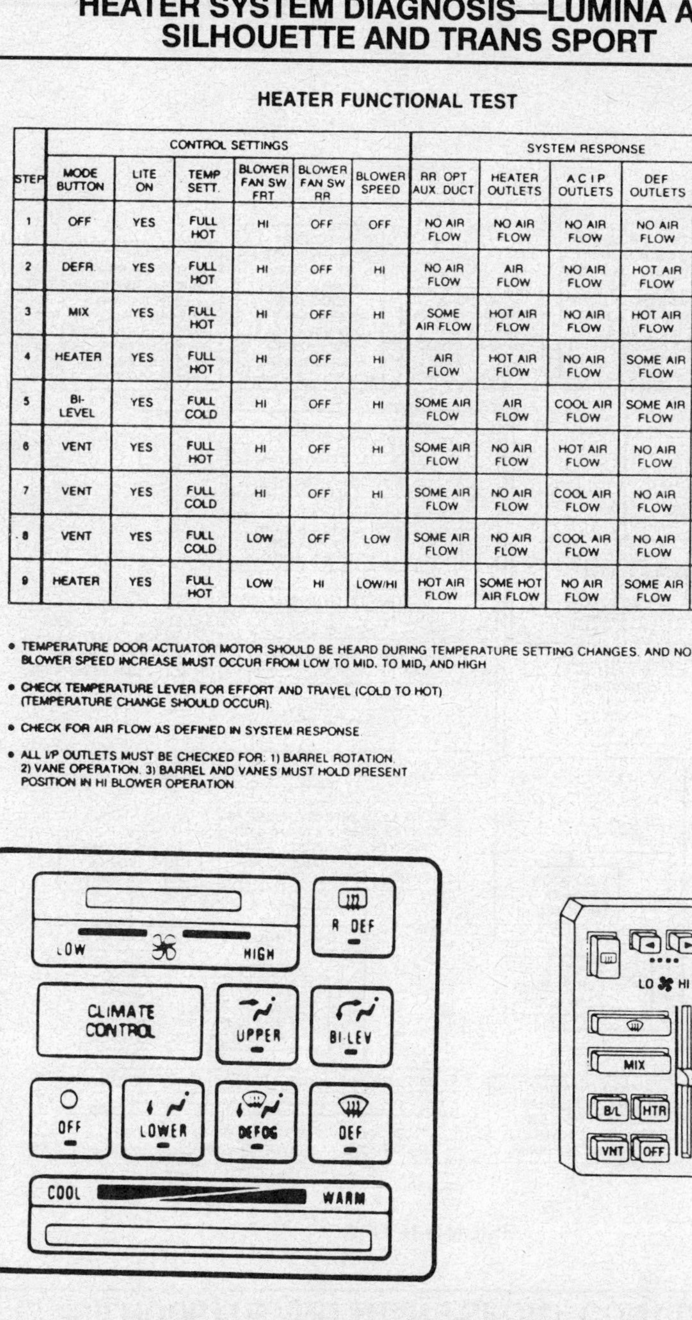

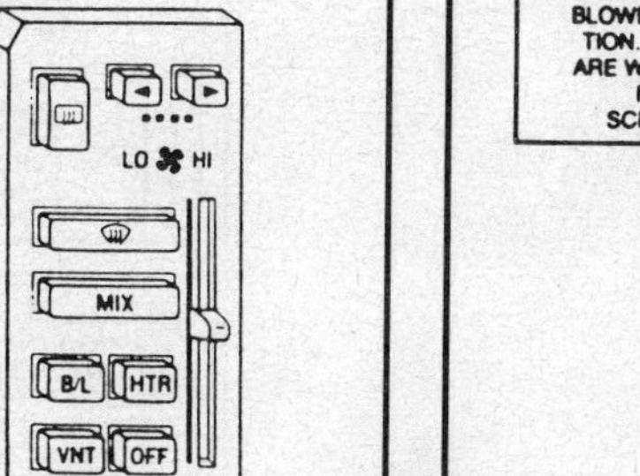

HEATER SYSTEM DIAGNOSIS—LUMINA APV, SILHOUETTE AND TRANS SPORT, CONT'D

4 BLOWER NOISE

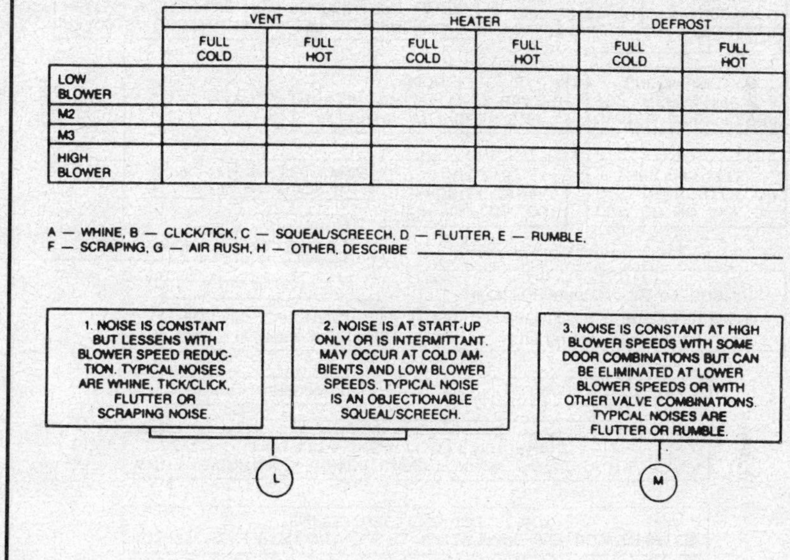

CHECK ALL ELECTRICAL CONNECTIONS AND GROUNDS FOR PROPER CONNECTION. REFER TO SECTION 8A.

SIT IN THE VEHICLE WITH THE DOORS AND WINDOWS CLOSED. WITH THE IGNITION ON AND THE ENGINE OFF, START WITH THE BLOWER ON HIGH, IN VENT MODE AND THE TEMPERATURE LEVER ON FULL COLD. CYCLE THROUGH BLOWER SPEEDS, MODES AND TEMPERATURE VALVE POSITIONS TO FIND WHERE THE NOISE OCCURS AND WHERE THE NOISE DOES NOT OCCUR. TRY TO DEFINE THE TYPE OF NOISE: AIR RUSH, WHINE, TICK/CLICK, SQUEAL/SCREECH, FLUTTER, RUMBLE OR SCRAPING NOISE. CHART BELOW SHOULD BE COMPLETELY FILLED IN AT COMPLETION.

A CONSTANT AIR RUSH NOISE IS TYPICAL OF ALL SYSTEMS ON HIGH BLOWER. SOME SYSTEMS AND MODES (USUALLY DEFROSTER) MAY BE WORSE THAN OTHERS. CHECK ANOTHER VEHICLE IF POSSIBLE (SAME MODEL) TO DETERMINE IF THE NOISE IS TYPICAL OF THE SYSTEM AS DESIGNED.

INDICATE THE TYPE OF NOISE AND WHERE IT OCCURS

	VENT		HEATER		DEFROST	
	FULL COLD	FULL HOT	FULL COLD	FULL HOT	FULL COLD	FULL HOT
LOW BLOWER						
M2						
M3						
HIGH BLOWER						

A — WHINE, B — CLICK/TICK, C — SQUEAL/SCREECH, D — FLUTTER, E — RUMBLE,
F — SCRAPING, G — AIR RUSH, H — OTHER, DESCRIBE ______

1. NOISE IS CONSTANT BUT LESSENS WITH BLOWER SPEED REDUCTION. TYPICAL NOISES ARE WHINE, TICK/CLICK, FLUTTER OR SCRAPING NOISE.

2. NOISE IS AT START-UP ONLY OR IS INTERMITTANT. MAY OCCUR AT COLD AMBIENTS AND LOW BLOWER SPEEDS. TYPICAL NOISE IS AN OBJECTIONABLE SQUEAL/SCREECH.

(L)

3. NOISE IS CONSTANT AT HIGH BLOWER SPEEDS WITH SOME DOOR COMBINATIONS BUT CAN BE ELIMINATED AT LOWER BLOWER SPEEDS OR WITH OTHER VALVE COMBINATIONS. TYPICAL NOISES ARE FLUTTER OR RUMBLE.

(M)

HEATER SYSTEM DIAGNOSIS—LUMINA APV, SILHOUETTE AND TRANS SPORT, CONT'D

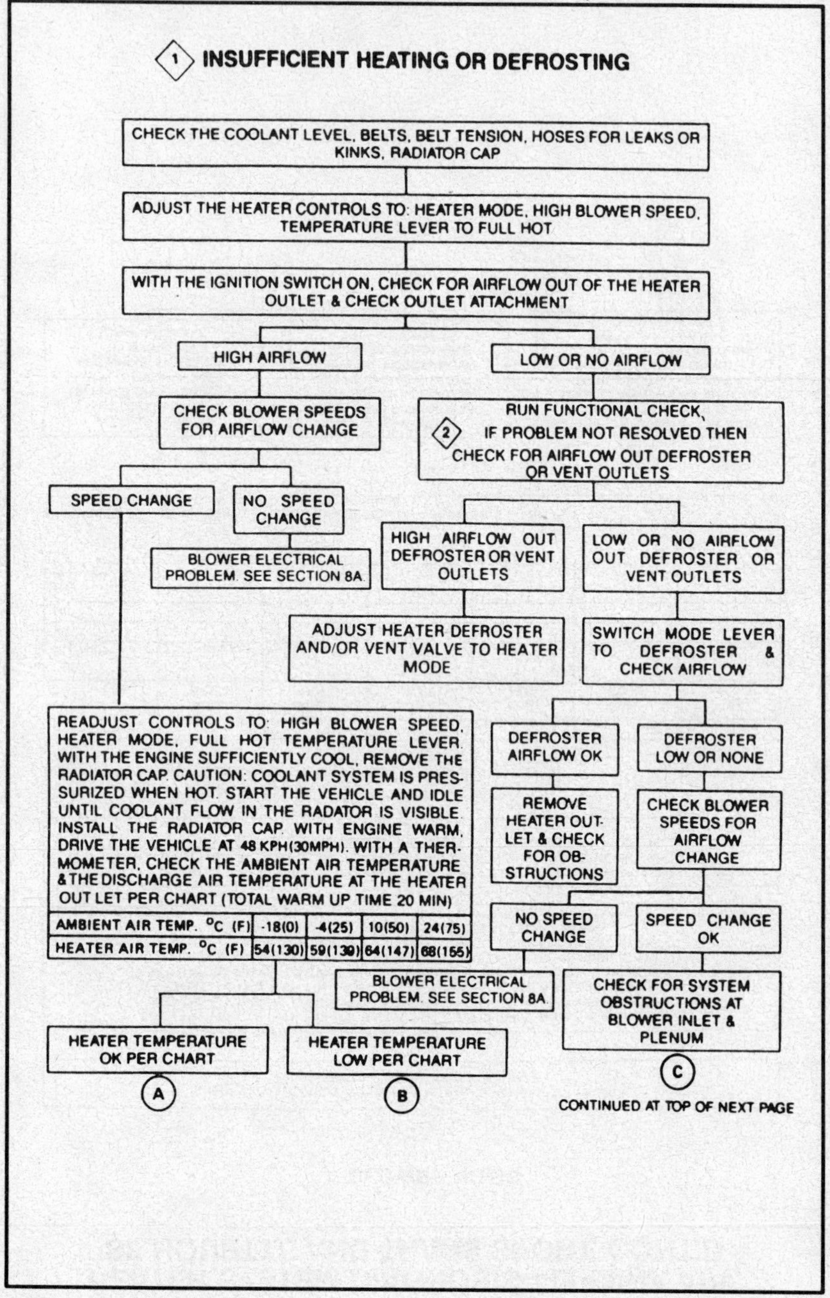

① INSUFFICIENT HEATING OR DEFROSTING

CHECK THE COOLANT LEVEL, BELTS, BELT TENSION, HOSES FOR LEAKS OR KINKS, RADIATOR CAP

ADJUST THE HEATER CONTROLS TO: HEATER MODE, HIGH BLOWER SPEED, TEMPERATURE LEVER TO FULL HOT

WITH THE IGNITION SWITCH ON, CHECK FOR AIRFLOW OUT OF THE HEATER OUTLET & CHECK OUTLET ATTACHMENT

HIGH AIRFLOW

CHECK BLOWER SPEEDS FOR AIRFLOW CHANGE

SPEED CHANGE

NO SPEED CHANGE

BLOWER ELECTRICAL PROBLEM. SEE SECTION 8A

LOW OR NO AIRFLOW

RUN FUNCTIONAL CHECK, ② IF PROBLEM NOT RESOLVED THEN CHECK FOR AIRFLOW OUT DEFROSTER OR VENT OUTLETS

HIGH AIRFLOW OUT DEFROSTER OR VENT OUTLETS

ADJUST HEATER DEFROSTER AND/OR VENT VALVE TO HEATER MODE

LOW OR NO AIRFLOW OUT DEFROSTER OR VENT OUTLETS

SWITCH MODE LEVER TO DEFROSTER & CHECK AIRFLOW

DEFROSTER AIRFLOW OK

REMOVE HEATER OUTLET & CHECK FOR OBSTRUCTIONS

DEFROSTER LOW OR NONE

CHECK BLOWER SPEEDS FOR AIRFLOW CHANGE

NO SPEED CHANGE

BLOWER ELECTRICAL PROBLEM. SEE SECTION 8A

SPEED CHANGE OK

CHECK FOR SYSTEM OBSTRUCTIONS AT BLOWER INLET & PLENUM

Ⓒ

READJUST CONTROLS TO: HIGH BLOWER SPEED, HEATER MODE, FULL HOT TEMPERATURE LEVER. WITH THE ENGINE SUFFICIENTLY COOL, REMOVE THE RADIATOR CAP. CAUTION: COOLANT SYSTEM IS PRESSURIZED WHEN HOT. START THE VEHICLE AND IDLE UNTIL COOLANT FLOW IN THE RADIATOR IS VISIBLE. INSTALL THE RADIATOR CAP. WITH ENGINE WARM, DRIVE THE VEHICLE AT 48 KPH(30MPH). WITH A THERMOMETER, CHECK THE AMBIENT AIR TEMPERATURE & THE DISCHARGE AIR TEMPERATURE AT THE HEATER OUTLET PER CHART (TOTAL WARM UP TIME 20 MIN)

AMBIENT AIR TEMP. °C (F)	-18(0)	-4(25)	10(50)	24(75)
HEATER AIR TEMP. °C (F)	54(130)	59(139)	64(147)	68(155)

HEATER TEMPERATURE OK PER CHART Ⓐ

HEATER TEMPERATURE LOW PER CHART Ⓑ

CONTINUED AT TOP OF NEXT PAGE

HEATER SYSTEM DIAGNOSIS—LUMINA APV, SILHOUETTE AND TRANS SPORT, CONT'D

④ BLOWER NOISE

Ⓛ

CHECK FOR MOTOR & FAN VIBRATION AT EACH BLOWER SPEED BY FEELING THE BLOWER ARMATURE

NO EXCESS VIBRATION

REMOVE BLOWER MOTOR & FAN ASSEMBLY AND CHECK FOR FOREIGN MATERIAL AT THE ORIFICE OF BLOWER INLET.

PROBLEM FOUND

REPAIR/REPLACE AS NECESSARY AND RECHECK

NONE FOUND

VIBRATION EXCESSIVE

EXAMINE BLOWER FAN FOR WEAR SPOTS, CRACKED BLADES OR HUB, LOOSE FAN RETAINING NUT AND ALIGNMENT. EXAMINE BLOWER CASE FOR WEAR SPOTS

PROBLEM FOUND

REPAIR/REPLACE AS NECESSARY AND RECHECK

NONE FOUND

LUBRICATE MOTOR

PROBLEM STILL EXISTS

REPLACE MOTOR AND FAN ASSEMBLY AND RECHECK

PROBLEM STILL EXISTS

IF NOISE IS A CLICK/TICK OR WHINE, TRY A SECOND NEW MOTOR, THEN PROCEED

REINSTALL ORIGINAL MOTOR AND PROCEED TO ② (NOISE IS CONSTANT. . .)

Ⓜ

ON HIGH BLOWER, CHECK FULL HOT TO FULL COLD TEMPERATURE POSITIONS IN DEFROST, HEATER AND VENT MODES

NOISE IN DEFROSTER MODE ONLY

NOISE IN HEATER MODE ONLY

NOISE IN VENT MODE ONLY

NOISE IN ALL MODES BUT NOT ALL TEMPERATURE POSITIONS

NOISE IN ALL MODES AND IN ALL TEMPERATURE POSITIONS

CHECK DUCTS FOR OBSTRUCTIONS OR FOREIGN MATERIALS AND REMOVE. CHECK HEATER/DEFROSTER DOOR SEALS REPAIR/REPLACE AS NECESSARY AND RECHECK

CHECK DUCTS FOR OBSTRUCTIONS OR FOREIGN MATERIALS AND REMOVE. CHECK VENT DOOR SEALS. REPAIR/REPLACE AS NECESSARY AND RECHECK

CHECK TEMPERATURE DOOR SEALS. REPAIR/REPLACE AS NECESSARY AND RECHECK

CHECK SYSTEM FOR OBSTRUCTIONS OR FOREIGN MATERIALS BETWEEN THE FAN AND THE TEMPERATURE DOOR. REMOVE, REPAIR OR REPLACE AS NECESSARY AND RECHECK.

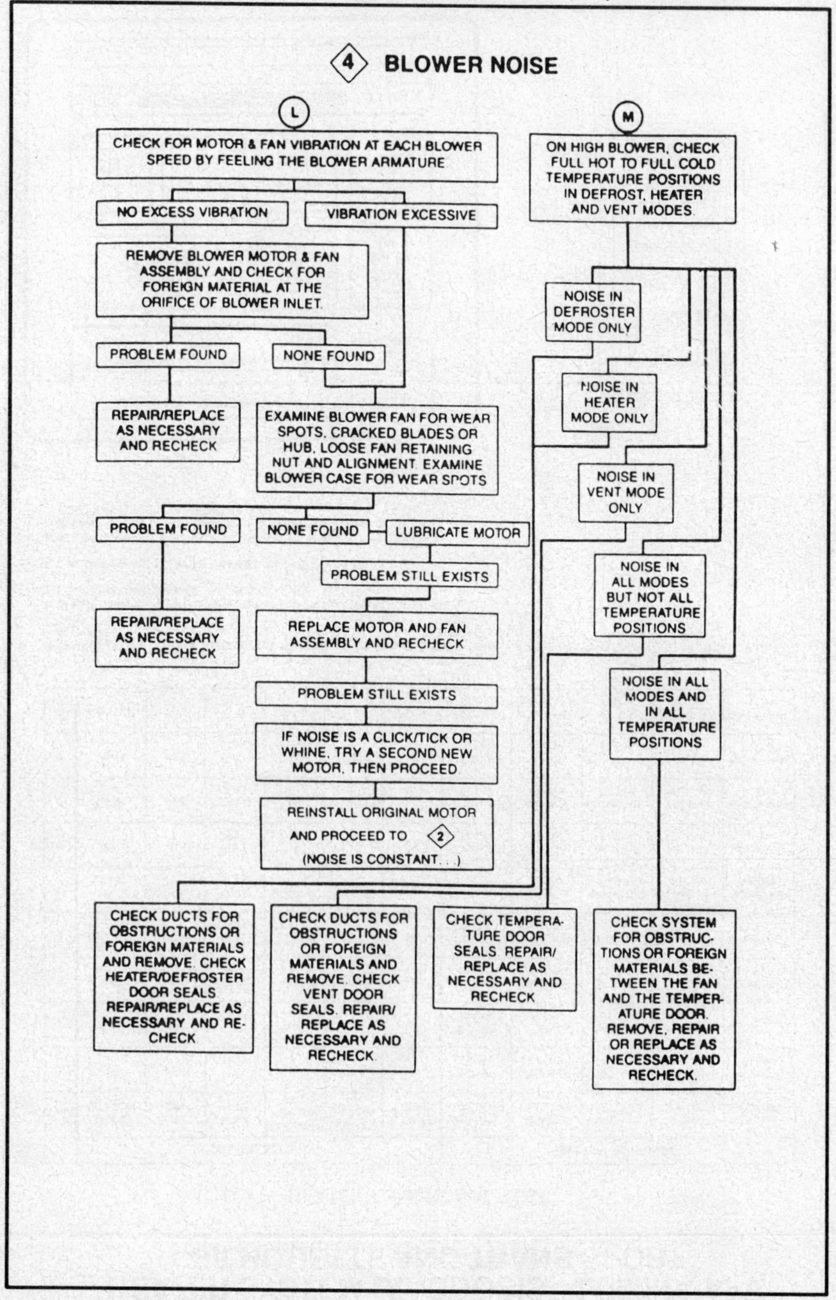

HEATER SYSTEM DIAGNOSIS—LUMINA APV, SILHOUETTE AND TRANS SPORT, CONT'D

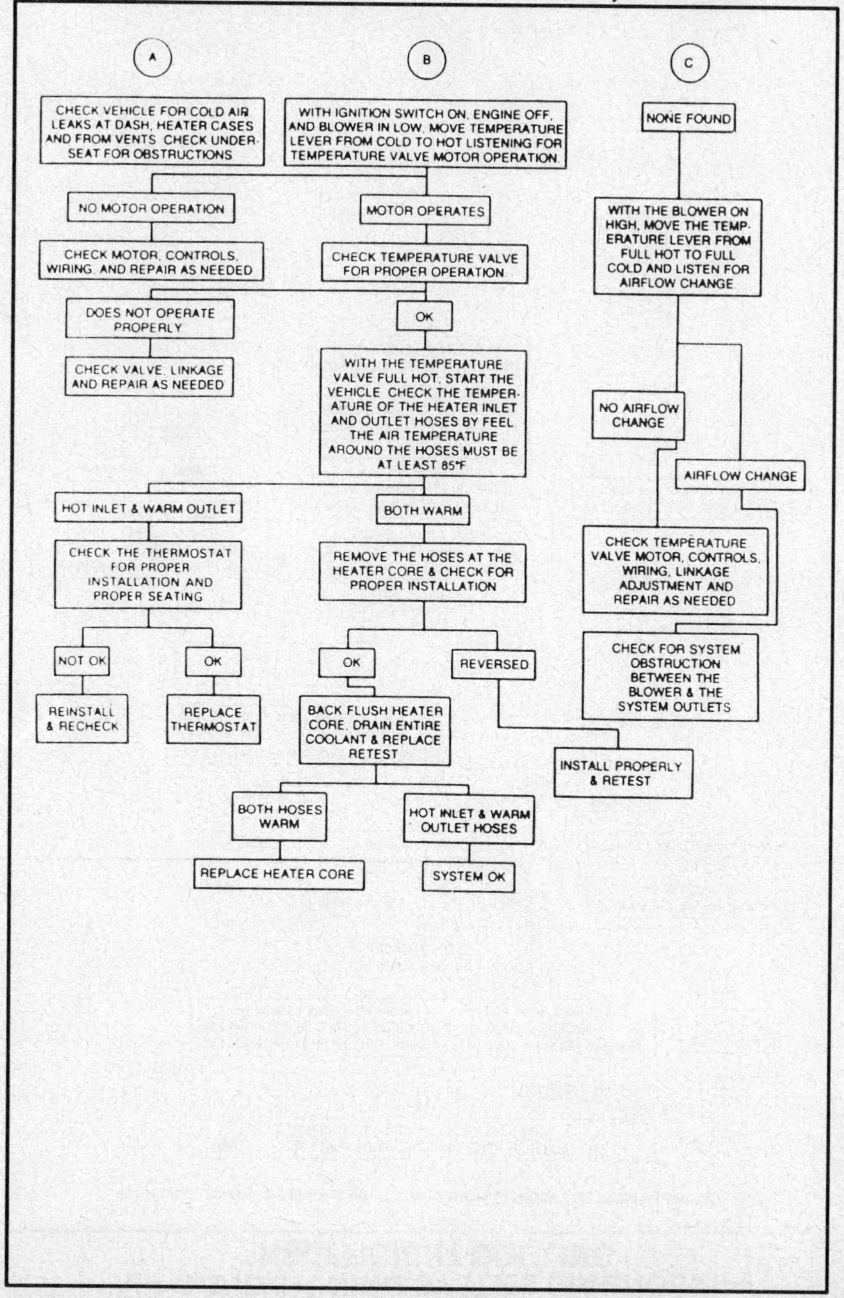

A
CHECK VEHICLE FOR COLD AIR LEAKS AT DASH, HEATER CASES AND FROM VENTS. CHECK UNDER-SEAT FOR OBSTRUCTIONS

B
WITH IGNITION SWITCH ON, ENGINE OFF, AND BLOWER IN LOW, MOVE TEMPERATURE LEVER FROM COLD TO HOT LISTENING FOR TEMPERATURE VALVE MOTOR OPERATION
NO MOTOR OPERATION
CHECK MOTOR, CONTROLS, WIRING, AND REPAIR AS NEEDED
MOTOR OPERATES
CHECK TEMPERATURE VALVE FOR PROPER OPERATION
DOES NOT OPERATE PROPERLY
CHECK VALVE, LINKAGE AND REPAIR AS NEEDED
OK
WITH THE TEMPERATURE VALVE FULL HOT, START THE VEHICLE. CHECK THE TEMPERATURE OF THE HEATER INLET AND OUTLET HOSES BY FEEL. THE AIR TEMPERATURE AROUND THE HOSES MUST BE AT LEAST 85°F
HOT INLET & WARM OUTLET
CHECK THE THERMOSTAT FOR PROPER INSTALLATION AND PROPER SEATING
NOT OK
REINSTALL & RECHECK
OK
REPLACE THERMOSTAT
BOTH WARM
REMOVE THE HOSES AT THE HEATER CORE & CHECK FOR PROPER INSTALLATION
OK
BACK FLUSH HEATER CORE, DRAIN ENTIRE COOLANT & REPLACE RETEST
BOTH HOSES WARM
REPLACE HEATER CORE
HOT INLET & WARM OUTLET HOSES
SYSTEM OK
REVERSED
INSTALL PROPERLY & RETEST

C
NONE FOUND
WITH THE BLOWER ON HIGH, MOVE THE TEMPERATURE LEVER FROM FULL HOT TO FULL COLD AND LISTEN FOR AIRFLOW CHANGE
NO AIRFLOW CHANGE
CHECK TEMPERATURE VALVE MOTOR, CONTROLS, WIRING, LINKAGE ADJUSTMENT AND REPAIR AS NEEDED
AIRFLOW CHANGE
CHECK FOR SYSTEM OBSTRUCTION BETWEEN THE BLOWER & THE SYSTEM OUTLETS

HEATER SYSTEM DIAGNOSIS—LUMINA APV, SILHOUETTE AND TRANS SPORT, CONT'D

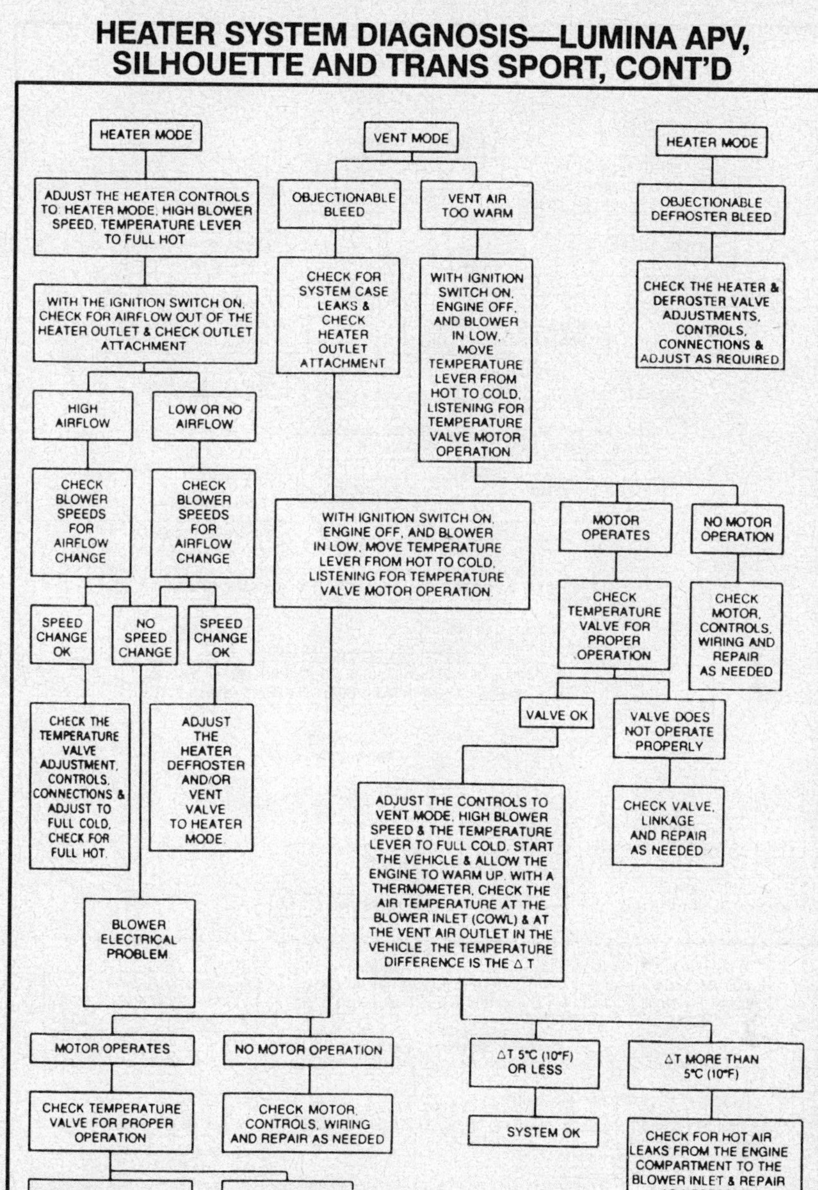
HEATER MODE
ADJUST THE HEATER CONTROLS TO HEATER MODE, HIGH BLOWER SPEED, TEMPERATURE LEVER TO FULL HOT
WITH THE IGNITION SWITCH ON, CHECK FOR AIRFLOW OUT OF THE HEATER OUTLET & CHECK OUTLET ATTACHMENT
HIGH AIRFLOW
CHECK BLOWER SPEEDS FOR AIRFLOW CHANGE
SPEED CHANGE OK
CHECK THE TEMPERATURE VALVE ADJUSTMENT, CONTROLS, CONNECTIONS & ADJUST TO FULL COLD, CHECK FOR FULL HOT.
LOW OR NO AIRFLOW
CHECK BLOWER SPEEDS FOR AIRFLOW CHANGE
NO SPEED CHANGE
BLOWER ELECTRICAL PROBLEM
SPEED CHANGE OK
ADJUST THE HEATER DEFROSTER AND/OR VENT VALVE TO HEATER MODE
VENT MODE
OBJECTIONABLE BLEED
CHECK FOR SYSTEM CASE LEAKS & CHECK HEATER OUTLET ATTACHMENT
WITH IGNITION SWITCH ON, ENGINE OFF, AND BLOWER IN LOW, MOVE TEMPERATURE LEVER FROM HOT TO COLD, LISTENING FOR TEMPERATURE VALVE MOTOR OPERATION
MOTOR OPERATES
CHECK TEMPERATURE VALVE FOR PROPER OPERATION
DOES NOT OPERATE PROPERLY
CHECK VALVE, LINKAGE AND REPAIR AS NEEDED
VALVE OK
ADJUST HEATER, DEFROSTER AND VENT VALVE TO VENT MODE
NO MOTOR OPERATION
CHECK MOTOR, CONTROLS, WIRING AND REPAIR AS NEEDED
VENT AIR TOO WARM
WITH IGNITION SWITCH ON, ENGINE OFF, AND BLOWER IN LOW, MOVE TEMPERATURE LEVER FROM HOT TO COLD, LISTENING FOR TEMPERATURE VALVE MOTOR OPERATION
MOTOR OPERATES
CHECK TEMPERATURE VALVE FOR PROPER OPERATION
VALVE OK
ADJUST THE CONTROLS TO VENT MODE, HIGH BLOWER SPEED & THE TEMPERATURE LEVER TO FULL COLD. START THE VEHICLE & ALLOW THE ENGINE TO WARM UP. WITH A THERMOMETER, CHECK THE AIR TEMPERATURE AT THE BLOWER INLET (COWL) & AT THE VENT AIR OUTLET IN THE VEHICLE. THE TEMPERATURE DIFFERENCE IS THE Δ T
Δ T 5°C (10°F) OR LESS
SYSTEM OK
Δ T MORE THAN 5°C (10°F)
CHECK FOR HOT AIR LEAKS FROM THE ENGINE COMPARTMENT TO THE BLOWER INLET & REPAIR AS NECESSARY
VALVE DOES NOT OPERATE PROPERLY
CHECK VALVE, LINKAGE AND REPAIR AS NEEDED
NO MOTOR OPERATION
CHECK MOTOR, CONTROLS, WIRING AND REPAIR AS NEEDED
HEATER MODE
OBJECTIONABLE DEFROSTER BLEED
CHECK THE HEATER & DEFROSTER VALVE ADJUSTMENTS, CONTROLS, CONNECTIONS & ADJUST AS REQUIRED

AIR CONDITIONING SYSTEM DIAGNOSIS—INSUFFICIENT COOLING

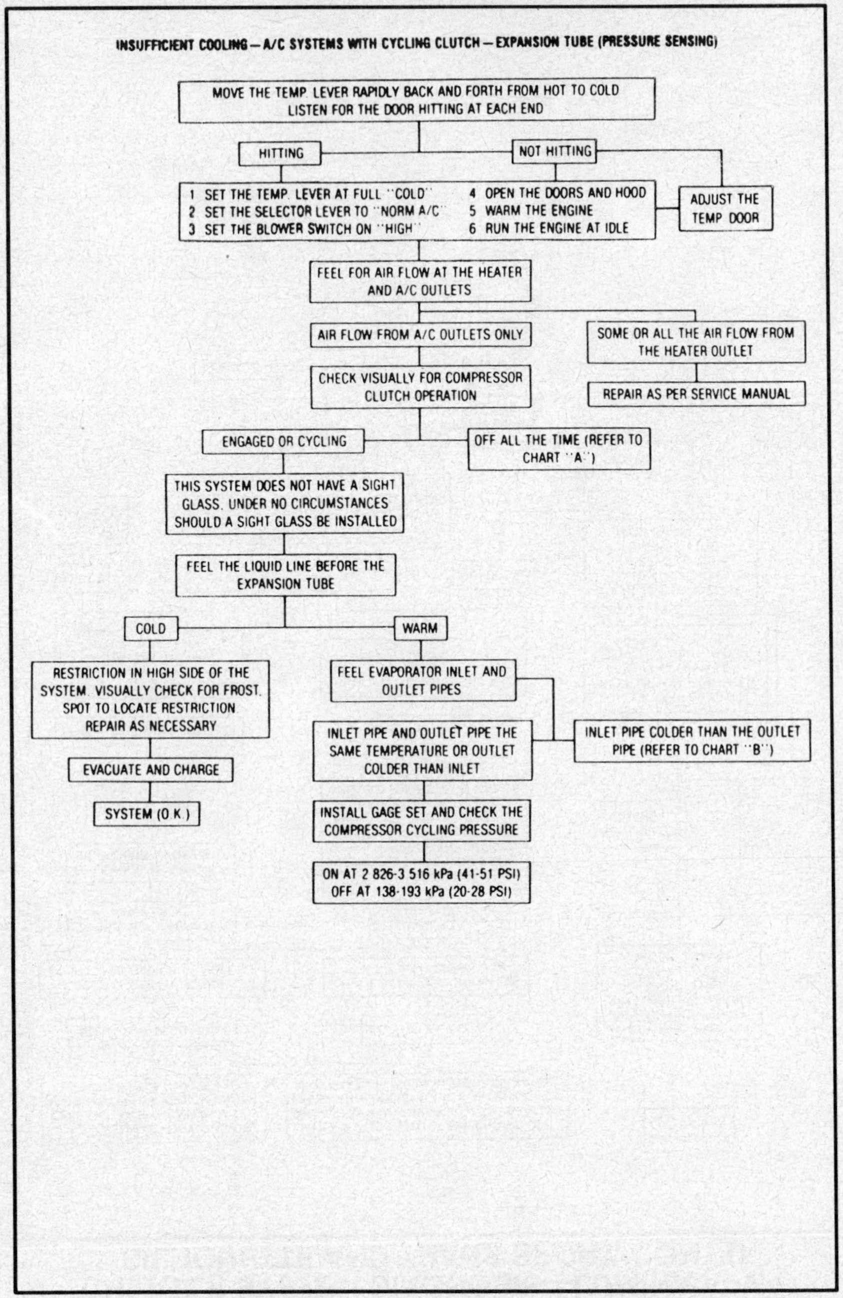

INSUFFICIENT COOLING — A/C SYSTEMS WITH CYCLING CLUTCH — EXPANSION TUBE (PRESSURE SENSING)

MOVE THE TEMP. LEVER RAPIDLY BACK AND FORTH FROM HOT TO COLD LISTEN FOR THE DOOR HITTING AT EACH END

HITTING

NOT HITTING — ADJUST THE TEMP. DOOR

1. SET THE TEMP. LEVER AT FULL "COLD"
2. SET THE SELECTOR LEVER TO "NORM A/C"
3. SET THE BLOWER SWITCH ON "HIGH"
4. OPEN THE DOORS AND HOOD
5. WARM THE ENGINE
6. RUN THE ENGINE AT IDLE

FEEL FOR AIR FLOW AT THE HEATER AND A/C OUTLETS

SOME OR ALL THE AIR FLOW FROM THE HEATER OUTLET — REPAIR AS PER SERVICE MANUAL

AIR FLOW FROM A/C OUTLETS ONLY — CHECK VISUALLY FOR COMPRESSOR CLUTCH OPERATION

OFF ALL THE TIME (REFER TO CHART "A")

ENGAGED OR CYCLING — THIS SYSTEM DOES NOT HAVE A SIGHT GLASS. UNDER NO CIRCUMSTANCES SHOULD A SIGHT GLASS BE INSTALLED — FEEL THE LIQUID LINE BEFORE THE EXPANSION TUBE

COLD — RESTRICTION IN HIGH SIDE OF THE SYSTEM. VISUALLY CHECK FOR FROST. SPOT TO LOCATE RESTRICTION. REPAIR AS NECESSARY — EVACUATE AND CHARGE — SYSTEM (O.K.)

WARM — FEEL EVAPORATOR INLET AND OUTLET PIPES

INLET PIPE COLDER THAN THE OUTLET PIPE (REFER TO CHART "B")

INLET PIPE AND OUTLET PIPE THE SAME TEMPERATURE OR OUTLET COLDER THAN INLET — INSTALL GAGE SET AND CHECK THE COMPRESSOR CYCLING PRESSURE — ON AT 2 826-3 516 kPa (41-51 PSI) OFF AT 138-193 kPa (20-28 PSI)

AIR CONDITIONING SYSTEM DIAGNOSIS—INSUFFICIENT COOLING, CONT'D

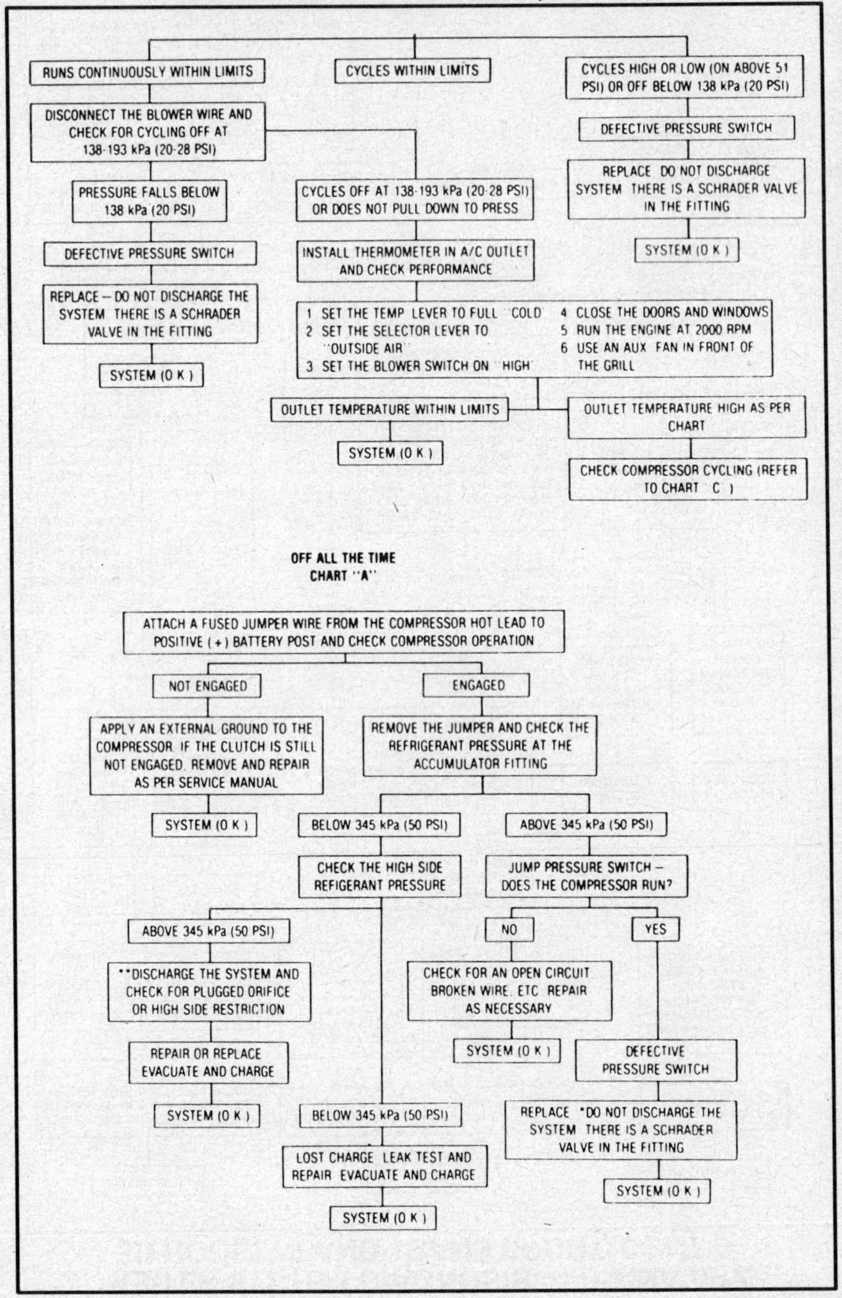

RUNS CONTINUOUSLY WITHIN LIMITS — DISCONNECT THE BLOWER WIRE AND CHECK FOR CYCLING OFF AT 138-193 kPa (20-28 PSI)

PRESSURE FALLS BELOW 138 kPa (20 PSI) — DEFECTIVE PRESSURE SWITCH — REPLACE — DO NOT DISCHARGE THE SYSTEM. THERE IS A SCHRADER VALVE IN THE FITTING — SYSTEM (O.K.)

CYCLES WITHIN LIMITS / CYCLES OFF AT 138-193 kPa (20-28 PSI) OR DOES NOT PULL DOWN TO PRESS — INSTALL THERMOMETER IN A/C OUTLET AND CHECK PERFORMANCE

1. SET THE TEMP. LEVER TO FULL "COLD"
2. SET THE SELECTOR LEVER TO "OUTSIDE AIR"
3. SET THE BLOWER SWITCH ON "HIGH"
4. CLOSE THE DOORS AND WINDOWS
5. RUN THE ENGINE AT 2000 RPM
6. USE AN AUX. FAN IN FRONT OF THE GRILL

OUTLET TEMPERATURE WITHIN LIMITS — SYSTEM (O.K.)

OUTLET TEMPERATURE HIGH AS PER CHART — CHECK COMPRESSOR CYCLING (REFER TO CHART "C")

CYCLES HIGH OR LOW (ON ABOVE 51 PSI) OR OFF BELOW 138 kPa (20 PSI) — DEFECTIVE PRESSURE SWITCH — REPLACE. DO NOT DISCHARGE SYSTEM. THERE IS A SCHRADER VALVE IN THE FITTING — SYSTEM (O.K.)

OFF ALL THE TIME
CHART "A"

ATTACH A FUSED JUMPER WIRE FROM THE COMPRESSOR HOT LEAD TO POSITIVE (+) BATTERY POST AND CHECK COMPRESSOR OPERATION

NOT ENGAGED — APPLY AN EXTERNAL GROUND TO THE COMPRESSOR. IF THE CLUTCH IS STILL NOT ENGAGED, REMOVE AND REPAIR AS PER SERVICE MANUAL — SYSTEM (O.K.)

ENGAGED — REMOVE THE JUMPER AND CHECK THE REFRIGERANT PRESSURE AT THE ACCUMULATOR FITTING

BELOW 345 kPa (50 PSI) — CHECK THE HIGH SIDE REFIGERANT PRESSURE

- ABOVE 345 kPa (50 PSI) — **DISCHARGE THE SYSTEM AND CHECK FOR PLUGGED ORIFICE OR HIGH SIDE RESTRICTION — REPAIR OR REPLACE EVACUATE AND CHARGE — SYSTEM (O.K.)
- BELOW 345 kPa (50 PSI) — LOST CHARGE. LEAK TEST AND REPAIR. EVACUATE AND CHARGE — SYSTEM (O.K.)

ABOVE 345 kPa (50 PSI) — JUMP PRESSURE SWITCH — DOES THE COMPRESSOR RUN?

- NO — CHECK FOR AN OPEN CIRCUIT BROKEN WIRE, ETC. REPAIR AS NECESSARY — SYSTEM (O.K.)
- YES — DEFECTIVE PRESSURE SWITCH — REPLACE. *DO NOT DISCHARGE THE SYSTEM. THERE IS A SCHRADER VALVE IN THE FITTING — SYSTEM (O.K.)

AIR CONDITIONING SYSTEM DIAGNOSIS INSUFFICIENT COOLING, CONT'D

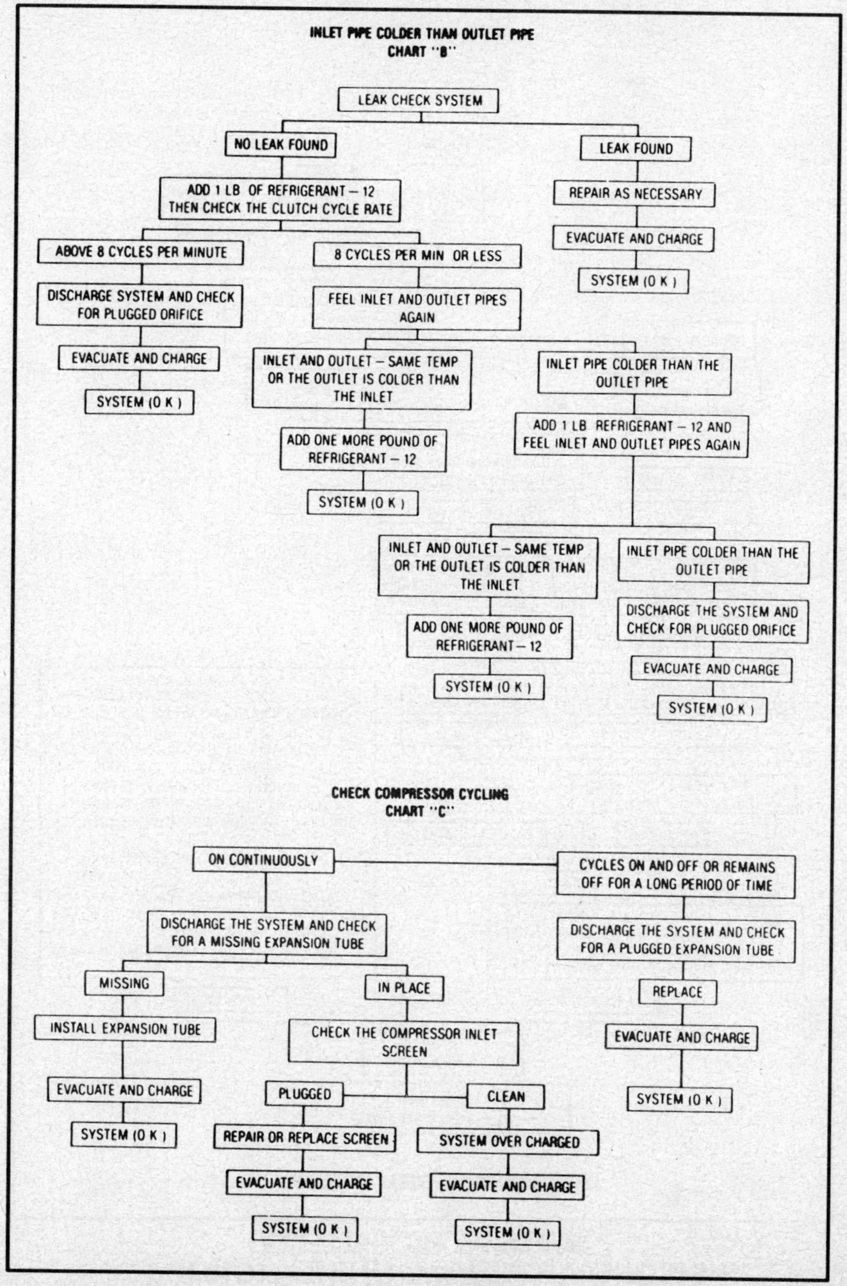

INLET PIPE COLDER THAN OUTLET PIPE
CHART "B"

LEAK CHECK SYSTEM

- NO LEAK FOUND
  - ADD 1 LB OF REFRIGERANT – 12 THEN CHECK THE CLUTCH CYCLE RATE
    - ABOVE 8 CYCLES PER MINUTE
      - DISCHARGE SYSTEM AND CHECK FOR PLUGGED ORIFICE
      - EVACUATE AND CHARGE
      - SYSTEM (O K)
    - 8 CYCLES PER MIN OR LESS
      - FEEL INLET AND OUTLET PIPES AGAIN
        - INLET AND OUTLET – SAME TEMP OR THE OUTLET IS COLDER THAN THE INLET
          - ADD ONE MORE POUND OF REFRIGERANT – 12
          - SYSTEM (O K)
        - INLET PIPE COLDER THAN THE OUTLET PIPE
          - ADD 1 LB REFRIGERANT – 12 AND FEEL INLET AND OUTLET PIPES AGAIN
            - INLET AND OUTLET – SAME TEMP OR THE OUTLET IS COLDER THAN THE INLET
              - ADD ONE MORE POUND OF REFRIGERANT – 12
              - SYSTEM (O K)
            - INLET PIPE COLDER THAN THE OUTLET PIPE
              - DISCHARGE THE SYSTEM AND CHECK FOR PLUGGED ORIFICE
              - EVACUATE AND CHARGE
              - SYSTEM (O K)
- LEAK FOUND
  - REPAIR AS NECESSARY
  - EVACUATE AND CHARGE
  - SYSTEM (O K)

CHECK COMPRESSOR CYCLING
CHART "C"

- ON CONTINUOUSLY
  - DISCHARGE THE SYSTEM AND CHECK FOR A MISSING EXPANSION TUBE
    - MISSING
      - INSTALL EXPANSION TUBE
      - EVACUATE AND CHARGE
      - SYSTEM (O K)
    - IN PLACE
      - CHECK THE COMPRESSOR INLET SCREEN
        - PLUGGED
          - REPAIR OR REPLACE SCREEN
          - EVACUATE AND CHARGE
          - SYSTEM (O K)
        - CLEAN
          - SYSTEM OVER CHARGED
          - EVACUATE AND CHARGE
          - SYSTEM (O K)
- CYCLES ON AND OFF OR REMAINS OFF FOR A LONG PERIOD OF TIME
  - DISCHARGE THE SYSTEM AND CHECK FOR A PLUGGED EXPANSION TUBE
  - REPLACE
  - EVACUATE AND CHARGE
  - SYSTEM (O K)

AIR CONDITIONING SYSTEM DIAGNOSIS COMPRESSOR

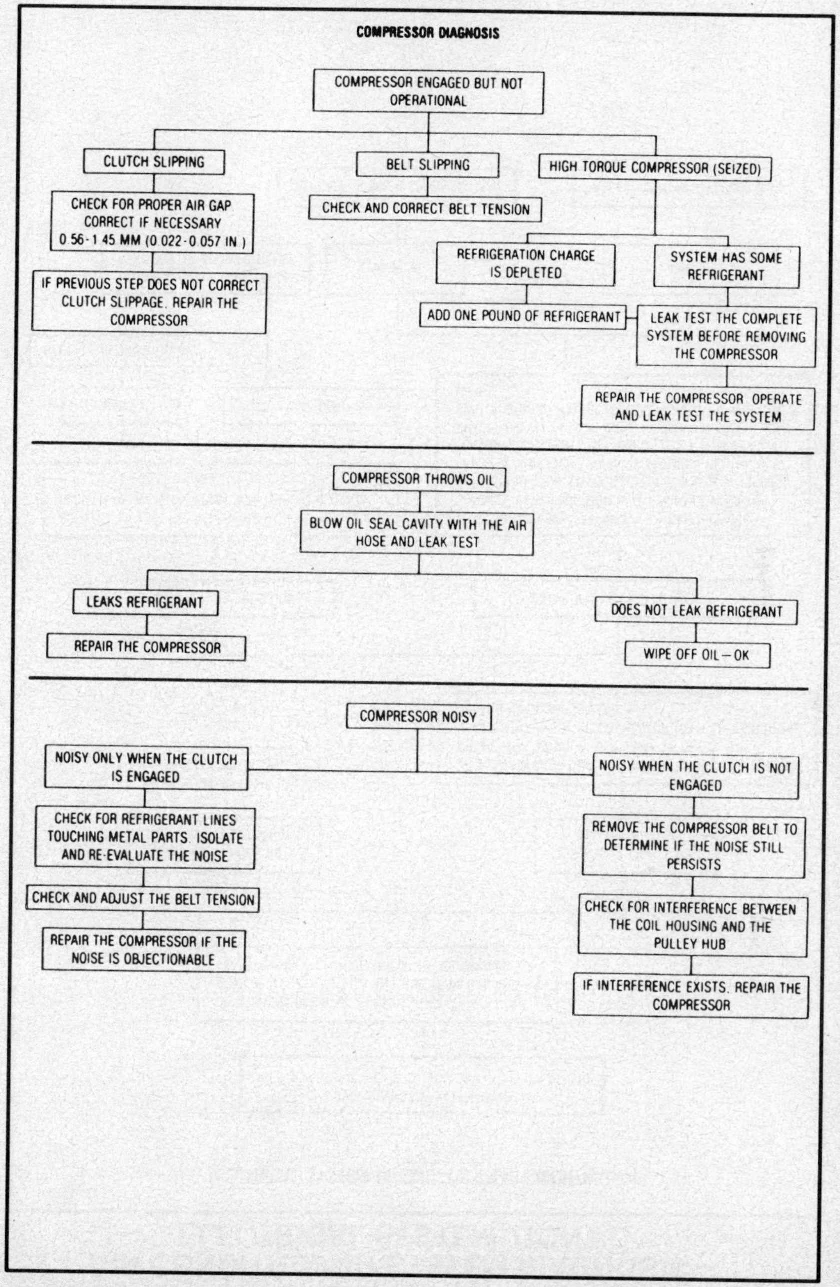

COMPRESSOR DIAGNOSIS

COMPRESSOR ENGAGED BUT NOT OPERATIONAL

- CLUTCH SLIPPING
  - CHECK FOR PROPER AIR GAP CORRECT IF NECESSARY 0 56-1 45 MM (0 022-0 057 IN)
  - IF PREVIOUS STEP DOES NOT CORRECT CLUTCH SLIPPAGE, REPAIR THE COMPRESSOR
- BELT SLIPPING
  - CHECK AND CORRECT BELT TENSION
- HIGH TORQUE COMPRESSOR (SEIZED)
  - REFRIGERATION CHARGE IS DEPLETED
    - ADD ONE POUND OF REFRIGERANT
  - SYSTEM HAS SOME REFRIGERANT
    - LEAK TEST THE COMPLETE SYSTEM BEFORE REMOVING THE COMPRESSOR
    - REPAIR THE COMPRESSOR OPERATE AND LEAK TEST THE SYSTEM

COMPRESSOR THROWS OIL

- BLOW OIL SEAL CAVITY WITH THE AIR HOSE AND LEAK TEST
  - LEAKS REFRIGERANT
    - REPAIR THE COMPRESSOR
  - DOES NOT LEAK REFRIGERANT
    - WIPE OFF OIL – OK

COMPRESSOR NOISY

- NOISY ONLY WHEN THE CLUTCH IS ENGAGED
  - CHECK FOR REFRIGERANT LINES TOUCHING METAL PARTS ISOLATE AND RE-EVALUATE THE NOISE
  - CHECK AND ADJUST THE BELT TENSION
  - REPAIR THE COMPRESSOR IF THE NOISE IS OBJECTIONABLE
- NOISY WHEN THE CLUTCH IS NOT ENGAGED
  - REMOVE THE COMPRESSOR BELT TO DETERMINE IF THE NOISE STILL PERSISTS
  - CHECK FOR INTERFERENCE BETWEEN THE COIL HOUSING AND THE PULLEY HUB
  - IF INTERFERENCE EXISTS, REPAIR THE COMPRESSOR

AIR CONDITIONING SYSTEM DIAGNOSIS—ELECTRICAL SYSTEM

ELECTRICAL SYSTEM DIAGNOSTIC CHART

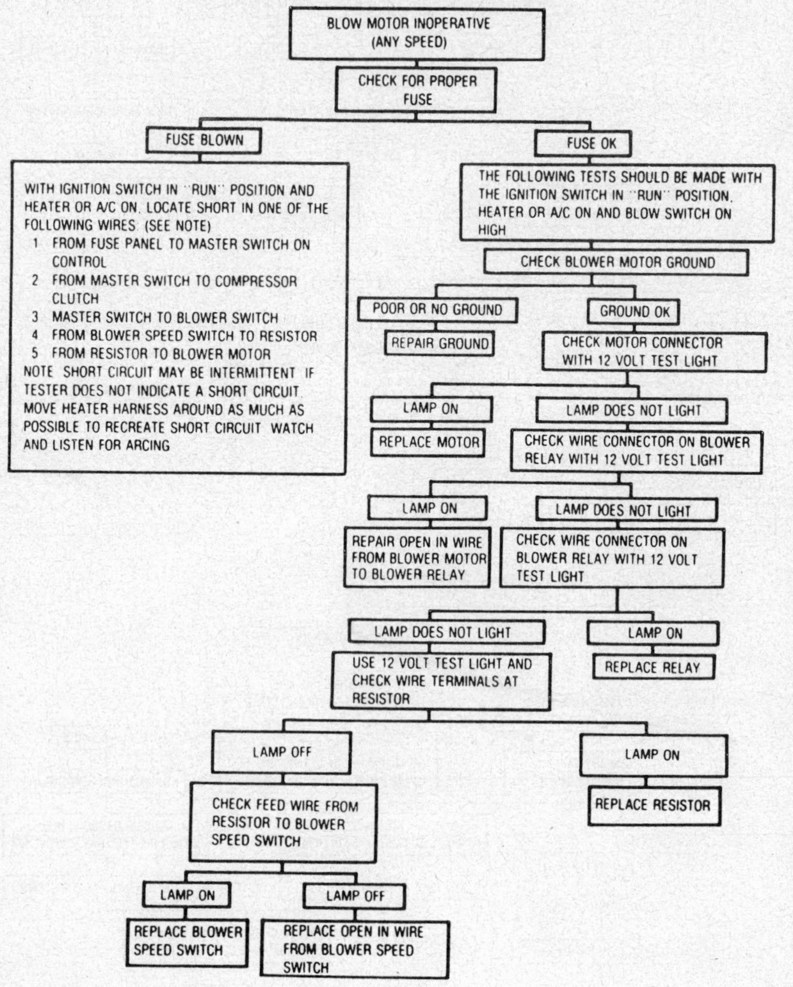

- BLOW MOTOR INOPERATIVE (ANY SPEED)
  - CHECK FOR PROPER FUSE
    - FUSE BLOWN
      - WITH IGNITION SWITCH IN "RUN" POSITION AND HEATER OR A/C ON, LOCATE SHORT IN ONE OF THE FOLLOWING WIRES. (SEE NOTE)
        1. FROM FUSE PANEL TO MASTER SWITCH ON CONTROL
        2. FROM MASTER SWITCH TO COMPRESSOR CLUTCH
        3. MASTER SWITCH TO BLOWER SWITCH
        4. FROM BLOWER SPEED SWITCH TO RESISTOR
        5. FROM RESISTOR TO BLOWER MOTOR

        NOTE: SHORT CIRCUIT MAY BE INTERMITTENT. IF TESTER DOES NOT INDICATE A SHORT CIRCUIT, MOVE HEATER HARNESS AROUND AS MUCH AS POSSIBLE TO RECREATE SHORT CIRCUIT. WATCH AND LISTEN FOR ARCING
    - FUSE OK
      - THE FOLLOWING TESTS SHOULD BE MADE WITH THE IGNITION SWITCH IN "RUN" POSITION, HEATER OR A/C ON AND BLOW SWITCH ON HIGH
        - CHECK BLOWER MOTOR GROUND
          - POOR OR NO GROUND
            - REPAIR GROUND
          - GROUND OK
            - CHECK MOTOR CONNECTOR WITH 12 VOLT TEST LIGHT
              - LAMP ON
                - REPLACE MOTOR
              - LAMP DOES NOT LIGHT
                - CHECK WIRE CONNECTOR ON BLOWER RELAY WITH 12 VOLT TEST LIGHT
                  - LAMP ON
                    - REPAIR OPEN IN WIRE FROM BLOWER MOTOR TO BLOWER RELAY
                  - LAMP DOES NOT LIGHT
                    - CHECK WIRE CONNECTOR ON BLOWER RELAY WITH 12 VOLT TEST LIGHT
                      - LAMP DOES NOT LIGHT
                        - USE 12 VOLT TEST LIGHT AND CHECK WIRE TERMINALS AT RESISTOR
                          - LAMP OFF
                            - CHECK FEED WIRE FROM RESISTOR TO BLOWER SPEED SWITCH
                              - LAMP ON
                                - REPLACE BLOWER SPEED SWITCH
                              - LAMP OFF
                                - REPLACE OPEN IN WIRE FROM BLOWER SPEED SWITCH
                          - LAMP ON
                            - REPLACE RESISTOR
                      - LAMP ON
                        - REPLACE RELAY

AIR CONDITIONING SYSTEM DIAGNOSIS—ELECTRICAL SYSTEM, CONT'D

ELECTRICAL SYSTEM DIAGNOSTIC CHART (CONTINUED)

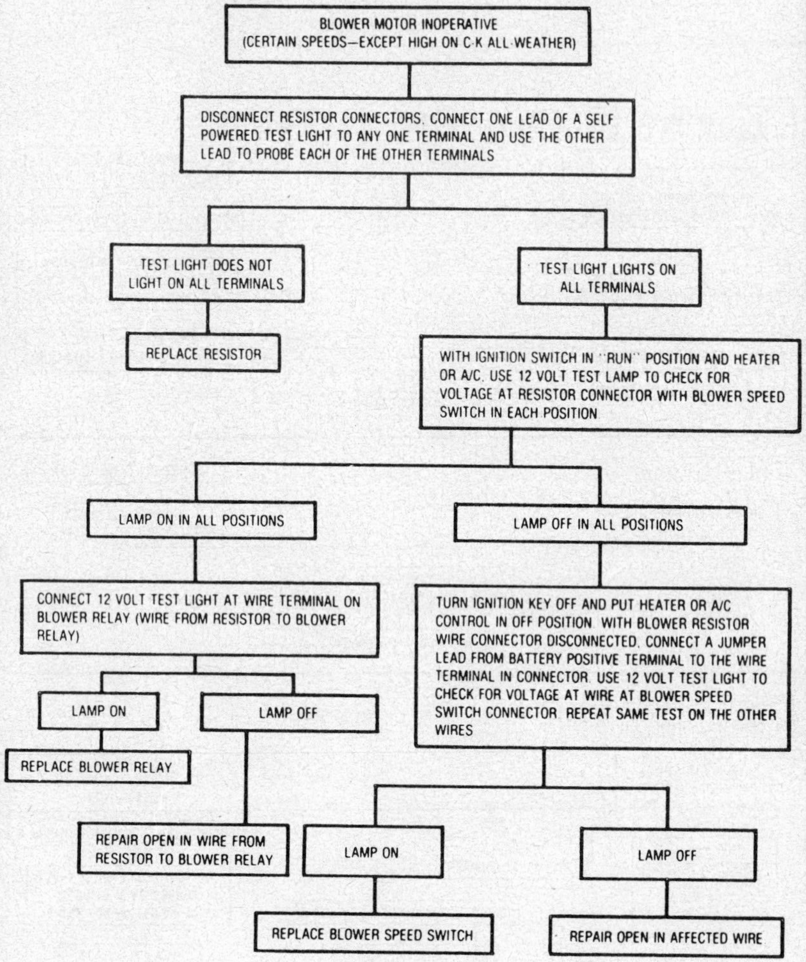

- BLOWER MOTOR INOPERATIVE (CERTAIN SPEEDS—EXCEPT HIGH ON C-K ALL-WEATHER)
  - DISCONNECT RESISTOR CONNECTORS. CONNECT ONE LEAD OF A SELF POWERED TEST LIGHT TO ANY ONE TERMINAL AND USE THE OTHER LEAD TO PROBE EACH OF THE OTHER TERMINALS
    - TEST LIGHT DOES NOT LIGHT ON ALL TERMINALS
      - REPLACE RESISTOR
    - TEST LIGHT LIGHTS ON ALL TERMINALS
      - WITH IGNITION SWITCH IN "RUN" POSITION AND HEATER OR A/C, USE 12 VOLT TEST LAMP TO CHECK FOR VOLTAGE AT RESISTOR CONNECTOR WITH BLOWER SPEED SWITCH IN EACH POSITION
        - LAMP ON IN ALL POSITIONS
          - CONNECT 12 VOLT TEST LIGHT AT WIRE TERMINAL ON BLOWER RELAY (WIRE FROM RESISTOR TO BLOWER RELAY)
            - LAMP ON
              - REPLACE BLOWER RELAY
            - LAMP OFF
              - REPAIR OPEN IN WIRE FROM RESISTOR TO BLOWER RELAY
        - LAMP OFF IN ALL POSITIONS
          - TURN IGNITION KEY OFF AND PUT HEATER OR A/C CONTROL IN OFF POSITION. WITH BLOWER RESISTOR WIRE CONNECTOR DISCONNECTED, CONNECT A JUMPER LEAD FROM BATTERY POSITIVE TERMINAL TO THE WIRE TERMINAL IN CONNECTOR. USE 12 VOLT TEST LIGHT TO CHECK FOR VOLTAGE AT WIRE AT BLOWER SPEED SWITCH CONNECTOR. REPEAT SAME TEST ON THE OTHER WIRES
            - LAMP ON
              - REPLACE BLOWER SPEED SWITCH
            - LAMP OFF
              - REPAIR OPEN IN AFFECTED WIRE

AIR CONDITIONING SYSTEM DIAGNOSIS—VACUUM SCHEMATIC—G SERIES

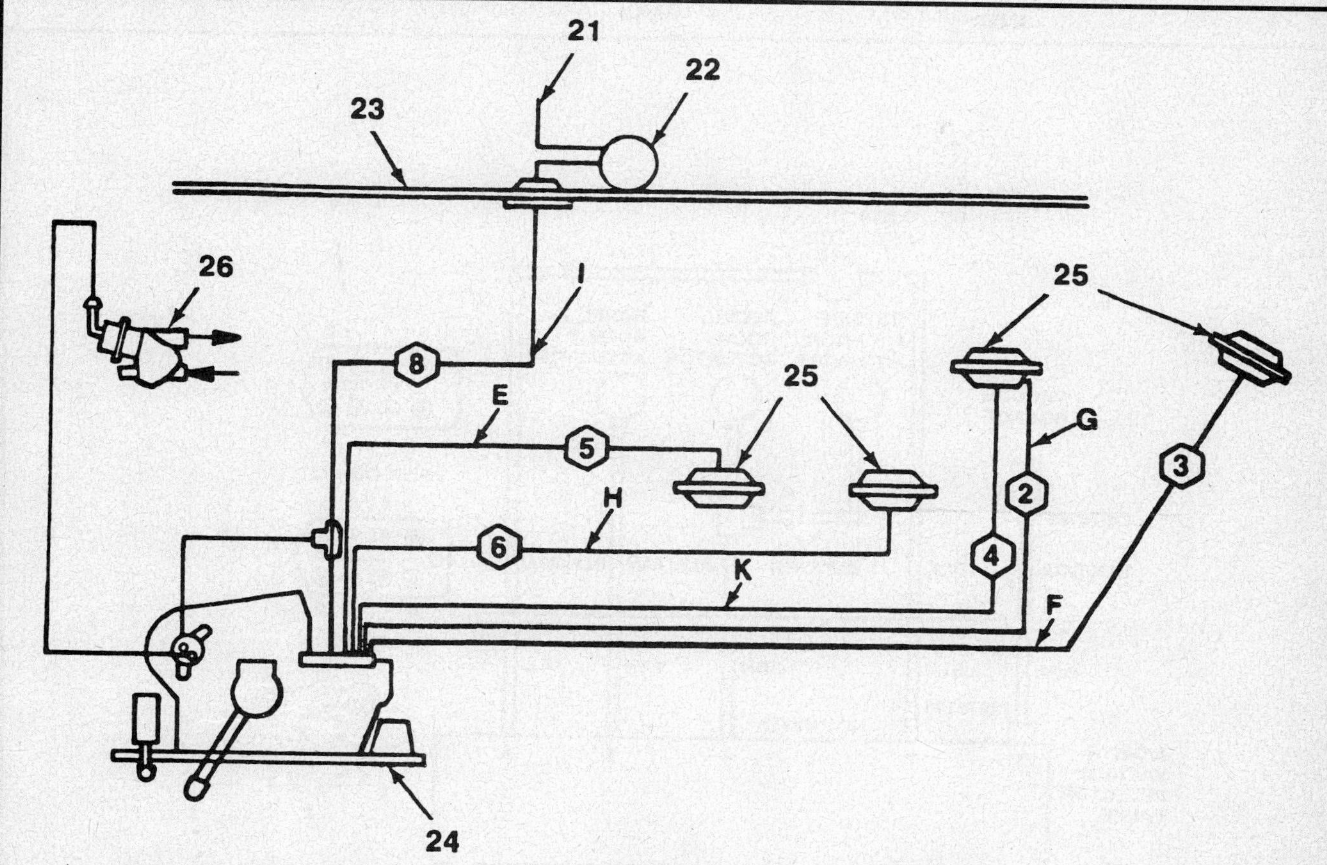

Connection	Port No.	Max	Norm	Bi Level	Vent	Heater	Blend	Defrost
Sealed	1	—	—	—	—	—	—	—
Defrost	2	Vent	Vent	Vent	Vent	Vent	Vent	Vac
O.S.A./Rec	3	Vac	Vent	Vent	Vent	Vent	Vent	Vent
Heat-Def	4	Vac	Vac	Vac	Vac	Vac	Vent	Vent
Bi-Level	5	Vac	Vac	Vac	Vac	Vent	Vent	Vent
A/C Mode	6	Vac	Vac	Vent	Vac	Vent	Vent	Vent
Sealed	7	—	—	—	—	—	—	—
Source	8	Vac	Vac	Vac	Vac	Vac	Vac	Vac
Sealed	9	—	—	—	—	—	—	—

Ports 1, 7 & 9 Not Used (Sealed On Vacuum Hose Assembly)

I. Vacuum Line—Tan (Source)
E. Vacuum Line—Gray (Bi Level)
H. Vacuum Line—Dark Blue (A/C)
K. Vacuum Line—Red (Heat/Defrost)
F. Vacuum Line—Orange (Recirculate)
G. Vacuum Line—Purple (Defrost)

21. Vacuum Source—Engine
22. Vacuum Tank
23. Cowl
24. Control
25. Actuator
26. Htr Water Bypass Valve

AIR CONDITIONING SYSTEM DIAGNOSIS—VACUUM SCHEMATIC—1993 S10/S15 SERIES AND BRAVADA

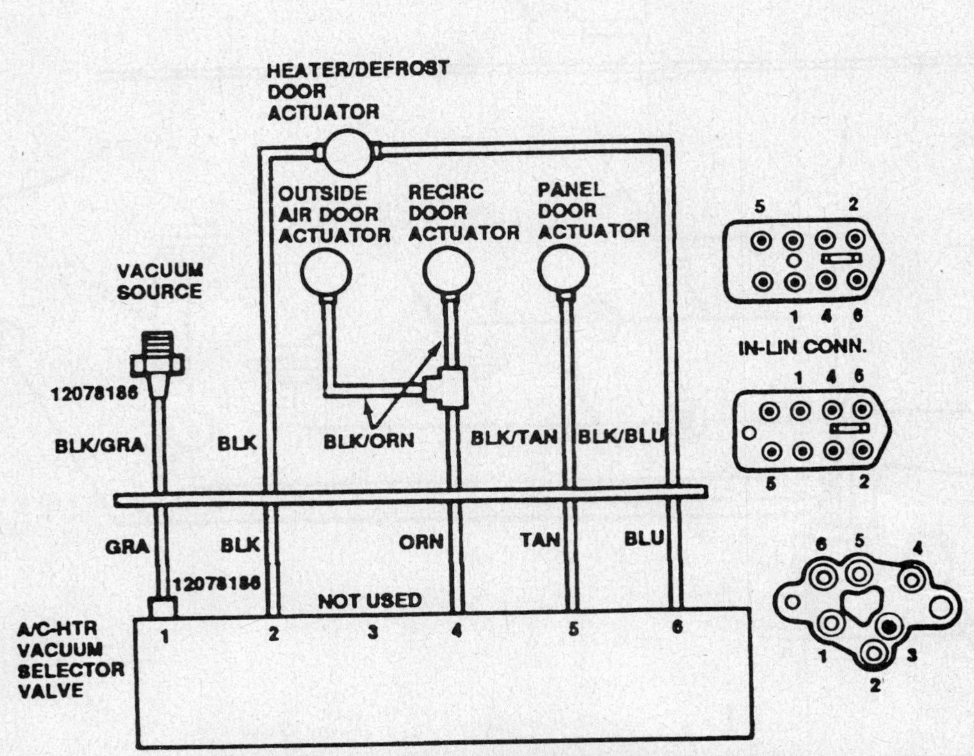

A/C-HTR VACUUM SELECTOR VALVE OPERATING CHART

CONNECTION	PORT	OFF	MAX A/C	NORM A/C	BI-LEV A/C	VENT	HEATER	DEFROST
SOURCE	1	VACUUM	VACUUM	VACUUM	VACUUM	VACUUM	VACUUM	VACUUM
HEATER	2	PARTIAL VAC.	VENT	VENT	VENT	VENT	PARTIAL VAC.	VENT
NOT USED	3	SEALED IN THE CONNECTOR						
OUTSIDE AIR/ RECIRCULATION	4	VENT	VACUUM	VENT	VENT	VENT	VENT	VENT
PANEL	5	VENT	VACUUM	VACUUM	VACUUM	VACUUM	VENT	VENT
DEFROST	6	VENT	VACUUM	VACUUM	VENT	VACUUM	VENT	VACUUM

AIR CONDITIONING SYSTEM DIAGNOSIS—VACUUM SCHEMATIC—1995 S/T SERIES

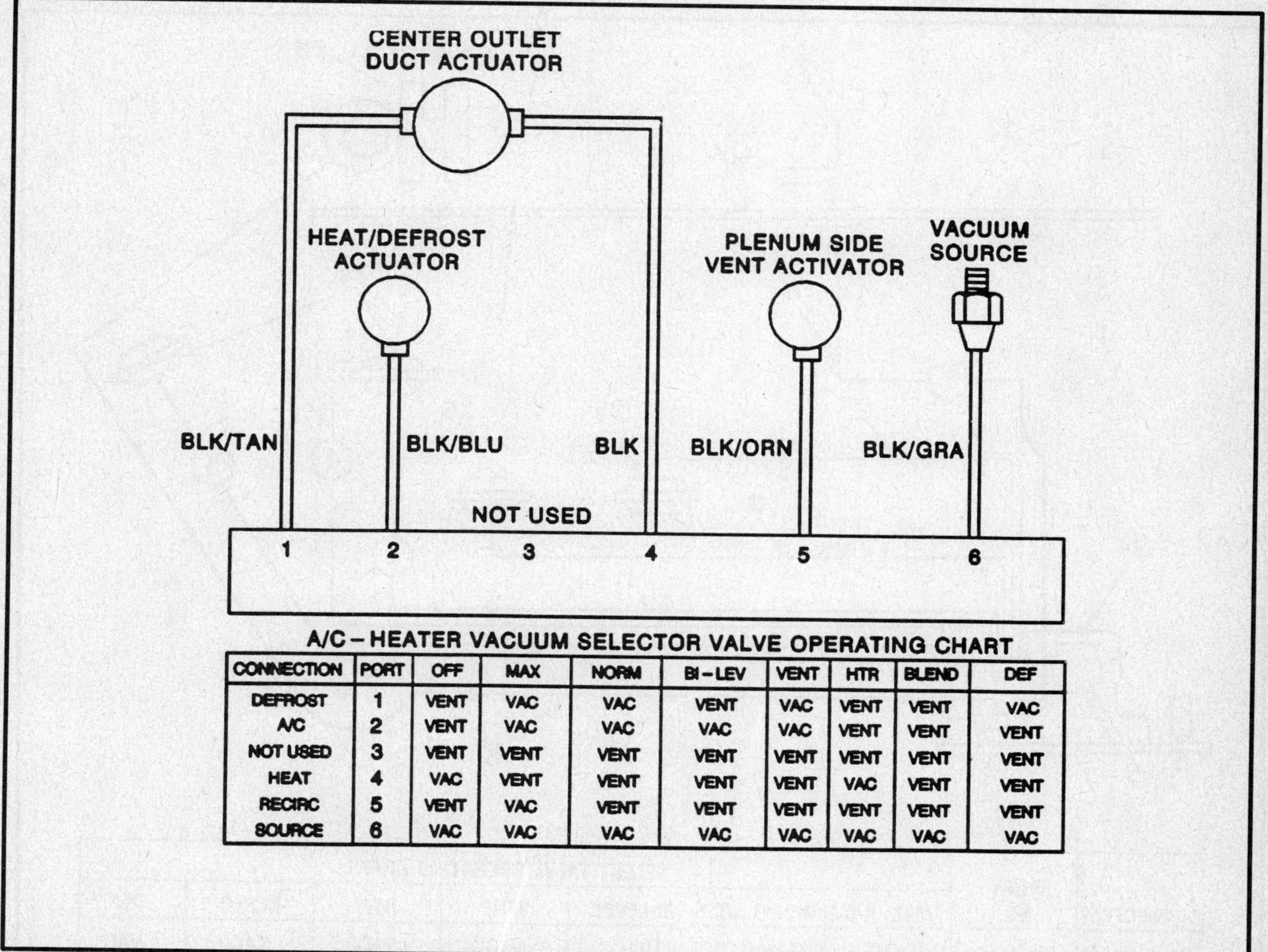

A/C – HEATER VACUUM SELECTOR VALVE OPERATING CHART

CONNECTION	PORT	OFF	MAX	NORM	BI – LEV	VENT	HTR	BLEND	DEF
DEFROST	1	VENT	VAC	VAC	VENT	VAC	VENT	VENT	VAC
A/C	2	VENT	VAC	VAC	VAC	VAC	VENT	VENT	VENT
NOT USED	3	VENT	VENT	VENT	VENT	VENT	VENT	VENT	VENT
HEAT	4	VAC	VENT	VENT	VENT	VENT	VAC	VENT	VENT
RECIRC	5	VENT	VAC	VENT	VENT	VENT	VENT	VENT	VENT
SOURCE	6	VAC	VAC	VAC	VAC	VAC	VAC	VAC	VAC

AIR CONDITIONING SYSTEM DIAGNOSIS—VACUUM SCHEMATIC—ASTRO AND SAFARI

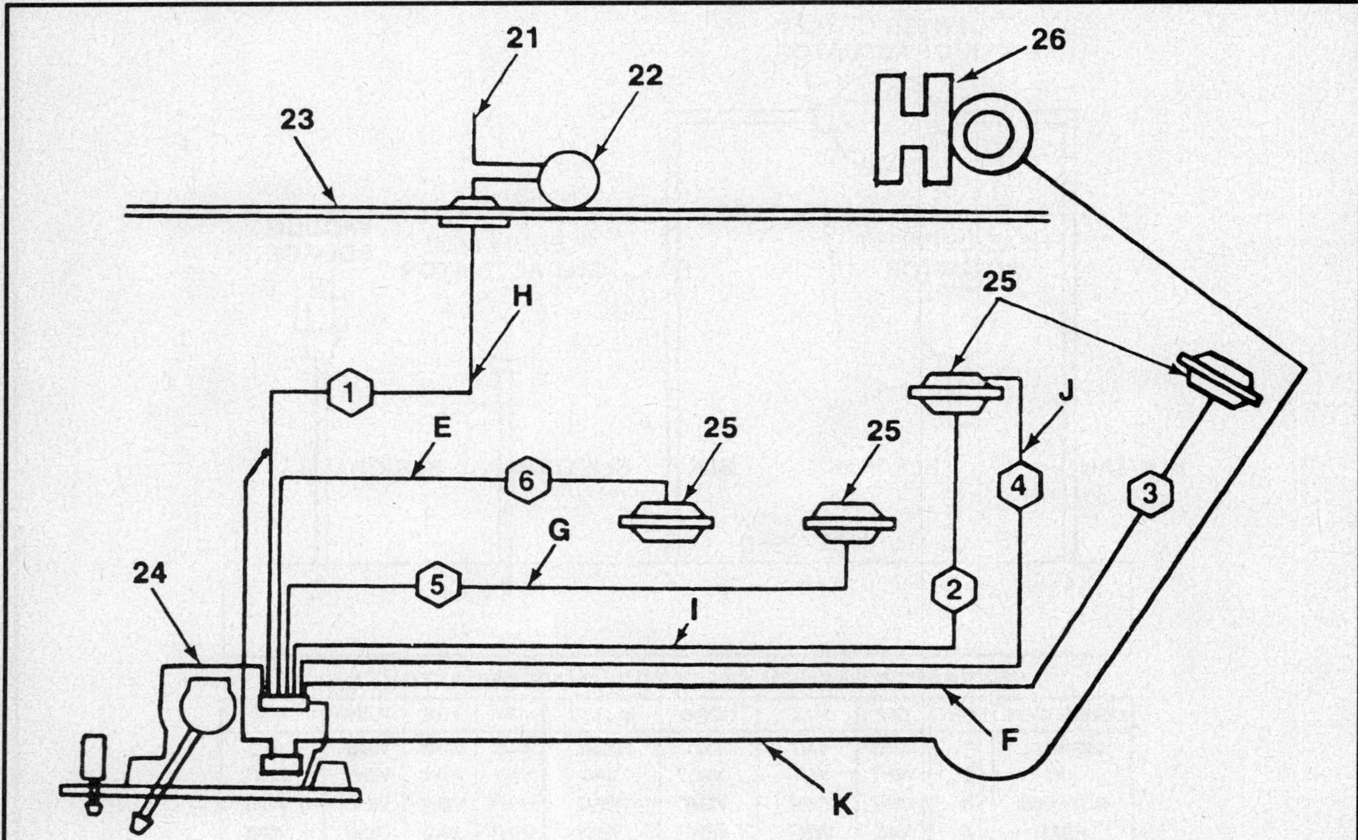

CONNECTION	PORT NO.	SELECT VALVE OPERATING CHART						
		MAX. A/C	NORM A/C	BI-LEVEL	VENT	HTR	BLEND	DEF.
Source	1	VAC	VAC	VAC	VAC	VAC	VAC	VAC
Def.	2	VENT	VENT	VENT	VENT	VENT	VENT	VAC
REC/OSA	3	VAC	VENT	VENT	VENT	VENT	VENT	VENT
HTR	4	VENT	VAC	VAC	VAC	VAC	VENT	VENT
BI-LEV	5	VAC	VAC	VAC	VAC	VENT	VENT	VENT
A/C	6	VAC	VAC	VENT	VAC	VENT	VENT	VENT

E. Vacuum Line - Bi-Level (Blue)
F. Vacuum Line - Recirculate (Brown)
G. Vacuum Line - A/C (Violet)
H. Vacuum Line - Source (Green)
I. Vacuum Line - Defrost (Pink)
J. Vacuum Line - Heat (Tan)
K. Vacuum Line - Water Valve (Black)

21. Vacuum Source - Engine
22. Vacuum Tank
23. Cowl
24. Control
25. Actuator
26. Water Valve

AIR CONDITIONING SYSTEM DIAGNOSIS—VACUUM SCHEMATIC—LUMINA APV, SILHOUETTE AND TRANS SPORT

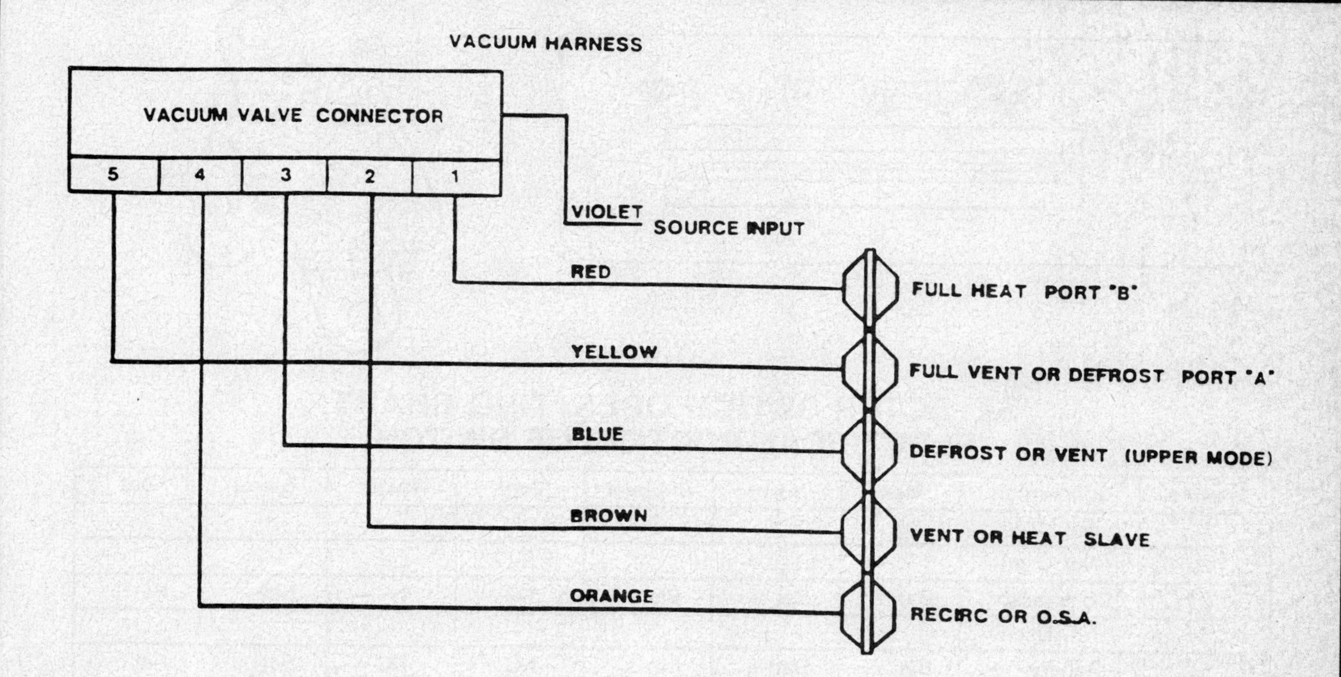

VACUUM VALVE LOGIC - MODE LEVER POSITIONS

PORT	OFF	MAX A/C	NORM A/C	BI LEVEL	VENT	HEATER	DEFROST	DEFOG
LOWER MODE HEATER	VENT	VENT	VENT	VENT	VENT	VAC	VENT	VENT
SLAVE DOOR	VENT	VAC	VAC	VAC	VAC	VENT	VENT	VENT
UPPER MODE DEFROST A/C	VENT	VAC	VAC	VAC	VAC	VENT	VENT	VENT
A.I.	VENT O.S.A.	VAC RECIRC	VENT O.S.A.	VENT O.S.A.	VENT O.S.A.	VENT O.S.A.	VENT O.S.A.	VENT O.S.A.
LOWER MODE A/C DEFROST	VENT	VAC	VAC	VENT	VAC	VENT	VAC	VENT

AIR CONDITIONING SYSTEM DIAGNOSIS—VACUUM ACTUATED CONTROL ASSEMBLY—G SERIES VAN

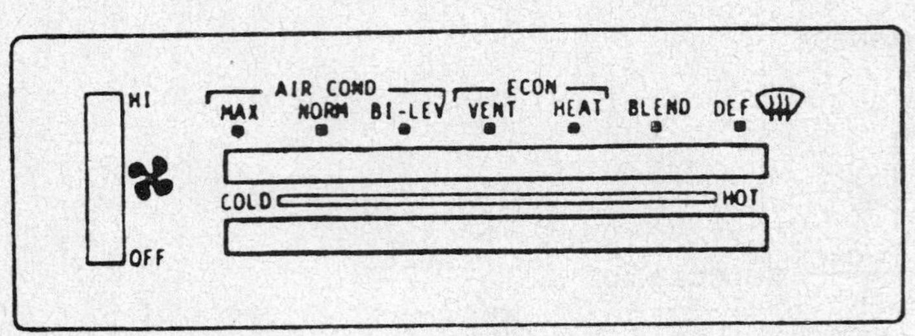

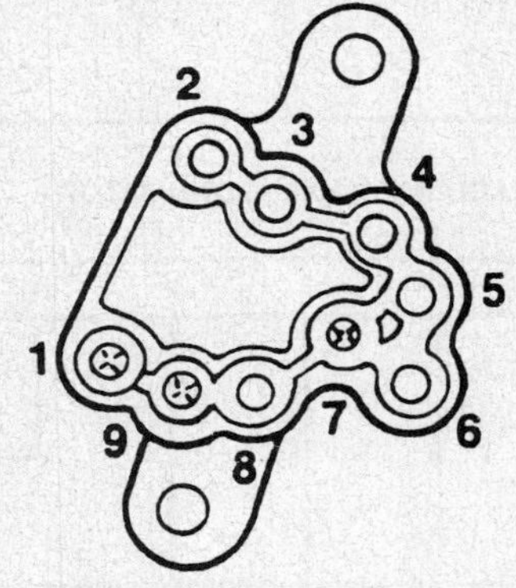

SELECTOR SWITCH OPERATING CHART (ELECTRICAL PORTION OF SWITCH)

Terminal	Connection	Max	Norm	Bi-Level	Vent	Heater	Blend	Def
1	Not Used							
2	Not Used							
3	Compressor	Bat +	Bat +	Bat +	NC	NC	Bat +	Bat +
4	Not Used							
5	Battery +	Bat +	Bat +	Bat +	NC	NC	Bat +	Bat +

SELECTOR VALVE OPERATING CHART (VACUUM PORTION OF SWITCH)

Connection	Port No.	Max	Norm	Bi Level	Vent	Heater	Blend	Defrost
Sealed	1	—	—	—	—	—	—	—
Defrost	2	Vent	Vent	Vent	Vent	Vent	Vent	Vac
O.S.A./Rec	3	Vac	Vent	Vent	Vent	Vent	Vent	Vent
Heat-Def	4	Vac	Vac	Vac	Vac	Vac	Vent	Vent
Bi-Level	5	Vac	Vac	Vac	Vac	Vent	Vent	Vent
A/C Mode	6	Vac	Vac	Vent	Vac	Vent	Vent	Vent
Sealed	7	—	—	—	—	—	—	—
Source	8	Vac	Vac	Vac	Vac	Vac	Vac	Vac
Sealed	9	—	—	—	—	—	—	—

FAN SWITCH OPERATING CHART

Terminal	Connection	Off	Lo	Med 1	Med 2	HI
A	Hi					Conn F, C, E
B	Med 2				Conn F, C, E	
C	Bat +		Conn F, E	Conn F, D, E	Conn F, B, E	Conn F, A, E
D	Med 1			Conn F, C, E		
E	Lo	Conn F	Conn F, C	Conn F, C, D	Conn F, B, C	Conn F, A, C
F	Common	Conn E	Conn C, E	Conn C, D, E	Conn B, C, E	Conn A, C, E

AIR CONDITIONING SYSTEM DIAGNOSIS VACUUM ACTUATED CONTROL ASSEMBLY— ASTRO VAN AND SAFARI

CONNECTION	PORT NO.	SELECT VALVE OPERATING CHART						
		MAX. A/C	NORM A/C	BI-LEVEL	VENT	HTR	BLEND	DEF.
Source	1	VAC	VAC	VAC	VAC	VAC	VAC	VAC
Def.	2	VENT	VENT	VENT	VENT	VENT	VENT	VAC
REC/OSA	3	VAC	VENT	VENT	VENT	VENT	VENT	VENT
HTR	4	VENT	VAC	VAC	VAC	VAC	VENT	VENT
MODE (A/C)	5	VAC	VAC	VAC	VAC	VENT	VENT	VENT
MODE (HTR)	6	VAC	VAC	VENT	VAC	VENT	VENT	VENT

BLOWER SWITCH

TERM	POSITION			
	OFF	M_1	M_2	HI
B+	No Continuity	Conn. To M_1	Conn. To M_2	Conn. To H
H	No Continuity	No Continuity	No Continuity	Conn. to B+
M_1	No Continuity	Conn. To B+	Continuity Optional	No Continuity
M_2	No Continuity	No Continuity	Conn. To B+	Continuity Optional

CONNECTION	TERM NO.	SELECT VALVE OPERATING CHART						
		MAX. A/C	NORM A/C	BI-LEVEL	VENT	HEAT	BLEND	DEFROST
Compressor	1	Conn. 3,5	Conn. 3,5	Conn. 3,5	No Conn.	No Conn.	Conn. 3,5	Conn. 3,5
No Used	2				No Conn.			
B+	3	Conn. 1,5	Conn. 1,5	Conn. 1,5	No Conn.	No Conn.	Conn. 1,5	Conn. 1,5
No Used	4				No Conn.			
Compressor	5	Conn. 1,3	Conn. 1,3	Conn. 1,3	No Conn.	No Conn.	Conn. 1,3	Conn. 1,3

AIR CONDITIONING SYSTEM DIAGNOSIS— VDOT SYSTEM

STEP 1

A/C FUNCTIONAL TEST

STEP	CONTROL SETTINGS						SYSTEM RESPONSE					
	MODE BUTTON	LITE ON	TEMP SETT	FAN SW FRT	FAN SW RR	FAN SPEED	RR. OPT AUX. DUCT	HEATER OUTLETS	A/C I.P. OUTLETS	DEF OUTLETS	SIDE WDO DEF	A.C COMPR
1	OFF	YES	FULL HOT	HI	OFF	OFF	NO AIR FLOW	NO AIR FLOW	NO AIR FLOW	NO AIR FLOW	NO AIR FLOW	OFF
2	DEFR	YES	FULL HOT	HI	OFF	HI	SOME AIR FLOW	SOME AIR FLOW	NO AIR FLOW	HOT AIR FLOW	SOME HOT AIR FLOW	ON
3	MIX	YES	FULL HOT	HI	OFF	HI	SOME AIR FLOW	AIR FLOW	NO AIR FLOW	HOT AIR FLOW	SOME HOT AIR FLOW	ON
4	HEATER	YES	FULL HOT	HI	OFF	HI	AIR FLOW	HOT AIR FLOW	NO AIR FLOW	SOME AIR FLOW	SOME HOT AIR FLOW	OFF
5	VENT	YES	FULL HOT	HI	OFF	HI	SOME AIR FLOW	NO AIR FLOW	HOT AIR FLOW	NO AIR FLOW	SOME AIR FLOW	OFF
6	BI-LEVEL	YES	FULL COLD	HI	OFF	HI	SOME AIR FLOW	AIR FLOW	COLD AIR FLOW	SOME AIR FLOW	SOME AIR FLOW	ON
7	NORMAL	YES	FULL COLD	LOW	OFF	HI	SOME AIR FLOW	NO AIR FLOW	COLD AIR FLOW	NO AIR FLOW	SOME AIR FLOW	ON
8	NORMAL	YES	FULL COLD	HI	OFF	LOW	SOME AIR FLOW	NO AIR FLOW	COLD AIR FLOW	NO AIR FLOW	SOME AIR FLOW	ON
9	MAX	YES	FULL COLD	HI	OFF	HI	SOME AIR FLOW	NO AIR FLOW	COLD AIR FLOW	NO AIR FLOW	SOME AIR FLOW	ON
10	MAX	YES	FULL COLD	LOW	OFF	LOW	SOME AIR FLOW	NO AIR FLOW	COLD AIR FLOW	NO AIR FLOW	SOME AIR FLOW	ON
11	HEATER	YES	FULL HOT	LOW	HI	LOW HI	HOT AIR FLOW	SOME AIR FLOW	NO AIR FLOW	SOME AIR FLOW	SOME AIR FLOW	OFF

- TEMPERATURE DOOR ACTUATOR MOTOR SHOULD BE HEARD DURING TEMPERATURE SETTING CHANGES AND NOTICEABLE BLOWER SPEED INCREASE MUST OCCUR FROM LOW TO MID. TO MID, AND HIGH
- CHECK TEMPERATURE LEVER FOR EFFORT AND TRAVEL (COLD TO HOT) (TEMPERATURE CHANGE SHOULD OCCUR)
- CHECK FOR AIR FLOW AS DEFINED IN SYSTEM RESPONSE
- ALL I/P OUTLETS MUST BE CHECKED FOR: 1) BARREL ROTATION. 2) VANE OPERATION. 3) BARREL AND VANES MUST HOLD PRESENT POSITION IN HI BLOWER OPERATION

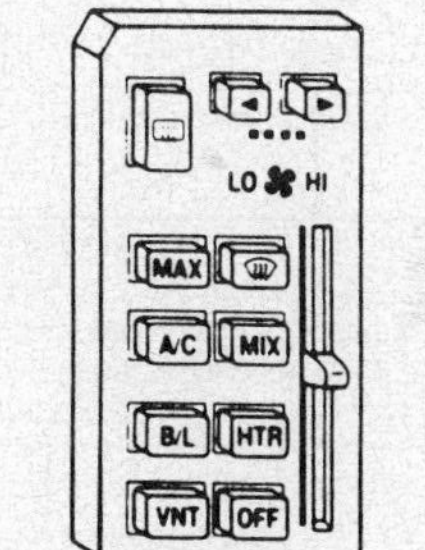

AIR CONDITIONING SYSTEM DIAGNOSIS—VDOT SYSTEM, CONT'D

STEP 2—*Checking Refrigerant Charge*

Note: Before proceeding with this step, pressure gauges must be properly calibrated, the ambient air temperature must be 60°F or above, and the engine must be warmed to operating temperature.

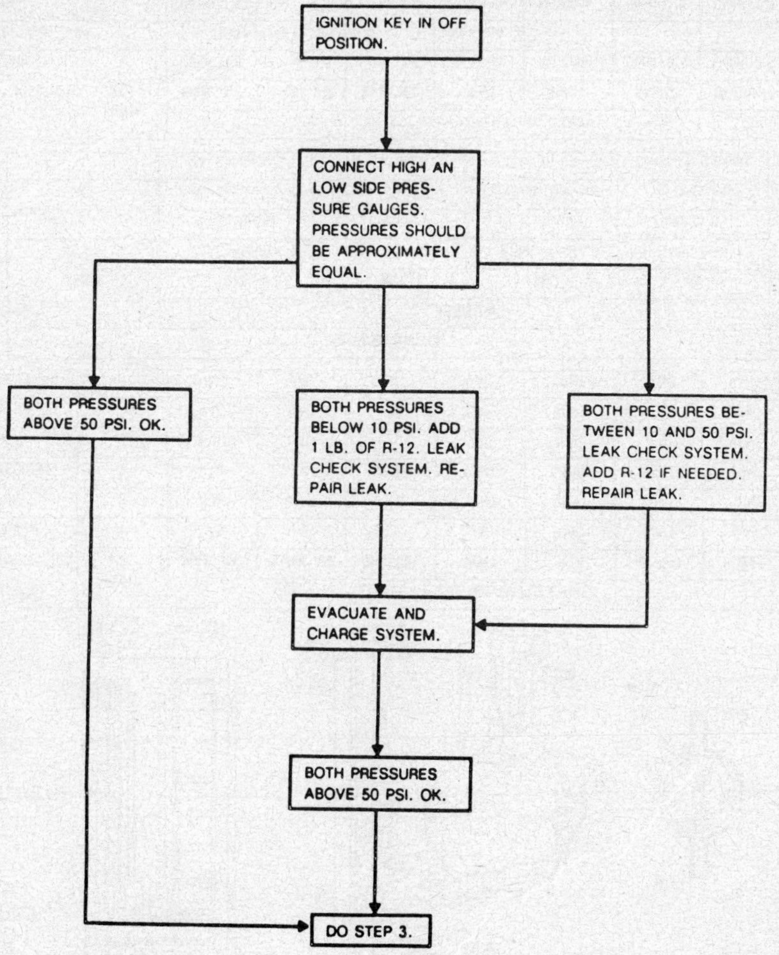

IGNITION KEY IN OFF POSITION.

↓

CONNECT HIGH AN LOW SIDE PRESSURE GAUGES. PRESSURES SHOULD BE APPROXIMATELY EQUAL.

- BOTH PRESSURES ABOVE 50 PSI. OK. → DO STEP 3.
- BOTH PRESSURES BELOW 10 PSI. ADD 1 LB. OF R-12. LEAK CHECK SYSTEM. REPAIR LEAK. → EVACUATE AND CHARGE SYSTEM.
- BOTH PRESSURES BETWEEN 10 AND 50 PSI. LEAK CHECK SYSTEM. ADD R-12 IF NEEDED. REPAIR LEAK. → EVACUATE AND CHARGE SYSTEM.

EVACUATE AND CHARGE SYSTEM. → BOTH PRESSURES ABOVE 50 PSI. OK. → DO STEP 3.

AIR CONDITIONING SYSTEM DIAGNOSIS—VDOT SYSTEM, CONT'D

STEP 3--*Checking Compressor Clutch Engagement*

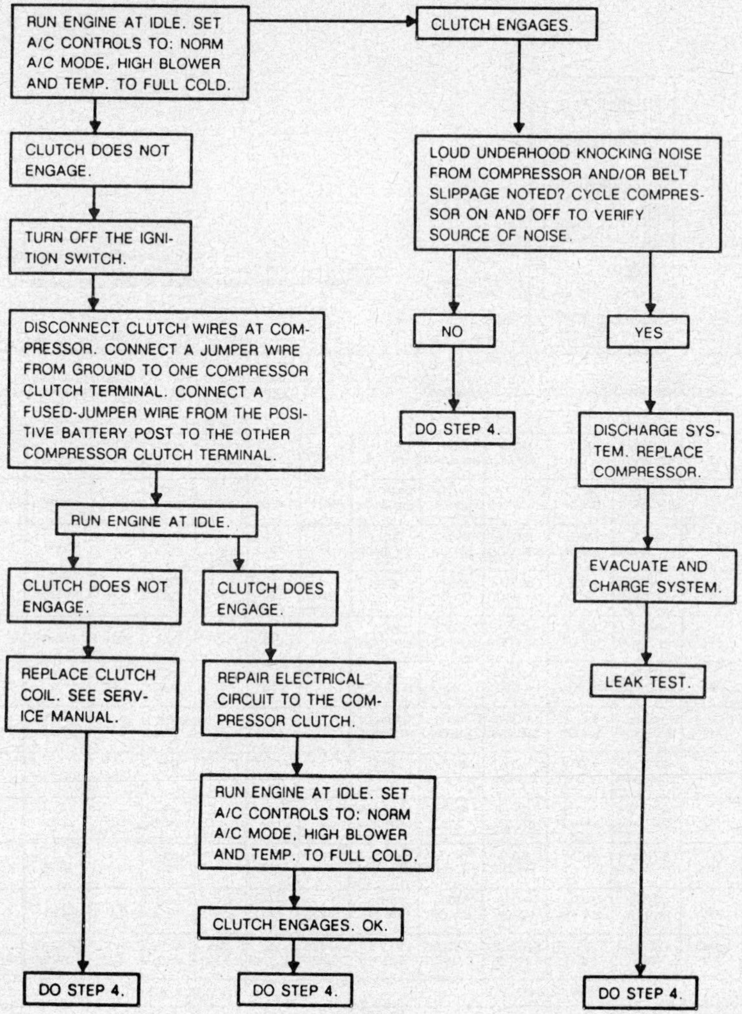

RUN ENGINE AT IDLE. SET A/C CONTROLS TO: NORM A/C MODE, HIGH BLOWER AND TEMP. TO FULL COLD.

- CLUTCH ENGAGES. → LOUD UNDERHOOD KNOCKING NOISE FROM COMPRESSOR AND/OR BELT SLIPPAGE NOTED? CYCLE COMPRESSOR ON AND OFF TO VERIFY SOURCE OF NOISE.
  - NO → DO STEP 4.
  - YES → DISCHARGE SYSTEM. REPLACE COMPRESSOR. → EVACUATE AND CHARGE SYSTEM. → LEAK TEST. → DO STEP 4.
- CLUTCH DOES NOT ENGAGE. → TURN OFF THE IGNITION SWITCH. → DISCONNECT CLUTCH WIRES AT COMPRESSOR. CONNECT A JUMPER WIRE FROM GROUND TO ONE COMPRESSOR CLUTCH TERMINAL. CONNECT A FUSED-JUMPER WIRE FROM THE POSITIVE BATTERY POST TO THE OTHER COMPRESSOR CLUTCH TERMINAL. → RUN ENGINE AT IDLE.
  - CLUTCH DOES NOT ENGAGE. → REPLACE CLUTCH COIL. SEE SERVICE MANUAL. → DO STEP 4.
  - CLUTCH DOES ENGAGE. → REPAIR ELECTRICAL CIRCUIT TO THE COMPRESSOR CLUTCH. → RUN ENGINE AT IDLE. SET A/C CONTROLS TO: NORM A/C MODE, HIGH BLOWER AND TEMP. TO FULL COLD. → CLUTCH ENGAGES. OK. → DO STEP 4.

AIR CONDITIONING SYSTEM DIAGNOSIS—VDOT SYSTEM, CONT'D

STEP 4--*Checking System Performance*

IMPORTANT
THIS TEST WAS DESIGNED FOR TYPICAL GARAGE CONDITIONS: 70-90°F AND NO SUN LOAD. NORMAL DISCHARGE AIR TEMPERATURE IS TYPICALLY AT LEAST 20°F COOLER THAN AMBIENT TEMPERATURE. FOLLOW THIS TEST PROCEDURE EXACTLY. IT IS DESIGNED TO CREATE ENOUGH COOLING LOAD TO CAUSE THE V5 COMPRESSOR TO OPERATE AT FULL STROKE. THIS IS ABSOLUTELY NECESSARY FOR ACCURATE TEST RESULTS.

CLOSE ALL VEHICLE WINDOWS AND DOORS. SET A/C CONTROLS TO: NORM A/C MODE, HIGH BLOWER AND TEMP. TO FULL COLD. RUN ENGINE AT IDLE FOR 5 MINUTES.

FEEL LIQUID LINE ON BOTH SIDES OF ORIFICE (EXPANSION) TUBE.

SAME TEMPERATURE. DISCHARGE SYSTEM.

ORIFICE (EXPANSION) TUBE MISSING.

INSTALL ORIFICE (EXPANSION) TUBE.

EVACUATE AND CHARGE SYSTEM.

LEAK TEST.

NOTE DISCHARGE AIR TEMPERATURE. IS IT WITHIN SPECIFICATIONS?

YES → END

NO → FOLLOW STEP 4 AGAIN.

NOTICEABLE TEMPERATURE DIFFERENCE.

RECORD LOW AND HIGH SIDE PRESSURES AFTER A/C SYSTEM HAS BEEN OPERATING FOR 5 MINUTES OR MORE. ON ENGINES WITH COOLING FANS THAT CYCLE, TAKE PRESSURE READINGS WITH ENGINE COOLING FAN ON.

LOCATE THE INTERSECTION OF THE LOW AND HIGH SIDE PRESSURES ON THE DIAGNOSTIC CHART (FIGURE 1).

CONTINUE TESTING WITH NEXT CHART.

AIR CONDITIONING SYSTEM DIAGNOSIS—VDOT SYSTEM, CONT'D

STEP 4--*Continued*

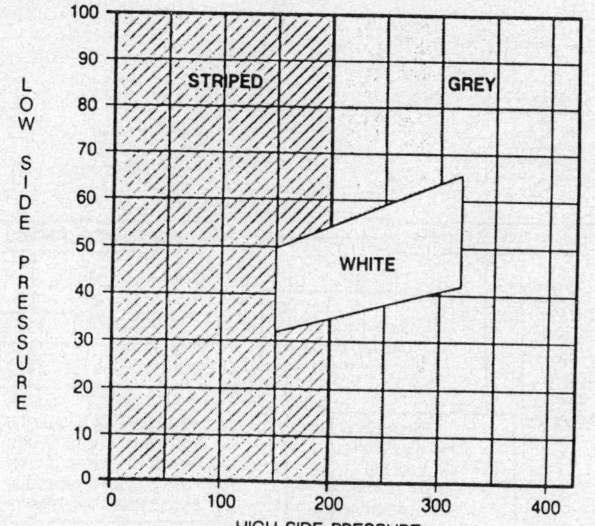

FIGURE 1

HUMIDITY AND TEMPERATURE VARIABLES CAN CREATE BORDERLINE DIAGNOSTIC CONDITIONS. IF THE DIAGNOSTIC CHART (FIGURE 1) DIRECTS YOU TO FOLLOW PROCEDURES IN ONE STEP, BUT THOSE PROCEDURES DO NOT LEAD YOU TO CORRECT THE PROBLEM, FOLLOW THE PROCEDURES FOR THE OTHER STEP.

LOW AND HIGH SIDE PRESSURES INTERSECT IN THE STRIPED AREA OF THE CHART. DO STEP 6.

LOW AND HIGH SIDE PRESSURES INTERSECT IN THE GREY AREA OF THE CHART. DO STEP 5.

LOW AND HIGH SIDE PRESSURES INTERSECT IN THE WHITE AREA OF THE CHART. WHITE AREA MEANS ALL COMPONENTS OF THE REFRIGERANT SYSTEM ARE FUNCTIONING PROPERLY. IF INSUFFICIENT COOLING EXISTS, AIR HANDLING SYSTEM IS AT FAULT.

AIR CONDITIONING SYSTEM DIAGNOSIS— VDOT SYSTEM, CONT'D

STEP 5--*Grey Area Diagnosis And Service*

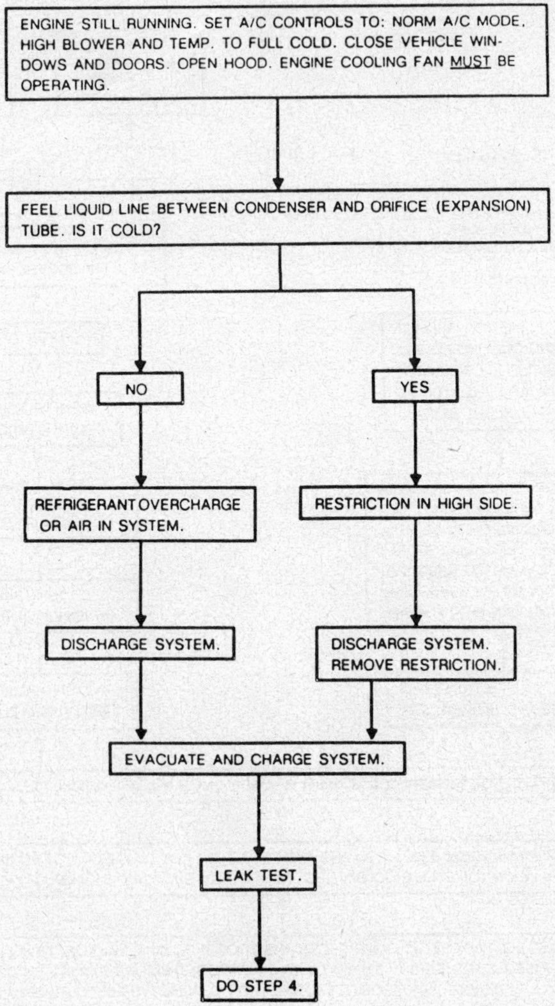

ENGINE STILL RUNNING. SET A/C CONTROLS TO: NORM A/C MODE, HIGH BLOWER AND TEMP. TO FULL COLD. CLOSE VEHICLE WINDOWS AND DOORS. OPEN HOOD. ENGINE COOLING FAN <u>MUST</u> BE OPERATING.

→ FEEL LIQUID LINE BETWEEN CONDENSER AND ORIFICE (EXPANSION) TUBE. IS IT COLD?

- NO → REFRIGERANT OVERCHARGE OR AIR IN SYSTEM. → DISCHARGE SYSTEM. → EVACUATE AND CHARGE SYSTEM.
- YES → RESTRICTION IN HIGH SIDE. → DISCHARGE SYSTEM. REMOVE RESTRICTION. → EVACUATE AND CHARGE SYSTEM.

EVACUATE AND CHARGE SYSTEM. → LEAK TEST. → DO STEP 4.

AIR CONDITIONING SYSTEM DIAGNOSIS— VDOT SYSTEM, CONT'D

STEP 6--*Striped Area Diagnosis And Service*

ARE COMPRESSOR HIGH AND LOW SIDE PRESSURES WITHIN 30 PSI. OF EACH OTHER?

- YES → RUN ENGINE AT 3,000 RPM. SET A/C CONTROLS TO: HIGH BLOWER AND TEMP. TO FULL COLD. CLOSE VEHICLE WINDOWS AND DOORS. CYCLE MODE LEVER FROM VENT TO A/C EVERY 20 SECONDS FOR 3 MINUTES. → ARE COMPRESSOR HIGH AND LOW SIDE PRESSURES WITHIN 30 PSI. OF EACH OTHER?
  - NO → DO STEP 4.
  - YES → ENGINE OFF. WITH COMPRESSOR CLUTCH DISENGAGED, DOES COMPRESSOR CLUTCH DRIVER (NOT PULLEY) TURN FREELY BY HAND?
    - YES → REPLACE COMPRESSOR. → EVACUATE AND CHARGE SYSTEM.
    - NO → PERFORM CONTROL VALVE DIAGNOSIS. DO STEP 7.
- NO → IS LOW SIDE PRESSURE 25 TO 35 PSI?
  - NO → PERFORM CONTROL VALVE DIAGNOSIS. DO STEP 7.
  - YES → REFRIGERANT UNDERCHARGED. ADD 14 OZ. OF REFRIGERANT TO SYSTEM. DOES COOLING PERFORMANCE IMPROVE?
    - NO → DISCHARGE SYSTEM. CHECK ORIFICE (EXPANSION) TUBE. IF PLUGGED, REMOVE. CLEAR LINES. REPLACE ORIFICE (EXPANSION) TUBE. IF ONLY LIGHT DEBRIS IS PRESENT, CLEAN TUBE WITH SHOP AIR AND REUSE. → EVACUATE AND CHARGE SYSTEM.
    - YES → LEAK TEST. → IF FOUND, REPAIR REFRIGERANT LEAK. IF NO LEAK IS FOUND, CONTINUE. → EVACUATE AND CHARGE SYSTEM.

EVACUATE AND CHARGE SYSTEM. → LEAK TEST. → DO STEP 4.

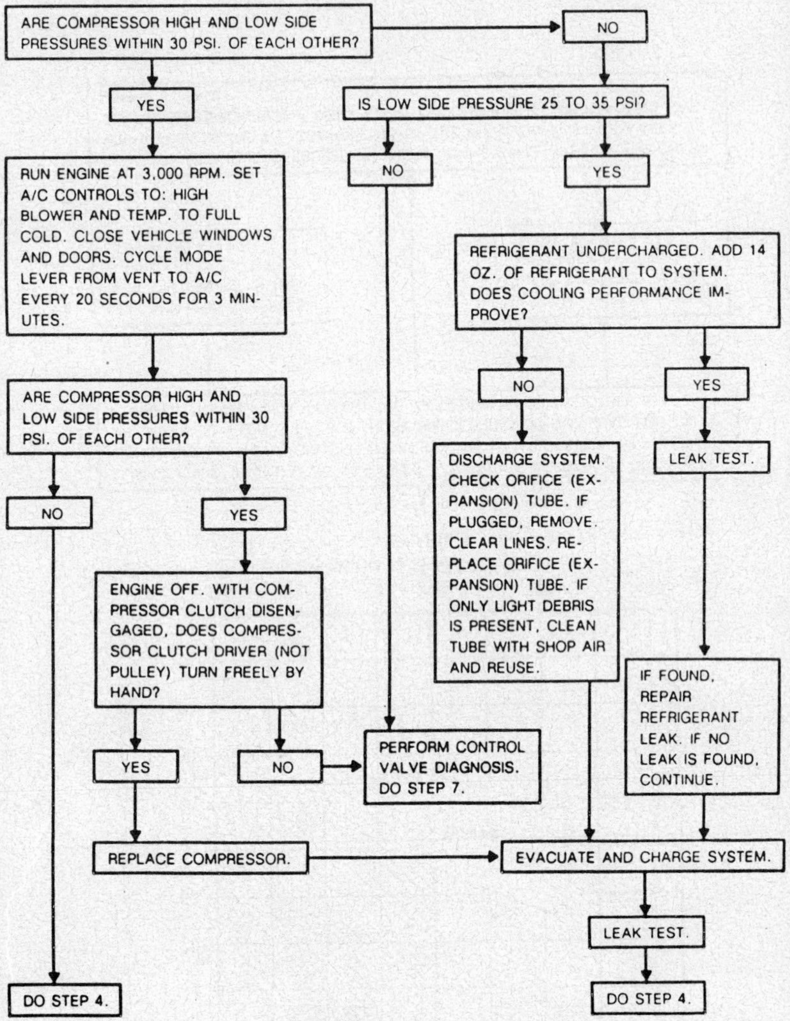

AIR CONDITIONING SYSTEM DIAGNOSIS—VDOT SYSTEM, CONT'D

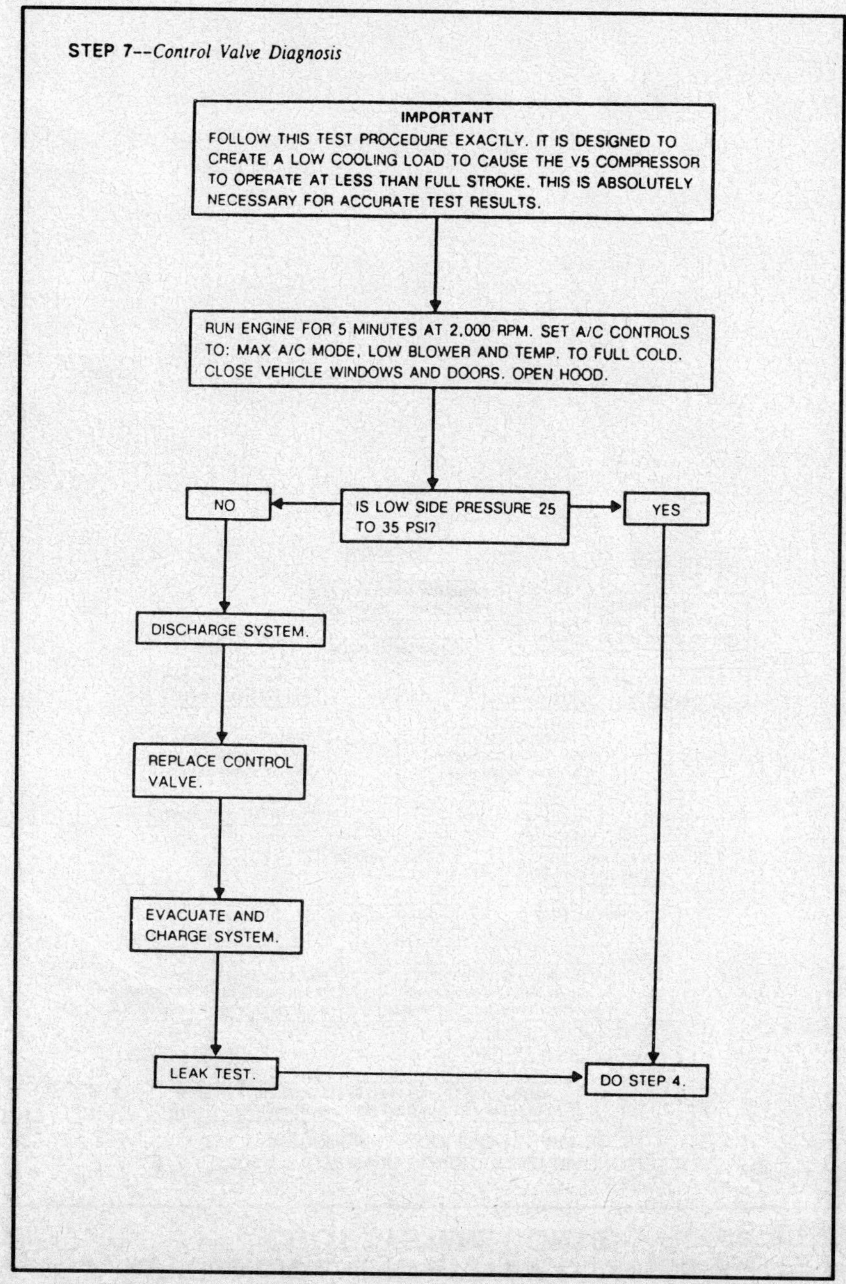

STEP 7--Control Valve Diagnosis
IMPORTANT
FOLLOW THIS TEST PROCEDURE EXACTLY. IT IS DESIGNED TO CREATE A LOW COOLING LOAD TO CAUSE THE V5 COMPRESSOR TO OPERATE AT LESS THAN FULL STROKE. THIS IS ABSOLUTELY NECESSARY FOR ACCURATE TEST RESULTS.
RUN ENGINE FOR 5 MINUTES AT 2,000 RPM. SET A/C CONTROLS TO: MAX A/C MODE, LOW BLOWER AND TEMP. TO FULL COLD. CLOSE VEHICLE WINDOWS AND DOORS. OPEN HOOD.
IS LOW SIDE PRESSURE 25 TO 35 PSI?
NO
YES
DISCHARGE SYSTEM.
REPLACE CONTROL VALVE.
EVACUATE AND CHARGE SYSTEM.
LEAK TEST.
DO STEP 4.

AIR CONDITIONING SYSTEM DIAGNOSIS—CCOT SYSTEM

C.C.O.T. SYSTEM AIR CONDITIONING DIAGNOSIS
INSUFFICIENT COOLING "CHART A"

CHECK FOR:
1. BLOWN A/C FUSE AND/OR GAGE FUSE.
2. LOOSE OR DISCONNECTED A/C WIRE CONNECTOR.
3. CHECK BLOWER FOR FAN OPERATION.
4. ENGINE COOLING FAN OPERATION (FAN OPERATES IN ALL A/C MODES AS FOLLOWS:
   A. DISCONNECT ENGINE COOLANT TEMPERATURE FAN SWITCH.
   B. WITH IGNITION ON AND ENGINE NOT RUNNING, SET A/C CONTROL TO A/C MODE.
   C. ENGINE COOLING FAN SHOULD RUN.
   D. RECONNECT ENGINE COOLANT TEMPERATURE FAN SWITCH.

CHECK FOR LOOSE, MISSING OR DAMAGED DRIVE BELT

BELT PROBLEM

BELT OK

CHECK FOR COMPRESSOR SEIZURE

COMPRESSOR SEIZED

REPLACE COMPRESSOR ASSEMBLY. REPLACE ORIFICE. EVACUATE AND CHARGE.

OK

NO SEIZURE

REPLACE OR TIGHTEN BELT AS REQUIRED

AMBIENT TEMPERATURE MUST BE ABOVE 10°C (50°F) FOR FOLLOWING DIAGNOSTIC PROCEDURE

CHECK FOR COMPRESSOR CLUTCH ENGAGEMENT AS FOLLOWS:
1. ENGINE RUNNING (APPROX. 1000 rpm).
2. SET A/C CONTROL TO 'NORM' AND 'HIGH' BLOWER.
3. PUT AUXILIARY FAN IN FRONT OF VEHICLE.
4. OBSERVE CLUTCH OPERATION FOR 5 MIN.

CLUTCH DOES ENGAGE OR CYCLES

OFF ALL THE TIME

SEE CHART B

FEEL LIQUID LINE BEFORE EXPANSION TUBE

COLD

RESTRICTION IN HIGH SIDE OF SYSTEM. VISUALLY CHECK FOR FROST SPOT TO LOCATE RESTRICTION. REPAIR.

EVACUATE AND CHARGE.

OK

WARM

FEEL EVAPORATOR INLET AND OUTLET PIPE

INLET PIPE AND OUTLET PIPE SAME TEMPERATURE OR OUTLET COLDER THAN INLET.

SEE CHART D

INLET COLDER THAN OUTLET PIPE.

LEAK CHECK SYSTEM

NO LEAK FOUND SEE CHART C

LEAK FOUND, REPAIR AS REQUIRED, EVACUATE AND CHARGE.

OK

AIR CONDITIONING SYSTEM DIAGNOSIS— CCOT SYSTEM, CONT'D

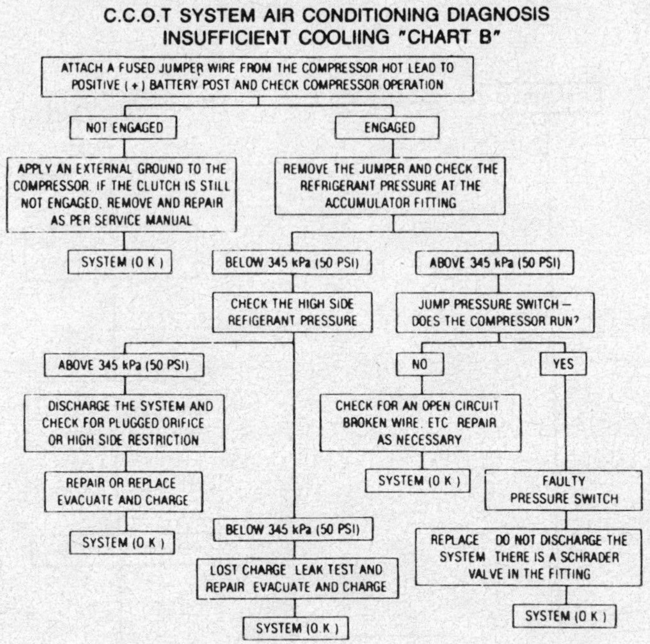

C.C.O.T SYSTEM AIR CONDITIONING DIAGNOSIS INSUFFICIENT COOLIING "CHART B"

ATTACH A FUSED JUMPER WIRE FROM THE COMPRESSOR HOT LEAD TO POSITIVE (+) BATTERY POST AND CHECK COMPRESSOR OPERATION

NOT ENGAGED

APPLY AN EXTERNAL GROUND TO THE COMPRESSOR. IF THE CLUTCH IS STILL NOT ENGAGED, REMOVE AND REPAIR AS PER SERVICE MANUAL

SYSTEM (O K)

ENGAGED

REMOVE THE JUMPER AND CHECK THE REFRIGERANT PRESSURE AT THE ACCUMULATOR FITTING

BELOW 345 kPa (50 PSI)

CHECK THE HIGH SIDE REFIGERANT PRESSURE

ABOVE 345 kPa (50 PSI)

DISCHARGE THE SYSTEM AND CHECK FOR PLUGGED ORIFICE OR HIGH SIDE RESTRICTION

REPAIR OR REPLACE EVACUATE AND CHARGE

SYSTEM (O K)

BELOW 345 kPa (50 PSI)

LOST CHARGE LEAK TEST AND REPAIR EVACUATE AND CHARGE

SYSTEM (O K)

ABOVE 345 kPa (50 PSI)

JUMP PRESSURE SWITCH — DOES THE COMPRESSOR RUN?

NO

CHECK FOR AN OPEN CIRCUIT BROKEN WIRE, ETC REPAIR AS NECESSARY

SYSTEM (O K)

YES

FAULTY PRESSURE SWITCH

REPLACE DO NOT DISCHARGE THE SYSTEM THERE IS A SCHRADER VALVE IN THE FITTING

SYSTEM (O K)

AIR CONDITIONING SYSTEM DIAGNOSIS— CCOT SYSTEM, CONT'D

C.C.O.T. SYSTEM AIR CONDITIONING DIAGNOSIS INSUFFICIENT COOLING "CHART C"

ADD .45 kg (ONE LB) OF REFRIGERANT-12 AND THEN CHECK CLUTCH CYCLE RATE

MORE THAN 8 CLUTCH CYCLES PER MINUTE

DISCHARGE SYSTEM AND CHECK FOR PLUGGED ORIFICE

REPAIR AS REQUIRED EVACUATE AND CHARGE

OK

8 OR LESS CLUTCH CYCLES PER MINUTE

FEEL INLET AND OUTLET PIPES AGAIN

INLET AND OUTLET SAME TEMPERATURE OR OUTLET COLDER THAN INLET

ADD .45 kg (ONE LB) OF REFRIGERANT—12

OK

INLET PIPE COLDER THAN OUTLET PIPE

ADD .45 kg (ONE LB) OF REFRIGERANT—12

OK

DISCHARGE SYSTEM AND CHECK FOR PLUGGED ORIFICE

REPAIR AS REQUIRED EVACUATE AND CHARGE

OK

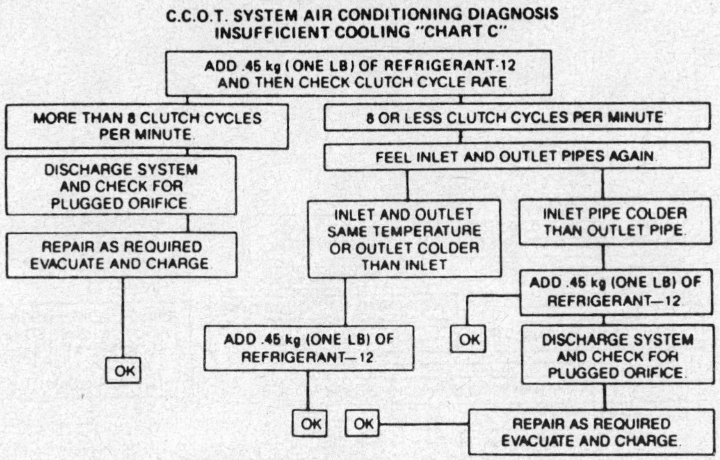

AIR CONDITIONING SYSTEM DIAGNOSIS—CCOT SYSTEM, CONT'D

C.C.O.T. SYSTEM AIR CONDITIONING DIAGNOSIS
INSUFFICIENT COOLING "CHART D"

INSTALL GAGE SET AND CHECK COMPRESSOR CYCLING PRESSURE

COMPRESSOR SHOULD CYCLE ON AT 280-350 kPa (41-51 PSI) CYCLE OFF AT 140-190 kPa (20-28 PSI)

COMPRESSOR RUNS CONTINUOUSLY WITHIN LIMITS

CYCLES HIGH OR LOW ON ABOVE 350 kPa (51 PSI) OR OFF BELOW 140 kPa (20 PSI)

COMPRESSOR CYCLES WITHIN LIMITS.

DISCONNECT BLOWER WIRE AND CHECK FOR COMPRESSOR CYCLING OFF AT 140-190 kPa (20-28 PSI)

INOPERATIVE PRESSURE CYCLING SWITCH-REPLACE. DO NOT DISCHARGE SYSTEM.

OK

PRESSURE FALLS BELOW 140 kPa (20 PSI)

CYCLES OFF AT 140-190 kPa (20-28 PSI) WILL NOT PULL DOWN TO PRESSURE.

INOPERATIVE PRESSURE CYCLING SWITCH-REPLACE. DO NOT DISCHARGE SYSTEM

RECONNECT BLOWER MOTOR WIRE

OK

1. SET A/C CONTROL TO MAX, FULL COLD, AND HIGH BLOWER.
2. CLOSE DOORS AND WINDOWS OF VEHICLE
3. RUN ENGINE AT 2000 RPM FOR 5 MINUTES.
4. USE AUXILIARY FAR IN FRONT OF VEHICLE

INSTALL THERMOMETER IN A/C OUTLET AND CHECK SYSTEM PERFORMANCE (SEE SYSTEM PERFORMANCE CHART BELOW AND REFER TO CHART E).

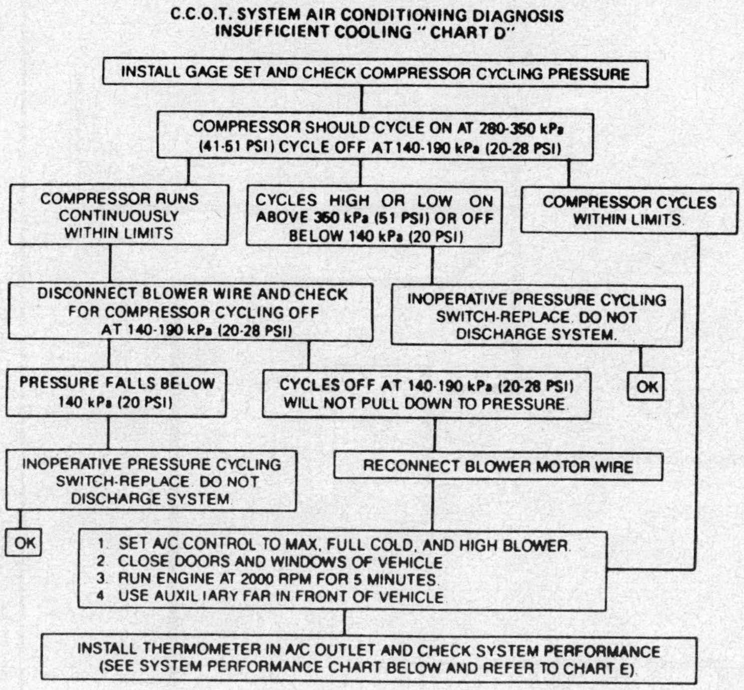

PERFORMANCE CHART FOR C.C.O.T. SYSTEMS

TEMPERATURE OF AIR ENTERING CONDENSER	°F (°C)	70 (21)	80 (27)	90 (32)	100 (38)
COMPRESSOR OUT PRESSURE	PSI (KPA)	135-170 (950-1200)	165-200 (1150-1400)	200-245 (1400-1700)	245-300 (1700-2050)
ACCUMULATOR PRESSURE	PSI (KPA)	22-28 (150-193)	22-29 (150-200)	26-35 (180-240)	30-40 (205-275)
AVERAGE A/C AIR DISCHARGE	°F (°C)	36-43 (2.2-6.0)	36-43 (2.2-6.0)	36-43 (2.2-6.0)	42-48 (5.5-9.0)

AIR CONDITIONING SYSTEM DIAGNOSIS—CCOT SYSTEM, CONT'D

C.C.O.T. SYSTEM AIR CONDITIONING DIAGNOSIS
INSUFFICIENT COOLING "CHART E"

TEMPERATURE PERFORMANCE WITHIN LIMITS.

OK

OUTLET TEMPERATURE ABOVE LIMITS.

CHECK COMPRESSOR CYCLING

ON CONTINUOUSLY

DISCHARGE SYSTEM AND CHECK FOR MISSING ORIFICE.

MISSING

INSTALL ORIFICE EVACUATE AND CHARGE.

OK

INPLACE

CYCLES ON AND OFF OR REMAINS OFF FOR A LONG PERIOD OF TIME.

DISCHARGE SYSTEM AND CHECK FOR PLUGGED ORIFICE.

REPLACE ORIFICE

EVACUATE AND CHARGE.

OK

CHECK FOR RESTRICTED SUCTION LINE

RESTRICTED

REPAIR AS REQUIRED EVACUATE AND CHARGE.

OK

CLEAN

SYSTEM OVERCHARGED EVACUATE AND CHARGE.

OK

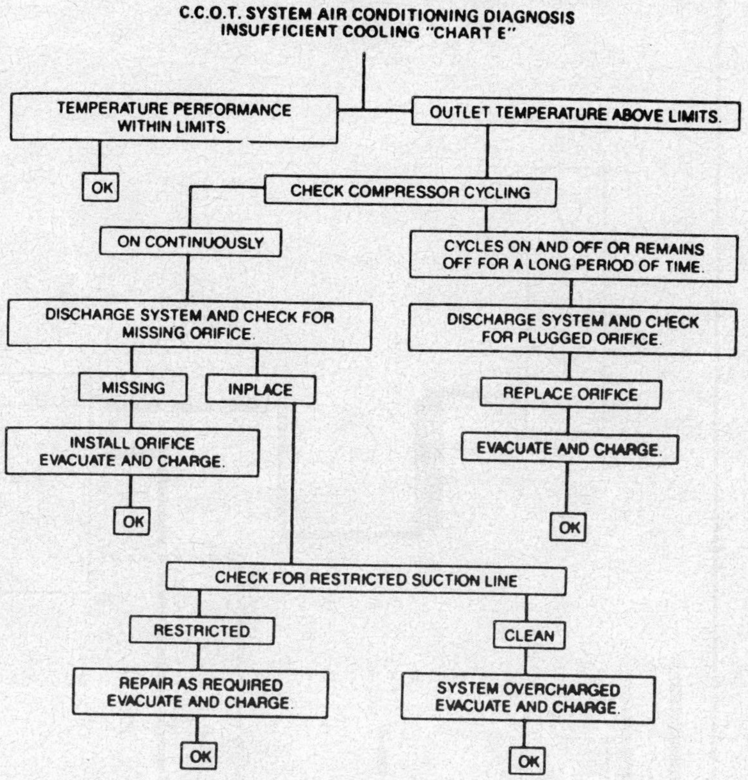

WIRING SCHEMATICS

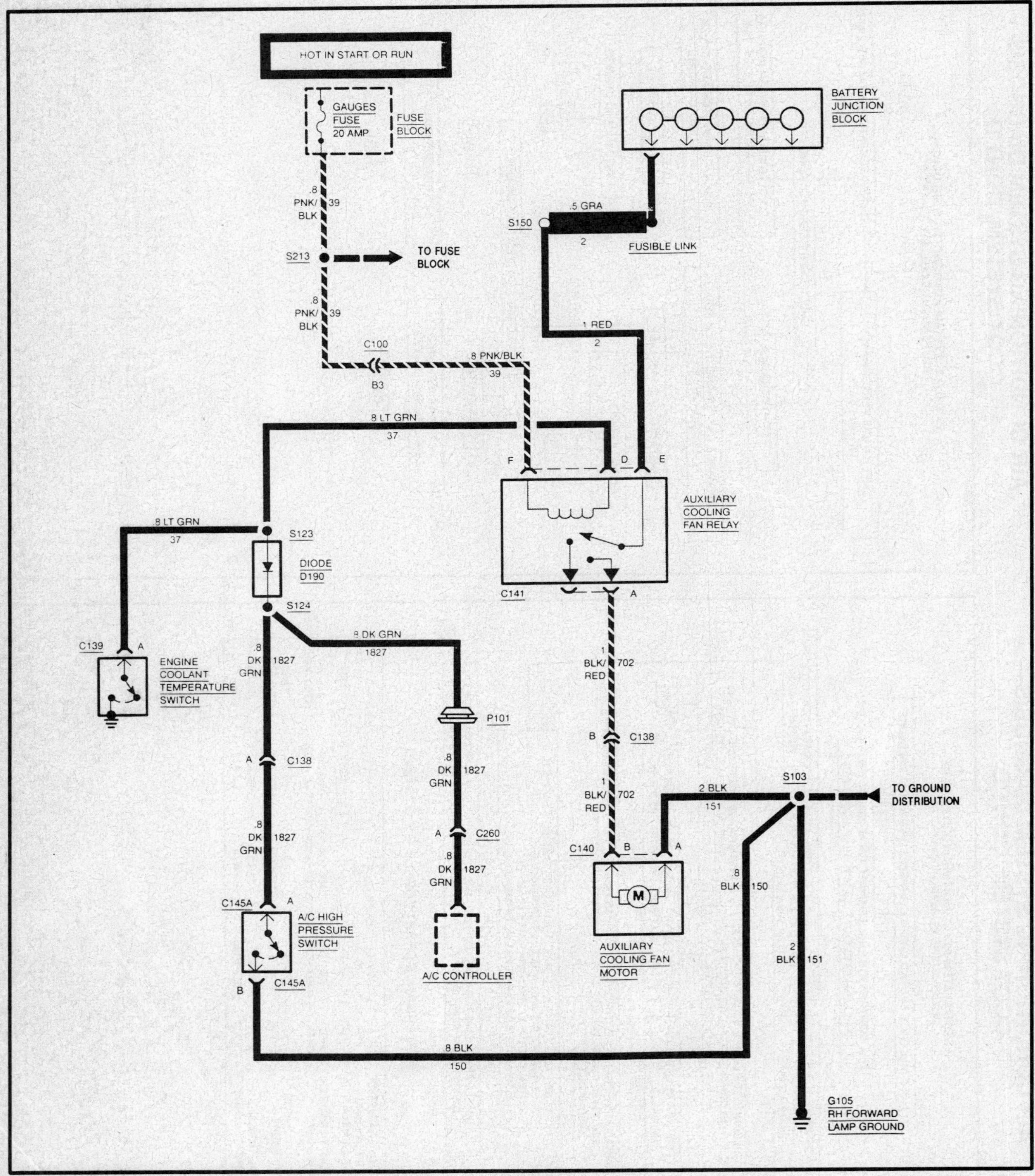

Auxiliary cooling fan wiring schematic—1994–95 C/K Series

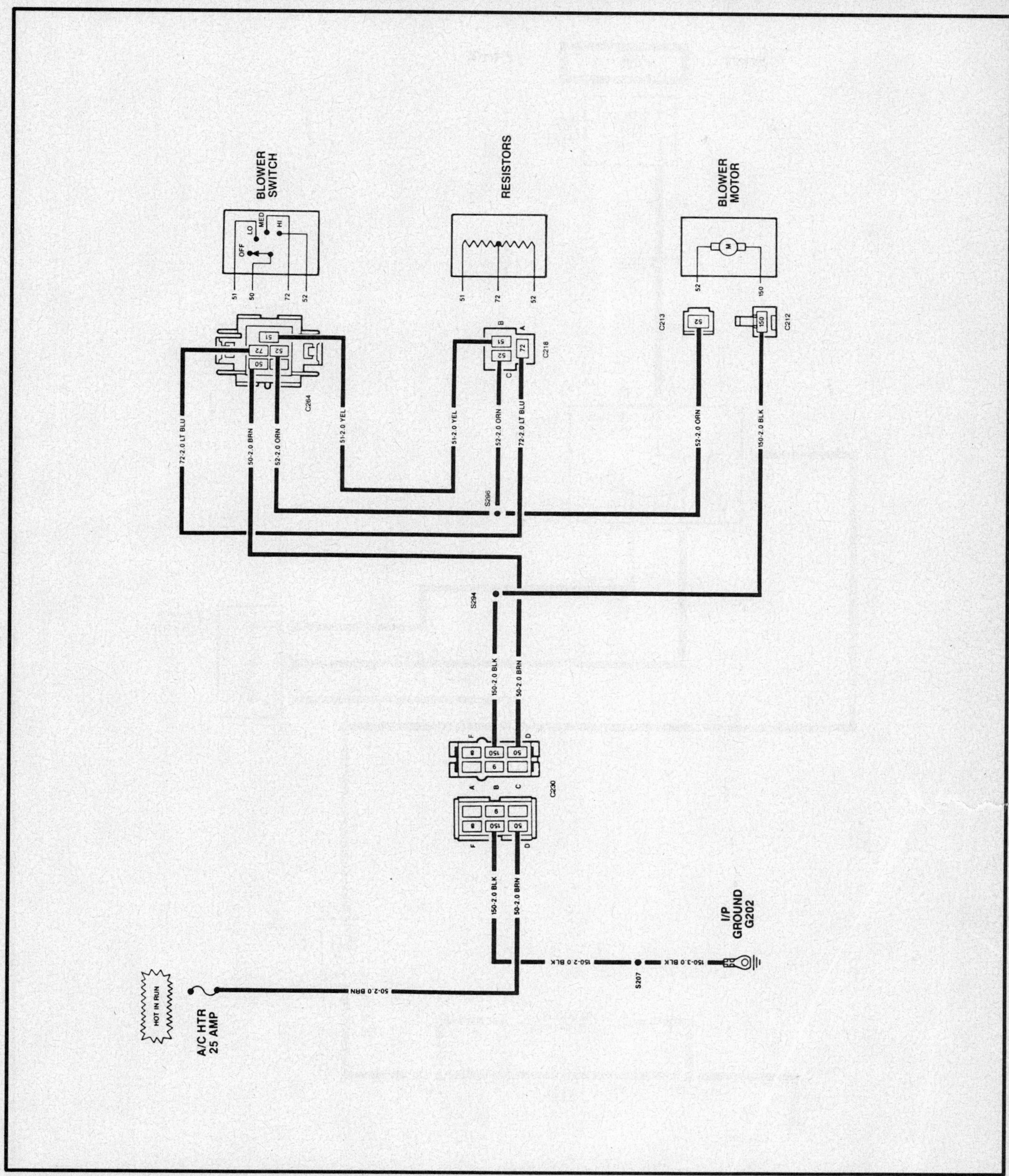

Heater only wiring schematic—1993 C/K Series (Pick-Up, Suburban, Blazer, Jimmy)

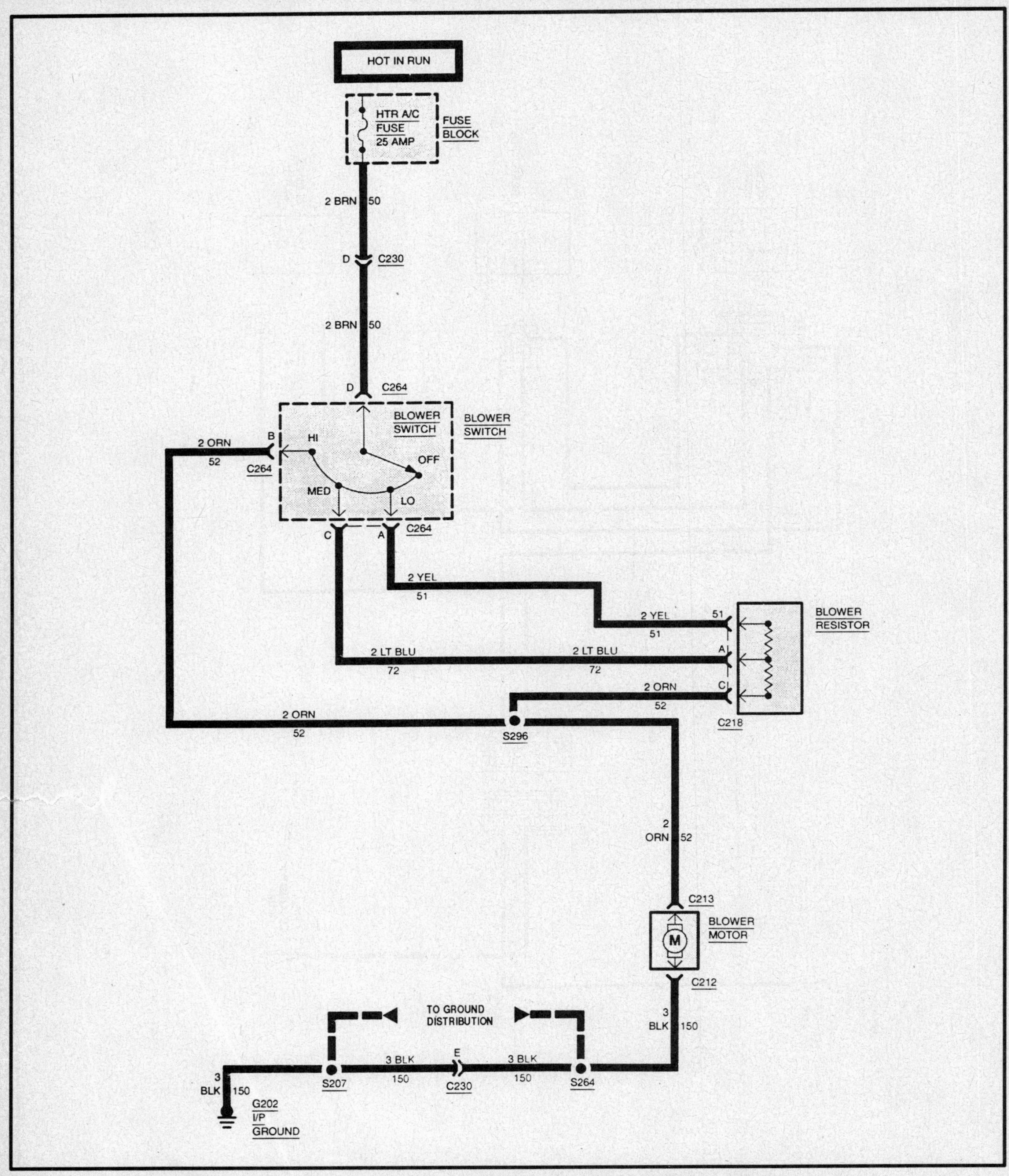

Heater only wiring schematic—1994–95 C/K Series (Pick-Up, Suburban, Blazer, Jimmy)

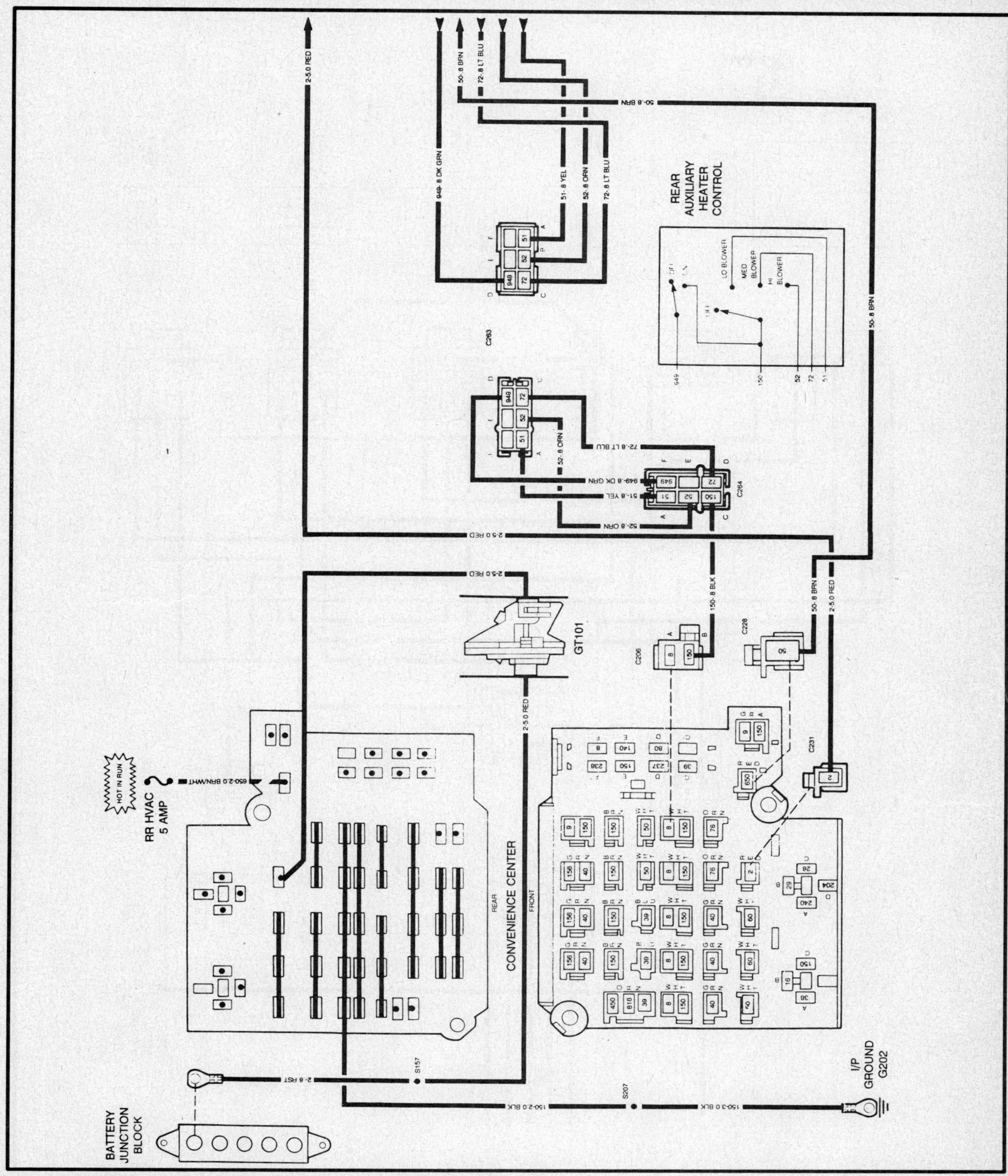

Auxiliary heater only wiring schematic—1993 Suburban

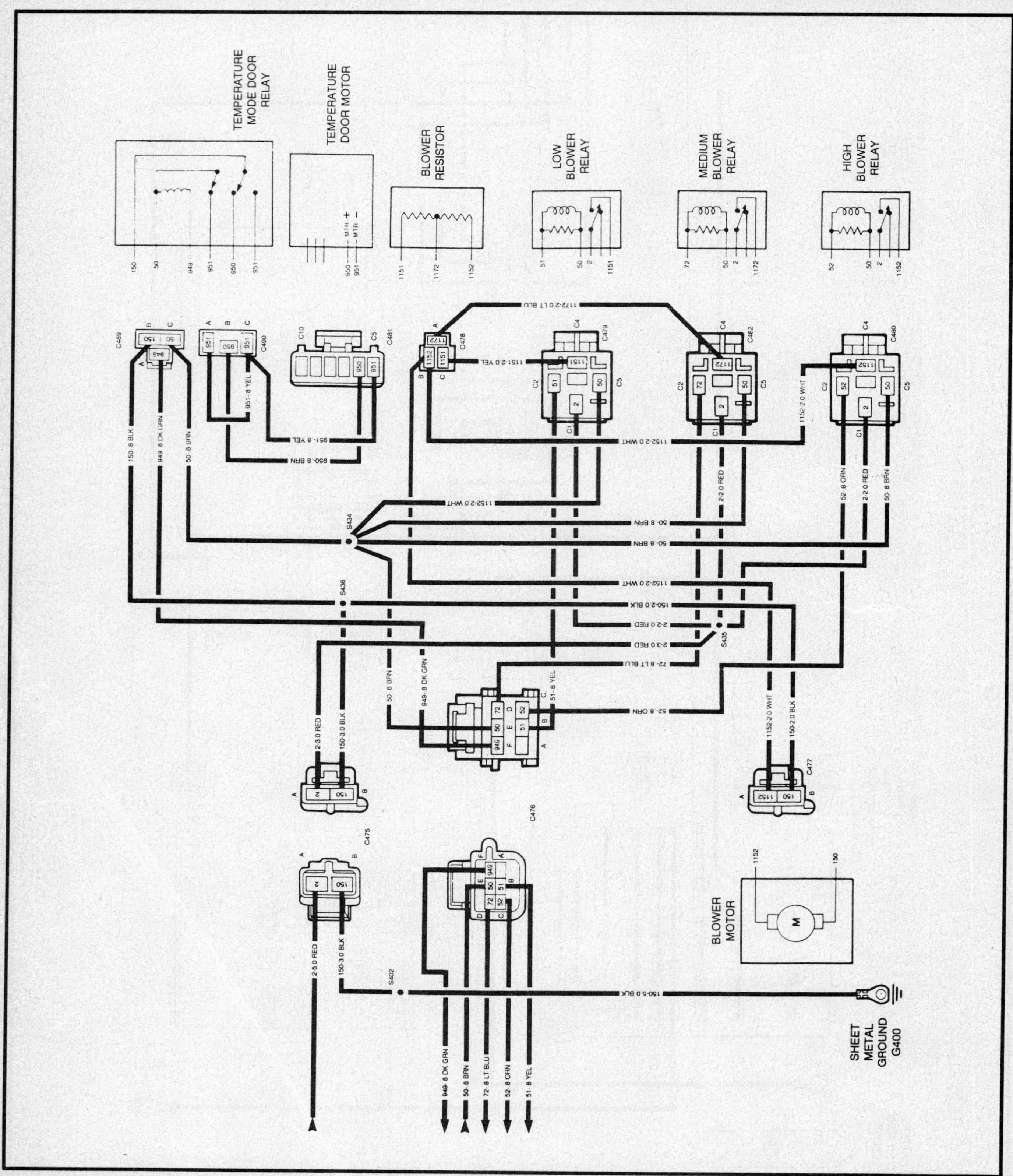

Auxiliary heater only wiring schematic—1993 Suburban, Cont'd

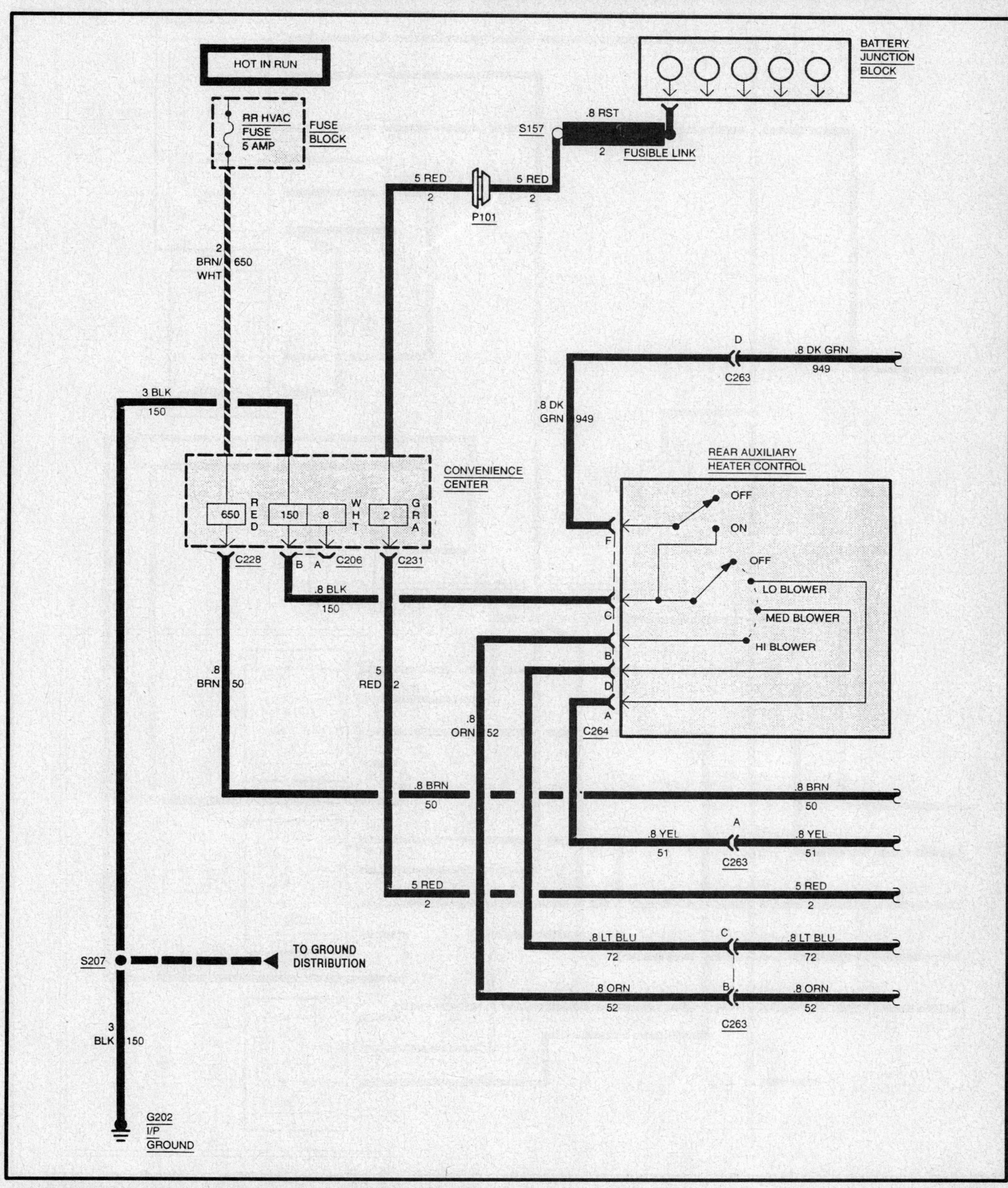

Auxiliary heater wiring schematic—1994 C/K Series

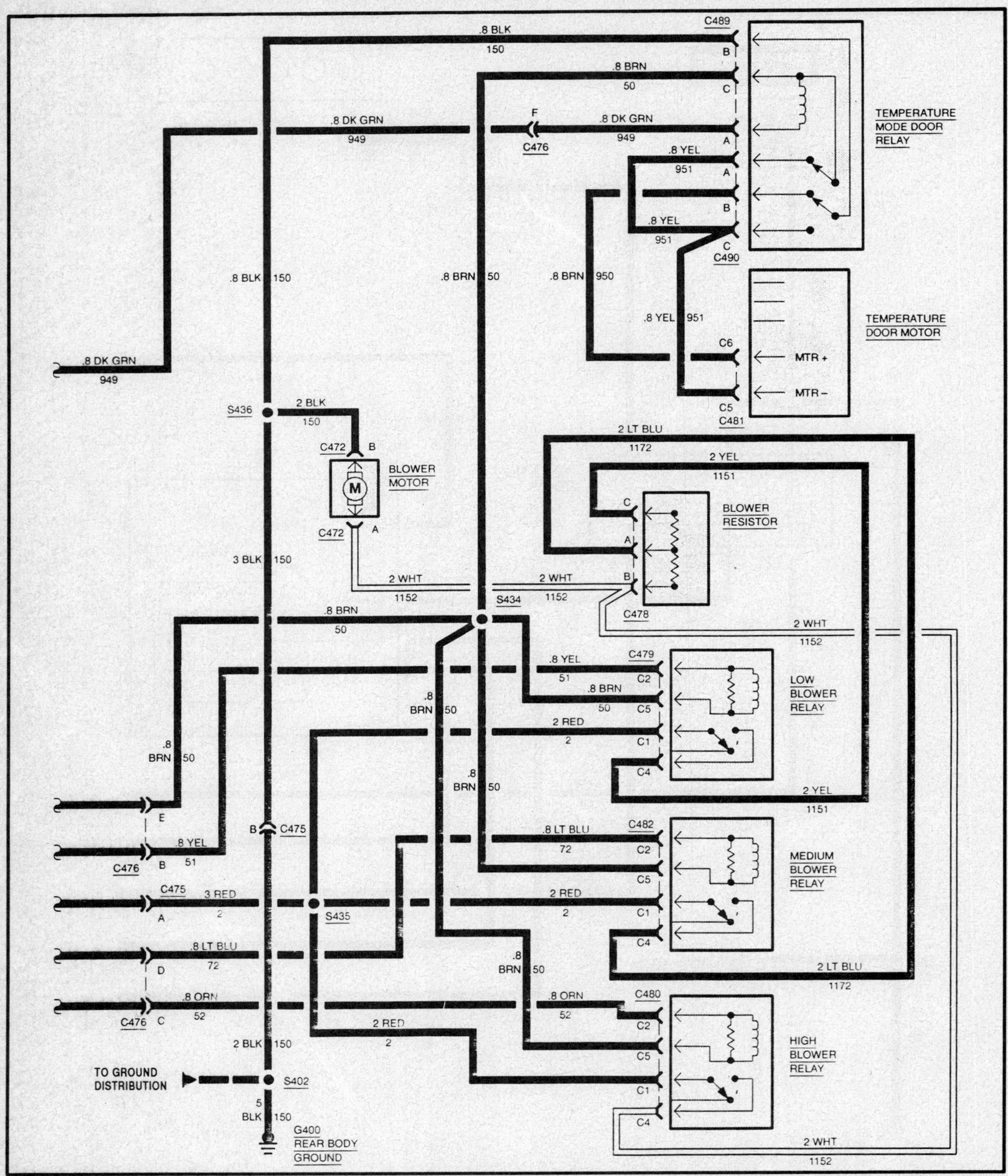

Auxiliary heater wiring schematic—1994 C/K Series, Cont'd

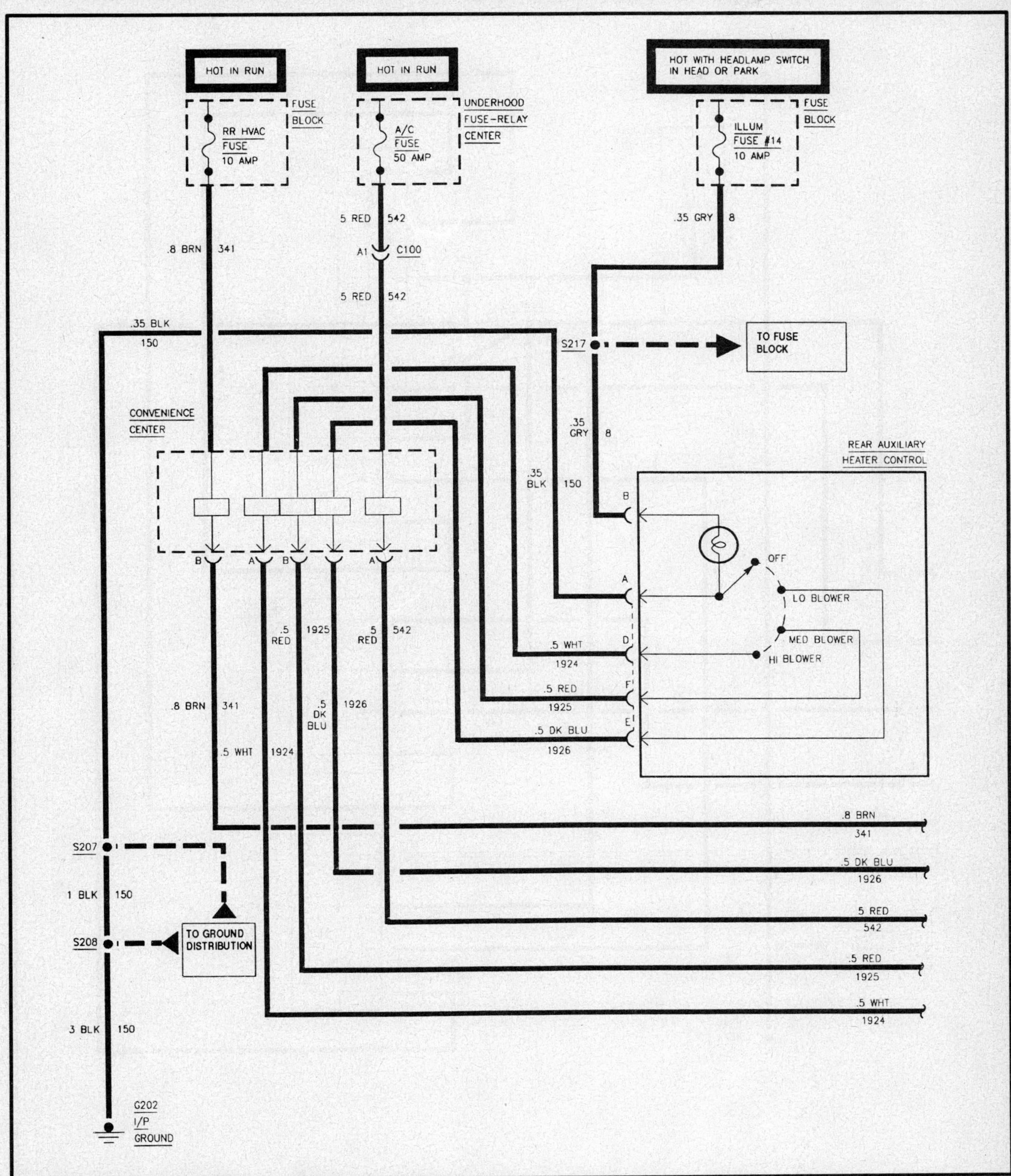

Auxiliary heater wiring schematic—1995 C/K Series

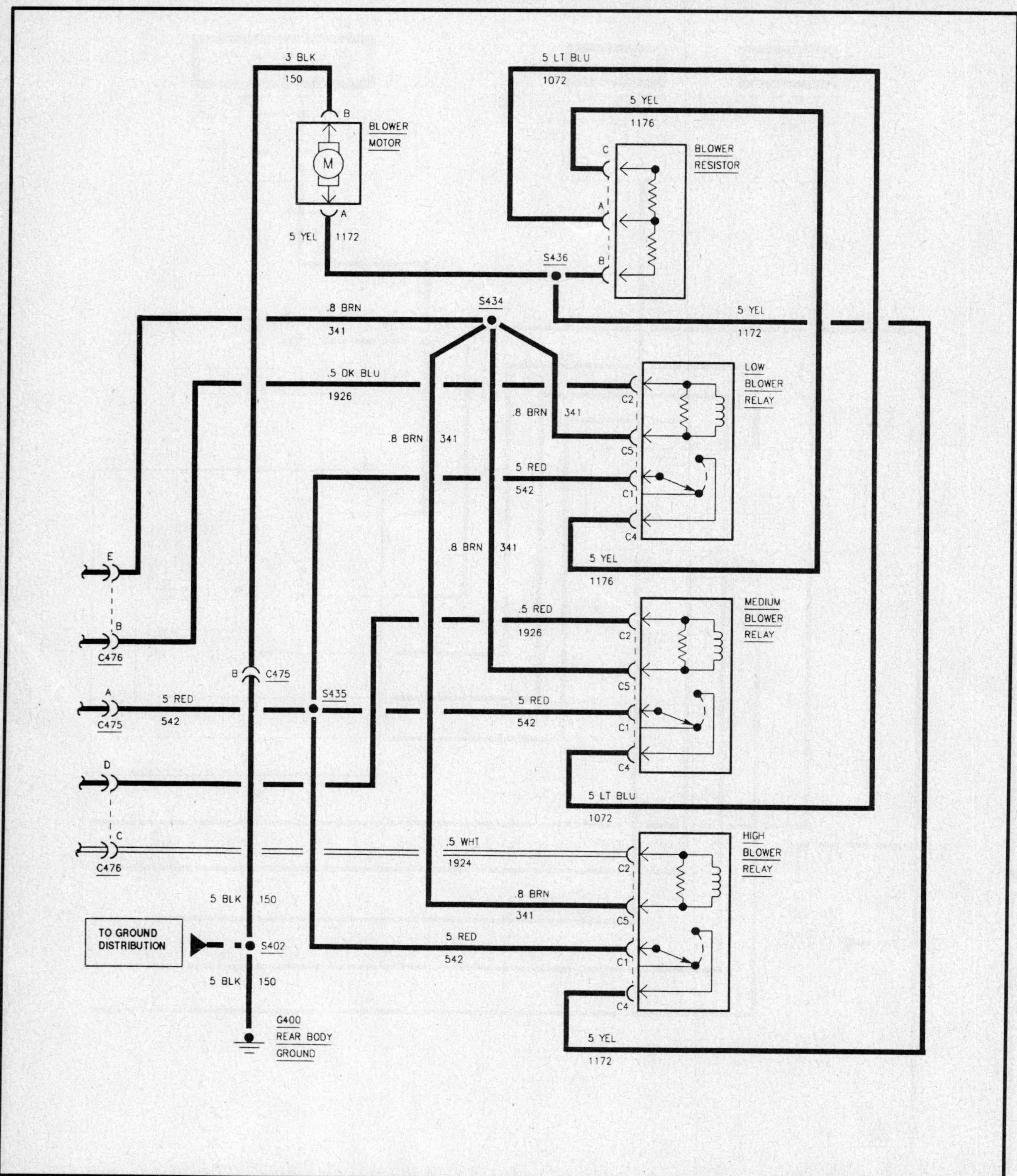

Auxiliary heater wiring schematic—1995 C/K Series, Cont'd

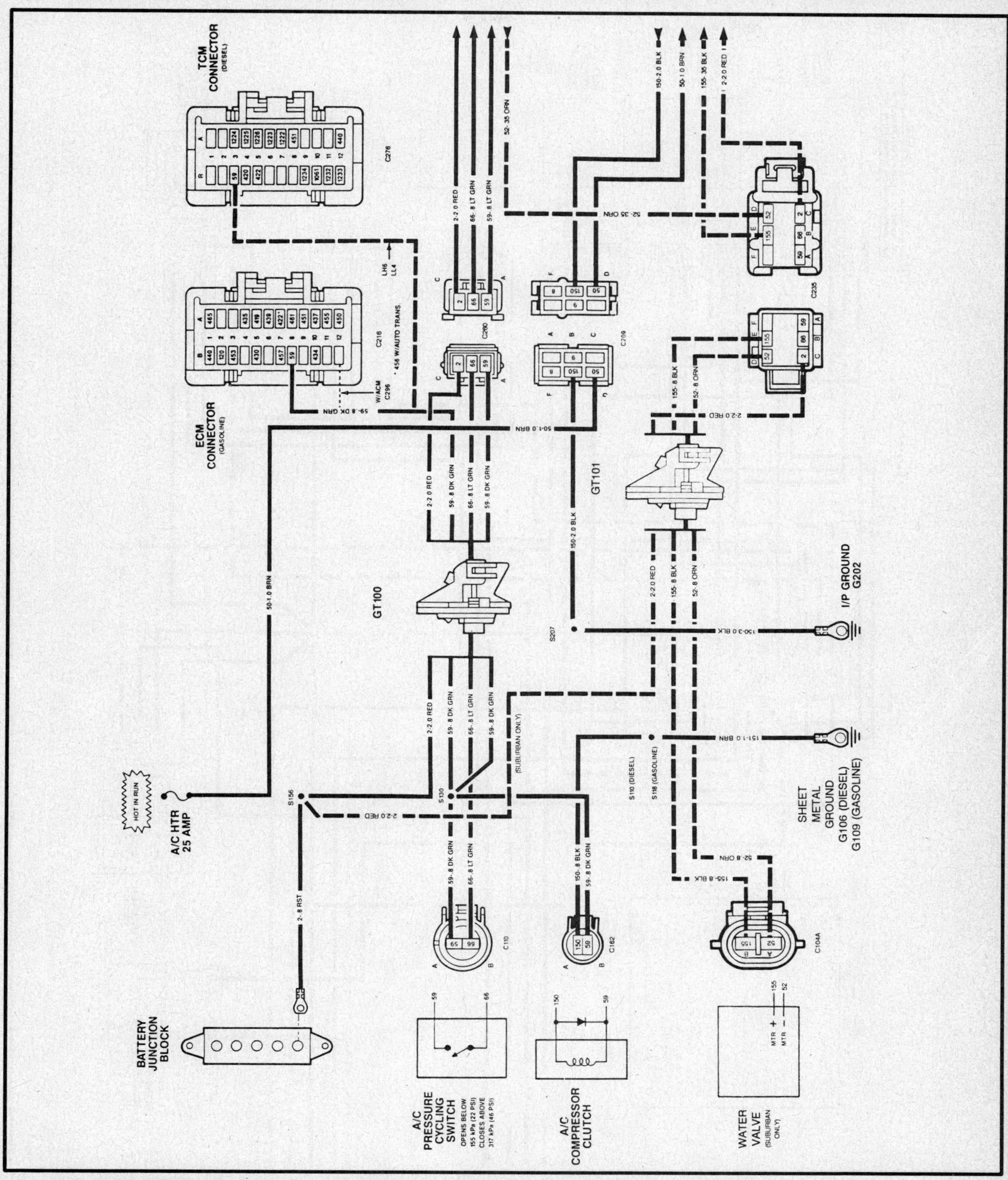

Air conditioning wiring schematic—1993 C/K Series (Pick-Up, Suburban, Blazer, Jimmy)

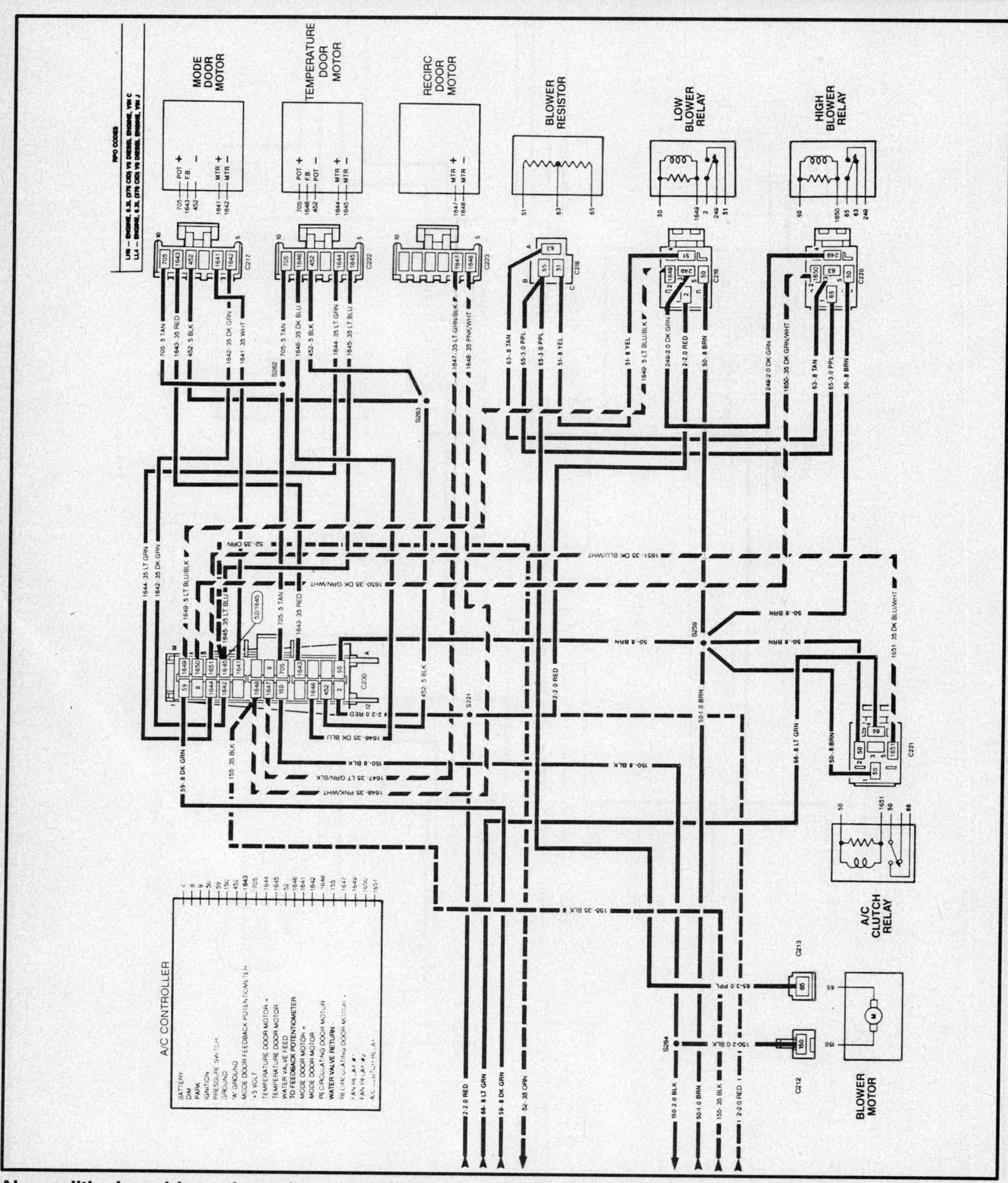

Air conditioning wiring schematic—1993 C/K Series (Pick-Up, Suburban, Blazer, Jimmy), Cont'd

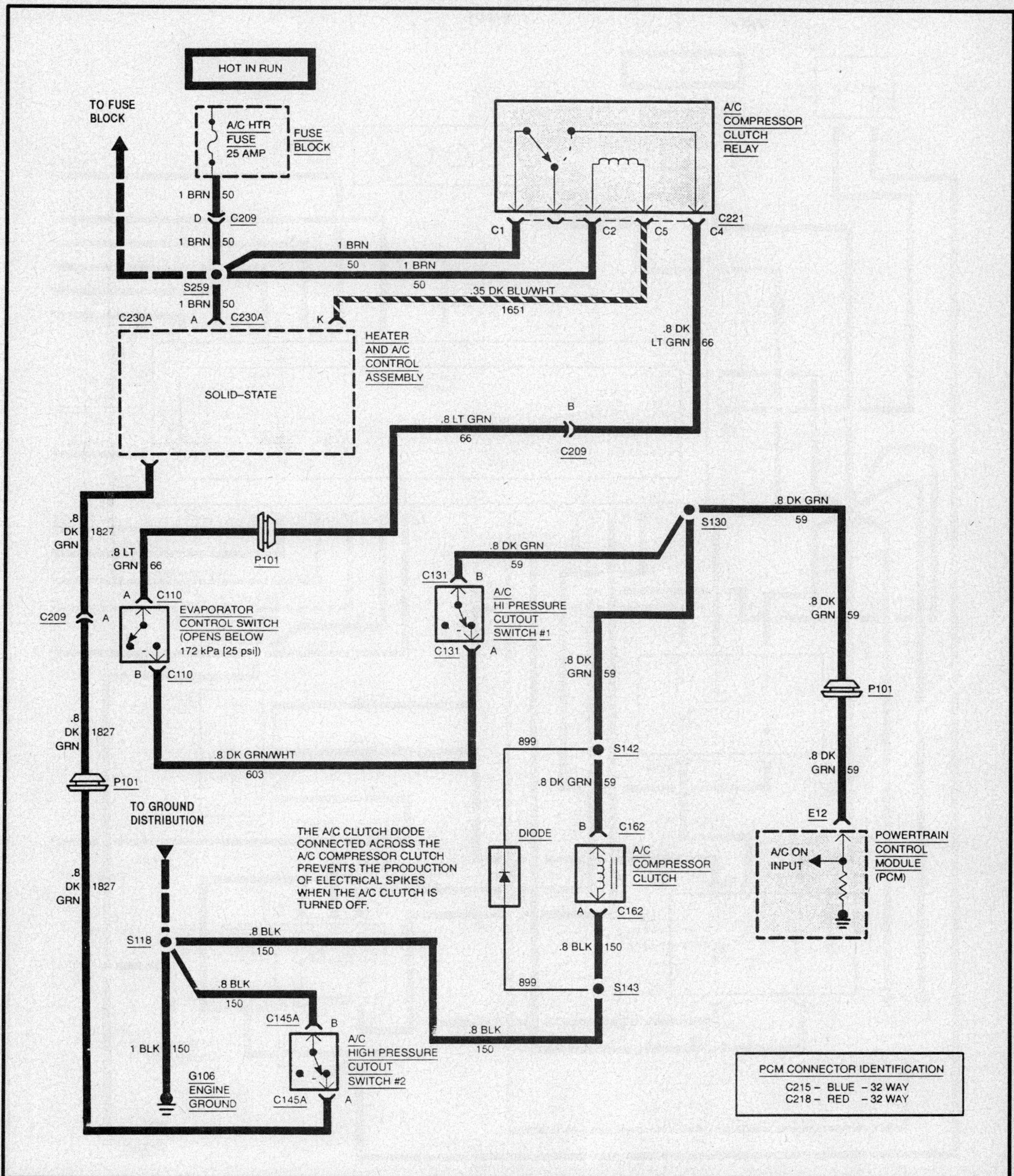

A/C compressor controls wiring schematic—1994 C/K Series (Pick-Up, Suburban, Blazer, Jimmy)

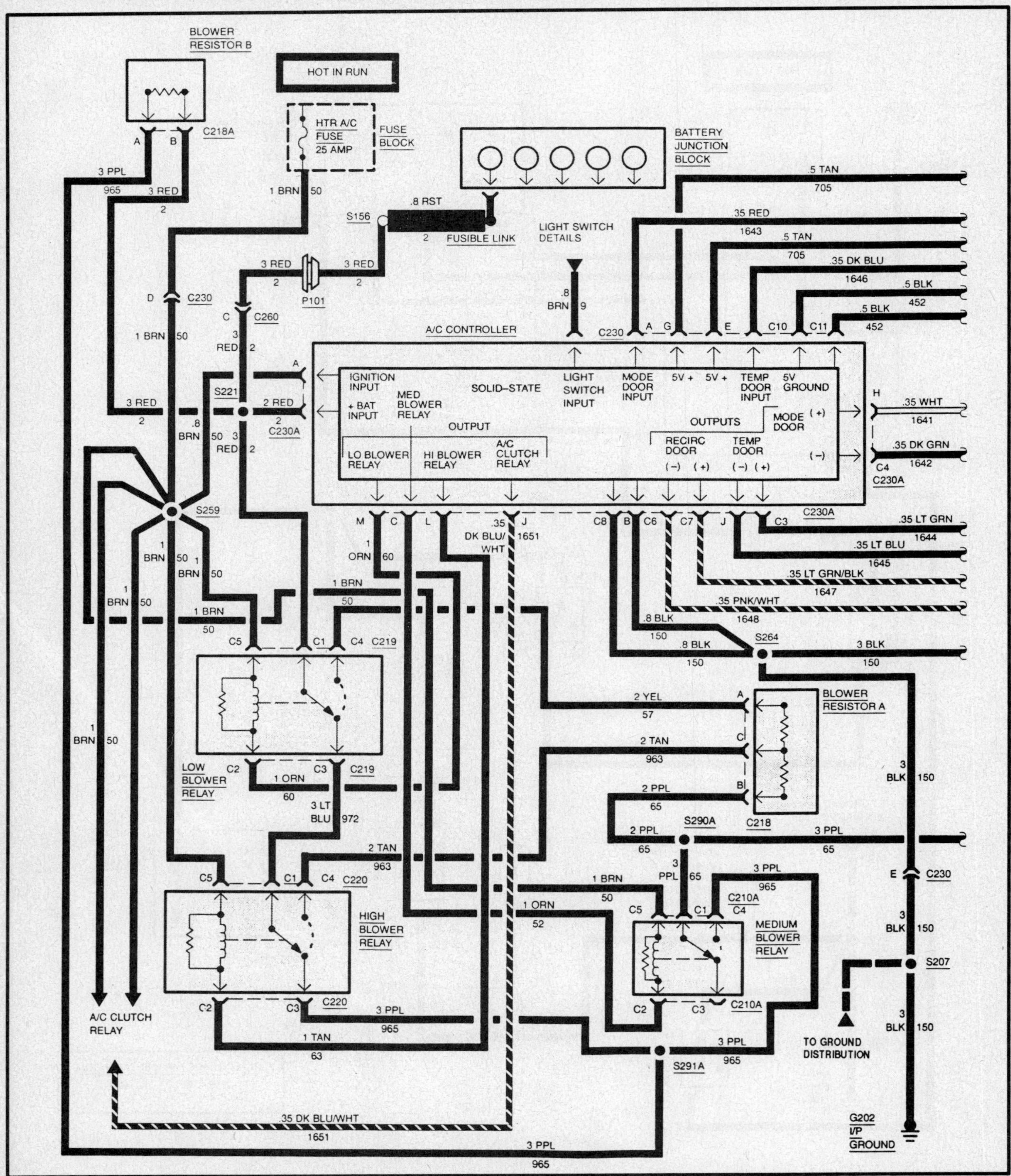

Heater and A/C blower controls wiring schematic—1994 C/K Series (Pick-Up, Suburban, Blazer, Jimmy)

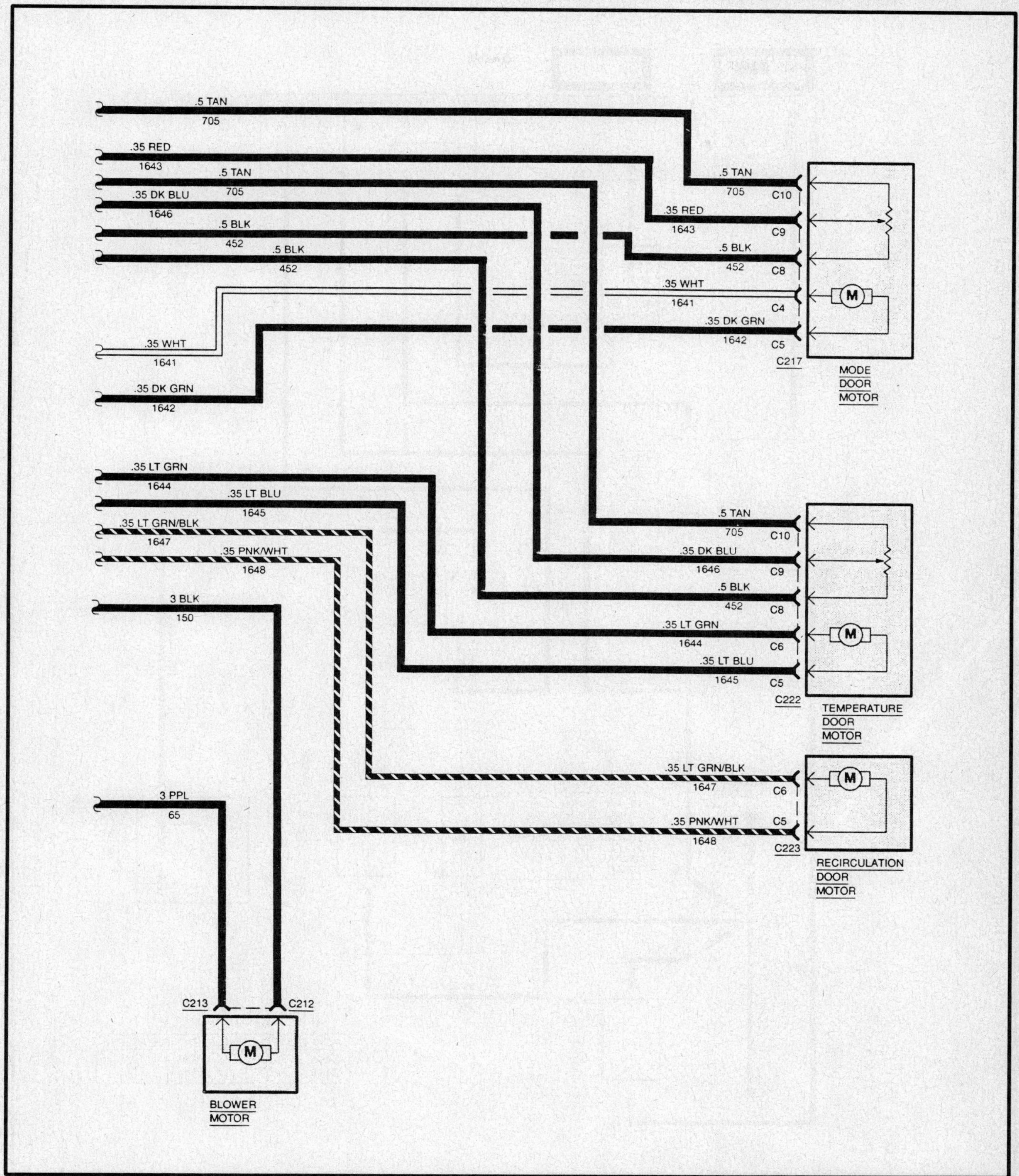

Heater and A/C blower controls wiring schematic—1994 C/K Series, (Pick-Up, Suburban, Blazer, Jimmy) Cont'd

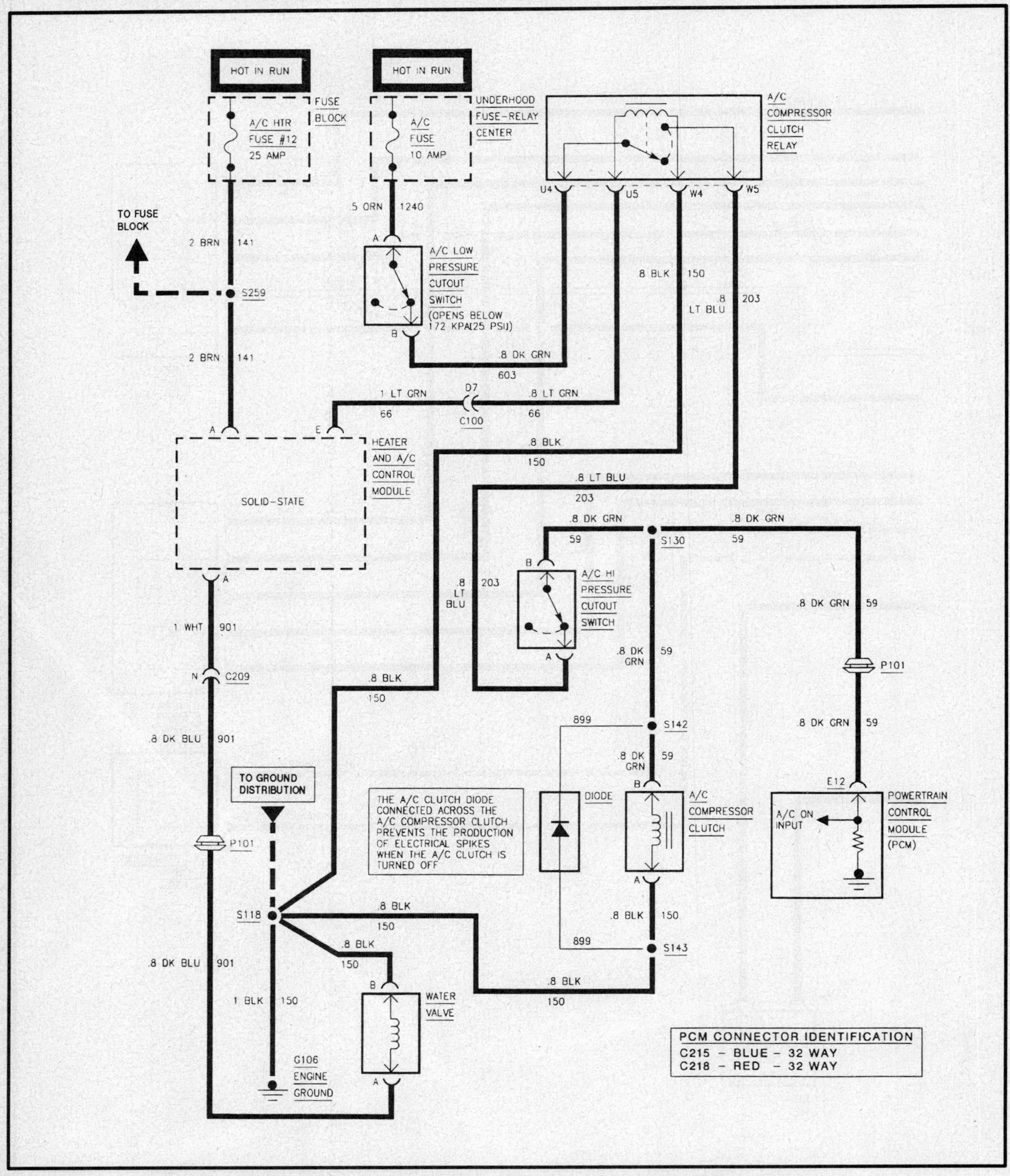

HVAC compressor wiring schematic—1995 C/K Series (Pick-up, Suburban, Blazer, Jimmy)

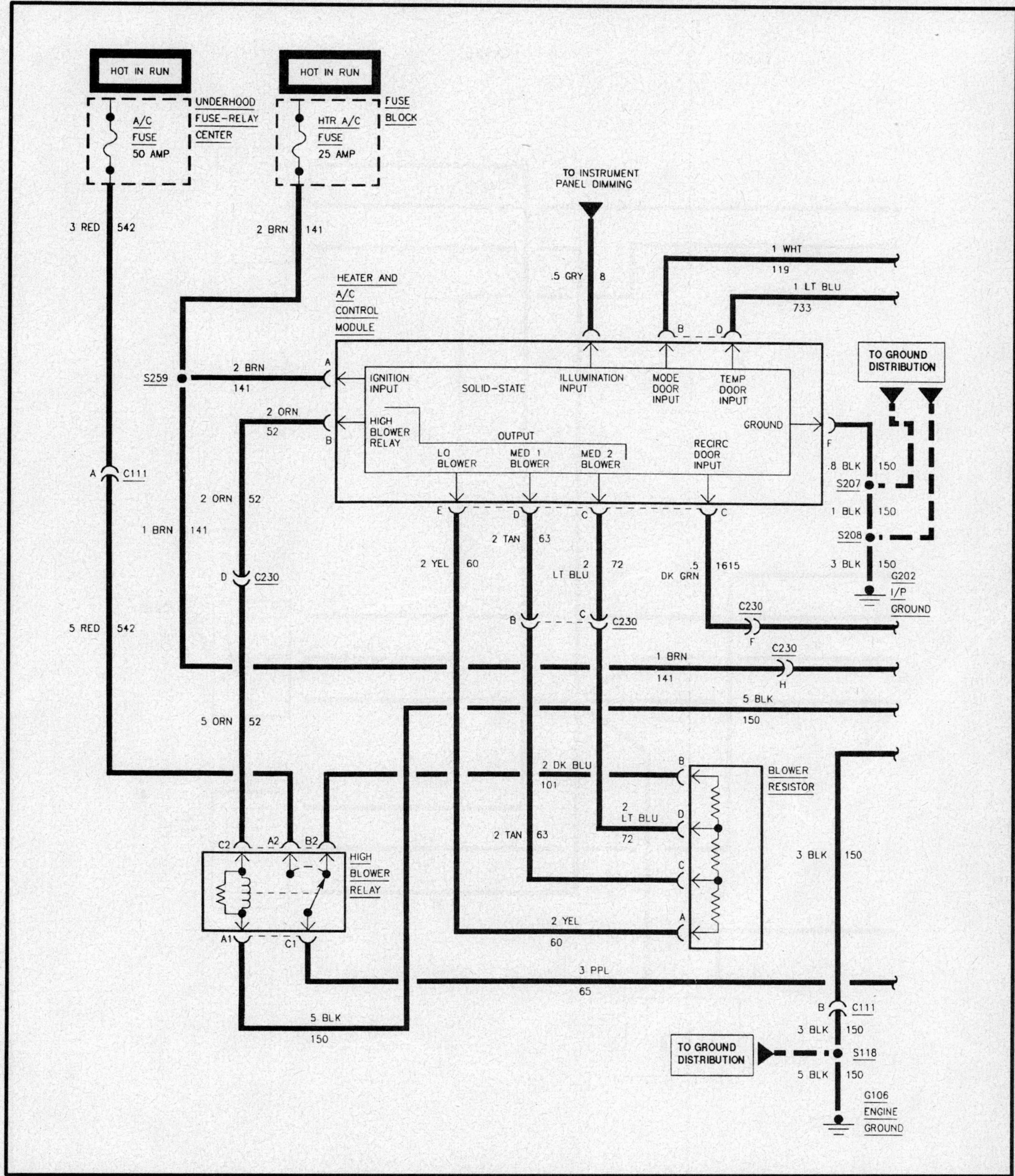

HVAC blower control wiring schematic—1995 C/K Series (Pick-up, Suburban, Blazer, Jimmy)

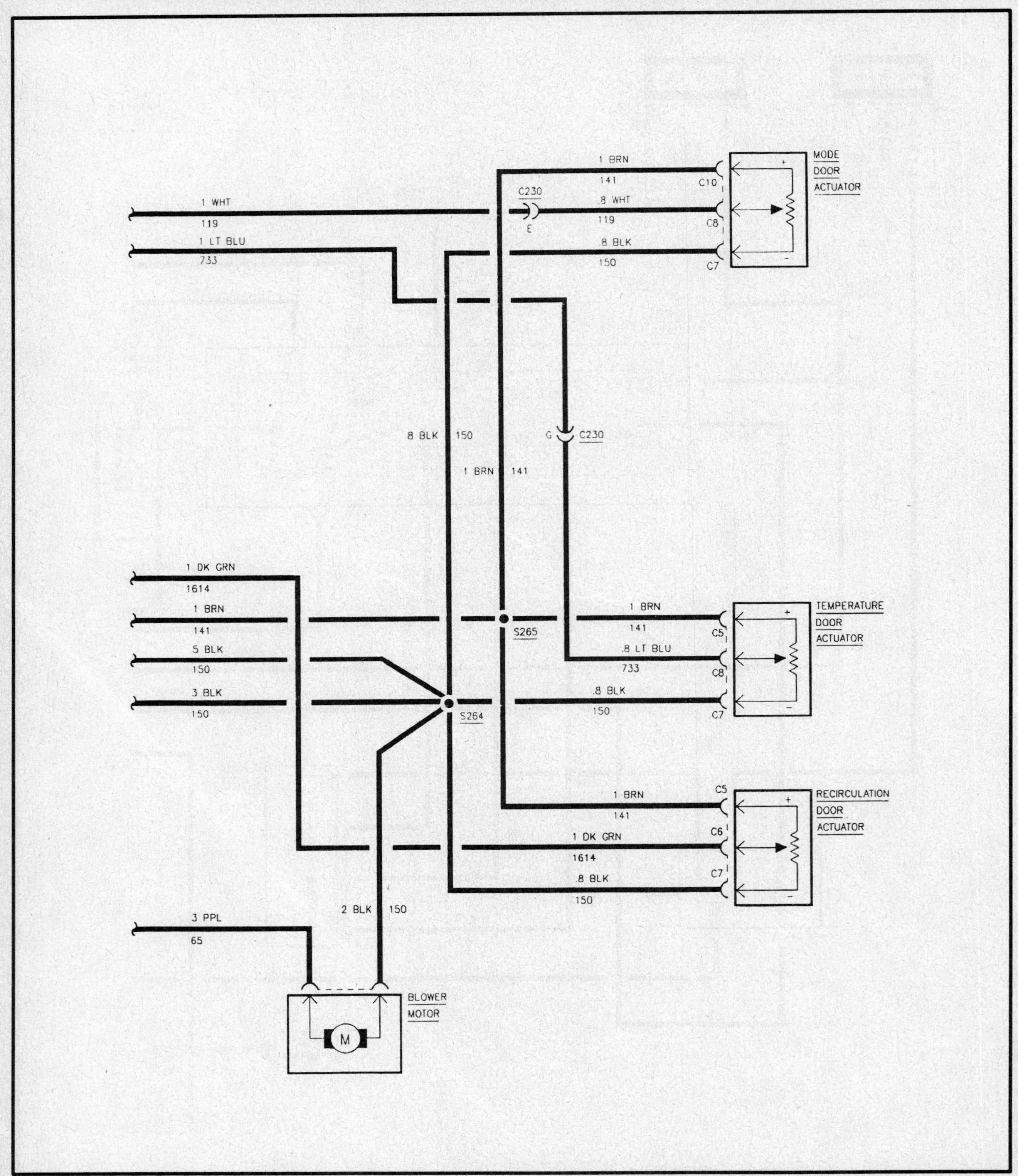

HVAC blower control wiring schematic—1995 C/K Series (Pick-up, Suburban, Blazer, Jimmy), Cont'd

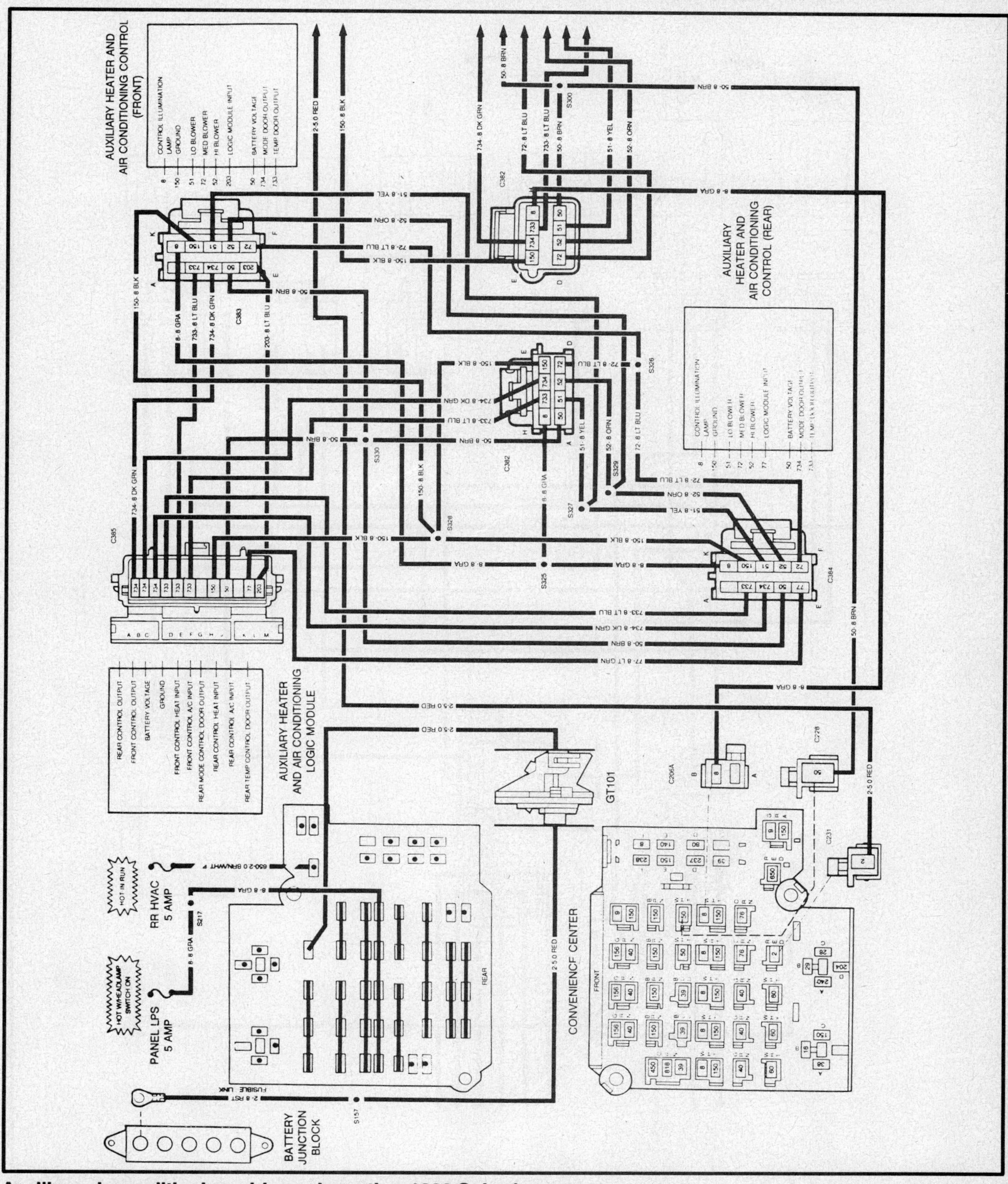

Auxiliary air conditioning wiring schematic—1993 Suburban

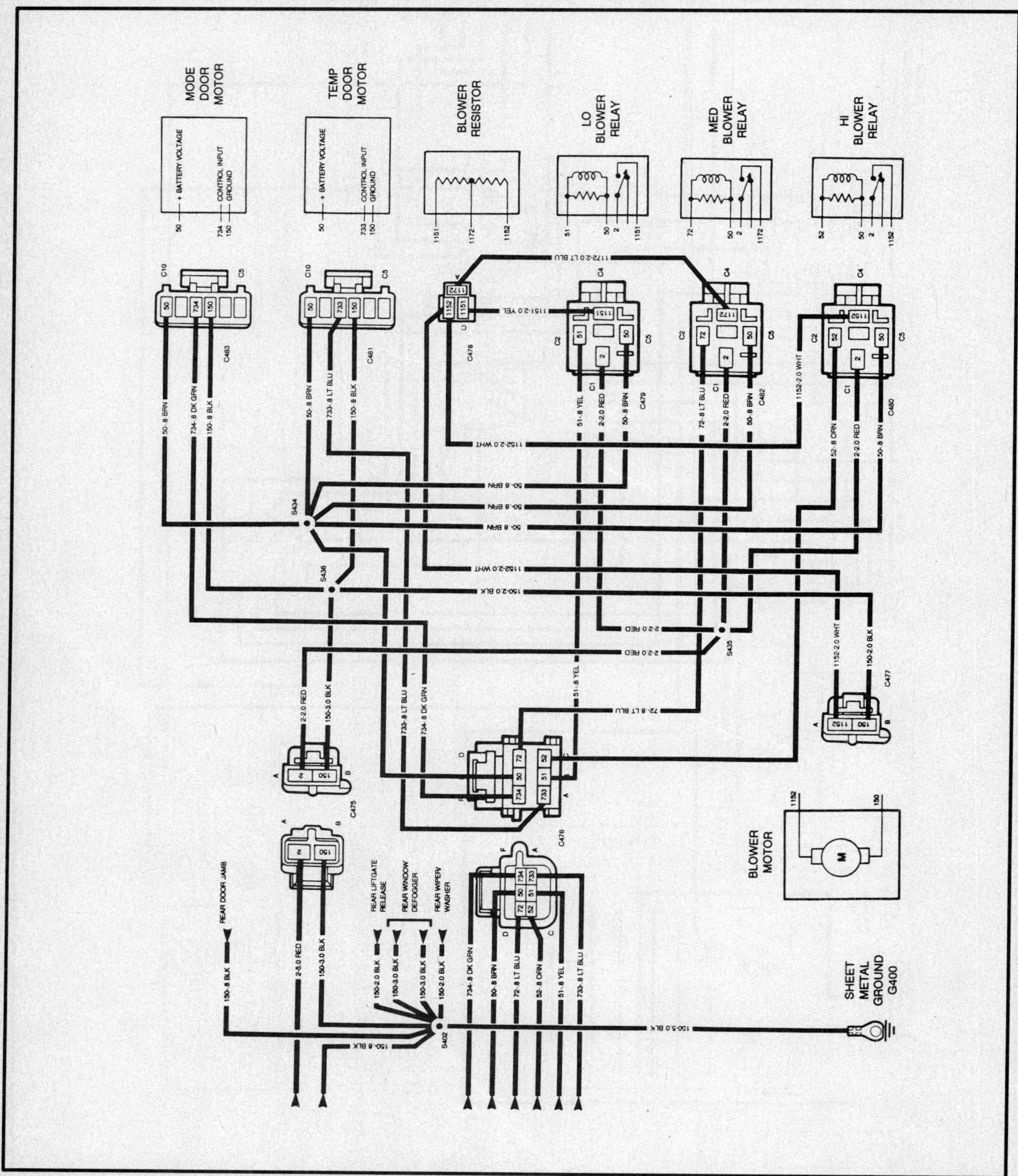

Auxiliary air conditioning wiring schematic—1993 Suburban, Cont'd

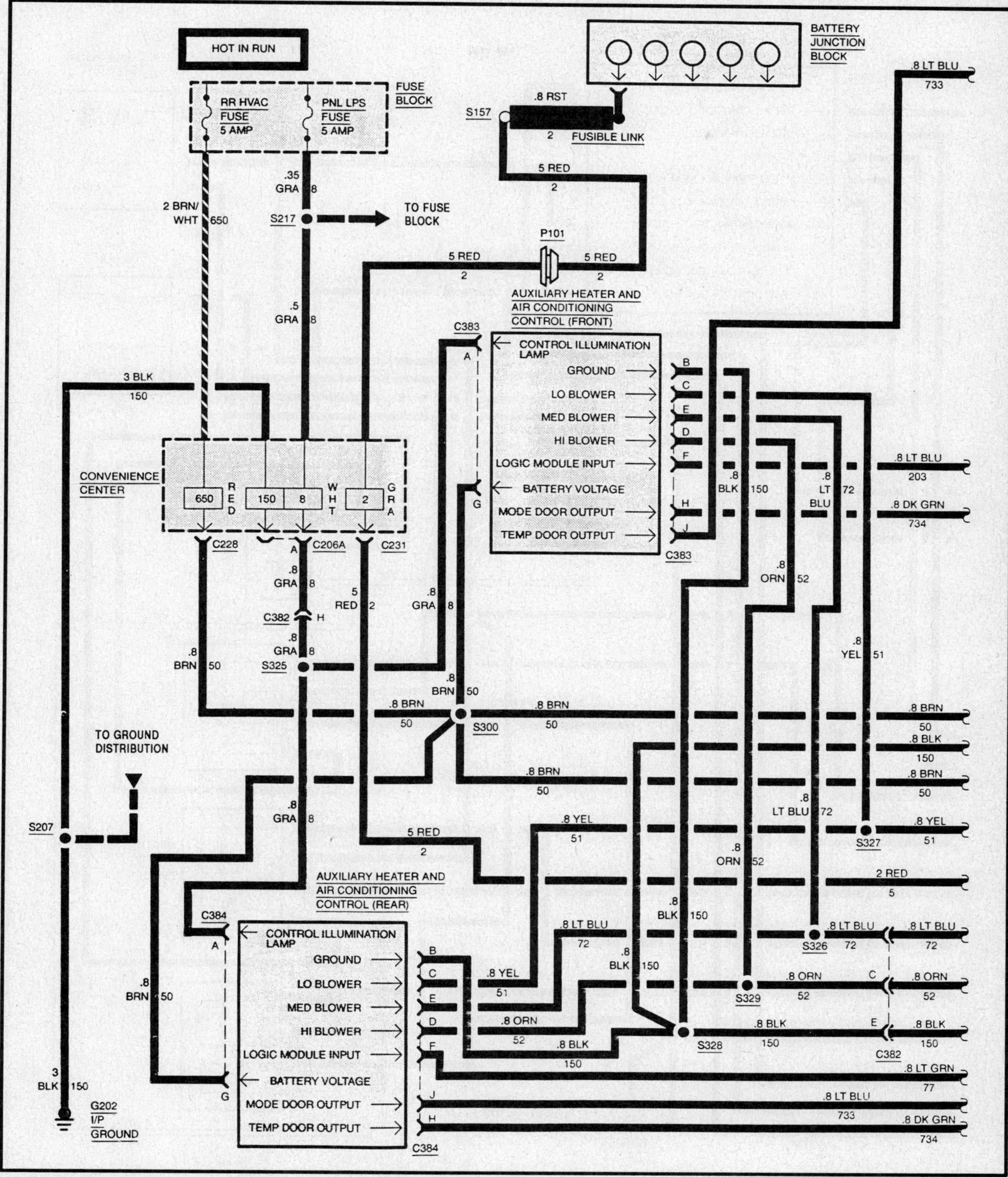

Auxiliary heater and air conditioning wiring schematic—1994 Suburban

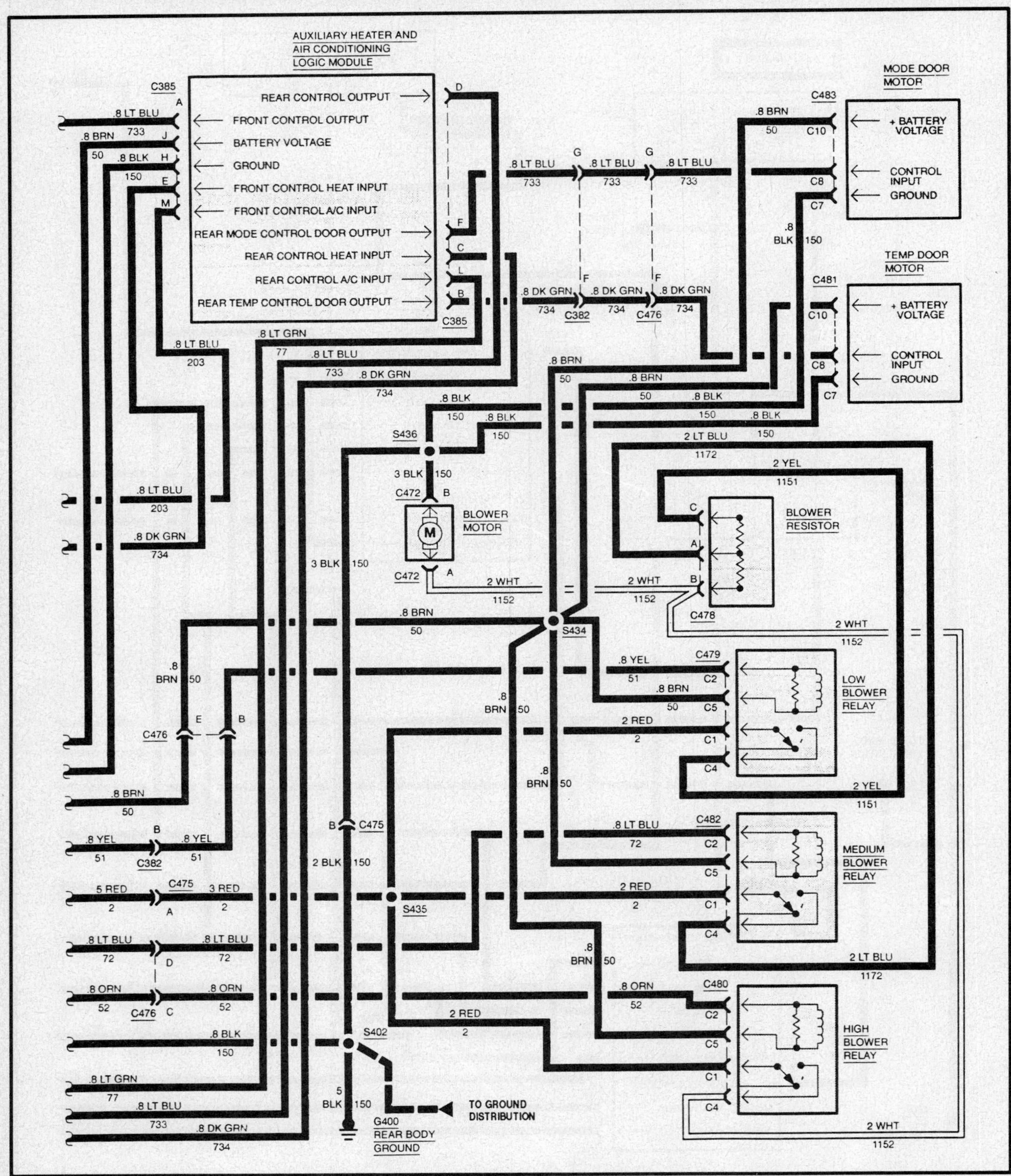

Auxiliary heater and air conditioning wiring schematic—1994 Suburban, Cont'd

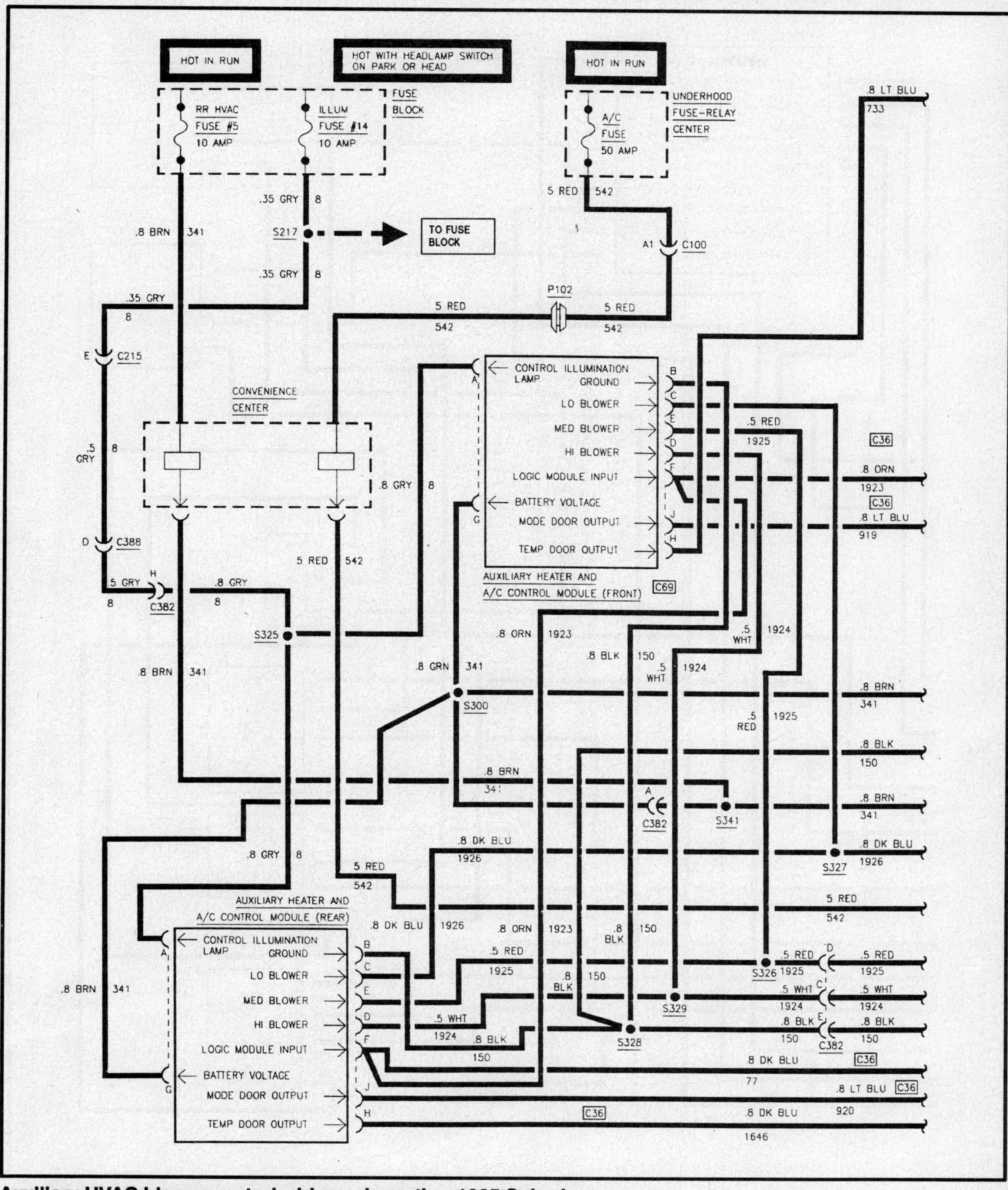

Auxiliary HVAC blower control wiring schematic—1995 Suburban

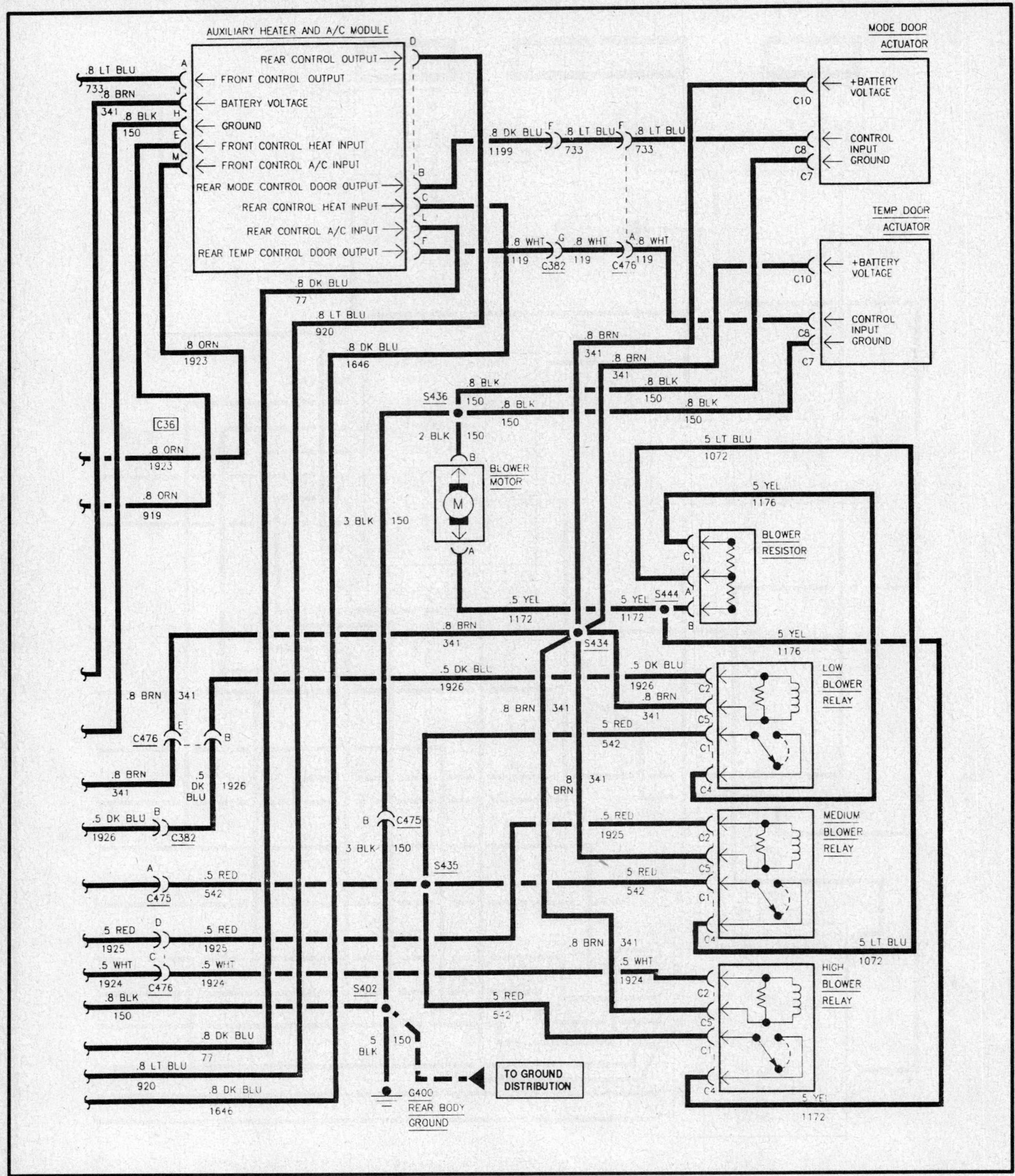

Auxiliary HVAC blower control wiring schematic—1995 Suburban, Cont'd

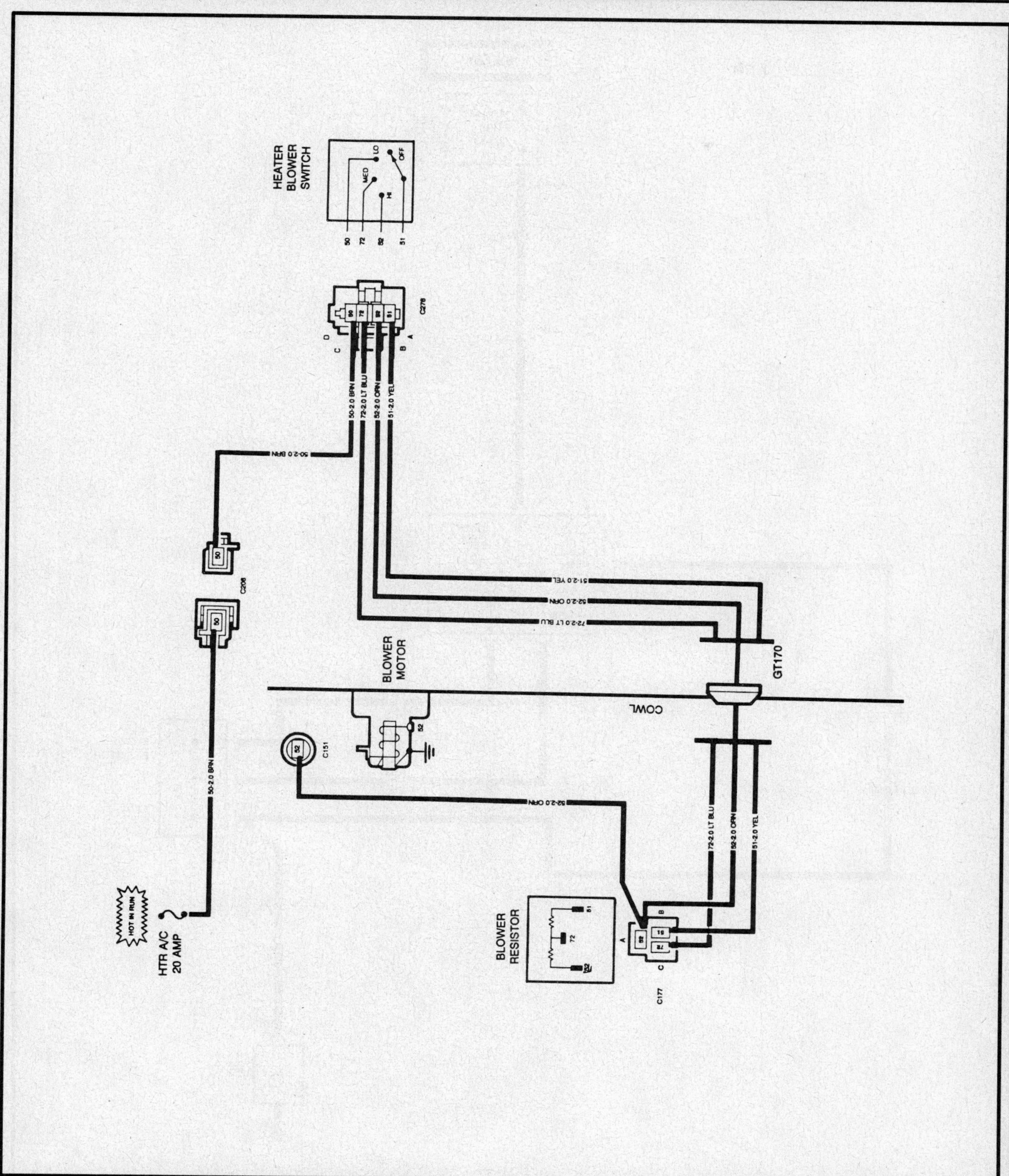

Heater only wiring schematic—1993 G Series Van

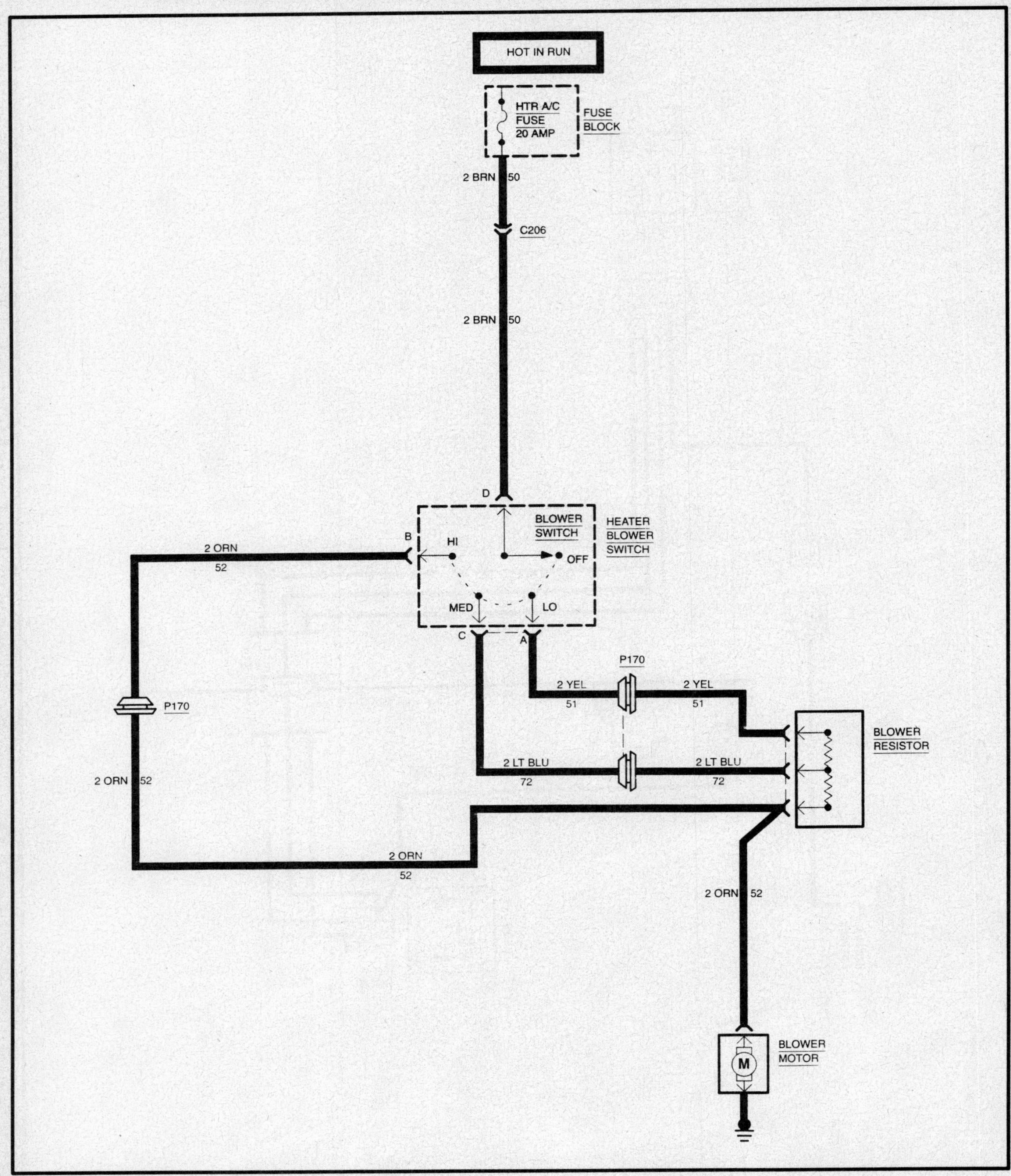

Heater only wiring schematic—1994–95 G Series Van

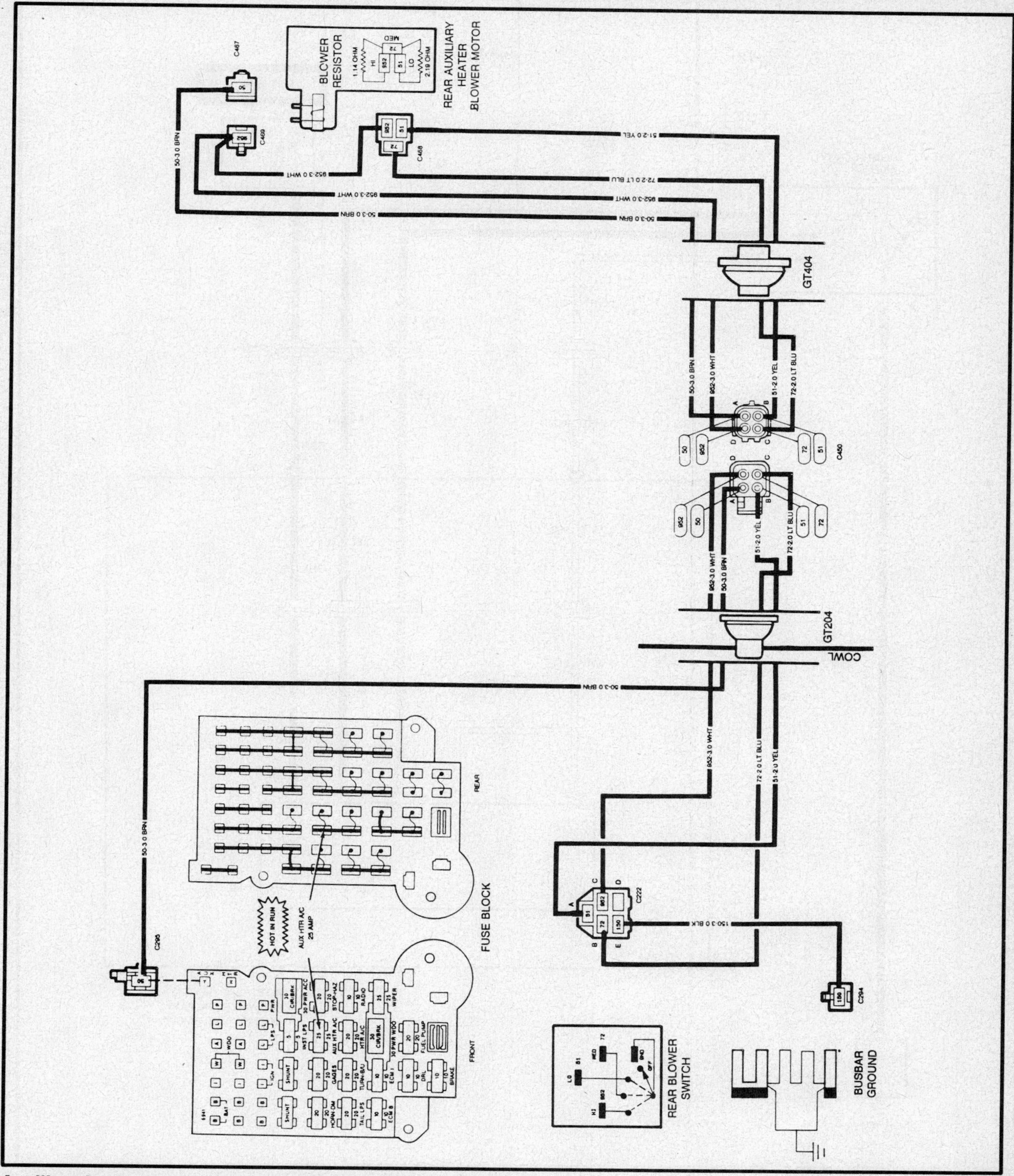

Auxiliary heater only wiring schematic—1993 G Series Van

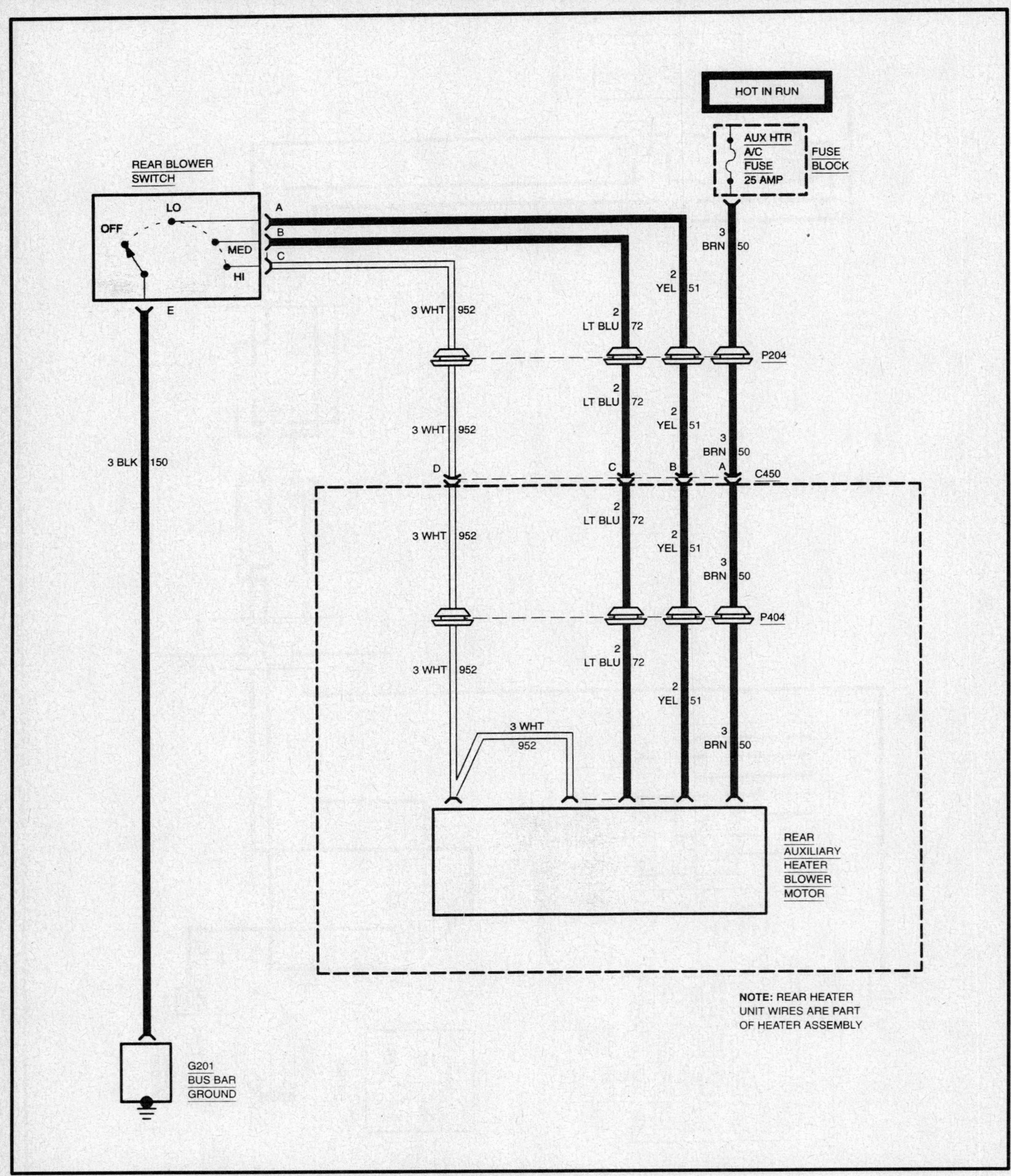

Auxiliary heater wiring schematic—1994–95 G Series Van

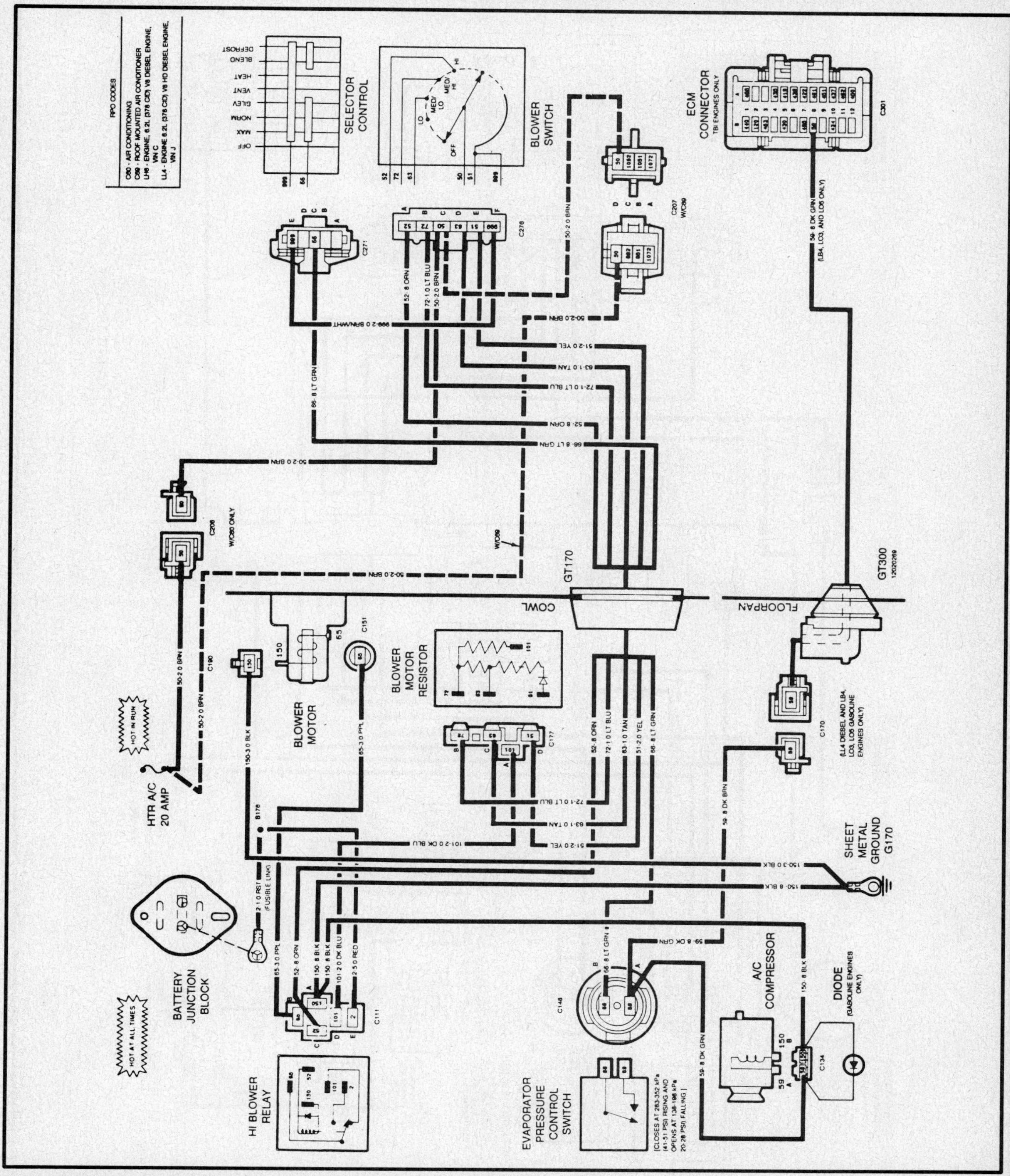

Air conditioning wiring schematic—1993 G Series Van (except 7.4L engine)

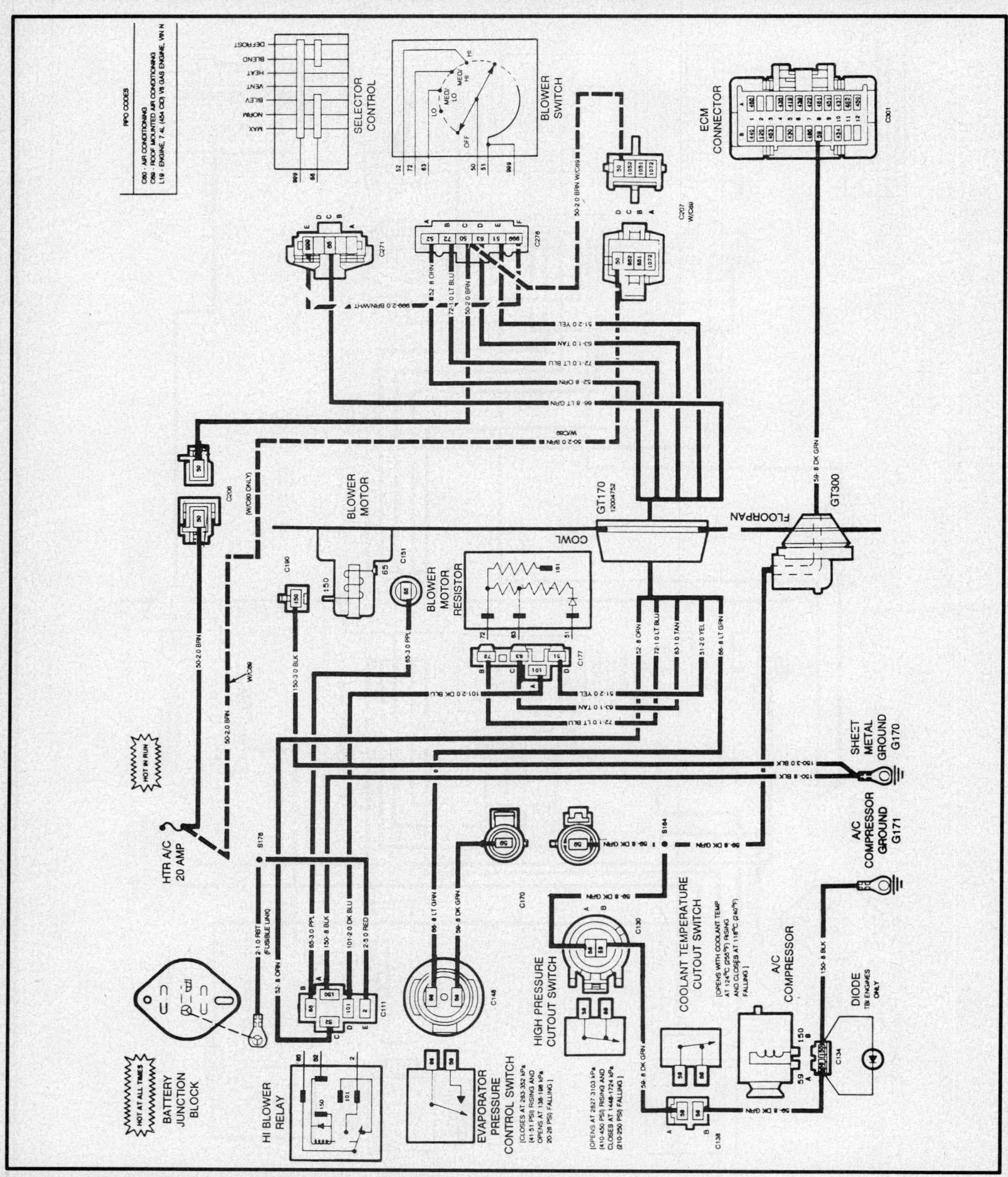

Air conditioning wiring schematic—1993 G Series Van (with 7.4L engine)

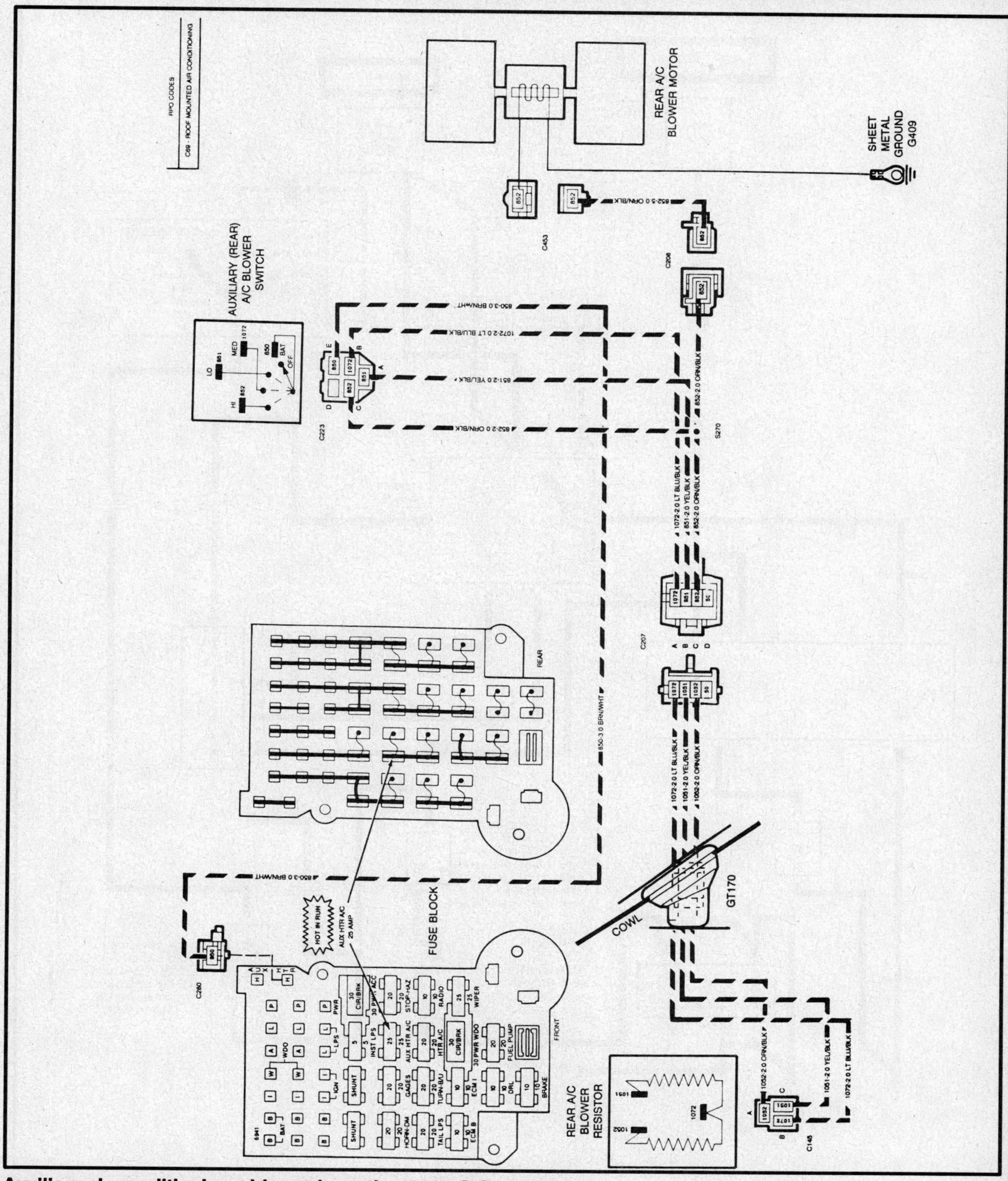

Auxiliary air conditioning wiring schematic—1993 G Series Van

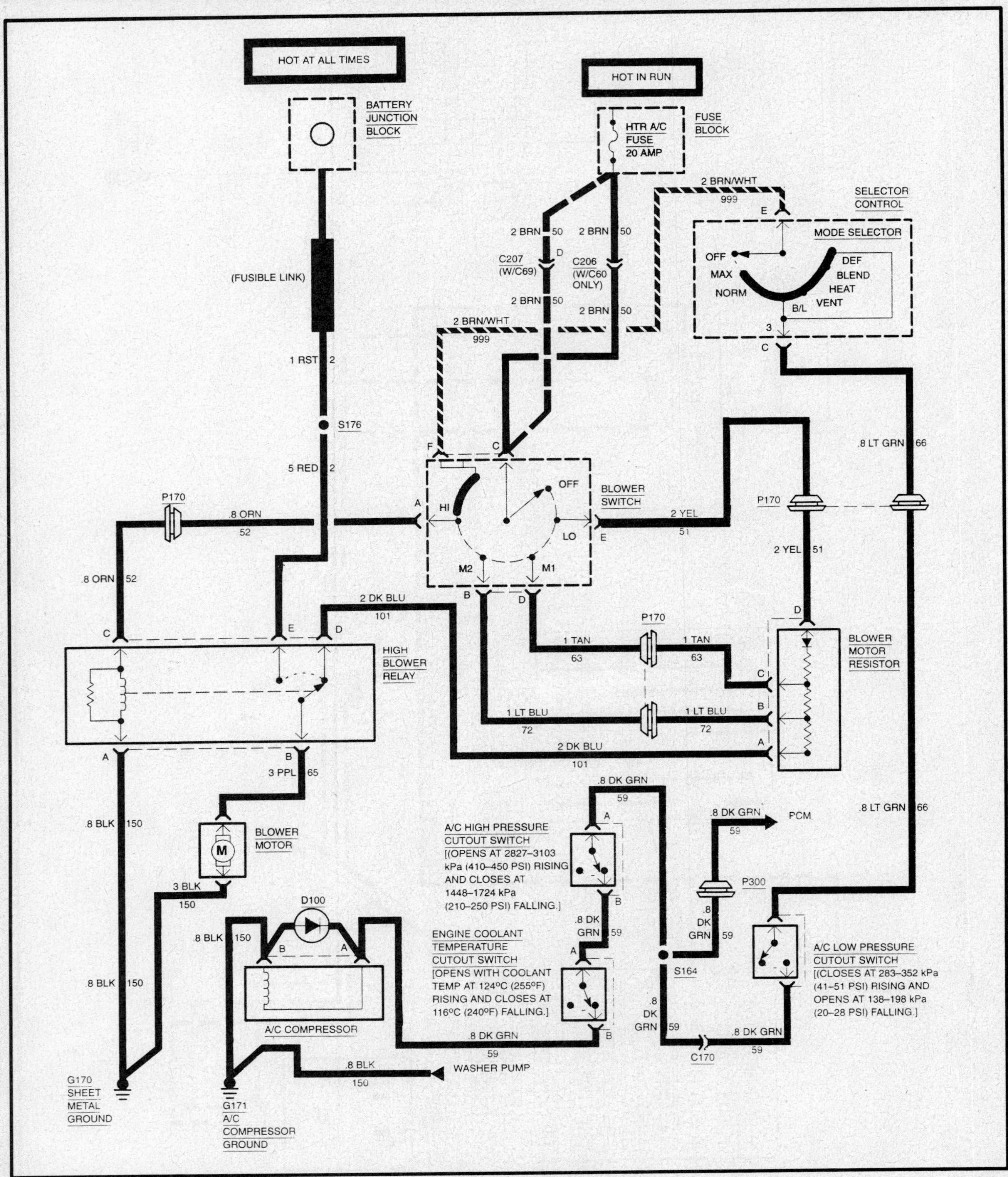

Heater and air conditioning wiring schematic—1994–95 G Series Van

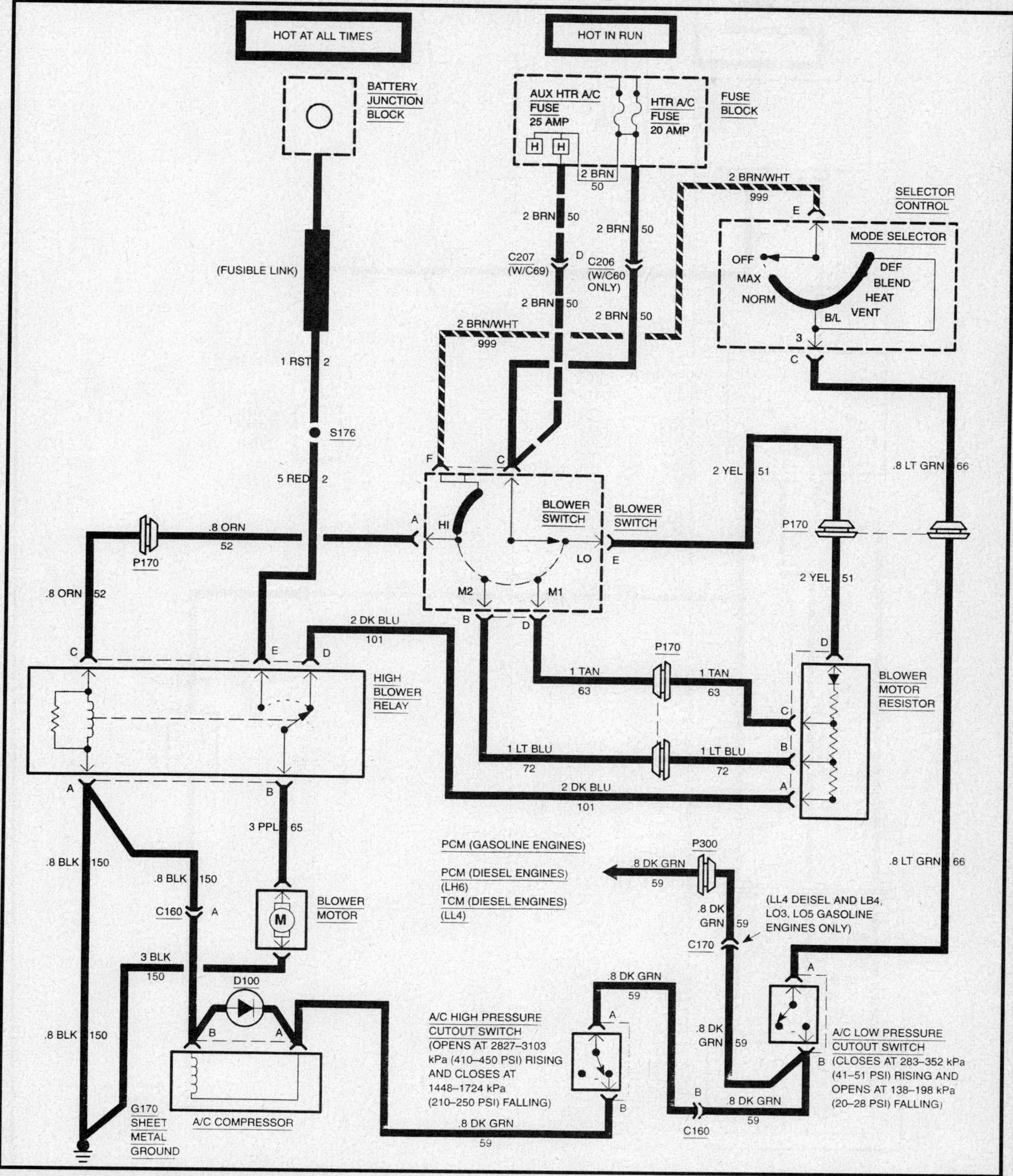

Heater and air conditioning wiring schematic—1994–95 G Series Van (with auxiliary system)

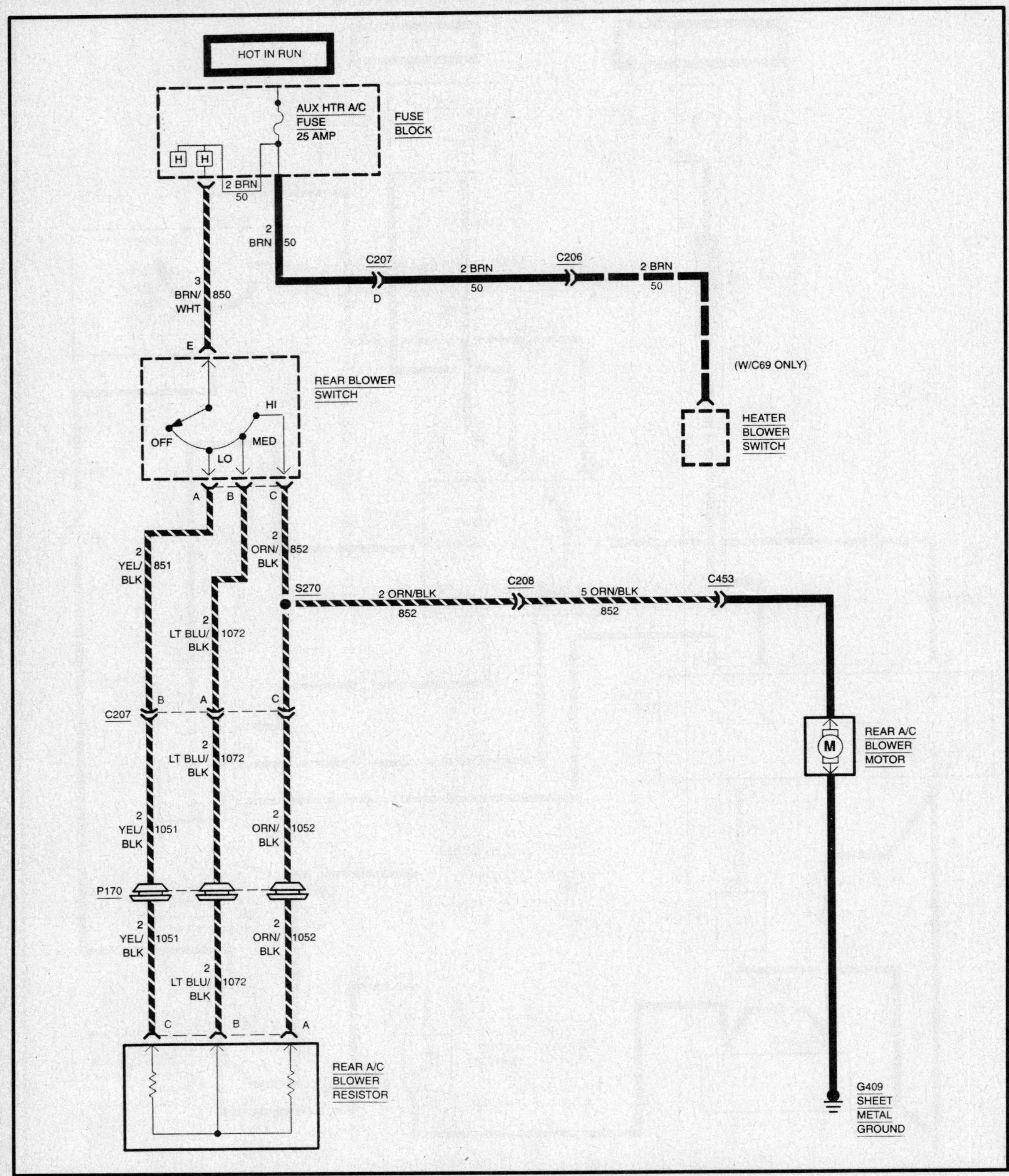

Auxiliary heater and air conditioning wiring schematic—1994–95 G Series Van

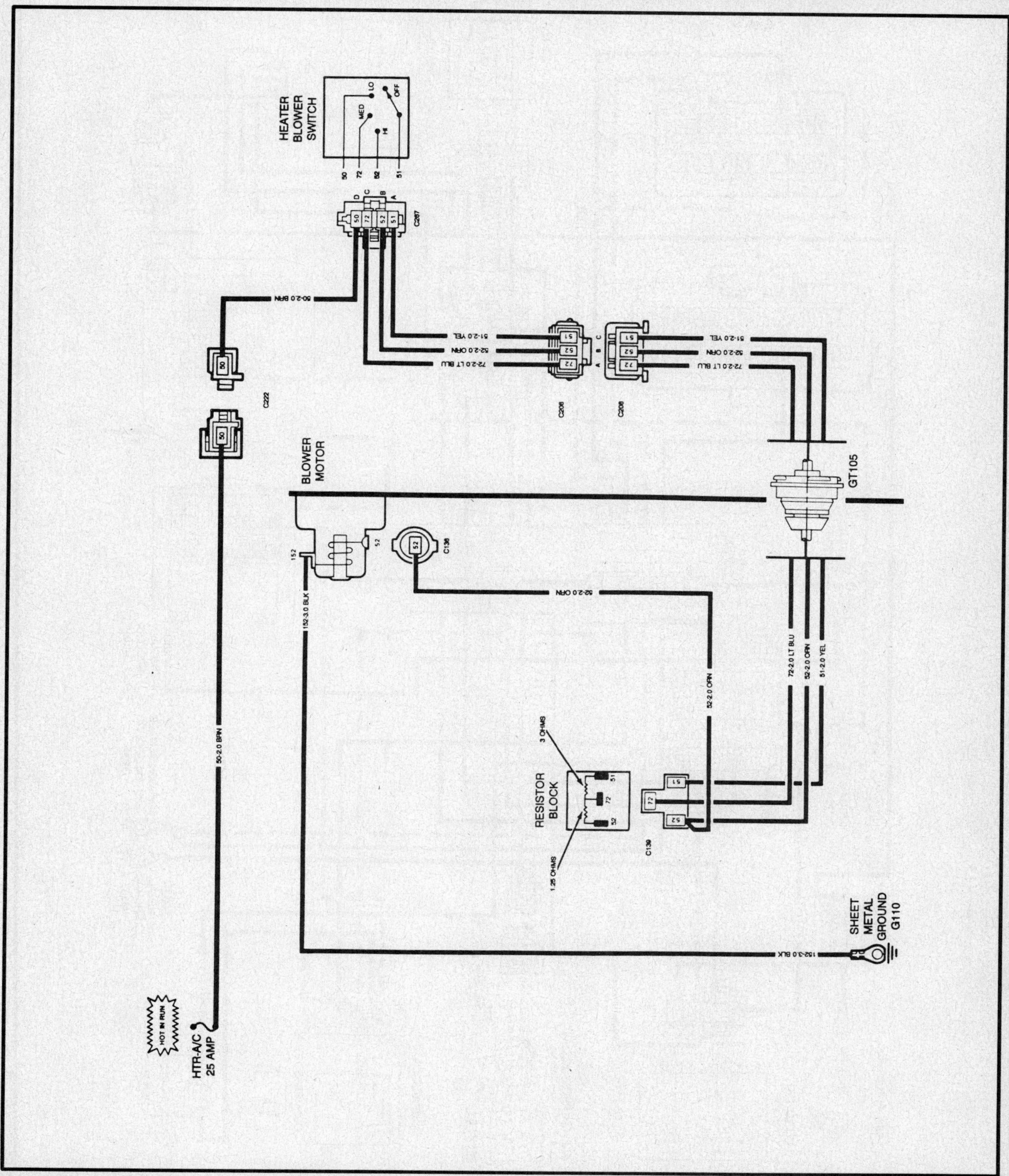

Heater only wiring schematic—S10/S15 Series and Bravada

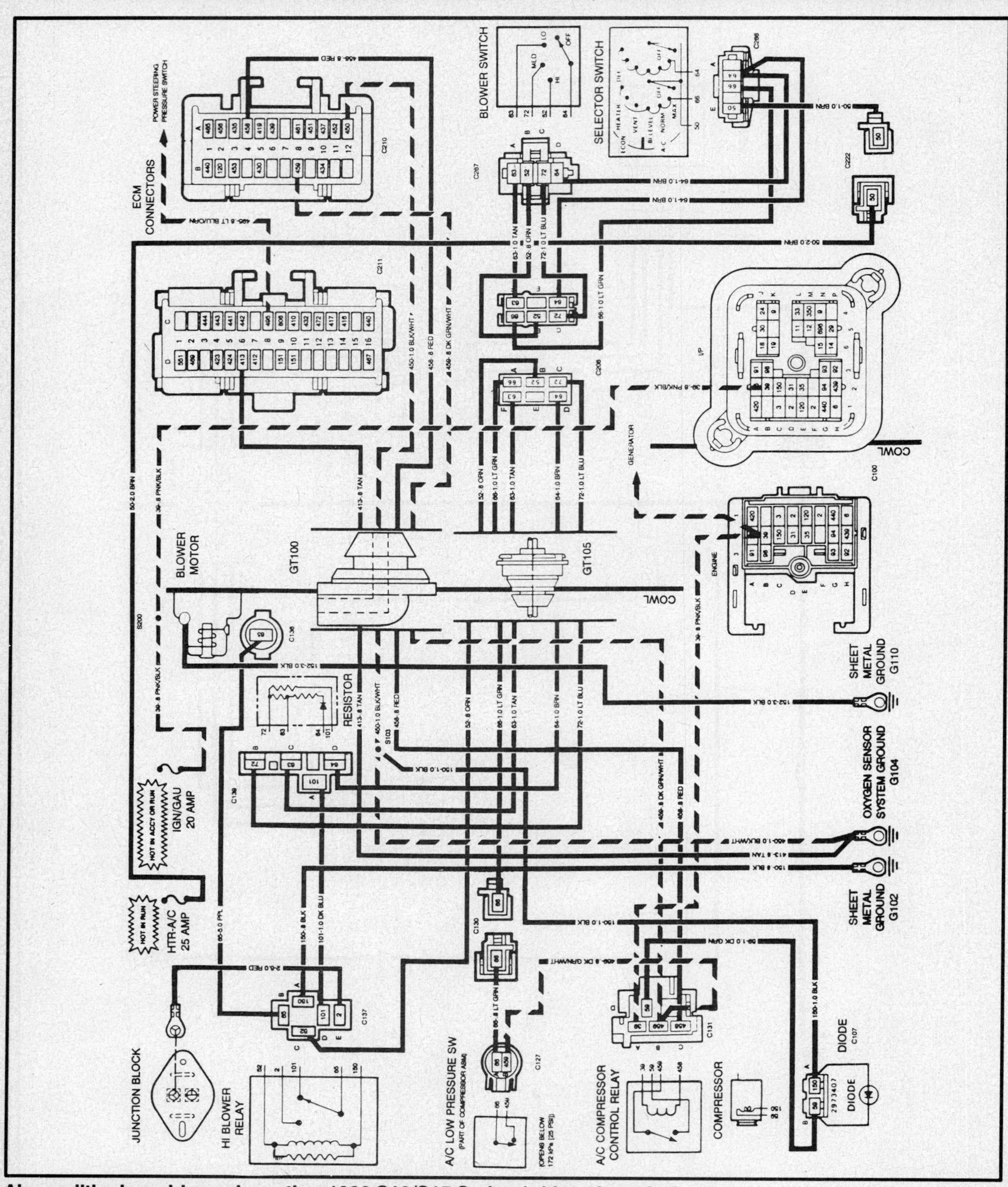

Air conditioning wiring schematic—1993 S10/S15 Series (with 2.5L engine)

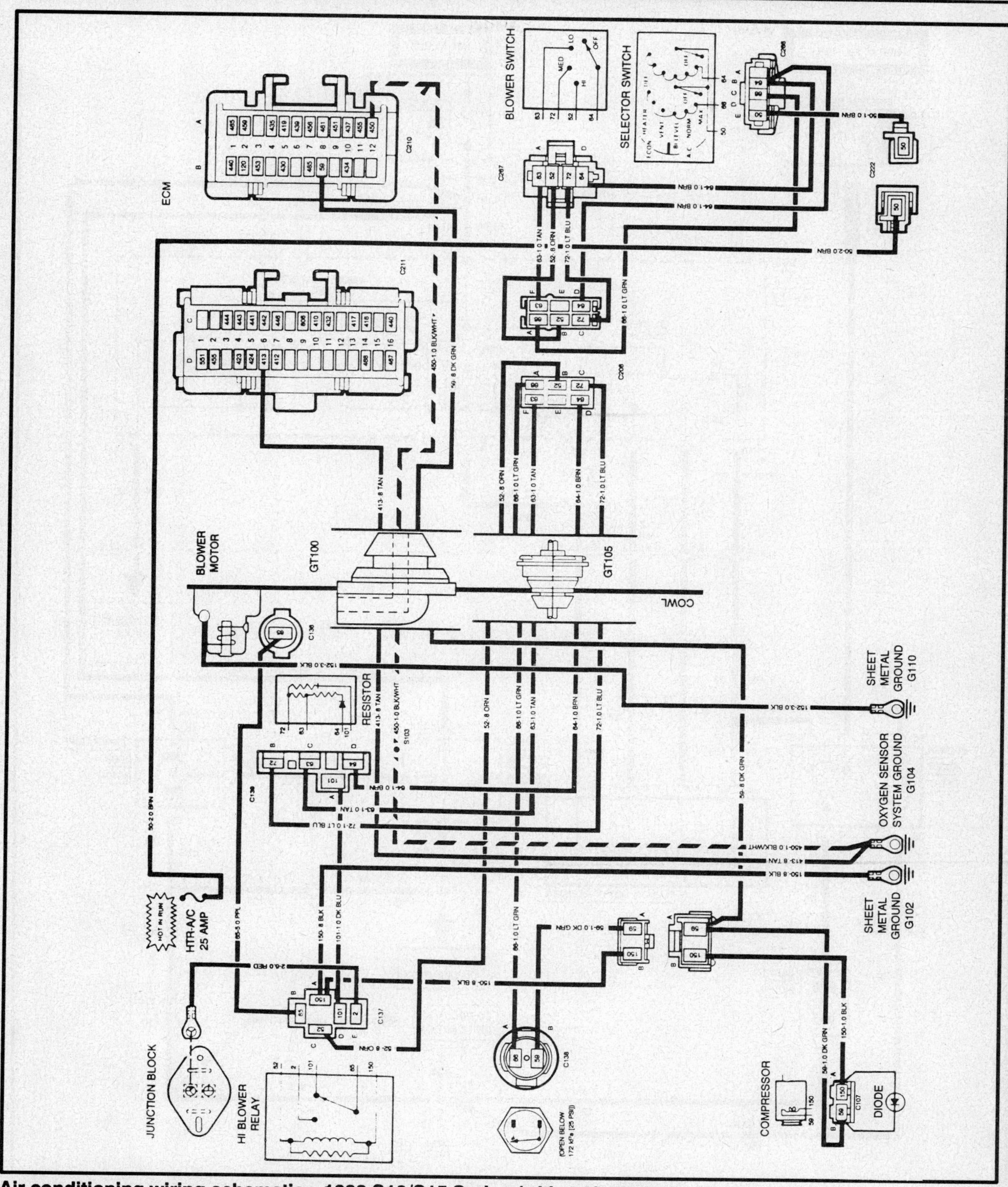

Air conditioning wiring schematic—1993 S10/S15 Series (with 4.3L engine)

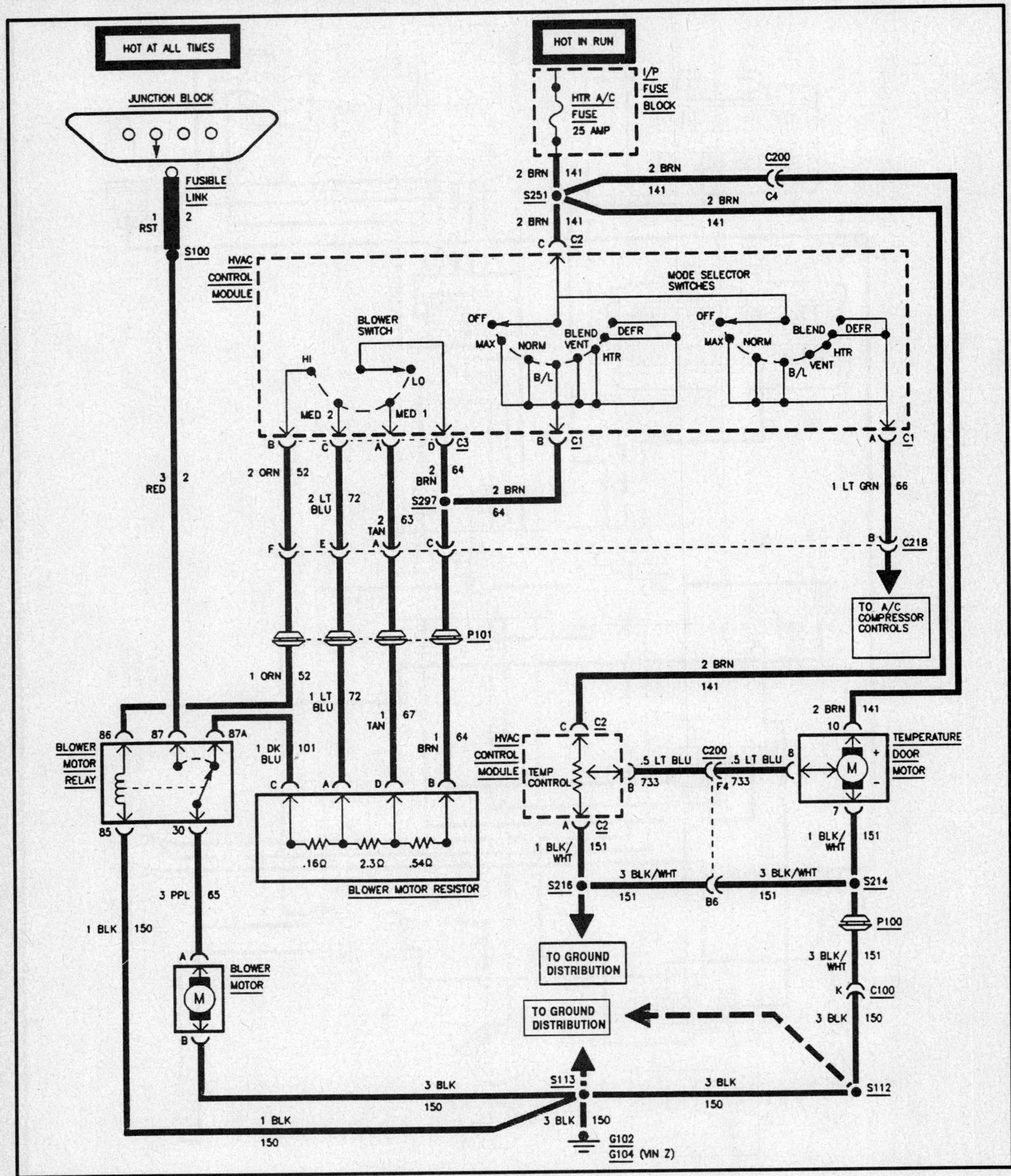

HVAC blower control (W/PCM) wiring schematic—S/T Series

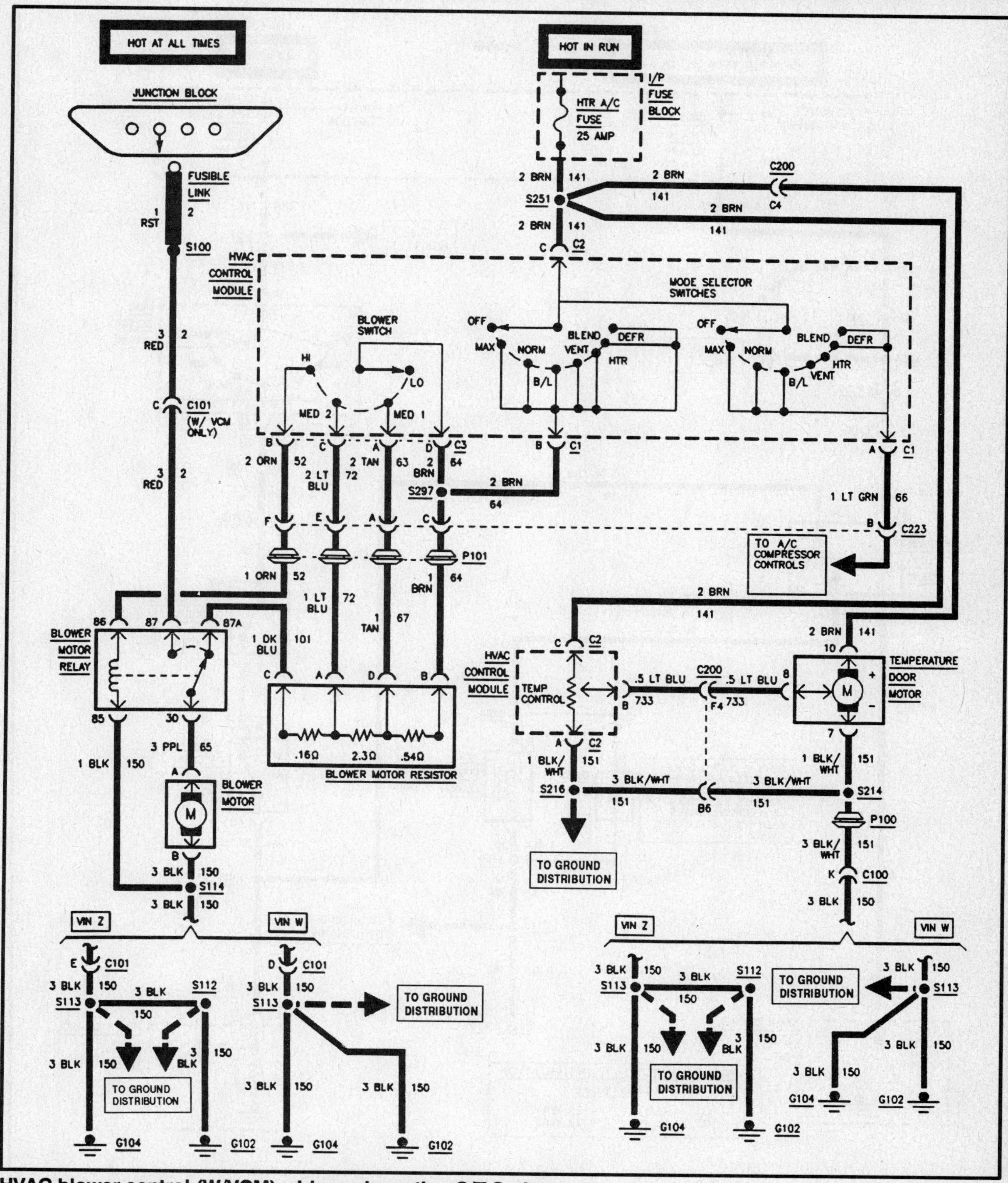

HVAC blower control (W/VCM) wiring schematic—S/T Series

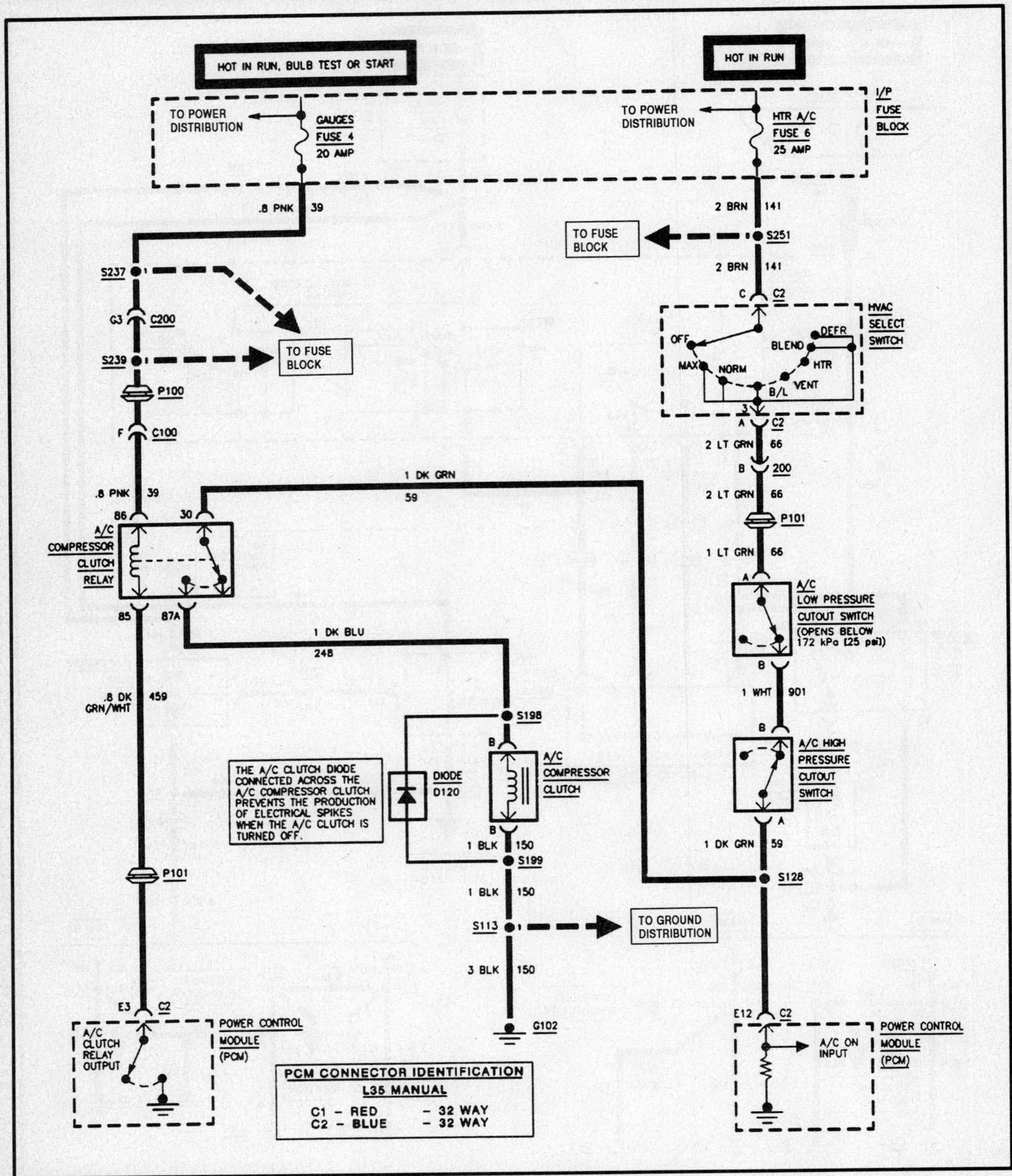

HVAC compressor control (L4 VIN 4) wiring schematic—S/T Series

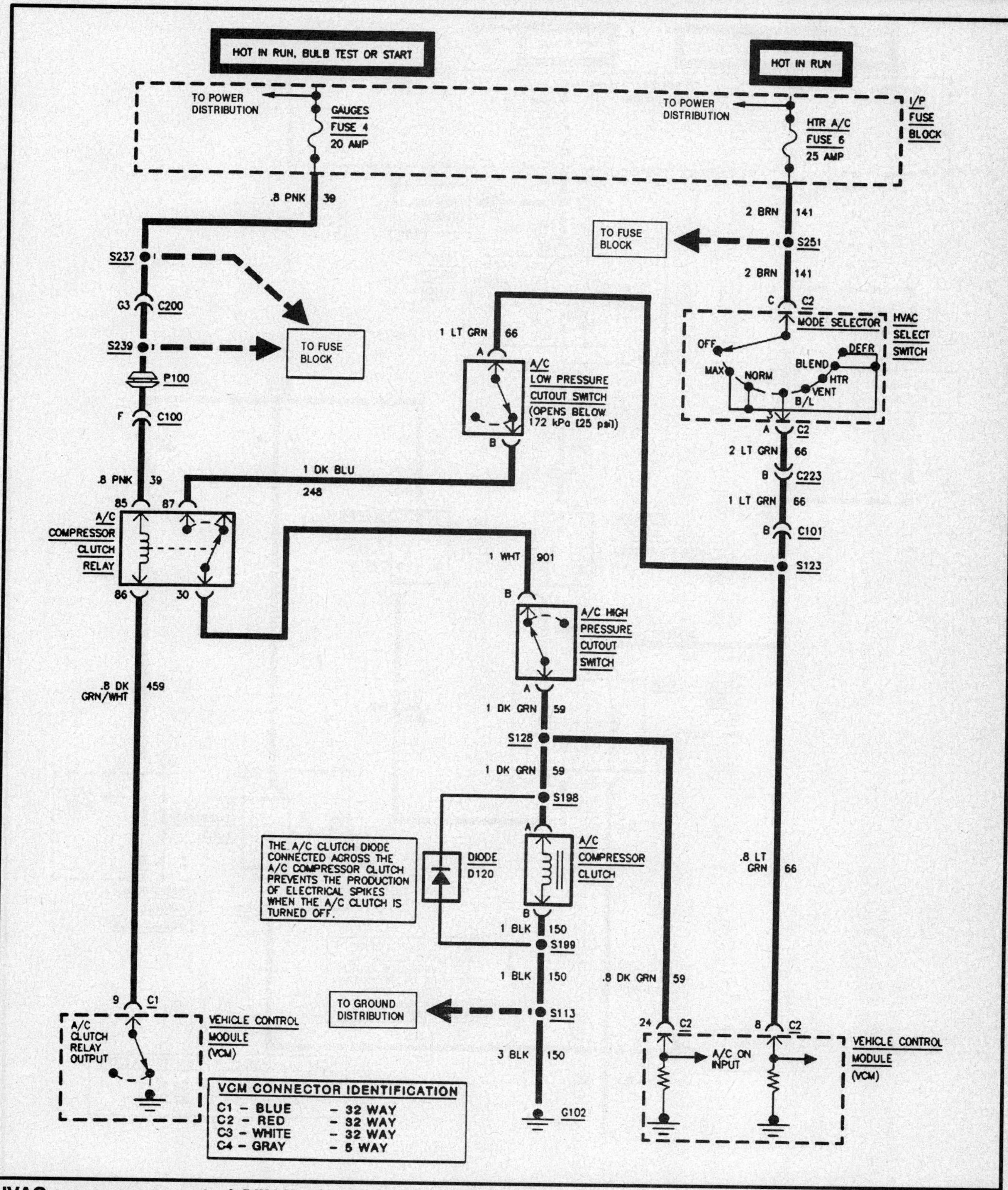

HVAC compressor control (VIN Z w/manual transmission) wiring schematic—S/T Series

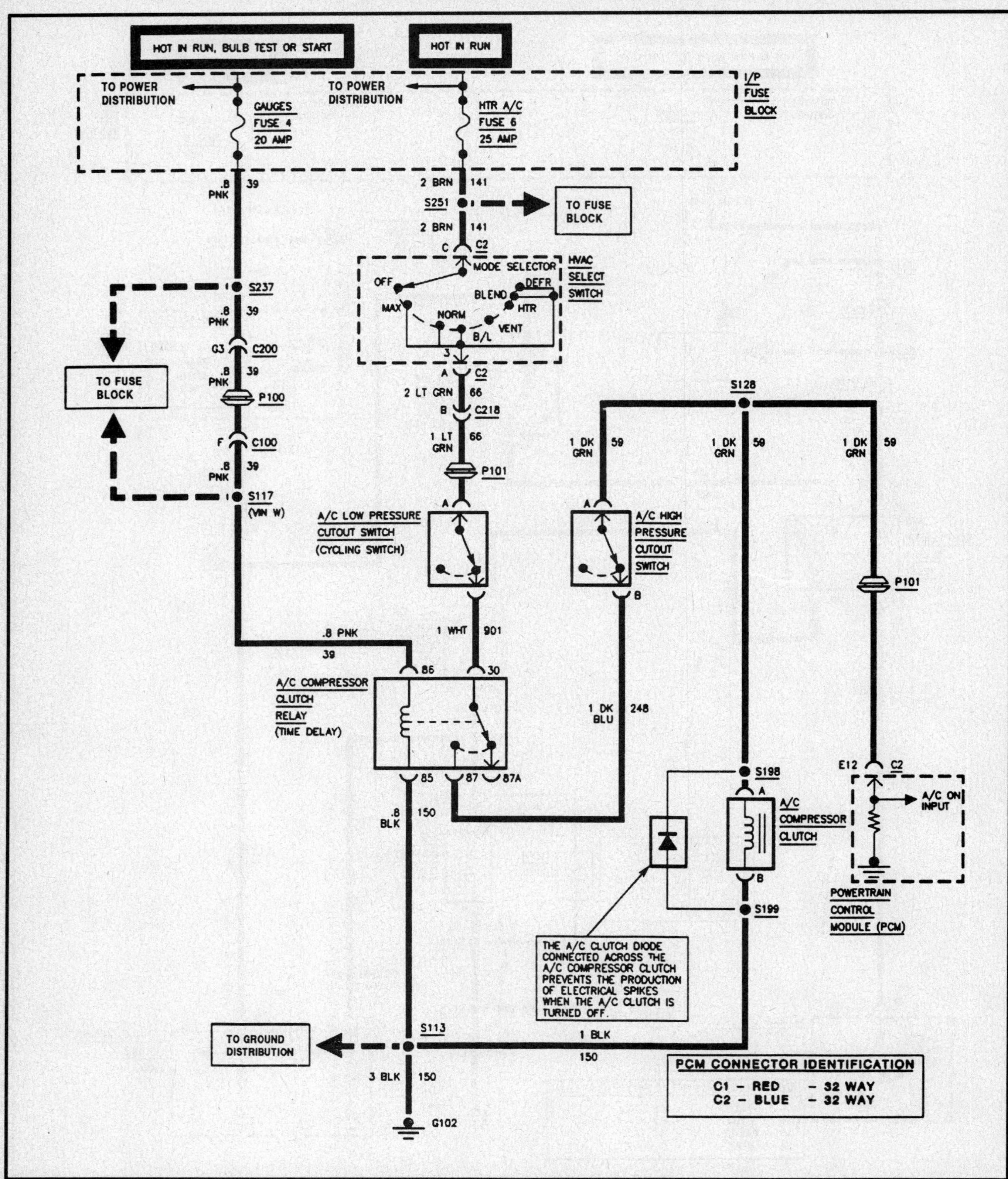

HVAC compressor control (VIN Z, W w/PCM) wiring schematic—S/T Series

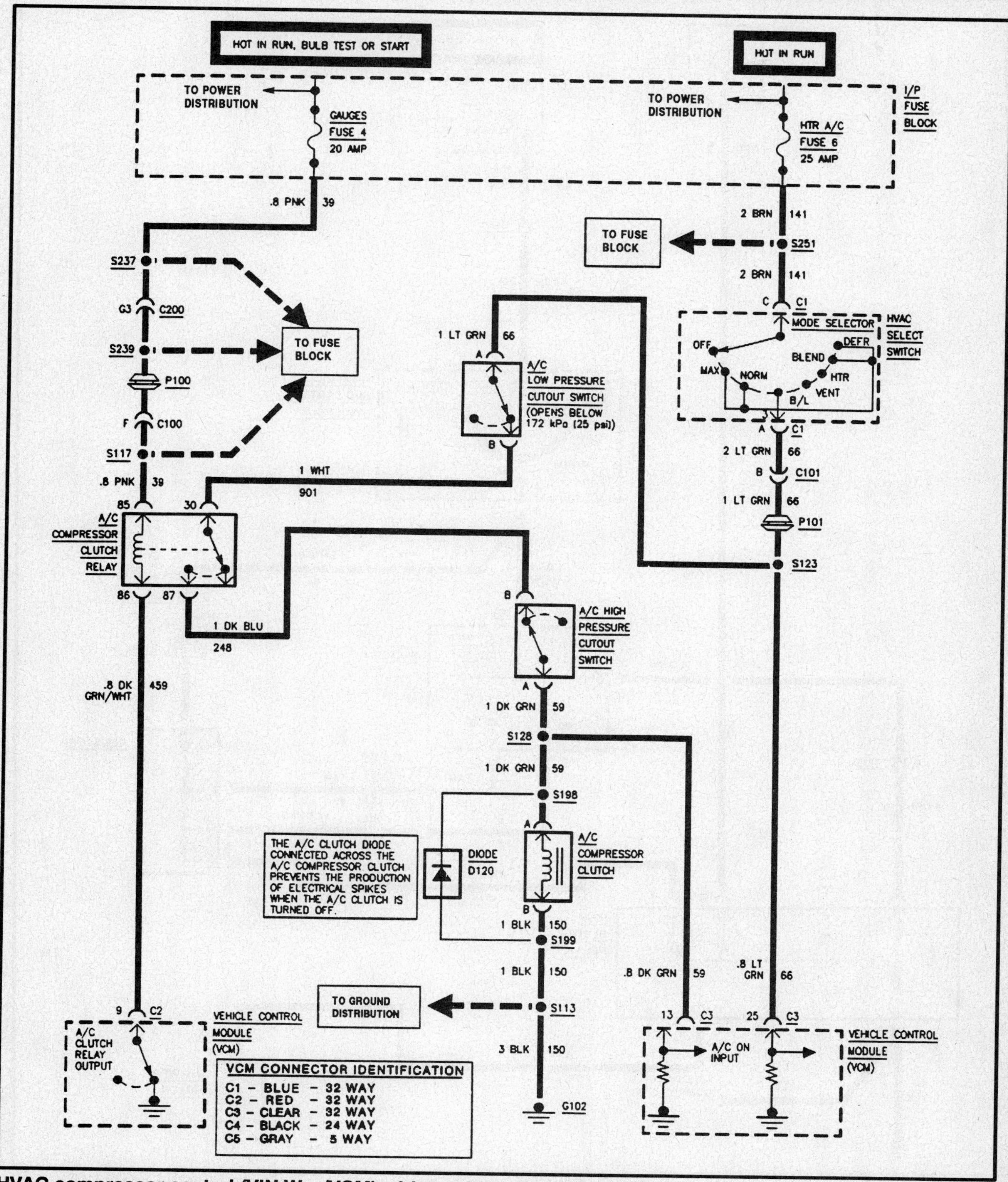

HVAC compressor control (VIN W w/VCM) wiring schematic—S/T Series

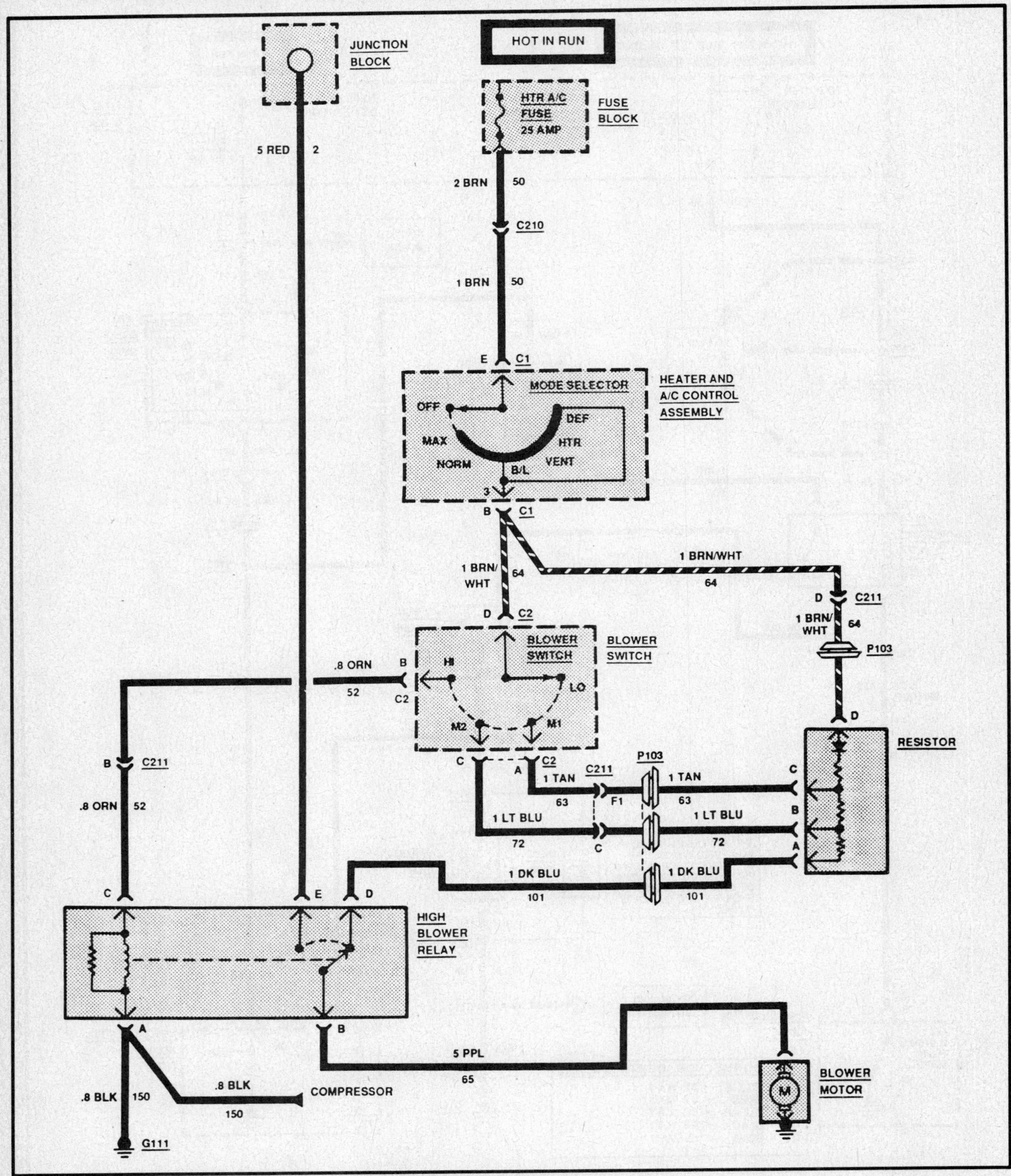

Heater and air conditioning blower controls wiring schematic—Bravada

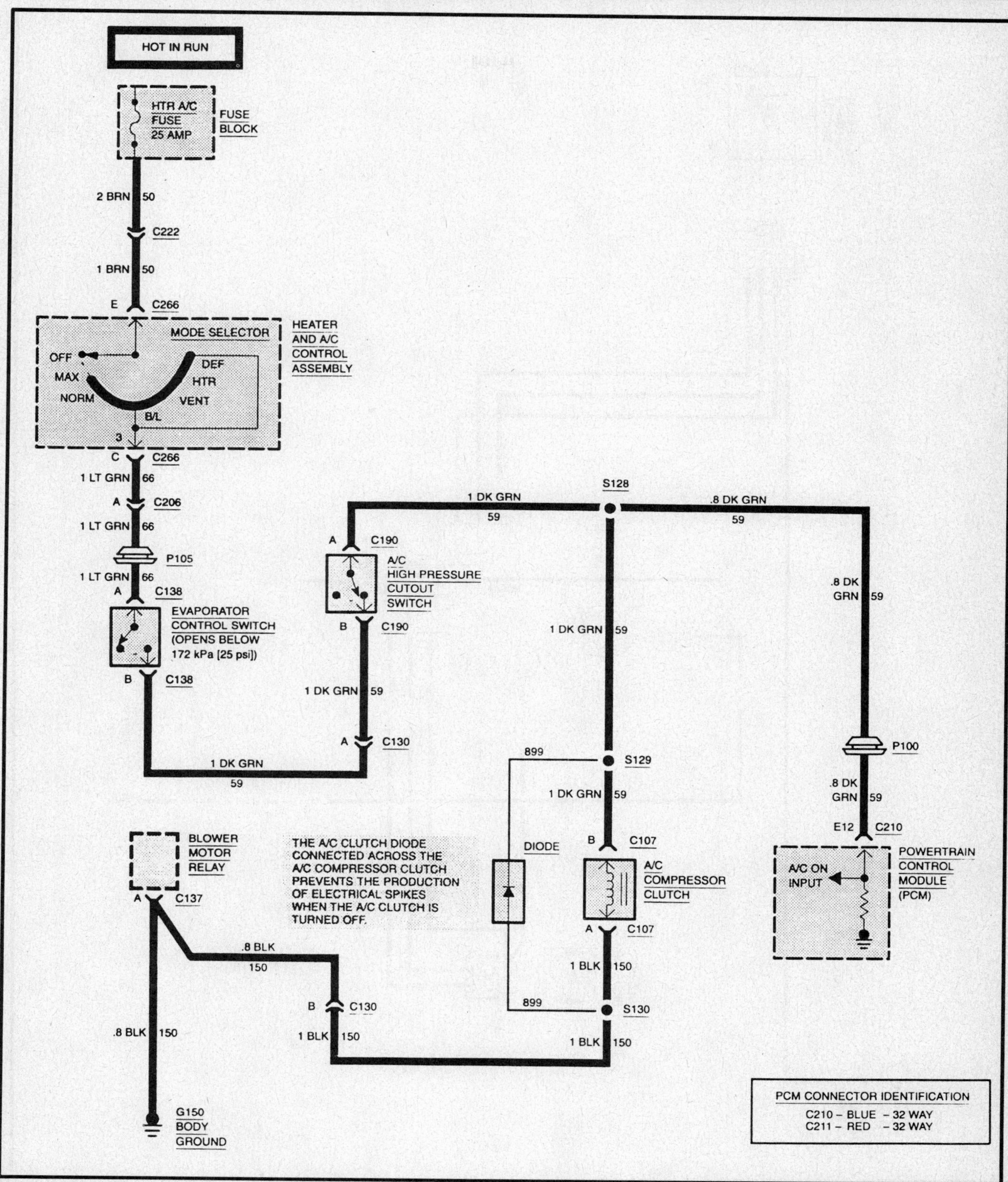

Air conditioning compressor controls wiring schematic—Bravada

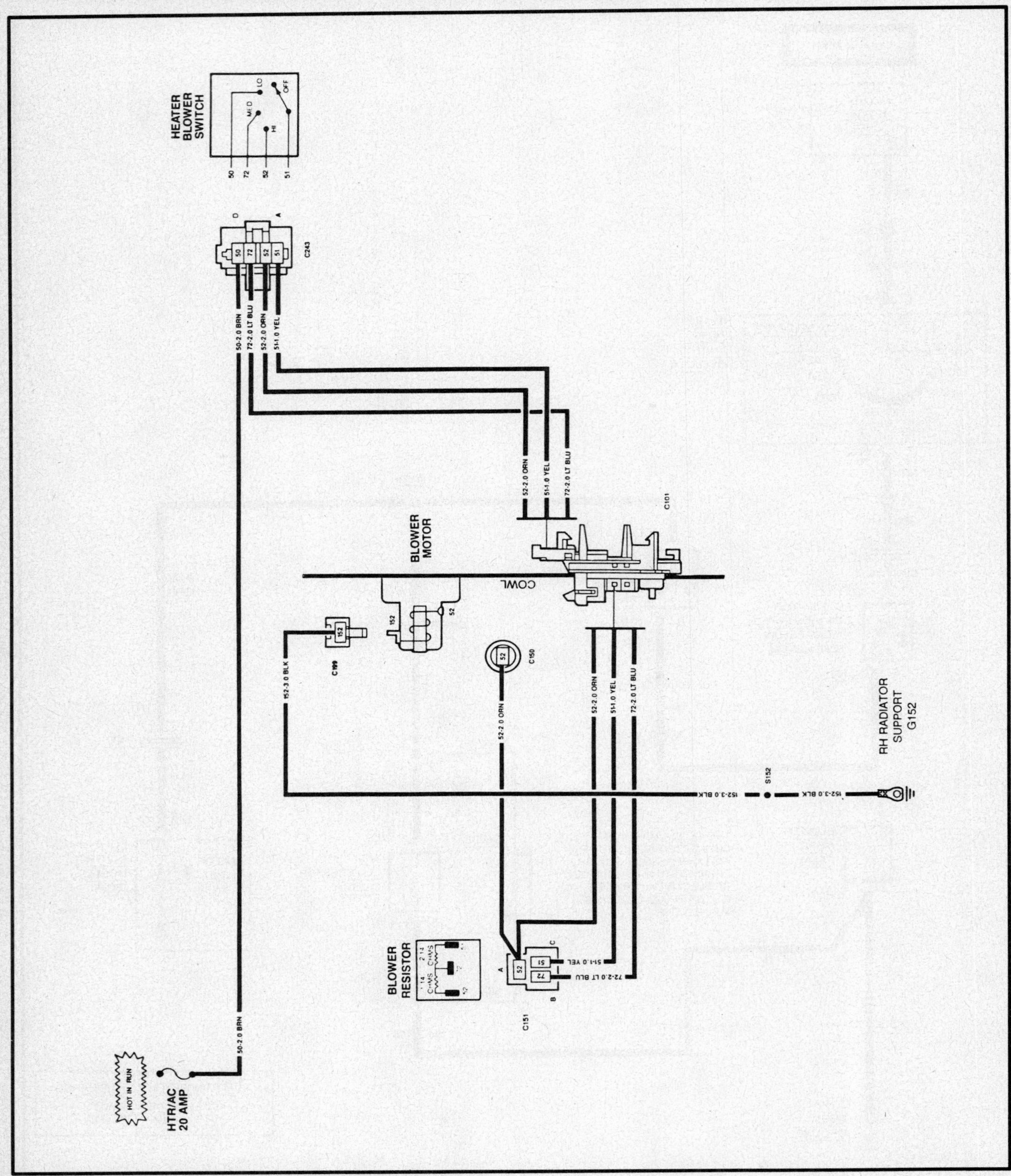

Heater only wiring schematic—1993 Astro and Safari

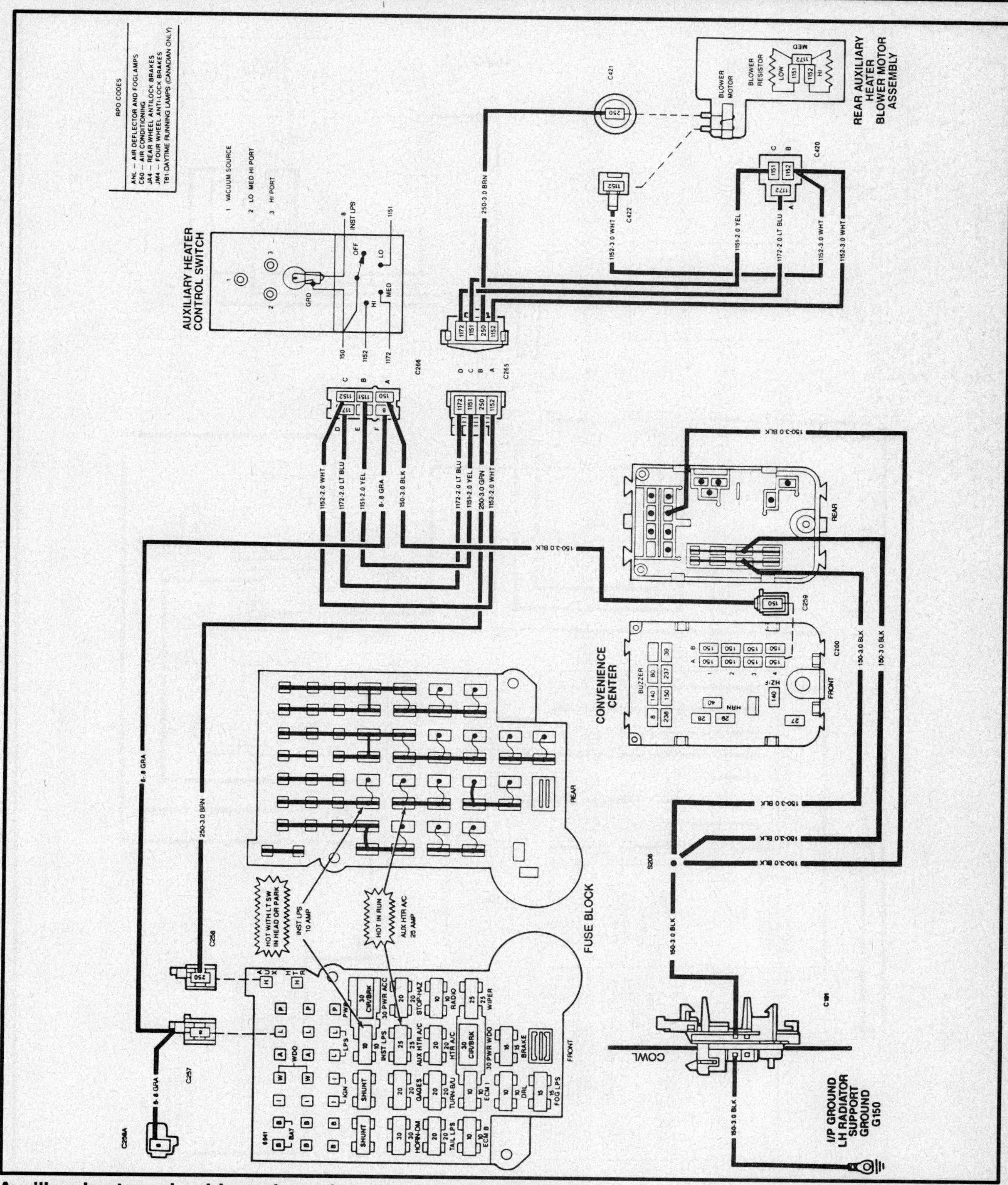

Auxiliary heater only wiring schematic—1993 Astro and Safari

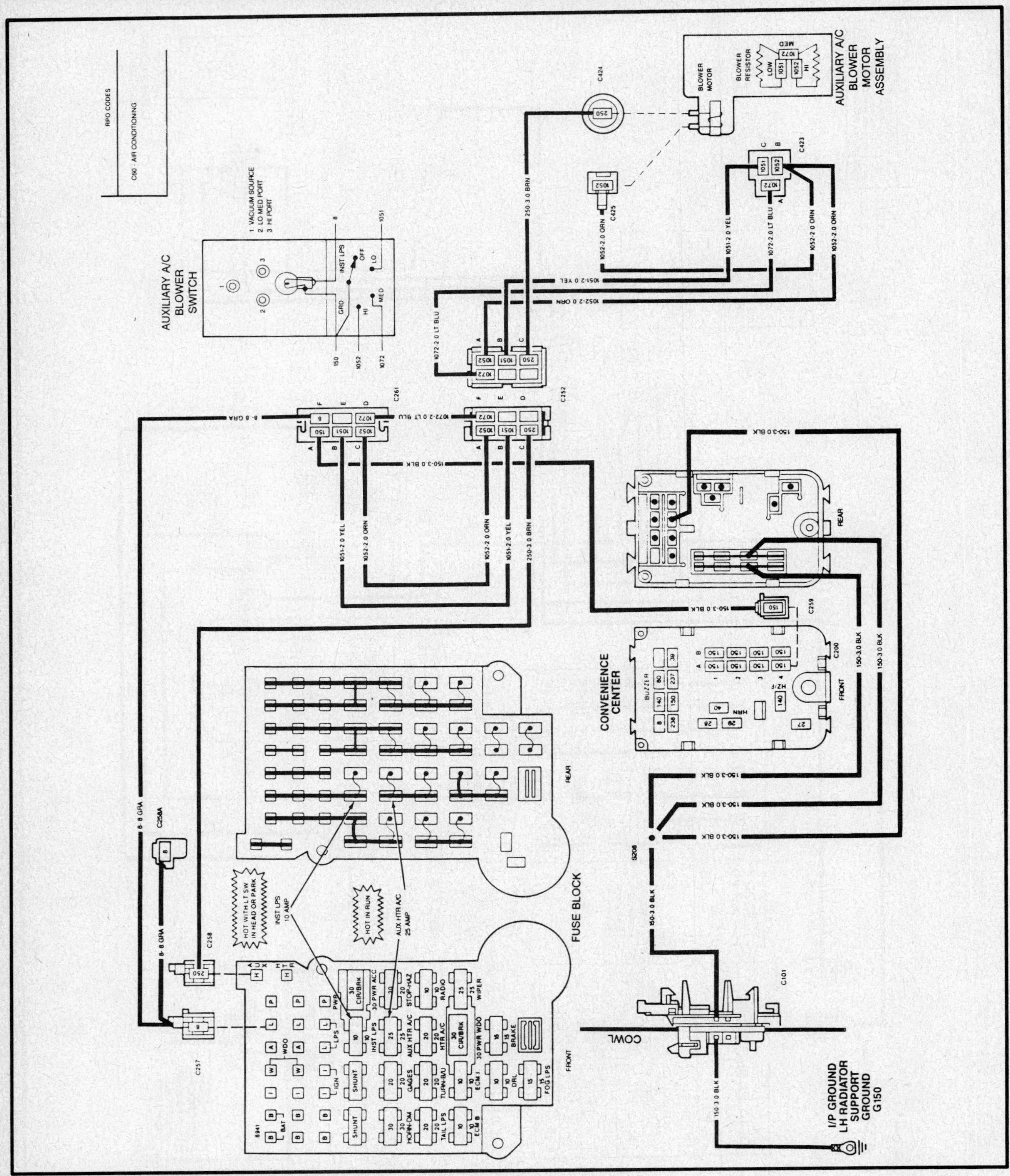

Auxiliary air conditioning wiring schematic—1993 Astro and Safari

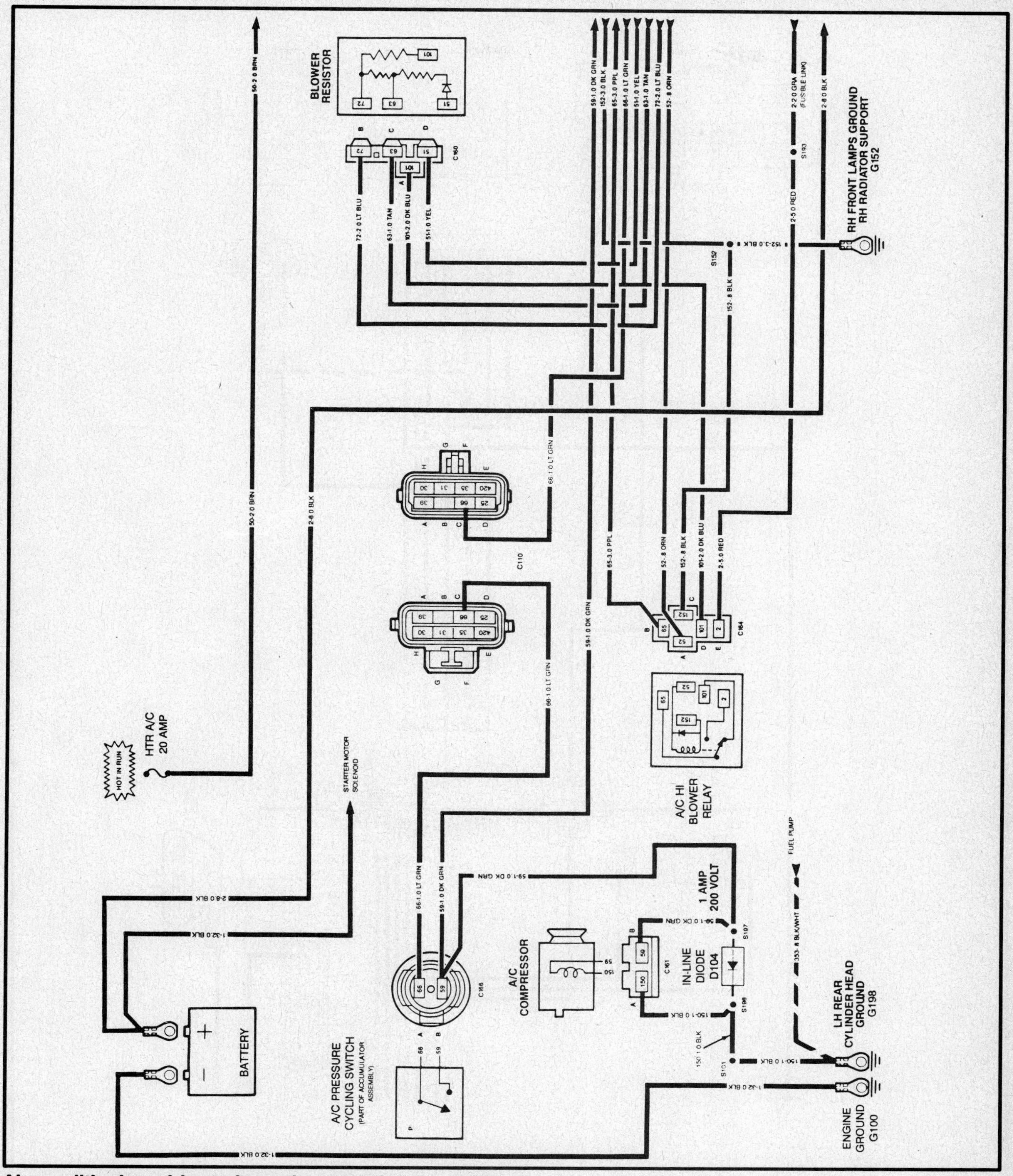

Air conditioning wiring schematic—1993 Astro and Safari

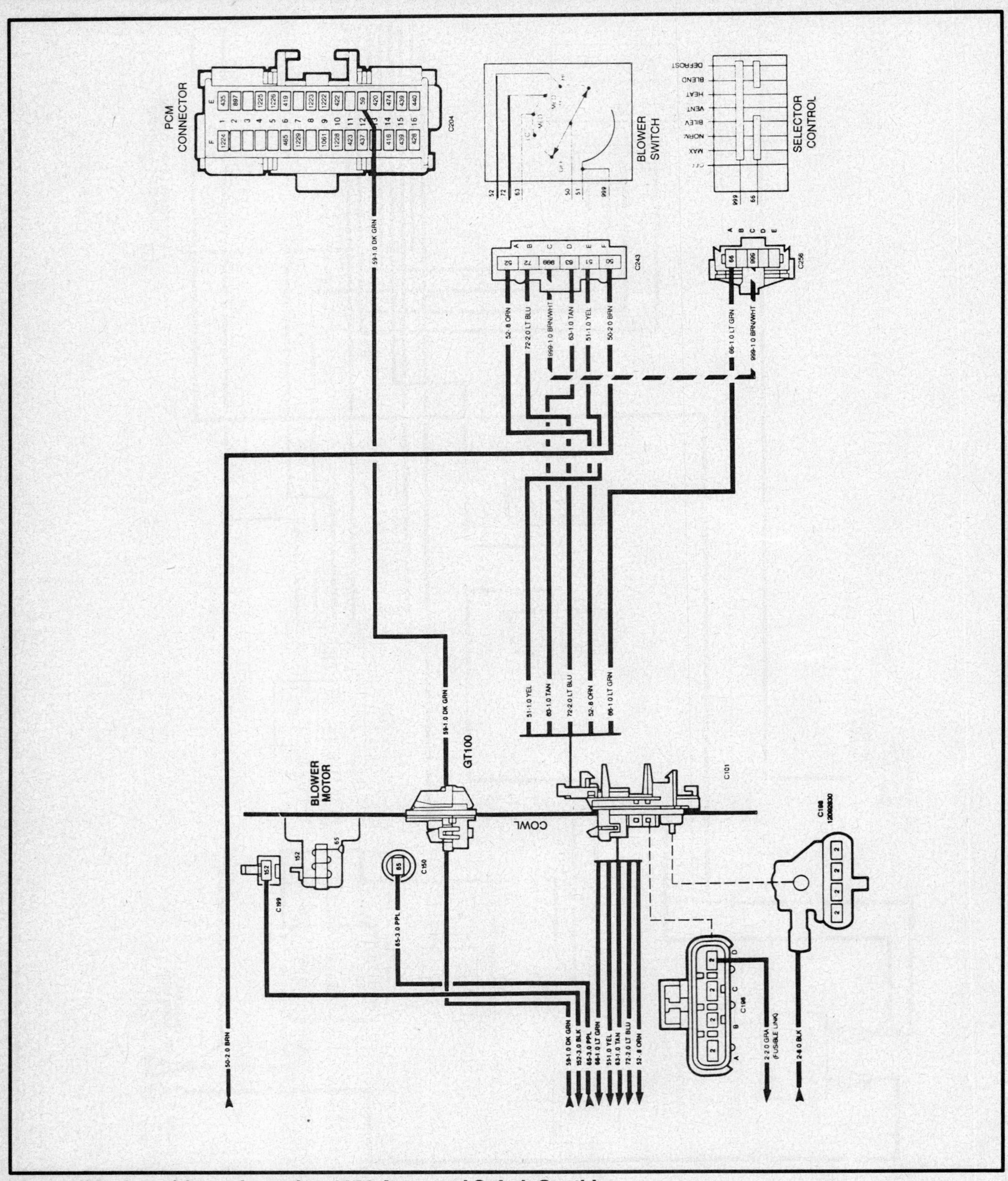

Air conditioning wiring schematic—1993 Astro and Safari, Cont'd

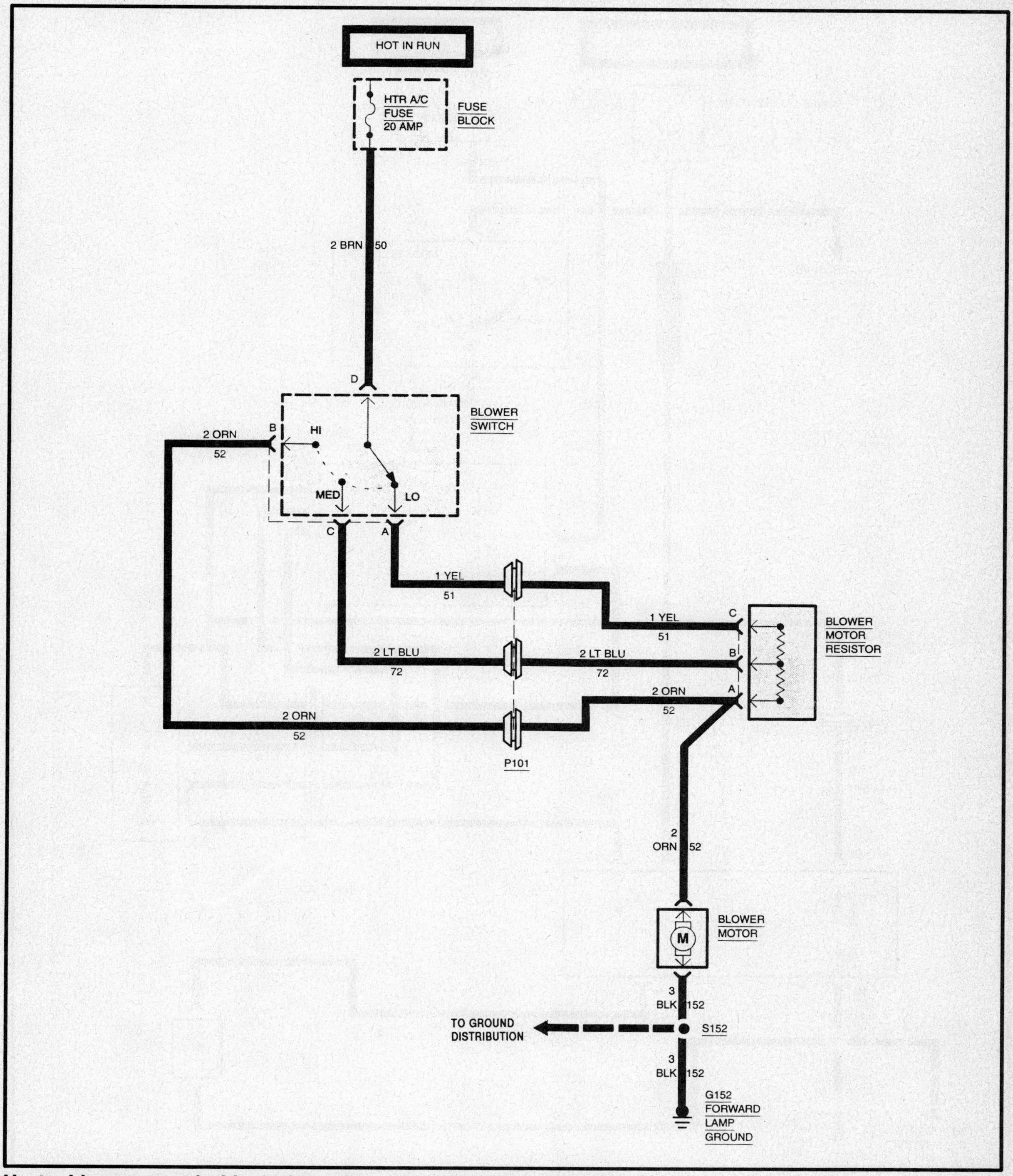

HOT IN RUN
HTR A/C FUSE 20 AMP
FUSE BLOCK
2 BRN 150
D
BLOWER SWITCH
B
HI
2 ORN 52
MED
LO
C
A
1 YEL 51
1 YEL 51
C
BLOWER MOTOR RESISTOR
2 LT BLU 72
2 LT BLU 72
B
2 ORN 52
A
2 ORN 52
P101
2 ORN 52
BLOWER MOTOR
M
3 BLK 152
TO GROUND DISTRIBUTION
S152
3 BLK 152
G152 FORWARD LAMP GROUND

Heater blower control wiring schematic—1994–95 Astro and Safari

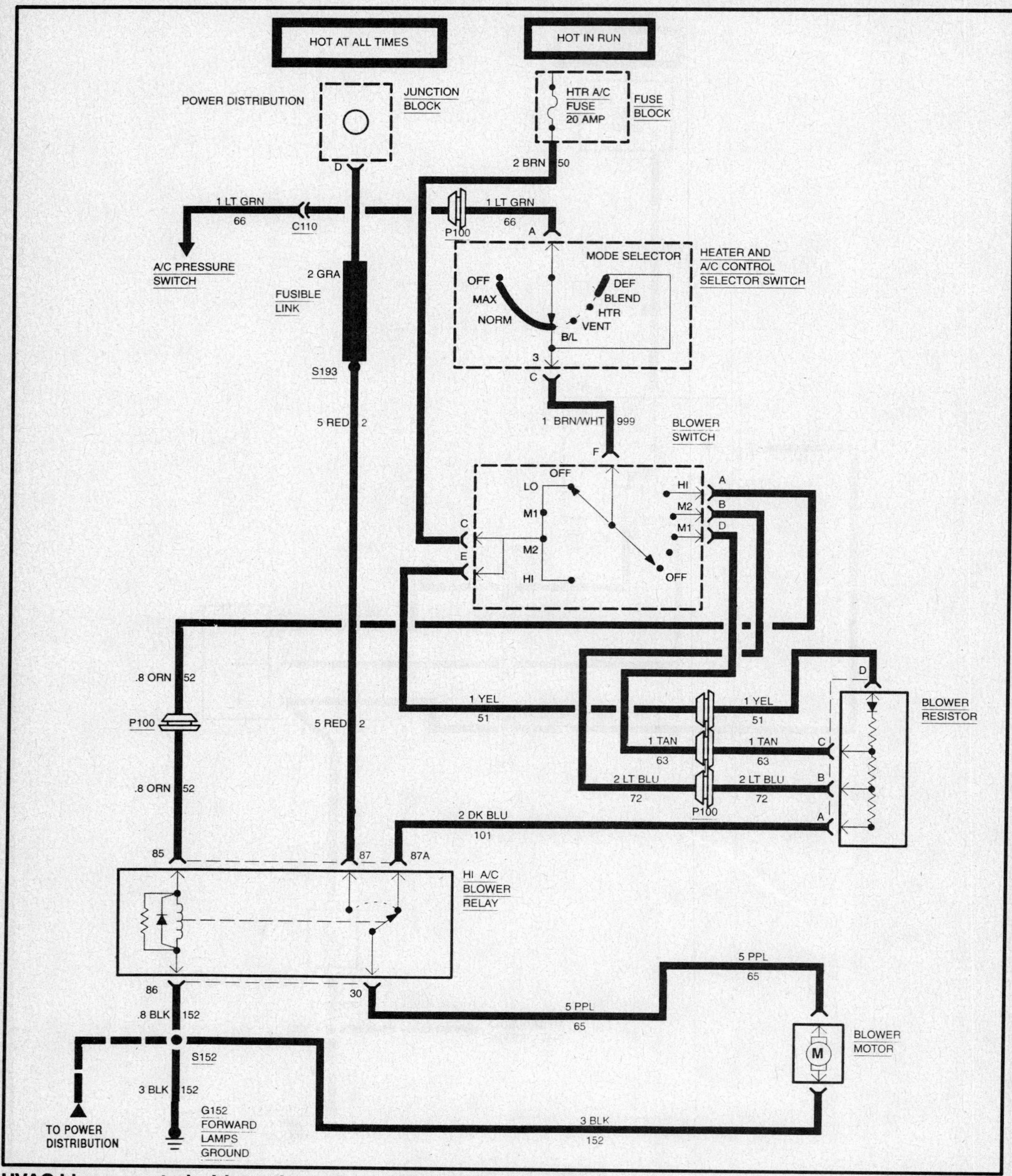

HVAC blower control wiring schematic—1994–95 Astro and Safari

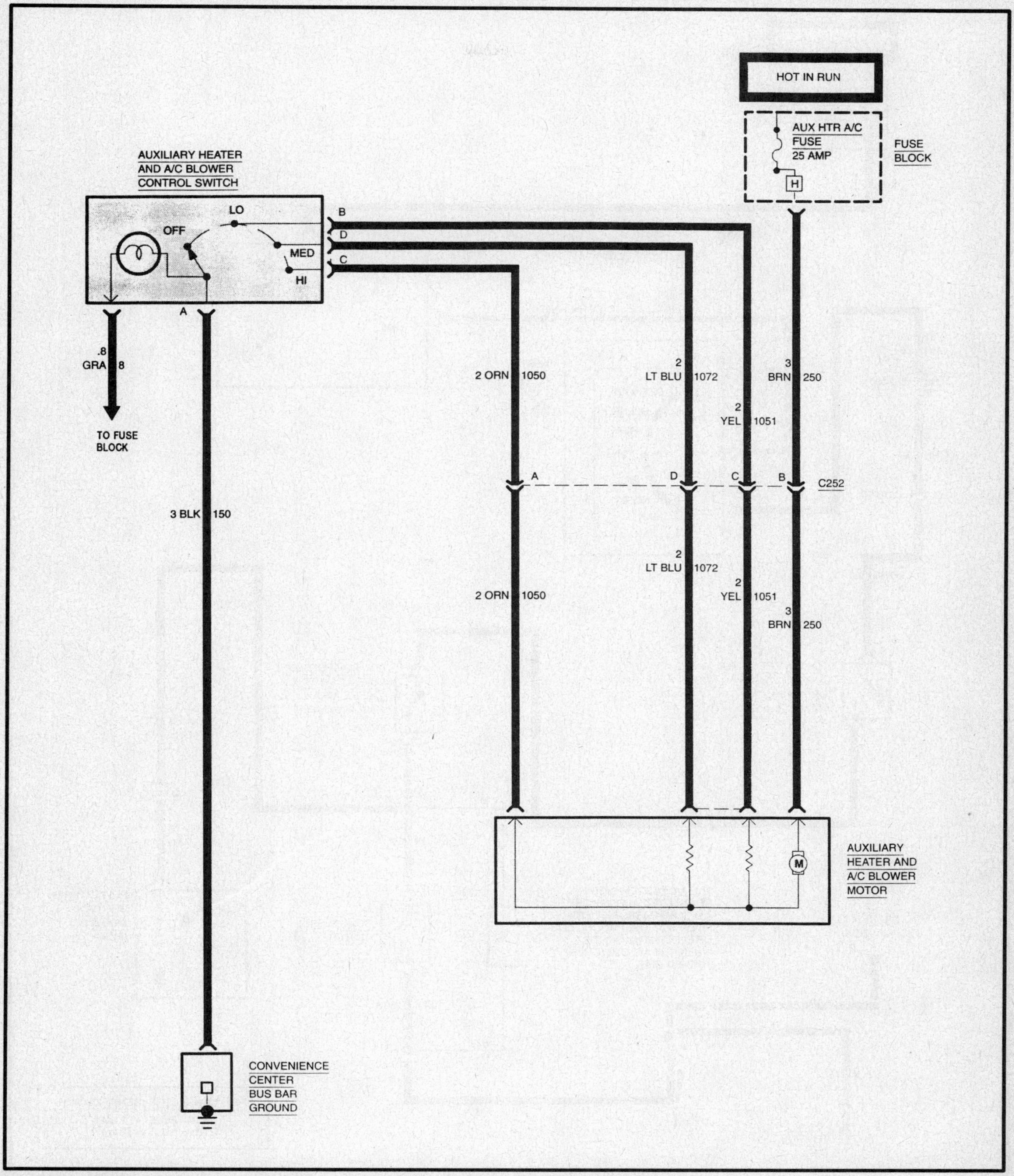

HOT IN RUN

AUX HTR A/C FUSE 25 AMP

H

FUSE BLOCK

AUXILIARY HEATER AND A/C BLOWER CONTROL SWITCH

OFF
LO
MED
HI

B
D
C
A

.8 GRA 8

TO FUSE BLOCK

2 ORN 1050

2 LT BLU 1072

3 BRN 250

2 YEL 1051

A D C B C252

3 BLK 150

2 LT BLU 1072

2 ORN 1050

2 YEL 1051

3 BRN 250

M

AUXILIARY HEATER AND A/C BLOWER MOTOR

CONVENIENCE CENTER BUS BAR GROUND

Auxiliary HVAC blower control wiring schematic—1994–95 Astro and Safari

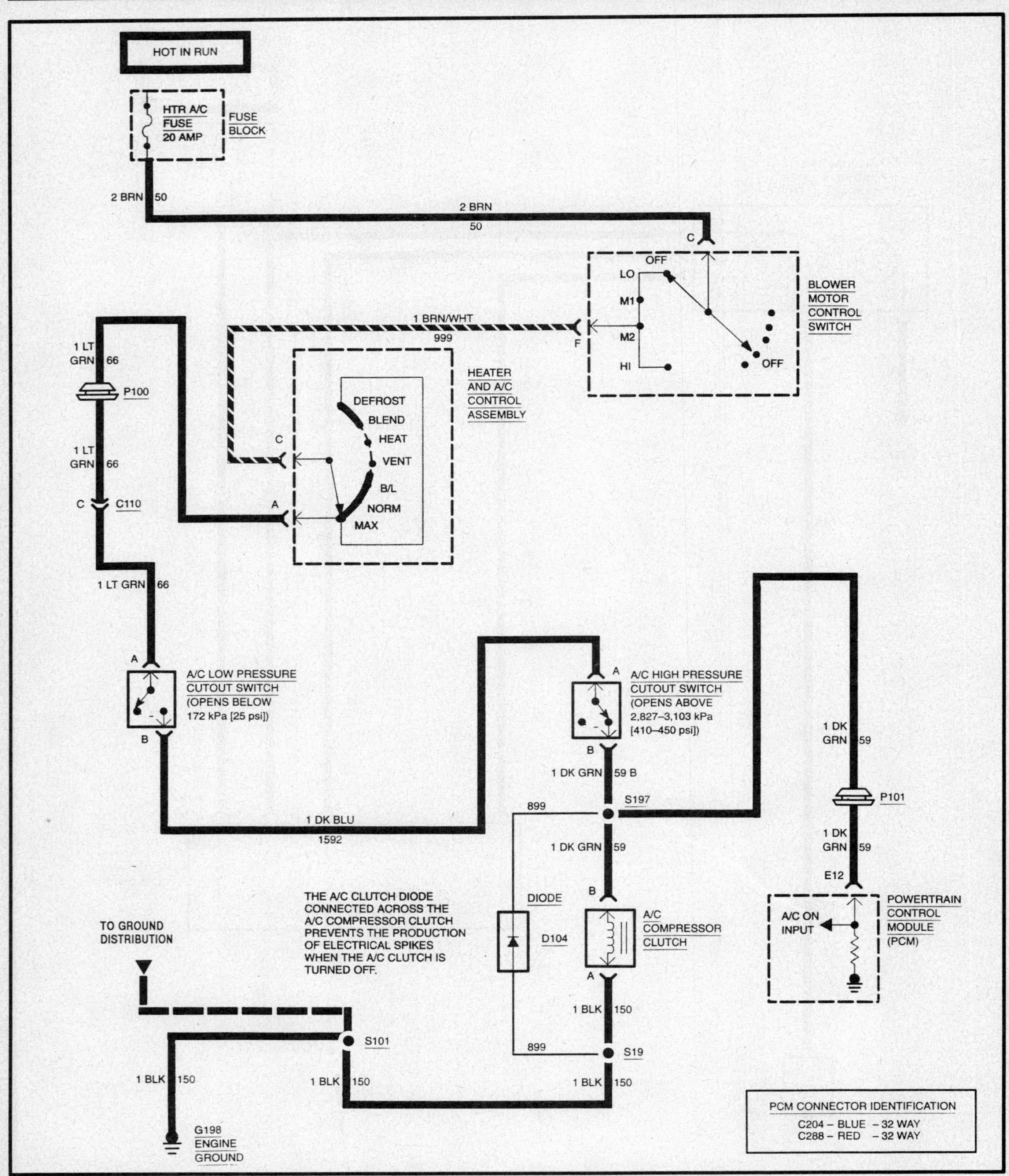

HVAC compressor control wiring schematic—1994–95 Astro and Safari

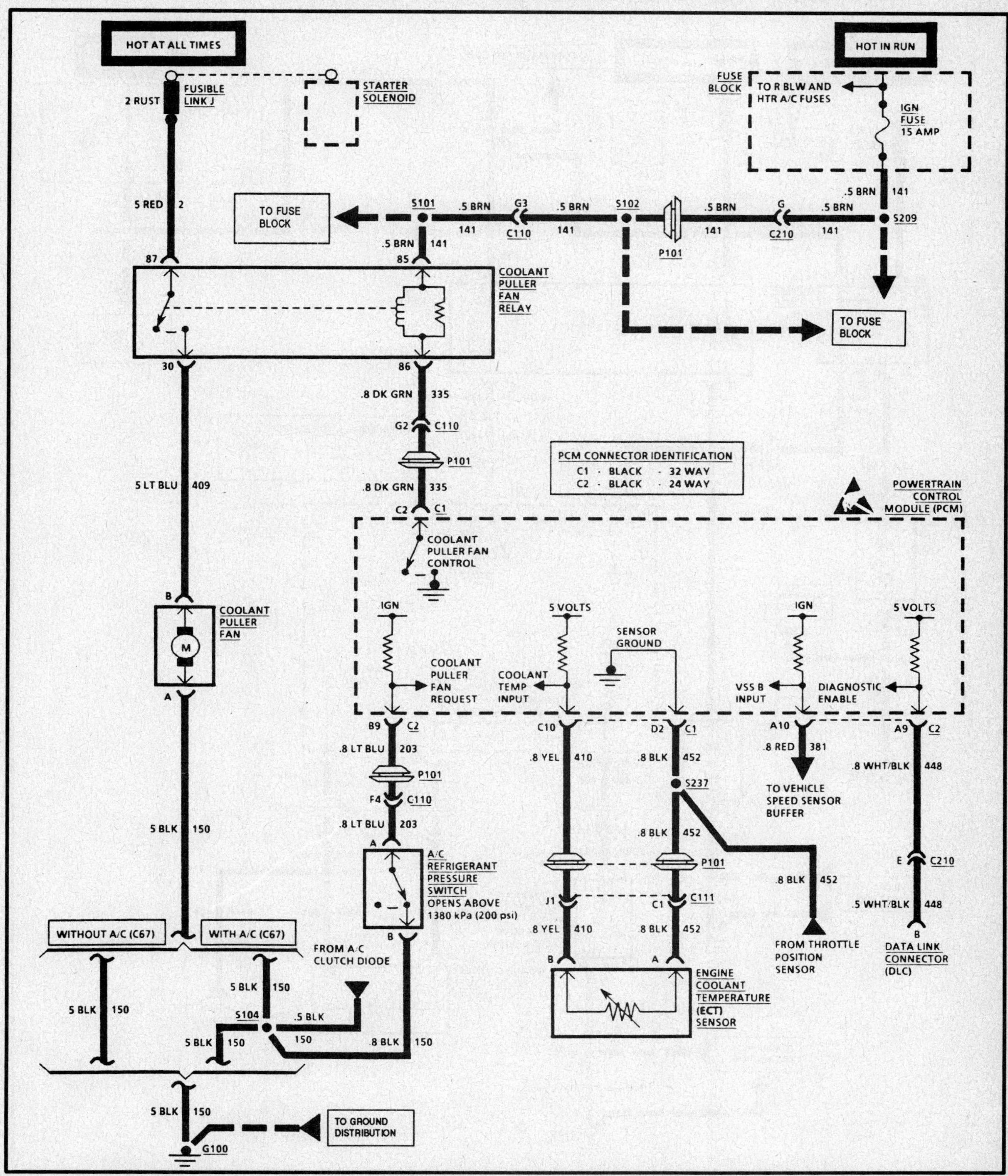

Coolant fan (3.1L VIN D engine) wiring schematic—Lumina APV, Silhouette and Trans Sport

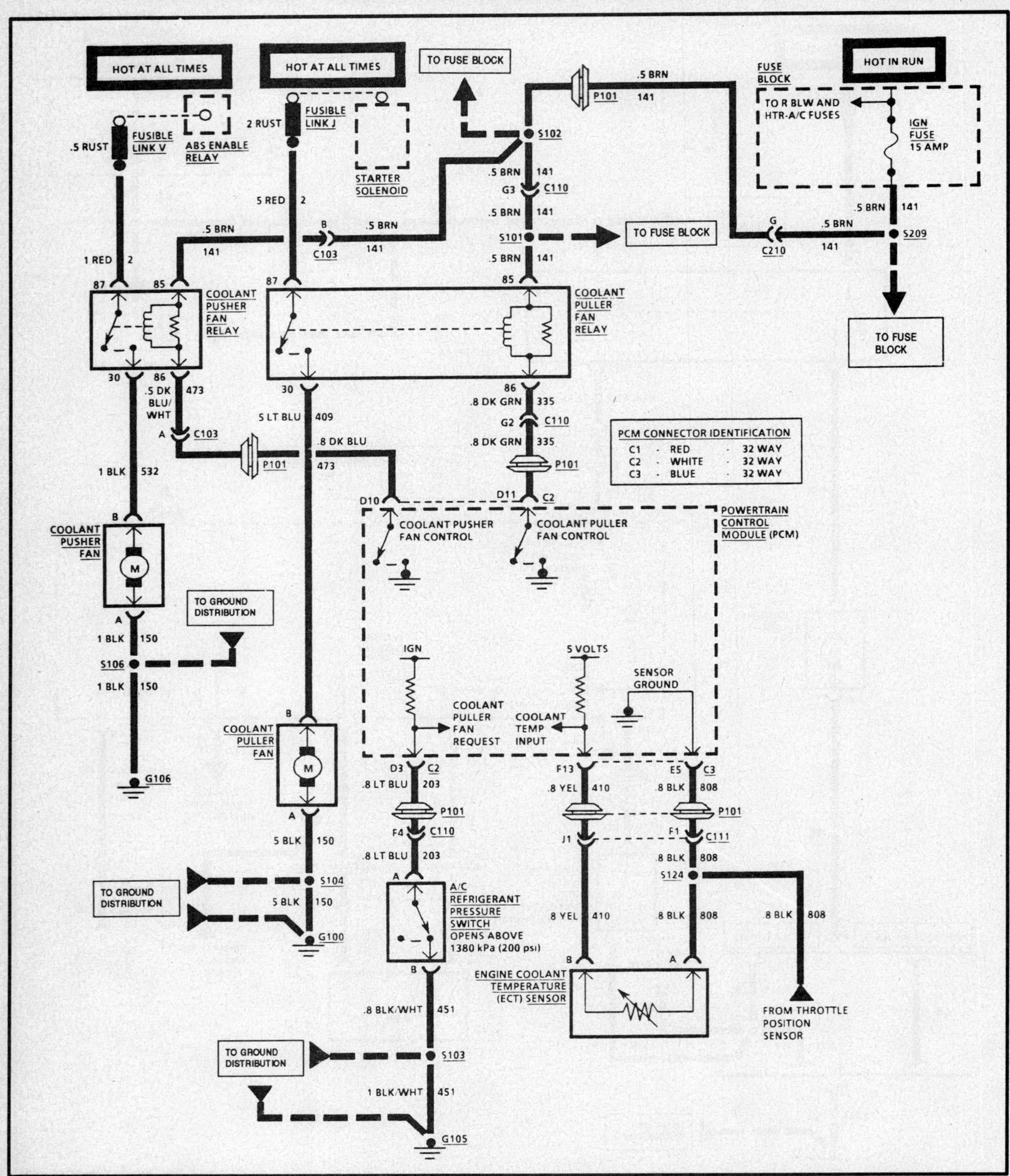

Coolant fan (3.8L VIN L engine) wiring schematic—Lumina APV, Silhouette and Trans Sport

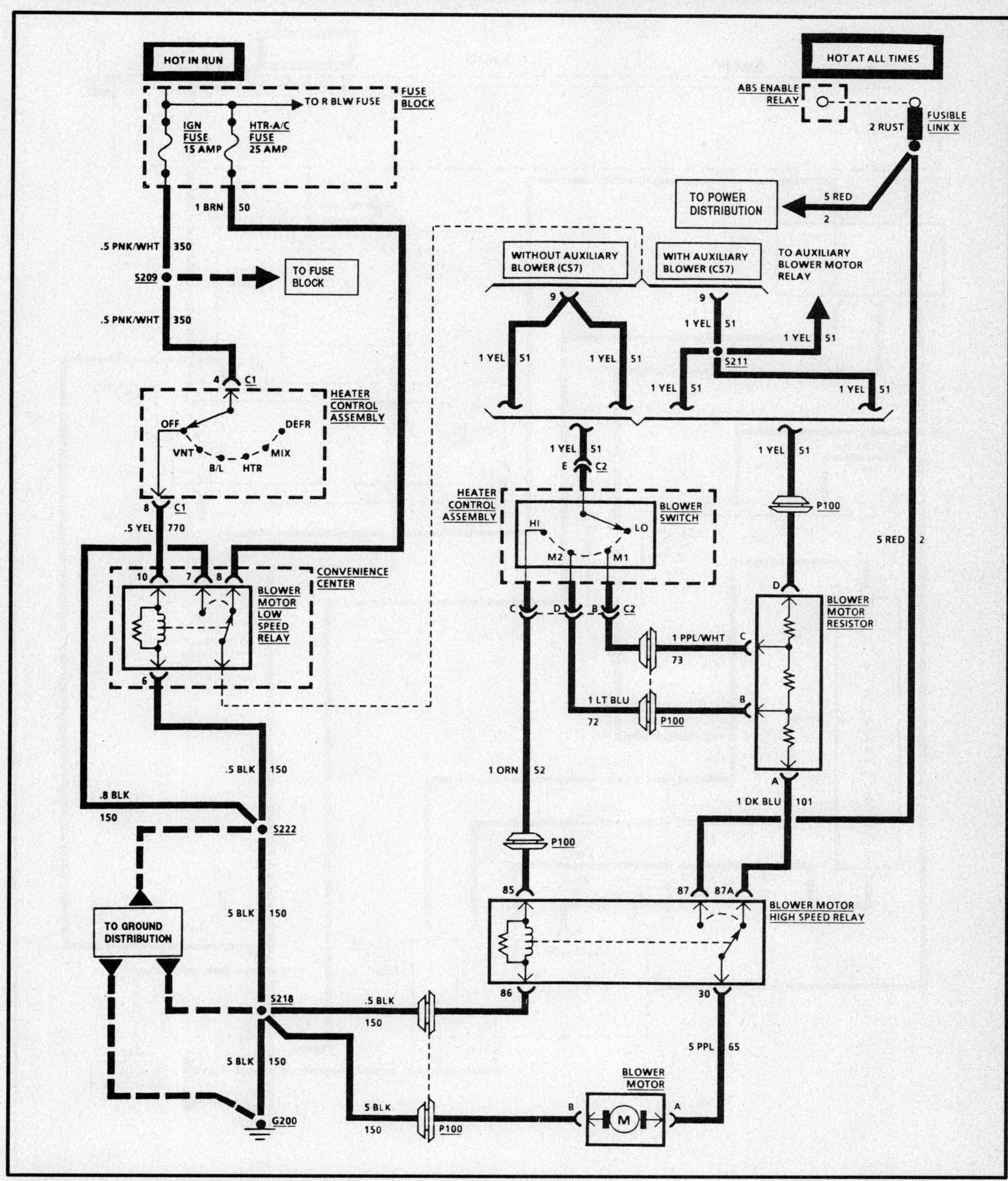

Heater only wiring schematic—Lumina APV and Trans Sport

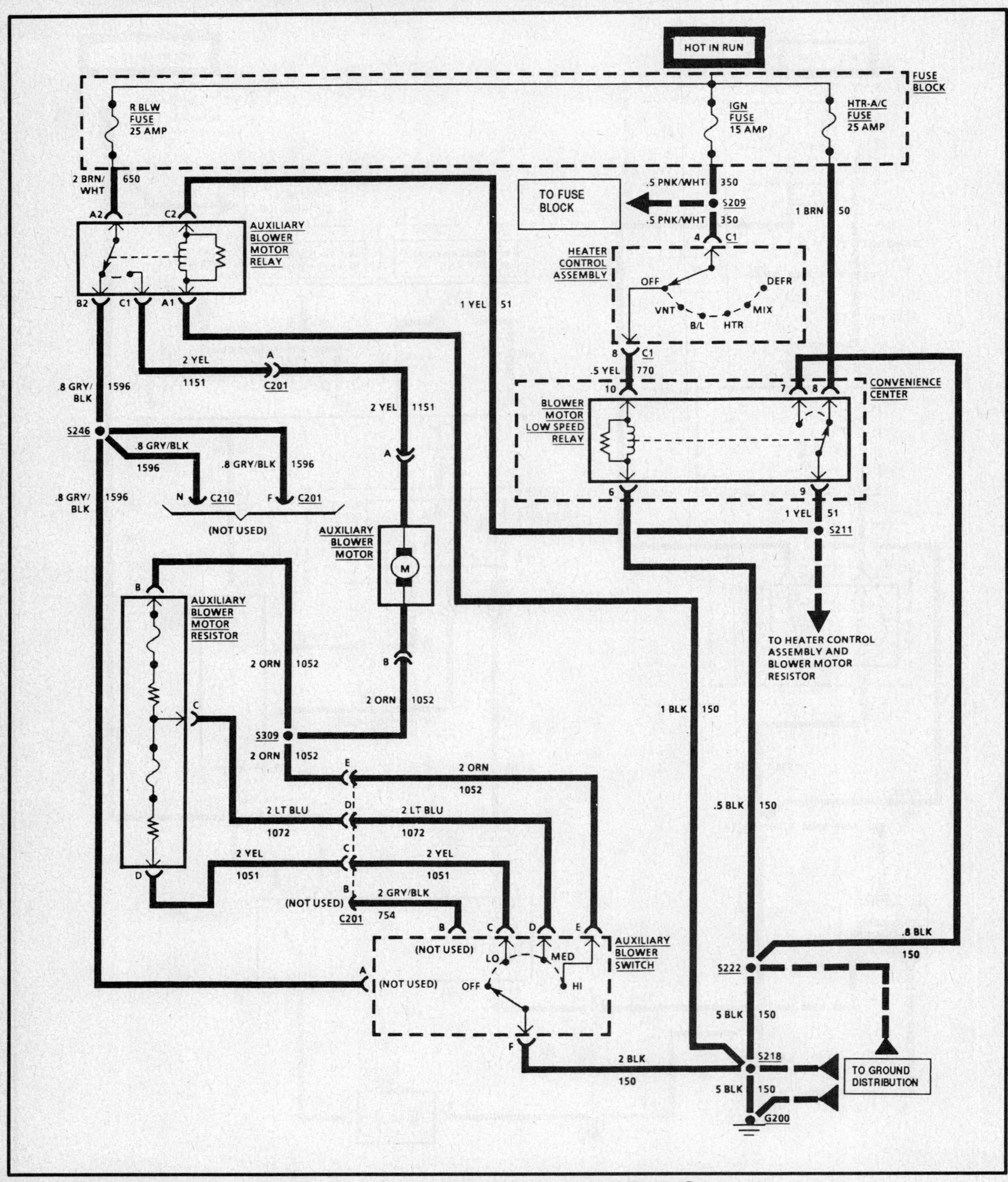

Auxiliary heater only wiring schematic—Lumina APV, Silhouette and Trans Sport

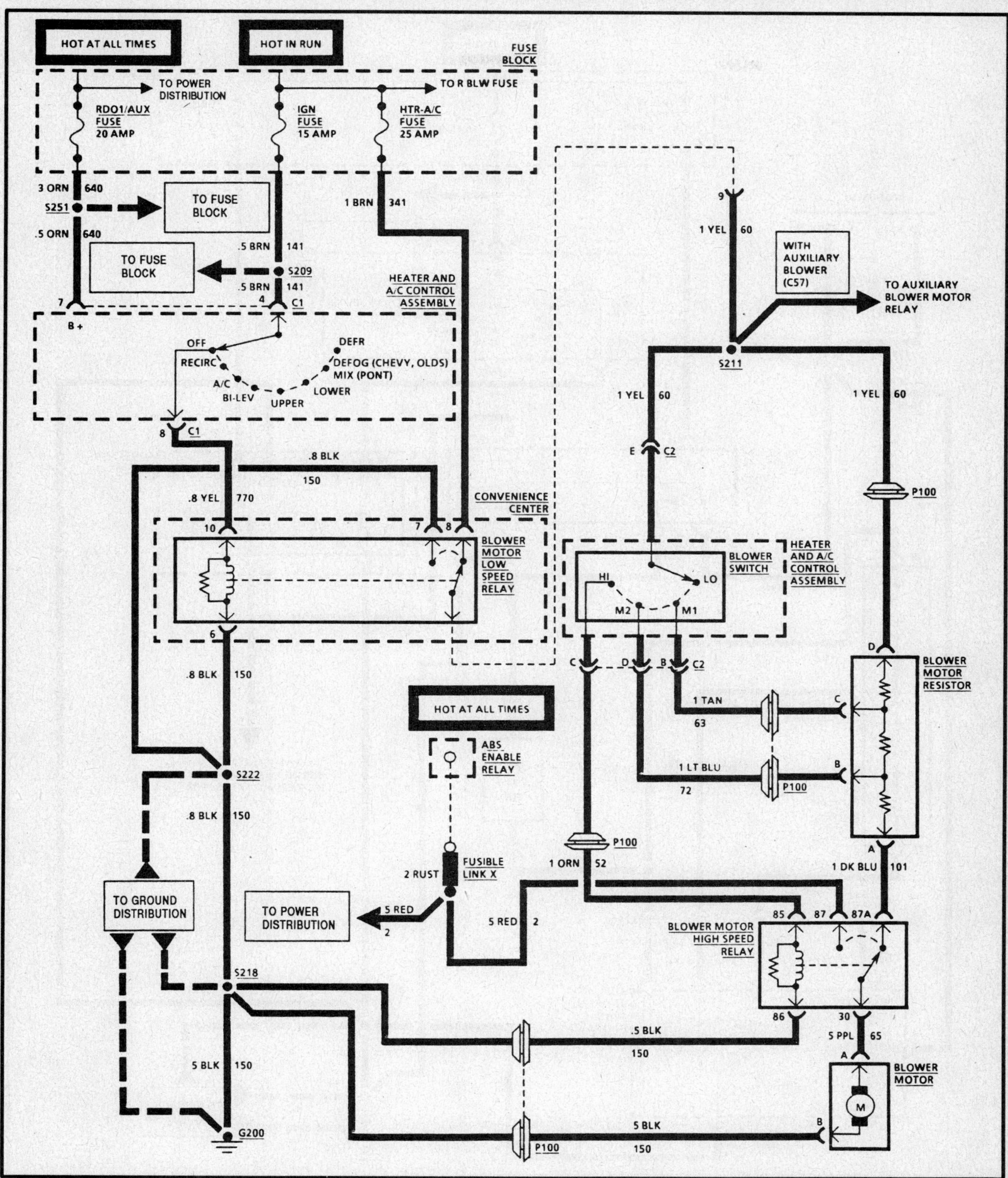

Blower motor control (C67) wiring schematic—1994–95 Lumina APV, Silhouette and Trans Sport

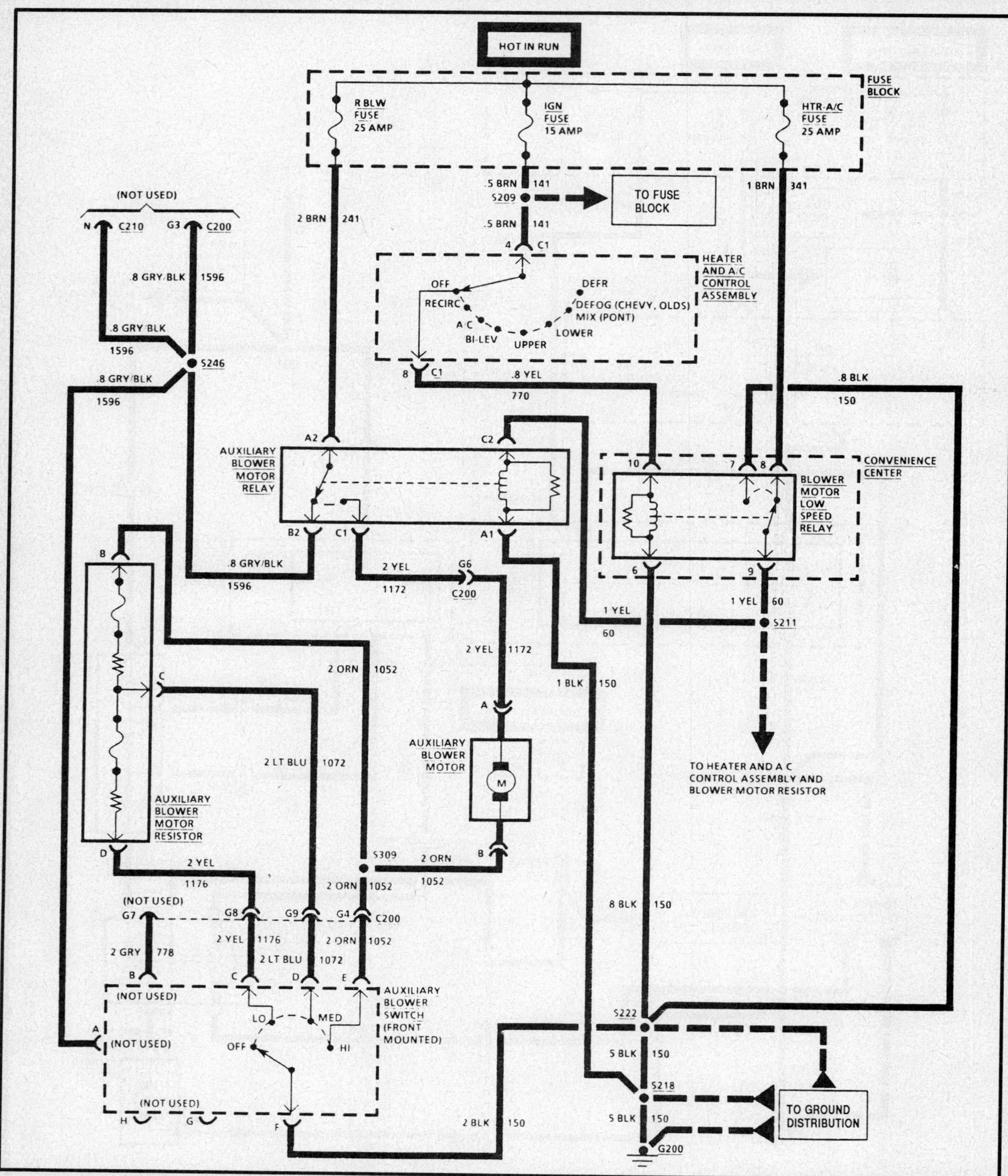

Auxiliary blower motor control (C57) wiring schematic—1994–95 Lumina APV, Silhouette and Trans Sport

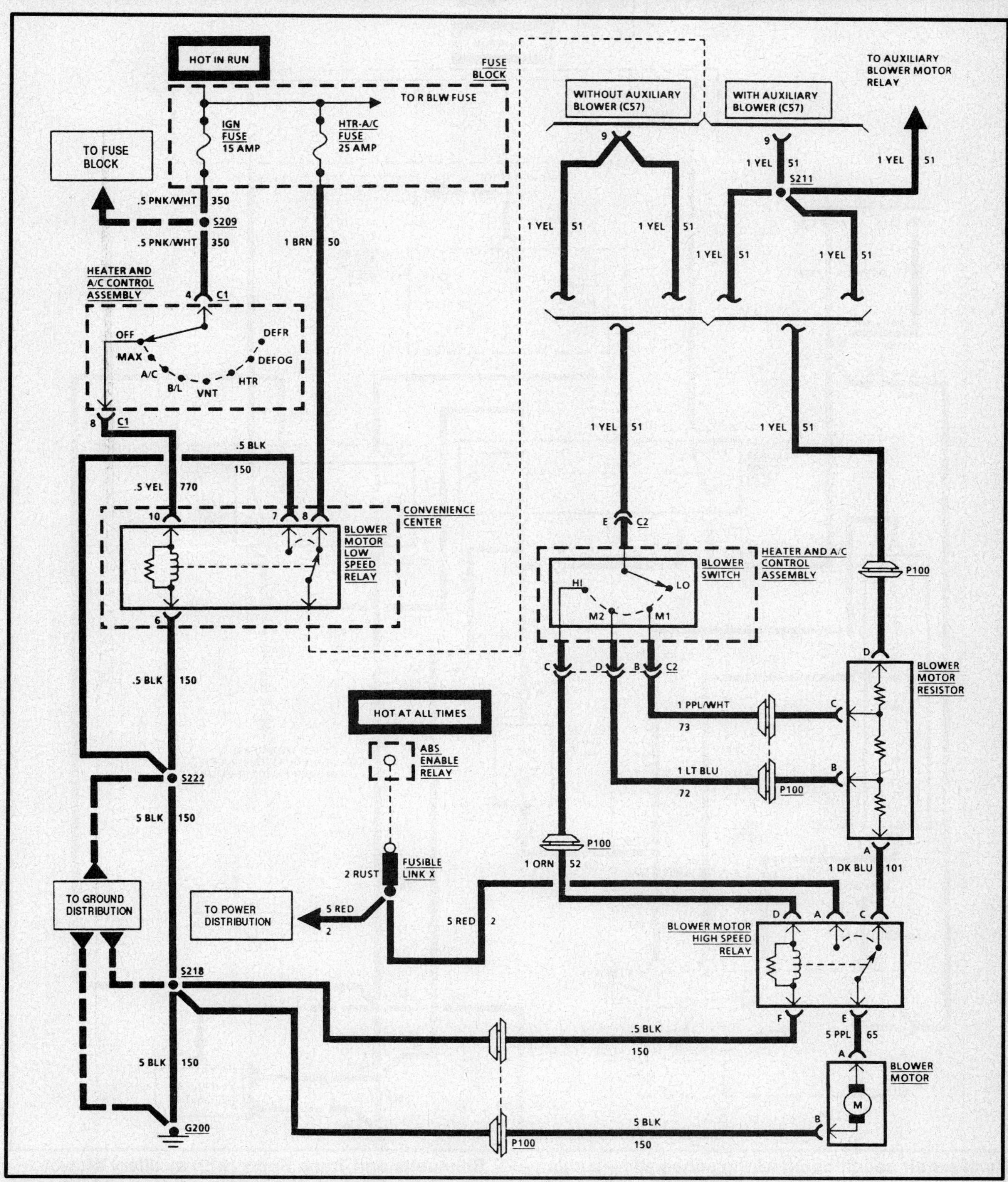

Air conditioning wiring schematic—1993 Lumina APV, Silhouette and Trans Sport

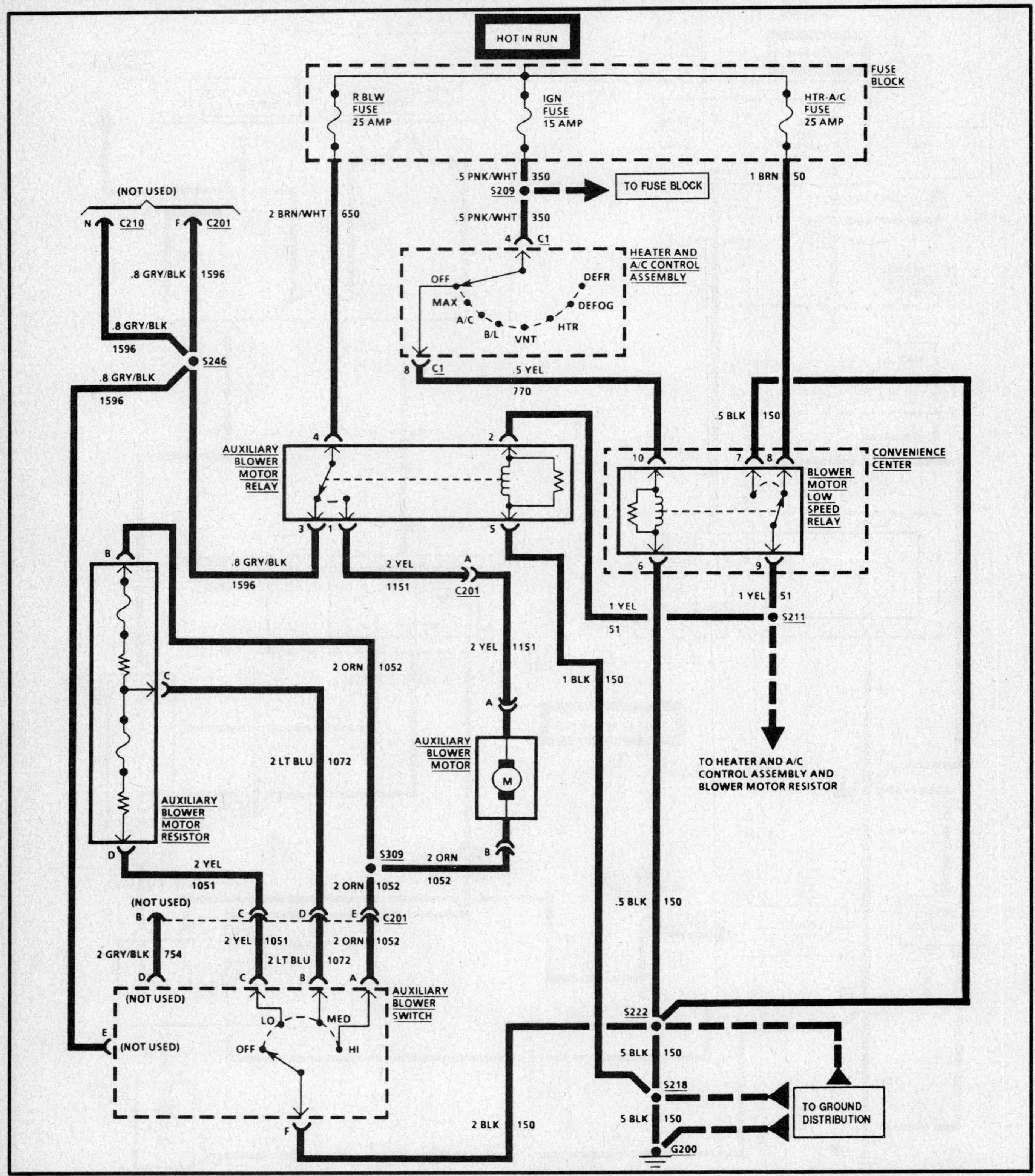

Auxiliary air conditioning wiring schematic—Lumina APV, Silhouette and Trans Sport (with auxiliary blower only)

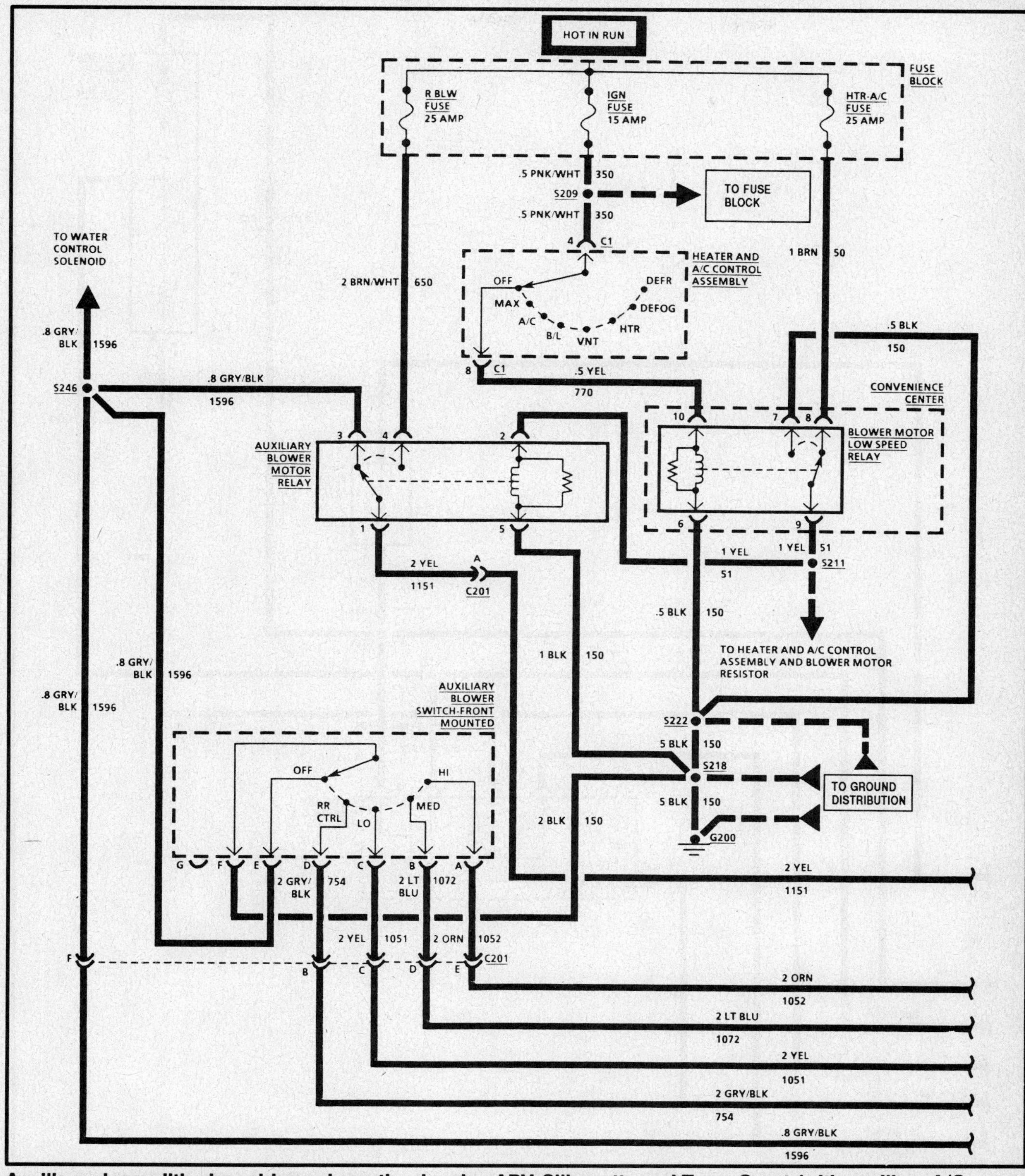

Auxiliary air conditioning wiring schematic—Lumina APV, Silhouette and Trans Sport (with auxiliary A/C components and blower)

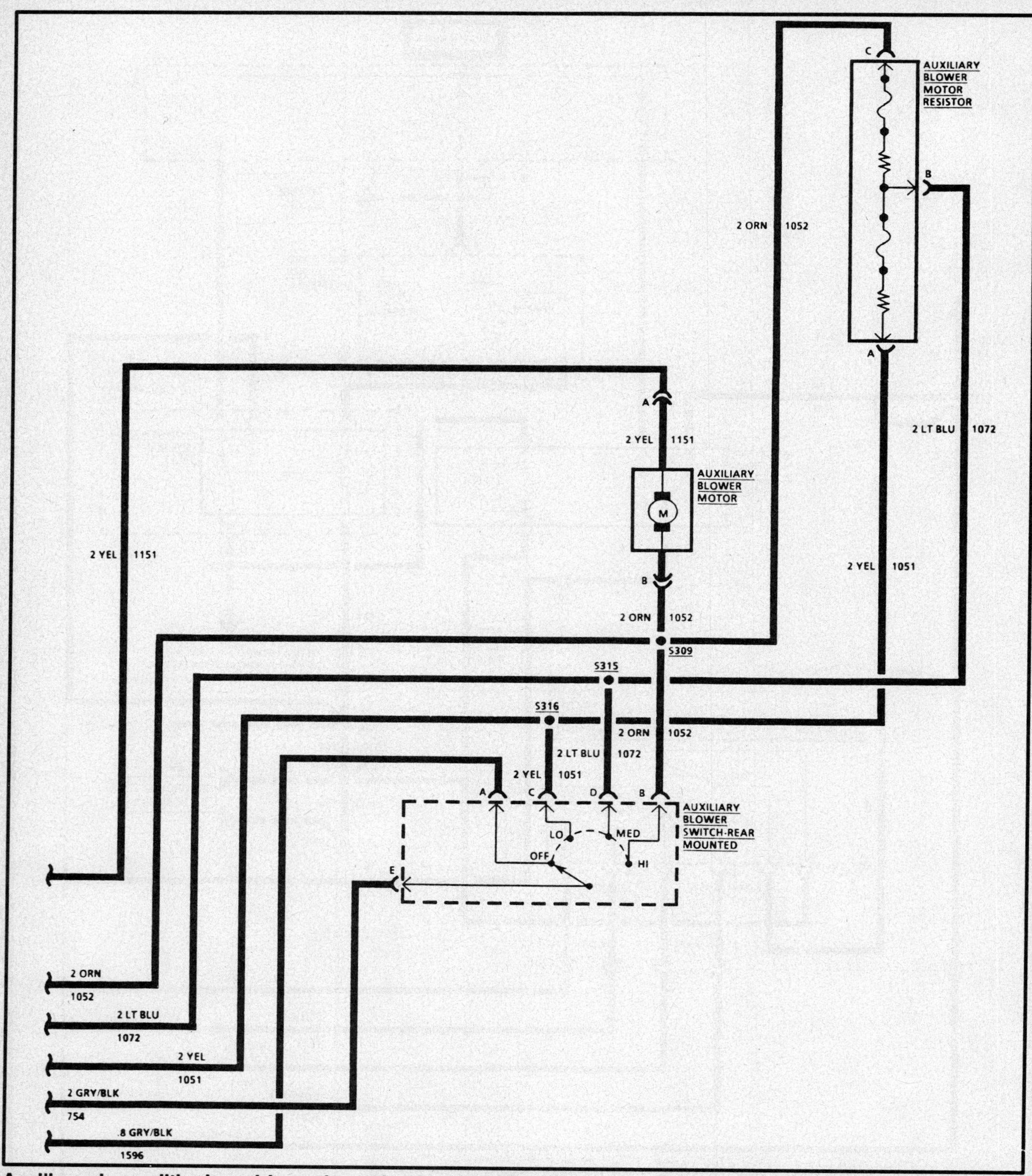

Auxiliary air conditioning wiring schematic—Lumina APV, Silhouette and Trans Sport (with auxiliary A/C components and blower), Cont'd

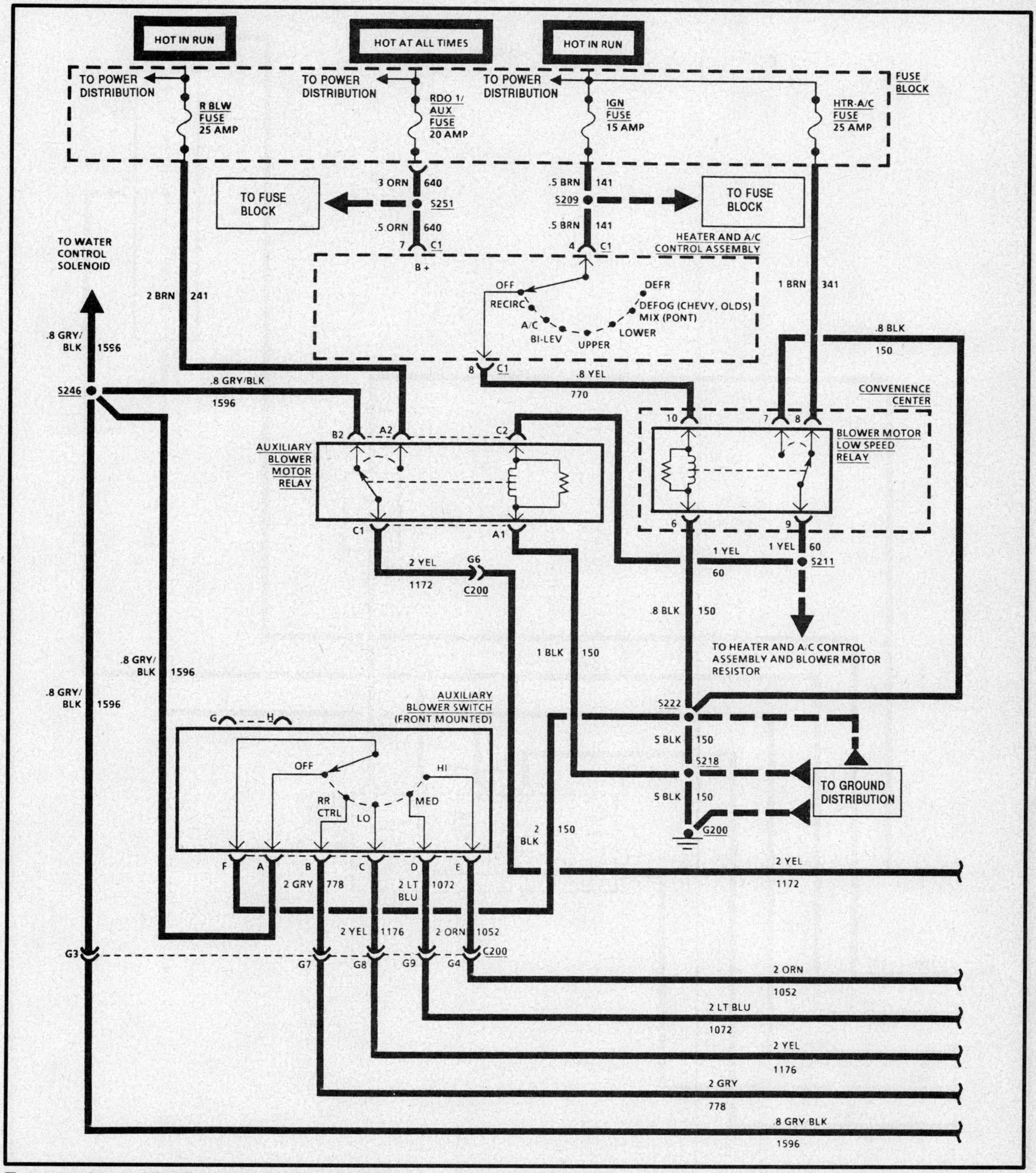

Front and rear HVAC auxiliary blower motor control (C34 or C34/C36) wiring schematic—1994–95 Lumina APV, Silhouette and Trans Sport

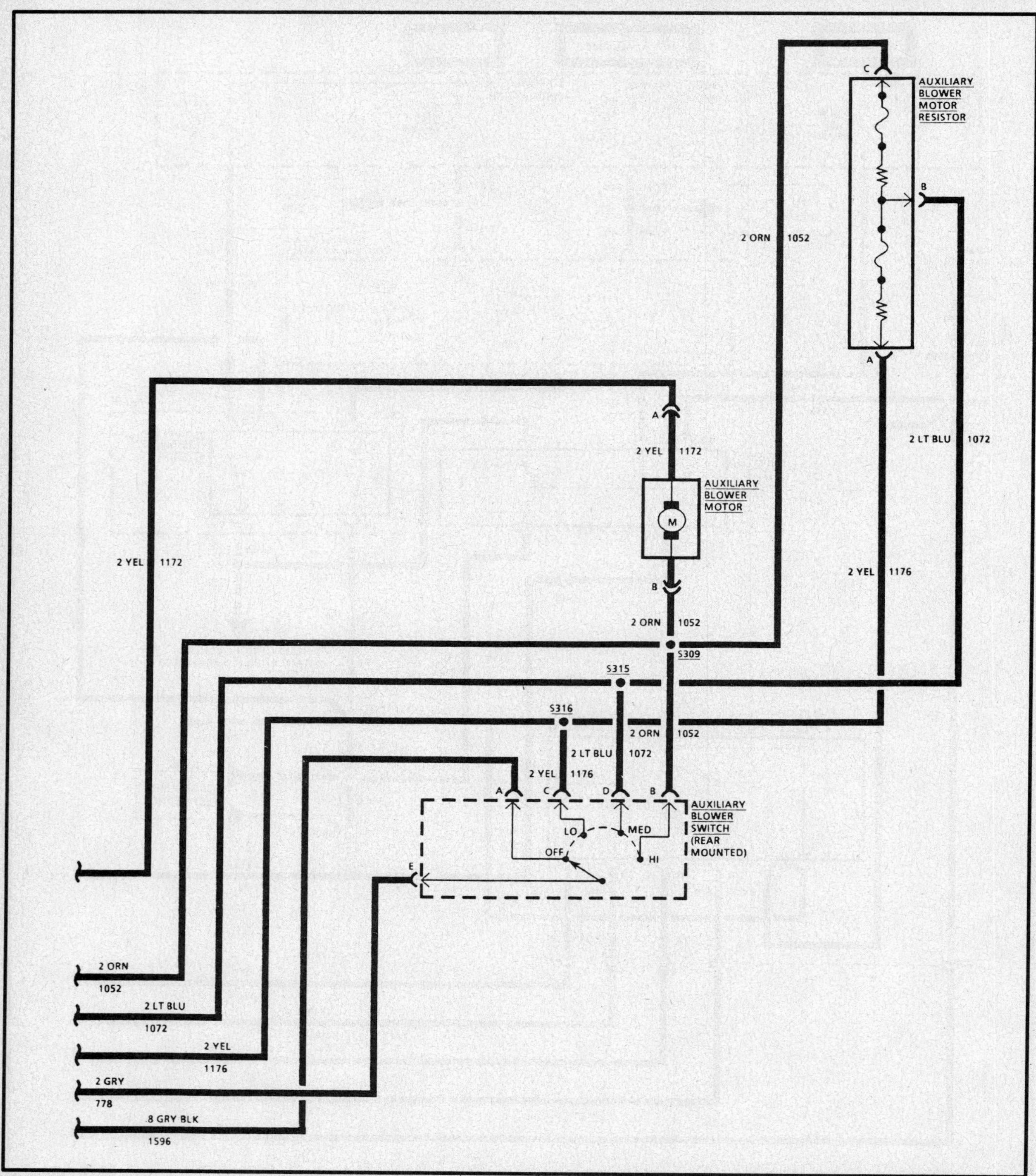

Front and rear HVAC auxiliary blower motor control (C34 or C34/C36) wiring schematic—1994–95 Lumina APV, Silhouette and Trans Sport, Cont'd

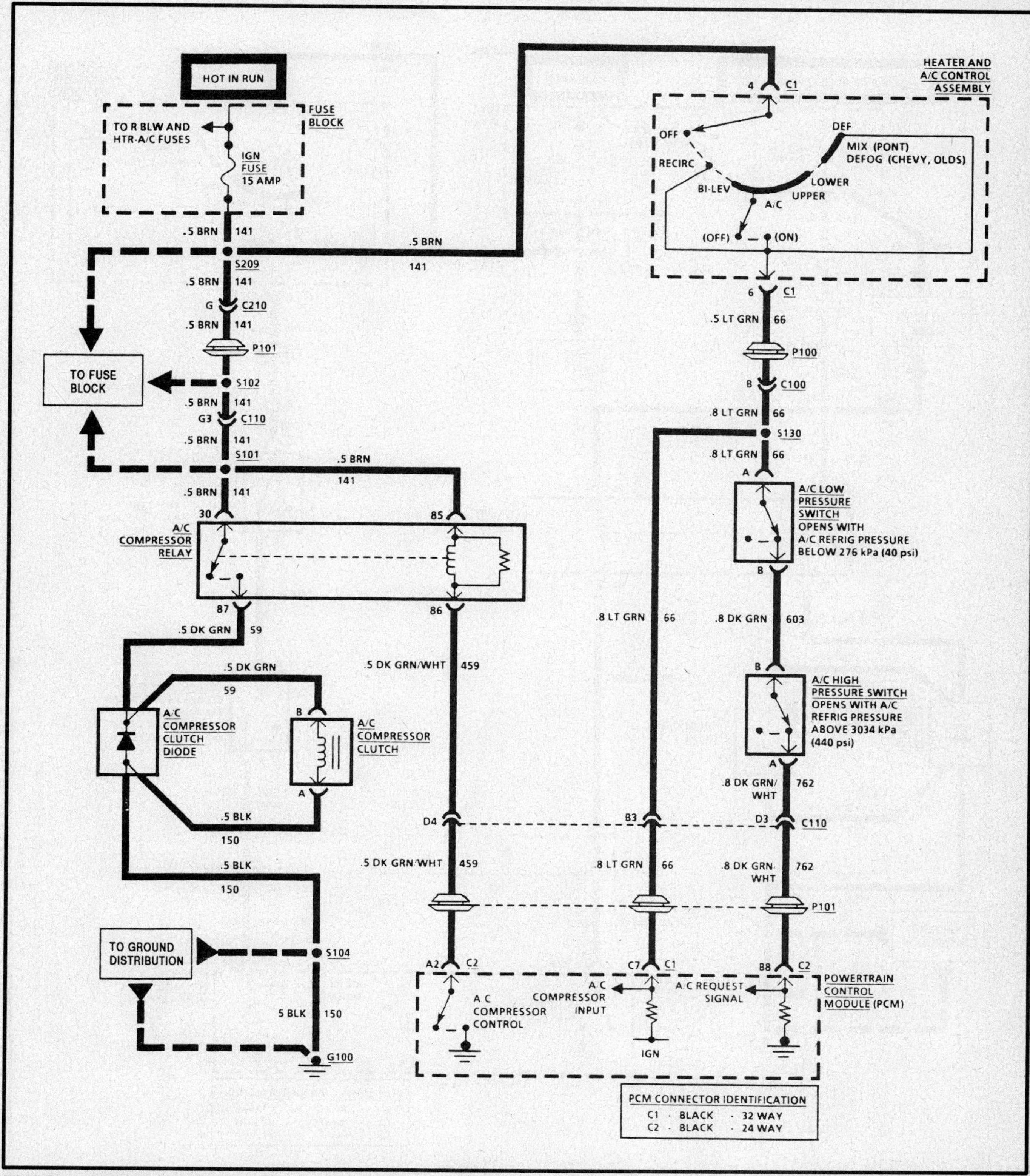

HVAC compressor control (C67), (3.1L VIN D engine) wiring schematic—1994–95 Lumina APV, Silhouette and Trans Sport

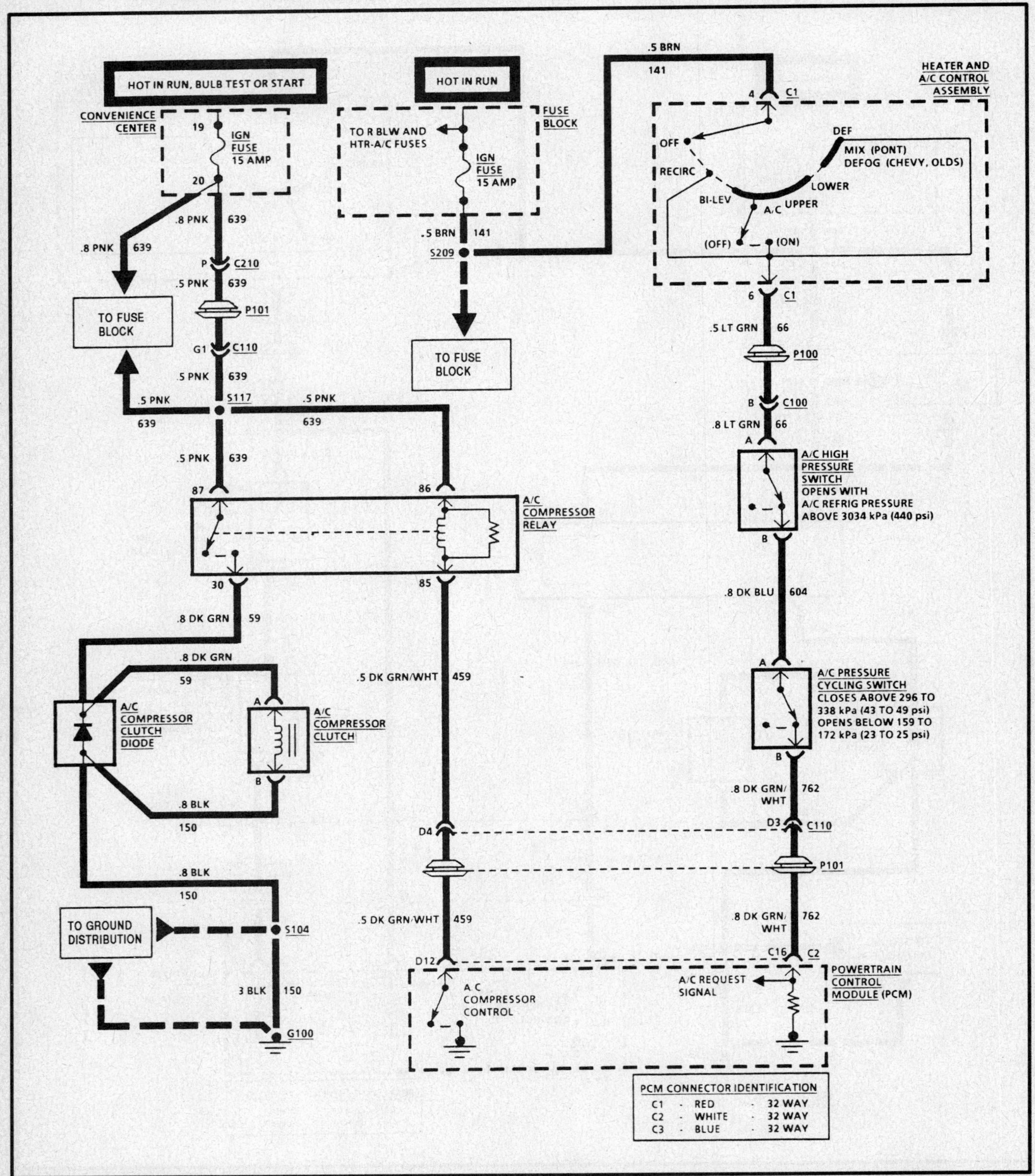

HVAC compressor control (C67 and C34), (3.8L VIN L engine) wiring schematic—1994–95 Lumina APV, Silhouette and Trans Sport

11 GEO 11

METRO • PRIZM • STORM • TRACKER

SPECIFICATIONS

ENGINE IDENTIFICATION

Year	Model	Engine Displacement Liters (cc)	Engine Series (ID/VIN)	Fuel System	No. of Cylinders	Engine Type
1993	Metro	1.0 (1000)	6	TBI	3	SOHC
	Prizm	1.6 (1600)	6	MFI	4	SOHC
	Prizm GSi	1.8 (1800)	8	MFI	4	DOHC
	Storm	1.6 (1600)	6	MFI	4	SOHC
	Storm GSi	1.8 (1800)	8	MFI	4	DOHC
	Tracker	1.6 (1600)	U	TBI	4	SOHC
1994	Metro	1.0 (1000)	6	TBI	3	SOHC
	Prizm	1.6 (1600)	6	MFI	4	DOHC
	Prizm GSi	1.8 (1800)	8	MFI	4	DOHC
	Tracker	1.6 (1600)	U	TBI ①	4	SOHC ②
1995	Metro	1.0 (1000)	6	TBI	3	SOHC
	Metro	1.3 (1300)	9	TBI	4	SOHC
	Prizm	1.6 (1600)	6	MFI	4	DOHC
	Prizm GSi	1.8 (1800)	8	MFI	4	DOHC
	Tracker	1.6 (1600)	U	TBI	4	SOHC
	Tracker	1.6 (1600)	6	MFI	4	DOHC

TBI–Throttle Body Injection
MFI–Multi-Point Fuel Injection
SOHC–Single Overhead Camshaft
DOHC–Dual Overhead Camshaft
① MFI for California
② DOHC for California

REFRIGERANT CAPACITIES

Year	Model	Refrigerant (oz.)	Oil (fl. oz.)	Compressor Type
1993	Metro	17.6	2.7	Swash-plate type
	Prizm	NA	NA	NA
	Storm	21.1	5.1	Rotary vane: KC-50
	Tracker	21.1	2.7	Swash-plate type
1994	Metro	17.6	3.4	Swash-plate type
	Prizm	25	NA	NA
	Tracker	21.2 (600 g)	3.4	Swash-plate type
1995	Metro	17.6	3.4	NA
	Prizm	25	NA	NA
	Tracker	21.2 (600 g)	5.5	Swash-plate type

NA–Not available.
g=grams

AIR CONDITIONING BELT TENSION

Year	Model	Engine Liters (cc)	Belt Type	Specifications	
				New (lbs.)	Used (lbs.)
1993	Metro	1.0 (1000)	Poly-V	0.20-0.25①	0.20-0.25①
	Prizm	1.6 (1600)	Poly-V	140-180①	80-120①
	Prizm GSi	1.8 (1800)	Serpentine	②	②
	Storm	1.6 (1600)	Poly-V	0.31-0.47①	0.31-0.47①
	Storm GSi	1.8 (1800)	Serpentine	②	②
	Tracker	1.6 (1600)	Poly-V	0.20-0.25①	0.20-0.25①
1994	Metro	1.0 (1000)	Poly-V	0.20-0.25①	0.20-0.25①
	Prizm	1.6 (1600)	Poly-V	140-180①	80-120①
	Prizm GSi	1.8 (1800)	Serpentine	②	②
	Tracker	1.6 (1600)	Poly-V	0.20-0.25①	0.20-0.25①
1995	Metro	1.0 (1000)	Poly-V	0.20-0.25①	0.20-0.25①
	Metro	1.3 (1300)	Poly-V	0.30-0.40①	0.30-0.40①
	Prizm	1.6 (1600)	Poly-V	140-180①	80-120①
	Prizm GSi	1.8 (1800)	Serpentine	②	②
	Tracker	1.6 (1600)	Poly-V	0.20-0.35①	0.20-0.25①

① Specifications given in inches of deflection or pounds of tension; each is measured using appropriate belt gauge.
② Equipped with automatic tensioner; no adjustment required.

SYSTEM DESCRIPTION

General Information

The compressor is driven by a drive belt from the engine crankshaft through an electromagnetic clutch. When voltage is applied to energize the clutch coil, a clutch plate and hub assembly are drawn rearward toward the pulley. As the compressor shaft turns, the compressor performs 2 functions. One is to compress the low pressure refrigerant vapor from the evaporator into a high pressure/temperature vapor. The other function is to pump refrigerant oil through the system to lubricate all components.

The condenser is mounted in front of the radiator and is comprised of small coils and cooling fins. When the high pressure/temperature vapor, from the compressor, enters the condenser, heat is transferred from the refrigerant to the air passing through the front of the vehicle. The refrigerant is cooled and condensed into a liquid.

The receiver/drier is mounted on the fender and is connected to the condenser outlet and evaporator inlet. The receiver/drier is a temporary storage container for condensed liquid refrigerant, a filter which removes moisture and contaminants from the system and it incorporates a sight glass for checking the system's refrigerant charge.

The expansion valve regulates the flow of liquid refrigerant into the core of the evaporator. The condensed liquid is released through the expansion valve, the pressure is decreased and the temperature drops causing the cooling affect.

The evaporator is housed in the evaporator case, located behind the right side of the instrument panel. During the air conditioning operation, ambient air is directed through the fins of the evaporator and into the vehicle's passenger compartment.

NOTE: The refrigeration system on this vehicle uses R-134a which is not compatible with R-12. Before servicing the system, always make sure the proper servicing equipment is used or the system could become severely damaged. Always refer to the service text and manufacturer's instructions included with service equipment before proceeding.

CAUTION

Avoid breathing A/C Refrigerant-134a and lubricant vapor or mist. Exposure may irritate eyes, nose and throat. To remove R-134a from the A/C system, use service equipment certified to meet the requirements of SAE J2210 (R-134a recycling equipment). If accidental system discharge occurs, ventilate work area before resuming service. Additional health and safety information may be obtained from refrigerant and lubricant manufacturers.

Air Bag System Information

CAUTION

When performing service on or around the Supplemental Inflatable Restraint (SIR), or "air bag", system components or wiring, the following disabling procedure must be completed before work begins and the enabling procedure completed after work is finished. Failure to follow procedures could result in possible air bag deployment, personal injury or otherwise unneeded SIR system repairs.

Metro

1. Disable the SIR system as follows:
   - Turn the ignition switch **OFF** or **LOCK**.

- Disconnect the negative battery cable and remove the SIR IG fuse from the SIR fuse block.
- Remove the access cover at the back of the steering wheel to access the 2-way connector.
- Remove the Connector Positive Assurance (CPA) lock on the yellow 2-way connector at the back of the steering wheel.
- Disconnect the yellow 2-way connector.

2. Enable the SIR system as follows:
- Connect the yellow 2-way connector at the back of the steering wheel.
- Install the CPA lock on the yellow 2-way connector.
- Connect the negative battery cable. Install SIR IG fuse.
- Install the access cover on the back of the steering wheel.
- Turn the ignition switch to **ON** and make sure the "Inflatable Restraint" light flashes 7-9 times and then goes out.

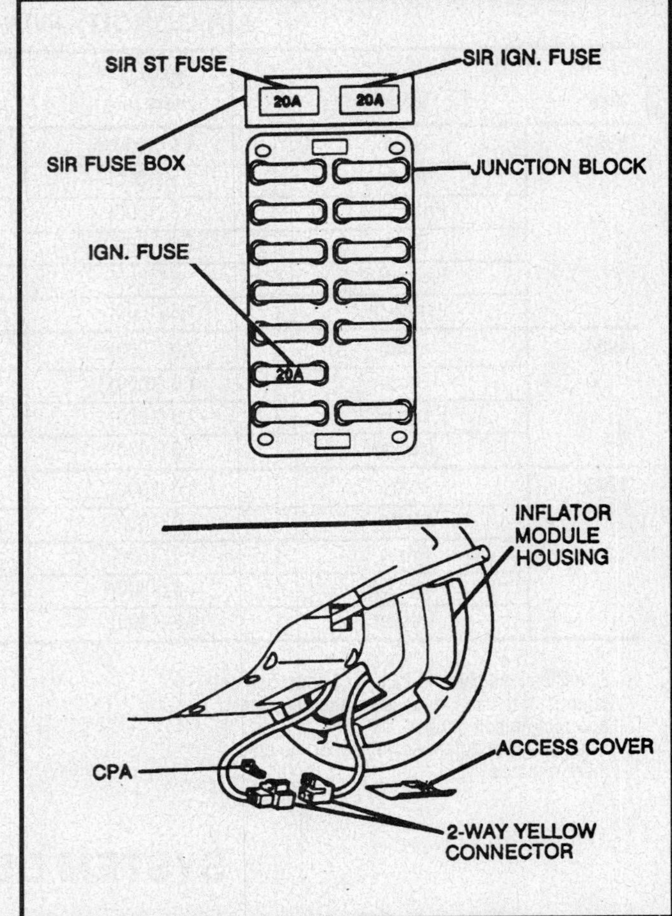

SIR fuse, access cover and 2-way connector–Metro

Storm

1. Disable the SIR system as follows:
- Set front wheels to straight ahead position. Turn ignition switch to **OFF**.
- Remove the meter fuse (C-22) and the SIR fuse (C-23) from the fuse box.
- Pry out the switch bezel and cigar light bezel and disconnect electrical connections. Remove the hood release handle, then remove the lower panel bolster from beneath the steering column (disconnect the lap cooler air duct in the process).
- Remove the CPA (connector positive assurance) lock on the yellow 3-way connector at the base of the steering column.
- Disconnect the orange 3-way connector.

2. Enable the SIR system as follows:
- Install the lower panel bolster, connect the wiring for the cigar lighter and switches and reinstall the bezels.
- Install the lower panel bolster, connect the wiring for the cigar lighter and switches and reinstall the bezels.
- Install the meter fuse and SIR fuse.
- Turn the ignition switch to **ON** and be sure the "Inflatable Restraint" light flashes 7-9 times and then goes out.

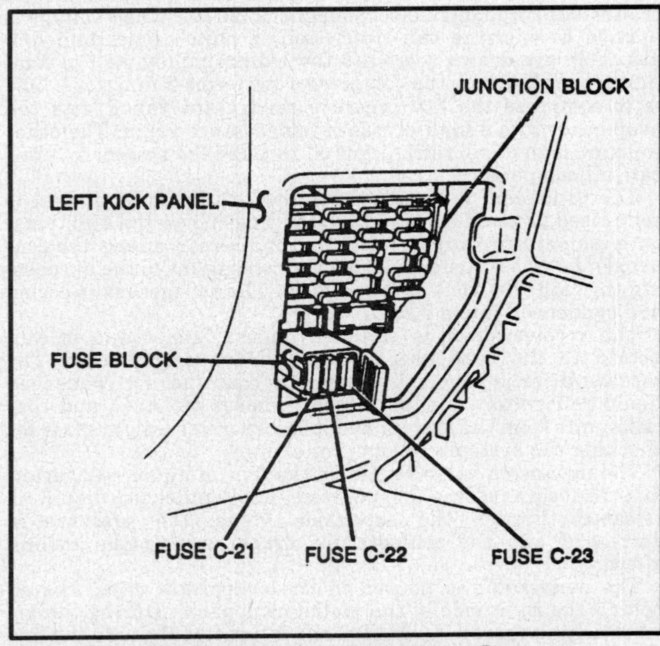

Fuse block for disabling SIR system–Storm

1994-95 Prizm

1. Disable the SRS as follows:
- Turn the ignition to **LOCK.**
- Disconnect the IGN fuse and CIG & RADIO fuse.
- Remove the Connector Positive Assurance (CPA) lock and lower the steering column (yellow two-cavity) connector at the base of the steering column.
- Open the glove box and gently pry off the passenger inflator module connector retainer.
- Remove the CPA lock and disconnect the passenger inflator module (yellow-2 cavity) connector.

2. Enable the SRS as follows:
- Turn the ignition switch to **LOCK.**
- Connect the passenger inflator module connector and secure it with the CPA lock. Then close the glove box.
- Connect the lower steering column connector and secure it with the CPA lock. Replace fuses.
- Turn the ignition switch to **ACC** or **ON.** Verify AIR BAG lights for six seconds then turns off.

Service Valve Location

The low side service valve is located in the suction hose (hose between the evaporator and compressor). The high side service valve is located in the hose between the condenser and receiver/drier.

The Air Conditioning Refrigerant Recovery, Recycling and Recharging (ACR4) System (J 39500) removes Refrigerant-134a from the vehicle A/C system, recycles and recharges all with one hook-up.

Single pass filtering during recovery cycle, plus automatic multiple pass filtering during the evacuation cycle assures constant supply of clean/dry refrigerant for A/C system charging.

NOTE: R-12 and R-134a require separate and non-interchangeable sets of recovery, recycling and recharging equipment because the refrigerants and lubricants are not compatible and cannot be mixed even in the smallest amounts.

NOTE: Do not attempt to use one set of equipment for both R-12 and R-134a. All equipment will contain residue amounts of refrigerant and/or lubricant, which will result in contamination and damage to the recovery/recycling equipment.

NOTE: Refrigerant-134a systems have special fittings (per SAE specifications) to avoid cross-contamination with Refrigerant-12 systems. Do not attempt to adapt this unit to Refrigerant-12 systems. Severe system failure will result.

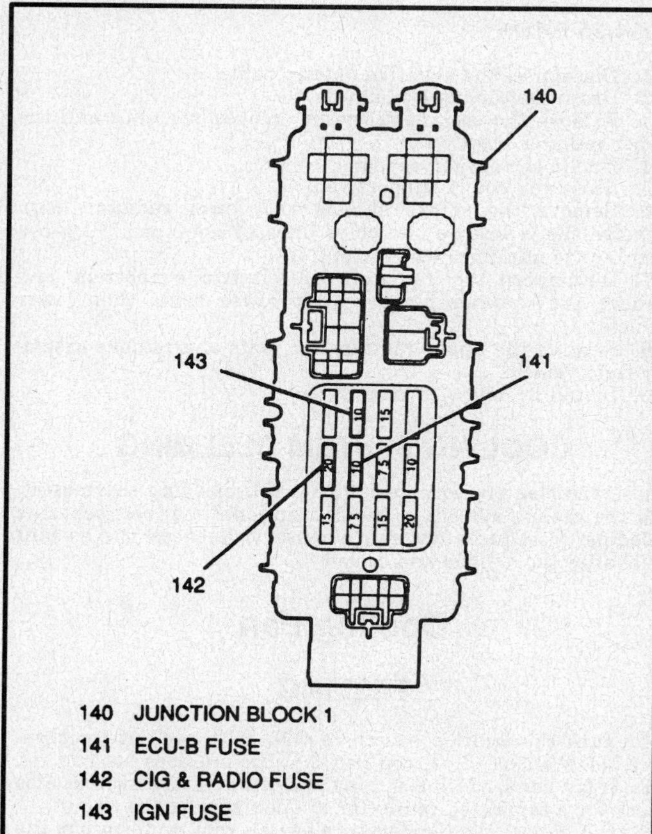

Fuse block for 1994-95 Prizm

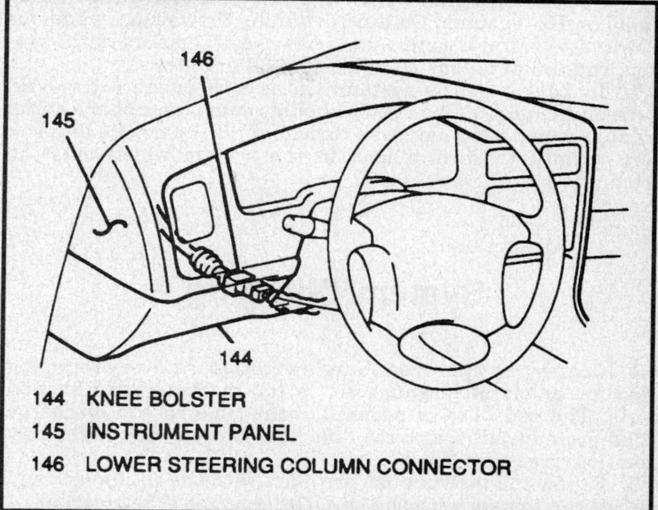

Lower steering column connector 1994-95 Prizm

CAUTION

Always wear goggles and gloves when doing work that involves opening the refrigeration system. If liquid refrigerant comes into contact with the skin or eyes, injury may result.

Use only authorized 23 kg (50 lb.) refillable refrigerant tanks (J 39500-50). Use of other tanks could cause personal injury and void the warranty.

1. Connect the high side (red) and low side (blue) hoses to their respective ports on the vehicle (Figure 15).
2. Refer to the ACR4 instruction manual for all initial setup procedures and operating instructions.

System Discharging

1. Remove the caps from the high and low pressure charging valves in the high and low pressure lines.
2. Turn both manifold gauge set hand valves to the FULLY CLOSED (clockwise) position.
3. Connect the manifold gauge set.
4. If the gauge set hoses do not have the gauge port actuating pins, install fitting adapters on the manifold gauge set hoses. If the vehicle does not have a service access gauge port valve, connect the gauge set low pressure hose to the evaporator service access gauge port valve. A special adapter may be required to attach the manifold gauge set to the high pressure service access gauge port valve.
5. Connect the center hose to the refrigerant recycling station.
6. Open the low pressure gauge valve slightly and allow the system pressure to bleed into the recycling station.
7. When the system is just about empty, open the high pressure valve very slowly to avoid losing an excessive amount of refrigerant oil. Allow any remaining refrigerant to escape.

System Evacuating

1. Connect the manifold gauge set.
2. Discharge the system into the refrigerant recycling station.
3. Connect the center hose to the recycling center or an air conditioning evacuator pump.
4. Turn both gauge set valves to the WIDE OPEN position.
5. Start the pump and note the low side gauge reading.

6. Operate the pump until the low pressure gauge reads 25-30 in. Hg. vacuum. Continue running the vacuum pump for 10 minutes more. If components have been replaced in the system, run the pump for an additional 30 minutes.
7. To Leak test the system. Close both gauge set valves. Turn off the pump. The needle should remain stationary at the point at which the pump was turned off. If the needle drops to zero rapidly, there is a leak in the system which must be repaired.

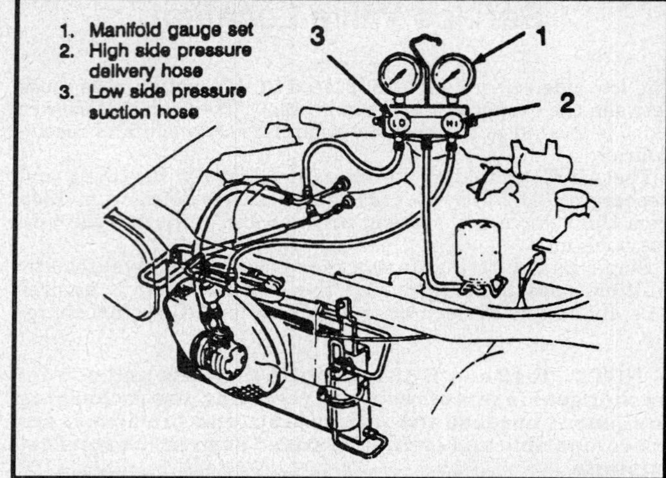

Air conditioning system service valves with manifold gauge set connected

System Charging

1. Connect an approved charging station, recovery/recycling machine or manifold gauge set to the discharge and suction ports. The red hose is normally connected to the discharge (high pressure) line, and the blue hose is connected to the suction (low pressure) line.
2. Follow the instructions provided with the equipment and charge the system with the specified amount of refrigerant.
3. Perform a leak test.

SYSTEM COMPONENTS

Radiator

REMOVAL AND INSTALLATION

Except Tracker and 1994-95 Prizm

1. Disconnect the negative battery cable.
2. Drain the cooling system.
3. Remove the coolant reservoir or overflow line and the upper and lower radiator hoses.
4. Disconnect the transaxle oil cooler lines, if equipped. Plug the openings to minimize leakage of fluid.
5. Remove the upper radiator brackets.
6. Disconnect the cooling fan electrical connectors.
7. Remove the radiator and fan assembly.

To install:

8. Install the radiator and fan assembly.
9. Connect the cooling fan electrical connectors.
10. Install the upper radiator brackets.
11. Connect the transaxle oil cooler lines, if equipped.
12. Install the coolant reservoir or line and the upper and lower radiator hoses.
13. Refill the cooling system.
14. Connect the negative battery cable.

Tracker

1. Remove the radiator cap. Raise and support the vehicle. Properly drain the cooling system.
2. Remove the hose clamps and disconnect the transmission cooler lines. Plug the lines to minimize leakage of fluid.
3. Remove 2 lower shroud bolts. Remove the lower radiator hose. Lower the vehicle.
4. Remove 2 bolts and reposition the refrigerant flex hose (if equipped with A/C).
5. Remove 2 bolts and position the power steering reservoir out of the way.
6. Remove 2 screws and move the fan shroud to the rear.
7. Remove the upper radiator hose and the coolant overflow hose.
8. Remove 4 bolts and remove the radiator assembly.
9. Installation is the reverse of the removal procedure. Refill the cooling system. Check the transmission fluid level.

1994-95 Prizm

1. Disconnect the negative battery cable.
2. Drain the cooling system.
3. Remove the coolant reservoir or overflow lines and the upper radiator hose.
4. Unclip the oxygen sensor.
5. Raise and safely support vehicle.
6. Remove the splash shields and lower radiator hose. Remove the transaxle oil cooler lines, if equipped. Plug the openings to minimize leakage of fluid.
7. Disconnect the radiator fan electric connection and remove the radiator fan assembly lower bolts, then lower vehicle.
8. Remove the upper radiator fan bolts and remove assembly from vehicle.
9. Install in reverse order.

COOLING SYSTEM BLEEDING

These vehicles are equipped with a self-bleeding thermostat. Fill the cooling system in the conventional manner; separate bleeding procedures are not necessary. Recheck the coolant level after the vehicle and cooled.

Cooling Fan

TESTING

1. Turn the ignition switch to **ON**. With coolant temperature below about 180°F, confirm that the fan does not run.
2. If fan runs, check fan relay and temperature switch. Also check for a separated connector or open wire in the circuit.
3. Disconnect the temperature switch wire and confirm the fan rotates. If not, check the fan relay, fan motor, ignition relay and fuse. Also check for a short between the fan relay and temperature switch.

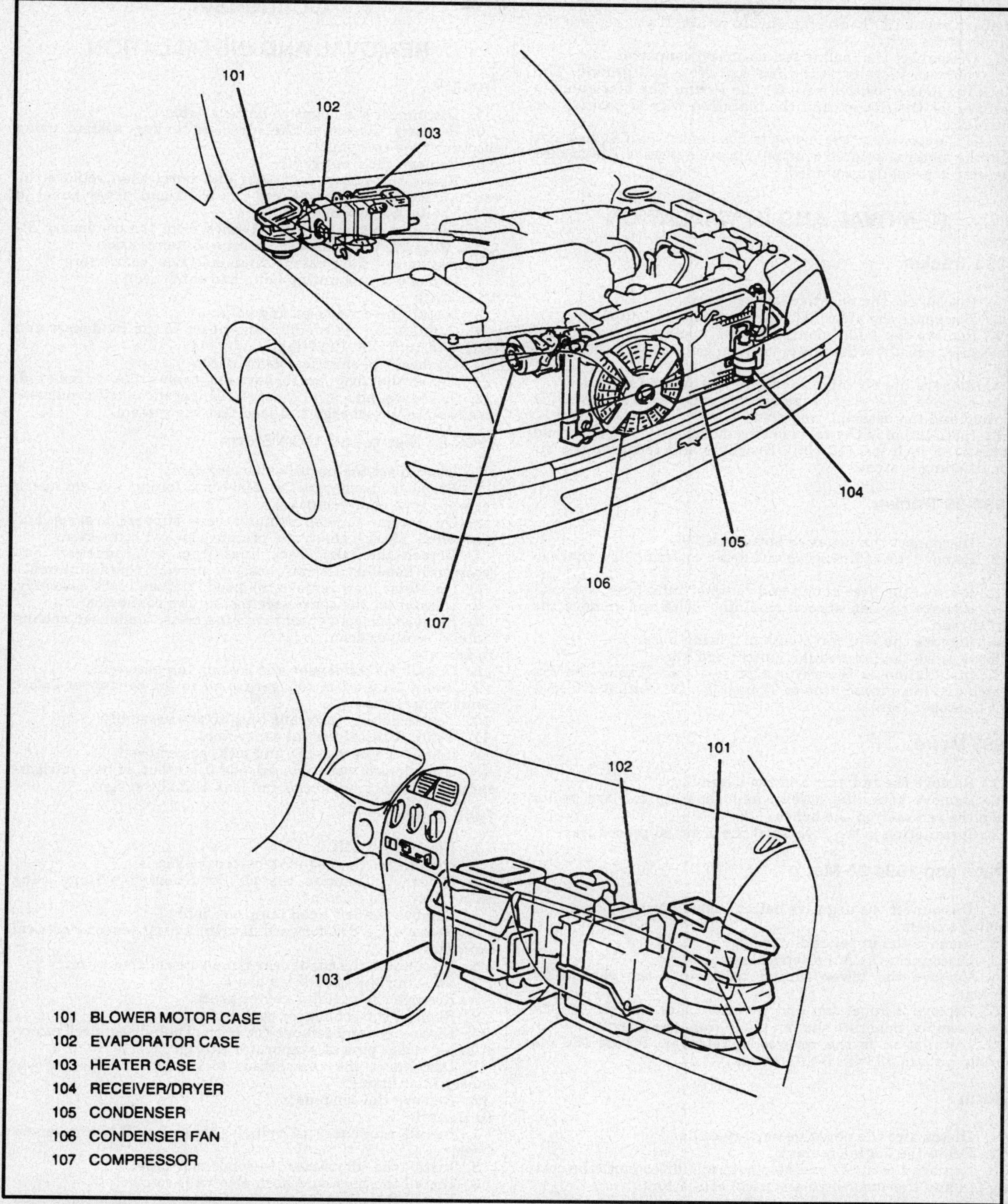

1995 Prizm Air Conditioning System Components

4. Connect the temperature switch wire. Raise temperature to above about 190°F. The fan should rotate. If not, replace the temperature switch.

5. Disconnect the cooling fan electrical connector.

6. Connect 12 volts to the fan connector and ground. The black/red is the positive wire for the Prizm. The black/blue is positive for the Storm, and the black/red wire is positive for the Metro.

7. If the fan runs, the motor is not defective; if it does not run, the motor or related components are defective. Make sure the unit is properly grounded.

REMOVAL AND INSTALLATION

1993 Tracker

1. Disconnect the negative battery cable.
2. Discharge the air conditioning system, if equipped.
3. Remove the 4 fan mounting nuts, cooling fan and pump pulley. Do not allow the fan to come in contact with the radiator.
4. Remove the air conditioning line above the shroud.
5. Remove the shroud retaining bolts and remove the shroud and fan assembly together.
6. Installation is the reverse of removal. Torque the shroud bolts to 89 inch lbs. (10 Nm). Evacuate and recharge the air conditioning system.

1994-95 Tracker

1. Disconnect the negative battery cable.
2. Remove the radiator cap and drain coolant below thermostat.
3. Remove the hose clamp and radiator inlet hose.
4. Remove the fan shroud retaining bolts and remove the fan shroud.
5. Remove the four fan clutch mounting nuts.
6. Remove the fan and fan clutch together.
7. Installation is the reverse of removal. Torque the fan clutch and fan shroud nuts to 97 inch lbs. (11 Nm). Refill coolant to proper level.

1993 Metro

1. Remove the radiator and fan assembly.
2. Remove retaining screws and separate the fan motor from the radiator on the bench.
3. Installation is the reverse of the removal procedure.

Prizm and 1994-95 Metro

1. Disconnect the negative battery cable. Properly drain the cooling system.
2. Remove the upper radiator hose.
3. Disconnect the fan electrical connectors.
4. Remove the lower shroud bolt (raise the vehicle for access).
5. Remove 2 upper fan and radiator bolts and remove the fan assembly. Separate the fan blade from the motor.
6. Installation is the reverse of removal. Torque the fan shroud nuts to 89 inch lbs. (10 Nm).

Storm

1. Disconnect the negative battery cable.
2. Drain the engine coolant.
3. Remove the upper radiator hose and disconnect the cooling fan and thermo switch electrical connectors.
4. Remove the cooling fan and motor assembly.
5. Installation is the reverse of removal.

Condenser

REMOVAL AND INSTALLATION

Tracker

1. Disconnect the negative battery cable.
2. Properly discharge the air conditioning system using recovery type equipment.
3. Remove the front grille.
4. Remove the horn connector and horn, then remove the radiator core center brace and the front end upper panel (6 upper bolts, 4 lower bolts).
5. Disconnect the refrigerant lines from the condenser fittings. Plug the open lines to prevent contamination.
6. Disconnect the condenser fan electrical connectors.
7. Remove the mounting bolts and condenser.

To install:

8. Install the condenser and bolts.
9. Connect the air conditioning hoses to the condenser and torque to 18 ft. lbs. (25 Nm).
10. Connect the electrical connections.
11. Install the cover, brace, horn and front grille, as removed.
12. Evacuate, add 0.7-1.0 oz. of refrigerant oil (if condenser was replaced), recharge and lead test the system.

1993-94 Metro and 1993 Storm

1. Disconnect the negative battery cable.
2. Properly discharge the air conditioning system using recovery type equipment.
3. On Storm, remove radiator core support bracket and hood latch. Detach the triple pressure switch connector.
4. Detach the refrigerant lines from the condenser and receiver/drier. Plug all open hoses to prevent contamination.
5. On Metro, now remove the hood latch and lock assembly.
6. Disconnect the condenser cooling fan connector.
7. Remove the condenser retaining bolts, condenser, cooling fan and receiver/drier.

To install:

8. Install the condenser and cooling fan assembly.
9. Add 0.7-1.0 oz. of refrigerant oil to the condenser before connecting hoses.
10. Connect the refrigerant lines to the assembly.
11. Connect the electrical connectors.
12. Install the hood latch and lock, as removed.
13. If condenser was replaced, add 0.7-1.0 oz. of new refrigerant oil. Evacuate, recharge and leak test the system.

1995 Metro

1. Disable the SIR.
2. Disconnect the negative battery cable.
3. Properly discharge the air conditioning system using recovery type equipment.
4. Remove the left head lamp assembly.
5. Remove the SIR forward discriminating sensor electrical connector.
6. Disconnect the condenser fan electrical connector.
7. Slide out the hood latch cable.
8. Remove the radiator center brace.
9. Remove the condenser cooling fan.
10. Disconnect and remove the horn. Then disconnect receiver/dryer outlet pipe at evaporator fitting.
11. Disconnect the compressor to condenser pipe at condenser inlet fitting.
12. Remove the condenser.

To install:

1. Install condenser to vehicle; then install the receiver/dryer.
2. Install the compressor-to-condenser pipe.
3. Install the horn and horn electrical connectors.
4. Install the condenser cooling fan to the condenser. Install the center brace and the hood latch cable.

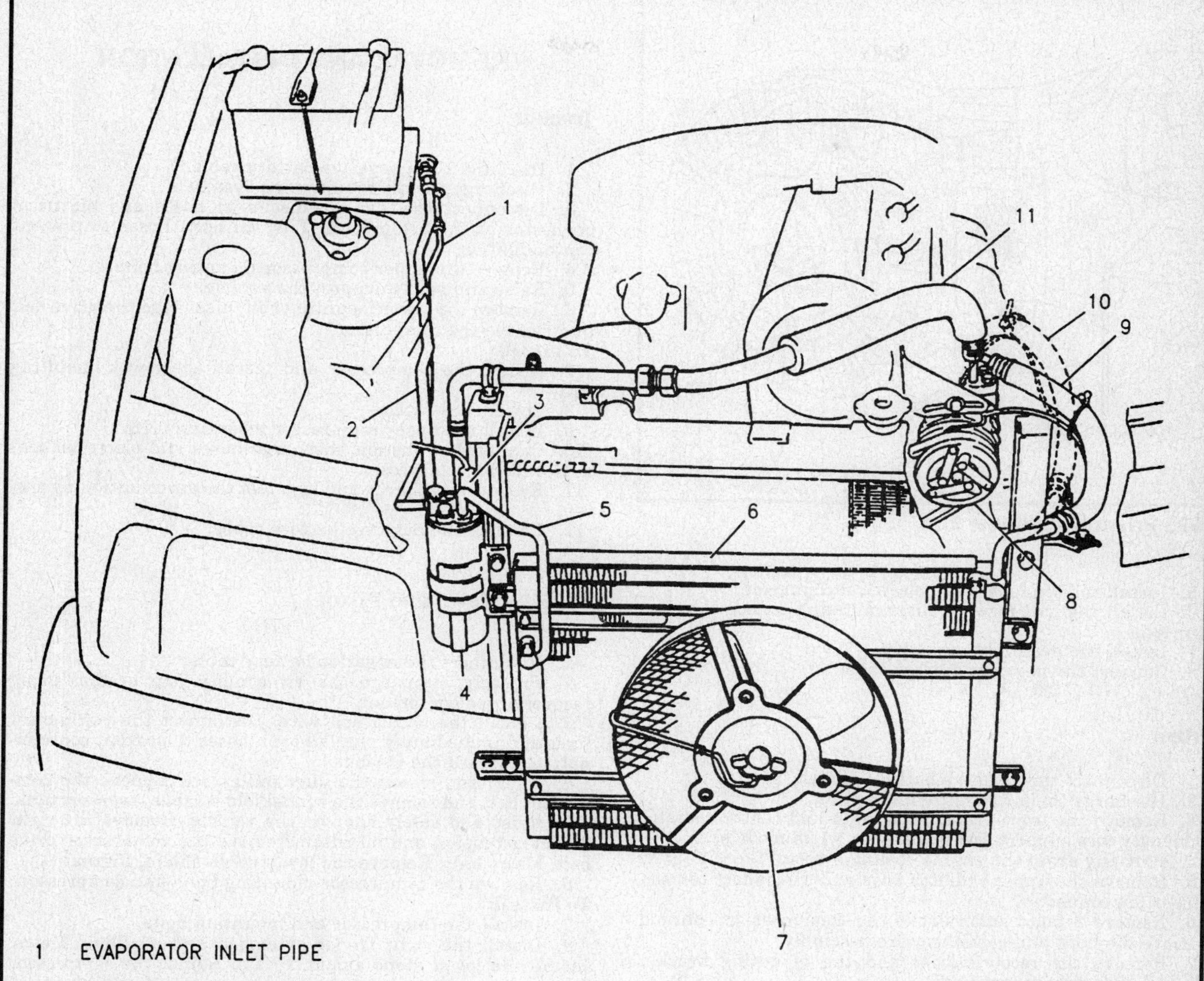

1 EVAPORATOR INLET PIPE
2 EVAPORATOR OUTLET PIPE
3 DUAL PRESSURE SWITCH
4 RECEIVER/DRYER
5 RECEIVER/DRYER INLET PIPE
6 CONDENSER
7 CONDENSER FAN
8 COMPRESSOR
9 COMPRESSOR DISCHARGE PIPE (8-VALVE ENGINE)
10 COMPRESSOR DISCHARGE PIPE (16-VALVE ENGINE)
11 COMPRESSOR SUCTION PIPE

1995 Tracker – A/C Components

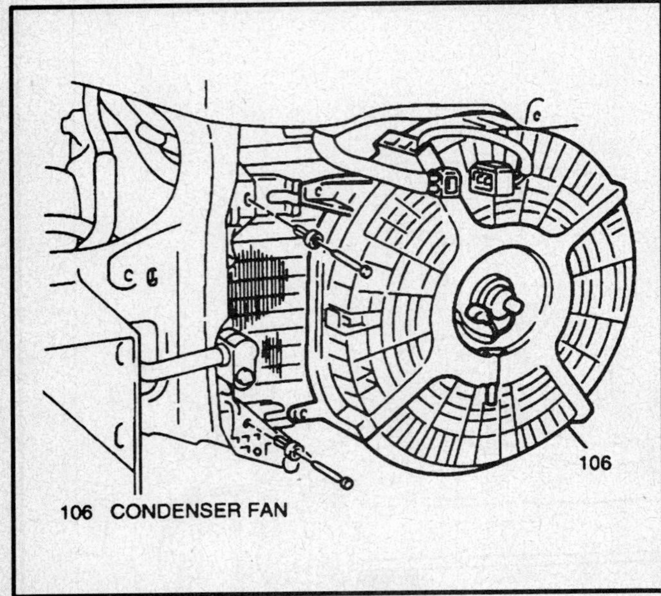

1995 Prizm Condenser Fan

5. Install the condenser fan electrical connector.
6. Install the SIR forward discriminating sensor electrical connector.
7. Install the headlight assembly.
8. Connect the negative battery cable.

Prizm

1. Disconnect the negative battery cable.
2. Discharge the air conditioning system.
3. Remove the front grille, hood latch and center radiator/condenser core support and battery for 94-95 models.
4. Partially drain the engine cooling system.
5. Remove the upper radiator hose and disconnect the condenser fan connector.
6. Remove 3 bolts and remove the condenser fan shroud. Remove the horn and condenser fan assembly.
7. Remove the receiver/drier and the mounting bracket. Plug all open refrigerant hoses.
8. Remove the receiver-to-condenser pipe from the condenser and oxygen sensor for 94-95 models.
9. Disconnect the compressor discharge pipe from the condenser.
10. Remove the upper condenser mounting brackets and slide the condenser to the left and remove the receiver/drier outlet pipe hold-down bracket. Remove the condenser from the vehicle. Drain and measure the refrigerant oil from the condenser.

To install:

11. Install the condenser and upper condenser mounting brackets.
12. Connect the compressor discharge pipe to the condenser.
13. Install the receiver-to-condenser pipe to the condenser.
14. Install the receiver/drier and mounting bracket.
15. Install the horn and condenser fan assembly.
16. Install the upper radiator hose and connect the condenser fan connector.
17. Refill the engine cooling system.
18. Install the hood latch and front grille.
19. Install same amount of oil as was drained and measured during removal. Evacuate, recharge and leak test the system.
20. Connect the negative battery cable.

Compressor

REMOVAL AND INSTALLATION

Tracker

1. Disconnect the negative battery cable.
2. Discharge the air conditioning system.
3. Disconnect the suction, discharge hoses and electrical connector at the compressor. Plug all open hoses to prevent contamination.
4. Remove the upper compressor mounting bolts.
5. Raise and safely support the vehicle.
6. Remove the lower mounting bolt, disengage the drive belt and remove the compressor.

To install:

7. Install the compressor and install the lower mounting bolt.
8. Lower the vehicle.
9. Install the upper compressor mounting bolts.
10. Connect the suction, discharge hoses and electrical connector at the compressor.
11. Evacuate, recharge and leak test the air conditioning system.
12. Connect the negative battery cable.

1993-94 Metro and Prizm

1. Disconnect the negative battery cable.
2. Properly discharge the air conditioning system using recovery type equipment.
3. Detach the clutch coil wire. Disconnect the refrigerant lines and immediately plug all open hoses to prevent contamination. Discard the O-rings.
4. On Prizm, loosen the idler pulley and remove the compressor belt and remove the windshield washer reservoir tank.
5. Raise and safely support the vehicle. Remove the right fender extension and oil filter. Remove the compressor drive belt, Metro only. Remove the lower stone shield, Prizm.
6. Remove the compressor mounting bolts and compressor.

To install:

7. Install the compressor and mounting bolts.
8. Install the right fender extension and oil filter, Metro. Install the lower stone shield, Prizm. Adjust the compressor drive belt.
9. Lower the vehicle.
10. Connect the suction, discharge hoses and electrical connector at the compressor.
11. Evacuate and recharge the air conditioning system.
12. Connect the negative battery cable.

1995 Metro

1. Disconnect the negative battery cable.
2. Properly discharge the air conditioning system using recovery type equipment.
3. Remove the compressor clutch coil electrical connector.
4. Raise and safely support the vehicle.
5. Remove the right front wheel and lower splash shield.
6. Loosen the idle pulley bolt and remove the compressor drive belt.
7. Remove the discharge pipe from the compressor service and suction pipe, and immediately plug all open hoses, discard all O-rings.
8. Remove the compressor mounting bolts and compressor.

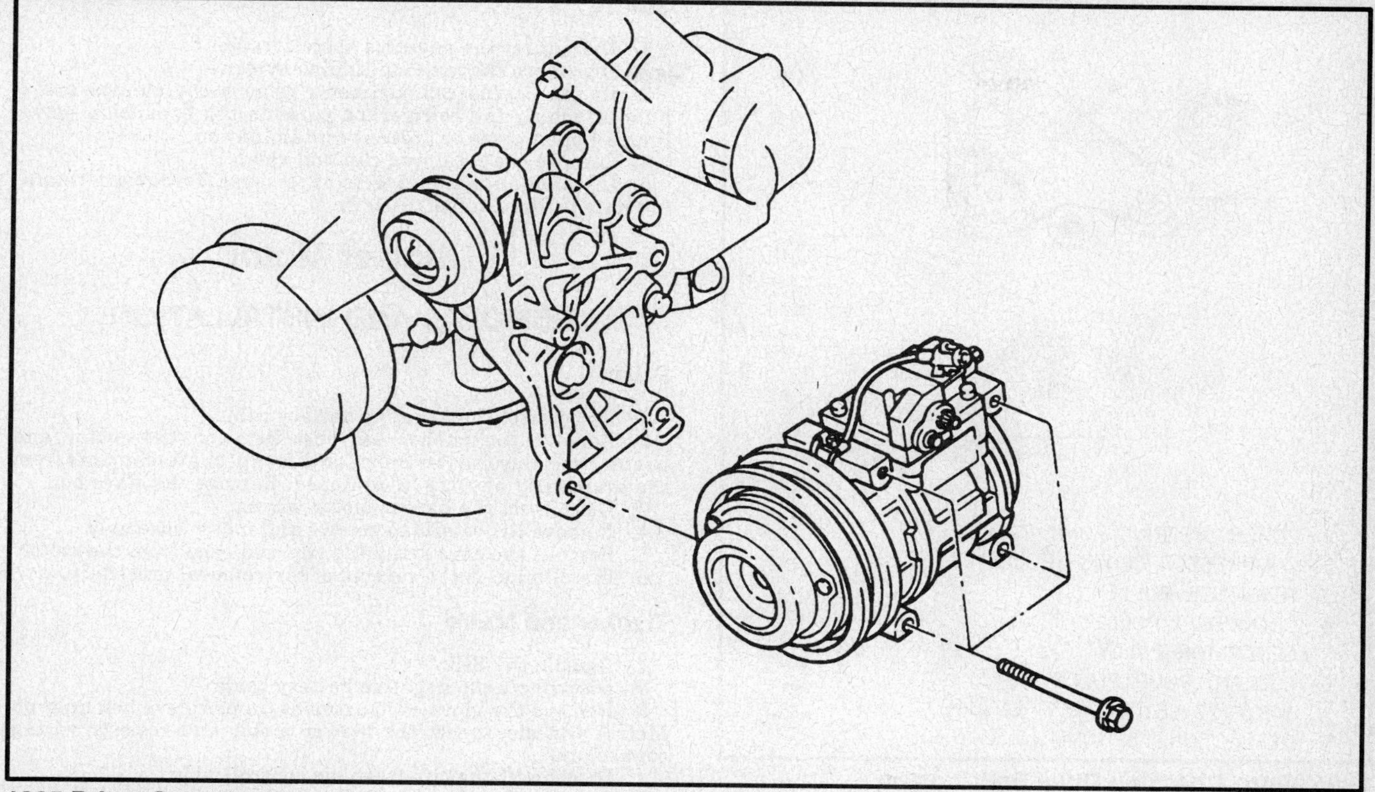

1995 Prizm Compressor

To install:

9. Install the compressor and compressor mounting bolts.
10. Install new O-rings coated with clean refrigerant oil, then the compressor suction and discharge pipes.
11. Install the compressor drive belt and adjust the drive bolt tension.
12. Install the lower splash shield and right front wheel; lower vehicle.
13. Connect the compressor clutch electrical connector and negative battery cable.

Storm

1. Disconnect the negative battery cable.
2. Discharge the air conditioning system.
3. Remove the power steering drive belt. If equipped with serpentine belt, lever up the tensioner and remove the belt from the compressor.
4. Detach the electrical connection from the compressor. Disconnect the refrigerant lines from the compressor. Plug all open hoses to prevent contamination.
5. Raise and safely support the vehicle.
6. Remove the right undercover and 2 compressor mounting bolt.
7. Remove the compressor from the vehicle.

To install:

8. Install the compressor into the vehicle.
9. Install the compressor mounting bolts and right undercover.
10. Lower the vehicle.
11. Connect the suction, discharge hoses and electrical connector at the compressor.
12. Install the power steering drive belt and serpentine belt, as removed.
13. Evacuate, recharge and leak test the system.
14. Connect the negative battery cable.

Receiver/Drier

REMOVAL AND INSTALLATION

1. Disconnect the negative battery cable.
2. Discharge the air conditioning system.
3. Remove the front grille and horn from the vehicle for Prizm only. Remove the condenser support bracket and 2 condenser retaining bolts for Storm only.
4. Detach electrical wires from the receiver/drier. Disconnect the inlet and outlet from the receiver/drier. Plug the open pipes to prevent contamination.
5. Remove the assembly from the mounting bracket.
6. Installation is the reverse of removal. Add 0.3 oz. (10ml) of refrigerant oil to the inlet. Transfer electrical switch and use sealing tape on the threads.

Expansion Valve

REMOVAL AND INSTALLATION

Except Storm

1. Disconnect the negative battery cable.
2. Discharge the air conditioning system.
3. Remove the evaporator assembly from the vehicle.
4. On Metro, remove the A/C amplifier from the evaporator housing.
5. Remove the clamps to separate the upper and lower halves.
6. Using backup wrenches, remove the expansion valve from the evaporator.
7. Installation is the reverse of removal. Torque the fittings to 18 ft. lbs. (25 Nm).

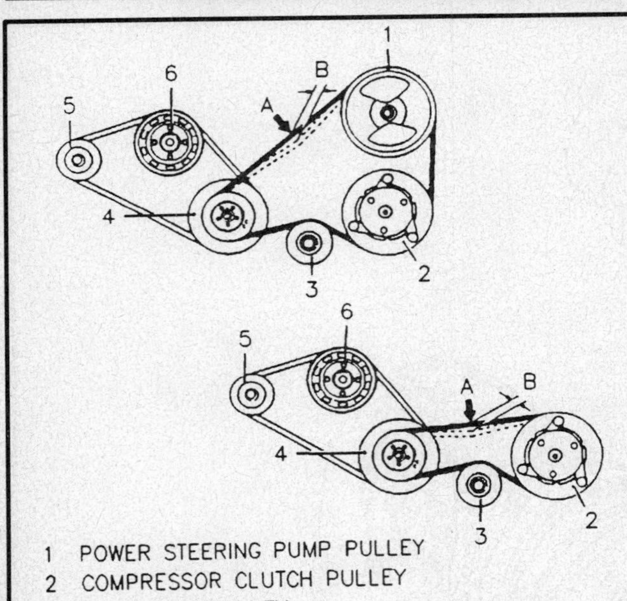

1995 Metro Checking Drive Belt Tension

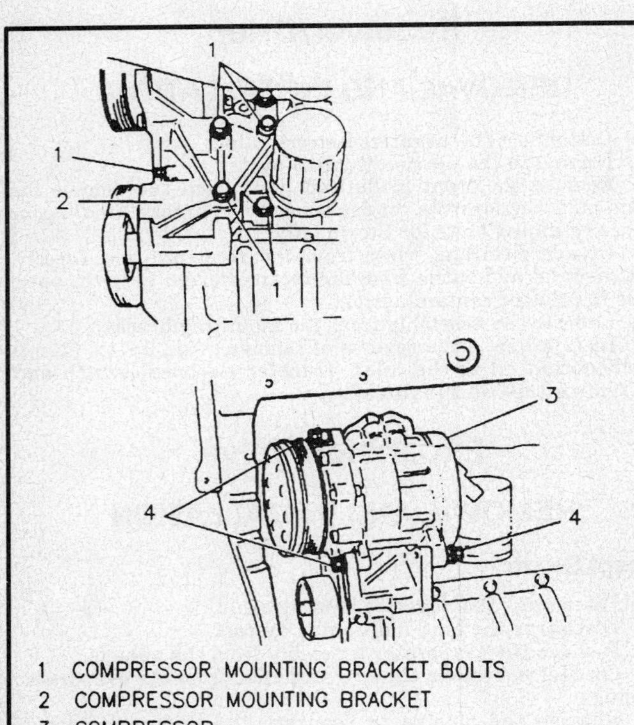

1995 Metro Compressor Mounting Bracket

Storm

1. Disconnect the negative battery cable.
2. Discharge the air conditioning system.
3. In the engine compartment, remove the clamps and 2 nuts attaching the refrigerant pipes to the expansion valve. Plug all open pipes to prevent contamination.
4. Remove the retaining clip and valve.
5. Installation is the reverse of removal. Torque the retaining nuts to 70 inch lbs. (8 Nm).

Blower Motor

REMOVAL AND INSTALLATION

Prizm

1. Disconnect the negative battery cable.
2. Remove the rubber air duct between the motor and heater assembly (heater only), or disconnect attachments from the evaporator housing, if equipped. Remove the glove box.
3. Disconnect the blower motor wiring.
4. Remove the retaining screws and motor assembly.
5. Remove the cage retaining clip and cage from the motor.
6. Installation is the reverse of the removal procedure.

Tracker and Metro

1. Disable the SIR.
2. Disconnect the negative battery cable.
3. Remove the glove compartment (upper glove box liner on Metro) and disconnect the blower motor and resistor wiring connectors.
4. Disconnect the circ-fresh air control cable.
5. Remove the blower case mounting bolts and case from the vehicle.
6. Remove the three motor retaining screws and blower motor. Disconnect the air hose, if equipped.
7. Installation is the reverse of removal.

Storm

1. Disconnect the negative battery cable.
2. Disconnect the blower motor connector.
3. Remove the 4 retaining screws and motor assembly.
4. Installation is the reverse of removal.

Blower Motor Resistor

REMOVAL AND INSTALLATION

Tracker and Prizm

1. Disconnect the negative battery cable.
2. Remove the glove compartment.
3. Disconnect the resistor connector.
4. Remove the retaining screws and resistor.
5. Installation is the reverse of removal.

Metro

1. Disable the SIR.
2. Disconnect the negative battery cable.
3. Remove the glove box.
4. Disconnect the electrical connector and remove the resistor.
5. Installation is the reverse of removal.

Storm

1. Disconnect the negative battery cable.

2. Disconnect the harness connector, remove the plate and remove the resistor.
3. Installation is the reverse of removal.

Heater Core

NOTE: On vehicles equipped with SIR (air bag) systems, perform the specific disabling procedure described in this article before proceeding with removal and installation of this component.

REMOVAL AND INSTALLATION

Tracker

1. Disconnect the negative battery cable.
2. Drain the engine coolant.
3. Remove the steering column.
4. Remove the center console.
5. Remove the instrument panel and center supports.
6. Disconnect all electrical connectors and cables from the heater case.
7. Disconnect the heater core hoses.
8. Remove the defrost duct and speedometer retaining bracket from the heater case.
9. Remove the fastening bolts, grommets and floor duct, if equipped, from the case and remove the case from the vehicle.
10. Separate the heater case and remove the heater core.

To install:

11. Install the core and assemble the heater case.
12. Install the fastening bolts, grommets and floor duct to the case after installation.
13. Install the defrost duct and speedometer retaining bracket to the heater case.
14. Connect the heater core hoses.
15. Connect all electrical connectors and cables to the heater case.
16. Install the center supports and instrument panel.
17. Install the center console.
18. Install the steering column.
19. Refill the engine coolant.
20. Connect the negative battery cable.

Metro

1. Disconnect the negative battery cable.
2. Properly drain the cooling system.
3. Remove the instrument panel.
4. Remove the heater hoses from the heater core tubes at the firewall.
5. Detach the temperature and mode control cables from the heater housing.
6. If heater only, remove the air duct from the heater housing to the blower assembly; otherwise, detach the heater housing from the evaporator assembly.
7. Remove 2 bolts and 2 nuts and remove the heater assembly.
8. Separate the heater case halves.
9. Installation is the reverse of the removal procedure. Adjust control cables as needed.

Prizm

1. Disconnect the negative battery cable.
2. Drain the engine coolant.
3. Remove the steering wheel.
4. Remove the trim bezel from the instrument panel.
5. Remove the cup holder from the console.
6. Remove the radio.
7. Remove the instrument cluster, instrument panel, console and all console trim.
8. Remove the lower dash trim and side window air deflectors.
9. Disconnect all instrument panel wiring harnesses and cables.
10. Remove the 2 center console support braces.
11. Remove the 2 heater hoses from the core.
12. Remove all mounting bolts, nuts and clips from the heater and air distribution cases.
13. Remove the screws and clips from the case and separate.
14. Remove the heater core from the case.

To install:

15. Install the heater core to the case.
16. Install the screws and clips to the case.
17. Install all mounting bolts, nuts and clips to the heater and air distribution cases.
18. Install the 2 heater hoses to the core.
19. Install the 2 center console support braces.
20. Connect all instrument panel wiring harnesses and cables.
21. Install the lower dash trim and side window air deflectors.
22. Install the instrument panel, console and all console trim.
23. Install the radio.
24. Install the cup holder to the console.
25. Install the trim bezel to the instrument panel.
26. Install the steering wheel.
27. Refill the engine coolant.
28. Connect the negative battery cable.

Storm

1. Disconnect the negative battery cable.
2. Drain the engine coolant.
3. Disconnect the hoses at the heater core.
4. Remove the instrument panel.
5. Remove the evaporator assembly, air conditioning only.
6. On heater only systems, remove the duct between the blower assembly and heater unit.
7. Remove the center ventilation duct.
8. Remove the 4 heater unit retaining nuts and heater unit.
9. Remove the duct between the blower and heater unit.
10. Detach the control cables from the heater unit.
11. Remove the 5 mode control case-to-heater core case retaining screws. Do not remove the link.
12. Separate the 2 halves and remove the core.

To install:

13. Install the heater core and assemble the 2 case halves. Install the five mode control case-to-heater core case retaining screws.
14. Install the duct between the blower and heater unit (heater only).
15. Install the heater unit and 4 heater unit retaining nuts.
16. Install the center ventilation duct.
17. Install the duct between the blower assembly and heater unit.
18. Install the evaporator assembly, air conditioning only.
19. Install the instrument panel.
20. Connect the hoses at the heater core.
21. Refill the engine coolant.
22. Connect the negative battery cable.

Evaporator

NOTE: On vehicles equipped with SIR (air bag) systems, perform the specific disabling procedure described in this article before proceeding with removal and installation of this component.

REMOVAL AND INSTALLATION

Tracker

1. Properly discharge the air conditioning system using recovery type equipment. Disconnect the negative battery cable.
2. Disconnect the inlet and outlet A/C pipes from the evaporator core tubes at the firewall.

3. Remove the evaporator case mounting nut at the firewall.
4. Remove the glove box.
5. Loosen the blower motor housing support (2 bolts). Loosen the evaporator to heater connector band and slide the band onto the heater housing.
6. Remove the condensation drain hose. Remove the A/C amplifier and thermistor connectors.
7. Remove 2 evaporator case upper mounting bolts and remove the evaporator case.
8. Separate the upper and lower case halves. Remove the pipe retaining clamp from the lower case, then remove the lower case screws. Remove the expansion valve and the evaporator core.
9. Installation is the reverse of the removal procedure. Add 1.0 oz. of refrigerant oil if the evaporator core was replaced. Evacuate, recharge and leak test the system.

Metro

1. Disconnect the negative battery cable.
2. Properly discharge the air conditioning system using recovery type equipment.
3. Remove the glove compartment.
4. Remove blower motor case.
5. Disconnect all electrical wiring and cables from the blower case.
6. Detach the connectors for the amplifier and thermistor. Disconnect and plug the inlet and outlet refrigerant lines from the evaporator.
7. Remove the drain hose and the 2 retaining nuts and remove the evaporator assembly from the vehicle.
8. Remove the amplifier, then separate the case housing and remove the evaporator core.

To install:

9. Install the evaporator core and assemble the case housing.
10. Install the housing, upper and lower housing retaining bolts.
11. Connect the inlet and outlet lines to the evaporator.
12. Install the blower case and retaining bolts.
13. Connect all electrical wiring and cables to the blower case.
14. Install the glove compartment. Install the upper panel and attaching screw at the rear of the glove compartment upper panel.
15. Evacuate and recharge the air conditioning system.
16. Connect the negative battery cable.

Prizm

1. Disconnect the negative battery cable.
2. Discharge the air conditioning system.
3. Disconnect and plug the inlet and outlet pipes from the evaporator.
4. Remove the hold-down brackets for the evaporator pipes.
5. Remove the right lower instrument panel trim.
6. Disconnect all electrical wiring and cables from the housing.
7. Remove the air conditioning amplifier from the housing.
8. Remove the mounting bolts and evaporator assembly.
9. Separate the housing halves and remove the thermistor, expansion valve and evaporator core.

To install:

10. Install the evaporator core, expansion valve and thermistor, and assemble the housing halves.
11. Install the housing and mounting bolts.
12. Install the air conditioning amplifier to the housing.
13. Connect all electrical wiring and cables to the housing.
14. Install the right lower instrument panel trim.
15. Connect the inlet and outlet pipe to the evaporator.
16. Install the hold-down brackets for the evaporator pipes.
17. Evacuate and recharge the air conditioning system.
18. Connect the negative battery cable.

Storm

1. Disconnect the negative battery cable.
2. Properly discharge the air conditioning system using recovery type equipment.
3. Disconnect and plug the pipes from the expansion valve.
4. Remove retaining clip and expansion valve from the evaporator. While in the engine compartment, remove the evaporator case retaining nut on the firewall.
5. Remove the glove compartment.
6. Remove the lower instrument panel reinforcement bracket.
7. Disconnect all electrical wiring and cables from the evaporator housing.
8. Remove the retaining nuts and then the evaporator housing.
9. Separate the housing halves and remove the evaporator core.

To install:

10. Install the evaporator core and assemble the housing halves.
11. Install the housing and retaining clips.
12. Connect all electrical wiring and cables to the evaporator housing.
13. Install the lower instrument panel reinforcement bracket.
14. Install the glove compartment.
15. Connect the pipes to the expansion valve. Install the evaporator case engine compartment nut.
16. Install expansion valve and retaining clip to the evaporator.
17. Evacuate and recharge the air conditioning system.
18. Connect the negative battery cable.

Refrigerant Lines

REMOVAL AND INSTALLATION

1. Disconnect the negative battery cable.
2. Properly discharge the air conditioning system.
3. Remove the radiator grille if required for front refrigerant lines.
4. Remove components as required for access. Loosen the connector at the compressor and attaching points. Use a backup wrench on pipes with flare nut fittings.
5. Remove the pipe retaining clips.
6. Installation is the reverse of removal. Install new replacement O-rings whenever a joint or fitting is disconnected. Lubricate with refrigerant oil during installation. Torque the 3/8 in. O.D. pipes to 11-18 ft. lbs. (15-25 Nm), 1/2 in. O.D. pipes to 15-22 ft. lbs. (20-30 Nm) and 5/8 in. O.D. pipes to 22-29 ft. lbs. (30-40 Nm).

Manual Control Head

REMOVAL AND INSTALLATION

Tracker

1. Disconnect the negative battery cable.
2. Pull the control knobs from the levers.
3. Remove the bezel from the control panel. Remove the control assembly lens and disconnect the bulb.

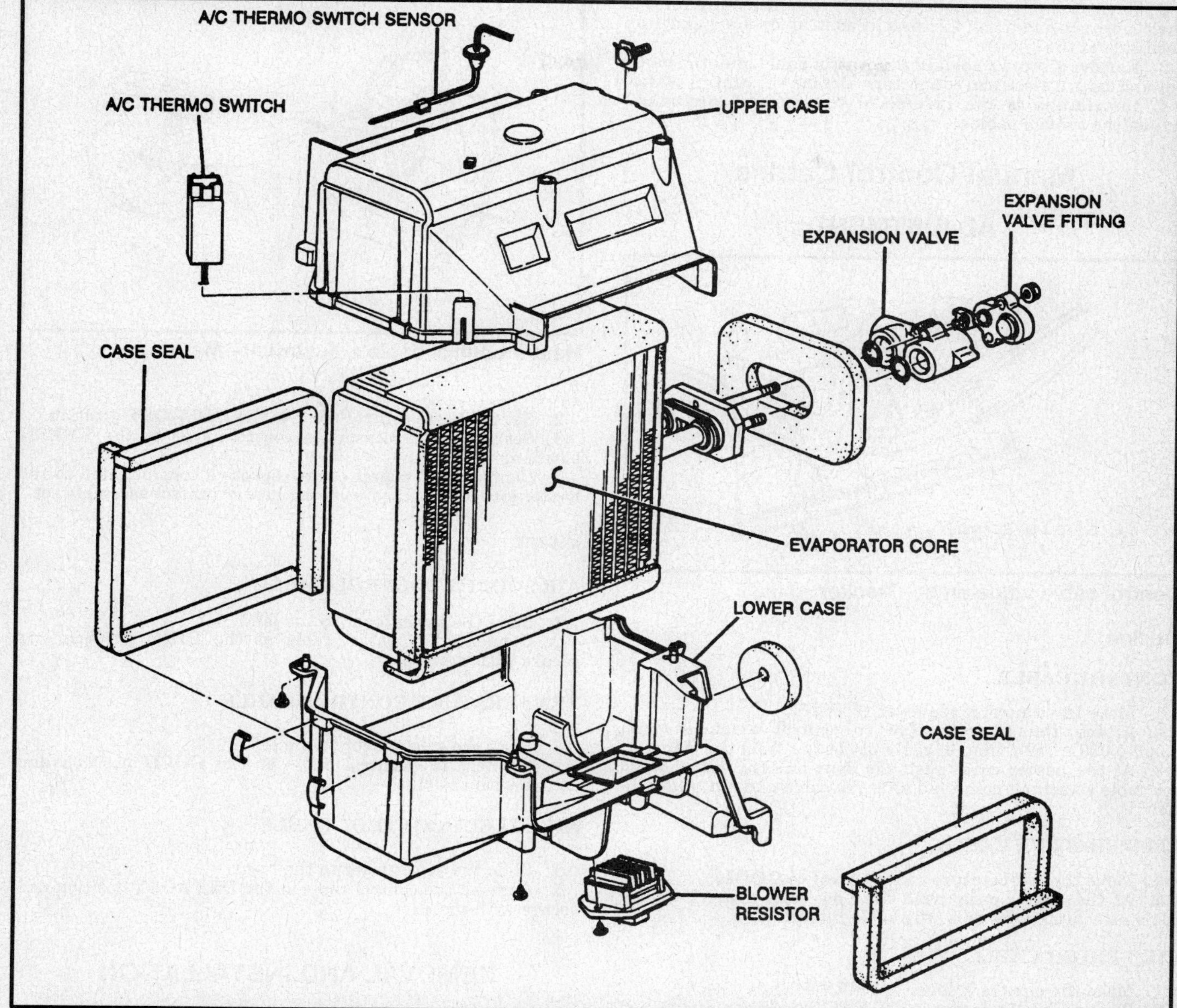

Evaporator Case disassembled–Storm shown; others similar

4. Remove the glove box. Disconnect the control cables at the blower and heater assembly.
5. Remove the control assembly fasteners.
6. Pull the control assembly out and disconnect the electrical connections.
7. Disconnect the control cables from the levers, if needed.
8. Remove the blower, air conditioning and heater switch.

To install:

9. Install the blower, air conditioning and heater switch.
10. Connect the control cables to the levers.
11. Connect the electrical connections and install the control assembly.
12. Install the control assembly fasteners.
13. Connect the control cables at the blower and heater assembly.
14. Connect the bulb and install the control assembly lens.
15. Install the control knobs. Adjust the control cables.
16. Connect the negative battery cable.

Metro

1. Disconnect the negative battery cable.
2. Remove the cigar lighter. Remove the center instrument panel trim.
3. Remove the A/C switch, if equipped. Pull off the control knobs.
4. Remove the radio.
5. Remove the panel bezel (2 screws). Remove 2 control panel mounting screws, pull the panel out, disconnect electrical connectors and cables.
6. Installation is the reverse of the removal procedure. Adjust the control cables.

Storm

1. Disconnect the negative battery cable.

2. Remove the lever knobs, remove the ashtray and remove the center console trim (4 screws in ashtray opening and 1 on each side of the bezel).
3. Remove 4 screws holding the control panel, pull the panel out and detach electrical connectors. Detach the control cables.
4. Installation is the reverse of the removal procedure. Adjust the control cables.

Manual Control Cables

ADJUSTMENT

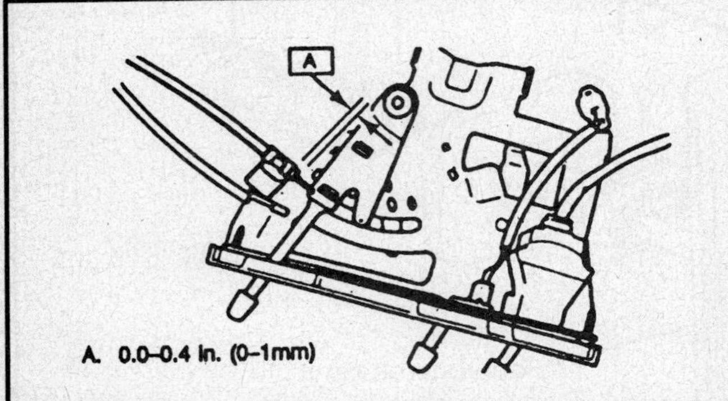

Control cable adjustment–Tracker

Tracker

CONTROL CABLE

1. Move the control mode lever to **VENT**.
2. Attach the control cable to control assembly with 0.000-0.039 in. (0-1 mm) of cable projecting from the clamp.
3. At the heater case, push the door linkage fully toward the cable attaching point and affix the cable and rod into position.

TEMPERATURE CABLE

1. Move the temperature control lever to **COOL**.
2. At the heater case, push the door fully away from the cable attaching point and affix cable into position.

CIRC-FRESH CABLE

1. Move the circ-fresh lever to **FRESH**.
2. Be sure the air door is in the FRESH position and attach the cable at the heater case.

Metro

1. After installation of the cables to the heater control assembly, set the temperature control lever to **HOT**.

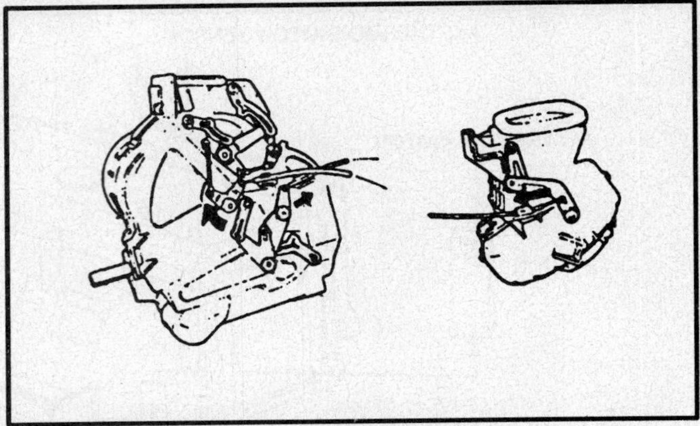

Heater control cable adjustment–Metro

2. Set the mode control lever to the **DEFROST** position.
3. Set the fresh/recirculate control lever to the **FRESH** position.
4. Connect and clamp each respective control cable to the heater and blower case with the heater control assembly set.

Storm

AIR SOURCE CONTROL CABLE

1. Slide the select lever to the left.
2. Connect the control cable at the **CIRC** position and secure with the clip.

TEMPERATURE CONTROL CABLE

1. Slide the select lever to the left.
2. Connect the control cable at the **COLD** position and secure with the clip.

AIR SELECT CONTROL CABLE

1. Slide the select lever to the right.
2. Connect the control cable at the **DEFROST** position and secure with the clip.

REMOVAL AND INSTALLATION

1. Remove the heater control panel, glove box or other components necessary to access cable attaching points.
2. Unlatch the cable from the retaining clip and slide the cable from the lever.
3. Route the cable through the vehicle.
4. Install the cable and adjust; do not overbend the cable.

SENSORS AND SWITCHES

Dual Pressure or Triple Switch

OPERATION

When the cycling refrigerant pressure drops due to leakage, a control switch stops further compressor rotation by turning off the compressor and condenser fan. The switch is located on top of the receiver/drier assembly, for 94-95 Prizm the switch is located along the right front inner fender. The switch opens when the pressure goes below approximately 28 psi (196 kPa) and above approximately 455 psi (3137 kPa).

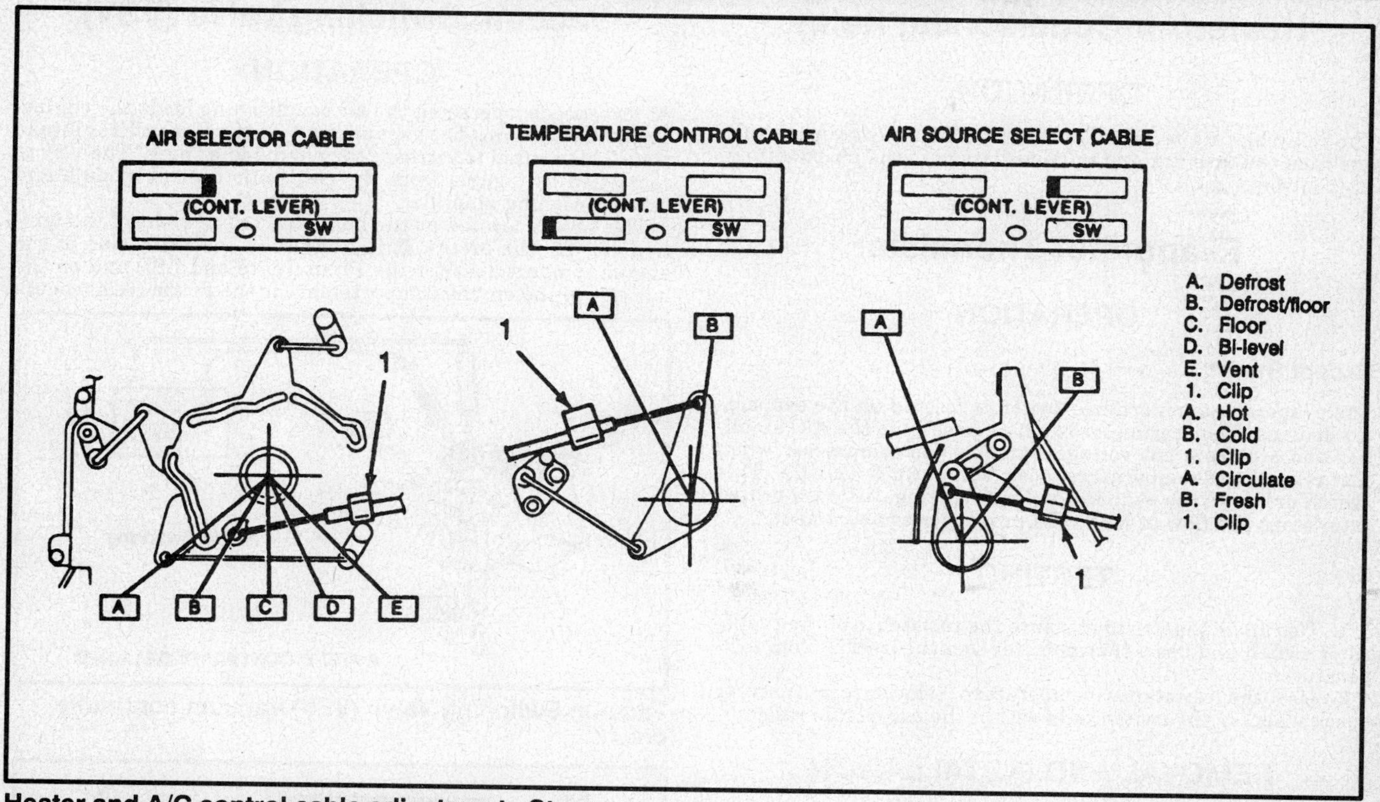

AIR SELECTOR CABLE
(CONT. LEVER)
SW

TEMPERATURE CONTROL CABLE
(CONT. LEVER)
SW

AIR SOURCE SELECT CABLE
(CONT. LEVER)
SW

A. Defrost
B. Defrost/floor
C. Floor
D. Bi-level
E. Vent
1. Clip
A. Hot
B. Cold
1. Clip
A. Circulate
B. Fresh
1. Clip

Heater and A/C control cable adjustment—Storm

TESTING

Storm

1. Back probe the triple switch connector with a test light from pin No. 3 (green/white) wire to ground.
2. If the lamp lights, repair the open in the green/white wire between the switch and the air conditioning thermo relay.
3. If the lamp does not light, back probe the switch connector from pin 4 (brown) wire to ground. If the lamp lights, replace the triple switch.

Prizm, Tracker and Metro

1. When the ignition key and air conditioning switch **ON**, disconnect the dual pressure switch connector and install a jumper wire between the 2 terminals.
2. If the compressor engages and the refrigerant pressures are normal, the switch is defective.
3. Also check for continuity at the switch while the system is in operation: no continuity below approximately 28 psi or above approximately 455 psi; continuity between these pressures.

REMOVAL AND INSTALLATION

1. Disconnect the negative battery cable. Remove components restricting access to the receiver/drier.
2. Disconnect the switch connector at the receiver/drier.
3. Properly discharge the air conditioning system.
4. Remove the switch from the receiver/drier, for Prizm unscrew CCW.
5. Installation is the reverse of removal. Use thread sealing tape before installing the dual pressure or triple switch.

Compressor Relay

OPERATION

The location of the relay is the right front corner of the engine compartment on the Tracker, on the left inner fender block 5 on Prizm, in the relay box behind the battery on Metro, and in the relay panel near the battery or on the right strut tower for Storm. The relay has a 4 terminal connector. The relay is used to direct voltage to the compressor clutch through the ground circuit.

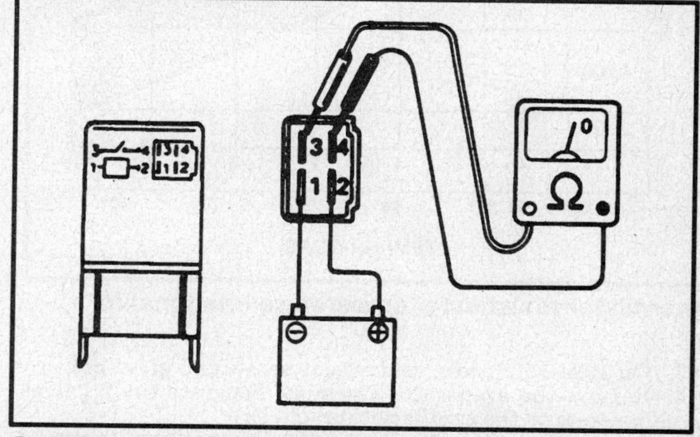

Condenser fan or compressor relay continuity check

Heater/Air Conditioning Relay

OPERATION

The relay has a 4 terminal connector. The relay receives voltage from the fuse box and applies voltage to the air conditioning controls.

Evaporator Thermistor

OPERATION

Except Storm

The evaporator temperature switch is located on the evaporator housing. The thermistor is wired directly to the A/C amplifier and creates a cut voltage signal to the compressor when the evaporator temperature goes below 34°F (1.1°C). This switch prevents the evaporator from freezing. A frozen evaporator stops the flow of air to the passenger compartment.

TESTING

1. Use an ohmmeter to measure the resistance of the evaporator switch and use a thermometer to measure the room temperature.
2. Use the resistance temperature relationship chart to check whether the switch falls within the acceptable range.

REMOVAL AND INSTALLATION

1. Disconnect the negative battery cable. Properly discharge the air conditioning system using recovery type equipment.
2. On 1994-95 models, remove evaporator inlet and outlet pipes at bulkhead by loosening pipe nuts and mounting nuts on engine side of bulkhead.

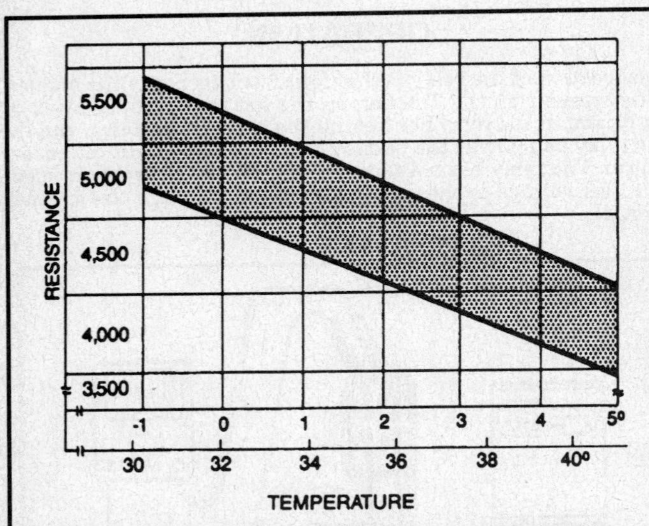

Thermistor resistance/temperature relationship

3. On 1994-95 models, remove one screw and glove box.
4. Remove the evaporator assembly. Separate the 2 halves to gain access to the capillary tube.
5. Remove the amplifier, expansion valve, and capillary tube from the evaporator.
6. Installation is the reverse of removal.

Vacuum Switching Valve (VSV)

OPERATION

At low speeds, operating the air conditioning loads the engine. To prevent stalling, the vacuum switching valve utilizes intake manifold vacuum to increase the engine idle speed. The VSV is controlled by signals from the electronic control module and air conditioning amplifier.

The VSV is located at the bulkhead to the right of the ignition coil for the Metro. It is located on the right side of the engine compartment for the Prizm (base and LSi) and on the left side of the engine compartment for the Prizm (GSi model).

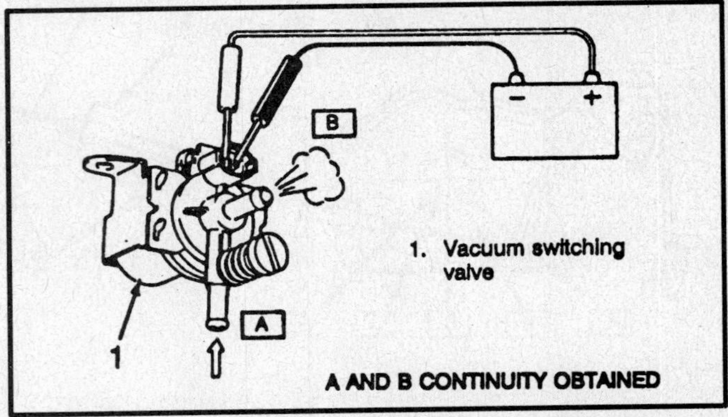

Vacuum Switching Valve (VSV) vacuum continuity check

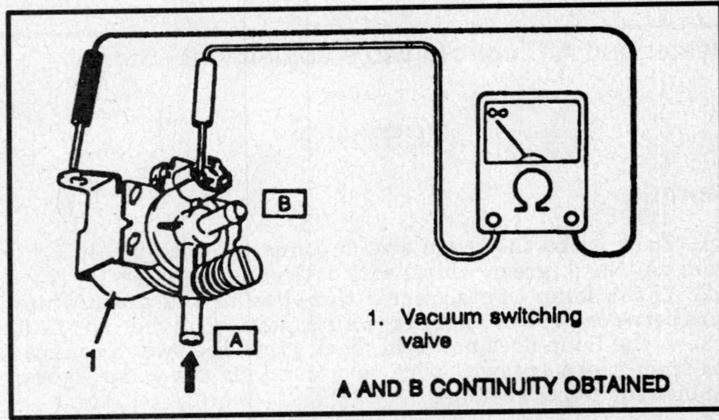

Vacuum Switching Valve (VSV) short circuit check

TESTING

Metro

1. Check for proper vacuum continuity using a 12 volt supply to the VSV terminals.
2. Check the VSV for a short circuit using an ohmmeter. No continuity should exist between each terminal and valve housing.
3. Check the valve for opens by measuring the resistance between the terminals; replace the valve, if any problems are found.

REMOVAL AND INSTALLATION

1. Disconnect the negative battery cable.
2. Remove the 2 retaining clamps and vacuum hose. Mark the vacuum hoses.
3. Disconnect the electrical connector and remove the valve from the mounting.
4. Installation is the reverse of removal.

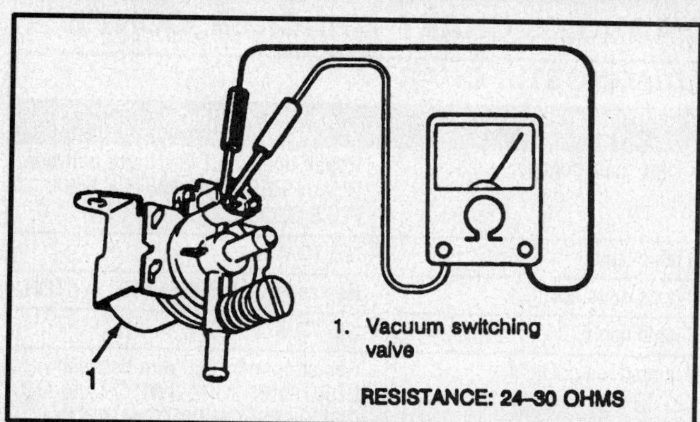

Vacuum Switching Valve (VSV) open circuit check

Air Conditioning Coolant Temperature Sensor

OPERATION

The coolant temperature sensor is located on the right side of the engine compartment behind the radiator for the Tracker.

The sensor is located on the right rear of the engine on the intake manifold. (1993)

The sensor monitors engine temperature and signals the ECM to turn the compressor off is the temperature rises above normal.

Air Conditioning Amplifier/Controller

OPERATION

The amplifier/controller is located behind the right instrument panel above the evaporator case on the Prizm, Metro and Tracker. This unit is solid state and is performs many functions such as, controlling the vacuum switching valve, compressor clutch and condenser cooling fan motor based on signals received from various sensors and relays.

Revolution Detection Sensor

OPERATION

The sensor is located on the rear of the compressor for the Prizm (GSi). The sensor monitors compressor rpm. If excessive, the sensor sends a signal to the ECM to turn off the compressor.

SYSTEM DIAGNOSIS AND WIRING SCHEMATICS

AIR CONDITIONING SYSTEM ELECTRICAL DIAGNOSIS CHART-TRACKER

AIR CONDITIONING: COMPRESSOR CONTROLS DIAGNOSTIC CHART A

	TEST	RESULT	ACTION
A1.	Start engine, push A/C SWITCH "ON," move BLOWER SPEED SELECTOR SWITCH to any position except "OFF."	AC COMPRESSOR CLUTCH engages and BLOWER MOTOR operates at desired speed.	All systems diagnosed in this cell are functioning normally.
		AC COMPRESSOR CLUTCH engages but BLOWER MOTOR does not operate.	Refer to Cell 60 for BLOWER MOTOR and Heater System Diagnosis.
		BLOWER MOTOR operates but A/C COMPRESSOR CLUTCH does not engage.	Turn IGNITION SWITCH to "LOCK," then turn on "ON," and GO TO **A2**.
		(1994-95) AC COMPRESSOR CLUTCH remains engaged with A/C OFF.	GO TO **A3**.
A2.	Backprobe A/C COMPRESSOR CLUTCH connector with a test lamp from connector cavity to chassis ground.	Test lamp lights.	Replace A/C COMPRESSOR CLUTCH.
		Test lamp does not light.	GO TO **A3**.
A3.	Backprobe A/C COMPRESSOR CLUTCH RELAY connector with a test lamp from connector cavity 4 to chassis ground.	Test lamp lights.	Repair open in BLK/WHT wire between A/C COMPRESSOR CLUTCH RELAY and A/C COMPRESSOR CLUTCH.
		Test lamp does not light.	GO TO **A4**.
A4.	Backprobe A/C COMPRESSOR CLUTCH RELAY connector with a test lamp from connector cavity 2 to chassis ground.	Test lamp does not light.	Repair open in RED wire between A/C COMPRESSOR CLUTCH RELAY and A/C FUSE HOLDER.
		Test lamp lights.	GO TO **A5**.

AIR CONDITIONING SYSTEM ELECTRICAL DIAGNOSIS CHART—TRACKER, CONT'D

AIR CONDITIONING: COMPRESSOR CONTROLS DIAGNOSTIC CHART A

	TEST	RESULT	ACTION
A5.	Backprobe DUAL PRESSURE SWITCH connector with a test lamp from cavity 1 to chassis ground.	Test lamp does not light.	Repair open in LT GRN wire between DUAL PRESSURE SWITCH and FUSE BLOCK.
		Test lamp lights.	GO TO **A6**.
A6.	Backprobe DUAL PRESSURE SWITCH connector with a test lamp from cavity 2 to chassis ground.	Test lamp does not light.	Replace DUAL PRESSURE SWITCH.
		Test lamp lights.	GO TO **A7**.
A7.	Backprobe A/C COMPRESSOR CLUTCH RELAY connector with a test lamp from terminal 1 to chassis ground.	Test lamp does not light.	Repair open in YEL wire between DUAL PRESSURE SWITCH and A/C COMPRESSOR CLUTCH RELAY.
		Test lamp lights.	GO TO **A8**.
A8.	Disconnect A/C COMPRESSOR CLUTCH RELAY connector. Connect a test lamp from connector cavity 3 to Battery voltage.	Test lamp lights.	Replace A/C COMPRESSOR CLUTCH RELAY.
		Test lamp does not light.	GO TO **A9**.
A9.	Connect a digital multimeter from A/C COMPRESSOR CLUTCH RELAY connector cavity 3 to A/C AMPLIFIER connector cavity 7. Measure resistance.	More than 0.5 ohms.	Repair open in PNK wire.
		Less than 0.5 ohms.	GO TO **A10**.
A10.	Disconnect A/C AMPLIFIER connector. Connect a digital multimeter from connector cavity 9 to chassis ground. Measure resistance.	More than 3.0 ohms.	Repair BLK wire between G201 and A/C AMPLIFIER.
		Less than 3.0 ohms.	GO TO **A11**.
A11.	Backprobe BLOWER SPEED SELECTOR SWITCH connector with a test lamp from cavity 1 to chassis ground.	Test lamp does not light.	Repair open in LT GRN wire between BLOWER SPEED SELECTOR SWITCH and S209.
		Test lamp lights.	GO TO **A12**.
A12.	Backprobe BLOWER SPEED SELECTOR SWITCH connector with a test lamp from cavity 4 to chassis ground.	Test lamp does not light.	Replace BLOWER SPEED SELECTOR SWITCH.
		Test lamp lights.	GO TO **A13**.
A13.	Backprobe A/C SWITCH connector with a test lamp from cavity 1 to chassis ground.	Test lamp does not light.	Repair open in A/C SWITCH FUSE or PNK/BLK wire between BLOWER SPEED SELECTOR SWITCH and A/C SWITCH.
		Test lamp lights.	GO TO **A14**.
A14.	Backprobe A/C SWITCH connector with a test lamp from cavity 2 to chassis ground.	Test lamp does not light.	Replace A/C SWITCH.
		Test lamp lights.	GO TO **A15**.
A15.	With A/C AMPLIFIER connector disconnected, connect a test lamp from connector cavity 11 to chassis ground.	Test lamp does not light.	Repair open in BLU wire between A/C AMPLIFIER and A/C SWITCH.
		Test lamp lights.	GO TO **A16**.
A16.	Connect a digital multimeter from A/C AMPLIFIER connector cavity 12 to chassis ground. Measure resistance.	Less than 5.0 ohms.	GO TO **A17**.
		More than 5.0 ohms.	GO TO **A18**.
A17.	Backprobe COOLANT HIGH TEMPERATURE SWITCH connector with a digital multimeter from connector cavity to chassis ground. Measure resistance.	Less than 5.0 ohms.	Replace COOLANT HIGH TEMPERATURE SWITCH.
		More than 5.0 ohms.	Repair short to ground in YEL/BLU wire between COOLANT HIGH TEMPERATURE SENSOR and A/C AMPLIFIER.
A18.	Turn IGNITION SWITCH to "LOCK." Connect a test lamp from A/C AMPLIFIER connector cavity 2 to chassis ground.	Test lamp does not light.	GO TO **A23**.
		Test lamp lights.	GO TO **A19** with Automatic Transmission. GO TO **A21** with Manual Transmission.

AIR CONDITIONING SYSTEM ELECTRICAL DIAGNOSIS CHART—TRACKER, CONT'D

AIR CONDITIONING: COMPRESSOR CONTROLS DIAGNOSTIC CHART A

	TEST	RESULT	ACTION
A19.	Disconnect TRANSMISSION POSITION SWITCH connector. Connect a test lamp from A/C AMPLIFIER connector cavity 2 to chassis ground.	Test lamp lights.	Repair short to voltage in BLK/RED wire between TRANSMISSION POSITION SWITCH and A/C AMPLIFIER.
		Test lamp does not light.	GO TO **A20**.
A20.	Disconnect IGNITION SWITCH connector. Connect a test lamp from TRANSMISSION POSITION SWITCH connector C1 cavity 1 to chassis ground.	Test lamp lights.	Repair short to voltage in BLK/YEL wire between TRANSMISSION POSITION SWITCH and IGNITION SWITCH.
		Test lamp does not light.	Replace IGNITION SWITCH.
A21.	Disconnect CLUTCH START SWITCH. Connect a test lamp from A/C AMPLIFIER connector cavity 2 to chassis ground.	Test lamp lights.	Repair short to voltage in BLK/RED wire between CLUTCH START SWITCH and A/C AMPLIFIER.
		Test lamp does not light.	GO TO **A22**.
A22.	Disconnect IGNITION SWITCH connector. Connect a test lamp from CLUTCH START SWITCH connector BLK/YEL wire to chassis ground.	Test lamp lights.	Repair short to voltage in BLK/YEL wire between CLUTCH START SWITCH and IGNITION SWITCH.
		Test lamp does not light.	Replace IGNITION SWITCH.
A23.	With A/C AMPLIFIER connector disconnected, connect a digital multimeter from connector cavity 10 to connector cavity 4. Measure resistance.	Less than 2000 ohms.	Replace A/C AMPLIFIER.
		More than 2000 ohms.	GO TO **A24**.
A24.	Disconnect EVAPORATOR THERMISTOR connector. Connect a digital multimeter from EVAPORATOR THERMISTOR connector cavity 2 to A/C AMPLIFIER connector cavity 10. Measure resistance.	More than 5.0 ohms.	Repair open in YEL/GRN wire between A/C AMPLIFIER and EVAPORATOR THERMISTOR.
		Less than 5.0 ohms.	
A25.	Connect a digital multimeter from A/C AMPLIFIER connector cavity 4 to EVAPORATOR THERMISTOR connector cavity 1. Measure resistance. (1994-95)	More than 5.0 ohms.	Repair open in WHT/BLU wire.
		Less than 5.0 ohms.	Replace EVAPORATOR THERMISTOR.
A26.	Disconnect A/C AMPLIFIER connector.	A/C COMPRESSOR CLUTCH is still engaged.	Check for a short to ground in PNK wire between A/C COMPRESSOR CLUTCH RELAY and A/C AMPLIFIER. Check for a short to voltage in BLK/WHT wire between A/C COMPRESSOR CLUTCH RELAY and A/C COMPRESSOR CLUTCH. If both are OK, replace A/C COMPRESSOR CLUTCH RELAY.
		A/C COMPRESSOR CLUTCH is disengaged.	GO TO **A27**.
A27.	Make sure A/C SWITCH is OFF. Connect a test lamp from A/C AMPLIFIER connector cavity 11 to chassis ground.	Test lamp does not light.	Replace A/C AMPLIFIER.
		Test lamp lights.	Check for a short to voltage in BLU wire between A/C SWITCH and A/C AMPLIFIER. If OK, replace A/C SWITCH.

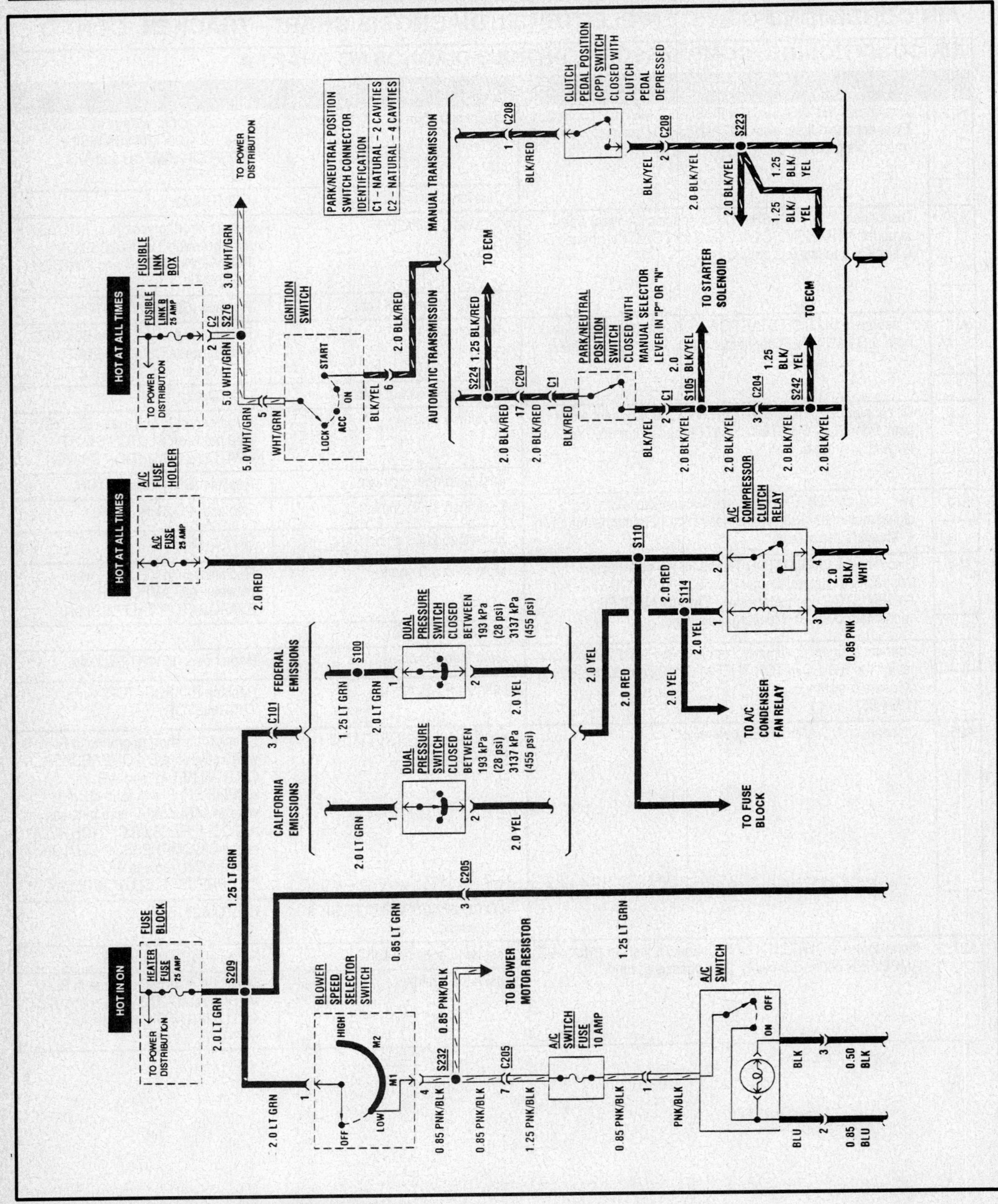

Air conditioning wiring schematic—Tracker

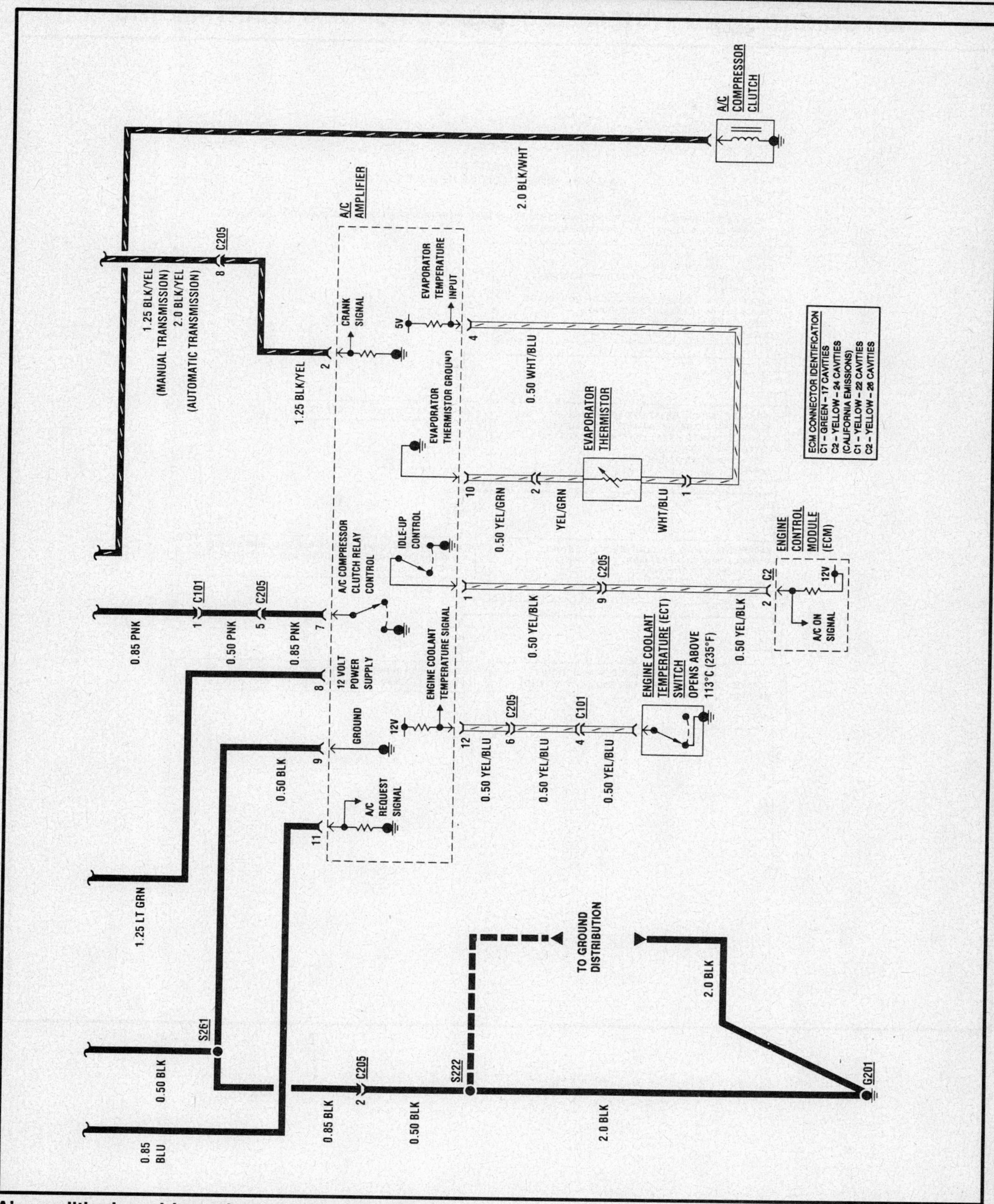

Air conditioning wiring schematic–Tracker, Cont'd

AIR CONDITIONING SYSTEM ELECTRICAL DIAGNOSIS CHART–METRO

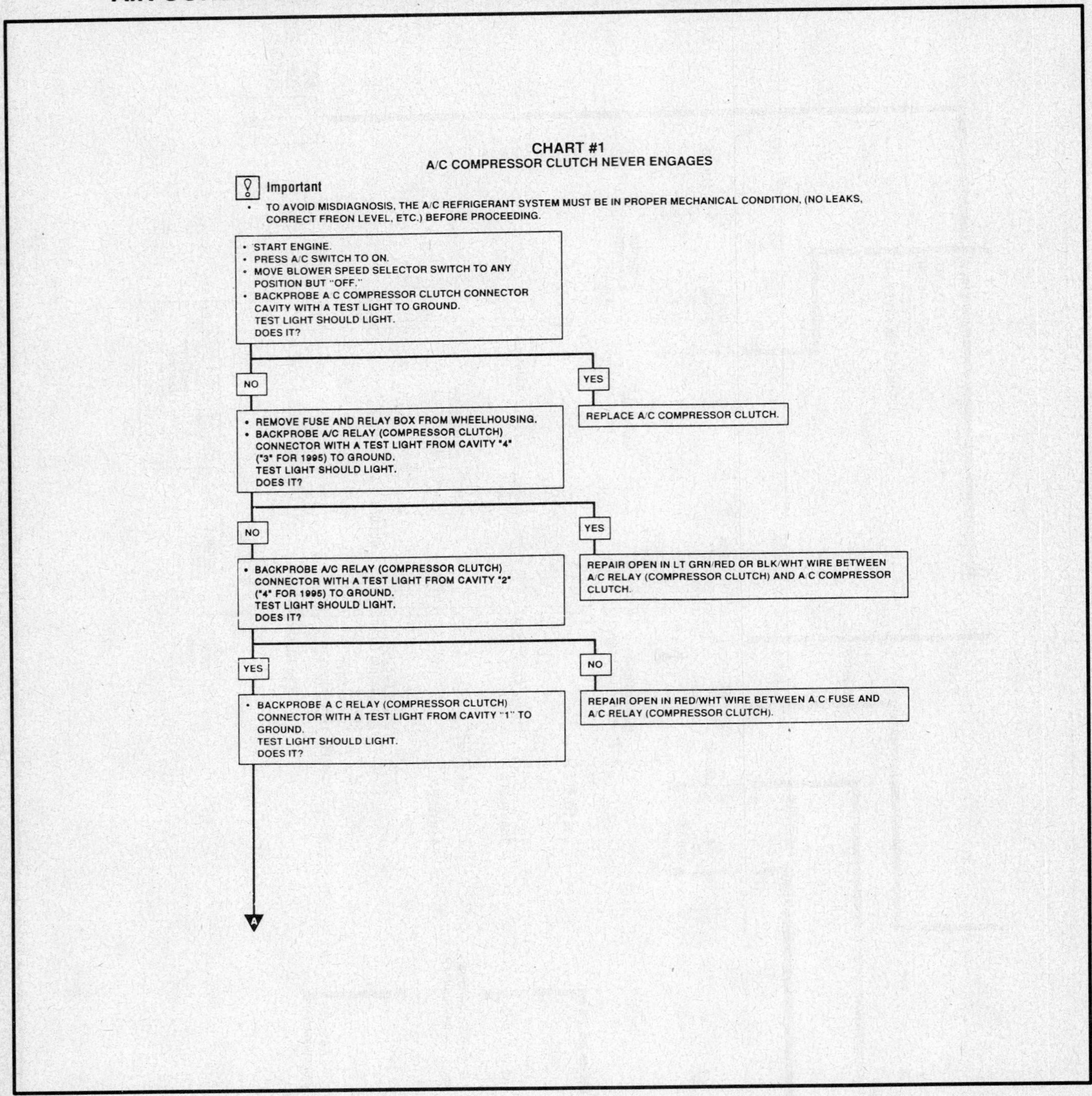

CHART #1
A/C COMPRESSOR CLUTCH NEVER ENGAGES
Important
• TO AVOID MISDIAGNOSIS, THE A/C REFRIGERANT SYSTEM MUST BE IN PROPER MECHANICAL CONDITION, (NO LEAKS, CORRECT FREON LEVEL, ETC.) BEFORE PROCEEDING.
• START ENGINE.
• PRESS A/C SWITCH TO ON.
• MOVE BLOWER SPEED SELECTOR SWITCH TO ANY POSITION BUT "OFF."
• BACKPROBE A C COMPRESSOR CLUTCH CONNECTOR CAVITY WITH A TEST LIGHT TO GROUND. TEST LIGHT SHOULD LIGHT. DOES IT?
NO
YES
REPLACE A/C COMPRESSOR CLUTCH.
• REMOVE FUSE AND RELAY BOX FROM WHEELHOUSING.
• BACKPROBE A/C RELAY (COMPRESSOR CLUTCH) CONNECTOR WITH A TEST LIGHT FROM CAVITY "4" ("3" FOR 1995) TO GROUND. TEST LIGHT SHOULD LIGHT. DOES IT?
NO
YES
REPAIR OPEN IN LT GRN/RED OR BLK/WHT WIRE BETWEEN A/C RELAY (COMPRESSOR CLUTCH) AND A C COMPRESSOR CLUTCH.
• BACKPROBE A/C RELAY (COMPRESSOR CLUTCH) CONNECTOR WITH A TEST LIGHT FROM CAVITY "2" ("4" FOR 1995) TO GROUND. TEST LIGHT SHOULD LIGHT. DOES IT?
YES
NO
REPAIR OPEN IN RED/WHT WIRE BETWEEN A C FUSE AND A/C RELAY (COMPRESSOR CLUTCH).
• BACKPROBE A C RELAY (COMPRESSOR CLUTCH) CONNECTOR WITH A TEST LIGHT FROM CAVITY "1" TO GROUND. TEST LIGHT SHOULD LIGHT. DOES IT?
A

AIR CONDITIONING SYSTEM ELECTRICAL DIAGNOSIS CHART–METRO, CONT'D

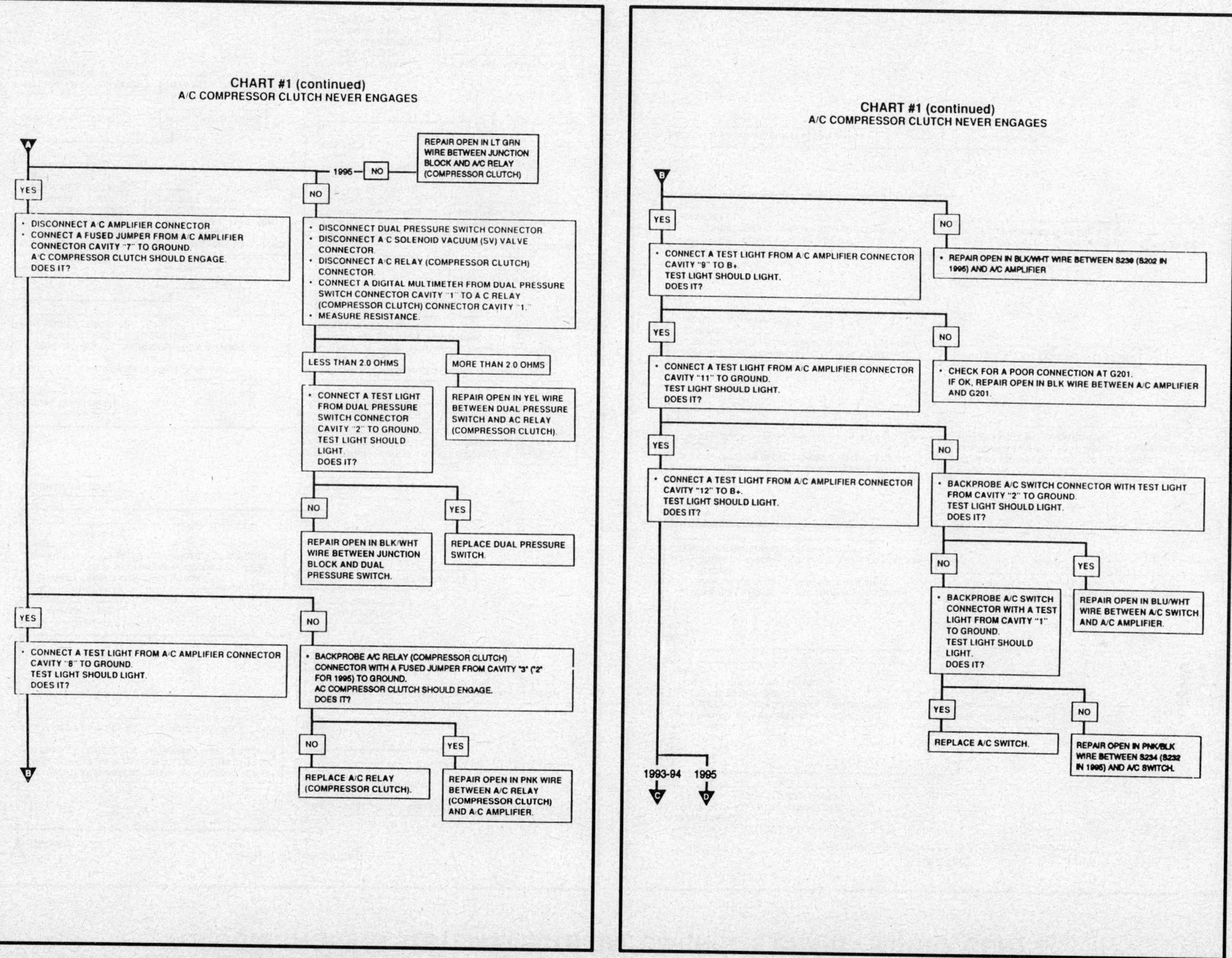
CHART #1 (continued)
A/C COMPRESSOR CLUTCH NEVER ENGAGES
A
YES
• DISCONNECT A/C AMPLIFIER CONNECTOR
• CONNECT A FUSED JUMPER FROM A/C AMPLIFIER CONNECTOR CAVITY "7" TO GROUND. A/C COMPRESSOR CLUTCH SHOULD ENGAGE. DOES IT?
NO
1995
NO
REPAIR OPEN IN LT GRN WIRE BETWEEN JUNCTION BLOCK AND A/C RELAY (COMPRESSOR CLUTCH)
• DISCONNECT DUAL PRESSURE SWITCH CONNECTOR
• DISCONNECT A/C SOLENOID VACUUM (SV) VALVE CONNECTOR
• DISCONNECT A/C RELAY (COMPRESSOR CLUTCH) CONNECTOR.
• CONNECT A DIGITAL MULTIMETER FROM DUAL PRESSURE SWITCH CONNECTOR CAVITY "1" TO A/C RELAY (COMPRESSOR CLUTCH) CONNECTOR CAVITY "1."
• MEASURE RESISTANCE.
LESS THAN 2.0 OHMS
MORE THAN 2.0 OHMS
• CONNECT A TEST LIGHT FROM DUAL PRESSURE SWITCH CONNECTOR CAVITY "2" TO GROUND. TEST LIGHT SHOULD LIGHT. DOES IT?
REPAIR OPEN IN YEL WIRE BETWEEN DUAL PRESSURE SWITCH AND AC RELAY (COMPRESSOR CLUTCH).
NO
YES
REPAIR OPEN IN BLK/WHT WIRE BETWEEN JUNCTION BLOCK AND DUAL PRESSURE SWITCH.
REPLACE DUAL PRESSURE SWITCH.
YES
• CONNECT A TEST LIGHT FROM A/C AMPLIFIER CONNECTOR CAVITY "8" TO GROUND. TEST LIGHT SHOULD LIGHT. DOES IT?
NO
• BACKPROBE A/C RELAY (COMPRESSOR CLUTCH) CONNECTOR WITH A FUSED JUMPER FROM CAVITY "3" ("2" FOR 1995) TO GROUND. AC COMPRESSOR CLUTCH SHOULD ENGAGE. DOES IT?
NO
YES
REPLACE A/C RELAY (COMPRESSOR CLUTCH).
REPAIR OPEN IN PNK WIRE BETWEEN A/C RELAY (COMPRESSOR CLUTCH) AND A/C AMPLIFIER.
B
CHART #1 (continued)
A/C COMPRESSOR CLUTCH NEVER ENGAGES
B
YES
• CONNECT A TEST LIGHT FROM A/C AMPLIFIER CONNECTOR CAVITY "9" TO B+. TEST LIGHT SHOULD LIGHT. DOES IT?
NO
• REPAIR OPEN IN BLK/WHT WIRE BETWEEN S230 (S202 IN 1995) AND A/C AMPLIFIER
YES
• CONNECT A TEST LIGHT FROM A/C AMPLIFIER CONNECTOR CAVITY "11" TO GROUND. TEST LIGHT SHOULD LIGHT. DOES IT?
NO
• CHECK FOR A POOR CONNECTION AT G201. IF OK, REPAIR OPEN IN BLK WIRE BETWEEN A/C AMPLIFIER AND G201.
YES
• CONNECT A TEST LIGHT FROM A/C AMPLIFIER CONNECTOR CAVITY "12" TO B+. TEST LIGHT SHOULD LIGHT. DOES IT?
NO
• BACKPROBE A/C SWITCH CONNECTOR WITH TEST LIGHT FROM CAVITY "2" TO GROUND. TEST LIGHT SHOULD LIGHT. DOES IT?
NO
YES
• BACKPROBE A/C SWITCH CONNECTOR WITH A TEST LIGHT FROM CAVITY "1" TO GROUND. TEST LIGHT SHOULD LIGHT. DOES IT?
REPAIR OPEN IN BLU/WHT WIRE BETWEEN A/C SWITCH AND A/C AMPLIFIER.
YES
NO
REPLACE A/C SWITCH.
REPAIR OPEN IN PNK/BLK WIRE BETWEEN S234 (S232 IN 1995) AND A/C SWITCH.
1993-94
1995
C
D

AIR CONDITIONING SYSTEM ELECTRICAL DIAGNOSIS CHART–METRO, CONT'D

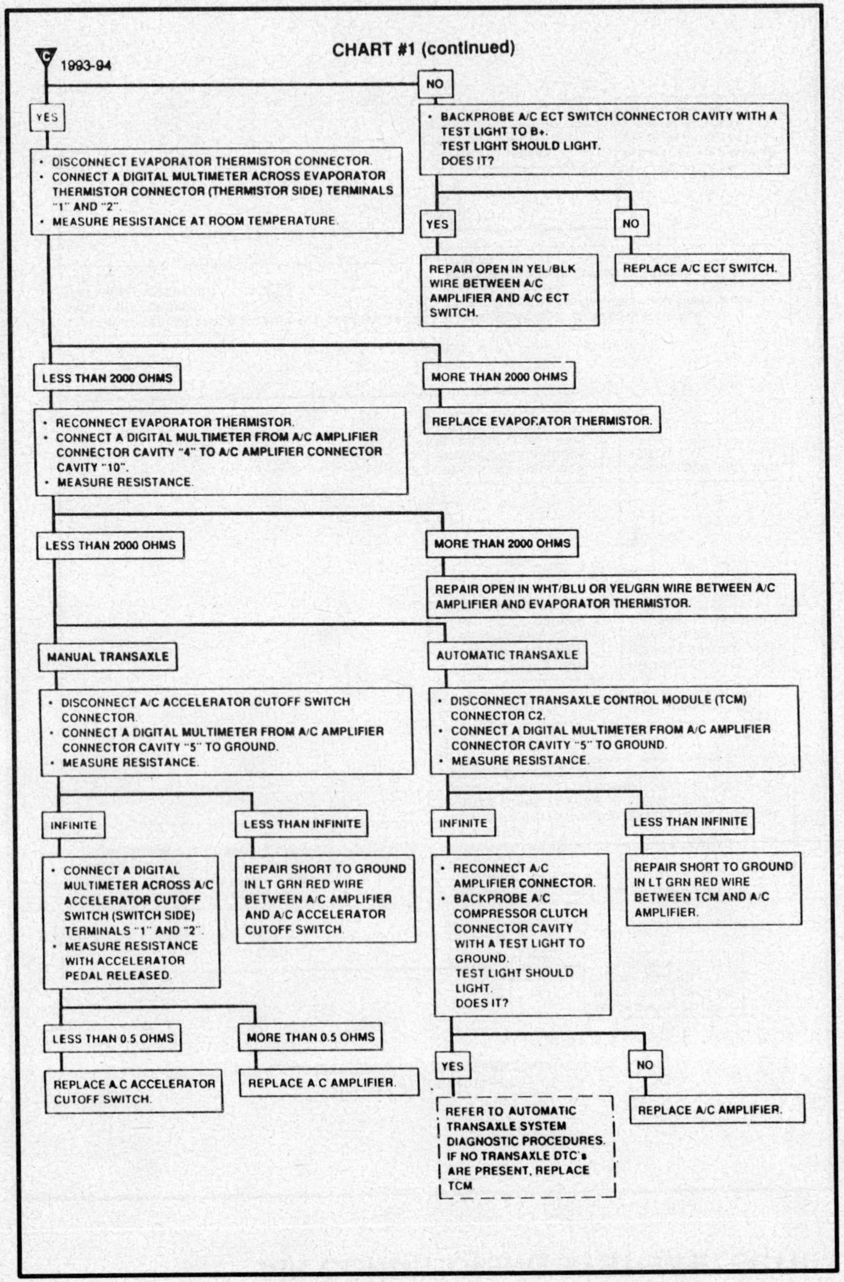

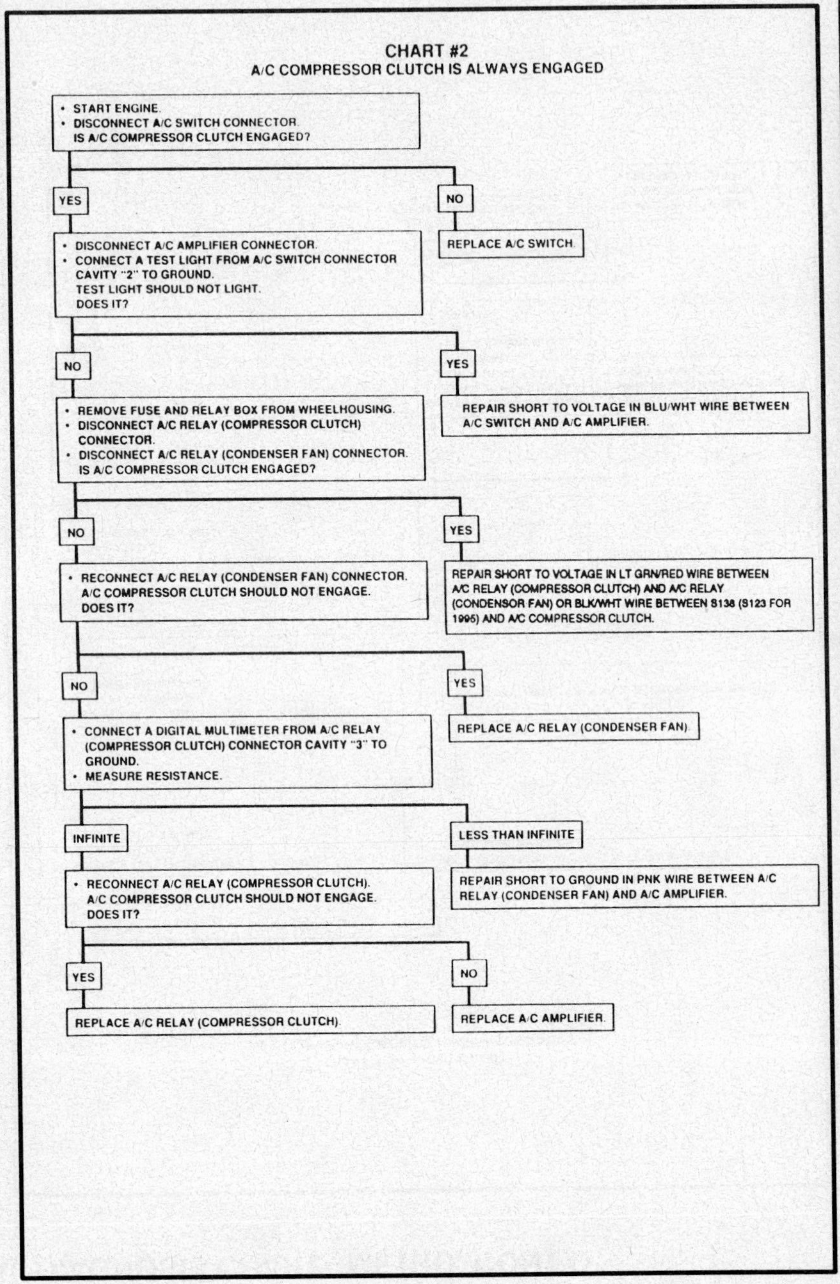

CHART #1 (continued)

C 1993-94

YES

- DISCONNECT EVAPORATOR THERMISTOR CONNECTOR.
- CONNECT A DIGITAL MULTIMETER ACROSS EVAPORATOR THERMISTOR CONNECTOR (THERMISTOR SIDE) TERMINALS "1" AND "2".
- MEASURE RESISTANCE AT ROOM TEMPERATURE.

NO

- BACKPROBE A/C ECT SWITCH CONNECTOR CAVITY WITH A TEST LIGHT TO B+. TEST LIGHT SHOULD LIGHT. DOES IT?

YES

REPAIR OPEN IN YEL/BLK WIRE BETWEEN A/C AMPLIFIER AND A/C ECT SWITCH.

NO

REPLACE A/C ECT SWITCH.

LESS THAN 2000 OHMS

- RECONNECT EVAPORATOR THERMISTOR.
- CONNECT A DIGITAL MULTIMETER FROM A/C AMPLIFIER CONNECTOR CAVITY "4" TO A/C AMPLIFIER CONNECTOR CAVITY "10".
- MEASURE RESISTANCE.

MORE THAN 2000 OHMS

REPLACE EVAPORATOR THERMISTOR.

LESS THAN 2000 OHMS

MORE THAN 2000 OHMS

REPAIR OPEN IN WHT/BLU OR YEL/GRN WIRE BETWEEN A/C AMPLIFIER AND EVAPORATOR THERMISTOR.

MANUAL TRANSAXLE

- DISCONNECT A/C ACCELERATOR CUTOFF SWITCH CONNECTOR.
- CONNECT A DIGITAL MULTIMETER FROM A/C AMPLIFIER CONNECTOR CAVITY "5" TO GROUND.
- MEASURE RESISTANCE.

INFINITE

- CONNECT A DIGITAL MULTIMETER ACROSS A/C ACCELERATOR CUTOFF SWITCH (SWITCH SIDE) TERMINALS "1" AND "2".
- MEASURE RESISTANCE WITH ACCELERATOR PEDAL RELEASED.

LESS THAN 0.5 OHMS

REPLACE A/C ACCELERATOR CUTOFF SWITCH.

MORE THAN 0.5 OHMS

REPLACE A/C AMPLIFIER.

LESS THAN INFINITE

REPAIR SHORT TO GROUND IN LT GRN RED WIRE BETWEEN A/C AMPLIFIER AND A/C ACCELERATOR CUTOFF SWITCH.

AUTOMATIC TRANSAXLE

- DISCONNECT TRANSAXLE CONTROL MODULE (TCM) CONNECTOR C2.
- CONNECT A DIGITAL MULTIMETER FROM A/C AMPLIFIER CONNECTOR CAVITY "5" TO GROUND.
- MEASURE RESISTANCE.

INFINITE

- RECONNECT A/C AMPLIFIER CONNECTOR.
- BACKPROBE A/C COMPRESSOR CLUTCH CONNECTOR CAVITY WITH A TEST LIGHT TO GROUND. TEST LIGHT SHOULD LIGHT. DOES IT?

YES

REFER TO AUTOMATIC TRANSAXLE SYSTEM DIAGNOSTIC PROCEDURES. IF NO TRANSAXLE DTC's ARE PRESENT, REPLACE TCM.

NO

REPLACE A/C AMPLIFIER.

LESS THAN INFINITE

REPAIR SHORT TO GROUND IN LT GRN RED WIRE BETWEEN TCM AND A/C AMPLIFIER.

CHART #2

A/C COMPRESSOR CLUTCH IS ALWAYS ENGAGED

- START ENGINE.
- DISCONNECT A/C SWITCH CONNECTOR. IS A/C COMPRESSOR CLUTCH ENGAGED?

YES

- DISCONNECT A/C AMPLIFIER CONNECTOR.
- CONNECT A TEST LIGHT FROM A/C SWITCH CONNECTOR CAVITY "2" TO GROUND. TEST LIGHT SHOULD NOT LIGHT. DOES IT?

NO

REPLACE A/C SWITCH.

NO

- REMOVE FUSE AND RELAY BOX FROM WHEELHOUSING.
- DISCONNECT A/C RELAY (COMPRESSOR CLUTCH) CONNECTOR.
- DISCONNECT A/C RELAY (CONDENSER FAN) CONNECTOR. IS A/C COMPRESSOR CLUTCH ENGAGED?

YES

REPAIR SHORT TO VOLTAGE IN BLU/WHT WIRE BETWEEN A/C SWITCH AND A/C AMPLIFIER.

NO

- RECONNECT A/C RELAY (CONDENSER FAN) CONNECTOR. A/C COMPRESSOR CLUTCH SHOULD NOT ENGAGE. DOES IT?

YES

REPAIR SHORT TO VOLTAGE IN LT GRN/RED WIRE BETWEEN A/C RELAY (COMPRESSOR CLUTCH) AND A/C RELAY (CONDENSOR FAN) OR BLK/WHT WIRE BETWEEN S138 (S123 FOR 1995) AND A/C COMPRESSOR CLUTCH.

NO

- CONNECT A DIGITAL MULTIMETER FROM A/C RELAY (COMPRESSOR CLUTCH) CONNECTOR CAVITY "3" TO GROUND.
- MEASURE RESISTANCE.

YES

REPLACE A/C RELAY (CONDENSER FAN).

INFINITE

- RECONNECT A/C RELAY (COMPRESSOR CLUTCH). A/C COMPRESSOR CLUTCH SHOULD NOT ENGAGE. DOES IT?

YES

REPLACE A/C RELAY (COMPRESSOR CLUTCH).

NO

REPLACE A/C AMPLIFIER.

LESS THAN INFINITE

REPAIR SHORT TO GROUND IN PNK WIRE BETWEEN A/C RELAY (CONDENSER FAN) AND A/C AMPLIFIER.

AIR CONDITIONING SYSTEM ELECTRICAL DIAGNOSIS CHART—METRO, CONT'D
CHART #1 (continued)
A/C COMPRESSOR CLUTCH NEVER ENGAGES

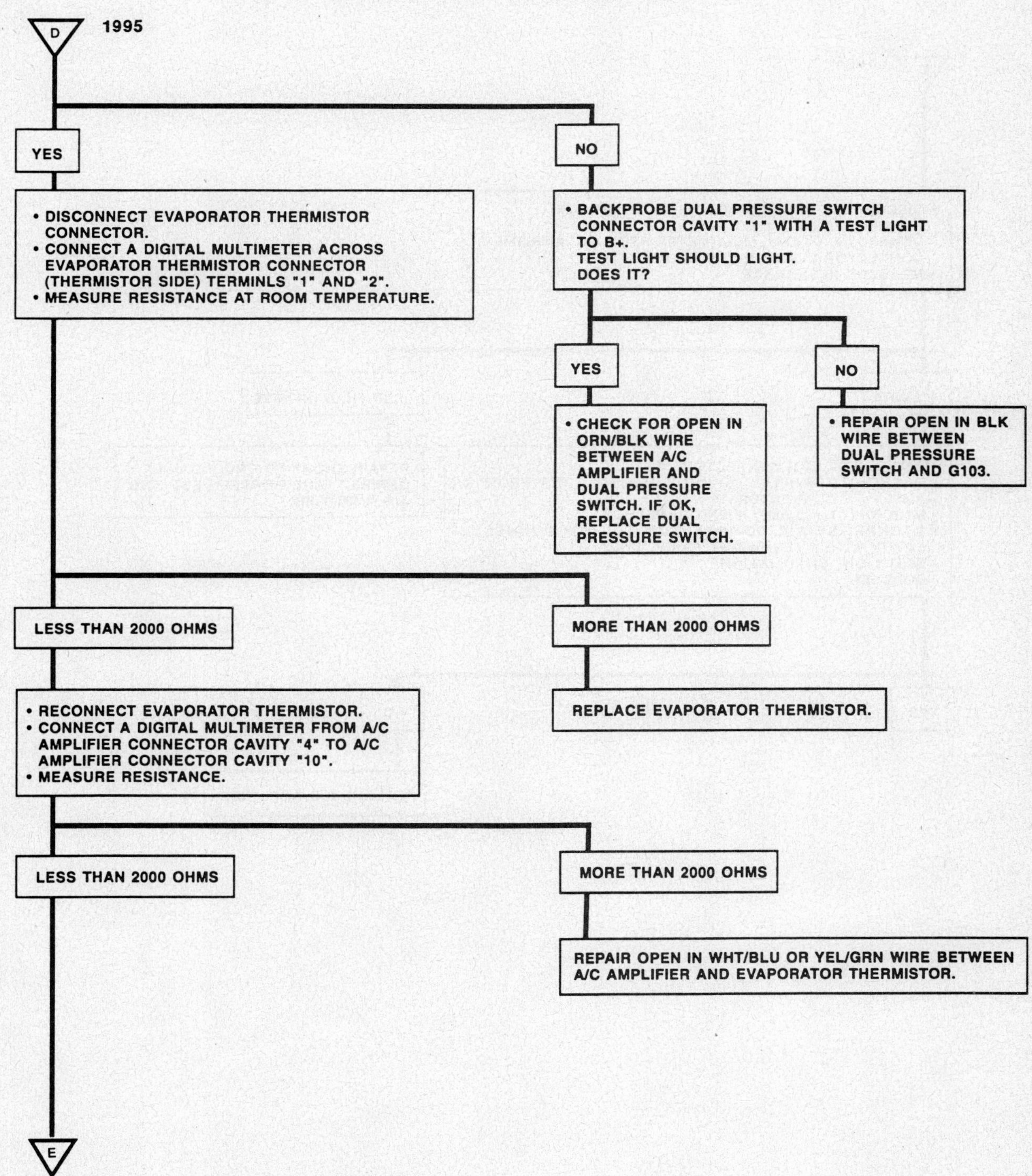
D
1995
YES
NO
• DISCONNECT EVAPORATOR THERMISTOR CONNECTOR.
• CONNECT A DIGITAL MULTIMETER ACROSS EVAPORATOR THERMISTOR CONNECTOR (THERMISTOR SIDE) TERMINLS "1" AND "2".
• MEASURE RESISTANCE AT ROOM TEMPERATURE.
• BACKPROBE DUAL PRESSURE SWITCH CONNECTOR CAVITY "1" WITH A TEST LIGHT TO B+.
TEST LIGHT SHOULD LIGHT.
DOES IT?
YES
NO
• CHECK FOR OPEN IN ORN/BLK WIRE BETWEEN A/C AMPLIFIER AND DUAL PRESSURE SWITCH. IF OK, REPLACE DUAL PRESSURE SWITCH.
• REPAIR OPEN IN BLK WIRE BETWEEN DUAL PRESSURE SWITCH AND G103.
LESS THAN 2000 OHMS
MORE THAN 2000 OHMS
• RECONNECT EVAPORATOR THERMISTOR.
• CONNECT A DIGITAL MULTIMETER FROM A/C AMPLIFIER CONNECTOR CAVITY "4" TO A/C AMPLIFIER CONNECTOR CAVITY "10".
• MEASURE RESISTANCE.
REPLACE EVAPORATOR THERMISTOR.
LESS THAN 2000 OHMS
MORE THAN 2000 OHMS
REPAIR OPEN IN WHT/BLU OR YEL/GRN WIRE BETWEEN A/C AMPLIFIER AND EVAPORATOR THERMISTOR.
E

AIR CONDITIONING SYSTEM ELECTRICAL DIAGNOSIS CHART–METRO, CONT'D

CHART #1 (continued)

A/C COMPRESSOR CLUTCH NEVER ENGAGES

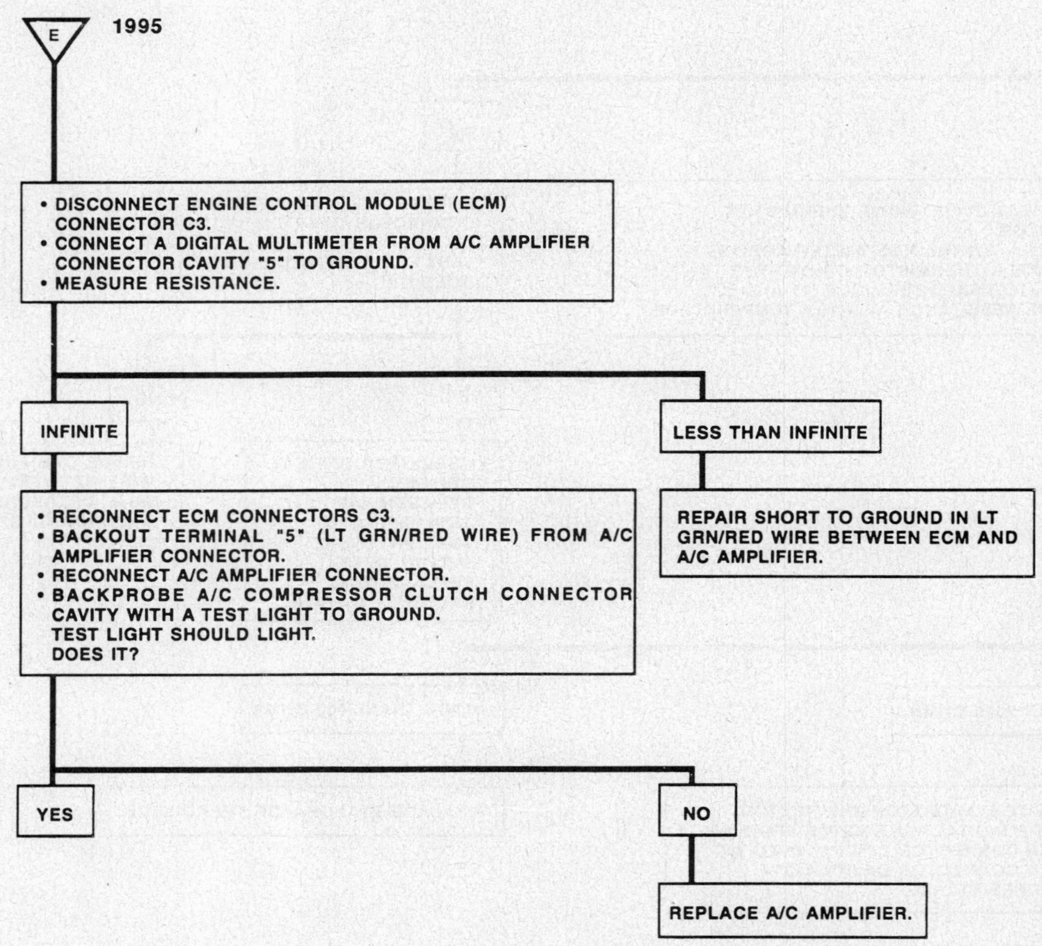

E
1995
• DISCONNECT ENGINE CONTROL MODULE (ECM) CONNECTOR C3.
• CONNECT A DIGITAL MULTIMETER FROM A/C AMPLIFIER CONNECTOR CAVITY "5" TO GROUND.
• MEASURE RESISTANCE.
INFINITE
LESS THAN INFINITE
• RECONNECT ECM CONNECTORS C3.
• BACKOUT TERMINAL "5" (LT GRN/RED WIRE) FROM A/C AMPLIFIER CONNECTOR.
• RECONNECT A/C AMPLIFIER CONNECTOR.
• BACKPROBE A/C COMPRESSOR CLUTCH CONNECTOR CAVITY WITH A TEST LIGHT TO GROUND.
TEST LIGHT SHOULD LIGHT.
DOES IT?
REPAIR SHORT TO GROUND IN LT GRN/RED WIRE BETWEEN ECM AND A/C AMPLIFIER.
YES
NO
REPLACE A/C AMPLIFIER.

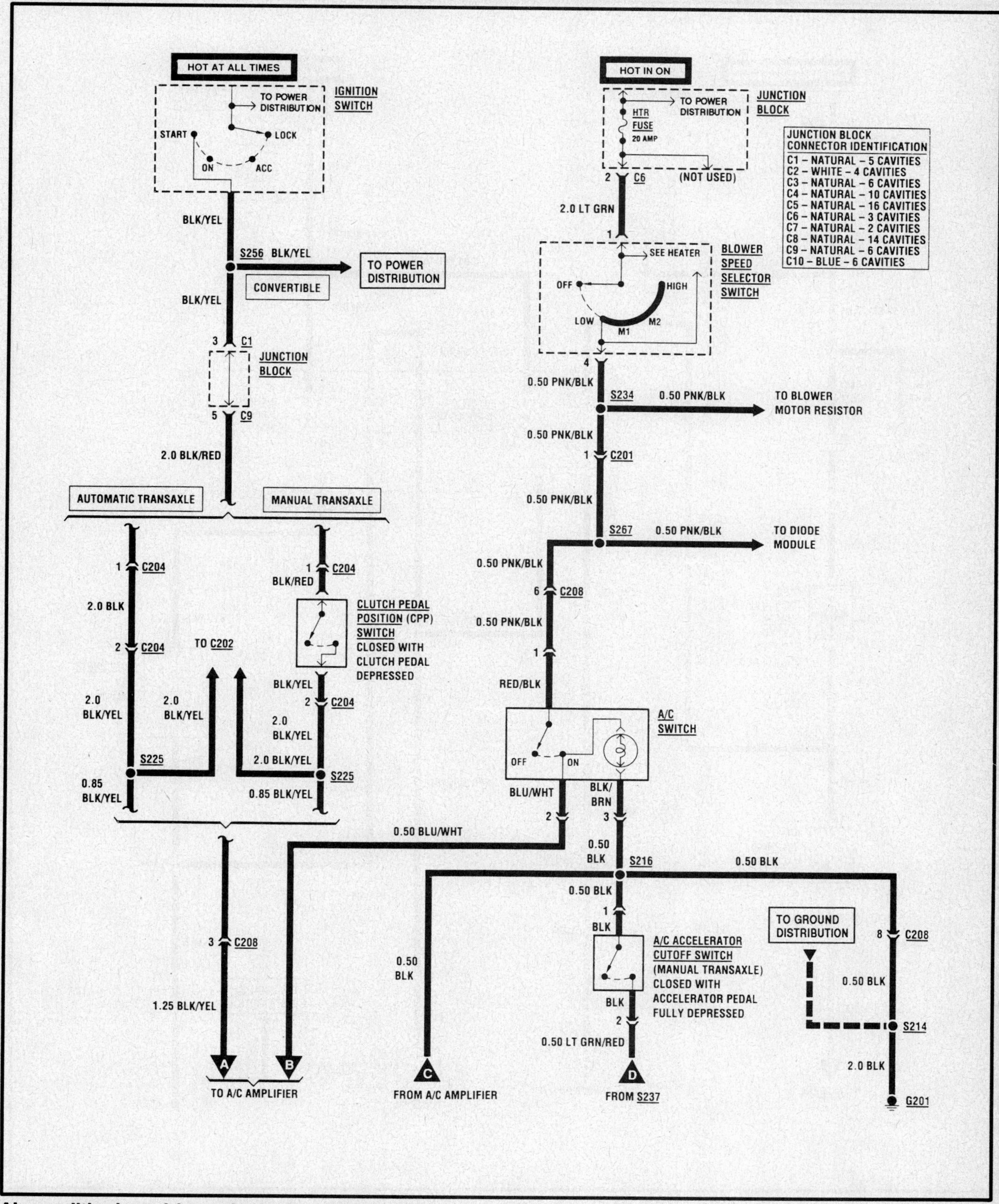

Air conditioning wiring schematic—1993-94 Metro

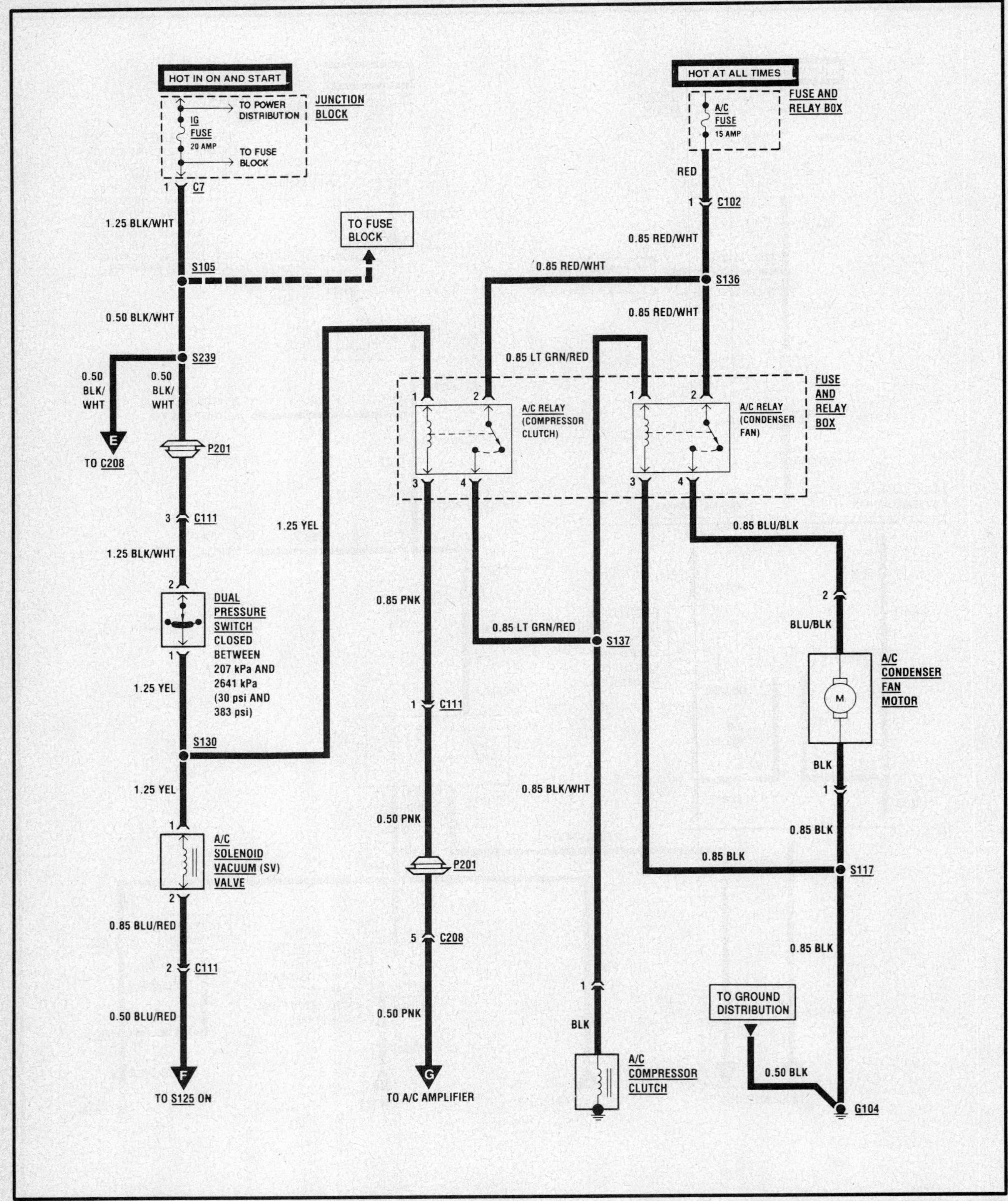

Air conditioning wiring schematic—1993-94 Metro, Cont'd

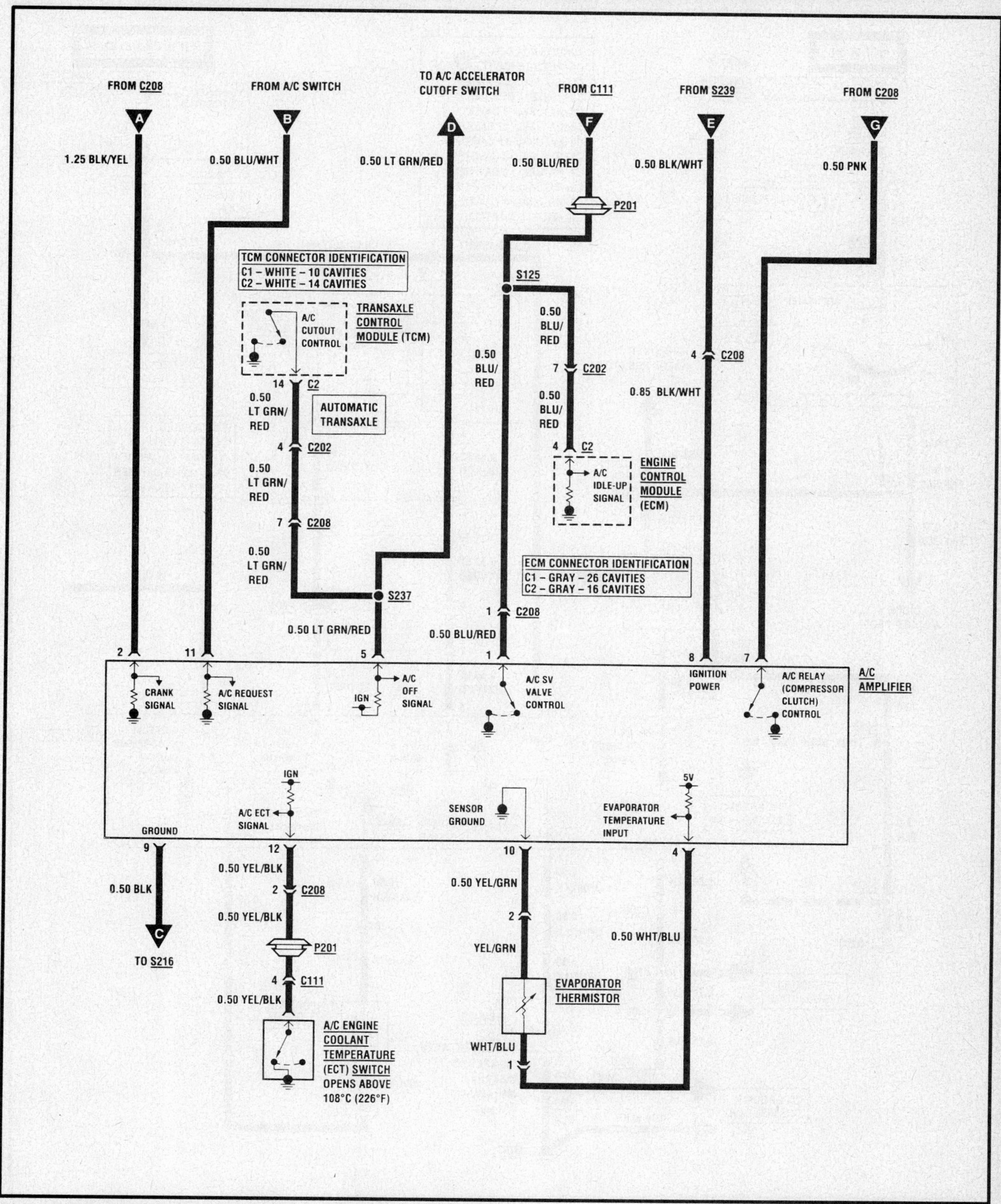

Air conditioning wiring schematic—1993-94 Metro, Cont'd

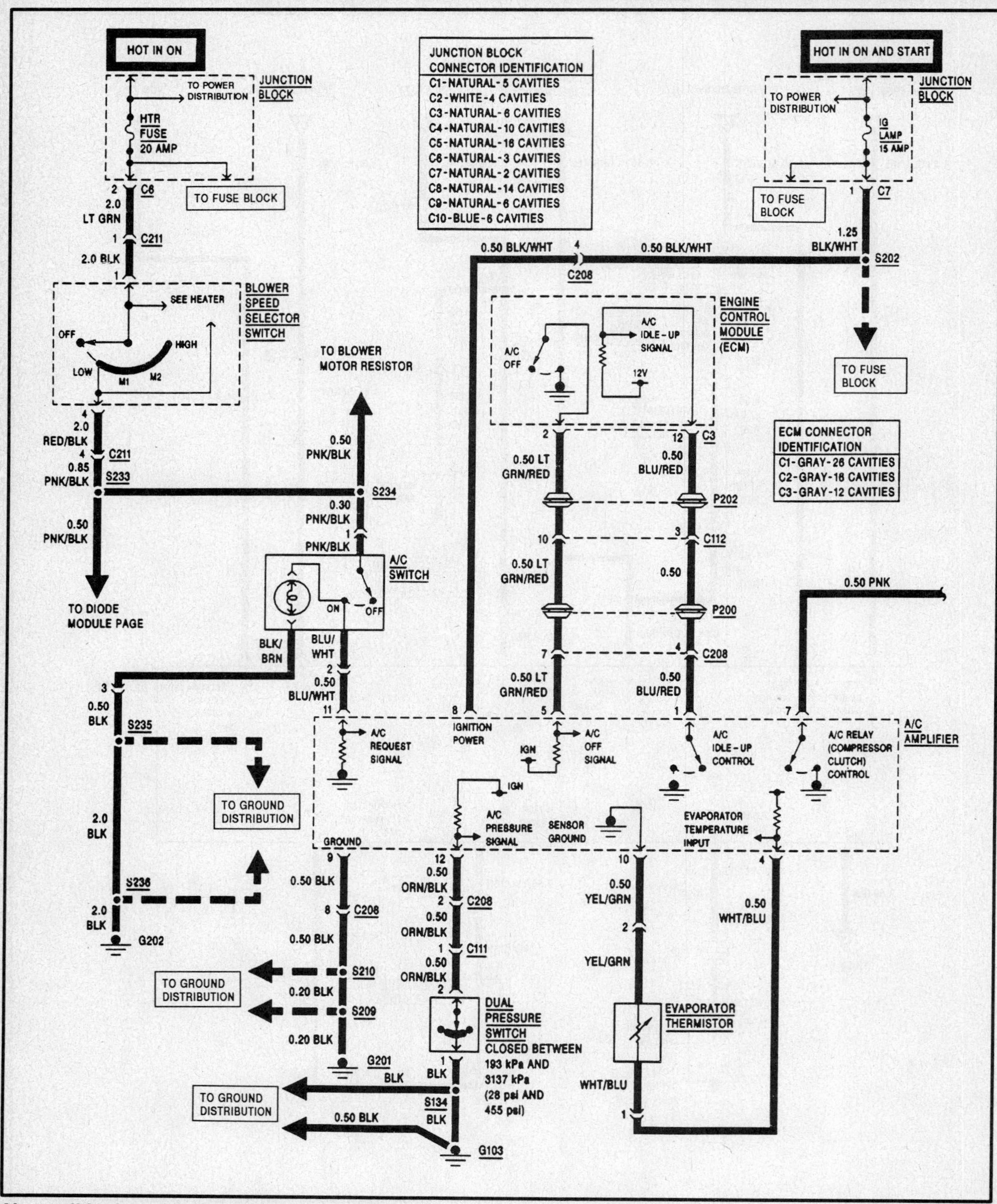

Air conditioning wiring schematic—1995 Metro

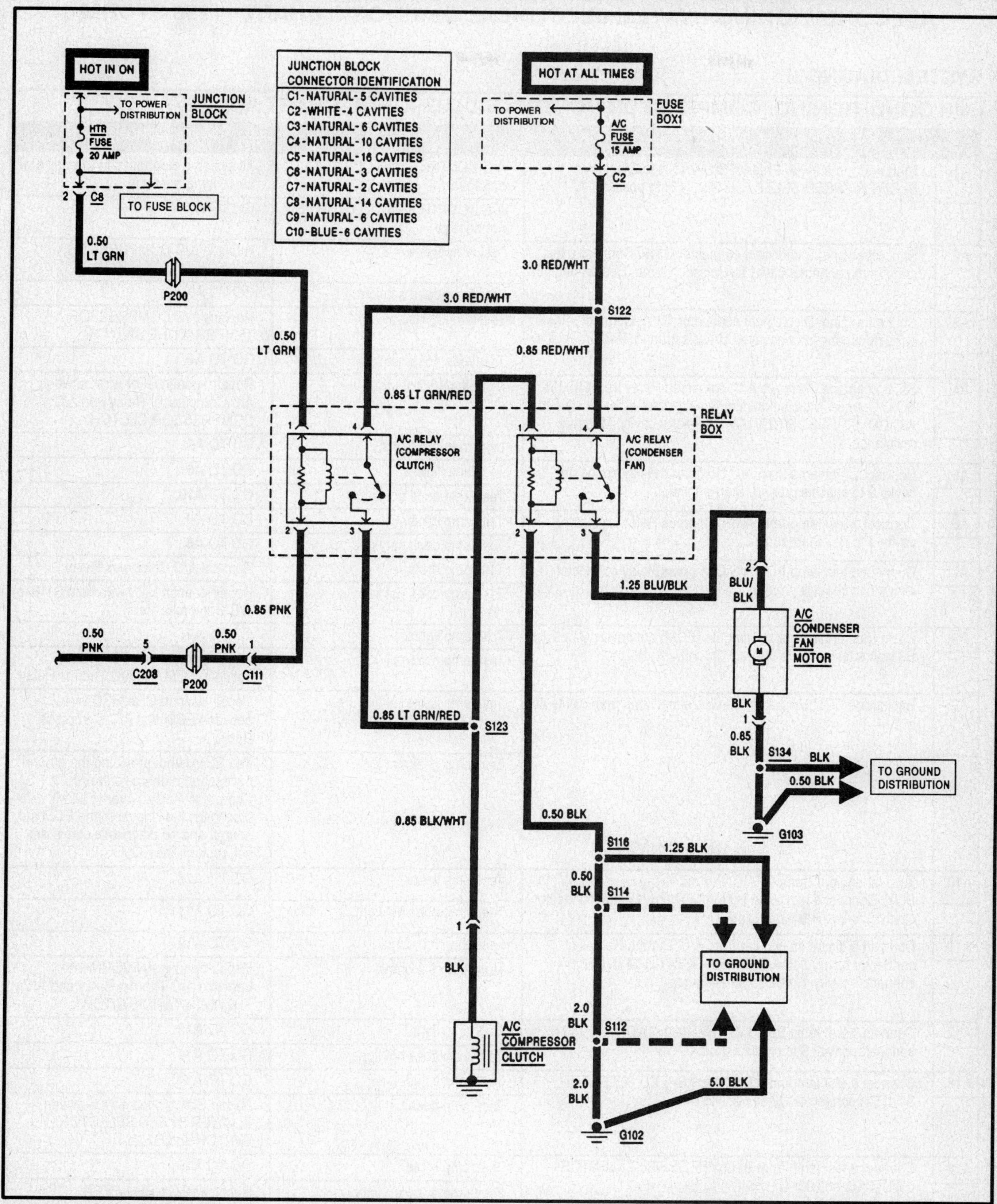

Air conditioning wiring schematic—1995 Metro, Cont'd

AIR CONDITIONING SYSTEM ELECTRICAL DIAGNOSIS CHART–1993 STORM

SYSTEM DIAGNOSIS

AIR CONDITIONING: COMPRESSOR CONTROLS DIAGNOSTIC CHART A

	TEST	RESULT	ACTION
A1.	Start and run engine. Press A/C SWITCH to ON. Move BLOWER SPEED SELECTOR SWITCH to position "1."	A/C COMPRESSOR CLUTCH engages.	All systems diagnosed in this cell are functioning normally.
		A/C COMPRESSOR CLUTCH does not engage.	GO TO **A2**.
A2.	Shut off engine. Disconnect connector C112. Connect a test lamp from connector cavity to chassis ground. Restart engine.	Test lamp lights.	Replace A/C COMPRESSOR CLUTCH.
		Test lamp does not light.	GO TO **A3**.
A3.	Shut off engine. Disconnect connector C111. Connect a test lamp from connector cavity to chassis ground. Restart engine.	Test lamp lights.	Replace A/C COMPRESSOR TEMPERATURE SWITCH.
		Test lamp does not light.	GO TO **A4**.
A4.	Shut off engine. Remove A/C Compress Relay from RELAY BOX. Connect a digital multimeter from connector cavity 4 to A/C COMPRESSOR CLUTCH connector cavity. Measure resistance.	More than 5.0 ohms.	Repair open in GRN wire between A/C Compressor Relay and A/C COMPRESSOR CLUTCH.
		Less than 5.0 ohms.	GO TO **A5**.
A5.	Connect a test lamp from A/C Compress Relay connector cavity 2 to chassis ground. Start engine.	Test lamp lights.	GO TO **A6**.
		Test lamp does not light.	GO TO **A10**.
A6.	Connect a test lamp from A/C Compress Relay connector cavity 3 to B+. Start engine.	Test lamp lights.	GO TO **A7**.
		Test lamp does not light.	GO TO **A8**.
A7.	Connect a test lamp from A/C Compress Relay connector cavity 1 to chassis ground.	Test lamp lights.	Replace A/C Compress Relay.
		Test lamp does not light.	Repair open in BRN wire from S113 to A/C Compress Relay.
A8.	Backprobe engine control module (ECM) connector C1 cavity B8 with a test lamp to chassis ground.	Test lamp lights.	GO TO **A9**.
		Test lamp does not light.	Repair open in GRN/ORN wire between ECM and A/C Thermo Relay.
A9.	Backprobe ECM connector C1 with a test lamp from cavity A2 to B+.	Test lamp lights.	Repair open in GRA/RED wire between ECM and A/C Compress Relay.
		Test lamp does not light.	The ECM is not providing the ground necessary to energize the A/C Compress Relay. Refer to ECM diagnosis. If all inputs to the ECM are normal and no diagnostic codes are set, replace the ECM.
A10.	Turn off engine. Remove A/C Thermo Relay from RELAY BOX. Connect a test lamp from A/C Thermo Relay connector cavity 3 to B+. Restart engine.	Test lamp lights.	GO TO **A24**.
		Test lamp does not light.	GO TO **A11**.
A11.	Connect a digital multimeter from A/C Thermo Relay connector cavity 3 to A/C THERMOSTATIC SWITCH connector cavity 1. Measure resistance.	Less than 5.0 ohms.	GO TO **A12**.
		More than 5.0 ohms.	Repair open in PNK/GRN wire between A/C Thermo Relay and A/C THERMOSTATIC SWITCH.
A12.	Connect a test lamp from A/C THERMOSTATIC SWITCH connector cavity 3 to chassis ground.	Test lamp lights.	GO TO **A13**.
		Test lamp does not light.	GO TO **A16**.
A13.	Connect a test lamp from BLOWER SPEED SELECTOR SWITCH connector C2 cavity 2 to B+.	Test lamp lights.	GO TO **A14**.
		Test lamp does not light.	Repair BLK ground wire between BLOWER SPEED SELECTOR SWITCH and G202.
A14.	Connect a test lamp from BLOWER SPEED SELECTOR SWITCH connector C1 cavity 5 to B+.	Test lamp lights.	GO TO **A15**.
		Test lamp does not light.	Replace BLOWER SPEED SELECTOR SWITCH.

AIR CONDITIONING SYSTEM ELECTRICAL DIAGNOSIS CHART—1993 STORM, CONT'D

AIR CONDITIONING: COMPRESSOR CONTROLS DIAGNOSTIC CHART A			
	TEST	RESULT	ACTION
A15.	Connect a test lamp from A/C THERMOSTATIC SWITCH connector cavity 2 to B+.	Test lamp lights.	Replace A/C THERMOSTATIC SWITCH.
		Test lamp does not light.	Repair open in GRN/YEL wire between A/C THERMOSTATIC SWITCH and BLOWER SPEED SELECTOR SWITCH.
A16.	Shut off engine. Connect a digital multimeter from A/C THERMOSTATIC SWITCH connector cavity 3 to A/C SWITCH connector cavity 2. Measure resistance.	Less than 5.0 ohms.	GO TO **A17**.
		More than 5.0 ohms.	Repair open in LT GRN wire between A/C THERMOSTATIC SWITCH and A/C SWITCH.
A17.	Connect a test lamp from A/C SWITCH connector cavity 1 to chassis ground.	Test lamp lights.	Replace A/C SWITCH.
		Test lamp does not light.	GO TO **A18**.
A18.	Shut off engine. Remove Heater and A/C Relay from FUSE AND RELAY BOX. Connect a test lamp from connector cavity 2 to chassis ground. Start engine.	Test lamp lights.	GO TO **A19**.
		Test lamp does not light.	Repair open in WHT wire between FL-2 and Heater and A/C Relay.
A19.	Shut off engine. Connect a digital multimeter from Heater and A/C Relay connector cavity 4 to A/C SWITCH connector cavity 1. Measure resistance.	Less than 5.0 ohms.	GO TO **A20**.
		More than 5.0 ohms.	Repair open in BLU wire between Heater and A/C Relay and Fuse E-2 or BRN wire between Fuse E-2 and A/C SWITCH.
A20.	Connect a digital multimeter from Heater and A/C Relay connector cavity 3 to chassis ground. Measure resistance.	Less than 5.0 ohms.	GO TO **A21**.
		More than 5.0 ohms.	Repair BLK ground wire between Heater and A/C Relay and G102.
A21.	Connect a test lamp from Heater and A/C Relay connector cavity 1 to chassis ground. Start engine.	Test lamp lights.	Replace Heater and A/C Relay.
		Test lamp does not light.	GO TO **A22**.
A22.	Shut off engine. Connect a digital multimeter from Restart Relay connector cavity 5 to Heater and A/C Relay connector cavity 1. Measure resistance.	Less than 5.0 ohms.	GO TO **A23**.
		More than 5.0 ohms.	Repair open in WHT/RED wire between Restart Relay and Heater and A/C Relay.
A23.	Connect a test lamp from Restart Relay connector cavity 4 to chassis ground. Start engine.	Test lamp lights.	Replace Restart Relay.
		Test lamp does not light.	Repair open in WHT/BLU wire between Restart Relay and GENERATOR.
A24.	Connect a test lamp from A/C Thermo Relay connector cavity 2 to chassis ground.	Test lamp lights.	GO TO **A25**.
		Test lamp does not light.	GO TO **A27**.
A25.	Connect a test lamp from A/C Thermo Relay connector cavity 1 to chassis ground.	Test lamp lights.	GO TO **A26**.
		Test lamp does not light.	Repair open in LT GRN wire between A/C Thermo Relay and A/C SWITCH.
A26.	Connect a digital multimeter from A/C Thermo Relay connector cavity 4 to A/C Compress Relay connector cavity 2. Measure resistance.	Less than 5.0 ohms.	Replace A/C Thermo Relay.
		More than 5.0 ohms.	Repair open in GRN/ORN wire between A/C Thermo Relay and A/C Compress Relay.
A27.	Backprobe TRIPLE SWITCH at connector cavity 2 with a test lamp to chassis ground.	Test lamp lights.	Repair open in GRN/WHT wire.
		Test lamp does not light.	GO TO **A28**.
A28.	Backprobe TRIPLE SWITCH at connector cavity 4 with a test lamp to chassis ground.	Test lamp lights.	Check for poor connection at TRIPLE SWITCH. If OK, replace TRIPLE SWITCH.
		Test lamp does not light.	Repair open in BRN wire between S1121 and TRIPLE SWITCH.

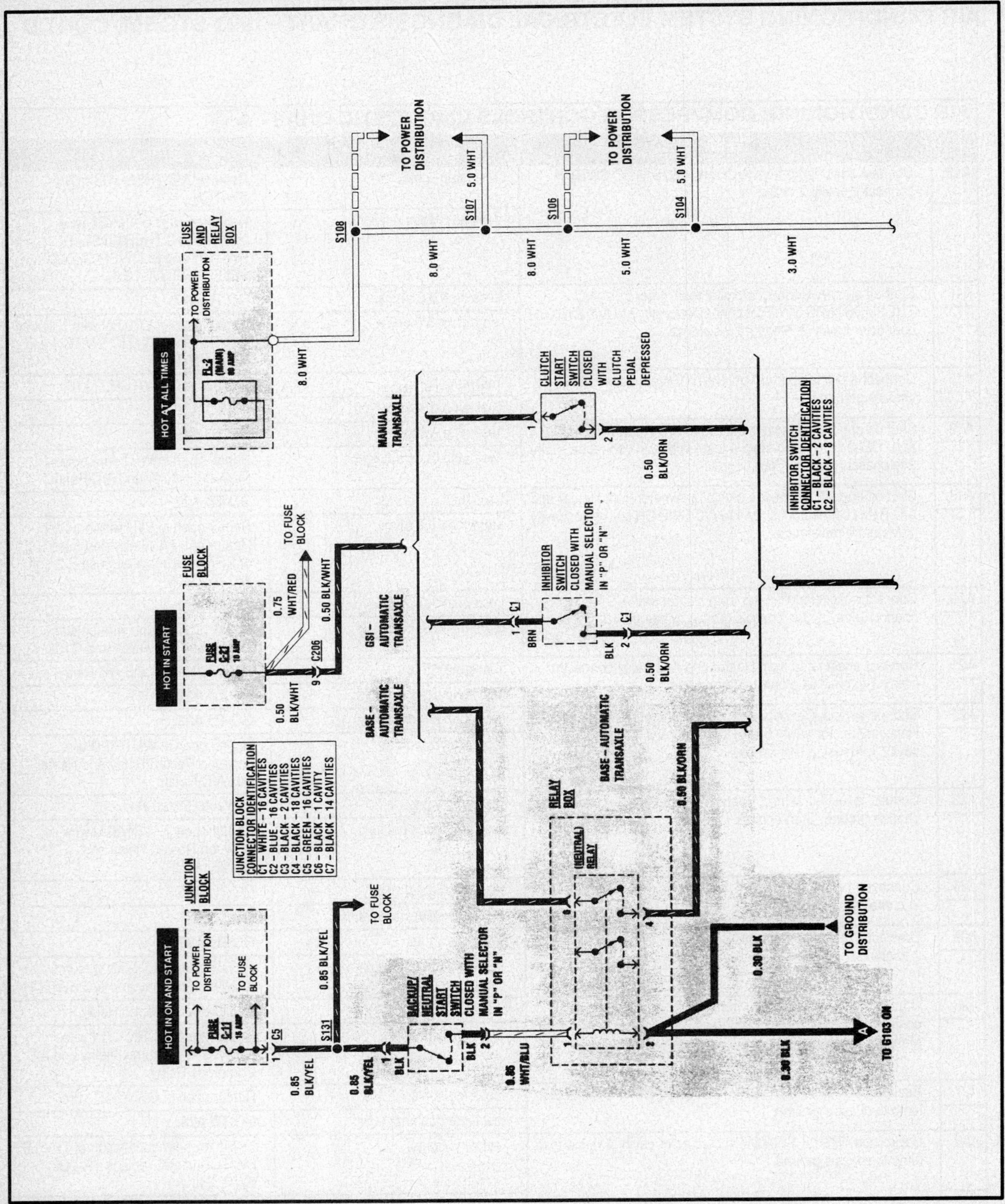

Air conditioning wiring schematic—Storm

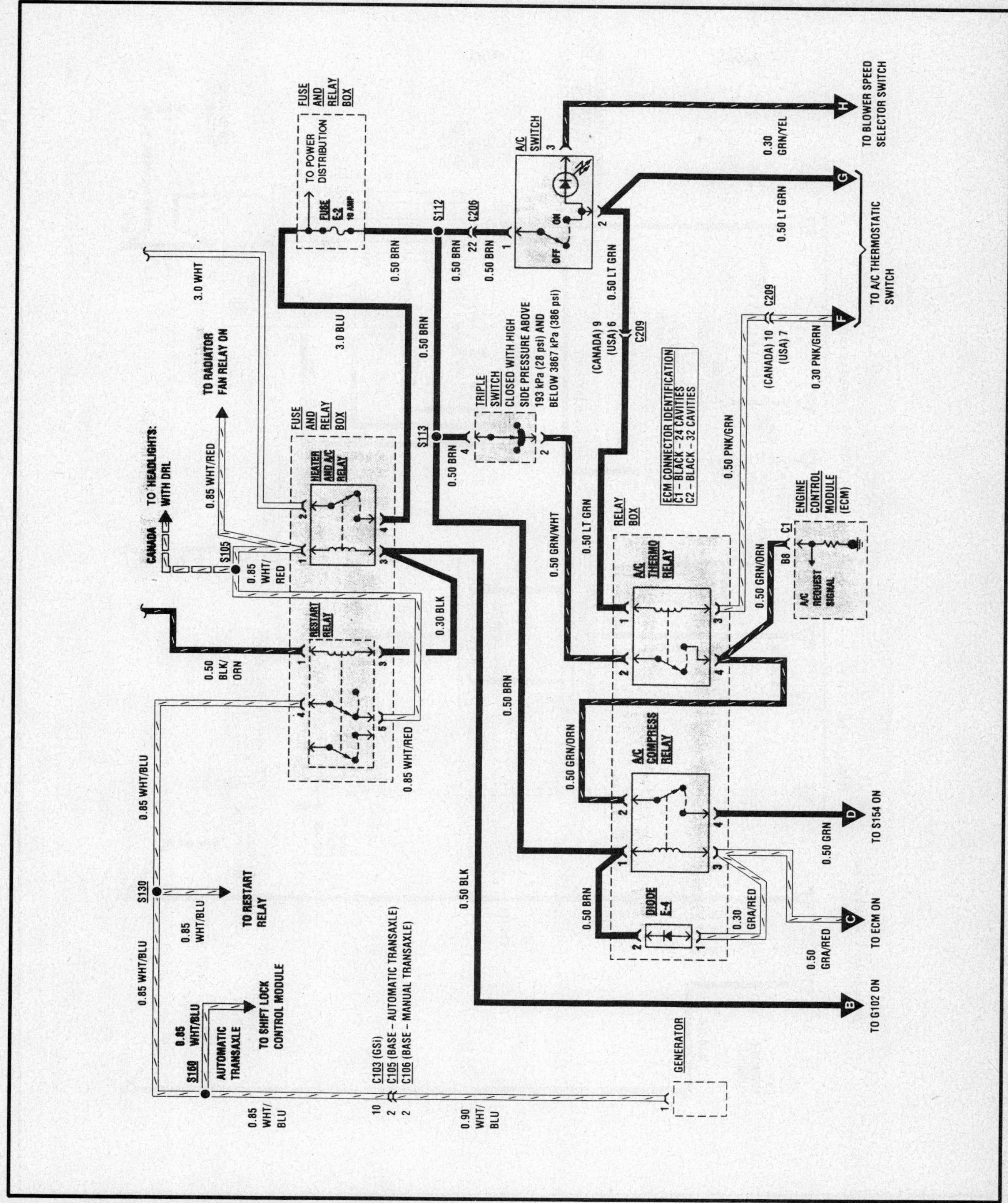

Air conditioning wiring schematic—Storm, Cont'd

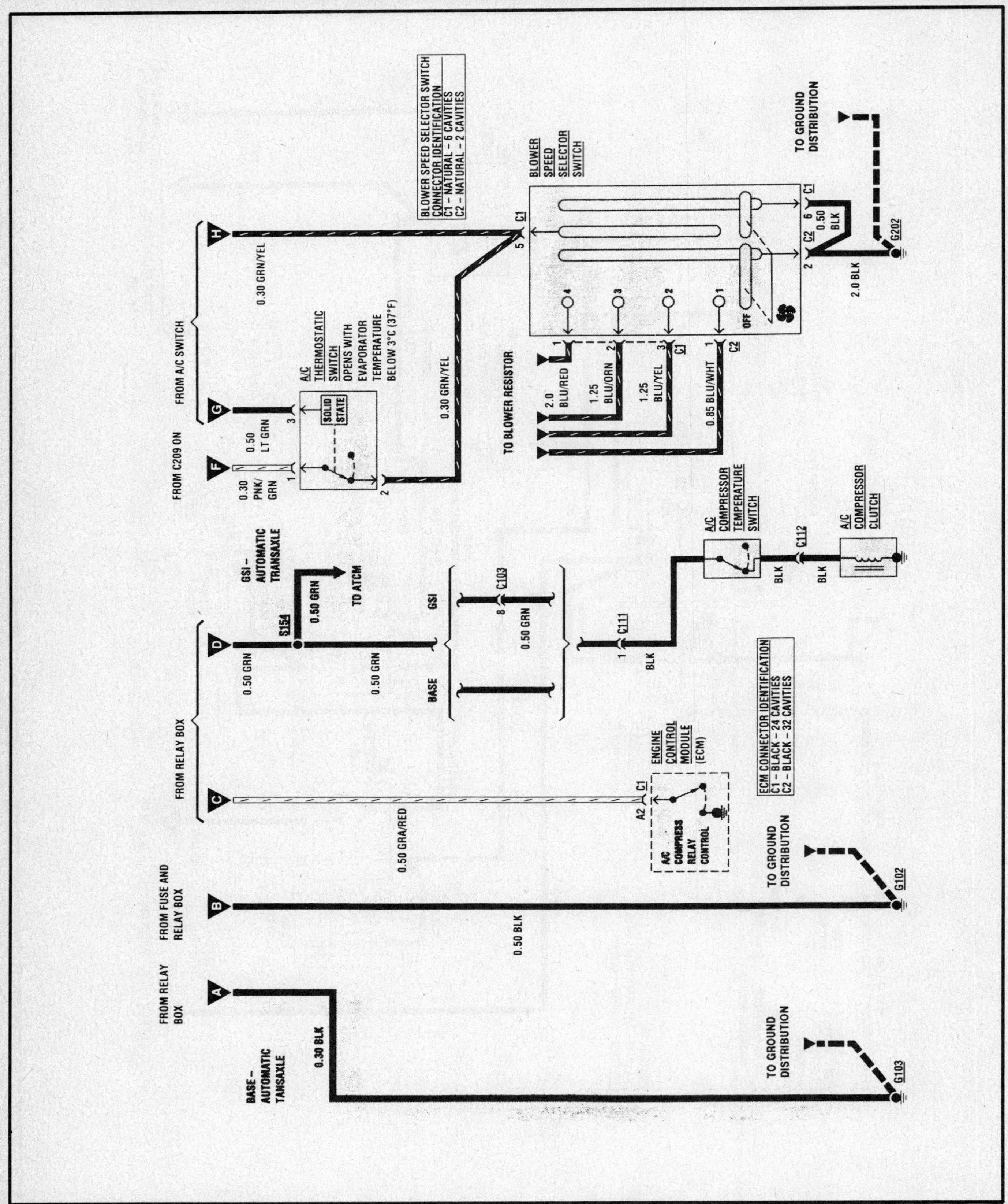

Air conditioning wiring schematic–Storm, Cont'd

COOLANT FAN ELECTRICAL DIAGNOSIS CHART–PRIZM
CHART #1
RADIATOR FAN MOTOR DOES NOT RUN

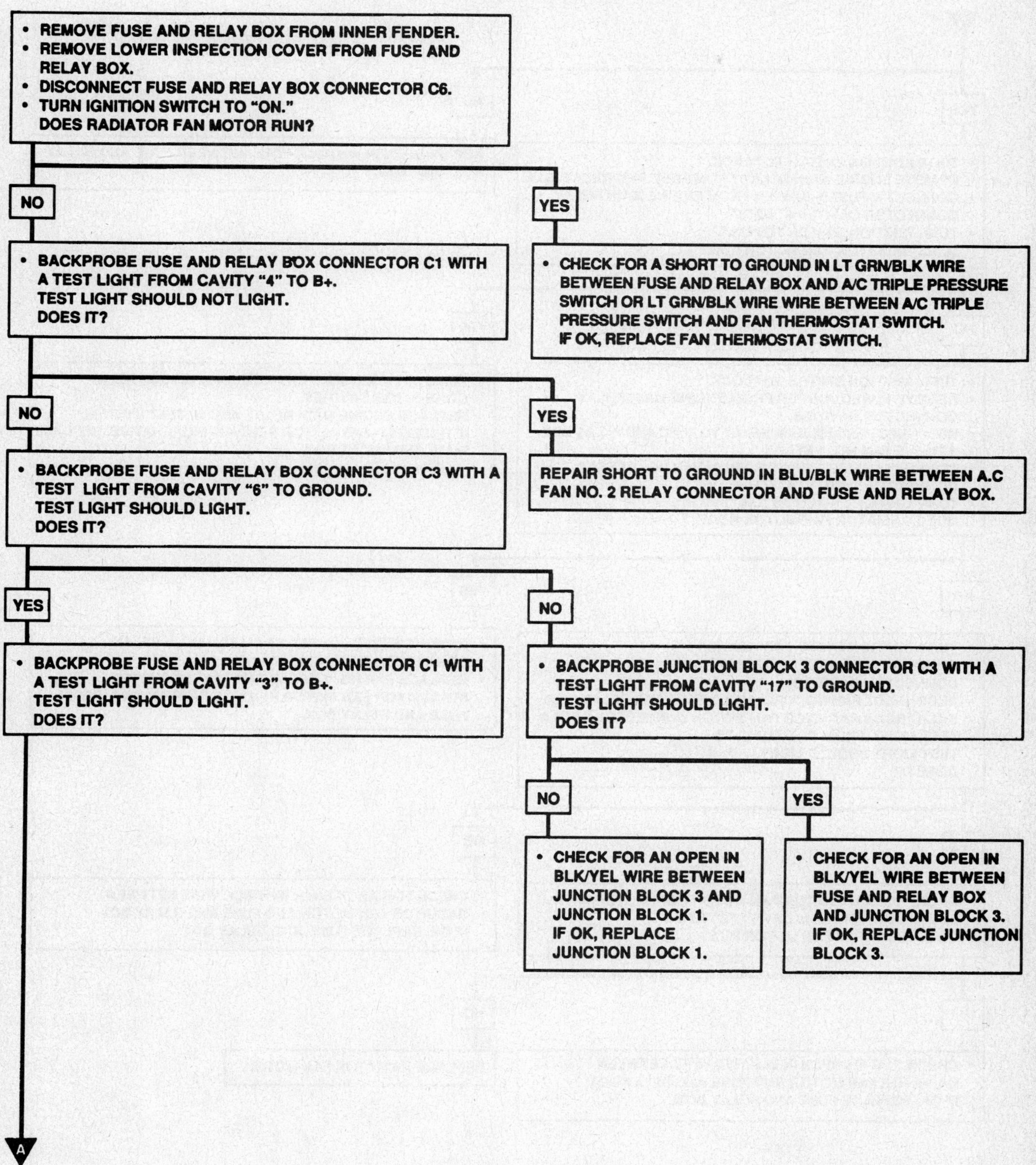

• REMOVE FUSE AND RELAY BOX FROM INNER FENDER.
• REMOVE LOWER INSPECTION COVER FROM FUSE AND RELAY BOX.
• DISCONNECT FUSE AND RELAY BOX CONNECTOR C6.
• TURN IGNITION SWITCH TO "ON."
DOES RADIATOR FAN MOTOR RUN?
NO
YES
• BACKPROBE FUSE AND RELAY BOX CONNECTOR C1 WITH A TEST LIGHT FROM CAVITY "4" TO B+.
TEST LIGHT SHOULD NOT LIGHT.
DOES IT?
• CHECK FOR A SHORT TO GROUND IN LT GRN/BLK WIRE BETWEEN FUSE AND RELAY BOX AND A/C TRIPLE PRESSURE SWITCH OR LT GRN/BLK WIRE WIRE BETWEEN A/C TRIPLE PRESSURE SWITCH AND FAN THERMOSTAT SWITCH.
IF OK, REPLACE FAN THERMOSTAT SWITCH.
NO
YES
• BACKPROBE FUSE AND RELAY BOX CONNECTOR C3 WITH A TEST LIGHT FROM CAVITY "6" TO GROUND.
TEST LIGHT SHOULD LIGHT.
DOES IT?
REPAIR SHORT TO GROUND IN BLU/BLK WIRE BETWEEN A.C FAN NO. 2 RELAY CONNECTOR AND FUSE AND RELAY BOX.
YES
NO
• BACKPROBE FUSE AND RELAY BOX CONNECTOR C1 WITH A TEST LIGHT FROM CAVITY "3" TO B+.
TEST LIGHT SHOULD LIGHT.
DOES IT?
• BACKPROBE JUNCTION BLOCK 3 CONNECTOR C3 WITH A TEST LIGHT FROM CAVITY "17" TO GROUND.
TEST LIGHT SHOULD LIGHT.
DOES IT?
NO
YES
• CHECK FOR AN OPEN IN BLK/YEL WIRE BETWEEN JUNCTION BLOCK 3 AND JUNCTION BLOCK 1.
IF OK, REPLACE JUNCTION BLOCK 1.
• CHECK FOR AN OPEN IN BLK/YEL WIRE BETWEEN FUSE AND RELAY BOX AND JUNCTION BLOCK 3.
IF OK, REPLACE JUNCTION BLOCK 3.
A

COOLANT FAN ELECTRICAL DIAGNOSIS CHART–PRIZM, CONT'D
CHART #1 (continued)
RADIATOR FAN MOTOR DOES NOT RUN

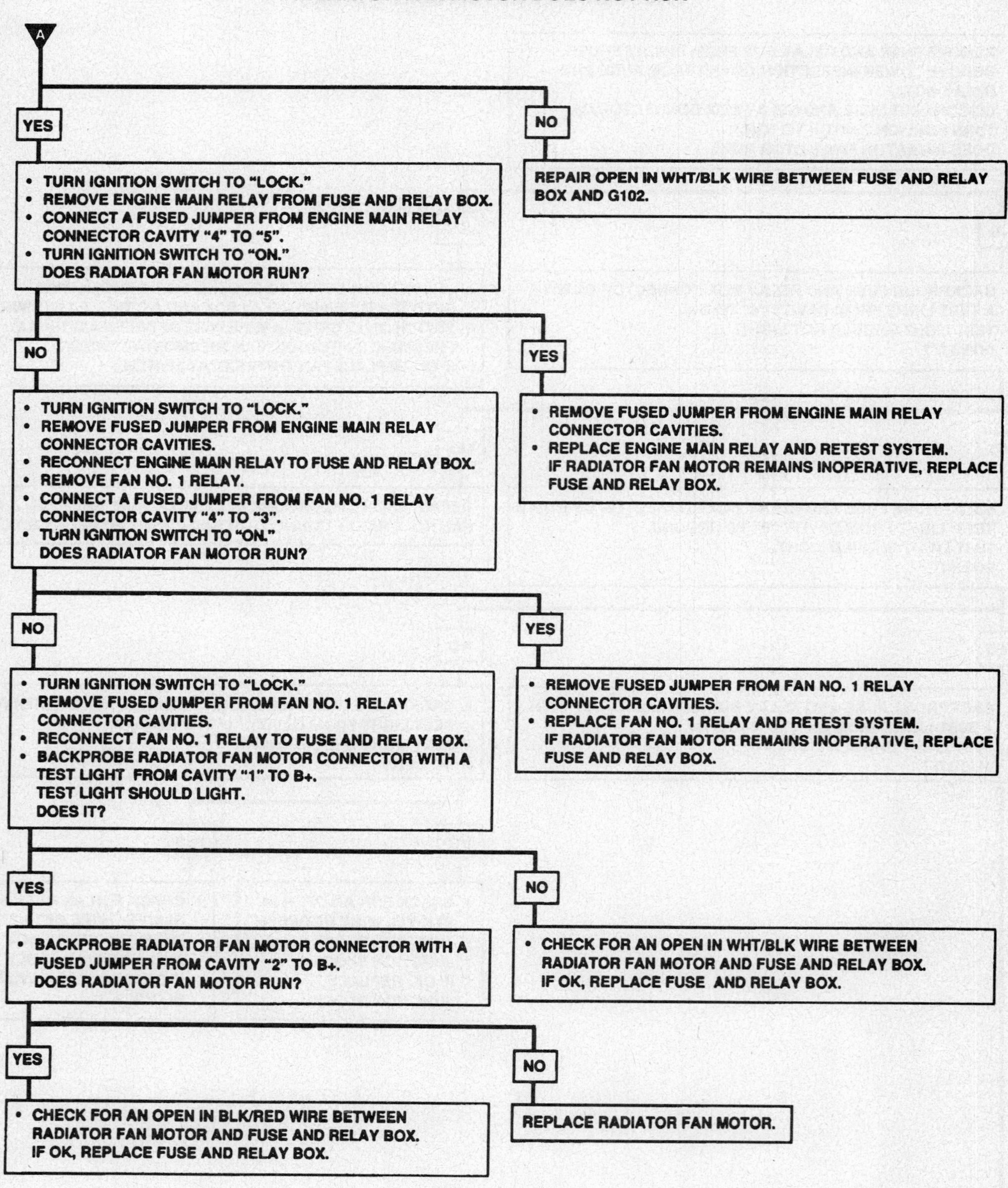

A
YES
NO
REPAIR OPEN IN WHT/BLK WIRE BETWEEN FUSE AND RELAY BOX AND G102.
• TURN IGNITION SWITCH TO "LOCK."
• REMOVE ENGINE MAIN RELAY FROM FUSE AND RELAY BOX.
• CONNECT A FUSED JUMPER FROM ENGINE MAIN RELAY CONNECTOR CAVITY "4" TO "5".
• TURN IGNITION SWITCH TO "ON."
DOES RADIATOR FAN MOTOR RUN?
NO
YES
• TURN IGNITION SWITCH TO "LOCK."
• REMOVE FUSED JUMPER FROM ENGINE MAIN RELAY CONNECTOR CAVITIES.
• RECONNECT ENGINE MAIN RELAY TO FUSE AND RELAY BOX.
• REMOVE FAN NO. 1 RELAY.
• CONNECT A FUSED JUMPER FROM FAN NO. 1 RELAY CONNECTOR CAVITY "4" TO "3".
• TURN IGNITION SWITCH TO "ON."
DOES RADIATOR FAN MOTOR RUN?
• REMOVE FUSED JUMPER FROM ENGINE MAIN RELAY CONNECTOR CAVITIES.
• REPLACE ENGINE MAIN RELAY AND RETEST SYSTEM. IF RADIATOR FAN MOTOR REMAINS INOPERATIVE, REPLACE FUSE AND RELAY BOX.
NO
YES
• TURN IGNITION SWITCH TO "LOCK."
• REMOVE FUSED JUMPER FROM FAN NO. 1 RELAY CONNECTOR CAVITIES.
• RECONNECT FAN NO. 1 RELAY TO FUSE AND RELAY BOX.
• BACKPROBE RADIATOR FAN MOTOR CONNECTOR WITH A TEST LIGHT FROM CAVITY "1" TO B+.
TEST LIGHT SHOULD LIGHT.
DOES IT?
• REMOVE FUSED JUMPER FROM FAN NO. 1 RELAY CONNECTOR CAVITIES.
• REPLACE FAN NO. 1 RELAY AND RETEST SYSTEM. IF RADIATOR FAN MOTOR REMAINS INOPERATIVE, REPLACE FUSE AND RELAY BOX.
YES
NO
• BACKPROBE RADIATOR FAN MOTOR CONNECTOR WITH A FUSED JUMPER FROM CAVITY "2" TO B+.
DOES RADIATOR FAN MOTOR RUN?
• CHECK FOR AN OPEN IN WHT/BLK WIRE BETWEEN RADIATOR FAN MOTOR AND FUSE AND RELAY BOX.
IF OK, REPLACE FUSE AND RELAY BOX.
YES
NO
• CHECK FOR AN OPEN IN BLK/RED WIRE BETWEEN RADIATOR FAN MOTOR AND FUSE AND RELAY BOX.
IF OK, REPLACE FUSE AND RELAY BOX.
REPLACE RADIATOR FAN MOTOR.

COOLANT FAN ELECTRICAL DIAGNOSIS CHART–PRIZM, CONT'D
CHART #2
RADIATOR FAN MOTOR RUNS CONTINUOUSLY AT FULL SPEED WITH IGNITION SWITCH IN "ON"

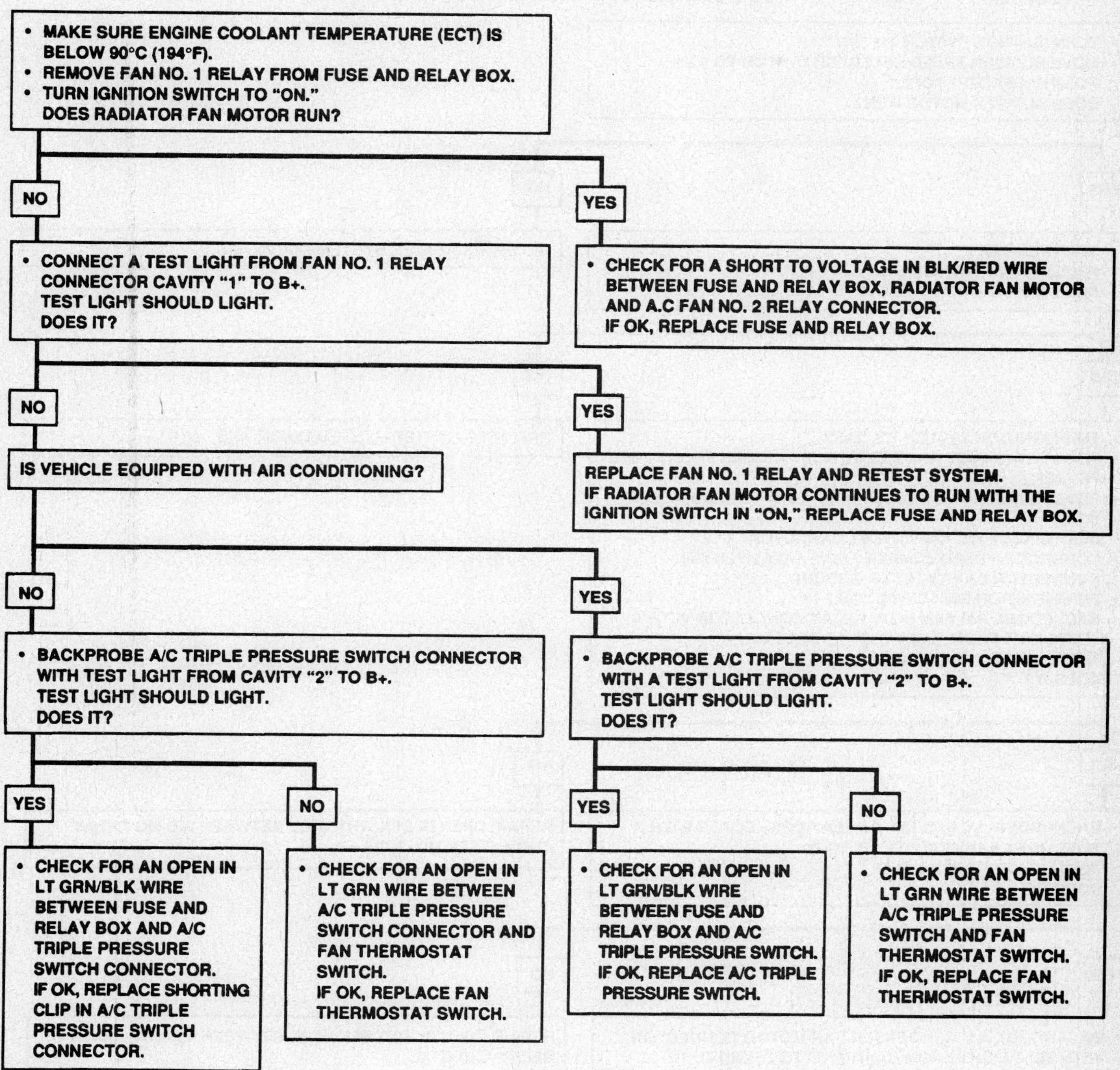

• MAKE SURE ENGINE COOLANT TEMPERATURE (ECT) IS BELOW 90°C (194°F).
• REMOVE FAN NO. 1 RELAY FROM FUSE AND RELAY BOX.
• TURN IGNITION SWITCH TO "ON."
DOES RADIATOR FAN MOTOR RUN?
NO
YES
• CONNECT A TEST LIGHT FROM FAN NO. 1 RELAY CONNECTOR CAVITY "1" TO B+.
TEST LIGHT SHOULD LIGHT.
DOES IT?
• CHECK FOR A SHORT TO VOLTAGE IN BLK/RED WIRE BETWEEN FUSE AND RELAY BOX, RADIATOR FAN MOTOR AND A.C FAN NO. 2 RELAY CONNECTOR.
IF OK, REPLACE FUSE AND RELAY BOX.
NO
YES
IS VEHICLE EQUIPPED WITH AIR CONDITIONING?
REPLACE FAN NO. 1 RELAY AND RETEST SYSTEM.
IF RADIATOR FAN MOTOR CONTINUES TO RUN WITH THE IGNITION SWITCH IN "ON," REPLACE FUSE AND RELAY BOX.
NO
YES
• BACKPROBE A/C TRIPLE PRESSURE SWITCH CONNECTOR WITH TEST LIGHT FROM CAVITY "2" TO B+.
TEST LIGHT SHOULD LIGHT.
DOES IT?
• BACKPROBE A/C TRIPLE PRESSURE SWITCH CONNECTOR WITH A TEST LIGHT FROM CAVITY "2" TO B+.
TEST LIGHT SHOULD LIGHT.
DOES IT?
YES
NO
YES
NO
• CHECK FOR AN OPEN IN LT GRN/BLK WIRE BETWEEN FUSE AND RELAY BOX AND A/C TRIPLE PRESSURE SWITCH CONNECTOR.
IF OK, REPLACE SHORTING CLIP IN A/C TRIPLE PRESSURE SWITCH CONNECTOR.
• CHECK FOR AN OPEN IN LT GRN WIRE BETWEEN A/C TRIPLE PRESSURE SWITCH CONNECTOR AND FAN THERMOSTAT SWITCH.
IF OK, REPLACE FAN THERMOSTAT SWITCH.
• CHECK FOR AN OPEN IN LT GRN/BLK WIRE BETWEEN FUSE AND RELAY BOX AND A/C TRIPLE PRESSURE SWITCH.
IF OK, REPLACE A/C TRIPLE PRESSURE SWITCH.
• CHECK FOR AN OPEN IN LT GRN WIRE BETWEEN A/C TRIPLE PRESSURE SWITCH AND FAN THERMOSTAT SWITCH.
IF OK, REPLACE FAN THERMOSTAT SWITCH.

COOLANT FAN ELECTRICAL DIAGNOSIS CHART–PRIZM, CONT'D
CHART #3
RADIATOR FAN MOTOR AND A/C CONDENSER FAN MOTOR DO NOT RUN AT HALF SPEED DURING A/C SYSTEM OPERATION (WITH A/C)

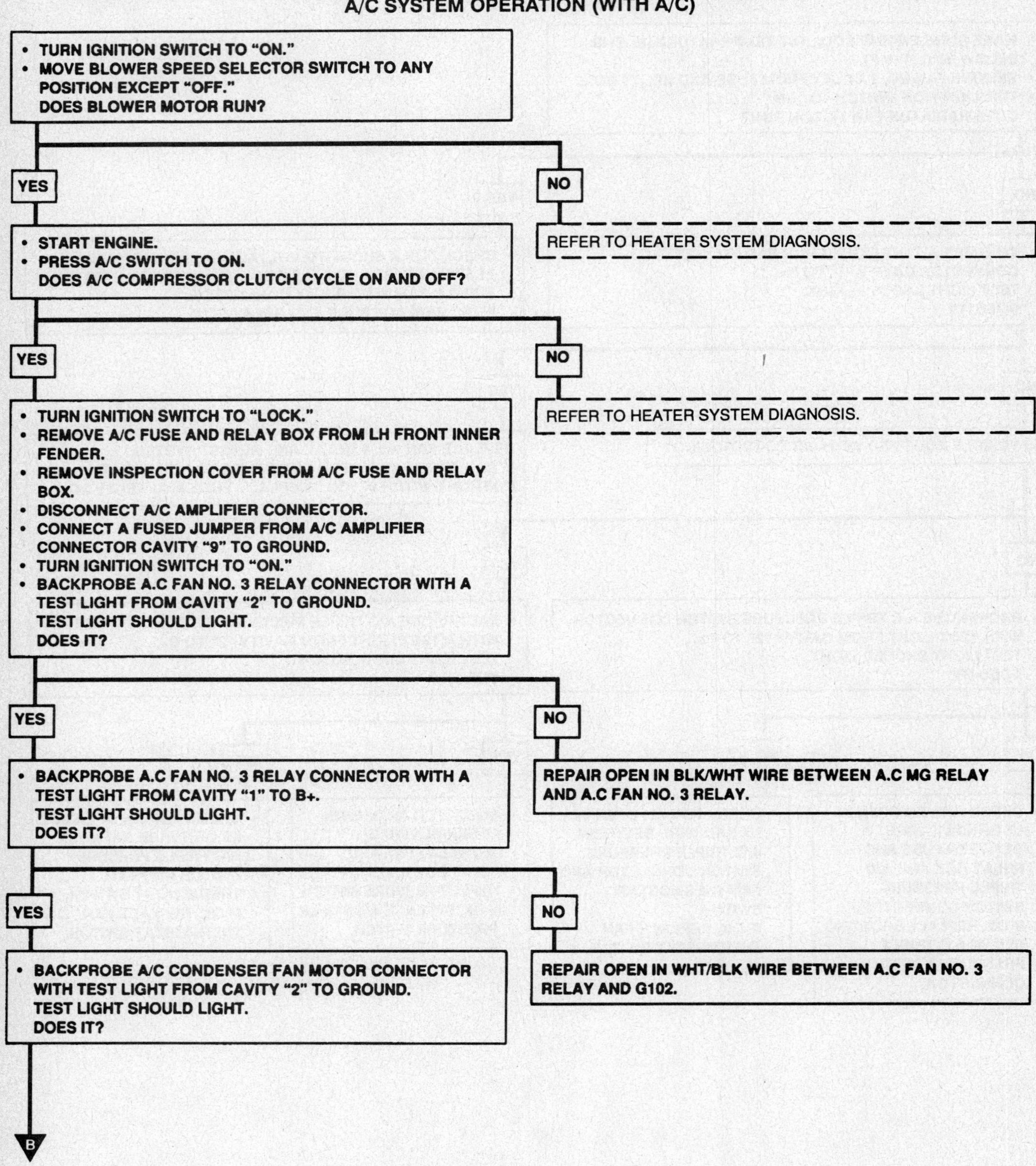

• TURN IGNITION SWITCH TO "ON."
• MOVE BLOWER SPEED SELECTOR SWITCH TO ANY POSITION EXCEPT "OFF."
DOES BLOWER MOTOR RUN?
YES
NO
REFER TO HEATER SYSTEM DIAGNOSIS.
• START ENGINE.
• PRESS A/C SWITCH TO ON.
DOES A/C COMPRESSOR CLUTCH CYCLE ON AND OFF?
YES
NO
REFER TO HEATER SYSTEM DIAGNOSIS.
• TURN IGNITION SWITCH TO "LOCK."
• REMOVE A/C FUSE AND RELAY BOX FROM LH FRONT INNER FENDER.
• REMOVE INSPECTION COVER FROM A/C FUSE AND RELAY BOX.
• DISCONNECT A/C AMPLIFIER CONNECTOR.
• CONNECT A FUSED JUMPER FROM A/C AMPLIFIER CONNECTOR CAVITY "9" TO GROUND.
• TURN IGNITION SWITCH TO "ON."
• BACKPROBE A.C FAN NO. 3 RELAY CONNECTOR WITH A TEST LIGHT FROM CAVITY "2" TO GROUND.
TEST LIGHT SHOULD LIGHT.
DOES IT?
YES
NO
REPAIR OPEN IN BLK/WHT WIRE BETWEEN A.C MG RELAY AND A.C FAN NO. 3 RELAY.
• BACKPROBE A.C FAN NO. 3 RELAY CONNECTOR WITH A TEST LIGHT FROM CAVITY "1" TO B+.
TEST LIGHT SHOULD LIGHT.
DOES IT?
YES
NO
REPAIR OPEN IN WHT/BLK WIRE BETWEEN A.C FAN NO. 3 RELAY AND G102.
• BACKPROBE A/C CONDENSER FAN MOTOR CONNECTOR WITH TEST LIGHT FROM CAVITY "2" TO GROUND.
TEST LIGHT SHOULD LIGHT.
DOES IT?
B

COOLANT FAN ELECTRICAL DIAGNOSIS CHART–PRIZM, CONT'D
CHART #3 (continued)
RADIATOR FAN MOTOR AND A/C CONDENSER FAN MOTOR DO NOT RUN AT HALF SPEED DURING A/C SYSTEM OPERATION (WITH A/C)

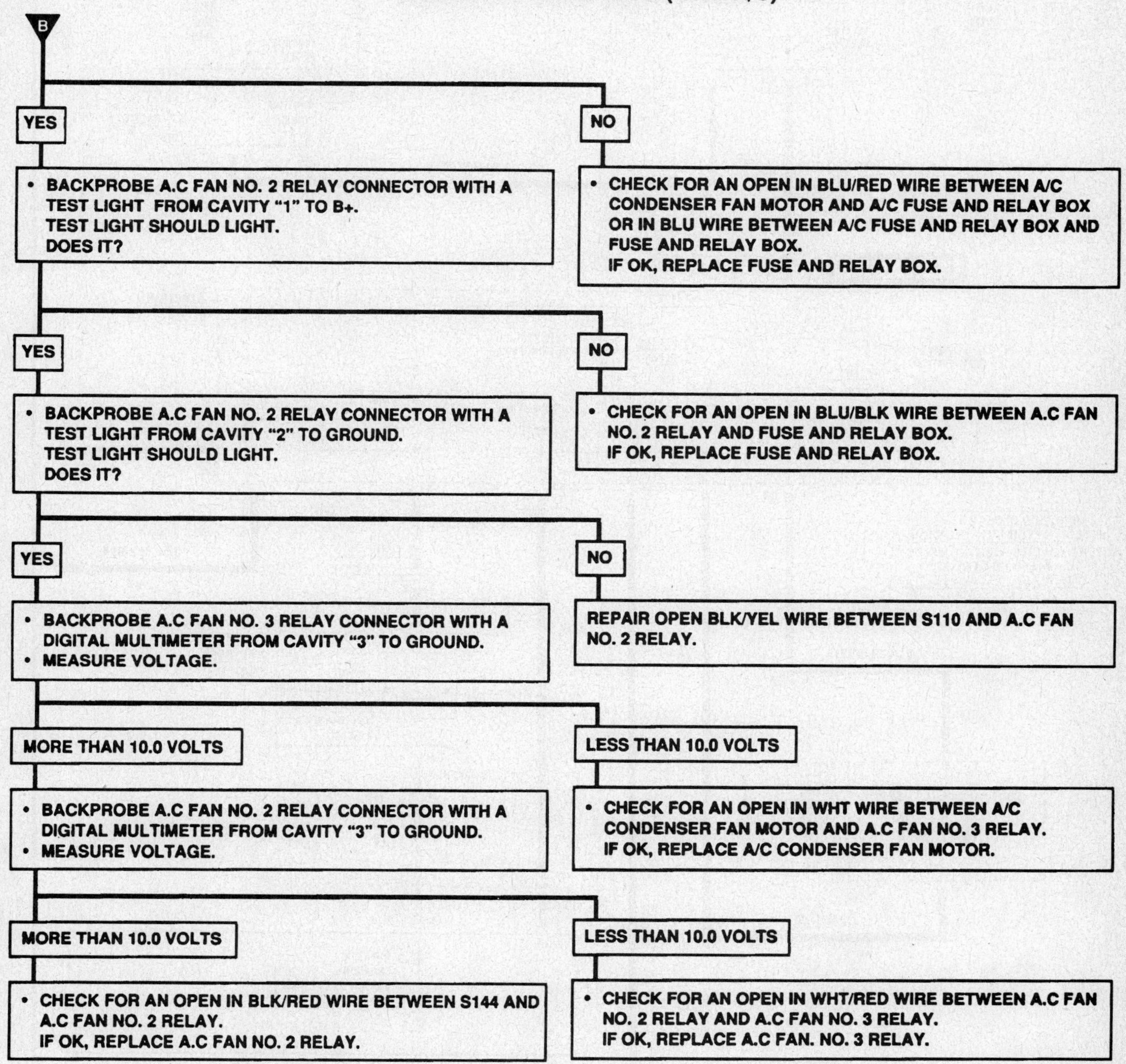

B
YES
NO
• BACKPROBE A.C FAN NO. 2 RELAY CONNECTOR WITH A TEST LIGHT FROM CAVITY "1" TO B+. TEST LIGHT SHOULD LIGHT. DOES IT?
• CHECK FOR AN OPEN IN BLU/RED WIRE BETWEEN A/C CONDENSER FAN MOTOR AND A/C FUSE AND RELAY BOX OR IN BLU WIRE BETWEEN A/C FUSE AND RELAY BOX AND FUSE AND RELAY BOX. IF OK, REPLACE FUSE AND RELAY BOX.
YES
NO
• BACKPROBE A.C FAN NO. 2 RELAY CONNECTOR WITH A TEST LIGHT FROM CAVITY "2" TO GROUND. TEST LIGHT SHOULD LIGHT. DOES IT?
• CHECK FOR AN OPEN IN BLU/BLK WIRE BETWEEN A.C FAN NO. 2 RELAY AND FUSE AND RELAY BOX. IF OK, REPLACE FUSE AND RELAY BOX.
YES
NO
• BACKPROBE A.C FAN NO. 3 RELAY CONNECTOR WITH A DIGITAL MULTIMETER FROM CAVITY "3" TO GROUND.
• MEASURE VOLTAGE.
REPAIR OPEN BLK/YEL WIRE BETWEEN S110 AND A.C FAN NO. 2 RELAY.
MORE THAN 10.0 VOLTS
LESS THAN 10.0 VOLTS
• BACKPROBE A.C FAN NO. 2 RELAY CONNECTOR WITH A DIGITAL MULTIMETER FROM CAVITY "3" TO GROUND.
• MEASURE VOLTAGE.
• CHECK FOR AN OPEN IN WHT WIRE BETWEEN A/C CONDENSER FAN MOTOR AND A.C FAN NO. 3 RELAY. IF OK, REPLACE A/C CONDENSER FAN MOTOR.
MORE THAN 10.0 VOLTS
LESS THAN 10.0 VOLTS
• CHECK FOR AN OPEN IN BLK/RED WIRE BETWEEN S144 AND A.C FAN NO. 2 RELAY. IF OK, REPLACE A.C FAN NO. 2 RELAY.
• CHECK FOR AN OPEN IN WHT/RED WIRE BETWEEN A.C FAN NO. 2 RELAY AND A.C FAN NO. 3 RELAY. IF OK, REPLACE A.C FAN. NO. 3 RELAY.

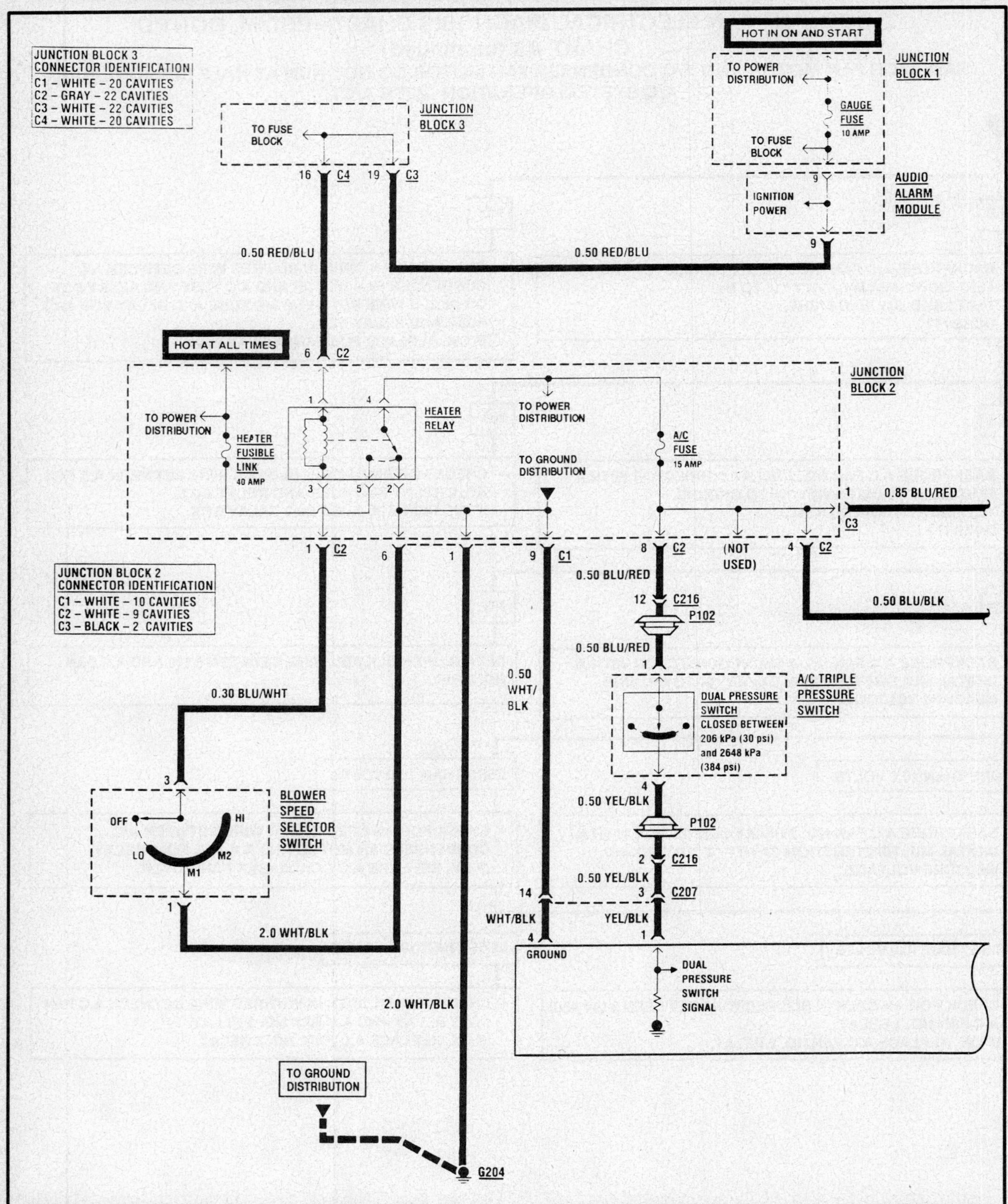

Air conditioning wiring schematic—1994-95 Prizm

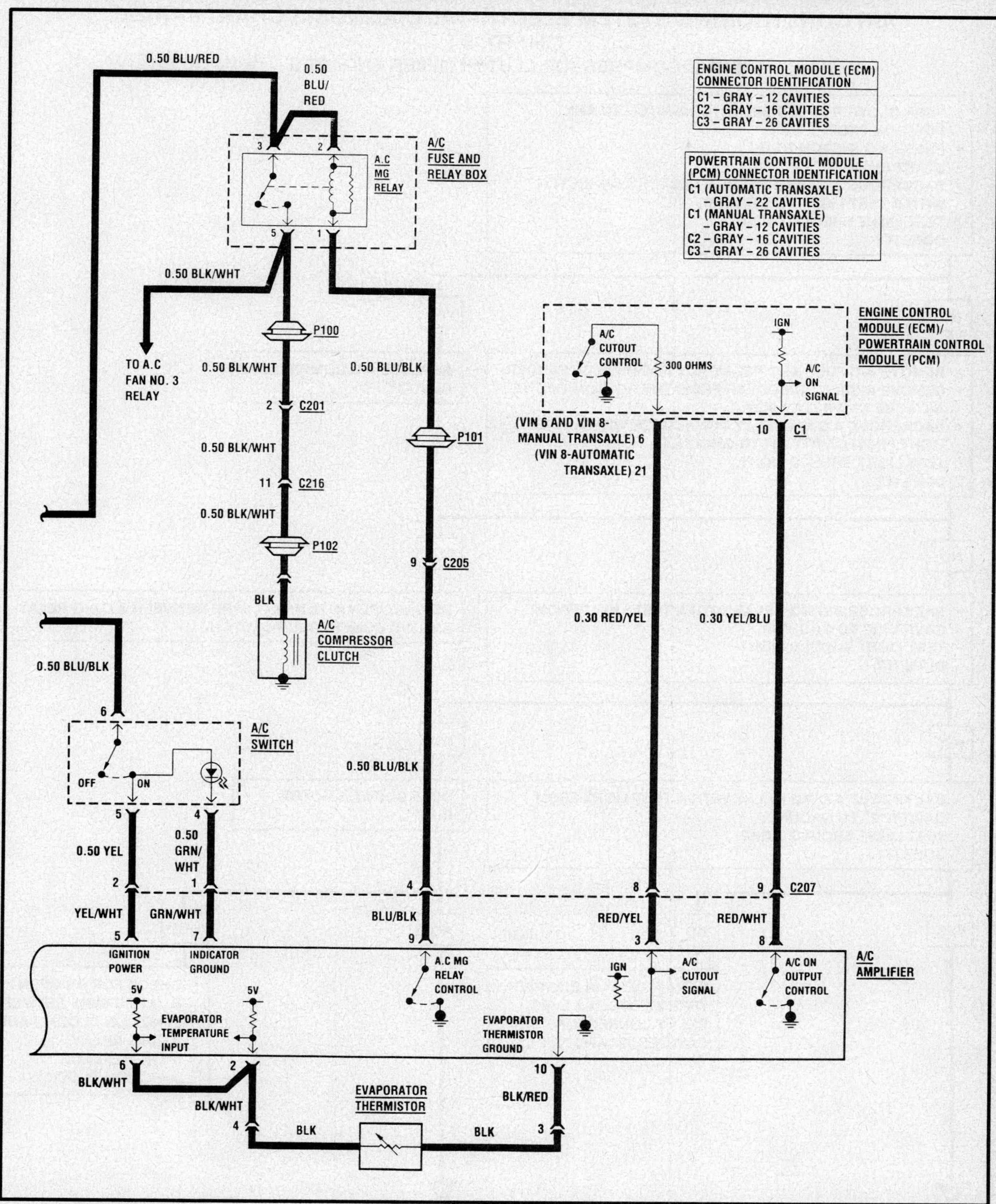

Air conditioning wiring schematic–1994-95 Prizm, Cont'd

AIR CONDITIONING SYSTEM ELECTRICAL DIAGNOSIS CHART–PRIZM
CHART #1
A/C COMPRESSOR CLUTCH NEVER ENGAGES

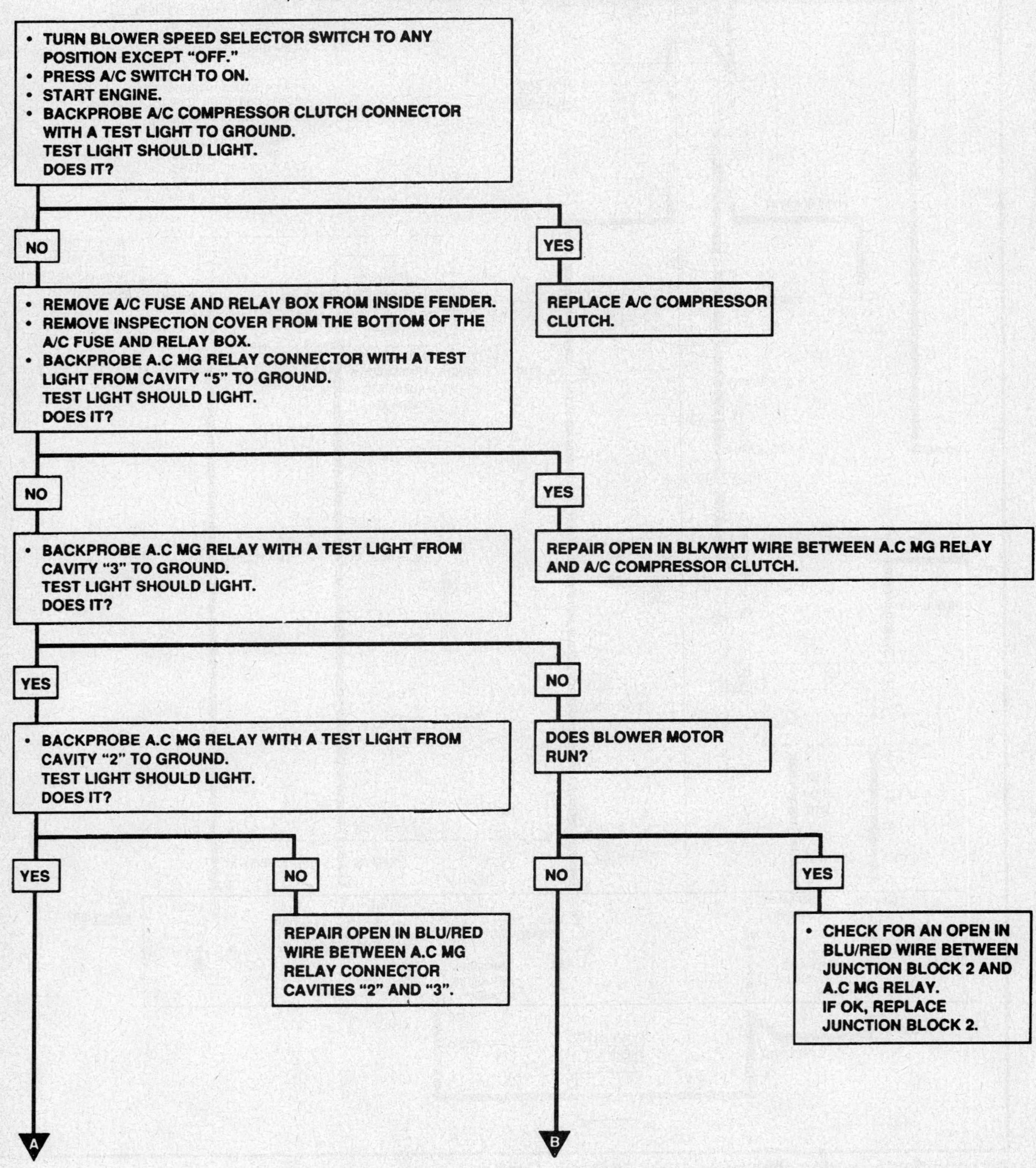

• TURN BLOWER SPEED SELECTOR SWITCH TO ANY POSITION EXCEPT "OFF."
• PRESS A/C SWITCH TO ON.
• START ENGINE.
• BACKPROBE A/C COMPRESSOR CLUTCH CONNECTOR WITH A TEST LIGHT TO GROUND.
TEST LIGHT SHOULD LIGHT.
DOES IT?
NO
YES
• REMOVE A/C FUSE AND RELAY BOX FROM INSIDE FENDER.
• REMOVE INSPECTION COVER FROM THE BOTTOM OF THE A/C FUSE AND RELAY BOX.
• BACKPROBE A.C MG RELAY CONNECTOR WITH A TEST LIGHT FROM CAVITY "5" TO GROUND.
TEST LIGHT SHOULD LIGHT.
DOES IT?
REPLACE A/C COMPRESSOR CLUTCH.
NO
YES
• BACKPROBE A.C MG RELAY WITH A TEST LIGHT FROM CAVITY "3" TO GROUND.
TEST LIGHT SHOULD LIGHT.
DOES IT?
REPAIR OPEN IN BLK/WHT WIRE BETWEEN A.C MG RELAY AND A/C COMPRESSOR CLUTCH.
YES
NO
• BACKPROBE A.C MG RELAY WITH A TEST LIGHT FROM CAVITY "2" TO GROUND.
TEST LIGHT SHOULD LIGHT.
DOES IT?
DOES BLOWER MOTOR RUN?
YES
NO
NO
YES
REPAIR OPEN IN BLU/RED WIRE BETWEEN A.C MG RELAY CONNECTOR CAVITIES "2" AND "3".
• CHECK FOR AN OPEN IN BLU/RED WIRE BETWEEN JUNCTION BLOCK 2 AND A.C MG RELAY.
IF OK, REPLACE JUNCTION BLOCK 2.
A
B

AIR CONDITIONING SYSTEM ELECTRICAL DIAGNOSIS CHART–PRIZM
CHART #1 (continued)
A/C COMPRESSOR CLUTCH NEVER ENGAGES

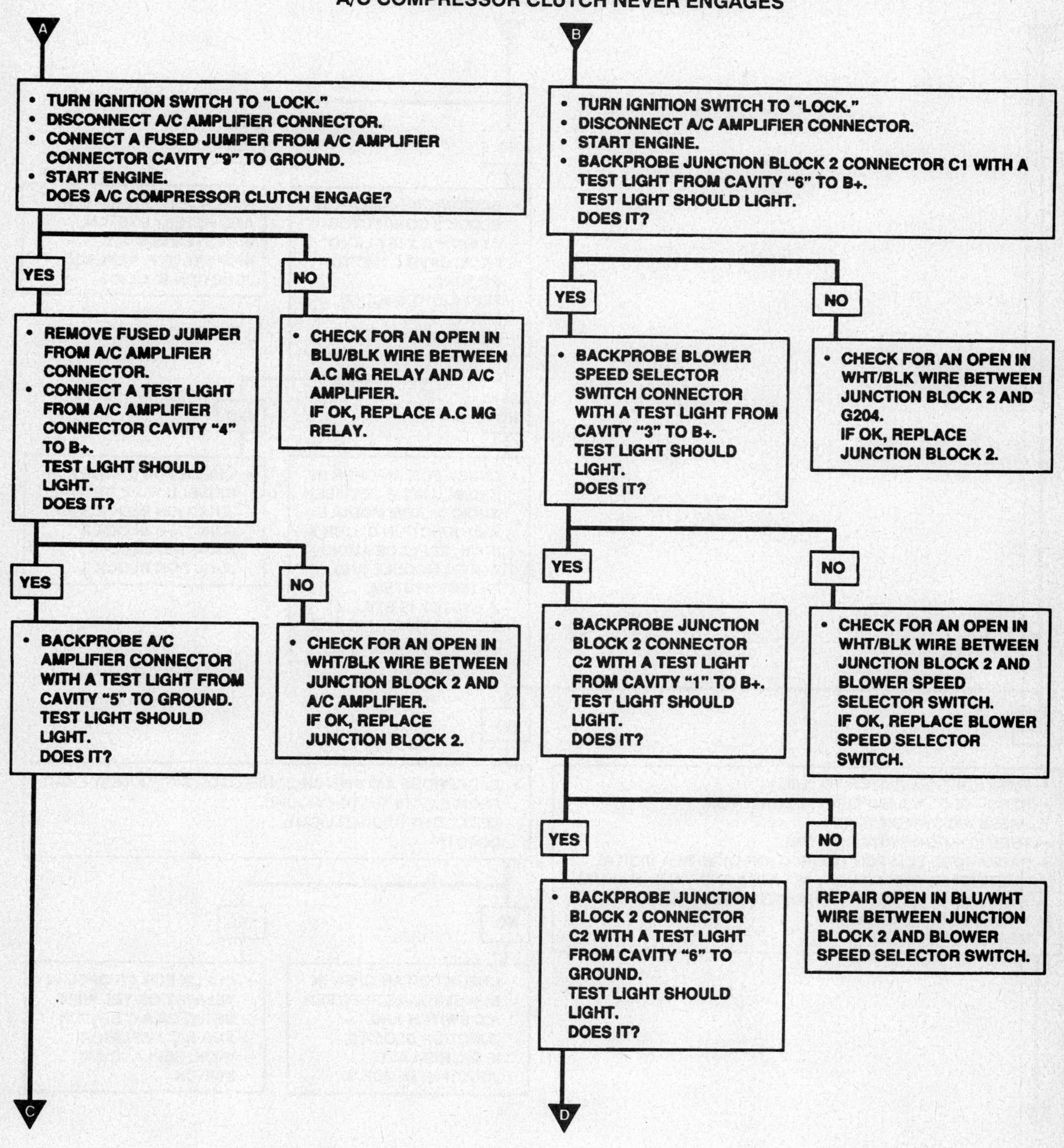
A
• TURN IGNITION SWITCH TO "LOCK."
• DISCONNECT A/C AMPLIFIER CONNECTOR.
• CONNECT A FUSED JUMPER FROM A/C AMPLIFIER CONNECTOR CAVITY "9" TO GROUND.
• START ENGINE.
DOES A/C COMPRESSOR CLUTCH ENGAGE?
YES
NO
• REMOVE FUSED JUMPER FROM A/C AMPLIFIER CONNECTOR.
• CONNECT A TEST LIGHT FROM A/C AMPLIFIER CONNECTOR CAVITY "4" TO B+.
TEST LIGHT SHOULD LIGHT.
DOES IT?
• CHECK FOR AN OPEN IN BLU/BLK WIRE BETWEEN A.C MG RELAY AND A/C AMPLIFIER.
IF OK, REPLACE A.C MG RELAY.
YES
NO
• BACKPROBE A/C AMPLIFIER CONNECTOR WITH A TEST LIGHT FROM CAVITY "5" TO GROUND.
TEST LIGHT SHOULD LIGHT.
DOES IT?
• CHECK FOR AN OPEN IN WHT/BLK WIRE BETWEEN JUNCTION BLOCK 2 AND A/C AMPLIFIER.
IF OK, REPLACE JUNCTION BLOCK 2.
C
B
• TURN IGNITION SWITCH TO "LOCK."
• DISCONNECT A/C AMPLIFIER CONNECTOR.
• START ENGINE.
• BACKPROBE JUNCTION BLOCK 2 CONNECTOR C1 WITH A TEST LIGHT FROM CAVITY "6" TO B+.
TEST LIGHT SHOULD LIGHT.
DOES IT?
YES
NO
• BACKPROBE BLOWER SPEED SELECTOR SWITCH CONNECTOR WITH A TEST LIGHT FROM CAVITY "3" TO B+.
TEST LIGHT SHOULD LIGHT.
DOES IT?
• CHECK FOR AN OPEN IN WHT/BLK WIRE BETWEEN JUNCTION BLOCK 2 AND G204.
IF OK, REPLACE JUNCTION BLOCK 2.
YES
NO
• BACKPROBE JUNCTION BLOCK 2 CONNECTOR C2 WITH A TEST LIGHT FROM CAVITY "1" TO B+.
TEST LIGHT SHOULD LIGHT.
DOES IT?
• CHECK FOR AN OPEN IN WHT/BLK WIRE BETWEEN JUNCTION BLOCK 2 AND BLOWER SPEED SELECTOR SWITCH.
IF OK, REPLACE BLOWER SPEED SELECTOR SWITCH.
YES
NO
• BACKPROBE JUNCTION BLOCK 2 CONNECTOR C2 WITH A TEST LIGHT FROM CAVITY "6" TO GROUND.
TEST LIGHT SHOULD LIGHT.
DOES IT?
REPAIR OPEN IN BLU/WHT WIRE BETWEEN JUNCTION BLOCK 2 AND BLOWER SPEED SELECTOR SWITCH.
D

AIR CONDITIONING SYSTEM ELECTRICAL DIAGNOSIS CHART—PRIZM, CONT'D

CHART #1 (continued)

A/C COMPRESSOR CLUTCH NEVER ENGAGES

C

D

NO

- BACKPROBE JUNCTION BLOCK 3 CONNECTOR C3 WITH A TEST LIGHT FROM CAVITY "19" TO GROUND. TEST LIGHT SHOULD LIGHT. DOES IT?

NO

- CHECK FOR AN OPEN IN RED/BLU WIRE BETWEEN AUDIO ALARM MODULE AND JUNCTION BLOCK 3. IF OK, REPLACE AUDIO ALARM MODULE AND RETEST SYSTEM. IF SYSTEM IS STILL INOPERATIVE, REPLACE JUNCTION BLOCK 1.

YES

- CHECK FOR AN OPEN IN RED/BLU WIRE BETWEEN JUNCTION BLOCK 3 AND JUNCTION BLOCK 2. IF OK, REPLACE JUNCTION BLOCK 3.

YES

REPLACE HEATER RELAY AND RETEST SYSTEM. IF SYSTEM IS STILL INOPERATIVE, REPLACE JUNCTION BLOCK 2.

YES

- TURN IGNITION SWITCH TO "LOCK."
- RECONNECT A/C AMPLIFIER CONNECTOR.
- PRESS A/C SWITCH TO OFF
- TURN IGNITION SWITCH TO "ON."
- BACKPROBE ECM/PCM CONNECTOR C1 WITH A DIGITAL MULTIMETER FROM CAVITY "6" (VIN 6 AND VIN 8 - MANUAL TRANSAXLE) OR FROM CAVITY "21" (VIN 8 - AUTOMATIC TRANSAXLE) TO GROUND.
- MEASURE VOLTAGE.

E

NO

- BACKPROBE A/C SWITCH CONNECTOR WITH A TEST LIGHT FROM CAVITY "6" TO GROUND. TEST LIGHT SHOULD LIGHT. DOES IT?

NO

- CHECK FOR AN OPEN IN BLU/BLK WIRE BETWEEN A/C SWITCH AND JUNCTION BLOCK 2. IF OK, REPLACE JUNCTION BLOCK 2.

YES

- CHECK FOR AN OPEN IN YEL/WHT OR YEL WIRE BETWEEN A/C SWITCH AND A/C AMPLIFIER. IF OK, REPLACE A/C SWITCH.

AIR CONDITIONING SYSTEM ELECTRICAL DIAGNOSIS CHART–PRIZM, CONT'D
CHART #1 (continued)
A/C COMPRESSOR CLUTCH NEVER ENGAGES

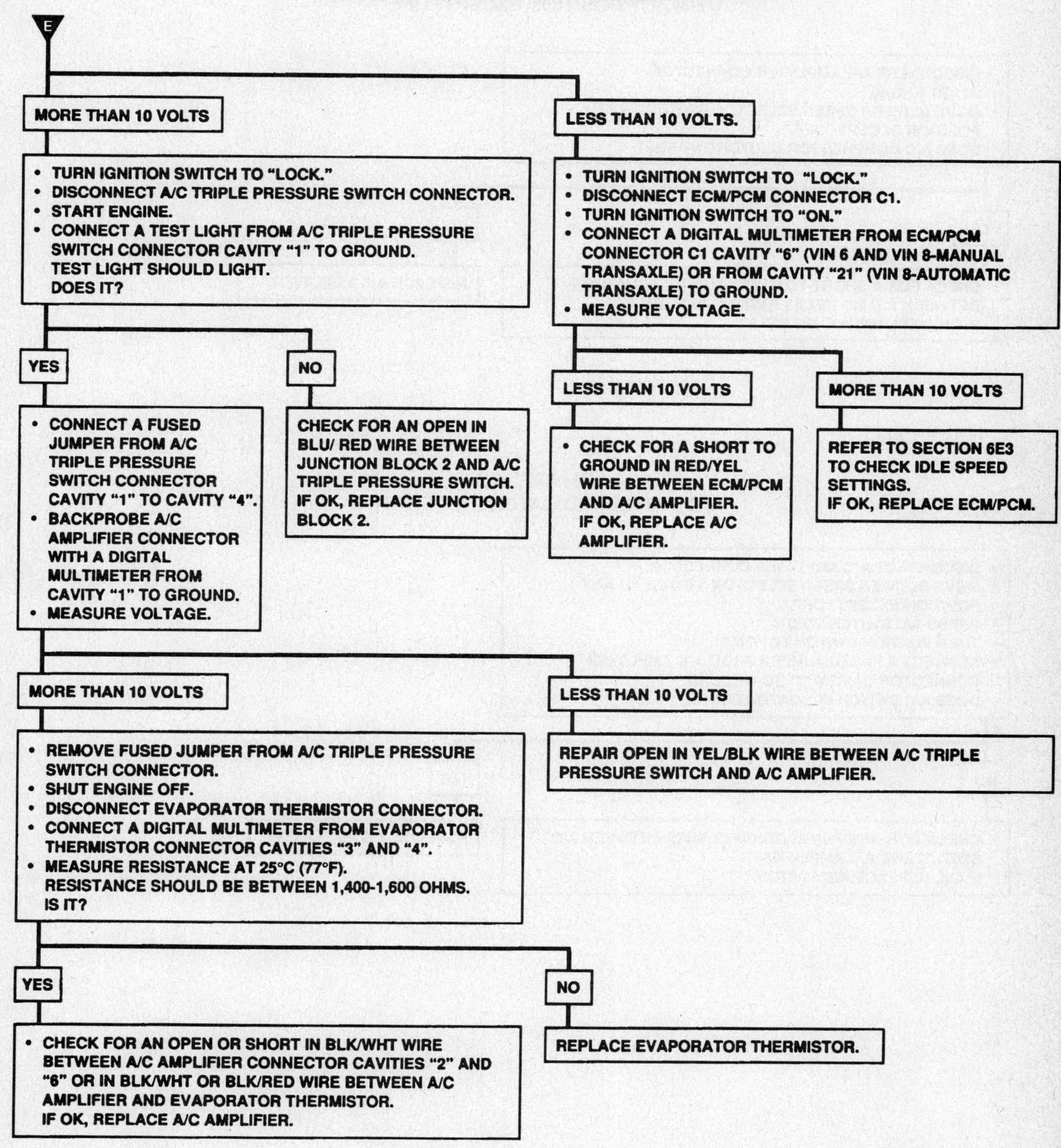

E
MORE THAN 10 VOLTS
• TURN IGNITION SWITCH TO "LOCK."
• DISCONNECT A/C TRIPLE PRESSURE SWITCH CONNECTOR.
• START ENGINE.
• CONNECT A TEST LIGHT FROM A/C TRIPLE PRESSURE SWITCH CONNECTOR CAVITY "1" TO GROUND. TEST LIGHT SHOULD LIGHT. DOES IT?
YES
• CONNECT A FUSED JUMPER FROM A/C TRIPLE PRESSURE SWITCH CONNECTOR CAVITY "1" TO CAVITY "4".
• BACKPROBE A/C AMPLIFIER CONNECTOR WITH A DIGITAL MULTIMETER FROM CAVITY "1" TO GROUND.
• MEASURE VOLTAGE.
MORE THAN 10 VOLTS
• REMOVE FUSED JUMPER FROM A/C TRIPLE PRESSURE SWITCH CONNECTOR.
• SHUT ENGINE OFF.
• DISCONNECT EVAPORATOR THERMISTOR CONNECTOR.
• CONNECT A DIGITAL MULTIMETER FROM EVAPORATOR THERMISTOR CONNECTOR CAVITIES "3" AND "4".
• MEASURE RESISTANCE AT 25°C (77°F). RESISTANCE SHOULD BE BETWEEN 1,400-1,600 OHMS. IS IT?
YES
• CHECK FOR AN OPEN OR SHORT IN BLK/WHT WIRE BETWEEN A/C AMPLIFIER CONNECTOR CAVITIES "2" AND "6" OR IN BLK/WHT OR BLK/RED WIRE BETWEEN A/C AMPLIFIER AND EVAPORATOR THERMISTOR. IF OK, REPLACE A/C AMPLIFIER.
NO
REPLACE EVAPORATOR THERMISTOR.
LESS THAN 10 VOLTS
REPAIR OPEN IN YEL/BLK WIRE BETWEEN A/C TRIPLE PRESSURE SWITCH AND A/C AMPLIFIER.
NO
CHECK FOR AN OPEN IN BLU/ RED WIRE BETWEEN JUNCTION BLOCK 2 AND A/C TRIPLE PRESSURE SWITCH. IF OK, REPLACE JUNCTION BLOCK 2.
LESS THAN 10 VOLTS.
• TURN IGNITION SWITCH TO "LOCK."
• DISCONNECT ECM/PCM CONNECTOR C1.
• TURN IGNITION SWITCH TO "ON."
• CONNECT A DIGITAL MULTIMETER FROM ECM/PCM CONNECTOR C1 CAVITY "6" (VIN 6 AND VIN 8-MANUAL TRANSAXLE) OR FROM CAVITY "21" (VIN 8-AUTOMATIC TRANSAXLE) TO GROUND.
• MEASURE VOLTAGE.
LESS THAN 10 VOLTS
• CHECK FOR A SHORT TO GROUND IN RED/YEL WIRE BETWEEN ECM/PCM AND A/C AMPLIFIER. IF OK, REPLACE A/C AMPLIFIER.
MORE THAN 10 VOLTS
REFER TO SECTION 6E3 TO CHECK IDLE SPEED SETTINGS. IF OK, REPLACE ECM/PCM.

AIR CONDITIONING SYSTEM ELECTRICAL DIAGNOSIS CHART–PRIZM, CONT'D

CHART #2

A/C COMPRESSOR CLUTCH ENGAGES WITH A/C SWITCH OFF AND BLOWER SPEED SELECTOR SWITCH IN ANY POSITION EXCEPT "OFF"

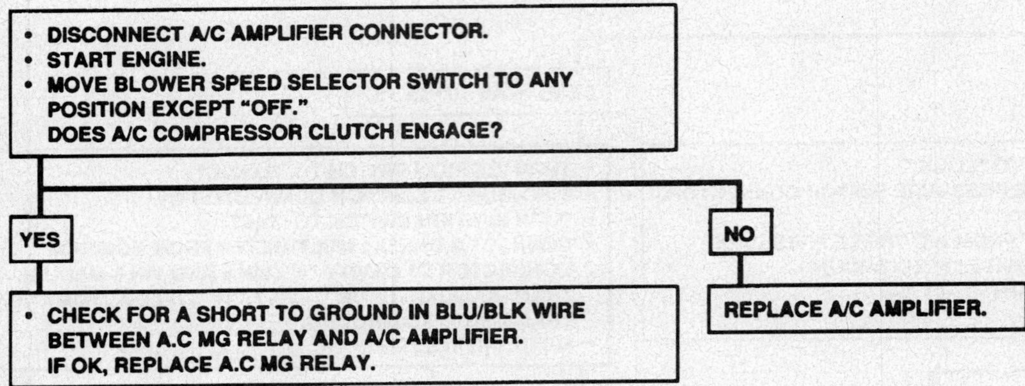

CHART #3

A/C SWITCH INDICATOR INOPERATIVE

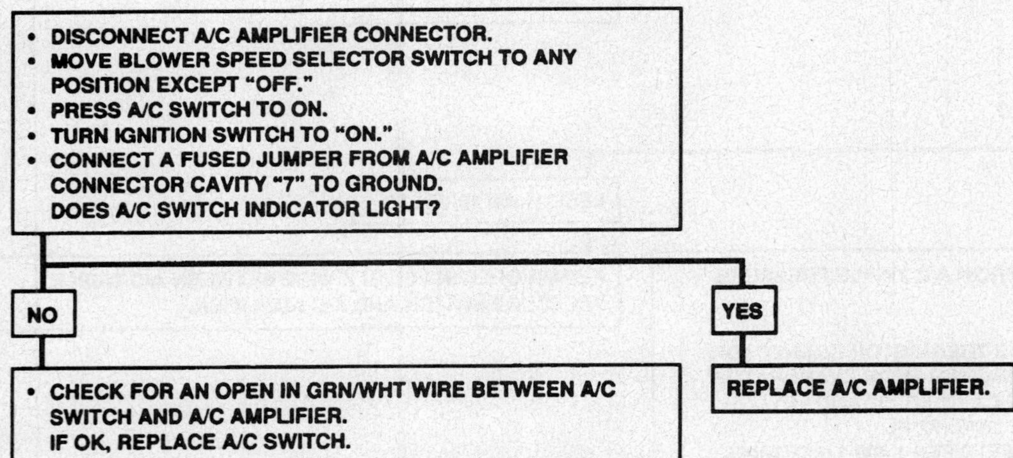

• DISCONNECT A/C AMPLIFIER CONNECTOR.
• MOVE BLOWER SPEED SELECTOR SWITCH TO ANY POSITION EXCEPT "OFF."
• PRESS A/C SWITCH TO ON.
• TURN IGNITION SWITCH TO "ON."
• CONNECT A FUSED JUMPER FROM A/C AMPLIFIER CONNECTOR CAVITY "7" TO GROUND.
DOES A/C SWITCH INDICATOR LIGHT?
NO
YES
• CHECK FOR AN OPEN IN GRN/WHT WIRE BETWEEN A/C SWITCH AND A/C AMPLIFIER.
IF OK, REPLACE A/C SWITCH.
REPLACE A/C AMPLIFIER.

COOLANT FANS
WITH AIR CONDITIONING

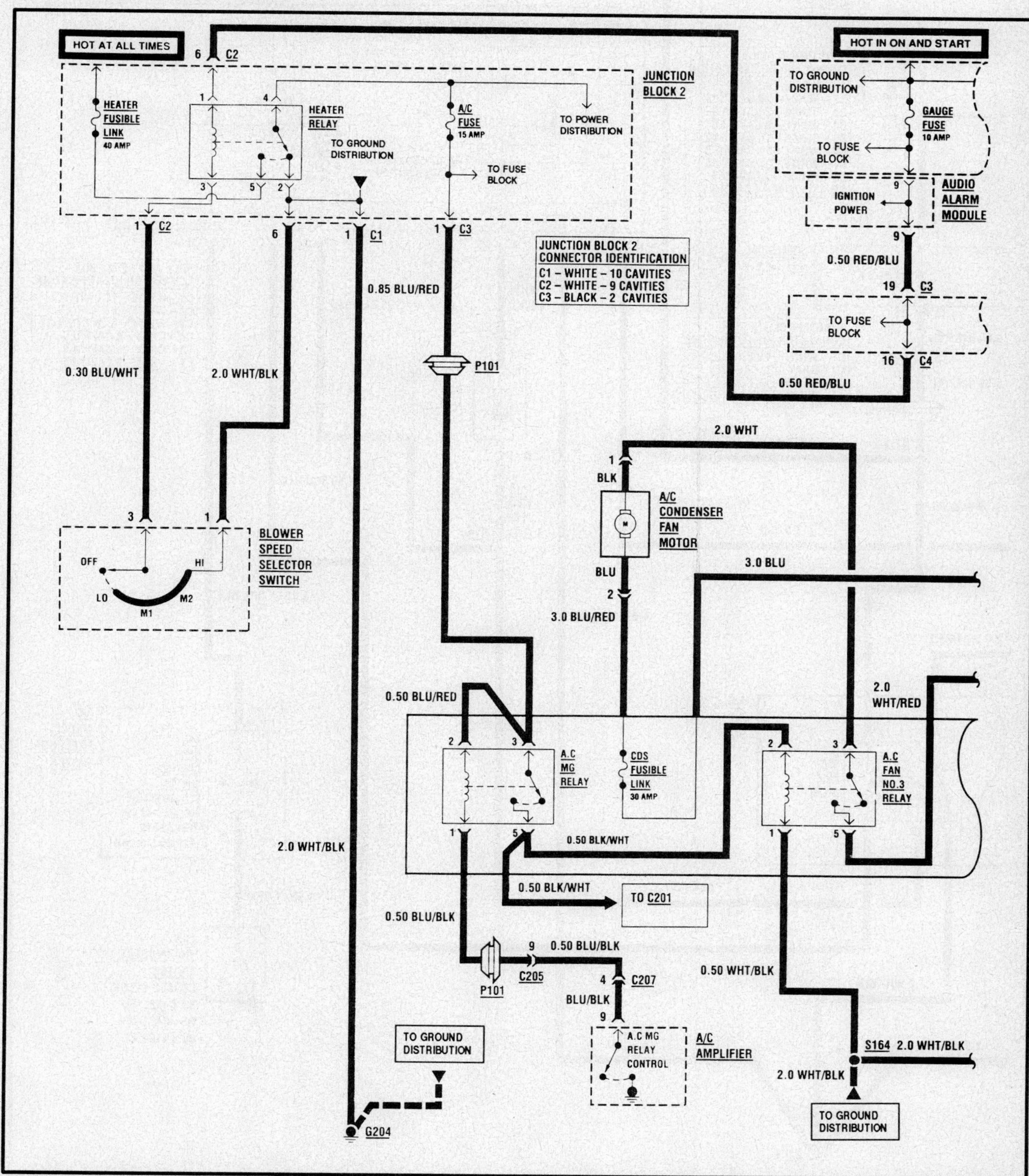

Coolant fan wiring schematic—1994-95 Prizm

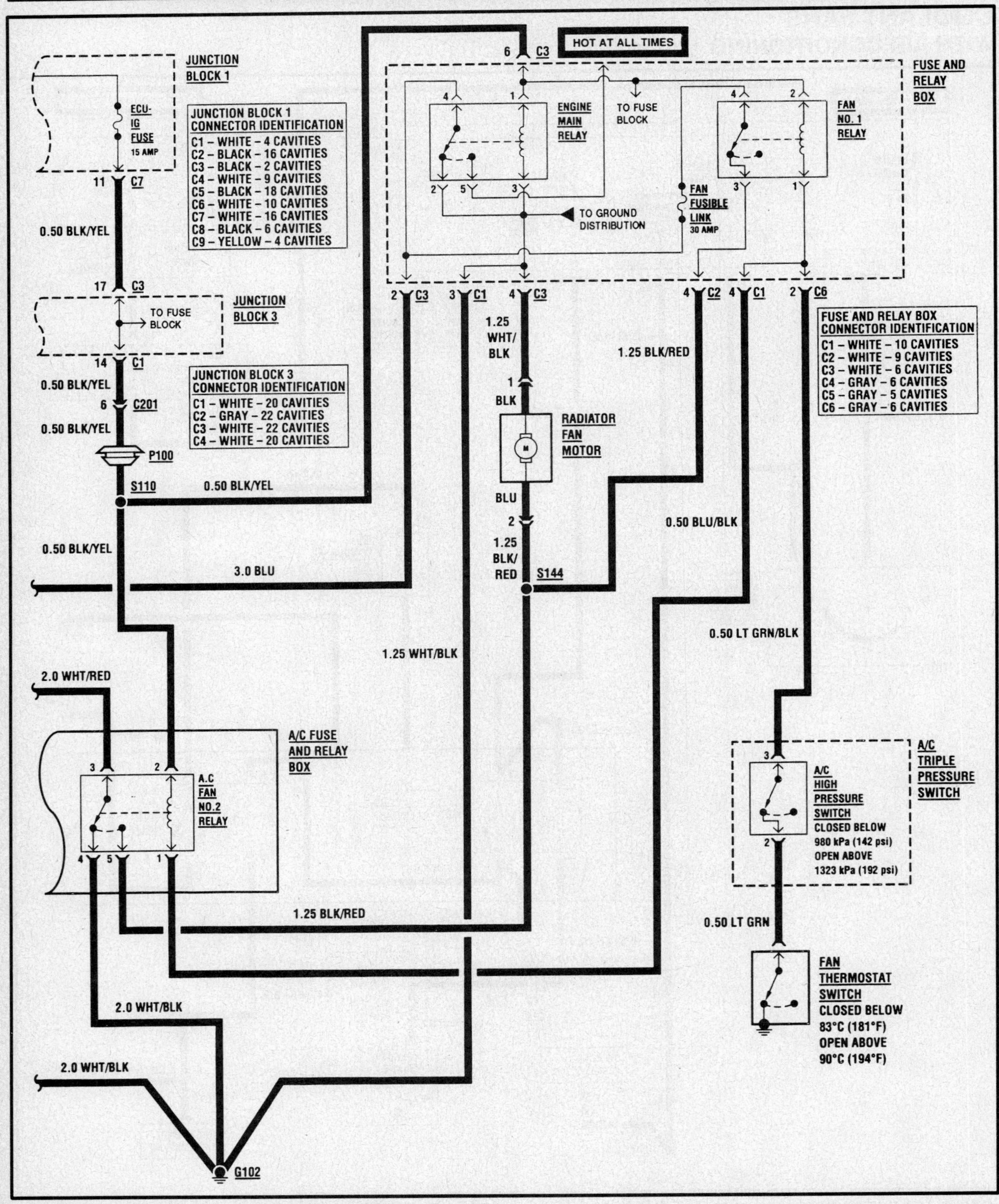

Coolant fan wiring schematic—1994-95 Prizm, Cont'd

12 SATURN 12

SC1 • SC2 • SL • SL1 • SL2 • SW1 • SW2

SPECIFICATIONS

ENGINE IDENTIFICATION

Year	Model	Engine Displacement Liters (cc)	Engine Series (ID/VIN)	Fuel System	No. of Cylinders	Engine Type
1993	Sedan SL/SL1	1.9 (1901)	LKO (9)	TBI	4	SOHC
	Sedan SL2	1.9 (1901)	LLO (7)	MFI	4	DOHC
	Wagon SW1	1.9 (1901)	LKO (9)	TBI	4	SOHC
	Wagon SW2	1.9 (1901)	LLO (7)	MFI	4	DOHC
	Coupe SC1	1.9 (1901)	LKO (9)	TBI	4	SOHC
	Coupe SC2	1.9 (1901)	LKO (7)	MFI	4	DOHC
1994	Sedan SL/SL1	1.9 (1901)	LKO (9)	TBI	4	SOHC
	Sedan SL2	1.9 (1901)	LLO (7)	MFI	4	DOHC
	Wagon SW1	1.9 (1901)	LKO (9)	TBI	4	SOHC
	Wagon SW2	1.9 (1901)	LLO (7)	MFI	4	DOHC
	Coupe SC1	1.9 (1901)	LKO (9)	TBI	4	SOHC
	Coupe SC2	1.9 (1901)	LKO (7)	MFI	4	DOHC
1995	Sedan SL/SL1	1.9 (1901)	L24 (8)	MFI	4	SOHC
	Sedan SL2	1.9 (1901)	LLO (7)	MFI	4	DOHC
	Wagon SW1	1.9 (1901)	L24 (8)	MFI	4	SOHC
	Wagon SW2	1.9 (1901)	LLO (7)	MFI	4	DOHC
	Coupe SC1	1.9 (1901)	L24 (8)	MFI	4	SOHC
	Coupe SC2	1.9 (1901)	LLO (7)	MFI	4	DOHC

TBI—Throttle Body Injection
MFI—Multi-Port Fuel Injection
SOHC—Single Overhead Cam
DOHC—Dual Overhead Cam

REFRIGERANT CAPACITIES

Year	Model	Refrigerant (oz.)	Oil (cc)	Compressor Type
1993	Sedan SL/SL1	34	200	Variable displ.; rotary vane
	Sedan SL2	34	200	Variable displ.; rotary vane
	Wagon SW1	34	200	Variable displ.; rotary vane
	Wagon SW2	34	200	Variable displ.; rotary vane
	Coupe SC1	34	200	Variable displ.; rotary vane
	Coupe SC2	34	200	Variable displ.; rotary vane
1994	Sedan SL/SL1	34	200	Variable displ.; rotary vane
	Sedan SL2	34	200	Variable displ.; rotary vane
	Wagon SW1	34	200	Variable displ.; rotary vane
	Wagon SW2	34	200	Variable displ.; rotary vane
	Coupe SC1	34	200	Variable displ.; rotary vane
	Coupe SC2	34	200	Variable displ.; rotary vane
1995	Sedan SL/SL1	24	200	Variable displ.; rotary vane
	Sedan SL2	24	200	Variable displ.; rotary vane
	Wagon SW1	24	200	Variable displ.; rotary vane
	Wagon SW2	24	200	Variable displ.; rotary vane

REFRIGERANT CAPACITIES, CONT'D

Year	Model	Refrigerant (oz.)	Oil (cc)	Compressor Type
1995	Coupe SC1	24	200	Variable displ.; rotary vane
	Coupe SC2	24	200	Variable displ.; rotary vane

AIR CONDITIONING BELT TENSION

Year	Model	Engine Liters (cc)	Belt Type	Specifications New ①	Used ①
1993	Sedan SL/SL1	1.9 ②	Serpentine	50-65 lbs.	45 lbs. min.
	Sedan SL2	1.9 ③	Serpentine	50-65 lbs.	45 lbs. min.
	Wagon SW1	1.9 ②	Serpentine	50-65 lbs.	45 lbs. min.
	Wagon SW2	1.9 ③	Serpentine	50-65 lbs.	45 lbs. min.
	Coupe SC1	1.9 ②	Serpentine	50-65 lbs.	45 lbs. min.
	Coupe SC2	1.9 ③	Serpentine	50-65 lbs.	45 lbs. min.
1994	Sedan SL/SL1	1.9 ②	Serpentine	50-65 lbs.	45 lbs. min.
	Sedan SL2	1.9 ③	Serpentine	50-65 lbs.	45 lbs. min.
	Wagon SW1	1.9 ②	Serpentine	50-65 lbs.	45 lbs. min.
	Wagon SW2	1.9 ③	Serpentine	50-65 lbs.	45 lbs. min.
	Coupe SC1	1.9 ②	Serpentine	50-65 lbs.	45 lbs. min.
	Coupe SC2	1.9 ③	Serpentine	50-65 lbs.	45 lbs. min.
1995	Sedan SL/SL1	1.9 ②	Serpentine	50-65 lbs.	45 lbs. min.
	Sedan SL2	1.9 ③	Serpentine	50-65 lbs.	45 lbs. min.
	Wagon SW1	1.9 ②	Serpentine	50-65 lbs.	45 lbs. min.
	Wagon SW2	1.9 ③	Serpentine	50-65 lbs.	45 lbs. min.
	Coupe SC1	1.9 ②	Serpentine	50-65 lbs.	45 lbs. min.
	Coupe SC2	1.9 ③	Serpentine	50-65 lbs.	45 lbs. min.

① Inches of deflection at midpoint of the belt
② SOHC engine
③ DOHC engine

SYSTEM DESCRIPTION

General Information

The Heating, Ventilating, Air Conditioning, and Controls (HVAC) module consists of a recirc motor, blower motor and fan, blower motor resistor, heater core and evaporator core. The operations of these assemblies are controlled by the levers and switches on the HVAC control panel.

Distribution of the air is controlled by the mode levers and buttons on the control assembly. The various positions of the mode levers and buttons direct cooled, heated, blended, outside or inside air through the air ducts. The flow of air during the various modes of operations is as follows:

Face—Instrument panel outlets with a small amount of bleed air to the heater

Face and Feet—Instrument panel outlets and floor outlets

Feet—Floor outlets with a small amount of bleed air to defroster

Top—Defroster ducts with a small amount of bleed air to the heater

Service Valve Locations

The suction valve and the discharge valves are located near the compressor on the suction and discharge lines.

System Discharging

NOTE: 1994 and later models use R134a, a non-CFC refrigerant. Although both R12 and R134a should be recovered and recycled, the two refrigerants and their respective lubricants are not be be mixed under any circumstances. Seperate recovery/recycling systems, gauges and manifolds must be used for each type of refrigerant.

1. Before removing or replacing any of the A/C refrigerant lines or components, the refrigerant must be completely recovered.
2. The refrigerant system must be discharged using an air conditioning refrigerant recovery and recycling system. Follow

the manufacturers operating instructions for the system being used.

3. Always check the A/C system for pressure with a manifold gauge set to determine if refrigerant is present in the system.

4. Performing recovery on an A/C system which is open to the atmosphere as a result of a leak, would allow the recovery station to pull only air into the tank.

System Evacuating

1. Connect the manifold gauge set and vacuum pump to high and low side Schrader valves. Turn ON vacuum pump and slowly open high and low side valves to pump. Allow system to evacuate for 20-30 minutes. Note vacuum reading.
2. Close high and low side valves. Shut OFF vacuum pump.
3. Watch low side gauge for vacuum loss (1-3 minutes). If loss is less than 1 in. Hg (3.38 kPa) from level recorded in Step 1, proceed to charging the A/C system.
4. If vacuum loss is greater than 1 in. Hg (3.38 kPa) from level recorded in Step 1, charge with 1/2 lb. (0.23 kg) of refrigerant. Leak test, and retest.

NOTE: Disconnect high side adapter from service port and check for vacuum loss before charging.

System Charging

1. Open the refrigerant source valve(s) and allow 1 lb. (0.50 kg) of liquid refrigerant to flow into system through low-side service fitting.
2. As soon as 1 lb. (0.50 kg) has been added to the system, start engine, set the A/C control to upper outlets, temperature lever to **MAX COLD**, blower speed on **HIGH**, and push A/C compressor button to the **ON** position (A/C control button light **ON**). Slowly draw in the remainder of the refrigerant charge.
3. Turn OFF refrigerant source valve and run engine for 30 seconds to clear the lines and gauges.
4. With the engine running, remove the charging low-side hose adapter from the suction pipe service fitting. Unscrew rapidly to avoid excess refrigerant escaping from the system.

NOTE: Make sure there is an O-ring seal inside of caps before installation because cap is primary seal for A/C service fittings.

5. Install protective caps on service fittings.
6. Turn engine OFF.
7. Leak check system with electronic leak detector or equivalent.
8. With system fully charged and leak-checked, conduct a functional and performance test.

Supplemental Inflatable Restraint

Air Bag System Disabling

CAUTION

When performing service around the Supplemental Inflatable Restraint (SIR) system components or wiring, follow the procedures listed below to temporarily disable the SIR system. Failure to follow procedures could result in possible air bag deployment, personal injury, or otherwise unneeded SIR system repairs.

1. Turn the steering wheel so that the wheels are straight ahead. Turn ignition switch to **OFF** (1995 **LOCK**) position.
2. Remove "Air Bag" fuse.
3. Remove connector position assurance device from yellow 2-way SIR connector at the base of the steering column and disconnect.

NOTE: With the Air Bag fuse removed and the ignition switch ON the "Air Bag" telltale light will be ON. This is normal operation and does not indicate an SIR fault.

Enabling the SIR system

1. Turn ignition switch to **OFF** (1995 **LOCK**) position.
2. Connect the yellow 2-way SIR connector at the base of the steering column and install connector position assurance device to connector.
3. Install "Air Bag" fuse.
4. Turn ignition switch to **RUN** position and make sure the "Air Bag" telltale lamp flashes 7 times and then remains OFF.

SYSTEM COMPONENTS

NOTE: If equipped with Supplemental Inflatable Restraint system (air bag) be sure to properly disable the system before removing key components, especially those in or around the instrument panel, steering column or the air bag sensors.

Radiator

REMOVAL AND INSTALLATION

1. Drain cooling system.
2. Disconnect negative battery terminal.
3. Remove air intake ducts. If equipped with a DOHC (LLO) engine, remove the air cleaner housing and temperature sensor connector.
4. Remove upper radiator hose.
5. On models with automatic transaxles, disconnect upper transaxle oil cooler line.
6. Remove electric cooling fan assembly.
7. Remove lower radiator hose.
8. Raise and properly support vehicle.
9. Remove lower splash shield.
10. On models with automatic transaxle, disconnect lower transaxle cooler line.
11. Remove 4 condenser bracket-to-radiator bolts.

NOTE: Wire condenser up to vehicle to keep in place.

12. Lower vehicle.
13. Remove upper radiator nuts and brackets.
14. On A/C equipped vehicles, remove upper radiator seal.
15. Remove radiator from vehicle.

To install:

16. Install radiator in vehicle.
17. On A/C equipped vehicles, install upper radiator seal.
18. Install upper radiator brackets and nuts.

NOTE: The L-shaped brackets must not pinch the radiator locating pins. The radiator must be able to move freely in the grommets after installation.

19. Raise and properly support vehicle.
20. Install condenser bracket-to-radiator bolts.
21. On models with automatic transaxle, connect lower transaxle oil cooler line.
22. Install lower splash shield.
23. Lower vehicle.

24. Install lower radiator hose.
25. Install fan assembly.
26. Connect upper transaxle oil cooler line at a 35 degree angle.

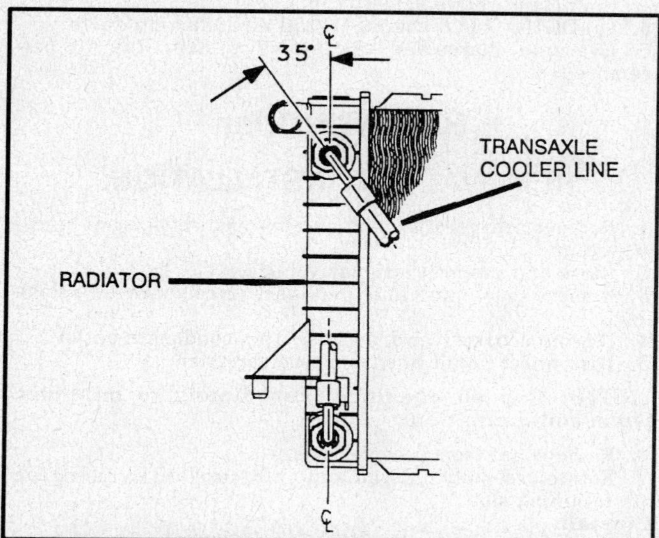

Transaxle cooler line installation

27. Install upper radiator hose.
28. If equipped with a DOHC (LLO) engine, install air cleaner housing.
29. Install intake air ducts and temperature sensor connector.
30. Connect negative battery terminal.
31. Fill with coolant and leak test.

Cooling Fan

REMOVAL AND INSTALLATION

1. Disconnect negative battery cable.
2. If equipped with a DOHC (LLO) engine, remove intake air ducts and temperature sensor connector.
3. Remove wiring harness from fan motor.
4. Remove top hold down bolts from coolant fan assembly.

NOTE: On models with automatic transaxle, it may be necessary to loosen top automatic transaxle oil cooler line and move it out of the way.

5. Lift coolant fan off lower mounting brackets. Move assembly to the left and rotate counter-clockwise lifting right side up past upper radiator hose.
6. Remove fan from vehicle.

To install:

7. Install cooling fan in vehicle with lower left corner first.
8. Rotate assembly clockwise to place lower left fan mount under radiator hose.
9. Position cooling fan assembly on lower mounting brackets.
10. Install upper hold down bolts.

NOTE: Tighten upper automatic transaxle oil cooler line if necessary. On 1993 vehicles, position upper transaxle oil cooler line at 35 degrees.

11. Install the wiring harness on the fan motor.
12. If equipped with a DOHC (LLO) engine, install intake air ducts and temperature sensor connector.
13. Connect negative battery cable.

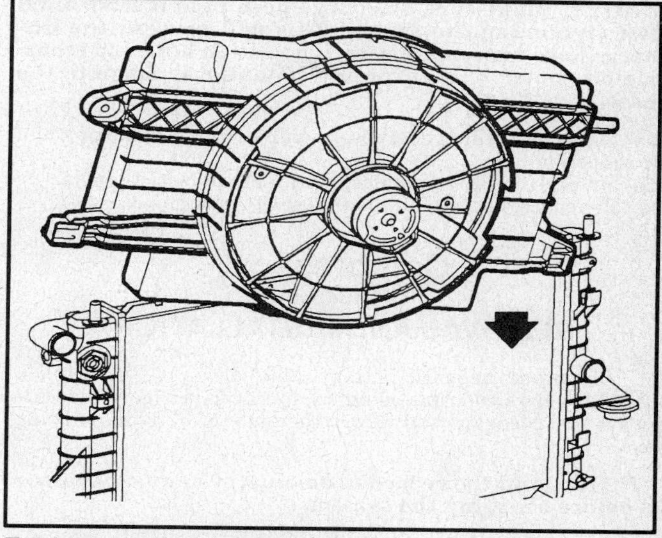
Engine cooling fan installation

Condenser

REMOVAL AND INSTALLATION

1. Recover refrigerant using an approved refrigerant recovery system.
2. On DOHC (LLO) engines, remove air cleaner housing and air induction hose at intake manifold.
3. On SOHC (LKO, L24) engines, remove air induction ducts.
4. Remove compressor discharge hose from condenser inlet.

NOTE: For 1995 Sedans/Wagons and SC1 models, remove left front headlamp assembly to gain access to fitting. For 1995 SC2, remove lower splash shield assembly and gain access to fitting from under the vehicle.

5. Raise and properly support vehicle.
6. Remove lower splash shield.
7. Remove receiver-drier hose from condenser outlet.
8. Remove condenser bracket-to-radiator bolts.
9. Facing the vehicle, pull the condenser back slightly to release it from the mounting pads. Slide condenser straight down.
10. Rotate left end of condenser down so inlet pipe is straight up.
11. Rotate bottom of condenser rearward to unhook inlet pipe from the lower radiator mount.
12. Remove condenser from vehicle.

To install:

13. Install condenser by holding it at a right angle to the radiator with the inlet pointing upward. Hook the inlet over the lower radiator mount and rotate to a position parallel with the radiator.
14. Slide condenser up and position on mounting pads.
15. Install condenser bracket-to-radiator bolts.
16. Lubricate new O-ring on receiver-drier hose and connect hose to condenser outlet.

NOTE: Make sure receiver-drier hose is parallel with the condenser after tightening the fitting. This will provide hose clearance to the body and frame, avoiding potential damage to hose.

17. Install lower splash shield.
18. Lower vehicle.
19. Lubricate and install new O-ring on compressor discharge hose and connect hose to condenser outlet.

NOTE: Make sure discharge hose pipe is horizontal after tightening the fitting. This will prevent the discharge hose from contacting the suction hose and transaxle oil cooler lines, avoiding potential damage to the hoses.

20. On DOHC (LLO) engines, install air cleaner housing and air induction hose.
21. On SOHC (LKO) engines, install air induction ducts.
22. Evacuate, charge, and leak test A/C system.

Compressor

REMOVAL AND INSTALLATION

1. Disconnect negative battery cable.
2. Recover refrigerant using an approved refrigerant recovery system. Measure and record the amount of oil lost during recovery.

NOTE: Add the recorded amount of new compressor oil before charging the system.

3. On DOHC (LLO) engine, remove air induction ducts.
4. Remove accessory drive belt from compressor clutch pulley by rotating belt tensioner clockwise.
5. Disconnect compressor clutch electrical connector.
6. Disconnect low and high side hoses at compressor.

NOTE: Cap all openings immediately to minimize system contamination.

7. Remove compressor.

NOTE: Keep compressor level during removal to avoid any oil loss from the low or high side ports.

To install:

NOTE: Keep compressor level during installation to avoid any oil loss from the low or high side ports.

8. Install compressor to front bracket with 3 bolts. Finger tighten only.
9. Install compressor to rear bracket with 3 bolts. Tighten front bolts to 36 ft. lbs. (49 Nm) and rear bolts to 19 ft. lbs. (25 Nm).
10. Lubricate and install new O-rings.

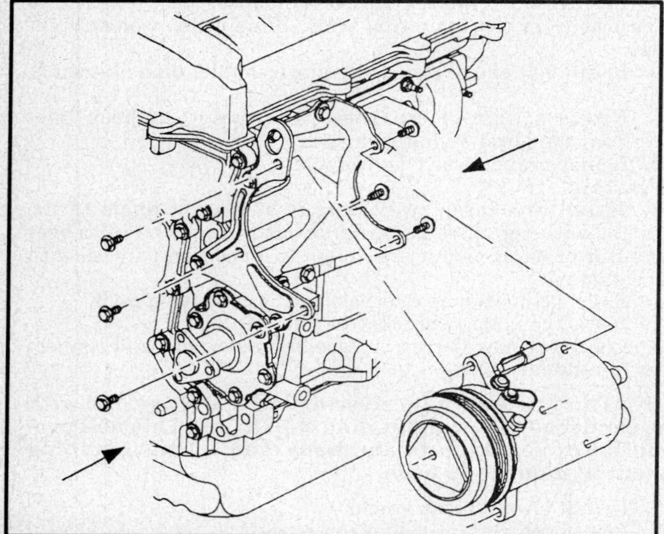

Compressor and mounting bracket

11. Tighten suction hose and discharge nose to 19 ft. lbs. (25 Nm).
12. Connect compressor clutch electrical connector.
13. Install accessory drive belt.
14. Connect negative battery cable.
15. On DOHC (LLO) engine, install air induction ducts.
16. Evacuate, charge and leak test A/C system. Run A/C performance test.

Receiver/Drier

REMOVAL AND INSTALLATION

1. Recover refrigerant using an approved refrigerant recovery system.
2. Raise and properly support vehicle.
3. Remove push nut and pull back receiver/drier splash shield.
4. Disconnect receiver/drier hose from condenser outlet.
5. Disconnect liquid line from receiver/drier.

NOTE: Cap all openings immediately to minimize system contamination.

6. Remove nut from receiver/drier.
7. Rotate assembly off stud and pull rearward to disengage from retaining slot.

To install:

8. Feed receiver/drier hose up over vehicle frame and down to condenser outlet.
9. Install receiver/drier in retaining slot, rotate onto stud, and install nut.

NOTE: Installed position is with tab all the way forward and at the bottom of the slot. Make sure pipe does not touch the frame rail.

10. Lubricate new O-ring and connect receiver/drier hose on condenser outlet.

NOTE: Make sure receiver/drier hose is parallel with the condenser after tightening the fitting. This will provide hose clearance to the body and frame, avoiding potential damage to the hose.

11. Lubricate and install new O-ring and connect liquid line on receiver/drier.

NOTE: Make sure liquid line is not touching sheet metal in the body cut out after tightening the fitting.

12. Rotate receiver/drier splash shield into place and install push nut.
13. Lower vehicle. Evacuate, charge, and leak test A/C system.

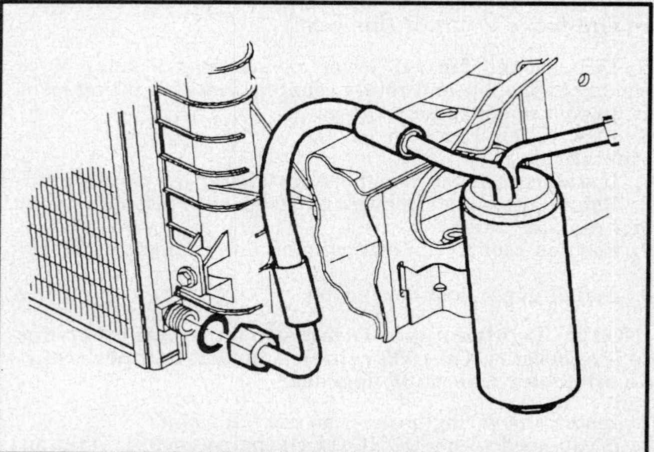

Receiver/drier installation

Thermal Expansion Valve (TXV)

REMOVAL AND INSTALLATION

1. Recover refrigerant using an approved refrigerant recovery system.
2. On DOHC (LLO) engines, remove air cleaner cover and air induction hose at intake manifold.
3. On SOHC (LKO, L24) engines, remove air cleaner housing.
4. Remove suction hose from TXV.
5. Remove liquid line from TXV.

NOTE: Cap all openings immediately to minimize system contamination.

6. Remove TXV from evaporator.

To install:

7. Lubricate and install new O-rings on evaporator pipes.
8. Install TXV on evaporator.
9. Lubricate and install new O-rings on suction hose and liquid line.
10. Install liquid line to TXV.
11. Install suction hose to TXV.
12. On DOHC (LLO) engines, install air cleaner cover and air induction hose.
13. On SOHC (LKO, L24) engines, install air cleaner housing.
14. Evacuate, charge, and leak test A/C system.
15. Run system performance test.

Blower Motor

REMOVAL AND INSTALLATION

1. Disconnect blower motor electrical connector.
2. Remove blower motor mounting screws and blower motor assembly.
3. Installation is a reversal of removal procedures.

Blower Motor Resistor

REMOVAL AND INSTALLATION

1. Disable the SIR system.
2. Remove upper trim panel screw caps and screws.
3. Lift upper trim panel and pull out to remove.
4. Remove screws and unsnap windshield defroster duct from mode valve assembly. Lift up on defroster duct and move it to the right to allow access to resistor assembly.
5. Disconnect blower motor resistor connector.
6. Remove screws and blower motor resistor.
7. Installation is a reversal of removal procedures.

Heater Core

REMOVAL AND INSTALLATION

NOTE: If equipped with an SIR system, the air bag must be disabled before removing key components on or under the instrument panel.

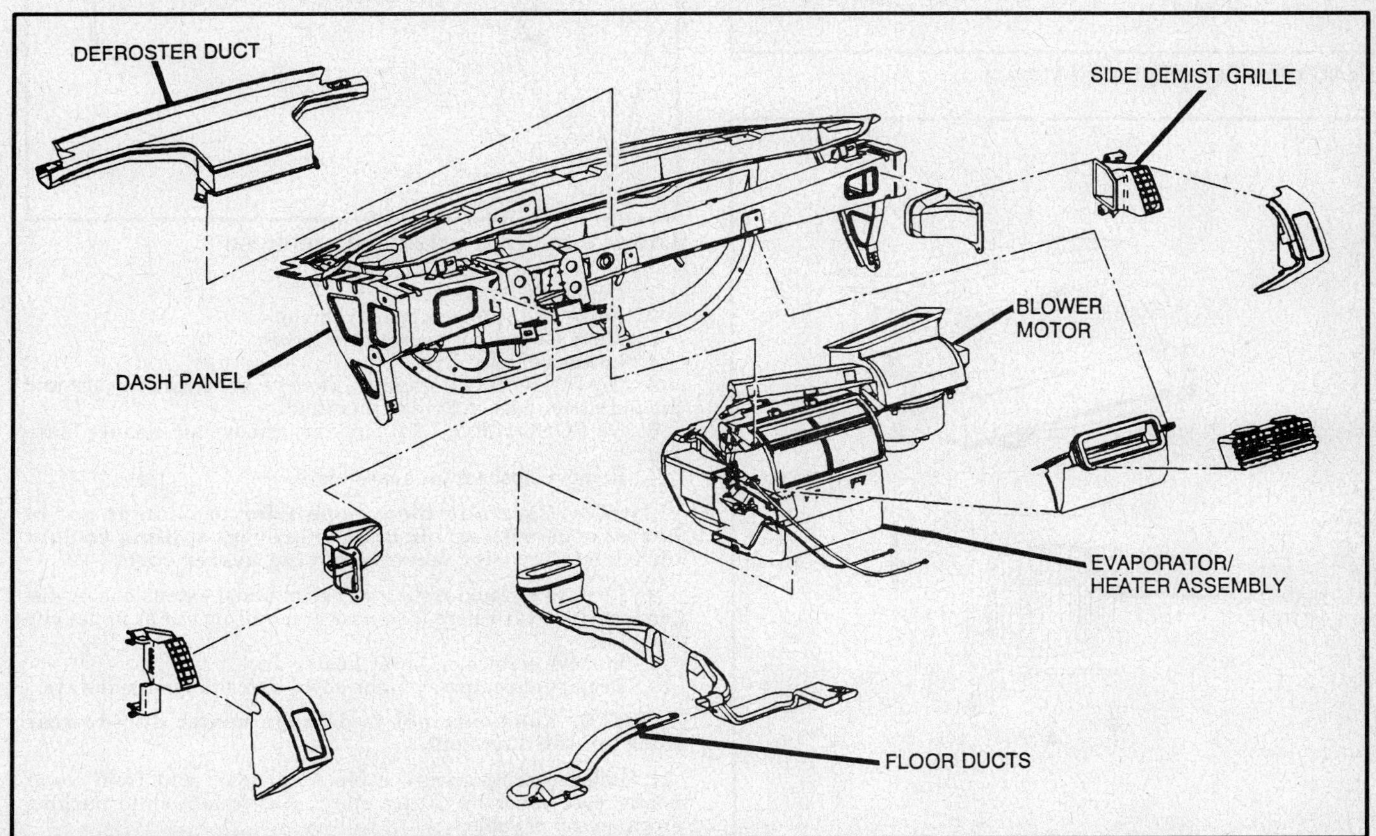

System component view—instrument panel removed

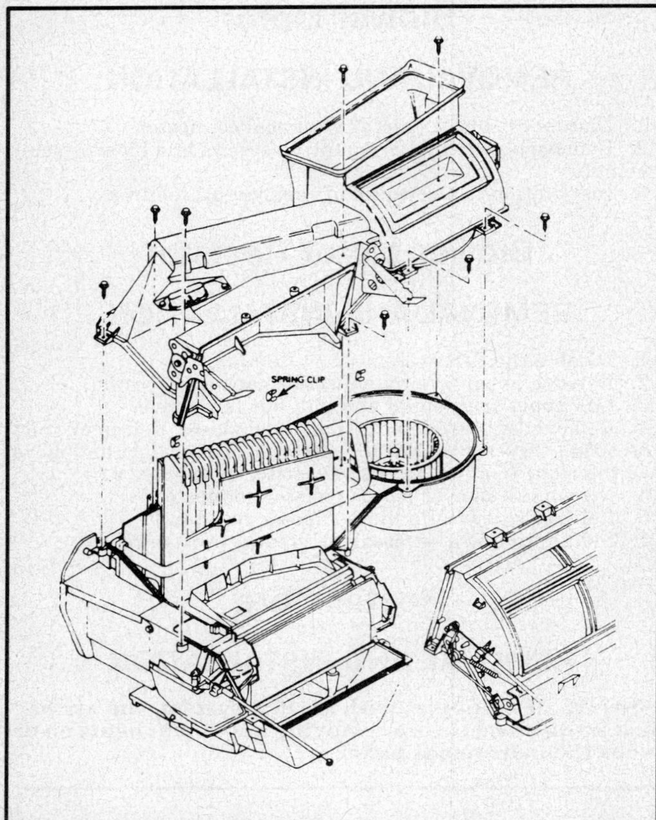

HVAC module—exploded view

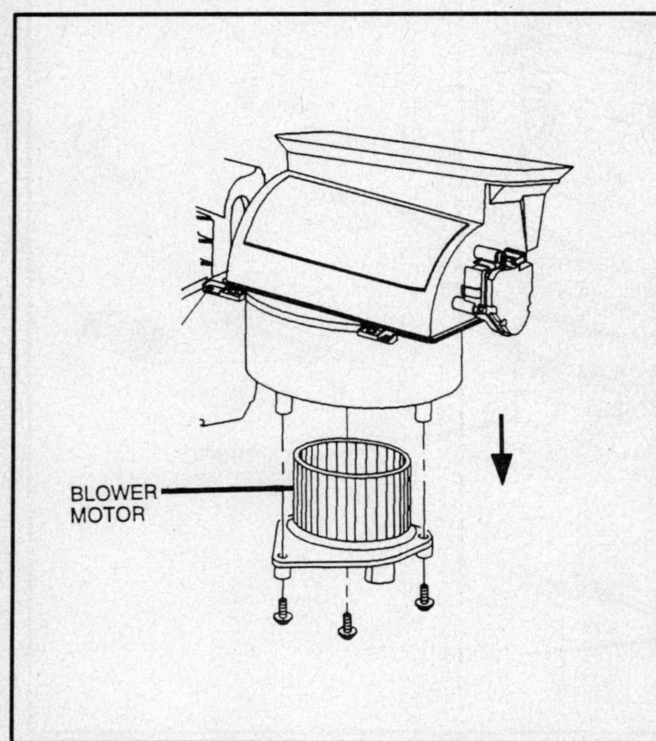

Blower motor removal

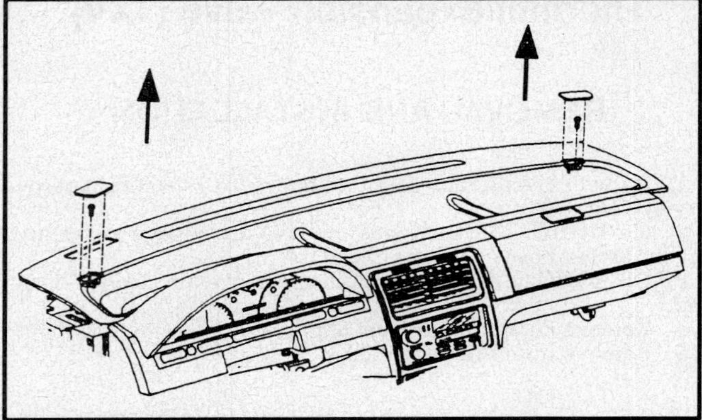

Upper trim panel caps and screws

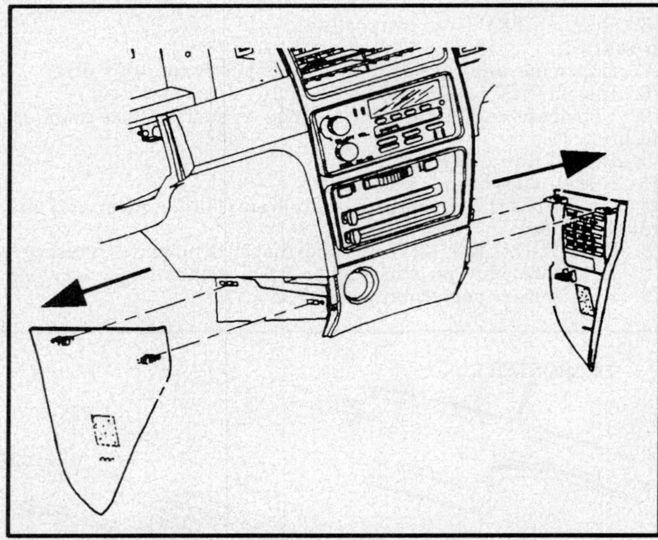

Lower trim panel extensions removal

1. Drain cooling system.
2. Raise and safely support vehicle.
3. Move clamps up heater core hoses.
4. Lower vehicle.
5. On DOHC (LLO) engines, remove air cleaner cover and air induction hose at intake manifold.
6. On SOHC (LKO, L24) engines, remove air cleaner housing.
7. Remove hoses from heater core.

NOTE: Carefully blow remainder of coolant out of heater core with an air hose to prevent spilling coolant on vehicle interior when removing heater core.

8. Remove left and right lower trim panel extensions by disconnecting lower velcro fasteners and pulling out at upper clip locations.
9. Remove screws on lower heater duct.
10. Drop heater duct straight down and slide out sideways.

NOTE: Take care not to damage heater duct-to-rear floor heater duct seal.

11. Release temperature cable hold down clip from lower heater core cover by lifting up on plastic tab while pushing down on top of cable.
12. Squeeze temperature valve pin and pull temperature cable straight off.
13. Remove heater core side cover.

14. Remove lower heater core cover.
15. Remove heater core pipe clamp.
16. Remove lower heater core retainer.
17. Remove heater core.

To install:

18. Install heater core in the housing.

NOTE: Be careful not to damage heater core pipe seal when installing pipes through cowl. Lubricate pipes with petroleum jelly.

19. Install lower heater core retainer.
20. Install heater core pipe clamp.
21. Install lower heater core cover and screws.
22. Install heater core side cover.
23. Push temperature cable over pin and snap hold down clip over temperature cable holder.
24. Install heater duct by sliding in sideways and up into position.

NOTE: Take care not to damage rear floor heater duct seal.

25. Install screws on lower heater duct.
26. Install left and right lower trim panel extensions.
27. Raise and properly support vehicle.
28. Install hoses and clamps on heater core outlet and inlet.
29. Lower vehicle.
30. On DOHC (LLO) engines, install air cleaner housing cover and air induction hose.
31. On SOHC (LKO, L24) engines, install air cleaner housing.
32. Fill and pressure test the cooling system.

NOTE: Enable the air bag system, if equipped.

Evaporator

REMOVAL AND INSTALLATION

1993–94

NOTE: If equipped with an SIR system, the air bag must be disabled before removing key components on or under the instrument panel.

1. Disconnect negative battery cable.
2. Recover refrigerant using an approved refrigerant recovery system.
3. Drain cooling system.
4. On DOHC (LLO) engines, remove air cleaner cover and air induction hose at intake manifold.
5. On SOHC (LKO, L24) engines, remove air cleaner housing.
6. Remove suction hose and liquid line from thermal expansion valve (TXV).
7. Remove TXV from evaporator.

NOTE: Cap all openings immediately to minimize system contamination.

8. Raise and safely support the vehicle.
9. Move clamps up heater core inlet and outlet hoses.
10. Lower vehicle.
11. Remove hoses from heater core.

NOTE: Carefully blow remainder of coolant out of heater core with an air hose to prevent spilling coolant on vehicle interior when removing HVAC module.

12. Remove left and right end cap assemblies.
13. Remove left and right lower trim panel extensions by disconnecting lower velcro fasteners and pulling out at the upper clip locations.
14. Remove cigarette lighter trim bezel.

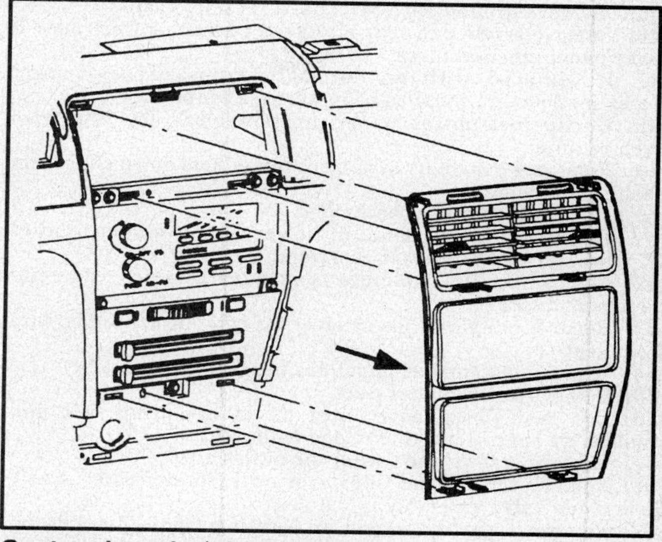

Center air outlet/trim panel removal

15. Remove center air outlet/trim panel by pulling outward at clip locations.

NOTE: Start at the bottom and work up to the top clips.

16. Remove upper trim panel screw caps and screws.
17. Lift upper trim panel to disengage clips at rear edge and pull panel rearward out of clips at the bottom of the windshield to remove upper trim panel.
18. Open glove box.
19. Tilt steering wheel down.
20. Remove screws and pull cluster trim panel rearward to disengage retainers.
21. Disconnect electrical connectors from panel lighting rheostat and rear window defogger switches.
22. Remove Cluster trim panel.
23. Remove glove box and striker.
24. Remove screws and ALDL connector.
25. Remove screws and steering column filler panel.
26. Remove hood release lever screw.
27. Remove screws and pull instrument panel cluster out far enough to disconnect electrical connectors.
28. Disconnect electrical connectors and remove instrument panel cluster.
29. Unclip instrument panel cluster wiring harness from vehicle cross beam and dash retainer.
30. Remove radio and HVAC control.
31. Disconnect cigarette lighter connector.
32. Remove cigarette lighter bulb holder by rotating counterclockwise and pulling straight out.
33. Apply parking brake.
34. Remove parking brake filler panel by lifting at rear edge.
35. If equipped with a manual transaxle, remove gear shift knob by pulling straight up.
36. Remove ashtray.
37. Unclip ashtray bulb holder.
38. Remove window/mirror switch, if equipped, by sliding switch forward then lifting rear edge.
39. Disconnect window/mirror electrical connectors, if equipped.
40. Remove liner from rear storage compartment of console.
41. Remove console side screws and console rear compartment screws.
42. Lift the back of the console. Reach under console and push out seat belt bezels.
43. Feed seat belts through cutouts while removing console.
44. Remove fuse block from dash reinforcement.

45. Remove ground wire from dash reinforcement.
46. Remove screw and rear electrical connector from instrument panel junction block.
47. If equipped with an automatic transaxle, disconnect 2-way instrument panel-to-body harness connector.
48. Unclip instrument panel junction block harness from dash retainer.
49. Remove wiring harness and antenna hold down clips from dash reinforcement.
50. Loosen floor shifter assembly.
51. Remove nuts and bolts, lift lower reinforcement bracket off studs, and slide bracket rearward.
52. Remove screws and nuts from dash retainer and reinforcement bracket.
53. Remove bolts and lower steering column assembly onto front seat.
54. Remove instrument panel/dash assembly.
55. Remove lower heater duct.
56. Lift rear floor heater duct off of mounting bolt and remove. Be careful not to damage foam seal.
57. Remove screws and center air outlet duct.
58. Remove screws and unsnap windshield defroster nozzle from mode valve assembly.
59. Remove defroster nozzle by rotating front of nozzle up and away from windshield.
60. Disconnect blower motor resistor connector.
61. Disconnect blower motor and recirc motor electrical connectors.

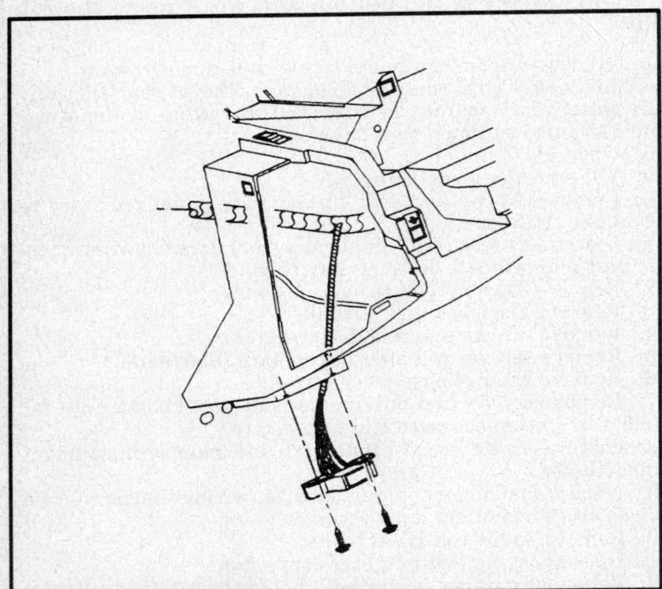
ALDL connector removal

62. Remove wiring harness and hold down clips from HVAC module.
63. Remove fuel vapor line and clip from HVAC module stud to gain access to nut.
64. Remove 3 screws and 2 nuts holding HVAC module to cowl.
65. Remove HVAC module from vehicle.
66. Remove and discard front of dash seals.
67. Separate the case halves, note the position of seals for reinstallation, and remove the evaporator core.

To install:

68. Assemble the water filter, retainers, evaporator seal and spacer pad to the evaporator. If the evaporator core was replaced, add 1.5 ounces of refrigerant oil and replace pipe cover.

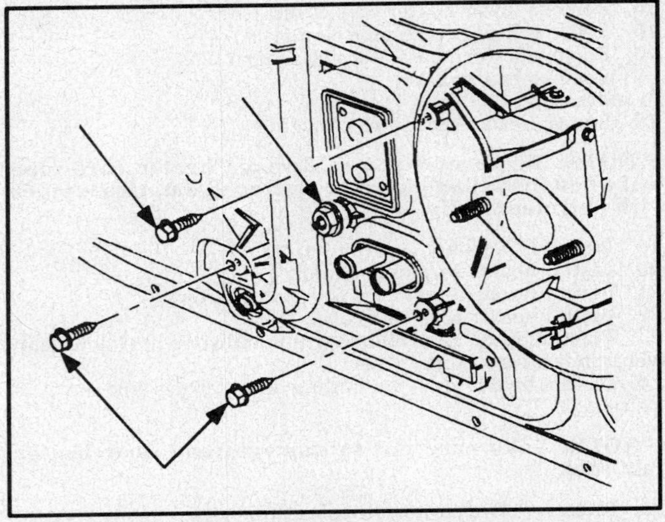
HVAC module mounting screws and nuts locations

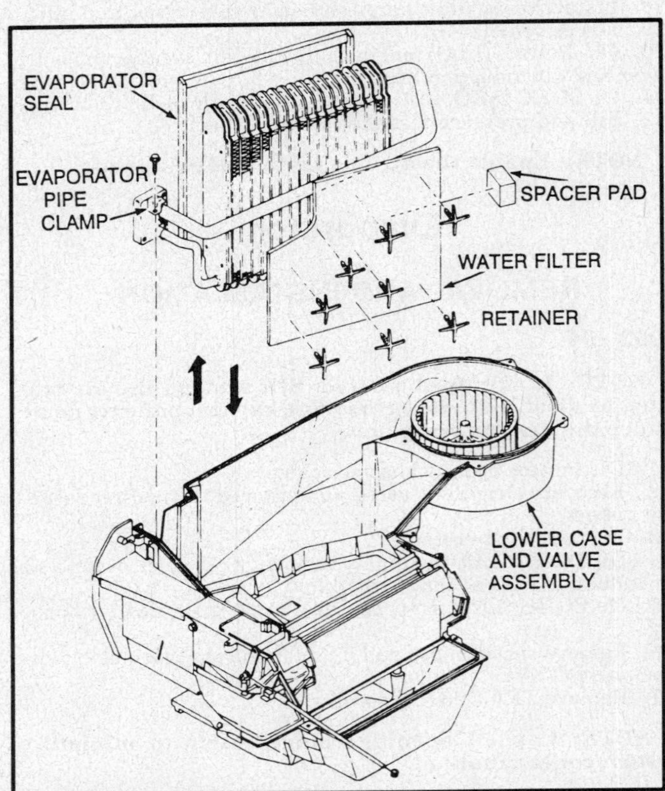

Evaporator core removed

NOTE: For 1993–94 vehicles, evaporator core will have filter and pad already installed. 1.5 ounces of refrigerant oil will still have to be added to the new evaporator.

69. Install evaporator into case halves and connect.

NOTE: Make sure all tongue and groove parts fit properly before tightening to avoid case damage.

70. Install mode valve and screws.

71. Install front of dash seals on heater core pipes, case drain and evaporator block.
72. Install HVAC module through the cowl. Install screws and nuts.
73. Install fuel vapor line and clip.
74. Connect blower motor and recirc motor electrical connectors.
75. Install wire harness hold down clips on HVAC module.
76. Connect blower motor resistor electrical connector.
77. Install windshield defroster nozzle onto mode valve.
78. Install center air outlet duct and screws.
79. Install rear floor heater duct.
80. Install lower heater duct.
81. Install instrument panel assembly.

NOTE: When installing instrument panel/dash assembly, feed fuse block and wire harness through lower dash reinforcement.

82. Raise and install steering column assembly.
83. Install lower reinforcement bracket.
84. Tighten floor shifter assembly.
85. Install wire harness and antenna hold-down clips on dash reinforcement.
86. Connect rear electrical connector on instrument panel fuse block.
87. If equipped with an automatic transaxle, connect 2-way instrument panel-to-body harness connector and install lock pin.
88. Install fuse block and ground wire on dash reinforcement.
89. Install console by feeding seat belts and wire harness through console cutouts, snap seat belt bezels into place and install console rear compartment screws and console side screws.
90. Install liner in the rear storage compartment of console.
91. Install window/mirror switch, if equipped.
92. Install ashtray.
93. If equipped with a manual transaxle, install gear shift knob, parking brake filler panel, and connect cigarette lighter connector.
94. Install HVAC control, adjust temperature and mode cables, and install radio. Connect electrical connectors on instrument panel cluster.

NOTE: Make sure electrical connectors for lighting rheostat and rear window defogger switches are in place.

95. Install instrument panel cluster.
96. Install hood release lever, steering column filler panel, ALDL connector and glove box.
97. Install cluster trim panel. Connect electrical connectors on lighting rheostat and rear window defogger switches.
98. Install upper trim panel into clips.
99. Install center air outlet/trim panel, left and right lower trim panel extensions and end caps.
100. Install cigarette lighter trim bezel.
101. Raise and safely support vehicle. Install hoses and clamps on heater core inlet and outlet. Lower vehicle.
102. Install the TXV, using new O-rings.
103. Install suction hose and liquid line on TXV, using new O-rings.
104. On DOHC engine, install air cleaner housing cover and air induction hose. On SOHC engine, install air cleaner housing.
105. Fill and pressure test the cooling system.
106. Evacuate, charge, and leak test A/C system. Perform A/C performance test. Connect negative battery cable.

NOTE: Enable the air bag system, if equipped.

1995

1. Disable the SIR system.
2. Disconnect negative battery cable.
3. Recover refrigerant using an approved refrigerant recovery system.
4. Drain cooling system.
5. Remove air cleaner housing cover and air induction hose at intake manifold.
6. Remove suction hose and liquid line from the thermal expansion valve.
7. Remove thermal expansion valve from evaporator.

NOTE: Place protective covers over A/C hoses, lines, TXV, and HVAC module to prevent contamination of A/C system.

8. Raise and safely support the vehicle.
9. Move clamps up heater core inlet and outlet hoses.
10. Lower vehicle.
11. Remove hoses from heater core.

NOTE: Blow remainder of coolant out of heater core with an air hose to prevent spilling coolant on vehicle interior when removing HVAC module.

12. Remove screws and carefully pull right and left end cap assemblies outward at clip locations.
13. Remove parking brake cover.
14. Move shifter to neutral. Remove ashtray from cup holder and cup holder.
15. Remove ashtray bulb socket by lifting tab while sliding socket upwards. Then pull socket straight out.
16. Remove wiring harness from cup holder.
17. Remove window/mirror switch, if equipped. Disconnect electrical connectors.
18. Remove rear screw cover by lifting at cut out.
19. Remove rear console screws.
20. Remove left and right lower trim panel extensions.
21. Remove front console screws.
22. Move console rearward.
23. Disconnect cigarette lighter electrical connector.
24. Remove bulb socket from cigarette lighter.
25. Lift console at rear. Slide console rearward and lift straight up to remove.
26. Depress center pins inward to release radio/HVAC controller cover push pin fasteners.

NOTE: Do not push center pins through fasteners.

27. Remove fasteners and pull radio/HVAC controller cover rearward.
28. Disconnect traction control-fog lamp-rear defog electrical connector if equipped.
29. Remove radio screws.
30. Push spring clips in through D holes on both sides of radio brace.
31. Pull radio out slightly to access rear of radio.
32. Disconnect electrical connector and antenna and remove radio.
33. Disconnect blower switch, A/C-Recirc and lighting electrical connectors. Remove electrical harness clip from H-bracket.
34. Remove temperature and mode cables from HVAC control by squeezing lock tabs together while pulling cable housing straight up.
35. Remove cables from pins by pulling straight up.
36. Remove screws and HVAC controller.
37. Remove closeout seal by releasing from tabs.
38. Remove screw and ground wire from H-bracket.
39. Remove wiring harness from H-bracket.
40. Remove screw and disconnect rear electrical connector from instrument panel junction block.
41. Remove instrument panel junction block screw.
42. Release lock tabs on instrument panel junction block and slide off of mounting pads.
43. Feed instrument panel junction block through H-bracket towards front of car.

44. Remove screws from H-bracket and nuts from reinforcement bracket.
45. Lift reinforcement bracket off studs and move rearward.
46. Remove screws from datta link connector (DLC) connector and steering column filler panel.
47. Remove hood release cable from lever.
48. Remove steering column filler panel.
49. Disconnect ignition switch electrical connector at right steering column bolt.
50. Remove steering column bolts and lower column on front seat.
51. Remove fasteners and pull instrument cluster trim bezel rearward at clip locations.
52. Disconnect electrical connector from instrument panel dimmer switch.
53. Remove connector position assurance (CPA) devices and disconnect electrical connectors from instrument cluster by squeezing tabs on each side of connector.
54. Remove instrument cluster.
55. Remove dimmer switch wiring harness from instrument panel reinforcement, and feed connector through reinforcement towards front of car.
56. Remove passenger side air bag harness from cross car beam and energy absorber.
57. Remove glove box door stops and let door hang down.
58. Remove glove box assembly.
59. Disconnect antenna cable at lower right side of instrument panel reinforcement.

NOTE: Put instrument panel pad/reinforcement on a clean surface so that the surface does not become damaged.

60. Remove nut, screws and instrument panel pad/reinforcement assembly.
61. For Sedans and Wagons, remove lower heater duct.
62. Lift rear floor heater duct off of mounting bolt and remove.
63. Remove screws and center air outlet duct.
64. Remove screws and unsnap windshield defroster nozzle from mode valve assembly.
65. Remove defroster nozzle.

NOTE: For SC1 and SC2 vehicles, leave defroster nozzle in place after disconnecting. Nozzle cannot be removed because of windshield rake angle.

66. Remove connector position assurance (CPA) devices and disconnect blower motor resistor connector.
67. Remove wire harness and hold down clips from HVAC module.
68. Disconnect blower motor and recirc motor electrical connectors.
69. Remove wiring harness and hold down clips from HVAC module.
70. Remove fuel vapor line and clip from HVAC module stud.
71. Remove three screws and two nuts holding HVAC module to the cowl.
72. Remove HVAC module from vehicle.
73. Remove and discard cowl panel seals.
74. Remove valve assembly from HVAC module.
75. Remove upper air inlet case screws and spring clips and separate the halves.
76. Remove evaporator pipe clamp and screw.
77. Lift evaporator straight up to remove from lower case assembly.

To install:

78. Assemble the water filter, retainers, evaporator seal and spacer pad to the new evaporator. Add 67 ml (2.25 oz.) of new *Saturn* Refrigerant Oil and replace evaporator pipe cover.

NOTE: 1995 evaporator part will come with filter and pad already installed. 2.25 oz. (67 ml) of oil will still have to be added to the evaporator.

79. Lower evaporator into the lower case assembly.
80. Install evaporator pipe clamp and screw.

NOTE: Make sure evaporator pipes are wrapped with mastic on part being installed.
Make sure all tongue and groove parts fit properly before tightening screws to avoid case damage.

81. Install upper air inlet case, screws and spring clips.
82. Install mode valve and screws.
83. Install new cowl panel seals on heater core pipes, case drain, and evaporator block.
84. Install HVAC module through the cowl. Install screws and nuts.
85. Install fuel vapor line and clip to stud below TXV.
86. Connect blower motor and recirc motor electrical connectors.
87. Install wire harness hold down clips on HVAC module.
88. Connect blower motor resistor electrical connector and install CPA devices.
89. Install wire harness hold down clips on HVAC module and defroster nozzle.
90. Install center air outlet duct and screws.
91. For SL and SW only, install rear floor heater duct and place on mounting stud.

NOTE: Be careful not to damage foam seal.

92. Install lower heater duct.
93. Install lower reinforcement bracket and nuts.
94. Install instrument panel pad/reinforcement assembly. Torque to 89 inch lbs. (10 Nm).
95. Install glove box and snap in at clip locations.
96. Install glove box door stops.
97. Connect antenna cable at lower right side of instrument panel reinforcement.
98. Install passenger side air bag harness to energy absorber and cross-car beam.
99. Install dimmer switch wiring harness to instrument panel reinforcement.
100. Install instrument cluster.
101. Connect electrical connectors to instrument cluster.
102. Install CPA's.
103. Connect electrical connector to dimmer switch.
104. Install instrument cluster trim bezel. Push in at clip locations.
105. Install push pin fasteners.
106. Install steering column into position, torque to 26 ft. lbs. (35 Nm).
107. Connect ignition switch electrical connector at right steering column bolt.
108. Install hood release cable to lever.
109. Install steering column filler panel and DLC connector.
110. Install lower reinforcement on studs.
111. Feed instrument panel junction block through H-bracket towards rear of car.
112. Install IPJB on mounting pads to lock tabs.
113. Connect rear electrical connector to IPJB.
114. Install wiring harness, ground wire and screw to H-bracket and seal.
115. Install HVAC control.
116. Install temperature and mode cables over pins.

Cable Identification:

- Temperature cable — white
- Mode cable — black

117. Install cable housings into channel and push down to lock.
118. Connect blower switch, A/C-Recirc and lighting electrical connectors.

NOTE: Make sure wiring harnesses do not interfere with control lever movement.

119. Install electrical harness clip to H-bracket.
120. Connect electrical connector and antenna to radio and install radio.
121. Connect traction control fog lamp-rear defog electrical connector, if equipped.
122. Install radio/HVAC control cover. Push in at clip locations.
123. Lower front of console over shifter, and onto rear mounting pad.
124. Move console rearward.
125. Install cigarette lighter bulb through opening and connect to electrical wires.
126. Move console forward into position.
127. Install and tighten front console screws.
128. Install left and right lower trim panel extensions.
129. Align rear of console with pin on mounting pad and install screws and screw cover.
130. Connect window/mirror switch electrical connectors.
131. Install window/mirror switch by inserting front edge into opening. Then push rear edge down into position.
132. Insert bulb through opening until bulb socket is flush with cup holder. Push socket down to engage lock tab.
133. Install wiring harness to cup holder, then install cup holder.
134. Install parking brake cover over lever.
135. Install right and left end cap assemblies.
136. Raise and safely support the vehicle.
137. Install hose and clamp on heater core outlet.
138. Install hose and clamp on heater core inlet.
139. Lower vehicle.
140. Remove protective covers. Lubricate and install new O-rings on evaporator pipes.
141. Install thermal expansion valve (TXV) on evaporator, torque to 89 ft. lbs. (10 Nm).
142. Lubricate and install new O-rings on suction hose and liquid line, install liquid line and suction hose, both are torqued to 19 ft. lbs. (25 Nm).
143. Install air cleaner housing cover and air induction hose.
144. Fill and pressure test the cooling system.
145. Evacuate, charge, and leak test A/C system. Perform A/C Performance Test.
146. Connect negative battery cable.
147. Enable the SIR system.

Refrigerant Lines

REMOVAL AND INSTALLATION

1. Properly discharge the air conditioning system.
2. Remove air cleaner components, battery and junction block as required for access.
3. Remove suction hose from thermal expansion valve (TXV), compressor inlet, compressor outlet and/or condenser attachments as required.

NOTE: Cap all openings immediately as they are disconnected to minimize contamination of dirt and moisture to the system.

4. Installation is the reverse of the removal procedure. Use new O-rings at all fittings.
5. Evacuate, recharge and leak test the system.

Manual Control Head (HVAC Controller)

REMOVAL AND INSTALLATION

1993–94

1. Disconnect negative battery cable.
2. Remove center air outlet/trim panel by pulling outward at clip locations.

NOTE: Start at the bottom and work up to top clips.

3. Remove 2 radio screws and slide radio out.
4. Disconnect radio electrical connector and antenna.
5. Disconnect blower motor switch electrical connector.
6. Release temperature and mode cable hold down/adjustment clips.
7. Remove control panel screws and pull control panel out slightly.
8. Squeeze mode cable and temperature cable controller pins and lift cables straight off pins.

NOTE: Move temperature lever to FULL COLD to gain better access to cable pin.

9. Slide HVAC control further out of dash, release 6-way connector lock and disconnect.
10. Remove HVAC controller.

To install:

11. Install HVAC control head.
12. Install temperature and mode cables over pins.

NOTE: For proper cable installation, note that the temperature cable is blue and the mode cable is black.

13. Position temperature lever in the **FULL COLD** position and the mode lever in the **FULL VENT** position.
14. Align cables in grooves and push hold down/adjustment clips over cables to lock.
15. Check temperature and mode levers for full travel. Adjust as necessary by pushing the lever to the end that springs back. While holding the lever, lift up the hold down/adjustment clip, let the cable adjust and push clip down to lock.
16. Connect 6-way and blower switch electrical connectors.

NOTE: Make sure wiring harnesses do not interfere with control lever movement.

17. Connect radio electrical connector and antenna, and install radio.
18. Install center air outlet/trim panel.
19. Connect negative battery cable.

1995

1. Release radio/HVAC controllerr cover push pin fasteners.
2. Remove fasteners and pull radio/HVAC controller cover rearward.
3. Disconnect traction control-fog rear defog electrical connector, if equipped.
4. Remove radio screws, push spring clips in through D holes and pull radio out slightly.
5. Disconnect electrical connector and antenna. Remove radio.
6. Disconnect blower switch, A/C-Recirc and lighting electrical connectors. Remove electrical harness clip from H-bracket.
7. Remove temperature and mode cables from HVAC and from pins.

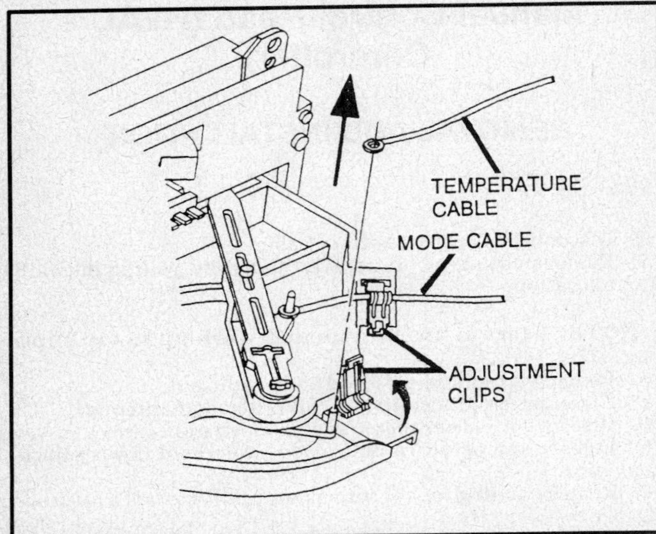

Temperature/mode cable removal at control panel

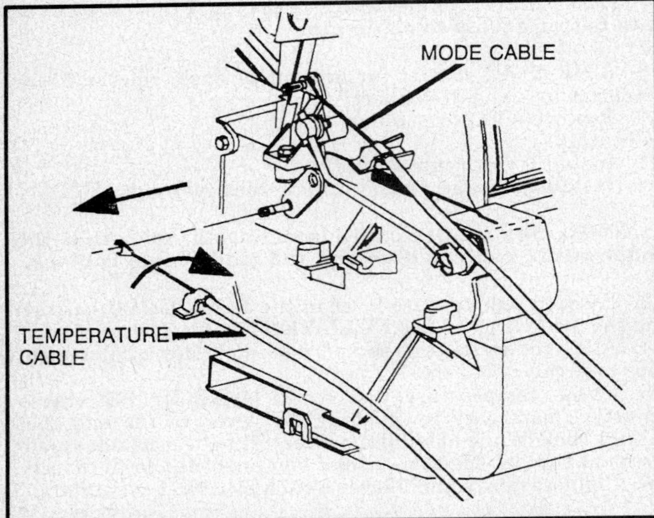

Temperature/mode cable removal at evaporator case

8. Remove screws and HVAC controller.
9. Install in reverse order.

Manual Control Cables

REMOVAL, INSTALLATION, AND ADJUSTMENTS

NOTE: Both temperature and mode cables are removed, installed and adjusted in the same manner. Temperature cable is blue, 1995 is white and mode cable is black.

1. Disconnect negative battery cable.
2. Remove center air outlet/trim panel by pulling outward at clip locations.

NOTE: Start at the bottom and work up to top clips.

3. Remove 2 radio screws and slide radio out.
4. Disconnect radio electrical connector and antenna.
5. Remove blower motor switch electrical connector.
6. Release temperature and/or mode cable hold down/adjustment clips.
7. Squeeze temperature and/or mode cable controller pin and lift cable straight off pin.
8. Reach under dash and release temperature and/or mode cable hold down clip by pushing up on plastic tab while pushing down on top of cable.
9. Remove clip from temperature door pin/mode valve pin and pull cable straight off pin.
10. Remove cable.

To Install and Adjust:

11. Install cable on pin under dash.
12. Install pin clip and lock down.
13. Install cable over controller pin.
14. Position the temperature lever to **FULL COLD** and the mode lever to **FULL VENT** positions.
15. Align cables in grooves and push hold down/adjustment clips over cables to lock.
16. Check temperature and mode levers for full travel. Adjust as necessary by pushing the lever to the end that springs back. While holding the lever, lift the hold down/adjustment clip, let the cable adjust and push clip down to lock.
17. Connect blower switch electrical connector.

NOTE: Make sure wiring harnesses do not interfere with control lever movement.

18. Connect radio electrical connector and antenna, and install radio.
19. Install center air outlet/trim panel.
20. Connect negative battery cable.

SENSORS AND SWITCHES

Air Conditioner Clutch Control

OPERATION

The A/C clutch control relay is used by the Powertrain Control Module (PCM) to turn ON or OFF the A/C compressor clutch coil. When the PCM receives an A/C request signal, it will supply a ground to the A/C clutch control relay, energizing the relay and allowing the A/C compressor to be turned ON. During certain driving conditions, the PCM will turn OFF the A/C compressor by removing the ground for the A/C compressor clutch control relay.

Air Temperature Sensor

OPERATION

The air temperature sensor is a thermistor-type sensor mounted in the engine inlet air system. The sensor input is used by the Powertrain Control Module (PCM) for various functions including the operation of the A/C compressor.

REMOVAL AND INSTALLATION

1. Disconnect negative battery cable.
2. Remove fasteners and rotate the air inlet tube to access the inlet air temperature sensor.

3. Disconnect the electrical connector from the air temperature sensor.
4. Remove air inlet temperature sensor using a deep well 13 mm socket.
5. Reverse procedures to install.

Coolant Temperature Sensor

OPERATION

The coolant temperature sensor is identical to the air temperature sensor. It is mounted in a coolant passage located in the cylinder head. The signal received by the PCM indicates the temperature of the engine coolant which is an indication of the engine operating temperature. If the coolant temperature exceeds 244°F (118°C) the PCM will shut down the A/C operation. The A/C will be turned **ON** again when the coolant temperature decreases to 234°F (113°C).

REMOVAL AND INSTALLATION

NOTE: The coolant temperature sensor used by the PCM and the coolant temperature sensor used by the temperature gauge in the instrument cluster are similar. The sensor used by the PCM uses two wires and the sensor for the instrument cluster has a single wire.

1. Disconnect the negative battery cable. Partially drain the cooling system.
2. Disconnect electrical connector from coolant temperature sensor.
3. Remove coolant temperature sensor.
4. Reverse procedures to install.

Fan Control Relay

OPERATION

The fan control relay is used by the PCM to control engine cooling fan operation. The engine cooling fan will be turned ON or OFF by the PCM, dependent upon engine coolant temperature, vehicle speed, or A/C "ON". The fan control relay is located in the underhood junction block.

Compressor Temperature Sensor

OPERATION

Mounted in the front head of the compressor is a high temperature sensor to protect the compressor from overheating. The sensor will open the clutch circuit at about 302°F (150°C).

REMOVAL AND INSTALLATION

NOTE: The air conditioning system does not have to be discharged to remove the temperature sensor.

1. Remove the electrical connector.
2. Remove the 2-wire retaining screws on compressor body.
3. Remove temperature sensor.
4. Reverse procedures to install.

SYSTEM DIAGNOSIS

ENGINE COOLING FAN INOPERATIVE DIAGNOSIS

ENGINE COOLING FAN OPERATES ALL THE TIME DIAGNOSIS

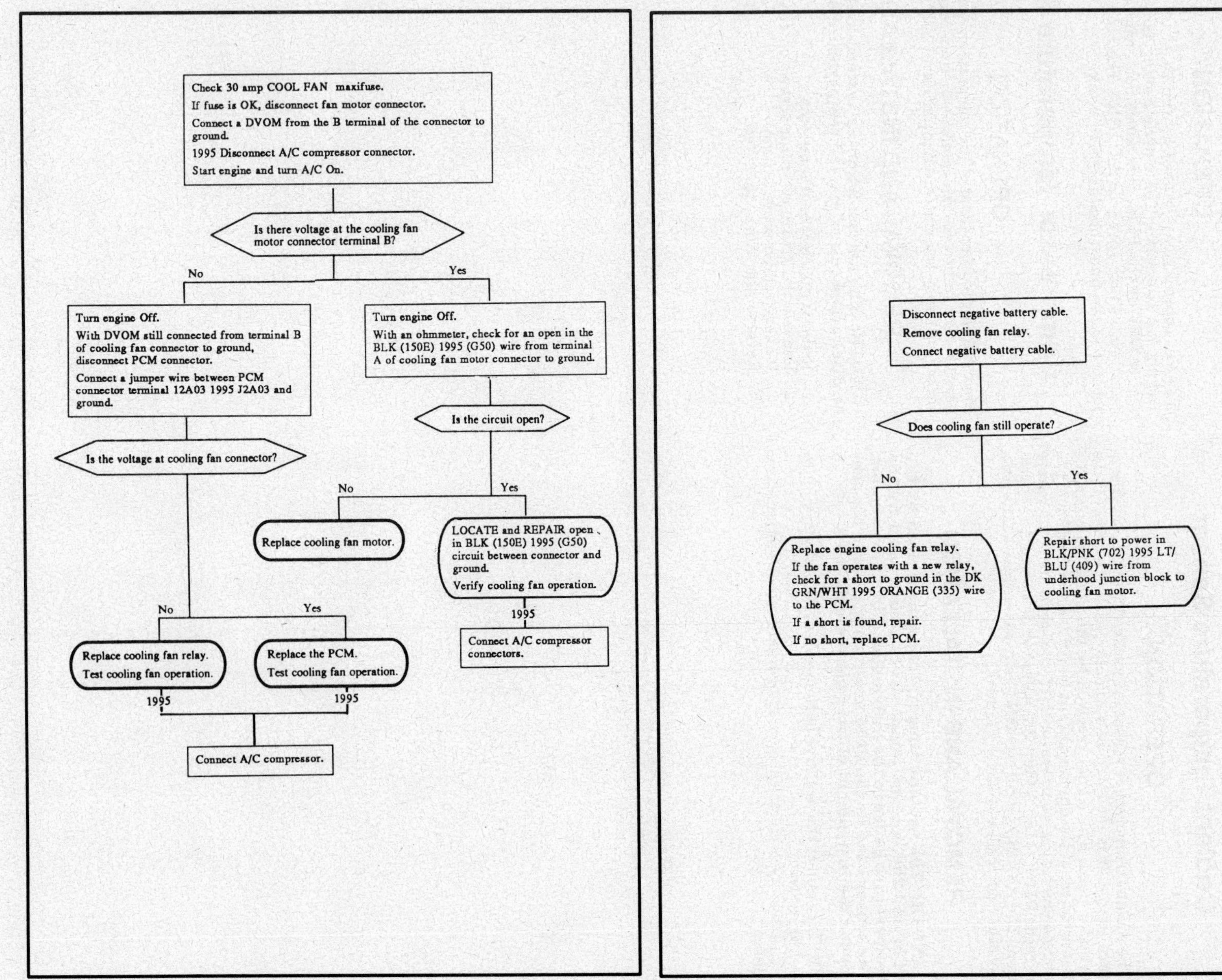

Check 30 amp COOL FAN maxifuse.
If fuse is OK, disconnect fan motor connector.
Connect a DVOM from the B terminal of the connector to ground.
1995 Disconnect A/C compressor connector.
Start engine and turn A/C On.
Is there voltage at the cooling fan motor connector terminal B?
No
Yes
Turn engine Off.
With DVOM still connected from terminal B of cooling fan connector to ground, disconnect PCM connector.
Connect a jumper wire between PCM connector terminal 12A03 1995 J2A03 and ground.
Turn engine Off.
With an ohmmeter, check for an open in the BLK (150E) 1995 (G50) wire from terminal A of cooling fan motor connector to ground.
Is the circuit open?
Is the voltage at cooling fan connector?
No
Yes
Replace cooling fan motor.
LOCATE and REPAIR open in BLK (150E) 1995 (G50) circuit between connector and ground.
Verify cooling fan operation.
1995
Connect A/C compressor connectors.
No
Yes
Replace cooling fan relay.
Test cooling fan operation.
Replace the PCM.
Test cooling fan operation.
1995
1995
Connect A/C compressor.
Disconnect negative battery cable.
Remove cooling fan relay.
Connect negative battery cable.
Does cooling fan still operate?
No
Yes
Replace engine cooling fan relay.
If the fan operates with a new relay, check for a short to ground in the DK GRN/WHT 1995 ORANGE (335) wire to the PCM.
If a short is found, repair.
If no short, replace PCM.
Repair short to power in BLK/PNK (702) 1995 LT/BLU (409) wire from underhood junction block to cooling fan motor.

BLOWER MOTOR INOPERATIVE DIAGNOSIS

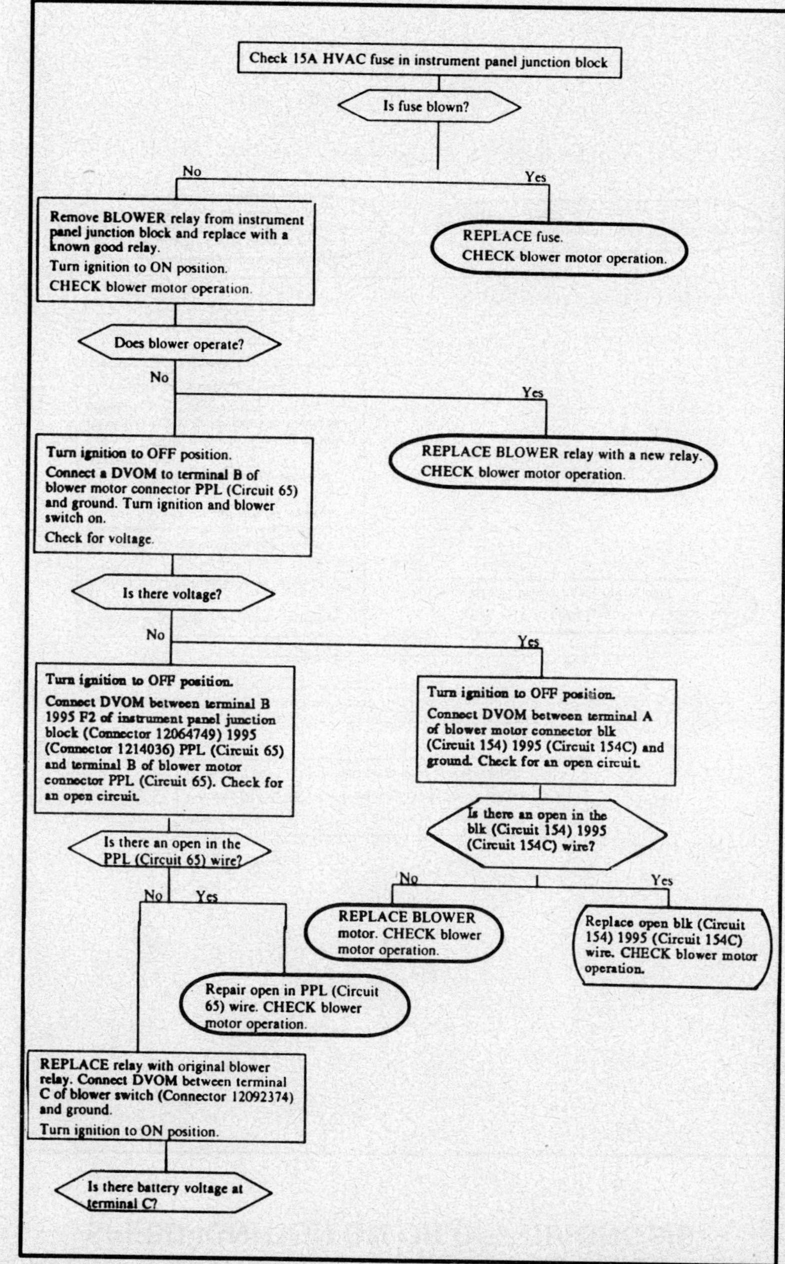

Check 15A HVAC fuse in instrument panel junction block
Is fuse blown?
No
Yes
REPLACE fuse.
CHECK blower motor operation.
Remove BLOWER relay from instrument panel junction block and replace with a known good relay.
Turn ignition to ON position.
CHECK blower motor operation.
Does blower operate?
No
Yes
REPLACE BLOWER relay with a new relay.
CHECK blower motor operation.
Turn ignition to OFF position.
Connect a DVOM to terminal B of blower motor connector PPL (Circuit 65) and ground. Turn ignition and blower switch on.
Check for voltage.
Is there voltage?
No
Yes
Turn ignition to OFF position.
Connect DVOM between terminal B 1995 F2 of instrument panel junction block (Connector 12064749) 1995 (Connector 1214036) PPL (Circuit 65) and terminal B of blower motor connector PPL (Circuit 65). Check for an open circuit.
Turn ignition to OFF position.
Connect DVOM between terminal A of blower motor connector blk (Circuit 154) 1995 (Circuit 154C) and ground. Check for an open circuit.
Is there an open in the PPL (Circuit 65) wire?
No
Yes
Is there an open in the blk (Circuit 154) 1995 (Circuit 154C) wire?
No
Yes
REPLACE BLOWER motor. CHECK blower motor operation.
Replace open blk (Circuit 154) 1995 (Circuit 154C) wire. CHECK blower motor operation.
Repair open in PPL (Circuit 65) wire. CHECK blower motor operation.
REPLACE relay with original blower relay. Connect DVOM between terminal C of blower switch (Connector 12092374) and ground.
Turn ignition to ON position.
Is there battery voltage at terminal C?

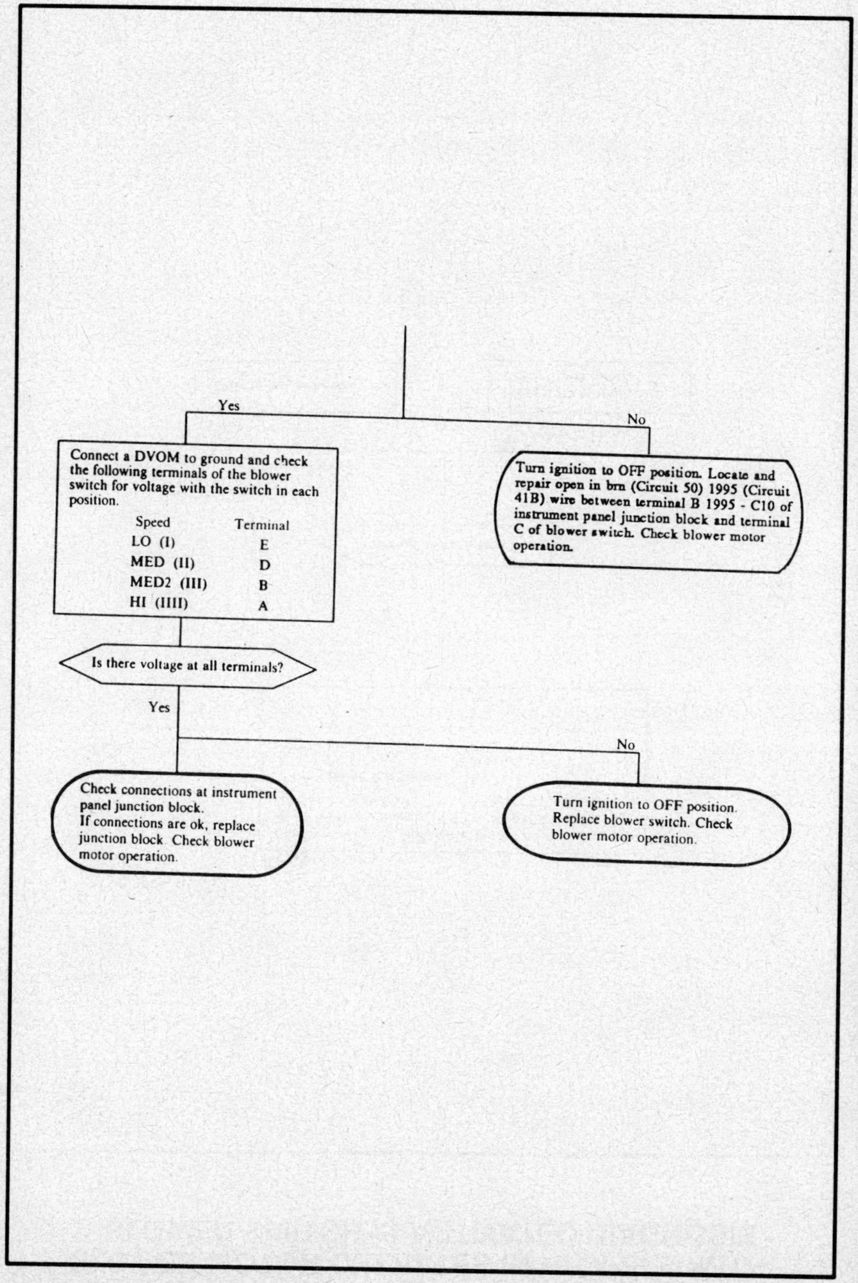

Yes

No

Connect a DVOM to ground and check the following terminals of the blower switch for voltage with the switch in each position.

Speed	Terminal
LO (I)	E
MED (II)	D
MED2 (III)	B
HI (IIII)	A

Turn ignition to OFF position. Locate and repair open in brn (Circuit 50) 1995 (Circuit 41B) wire between terminal B 1995 - C10 of instrument panel junction block and terminal C of blower switch. Check blower motor operation.

Is there voltage at all terminals?

Yes

No

Check connections at instrument panel junction block.
If connections are ok, replace junction block. Check blower motor operation.

Turn ignition to OFF position.
Replace blower switch. Check blower motor operation.

BLOWER MOTOR OPERATES AT ALL TIMES IN HI SPEED IGNITION ON OR OFF DIAGNOSIS

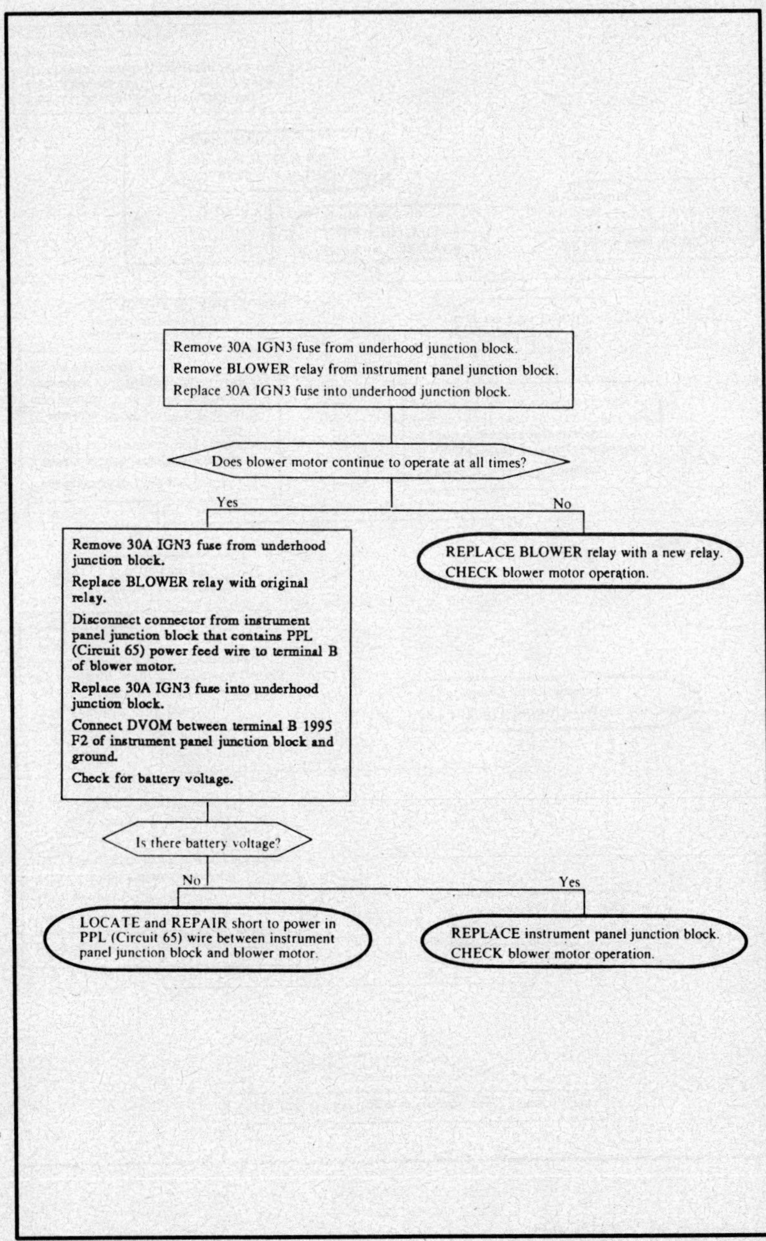

Remove 30A IGN3 fuse from underhood junction block.
Remove BLOWER relay from instrument panel junction block.
Replace 30A IGN3 fuse into underhood junction block.
Does blower motor continue to operate at all times?
Yes
No
Remove 30A IGN3 fuse from underhood junction block.
Replace BLOWER relay with original relay.
Disconnect connector from instrument panel junction block that contains PPL (Circuit 65) power feed wire to terminal B of blower motor.
Replace 30A IGN3 fuse into underhood junction block.
Connect DVOM between terminal B 1995 F2 of instrument panel junction block and ground.
Check for battery voltage.
REPLACE BLOWER relay with a new relay.
CHECK blower motor operation.
Is there battery voltage?
No
Yes
LOCATE and REPAIR short to power in PPL (Circuit 65) wire between instrument panel junction block and blower motor.
REPLACE instrument panel junction block.
CHECK blower motor operation.

BLOWER MOTOR OPERATES IN HI SPEED WITH BLOWER SWITCH IS ACTIVATED DIAGNOSIS

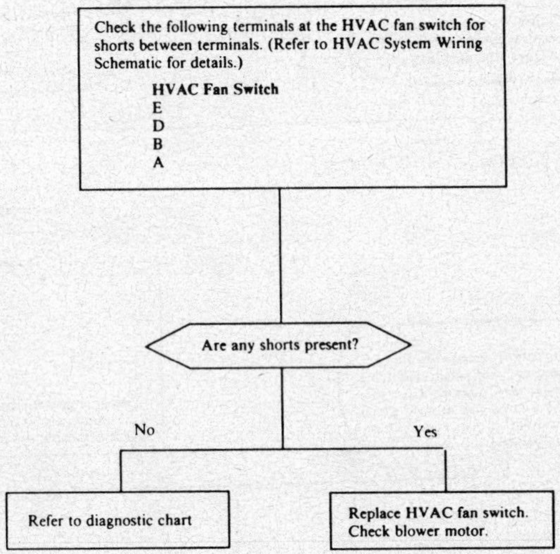

Check the following terminals at the HVAC fan switch for shorts between terminals. (Refer to HVAC System Wiring Schematic for details.)

HVAC Fan Switch
E
D
B
A

Are any shorts present?

No — Refer to diagnostic chart

Yes — Replace HVAC fan switch. Check blower motor.

BLOWER MOTOR OPERATES IN HI, BUT NOT IN ONE OR MORE OF THE OTHER SPEEDS DIAGNOSIS

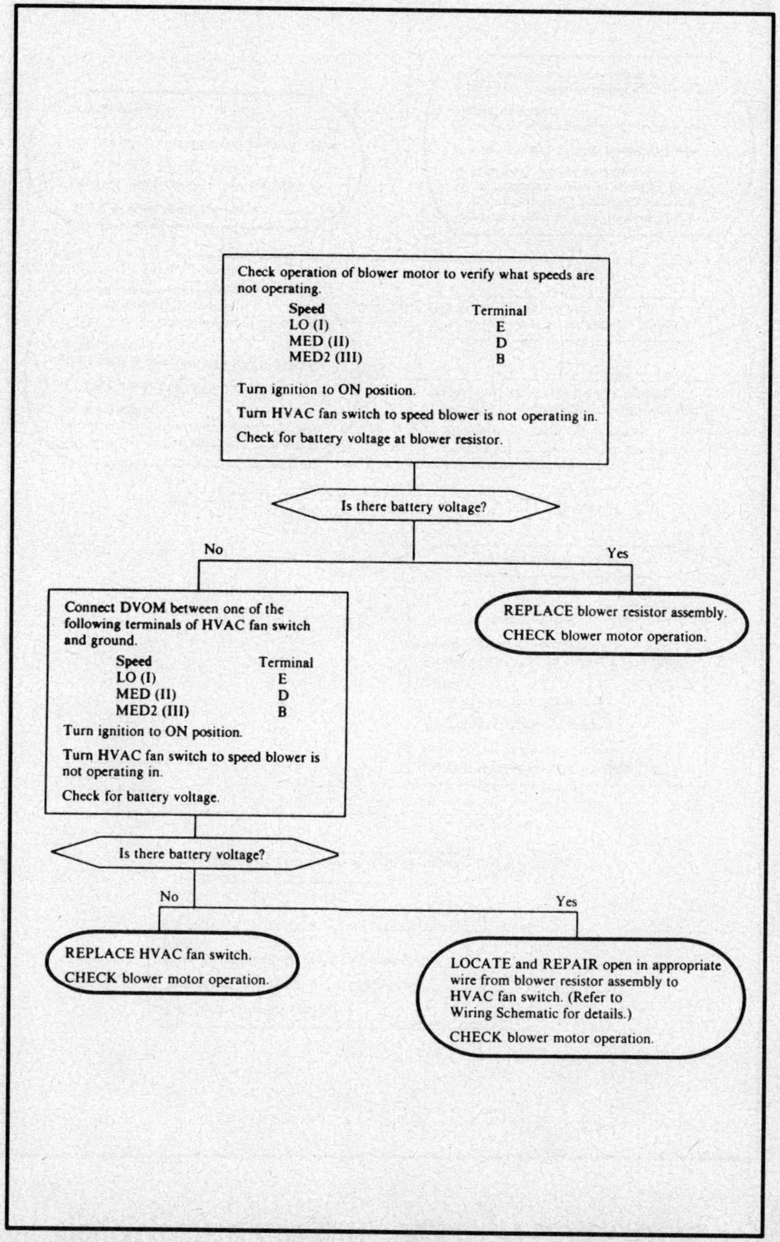

Check operation of blower motor to verify what speeds are not operating.

Speed	Terminal
LO (I)	E
MED (II)	D
MED2 (III)	B

Turn ignition to ON position.

Turn HVAC fan switch to speed blower is not operating in.

Check for battery voltage at blower resistor.

Is there battery voltage?

- **Yes:** REPLACE blower resistor assembly. CHECK blower motor operation.
- **No:** Connect DVOM between one of the following terminals of HVAC fan switch and ground.

Speed	Terminal
LO (I)	E
MED (II)	D
MED2 (III)	B

Turn ignition to ON position.

Turn HVAC fan switch to speed blower is not operating in.

Check for battery voltage.

Is there battery voltage?

- **No:** REPLACE HVAC fan switch. CHECK blower motor operation.
- **Yes:** LOCATE and REPAIR open in appropriate wire from blower resistor assembly to HVAC fan switch. (Refer to Wiring Schematic for details.) CHECK blower motor operation.

BLOWER MOTOR OPERATES IN LO, MED AND MED2, BUT NOT IN HI DIAGNOSIS

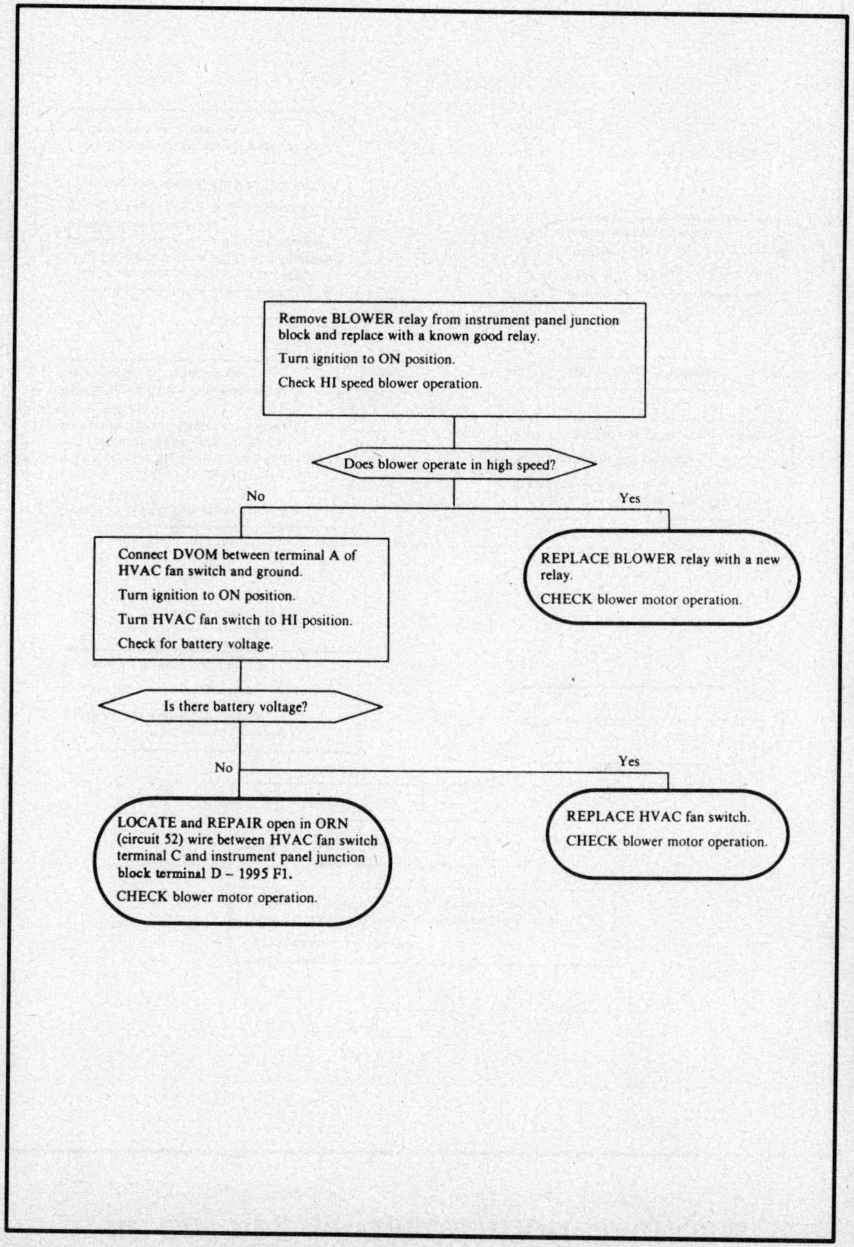

Remove BLOWER relay from instrument panel junction block and replace with a known good relay.

Turn ignition to ON position.

Check HI speed blower operation.

Does blower operate in high speed?

- **Yes:** REPLACE BLOWER relay with a new relay. CHECK blower motor operation.
- **No:** Connect DVOM between terminal A of HVAC fan switch and ground. Turn ignition to ON position. Turn HVAC fan switch to HI position. Check for battery voltage.

Is there battery voltage?

- **No:** LOCATE and REPAIR open in ORN (circuit 52) wire between HVAC fan switch terminal C and instrument panel junction block terminal D – 1995 F1. CHECK blower motor operation.
- **Yes:** REPLACE HVAC fan switch. CHECK blower motor operation.

NO OUTSIDE AIR CIRCULATION DIAGNOSIS

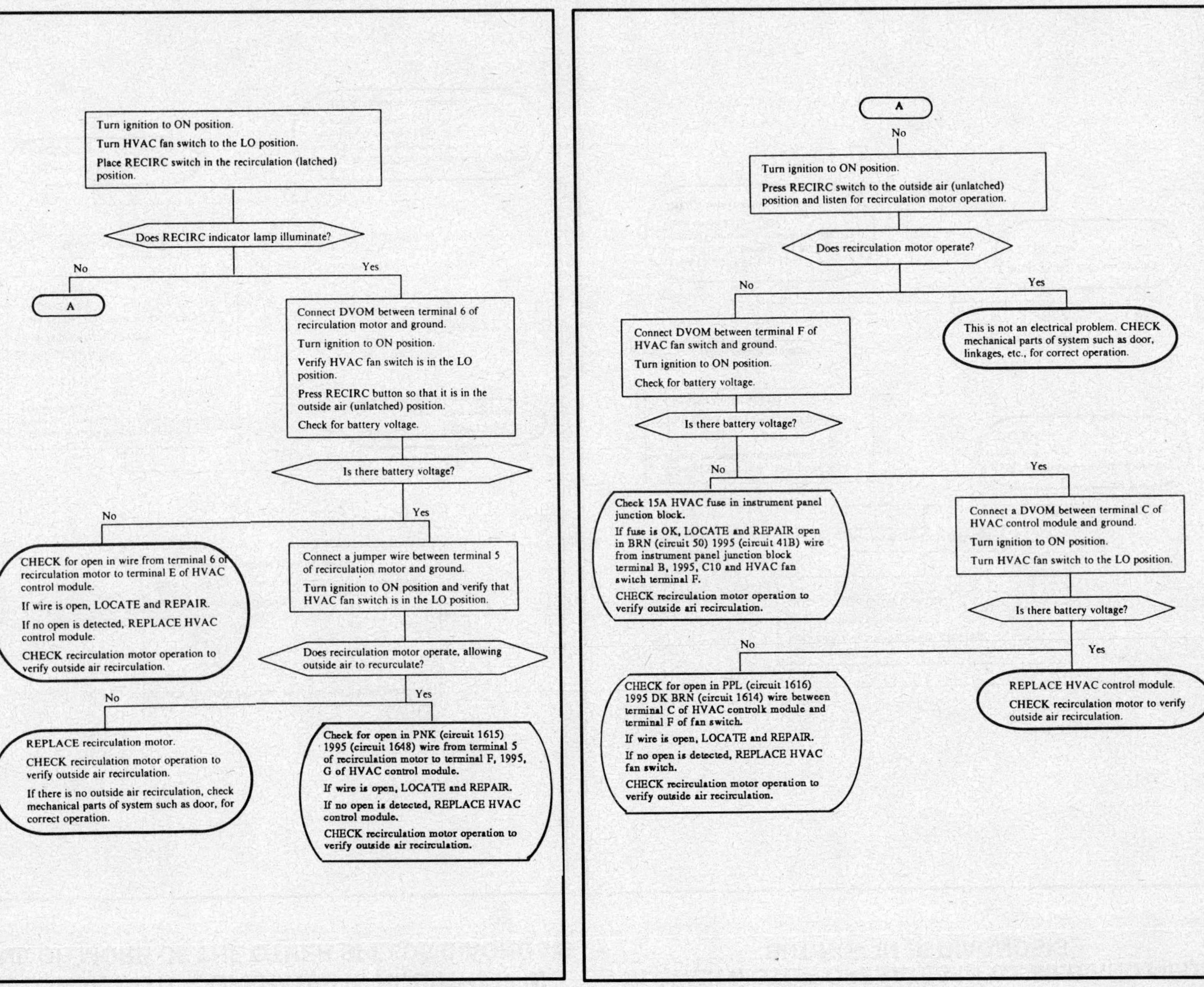

Turn ignition to ON position.
Turn HVAC fan switch to the LO position.
Place RECIRC switch in the recirculation (latched) position.
Does RECIRC indicator lamp illuminate?
No
A
Yes
Connect DVOM between terminal 6 of recirculation motor and ground.
Turn ignition to ON position.
Verify HVAC fan switch is in the LO position.
Press RECIRC button so that it is in the outside air (unlatched) position.
Check for battery voltage.
Is there battery voltage?
No
CHECK for open in wire from terminal 6 of recirculation motor to terminal E of HVAC control module.
If wire is open, LOCATE and REPAIR.
If no open is detected, REPLACE HVAC control module.
CHECK recirculation motor operation to verify outside air recirculation.
Yes
Connect a jumper wire between terminal 5 of recirculation motor and ground.
Turn ignition to ON position and verify that HVAC fan switch is in the LO position.
Does recirculation motor operate, allowing outside air to recurculate?
No
REPLACE recirculation motor.
CHECK recirculation motor operation to verify outside air recirculation.
If there is no outside air recirculation, check mechanical parts of system such as door, for correct operation.
Yes
Check for open in PNK (circuit 1615) 1995 (circuit 1648) wire from terminal 5 of recirculation motor to terminal F, 1995, G of HVAC control module.
If wire is open, LOCATE and REPAIR.
If no open is detected, REPLACE HVAC control module.
CHECK recirculation motor operation to verify outside air recirculation.

NO OUTSIDE AIR CIRCULATION DIAGNOSIS

A
No
Turn ignition to ON position.
Press RECIRC switch to the outside air (unlatched) position and listen for recirculation motor operation.
Does recirculation motor operate?
Yes
This is not an electrical problem. CHECK mechanical parts of system such as door, linkages, etc., for correct operation.
No
Connect DVOM between terminal F of HVAC fan switch and ground.
Turn ignition to ON position.
Check for battery voltage.
Is there battery voltage?
No
Check 15A HVAC fuse in instrument panel junction block.
If fuse is OK, LOCATE and REPAIR open in BRN (circuit 50) 1995 (circuit 41B) wire from instrument panel junction block terminal B, 1995, C10 and HVAC fan switch terminal F.
CHECK recirculation motor operation to verify outside ari recirculation.
Yes
Connect a DVOM between terminal C of HVAC control module and ground.
Turn ignition to ON position.
Turn HVAC fan switch to the LO position.
Is there battery voltage?
No
CHECK for open in PPL (circuit 1616) 1995 DK BRN (circuit 1614) wire between terminal C of HVAC controlk module and terminal F of fan switch.
If wire is open, LOCATE and REPAIR.
If no open is detected, REPLACE HVAC fan switch.
CHECK recirculation motor operation to verify outside air recirculation.
Yes
REPLACE HVAC control module.
CHECK recirculation motor to verify outside air recirculation.

NO INSIDE AIR CIRCULATION DIAGNOSIS

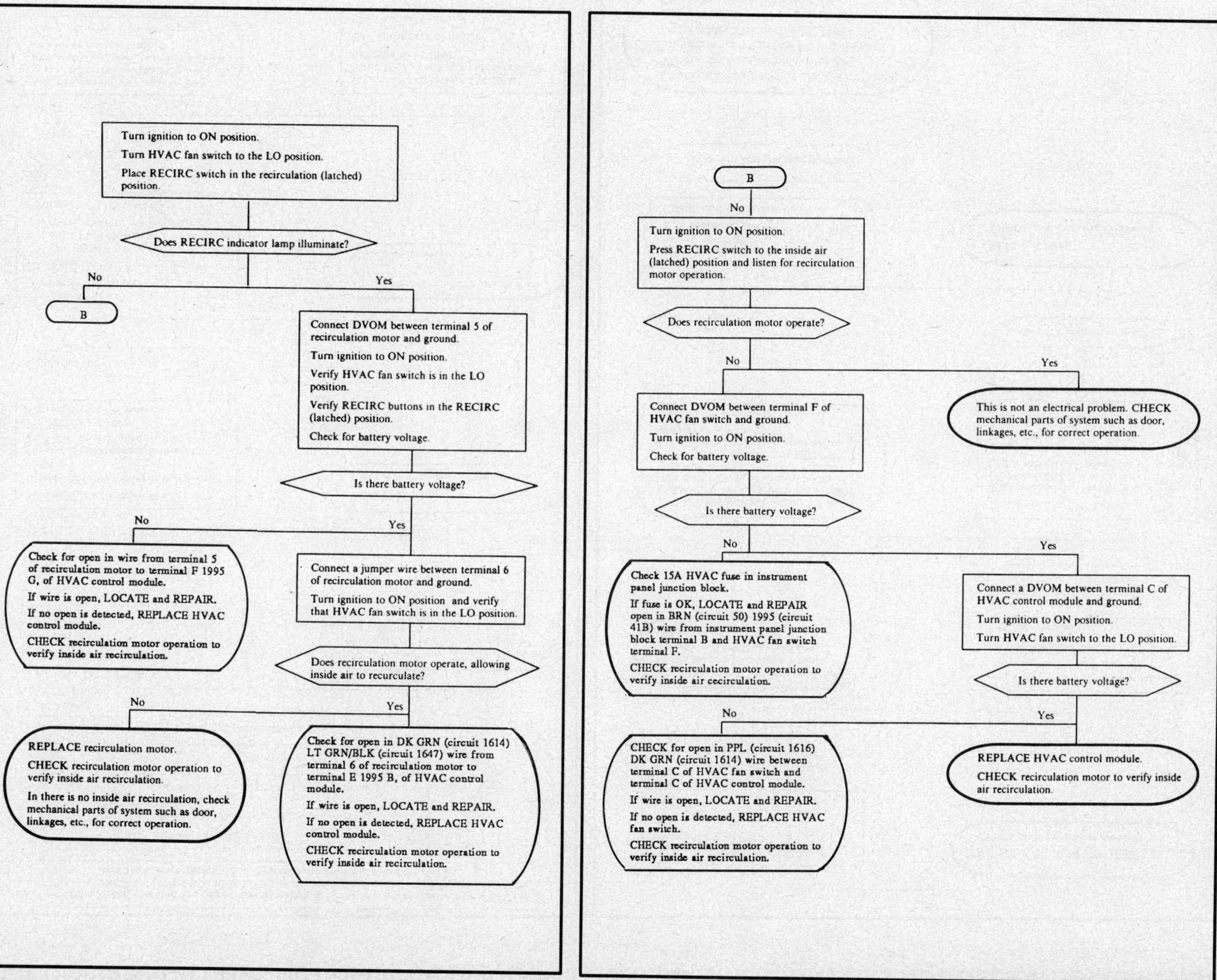
Turn ignition to ON position.
Turn HVAC fan switch to the LO position.
Place RECIRC switch in the recirculation (latched) position.
Does RECIRC indicator lamp illuminate?
No
B
Yes
Connect DVOM between terminal 5 of recirculation motor and ground.
Turn ignition to ON position.
Verify HVAC fan switch is in the LO position.
Verify RECIRC buttons in the RECIRC (latched) position.
Check for battery voltage.
Is there battery voltage?
No
Check for open in wire from terminal 5 of recirculation motor to terminal F 1995 G, of HVAC control module.
If wire is open, LOCATE and REPAIR.
If no open is detected, REPLACE HVAC control module.
CHECK recirculation motor operation to verify inside air recirculation.
Yes
Connect a jumper wire between terminal 6 of recirculation motor and ground.
Turn ignition to ON position and verify that HVAC fan switch is in the LO position.
Does recirculation motor operate, allowing inside air to recurculate?
No
REPLACE recirculation motor.
CHECK recirculation motor operation to verify inside air recirculation.
In there is no inside air recirculation, check mechanical parts of system such as door, linkages, etc., for correct operation.
Yes
Check for open in DK GRN (circuit 1614) LT GRN/BLK (circuit 1647) wire from terminal 6 of recirculation motor to terminal E 1995 B, of HVAC control module.
If wire is open, LOCATE and REPAIR.
If no open is detected, REPLACE HVAC control module.
CHECK recirculation motor operation to verify inside air recirculation.

NO INSIDE AIR CIRCULATION DIAGNOSIS

B
No
Turn ignition to ON position.
Press RECIRC switch to the inside air (latched) position and listen for recirculation motor operation.
Does recirculation motor operate?
Yes
This is not an electrical problem. CHECK mechanical parts of system such as door, linkages, etc., for correct operation.
No
Connect DVOM between terminal F of HVAC fan switch and ground.
Turn ignition to ON position.
Check for battery voltage.
Is there battery voltage?
No
Check 15A HVAC fuse in instrument panel junction block.
If fuse is OK, LOCATE and REPAIR open in BRN (circuit 50) 1995 (circuit 41B) wire from instrument panel junction block terminal B and HVAC fan switch terminal F.
CHECK recirculation motor operation to verify inside air cecirculation.
Yes
Connect a DVOM between terminal C of HVAC control module and ground.
Turn ignition to ON position.
Turn HVAC fan switch to the LO position.
Is there battery voltage?
No
CHECK for open in PPL (circuit 1616) DK GRN (circuit 1614) wire between terminal C of HVAC fan switch and terminal C of HVAC control module.
If wire is open, LOCATE and REPAIR.
If no open is detected, REPLACE HVAC fan switch.
CHECK recirculation motor operation to verify inside air recirculation.
Yes
REPLACE HVAC control module.
CHECK recirculation motor to verify inside air recirculation.

A/C COMPRESSOR DOES NOT OPERATE DIAGNOSIS

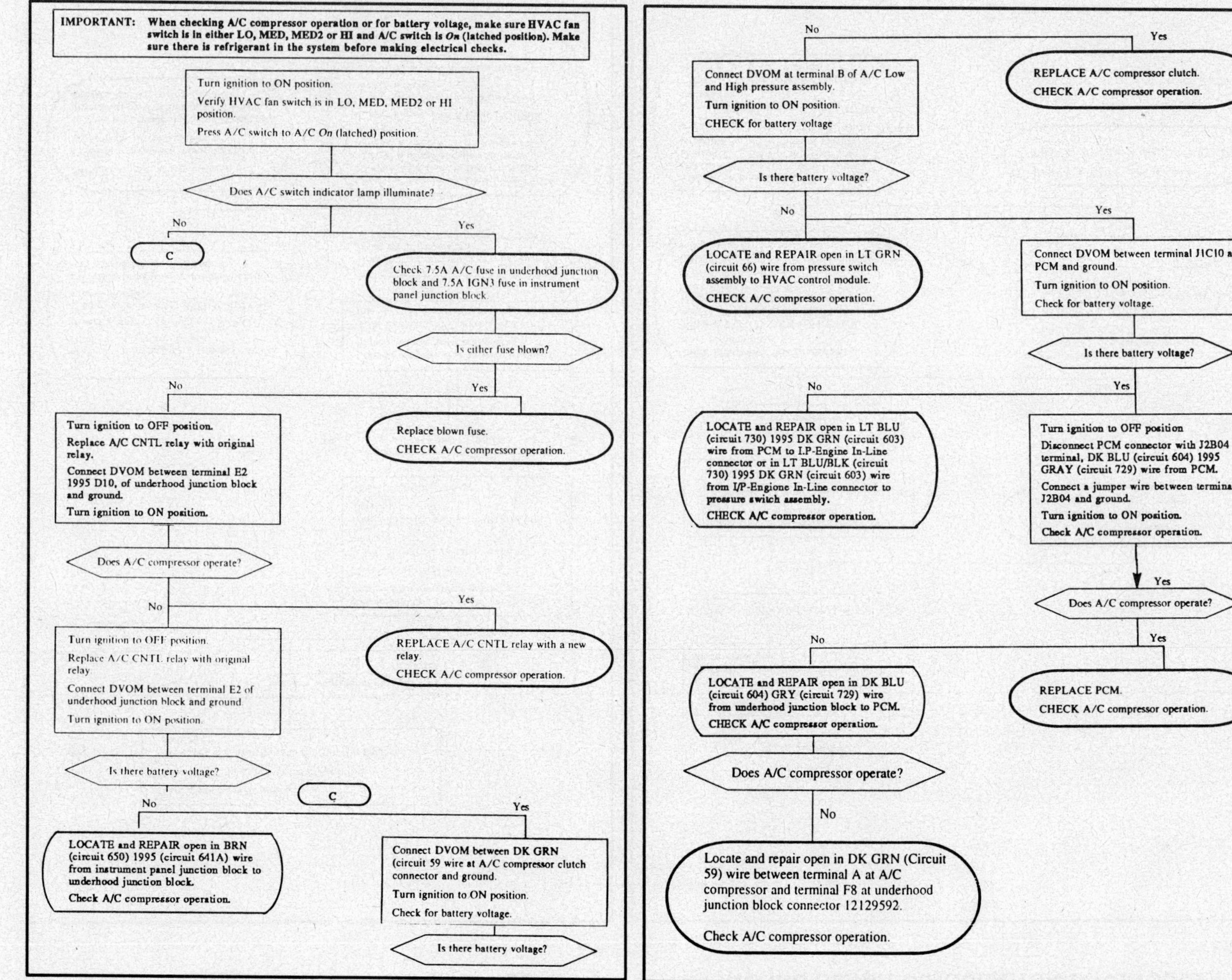
IMPORTANT: When checking A/C compressor operation or for battery voltage, make sure HVAC fan switch is in either LO, MED, MED2 or HI and A/C switch is On (latched position). Make sure there is refrigerant in the system before making electrical checks.
Turn ignition to ON position.
Verify HVAC fan switch is in LO, MED, MED2 or HI position.
Press A/C switch to A/C On (latched) position.
Does A/C switch indicator lamp illuminate?
No
C
Yes
Check 7.5A A/C fuse in underhood junction block and 7.5A IGN3 fuse in instrument panel junction block.
Is either fuse blown?
Yes
Replace blown fuse.
CHECK A/C compressor operation.
No
Turn ignition to OFF position.
Replace A/C CNTL relay with original relay.
Connect DVOM between terminal E2 1995 D10, of underhood junction block and ground.
Turn ignition to ON position.
Does A/C compressor operate?
Yes
REPLACE A/C CNTL relay with a new relay.
CHECK A/C compressor operation.
No
Turn ignition to OFF position.
Replace A/C CNTL relay with original relay.
Connect DVOM between terminal E2 of underhood junction block and ground.
Turn ignition to ON position.
Is there battery voltage?
No
LOCATE and REPAIR open in BRN (circuit 650) 1995 (circuit 641A) wire from instrument panel junction block to underhood junction block.
Check A/C compressor operation.
C
Yes
Connect DVOM between DK GRN (circuit 59 wire at A/C compressor clutch connector and ground.
Turn ignition to ON position.
Check for battery voltage.
Is there battery voltage?

A/C COMPRESSOR DOES NOT OPERATE DIAGNOSIS

Yes
REPLACE A/C compressor clutch.
CHECK A/C compressor operation.
No
Connect DVOM at terminal B of A/C Low and High pressure assembly.
Turn ignition to ON position.
CHECK for battery voltage
Is there battery voltage?
No
LOCATE and REPAIR open in LT GRN (circuit 66) wire from pressure switch assembly to HVAC control module.
CHECK A/C compressor operation.
Yes
Connect DVOM between terminal J1C10 at PCM and ground.
Turn ignition to ON position.
Check for battery voltage.
Is there battery voltage?
No
LOCATE and REPAIR open in LT BLU (circuit 730) 1995 DK GRN (circuit 603) wire from PCM to I.P-Engine In-Line connector or in LT BLU/BLK (circuit 730) 1995 DK GRN (circuit 603) wire from I/P-Engione In-Line connector to pressure switch assembly.
CHECK A/C compressor operation.
Yes
Turn ignition to OFF position
Disconnect PCM connector with J2B04 terminal, DK BLU (circuit 604) 1995 GRAY (circuit 729) wire from PCM.
Connect a jumper wire between terminal J2B04 and ground.
Turn ignition to ON position.
Check A/C compressor operation.
Yes
Does A/C compressor operate?
Yes
REPLACE PCM.
CHECK A/C compressor operation.
No
LOCATE and REPAIR open in DK BLU (circuit 604) GRY (circuit 729) wire from underhood junction block to PCM.
CHECK A/C compressor operation.
Does A/C compressor operate?
No
Locate and repair open in DK GRN (Circuit 59) wire between terminal A at A/C compressor and terminal F8 at underhood junction block connector 12129592.
Check A/C compressor operation.

A/C COMPRESSOR DOES NOT OPERRATE DIAGNOSIS, CONT'D

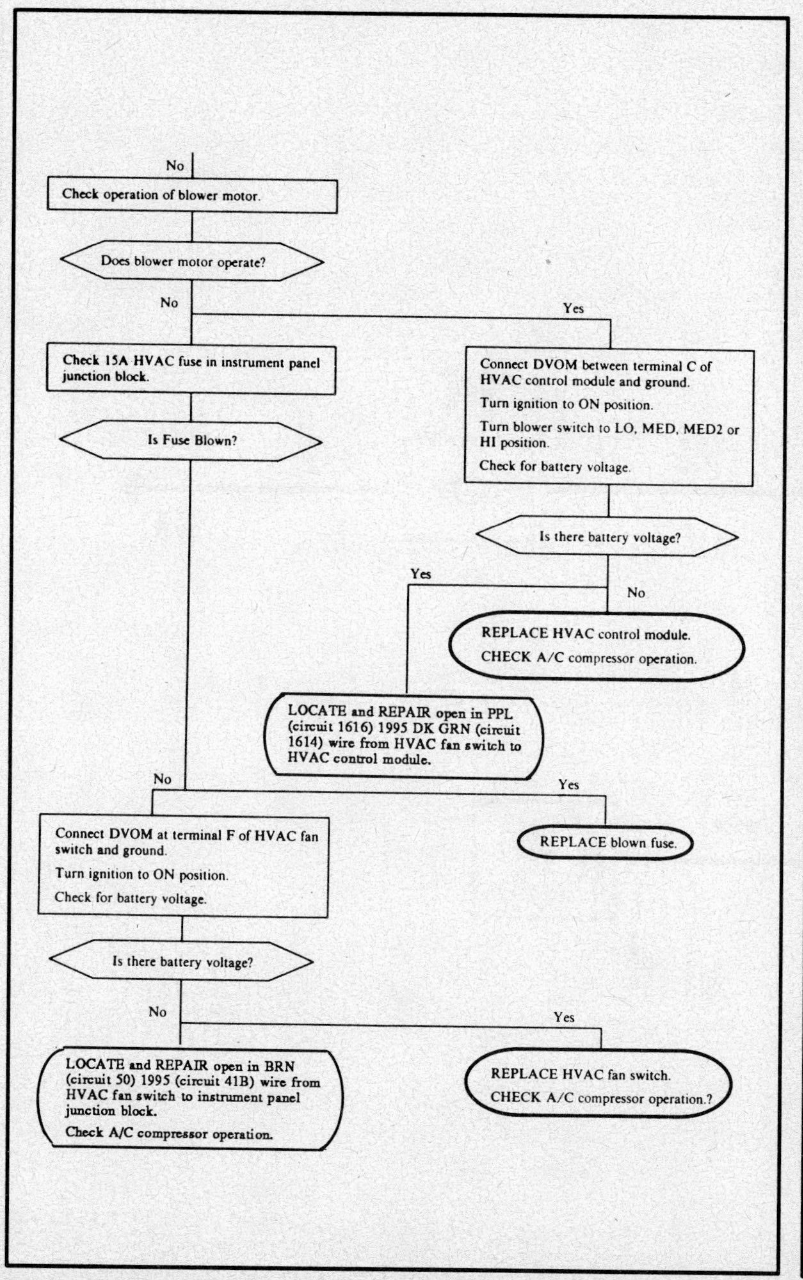
No
Check operation of blower motor.
Does blower motor operate?
No
Yes
Check 15A HVAC fuse in instrument panel junction block.
Connect DVOM between terminal C of HVAC control module and ground.
Turn ignition to ON position.
Turn blower switch to LO, MED, MED2 or HI position.
Check for battery voltage.
Is Fuse Blown?
Is there battery voltage?
Yes
No
REPLACE HVAC control module.
CHECK A/C compressor operation.
LOCATE and REPAIR open in PPL (circuit 1616) 1995 DK GRN (circuit 1614) wire from HVAC fan switch to HVAC control module.
No
Yes
Connect DVOM at terminal F of HVAC fan switch and ground.
Turn ignition to ON position.
Check for battery voltage.
REPLACE blown fuse.
Is there battery voltage?
No
Yes
LOCATE and REPAIR open in BRN (circuit 50) 1995 (circuit 41B) wire from HVAC fan switch to instrument panel junction block.
Check A/C compressor operation.
REPLACE HVAC fan switch.
CHECK A/C compressor operation.?

A/C COMPRESSOR OPERATES ALL THE TIME DIAGNOSIS

Turn ignition to OFF position.
Remove A/C CNTL relay from underhood junction block and replace with a known good relay.
Turn ignition to ON position.
CHECK A/C compressor operation.

Does A/C compressor operate?

No

REPLACE A/C CNTL relay with a new relay.
CHECK A/C compressor operation.

Yes

Turn ignition to OFF position
Replace relay with original A/C CNTL relay.
Disconnect connector at underhood junction block that contains DK BLU (circuit 604) GRAY (circuit 729) wire from PCM.
Turn ignition to ON position.

Does A/C compressor still operate?

No

CHECK for short to ground in DK BLU (circuit 604) 1995 GRA (circuit 729) wire from underhood junction block to PCM.
If short in wire, LOCATE and REPAIR.
If no short is detected, REPLACE PCM.
CHECK A/C compressor operation.

Yes

CHECK for short to power in DK GRN (circuit 59) wire from underhood junction block to A/C compressor.
If short in wire, LOCATE and REPAIR.
If no short is detected, REPLACE A/C compressor clutch.
CHECK A/C compressor operation.

WIRING SCHEMATICS

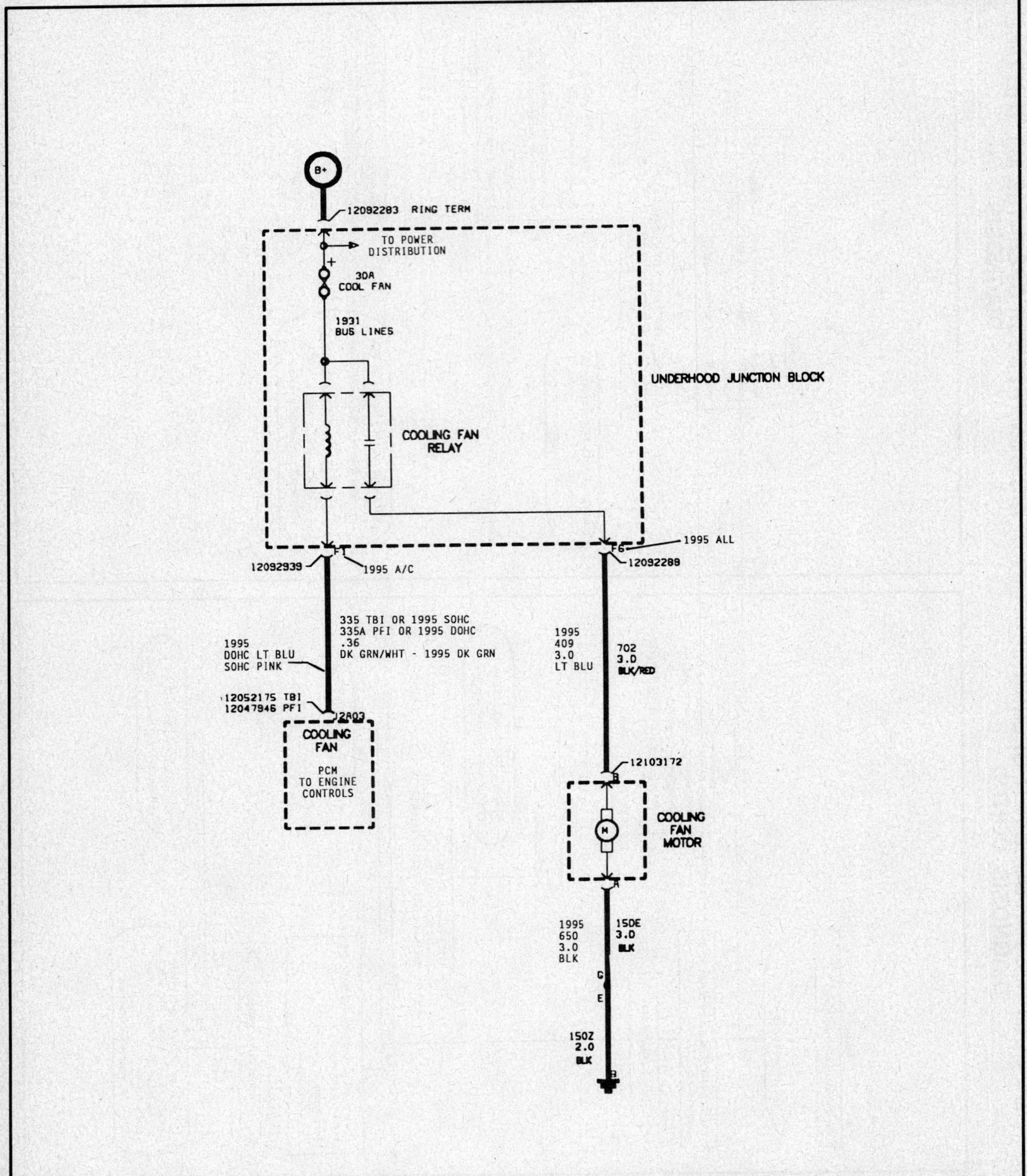

Cooling fan wiring schematic—1993–95 models

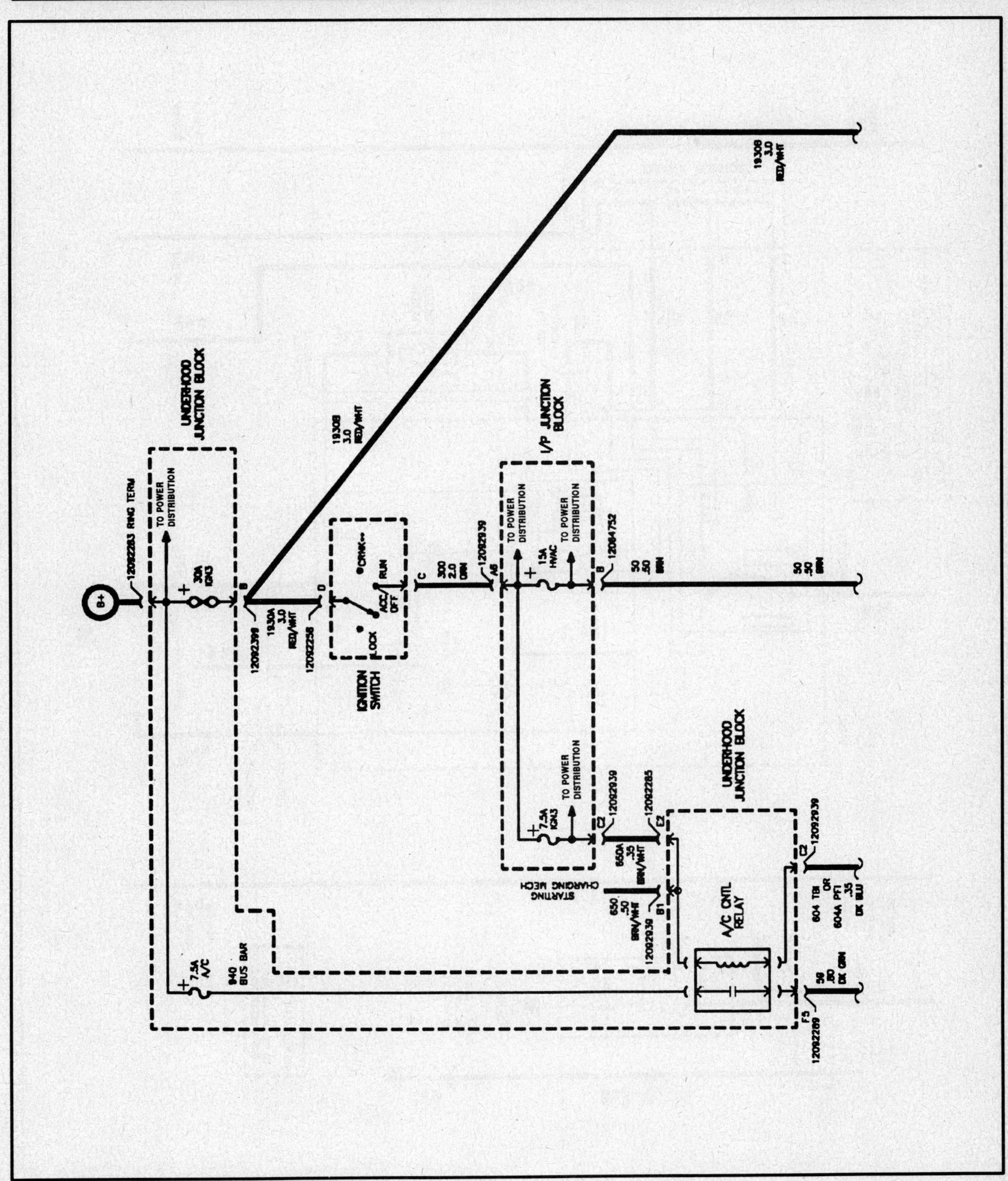

Air conditioning wiring schematic—1993–94 models

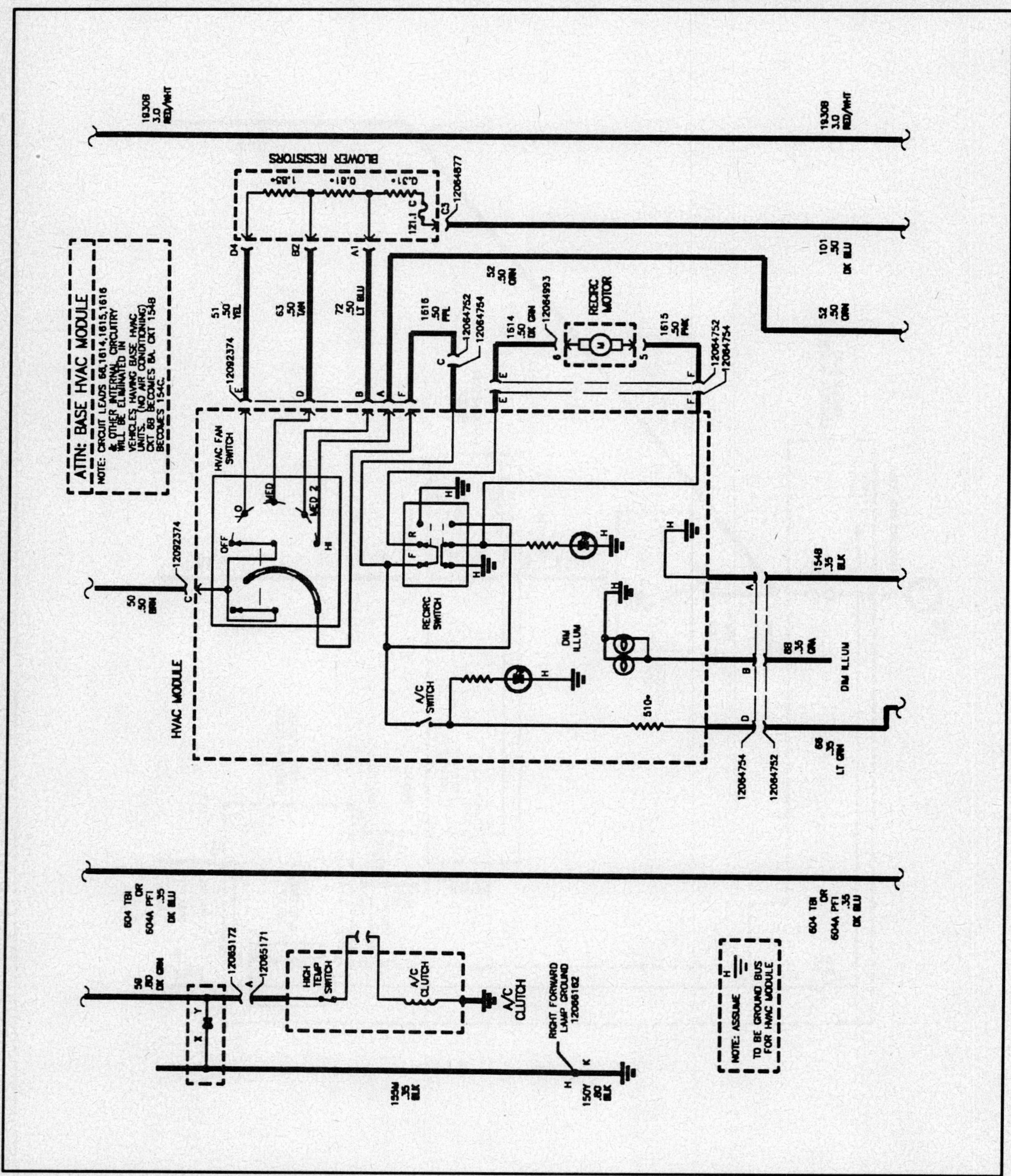

Air conditioning wiring schematic—1993–94 models, Cont'd

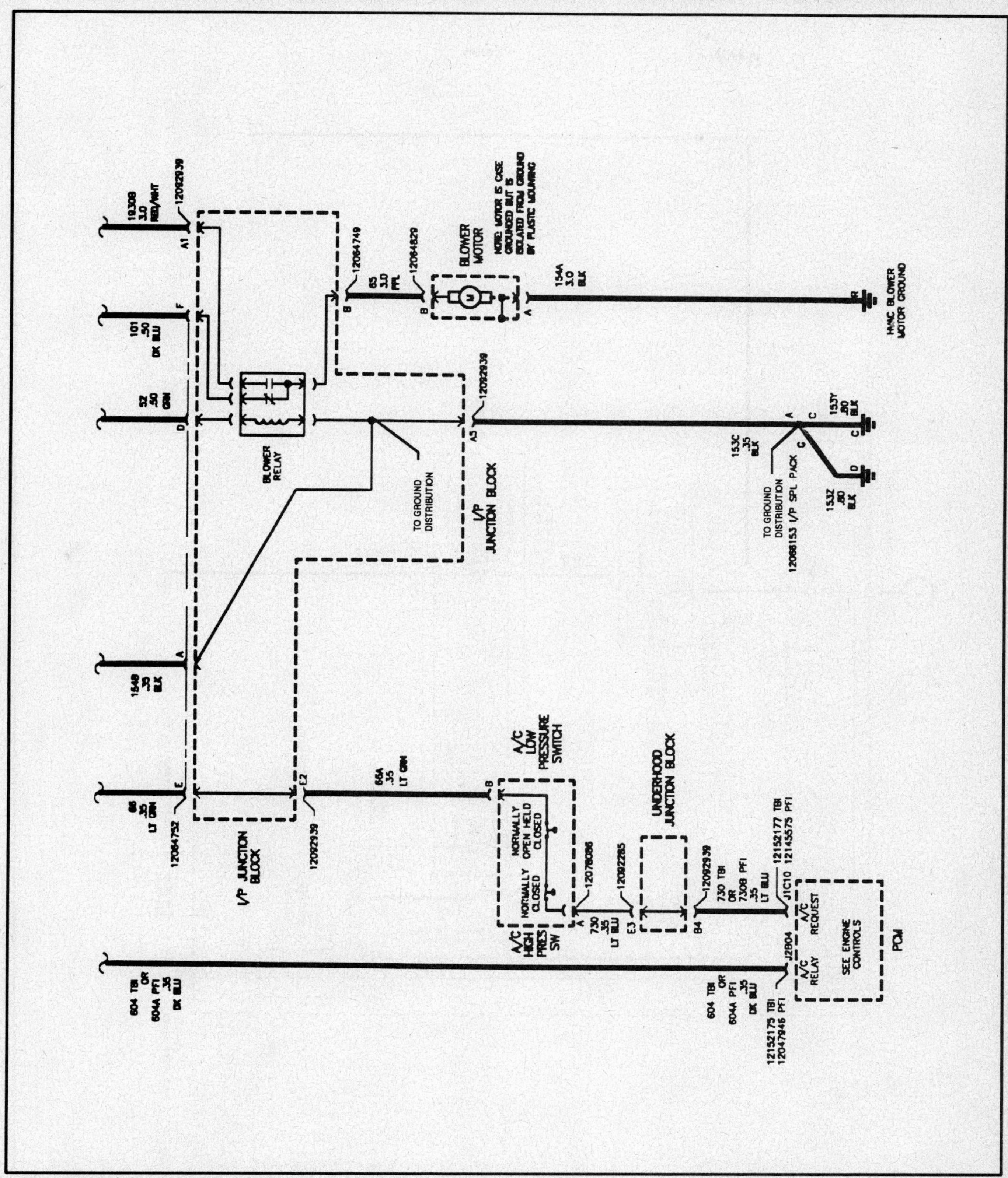

Air conditioning wiring schematic—1993–94 models, Cont'd

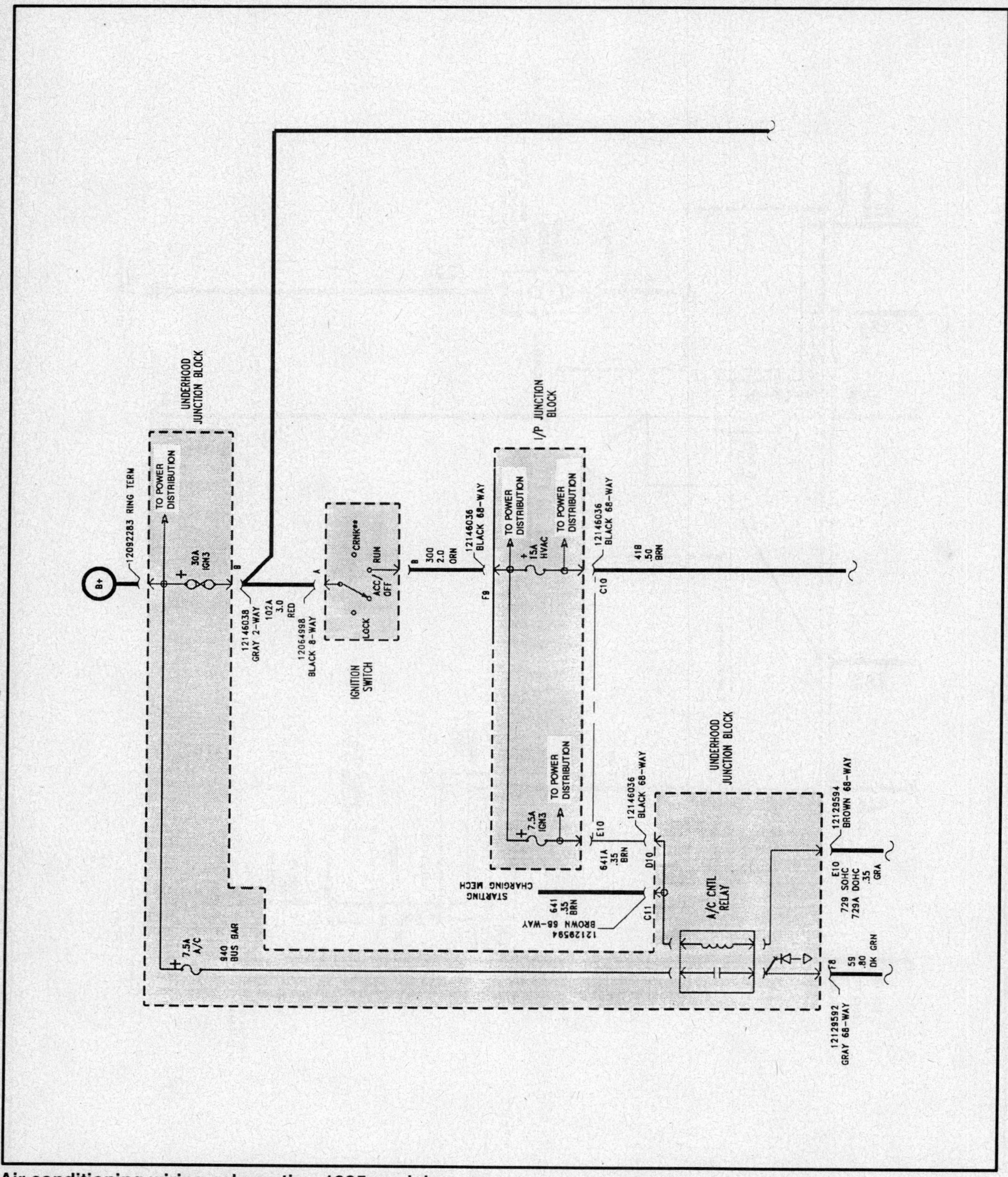

Air conditioning wiring schematic—1995 models

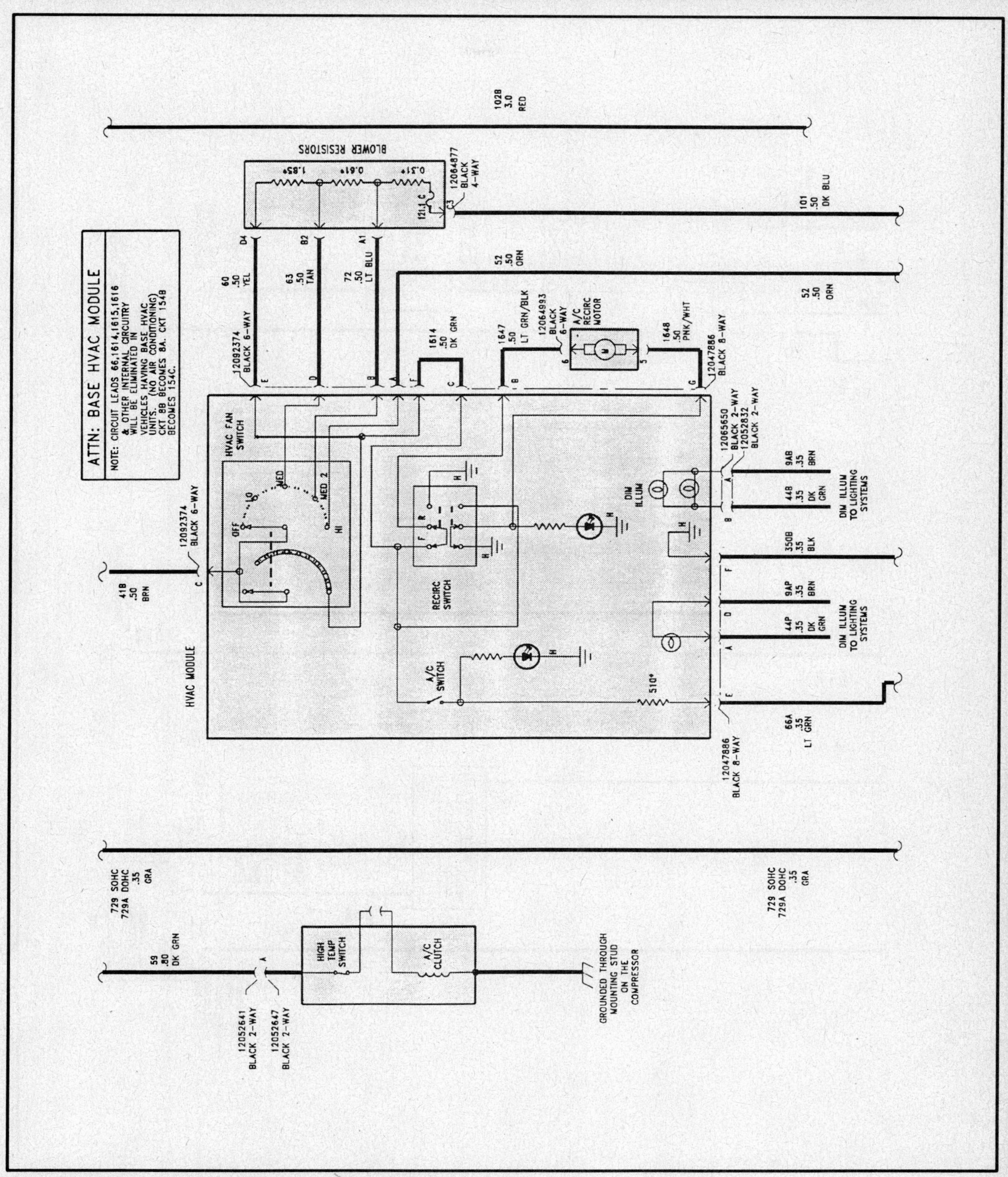

Air conditioning wiring schematic—1995 models, Cont'd

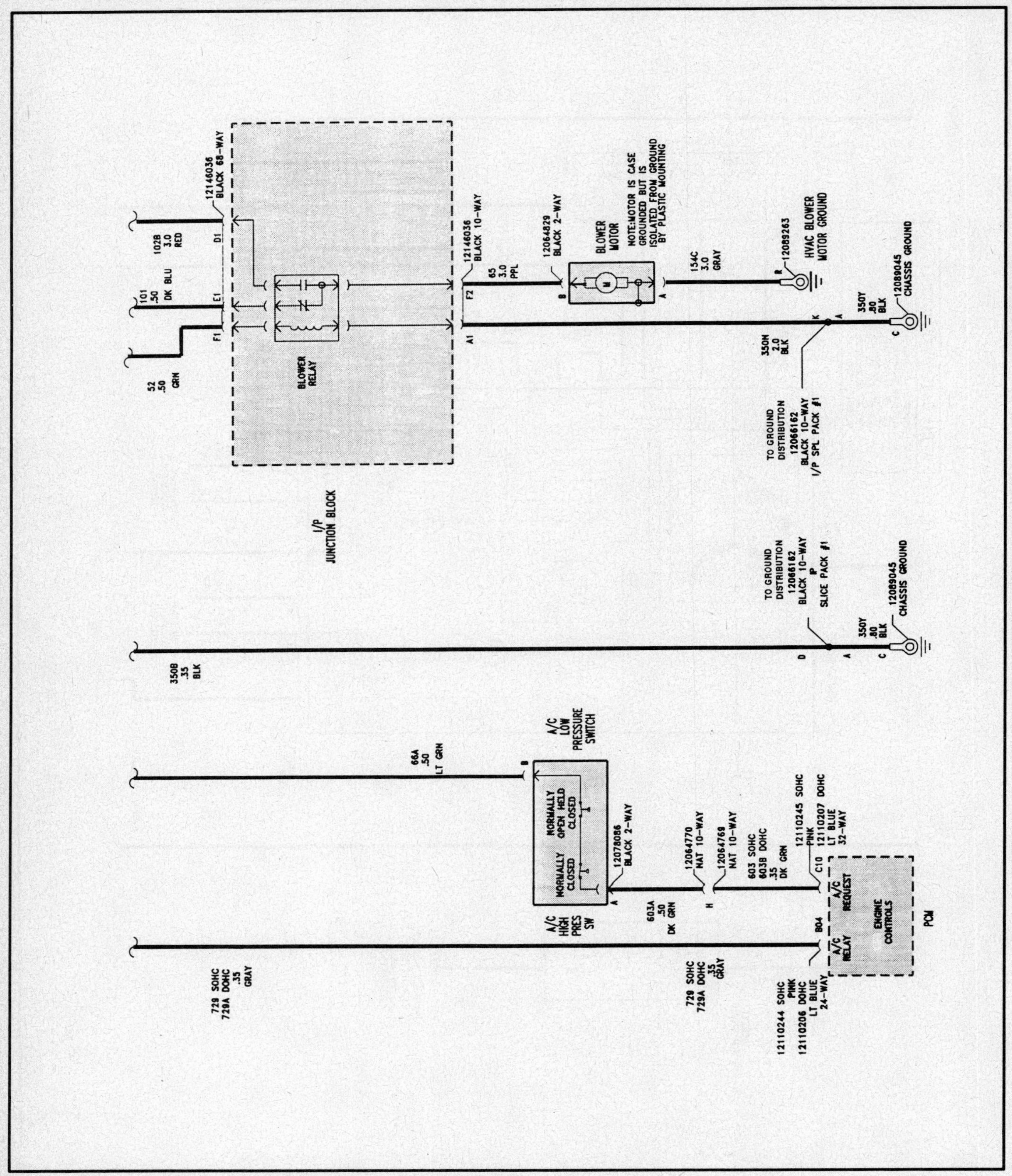

Air conditioning wiring schematic—1995 models, Cont'd

13 DOMESTIC VEHICLES 13

LABOR OPERATIONS

CHRYSLER CORPORATION/JEEP/EAGLE

FORD MOTOR COMPANY

GENERAL MOTORS CORPORATION

CHRYSLER CORPORATION/EAGLE-FWD
EAGLE SUMMIT

LABOR COOLING SYSTEM LABOR

(Factory Time) Chilton Time

SERVICE

(G) Belt, Drive, Adjust
All models
one .3
each adtnl. .1

(G) Belt, Drive, Renew
All models
serpentine
Four (.3) .5
V6 (.5) .8
V-belt
one (.3) .4
each adtnl. .1
w/AC add (.1) .1

(G) Core, Heater, R&R or Renew
1993-95 Summit (3.2) 5.0
Boil & Repair, add 1.2
Repair Core, add .9
Recore, add 1.2

(G) Expansion (Freeze) Plugs, Water Jacket, Renew
Add appropriate time to access plug.
All models .5

(G) Gauge, Temperature (Dash Unit), Renew
1993-95 Summit (.6) .9
1993-95 Summit Wagon (.3) .5

(G) Gauge, Temperature (Engine Unit), Renew
All models (.3) .4

(G) Hoses, Heater, Renew
All models
one (.4) .6
each adtnl. .1

(G) Hoses, Radiator, Renew
Includes: Drain and refill cooling system as required.
1993-95 Summit
upper (.3) .4
lower (.4) .5

(G) Motor, Heater Blower, Renew
1993-95 Summit (.3) .5

(G) Motor, Radiator Fan and/or Fan, Renew
1993-95 Summit (.5) .7
Test system, add (.3) .3

(G) Pump and/or Gasket, Water, Renew
Includes: Drain and refill cooling system.
1993-95 Summit
1.5L, 2.4L (2.1) 3.0
w/AC add .6
w/PS add .3

(G) Radiator Assy., R&R or Renew
1993-95 Summit (.7) 1.1
w/AT add .1
Boil & Repair, add 1.5
Rod Clean, add 1.9
Repair Core, add 1.3
Renew Tank, add 1.6
Renew Trans. Oil Cooler, add 1.9
Recore Radiator, add 1.7

(G) Relay, Radiator Fan Motor, Renew
All models (.2) .3

(G) Resistor, Heater Blower Motor, Renew
All models (.3) .4

(G) Switch, Heater Blower Motor, Renew
1993-95 Summit (.5) .8

(G) Thermostat, Coolant, Renew
1993-95 Summit (.3) .4

(G) Winterize Cooling System
Includes: Run engine to check for leaks, tighten all hose connections. Test radiator and pressure cap, drain radiator and engine block. Add antifreeze and refill system.
All models .5

LABOR AIR CONDITIONING LABOR

(Factory Time) Chilton Time

Note: If more than one item requires replacement where evacuation and discharging the system is already included in the operation, deduct 1.0 hour for each additional item from the time listed.

SERVICE AND TESTING

(G) Drain, Evacuate and Recharge System
All models 1.0

(G) Flush Refrigerant System, Complete
To be used in conjunction with component replacement which could contaminate system. Includes evacuate and recharge.
All models 1.3

(G) Recover and/or Recycle AC Refrigerant
Add to evacuate and charge the AC system, as required.
All models .2

(G) Refrigerant, Add (Partial Charge)
All models .6

COMPONENTS

(G) Blower Motor, Renew
1993-95 Summit 1.1

(G) Clutch Assy., Compressor, Renew
1993-95 Summit (1.4) 2.0

(G) Coil, Evaporator, Renew
Includes: Evacuate and charge system.
1993-95 Summit (2.2) 4.0

(G) Compressor Assy., Renew
Includes: Transfer parts as required. Evacuate and charge system.
1993-95 Summit (1.7) 2.5
Recondition add (1.8) 2.5

(G) Condenser Assy., Renew
Includes: Evacuate and charge system.
1993-95 Summit (1.1) 2.0
Renew receiver drier add .2

(G) Control Assy., AC, Renew
1993-95 Summit (.9) 1.5

(G) Hoses, AC, Renew
Includes: Evacuate and charge system.
1993-95 Summit
suction or discharge (1.8) 2.4
to drier (1.0) 1.8

(G) Module, Automatic Compressor Control, Renew
1993-95 Summit (.6) 1.0

(G) Motor, Condenser Fan, Renew
1993-95 Summit (.4) .6

(G) Receiver/Drier Assy., Renew
Includes: Evacuate and charge system.
1993-95 Summit (.8) 1.5

(G) Resistor, Blower Motor, Renew
All models (.3) .5

(G) Seal, Compressor Shaft, Renew
Includes: R&R compressor. Evacuate and charge system.
All models (1.3) 1.9

(G) Switch, Blower Motor, Renew
1993-95 Summit (1.0) 1.5

(G) Switch, Dual Pressure, Renew
1993-95 Summit (.7) 1.0

(G) Switch, High Pressure Cut-Off, Renew
1993-95 Summit (.7) 1.0

(G) Valve, Expansion, Renew
Includes: Evacuate and charge system.
1993-95 Summit (2.1) 3.0
Renew receiver drier, add .2

CHRYSLER CORPORATION/EAGLE-FWD

CHRYSLER CONCORDE • CHRYSLER NEW YORKER/LHS • DODGE INTREPID • EAGLE VISION

LABOR — COOLING SYSTEM — LABOR

(Factory Time) Chilton Time

SERVICE

(G) Belt, Drive, Adjust
All models (.2) 4

(G) Belt, Serpentine Drive, Renew
All models (.2) 3
w/AC add 2

(G) Blade, Fan, Renew
All models (.5) 7

(G) Control Assy., Temperature, Renew
All models
heater or AC (.3) 5
ATC (.3) 5

(G) Cooler, Transaxle Auxiliary Oil, Renew
All models (.3) 6

(G) Core, Heater, R&R or Renew
All models
wo/AC (3.1) 5.5
w/AC (3.9) 6.5
w/console add 3
Boil & Repair, add 1.2
Repair Core, add 9
Recore, add 1.2

(G) Expansion (Freeze) Plugs, Water Jacket, Renew
Add appropriate time to access plug.
All models, each 5

(G) Gauge, Temperature (Dash Unit), Renew
All models (.8) 1.2

(G) Gauge, Temperature (Engine Unit), Renew
All models (.3) 4

(G) Hoses, Heater, Renew
All models
one (.4) 6
each adtnl. 1

(G) Hoses, Radiator, Renew
Includes: Drain and refill cooling system as required.
All models
upper (.4) 5
lower (.5) 6
water pump to intake (.5) 7

(G) Motor, Heater Blower, Renew
All models (.8) 1.0

(G) Motor, Radiator Fan and/or Fan, Renew
All models (.9) 1.4
Test system add (.3) 3

(G) Pump and/or Gasket, Water, Renew
Includes: Drain and refill cooling system.
All models
3.3L (.6) 1.0
3.5L (2.4) 4.0
w/AC add 3

(G) Radiator Assy., R&R or Renew
All models (1.0) 1.4
Boil & Repair, add 1.5
Rod Clean, add 1.9
Repair Core, add 1.3
Renew Tank, add 1.6
Renew Trans. Oil Cooler, add 1.9
Recore Radiator, add 1.7

(G) Relay, Radiator Fan Motor, Renew
All models (.2) 4

(G) Resistor, Heater Blower Motor, Renew
All models (.4) 6

(G) Tensioner, Drive Belt, Renew
All models (.4) 6

(G) Thermostat, Coolant, Renew
All models (.5) 6

(G) Winterize Cooling System
Includes: Run engine to check for leaks, tighten all hose connections. Test radiator and pressure cap, drain radiator and engine block. Add antifreeze and refill system.
All models 5

LABOR — AIR CONDITIONING — LABOR

(Factory Time) Chilton Time

Note: If more than one item requires replacement where evacuation and discharging the system is already included in the operation, deduct 1.0 hour for each additional item from the time listed.

SERVICE AND TESTING

(G) Drain, Evacuate and Recharge System
All models 1.0

(G) Flush Refrigerant System, Complete
To be used in conjunction with component replacement which could contaminate system. Includes evacuate and recharge.
All models 1.3

(G) Recover and/or Recycle AC Refrigerant
Add to evacuate and charge the AC system, as required.
All models 2

(G) Refrigerant, Add (Partial Charge)
All models 6

COMPONENTS

(G) Belt, Compressor Drive, Renew
All models (.3) 4

(G) Blower Motor, Renew
All models (.8) 1.0

(G) Clutch Assy., Compressor, Renew
All models (.6) 9

(G) Coil, Compressor Clutch Field, Renew
All models (.5) 8

(G) Coil, Evaporator, Renew
Includes: Evacuate and charge system.
All models (4.1) 7.0
w/console add 3
w/bench seats add 1.0

(G) Compressor Assy., Renew
Includes: Transfer parts as required. Evacuate and charge system.
All models (1.0) 1.8
Renew receiver/drier add 5

(G) Condenser Assy., Renew
Includes: Evacuate and charge system.
All models (1.1) 2.0
Renew receiver/drier add 2

(G) Hoses, AC, Renew
Includes: Evacuate and charge system.
All models
suction or discharge, each (.9) 1.7
tube assy. (.9) 1.7

(G) Manifold and/or Gasket, Compressor, Renew
All models
3.3L (.9) 1.4
3.5L (1.1) 1.6

(G) Module, Blower Motor and Compressor Control, Renew
All models (.4) 6

(G) Motor, AC Door Actuator, Renew
All models (2.6) 4.0

(G) Receiver/Drier Assy., Renew
Includes: Evacuate and charge system.
All models (1.1) 1.6

LABOR — AIR CONDITIONING — LABOR

(Factory Time) Chilton Time

(G) Resistor, Blower Motor, Renew
All models (.3) 5

(G) Sensor, Sun/Photo, Renew
All models (.3) 5

(G) Switch, Clutch Cycling Pressure, Renew
All models (.9) 1.5
w/console add 3

(G) Valve, Expansion, Renew
Includes: Evacuate and charge system.
All models (.8) 1.4
Renew receiver/drier add 5

(G) Valve, High Pressure Relief, Renew
All models (.8) 1.2

CHRYSLER CORPORATION/EAGLE-FWD
PLYMOUTH LASER • EAGLE TALON

LABOR — COOLING SYSTEM — LABOR

(Factory Time) Chilton Time

TESTING

(M) Pressure Test Cooling System
All models 3

SERVICE

(G) Belt, Drive, Adjust
All models 3

(G) Belt, Drive, Renew
1993-94 (.3) 4
1995
Generator
wo/Turbo (.4) 6
w/Turbo (.5) 7
Power Steering (.2) 3

(G) Control Assy., Temperature, Renew
All models (.9) 1.4

(G) Core, Heater, R&R or Renew
All models
wo/AC (5.2) 10.0
w/AC (6.2) 11.0
Boil & Repair, add 1.2
Repair Core, add 9
Recore, add 1.2

(G) Expansion (Freeze) Plugs, Water Jacket, Renew (Engine Block)
Add appropriate time to access plug.
All models, Four
right side
front (.6) 9
center or rear (1.2) 1.5
left side
upper or lower, front or center (.6) .9
rear (.8) 1.1
rear of engine (2.6) 3.5

(G) Gauge, Temperature (Dash Unit), Renew
All models (.5) 9

(G) Hoses, Heater, Renew
All models
one (.4) 5
each adtnl. 2

(G) Hoses, Radiator, Renew
Includes: Drain and refill cooling system as required.
All models
upper (.3) 4
lower (.4) 5

(G) Motor, Condenser Fan, Renew
All models (.4) 6

(G) Motor, Heater Blower, Renew
All models (.3) 6

(G) Motor, Radiator Fan and/or Fan, Renew
All models (.5) 7

(G) Pump and/or Gasket, Water, Renew
Includes: Drain and refill cooling system.
1993-94
1.8L (2.1) 3.0
2.0L DOHC (3.2) 4.5
w/PS add (.2) 2
1995
2.0L (2.5) 3.5
2.0L DOHC Turbo (3.2) 4.5
w/PS add (.3) 3
w/AC add (.2) 2

(G) Radiator Assy., R&R or Renew
All models (.7) 1.2
w/AT add (.1) 1
w/AC add (.1) 1
Boil & Repair, add 1.5
Rod Clean, add 1.9
Repair Core, add 1.3
Renew Tank, add 1.6
Renew Trans. Oil Cooler, add 1.9
Recore Radiator, add 1.7

(G) Relay, Radiator Fan Motor, Renew
All models (.2) 3

(G) Resistor, Heater Blower Motor, Renew
1993-95 (.3) 5

(G) Sending Unit, Engine Coolant Temp., Renew
All models (.3) 4

(G) Switch, Heater Blower Motor, Renew
All models
wo/AC (.5) 7
w/AC (1.0) 1.5

(G) Thermostat, Coolant, Renew
1993-94 (.3) 5
1995 (.4) 6

(G) Winterize Cooling System
Includes: Run engine to check for leaks, tighten all hose connections. Test radiator and pressure cap, drain radiator and engine block. Add antifreeze and refill system.
All models .... .528

LABOR — AIR CONDITIONING — LABOR

(Factory Time) Chilton Time

Note: If more than one item requires replacement where evacuation and discharging the system is already included in the operation, deduct 1.0 hour for each additional item from the time listed.

SERVICE AND TESTING

(G) Drain, Evacuate and Recharge System
All models 1.0

(G) Flush Refrigerant System, Complete
To be used in conjunction with component replacement which could contaminate system. Includes evacuate and recharge.
All models 1.3

(G) Recover and/or Recycle AC Refrigerant
Add to evacuate and charge the AC system, as required.
All models 2

LABOR — AIR CONDITIONING — LABOR

(Factory Time) Chilton Time

(G) Refrigerant, Add (Partial Charge)
All models 6

COMPONENTS

(G) Belt, Compressor Drive, Renew
1993-94 (.2) 3
w/DOHC add (.4) 4

(G) Blower Motor, Renew
All models (.3) 6

(G) Clutch Assy., Compressor, Renew
All models (1.4) 2.3

(G) Coil, Compressor Clutch Field, Renew
All models (1.4) 2.3

(G) Coil, Evaporator, Renew
Includes: Evacuate and charge system.
All models (1.5) 2.5

(G) Compressor Assy., Renew
Includes: Transfer parts as required. Evacuate and charge system.
All models (1.7) 2.8

(G) Condenser Assy., Renew
Includes: Evacuate and charge system.
All models (1.1) 2.0
Renew receiver drier, add 2

(G) Control Assy., Temperature, Renew
All models (.9) 1.4

(G) Cylinder Head and/or Valve Plate, Compressor, Renew
Includes: Evacuate and charge system.
All models (1.6) 2.8
Renew receiver drier, add 5

(G) Hoses, AC, Renew
Includes: Evacuate and charge system.
All models
suction (1.8) 2.5
tube
condenser to receiver (1.0) 1.7
expansion valve to receiver (1.8) 2.5
discharge (1.0) 1.8

(G) Module, Automatic Compressor Control, Renew
All models (.5) 7

(G) Motor, Condenser Fan, Renew
All models (.4) 6

(G) Receiver/Drier Assy., Renew
Includes: Evacuate and charge system.
1993-94 (1.1) 1.8
1995 (.8) 1.5

(G) Relay, Condenser Fan Motor, Renew
All models (.2) 3

(G) Resistor, Blower Motor, Renew
1993-95 (.3) 5

(G) Sensor, Air Inlet, Renew
All models (1.3) 2.0

(G) Sensor, Air Thermo, Renew
Includes: R&R evaporator.
All models (1.3) 2.0

(G) Switch, AC On/Off Control, Renew
All models (.4) 7

(G) Switch, Blower Motor, Renew
All models
wo/AC (.5) 7
w/AC (1.0) 1.5

(G) Switch, Dual Pressure, Renew
All models (.7) 1.0

(G) Valve, Expansion, Renew
Includes: Evacuate and charge system.
All models (1.5) 2.5
Renew receiver drier, add 5

(G) Valve, Pressure Relief, Renew
Includes: Evacuate and charge system.
All models (.8) 1.4

CHRYSLER CORPORATION-FWD
DODGE STEALTH

LABOR — COOLING SYSTEM — LABOR

(Factory Time) Chilton Time

TESTING

(M) Pressure Test Cooling System
All models 3

SERVICE

(G) Belt, Drive, Adjust
All models 3

(G) Belt, Drive, Renew
All models
SOHC 2
DOHC 7

(G) Control Assy., Temperature, Renew
All models (.9) 1.4

(G) Core, Heater, R&R or Renew
All models
wo/AC (3.3) 6.0
w/AC (3.5) 6.5
Boil & Repair, add 1.2
Repair Core, add 9
Recore, add 1.2

(G) Expansion (Freeze) Plugs, Water Jacket, Renew (Engine Block)
Add appropriate time to access plug.
All models
right side
front (.7) 1.0
center or rear (1.1) 1.5
left side
upper front or center (2.1) 3.0
lower front or center (.3) 5
rear (1.0) 1.4
rear of engine (3.5) 5.0

(G) Gauge, Temperature (Dash Unit), Renew
All models (3.0) 4.5

(G) Hoses, Heater, Renew
All models, each (.4) 5

(G) Hoses, Radiator, Renew
Includes: Drain and refill cooling system as required.
All models
upper (.3) 4
lower (.4) 5

(G) Motor, Condenser Fan, Renew
All models (.4) 6

(G) Motor, Heater Blower, Renew
All models (.3) 5

(G) Motor, Radiator Fan and/or Fan, Renew
All models (.5) 7
w/Turbo add (.2) 2

(G) Pump and/or Gasket, Water, Renew
Includes: Drain and refill cooling system.
All models
SOHC (2.2) 3.2
DOHC (2.8) 4.0
w/AC add (.2) 2
w/Turbo add (.3) 3

(G) Radiator Assy., R&R or Renew
All models (.7) 1.2
w/AT add (.1) 1
w/intercooler, add (.1) 1
Boil & Repair, add 1.5
Rod Clean, add 1.9
Repair Core, add 1.3
Renew Tank, add 1.6
Renew Trans. Oil Cooler, add 1.9
Recore Radiator, add 1.7

LABOR COOLING SYSTEM LABOR

(Factory Time) Chilton Time

(G) Relay, Radiator Fan Motor, Renew
All models (.2) 3

(G) Resistor, Heater Blower Motor, Renew
All models (.3) 6

(G) Sending Unit, Engine Coolant Temp., Renew
All models (.3) 4

(G) Switch, Heater Blower Motor, Renew
All models (1.0) 1.5

(G) Thermostat, Coolant, Renew
All models (.4) 6

(G) Winterize Cooling System
Includes: Run engine to check for leaks, tighten all hose connections. Test radiator and pressure cap, drain radiator and engine block. Add antifreeze and refill system.
All models 5

LABOR AIR CONDITIONING LABOR

(Factory Time) Chilton Time

Note: If more than one item requires replacement where evacuation and discharging the system is already included in the operation, deduct 1.0 hour for each additional item from the time listed.

SERVICE AND TESTING

(G) Drain, Evacuate and Recharge System
All models 1.0

(G) Flush Refrigerant System, Complete
To be used in conjunction with component replacement which could contaminate system. Includes evacuate and recharge.
All models 1.3

(G) Recover and/or Recycle AC Refrigerant
Add to evacuate and charge the AC system, as required.
All models 2

(G) Refrigerant, Add (Partial Charge)
All models 6

COMPONENTS

(G) Actuator or Damper, Mode Door, Renew
All models (1.0) 1.5

(G) Belt, Compressor Drive, Renew
All models
SOHC (.2) 3
DOHC (.4) 5

(G) Blower Motor, Renew
All models (.3) 6

(G) Clutch Assy., Compressor, Renew
All models (1.4) 2.3

(G) Coil, Compressor Clutch Field, Renew
All models (1.4) 2.3

(G) Coil, Evaporator, Renew
Includes: Evacuate and charge system.
All models (1.5) 2.5

(G) Compressor Assy., Renew
Includes: Transfer parts as required. Evacuate and charge system.
All models (1.7) 2.8

(G) Condenser Assy., Renew
Includes: Evacuate and charge system.
All models
SOHC (1.0) 2.0
DOHC (2.0) 3.0
w/intercooler, add (.2) 2
Renew receiver drier, add 2

(G) Control Assy., Temperature, Renew
All models
wo/ATC (.9) 1.4
w/ATC (.8) 1.3

(G) Controller, Automatic, Renew
All models (.8) 1.2

(G) Hoses, AC, Renew
Includes: Evacuate and charge system.
All models
suction (1.0) 1.7
tube (1.2) 1.9
condenser to receiver (1.0) 1.7
discharge (1.0) 1.7
to condenser (1.2) 1.9
to drier (1.1) 1.8
to evaporator (1.2) 1.9

(G) Motor, Condenser Fan, Renew
All models (.4) 6
w/Turbo add (.2) 2

(G) Receiver/Drier Assy., Renew
Includes: Evacuate and charge system.
1993-95 (1.1) 1.8

(G) Relay, Condenser Fan Motor, Renew
All models (.2) 3

(G) Resistor, Blower Motor, Renew
1993-95 (.3) 5

(G) Seal, Compressor Shaft, Renew
Includes: R&R compressor. Evacuate and charge system.
All models (1.6) 2.7

(G) Sensor, Air Inlet, Renew
All models (1.3) 2.0

(G) Sensor, Air Thermo, Renew
Includes: R&R evaporator.
All models (1.3) 2.0

(G) Sensor, In-Vehicle, Renew
All models (.2) 4

(G) Sensor, Sun/Photo, Renew
All models (.3) 5

(G) Switch, AC On/Off Control, Renew
All models (.4) 7

(G) Switch, Blower Motor, Renew
All models (1.0) 1.5

(G) Switch, Dual Pressure, Renew
All models (.7) 1.0

(G) Thermal Limiter, Renew
All models (.2) 3

(G) Valve, Expansion, Renew
Includes: Evacuate and charge system.
All models (1.5) 2.5
Renew receiver drier, add 2

(G) Valve, Pressure Relief, Renew
Includes: Evacuate and charge system.
All models (.8) 1.2

CHRYSLER CORPORATION-FWD
DODGE DAYTONA • CHRYSLER LEBARON (J)

LABOR — COOLING SYSTEM — LABOR

(Factory Time) Chilton Time

SERVICE

(G) Belt, Drive, Adjust
All models
one 2
each adtnl. 1

(G) Belt, Drive, Renew
All models
V belt
Fan & Alternator (.2) 3
PS (.4) 6
w/AC add (.1) 1
AC (.3) 4
Serpentine belt (.2) 4

(G) Blade, Fan, Renew
All models (.2) 5

(G) Control Assy., Heater, Renew
1993-95
wo/AC (.4) 7
w/AC (.3) 6

(G) Cooler, Transaxle Auxiliary Oil, Renew
1993-95 (.3) 6

(G) Core, Heater, R&R or Renew
1993 Daytona
wo/AC (2.6) 5.0
w/AC (3.4) 6.5
1993-95 LeBaron
wo/AC (3.3) 6.0
w/AC (4.1) 8.0
Convertible add 6
w/console add (.2) 2
Boil & Repair, add 1.2
Repair Core, add 9
Recore, add 1.2

(G) Expansion (Freeze) Plugs, Water Jacket, Renew (Cylinder Head)
All models, Four
front (.6) 9
rear (.8) 1.1

(G) Expansion (Freeze) Plugs, Water Jacket, Renew (Engine Block)
Add appropriate time to access plug.
All models
Four
left side
front (.7) 1.0
rear (.4) 6
right side
front or center (.6) 9
rear (1.0) 1.4
V6
left side
front or center
upper (2.1) 3.1
lower (.3) 5
rear (1.0) 1.5
right side
front (.7) 1.1
center or rear (1.1) 1.6
rear of engine (3.5) 5.0
w/PS add (.3) 3

(G) Gauge, Temperature (Dash Unit), Renew
All models (.3) 6

(G) Gauge, Temperature (Engine Unit), Renew
All models (.3) 4

(G) Hoses, Heater, Renew
All models
one (.4) 4
each adtnl. (.1) 2

(G) Hoses, Radiator, Renew
Includes: Drain and refill cooling system as required.
All models
upper (.3) 4
lower (.4) 6

(G) Motor, Heater Blower, Renew
1993-95
wo/AC (.8) 1.2
w/AC (1.0) 1.4
w/console add (.2) 2

(G) Motor, Radiator Fan and/or Fan, Renew
All models (.4) 5

(G) Pump and/or Gasket, Water, Renew
Includes: Drain and refill cooling system.
All models
Four (1.0) 1.6
w/AC add (.3) 3
V6 (2.2) 4.0
w/AC add (.2) 2

(G) Radiator Assy., R&R or Renew
All models (.7) 9
w/AT add (.1) 1
w/AC add 2
Boil & Repair, add 1.5
Rod Clean, add 1.9
Repair Core, add 1.3
Renew Tank, add 1.6
Renew Trans Oil Cooler, add 1.9
Recore Radiator, add 1.7

(G) Relay, Radiator Fan Motor, Renew
All models (.2) 3

(G) Resistor, Heater Blower Motor, Renew
1993-95 (.4) 5

(G) Sending Unit, Engine Coolant Temp., Renew
All models (.3) 5

(G) Switch, Heater Blower Motor, Renew
1993-95 (.5) 8

(G) Tensioner, Drive Belt, Renew
1993-95 V6 (.4) 6

(G) Thermostat, Coolant, Renew
1993-95 (.4) 6

(G) Winterize Cooling System
Includes: Run engine to check for leaks, tighten all hose connections. Test radiator and pressure cap, drain radiator and engine block. Add antifreeze and refill system.
All models 5

LABOR — AIR CONDITIONING — LABOR

(Factory Time) Chilton Time

Note: If more than one item requires replacement where evacuation and discharging the system is already included in the operation, deduct 1.0 hour for each additional item from the time listed.

SERVICE AND TESTING

(G) Drain, Evacuate and Recharge System
All models 1.0

(G) Flush Refrigerant System, Complete
To be used in conjunction with component replacement which could contaminate system. Includes evacuate and recharge.
All models 1.3

(G) Performance Test
All models 8

(G) Recover and/or Recycle AC Refrigerant
Add to evacuate and charge the AC system, as required.
All models 2

(G) Refrigerant, Add (Partial Charge)
All models 6

(G) Vacuum Leak Test
All models 8

COMPONENTS

(G) Actuator, Vacuum, Renew
1993-95
outside air door (.7) 1.2
heater/defroster door (.3) 6
A/C mode door (.7) 1.2

LABOR — AIR CONDITIONING — LABOR

(Factory Time) Chilton Time

(G) Belt, Compressor Drive, Renew
1993-95
V belt (.2) 3
Serpentine belt (.3) 5

(G) Blower Motor, Renew
1993-95 (1.0) 1.4

(G) Cable, Temperature Control, Renew
1993-95 (.7) 1.1

(G) Clutch Assy., Compressor, Renew
1993-95
w/10PA17 (.3) 5
w/Scroll (.5) 8
w/Sanden (1.4) 1.7

(G) Coil, Compressor Clutch Field, Renew
1993-95
w/10PA17 (.4) 7
w/Scroll (.5) 8
w/Sanden (1.4) 1.7

(G) Coil, Evaporator, Renew
Includes: Evacuate and charge system.
1993-95
Daytona (3.4) 6.5
LeBaron (4.1) 8.0
w/console add (.2) 2
w/folding top add (.6) 6

(G) Compressor Assy., Renew
Includes: Transfer parts as required. Evacuate and charge system.
1993-95
w/10PA17 (1.1) 2.0
w/Scroll (1.1) 2.4
w/Sanden (1.1) 2.0

(G) Condenser Assy., Renew
Includes: Evacuate and charge system.
1993-95 (1.5) 2.4
Renew receiver drier add (.2) 2

(G) Control Assy., Temperature, Renew
1993-95 (.3) 6

(G) Hoses, AC, Renew
Includes: Evacuate and charge system.
1993-95 (1.1) 1.6
Renew receiver drier add 2

(G) Pulley (w/Hub), Compressor Clutch, Renew
All models (.4) 7

(G) Receiver/Drier Assy., Renew
Includes: Evacuate and charge system.
All models (.9) 1.4

(G) Resistor, Blower Motor, Renew
1993-95 (.4) 5

(G) Switch, AC On/Off Control, Renew
All models (.5) 8

(G) Switch, Blower Motor, Renew
1993-95 (.5) 8

(G) Switch, Clutch Cycling (Thermostatic Control), Renew
1993-95 (.8) 1.2

(G) Switch, High Pressure Cut-Off, Renew
1993-95 (.9) 1.4

(G) Switch, Low Pressure Cut-Off, Renew
Includes: Evacuate and charge system.
All models (.9) 1.4

(G) Switch, Push Button Vacuum, Renew
All models (.5) 9

(G) Valve, Expansion, Renew
Includes: Evacuate and charge system.
1993-95 (.8) 1.3
Renew receiver drier add 2

CHRYSLER CORPORATION-FWD
PLYMOUTH ACCLAIM • CHRYSLER LEBARON (A) • DODGE SPIRIT

LABOR — COOLING SYSTEM — LABOR

(Factory Time) Chilton Time

SERVICE

(G) Belt, Drive, Adjust
All models
one 2
each adtnl. 1

(G) Belt, Drive, Renew
All models
V belt
Fan & alternator (.2) 3
PS (.4) 6
w/AC add (.1) 1
AC (.2) 3
Serpentine (.2) 4

(G) Blade, Fan, Renew
All models (.2) 5

(G) Control Assy., Heater, Renew
1993-95
wo/AC (.4) 7
w/AC (.3) 6

(G) Cooler, Transaxle Auxiliary Oil, Renew
All models (.3) 6

(G) Core, Heater, R&R or Renew
All models
wo/AC (1.9) 3.3
w/AC (2.7) 5.5
w/console add (.2) 2
Boil & Repair, add 1.2
Repair Core, add 9
Recore, add 1.2

(G) Expansion (Freeze) Plugs, Water Jacket, Renew (Cylinder Head)
All models, Four
front (.6) 9
rear (.8) 1.1

(G) Expansion (Freeze) Plugs, Water Jacket, Renew (Engine Block)
Add appropriate time to access plug.
All models
V6
right side
front (.7) 1.0
center or rear (1.1) 1.5
left side
front or center
upper (2.1) 3.0
lower (.3) 5
rear (1.0) 1.4
rear of engine (3.7) 5.0

Four
left side
front (.7) 1.0
rear (.4) 6
right side
front or center (.6) 9
rear (1.0) 1.4
w/PS add (.3) 3

(G) Gauge, Temperature (Dash Unit), Renew
All models (.3) 5

(G) Gauge, Temperature (Engine Unit), Renew
All models (.3) 5

(G) Hoses, Heater, Renew
All models
one (.4) 4
each adtnl. (.1) 2

(G) Hoses, Radiator, Renew
Includes: Drain and refill cooling system as required.
All models
upper (.3) 4
lower (.4) 6

LABOR — COOLING SYSTEM — LABOR

(Factory Time) Chilton Time

(G) Motor, Heater Blower, Renew
All models
wo/AC (.4) .6
w/AC (.7) 1.2

(G) Motor, Radiator Fan and/or Fan, Renew
All models (.4) .5

(G) Pump and/or Gasket, Water, Renew
Includes: Drain and refill cooling system.
All models
Four (1.0) 1.6
w/AC add (.3) .3
V6 (2.2) 4.0
w/AC add (.2) .2

(G) Radiator Assy., R&R or Renew
All models (.5) .9
w/AT add (.1) .1
w/AC add .2
Boil & Repair, add 1.5
Rod Clean, add 1.9
Repair Core, add 1.3
Renew Tank, add 1.6
Renew Trans. Oil Cooler, add 1.9
Recore Radiator, add 1.7

(G) Relay, Radiator Fan Motor, Renew
All models (.2) .3

(G) Resistor, Heater Blower Motor, Renew
All models (.5) .8

(G) Sending Unit, Engine Coolant Temp., Renew
All models (.3) .5

(G) Switch, Heater Blower Motor, Renew
All models (.5) .8

(G) Switch, Vacuum (Push Button), Renew
All models (.5) .9

(G) Tensioner, Drive Belt, Renew
All models
Serpentine
Four (.9) 1.3
V6 (.4) .6

(G) Thermostat, Coolant, Renew
All models (.4) .6

(G) Winterize Cooling System
Includes: Run engine to check for leaks, tighten all hose connections. Test radiator and pressure cap, drain radiator and engine block. Add antifreeze and refill system.
All models .5

LABOR — AIR CONDITIONING — LABOR

(Factory Time) Chilton Time

Note: If more than one item requires replacement where evacuation and discharging the system is already included in the operation, deduct 1.0 hour for each additional item from the time listed.

SERVICE AND TESTING

(G) Drain, Evacuate and Recharge System
All models 1.0

(G) Flush Refrigerant System, Complete
To be used in conjunction with component replacement which could contaminate system. Includes evacuate and recharge.
All models 1.3

(G) Recover and/or Recycle AC Refrigerant
Add to evacuate and charge the AC system, as required.
All models .2

(G) Refrigerant, Add (Partial Charge)
All models (.4) .6

(G) Vacuum Leak Test
All models .8

COMPONENTS

(G) Actuator, Vacuum, Renew
All models
outside air door (.2) .4
heater/defroster door (.3) .6
A/C mode door (.8) 1.5

(G) Belt, Compressor Drive, Renew
All models
V belt (.2) .3
Serpentine belt (.3) .5

(G) Blower Motor, Renew
All models (.7) 1.2

(G) Cable, Temperature Control, Renew
All models (.6) 1.0

(G) Clutch Assy., Compressor, Renew
1993-95 10PA17 (.3) .5

(G) Coil, Compressor Clutch Field, Renew
1993-95 10PA17 (.4) .7

(G) Coil, Evaporator, Renew
Includes: Evacuate and charge system.
1993-95 (2.7) 6.0
w/console add (.2) .2

(G) Compressor Assy., Renew
Includes: Transfer parts as required. Evacuate and charge system.
1993-95 10PA17 (1.1) 2.0

(G) Condenser Assy., Renew
Includes: Evacuate and charge system.
All models (1.5) 2.4

(G) Control Assy., Temperature, Renew
1993-95 (.3) .5

(G) Hoses, AC, Renew
Includes: Evacuate and charge system.
All models, each (1.1) 1.5
Renew receiver drier add .2

(G) Pulley (w/Hub), Compressor Clutch, Renew
All models (.4) .7

(G) Receiver/Drier Assy., Renew
Includes: Evacuate and charge system.
All models (.9) 1.4

(G) Resistor, Blower Motor, Renew
All models (.5) .8

(G) Seal, Compressor Shaft, Renew
Includes: R&R compressor. Evacuate and charge system.
1993-95 (1.5) 2.5

(G) Switch, AC On/Off Control, Renew
All models (.5) .9

(G) Switch, Ambient Sensor, Renew
1993-95 (.3) .5

(G) Switch, Blower Motor, Renew
All models (.5) .8

(G) Switch, Clutch Cycling (Thermostatic Control), Renew
All models (.8) 1.2

(G) Switch, High Pressure Cut-Off, Renew
1993-95 (.9) 1.4

(G) Switch, Low Pressure and/or Cycling, Renew
All models (.9) 1.4

(G) Switch, Push Button Vacuum, Renew
All models (.5) .9

(G) Valve, Expansion, Renew
Includes: Evacuate and charge system.
All models (.8) 1.3
Renew receiver drier add .2

CHRYSLER CORPORATION-FWD
DODGE/PLYMOUTH NEON

LABOR — COOLING SYSTEM — LABOR

(Factory Time) Chilton Time

SERVICE

(G) Assembly, Dial & Gauge, Renew
All models (.4) .7

(G) Belt, Drive, Adjust
All models
one (.2) .3
each adtnl. .1

(G) Belt, Drive, Renew
All models
alternator
SOHC (.4) .5
DOHC (.5) .6
PS (.2) .3

(G) Blade, Fan, Renew
All models (.3) .4

(G) Control Assy., Temperature, Renew
All models, heater or AC (.3) .5

(G) Cooler, Transaxle Auxiliary Oil, Renew
All models (.3) .6

(G) Core, Heater, R&R or Renew
All models
wo/AC (3.2) 5.5
w/AC (3.8) 6.5
w/console, add (.1) .2
Boil & Repair, add 1.2
Repair Core, add .9
Recore, add 1.2

(G) Gauge, Temperature (Engine Unit), Renew
All models (.2) .4

(G) Hoses, Heater, Renew
All models
inlet or outlet
one (.3) .4
each adtnl. .2
return to pump (.3) .4
head to tube (.8) 1.1

(G) Hoses, Radiator, Renew
Includes: Drain and refill cooling system as required.
All models
upper (.3) .5
lower (.5) .6
w/AC add (.2) .2

(G) Motor, Heater Blower, Renew
All models (.2) .4
w/console, add (.2) .2

(G) Motor, Radiator Fan and/or Fan, Renew
All models (.4) .6

(G) Pump and/or Gasket, Water, Renew
Includes: Drain and refill cooling system.
All models
SOHC (1.9) 2.9
DOHC (2.0) 3.0

(G) Radiator Assy., R&R or Renew
All models
SOHC (.5) .8
DOHC (.8) 1.1
w/AC add .1
Boil & Repair, add 1.5
Rod Clean, add 1.9
Repair Core, add 1.3
Renew Tank, add 1.6
Renew Trans. Oil Cooler, add 1.9
Recore Radiator, add 1.7

(G) Relay, Radiator Fan Motor, Renew
All models (.2) .4

(G) Resistor, Heater Blower Motor, Renew
All models (.2) .4

(G) Thermostat, Coolant, Renew
All models (.3) .5

(G) Winterize Cooling System
Includes: Run engine to check for leaks, tighten all hose connections. Test radiator and pressure cap, drain radiator and engine block. Add antifreeze and refill system.
All models .5

LABOR — AIR CONDITIONING — LABOR

(Factory Time) Chilton Time

Note: If more than one item requires replacement where evacuation and discharging the system is already included in the operation, deduct 1.0 hour for each additional item from the time listed.

SERVICE AND TESTING

(G) Drain, Evacuate and Recharge System
All models 1.0

(G) Flush Refrigerant System, Complete
To be used in conjunction with component replacement which could contaminate system. Includes evacuate and recharge.
All models 1.3

(G) Recover and/or Recycle AC Refrigerant
Add to evacuate and charge the AC system, as required.
All models .2

(G) Refrigerant, Add (Partial Charge)
All models .6

COMPONENTS

(G) Blower Motor, Renew
All models (.2) .4
w/console, add (.2) .2

(G) Clutch Assy., Compressor, Renew
All models (.5) .8

(G) Coil, Compressor Clutch Field, Renew
All models (.5) .8

(G) Coil, Evaporator, Renew
Includes: Evacuate and charge system.
All models (3.9) 7.0
w/console, add (.1) .1

(G) Compressor Assy., Renew
Includes: Transfer parts as required. Evacuate and charge system.
All models (1.1) 1.8
Renew receiver/drier, add (.2) .2

(G) Condenser Assy., Renew
Includes: Evacuate and charge system.
All models (1.0) 1.7
Renew receiver/drier, add (.2) .2

(G) Control Assy., Temperature, Renew
All models (.3) .5

(G) Hoses, AC, Renew
Includes: Evacuate and charge system.
All models
one (.8) 1.5
each adtnl. .5

(G) Manifold and/or Gasket, Compressor, Renew
All models (.9) 1.6

(G) Receiver/Drier Assy., Renew
Includes: Evacuate and charge system.
All models (1.1) 1.8

(G) Resistor, Blower Motor, Renew
All models (.2) .4

(G) Switch, AC Low Pressure, Renew
All models (.8) 1.5

(G) Switch, Clutch Cycling Pressure, Renew
All models (.2) .4

LABOR — AIR CONDITIONING — LABOR

(Factory Time) Chilton Time

(G) Switch, High Pressure Cut-Off, Renew
All models (.7) 1.4

(G) Valve, Expansion, Renew
Includes: Evacuate and charge system.
All models (.8) 1.5
Renew receiver/drier, add 2

(G) Valve, High Pressure Relief, Renew
All models (1.4) 2.2

CHRYSLER CORPORATION-FWD
DODGE SHADOW • PLYMOUTH SUNDANCE

LABOR — COOLING SYSTEM — LABOR

(Factory Time) Chilton Time

SERVICE

(G) Belt, Drive, Adjust
All models
one 2
each adtnl. 1

(G) Belt, Drive, Renew
All models
V-belt
Fan & Alternator (.2) 3
Power steering (.4) 6
w/AC add (.1) 1
AC (.2) 3
Serpentine belt (.2) 4

(G) Blade, Fan, Renew
All models (.2) 5

(G) Control Assy., Heater, Renew
All models
wo/AC (.4) 7
w/AC (.3) 6

(G) Cooler, Transaxle Auxiliary Oil, Renew
All models (.3) 6

(G) Core, Heater, R&R or Renew
1993-94
wo/AC (2.3) 3.7
w/AC (2.9) 5.5
w/console add (.2) 2
Includes recharge AC system.
Boil & Repair, add 1.2
Repair Core, add 9
Recore, add 1.2

(G) Expansion (Freeze) Plugs, Water Jacket, Renew (Cylinder Head)
All models, Four
front (.6) 9
rear (.8) 1.1

(G) Expansion (Freeze) Plugs, Water Jacket, Renew (Engine Block)
Add appropriate time to access plug.
All models
Four
left side
front (.7) 1.0
rear (.4) 6
right side
front or center (.6) 9
rear (1.0) 1.4
V6
left side
front or center
upper (2.1) 3.1
lower (.3) 5
rear (1.0) 1.5
right side
front (.7) 1.1
center or rear (1.1) 1.6
rear of engine (3.5) 5.0
w/PS add (.3) 3

(G) Gauge, Temperature (Dash Unit), Renew
All models (.3) 5

(G) Gauge, Temperature (Engine Unit), Renew
All models (.2) 4

(G) Hoses, Heater, Renew
All models
one (.4) 4
each adtnl. (.1) 2

(G) Hoses, Radiator, Renew
Includes: Drain and refill cooling system as required.
All models
upper (.3) 4
lower (.4) 6

(G) Motor, Heater Blower, Renew
All models
wo/AC (.4) 6
w/AC (.6) 1.2
w/console add (.2) 2

(G) Motor, Radiator Fan and/or Fan, Renew
All models (.4) 5

(G) Pump and/or Gasket, Water, Renew
Includes: Drain and refill cooling system.
All models
Four (1.0) 1.6
w/AC add (.3) 3
V6 (2.2) 4.0
w/AC add (.2) 2

(G) Radiator Assy., R&R or Renew
All models (.7) 9
w/AT add (.1) 1
w/AC add (.2) 2
Boil & Repair, add 1.5
Rod Clean, add 1.9
Repair Core, add 1.3
Renew Tank, add 1.6
Renew Trans. Oil Cooler, add 1.9
Recore Radiator, add 1.7

(G) Relay, Radiator Fan Motor, Renew
All models (.2) 3

(G) Resistor, Heater Blower Motor, Renew
All models
wo/AC (.2) 3
w/AC (.3) 4

(G) Sending Unit, Engine Coolant Temp., Renew
All models (.3) 5

(G) Switch, Heater Blower Motor, Renew
1993-94 (.5) 8

(G) Tensioner, Drive Belt, Renew
1993-94 V6 (.4) 6

(G) Thermostat, Coolant, Renew
All models (.4) 6

(G) Winterize Cooling System
Includes: Run engine to check for leaks, tighten all hose connections. Test radiator and pressure cap, drain radiator and engine block. Add antifreeze and refill system.
All models 5

LABOR — AIR CONDITIONING — LABOR

(Factory Time) Chilton Time

Note: If more than one item requires replacement where evacuation and discharging the system is already included in the operation, deduct 1.0 hour for each additional item from the time listed.

SERVICE AND TESTING

(G) Drain, Evacuate and Recharge System
All models 1.0

(G) Flush Refrigerant System, Complete
To be used in conjunction with component replacement which could contaminate system. Includes evacuate and recharge.
All models 1.3

(G) Performance Test
All models 8

(G) Recover and/or Recycle AC Refrigerant
Add to evacuate and charge the AC system, as required.
All models 2

(G) Refrigerant, Add (Partial Charge)
All models (.5) 6

(G) Vacuum Leak Test
All models 8

COMPONENTS

(G) Actuator, Vacuum, Renew
1993-94
outside air door (.7) 1.2
heater/defroster door (.3) 6
A/C mode door (.8) 1.5

(G) Belt, Compressor Drive, Renew
All models (.2) 3
V belt (.2) 3
Serpentine belt (.3) 5

(G) Blower Motor, Renew
All models (.6) 9

(G) Cable, Temperature Control, Renew
All models (.6) 1.0

(G) Clutch Assy., Compressor, Renew
1993-94
10PA17 (.3) 5
Sanden (1.4) 1.7

(G) Coil, Compressor Clutch Field, Renew
1993-94
10PA17 (.4) 7
Sanden (1.4) 1.7

(G) Coil, Evaporator, Renew
Includes: Evacuate and charge system.
All models (2.9) 5.5
w/console add (.2) 2

(G) Compressor Assy., Renew
Includes: Transfer parts as required. Evacuate and charge system.
1993-94
10PA17 (1.2) 2.0
Sanden (1.1) 2.0

(G) Condenser Assy., Renew
Includes: Evacuate and charge system.
1993-94 (1.5) 2.4
Renew receiver drier add (.2) 2

(G) Control Assy., Temperature, Renew
1993-94 (.3) 6

(G) Hoses, AC, Renew
Includes: Evacuate and charge system.
All models, one (1.1) 1.6
Renew receiver drier add (.2) 2

(G) Pulley (w/Hub), Compressor Clutch, Renew
All models (.4) 7

(G) Receiver/Drier Assy., Renew
Includes: Evacuate and charge system.
All models (.9) 1.4

(G) Resistor, Blower Motor, Renew •
All models (.3) 4

(G) Switch, AC On/Off Control, Renew
All models (.5) 9

(G) Switch, Blower Motor, Renew
All models (.5) 8

(G) Switch, Clutch Cycling (Thermostatic Control), Renew
1993-94 (.8) 1.2

(G) Switch, High Pressure Cut-Off, Renew
1993-94 (.9) 1.4

(G) Switch, Low Pressure Cut-Off, Renew
Includes: Evacuate and charge system.
All models (.9) 1.4

(G) Switch, Push Button Vacuum, Renew
All models (.5) 9

(G) Valve, Expansion, Renew
Includes: Evacuate and charge system.
1993-94 (.8) 1.3
Renew receiver drier add (.2) 2

CHRYSLER CORPORATION-FWD

DODGE DYNASTY • CHRYSLER IMPERIAL • CHRYSLER NEW YORKER

LABOR — COOLING SYSTEM — LABOR

(Factory Time) Chilton Time

SERVICE

(G) Belt, Drive, Adjust
All models
one 2
each adtnl. 1

(G) Belt, Drive, Renew
All models
V belt
Fan & Alternator (.2) 3
PS (.4) 6
w/AC add (.1) 1
AC (.2) 3
Serpentine belt (.2) 4
w/AC add (.1) 1

(G) Blade, Fan, Renew
All models (.2) 5

(G) Control Assy., Heater, Renew
All models
wo/AC (.4) 7
w/AC (.6) 9
w/ATC (.3) 5

(G) Cooler, Transaxle Auxiliary Oil, Renew
All models (.3) 6

(G) Core, Heater, R&R or Renew
1993
wo/AC (1.6) 3.2
w/AC (2.0) 3.8
w/console add (.2) 2
Boil & Repair, add 1.2
Repair Core, add 9
Recore, add 1.2

(G) Expansion (Freeze) Plugs, Water Jacket, Renew (Cylinder Head)
All models
2.5L
front (.6) 9
rear (.8) 1.1
3.3L, 3.8L
front head
front (.3) 5
rear (.7) 9

LABOR — COOLING SYSTEM — LABOR

(Factory Time) Chilton Time

rear head
front (1.1) 1.5
rear (.7) 1.1

(G) Expansion (Freeze) Plugs, Water Jacket, Renew (Engine Block)

Add appropriate time to access plug.

All models
2.5L
left side
front (.7) 1.0
rear (.4) 6
right side
front or center (.6) 9
rear (1.0) 1.4
3.0L
left side
front or center
upper (2.1) 3.1
lower (.3) 5
right side
front (.7) 1.1
center or rear (1.1) 1.6
rear of engine (3.5) 5.0
3.3L, 3.8L
rear (.5) 7
all others (1.1) 1.6
w/PS add (.3) 3

(G) Gauge, Temperature (Dash Unit), Renew

1993 (.6) 1.0

(G) Gauge, Temperature (Engine Unit), Renew

All models (.3) 5

(G) Hoses, Heater, Renew

All models
one (.4) 4
each adtnl. (.1) 2

(G) Hoses, Radiator, Renew

Includes: Drain and refill cooling system as required.

All models
upper (.3) 4
lower (.4) 6

(G) Motor, Heater Blower, Renew

1993 (1.0) 1.5
w/console add (.2) 2

(G) Motor, Radiator Fan and/or Fan, Renew

All models (.4) 5

(G) Pump and/or Gasket, Water, Renew

Includes: Drain and refill cooling system.

All models
2.5L (1.0) 1.6
w/AC, add (.3) 3
3.0L (2.2) 4.0
w/AC add (.2) 2
3.3L, 3.8L (.6) 1.0

(G) Radiator Assy., R&R or Renew

All models (.5) 9
w/AT add (.1) 1
Boil & Repair, add 1.5
Rod Clean, add 1.9
Repair Core, add 1.3
Renew Tank, add 1.6
Renew Trans. Oil Cooler, add 1.9
Recore Radiator, add 1.7

(G) Relay, Radiator Fan Motor, Renew

1993 (.5) 1.0

(G) Resistor, Heater Blower Motor, Renew

1993 (.5) 8

(G) Sending Unit, Engine Coolant Temp., Renew

All models (.3) 5

(G) Switch, Heater Blower Motor, Renew

All models (.5) 8

(G) Switch, Vacuum (Push Button), Renew

All models (.5) 9

(G) Tensioner, Drive Belt, Renew

All models (.4) 6

(G) Thermostat, Coolant, Renew

All models (.4) 6

(G) Winterize Cooling System

Includes: Run engine to check for leaks, tighten all hose connections. Test radiator and pressure cap, drain radiator and engine block. Add antifreeze and refill system.

All models 5

LABOR — AIR CONDITIONING — LABOR

(Factory Time) Chilton Time

Note: If more than one item requires replacement where evacuation and discharging the system is already included in the operation, deduct 1.0 hour for each additional item from the time listed.

SERVICE AND TESTING

(G) Drain, Evacuate and Recharge System

All models 1.0

(G) Flush Refrigerant System, Complete

To be used in conjunction with component replacement which could contaminate system. Includes evacuate and recharge.

All models 1.3

(G) Recover and/or Recycle AC Refrigerant

Add to evacuate and charge the AC system, as required.

All models 2

(G) Refrigerant, Add (Partial Charge)

All models (.4) 6

(G) Vacuum Leak Test

All models 8

COMPONENTS

(G) Actuator, Vacuum, Renew

All models
outside air door (.2) 4
heater/defroster door (.3) 6
A/C mode door (.8) 1.5

(G) Belt, Compressor Drive, Renew

All models (.2) 3
V belt (.2) 3
Serpentine belt (.3) 5

(G) Blower Motor, Renew

All models
wo/ATC (.7) 1.2
w/ATC (1.0) 1.4

(G) Cable, Temperature Control, Renew

All models (.6) 1.0

(G) Clutch Assy., Compressor, Renew

1993 A590 (.6) 9
1993 10PA17 (.3) 5

(G) Coil, Compressor Clutch Field, Renew

1993 A590 (.6) 9
1993 10PA17 (.4) 7

(G) Coil, Evaporator, Renew

Includes: Evacuate and charge system.

All models (2.0) 4.0

(G) Compressor Assy., Renew

Includes: Transfer parts as required. Evacuate and charge system.

1993 A590 (1.6) 2.5
1993 10PA17 (1.1) 2.0

(G) Condenser Assy., Renew

Includes: Evacuate and charge system.

All models (1.5) 2.4

(G) Control Assy., Temperature, Renew

All models
wo/ATC (.6) 1.0
w/ATC (.3) 5

(G) Hoses, AC, Renew

Includes: Evacuate and charge system.

All models
suction hose (1.1) 1.5
discharge hose (1.1) 1.5
Renew receiver drier add 2

(G) Module, Power and/or Vacuum Assy., Renew

1993 (.4) 7

(G) Motor, Blend Air Door, Renew

All models (.6) 1.0

(G) Pulley (w/Hub), Compressor Clutch, Renew

All models (.4) 7

LABOR — AIR CONDITIONING — LABOR

(Factory Time) Chilton Time

(G) Receiver/Drier Assy., Renew
Includes: Evacuate and charge system.
All models (.9) 1.4

(G) Resistor, Blower Motor, Renew
1993 (.5) 8

(G) Sensor, Ambient Temperature, Renew
All models (.3) 6

(G) Sensor, In-Vehicle, Renew
All models (.5) 9

(G) Switch, AC On/Off Control, Renew
All models (.5) 9

(G) Switch, Ambient Sensor, Renew
1993 (.3) 5

(G) Switch, Blower Motor, Renew
All models (.5) 8

(G) Switch, Clutch Cycling (Thermostatic Control), Renew
All models (.3) 5

(G) Switch, High Pressure Cut-Off, Renew
1993 (.9) 1.4

(G) Switch, Low Pressure and/or Cycling, Renew
All models (.9) 1.4

(G) Switch, Push Button Vacuum, Renew
All models (.5) 9

(G) Valve, Expansion, Renew
Includes: Evacuate and charge system.
All models (.8) 1.3
Renew receiver drier add 2

CHRYSLER CORPORATION/JEEP

CHEROKEE • GRAND CHEROKEE • GRAND WAGONEER • WRANGLER

LABOR — COOLING SYSTEM — LABOR

(Factory Time) Chilton Time

TESTING

(M) Pressure Test Cooling System
All models 3

SERVICE

(G) Belt, Drive, Adjust
All models
V-belt
one 3
each adtnl. 1
serpentine 4

(G) Belt, Drive, Renew
All models
V-belt
one (.2) 4
each adtnl. 1
serpentine (.4) 6

(G) Blades, Fan or Clutch Assy., Renew
All models (.6) 8

(G) Control Assy., Temperature, Renew
1993-95 Wagoneer, Cherokee (.4) 7
1993-95 Grand Cherokee (.5) 8
1993-95 Wrangler (.5) 8

(G) Core, Heater, R&R or Renew
1993-95 Wagoneer, Cherokee
w/AC (2.3) 4.4
wo/AC (2.0) 3.9
1993-95 Grand Cherokee
wo/AC (2.5) 4.7
w/AC (3.1) 5.5
1993-95 Wrangler (1.2) 2.3
Boil & Repair, add 1.2
Repair Core, add 9
Recore, add 1.2

(G) Expansion (Freeze) Plugs, Water Jacket, Renew
Add appropriate time to access plug.
All models, each 5

(G) Gauge, Temperature (Dash Unit), Renew
1993-95 Wagoneer, Cherokee (.7) 1.0
1993-95 Grand Cherokee (.7) 1.1
1993-95 Wrangler (.3) 5
w/column shift, add 2

(G) Hoses, Heater, Renew
All models, one or all (.5) 7

(G) Hoses, Radiator, Renew
Includes: Drain and refill cooling system as required.
All models
upper (.4) 5
lower (.4) 6
w/AC, add 1

(G) Motor, Heater Blower, Renew
1993-95 Wagoneer, Cherokee (.4) 7
1993-95 Grand Cherokee (.5) 8
1993-95 Wrangler (1.0) 1.6

(G) Motor, Radiator Fan and/or Fan, Renew
1993-95 Wagoneer, Cherokee (.3) 5
1993-95 Grand Cherokee (.5) 8

(G) Pump and/or Gasket, Water, Renew
Includes: Drain and refill cooling system.
1993-95 Wrangler
Four (1.1) 1.7
Six
244 (1.2) 1.7
1993-95 Grand Cherokee (1.2) 1.7

(G) Radiator Assy., R&R or Renew
1993-95 Wagoneer, Cherokee
Four
wo/AC (.8) 1.2
w/AC (1.5) 2.2
Six (1.3) 1.8
1993-95 Grand Cherokee (.7) 1.1
1993-95 Wrangler (.7) 1.1
w/AT, add 1

Boil & Repair, add 1.5
Rod Clean, add 1.9
Repair Core, add 1.3
Renew Tank, add 1.6
Renew Trans. Oil Cooler, add 1.9
Recore Radiator, add 1.7

(G) Relay, Radiator Fan Motor, Renew
1993-95 (.2) 3

(G) Resistor, Heater Blower Motor, Renew
All models (.2) 4

(G) Sending Unit, Engine Coolant Temp., Renew
All models (.4) 5

(G) Switch, Heater Blower Motor, Renew
1993-95 Wagoneer, Cherokee (.5) 8
1993-95 Grand Cherokee
heater (.7) 1.2
AC (.4) 7
1993-95 Wrangler
heater (.3) 5
AC (.6) 1.1

(G) Switch, Radiator Fan Motor (Coolant Temp.), Renew
1993-95 (.5) 8

(G) Tensioner, Drive Belt, Renew
1993-95 (.4) 6

(G) Thermostat, Coolant, Renew
All models (.4) 6
w/AC, add 5

(G) Valve, Heater Water Shut-Off, Renew
All models (.4) 5

(G) Winterize Cooling System
Includes: Run engine to check for leaks, tighten all hose connections. Test radiator and pressure cap, drain radiator and engine block. Add antifreeze and refill system.
All models 5

LABOR AIR CONDITIONING LABOR

(Factory Time) Chilton Time

Note: If more than one item requires replacement where evacuation and discharging the system is already included in the operation, deduct 1.0 hour for each additional item from the time listed.

SERVICE AND TESTING

(G) Drain, Evacuate and Recharge System

All models (.8) **1.0**
Recover refrigerant, add .... **.2**

(G) Flush Refrigerant System, Complete

To be used in conjunction with component replacement which could contaminate system. Includes evacuate and recharge.

All models **1.3**
Recover refrigerant, add .... **.2**

(G) Recover and/or Recycle AC Refrigerant

Add to evacuate and charge the AC system, as required.

All models .... **.2**

(G) Refrigerant, Add (Partial Charge)

All models (.5) .... **.6**

COMPONENTS

(G) Accumulator Assy., Renew

Includes: Evacuate and charge system.

1993-95 Grand Cherokee (1.4) **2.1**
Recover refrigerant, add .... **.2**

(G) Belt, Compressor Drive, Renew

All models
V belt (.2) .... **.4**
serpentine (.4) .... **.6**

(G) Blower Motor, Renew

1993-95 Wagoneer, Cherokee (.4) .... **.7**
1993-95 Wrangler (.6) .... **.9**

(G) Clutch Assy., Compressor, Renew

1993-95 (.7) **1.2**
Add time to evacuate & charge
AC system, as needed
Recover refrigerant, add .... **.2**

(G) Coil, Compressor Clutch Field, Renew

1993-95 (.7) **1.2**
Add time to evacuate & charge
AC system, as needed
Recover refrigerant, add .... **.2**

(G) Coil, Evaporator, Renew

Includes: Evacuate and charge system.

1993-95 Wagoneer, Cherokee (2.3) . **4.1**
1993-95 Grand Cherokee (3.1) **5.0**
1993-95 Wrangler (2.1) **3.9**
Recover refrigerant, add .... **.2**

(G) Compressor Assy., Renew

Includes: Transfer parts as required. Evacuate and charge system.

1993-95
gas (1.7) **2.5**
Renew receiver-drier, add .... **.2**
Recover refrigerant, add .... **.2**

(G) Condenser Assy., Renew

Includes: Evacuate and charge system.

1993-95 Wagoneer, Cherokee (1.8) . **2.7**
1993-95 Grand Cherokee (1.8) **2.7**
1993-95 Wrangler (1.4) **2.0**
Renew receiver-drier, add .... **.2**
Recover refrigerant, add .... **.2**

(G) Control Assy., AC, Renew

1993-95 Wagoneer, Cherokee (.4) .... **.6**
1993-95 Grand Cherokee (.5) .... **.8**
1993-95 Wrangler (.5) .... **.8**

(G) Hoses, AC, Renew

Includes: Evacuate and charge system.

All models
one **1.7**
each adtnl. .... **.3**
Renew receiver-drier, add .... **.2**
Recover refrigerant, add .... **.2**

(G) Module, AC Control, Renew

1993-95 Cherokee (.2) .... **.4**

(G) Orifice Valve (Tube), Renew

Includes: Evacuate and charge system.

1993-95 Grand Cherokee (1.3) **1.8**
Recover refrigerant, add .... **.2**

(G) Receiver/Drier Assy., Renew

Includes: Evacuate and charge system.

1993-95 Wagoneer, Cherokee (.8) .. **1.4**
1993-95 Grand Cherokee (1.4) **2.0**
1993-95 Wrangler (1.2) **1.7**
Recover refrigerant, add .... **.2**

(G) Resistor, Blower Motor, Renew

All models (.3) .... **.4**

(G) Switch, Blower Motor, Renew

1993-95 Wagoneer, Cherokee (.5) .... **.8**
1993-95 Grand Cherokee (.5) .... **.8**
1993-95 Wrangler (.6) .... **.9**

(G) Switch, Clutch Cycling (Thermostatic Control), Renew

1993-95 Wagoneer, Cherokee (.4) .... **.6**
1993-95 Grand Cherokee (.4) .... **.6**
1993-95 Wrangler (.5) .... **.8**
Add time to evacuate & charge
AC system, as needed
Recover refrigerant, add .... **.2**

(G) Switch, High Pressure Cut-Off, Renew

1993-95 Grand Cherokee (.2) .... **.5**
Add time to evacuate & charge
AC system, as needed
Recover refrigerant, add .... **.2**

(G) Switch, Low Pressure Cut-Off, Renew

Includes: Evacuate and charge system.

All models (.8) **1.4**
Recover refrigerant, add .... **.2**

(G) Valve, Expansion, Renew

Includes: Evacuate and charge system.

1993-95 Wagoneer, Cherokee (1.3) . **1.8**
1993-95 Wrangler (.9) **1.5**
Renew receiver-drier, add .... **.2**
Recover refrigerant, add .... **.2**

CHRYSLER CORPORATION/DODGE TRUCKS (RWD)

PICKUPS • RAMCHARGER • VANS

LABOR COOLING SYSTEM LABOR

(Factory Time) Chilton Time

SERVICE

(G) Belt, Fan Drive, Renew

1993-95 V belt (.3) .... **.6**
1993-95 Serpentine belt (.2) .... **.4**
w/AIR, add .... **.1**
w/PS, add .... **.2**

(G) Blades, Fan or Clutch Assy., Renew

All models
Vans (.8) **1.1**
Pickups (.5) .... **.7**
w/AIR, add .... **.1**
w/AC, add .... **.1**

(G) Control Assy., Heater, Renew

All models
wo/AC
Vans (.4) .... **.6**
Pickups (.3) .... **.5**
w/AC
Vans (.6) .... **.9**
Pickups (.5) .... **.8**

(G) Core, Heater, R&R or Renew

Front
1993-95 Vans
wo/AC (.7) **1.6**
w/AC
wo/front & rear AC (2.7) **5.0**
w/front & rear AC (2.9) **5.5**
1993 Pickups
wo/AC (1.3) **2.2**
w/AC (2.1) **4.0**
1994-95 Pickups
wo/AC (2.3) **2.6**

COOLING SYSTEM

(Factory Time) Chilton Time

w/AC (3.1) 3.5
Rear
All models
wo/AC (.8) 1.5
w/AC (1.5) 3.0
Boil & Repair, Add 1.2
Repair Core, add 9
Recore, add 1.2

(G) Expansion (Freeze) Plugs, Water Jacket, Renew (Cylinder Head)

Front
1993-95 V6, V8
Vans (.3) 5
Pickups (.3) 5
1993-95 diesel
one (.2) 4
each adtnl. 1
Rear
1993-95 V6, V8
Vans (.3) 6
Pickups (3.1) 4.2
1993-95 diesel
one (.2) 4
each adtnl. 1

(G) Expansion (Freeze) Plugs, Water Jacket, Renew (Engine Block)

Add appropriate time to access plug.

1993-95 V6, V8
front right or left one (.6) 1.1
center right or left one (1.1) 1.4
rear right side (.5) 1.0
rear left side (.8) 1.2
engine rear one or both
MT
Vans (2.4) 3.4
Pickups
AT
Vans (2.4) 3.4
Pickups (2.9) 4.2

(G) Gauge, Temperature (Dash Unit), Renew

Vans
1993-95 (.6) 1.2
Pickups
1993-95 (.6) 1.2

(G) Hoses, Heater, Renew

Vans
1993-95
front (.3) 5
rear (.4) 6
Pickups
1993-95 (.6) 8

(G) Hoses, Radiator, Renew

Includes: Drain and refill cooling system as required.

Upper
1993-95 Vans (.5) 7
1993-95 Pickups (.4) 6
Lower
All models (.4) 6
By-pass
All models
1993-95 Vans (.5) 7
1993-95 Pickups-V6, V8 (.3) 5
w/AC, add 2

(G) Motor, Heater Blower, Renew

Front
1993-95 Vans (.6) 1.0
1993-95 Pickups (.4) 8
Rear (.4) 8

(G) Pulley, Fan, Renew

1993-95 (.3) 5
w/AC, add 3

(G) Pulley, Idler, Renew

All models (.3) 5

(G) Pump and/or Gasket, Water, Renew

Includes: Drain and refill cooling system.

Vans
1993-95 V6, V8 (1.3) 1.8
Pickups
1993-95 V6, V8 (1.0) 1.5
1993-95 diesel (.6) 1.0
w/AC, add 5
w/PS, add 2
w/100A alternator, add 6
w/AIR, add 2
w/snow commander pkg., add 1

(G) Radiator Assy., R&R or Renew

Vans
1993-95 (1.0) 1.5
Pickups
1993-95 gas (.7) 1.3
1993-95 diesel (1.2) 2.0
w/aux. oil cooler, add 1
Boil & Repair, add 1.5
Rod Clean, add 1.9
Repair Core, add 1.3
Renew Tank, add 1.6
Renew Trans. Oil Cooler, add 1.9
Recore Radiator, add 1.7

(G) Resistor, Heater Blower Motor, Renew

1993-95 (.2) 5

(G) Sending Unit, Engine Coolant Temp., Renew

1993-95 (.3) 5

(G) Switch, Heater Blower Motor, Renew

Vans
1993-95 (.4) 6
Pickups
1993-95 (.3) 6

(G) Tank, Coolant Reserve, Renew

1993-95 (.3) 5

(G) Thermostat, Coolant, Renew

Vans
1993-95 (.9) 1.2
Pickups
1993-95
gas (.4) 6
diesel (.6) 1.0
w/AC, add (.1) 1

(G) Valve, Heater Water Shut-Off, Renew

All models
wo/AC (.4) 7
w/AC
Vans
front (.5) 9
rear (.4) 7
Pickups (.4) 7

(G) Winterize Cooling System

Includes: Run engine to check for leaks, tighten all hose connections. Test radiator and pressure cap, drain radiator and engine block. Add antifreeze and refill system.

All models 5

AIR CONDITIONING

(Factory Time) Chilton Time

Note: If more than one item requires replacement where evacuation and discharging the system is already included in the operation, deduct 1.0 hour for each additional item from the time listed.

SERVICE AND TESTING

(G) Drain, Evacuate and Recharge System

All models 1.7
Recover refrigerant, add 2

(G) Flush Refrigerant System, Complete

To be used in conjunction with component replacement which could contaminate system. Includes evacuate and recharge.

All models 1.3
Recover refrigerant, add 2

(G) Performance Test

All models 8

(G) Recover and/or Recycle AC Refrigerant

Add to evacuate and charge the AC system, as required.

All models 2

(G) Refrigerant, Add (Partial Charge)

All models
front unit (.5) 1.1
front & rear unit (.9) 1.4

(G) Vacuum Leak Test

All models 9

COMPONENTS

(G) Belt, Compressor Drive, Renew

1993-95 V belt (.3) 6
1993-95 Serpentine belt (.2) 4
w/AIR, add 1
w/PS, add 1

(G) Blower Motor, Renew

Vans
1993-95
front (.6) 1.1
rear (.4) 9

(Factory Time) Chilton Time

Pickups
1993-95 (.4) 9

(G) Clutch Assy., Compressor, Renew

1993-95
gas (.6) 9
diesel (.7) 1.1

(G) Coil, Compressor Clutch Field, Renew

1993-95
gas (.5) 9
diesel (.7) 1.2

(G) Coil, Evaporator, Renew

Includes: Evacuate and charge system.

Vans
1993-95
front (2.9) 5.4
rear (1.6) 2.8
Pickups
1993 (2.3) 4.7
1994 (3.3) 5.5
Recover refrigerant, add 2

(G) Compressor Assy., Renew

Includes: Transfer parts as required. Evacuate and charge system.

Vans
1993-95 V6, V8 (2.1) 3.7
Pickups
1993-95 V6, V8 (2.0) 3.3
w/rear AC, add 3
w/114A alternator, add 6
Recover refrigerant, add 2

(G) Condenser Assy., Renew

Includes: Evacuate and charge system.

All models
Vans
front AC (1.6) 2.5
front & rear AC (1.9) 3.0
Pickups (1.2) 2.2
Renew receiver-drier, add 2
Recover refrigerant, add 2

(G) Control Assy., Temperature, Renew

All models
Vans (.6) 1.0
Pickups (.5) 9

(G) Hoses, AC, Renew

Includes: Evacuate and charge system.

All models
front heater
suction
Vans (1.2) 2.0
Pickups (1.1) 1.9
discharge (1.1) 1.9
rear heater
rear unit tube assy. (3.7) 5.0
rear unit to rear evap. (1.3) 2.1
w/rear AC, add 3
Renew receiver-drier, add 2
Recover refrigerant, add 2

(G) Pulley (w/Hub), Compressor Clutch, Renew

1993-95
gas (.4) 8
diesel (.6) 1.0

(G) Receiver/Drier Assy., Renew

Includes: Evacuate and charge system.

All models
front AC (1.1) 1.9
front & rear AC (1.5) 2.3
Recover refrigerant, add 2

(G) Resistor, Blower Motor, Renew

All models (.3) 4

(G) Seal, Compressor Front Cover, Renew

Includes: R&R compressor. Evacuate and charge system.

Vans
1993-95 V6, V8
Standen comp. (2.4) 3.7
Pickups
1993-95
Standen comp. (1.7) 2.9
1993-95 diesel (2.4) 3.7
w/114A alternator, add 6
w/rear AC, add 3
Recover refrigerant, add 2

(G) Seal, Compressor Rear Cover, Renew

Includes: R&R compressor. Evacuate and charge system.

Vans
1993-95
Standen comp. (2.4) 3.7
Pickups
1993-95 V6, V8
Standen comp. (1.7) 3.0
1993-95 diesel (2.0) 3.4
w/114A alternator, add 6
w/rear AC, add 3
Recover refrigerant, add 3

(G) Seal, Compressor Shaft, Renew

Includes: R&R compressor. Evacuate and charge system.

Vans
1993-95 V6, V8
Standen comp. (2.4) 3.6
Pickups
1993-95 V6, V8
Sanden comp. (1.7) 2.9
1993-95 diesel (2.3) 3.6
w/114A alternator, add 6
w/rear AC, add 3
Recover refrigerant, add 2

(G) Switch, Blower Motor, Renew

All models
front unit (.5) 9
rear unit (.3) 6

(G) Switch, Clutch Cycling (Thermostatic Control), Renew

1993-95
Vans (2.7) 3.1
Pickups (.3) 5

(G) Switch, Low Pressure Cut-Off, Renew

Includes: Evacuate and charge system.

All models
front AC (1.0) 1.8
front & rear AC (1.3) 2.1
Recover refrigerant, add 2

(G) Switch, Push Button Vacuum, Renew

All models (.6) 1.0

(G) Valve Plate and/or Gasket, Compressor, Renew

Includes: Add partial charge, leak test, charge system and renew cylinder head gasket.

Recover refrigerant, add 2

(G) Valve, Expansion, Renew

Includes: Evacuate and charge system.

Vans
1993-95
front unit (.9) 1.8
rear unit (1.9) 2.8
Pickups
1993-95 (1.1) 2.0
Renew receiver-drier, add 2
Recover refrigerant, add 2

CHRYSLER CORPORATION/CHRYSLER/DODGE/PLYMOUTH TRUCKS (FWD)

RAM VAN • CARAVAN • TOWN & COUNTRY • VOYAGER

LABOR — COOLING SYSTEM — LABOR

(Factory Time) Chilton Time

SERVICE

(G) Belt, Drive, Adjust
All models
one 2
each adtnl. 1

(G) Belt, Drive, Renew
All models
fan & alternator (.2) 3
w/AC, add 1
power steering (.4) 6
w/AC, add 1
AC (.2) 3

(G) Belt, Serpentine Drive, Renew
1993-95 (.2) 4
w/AC, add 1

(G) Control Assy., Front Heater, Renew
1993 (.4) 7
1994-95 (.2) 4

(G) Control Assy., Rear Heater, Renew
1993-95
wo/AC (.8) 1.2
w/AC (.3) 5

(G) Cooler, Transaxle Auxiliary Oil, Renew
All models (.5) 9

(G) Core, Front Heater, R&R or Renew
All models
wo/AC (1.8) 3.5
w/AC (3.8) 5.5
w/console, add 2
Boil & Repair, add 1.2
Repair Core, add 9
Recore, add 1.2

(G) Core, Rear Heater, R&R or Renew
1993-95 (1.2) 2.0

(G) Expansion (Freeze) Plugs, Water Jacket, Renew (Cylinder Head)
1993-95 2.2L, 2.5L
front (.6) 9
rear (.8) 1.1
1993-95 3.3L, 3.8L
front head
front (.3) 5
rear (.7) 1.0
rear head
front (1.1) 1.5
rear (.7) 1.0

(G) Expansion (Freeze) Plugs, Water Jacket, Renew (Engine Block)
Add appropriate time to access plug.
1993-95 2.2L, 2.5L
left side
front (.7) 1.0
rear (.4) 6
right side
front or center (.6) 9
rear (1.0) 1.4
w/pulse air, add 6
1993-95 2.6L, 3.0L
right side
front (.7) 1.0
center or rear (1.1) 1.5
left side
upper front or center (2.1) 3.0
lower front or center (.3) 5
rear (1.0) 1.4
rear of engine (3.7) 5.0
1993-95 3.3L, 3.8L
front (3.6) 5.0
rear
one (.5) 9
all (1.1) 1.7
w/PS, add 3

(G) Fan, Rear Heater Blower, Renew
1993-95 (.8) 1.2

(G) Gauge, Temperature (Dash Unit), Renew
1993-95 (.4) 6

(G) Hose, Rear Heater, Renew
1993-95 (.5) 8

(G) Hoses, Heater, Renew
All models
inlet or outlet (.4) 5
each adtnl. (.1) 2
by-pass (.5) 6
return to water pump (.4) 5

(G) Hoses, Radiator, Renew
Includes: Drain and refill cooling system as required.
All models
upper (.3) 4
lower (.4) 6

(G) Module/Fan, Assembly, Renew
1993-95 (.2) 4

(G) Motor, Front Heater Blower, Renew
1993-95 (.9) 1.3

(G) Motor, Radiator Fan and/or Fan, Renew
1993 (.4) 5

(G) Motor, Rear Heater & AC Mode, Renew
1993-95 (.9) 1.3

(G) Motor, Rear Heater Blower, Renew
1993-95 (.9) 1.3

(G) Pump and/or Gasket, Water, Renew
Includes: Drain and refill cooling system.
1993-95 2.5L (1.0) 1.6
w/AC add 3
w/AC, add 3
1993-95 3.0L (2.2) 4.5
w/AC add 2
1993-95 3.3L, 3.8L (.6) 1.0

(G) Radiator Assy., R&R or Renew
1993-95 (.7) 9
w/AT, add 1
w/AC, add 3
Boil & Repair, add 1.5
Rod Clean, add 1.9
Repair Core, add 1.3
Renew Tank, add 1.6
Renew Trans. Oil Cooler, add 1.9
Recore Radiator, add 1.7

(G) Relay, Radiator Fan Motor, Renew
1993-95 (.2) 3

(G) Resistor, Front Heater Blower Motor, Renew
All models
wo/AC (.2) 3
w/AC (.2) 4

(G) Resistor, Rear Heater Blower Motor, Renew
1993-95 (.8) 1.2

(G) Sending Unit, Engine Coolant Temp., Renew
All models (.3) 4

(G) Switch, Heater Blower Motor, Renew
All models (.5) 8

(G) Switch, Rear Heater Blower Motor, Renew
1993-95 (.4) 6

(G) Switch, Rear Heater Control, Renew
1993-95 (.3) 5

(G) Tensioner, Drive Belt, Renew
1993-95 V6 (.4) 6

(G) Thermostat, Coolant, Renew
All models (.4) 6

(G) Valve, Front Heater Water, Renew
All models (.3) 5

(G) Valve, Rear Heater Water, Renew
1993-95 (1.3) 1.7

(G) Winterize Cooling System
Includes: Run engine to check for leaks, tighten all hose connections. Test radiator and pressure cap, drain radiator and engine block. Add antifreeze and refill system.
All models 5

LABOR — AIR CONDITIONING — LABOR

(Factory Time) Chilton Time

Note: If more than one item requires replacement where evacuation and discharging the system is already included in the operation, deduct 1.0 hour for each additional item from the time listed.

SERVICE AND TESTING

(G) Drain, Evacuate and Recharge System

All models
- front 1.0
- front & rear 1.5

Recover refrigerant, add 2

(G) Flush Refrigerant System, Complete

To be used in conjunction with component replacement which could contaminate system. Includes evacuate and recharge.

All models 1.3
Recover refrigerant, add 2

(G) Performance Test

All models 8

(G) Recover and/or Recycle AC Refrigerant

Add to evacuate and charge the AC system, as required.

All models 2

(G) Refrigerant, Add (Partial Charge)

All models (.4) 6

(G) Vacuum Leak Test

All models 8

COMPONENTS

(G) Actuator, Vacuum, Renew

1993-95
- outside air door (.8) 1.3
- heater/defroster door (.3) 6
- A/C mode door (.3) 6

(G) Belt, Compressor Drive, Renew

V belt
1993-95 (.2) 3
1993-95 (.2) 4

(G) Blower Motor, Renew

1993-95 (.9) 1.2

(G) Cable, Temperature Control, Renew

1993-95 (1.7) 2.5

(G) Clutch Assy., Compressor, Renew

1993-95 10PA17 (.3) 5
Add time to evacuate & charge
AC system as needed
Recover refrigerant, add 2

(G) Coil, Compressor Clutch Field, Renew

1993-95 10PA17 (.4) 7
Add time to evacuate & charge
AC system as needed
Recover refrigerant, add 2

(G) Coil, Evaporator, Renew

Includes: Evacuate and charge system.

1993-95
- front (3.8) 5.5
- rear (1.7) 3.5

Recover refrigerant, add 2

(G) Compressor Assy., Renew

Includes: Transfer parts as required. Evacuate and charge system.

1993-95 10PA17 (1.1) 2.0
Renew receiver drier, add 2
Recover refrigerant, add 2

(G) Condenser Assy., Renew

Includes: Evacuate and charge system.

1993-95 (1.8) 3.0
Renew receiver drier, add 2
Recover refrigerant, add 2

(G) Control Assy., Temperature, Renew

1993 (.4) 7
1994-95 (.2) 4

(G) Hoses, AC, Renew

Includes: Evacuate and charge system.

1993-95
- suction, liquid hose (1.1) 1.5
- discharge, liquid hose (1.1) 1.5
- suction, liquid hose
  - rear (1.1) 1.5
- underbody (1.2) 1.6

Renew receiver drier, add 2
Recover refrigerant, add 2

(G) Pulley (w/Hub), Compressor Clutch, Renew

1993-95 All models (.4) 7
Add time to evacuate & charge
AC system as needed
Recover refrigerant, add 2

(G) Receiver/Drier Assy., Renew

Includes: Evacuate and charge system.

1993-95 (.9) 1.5
Recover refrigerant, add 2

(G) Resistor, Blower Motor, Renew

All models (.2) 4

(G) Seal, Compressor Center, Renew

Includes: R&R compressor, Pressure test and charge system.

Recover refrigerant, add 2

(G) Seal, Compressor Front Cover, Renew

Includes: R&R compressor. Evacuate and charge system.

Recover refrigerant, add 2

(G) Seal, Compressor Rear Cover, Renew

Includes: R&R compressor. Evacuate and charge system.

Recover refrigerant, add 2

(G) Seal, Compressor Shaft, Renew

Includes: R&R compressor. Evacuate and charge system.

Recover refrigerant, add 2

(G) Switch, Blower Motor, Renew

1993-95 (.5) 8

(G) Switch, High Pressure Cut-Off, Renew

Add time to evacuate & charge
AC system as needed
Recover refrigerant, add 2

(G) Switch, Low Pressure and/or Cycling, Renew

1993-95
- electric (.3) 5

Add time to evacuate & charge
AC system as needed
Recover refrigerant, add 2

(G) Switch, Low Pressure Cut-Off, Renew

Includes: Evacuate and charge system.

Add time to evacuate & charge
AC system as needed
Recover refrigerant, add 2

(G) Switch, Push Button Vacuum, Renew

1993-95 (.5) 7

(G) Valve, Expansion, Renew

Includes: Evacuate and charge system.

1993-95
- front (.8) 1.4
- rear (1.7) 2.4

Renew receiver drier, add 2
Recover refrigerant, add 2

CHRYSLER CORPORATION/DODGE TRUCKS
DAKOTA PICKUP

LABOR — COOLING SYSTEM — LABOR

(Factory Time) Chilton Time

TESTING

(M) Pressure Test Cooling System
All models 3

SERVICE

(G) Belt, Drive, Adjust
All models
one (.2) 3
each adtnl. 1

(G) Belt, Drive, Renew
V belt
1993-95
Alternator (.2) 3
w/PS, add 2
w/AC, add 1
w/AIR, add 1
Power Steering (.2) 3
w/AC, add 1
w/AIR, add 1
AC (.2) 3
w/PS, add 1
w/AIR, add 1
Air Pump (.2) 3
Serpentine belt
1993-95 (.2) 3

(G) Clutch, Viscous (Fluid) Fan Assy., Renew
All models (.5) 7
w/AC, add 1
w/AIR, add 1

(G) Control Assy., Temperature, Renew
All models
wo/AC (.3) 5
w/AC (.5) 8

(G) Core, Heater, R&R or Renew
All models
wo/AC (1.6) 3.0
w/AC (2.2) 5.0
Includes: Recharge AC system.
Boil & Repair, add 1.2
Repair Core, add 9
Recore, add 1.2

(G) Expansion (Freeze) Plugs, Water Jacket, Renew (Cylinder Head)
All models
Four (.8) 1.1
V8
front, one (.3) 6
rear (3.1) 4.2

(G) Expansion (Freeze) Plugs, Water Jacket, Renew (Engine Block)
Add appropriate time to access plug.
All models
Four
right side
one (.6) 9
all (1.0) 1.7
left side
upper (.9) 1.3
lower (.5) 8
V6, V8
engine side
front (.6) 1.1
right rear (.5) 1.0
left rear (.8) 1.2
engine front
right or left (.4) 7
engine rear
MT (2.6) 4.0
AT (3.8) 5.1
w/AC, add 3
w/4x4, add 2.8
w/two piece drive shaft, add 2

(G) Gauge, Temperature (Dash Unit), Renew
All models (.6) 1.1

(G) Hoses, Heater, Renew
1993-95 one (.6) 7
each adtnl. 2

(G) Hoses, Radiator, Renew
Includes: Drain and refill cooling system as required.
All models
upper or lower, each (.4) 6
1993-95 by-pass (.5) 7
w/AIR, add 1
w/AC, add 1

(G) Motor, Heater Blower, Renew
1993-95 (.9) 1.4

(G) Pump and/or Gasket, Water, Renew
Includes: Drain and refill cooling system.
All models
Four (1.1) 1.6
V6, V8 (1.0) 1.5
w/AC, add 3
w/PS, add 2
w/AIR, add 2

(G) Radiator Assy., R&R or Renew
All models (.7) 1.3
w/AT, add 1
w/aux. trans. cooler, add 1
Boil & Repair, add 1.5
Rod Clean, add 1.9
Repair Core, add 1.3
Renew Tank, add 1.6
Renew Trans. Oil Cooler, add 1.9
Recore Radiator, add 1.7

(G) Resistor, Heater Blower Motor, Renew
All models (.2) 4

(G) Sending Unit, Engine Coolant Temp., Renew
All models (.3) 5

(G) Switch, Coolant Temperature Sensor, Renew
All models (.3) 5

(G) Switch, Heater Blower Motor, Renew
All models (.4) 7

(G) Thermostat, Coolant, Renew
All models
Four, V6 (.4) 6
V8 (.8) 1.0
w/AC, add 1

(G) Winterize Cooling System
Includes: Run engine to check for leaks, tighten all hose connections. Test radiator and pressure cap, drain radiator and engine block. Add antifreeze and refill system.
All models 5

LABOR — AIR CONDITIONING — LABOR

(Factory Time) Chilton Time

Note: If more than one item requires replacement where evacuation and discharging the system is already included in the operation, deduct 1.0 hour for each additional item from the time listed.

SERVICE AND TESTING

(G) Drain, Evacuate and Recharge System
All models 1.0
Recover refrigerant, add 2

(G) Flush Refrigerant System, Complete
To be used in conjunction with component replacement which could contaminate system. Includes evacuate and recharge.
All models 1.3
Recover refrigerant, add 2

(G) Recover and/or Recycle AC Refrigerant
Add to evacuate and charge the AC system, as required.
All models 2

(G) Refrigerant, Add (Partial Charge)
All models 6

COMPONENTS

(G) Belt, Compressor Drive, Renew
All models (.2) 3
w/AIR, add 1
w/PS, add 1

(G) Blower Motor, Renew
1993-95 (.9) 1.3

LABOR — AIR CONDITIONING — LABOR

(Factory Time) Chilton Time

(G) Clutch Assy., Compressor, Renew
1993-95 (.7) 1.0

(G) Coil, Compressor Clutch Field, Renew
1993-95 (.7) 1.1

(G) Coil, Evaporator, Renew
Includes: Evacuate and charge system.
1993-95 (2.2) 3.2

(G) Compressor Assy., Renew
Includes: Transfer parts as required. Evacuate and charge system.
1993-95 (1.3) 2.7
w/114A alternator, add 6

(G) Condenser Assy., Renew
Includes: Evacuate and charge system.
1993-95 (1.0) 1.5
Renew receiver-drier, add 2

(G) Control Assy., Temperature, Renew
All models (.5) 9

(G) Hoses, AC, Renew
Includes: Evacuate and charge system.
All models
suction liquid line (1.1) 1.9
discharge liquid line (1.1) 1.9
Renew receiver-drier, add 2

(G) Receiver/Drier Assy., Renew
Includes: Evacuate and charge system.
All models (1.1) 1.6

(G) Resistor, Blower Motor, Renew
All models (.3) 4

(G) Seal, Compressor Front Cover, Renew
Includes: R&R compressor. Evacuate and charge system.
1993-95 (1.9) 2.8
w/114A alternator, add 6

(G) Seal, Compressor Rear Cover, Renew
Includes: R&R compressor. Evacuate and charge system.
1993-95 (1.6) 2.9
w/114A alternator, add 6

(G) Seal, Compressor Shaft, Renew
Includes: R&R compressor. Evacuate and charge system.
1993-95 (1.9) 3.0
w/114A alternator, add 6

(G) Switch, Blower Motor, Renew
All models (.5) 9

(G) Switch, Low Pressure Cut-Off, Renew
Includes: Evacuate and charge system.
All models (1.0) 1.5

(G) Switch, Push Button Vacuum, Renew
All models (.6) 1.0

(G) Switch, Thermostatic Control Clutch Cycling, Renew
1993-95 (1.1) 1.5

(G) Valve, Expansion, Renew
Includes: Evacuate and charge system.
All models (1.1) 1.6
Renew receiver-drier, add 2

FORD MOTOR COMPANY-FWD
FORD ESCORT

LABOR — COOLING SYSTEM — LABOR

(Factory Time) Chilton Time

TESTING

(M) Pressure Test Cooling System
All models 3

SERVICE

(G) Belt, Drive, Adjust
All models
one (.2) 3
each adtnl. (.1) 1

(G) Belt, Drive, Renew
1993-95
Power Steering (.5) 7
AC (.5) 7
Serpentine (.3) 4
Alternator (.5) 7

(G) Blade, Fan, Renew
1993-95 (.6) .8

(G) Bypass Tube and/or O-Ring, Heater, Renew
All models (.6) 1.0

(G) Cable, Temperature Control, Renew
1993-95 (.7) 1.0

(G) Control Assy., Heater, Renew
1993-94 (.6) 1.0
1995 (.5) 9

(G) Core, Heater, R&R or Renew
1993-95 (2.5) 4.5
Boil & Repair add 1.2
Repair Core add 9
Recore add 1.2

(G) Expansion (Freeze) Plugs, Water Jacket, Renew
Add appropriate time to access plug.
All models, each 5

(G) Gauge, Temperature (Dash Unit), Renew
1993-94 (.7) 1.2
1995 (.9) 1.7

(G) Hoses, Heater, Renew
All models, each (.4) 5

(G) Hoses, Radiator, Renew
Includes: Drain and refill cooling system as required.
1993-95
upper (.4) 5
lower (.6) 7
both (.7) 1.0

(G) Motor, Heater Blower, Renew
1993-95 (.7) 1.1

(G) Motor, Radiator Fan and/or Fan, Renew
1993-95 (.6) .8

(G) Pump and/or Gasket, Water, Renew
Includes: Drain and refill cooling system.
1993-95
1.8L (2.0) 3.7
1.9L (1.7) 3.2
Renew timing belt add 3

(G) Radiator Assy., R&R or Renew
1993-95
MTX (.9) 1.4
ATX (1.0) 1.5
Renew side tank add
one (.4) 4
both (.6) 6

(G) Resistor, Heater Blower Motor, Renew
All models (.3) 5

(G) Sending Unit, Engine Coolant Temp., Renew
1993-95 (.4) .5

(G) Switch, Heater Blower Motor, Renew
1993-95 (.6) 1.0

LABOR COOLING SYSTEM LABOR

(Factory Time) Chilton Time

(G) Switch, Radiator Fan Motor (Coolant Temp.), Renew
All models (.3) 4

(G) Tensioner, Drive Belt, Renew
1993-95 (.3) 5

(G) Thermostat, Coolant, Renew
1993-95
1.8L (.5) 7
1.9L (.8) 1.0

(G) Winterize Cooling System
Includes: Run engine to check for leaks, tighten all hose connections. Test radiator and pressure cap, drain radiator and engine block. Add antifreeze and refill system.
All models 5

LABOR AIR CONDITIONING LABOR

(Factory Time) Chilton Time

Note: If more than one item requires replacement where evacuation and discharging the system is already included in the operation, deduct 1.0 hour for each additional item from the time listed.

SERVICE AND TESTING

(G) Drain, Evacuate and Recharge System
All models (.7) 1.0

(G) Flush Refrigerant System, Complete
To be used in conjunction with component replacement which could contaminate system. Includes evacuate and recharge.
All models 1.3

(G) Performance Test
All models 6

(G) Recover and/or Recycle AC Refrigerant
Add to evacuate and charge the AC system, as required.
All models 2

(G) Refrigerant, Add (Partial Charge)
All models 6

COMPONENTS

(G) Belt, Compressor Drive, Renew
1993-95 (.5) 7

(G) Blower Motor, Renew
1993-95 (.7) 1.1

(G) Clutch & Pulley, Compressor, Renew
Includes: Evacuate and charge system.
1993-95 (1.9) 2.7

(G) Compressor Assy., R&R and Recondition
Includes: Evacuate and charge system.
1993-95 (2.9) 4.1

(G) Compressor Assy., Renew
Includes: Transfer parts as required. Evacuate and charge system.
1993-95 (1.4) 2.0

(G) Condenser Assy., Renew
Includes: Evacuate and charge system.
1993-95 (1.6) 2.5

(G) Control Assy., Temperature, Renew
1993-94 (.6) 1.0
1995 (.5) 9

(G) Core, Evaporator, Renew
Includes: Evacuate and charge system.
1993-94 (2.0) 4.5
1995 (1.7) 4.5

(G) Hoses, AC, Renew
Includes: Evacuate and charge system.
1993-95
liquid line (1.0) 1.7
suction (1.0) 1.7
discharge (1.1) 1.8

(G) Manifold Assy., Suction or Discharge, Renew
All models (.8) 1.5

(G) Orifice, Evaporator Core, Renew
Includes: Evacuate and charge system.
1993-95 (1.1) 1.6

(G) Resistor, Blower Motor, Renew
All models (.3) 5

(G) Seal, Compressor Shaft, Renew
Includes: R&R compressor. Evacuate and charge system.
1993-95 (2.3) 3.3

(G) Switch, Blower Motor, Renew
1993-95 (.6) 1.0

(G) Switch, Clutch Cycling Pressure, Renew
All models (.3) 4

FORD MOTOR COMPANY-FWD
MERCURY SABLE • FORD TAURUS

LABOR COOLING SYSTEM LABOR

(Factory Time) Chilton Time

TESTING

(M) Pressure Test Cooling System
All models 3

SERVICE

(G) Belt, Drive, Adjust
All models
one (.2) 3
each adtnl. 1

(G) Belt, Drive, Renew
All models
V belt, one (.3) 5
each adtnl. 1
Serpentine belt
3.2L SHO (.5) 7
3.8L (.6) 8

(G) Blade, Fan, Renew
All models (.5) 6

(G) Cable, Temperature Control, Renew
All models (.8) 1.3

(G) Control Assy., Heater, Renew
All models (1.0) 1.5

(G) Core, Heater, R&R or Renew
All models
w/AC (4.4) 8.0
Boil & Repair, add 1.2
Repair Core, add 9
Recore, add 1.2

(G) Expansion (Freeze) Plugs, Water Jacket, Renew
Add appropriate time to access plug.
All models, each 5

(G) Gauge, Temperature (Dash Unit), Renew
All models (1.0) 1.7

(G) Hoses, Heater, Renew
All models, each (.4) 5

LABOR — COOLING SYSTEM — LABOR

(Factory Time) Chilton Time

(G) Hoses, Radiator, Renew

Includes: Drain and refill cooling system as required.

All models
- upper (.4) .4
- lower (.5) .5
- both (.6) .6

(G) Motor, Radiator Fan and/or Fan, Renew

All models (.5) .7

(G) Pump and/or Gasket, Water, Renew

Includes: Drain and refill cooling system.

All models
- 3.0L (1.3) 2.0
- 3.0L SHO, 3.2L SHO (2.5) 3.7
- 3.8L (2.1) 3.0

(G) Radiator Assy., R&R or Renew

All models
- wo/SHO (.9) 1.4
- w/SHO (1.0) 1.6

Renew side tank, add
- one (.4) .5
- both (.6) .8

Renew oil cooler, add (.1) .2

(G) Resistor, Heater Blower Motor, Renew

All models (.3) .5

(G) Sending Unit, Engine Coolant Temp., Renew

All models (.3) .4

(G) Switch, Heater Blower Motor, Renew

All models (1.0) 1.5

(G) Tensioner, Drive Belt, Renew

All models
- 3.0L (.5) .7
- 3.0L SHO, 3.2L SHO
  - one (.3) .4
  - both (.5) .7
- 3.8L (.3) .4

(G) Thermostat, Coolant, Renew

All models
- 3.0L (.7) 1.0
- 3.0L SHO, 3.2L SHO (.5) .8
- 3.8L (.6) .8

(G) Winterize Cooling System

Includes: Run engine to check for leaks, tighten all hose connections. Test radiator and pressure cap, drain radiator and engine block. Add antifreeze and refill system.

All models .5

LABOR — AIR CONDITIONING — LABOR

(Factory Time) Chilton Time

Note: If more than one item requires replacement where evacuation and discharging the system is already included in the operation, deduct 1.0 hour for each additional item from the time listed.

SERVICE AND TESTING

(G) Drain, Evacuate and Recharge System

All models (.7) 1.0

(G) Flush Refrigerant System, Complete

To be used in conjunction with component replacement which could contaminate system. Includes evacuate and recharge.

All models 1.3

(G) Performance Test

All models .6

(G) Recover and/or Recycle AC Refrigerant

Add to evacuate and charge the AC system, as required.

All models .2

(G) Refrigerant, Add (Partial Charge)

All models .6

COMPONENTS

(G) Accumulator Assy., Renew

Includes: Evacuate and charge system.

All models (1.0) 1.5

Note: Also called receiver drier.

(G) Belt, Compressor Drive, Renew

All models
- V belt (.3) .5
- Serpentine belt
  - 3.2L SHO (.5) .7
  - 3.8L (.6) .8

(G) Blower Motor, Renew

All models
- wo/EATC (.8) 1.5
- w/EATC (1.0) 1.7

(G) Clutch and/or Pulley, Compressor, Renew

Includes: R&R compressor.

All models
- V6
  - 3.0L, 3.2L (2.8) 3.7
  - 3.8L (2.6) 3.5

(G) Compressor Assy., R&R and Recondition

Includes: Evacuate and charge system.

All models
- V6
  - 3.0L, 3.2L (3.6) 5.2
  - 3.8L (3.9) 5.2

(G) Compressor Assy., Renew

Includes: Transfer parts as required. Evacuate and charge system.

All models
- V6
  - 3.0L MFI (2.8) 3.6
  - 3.0L SHO, 3.2L SHO (2.4) 3.3
  - 3.8L (2.7) 3.6

(G) Condenser Assy., Renew

Includes: Evacuate and charge system.

All models (1.6) 2.2

(G) Control Assy., AC, Renew

All models (1.0) 1.5

(G) Controller, Blower Motor Speed, Renew

All models (.3) .5

(G) Core, Evaporator, Renew

Includes: Evacuate and charge system.

All models (3.2) 9.2

(G) Dehydrator and/or Receiver Tank, Renew

Includes: Evacuate and charge system.

1993-95 SHO models (2.1) 3.2

(G) Hoses, AC, Renew

Includes: Evacuate and charge system.

All models
- suction line
  - V6
    - wo/SHO (1.5) 2.3
  - w/SHO (1.7) 2.4
- liquid line
  - wo/SHO (1.0) 1.7
  - w/SHO (1.6) 2.4
- discharge line (1.2) 1.9

(G) Manifold Assy., Suction or Discharge, Renew

All models (1.1) 2.0

(G) Motor, Door Vacuum, Renew

All models, temperature door (3.0) 6.0

(G) Orifice Valve (Tube), Renew

Includes: Evacuate and charge system.

All models (1.1) 1.5

(G) Relay, Blower Motor, Renew

All models (.3) .4

(G) Resistor, Blower Motor, Renew

All models (.3) .5

(G) Seal, Compressor Shaft, Renew

Includes: R&R compressor. Evacuate and charge system.

All models
- V6 (3.1) 4.1

(G) Sensor, Ambient Temperature, Renew

All models (.3) .6

(G) Switch, Blower Motor, Renew

All models (1.0) 1.5

(G) Switch, Clutch Cycling Pressure, Renew

1993-95 (.5) .7

LABOR AIR CONDITIONING LABOR

(Factory Time) Chilton Time

AUTOMATIC TEMPERATURE CONTROL (ATC)

(G) ATC System Diagnosis
1993-94 (.5) 8

(G) Blower Motor, Speed Control, Renew
Does not include system test.
1993-94 (.3) 5

(G) Control, ATC, Renew
Does not include system test.
1993-94 (1.0) 1.4

(G) Motor, AC Blower, Renew
1993-94 (.9) 1.2

(G) Pin Point Test
1993-94 3

(G) Sensor, Ambient, Renew
Does not include system test.
1993-94 (.3) 5

(G) Sensor, ATC, Renew
Does not include system test.
1993-94 (.4) 6

(G) Sensor, Sunload, Renew
Does not include system test.
1993-94 (.3) 5

(G) Servo, ATC, Renew
Does not include system test.
1993-94 (.4) 6

(G) Switch, Clutch Cycling, Renew
Does not include system test.
1993-94 (.5) 7

(G) Switch, AC Blower Motor, Renew
Does not include system test.
1993-94 (1.0) 1.4

(G) Switch, Damper Door, Renew
Does not include system test.
1993-94 (1.0) 1.4

FORD MOTOR COMPANY-FWD
FORD TEMPO • MERCURY TOPAZ

LABOR COOLING SYSTEM LABOR

(Factory Time) Chilton Time

TESTING

(M) Pressure Test Cooling System
All models 3

SERVICE

(G) Belt, Drive, Adjust
All models
one (.2) 3
each adtnl. (.1) 1

(G) Belt, Drive, Renew
All models
AC (.4) 5
Alternator (.3) 4
PS (.4) 5
Thermactor (.3) 4
Water Pump
wo/AC (.4) 5
w/AC (.5) 6

(G) Blade, Fan, Renew
All models
wo/AC (.6) 1.0
w/AC (.4) 6

(G) Bypass Tube and/or O-Ring, Heater, Renew
All models (.6) 1.0

(G) Cable, Temperature Control, Renew
All models (.7) 1.1

(G) Control Assy., Heater, Renew
1993-94
wo/AC (.4) 6
w/AC (.7) 1.0

(G) Core, Heater, R&R or Renew
All models
wo/AC (.9) 1.9
w/AC (1.3) 3.0

Boil & Repair add 1.2
Repair Core add 9
Recore add 1.2

(G) Expansion (Freeze) Plugs, Water Jacket, Renew (Engine Block)
Add appropriate time to access plug.
All models, each (.3) 5

(G) Gauge, Temperature (Dash Unit), Renew
All models (.7) 1.2

(G) Hoses, Heater, Renew
All models
one (.6) 9
both (.7) 1.0

(G) Hoses, Radiator, Renew
Includes: Drain and refill cooling system as required.
All models
upper (.3) 4
lower (.4) 5
both (.5) 6

(G) Motor, Heater Blower, Renew
All models (.5) 9

(G) Motor, Radiator Fan and/or Fan, Renew
1993-94 Four
wo/AC (.5) 7
w/AC (.4) 6
1993-94 V6 (.5) 7

(G) Pump and/or Gasket, Water, Renew
Includes: Drain and refill cooling system.
1993-94 Four
gas (1.2) 2.0
1993-94 V6 (1.3) 2.1
w/AC add (.1) 1

(G) Radiator Assy., R&R or Renew
All models
wo/AC (.7) 1.2
w/AC (.6) 1.0
Renew oil cooler add (.1) 2
Renew side tanks, add
one (.4) 4
both (.6) 6

(G) Relay, Heater Blower Motor, Renew
All models (.3) 4

(G) Resistor, Heater Blower Motor, Renew
All models (.3) 5

(G) Sending Unit, Engine Coolant Temp., Renew
All models (.3) 4

(G) Switch, Heater Blower Motor, Renew
All models (.6) 1.0

(G) Switch, Radiator Fan Motor (Coolant Temp.), Renew
All models (.3) 4

(G) Tensioner, Drive Belt, Renew
1993 Four (1.2) 1.6
1994 Four (.6) 1.6
1993-94 V6 (.4) 7

(G) Thermostat, Coolant, Renew
1993-94 Four (.5) 7
1993-94 V6 (.7) 1.0

(G) Winterize Cooling System
Includes: Run engine to check for leaks, tighten all hose connections. Test radiator and pressure cap, drain radiator and engine block. Add antifreeze and refill system.
All models 5

LABOR AIR CONDITIONING LABOR

(Factory Time) Chilton Time

Note: If more than one item requires replacement where evacuation and discharging the system is already included in the operation, deduct 1.0 hour for each additional item from the time listed.

SERVICE AND TESTING

(G) Drain, Evacuate and Recharge System
All models (.7) 1.0

(G) Flush Refrigerant System, Complete
To be used in conjunction with component replacement which could contaminate system. Includes evacuate and recharge.
All models 1.3

(G) Performance Test
All models 6

(G) Recover and/or Recycle AC Refrigerant
Add to evacuate and charge the AC system, as required.
All models 2

(G) Refrigerant, Add (Partial Charge)
All models 6

COMPONENTS

(G) Accumulator Assy., Renew
Includes: Evacuate and charge system.
1993-94 (1.0) 1.5

(G) Belt, Compressor Drive, Renew
All models (.4) 6

(G) Blower Motor, Renew
1993-94 (.8) 1.2

(G) Clutch & Pulley, Compressor, Renew
Includes: Evacuate and charge system.
1993-94 Four (2.4) 3.4
1993-94 V6 (2.8) 3.8
Renew clutch bearing add (.1) 1
Renew clutch field add (.1) 1

(G) Compressor Assy., R&R and Recondition
Includes: Evacuate and charge system.
1993-94 Four (3.7) 4.8
1993-94 V6 (3.8) 4.9

(G) Compressor Assy., Renew
Includes: Transfer parts as required. Evacuate and charge system.
1993-94 Four (2.6) 3.6
1993-94 V6 (2.1) 3.1

(G) Condenser Assy., Renew
Includes: Evacuate and charge system.
All models (1.5) 2.4

(G) Control Assy., Temperature, Renew
All models (.7) 1.2

(G) Core, Evaporator, Renew
Includes: Evacuate and charge system.
1993 (5.2) 8.0
1994 (3.7) 8.0

(G) Hoses, AC, Renew
Includes: Evacuate and charge system.
All models
suction line (1.3) 2.0
compressor to condenser (1.0) ... 1.7
liquid line, condenser
to evaporator (1.4) 2.1

(G) Manifold Assy., Suction or Discharge, Renew
All models each (.8) 1.5

(G) Orifice Valve (Tube), Renew
Includes: Evacuate and charge system.
All models (1.4) 2.1

(G) Resistor, Blower Motor, Renew
All models (.3) 5

(G) Seal, Compressor Shaft, Renew
Includes: R&R compressor. Evacuate and charge system.
1993-94 Four (2.7) 3.8
1993-94 V6 (3.1) 4.1

(G) Switch, Blower Motor, Renew
All models (.6) 1.0

(G) Switch, Clutch Cycling Pressure, Renew
All models (.4) 6

FORD MOTOR COMPANY-FWD

FORD CONTOUR • MERCURY MYSTIQUE

LABOR COOLING SYSTEM LABOR

(Factory Time) Chilton Time

TESTING

(M) Pressure Test Cooling System
All models 3

SERVICE

(G) Belt, Serpentine Drive, Renew
All models
2.0L (.4) 5
2.5L (.3) 4

(G) Belt, Water Pump Drive, Renew
All models
2.5L (.3) 4

(G) Blade, Fan, Renew
All models
one (.5) 7
both (.7) 1.0

(G) Control Assy., Heater, Renew
All models (.6) 9

(G) Core, Heater, R&R or Renew
All models (1.3) 2.4
Boil & Repair add 1.2
Repair Core add 9
Recore add 1.2

(G) Expansion (Freeze) Plugs, Water Jacket, Renew
Add appropriate time to access plug.
All models, each 5

(G) Gauge, Temperature (Dash Unit), Renew
All models (.8) 1.2

(G) Hoses, Heater, Renew
All models
one (.6) 8
both (.7) 1.0

(G) Hoses, Radiator, Renew
Includes: Drain and refill cooling system as required.
All models
upper (.7) 8
lower (.9) 1.0
both (1.2) 1.5

(G) Motor, Heater Blower, Renew
All models (.3) 5

(G) Motor, Radiator Fan and/or Fan, Renew
All models
one (.5) 8
both (.6) 1.0

(G) Pump and/or Gasket, Water, Renew
Includes: Drain and refill cooling system.
All models
2.0L (1.5) 2.4
2.5L (.7) 1.2

LABOR COOLING SYSTEM LABOR

(Factory Time) Chilton Time

(G) Radiator Assy., R&R or Renew
All models
MT (1.1) 1.6
AT (1.2) 1.7
Renew side tanks add
one (.3) 4
both (.6) 7

(G) Resistor, Heater Blower Motor, Renew
All models (.3) 4

(G) Sending Unit, Engine Coolant Temp., Renew
All models (.5) 7

(G) Switch, Heater Blower Motor, Renew
All models (.6) 1.0

(G) Switch, Radiator Fan Motor (Coolant Temp.), Renew
All models (.3) 4

(G) Tensioner, Drive Belt, Renew
All models (.5) 8

(G) Thermostat, Coolant, Renew
All models
2.0L (.8) 1.0
2.5L (1.0) 1.3

(G) Winterize Cooling System
Includes: Run engine to check for leaks, tighten all hose connections. Test radiator and pressure cap, drain radiator and engine block. Add antifreeze and refill system.
All models 5

LABOR AIR CONDITIONING LABOR

(Factory Time) Chilton Time

Note: If more than one item requires replacement where evacuation and discharging the system is already included in the operation, deduct 1.0 hour for each additional item from the time listed.

SERVICE AND TESTING

(G) Drain, Evacuate and Recharge System
All models (.7) 1.0

(G) Flush Refrigerant System, Complete
To be used in conjunction with component replacement which could contaminate system. Includes evacuate and recharge.
All models 1.3

(G) Performance Test
All models 6

(G) Recover and/or Recycle AC Refrigerant
Add to evacuate and charge the AC system, as required.
All models 2

(G) Refrigerant, Add (Partial Charge)
All models 6

COMPONENTS

(G) Accumulator Assy., Renew
Includes: Evacuate and charge system.
All models (1.1) 1.6

(G) Blower Motor, Renew
All models (.3) 5

(G) Clutch and/or Pulley, Compressor, Renew
Includes: R&R compressor.
All models
2.0L (2.0) 2.8
2.5L (1.9) 2.7

(G) Coil, Evaporator, Renew
Includes: Evacuate and charge system.
All models (5.2) 7.5

(G) Compressor Assy., Renew
Includes: Transfer parts as required. Evacuate and charge system.
All models
2.0L (1.6) 2.2
2.5L (1.5) 2.1

(G) Condenser Assy., Renew
Includes: Evacuate and charge system.
All models (1.7) 2.4

(G) Control Assy., AC, Renew
All models (.6) 9

(G) Controller, Blower Motor Speed, Renew
All models (.3) 5

(G) Hoses, AC, Renew
Includes: Evacuate and charge system.
All models
Liquid line
2.0L (1.2) 1.7
2.5L (1.4) 1.9
Suction hose
2.0: (1.6) 2.2
2.5L (1.2) 1.7

(G) Manifold Assy., Suction or Discharge, Renew
All models (1.4) 2.0

(G) Orifice Valve (Tube), Renew
Includes: Evacuate and charge system.
All models (.9) 1.4

(G) Resistor, Blower Motor, Renew
All models (.7) 1.0

(G) Seal, Compressor Shaft, Renew
Includes: R&R compressor. Evacuate and charge system.
All models
2.0L (2.0) 2.9
2.5L (1.9) 2.8

(G) Switch, Blower Motor, Renew
All models (.6) 9

(G) Switch, Clutch Cycling Pressure, Renew
All models (.6) 9

FORD MOTOR COMPANY-FWD
LINCOLN CONTINENTAL

LABOR COOLING SYSTEM LABOR

(Factory Time) Chilton Time

TESTING

(M) Pressure Test Cooling System
All models 3

SERVICE

(G) Belt, Serpentine Drive, Renew
All models (.6) 8

(G) Blade, Fan, Renew
All models (.5) 6
Renew motor add (.1) 1

(G) Core, Heater, R&R or Renew
All models (3.9) 10.5
Boil & Repair, add 1.2
Repair Core, add 9
Recore, add 9

(G) Expansion (Freeze) Plugs, Water Jacket, Renew
Add appropriate time to access plug.
All models, each 5

(G) Hoses, Heater, Renew
All models, each (.4) 5

(G) Hoses, Radiator, Renew
Includes: Drain and refill cooling system as required.
All models
upper (.5) 6
lower (.6) 7
both (.7) 9

(G) Motor, Radiator Fan and/or Fan, Renew
All models (.5) 7

(G) Pump and/or Gasket, Water, Renew
Includes: Drain and refill cooling system.
All models (2.1) 4.0

(G) Radiator Assy., R&R or Renew
All models (1.1) 1.6

Renew side tank add
one (.4) 4
both (.6) 6
Renew oil cooler add (.1) 2

(G) Sending Unit, Engine Coolant Temp., Renew
All models (.3) 4

(G) Switch, Radiator Fan Motor (Coolant Temp.), Renew
All models (.3) 4

(G) Tensioner, Drive Belt, Renew
All models (.3) 4

(G) Thermostat, Coolant, Renew
All models (.6) 8

(G) Winterize Cooling System
Includes: Run engine to check for leaks, tighten all hose connections. Test radiator and pressure cap, drain radiator and engine block. Add antifreeze and refill system.
All models 5

LABOR AIR CONDITIONING LABOR

(Factory Time) Chilton Time

Note: If more than one item requires replacement where evacuation and discharging the system is already included in the operation, deduct 1.0 hour for each additional item from the time listed.

SERVICE AND TESTING

(G) Drain, Evacuate and Recharge System
All models (.7) 1.0

(G) Flush Refrigerant System, Complete
To be used in conjunction with component replacement which could contaminate system. Includes evacuate and recharge.
All models 1.3

(G) Performance Test
All models 6

(G) Recover and/or Recycle AC Refrigerant
Add to evacuate and charge the AC system, as required.
All models 2

(G) Refrigerant, Add (Partial Charge)
All models 6

COMPONENTS

(G) Accumulator Assy., Renew
Includes: Evacuate and charge system.
1993-95 (1.0) 1.5

(G) Belt, Compressor Drive, Renew
All models (.6) 8

(G) Blower Motor, Renew
All models (.9) 1.4

(G) Clutch & Pulley, Compressor, Renew
Includes: Evacuate and charge system.
All models (2.7) 3.5

(G) Compressor Assy., R&R and Recondition
Includes: Evacuate and charge system.
All models (3.6) 4.8

(G) Compressor Assy., Renew
Includes: Transfer parts as required. Evacuate and charge system.
All models (2.7) 3.5

(G) Condenser Assy., Renew
Includes: Evacuate and charge system.
All models (1.8) 2.5

(G) Control Assy., AC, Renew
All models (.4) 6

(G) Controller, Blower Motor Speed, Renew
All models (.9) 1.4

(G) Core, Evaporator, Renew
Includes: Evacuate and charge system.
1993 (6.6) 13.0
1994 (3.3) 6.0

(G) Hoses, AC, Renew
Includes: Evacuate and charge system.
All models
discharge line (1.2) 1.8
suction line (1.6) 2.2
liquid line (1.4) 2.0

(G) Manifold Assy., Suction or Discharge, Renew
All models, each (1.1) 1.7

LABOR AIR CONDITIONING LABOR

(Factory Time) Chilton Time

(G) Motor, AC Door Actuator, Renew
All models
outside/recirculation (.7) 1.1
panel/defrost (2.4) 3.5
temperature blend (3.2) 4.5
floor/panel (4.3) 8.0

(G) Orifice Valve (Tube), Renew
Includes: Evacuate and charge system.
1993 (1.1) 1.7

(G) Seal, Compressor Shaft, Renew
Includes: R&R compressor. Evacuate and charge system.
All models (3.0) 4.0

(G) Switch, Clutch Cycling Pressure, Renew
All models (.5) 7

AUTOMATIC TEMPERATURE CONTROL (ATC)

(G) ATC System Diagnosis
1993-95 (.5) 8

(G) Blower Motor, Speed Control, Renew
Does not include system test.
1993-95 (.9) 1.4

(G) Control, ATC, Renew
Does not include system test.
1993-95 (.5) 8

(G) Motor, AC Blower, Renew
1993-95 (.8) 1.1

(G) Pin Point Test
1993-95 3

(G) Sensor, Ambient, Renew
Does not include system test.
1993-95 (.3) 5

(G) Sensor, ATC, Renew
Does not include system test.
1993-95 (.9) 1.2

(G) Sensor, Sunload, Renew
Does not include system test.
1993-95 (.3) 5

(G) Servo, ATC, Renew
Does not include system test.
1993-95 (.4) 6

(G) Switch, Clutch Cycling, Renew
Does not include system test.
1993-95 (.3) 4

(G) Switch, AC Blower Motor, Renew
Does not include system test.
1993-95 (.5) 8

(G) Switch, Damper Door, Renew
Does not include system test.
1993-95 (.7) 1.0

FORD MOTOR COMPANY-FWD
FORD FESTIVA

LABOR COOLING SYSTEM LABOR

(Factory Time) Chilton Time

TESTING

(M) Pressure Test Cooling System
All models 3

SERVICE

(G) Belt, Drive, Adjust
All models
one (.2) 3
each adtnl. 1

(G) Belt, Drive, Renew
All models
alternator (.3) 4
power steering (.3) 4

(G) Blade, Fan, Renew
All models (.5) 8

(G) Cable, Temperature Control, Renew
All models (.5) 8

(G) Control Assy., Heater, Renew
All models (.4) 7

(G) Core, Heater, R&R or Renew
All models (1.9) 5.0
Boil & Repair, add 1.2
Repair Core, add 9
Recore, add 1.2

(G) Expansion (Freeze) Plugs, Water Jacket, Renew (Engine Block)
Add appropriate time to access plug.
All models, each (.3) 5

(G) Gauge, Temperature (Dash Unit), Renew
All models (.6) 1.0

(G) Hoses, Heater, Renew
All models
one (.4) 6
both (.5) 8

(G) Hoses, Radiator, Renew
Includes: Drain and refill cooling system as required.
All models
upper or lower each (.3) 4
both (.4) 6

(G) Motor, Heater Blower, Renew
All models (.4) 7

(G) Motor, Radiator Fan and/or Fan, Renew
All models
front (.3) 5
rear (.5) 8

(G) Pump and/or Gasket, Water, Renew
Includes: Drain and refill cooling system.
All models (1.8) 3.5
w/AC add (.1) 1
Renew timing belt add (.3) 3

(G) Radiator Assy., R&R or Renew
All models
MT (.7) 1.0
AT (.9) 1.3

(G) Resistor, Heater Blower Motor, Renew
All models 6

(G) Sending Unit, Engine Coolant Temp., Renew
All models (.4) 6

(G) Switch, Heater Blower Motor, Renew
All models (.5) 8

(G) Switch, Radiator Fan Motor (Coolant Temp.), Renew
All models (.3) 4

(G) Thermostat, Coolant, Renew
All models (.4) 5

(G) Winterize Cooling System
Includes: Run engine to check for leaks, tighten all hose connections. Test radiator and pressure cap, drain radiator and engine block. Add antifreeze and refill system.
All models 5

LABOR — AIR CONDITIONING — LABOR

(Factory Time) Chilton Time

Note: If more than one item requires replacement where evacuation and discharging the system is already included in the operation, deduct 1.0 hour for each additional item from the time listed.

SERVICE AND TESTING

(G) Drain, Evacuate and Recharge System

All models (.7) 1.0

(G) Flush Refrigerant System, Complete

To be used in conjunction with component replacement which could contaminate system. Includes evacuate and recharge.

All models 1.3

(G) Performance Test

All models 6

(G) Recover and/or Recycle AC Refrigerant

Add to evacuate and charge the AC system, as required.

All models 2

(G) Refrigerant, Add (Partial Charge)

All models 6

COMPONENTS

(G) Belt, Compressor Drive, Renew

All models (.3) 4

(G) Blower Motor, Renew

All models (.4) 7

(G) Clutch & Pulley, Compressor, Renew

Includes: Evacuate and charge system.

All models (1.9) 2.4
Renew clutch bearing, add (.3) 3
Renew clutch field, add (.1) 1

(G) Compressor Assy., R&R and Recondition

Includes: Evacuate and charge system.

All models (4.1) 5.5

(G) Compressor Assy., Renew

Includes: Transfer parts as required. Evacuate and charge system.

All models (1.5) 2.0

(G) Condenser Assy., Renew

Includes: Evacuate and charge system.

All models (1.1) 1.7

(G) Control Assy., Temperature, Renew

All models (.5) 7

(G) Core, Evaporator, Renew

Includes: Evacuate and charge system.

All models (1.3) 2.2

(G) Dehydrator and/or Receiver Tank, Renew

Includes: Evacuate and charge system.

All models (1.2) 1.7

(G) Hoses, AC, Renew

Includes: Evacuate and charge system.

All models
suction line (1.1) 1.8
liquid line (1.0) 1.7
discharge line (1.0) 1.7

(G) Manifold Assy., Suction or Discharge, Renew

All models (.8) 1.5

(G) Seal, Compressor Shaft, Renew

Includes: R&R compressor. Evacuate and charge system.

All models (2.2) 2.7

(G) Switch, Blower Motor, Renew

All models (.5) 8

(G) Switch, Clutch Cycling Pressure, Renew

All models (.7) 1.0

(G) Valve, Expansion, Renew

Includes: Evacuate and charge system.

All models (1.5) 2.1

FORD MOTOR COMPANY-FWD
FORD ASPIRE

LABOR — COOLING SYSTEM — LABOR

(Factory Time) Chilton Time

TESTING

(M) Pressure Test Cooling System

All models 3

SERVICE

(G) Belt, Drive, Adjust

All models
one (.2) 3
each adtnl. 1

(G) Belt, Drive, Renew

All models
alternator (.3) 4
power steering (.3) 4

(G) Blade, Fan, Renew

All models (.5) 8

(G) Cable, Temperature Control, Renew

All models (.5) 8

(G) Control Assy., Heater, Renew

All models (.5) 8

(G) Core, Heater, R&R or Renew

All models (2.3) 4.0

LABOR COOLING SYSTEM LABOR

(Factory Time) Chilton Time

(G) Expansion (Freeze) Plugs, Water Jacket, Renew

Add appropriate time to access plug.

All models, each 5

(G) Gauge, Temperature (Dash Unit), Renew

All models (.6) 1.0

(G) Hoses, Heater, Renew

All models
- one (.4) 6
- both (.5) 8

(G) Hoses, Radiator, Renew

Includes: Drain and refill cooling system as required.

All models
- one (.4) 5
- both (.5) 7

(G) Motor, Heater Blower, Renew

All models (.4) 6

(G) Motor, Radiator Fan and/or Fan, Renew

All models
- front (.3) 5
- rear (.6) 9

(G) Pump and/or Gasket, Water, Renew

Includes: Drain and refill cooling system.

All models (1.6) 3.1
w/AC add (.5) 5

(G) Radiator Assy., R&R or Renew

All models
- MT (.7) 1.0
- AT (.9) 1.3

(G) Sending Unit, Engine Coolant Temp., Renew

All models (.3) 5

(G) Switch, Heater Blower Motor, Renew

All models (.5) 8

(G) Switch, Radiator Fan Motor (Coolant Temp.), Renew

All models (.3) 5

(G) Thermostat, Coolant, Renew

All models (.5) 7

(G) Winterize Cooling System

Includes: Run engine to check for leaks, tighten all hose connections. Test radiator and pressure cap, drain radiator and engine block. Add antifreeze and refill system.

All models 5

LABOR AIR CONDITIONING LABOR

(Factory Time) Chilton Time

Note: If more than one item requires replacement where evacuation and discharging the system is already included in the operation, deduct 1.0 hour for each additional item from the time listed.

SERVICE AND TESTING

(G) Drain, Evacuate and Recharge System

All models (.7) 1.0

(G) Flush Refrigerant System, Complete

To be used in conjunction with component replacement which could contaminate system. Includes evacuate and recharge.

All models 1.3

(G) Performance Test

All models 6

(G) Recover and/or Recycle AC Refrigerant

Add to evacuate and charge the AC system, as required.

All models 2

(G) Refrigerant, Add (Partial Charge)

All models 6

COMPONENTS

(G) Belt, Compressor Drive, Renew

All models (.3) 4

(G) Blower Motor, Renew

All models (.4) 7

(G) Clutch & Pulley, Compressor, Renew

Includes: Evacuate and charge system.

All models (1.3) 1.8

(G) Compressor Assy., Renew

Includes: Transfer parts as required. Evacuate and charge system.

All models (1.4) 2.0

(G) Condenser Assy., Renew

Includes: Evacuate and charge system.

All models (1.2) 1.8

(G) Control Assy., Temperature, Renew

All models (.5) 8

(G) Core, Evaporator, Renew

Includes: Evacuate and charge system.

All models (1.4) 2.4

(G) Dehydrator and/or Receiver Tank, Renew

Includes: Evacuate and charge system.

All models (1.0) 1.5

(G) Hoses, AC, Renew

Includes: Evacuate and charge system.

All models
- suction line (1.1) 1.8
- liquid line (1.3) 2.1
- discharge line (1.0) 1.7

(G) Seal, Compressor Shaft, Renew

Includes: R&R compressor. Evacuate and charge system.

All models (1.4) 2.1

(G) Switch, Blower Motor, Renew

All models (.5) 8

(G) Switch, Clutch Cycling Pressure, Renew

All models (.8) 1.2

(G) Valve, Expansion, Renew

Includes: Evacuate and charge system.

All models (1.3) 1.8

FORD MOTOR COMPANY-FWD
FORD PROBE

COOLING SYSTEM

(Factory Time) Chilton Time

TESTING

(M) Pressure Test Cooling System
All models 5

SERVICE

(G) Belt, Drive, Adjust
All models
one (.2) 3
each adtnl. 1

(G) Belt, Drive, Renew
1993-95
Four (.4) 6
V6 (.3) 5

(G) Blade, Fan, Renew
1993-95 (.5) 7

(G) Bypass Tube and/or O-Ring, Heater, Renew
1993-95
Four (.6) 9
V6 (1.3) 1.8

(G) Cable, Temperature Control, Renew
All models (.5) 8

(G) Control Assy., Heater, Renew
1993-95 (.4) 7

(G) Core, Heater, R&R or Renew
1993-95 (2.1) 4.0
Add time to recharge AC system if required.
Boil & Repair, add 1.2
Repair Core, add 9
Recore, add 1.2

(G) Expansion (Freeze) Plugs, Water Jacket, Renew (Engine Block)
Add appropriate time to access plug.
All models, each (.3) 5

(G) Gauge, Temperature (Dash Unit), Renew
1993-95 (1.0) 1.8

(G) Hoses, Heater, Renew
All models
one (.4) 5
both (.5) 7

(G) Hoses, Radiator, Renew
Includes: Drain and refill cooling system as required.
All models
upper (.3) 4
lower (.4) 5
both (.5) 6

(G) Motor, Heater Blower, Renew
All models (.4) 7

(G) Motor, Radiator Fan and/or Fan, Renew
1993-95
Four (.5) 7
V6
one (.5) 7
both (.6) 9

(G) Pump and/or Gasket, Water, Renew
Includes: Drain and refill cooling system.
1993-95
Four (2.0) 3.8
V6 (2.2) 4.1
Renew timing belt add 5

(G) Radiator Assy., R&R or Renew
1993-95
MT (.7) 1.2
AT (.8) 1.4

(G) Resistor, Heater Blower Motor, Renew
All models (.3) 5

(G) Sending Unit, Engine Coolant Temp., Renew
All models (.3) 4

(G) Switch, Heater Blower Motor, Renew
1993-95 (.4) 8

(G) Switch, Radiator Fan Motor (Coolant Temp.), Renew
All models (.3) 5

(G) Thermostat, Coolant, Renew
1993-95
Four (.5) 7
V6 (.6) 8

(G) Winterize Cooling System
Includes: Run engine to check for leaks, tighten all hose connections. Test radiator and pressure cap, drain radiator and engine block. Add antifreeze and refill system.
All models 5

AIR CONDITIONING

(Factory Time) Chilton Time

Note: If more than one item requires replacement where evacuation and discharging the system is already included in the operation, deduct 1.0 hour for each additional item from the time listed.

SERVICE AND TESTING

(G) Drain, Evacuate and Recharge System
All models (.7) 1.0

(G) Flush Refrigerant System, Complete
To be used in conjunction with component replacement which could contaminate system. Includes evacuate and recharge.
All models 1.3

(G) Performance Test
All models 6

(G) Recover and/or Recycle AC Refrigerant
Add to evacuate and charge the AC system, as required.
All models 2

(G) Refrigerant, Add (Partial Charge)
All models 6

COMPONENTS

(G) Accumulator Assy., Renew
Includes: Evacuate and charge system.
All models (1.0) 1.5

(G) Belt, Compressor Drive, Renew
1993-95
Four (.3) 4
V6 (.4) 6

(G) Blower Motor, Renew
1993-95 (.4) 6

(G) Clutch & Pulley, Compressor, Renew
Includes: Evacuate and charge system.
1993-95 (1.7) 2.3
Renew clutch brg. add (.1) 1
Renew clutch field add (.1) 1

(G) Compressor Assy., R&R and Recondition
Includes: Evacuate and charge system.
1993-95 (3.9) 5.5

(G) Compressor Assy., Renew
Includes: Transfer parts as required. Evacuate and charge system.
1993-95 (1.6) 2.3

(G) Condenser Assy., Renew
Includes: Evacuate and charge system.
All models (1.3) 2.0

(G) Control Assy., Temperature, Renew
1993-95 (.4) 7

LABOR — AIR CONDITIONING — LABOR

(Factory Time) Chilton Time

(G) Core, Evaporator, Renew
Includes: Evacuate and charge system.
1993-95 (2.5) 5.0

(G) Hoses, AC, Renew
Includes: Evacuate and charge system.
All models (1.0) 1.7

(G) Orifice Valve (Tube), Renew
Includes: Evacuate and charge system.
1993-95 (.9) 1.5

(G) Resistor, Blower Motor, Renew
1993-95 (.3) 5

(G) Seal, Compressor Shaft, Renew
Includes: R&R compressor. Evacuate and charge system.
1993-95 (1.7) 2.5

(G) Switch, Blower Motor, Renew
1993-95 (.4) 8

(G) Switch, Clutch Cycling Pressure, Renew
All models (.3) 4

FORD MOTOR COMPANY-FWD
MERCURY TRACER

LABOR — COOLING SYSTEM — LABOR

(Factory Time) Chilton Time

TESTING

(M) Pressure Test Cooling System
All models 3

SERVICE

(G) Belt, Drive, Adjust
All models
one (.2) 3
each adtnl. 1

(G) Belt, Drive, Renew
1993-95
Alternator (.5) 7
PS (.5) 7
AC (.5) 7
Serpentine (.3) 4

(G) Blade, Fan, Renew
1993-95 (.6) 8

(G) Bypass Tube and/or O-Ring, Heater, Renew
1993-95 (.6) 1.0

(G) Cable, Temperature Control, Renew
All models (.7) 1.0

(G) Control Assy., Heater, Renew
1993-94 (.5) 8
1995 (.6) 9

(G) Core, Heater, R&R or Renew
1993-95 (2.5) 4.5
Boil & Repair add 1.2
Repair Core add 9
Recore add 1.2

(G) Expansion (Freeze) Plugs, Water Jacket, Renew
Add appropriate time to access plug.
All models, each 5

(G) Gauge, Temperature (Dash Unit), Renew
1993-94 (.7) 1.2
1995 (.9) 1.7

(G) Hoses, Heater, Renew
All models, each (.4) 5

(G) Hoses, Radiator, Renew
Includes: Drain and refill cooling system as required.
1993-95
upper (.4) 5
lower (.6) 7
both (.7) 1.0

(G) Motor, Heater Blower, Renew
1993-95 (.7) 1.1

(G) Motor, Radiator Fan and/or Fan, Renew
1993-95 (.6) 8

(G) Pump and/or Gasket, Water, Renew
Includes: Drain and refill cooling system.
1993-95
1.8L (2.0) 3.7
1.9L (1.7) 3.2
Renew timing belt add (.3) 3

(G) Radiator Assy., R&R or Renew
1993-95
MTX (.9) 1.4
ATX (1.0) 1.5
Renew side tank add
one (.4) 4
both (.6) 6

(G) Resistor, Heater Blower Motor, Renew
1993-95 (.3) 5

(G) Sending Unit, Engine Coolant Temp., Renew
All models (.4) 5

(G) Switch, Heater Blower Motor, Renew
All models (.6) 1.0

(G) Switch, Radiator Fan Motor (Coolant Temp.), Renew
All models (.3) 4

(G) Tensioner, Drive Belt, Renew
All models (.3) 5

(G) Thermostat, Coolant, Renew
1993-95
1.8L (.5) 7
1.9L (.8) 1.0

(G) Winterize Cooling System
Includes: Run engine to check for leaks, tighten all hose connections. Test radiator and pressure cap, drain radiator and engine block. Add antifreeze and refill system.
All models 5

LABOR — AIR CONDITIONING — LABOR

(Factory Time) Chilton Time

Note: If more than one item requires replacement where evacuation and discharging the system is already included in the operation, deduct 1.0 hour for each additional item from the time listed.

SERVICE AND TESTING

(G) Drain, Evacuate and Recharge System
All models (.7) 1.0

(G) Flush Refrigerant System, Complete
To be used in conjunction with component replacement which could contaminate system. Includes evacuate and recharge.
All models 1.3

(G) Performance Test
All models 6

(G) Recover and/or Recycle AC Refrigerant
Add to evacuate and charge the AC system, as required.
All models 2

(G) Refrigerant, Add (Partial Charge)
All models 6

COMPONENTS

(G) Belt, Compressor Drive, Renew
1993-95 (.5) 7

(G) Blower Motor, Renew
1993-95 (.7) 1.1

(G) Clutch & Pulley, Compressor, Renew
Includes: Evacuate and charge system.
1993-95 (1.9) 2.7

(G) Compressor Assy., Renew
Includes: Transfer parts as required. Evacuate and charge system.
1993-95 (1.4) 2.0

(G) Condenser Assy., Renew
Includes: Evacuate and charge system.
1993-95 (1.6) 2.5

(G) Control Assy., Temperature, Renew
1993-94 (.6) 1.0
1995 (.5) 9

(G) Core, Evaporator, Renew
Includes: Evacuate and charge system.
1993-94 (2.0) 4.5
1995 (1.7) 4.5

(G) Hoses, AC, Renew
Includes: Evacuate and charge system.
1993-95
suction (1.0) 1.7
discharge (1.1) 1.8
liquid line (1.0) 1.7

(G) Manifold Assy., Suction or Discharge, Renew
All models (.8) 1.5

(G) Orifice, Evaporator Core, Renew
Includes: Evacuate and charge system.
1993-95 (1.1) 1.6

(G) Resistor, Blower Motor, Renew
1993-95 (.3) 5

(G) Seal, Compressor Shaft, Renew
Includes: R&R compressor. Evacuate and charge system.
1993-95 (2.3) 3.3

(G) Switch, Blower Motor, Renew
1993-95 (.6) 1.0

(G) Switch, Clutch Cycling Pressure, Renew
1993-95 (.3) 4

FORD MOTOR COMPANY-FWD
MERCURY CAPRI

LABOR — COOLING SYSTEM — LABOR

(Factory Time) Chilton Time

TESTING

(M) Pressure Test Cooling System
All models 3

SERVICE

(G) Belt, Drive, Adjust
All models
one (.2) 3
each adtnl. 1

(G) Belt, Drive, Renew
All models
Alternator (.3) 4
PS (.3) 4
AC (.4) 5

(G) Belt, Serpentine Drive, Renew
All models (.3) 5

(G) Blades, Fan or Clutch Assy., Renew
All models (.5) 7

(G) Cable, Temperature Control, Renew
All models (.9) 1.3

(G) Control Assy., Temperature, Renew
All models (.8) 1.1

(G) Core, Heater, R&R or Renew
All models (2.5) 4.9
Boil & Repair add 1.2
Recore add 9
Repair Core add 1.2

(G) Expansion (Freeze) Plugs, Water Jacket, Renew
Add appropriate time to access plug.
All models, each 5

(G) Gauge, Temperature (Dash Unit), Renew
All models (1.2) 1.9

(G) Hoses, Heater, Renew
All models
one (.6) 8
both (.8) 1.2

(G) Hoses, Radiator, Renew
Includes: Drain and refill cooling system as required.
All models
upper (.4) 5
lower (.5) 6
both (.6) 8

(G) Motor, Heater Blower, Renew
1993 (1.0) 1.4
1994 (.4) 6

(G) Motor, Radiator Fan and/or Fan, Renew
All models (.6) 8

(G) Pump and/or Gasket, Water, Renew
Includes: Drain and refill cooling system.
All models (2.8) 4.5
w/AC add (.3) 3

(G) Radiator Assy., R&R or Renew
All models
MT (.8) 1.2
AT (.9) 1.3
Renew side tanks add

LABOR — COOLING SYSTEM — LABOR

(Factory Time) Chilton Time

one (.4) 4
both (.6) 6

(G) Resistor, Heater Blower Motor, Renew
All models (.4) 5

(G) Sending Unit, Engine Coolant Temp., Renew
All models (.3) 4

(G) Switch, Heater Blower Motor, Renew
All models (.8) 1.1

(G) Switch, Radiator Fan Motor (Coolant Temp.), Renew
All models (.3) 4

(G) Tensioner, Drive Belt, Renew
All models (1.4) 2.0
w/AC add (.6) 6

(G) Thermostat, Coolant, Renew
All models (.6) 8

(G) Winterize Cooling System
Includes: Run engine to check for leaks, tighten all hose connections. Test radiator and pressure cap, drain radiator and engine block. Add antifreeze and refill system.
All models 5

LABOR — AIR CONDITIONING — LABOR

(Factory Time) Chilton Time

Note: If more than one item requires replacement where evacuation and discharging the system is already included in the operation, deduct 1.0 hour for each additional item from the time listed.

SERVICE AND TESTING

(G) Drain, Evacuate and Recharge System
All models (.7) 1.0

(G) Flush Refrigerant System, Complete
To be used in conjunction with component replacement which could contaminate system. Includes evacuate and recharge.
All models 1.3

(G) Performance Test
All models 6

(G) Recover and/or Recycle AC Refrigerant
Add to evacuate and charge the AC system, as required.
All models 2

(G) Refrigerant, Add (Partial Charge)
All models 6

COMPONENTS

(G) Belt, Compressor Drive, Renew
All models (.4) 5

(G) Blower Motor, Renew
1993 (1.0) 1.4
1994 (.4) 6

(G) Clutch & Pulley, Compressor, Renew
Includes: Evacuate and charge system.
All models (2.0) 2.8

(G) Compressor Assy., Renew
Includes: Transfer parts as required. Evacuate and charge system.
All models (1.7) 2.5

(G) Condenser Assy., Renew
Includes: Evacuate and charge system.
All models (1.3) 2.0

(G) Core, Evaporator, Renew
Includes: Evacuate and charge system.
All models (1.7) 3.5

(G) Hoses, AC, Renew
Includes: Evacuate and charge system.
All models (1.2) 1.7

(G) Receiver/Drier Assy., Renew
Includes: Evacuate and charge system.
All models (1.1) 1.5

(G) Resistor, Blower Motor, Renew
All models (.4) 5

(G) Seal, Compressor Shaft, Renew
Includes: R&R compressor. Evacuate and charge system.
All models (2.5) 3.5

(G) Switch, Blower Motor, Renew
All models (.8) 1.1

(G) Valve, Expansion, Renew
Includes: Evacuate and charge system.
All models (2.6) 4.5

FORD MOTOR COMPANY-RWD
FORD MUSTANG

LABOR — COOLING SYSTEM — LABOR

(Factory Time) Chilton Time

TESTING

(M) Pressure Test Cooling System
All models 3

SERVICE

(G) Belt, Drive, Adjust
1993
one (.2) 3
each adtnl. 1

(G) Belt, Drive, Renew
1993
one (.3) 4
each adtnl. 1

(G) Belt, Serpentine Drive, Renew
1993-95 V6, V8 (.3) 5

(G) Bypass and/or Tube, Hose, Renew
1993 V8 (.3) 5

(G) Cable, Temperature Control, Renew
All models (.4) 6

(G) Clutch, Viscous (Fluid) Fan Assy., Renew
1993 (.4) 6

(G) Control Assy., Heater, Renew
All models (.4) 7

LABOR — COOLING SYSTEM — LABOR

(Factory Time) Chilton Time

(G) Core, Heater, R&R or Renew
1993
wo/AC (2.4) **5.0**
w/AC (3.8) **6.0**
1994-95 (3.2) **6.0**
Boil & Repair, add **1.2**
Repair Core, add .... **.9**
Recore, add **1.2**

(G) Expansion (Freeze) Plugs, Water Jacket, Renew
Add appropriate time to access plug.
All models, each .... **.5**

(G) Gauge, Temperature (Dash Unit), Renew
1993 (.7) **1.2**
1994 (.6) **1.0**

(G) Hoses, Heater, Renew
All models, each (.4) .... **.6**

(G) Hoses, Radiator, Renew
Includes: Drain and refill cooling system as required.
All models
upper (.3) .... **.4**
lower (.4) .... **.5**
both (.5) .... **.8**

(G) Motor, Heater Blower, Renew
1993 (.6) **1.1**
1994-95 (.5) .... **.8**

(G) Motor, Radiator Fan and/or Fan, Renew
1993 (.3) .... **.5**
1994-95 (.6) .... **.9**

(G) Pump and/or Gasket, Water, Renew
Includes: Drain and refill cooling system.
Four
1993 (.8) **1.2**
V6
1994-95 (1.1) **2.0**
V8
1993-95 (1.1) **2.0**
w/AC add (.1) .... **.2**

(G) Radiator Assy., R&R or Renew
1993 (.6) **1.0**
w/AC add .... **.1**
1994-95
MT (.8) **1.2**
AT (1.0) **1.4**
Boil & Repair, add **1.5**
Rod Clean, add **1.9**
Repair Core, add **1.3**
Renew Tank, add **1.6**
Renew Trans. Oil Cooler, add **1.9**
Recore Radiator, add **1.7**

(G) Resistor, Heater Blower Motor, Renew
All models (.3) .... **.5**

(G) Sending Unit, Engine Coolant Temp., Renew
All models (.3) .... **.4**

(G) Switch, Heater Blower Motor, Renew
All models (.4) .... **.6**

(G) Switch, Radiator Fan Motor (Coolant Temp.), Renew
1993 (.3) .... **.5**
1994-95 (.5) .... **.7**

(G) Tensioner, Drive Belt, Renew
1994-95 (.3) .... **.5**

(G) Thermostat, Coolant, Renew
Four
1993 (.5) .... **.7**
V6
1994-95 (.5) .... **.7**
V8
1993-95 (.9) **1.2**

(G) Winterize Cooling System
Includes: Run engine to check for leaks, tighten all hose connections. Test radiator and pressure cap, drain radiator and engine block. Add antifreeze and refill system.
All models .... **.5**

LABOR — AIR CONDITIONING — LABOR

(Factory Time) Chilton Time

Note: If more than one item requires replacement where evacuation and discharging the system is already included in the operation, deduct 1.0 hour for each additional item from the time listed.

SERVICE AND TESTING

(G) Drain, Evacuate and Recharge System
All models (.7) **1.0**

(G) Flush Refrigerant System, Complete
To be used in conjunction with component replacement which could contaminate system. Includes evacuate and recharge.
All models **1.3**

(G) Performance Test
All models .... **.6**

(G) Refrigerant, Add (Partial Charge)
All models .... **.6**

COMPONENTS

(G) Accumulator Assy., Renew
Includes: Evacuate and charge system.
1993-95 (1.0) **1.5**

(G) Belt, Compressor Drive, Renew
All models (.3) .... **.5**

(G) Blower Motor, Renew
All models (.4) .... **.8**

(G) Cable, Temperature Control, Renew
1993 (.4) .... **.7**

(G) Clutch Assy., Compressor, Renew
1993-95 (.5) .... **.8**
Renew clutch bearing add (.1) .... **.1**
Renew clutch field add (.1) .... **.1**

(G) Compressor Assy., Renew
Includes: Transfer parts as required. Evacuate and charge system.
1993
Four (1.4) **2.4**
V8 (1.4) **2.5**
Recondition compressor add (1.9) .. **3.0**
1994-95
V6 (1.1) **2.0**
V8 (1.4) **2.2**

(G) Condenser Assy., Renew
Includes: Evacuate and charge system.
All models (1.4) **2.0**

(G) Control Assy., Temperature, Renew
1993 (.5) .... **.8**
1994-95 (.6) **1.0**

(G) Core, Evaporator, Renew
Includes: Evacuate and charge system.
1993 (4.1) **6.0**
1994-95 (3.2) **5.0**

(G) Hoses, AC, Renew
Includes: Evacuate and charge system.
1993
condenser to evaporator (1.1) **1.7**
suction line (1.0) **1.9**
compressor to condenser. (.7) ... **1.6**
liquid line (.9) **1.8**
1994-95
condenser to evaporator
V6 (.9) **1.5**
V8 (1.1) **1.7**
suction line
V6 (1.0) **1.6**
V8 (1.1) **1.7**
discharge line (1.1) **1.7**

(G) Manifold Assy., Suction or Discharge, Renew
1993 (.8) **1.5**
1994-95
suction (1.1) **1.8**
discharge (.8) **1.5**

(G) Motor, Door Vacuum, Renew
Recirculating
1993 (.3) .... **.8**
Heat Defrost Door
1993 (1.3) **2.1**
Defroster Door, Floor
1993 (2.0) **3.0**
1994-95
recirculation door (.3) .... **.6**

LABOR AIR CONDITIONING LABOR

(Factory Time) Chilton Time

A/C heat door (2.0) 3.0
auxiliary heat door (1.3) 2.0
Add time to recharge AC system if required.

(G) Orifice Valve (Tube), Renew
Includes: Evacuate and charge system.
1993-95 (1.1) 1.7

(G) Resistor, Blower Motor, Renew
All models (.3) 4

(G) Seal, Compressor Shaft, Renew
Includes: R&R compressor. Evacuate and charge system.
1993
Four (1.6) 2.6
V8 (1.9) 2.8
1994-95
V6 (1.8) 2.7
V8 (1.9) 2.8

(G) Switch, Blower Motor, Renew
All models (.3) 5

(G) Switch, Clutch Cycling Pressure, Renew
1993-95 (.5) 7

(G) Valve, Pressure Relief, Renew
Includes: Evacuate and charge system.
All models (.9) 1.6

FORD MOTOR COMPANY-RWD
FORD THUNDERBIRD • MERCURY COUGAR

LABOR COOLING SYSTEM LABOR

(Factory Time) Chilton Time

TESTING

(M) Pressure Test Cooling System
All models 3

SERVICE

(G) Belt, Drive, Supercharger, Renew
1993-95 (.6) 9

(G) Belt, Serpentine Drive, Renew
1993-95
V6
wo/S/C (.3) 5
w/S/C (.5) 8
all 1.5
V8 (.3) 5

(G) Blades, Fan or Clutch Assy., Renew
All models (.4) 5
Renew clutch fan, add 1

(G) Clutch, Viscous (Fluid) Fan Assy., Renew
All models (.4) 6

(G) Control Assy., Heater and AC, Renew
1993-95 (.5) 1.0

(G) Core, Heater, R&R or Renew
1993-95 (4.0) 7.5
Add time to recharge AC system.
Boil & Repair, add 1.2
Repair Core, add 9
Recore, add 1.2

(G) Expansion (Freeze) Plugs, Water Jacket, Renew
Add appropriate time to access plug.
All models, each 5

(G) Gauge, Temperature (Dash Unit), Renew
1993-95 (1.2) 1.8

(G) Hoses, Heater, Renew
1993-95 each (.5) 6

(G) Hoses, Radiator, Renew
Includes: Drain and refill cooling system as required.
All models
upper (.3) 4
lower (.4) 6
both (.5) 7

(G) Motor, Heater Blower, Renew
1993-95 (1.0) 1.6

(G) Motor, Radiator Fan and/or Fan, Renew
1993-95 (.4) 6

(G) Pump and/or Gasket, Water, Renew
Includes: Drain and refill cooling system.
1993-95 V6
3.8L EFI (1.1) 2.0
3.8L S/C (1.9) 3.0
1993-95 V8 (.9) 1.7

(G) Radiator Assy., R&R or Renew
1993 (.6) 1.0
w/AT add 1
1994-95
V6 (.7) 1.1
V8 (1.2) 1.6
Boil & Repair, add 1.5
Rod Clean, add 1.9
Repair Core, add 1.3
Renew Tank, add 1.6
Renew Trans. Oil Cooler, add 1.9
Recore Radiator, add 1.7

(G) Resistor, Heater Blower Motor, Renew
All models (.3) 5

(G) Sending Unit, Engine Coolant Temp., Renew
All models (.3) 4

(G) Switch, Heater Blower Motor, Renew
All models (.4) 7

(G) Switch, Radiator Fan Motor (Coolant Temp.), Renew
1993-95 (.3) 4

(G) Tensioner, Drive Belt, Renew
V6
1993-95
3.8L EFI (.3) 5
3.8L S/C
one (.4) 6
both (.6) 9
V8
1993 (.3) 5
1994-95 (.5) 8

(G) Thermostat, Coolant, Renew
1993-95 (.5) 7

(G) Winterize Cooling System
Includes: Run engine to check for leaks, tighten all hose connections. Test radiator and pressure cap, drain radiator and engine block. Add antifreeze and refill system.
All models 5

LABOR — AIR CONDITIONING — LABOR

(Factory Time) Chilton Time

Note: If more than one item requires replacement where evacuation and discharging the system is already included in the operation, deduct 1.0 hour for each additional item from the time listed.

SERVICE AND TESTING

(G) Drain, Evacuate and Recharge System
All models (.7) 1.0

(G) Flush Refrigerant System, Complete
To be used in conjunction with component replacement which could contaminate system. Includes evacuate and recharge.
All models 1.3

(G) Performance Test
All models 6

(G) Recover and/or Recycle AC Refrigerant
Add to evacuate and charge the AC system, as required.
All models 2

(G) Refrigerant, Add (Partial Charge)
All models 6

COMPONENTS

(G) Accumulator Assy., Renew
Includes: Evacuate and charge system.
All models (1.0) 1.5

(G) Belt, Compressor Drive, Renew
1993-95
V6
wo/S/C (.3) 5
w/S/C (.5) 8
V8 (.3) 5

(G) Blower Motor, Renew
1993-95
wo/ATC (1.0) 1.6
w/ATC (.9) 1.2

(G) Blower Motor, Speed Control, Renew
1993-95 (1.5) 2.0

(G) Clutch and/or Pulley, Compressor, Renew
Does not include R&R compressor.
1993 (.6) 9
1994-95
V6 (.6) 9
V8 (.9) 1.3

(G) Compressor Assy., Renew
Includes: Transfer parts as required. Evacuate and charge system.
1993
V6 (1.7) 2.6
V8 (1.8) 2.7
1994-95
V6 (1.7) 2.6
V8 (1.4) 2.3

(G) Condenser Assy., Renew
Includes: Evacuate and charge system.
1993 (1.4) 2.0
1994-95 (1.6) 2.5

(G) Control, ATC, Renew
1993-95 (.5) 8

(G) Control Assy., Temperature, Renew
1993-95 (.5) 1.0

(G) Core, Evaporator, Renew
Includes: Evacuate and charge system.
1993 (4.9) 8.5
1994-95 (3.0) 7.0

(G) Hoses, AC, Renew
Includes: Evacuate and charge system.
1993
discharge line (1.1) 1.9
suction line (1.4) 2.1
liquid line (1.1) 1.9
1994-95
discharge line (1.1) 1.9
suction
V6 (1.4) 2.1
V8 (.9) 1.6

(G) Manifold Assy., Suction or Discharge, Renew
1993-95 (.8) 1.5

(G) Motor, AC Door Actuator, Renew
1993
temperature blend (.8) 1.5
floor panel (3.9) 5.0
panel/defrost (2.5) 3.2
1994-95
Recirculation door (.3) 6
AC/Heat door (2.3) 4.0
Auxiliary AC/Heat door (3.5) 6.0
Add time to recharge AC system if required.

(G) Orifice Valve (Tube), Renew
Includes: Evacuate and charge system.
1993-95 (1.1) 1.5

(G) Resistor, Blower Motor, Renew
All models (.3) 5

(G) Seal, Compressor Shaft, Renew
Includes: R&R compressor. Evacuate and charge system.
1993
V6 (1.9) 2.9
V8 (2.4) 3.3
1994-95
V6 (1.9) 2.9
V8 (2.3) 3.0

(G) Sensor, Ambient Temperature, Renew
1993-95 (.3) 5

(G) Sensor, ATC, Renew
1993-95 (.8) 1.1

(G) Sensor, Sun/Photo, Renew
1993-95 (.3) 5

(G) Servo, AC Automatic Temperature, Renew
1993-95 (.4) 6

(G) Switch, Blower Motor, Renew
All models
wo/ATC (.4) 7
w/ATC (.4) 7

(G) Switch, Clutch Cycling Pressure, Renew
1993-95
wo/ATC (.5) 7
w/ATC (.5) 7

(G) Switch, Damper Door, Renew
1993-95 (.5) 8

FORD MOTOR COMPANY-RWD
FORD CROWN VICTORIA • MERCURY GRAND MARQUIS

LABOR — COOLING SYSTEM — LABOR

(Factory Time) Chilton Time

TESTING

(M) Pressure Test Cooling System
All models 3

SERVICE

(G) Belt, Serpentine Drive, Renew
1993-95 (.3) 5

(G) Blade, Fan, Renew
1993-95 (.6) 8

(G) Cable, Temperature Control, Renew
1993-95
wo/ATC (.4) 7
w/ATC (.8) 1.4

(G) Control Assy., Heater, Renew
1993-95 (.7) 1.1

(G) Core, Heater, R&R or Renew
1993-95 (4.0) 6.0
Add time to recharge AC system if required.
Boil & Repair, add 1.2

LABOR COOLING SYSTEM LABOR

(Factory Time) Chilton Time

Repair Core, add 9
Recore, add 1.2

(G) Expansion (Freeze) Plugs, Water Jacket, Renew
Add appropriate time to access plug.
All models, each (.3) 5

(G) Gauge, Temperature (Dash Unit), Renew
1993-95 (1.0) 1.5

(G) Gauge, Temperature (Engine Unit), Renew
All models (.3) 4

(G) Hoses, Heater, Renew
1993-95
one (.5) 7
both (.6) 9

(G) Hoses, Radiator, Renew
Includes: Drain and refill cooling system as required.
1993-95
one (.5) 6
both (.6) 9

(G) Motor, Heater Blower, Renew
All models (.4) 8

(G) Pump and/or Gasket, Water, Renew
Includes: Drain and refill cooling system.
1993-95 (1.0) 2.0

(G) Radiator Assy., R&R or Renew
1993-95 (1.0) 1.5
Boil & Repair, add 1.5
Rod Clean, add 1.9
Repair Core, add 1.3
Renew Tank, add 1.6
Renew Trans. Oil Cooler, add 1.9
Recore Radiator, add 1.7

(G) Resistor, Heater Blower Motor, Renew
1993-95 (.4) 5

(G) Switch, Heater Blower Motor, Renew
1993-95 (.8) 1.2

(G) Tensioner, Drive Belt, Renew
1993-95 (.5) 7

(G) Thermostat, Coolant, Renew
1993-95 (.5) 7

(G) Winterize Cooling System
Includes: Run engine to check for leaks, tighten all hose connections. Test radiator and pressure cap, drain radiator and engine block. Add antifreeze and refill system.
All models 5

LABOR AIR CONDITIONING LABOR

(Factory Time) Chilton Time

Note: If more than one item requires replacement where evacuation and discharging the system is already included in the operation, deduct 1.0 hour for each additional item from the time listed.

SERVICE AND TESTING

(G) ATC System Diagnosis
1993-95 (.5) 8

(G) Drain, Evacuate and Recharge System
All models (.7) 1.0

(G) Flush Refrigerant System, Complete
To be used in conjunction with component replacement which could contaminate system. Includes evacuate and recharge.
All models 1.3

(G) Performance Test
All models 6

(G) Recover and/or Recycle AC Refrigerant
Add to evacuate and charge the AC system, as required.
All models 2

(G) Refrigerant, Add (Partial Charge)
All models 6

COMPONENTS

(G) Accumulator Assy., Renew
Includes: Evacuate and charge system.
1993-95 (1.0) 1.5

(G) Belt, Compressor Drive, Renew
All models
Serpentine (.3) 5

(G) Blower Motor, Renew
All models (.4) 8

(G) Blower Motor, Speed Control, Renew
1993-95 (.3) 5

(G) Cable, Temperature Control, Renew
All models
wo/ATC (.4) 7
w/ATC (.8) 1.4

(G) Clutch Assy., Compressor, Renew
1993-95 (.7) 1.1
Renew clutch bearing, add 1
Renew clutch field, add 1

(G) Compressor Assy., R&R and Recondition
Includes: Evacuate and charge system.
1993-95 (2.6) 3.8

(G) Compressor Assy., Renew
Includes: Transfer parts as required. Evacuate and charge system.
1993-95 (1.4) 2.5

(G) Condenser Assy., Renew
Includes: Evacuate and charge system.
1993-95 (1.7) 2.5

(G) Control, ATC, Renew
1993-95 (.2) 4

(G) Control Assy., Temperature, Renew
1993-95 (.7) 1.1

(G) Controller, Blower Motor Speed, Renew
1993-95 (1.0) 1.5

(G) Core, Evaporator, Renew
Includes: Evacuate and charge system.
1993-95 (2.5) 6.0

(G) Hoses, AC, Renew
Includes: Evacuate and charge system.
All models
one (.9) 1.7
each adtnl. (.3) 5

(G) Manifold Assy., Suction or Discharge, Renew
1993-95 (.8) 1.5

(G) Motor, Door Vacuum, Renew
1993-95 one (2.9) 5.5

(G) Orifice Valve (Tube), Renew
Includes: Evacuate and charge system.
1993-95 (.8) 1.4

(G) Resistor, Blower Motor, Renew
All models (.4) 5

(G) Seal, Compressor Shaft, Renew
Includes: R&R compressor. Evacuate and charge system.
1993-95 (1.1) 1.7

(G) Sensor, Ambient Temperature, Renew
1993-95 (.1) 3

(G) Sensor, ATC, Renew
1993-95 (.1) 3

(G) Sensor, Sun/Photo, Renew
1993-95 (.3) 5

(G) Servo, AC Automatic Temperature, Renew
1993-95 (3.5) 5.0

(G) Switch, Blower Motor, Renew
1993-95
wo/ATC (.7) 1.1
w/ATC (.3) 5

(G) Switch, Clutch Cycling Pressure, Renew
1993-95
wo/ATC (.3) 5
w/ATC (.1) 3

(G) Switch, Damper Door, Renew
1993-95 (.3) 5

(G) Valve, Pressure Relief, Renew
Includes: Evacuate and charge system.
1993-95 (.8) 1.5

FORD MOTOR COMPANY-RWD
LINCOLN MARK • TOWN CAR

LABOR — COOLING SYSTEM — LABOR

(Factory Time) Chilton Time

TESTING

(M) Pressure Test Cooling System
All models .3

SERVICE

(G) Belt, Serpentine Drive, Renew
1993-95 (.3) .5

(G) Blade, Fan, Renew
1993-95 Mark (.6) .8
1993-95 Town Car (.5) .7

(G) Clutch, Viscous (Fluid) Fan Assy., Renew
1993-95 Town Car (.6) .8
1993 Mark (.4) .6

(G) Control Assy., Heater and AC, Renew
Town Car
1993-95 (.9) 1.4
Mark
1993-95 (.4) .7

(G) Core, Heater, R&R or Renew
Town Car
1993-95 (4.0) 6.0
Mark
1993-95 (4.9) 8.5
Boil & Repair add 1.2
Repair Core add .9
Recore add 1.2
Drain, evacuate and charge AC system add 1.0

(G) Expansion (Freeze) Plugs, Water Jacket, Renew
Add appropriate time to access plug.
All models, each .5

(G) Gauge, Temperature (Dash Unit), Renew
1993-95 (1.0) 1.7

(G) Hoses, Heater, Renew
All models, each (.4) .6

(G) Hoses, Radiator, Renew
Includes: Drain and refill cooling system as required.
All models
upper (.4) .4
lower (.5) .6
both (.6) .9

(G) Motor, Heater Blower, Renew
Town Car
1993-95 (.4) .8
Mark
1993-95 (.6) .9

(G) Motor, Radiator Fan and/or Fan, Renew
1993-95 (.4) .6

(G) Pump and/or Gasket, Water, Renew
Includes: Drain and refill cooling system.
Town Car
1993-95 (.9) 1.7
Mark
1993-95 (1.0) 1.9

(G) Radiator Assy., R&R or Renew
Town Car
1993-94 (.9) 1.5
Mark
1993-95 (1.0) 1.6
Renew side tanks add
one (.5) .7
both (.9) 1.3
Renew Oil Cooler add (.1) .1
Boil & Repair add 1.5
Rod Clean add 1.9
Repair Core add 1.3
Renew Tank add 1.6
Renew Trans. Oil Cooler add 1.9
Recore Radiator add 1.7

(G) Resistor, Heater Blower Motor, Renew
All models (.4) .5

(G) Sending Unit, Engine Coolant Temp., Renew
All models (.3) .4

(G) Switch, Heater Blower Motor, Renew
Town Car
1993-95 (1.0) 1.5

(G) Switch, Radiator Fan Motor (Coolant Temp.), Renew
1993-95 (.3) .4

(G) Tensioner, Drive Belt, Renew
1993-95
4.6L (.5) .7

(G) Thermostat, Coolant, Renew
Mark
1993-95 (.6) .8
Town Car
1993-95 (.5) .7

(G) Winterize Cooling System
Includes: Run engine to check for leaks, tighten all hose connections. Test radiator and pressure cap, drain radiator and engine block. Add antifreeze and refill system.
All models .5

LABOR — AIR CONDITIONING — LABOR

(Factory Time) Chilton Time

Note: If more than one item requires replacement where evacuation and discharging the system is already included in the operation, deduct 1.0 hour for each additional item from the time listed.

SERVICE AND TESTING

(G) ATC System Diagnosis
1993-95 (.5) .8

(G) Drain, Evacuate and Recharge System
All models (.7) 1.0

(G) Flush Refrigerant System, Complete
To be used in conjunction with component replacement which could contaminate system. Includes evacuate and recharge.
All models 1.3

(G) Performance Test
All models .6

(G) Recover and/or Recycle AC Refrigerant
Add to evacuate and charge the AC system, as required.
All models .2

(G) Refrigerant, Add (Partial Charge)
All models .6

COMPONENTS

(G) Accumulator Assy., Renew
Includes: Evacuate and charge system.
1993-95 (1.0) 1.5

(G) Belt, Compressor Drive, Renew
All models (.3) .5

(G) Blower Motor, Renew
Town Car
1993-95 (.4) .8
Mark
1993-95
wo/ATC (.6) .9
w/ATC (.5) .8

(G) Blower Motor, Speed Control, Renew
1993-95
Town Car (1.0) 1.5
Mark (1.5) 2.0

(G) Clutch and/or Pulley, Compressor, Renew
Does not include R&R compressor.
Mark
1993-95 (.9) 1.2
Town Car
1993-95 (.7) 1.1

(Factory Time) Chilton Time

Renew clutch bearing add (.1) 1
Renew clutch field coil add (.1) 1

(G) Compressor Assy., R&R and Recondition
Includes: Evacuate and charge system.
1993-95 (2.7) 4.0

(G) Compressor Assy., Renew
Includes: Transfer parts as required. Evacuate and charge system.
1993-95 (1.7) 3.0

(G) Condenser Assy., Renew
Includes: Evacuate and charge system.
Mark
1993-95 (1.6) 2.5
Town Car
1993-94 (1.7) 2.6
1995 (1.5) 2.5

(G) Control Assy., AC, Renew
Mark
1993-95 (.4) 7
Town Car
1993-95 (.9) 1.4

(G) Control, ATC, Renew
1993-95
Town Car (.9) 1.2
Mark (.4) 6

(G) Controller, Blower Motor Speed, Renew
1993-95
Town Car (1.0) 1.5
Mark (1.5) 2.0

(G) Core, Evaporator, Renew
Includes: Evacuate and charge system.
Mark
1993-95 (5.0) 8.5
Town Car
1993-95 (2.4) 5.0

(G) Doors, Actuator, Renew
1993 Mark
outside/recirc. (.6) 1.1
panel/defroster (2.2) 4.0
temperature blend (.7) 1.3
floor/panel (2.7) 5.0
1993-95 Mark
panel/defrost (2.3) 4.0
temperature blend (.7) 1.1
floor/panel (2.8) 4.5
1993-95 Town Car
panel/defroster (2.9) 5.5
temperature blend (2.9) 5.5
floor/panel (2.9) 5.5
Add time to recharge AC system if required.

(Factory Time) Chilton Time

(G) Hoses, AC, Renew
Includes: Evacuate and charge system.
1993-95
suction line (1.1) 2.0
liquid line (.9) 1.8

(G) Manifold Assy., Suction or Discharge, Renew
1993-95 (.8) 1.5

(G) Orifice Valve (Tube), Renew
Includes: Evacuate and charge system.
1993-95 (.8) 1.6

(G) Resistor, Blower Motor, Renew
1993-95 (.4) 6

(G) Seal, Compressor Shaft, Renew
Includes: R&R compressor. Evacuate and charge system.
1993-94 (2.0) 3.2
1995
Town Car (1.1) 1.7
Mark (2.1) 3.2

(G) Sensor, Ambient Temperature, Renew
1993-95 (.3) 5

(G) Sensor, ATC, Renew
Instrument Panel
1993-95 Town Car (.1) 3
1993-95 Mark (.3) 6

(G) Sensor, Sun/Photo, Renew
1993-95 (.3) 5

(G) Servo, AC Automatic Temperature, Renew
1993-95 (.4) 7

(G) Switch, Blower Motor, Renew
Town Car
1993-95 (1.0) 1.5
1993-95 Mark (.5) 8

(G) Switch, Clutch Cycling Pressure, Renew
1993-95
Town Car (.3) 5

(G) Switch, Damper Door, Renew
1993-95
Town Car (1.0) 1.4
Mark (.5) 8

(Factory Time) Chilton Time

AUTOMATIC TEMPERATURE CONTROL (ATC)

(G) ATC System Diagnosis
1993-94 (.5) 8

(G) Blower Motor, Speed Control, Renew
Does not include system test.
1993-94
Town Car (1.0) 1.5
Mark (1.5) 2.0

(G) Control, ATC, Renew
Does not include system test.
1993-94
Town Car (.9) 1.2
Mark (.4) 6

(G) Motor, AC Blower, Renew
1993-94
Town Car (.4) 6
Mark (.5) 8

(G) Pin Point Test
1993-94 3

(G) Sensor, Ambient, Renew
Does not include system test.
1993-94 (.3) 5

(G) Sensor, ATC, Renew
Does not include system test.
1993-94
Town Car (.9) 1.2
Mark (.3) 4

(G) Sensor, Sunload, Renew
Does not include system test.
1993-94 (.3) 5

(G) Servo, ATC, Renew
Does not include system test.
1993-94 (.4) 6

(G) Switch, Clutch Cycling, Renew
Does not include system test.
1993-94 (.5) 7

(G) Switch, AC Blower Motor, Renew
Does not include system test.
1993-94
Town Car (1.0) 1.4
Mark (.5) 8

(G) Switch, Damper Door, Renew
Does not include system test.
1993-94
Town Car (1.0) 1.4
Mark (.5) 8

FORD MOTOR COMPANY-TRUCKS

AEROSTAR • BRONCO • ECONOLINE • F-SERIES • RANGER • SUPERDUTY

COOLING SYSTEM

LABOR

(Factory Time) Chilton Time

TESTING

(M) Pressure Test Cooling System

All models .3

SERVICE

(G) Belt, Drive, Adjust

All models
- one (.3) .4
- each adtnl. (.2) .3

(G) Belt, Drive, Renew

All models (.3) .4

(G) Belt, Serpentine Drive, Renew

1993-95 2.3L (.4) .5
1993-95 3.0L, 4.0L (.5) .6
1993-95 Six, V8
- Econoline (.4) .5
- F Series, Bronco (.3) .4
- diesel (.4) .5

(G) Blades, Fan or Clutch Assy., Renew

1993-95 V8 diesel (.7) 1.0
1993-95 Four, V6, V8
- wo/viscous drive (.4) .6
- w/viscous drive (.5) .7

(G) Control Assy., Heater, Renew

All models (.6) 1.1

(G) Core, Heater, R&R or Renew

Without AC
1993-95 Aerostar
- main (1.0) 2.0
- auxiliary (1.1) 2.2

With AC
1993-95 Ranger 1.2
1993-95 Bronco, F Series 2.5
1993-95 Econoline 2.7
1993-95 Aerostar 1.5

(G) Expansion (Freeze) Plugs, Water Jacket, Renew

Add appropriate time to access plug.
All models, each .5
Add time to gain access to plug.

(G) Gauge, Temperature (Dash Unit), Renew

1993-95
- F Series, Bronco (.7) 1.1
- Econoline (.8) 1.2
- Ranger, Aerostar (.6) 1.0

(G) Gauge, Temperature (Engine Unit), Renew

1993-95
- Econoline, Aerostar (.5) .7
- Ranger, F Series, Bronco (.3) .5

(G) Hoses, Radiator, Renew

Includes: Drain and refill cooling system as required.

1993-95 Ranger
- upper (.3) .4
- lower (.4) .5
- both (.5) .6

1993-95 F Series, Bronco, Econoline
- upper or lower (.4) .5
- both (.5) .7

1993-95 Aerostar
- upper or lower (.4) .5
- both (.5) .7

(G) Motor, Heater Blower, Renew

1993-95
- Aerostar
  - main (.5) .9
  - auxiliary (.7) 1.0
- Ranger, Bronco (.5) .7
- Econoline
  - main (.5) .9
  - auxiliary (.7) 1.0
- F Series (.3) .6

(G) Pump and/or Gasket, Water, Renew

Includes: Drain and refill cooling system.

1993-95 Ranger
- Four (1.1) 1.7
- w/AC add (.5) .5
- w/PS add (.2) .2
- V6 (1.4) 2.0
- w/AC add (.2) .2

1993-95 Aerostar
- V6 (1.3) 2.0
- w/AC add (.3) .3

1993-95 Bronco
- Six (.9) 1.5
- w/AC add (.4) .4
- V8 (1.3) 1.9

1993-95 Econoline
- Six (1.1) 2.0
- w/FI, add .5
- V8
  - 5.0L, 5.8L (1.5) 2.7
  - 7.5L (2.1) 3.4
  - diesel (1.7) 2.7

1993-95 F Series
- Six (.9) 1.6
- V8
  - 5.0L, 5.8L (1.3) 2.0
  - 7.5L (1.7) 2.7
  - diesel (1.6) 2.9

(G) Radiator Assy., R&R or Renew

1993-95 Ranger, Aerostar
- gas (.6) 1.0

1993-95 Bronco
- V8 (.7) 1.0

1993-95 Econoline (1.2) 1.7
1993-95 F Series
- Six (1.0) 1.5
- V8 (.7) 1.0
- diesel (1.5) 2.0

(G) Resistor, Heater Blower Motor, Renew

1993-95
- Ranger, Bronco (.3) .6
- Econoline
  - main (.4) .6
  - auxiliary (.6) .8
- F Series (.3) .6

1993-95 Aerostar
- main (.4) .6
- auxiliary (.6) .8

(G) Switch, Heater Blower Motor, Renew

1993-95 Aerostar
- front (.6) .9
- rear (.4) .6

1993-95
- Ranger, Econoline (.5) .9
- Bronco, F Series (.4) .7

(G) Tensioner, Drive Belt, Renew

1993-95 (.3) .5

(G) Thermostat, Coolant, Renew

All models
- gas
  - Four (.5) .6
  - Six (.4) .6
  - V6 (.7) .9
  - V8 (.9) 1.0
- diesel
  - V8 (1.1) 1.4
- Econoline, add .5

(G) Valve, Heater Control, Renew

All models (.4) .6

(G) Winterize Cooling System

Includes: Run engine to check for leaks, tighten all hose connections. Test radiator and pressure cap, drain radiator and engine block. Add antifreeze and refill system.

All models .5

LABOR — AIR CONDITIONING — LABOR

(Factory Time) Chilton Time

Note: If more than one item requires replacement where evacuation and discharging the system is already included in the operation, deduct 1.0 hour for each additional item from the time listed.

SERVICE AND TESTING

(G) Drain, Evacuate and Recharge System

All models (.7) **1.0**

(G) Flush Refrigerant System, Complete

To be used in conjunction with component replacement which could contaminate system. Includes evacuate and recharge.

All models **1.3**

(G) Performance Test

All models .... **.6**

(G) Recover and/or Recycle AC Refrigerant

Add to evacuate and charge the AC system, as required.

All models .... **.2**

(G) Refrigerant, Add (Partial Charge)

All models .... **.6**

COMPONENTS

(G) Accumulator Assy., Renew

Includes: Evacuate and charge system.

1993-95 Ranger (.9) **1.6**
1993-95 Aerostar (1.4) **1.8**
1993-95 Bronco, F Series (.9) **1.6**
Note: Also called receiver/drier.

(G) Belt, Compressor Drive, Renew

1993-95
V belt (.3) .... **.4**
serpentine
2.3L (.4) .... **.5**
3.0L, 4.0L (.5) .... **.6**
Six, V8
Econoline (.4) .... **.5**
F Series, Bronco (.3) .... **.4**
diesel (.4) .... **.5**

(G) Blower Motor, Renew

Ranger
1993-95 (.5) .... **.9**
Bronco
1993-95 (.3) .... **.5**
Econoline
1993-95
main (.4) **1.0**
auxiliary (.7) **1.1**
Aerostar
1993-95
main (.4) .... **.7**
auxiliary (.5) .... **.8**
F Series
1993-95 (.3) .... **.5**

(G) Compressor Assy., Renew

Includes: Transfer parts as required. Evacuate and charge system.

Four
1993-95
gas
2.0L **3.0**
2.3L
Ranger (2.1) **3.1**
Aerostar (2.6) **3.7**
diesel (1.5) **2.3**
Six
1993-95
F Series (1.8) **2.5**
Econoline (2.1) **3.0**
V6
1993-95
Ranger (1.6) **2.3**
Aerostar
3.0L (2.0) **2.7**
4.0L (1.6) **2.3**
V8
1993-95
gas (1.6) **2.3**
diesel (1.8) **2.5**
Recondition compressor, add (1.2) **1.5**

(G) Condenser Assy., Renew

Includes: Evacuate and charge system.

1993-95 Ranger (1.3) **2.0**
1993-95 Aerostar
4x2 (1.4) **2.7**
4x4 (1.7) **3.0**
1993-95 Bronco, F Series (1.4) **2.7**
1993-95 Econoline (1.4) **2.7**

(G) Core, Evaporator, Renew

Includes: Evacuate and charge system.

Ranger
1993-95 (1.5) **2.9**
Aerostar
1993-95
main (1.6) **3.0**
auxiliary (1.4) **2.8**
Bronco
1993-95 (1.4) **2.6**
Econoline
1993-95
main (1.8) **3.4**
auxiliary (1.9) **3.5**
F Series
1993-95 (1.4) **2.6**

(G) Dehydrator and/or Receiver Tank, Renew

Includes: Evacuate and charge system.

1993-95 Econoline (1.3) **1.9**

(G) Hoses, AC, Renew

Includes: Evacuate and charge system.

All models
one (.9) **1.7**
each adtnl. (.3) .... **.5**

(G) Manifold Assy., Suction or Discharge, Renew

1993-95 (.8) **1.5**

(G) Orifice Valve (Tube), Renew

Includes: Evacuate and charge system.

1993-95 Ranger (1.0) **1.7**
1993-95 Aerostar
main (1.0) **1.5**
auxiliary (1.2) **1.8**
1993-95 Bronco, F Series (.9) **1.5**
1993-95 Econoline (.9) **1.5**

(G) Seal, Compressor Shaft, Renew

Includes: R&R compressor. Evacuate and charge system.

Four
1993-95
gas
2.3L
Ranger (2.6) **3.4**
Six
1993-95 (1.9) **2.6**
V6
1993-95
3.0L (2.3) **3.0**
4.0L (1.7) **2.5**
V8
1993-95 gas (1.9) **2.6**
1993-95 diesel (2.1) **2.9**

(G) Switch, Blower Motor, Renew

1993-95 Ranger (.5) .... **.7**
1993-95 Aerostar
main (.6) .... **.9**
auxiliary (.4) .... **.6**
1993-95 Bronco, Econoline (.5) .... **.7**
1993-95 F Series (.4) .... **.7**

(G) Switch, Clutch Cycling Pressure, Renew

All models (.4) .... **.5**

(G) Valve Assy., Evaporator, Renew

Includes: Evacuate and charge system.

1993-95 Aerostar
w/auxiliary AC (1.3) **2.0**

(G) Valve, Expansion, Renew

Includes: Evacuate and charge system.

1993-95 w/auxiliary AC (1.9) **3.0**

FORD MOTOR COMPANY-TRUCKS
FORD WINDSTAR

LABOR — COOLING SYSTEM — LABOR

(Factory Time) Chilton Time

TESTING

(M) Pressure Test Cooling System
All models .3

SERVICE

(G) Belt, Serpentine Drive, Renew
All models (.3) .4

(G) Control Assy., Heater, Renew
All models (.4) .6

(G) Core, Heater, R&R or Renew
All models (1.8) 3.5
Boil & Repair, add 1.2
Repair Core, add .9
Recore, add 1.2

(G) Gauge, Temperature (Dash Unit), Renew
All models (.6) 1.0

(G) Hoses, Heater, Renew
All models
one (.6) 1.0
both (.7) 1.2

(G) Hoses, Radiator, Renew
Includes: Drain and refill cooling system as required.
All models
upper (.5) .6
lower (.6) .7
both (.7) 1.0

(G) Motor, Electric Cooling Fan, Renew
All models (.4) .6

(G) Pump and/or Gasket, Water, Renew
Includes: Drain and refill cooling system.
All models (2.2) 3.5

(G) Radiator Assy., R&R or Renew
All models (1.2) 1.7
Renew side tanks, add
one .5
both .9

(G) Resistor, Heater Blower Motor, Renew
All models
main (.3) .4
auxiliary (.9) 1.4

(G) Sending Unit, Engine Coolant Temp., Renew
All models (.3) .5

(G) Switch, Heater Blower Motor, Renew
All models
main (.3) .5
auxiliary (.4) .6

(G) Tensioner, Drive Belt, Renew
All models (.4) .6

(G) Thermostat, Coolant, Renew
All models (.4) .6

(G) Winterize Cooling System
Includes: Run engine to check for leaks, tighten all hose connections. Test radiator and pressure cap, drain radiator and engine block. Add antifreeze and refill system.
All models .5

LABOR — AIR CONDITIONING — LABOR

(Factory Time) Chilton Time

Note: If more than one item requires replacement where evacuation and discharging the system is already included in the operation, deduct 1.0 hour for each additional item from the time listed.

SERVICE AND TESTING

(G) Drain, Evacuate and Recharge System
All models 1.0
Recover refrigerant, add .2

(G) Flush Refrigerant System, Complete
To be used in conjunction with component replacement which could contaminate system. Includes evacuate and recharge.
All models 1.3
Recover refrigerant, add .2

(G) Leak Check
Includes: Check all lines and connections.
All models .5

(G) Recover and/or Recycle AC Refrigerant
Add to evacuate and charge the AC system, as required.
All models .2

(G) Refrigerant, Add (Partial Charge)
All models .6

COMPONENTS

(G) Accumulator Assy., Renew
Includes: Evacuate and charge system.
All models (1.0) 1.5
Recover refrigerant, add .2

(G) Belt, Compressor Drive, Renew
All models (.3) .4

(G) Blower Motor, Renew
All models
main (.4) .6
auxiliary (.9) 1.4

(G) Clutch and/or Pulley, Compressor, Renew
Includes: R&R compressor.
All models (2.6) 3.7
Note: Includes evacuate and charge system.
Recover refrigerant, add .2

(G) Compressor Assy., Renew
Includes: Transfer parts as required. Evacuate and charge system.
All models (1.7) 2.5
Recover refrigerant, add .2

(G) Condenser Assy., Renew
Includes: Evacuate and charge system.
All models (1.6) 3.0
Recover refrigerant, add .2

(G) Control Assy., Temperature, Renew
All models (.4) .6

(G) Core, Evaporator, Renew
Includes: Evacuate and charge system.
All models
front (5.0) 8.0
rear (2.2) 4.0
Recover refrigerant, add .3

(G) Hoses, AC, Renew
Includes: Evacuate and charge system.
All models
suction
front (1.1) 1.7
auxiliary (1.5) 2.0
discharge (1.1) 1.7
Recover refrigerant, add .2

(G) Manifold Assy., Suction or Discharge, Renew
All models (.8) 1.5
Add time to evacuate & charge AC system as needed
Recover refrigerant, add .2

(G) Seal, Compressor Shaft, Renew
Includes: R&R compressor. Evacuate and charge system.
All models (3.0) 4.0
Recover refrigerant, add .2

LABOR — AIR CONDITIONING — LABOR

(Factory Time) Chilton Time

(G) Switch, Blower Motor, Renew
All models
main (.4) 6
auxiliary (.3) 5

(G) Switch, Clutch Cycling Pressure, Renew
All models (.3) 5
Add time to evacuate & charge AC system as needed
Recover refrigerant, add 2

(G) Valve, Expansion, Renew
Includes: Evacuate and charge system.
All models (1.7) 2.6
Recover refrigerant, add 2

FORD MOTOR COMPANY-TRUCKS
FORD EXPLORER

LABOR — COOLING SYSTEM — LABOR

(Factory Time) Chilton Time

TESTING

(M) Pressure Test Cooling System
All models 3

SERVICE

(G) Belt, Drive, Adjust
All models
one (.2) 3
each adtnl. 1

(G) Belt, Drive, Renew
All models
Serpentine belt (.5) 7

(G) Blades, Fan or Clutch Assy., Renew
All models (.5) 7

(G) Control Assy., Heater, Renew
All models (.6) 1.1

(G) Core, Heater, R&R or Renew
All models (.7) 1.2
Boil & Repair, add 1.2
Repair Core, add 9
Recore, add 1.2

(G) Expansion (Freeze) Plugs, Water Jacket, Renew
Add appropriate time to access plug.
All models, each (.3) 5

(G) Gauge, Temperature (Dash Unit), Renew
All models (.6) 1.0

(G) Hoses, Heater, Renew
All models
one (.4) 7
both (.5) 9

(G) Hoses, Radiator, Renew
Includes: Drain and refill cooling system as required.
All models
upper (.3) 4
lower (.4) 5
both (.5) 6

(G) Motor, Heater Blower, Renew
All models (.5) 7

(G) Pump and/or Gasket, Water, Renew
Includes: Drain and refill cooling system.
All models (1.4) 2.0
w/AC, add 2

(G) Radiator Assy., R&R or Renew
All models (.7) 1.1
Boil & Repair, add 1.5
Rod Clean, add 1.9
Repair Core, add 1.3
Renew Trans. Oil Cooler, add 1.9
Renew Tank, add 1.6
Renew Side Tank, add 7
Recore Radiator, add 1.7

(G) Resistor, Heater Blower Motor, Renew
All models (.3) 4

(G) Sending Unit, Engine Coolant Temp., Renew
All models (.3) 5

(G) Switch, Heater Blower Motor, Renew
All models (.5) 9

(G) Thermostat, Coolant, Renew
All models
4.0L (.7) 9

(G) Winterize Cooling System
Includes: Run engine to check for leaks, tighten all hose connections. Test radiator and pressure cap, drain radiator and engine block. Add antifreeze and refill system.
All models 5

LABOR — AIR CONDITIONING — LABOR

(Factory Time) Chilton Time

Note: If more than one item requires replacement where evacuation and discharging the system is already included in the operation, deduct 1.0 hour for each additional item from the time listed.

SERVICE AND TESTING

(G) Drain, Evacuate and Recharge System
All models (.7) 1.0
Recover refrigerant, add 2

(G) Flush Refrigerant System, Complete
To be used in conjunction with component replacement which could contaminate system. Includes evacuate and recharge.
All models 1.3
Recover refrigerant, add 2

(G) Performance Test
All models 6

(G) Recover and/or Recycle AC Refrigerant
Add to evacuate and charge the AC system, as required.
All models 2

(G) Refrigerant, Add (Partial Charge)
All models 6

COMPONENTS

(G) Accumulator Assy., Renew
Includes: Evacuate and charge system.
All models (.9) 1.5
Recover refrigerant, add 2

(G) Belt, Compressor Drive, Renew
All models
Serpentine belt (.5) 6

LABOR AIR CONDITIONING LABOR

(Factory Time) Chilton Time

(G) Blower Motor, Renew

All models (.5) 9

(G) Clutch and/or Pulley, Compressor, Renew

Does not include R&R compressor.

1993-95 Explorer (.8) 1.2
Renew pulley brg., add 1
Renew clutch coil kit, add 1
Recover refrigerant, add 2
Add time to evacuate & charge AC system as needed

(G) Compressor Assy., Renew

1993-95 Explorer (1.6) 2.4
Add time to evacuate & charge AC system as needed
Recover refrigerant, add 2

(G) Condenser Assy., Renew

Includes: Evacuate and charge system.

1993-95 Explorer (1.1) 1.7
Recover refrigerant, add 2

(G) Control Assy., Temperature, Renew

All models (.6) 9

(G) Core, Evaporator, Renew

Includes: Evacuate and charge system.

All models (1.5) 2.9
Recover refrigerant, add 2

(G) Hoses, AC, Renew

Includes: Evacuate and charge system.

All models
one (.9) 1.7
each adtnl. (.3) 5
Recover refrigerant, add 2

(G) Manifold Assy., Suction or Discharge, Renew

All models, each (.8) 1.5
Add time to evacuate & charge AC system as needed
Recover refrigerant, add 2

(G) Orifice Valve (Tube), Renew

Includes: Evacuate and charge system.

All models (1.0) 1.7
Recover refrigerant, add 2

(G) Resistor, Blower Motor, Renew

All models (.3) 4

(G) Seal, Compressor Shaft, Renew

Includes: R&R compressor. Evacuate and charge system.

1993-95 Explorer (1.7) 2.5
Recover refrigerant, add 2

(G) Switch, Blower Motor, Renew

All models (.5) 7

(G) Switch, Clutch Cycling Pressure, Renew

All models (.4) 6
Add time to evacuate & charge AC system as needed
Recover refrigerant, add 2

(G) Valve, Low Pressure, Renew

All models (.7) 1.2
Add time to evacuate & charge AC system as needed
Recover refrigerant, add 2

(G) Valve, Pressure Relief, Renew

Includes: Evacuate and charge system.

All models (.8) 1.3
Recover refrigerant, add 2

FORD MOTOR COMPANY-TRUCKS

MERCURY VILLAGER

LABOR COOLING SYSTEM LABOR

(Factory Time) Chilton Time

SERVICE

(G) Belt, Drive, Adjust

All models
one or two (.2) 3
all (.3) 4

(G) Belt, Drive, Renew

All models
one or two (.2) 4
all (.3) 5

(G) Blade, Fan, Renew

All models (.5) 7

(G) Control Assy., Heater, Renew

All models (.5) 8

(G) Core, Heater, R&R or Renew

All models (2.6) 3.8

(G) Expansion (Freeze) Plugs, Water Jacket, Renew

Add appropriate time to access plug.

All models
one (.3) 5
each adntl. (.1) 1

(G) Gauge, Temperature (Dash Unit), Renew

All models (.6) 9

(G) Gauge, Temperature (Engine Unit), Renew

All models (.3) 4

(G) Hoses, Heater, Renew

All models
one (.5) 7
both (.6) 9

(G) Hoses, Radiator, Renew

Includes: Drain and refill cooling system as required.

All models
upper (.5) 7
lower (.6) 8
both (.7) 9

(G) Motor, Electric Cooling Fan, Renew

All models (.6) 9

(G) Motor, Heater Blower, Renew

All models (.3) 5

(G) Pulley, Idler, Renew

All models
upper (.9) 1.3
lower (1.1) 1.6
both (1.2) 1.7

(G) Pump and/or Gasket, Water, Renew

Includes: Drain and refill cooling system.

All models (1.4) 2.1
w/AC, add 1

(G) Radiator Assy., R&R or Renew

All models (1.0) 1.4

(G) Resistor, Heater Blower Motor, Renew

All models (.3) 5

(G) Switch, Coolant Temperature Sensor, Renew

All models (.2) 3

(G) Switch, Electric Fan Thermo, Renew

All models (.5) 7

(G) Switch, Heater Blower Motor, Renew

All models (.6) 9

(G) Thermostat, Coolant, Renew

All models (.9) 1.3

(G) Valve, Heater Control, Renew

All models (.5) 7

(G) Winterize Cooling System

Includes: Run engine to check for leaks, tighten all hose connections. Test radiator and pressure cap, drain radiator and engine block. Add antifreeze and refill system.

All models 5

LABOR — AIR CONDITIONING — LABOR

(Factory Time) Chilton Time

Note: If more than one item requires replacement where evacuation and discharging the system is already included in the operation, deduct 1.0 hour for each additional item from the time listed.

SERVICE AND TESTING

(G) Drain, Evacuate and Recharge System

All models 1.0
Recover refrigerant, add 2

(G) Flush Refrigerant System, Complete

To be used in conjunction with component replacement which could contaminate system. Includes evacuate and recharge.

All models 1.3
Recover refrigerant, add 2

(G) Leak Check

Includes: Check all lines and connections.

All models 2

(G) Performance Test

All models 6

COMPONENTS

(G) Accumulator Assy., Renew

Includes: Evacuate and charge system.

Note: Also called receiver drier.
All models (.9) 1.2
Recover refrigerant, add 2

(G) Actuator or Damper, Mode Door, Renew

All models
outside/recirculation (.5) 7
panel/defrost (.3) 4
temperature blend (.5) 7

(G) Belt, Compressor Drive, Renew

All models (.5) 7

(G) Blower Motor, Renew

All models
front (.3) 4
rear (.5) 7

(G) Clutch & Pulley, Compressor, Renew

Includes: Evacuate and charge system.

All models (1.3) 1.8
Recover refrigerant, add 2

(G) Compressor Assy., R&R and Recondition

Includes: Evacuate and charge system.

All models (1.9) 2.6
Recover refrigerant, add 2

(G) Compressor Assy., Renew

Includes: Transfer parts as required. Evacuate and charge system.

All models (1.3) 2.0
Recover refrigerant, add 2

(G) Condenser Assy., Renew

Includes: Evacuate and charge system.

All models (1.7) 2.3
Recover refrigerant, add 2

(G) Control Assy., Temperature, Renew

All models
front (.5) 7
rear (.4) 5

(G) Core, Evaporator, Renew

Includes: Evacuate and charge system.

All models
front (1.2) 1.6
rear (2.2) 3.0
Recover refrigerant, add 2

(G) Hoses, AC, Renew

Includes: Evacuate and charge system.

All models
liquid or suction
front (1.2) 1.7
rear (1.1) 1.5
discharge (.9) 1.2
Recover refrigerant, add 2

(G) Seal, Compressor Shaft, Renew

Includes: R&R compressor. Evacuate and charge system.

All models (1.4) 1.9
Recover refrigerant, add 2

(G) Switch, Low Pressure and/or Cycling, Renew

All models (.3) 4
Add time to evacuate & charge AC system as needed
Recover refrigerant, add 2

(G) Valve, Expansion, Renew

Includes: Evacuate and charge system.

All models, rear (1.5) 2.0
Recover refrigerant, add 2

GENERAL MOTORS CORPORATION-"A"BODY (FWD)

OLDSMOBILE CUTLASS CIERA • OLDSMOBILE CUTLASS CRUISER

LABOR — COOLING SYSTEM — LABOR

(Factory Time) Chilton Time

TESTING

(M) Pressure Test Cooling System

All models 3

SERVICE

(G) Belt, Serpentine Drive, Renew

1993-95 (.3) 5

(G) Bypass and/or Tube, Hose, Renew

1993 V6 (.5) 9
1994-95 (.4) 6

(G) Control Assy., Temperature, Renew

Century
1993-95 (.6) 9
Ciera
1993-95 (.5) 9

(G) Core, Heater, R&R or Renew

1993-95 wo/AC (.7) 1.4
1993-95 w/AC (.8) 1.5
Boil & Repair, add 1.2
Repair Core, add 9
Recore, add 1.2

(G) Expansion (Freeze) Plugs, Water Jacket, Renew

Add appropriate time to access plug.

All models, each 5

(G) Gauge, Temperature (Engine Unit), Renew

1993-95 (.4) 6

(G) Hoses, Heater, Renew

1993-95
one (.6) 8
all (.8) 1.2

(G) Hoses, Radiator, Renew

Includes: Drain and refill cooling system as required.

All models
upper (.4) 4
lower (.5) 5
both (.6) 7

(G) Motor, Heater Blower, Renew

1993-95
Four (.3) 4
V6 (.7) 1.0

COOLING SYSTEM

LABOR — Factory Time / Chilton Time

(G) Motor, Radiator Fan and/or Fan, Renew
1993
one (.4) 6
both (.6) 1.0
1994-95
right or single
Four (.4) 6
V6 (.7) 1.0
left (.5) 8
both (.6) 9

(G) Pump and/or Gasket, Water, Renew
Includes: Drain and refill cooling system.
1993-95 Four (.6) 1.0
1993 V6 (.9) 1.4
1994-95 V6 (.6) 1.0

(G) Radiator Assy., R&R or Renew
1993
Four (.6) 9
V6 (.8) 1.2
w/AT add 1
1994-95 (.9) 1.3
Boil & Repair, add 1.5
Rod Clean, add 1.9
Repair Core, add 1.3
Renew Tank, add 1.6
Renew Trans. Oil Cooler, add 1.9
Recore Radiator, add 1.7

(G) Relay, Radiator Fan Motor, Renew
All models (.2) 3

(G) Resistor, Fan Motor, Renew
All V6 models (.2) 3

(G) Resistor, Heater Blower Motor, Renew
All models (.2) 3

(G) Sending Unit, Engine Coolant Temp., Renew
All models (.4) 6

(G) Switch, Heater Blower Motor, Renew
Century, Ciera, Cutlass Cruiser
1993-95 (.5) 6

(G) Switch, Radiator Fan Motor (Coolant Temp.), Renew
All models (.3) 5

(G) Tensioner, Drive Belt, Renew
All models
Four (.6) 1.1
V6
code N (.7) 1.2
code M (.3) 4

(G) Thermostat, Coolant, Renew
1993-95 Four (.4) 6
1993 V6 (.6) 8
1994-95 V6 (.7) 1.0

(G) Valve, Heater Control, Renew
1993-95 gas (.4) 7

(G) Winterize Cooling System
Includes: Run engine to check for leaks, tighten all hose connections. Test radiator and pressure cap, drain radiator and engine block. Add antifreeze and refill system.
All models 5

AIR CONDITIONING

LABOR — Factory Time / Chilton Time

Note: If more than one item requires replacement where evacuation and discharging the system is already included in the operation, deduct 1.0 hour for each additional item from the time listed.

SERVICE AND TESTING

(G) Drain, Evacuate and Recharge System
All models (.5) 1.0
Recover refrigerant add 2

(G) Flush Refrigerant System, Complete
To be used in conjunction with component replacement which could contaminate system. Includes evacuate and recharge.
All models 1.3
Recover refrigerant add 2

(G) Leak Check
Includes: Check all lines and connections.
All models 5

(G) Recover and/or Recycle AC Refrigerant
Add to evacuate and charge the AC system, as required.
All models 2

(G) Refrigerant, Add (Partial Charge)
All models 6

COMPONENTS

(G) Accumulator Assy., Renew
Includes: Evacuate and charge system.
All models (1.0) 1.5
Recover refrigerant add 2

(G) Actuator, Vacuum, Renew
1993-95
defroster (1.0) 1.5
upper & lower mode (.4) 9
air inlet (.4) 9

(G) Belt, Compressor Drive, Renew
1993-95 serpentine (.3) 5

(G) Blower Motor, Renew
1993-95
Four (.3) 4
V6 (.5) 1.0

(G) Clutch Plate & Hub Assy., Compressor, Renew
Includes: R&R hub and drive plate assy. Check air gap.
All models
HR6, DA6 compressor (.9) 1.3
V5 compressor (.8) 1.2
Add time to recharge AC system if required.
Recover refrigerant add 2

(G) Coil and/or Pulley Rim, Compressor Clutch, Renew
Includes: R&R hub and drive plate assy.
All models
HR6, DA6 compressor (1.2) 1.5
V5 compressor (1.0) 1.5
Renew pulley or bearing add 2
Add time to recharge AC system if required.
Recover refrigerant add 2

(G) Compressor Assy., Renew
Includes: Transfer parts as required. Evacuate and charge system.
All models
HR6, DA6 compressor (1.3) 2.0
V5 compressor (1.4) 2.1
Install liq. line filter add (1.1) 1.5
Recover refrigerant add 2

(G) Condenser Assy., Renew
Includes: Evacuate and charge system.
1993-95 (1.0) 1.5
Recover refrigerant add 2

(G) Control Assy., Temperature, Renew
1993-95 (.6) 9

(G) Core, Evaporator, Renew
Includes: Evacuate and charge system.
1993-95
Four (1.7) 3.5
V6 (3.4) 6.5
Recover refrigerant add 2

(G) Cylinder & Shaft Assy., Compressor, Renew
Includes: R&R compressor. Transfer parts as required. Evacuate and charge system.
All models
HR6, DA6 compressor (2.0) 2.8
Recover refrigerant add 2

(G) Expansion Tube & Screen, Clean and Inspect or Renew
Includes: Evacuate and charge system.
All models (.8) 1.4
Install liq. line filter add (1.1) 1.2
Recover refrigerant add 2

(G) Head and/or Seal, Compressor Front, Renew
Includes: R&R compressor. R&R clutch pulley assy., R&R shaft seal assy. Clean and inspect parts. Evacuate and charge system.
All models
HR6, DA6 compressor (1.9) 2.6
Recover refrigerant add 2

LABOR AIR CONDITIONING LABOR

(Factory Time) Chilton Time

(G) Hoses, AC, Renew

Includes: Evacuate and charge system.

All models
suction or discharge (1.3) 2.0
liquid line
Four (1.4) 2.1
V6 (1.9) 2.6
evaporator to accumulator
Four (1.4) 2.1
V6 (1.5) 2.2
Recover refrigerant add 2

(G) Relay, Blower Motor, Renew

All models (.2) 3

(G) Resistor, Blower Motor, Renew

All models (.2) 3

(G) Rotor and/or Bearing, Compressor Clutch, Renew

Includes: R&R hub and drive plate assy.

All models
HR6, DA6 compressor (1.2) 1.7
V5 compressor (1.0) 1.5
Add time to recharge AC system if required.
Recover refrigerant add 2

(G) Seal, Compressor Shaft, Renew

Includes: R&R compressor. Evacuate and charge system.

1993-95 V5 compressor (1.5) 2.2
Recover refrigerant add 2

(G) Seal, Seat and O-Ring, Compressor Front, Renew

Includes: R&R clutch hub and drive plate assy. Evacuate and charge system.

All models
HR6, DA6 compressor (1.7) 2.5
Recover refrigerant add 2
R&R accumulator, add 3

(G) Switch, Blower Motor, Renew

Century
1993-95 (.5) 8
Ciera
1993-95 (.5) 8

(G) Switch, Clutch Cycling Pressure, Renew

All models (.2) 3

(G) Switch, High Pressure Cut-Off, Renew

1993 (.5) 6
1994-95 (.2) 3
Add time to recharge AC system if required.
Recover refrigerant add 2

(G) Switch, Master Electrical, Renew

All models (.6) 9

(G) Valve, Vacuum Selector, Renew

1993-95 (.5) 8

GENERAL MOTORS CORPORATION-"C"BODY (FWD)

BUICK PARK AVENUE • CADILLAC DEVILLE • CADILLAC FLEETWOOD OLDSMOBILE NINETY EIGHT

LABOR COOLING SYSTEM LABOR

(Factory Time) Chilton Time

TESTING

(M) Pressure Test Cooling System

All models 3

SERVICE

(G) Belt, Fan Drive, Renew

1993-95 (.2) 4

(G) Core, Heater, R&R or Renew

98 Regency, Electra, Park Ave.
1993-95 (.8) 1.8
Deville, Fleetwood
1993 (1.0) 1.8
Add time to evacuate & charge AC system if required.
Boil & Repair, add 1.2
Repair Core, add 9
Recore, add 1.2

(G) Expansion (Freeze) Plugs, Water Jacket, Renew

Add appropriate time to access plug.

All models, each 5

(G) Hoses, Heater, Renew

98 Regency, Electra, Park Ave.
1993-95
one (.4) 5
all (.6) 9
Deville, Fleetwood
1993
water valve to core (.4) 6
manifold to core (.4) 6
cyl. block to core (.4) 6
cyl. block to water valve (.4) 6
all (.9) 1.2

(G) Hoses, Radiator, Renew

Includes: Drain and refill cooling system as required.

All models
upper (.3) 4
lower (.4) 5
both (.5) 7
by-pass (.5) 7

(G) Motor, Radiator Fan and/or Fan, Renew

98 Regency, Electra, Park Ave.
1993-95
one (.5) 7
both (.7) 1.0
Deville, Fleetwood
1993
one (.3) 5
both (.4) 6

(G) Pump and/or Gasket, Water, Renew

Includes: Drain and refill cooling system.

1993-95 V6
3.8L code L (1.9) 3.0
3.8L code 1 (2.9) 4.0
1993 V8 (1.7) 3.8

(G) Radiator Assy., R&R or Renew

1993 Deville (.6) 1.0
1993 Fleetwood (.6) 1.0
1993-95 Park Ave. (.7) 1.2
1993-95 98 Regency (.7) 1.2
Renew side tank and/or gasket, add
one side (.7) 1.0
both sides (1.2) 1.7
Boil & Repair, add 1.5
Rod Clean, add 1.9
Repair Core, add 1.3
Renew Trans. Oil Cooler, add 1.9
Recore Radiator, add 1.7

(G) Relay, Radiator Fan Motor, Renew

1993-95 Park Ave. (.2) 3
1993-95 98 Regency (.2) 3

(G) Resistor, Fan Motor, Renew

All V6 models (.2) 4

(G) Sending Unit, Engine Coolant Temp., Renew

1993-95
V6 (.4) 7
V8 (.2) 4

LABOR COOLING SYSTEM LABOR

(Factory Time) Chilton Time

(G) Switch, Radiator Fan Motor (Coolant Temp.), Renew

98 Regency, Electra, Park Ave.
1993-95 (.2) 5

(G) Tensioner, Drive Belt, Renew

1993-95
V6 (.8) 1.4
V8 (.3) 5

(G) Thermostat, Coolant, Renew

1993-95
V6 (.4) 5
V8 (.3) 4

(G) Valve, Heater Control, Renew

All models
gas (.4) 6

(G) Winterize Cooling System

Includes: Run engine to check for leaks, tighten all hose connections. Test radiator and pressure cap, drain radiator and engine block. Add antifreeze and refill system.

All models 5

LABOR AIR CONDITIONING LABOR

(Factory Time) Chilton Time

Note: If more than one item requires replacement where evacuation and discharging the system is already included in the operation, deduct 1.0 hour for each additional item from the time listed.

SERVICE AND TESTING

(G) Drain, Evacuate and Recharge System

All models (.5) 1.0
Recover refrigerant, add 2

(G) Flush Refrigerant System, Complete

To be used in conjunction with component replacement which could contaminate system. Includes evacuate and recharge.

All models 1.3
Recover refrigerant, add 2

(G) Leak Check

Includes: Check all lines and connections.

All models 5

(G) Performance Test

All models 8

(G) Recover and/or Recycle AC Refrigerant

Add to evacuate and charge the AC system, as required.

All models 2

(G) Refrigerant, Add (Partial Charge)

All models 6

COMPONENTS

(G) Accumulator Assy., Renew

Includes: Evacuate and charge system.

All models (.9) 1.5
Recover refrigerant, add 2

(G) Actuator, Electric, Renew

Regency
1993-95 temp. door (.8) 1.2

(G) Actuator, Vacuum, Renew

1993-95
defroster (.8) 1.4
upper or lower mode (.5) 1.0
air inlet (1.6) 2.4
slave valve (.8) 1.4

(G) Aspirator, Renew

1993-95 (.7) 1.1
Deville, Fleetwood
1993 (.3) 4

(G) Belt, Compressor Drive, Renew

1993-95 V6 (.2) 4
1993 V8 (.2) 4

(G) Blower Motor, Renew

1993-95
w/bolt on cage (.4) 6
w/press on cage 1.1

(G) Clutch Plate & Hub Assy., Compressor, Renew

Includes: R&R hub and drive plate assy. Check air gap.

All models
DA6, HR6 compressor (.6) 9
Add time to evacuate and charge system if required.
Recover refrigerant, add 2

(G) Coil and/or Pulley Rim, Compressor Clutch, Renew

Includes: R&R hub and drive plate assy.

All models
DA6, HR6 compressor (1.0) 1.4
Add time to evacuate and charge system if required.
Renew pulley or bearing, add 2
Recover refrigerant, add 2

(G) Compressor Assy., Renew

Includes: Transfer parts as required. Evacuate and charge system.

All models
DA6, HR6 compressor (1.1) 1.9
Install liquid line & filter
add (.4) 5
Install liquid line filter
add (.7) 1.0
Recover refrigerant, add 2

(G) Condenser Assy., Renew

Includes: Evacuate and charge system.

1993 Deville (1.3) 2.2
1993 Deville (1.3) 2.2
1993 Fleetwood (1.3) 2.2
1993-95 Park Ave. (1.2) 2.0
1993-95 98 Regency (1.2) 2.0
Recover refrigerant, add 2

(G) Control Assy., AC, Renew

98 Regency, Electra, Park Ave.
1993-95
touch control (.3) 5
comfort control (.4) 6
Deville, Fleetwood
custom air (.5) 8
tempmatic (.4) 6
1993 (.5) 8

(G) Core, Evaporator, Renew

Includes: Evacuate and charge system.

1993 Deville (3.6) 6.5
1993 Fleetwood (3.6) 6.5
1993-95 Park Ave. (3.7) 6.5
1993-95 98 Regency (3.7) 6.5
Recover refrigerant, add 2

(G) Cylinder & Shaft Assy., Compressor, Renew

Includes: R&R compressor. Transfer parts as required. Evacuate and charge system.

All models
DA6, HR6 compressor (2.0) 3.1
Recover refrigerant, add 2

(G) Expansion Tube (Orifice), Clean & Inspect or Renew

Includes: Evacuate and charge system.

All models (.8) 1.4
Install liquid line & filter
add (.3) 5
Install liquid line filter
add (.4) 6
Recover refrigerant, add 2

(G) Head and/or Seal, Compressor Front, Renew

Includes: R&R compressor. R&R clutch pulley assy., R&R shaft seal assy. Clean and inspect parts. Evacuate and charge system.

All models
DA6, HR6, R4 compressor (1.7) .. 2.8
Recover refrigerant, add 2

(G) Hose, Aspirator, R&R or Renew

98 Regency, Electra, Park Ave.
1993-95 (.7) 1.1
Deville, Fleetwood
1993 (.3) 5

(G) Hoses, AC, Renew

Includes: Evacuate and charge system.

All models
liquid line (.9) 1.5
suction (1.0) 1.7
discharge (1.0) 1.7
evaporator to accumulator (.8) ... 1.5
Recover refrigerant, add 2

(G) Module, Blower Motor and Compressor Control, Renew

1993-95 (.5) 8

(G) Module, EEC Power, Renew

1993 (.4) 6

(G) Programmer, R&R or Renew

1993 Deville (.4) 6

LABOR — AIR CONDITIONING — LABOR

(Factory Time)	Chilton Time
1993 Fleetwood (.4)	.6
1993-95 Park Ave. (.6)	1.1
1993-95 98 Regency (.6)	1.1
Renew vacuum relay, add (.1)	.1
Renew motor, add (.2)	.2
Renew output shaft, add (.2)	.2
Renew compensator, add (.1)	.1

(G) Relay, Blower Motor, Renew

1993-95 Park Ave. (.3)	.4
1993-95 98 Regency (.3)	.4

(G) Resistor, Blower Motor, Renew

All models (.3)	.4

(G) Rotor and/or Bearing, Compressor Clutch, Renew

Includes: R&R hub and drive plate assy.

All models	
DA6, HR6 compressor (1.0)	1.5
Add time to evacuate and charge system if required.	
Recover refrigerant, add	.2

(G) Seal, Seat and O-Ring, Compressor Front, Renew

Includes: R&R clutch hub and drive plate assy. Evacuate and charge system.

All models	
DA6, HR6 compressor (1.4)	2.5
Recover refrigerant, add	.2

(G) Sensor, In-Vehicle, Renew

98 Regency, Electra, Park Ave.	
1993-95 (.4)	.7
Deville, Fleetwood	
1993 (.3)	.5

(G) Switch, AC Dual Zone, Renew

1993-95 (.2)	.5

(G) Switch, Clutch Cycling Pressure, Renew

1993-95 Park Ave. (.2)	.4
1993-95 98 Regency (.2)	.4

(G) Switch, High Pressure Cut-Off, Renew

1993-95 Park Ave. (.2)	.4
1993-95 98 Regency (.2)	.4
Add time to evacuate and charge system if required.	

GENERAL MOTORS CORPORATION-"E", "K"BODY (FWD)

BUICK RIVIERA • CADILLAC ALLANTE • CADILLAC ELDORADO • CADILLAC SEVILLE

LABOR — COOLING SYSTEM — LABOR

TESTING

(M) Pressure Test Cooling System

(Factory Time)	Chilton Time
All models	.3

SERVICE

(G) Belt, Drive, Renew

1994-95 V8	
coolant pump (.2)	.3

(G) Belt, Serpentine Drive, Renew

All models (.3)	.4

(G) Bypass and/or Tube, Hose, Renew

1993-95 V8 4.6L (.5)	.9

(G) Core, Heater, R&R or Renew

Allante	
1993 (1.9)	4.0
Eldorado, Seville	
1993-95 (1.2)	2.7
1993 (1.1)	2.0
Concours	
1994-95 (1.2)	2.7
Deville	
1994-95 (1.3)	3.0
Add time to evacuate & charge AC system if required.	
Boil & Repair, add	1.2
Repair Core, add	.9
Recore, add	1.2

(G) Expansion (Freeze) Plugs, Water Jacket, Renew

Add appropriate time to access plug.

All models, each	.5

(G) Hoses, Heater, Renew

1993	
V6	
one (.3)	.4
all (.6)	.9
V8	
Eldorado, Seville	
inlet or outlet (.5)	.8
valve to core (1.0)	1.5
manifold to core (.3)	.5
block or head to core (.3)	.5
Allante	
block or head to core (.8)	1.2
all (1.0)	1.5
1994-95	
one (.6)	.9
all (1.2)	1.8

(G) Hoses, Radiator, Renew

Includes: Drain and refill cooling system as required.

1993	
upper (.3)	.4
lower (.4)	.5
w/4.6L add	.1
both (.5)	.7
by-pass (.5)	.7
1994-95	
upper (.4)	.6
lower (.6)	.8
both (.6)	1.0
throttle body	
inlet (.4)	.6
outlet (.7)	1.0

(G) Inlet, Coolant Pump, Renew

Includes: Evacuate and recharge AC system.

1993 V8 (3.5)	4.9
1994-95 V8	
Eldorado, Seville (3.5)	4.9
Deville (2.9)	3.9
Concours (.7)	1.1
Recover refrigerant, add	.2

(G) Motor, Radiator Fan and/or Fan, Renew

1993 V6	
single (.6)	.8
dual	
one (.5)	.7
both (.8)	1.0
1993	
4.5L, 4.9L	
Eldorado, Seville	
right (.6)	.8
left (.3)	.5
both (1.0)	1.4
Allante	
single (.3)	.5
dual	
one (.2)	.4
both (.3)	.5
4.6L	
one (.5)	.8
both (.7)	1.1
1994-95 V8	
Eldorado, Seville	
one (.5)	.7
both (.6)	.9
Deville	
one (.4)	.6

LABOR **COOLING SYSTEM** LABOR

(Factory Time) Chilton Time

both (.6) 9
Concours
one (.5) 7
both (.7) 1.0

(G) Pump and/or Gasket, Water, Renew

Includes: Drain and refill cooling system.

1993
V6 (.9) 1.5
w/AC add (.2) 2
V8
4.1L, 4.5L, 4.9L
Eldorado, Seville (1.3) 3.8
Allante (1.0) 1.7
4.6L (1.0) 1.7
1994-95
Eldorado, Seville (1.0) 1.7
Deville (1.5) 3.0
Concours (.9) 1.6

(G) Radiator Assy., R&R or Renew

1993
V6 (.5) 9
V8
4.1L, 4.5L, 4.9L (.9) 1.4
4.6L
Eldorado, Seville (.9) 1.4
Allante (1.1) 1.6
1994-95
Eldorado, Seville (1.6) 2.3
Concours (1.6) 2.3
Deville (.7) 1.2
Renew side tank and/or gasket, add
one side (.7) 7
both sides (1.2) 1.2
Boil & Repair, add 1.5
Rod Clean, add 1.9
Repair Core, add 1.3
Renew Trans. Oil Cooler, add 1.9
Recore Radiator, add 1.7

(G) Relay, Radiator Fan Motor, Renew

1993 V6 (.2) 4
w/HD cooling, add (.1) 1

(G) Sending Unit, Engine Coolant Temp., Renew

All models (.2) 5

(G) Tensioner, Drive Belt, Renew

1993
V6 (.5) 7
V8
4.1L, 4.5L, 4.9L (.2) 4
4.6L (.4) 6
1994-95 V8 (.4) 6

(G) Thermostat, Coolant, Renew

1993
V6 (.4) 6
V8 (.3) 5
1994-95 V8 (.6) 9

(G) Winterize Cooling System

Includes: Run engine to check for leaks, tighten all hose connections. Test radiator and pressure cap, drain radiator and engine block. Add antifreeze and refill system.

All models 5

LABOR **AIR CONDITIONING** LABOR

(Factory Time) Chilton Time

Note: If more than one item requires replacement where evacuation and discharging the system is already included in the operation, deduct 1.0 hour for each additional item from the time listed.

SERVICE AND TESTING

(G) Drain, Evacuate and Recharge System

All models (.5) 1.0
Recover refrigerant, add 2

(G) Flush Refrigerant System, Complete

To be used in conjunction with component replacement which could contaminate system. Includes evacuate and recharge.

All models 1.3
Recover refrigerant, add 2

(G) Leak Check

Includes: Check all lines and connections.

All models 5

(G) Recover and/or Recycle AC Refrigerant

Add to evacuate and charge the AC system, as required.

All models 2

(G) Refrigerant, Add (Partial Charge)

All models 6

COMPONENTS

(G) Accumulator Assy., Renew

Includes: Evacuate and charge system.

1993 V6 (.8) 1.5
1993 V8
Eldorado, Seville (1.3) 2.0
Allante (.7) 1.4
1994-95 V8 (.7) 1.4
Recover refrigerant, add 2

(G) Actuator, Electric, Renew

1993 Allante
defroster (.4) 7
air inlet (.6) 1.0

(G) Actuator, Vacuum, Renew

Allante
1993
defroster or air inlet (.4) 7
upper or lower mode (.2) 4
Eldorado, Seville
1993
defroster or air inlet (.4) 7
upper or lower mode (.2) 4
1994-95 (.6) 1.0
Riviera
1993
defroster (1.7) 3.2
upper or lower mode (1.6) 3.0
air inlet (1.0) 1.5
Deville, Concours
1994-95 (.6) 1.0

(G) Aspirator, Renew

Eldorado, Seville
1993 (.5) 8
1994-95 (.6) 1.0
Allante
1993 (.8) 1.1
Riviera
1993 (.5) 8
Deville
1994-95 (1.1) 1.6
Concours
1994-95 (1.0) 1.5

(G) Belt, Compressor Drive, Renew

All models (.2) 4

(G) Blower Motor, Renew

Eldorado, Seville
1993
4.1L, 4.5L, 4.9L (.8) 1.1
4.6L (.6) 1.0
1994-95
front (.7) 1.1
rear (1.2) 1.7
Allante
1993
4.1L, 4.5L, 4.9L (1.3) 1.8
4.6L (.6) 1.0
Reatta, Riviera
1993
AC (.6) 1.1
Deville, Concours
1994-95 (.7) 1.0

(G) Clutch Plate & Hub Assy., Compressor, Renew

Includes: R&R hub and drive plate assy. Check air gap.

1993 (1.2) 1.6
Allante add 3
1994-95 (.8) 1.2
Add time to evacuate and charge system if required.
Recover refrigerant, add 2

(G) Coil and/or Pulley Rim, Compressor Clutch, Renew

Includes: R&R hub and drive plate assy.

1993 (1.1) 1.5
Allante add 6
1994-95 (1.4) 2.0
Renew pulley or bearing add 1
Add time to evacuate and charge system if required
Recover refrigerant, add 2

(G) Coil, Evaporator, Renew

Includes: Evacuate and charge system.

Reatta, Riviera
1993 (2.7) 5.5
Eldorado, Seville
1993
4.9L (4.1) 5.7
4.6L (6.2) 8.5

LABOR AIR CONDITIONING LABOR

(Factory Time) Chilton Time

1994-95 (5.5) 8.0
Allante
1993
exc. 4.6L (4.1) 7.0
4.6L (6.9) 9.7
Recover refrigerant, add 2
Deville
1994-95 (3.5) 5.5
Concours
1994-95 (5.5) 8.0

(G) Compressor Assy., Renew

Includes: Transfer parts as required. Evacuate and charge system.

1993
V6 (1.1) 1.9
V8
4.1L, 4.5L, 4.9L (1.5) 2.5
4.6L (1.7) 2.7
1994-95
Eldorado, Seville (1.7) 2.7
Concours (1.7) 2.7
Deville (1.5) 2.5
Install liquid line & filter
add (1.0) 1.2
Recover refrigerant, add 2

(G) Condenser Assy., Renew

Includes: Evacuate and charge system.

Reatta, Riviera
1993 (1.5) 2.0
Eldorado, Seville
1993
4.1L, 4.5L, 4.9L (1.7) 2.6
4.6L (1.9) 2.8
1994-95 (1.9) 2.8
Allante
1993 (1.9) 2.8
Deville
1994-95 (1.5) 2.5
Concours
1994-95 (2.2) 3.3
Recover refrigerant, add 2

(G) Control Assy., Temperature, Renew

1993 Riviera, Reatta (.3) 6

(G) Expansion Tube (Orifice), Clean & Inspect or Renew

Includes: Evacuate and charge system.

All models (.8) 1.5
Install liquid line & filter
add (1.0) 1.2
Recover refrigerant, add 2

(G) Head and/or Seal, Compressor Front, Renew

Includes: R&R compressor. R&R clutch pulley assy., R&R shaft seal assy. Clean and inspect parts. Evacuate and charge system.

All models (1.9) 2.8
Allante add 3
Recover refrigerant, add 2

(G) Hose, Aspirator, R&R or Renew

Eldorado, Seville
1993-95 (.6) 1.0
Allante
1993 (1.3) 1.8
Riviera
1993 (.5) 9
Deville
1994-95 (.9) 1.4
Concours
1994-95 (.8) 1.3

(G) Hoses, AC, Renew

Includes: Evacuate and charge system.

All models
liquid line (.9) 1.6
suction, inlet (.8) 1.5
evaporator to accumulator (1.0) . . 1.7
suction & discharge
V6 (1.6) 2.3
V8 (1.1) 1.8
Recover refrigerant, add 2

(G) Module, EEC Power, Renew

1993 Allante (.5) 8
1993 Eldorado (.5) 8
1993 Seville (.5) 8
1993 Riviera, Reatta (.6) 9

(G) Module, HVAC or EEC Power, Renew

1993 Riviera, Reatta (.5) 8

(G) Programmer, R&R or Renew

Eldorado, Seville
1993-95 (.6) 1.0
Allante
1993 (.6) 1.0
Deville, Concours
1994-95 (.6) 1.0

(G) Rotor and/or Bearing, Compressor Clutch, Renew

Includes: R&R hub and drive plate assy.

All models
V6 (1.3) 1.7
V8 (1.3) 1.7
Allante add 4
Add time to evacuate & recharge AC system
if required.

(G) Seal, Seat and O-Ring, Compressor Front, Renew

Includes: R&R clutch hub and drive plate assy. Evacuate and charge system.

All models
V6 (1.3) 2.5
V8 (1.8) 3.0
Allante add 3
Recover refrigerant, add 2

(G) Sensor, In-Vehicle, Renew

Eldorado, Seville
1993 (.6) 9
Riviera, Reatta
1993 (.3) 6
Allante
1993 (.8) 1.1

(G) Sensor, Outside Temperature, Renew

All models (.2) 5

(G) Sensor, Refrigerant Temperature, Renew

All models (.2) 4
Add time to evacuate and charge system
if required.

(G) Shaft & Cylinder Assy., Compressor, Renew

Includes: R&R compressor. Evacuate and charge system.

All models
V6 (1.5) 2.9
V8 (2.0) 3.0
Allante add 3
Recover refrigerant, add 2

(G) Switch, Refrigerant, Renew

All models (.2) 4
Add time to evacuate and charge system
if required.
Recover refrigerant, add 2

GENERAL MOTORS CORPORATION-"G"BODY (FWD)

BUICK RIVIERA • OLDSMOBILE AURORA

LABOR COOLING SYSTEM LABOR

(Factory Time) Chilton Time

TESTING

(M) Pressure Test Cooling System

All models 3

SERVICE

(G) Belt, Drive, Renew

1995 4.0L Aurora
water pump (.3) 4
Serpentine (.6) 9

(G) Belt, Serpentine Drive, Renew

All models
3.8L
outer (.2) 3
inner (.3) 4
4.0L (.6) 9

LABOR — COOLING SYSTEM — LABOR

(Factory Time) Chilton Time

(G) Control Assy., Temperature, Renew
All models (.3) 5

(G) Core, Heater, R&R or Renew
All models (.7) 1.5
Boil & Repair, add 1.2
Repair Core, add 9
Recore, add 1.2

(G) Hoses, By-Pass, Renew
All 4.0L models (.7) 1.0

(G) Hoses, Heater, Renew
All models
inlet or outlet (.5) 8
water pump to core (.3) 5
all (.6) 9

(G) Hoses, Radiator, Renew
Includes: Drain and refill cooling system as required.
All models
3.8L
upper or lower (.7) 9
throttle body to thermostat housing (.5) 7
4.0L
upper or lower (.7) 9
throttle body to thermostat housing (.8) 1.0

intake manifold (.4) 6
all (.8) 1.2

(G) Motor, Heater or AC Blower, Renew
All models (.3) 5

(G) Motor, Radiator Fan and/or Fan, Renew
All models
3.8L
one (.6) 8
both (.8) 1.1
4.0L
one (.5) 7
both (.7) 1.0

(G) Pump and/or Gasket, Water, Renew
Includes: Drain and refill cooling system.
All models
3.8L code 1 (2.9) 4.0
3.8L code K (1.9) 3.0
4.0L (.9) 1.4

(G) Radiator Assy., R&R or Renew
All models (1.1) 1.5
Boil & Repair, add 1.5
Rod Clean, add 1.9
Repair Core, add 1.3
Renew Trans. Oil cooler, add 1.9
Recore Radiator, add 1.7

(G) Relay, Heater Blower Motor, Renew
1995 Riviera (.2) 4

(G) Relay, Radiator Fan Motor, Renew
All models (.2) 3

(G) Resistor, Fan Motor, Renew
1995 Riviera (.2) 3

(G) Resistor, Heater Blower Motor, Renew
1995 Riviera (.3) 5

(G) Switch, Radiator Fan Motor (Coolant Temp.), Renew
All models (.4) 6

(G) Tensioner, Drive Belt, Renew
All models
3.8L (.5) 7
4.0L (2.0) 2.9

(G) Thermostat, Coolant, Renew
All models (.6) 9

(G) Winterize Cooling System
Includes: Run engine to check for leaks, tighten all hose connections. Test radiator and pressure cap, drain radiator and engine block. Add antifreeze and refill system.
All models 5

LABOR — AIR CONDITIONING — LABOR

(Factory Time) Chilton Time

Note: If more than one item requires replacement where evacuation and discharging the system is already included in the operation, deduct 1.0 hour for each additional item from the time listed.

SERVICE AND TESTING

(G) Drain, Evacuate and Recharge System
All models 1.0

(G) Flush Refrigerant System, Complete
To be used in conjunction with component replacement which could contaminate system. Includes evacuate and recharge.
All models 1.3

(G) Leak Check
Includes: Check all lines and connections.
All models 5

(G) Recover and/or Recycle AC Refrigerant
Add to evacuate and charge the AC system, as required.
All models 2

(G) Refrigerant, Add (Partial Charge)
All models 6

COMPONENTS

(G) Accumulator Assy., Renew
Includes: Evacuate and charge system.
All models (1.1) 1.6

(G) Actuator and/or Motor, Electric, Renew
All models (.8) 1.3

(G) Aspirator, Renew
All models (.5) 8

(G) Blower Motor, Renew
All models (.3) 5

(G) Clutch Plate & Hub Assy., Compressor, Renew
Includes: R&R hub and drive plate assy. Check air gap.
All models (1.2) 1.7
Add time to evacuate & recharge AC system if required.

(G) Coil and/or Pulley Rim, Compressor Clutch, Renew
Includes: R&R hub and drive plate assy.
All models (1.1) 1.5
Replace pulley and/or bearing, add 2
Add time to evacuate & recharge AC system if required.

(G) Coil, Evaporator, Renew
Includes: Evacuate and charge system.
All models (3.5) 6.0

(G) Compressor Assy., Renew
Includes: Transfer parts as required. Evacuate and charge system.
All models (1.4) 2.0
Install liquid line filter, add 1

(G) Condenser Assy., Renew
Includes: Evacuate and charge system.
All models (1.2) 2.0

(G) Control Assy., Temperature, Renew
All models (.3) 5

(G) Cylinder & Shaft Assy., Compressor, Renew
Includes: R&R compressor. Transfer parts as required. Evacuate and charge system.
All models (2.2) 3.0

(G) Expansion Tube (Orifice), Clean & Inspect or Renew
Includes: Evacuate and charge system.
All models (1.0) 1.5
Install liquid line filter, add 3

(G) Head and/or Seal, Compressor Front, Renew
Includes: R&R compressor. R&R clutch pulley assy., R&R shaft seal assy. Clean and inspect parts. Evacuate and charge system.
All models (1.8) 2.5

(G) Hose, Aspirator, R&R or Renew
All models (.5) 8

(G) Hoses, AC, Renew
Includes: Evacuate and charge system.
All models
liquid line (1.3) 2.0
evaporator to accumulator (1.1) 1.7
suction & discharge hose (1.8) 2.4

LABOR — AIR CONDITIONING — LABOR

(Factory Time) Chilton Time

(G) Module, AC Programmer, Renew
All models (.6) 1.0

(G) Module, Blower Motor and Compressor Control, Renew
All models (.6) 1.0

(G) Programmer, R&R or Renew
All models (.6) 1.0

(G) Relay, Blower Motor, Renew
1995 Riviera (.2) 4

(G) Resistor, Blower Motor, Renew
1995 Riviera (.3) 5

(G) Rotor and/or Bearing, Compressor Clutch, Renew
Includes: R&R hub and drive plate assy.
All models (1.3) 1.8
Add time to evacuate & recharge AC system if required.

(G) Seal, Seat and O-Ring, Compressor Front, Renew
Includes: R&R clutch hub and drive plate assy. Evacuate and charge system.
All models (2.0) 2.4

(G) Sensor, AC Pressure, Renew
All models (.2) 4

(G) Sensor, In-Vehicle, Renew
All models (.3) 5

(G) Sensor, Outside Temperature, Renew
All models (.2) 4

(G) Sensor, Sun/Photo, Renew
All models (.4) 6

(G) Switch, AC Dual Zone, Renew
1995
Riviera (.5) 7
Aurora (.2) 3

(G) Switch, High Pressure Cut-Off, Renew
All models (.3) 5
Add time to evacuate & recharge AC system if required.

(G) Switch, Low Pressure Cut-Off, Renew
Includes: Evacuate and charge system.
All models (1.0) 1.5

GENERAL MOTORS CORPORATION-"H"BODY (FWD)
BUICK LESABRE • OLDSMOBILE DELTA 88 • PONTIAC BONNEVILLE

LABOR — COOLING SYSTEM — LABOR

(Factory Time) Chilton Time

TESTING

(M) Pressure Test Cooling System
All models 3

SERVICE

(G) Belt, Serpentine Drive, Renew
All models (.2) 4

(G) Core, Heater, R&R or Renew
1993-95 (.8) 1.8
Add time to evacuate and charge AC system if required.
Boil & Repair, add 1.2
Repair Core, add 9
Recore, add 1.2

(G) Expansion (Freeze) Plugs, Water Jacket, Renew
Add appropriate time to access plug.
All models, each 5

(G) Hoses, Heater, Renew
All models
one (.3) 4
all (.6) 9

(G) Hoses, Radiator, Renew
Includes: Drain and refill cooling system as required.
All models
upper (.3) 4
lower (.4) 5
both (.5) 7
by-pass (.5) 7

(G) Motor, Radiator Fan and/or Fan, Renew
1993-95
one (.5) 7
both (.7) 1.0

(G) Pump and/or Gasket, Water, Renew
Includes: Drain and refill cooling system.
1993-95 (1.9) 3.0

(G) Radiator Assy., R&R or Renew
1993-95 (.7) 1.2
Renew side tank and/or gasket, add
one side (.7) 7
both sides (1.2) 1.2
Boil & Repair, add 1.5
Rod Clean, add 1.9
Repair Core, add 1.3
Renew Trans. Oil Cooler, add 1.9
Recore Radiator, add 1.7

(G) Relay, Radiator Fan Motor, Renew
All models (.2) 3

(G) Resistor, Fan Motor, Renew
All models (.2) 4

(G) Sending Unit, Engine Coolant Temp., Renew
All models (.4) 7

(G) Switch, Radiator Fan Motor (Coolant Temp.), Renew
All models (.2) 5

(G) Tensioner, Drive Belt, Renew
1993-95 (.9) 1.4

(G) Thermostat, Coolant, Renew
All models (.4) 5

(G) Valve, Heater Control, Renew
All models (.4) 6

(G) Winterize Cooling System
Includes: Run engine to check for leaks, tighten all hose connections. Test radiator and pressure cap, drain radiator and engine block. Add antifreeze and refill system.
All models 5

LABOR — AIR CONDITIONING — LABOR

(Factory Time) Chilton Time

Note: If more than one item requires replacement where evacuation and discharging the system is already included in the operation, deduct 1.0 hour for each additional item from the time listed.

SERVICE AND TESTING

(G) Drain, Evacuate and Recharge System

All models (.5) 1.0
Recover refrigerant add 2

(G) Flush Refrigerant System, Complete

To be used in conjunction with component replacement which could contaminate system. Includes evacuate and recharge.

All models 1.3
Recover refrigerant add 2

(G) Leak Check

Includes: Check all lines and connections.

All models 5

(G) Recover and/or Recycle AC Refrigerant

Add to evacuate and charge the AC system, as required.

All models 2

(G) Refrigerant, Add (Partial Charge)

All models 6

COMPONENTS

(G) Accumulator Assy., Renew

Includes: Evacuate and charge system.

All models (.9) 1.5
Recover refrigerant, add 2

(G) Actuator, Vacuum, Renew

1993-95
defroster (.8) 1.4
upper or lower mode (.5) 1.0
air inlet (1.6) 2.4
slave valve (.8) 1.4

(G) Aspirator, Renew

1993-95
LeSabre (.2) 4
Delta 88 (.7) 1.1

(G) Belt, Compressor Drive, Renew

All models (.2) 4

(G) Blower Motor, Renew

heater (.8) 1.2
AC (.2) 4
1993-95 (.4) 6
w/press-on cage, add 5

(G) Clutch Plate & Hub Assy., Compressor, Renew

Includes: R&R hub and drive plate assy. Check air gap.

All models
HR6, DA6 compressor (.6) 9
Add time to evacuate and charge system if required.
Recover refrigerant, add 2

(G) Coil and/or Pulley Rim, Compressor Clutch, Renew

Includes: R&R hub and drive plate assy.

All models
HR6, DA6 compressor (1.0) 1.4
Renew pulley or bearing, add 2
Add time to evacuate and charge system if required.
Recover refrigerant, add 2

(G) Compressor Assy., Renew

Includes: Transfer parts as required. Evacuate and charge system.

All models (1.1) 1.9
HR6, DA6 compressor (1.1) 1.9
Install liquid line & filter, add (.4) 5
Recover refrigerant, add 2

(G) Condenser Assy., Renew

Includes: Evacuate and charge system.

All models (1.2) 2.0
Recover refrigerant, add 2

(G) Control Assy., Temperature, Renew

All models
wo/touch control (.6) 8
touch control (.5) 8
custom air (.5) 8
electronic (.3) 5
comfort control (.5) 8

(G) Core, Evaporator, Renew

Includes: Evacuate and charge system.

All models (3.7) 6.5
Recover refrigerant, add 2

(G) Expansion Tube (Orifice), Clean & Inspect or Renew

Includes: Evacuate and charge system.

All models (.8) 1.4
Recover refrigerant, add 2

(G) Head and/or Seal, Compressor Front, Renew

Includes: R&R compressor. R&R clutch pulley assy., R&R shaft seal assy. Clean and inspect parts. Evacuate and charge system.

All models
HR6, DA6 compressor (1.7) 2.8
Recover refrigerant, add 2

(G) Hose, Aspirator, R&R or Renew

1993-95
LeSabre (.3) 7
Delta 88 (.7) 1.1

(G) Hoses, AC, Renew

Includes: Evacuate and charge system.

All models
liquid line (.9) 1.5
evaporator to accumulator (.8) . . . 1.5
suction or discharge (1.0) 1.7
Recover refrigerant, add 2

(G) Module, Blower Motor and Compressor Control, Renew

1993-95 (.5) 8

(G) Module, EEC Power, Renew

1993 (.4) 6

(G) Programmer, R&R or Renew

1993
Bonneville (2.1) 3.0
LeSabre, Delta 88 (.8) 1.1
1994-95
Bonneville (1.9) 3.0
w/console add 7
Delta 88 (.6) 1.1
LeSabre (.4) 7

(G) Relay, Blower Motor, Renew

All models (.3) 4

(G) Resistor, Blower Motor, Renew

All models (.3) 4

(G) Rotor and/or Bearing, Compressor Clutch, Renew

Includes: R&R hub and drive plate assy.

All models
HR6, DA6 compressor (1.0) 1.5
Add time to evacuate and charge system if required.
Recover refrigerant, add 2

(G) Seal, Seat and O-Ring, Compressor Front, Renew

Includes: R&R clutch hub and drive plate assy. Evacuate and charge system.

All models
HR6, DA6 compressor (1.4) 2.5
Recover refrigerant, add 2

(G) Sensor, Ambient Temperature, Renew

1993-95 (.2) 4

(G) Sensor, In-Vehicle, Renew

1993-95 (.4) 7

(G) Sensor, Outside Temperature, Renew

1993-95 (.2) 5

(G) Shaft & Cylinder Assy., Compressor, Renew

Includes: R&R compressor. Evacuate and charge system.

All models
HR6, DA6 compressor (2.0) 3.1
Recover refrigerant, add 2

(G) Switch, Blower Motor, Renew

1993-95 (.5) 7

(G) Switch, Master Electrical, Renew

All models (.3) 6

(G) Switch, Refrigerant, Renew

All models
high pressure (.3) 4
low pressure (.2) 4
pressure cycling (.3) 4
Add time to evacuate and charge system if required.

(G) Valve, Heater Water Control, Renew

All models (.4) 6

(G) Valve, Vacuum Selector, Renew

All models (.3) 6

GENERAL MOTORS CORPORATION-"J"BODY (FWD)
CHEVROLET CAVALIER • PONTIAC SUNBIRD

LABOR — COOLING SYSTEM — LABOR

(Factory Time) Chilton Time

TESTING

(M) Pressure Test Cooling System
All models 3

SERVICE

(G) Belt, Drive, Adjust
All models, V-belt
one (.2) 3
each adtnl. (.1) 1

(G) Belt, Drive, Renew
Four, OHC
1993-94
AC (.2) 3
serpentine (.2) 3
w/AC add (.1) 1
Four, OHV
1993-94 (.2) 3
V6
1993-94 (.3) 4

(G) Control Assy., Temperature, Renew
1993-94
wo/AC (.4) 1.0
w/AC
wo/touch control (.6) 1.1
w/touch control (.3) 5

(G) Core, Heater, R&R or Renew
1993-94 (1.2) 2.0
Boil & Repair, add 1.2
Repair Core, add 9
Recore, add 1.2

(G) Expansion (Freeze) Plugs, Water Jacket, Renew
Add appropriate time to access plug.
All models, each 5

(G) Gauge, Temperature (Engine Unit), Renew
1993-94 (.3) 6

(G) Hoses, Heater, Renew
All models
one (.6) 9
both (.7) 1.0

(G) Hoses, Radiator, Renew
Includes: Drain and refill cooling system as required.
1993-94
upper (.3) 4
lower (.7) 8
both (.8) 1.0

(G) Motor, Heater Blower, Renew
1993-94 (.7) 1.1

(G) Motor, Radiator Fan and/or Fan, Renew
1993-94
Four
OHV (.6) 8
OHC (.8) 1.2
w/AT add 1
V6 (.8) 1.0

(G) Pump and/or Gasket, Water, Renew
Includes: Drain and refill cooling system.
1993-94
Four
OHC (2.2) 3.5
w/AC add 1
OHV (1.3) 2.0
w/AT add 4
V6 (.7) 1.3

(G) Radiator Assy., R&R or Renew
1993-94
Four (1.0) 1.5
V6 (1.6) 2.3
w/AC add (.2) 2
w/AT add (.2) 2
Renew side tank and/or gasket, add
one (.7) 7
both (1.2) 1.2
Boil & Repair, add 1.5
Rod Clean, add 1.9
Repair Core, add 1.3
Renew Tank, add 1.6
Renew Trans. Oil Cooler, add 1.9
Recore Radiator, add 1.7

(G) Relay, Heater Blower Motor, Renew
All models (.2) 3

(G) Relay, Radiator Fan Motor, Renew
1993-94 (.4) 6

(G) Resistor, Heater Blower Motor, Renew
All models (.3) 5

(G) Switch, Heater Blower Motor, Renew
All models (.4) 6
w/cruise control add (.2) 2

(G) Switch, Radiator Fan Motor (Coolant Temp.), Renew
All models (.2) 4

(G) Tensioner, Drive Belt, Renew
1993-94 Four, OHC (.3) 5
1993-94 Four, OHV (1.0) 1.5
1993-94 V6 (.6) 8

(G) Thermostat, Coolant, Renew
1993-94
Four
OHC (.2) 4
OHV (.4) 6
V6 (.5) 7

(G) Winterize Cooling System
Includes: Run engine to check for leaks, tighten all hose connections. Test radiator and pressure cap, drain radiator and engine block. Add antifreeze and refill system.
All models 5

LABOR — AIR CONDITIONING — LABOR

(Factory Time) Chilton Time

Note: If more than one item requires replacement where evacuation and discharging the system is already included in the operation, deduct 1.0 hour for each additional item from the time listed.

SERVICE AND TESTING

(G) Drain, Evacuate and Recharge System
All models (.5) 1.0
Recover refrigerant, add 2

(G) Flush Refrigerant System, Complete
To be used in conjunction with component replacement which could contaminate system. Includes evacuate and recharge.
All models 1.3
Recover refrigerant, add 2

(G) Leak Check
Includes: Check all lines and connections.
All models 5

(G) Recover and/or Recycle AC Refrigerant
Add to evacuate and charge the AC system, as required.
All models 2

(G) Refrigerant, Add (Partial Charge)
All models 6

COMPONENTS

(G) Accumulator Assy., Renew
Includes: Evacuate and charge system.
All models (.7) 1.5
Recover refrigerant, add 2

(G) Actuator, Vacuum, Renew
1993
defroster (.4) 6
upper or lower mode (.5) 1.0
recirculation (.5) 1.0
1994
defroster (.2) 4
upper or lower mode (2.3) 4.0
air inlet (.3) 5

LABOR AIR CONDITIONING LABOR

(Factory Time) Chilton Time

(G) Belt, Compressor Drive, Renew

1993-94 (.2) 3
w/AC add (.1) 1
Four, OHV
1993-94 (.2) 3
V6
1993-94 (.3) 4

(G) Blower Motor, Renew

1993-94
Four (.6) 9
V6 (.7) 1.0

(G) Clutch Plate & Hub Assy., Compressor, Renew

Includes: R&R hub and drive plate assy. Check air gap.

1993-94
V5 compressor (.8) 1.2
Add time to evacuate and charge system if required.
Recover refrigerant, add 2

(G) Coil and/or Pulley Rim, Compressor Clutch, Renew

Includes: R&R hub and drive plate assy.

1993-94
V5 compressor (1.0) 1.5
Renew pulley or bearing add (.2) 2
Add time to evacuate and charge system if required.
Recover refrigerant, add 2

(G) Compressor Assy., Renew

Includes: Transfer parts as required. Evacuate and charge system.

1993-94 (1.2) 2.0
Install liquid line filter
add (.9) 1.2
Recover refrigerant, add 2

(G) Condenser Assy., Renew

Includes: Evacuate and charge system.

Cavalier, Cimarron
1993 (1.4) 2.5
1994 (.9) 2.0
Sunbird
1993-94 (.9) 2.0
w/AT add (.1) 1
Recover refrigerant add 2

(G) Control Assy., Temperature, Renew

1993 (.6) 9
1994 (.3) 7
w/cruise control add (.2) 2

(G) Core, Evaporator, Renew

Includes: Evacuate and charge system.

1993-94 (2.1) 4.1
Recover refrigerant, add 2

(G) Expansion Tube (Orifice), Clean & Inspect or Renew

Includes: Evacuate and charge system.

All models (.8) 1.4
Install liquid line filter
add (.9) 1.2
Recover refrigerant, add 2

(G) Hoses, AC, Renew

Includes: Evacuate and charge system.

All models
liquid line (1.2) 1.9
evap. to accumulator (1.0) 1.7
suction & discharge hose (1.2) 1.8
Recover refrigerant, add 2

(G) Relay, AC, Renew

All models, each (.2) 4

(G) Relay, Blower Motor, Renew

All models (.2) 3

(G) Resistor, Blower Motor, Renew

All models (.3) 5

(G) Rotor and/or Bearing, Compressor Clutch, Renew

Includes: R&R hub and drive plate assy.

1993-94
V5 compressor (1.2) 1.5
Add time to evacuate and charge system if required.
Recover refrigerant, add 2

(G) Seal, Compressor Shaft, Renew

Includes: R&R compressor. Evacuate and charge system.

1993-94
V5 compressor (1.6) 2.2
Recover refrigerant, add 2

(G) Sensor, AC Pressure, Renew

1993-94 (.2) 3

(G) Switch, Blower Motor, Renew

1993 (.6) 9
1994 (.4) 7
w/cruise control add (.2) 2

(G) Switch, Master Electrical, Renew

1993 (.6) 9
1994 (.4) 7
w/cruise control add (.2) 2

(G) Valve, Vacuum Selector, Renew

1993 (.6) 9
1994 (.5) 7
w/cruise control add (.2) 2

GENERAL MOTORS CORPORATION-"L"BODY (FWD)

CHEVROLET BERETTA • CHEVROLET CORSICA

LABOR COOLING SYSTEM LABOR

(Factory Time) Chilton Time

TESTING

(M) Pressure Test Cooling System

All models 3

SERVICE

(G) Belt, Drive, Renew

All models, serpentine (.3) 5

(G) Bypass and/or Tube, Hose, Renew

All models (.5) 7

(G) Cluster, Instrument Assy., R&R or Renew

1993-95 (.3) 7

(G) Control Assy., Temperature, Renew

1993-95 (.3) 5

(G) Core, Heater, R&R or Renew

1993-95 (1.2) 2.0
Add time to recharge AC system if required.
Recover Refrigerant, add 2
Boil & Repair, add 1.2
Repair Core, add 9
Recore, add 1.2

(G) Expansion (Freeze) Plugs, Water Jacket, Renew

Add appropriate time to access plug.

All models, each 5

(G) Gauge, Temperature (Engine Unit), Renew

All models (.4) 5

(G) Hoses, Heater, Renew

All models
wo/AC
one (.5) 6
all (.7) 9
w/AC
one (.5) 6
all (.9) 1.2

(G) Hoses, Radiator, Renew

Includes: Drain and refill cooling system as required.

All models
upper (.5) 6
lower (.4) 5
both (.5) 7

LABOR COOLING SYSTEM LABOR

(Factory Time) Chilton Time

(G) Motor, Heater Blower, Renew
1993-95
wo/AC (.5) .7
w/AC (.6) .8

(G) Motor, Radiator Fan and/or Fan, Renew
1993 (.7) .9
1994-95
2.2L code G, 4 (.5) .7
2.3L code A (.3) .5
3.1L (.8) 1.0

(G) Pump and/or Gasket, Water, Renew
Includes: Drain and refill cooling system.
1993
Four
2.2L codes G, 4 (1.3) 2.0
2.3L code A (1.4) 2.1
Renew pump body, add .1
V6 2.8L, 3.1L (1.2) 1.9
1994-95
Four 2.2L, 2.3L (.9) 1.4
V6 3.1L (1.4) 2.1

(G) Radiator Assy., R&R or Renew
All models (1.0) 1.5
w/AC add .2
w/AT add (.1) .2
Renew side tank and/or gasket, add
one side (.7) .7
both sides (1.2) 1.2
Boil & Repair, add 1.5
Rod Clean, add 1.9
Repair Core, add 1.3
Renew Tank, add 1.6
Renew Trans. Oil Cooler, add 1.9
Recore Radiator, add 1.7

(G) Relay, Heater Blower Motor, Renew
All models (.2) .4

(G) Relay, Radiator Fan Motor, Renew
All models (.2) .4

(G) Resistor, Heater Blower Motor, Renew
All models (.3) .4

(G) Switch, Heater Blower Motor, Renew
1993
wo/AC (.6) .8
w/AC (.4) .6
1994-95 (.3) .5

(G) Switch, Radiator Fan Motor (Coolant Temp.), Renew
All models (.3) .4

(G) Tensioner, Drive Belt, Renew
1993-95 Four
2.3L code A (1.4) 2.1
2.2L code 4 (.3) .5
1993-95 V6 (.7) 1.0

(G) Thermostat, Coolant, Renew
1993-95 (.4) .5

(G) Winterize Cooling System
Includes: Run engine to check for leaks, tighten all hose connections. Test radiator and pressure cap, drain radiator and engine block. Add antifreeze and refill system.
All models .5

LABOR AIR CONDITIONING LABOR

(Factory Time) Chilton Time

Note: If more than one item requires replacement where evacuation and discharging the system is already included in the operation, deduct 1.0 hour for each additional item from the time listed.

SERVICE AND TESTING

(G) Drain, Evacuate and Recharge System
All models (.5) 1.0
Recover refrigerant, add .2

(G) Flush Refrigerant System, Complete
To be used in conjunction with component replacement which could contaminate system. Includes evacuate and recharge.
All models 1.3

(G) Leak Check
Includes: Check all lines and connections.
All models .5

(G) Recover and/or Recycle AC Refrigerant
Add to evacuate and charge the AC system, as required.
All models .2

(G) Refrigerant, Add (Partial Charge)
All models .6

COMPONENTS

(G) Accumulator Assy., Renew
Includes: Evacuate and charge system.
All models (.8) 1.5
Recover refrigerant, add .2

(G) Actuator, Electric, Renew
1993-95 temperature door (.4) .7

(G) Actuator, Vacuum, Renew
1993
defroster (.4) .7
upper or lower mode (.4) .7
air inlet (.4) .7
1994-95
defroster (2.2) 3.0
upper or lower mode (.3) .6
air inlet (.3) .6

(G) Belt, Compressor Drive, Renew
All models, serpentine (.3) .5

(G) Blower Motor, Renew
All models
Four (.5) .7
V6 (.6) .8

(G) Clutch Plate & Hub Assy., Compressor, Renew
Includes: R&R hub and drive plate assy. Check air gap.
All models (1.3) 2.2
Recover refrigerant, add .2

(G) Coil and/or Pulley Rim, Compressor Clutch, Renew
Includes: R&R hub and drive plate assy.
All models (1.5) 2.5
Recover refrigerant, add .2

(G) Compressor Assy., Renew
Includes: Transfer parts as required. Evacuate and charge system.
All models
Four
2.3L code A (1.5) 2.5
2.2L codes 4, G (1.3) 2.0
V6
2.8L, 3.1L (1.4) 2.4
Install liquid line filter, add (.9) 1.2
Recover refrigerant, add .2

(G) Condenser Assy., Renew
Includes: Evacuate and charge system.
All models (1.5) 2.4
Recover refrigerant, add .2

(G) Control Assy., Temperature, Renew
All models (.3) .5

(G) Core, Evaporator, Renew
Includes: Evacuate and charge system.
1993 (2.0) 3.0
1994-95 (2.4) 3.4
Recover refrigerant, add .2

(G) Expansion Tube (Orifice), Clean & Inspect or Renew
Includes: Evacuate and charge system.
All models (1.0) 1.5
Recover refrigerant, add .2
Install liquid line filter
add (.9) 1.2

(G) Hoses, AC, Renew
Includes: Evacuate and charge system.
All models
liquid line (1.1) 1.7
evap. to accumulator (1.3) 1.8
2.3L code A, add .2
discharge hose assy. (1.2) 1.6
Recover refrigerant, add .2

(G) Receiver/Drier Assy., Renew
Includes: Evacuate and charge system.
1993-95 (1.2) 1.7

(G) Relay, Blower Motor, Renew
All models (.2) .4

(G) Resistor, Blower Motor, Renew
All models (.3) .4

LABOR — AIR CONDITIONING — LABOR

(Factory Time) Chilton Time

(G) Rotor and/or Bearing, Compressor Clutch, Renew

Includes: R&R hub and drive plate assy.

All models (1.7) 2.6
Recover refrigerant, add 2

(G) Seal, Seat and O-Ring, Compressor Front, Renew

Includes: R&R clutch hub and drive plate assy. Evacuate and charge system.

All models (1.8) 2.5
Recover refrigerant, add 2

(G) Switch, Blower Motor, Renew

All models (.3) 6

(G) Switch, Compressor Cut-Off, Renew

All models, each (.3) 4
Add time to recharge AC system if required.
Recover refrigerant, add 2

(G) Switch, Mode Selector, Renew

All models (.3) 6

(G) Switch, Temperature Selector, Renew

All models (.3) 6

(G) Valve, Expansion, Renew

Includes: Evacuate and charge system.

1993-95 (1.9) 2.3

(G) Valve, Vacuum Selector, Renew

All models (.3) 5

GENERAL MOTORS CORPORATION-"N"BODY (FWD)

OLDSMOBILE ACHIEVA • PONTIAC GRAND AM • BUICK SKYLARK

LABOR — COOLING SYSTEM — LABOR

(Factory Time) Chilton Time

TESTING

(M) Pressure Test Cooling System

All models 3

SERVICE

(G) Belt, Drive, Adjust

1993-95 Four, one (.2) 3

(G) Belt, Drive, Renew

1993-95 Four
PS (.3) 5
serpentine (.2) 4
1993 V6
serpentine (.7) 1.0
1994-95 V6
serpentine (.5) 7

(G) Cluster, Instrument Assy., R&R or Renew

1993-95 Somerset, Skylark (.4) 9
w/console, add (.3) 3
w/standard column, add (.3) 3
1993-95 Grand Am (.7) 1.4
1993 Achieva (.4) 7
1994-95 Achieva (.6) 1.0

(G) Control Assy., Temperature, Renew

1993-95 (.5) 9

(G) Core, Heater, R&R or Renew

1993-95 (1.6) 3.0
Boil & Repair, add 1.2
Repair Core, add 9
Recore, add 1.2

(G) Expansion (Freeze) Plugs, Water Jacket, Renew

Add appropriate time to access plug.

All models, each 5

(G) Gauge, Temperature (Engine Unit), Renew

All models (.2) 3

(G) Hoses, Heater, Renew

1993-95
wo/AC
one (.6) 8
both (.8) 1.0
w/AC
inlet or outlet (.6) 8
water pump to core (.4) 6
manifold to core
Four (.4) 6
V6 (.6) 8
all (.8) 1.1

(G) Hoses, Radiator, Renew

Includes: Drain and refill cooling system as required.

1993-95
upper (.3) 4
lower
Four (.5) 6
V6 (.8) 1.0

(G) Motor, Heater Blower, Renew

All models
Four (.3) 5
V6 (.6) 8

(G) Motor, Radiator Fan and/or Fan, Renew

1993 (.4) 6
1994-95
Four (.4) 6
V6 (.8) 1.1

(G) Pump and/or Gasket, Water, Renew

Includes: Drain and refill cooling system.

1993-95 Four
2.3L codes A, D, 3 (1.5) 2.1
Renew pump body, add 1
1993-95 V6 (1.8) 2.9

(G) Radiator Assy., R&R or Renew

1993-95
Four (1.0) 1.5
V6 (1.1) 1.6
Renew side tank and/or gasket, add
one side (.7) 7
both sides (1.2) 1.2
Boil & Repair, add 1.5
Rod Clean, add 1.9
Renew Tank, add 1.3
Renew Trans. Oil Cooler, add 1.9
Recore Radiator, add 1.7

(G) Relay, Heater Blower Motor, Renew

All models (.2) 3

(G) Relay, Radiator Fan Motor, Renew

All models (.2) 3

(G) Resistor, Heater Blower Motor, Renew

All models (.3) 4

(G) Switch, Heater Blower Motor, Renew

All models
wo/AC (.5) 8
w/AC (.6) 9

(G) Tensioner, Drive Belt, Renew

1993-95 Four 2.3L (.7) 1.1
1993 V6 (.8) 1.2
1994-95 V6 (.5) 8

(G) Thermostat, Coolant, Renew

1993-95
Four (.6) 8
V6 (.8) 1.0

(G) Valve, Heater Control, Renew

1993 (.6) 1.0
1994-95 (.9) 1.2

(G) Winterize Cooling System

Includes: Run engine to check for leaks, tighten all hose connections. Test radiator and pressure cap, drain radiator and engine block. Add antifreeze and refill system.

All models 5

LABOR — AIR CONDITIONING — LABOR

(Factory Time) Chilton Time

Note: If more than one item requires replacement where evacuation and discharging the system is already included in the operation, deduct 1.0 hour for each additional item from the time listed.

SERVICE AND TESTING

(G) Drain, Evacuate and Recharge System

All models (.5) 1.0
Recover refrigerant, add 2

(G) Flush Refrigerant System, Complete

To be used in conjunction with component replacement which could contaminate system. Includes evacuate and recharge.

All models 1.3
Recover refrigerant, add 2

(G) Leak Check

Includes: Check all lines and connections.

All models 5

(G) Recover and/or Recycle AC Refrigerant

Add to evacuate and charge the AC system, as required.

All models 2

(G) Refrigerant, Add (Partial Charge)

All models 6

COMPONENTS

(G) Actuator, Vacuum, Renew

All models
defroster (.4) 7
upper or lower mode (.6) 9
air inlet (.5) 9

(G) Belt, Compressor Drive, Renew

1993-95 serpentine (.2) 5

(G) Blower Motor, Renew

1993-95
Four (.3) 7
V6 (.6) 9

(G) Clutch Plate & Hub Assy., Compressor, Renew

Includes: R&R hub and drive plate assy. Check air gap.

1993-95
HR6 compressor (1.0) 1.3
V5 compressor
Four (1.0) 1.3
V6 (1.2) 1.5
Add time to evacuate and charge system if required.
Recover refrigerant, add 2

(G) Coil and/or Pulley Rim, Compressor Clutch, Renew

Includes: R&R hub and drive plate assy.

1993-95
HR6 compressor (1.2) 1.5
V5 compressor
Four (1.2) 1.5
V6 (1.4) 1.7
Renew pulley or bearing, add 2
Add time to evacuate & charge system if required.
Recover refrigerant, add 2

(G) Compressor Assy., Renew

Includes: Transfer parts as required. Evacuate and charge system.

1993-95 (1.3) 2.0
Recover refrigerant, add 2
Install liq. line filter, add (.9) 1.2

(G) Condenser Assy., Renew

Includes: Evacuate and charge system.

1993-95 (1.3) 2.0
w/AT add (.1) 1
Recover refrigerant, add 2

(G) Control Assy., Temperature, Renew

1993-95 (.5) 8

(G) Core, Evaporator, Renew

Includes: Evacuate and charge system.

R&R center console, add 5
1993-95
Four (2.6) 4.8
V6 (2.4) 4.5
Recover refrigerant, add 2

(G) Cylinder & Shaft Assy., Compressor, Renew

Includes: R&R compressor. Transfer parts as required. Evacuate and charge system.

All models
HR6 compressor (2.0) 3.3
Recover refrigerant, add 2

(G) Head and/or Seal, Compressor Front, Renew

Includes: R&R compressor. R&R clutch pulley assy., R&R shaft seal assy. Clean and inspect parts. Evacuate and charge system.

All models
HR6 compressor (1.7) 3.0
Recover refrigerant, add 2

(G) Hoses, AC, Renew

Includes: Evacuate and charge system.

All models
one (.9) 1.7
each adtnl. (.3) 5
Recover refrigerant, add 2

(G) Receiver/Drier Assy., Renew

Includes: Evacuate and charge system.

1993-95 (1.2) 1.7
Recover refrigerant, add 2

(G) Relay, AC, Renew

1993-95 (.3) 5

(G) Resistor, Blower Motor, Renew

All models (.3) 4

(G) Rotor and/or Bearing, Compressor Clutch, Renew

Includes: R&R hub and drive plate assy.

1993-95
V5 compressor
Four (1.8) 2.2
V6 (1.9) 2.3
HR6 compressor (1.8) 2.5
Add time to evacuate and charge system if required.
Recover refrigerant, add 2

(G) Seal, Seat and O-Ring, Compressor Front, Renew

Includes: R&R clutch hub and drive plate assy. Evacuate and charge system.

1993-95
HR6 compressor (1.7) 2.8
V5 compressor
Four (1.7) 2.8
V6 (1.8) 2.9
Recover refrigerant, add 2

(G) Sensor, AC Pressure, Renew

1993-95 (.2) 4

(G) Switch, Blower Motor, Renew

1993-95 (.6) 1.0

(G) Switch, Master Electrical, Renew

All models (.5) 8

(G) Switch, Mode Selector, Renew

1994-95 Grand Am (.7) 1.0

(G) Switch, Temperature Selector, Renew

1994-95 Grand Am (.6) 9

(G) Valve, Expansion, Renew

Includes: Evacuate and charge system.

1993-95 (1.7) 2.5
Recover refrigerant, add 2

(G) Valve, Vacuum Selector, Renew

All models (.6) 8

GENERAL MOTORS CORPORATION-"T"BODY (FWD)
PONTIAC LEMANS

LABOR — COOLING SYSTEM — LABOR

(Factory Time) Chilton Time

TESTING

(M) Pressure Test Cooling System
All models 3

SERVICE

(G) Belt, Drive, Adjust
All models
one (.4) 5
each adtnl. 1

(G) Belt, Drive, Renew
All models
AC (.4) 5
fan, alternator (.2) 3

(G) Blades, Fan or Clutch Assy., Renew
All models (.4) 6

(G) Control Assy., Heater, Renew
All models (.9) 1.5

(G) Core, Heater, R&R or Renew
All models (1.5) 2.7
Add time to recharge AC system, if required.
Boil & Repair, add 1.2
Repair Core, add 9
Recore, add 1.2

(G) Expansion (Freeze) Plugs, Water Jacket, Renew
Add appropriate time to access plug.
All models, each (.3) 5

(G) Gauge, Temperature (Dash Unit), Renew
All models (.6) 1.0

(G) Hoses, Heater, Renew
All models
one (.3) 4
each adtnl. 2

(G) Hoses, Radiator, Renew
Includes: Drain and refill cooling system as required.
All models
upper (.3) 4
lower (.4) 5
both (.5) 7

(G) Motor, Heater Blower, Renew
All models (.3) 5

(G) Motor, Radiator Fan and/or Fan, Renew
All models (.3) 6

(G) Pump and/or Gasket, Water, Renew
Includes: Drain and refill cooling system.
All models (1.7) 2.5
w/AC add (.1) 1
w/PS add (.6) 6

(G) Radiator Assy., R&R or Renew
All models (.9) 1.4
w/AT add (.1) 1
Boil & Repair, add 1.5
Rod Clean, add 1.9
Repair Core, add 1.3
Renew Tank, add 1.6
Renew Trans. Oil Cooler, add 1.9
Recore Radiator, add 1.7

(G) Relay, Radiator Fan Motor, Renew
All models (.2) 3

(G) Resistor, Fan Motor, Renew
All models (.2) 3

(G) Resistor, Heater Blower Motor, Renew
All models (.2) 3

(G) Sending Unit, Engine Coolant Temp., Renew
All models (.4) 6

(G) Switch, Heater Blower Motor, Renew
All models (.5) 7

(G) Thermostat, Coolant, Renew
All models (2.0) 2.8
w/AC add (.2) 2

(G) Winterize Cooling System
Includes: Run engine to check for leaks, tighten all hose connections. Test radiator and pressure cap, drain radiator and engine block. Add antifreeze and refill system.
All models 5

LABOR — AIR CONDITIONING — LABOR

(Factory Time) Chilton Time

Note: If more than one item requires replacement where evacuation and discharging the system is already included in the operation, deduct 1.0 hour for each additional item from the time listed.

SERVICE AND TESTING

(G) Drain, Evacuate and Recharge System
All models (.5) 1.0

(G) Flush Refrigerant System, Complete
To be used in conjunction with component replacement which could contaminate system. Includes evacuate and recharge.
All models 1.3

(G) Recover and/or Recycle AC Refrigerant
Add to evacuate and charge the AC system, as required.
All models 2

(G) Refrigerant, Add (Partial Charge)
All models 6

COMPONENTS

(G) Accumulator Assy., Renew
Includes: Evacuate and charge system.
All models (.8) 1.5

(G) Actuator, Vacuum, Renew
All models
defroster door (.3) 5
upper or lower mode door (.5) 9
air inlet door (.5) 9

(G) Belt, Compressor Drive, Renew
All models (.4) 5

(G) Blower Motor, Renew
All models (.3) 5

(G) Clutch Plate & Hub Assy., Compressor, Renew
Includes: R&R hub and drive plate assy. Check air gap.
All models (1.4) 2.2
Recover refrigerant add 2

(G) Coil and/or Pulley Rim, Compressor Clutch, Renew
Includes: R&R hub and drive plate assy.
All models (1.5) 2.3
Renew pulley or bearing add 2
Recover refrigerant add 2

(G) Compressor Assy., Renew
Includes: Transfer parts as required. Evacuate and charge system.
All models (1.2) 2.0
Install liquid line filter add (.9) 1.2
Recover refrigerant add 2

(G) Condenser Assy., Renew
Includes: Evacuate and charge system.
All models (2.5) 3.5
w/AT add (.1) 1

(G) Control Assy., Temperature, Renew
All models (.9) 1.5

(G) Core, Evaporator, Renew
Includes: Evacuate and charge system.
All models (3.0) 4.0

LABOR — AIR CONDITIONING — LABOR

(Factory Time) Chilton Time

(G) Expansion Tube (Orifice), Clean & Inspect or Renew

Includes: Evacuate and charge system.

All models (.8) 1.5
Install liquid line filter add (.9) 1.2

(G) Hoses, AC, Renew

Includes: Evacuate and charge system.

All models
one (.8) 1.5
each adtnl. (.3) 5

(G) Relay, Blower Motor, Renew

All models (.2) 3

(G) Resistor, Blower Motor, Renew

All models (.2) 3

(G) Rotor and/or Bearing, Compressor Clutch, Renew

Includes: R&R hub and drive plate assy.

All models (1.5) 2.3
Recover refrigerant add 2

(G) Seal, Compressor Shaft, Renew

Includes: R&R compressor. Evacuate and charge system.

All models (1.5) 2.4

(G) Switch, Blower Motor, Renew

1993 (.3) 6

(G) Switch, Compressor Cut-Off, Renew

All models
low pressure (.2) 4
high pressure (.3) 5
Add time to recharge AC system if required.

(G) Switch, Master Electrical, Renew

All models (.6) 1.0

(G) Valve, Vacuum Selector, Renew

All models (.4) 6

GENERAL MOTORS CORPORATION-"W"BODY (FWD)

OLDSMOBILE CUTLASS SUPREME • PONTIAC GRAND PRIX
CHEVROLET LUMINA • BUICK REGAL

LABOR — COOLING SYSTEM — LABOR

(Factory Time) Chilton Time

TESTING

(M) Pressure Test Cooling System

All models 3

SERVICE

(G) Belt, Drive, Renew

1993-95 V6
2.8L (W), 3.1L (T) (.3) 5
w/AIR add 1
3.4L (X) (.3) 5
3.8L (L) (.2) 4
3.1L (M) (.2) 4
w/AIR add 1

(G) Bypass and/or Tube, Hose, Renew

All models (.5) 9

(G) Control Assy., Temperature, Renew

1993-95 (.5) 8

(G) Core, Heater, R&R or Renew

1993-95 (1.2) 2.0
Add time to recharge AC system if required.
Recover refrigerant, add 2
Boil & Repair, add 1.2
Repair Core, add 9
Recore, add 1.2

(G) Expansion (Freeze) Plugs, Water Jacket, Renew

Add appropriate time to access plug.

All models, each 5

(G) Hoses, Heater, Renew

1994-95 (.9) 1.4

(G) Hoses, Radiator, Renew

Includes: Drain and refill cooling system as required.

All models
upper (.3) 4
lower (.4) 5
both (.5) 7

(G) Motor, Heater Blower, Renew

1993-95 (.6) 1.1

(G) Motor, Radiator Fan and/or Fan, Renew

All models
single (.3) 5
dual
one (.6) 8
both (.8) 1.1

(G) Pump and/or Gasket, Water, Renew

Includes: Drain and refill cooling system.

1993-95 V6 (.7) 1.2

(G) Radiator Assy., R&R or Renew

1993-95 Four (.5) 8
1993-95 V6 (1.1) 1.5
Renew side tank and/or gasket, add
one (.7) 1.0
both (1.2) 1.7
w/AT add 2
Boil & Repair, add 1.5
Rod Clean, add 1.9
Repair Core, add 1.3
Renew Tank, add 1.6
Renew Trans. Oil Cooler, add 1.9
Recore Radiator, add 1.7

(G) Relay, Heater Blower Motor, Renew

All models (.2) 3

(G) Resistor, Heater Blower Motor, Renew

All models (.4) 7

(G) Sending Unit, Engine Coolant Temp., Renew

All models (.4) 7

(G) Switch, Heater Blower Motor, Renew

All models (.5) 7

(G) Tensioner, Drive Belt, Renew

1993-95 V6
2.8L (W), 3.1L (T) (.2) 4
3.4L (X) (.4) 6
3.8L (L) (.9) 1.4
3.1L (M) (.3) 4

(G) Thermostat, Coolant, Renew

1993-95 Four (.5) 6
1993-95 V6
2.8L (W), 3.1L (T) (.5) 6
3.4L (X) (.8) 1.2
3.8L (L) (.5) 6
3.1L (M) (.3) 5

(G) Winterize Cooling System

Includes: Run engine to check for leaks, tighten all hose connections. Test radiator and pressure cap, drain radiator and engine block. Add antifreeze and refill system.

All models 5

(Factory Time) Chilton Time

Note: If more than one item requires replacement where evacuation and discharging the system is already included in the operation, deduct 1.0 hour for each additional item from the time listed.

SERVICE AND TESTING

(G) Drain, Evacuate and Recharge System

All models (.5) 1.0
Recover refrigerant add 2

(G) Flush Refrigerant System, Complete

To be used in conjunction with component replacement which could contaminate system. Includes evacuate and recharge.

All models 1.3
Recover refrigerant add 2

(G) Leak Check

Includes: Check all lines and connections.

All models 5

(G) Recover and/or Recycle AC Refrigerant

Add to evacuate and charge the AC system, as required.

All models 2

(G) Refrigerant, Add (Partial Charge)

All models 6

COMPONENTS

(G) Accumulator Assy., Renew

Includes: Evacuate and charge system.

All models (.9) 1.5
Recover refrigerant, add 2

(G) Actuator, Vacuum, Renew

1993-95
defroster (.8) 1.4
upper or lower mode (.5) 1.0
air inlet (1.6) 2.4
slave valve (.8) 1.4

(G) Aspirator, Renew

1993-95
LeSabre (.2) 4
Delta 88 (.7) 1.1

(G) Belt, Compressor Drive, Renew

All models (.2) 4

(G) Blower Motor, Renew

heater (.8) 1.2
AC (.2) 4
1993-95 (.4) 6
w/press-on cage, add 5

(G) Clutch Plate & Hub Assy., Compressor, Renew

Includes: R&R hub and drive plate assy. Check air gap.

All models
HR6, DA6 compressor (.6) 9
Add time to evacuate and charge system if required.
Recover refrigerant, add 2

(G) Coil and/or Pulley Rim, Compressor Clutch, Renew

Includes: R&R hub and drive plate assy.

All models
HR6, DA6 compressor (1.0) 1.4
Renew pulley or bearing, add 2
Add time to evacuate and charge system if required.
Recover refrigerant, add 2

(G) Compressor Assy., Renew

Includes: Transfer parts as required. Evacuate and charge system.

All models (1.1) 1.9
HR6, DA6 compressor (1.1) 1.9
Install liquid line & filter, add (.4) 5
Recover refrigerant, add 2

(G) Condenser Assy., Renew

Includes: Evacuate and charge system.

All models (1.2) 2.0
Recover refrigerant, add 2

(G) Control Assy., Temperature, Renew

All models
wo/touch control (.6) 8
touch control (.5) 8
custom air (.5) 8
electronic (.3) 5
comfort control (.5) 8

(G) Core, Evaporator, Renew

Includes: Evacuate and charge system.

All models (3.7) 6.5
Recover refrigerant, add 2

(G) Expansion Tube (Orifice), Clean & Inspect or Renew

Includes: Evacuate and charge system.

All models (.8) 1.4
Recover refrigerant, add 2

(G) Head and/or Seal, Compressor Front, Renew

Includes: R&R compressor. R&R clutch pulley assy., R&R shaft seal assy. Clean and inspect parts. Evacuate and charge system.

All models
HR6, DA6 compressor (1.7) 2.8
Recover refrigerant, add 2

(G) Hose, Aspirator, R&R or Renew

1993-95
LeSabre (.3) 7
Delta 88 (.7) 1.1

(G) Hoses, AC, Renew

Includes: Evacuate and charge system.

All models
liquid line (.9) 1.5
evaporator to accumulator (.8) 1.5
suction or discharge (1.0) 1.7
Recover refrigerant, add 2

(G) Module, Blower Motor and Compressor Control, Renew

1993-95 (.5) 8

(G) Module, EEC Power, Renew

1993 (.4) 6

(G) Programmer, R&R or Renew

1993
Bonneville (2.1) 3.0
LeSabre, Delta 88 (.8) 1.1
1994-95
Bonneville (1.9) 3.0
w/console add 7
Delta 88 (.6) 1.1
LeSabre (.4) 7

(G) Relay, Blower Motor, Renew

All models (.3) 4

(G) Resistor, Blower Motor, Renew

All models (.3) 4

(G) Rotor and/or Bearing, Compressor Clutch, Renew

Includes: R&R hub and drive plate assy.

All models
HR6, DA6 compressor (1.0) 1.5
Add time to evacuate and charge system if required.
Recover refrigerant, add 2

(G) Seal, Seat and O-Ring, Compressor Front, Renew

Includes: R&R clutch hub and drive plate assy. Evacuate and charge system.

All models
HR6, DA6 compressor (1.4) 2.5
Recover refrigerant, add 2

(G) Sensor, Ambient Temperature, Renew

1993-95 (.2) 4

(G) Sensor, In-Vehicle, Renew

1993-95 (.4) 7

(G) Sensor, Outside Temperature, Renew

1993-95 (.2) 5

(G) Shaft & Cylinder Assy., Compressor, Renew

Includes: R&R compressor. Evacuate and charge system.

All models
HR6, DA6 compressor (2.0) 3.1
Recover refrigerant, add 2

(G) Switch, Blower Motor, Renew

1993-95 (.5) 7

(G) Switch, Master Electrical, Renew

All models (.3) 6

(G) Switch, Refrigerant, Renew

All models
high pressure (.3) 4
low pressure (.2) 4
pressure cycling (.3) 4
Add time to evacuate and charge system if required.

(G) Valve, Heater Water Control, Renew

All models (.4) 6

(G) Valve, Vacuum Selector, Renew

All models (.3) 6

SATURN

SC1 • SC2 • SL1 • SL2 • SW1 • SW2

LABOR — COOLING SYSTEM — LABOR

(Factory Time) Chilton Time

TESTING

(M) Pressure Test Cooling System

All models 3

SERVICE

(G) Belt, Serpentine Drive, Renew

All models (.2) 3

(G) Control Assy., Heater, Renew

All models (.6) 8

(G) Core, Heater, R&R or Renew

All models (1.5) 2.0
Boil & Repair, add 1.2
Repair Core, add 9
Recore, add 1.2

(G) Expansion (Freeze) Plugs, Water Jacket, Renew

Add appropriate time to access plug.

All models, each 5

(G) Hoses, Heater, Renew

All models
inlet
SOHC (.6) 8
DOHC (.8) 1.0
outlet (.6) 8

(G) Hoses, Radiator, Renew

Includes: Drain and refill cooling system as required.

All models
upper (.5) 6
lower (.6) 7
both (.7) 1.0

(G) Motor, Heater Blower, Renew

All models (.3) 5

(G) Motor, Radiator Fan and/or Fan, Renew

All models
MT (.4) 6
AT (.5) 7
w/AC, add 1

(G) Pump and/or Gasket, Water, Renew

Includes: Drain and refill cooling system.

All models (1.1) 1.5

(G) Radiator Assy., R&R or Renew

All models
SOHC (.8) 1.1
DOHC (.9) 1.2
w/AC, add 1
w/AT, add 2
Boil & Repair, add 1.5
Rod Clean, add 1.9
Repair Core, add 1.3
Renew Tank, add 1.6
Renew Trans. Oil Cooler, add 1.9
Recore Radiator, add 1.7

(G) Relay, Heater Blower Motor, Renew

All models (.2) 3

(G) Relay, Radiator Fan Motor, Renew

All models (.2) 3

(G) Resistor, Heater Blower Motor, Renew

All models (.5) 6

(G) Sending Unit, Engine Coolant Temp., Renew

All models (.7) 9

(G) Sensor, Engine Coolant Temperature Indicator, Renew

All models (.7) 9

(G) Switch, Heater Blower Motor, Renew

All models (.6) 8

(G) Tensioner, Drive Belt, Renew

All models
SOHC (.4) 5
w/PS, add 3
DOHC (1.0) 1.3

(G) Thermostat, Coolant, Renew

All models (.6) 8

(G) Winterize Cooling System

Includes: Run engine to check for leaks, tighten all hose connections. Test radiator and pressure cap, drain radiator and engine block. Add antifreeze and refill system.

All models 5

LABOR — AIR CONDITIONING — LABOR

(Factory Time) Chilton Time

Note: If more than one item requires replacement where evacuation and discharging the system is already included in the operation, deduct 1.0 hour for each additional item from the time listed.

SERVICE AND TESTING

(G) Drain, Evacuate and Recharge System

All models 1.2

(G) Flush Refrigerant System, Complete

To be used in conjunction with component replacement which could contaminate system. Includes evacuate and recharge.

All models 1.3

(G) Leak Check

Includes: Check all lines and connections.

All models 5

(G) Recover and/or Recycle AC Refrigerant

Add to evacuate and charge the AC system, as required.

All models, add 2

(G) Refrigerant, Add (Partial Charge)

All models 6

COMPONENTS

(G) Actuator, Electric, Renew

All models, air inlet (.6) 9

(G) Belt, Compressor Drive, Renew

All models (.2) 3

(G) Blower Motor, Renew

All models (.3) 5

(G) Coil, Evaporator, Renew

Includes: Evacuate and charge system.

All models (5.9) 7.5

(G) Compressor Assy., Renew

Includes: Transfer parts as required. Evacuate and charge system.

All models (1.7) 2.2

(G) Condenser Assy., Renew

Includes: Evacuate and charge system.

All models (1.3) 1.8

(G) Control Assy., AC, Renew

All models (.6) 8

(G) Hoses, AC, Renew

Includes: Evacuate and charge system.

All models
discharge (1.1) 1.6
suction (1.0) 1.5
expansion valve to receiver (1.7) 2.1

(G) Receiver/Drier Assy., Renew

Includes: Evacuate and charge system.

All models (1.2) 1.7

LABOR — AIR CONDITIONING — LABOR

(Factory Time) Chilton Time

(G) Relay, Blower Motor, Renew
All models (.2) 3

(G) Resistor, Blower Motor, Renew
All models (.5) 6

(G) Switch, Blower Motor, Renew
All models (.6) 8

(G) Switch, Compressor Cut-Off, Renew
All models
high/low pressure (.2) 3

(G) Valve, Expansion, Renew
Includes: Evacuate and charge system.
All models (1.7) 2.4

GENERAL MOTORS CORPORATION-(RWD)
BUICK ROADMASTER

LABOR — COOLING SYSTEM — LABOR

(Factory Time) Chilton Time

TESTING

(M) Pressure Test Cooling System
All models 3

SERVICE

(G) Belt, Drive, Renew
All models
serpentine (.2) 3

(G) Blades, Fan or Clutch Assy., Renew
All models (.3) 5

(G) Control Assy., Heater, Renew
1993-95
w/touch control (.6) 9
wo/touch control (.5) 8

(G) Core, Heater, R&R or Renew
1993-95
w/AC (.9) 2.5
Boil & Repair, add 1.2
Repair Core, add 9
Recore, add 1.2

(G) Expansion (Freeze) Plugs, Water Jacket, Renew
Add appropriate time to access plug.
All models, each 5

(G) Gauge, Temperature (Dash Unit), Renew
1993-95 (.8) 1.2

(G) Gauge, Temperature (Engine Unit), Renew
1993-95 (.4) 5

(G) Hoses, Heater, Renew
1993-95
water pump to core (.3) 4
water valve to core (.3) 4
manifold to core (.8) 1.0
all (.7) 1.3

(G) Hoses, Radiator, Renew
Includes: Drain and refill cooling system as required.
All models
upper (.3) 4
lower (.4) 5
both (.5) 7
by-pass (.5) 6

(G) Motor, Heater Blower, Renew
1993-95 (.4) 6

(G) Pump and/or Gasket, Water, Renew
Includes: Drain and refill cooling system.
1993-95 V8 (.8) 1.3

(G) Radiator Assy., R&R or Renew
1993-95 (.6) 1.0
Boil & Repair, add 1.5
Rod Clean, add 1.9
Repair Core, add 1.3
Renew Tank, add 1.6
Renew Trans. Oil Cooler, add 1.9
Recore Radiator, add 1.7

(G) Relay, Heater Blower Motor, Renew
1993-95 (.3) 4

(G) Resistor, Heater Blower Motor, Renew
1993-95 (.3) 4

(G) Sending Unit, Engine Coolant Temp., Renew
All models (.4) 5

(G) Switch, Heater Blower Motor, Renew
1993-95 (.7) 1.0

(G) Tensioner, Drive Belt, Renew
1993-95 serpentine (.2) 4

(G) Thermostat, Coolant, Renew
1993-95 (.6) 7

(G) Valve, Heater Control, Renew
1993-95 (.4) 5

(G) Winterize Cooling System
Includes: Run engine to check for leaks, tighten all hose connections. Test radiator and pressure cap, drain radiator and engine block. Add antifreeze and refill system.
All models 5

LABOR — AIR CONDITIONING — LABOR

(Factory Time) Chilton Time

Note: If more than one item requires replacement where evacuation and discharging the system is already included in the operation, deduct 1.0 hour for each additional item from the time listed.

SERVICE AND TESTING

(G) Drain, Evacuate and Recharge System
All models 1.0
Recover refrigerant add 2

(G) Flush Refrigerant System, Complete
To be used in conjunction with component replacement which could contaminate system. Includes evacuate and recharge.
All models 1.3
Recover refrigerant add 2

(G) Leak Check
Includes: Check all lines and connections.
All models 5

(G) Recover and/or Recycle AC Refrigerant
Add to evacuate and charge the AC system, as required.
All models 2

(G) Refrigerant, Add (Partial Charge)
All models 6

LABOR AIR CONDITIONING LABOR

(Factory Time) Chilton Time

COMPONENTS

(G) Accumulator Assy., Renew
Includes: Evacuate and charge system.
1993-95 (.8) **1.5**
Recover refrigerant, add .... **.2**

(G) Actuator, Electric, Renew
1993-95 temp. door (.8) **1.1**

(G) Actuator, Vacuum, Renew
1993-95
defroster (.2) .... **.4**
upper or lower mode (.2) .... **.4**
air inlet (3.2) **4.8**

(G) Bearing, Compressor, Main, Renew
Includes: R&R compressor. Evacuate and charge system.
All models (1.5) **2.8**
Recover refrigerant, add .... **.2**

(G) Belt, Compressor Drive, Renew
1993-95 serpentine (.2) .... **.3**

(G) Blower Motor, Renew
1993-95 (.4) .... **.6**

(G) Clutch Plate & Hub Assy., Compressor, Renew
Includes: R&R hub and drive plate assy. Check air gap.
1993 (.3) .... **.8**

(G) Coil and/or Pulley Rim, Compressor Clutch, Renew
Includes: R&R hub and drive plate assy.
1993 (.5) **1.0**
Renew pulley or bearing, add (.1) .... **.2**

(G) Compressor Assy., Renew
Includes: Transfer parts as required. Evacuate and charge system.
1993-95 (1.0) **2.0**
Recover refrigerant, add .... **.2**
Install liquid line filter, add **1.2**

(G) Condenser Assy., Renew
Includes: Evacuate and charge system.
1993-95 (1.6) **2.0**
Recover refrigerant, add .... **.2**

(G) Control Assy., AC, Renew
1993-95
wo/touch control (.6) .... **.9**
w/touch control (.5) .... **.8**

(G) Core, Evaporator, Renew
Includes: Evacuate and charge system.
1993-95 (1.3) **3.5**
Recover refrigerant, add .... **.2**

(G) Expansion Tube (Orifice), Clean & Inspect or Renew
Includes: Evacuate and charge system.
1993-95 (.9) **1.4**
Recover refrigerant, add .... **.2**

(G) Head and/or Seal, Compressor Front, Renew
Includes: R&R compressor. R&R clutch pulley assy., R&R shaft seal assy. Clean and inspect parts. Evacuate and charge system.
1993 (1.7) **2.8**
Recover refrigerant, add .... **.2**

(G) Hoses, AC, Renew
Includes: Evacuate and charge system.
1993-95
one (.8) **1.7**
each adtnl. (.3) .... **.5**
Assemble replacement hose, (.3) add ..... **.4**
Recover refrigerant, add .... **.2**

(G) Relay, Blower Motor, Renew
1993-95 (.3) .... **.4**

(G) Resistor, Blower Motor, Renew
1993-95 (.3) .... **.4**

(G) Rotor and/or Bearing, Compressor Clutch, Renew
Includes: R&R hub and drive plate assy.
1993 (.6) **1.2**

(G) Seal, Seat and O-Ring, Compressor Front, Renew
Includes: R&R clutch hub and drive plate assy. Evacuate and charge system.
1993 (1.2) **2.5**
Recover refrigerant, add .... **.2**

(G) Sensor, In-Vehicle, Renew
1993-95 (.6) .... **.8**

(G) Switch, Blower Motor, Renew
1993-95 (.7) **1.0**

(G) Switch, Low Pressure and/or Cycling, Renew
1993-95 (.2) .... **.4**

(G) Switch, Master Electrical, Renew
1993-95 (.7) .... **.9**

(G) Valve, Pressure Relief, Renew
Includes: Evacuate and charge system.
All models (1.0) **1.4**
Recover refrigerant, add .... **.2**

(G) Valve, Vacuum Selector, Renew
1993-95 (.6) .... **.8**

GENERAL MOTORS CORPORATION-(RWD)
CADILLAC FLEETWOOD

LABOR COOLING SYSTEM LABOR

(Factory Time) Chilton Time

TESTING

(M) Pressure Test Cooling System
All models .... **.3**

SERVICE

(G) Belt, Serpentine Drive, Renew
1993-95 (.2) .... **.5**

(G) Blades, Fan or Clutch Assy., Renew
1993 (.6) .... **.8**
1994 (.4) .... **.6**

(G) Bypass and/or Tube, Hose, Renew
1993-95 (.5) .... **.8**

(G) Core, Heater, R&R or Renew
1993-95 (1.2) **2.3**
Boil & Repair, add **1.2**
Repair Core, add .... **.9**
Recore, add **1.2**

(G) Expansion (Freeze) Plugs, Water Jacket, Renew
Add appropriate time to access plug.
All models, each .... **.5**

(G) Hoses, Heater, Renew
All models
pipe
inlet (.5) .... **.7**
outlet (.4) .... **.6**
both (.9) **1.3**
w/HD cooling add .... **.3**

(G) Hoses, Radiator, Renew
Includes: Drain and refill cooling system as required.
1993-95
upper (.3) .... **.4**

LABOR — COOLING SYSTEM — LABOR

(Factory Time) Chilton Time

lower (.5) 6
both (.5) 8

(G) Pump and/or Gasket, Water, Renew
Includes: Drain and refill cooling system.
1993 (1.1) 2.0
1994 (1.4) 2.3
Renew pump drive seal, add 5
w/HD cooling, add 5

(G) Radiator Assy., R&R or Renew
1993-95 (.6) 1.1

Boil & Repair, add 1.5
Rod Clean, add 1.9
Repair Core, add 1.3
Renew Tank, add 1.6
Renew Trans. Oil Cooler, add 1.9
Recore Radiator, add 1.7

(G) Tensioner, Drive Belt, Renew
1993-95 (.2) 5
w/HD cooling add (.2) 2

(G) Thermostat, Coolant, Renew
1993 (.5) 7
1994 (.6) 8
w/cruise control add (.1) 1

(G) Winterize Cooling System
Includes: Run engine to check for leaks, tighten all hose connections. Test radiator and pressure cap, drain radiator and engine block. Add antifreeze and refill system.
All models 5

LABOR — AIR CONDITIONING — LABOR

(Factory Time) Chilton Time

Note: If more than one item requires replacement where evacuation and discharging the system is already included in the operation, deduct 1.0 hour for each additional item from the time listed.

SERVICE AND TESTING

(G) Drain, Evacuate and Recharge System
All models 1.0
Recover refrigerant add 2

(G) Flush Refrigerant System, Complete
To be used in conjunction with component replacement which could contaminate system. Includes evacuate and recharge.
All models 1.3
Recover refrigerant add 2

(G) Pressure Test System
All models 6

(G) Recover and/or Recycle AC Refrigerant
Add to evacuate and charge the AC system, as required.
All models 2

(G) Refrigerant, Add (Partial Charge)
All models 6

COMPONENTS

(G) Accumulator Assy., Renew
Includes: Evacuate and charge system.
All models (.8) 1.5
Recover refrigerant add 2

(G) Actuator, Vacuum, Renew
1993-95
defroster (.4) 7
heater shut-off (3.2) 4.5
upper or lower mode (.3) 6
air inlet (2.6) 4.0

(G) Aspirator, Renew
1993-95 (.5) 7

(G) Belt, Compressor Drive, Renew
1993-95 serpentine (.2) 5

(G) Blower Motor, Renew
1993-95 (.4) 6

(G) Compressor Assy., Renew
Includes: Transfer parts as required. Evacuate and charge system.
1993-95 (1.1) 2.0
Install liquid line filter,
add 4
Recover refrigerant add 2

(G) Condenser Assy., Renew
Includes: Evacuate and charge system.
1993-95 (1.0) 2.0
Recover refrigerant add 2

(G) Control Assy., AC, Renew
1993-95 (.6) 9

(G) Core, Evaporator, Renew
Includes: Evacuate and charge system.
1993-95 (1.7) 3.0
Recover refrigerant add 2

(G) Expansion Tube (Orifice), Clean & Inspect or Renew
Includes: Evacuate and charge system.
All models (.8) 1.4
Recover refrigerant add 2

(G) Hose, Aspirator, R&R or Renew
1993-95 (.6) 1.0

(G) Hoses, AC, Renew
Includes: Evacuate and charge system.
1993-95
one (.8) 1.7
each adtnl. 5
Recover refrigerant add 2

(G) Module, HVAC Power, Renew
1993-95 (.2) 5

(G) Seal, Compressor Shaft, Renew
Includes: R&R compressor. Evacuate and charge system.
1993-95 (1.0) 2.5
Recover refrigerant add 2

(G) Sensor, In-Vehicle, Renew
1993-95 (.5) 8

(G) Switch, Compressor Cut-Off, Renew
1993-95 (.3) 4

(G) Switch, High Pressure Cut-Off, Renew
1993-95 (.2) 3
Add time to recharge AC system if required.

GENERAL MOTORS CORPORATION-(RWD)
CHEVROLET CAMARO • PONTIAC FIREBIRD

LABOR — COOLING SYSTEM — LABOR

(Factory Time) Chilton Time

TESTING

(M) Pressure Test Cooling System
All models 3

SERVICE

(G) Belt, Drive, Renew
1993-95 serpentine (.2) 3

(G) Control Assy., Heater, Renew
1993 (.3) 6
1994-95 (.7) 1.0

LABOR — COOLING SYSTEM — LABOR

(Factory Time) Chilton Time

(G) Core, Heater, R&R or Renew
1993-95 (1.3) 2.5
Add time to recharge AC system if required.

(G) Expansion (Freeze) Plugs, Water Jacket, Renew
Add appropriate time to access plug.
All models (.3) 5

(G) Hoses, Heater, Renew
1993-95
wo/AC
one (1.0) 1.3
both (1.2) 1.5
w/AC, each
inlet or outlet (.7) 1.0

(G) Hoses, Radiator, Renew
Includes: Drain and refill cooling system as required.
1993-95
upper (.5) 6
lower (.8) 9
both (.9) 1.1

(G) Motor, Heater Blower, Renew
All models (.5) 7

(G) Motor, Radiator Fan and/or Fan, Renew
1993-95
right or single
V6 (.5) 7
V8 (.6) 8
left (.5) 7
both (.8) 1.1

(G) Pump and/or Gasket, Water, Renew
Includes: Drain and refill cooling system.
1993
V6 (3.0) 3.5
V8 (1.8) 2.3
1994-95 (1.8) 2.3

(G) Radiator Assy., R&R or Renew
1993-95 (1.5) 1.9
w/AT, add 2

(G) Relay, Heater Blower Motor, Renew
All models (.3) 4

(G) Relay, Radiator Fan Motor, Renew
All models (.2) 4

(G) Resistor, Heater Blower Motor, Renew
1993 (.2) 3
1994-95 (.5) 7

(G) Sending Unit, Engine Coolant Temp., Renew
1993-95 (.7) 9

(G) Switch, Heater Blower Motor, Renew
1993 (.4) 6
1994-95 (.7) 9

(G) Tensioner, Drive Belt, Renew
1993-95 V8 (.3) 5

(G) Thermostat, Coolant, Renew
1993-95
V6 (.7) 9
V8 (.6) 8

(G) Winterize Cooling System
Includes: Run engine to check for leaks, tighten all hose connections. Test radiator and pressure cap, drain radiator and engine block. Add antifreeze and refill system.
All models 5

LABOR — AIR CONDITIONING — LABOR

(Factory Time) Chilton Time

Note: If more than one item requires replacement where evacuation and discharging the system is already included in the operation, deduct 1.0 hour for each additional item from the time listed.

SERVICE AND TESTING

(G) Drain, Evacuate and Recharge System
All models (.5) 1.0
Recover refrigerant, add 2

(G) Flush Refrigerant System, Complete
To be used in conjunction with component replacement which could contaminate system. Includes evacuate and recharge.
All models 1.3
Recover refrigerant, add 2

(G) Leak Check
Includes: Check all lines and connections.
All models 5

(G) Recover and/or Recycle AC Refrigerant
Add to evacuate and charge the AC system, as required.
All models 2

(G) Refrigerant, Add (Partial Charge)
All models 6

COMPONENTS

(G) Accumulator Assy., Renew
Includes: Evacuate and charge system.
1993 (.8) 1.5
Recover refrigerant, add 2

(G) Actuator, Vacuum, Renew
1993
defroster (2.3) 3.5
upper or lower mode (2.3) 3.5
air inlet (.6) 9
1994-95
defroster (2.6) 3.7
upper or lower mode (.6) 9
vent mode (2.7) 3.8

(G) Belt, Compressor Drive, Renew
1993-95 V6
serpentine (.2) 3
1993-95 V8
serpentine (.2) 3

(G) Blower Motor, Renew
All models (.3) 6

(G) Clutch Plate & Hub Assy., Compressor, Renew
Includes: R&R hub and drive plate assy. Check air gap.
1993-95 (1.3) 1.5
Add time to evacuate and charge AC system if required.

(G) Coil and/or Pulley Rim, Compressor Clutch, Renew
Includes: R&R hub and drive plate assy.
1993-95 (1.4) 1.6
Renew pulley or bearing, add 1
Add time to evacuate and charge AC system if required.

(G) Coil, Evaporator, Renew
Includes: Evacuate and charge system.
1993 (2.6) 3.5
Recover refrigerant, add 2

(G) Compressor Assy., Renew
Includes: Transfer parts as required. Evacuate and charge system.
1993-95
V6 (1.6) 2.4
V8 (1.8) 2.8
Recover refrigerant, add 2
Install liquid line filter, add (.9) 1.2

(G) Condenser Assy., Renew
Includes: Evacuate and charge system.
1993-95 (1.7) 2.5
w/AT, add (.2) 2
Recover refrigerant, add 2

(G) Control Assy., Temperature, Renew
1993-95 (.5) 7

(G) Hoses, AC, Renew
Includes: Evacuate and charge system.
1993-95
suction & discharge (1.7) 2.2
all others (.8) 1.5
Recover refrigerant, add 2

(G) Relay, Blower Motor, Renew
All models (.3) 4

(G) Resistor, Blower Motor, Renew
All models (.3) 4

(G) Rotor and/or Bearing, Compressor Clutch, Renew
Includes: R&R hub and drive plate assy.
1993-95 (1.3) 1.5
Add time to evacuate and charge AC system if required.
Recover refrigerant, add 2

LABOR — AIR CONDITIONING — LABOR

(Factory Time) Chilton Time

(G) Seal, Compressor Shaft, Renew
Includes: R&R compressor. Evacuate and charge system.
1993-95 (2.2) 2.6
R&R accumulator, add (.3) 3
Recover refrigerant, add 2

(G) Switch, Blower Motor, Renew
1993 (.5) 7

(G) Switch, Master Electrical, Renew
1993 (.5) 7

(G) Valve, Expansion, Renew
Includes: Evacuate and charge system.
1993-95 (.9) 1.4
Recover refrigerant, add 2

GENERAL MOTORS CORPORATION-(RWD)
CHEVROLET CAPRICE

LABOR — COOLING SYSTEM — LABOR

(Factory Time) Chilton Time

SERVICE

(G) Belt, Drive, Renew
1993-94 serpentine (.2) 3

(G) Blades, Fan or Clutch Assy., Renew
All models (.3) 5

(G) Cluster, Instrument Assy., R&R or Renew
1993-94 (.9) 1.2

(G) Control Assy., Heater, Renew
1993-94 (.5) 9

(G) Core, Heater, R&R or Renew
1993-94 (.9) 1.5
Boil & Repair, add 1.2
Repair Core, add 9
Recore, add 1.2
w/HD cooling, add 3

(G) Expansion (Freeze) Plugs, Water Jacket, Renew (Engine Block)
Add appropriate time to access plug.
1993-94 (.3) 5

(G) Gauge, Temperature (Dash Unit), Renew
1993-94 (.7) 1.0

(G) Gauge, Temperature (Engine Unit), Renew
1993-94 (.4) 5

(G) Hoses, Heater, Renew
1993-94 (.9) 1.1
w/HD cooling, add 3

(G) Hoses, Radiator, Renew
Includes: Drain and refill cooling system as required.
All models
upper (.3) 4
lower (.4) 5
both (.5) 7
w/HD cooling, add 3

(G) Motor, Heater Blower, Renew
1993-94 (.4) 5

(G) Pump and/or Gasket, Water, Renew
Includes: Drain and refill cooling system.
1993 V6
229, 262 (1.3) 1.7
1993 V8
code E, 7 (.8) 1.3
1994 V8 (1.8) 2.2
w/HD cooling, add 3

(G) Radiator Assy., R&R or Renew
1993 (.6) 1.1
1994 (1.1) 1.5
w/engine oil cooler, add 2
w/HD cooling, add 5
Boil & Repair, add 1.5
Rod Clean, add 1.9
Repair Core, add 1.3
Renew Tank, add 1.6
Renew Trans. Oil Cooler, add 1.9
Recore Radiator, add 1.7

(G) Resistor, Heater Blower Motor, Renew
1993-94 (.2) 3

(G) Switch, Heater Blower Motor, Renew
1993-94 (.6) 9

(G) Tensioner, Drive Belt, Renew
1993 V6 (.3) 5
1993-94 V8 (.2) 4

(G) Thermostat, Coolant, Renew
1993 V6
231, 262 (.7) 8
1993-94 V8 (.5) 7
w/HD cooling, add 3

(G) Valve, Heater Water Shut-Off, Renew
1993-94 (.6) 7
w/HD cooling, add 3

(G) Winterize Cooling System
Includes: Run engine to check for leaks, tighten all hose connections. Test radiator and pressure cap, drain radiator and engine block. Add antifreeze and refill system.
All models 5

LABOR — AIR CONDITIONING — LABOR

(Factory Time) Chilton Time

Note: If more than one item requires replacement where evacuation and discharging the system is already included in the operation, deduct 1.0 hour for each additional item from the time listed.

SERVICE AND TESTING

(G) Drain, Evacuate and Recharge System
1993-94 (.5) 1.0
Recover refrigerant add 2

(G) Flush Refrigerant System, Complete
To be used in conjunction with component replacement which could contaminate system. Includes evacuate and recharge.
All models 1.3
Recover refrigerant add 2

(G) Leak Check
Includes: Check all lines and connections.
All models 5

(G) Pressure Test System
All models 1.0

(G) Recover and/or Recycle AC Refrigerant
Add to evacuate and charge the AC system, as required.
All models 2

(G) Refrigerant, Add (Partial Charge)
All models 6

LABOR — AIR CONDITIONING — LABOR

(Factory Time) — Chilton Time

COMPONENTS

(G) Accumulator Assy., Renew
Includes: Evacuate and charge system.
All models (.7) 1.5
Recover refrigerant, add 2

(G) Actuator, Vacuum, Renew
1993-94
defroster door (.2) 4
upper or lower mode (2.3) 3.0
air inlet (3.2) 4.8

(G) Belt, Compressor Drive, Renew
1993-94 V8
V belt (.3) 4
serpentine belt (.2) 3
w/code Y, add 1

(G) Blower Motor, Renew
1993-94 (.4) 5

(G) Cable, Temperature Control, Renew
1993-94 (.5) 6

(G) Clutch and/or Pulley, Compressor, Renew
Does not include R&R compressor.
1993-94 (.5) 1.0
Renew pulley or bearing, add 2
Add time to recharge AC system if required.
Recover refrigerant add 2

(G) Clutch Plate & Hub Assy., Compressor, Renew
Includes: R&R hub and drive plate assy. Check air gap.
1993-94 (.3) 8

(G) Compressor Assy., Renew
Includes: Transfer parts as required. Evacuate and charge system.
1993 (1.1) 2.0
1994 (1.2) 1.5
w/HD cooling, add 2
Install liquid line filter add 9
Recover refrigerant, add 2

(G) Condenser Assy., Renew
Includes: Evacuate and charge system.
1993-94 (1.8) 2.2
Recover refrigerant, add 2

(G) Control Unit, Temperature, Renew
1993-94 (.5) 1.0

(G) Core, Evaporator, Renew
Includes: Evacuate and charge system.
1993-94 (1.5) 2.8
Recover refrigerant, add 2

(G) Expansion Tube (Orifice), Clean & Inspect or Renew
Includes: Evacuate and charge system.
1993-94 (1.1) 1.5

Install liquid line filter, add (.9) 1.2
Recover refrigerant, add 2

(G) Head and/or Seal, Compressor Front, Renew
Includes: R&R compressor. R&R clutch pulley assy., R&R shaft seal assy. Clean and inspect parts. Evacuate and charge system.
1993-94 (1.5) 2.6
Recover refrigerant, add 2

(G) Hoses, AC, Renew
Includes: Evacuate and charge system.
1993-94
one (.9) 1.7
each adtnl. (.3) 5
Recover refrigerant, add 2

(G) Relay, Blower Motor, Renew
1993-94 (.3) 4

(G) Resistor, Blower Motor, Renew
1993-94 (.3) 4

(G) Switch, Blower Motor, Renew
1993-94 (.7) 9

(G) Switch, Master Electrical, Renew
1993-94 (.7) 1.1

(G) Valve, Vacuum Selector, Renew
1993-94 (.6) 8

GENERAL MOTORS CORPORATION-(RWD)
CHEVROLET CORVETTE

LABOR — COOLING SYSTEM — LABOR

(Factory Time) — Chilton Time

SERVICE

(G) Bypass and/or Tube, Hose, Renew
1993-95 (.6) 7

(G) Cluster, Instrument Assy., R&R or Renew
1993 (1.0) 3.0
1994-95 (.7) 1.5

(G) Control Assy., Heater, Renew
1993-95
wo/touch control (1.0) 1.5
w/touch control (.5) 1.0

(G) Cooler, Engine Oil, Renew
1993-95 (2.2) 3.0

(G) Core, Heater, R&R or Renew
1993-95 (2.5) 5.5
Boil & Repair, add 1.2
Repair Core, add 9
Recore, add 1.2

(G) Expansion (Freeze) Plugs, Water Jacket, Renew (Engine Block)
Add appropriate time to access plug.
1993-95 (.5) 7

(G) Gauge, Temperature (Engine Unit), Renew
1993-95
codes 8, P (.4) 6
code J (1.4) 1.8

(G) Hoses, Heater, Renew
1993-95 (1.4) 2.0

(G) Hoses, Radiator, Renew
Includes: Drain and refill cooling system as required.
1993-95
upper & lower (.3) 4
both (.5) 7
radiator to thermostat (.6) 8
thermo to w/pump (.7) 9

(G) Motor, Heater Blower, Renew
1993-95 (.7) 1.1

(G) Motor, Radiator Fan and/or Fan, Renew
1993-95
code P
right (.7) 1.1
left (2.3) 3.5
both (.9) 1.4
code J
right (.7) 1.2
left (2.4) 3.7
both (1.4) 2.1

(G) Pump and/or Gasket, Water, Renew
Includes: Drain and refill cooling system.
1993
codes 8, P (1.8) 2.5
code J (1.4) 2.1
1994-95 (2.4) 3.0

LABOR — COOLING SYSTEM — LABOR

(Factory Time) Chilton Time

(G) Radiator Assy., R&R or Renew

1993-95
codes 8, P (1.8) **2.2**
code J (2.0) **2.8**
Boil & Repair, add **1.5**
Rod Clean, add **1.9**
Repair Core, add **1.3**
Renew Tank, add **1.6**
Renew Trans. Oil Cooler, add **1.9**
Recore Radiator, add **1.7**

(G) Resistor, Heater Blower Motor, Renew

1993-95 (.3) .... **.4**

(G) Sending Unit, Engine Coolant Temp., Renew

1993-95
codes 8, P (.6) **1.0**
code J (1.3) **1.8**

(G) Switch, Heater Blower Motor, Renew

1993 (.9) **1.4**

(G) Switch, Radiator Fan Motor (Coolant Temp.), Renew

1993-95
codes 8, P (.6) **1.0**
code J (1.3) **1.8**

(G) Tensioner, Drive Belt, Renew

1993-95
code P (.3) .... **.5**
code J (.5) .... **.7**

(G) Thermostat, Coolant, Renew

1993-95
codes 8, P (.7) **1.0**
code J (.5) .... **.8**

(G) Valve, Heater Water Shut-Off, Renew

1993-95 (.4) .... **.7**

(G) Winterize Cooling System

Includes: Run engine to check for leaks, tighten all hose connections. Test radiator and pressure cap, drain radiator and engine block. Add antifreeze and refill system.

All models .... **.5**

LABOR — AIR CONDITIONING — LABOR

(Factory Time) Chilton Time

Note: If more than one item requires replacement where evacuation and discharging the system is already included in the operation, deduct 1.0 hour for each additional item from the time listed.

SERVICE AND TESTING

(G) Drain, Evacuate and Recharge System

1993-95 (.5) **1.0**
Recover refrigerant, add .... **.2**

(G) Flush Refrigerant System, Complete

To be used in conjunction with component replacement which could contaminate system. Includes evacuate and recharge.

All models **1.3**
Recover refrigerant, add .... **.2**

(G) Leak Check

Includes: Check all lines and connections.

All models .... **.5**

(G) Pressure Test System

All models **1.0**

(G) Recover and/or Recycle AC Refrigerant

Add to evacuate and charge the AC system, as required.

All models .... **.2**

(G) Refrigerant, Add (Partial Charge)

All models .... **.6**

COMPONENTS

(G) Accumulator Assy., Renew

Includes: Evacuate and charge system.

1993-95 (1.0) **1.4**
Recover refrigerant, add .... **.2**

(G) Actuator, Vacuum, Renew

Defroster door
1993 (1.2) **1.8**
Heat A/C mode door
1993 (4.5) **7.0**
Air Inlet
1993 (.6) **1.0**
Temperature door
1994-95 (.5) .... **.9**

(G) Bearing, Compressor, Main, Renew

Includes: R&R compressor. Evacuate and charge system.

1993 10PA20 (1.7) **2.5**
Recover refrigerant, add .... **.2**

(G) Belt, Compressor Drive, Renew

1993-95 (.3) .... **.5**

(G) Blower Motor, Renew

1993-95 (.7) **1.1**

(G) Clutch and/or Pulley, Compressor, Renew

Does not include R&R compressor.

1993 10PA20 (.5) **1.0**
Renew pulley or brg., add .... **.2**
Add time to recharge AC system if required
Recover refrigerant, add .... **.2**

(G) Clutch Plate & Hub Assy., Compressor, Renew

Includes: R&R hub and drive plate assy. Check air gap.

1993 10PA20 (.5) **1.0**
1994-95
code P (1.1) **1.5**
code J (1.5) **2.0**
Recover refrigerant, add .... **.2**
Add time to charge AC system if required.

(G) Coil and/or Housing, Compressor Clutch, Renew

Includes: Evacuate and charge system.

1993 10PA20 (1.8) **2.6**
Recover refrigerant, add .... **.2**

(G) Coil and/or Pulley Rim, Compressor Clutch, Renew

Includes: R&R hub and drive plate assy.

1993 10PA20 (.4) .... **.7**
1994-95
code P (1.3) **1.5**
code J (3.1) **3.4**
Add time to charge AC system if required.
Recover refrigerant, add .... **.2**

(G) Coil, Compressor Clutch Field, Renew

1993 codes 8, P (1.8) **2.4**

(G) Compressor Assy., Renew

Includes: Transfer parts as required. Evacuate and charge system.

1993
codes 8, P (1.2) **2.0**
code J (2.0) **3.4**
1994-95
code P (1.5) **2.4**
code J (2.8) **3.9**
Recover refrigerant, add .... **.2**
Install liquid line filter, add (.7) **1.2**

(G) Condenser Assy., Renew

Includes: Evacuate and charge system.

1993-95
code P (2.5) **3.0**
code J (2.7) **3.5**
w/AT, add .... **.1**
Recover refrigerant, add .... **.2**

(G) Control Unit, Temperature, Renew

1993-95
wo/touch control (1.0) **1.5**
w/touch control (.6) **1.0**

(G) Core, Evaporator, Renew

Includes: Evacuate and charge system.

1993-95 (3.7) **4.9**
Recover refrigerant, add .... **.2**

(G) Cylinder & Shaft Assy., Compressor, Renew

Includes: R&R compressor. Transfer parts as required. Evacuate and charge system.

1993 (1.9) **2.8**
1993 codes 8, P (2.1) **3.0**
Recover refrigerant, add .... **.2**

LABOR AIR CONDITIONING LABOR

(Factory Time) Chilton Time

(G) Cylinder Head and/or Valve Plate, Compressor, Renew

Includes: Evacuate and charge system.

1993 (1.8) 2.6
Renew two or more valves, add 2
Recover refrigerant, add 2

(G) Expansion Tube (Orifice), Clean & Inspect or Renew

Includes: Evacuate and charge system.

1993-95 (1.6) 2.0
Install liquid line filter, add 1.2
Recover refrigerant, add 2

(G) Head and/or Seal, Compressor Front, Renew

Includes: R&R compressor. R&R clutch pulley assy., R&R shaft seal assy. Clean and inspect parts. Evacuate and charge system.

1993 (1.5) 2.8
Recover refrigerant, add 2

(G) Hoses, AC, Renew

Includes: Evacuate and charge system.

1993-95
codes 8, P
liquid line (.9) 1.7
evap. to accumulator (.7) 1.6
suction & discharge (.8) 1.7
code J
liquid line (.9) 1.9
evap. to accumulator (.9) 1.7
suction & discharge (1.2) 2.5
Recover refrigerant, add 2

(G) Module, HVAC Power, Renew

1993-95 (.3) 5

(G) Plates, Compressor Discharge Valve, Renew

Includes: R&R compressor. Evacuate and charge system.

1993
codes 8, P (2.0) 2.9
code J (1.8) 2.5
Renew two or more valves, add 2
Recover refrigerant, add 2

(G) Programmer, R&R or Renew

1993-95 ATC (.7) 1.0

(G) Relay, Blower Motor, Renew

1993-95
codes 8, P (.3) 4
code J (.6) 7

(G) Resistor, Blower Motor, Renew

1993-95 (.3) 3

(G) Rotor and/or Bearing, Compressor Clutch, Renew

Includes: R&R hub and drive plate assy.

1993
codes 8, P (.6) 1.2
code J (.3) 5
Add time to evacuate and charge system if required.
Recover refrigerant, add 2

(G) Seal, Compressor Shaft, Renew

Includes: R&R compressor. Evacuate and charge system.

1993-95 6
codes 8, P (2.5) 3.6
code J (1.0) 2.4
Recover refrigerant, add 2

(G) Seal, Seat and O-Ring, Compressor Front, Renew

Includes: R&R clutch hub and drive plate assy. Evacuate and charge system.

1993
codes 8, P (1.0) 2.2
code J (2.5) 3.7
Recover refrigerant, add 2

(G) Sensor, AC Pressure, Renew

1993-95 (.4) 6

(G) Sensor, In-Vehicle, Renew

1993-95 (.8) 1.2

(G) Shell and/or O-Rings, Compressor, Renew

Includes: R&R compressor. Evacuate and charge system.

1993
codes 8, P (1.7) 2.6
code J (1.9) 2.8
Recover refrigerant, add 2

(G) Switch, Blower Motor, Renew

1993-95 (.9) 1.4

(G) Switch, Clutch Cycling Pressure, Renew

1993-95 (.4) 6

(G) Switch, High Pressure Cut-Off, Renew

1993-95 (.4) 6

(G) Switch, Master Electrical, Renew

1993-95 (.9) 1.4

(G) Valve, Pressure Relief, Renew

Includes: Evacuate and charge system.

All models (.9) 1.4
Recover refrigerant, add 2

(G) Valve, Vacuum Selector, Renew

1993-95 (.9) 1.4

CHEVROLET IMPORTS/GEO

METRO

LABOR COOLING SYSTEM LABOR

(Factory Time) Chilton Time

TESTING

(M) Pressure Test Cooling System

All models 3

SERVICE

(G) Belt, Drive, Adjust

All models
one 3
each adtnl. 1

(G) Belt, Drive, Renew

1993-95 3
w/AC add 1

(G) Bypass and/or Tube, Hose, Renew

All models 6

(G) Control Assy., Temperature, Renew

1993-94 9
1995
wo/AC 1.4
w/AC 1.5

(G) Core, Heater, R&R or Renew

1993-95
wo/AC 4.0
w/AC 5.0
w/air bags add 1.0
Add time to drain & recharge AC system if required.
Boil & Repair, add 1.2
Repair Core, add 9
Recore, add 1.2

COOLING SYSTEM

LABOR | LABOR

(Factory Time) Chilton Time

(G) Expansion (Freeze) Plugs, Water Jacket, Renew
Add appropriate time to access plug.
All models .5

(G) Gauge, Temperature (Dash Unit), Renew
1993-94
wo/air bags 1.0
w/air bags 1.3
1995 1.1

(G) Hoses, Heater, Renew
1993-95
one .4
all .6

(G) Hoses, Radiator, Renew
Includes: Drain and refill cooling system as required.
All models
upper .4
lower .5
both .6

(G) Motor, Heater Blower, Renew
1993-95 .6

(G) Motor, Radiator Fan and/or Fan, Renew
All models .8

(G) Pump and/or Gasket, Water, Renew
Includes: Drain and refill cooling system.
1993-95 2.5
w/AC add .2

(G) Radiator Assy., R&R or Renew
All models .9
w/AT add .1
Boil & Repair, add 1.5
Rod Clean, add 1.9
Repair Core, add 1.3
Renew Tank, add 1.6
Renew Trans. Oil Cooler, add 1.9
Recore Radiator, add 1.7

(G) Resistor, Heater Blower Motor, Renew
1993-95 .3

(G) Sending Unit, Engine Coolant Temp., Renew
All models .4

(G) Switch, Heater Blower Motor, Renew
1993-94 .9
1995
wo/AC 1.4
w/AC 1.5

(G) Switch, Master Electrical (AC On/Off), Renew
1993-94 .4
1995 .9

(G) Switch, Radiator Fan Motor (Coolant Temp.), Renew
All models .4

(G) Thermostat, Coolant, Renew
1993-95 .5

(G) Winterize Cooling System
Includes: Run engine to check for leaks, tighten all hose connections. Test radiator and pressure cap, drain radiator and engine block. Add antifreeze and refill system.
All models .5

AIR CONDITIONING

LABOR | LABOR

(Factory Time) Chilton Time

Note: If more than one item requires replacement where evacuation and discharging the system is already included in the operation, deduct 1.0 hour for each additional item from the time listed.

SERVICE AND TESTING

(G) Drain, Evacuate and Recharge System
All models 1.0

(G) Flush Refrigerant System, Complete
To be used in conjunction with component replacement which could contaminate system. Includes evacuate and recharge.
All models 1.3

(G) Leak Check
Includes: Check all lines and connections.
All models .5

(G) Recover and/or Recycle AC Refrigerant
Add to evacuate and charge the AC system, as required.
All models .2

(G) Refrigerant, Add (Partial Charge)
All models .6

COMPONENTS

(G) Belt, Compressor Drive, Renew
1993-95 .3

(G) Blower Motor, Renew
1993-95
AC .6
AC condenser 1.0
Add time to recharge AC system if required.

(G) Clutch Plate & Hub Assy., Compressor, Renew
Includes: R&R hub and drive plate assy. Check air gap.
1993-95 2.0

(G) Coil and/or Pulley Rim, Compressor Clutch, Renew
Includes: R&R hub and drive plate assy.
1993-95 2.0

(G) Coil, Evaporator, Renew
Includes: Evacuate and charge system.
1993-95 2.5

(G) Compressor Assy., Renew
Includes: Transfer parts as required. Evacuate and charge system.
All models 1.8
Install liquid line filter add 1.2

(G) Condenser Assy., Renew
Includes: Evacuate and charge system.
All models 2.0

(G) Control Assy., Temperature, Renew
1993-94 .9
1995
wo/AC 1.4
w/AC 1.5

(G) Dryer, In-Line Filter, Renew
Includes: Evacuate and charge system.
All models 1.4

(G) Head and/or Seal, Compressor Front, Renew
Includes: R&R compressor. R&R clutch pulley assy., R&R shaft seal assy. Clean and inspect parts. Evacuate and charge system.
1993-95 2.7

(G) Hoses, AC, Renew
Includes: Evacuate and charge system.
1993-95
condenser inlet 1.2
compressor discharge 1.2
evaporator outlet 1.4
compressor suction 1.2
filter dryer to condenser 1.2
any one pipe 1.3
expansion valve inlet 1.7

(G) Resistor, Blower Motor, Renew
1993-95 .3

(G) Rotor and/or Bearing, Compressor Clutch, Renew
Includes: R&R hub and drive plate assy.
1993-95 2.1

(G) Seal, Seat and O-Ring, Compressor Front, Renew
Includes: R&R clutch hub and drive plate assy. Evacuate and charge system.
All models 2.5

(G) Shaft & Cylinder Assy., Compressor, Renew
Includes: R&R compressor. Evacuate and charge system.
1993-95 2.9

(G) Switch, AC Low Pressure, Renew
All models .3
Add time to recharge AC system if required.

(G) Switch, Blower Motor, Renew
1993-94 1.0
1995
wo/AC 1.4
w/AC 1.5

AIR CONDITIONING

(Factory Time) Chilton Time

(G) Switch, Master Electrical, Renew
1993-94 4
1995 9

(G) Switch, Thermostatic Control, Renew
All models 1.5

(G) Valve, Expansion, Renew
Includes: Evacuate and charge system.
1993-95 .... 1.6

CHEVROLET IMPORTS/GEO
STORM

COOLING SYSTEM

(Factory Time) Chilton Time

SERVICE

(G) Belt, Drive, Adjust
All models
one 3
all 4

(G) Belt, Drive, Renew
1993
1.6L code 5
1.6L code 6
fan/generator 3
AC or PS 3
1.8L code 8, serpentine 7

(G) Bypass and/or Tube, Hose, Renew
1993 5

(G) Control Assy., Temperature, Renew
1993 6

(G) Core, Heater, R&R or Renew
1993 .... 5.5
Add time to recharge AC system if required.
Boil & Repair, add 1.2
Repair Core, add 9
Recore, add 1.2

(G) Expansion (Freeze) Plugs, Water Jacket, Renew
Add appropriate time to access plug.
All models, each 5

(G) Gauge, Temperature (Dash Unit), Renew
1993 .... 1.2

(G) Hoses, Heater, Renew
All models
wo/AC
one 6
both 8
w/AC 9

(G) Hoses, Radiator, Renew
Includes: Drain and refill cooling system as required.
1993
upper or lower 4
both 6

(G) Motor, Heater Blower, Renew
All models 5

(G) Motor, Radiator Fan and/or Fan, Renew
1993 7

(G) Pump and/or Gasket, Water, Renew
Includes: Drain and refill cooling system.
1993
1.6L codes 5, 6 .... 2.8
1.8L code 8 .... 3.0

(G) Radiator Assy., R&R or Renew
1993 .... 1.2
w/AT add 1
Boil & Repair, add 1.5
Rod Clean, add 1.9
Repair Core, add 1.3
Renew Tank, add 1.6
Renew Trans. Oil Cooler, add 1.9
Recore Radiator, add 1.7

(G) Relay, Radiator Fan Motor, Renew
All models 3

(G) Resistor, Heater Blower Motor, Renew
All models 3

(G) Sending Unit, Engine Coolant Temp., Renew
All models 4

(G) Switch, Master Electrical (AC On/Off), Renew
1993 3

(G) Switch, Radiator Fan Motor (Coolant Temp.), Renew
1993 5

(G) Tensioner, Drive Belt, Renew
1993 1.8L code 8 .... 1.1

(G) Thermostat, Coolant, Renew
1993
1.6L codes 5, 6 6
1.8L code 8 9

(G) Winterize Cooling System
Includes: Run engine to check for leaks, tighten all hose connections. Test radiator and pressure cap, drain radiator and engine block. Add antifreeze and refill system.
All models 5

AIR CONDITIONING

(Factory Time) Chilton Time

Note: If more than one item requires replacement where evacuation and discharging the system is already included in the operation, deduct 1.0 hour for each additional item from the time listed.

SERVICE AND TESTING

(G) Drain, Evacuate and Recharge System
All models 1.0

(G) Flush Refrigerant System, Complete
To be used in conjunction with component replacement which could contaminate system. Includes evacuate and recharge.
All models 1.3

(G) Leak Check
Includes: Check all lines and connections.
All models 5

(G) Recover and/or Recycle AC Refrigerant
Add to evacuate and charge the AC system, as required.
All models 2

(G) Refrigerant, Add (Partial Charge)
All models 6

LABOR AIR CONDITIONING LABOR

(Factory Time) Chilton Time

COMPONENTS

(G) Belt, Compressor Drive, Renew
All models .3

(G) Blower Motor, Renew
All models .5

(G) Coil and/or Pulley Rim, Compressor Clutch, Renew
Includes: R&R hub and drive plate assy.
All models 2.2

(G) Coil, Evaporator, Renew
Includes: Evacuate and charge system.
1993 2.2

(G) Compressor Assy., Renew
Includes: Transfer parts as required. Evacuate and charge system.
1993 2.0
Install liquid line filter add 1.2

(G) Condenser Assy., Renew
Includes: Evacuate and charge system.
1993 1.8

(G) Control Assy., Temperature, Renew
1993 .7

(G) Hoses, AC, Renew
Includes: Evacuate and charge system.
1993
discharge 1.3
liquid line 1.5
evap. outlet 1.3
suction 1.2
suction and discharge 1.4

(G) Programmer, R&R or Renew
1993 .5

(G) Receiver/Drier Assy., Renew
Includes: Evacuate and charge system.
1993 1.8
Install liquid line filter add 1.2

(G) Relay, Blower Motor, Renew
1993 .3

(G) Resistor, Blower Motor, Renew
All models .3

(G) Switch, Clutch Cycling Pressure, Renew
1993 .5
Add time to recharge AC system if required.

(G) Switch, Low Pressure Cut-Off, Renew
Includes: Evacuate and charge system.
1993 1.3

(G) Switch, Master Electrical, Renew
1993 .4

(G) Switch, Thermostatic Control, Renew
1993 .7
Add time to recharge AC system if required.

(G) Valve, Expansion, Renew
Includes: Evacuate and charge system.
1993 1.4

CHEVROLET IMPORTS/GEO
PRIZM

LABOR COOLING SYSTEM LABOR

(Factory Time) Chilton Time

TESTING

(M) Pressure Test Cooling System
All models .3

SERVICE

(G) Belt, Drive, Adjust
All models
one .3
all .4

(G) Belt, Drive, Renew
1993-95
1.6L, 1.8L codes 6, 8
AC or PS .4
Alternator .2

(G) Bypass and/or Tube, Hose, Renew
1993-95 .8

(G) Control Assy., Temperature, Renew
1993-95 1.1

(G) Cooler, Engine Oil, Renew
1993-95 .9

(G) Core, Heater, R&R or Renew
1993-95 3.8
Boil & Repair, add 1.2
Repair Core, add .9
Recore, add 1.2
Add time to evacuate and recharge AC system if required.

(G) Expansion (Freeze) Plugs, Water Jacket, Renew
Add appropriate time to access plug.
All models, each .5

(G) Gauge, Temperature (Dash Unit), Renew
1993-95 1.5

(G) Hoses, Heater, Renew
1993-95
wo/AC
one .6
both .8
w/AC .8

(G) Hoses, Radiator, Renew
Includes: Drain and refill cooling system as required.
All models
upper .4
lower .5
both .6

(G) Motor, Heater Blower, Renew
1993-95 .5

(G) Motor, Radiator Fan and/or Fan, Renew
1993-95 .5

(G) Pump and/or Gasket, Water, Renew
Includes: Drain and refill cooling system.
1993-95
1.6L code 6 1.8
1.6L, 1.8L codes 5, 8 2.0
w/AC add .1
w/PS add .2

(G) Radiator Assy., R&R or Renew
All models 1.0
w/AC add .1
w/AT add .1
Boil & Repair, add 1.5
Rod Clean, add 1.9
Repair Core, add 1.3
Renew Tank, add 1.6
Renew Trans. Oil Cooler, add 1.9
Recore Radiator, add 1.7

(G) Relay, Heater Blower Motor, Renew
1993-95 .3

(G) Relay, Radiator Fan Motor, Renew
1993-95 .6

LABOR COOLING SYSTEM LABOR

(Factory Time) Chilton Time

(G) Resistor, Heater Blower Motor, Renew
1993-95 3

(G) Sending Unit, Engine Coolant Temp., Renew
All models 5

(G) Switch, Heater Blower Motor, Renew
1993-95 8

(G) Switch, Master Electrical (AC On/Off), Renew
1993-95 4

(G) Switch, Radiator Fan Motor (Coolant Temp.), Renew
All models 4

(G) Thermostat, Coolant, Renew
All models 5

(G) Valve, Heater Control, Renew
1993-95 5

(G) Winterize Cooling System
Includes: Run engine to check for leaks, tighten all hose connections. Test radiator and pressure cap, drain radiator and engine block. Add antifreeze and refill system.
All models 5

LABOR AIR CONDITIONING LABOR

(Factory Time) Chilton Time

Note: If more than one item requires replacement where evacuation and discharging the system is already included in the operation, deduct 1.0 hour for each additional item from the time listed.

SERVICE AND TESTING

(G) Drain, Evacuate and Recharge System
All models 1.0

(G) Flush Refrigerant System, Complete
To be used in conjunction with component replacement which could contaminate system. Includes evacuate and recharge.
All models 1.3

(G) Leak Check
Includes: Check all lines and connections.
All models 5

(G) Recover and/or Recycle AC Refrigerant
Add to evacuate and charge the AC system, as required.
All models 2

(G) Refrigerant, Add (Partial Charge)
All models 6

COMPONENTS

(G) Belt, Compressor Drive, Renew
1993-95 4

(G) Blower Motor, Renew
1993-95 5

(G) Clutch Plate & Hub Assy., Compressor, Renew
Includes: R&R hub and drive plate assy. Check air gap.
1993-95 5
Add time to evacuate and charge AC system if required.

(G) Coil and/or Pulley Rim, Compressor Clutch, Renew
Includes: R&R hub and drive plate assy.
1993-95 6
Add time to evacuate and charge AC system if required.

(G) Coil, Evaporator, Renew
Includes: Evacuate and charge system.
1993-95 .... 2.5

(G) Compressor Assy., Renew
Includes: Transfer parts as required. Evacuate and charge system.
All models 2.0
Install liquid line filter add 1.2

(G) Condenser Assy., Renew
Includes: Evacuate and charge system.
All models 2.4

(G) Control Assy., Temperature, Renew
1993-95 .... 1.3

(G) Cylinder & Shaft Assy., Compressor, Renew
Includes: R&R compressor. Transfer parts as required. Evacuate and charge system.
1993-95 .... 2.5

(G) Dryer, In-Line Filter, Renew
Includes: Evacuate and charge system.
All models 1.4

(G) Head and/or Seal, Compressor Front, Renew
Includes: R&R compressor. R&R clutch pulley assy., R&R shaft seal assy. Clean and inspect parts. Evacuate and charge system.
1993-95 .... 2.3

(G) Hoses, AC, Renew
Includes: Evacuate and charge system.
All models
- expansion valve inlet 1.9
- discharge 1.7
- evaporator to accumulator 1.7
- liquid line 1.5
- evaporator outlet 1.5
- suction 1.5
- dryer to condenser 1.5
- expansion valve inlet 1.8

(G) Motor, Condenser Fan, Renew
1993-95 8

(G) Programmer, R&R or Renew
1993-95 6

(G) Relay, Blower Motor, Renew
1993-95 3

(G) Resistor, Blower Motor, Renew
1993-95 3

(G) Rotor and/or Bearing, Compressor Clutch, Renew
Includes: R&R hub and drive plate assy.
1993-95 6
Add time to evacuate and charge AC system if required.

(G) Seal, Seat and O-Ring, Compressor Front, Renew
Includes: R&R clutch hub and drive plate assy. Evacuate and charge system.
1993-95 .... 2.2

(G) Switch, AC Low Pressure, Renew
All models 1.2

(G) Switch, Blower Motor, Renew
1993-95 8

(G) Switch, High Pressure Cut-Off, Renew
All models 1.2

(G) Switch, Pressure Cycling, Renew
All models 1.2

(G) Switch, Master Electrical, Renew
1993-95 4

(G) Switch, Thermostatic Control, Renew
1993-95 8
Add time to evacuate and charge AC system if reqiured.

(G) Valve, Expansion, Renew
Includes: Evacuate and charge system.
1993-95 .... 1.7

CHEVROLET IMPORTS/GEO
TRACKER

LABOR COOLING SYSTEM LABOR

(Factory Time) Chilton Time

TESTING

(M) Pressure Test Cooling System
All models .3

SERVICE

(G) Belt, Drive, Adjust
All models
one .3
all .4

(G) Belt, Drive, Renew
All models
AC .3
Fan or Alternator .5
PS .3

(G) Bypass and/or Tube, Hose, Renew
All models .5

(G) Control Assy., Temperature, Renew
1993-95
wo/AC .9
w/AC 1.0

(G) Core, Heater, R&R or Renew
All models
wo/AC 3.5
w/AC 4.0

Add time to evacuate and charge AC system if required.

(G) Expansion (Freeze) Plugs, Water Jacket, Renew
Add appropriate time to access plug.
All models, each .5

(G) Fan, Clutch and/or Pulley, Cooling, Renew
All models .5

(G) Gauge, Temperature (Dash Unit), Renew
All models .8

(G) Hoses, Heater, Renew
All models
one .4
all .5

(G) Hoses, Radiator, Renew
Includes: Drain and refill cooling system as required.
All models
upper .4
radiator to outlet pipe .5
outlet to inlet pipe .5
both .7

(G) Motor, Heater Blower, Renew
All models .6

(G) Pump and/or Gasket, Water, Renew
Includes: Drain and refill cooling system.
All models 2.0
w/AC add .8

(G) Radiator Assy., R&R or Renew
All models .9
w/AT add .1

(G) Resistor, Heater Blower Motor, Renew
All models .3

(G) Switch, Master Electrical (AC On/Off), Renew
1993-95 .9

(G) Thermostat, Coolant, Renew
All models .4

(G) Winterize Cooling System
Includes: Run engine to check for leaks, tighten all hose connections. Test radiator and pressure cap, drain radiator and engine block. Add antifreeze and refill system.
All models .5

LABOR AIR CONDITIONING LABOR

(Factory Time) Chilton Time

Note: If more than one item requires replacement where evacuation and discharging the system is already included in the operation, deduct 1.0 hour for each additional item from the time listed.

SERVICE AND TESTING

(G) Drain, Evacuate and Recharge System
All models 1.0

(G) Flush Refrigerant System, Complete
To be used in conjunction with component replacement which could contaminate system. Includes evacuate and recharge.
All models 1.3

(G) Recover and/or Recycle AC Refrigerant
Add to evacuate and charge the AC system, as required.
All models .2

(G) Refrigerant, Add (Partial Charge)
All models .6

(G) Vacuum Leak Test
All models .5

COMPONENTS

(G) Belt, Compressor Drive, Renew
All models .3

(G) Blower Motor, Renew
All models .6

(G) Clutch Plate & Hub Assy., Compressor, Renew
Includes: R&R hub and drive plate assy. Check air gap.
All models 1.9

(G) Coil and/or Pulley Rim, Compressor Clutch, Renew
Includes: R&R hub and drive plate assy.
All models 2.0

(G) Compressor Assy., Renew
Includes: Transfer parts as required. Evacuate and charge system.
All models 1.5
Install liquid line filter
add 1.2

(G) Condenser Assy., Renew
Includes: Evacuate and charge system.
All models 2.0

(G) Control Assy., Temperature, Renew
1993-95
wo/AC .9
w/AC 1.0

(G) Core, Evaporator, Renew
Includes: Evacuate and charge system.
All models 3.0

(G) Cylinder & Shaft Assy., Compressor, Renew
Includes: R&R compressor. Transfer parts as required. Evacuate and charge system.
All models 2.8

(G) Dryer, In-Line Filter, Renew
Includes: Evacuate and charge system.
All models 1.5

(G) Head and/or Seal, Compressor Front, Renew
Includes: R&R compressor. R&R clutch pulley assy., R&R shaft seal assy. Clean and inspect parts. Evacuate and charge system.
All models 2.5

(G) Hoses, AC, Renew
Includes: Evacuate and charge system.
All models
one 1.5
each adtnl. .5

LABOR — AIR CONDITIONING — LABOR

(Factory Time) Chilton Time

(G) Programmer, R&R or Renew
All models 4

(G) Resistor, Blower Motor, Renew
All models 3

(G) Rotor and/or Bearing, Compressor Clutch, Renew
Includes: R&R hub and drive plate assy.
All models 1.9

(G) Seal, Seat and O-Ring, Compressor Front, Renew
Includes: R&R clutch hub and drive plate assy. Evacuate and charge system.
All models 2.0

(G) Switch, Low Pressure and/or Cycling, Renew
All models 4
Add time to evacuate and charge system if reqiured.

(G) Switch, Master Electrical, Renew
1993-95 9

(G) Valve, Expansion, Renew
Includes: Evacuate and charge system.
All models 3.0

GENERAL MOTORS CORPORATION-TRUCKS

ASTRO • PICKUPS • SAFARI • SUBURBAN • VANS

LABOR — COOLING SYSTEM — LABOR

(Factory Time) Chilton Time

TESTING

(M) Pressure Test Cooling System
All models 3

SERVICE

(G) Belt, Drive, Adjust
All models
Six, V8, (.2) 3
each adtnl. (.1) 1

(G) Belt, Drive, Renew
All models
V6, serpentine (.2) 3
Renew tensioner, add 1
V8 305, 350
AC
P Vans (.3) 4
AIR
P Vans (.2) 3
Fan
P Vans (.2) 3
PS
P Vans (.5) 6
w/AC, add 3
serpentine (.2) 4
V8 454
AC (.3) 4
AIR & Fan (.2) 3
PS (.5) 6
Serpentine (.2) 4
V8 diesel
serpentine (.2) 4

(G) Blades, Fan or Clutch Assy., Renew
All models
C, K series
gas (.3) 5
diesel (.6) 8
Vans
gas (.7) 9
diesel (.7) 9
w/PS, add 1
w/one-piece shroud, add 3
Astro, Safari (.6) 8
w/AC, add 1

(G) Bypass and/or Tube, Hose, Renew
All models
C, K, R, V series (.3) 5
G, P Vans (.6) 9
Astro, Safari (.5) 8

(G) Control Assy., Heater, Renew
1993-95
G Vans, Astro, Safari (.4) 7
C, K series (.3) 5
P Vans (.3) 5

(G) Core, Heater, Auxiliary, Renew
All models
G Vans (.5) 9
Astro, Safari (.7) 1.3
R, V, C, K series (.6) 1.1
R&R rear seat, add 2

(G) Core, Heater, R&R or Renew
1993-95
wo/AC
C, K series
gas (.7) 1.5
diesel (.7) 1.5
Vans (2.1) 4.0
Astro, Safari (1.3) 2.5
w/AC
C, K series (.7) 1.5
Vans
gas (3.3) 6.5
diesel (2.7) 5.3
Astro, Safari (.9) 1.7
Add time to evacuate and charge AC system as needed.
Recover refrigerant, add 2
Boil & Repair, add 1.2
Repair Core, add 9
Recore, add 1.2

(G) Expansion (Freeze) Plugs, Water Jacket, Renew
Add appropriate time to access plug.
All models, one 5

(G) Gauge, Temperature (Dash Unit), Renew
1993
Astro, Safari (.9) 1.4
Vans (.8) 1.3
C, K, R, V series (.6) 1.2

(G) Hoses, Auxiliary Heater, Renew
All models, all (1.8) 2.4

(G) Hoses, Heater, Renew
All models
C, K series
one (.4) 5
both (.5) 7
G, P Vans
one (.3) 4
both (.5) 6
Astro, Safari
one (.9) 1.2
both (1.0) 1.4

(G) Hoses, Radiator, Renew
Includes: Drain and refill cooling system as required.
All models
upper (.4) 5
lower (.5) 6
both (.6) 9

(G) Motor, Auxiliary Heater Blower, Renew
All models
Vans, Astro, Safari (.5) 8
C, K series (.3) 5

(G) Motor, Heater Blower, Renew
1993-95 C, K series (.9) 1.2
1993-95 Astro, Safari
front
wo/AC (.5) 8
w/AC (.5) 8
auxiliary (.4) 6
A/C rear (.3) 5
1993-95 Vans
gas (.3) 5
diesel (.5) 7

LABOR — COOLING SYSTEM — LABOR

(Factory Time) Chilton Time

Add time to recharge AC system if required.
Recover refrigerant, add 2

(G) Motor, Radiator Fan and/or Fan, Renew
1993-95 right or single
Vans (.6) 9
C, K, R, V series (.5) 8

(G) Motor, Rear AC Blower, Renew
All models
Vans (.6) 9
Astro, Safari (.4) 7

(G) Pump and/or Gasket, Water, Renew
Includes: Drain and refill cooling system.
1993-95
C, K Series
gas (.8) 1.5
diesel (1.6) 2.4
w/AC, add 1
w/PS, add (.3) 3
G Vans
Six & V8 (1.4) 1.8
V6 (.9) 1.6
diesel (2.0) 3.0
w/AC, add 5
w/PS, add 4
w/AIR, add 2
Astro, Safari
V6 (1.1) 1.9
w/AC, add 2

(G) Radiator Assy., R&R or Renew
1993-95
C, K series
gas (.5) 9
diesel (.8) 1.2
G, P Vans
gas (.7) 1.1
diesel (1.0) 1.5
w/AC, add 3
Astro, Safari (.7) 1.1
w/eng. oil cooler, add 2
Renew side tank, add
one side 7
both sides 1.2
Boil & Repair, add 1.5
Rod Clean, add 1.9
Repair Core, add 1.3
Renew Tank, add 1.6
Renew Trans. Oil Cooler, add 1.9
Recore Radiator, add 1.7

(G) Relay, Heater Blower Motor, Renew
All models (.3) 4

(G) Relay, Radiator Fan Motor, Renew
1993-95 (.2) 3

(G) Resistor, Heater Blower Motor, Renew
All models (.2) 4

(G) Sending Unit, Engine Coolant Temp., Renew
All models
Vans, C, K, R, V series (.4) 5
Astro, Safari (.6) 9

(G) Switch, Heater Blower Motor, Renew
All models (.4) 7

(G) Thermostat, Coolant, Renew
1993-95
C, K series
gas (.5) 7
diesel (.4) 6
Vans
V6 (.5) 7
V8 (.8) 1.0
w/AC, add 5
diesel (.8) 1.0
Astro, Safari
V6 (.7) 9

(G) Valve, Auxiliary Heater Water Shut-Off, Renew
All models
Vans, C, K, R, V series (.7) 1.1
Astro, Safari (.9) 1.3

(G) Valve, Heater Control, Renew
All models (.6) 8

(G) Winterize Cooling System
Includes: Run engine to check for leaks, tighten all hose connections. Test radiator and pressure cap, drain radiator and engine block. Add antifreeze and refill system.
All models 8

LABOR — AIR CONDITIONING — LABOR

(Factory Time) Chilton Time

Note: If more than one item requires replacement where evacuation and discharging the system is already included in the operation, deduct 1.0 hour for each additional item from the time listed.

SERVICE AND TESTING

(G) Drain, Evacuate and Recharge System
All models (.5) 1.0
Recover refrigerant, add 2

(G) Flush Refrigerant System, Complete
To be used in conjunction with component replacement which could contaminate system. Includes evacuate and recharge.
All models 1.3
Recover refrigerant, add 2

(G) Leak Check
Includes: Check all lines and connections.
All models 6

(G) Recover and/or Recycle AC Refrigerant
Add to evacuate and charge the AC system, as required.
All models 2

(G) Refrigerant, Add (Partial Charge)
All models 6

COMPONENTS

(G) Accumulator Assy., Renew
Includes: Evacuate and charge system.
All models (.8) 1.5
Recover refrigerant, add 2

(G) Belt, Compressor Drive, Renew
All models
Four (.3) 4
1993-95 serpentine (.2) 3
V8
1993-95 serpentine (.2) 3
V8
1993-95 454
V belt (.3) 4
serpentine (.2) 3
1993-95 serpentine (.2) 3

(G) Blower Motor, Renew
1993
front unit
C, K series
wo/AC (.3) 5
w/AC (.7) 1.0
Astro, Safari
wo/AC (.6) 8
w/AC (.5) 7
Vans
gas (.3) 5
diesel (.5) 7

Add time to recharge AC system if required.
rear unit (.6) 1.1
1994-95
C, K series
front (.9) 1.2
rear (.3) 5
G Vans
front (.3) 5
rear (.6) 8
R&R rear seat, add 3
Astro, Safari
front (.5) 8
rear (.3) 5
P Vans (.3) 5

(G) Clutch Plate & Hub Assy., Compressor, Renew
Includes: R&R hub and drive plate assy. Check air gap.
1993
6 cyl. axial
C, K, R, V series (.3) 6
Vans (.8) 1.1
4 cyl. radial (.5) 8
HR6, DA6
Vans, Safari, Astro (.4) 7
C, K series (.3) 6
1994-95
C, K series (R4) (.4) 6

(Factory Time) Chilton Time

G Vans
G Vans (6 cyl. axial) (1.5) **2.2**
Add time to recharge system.
Astro, Safari (HR6) (.4) .... **.6**
P Vans
P Vans (R4) (.4) .... **.6**
Recover refrigerant, add .... **.2**

(G) Coil and/or Pulley Rim, Compressor Clutch, Renew

Includes: R&R hub and drive plate assy.

1993
6 cyl. axial
C, K, R, V series (.6) **1.1**
Vans (1.0) **1.4**
4 cyl. radial
Astro, Safari, Vans (1.4) **2.3**
C, K, R, V series (.6) .... **.8**
HR6, DA6
Vans, Safari, Astro (1.0) **1.5**
C, K, R, V series (.8) **1.3**
1994-95
C, K series (R4) (.4) .... **.6**
G Vans (HR6) (.6) .... **.8**
Astro, Safari (HR6) (.4) .... **.6**
P Vans (R4) (.4) .... **.6**
Add time to evacuate and charge system if required.
Recover refrigerant, add .... **.2**

(G) Coil, Evaporator, Renew

Includes: Evacuate and charge system.

1993
front unit
Vans
gas (1.8) **3.5**
diesel (2.0) **3.9**
Astro, Safari (1.6) **3.0**
C, K series
gas (2.5) **4.9**
diesel (1.1) **2.0**
rear unit
Astro, Safari (1.6) **3.6**
Vans (1.9) **4.3**
1994-95
C, K series
front
gas (2.9) **5.4**
diesel (2.7) **5.2**
rear (2.0) **3.9**
G Vans
front
gas (1.3) **2.4**
diesel (2.0) **3.9**
Astro, Safari
front (1.6) **3.0**
rear (1.3) **2.4**
P Vans
gas (1.5) **2.8**
diesel (2.0) **3.9**
Recover refrigerant, add .... **.2**

(G) Compressor Assy., Renew

Includes: Transfer parts as required. Evacuate and charge system.

1993
6 cyl. axial
C, K, R, V series (1.1) **2.0**
Vans
gas (1.3) **2.2**
diesel (1.7) **2.6**
4 cyl. radial
Astro, Safari, Vans (1.5) **2.5**
C, K, R, V series (1.0) **2.0**
HR6, DA6
Vans, Safari, Astro (1.3) **2.4**
C, K, R, V series (1.0) **2.0**
Astro, Safari w/AIR, add .... **.5**
1994-95
C, K series (R4) (1.0) **2.0**
G Vans
A6 (1.9) **2.8**
HR6 (1.6) **2.5**
Astro, Safari (HR6) (1.6) **2.5**
P Vans (R4) (1.5) **2.4**
Recover refrigerant, add .... **.2**

(G) Condenser Assy., Renew

Includes: Evacuate and charge system.

All models **2.3**
w/aux. oil cooler, add .... **.3**
Recover refrigerant, add .... **.2**

(G) Control Assy., Temperature, Renew

1993-95
G Vans (.5) .... **.7**
Astro, Safari (.4) .... **.6**
C, K, R, V series, P Vans (.3) ...... **.5**

(G) Cylinder & Shaft Assy., Compressor, Renew

Includes: R&R compressor. Transfer parts as required. Evacuate and charge system.

1993
4 cyl. radial
Astro, Safari, Vans (2.3) **3.5**
C, K, R, V series (1.9) **3.0**
HR6, DA6
Astro, Safari, Vans (2.3) **3.7**
C, K, R, V series (1.9) **3.3**
1994-95
C, K series (1.5) **2.5**
P Vans (2.3) **3.3**
Recover refrigerant, add .... **.2**

(G) Expansion Tube (Orifice), Clean & Inspect or Renew

Includes: Evacuate and charge system.

All models
C. K, R, V series (1.0) **1.7**
Vans, Astro, Safari (.7) **1.4**
Recover refrigerant, add .... **.2**

(G) Head and/or Seal, Compressor Front, Renew

Includes: R&R compressor. R&R clutch pulley assy., R&R shaft seal assy. Clean and inspect parts. Evacuate and charge system.

All models
6 cylinder axial
C, K, R, V series (2.2) **3.1**
Vans
gas (2.4) **3.3**
diesel (2.8) **3.7**
4 cyl. radial
Astro, Safari, Vans (2.0) **3.0**
C, K, R, V series (1.5) **2.8**
HR6, DA6
Vans, Safari, Astro (1.6) **3.0**
C, K, R, V series (1.4) **2.8**
1994-95
C, K series (R4) (1.4) **2.4**
G, Vans, Astro, Safari (HR6) (2.0) . **3.0**
P Vans (R4) (1.9) **2.9**
Recover refrigerant, add .... **.2**

(G) Hoses, AC, Renew

Includes: Evacuate and charge system.

Condenser Outlet
1993-95 Astro (1.1) **2.2**
Liquid Line
1993-95
Vans, Astro, Safari (1.1) **1.8**
C, K, R, V series (1.3) **2.0**
Suction & Discharge Hose Assy.
1993-95
w/front AC
Vans (1.1) **1.8**
Astro, Safari (1.1) **1.8**
C, K, R, V series (1.4) **2.1**
w/rear AC
Vans (2.0) **3.0**
Front to Rear Unit
1993-95
C, K series (1.9) **2.8**
G Vans (1.1) **1.8**
Astro, Safari (1.3) **2.0**
Hose & Plate Assy.
All models (1.4) **2.1**
R&R seat for rear AC, add .... **.2**
R&R trim panel for rear AC, add .... **.5**
Recover refrigerant, add .... **.2**

(G) Pulley and/or Bearing, Compressor, Renew

Includes: R&R hub and drive plate.

All models, 6 cylinder axial
C, K, R, V series (.5) .... **.9**
Vans (2.1) **3.2**
Add time to evacuate & charge AC system as needed
Recover refrigerant, add .... **.2**

(G) Relay, Blower Motor, Renew

All models (.3) .... **.5**

(G) Resistor, Blower Motor, Renew

All models
front unit (.3) .... **.4**
rear unit (.3) .... **.5**
R&R seat, add .... **.2**

(G) Rotor and/or Bearing, Compressor Clutch, Renew

Includes: R&R hub and drive plate assy.

1993
4 cyl. radial
Astro, Safari, Vans (1.4) **2.3**
C, K, R, V series (.6) **1.0**
HR6, DA6
Vans, Safari, Astro (.9) **1.4**
C, K, R, V series (.7) **1.2**
1994-95
C, K series (R4) (.5) .... **.8**
G Vans (HR6) (.6) .... **.9**
Astro, Safari (HR6) (.4) .... **.6**
P Vans (R4) (.4) .... **.6**
Add time to evacuate and charge system if required.
Recover refrigerant, add .... **.2**

(G) Seal, Compressor Shaft, Renew

Includes: R&R compressor. Evacuate and charge system.

1993
6 cyl. axial
C, K, R, V series (1.1) **2.0**

LABOR — AIR CONDITIONING — LABOR

(Factory Time) Chilton Time

Vans
gas (1.6) 2.5
diesel (1.9) 2.8
4 cyl. radial (1.3) 2.5
HR6, DA6
Vans, Safari, Astro (1.2) 2.6
C, K, R, V series (1.1) 2.5
1994-95
C, K series (R4) (1.0) 2.2
G Vans
A6 (2.2) 3.2
HR6 (1.1) 2.1
Astro, Safari (HR6) (.9) 2.2
P Vans (R4) (1.2) 2.2
Recover refrigerant, add 2

(G) Switch, Blower Motor, Renew
1993
front unit (.5) 9
rear unit (.3) 6
1994-95
front unit
C, K series (.3) 5
G Vans (.4) 6
Astro, Safari (.4) 6
P Vans (.3) 5
rear unit
C, K series (.2) 4
G Vans (.4) 6
Astro, Safari (.2) 4

(G) Switch, Clutch Cycling Pressure, Renew
All models (.2) 3
Add time to evacuate & charge AC system as needed
Recover refrigerant, add 2

(G) Valve, Expansion, Renew
Includes: Evacuate and charge system.
All models
G Vans (1.1) 2.0
C, K, R, V, series (1.7) 2.5
Astro, Safari (1.3) 2.2
Recover refrigerant, add 2

GENERAL MOTORS CORPORATION-TRUCKS
LUMINA APV • SILHOUETTE • TRANS SPORT

LABOR — COOLING SYSTEM — LABOR

(Factory Time) Chilton Time

TESTING

(M) Pressure Test Cooling System
All models 3

SERVICE

(G) Belt, Serpentine Drive, Renew
All models (.2) 4

(G) Bypass and/or Tube, Hose, Renew
All models (.6) 9

(G) Core, Heater, R&R or Renew
All models
w/AC (1.2) 2.3
auxiliary AC (1.4) 2.5
Add time to recharge AC system if required.
Boil & Repair, add 1.2
Repair Core, add 9
Recore, add 1.2

(G) Expansion (Freeze) Plugs, Water Jacket, Renew
Add appropriate time to access plug.
All models, each 5

(G) Hoses, Heater, Renew
All models
outlet (.4) 6
all (.7) 1.1
aux. heater inlet (1.3) 2.0

(G) Hoses, Radiator, Renew
Includes: Drain and refill cooling system as required.
All models
upper or lower (.3) 4
both (.4) 5

(G) Motor, Heater Blower, Renew
All models
AC
3.1L code D (.5) 8
3.8L code L (.7) 1.0
auxiliary (1.0) 1.3
rear (1.1) 1.4

(G) Motor, Radiator Fan and/or Fan, Renew
All models
one (.4) 6
both (.7) 1.1

(G) Pump and/or Gasket, Water, Renew
Includes: Drain and refill cooling system.
All models (.9) 1.4

(G) Radiator Assy., R&R or Renew
All models (.9) 1.3
Boil & Repair, add 1.5
Rod Clean, add 1.9
Repair Core, add 1.3
Renew Tank, add 1.6
Renew Trans. Oil Cooler, add 1.9
Recore Radiator, add 1.7

(G) Relay, Heater Blower Motor, Renew
All models (.2) 4

(G) Relay, Radiator Fan Motor, Renew
All models (.2) 4

(G) Resistor, Heater Blower Motor, Renew
All models
front (.2) 5
rear or auxiliary (.8) 1.1

(G) Sending Unit, Engine Coolant Temp., Renew
All models (.3) 6

(G) Switch, Heater Blower Motor, Renew
All models
auxiliary (.2) 4
AC (.5) 8
rear (.6) 9

(G) Tensioner, Drive Belt, Renew
All models
3.1L code D (.3) 5
3.8L code L (.9) 1.3

(G) Thermostat, Coolant, Renew
All models (.4) 5

(G) Valve, Heater Water Shut-Off, Renew
All models (.6) 1.0

(G) Winterize Cooling System
Includes: Run engine to check for leaks, tighten all hose connections. Test radiator and pressure cap, drain radiator and engine block. Add antifreeze and refill system.
All models 5

LABOR — AIR CONDITIONING — LABOR

(Factory Time) Chilton Time

Note: If more than one item requires replacement where evacuation and discharging the system is already included in the operation, deduct 1.0 hour for each additional item from the time listed.

SERVICE AND TESTING

(G) Drain, Evacuate and Recharge System
All models (.5) 1.0
Recover refrigerant, add 2

(G) Flush Refrigerant System, Complete
To be used in conjunction with component replacement which could contaminate system. Includes evacuate and recharge.
All models 1.3

(G) Leak Check
Includes: Check all lines and connections.
All models 5

(G) Recover and/or Recycle AC Refrigerant
Add to evacuate and charge the AC system, as required.
All models 2

(G) Refrigerant, Add (Partial Charge)
All models 6

COMPONENTS

(G) Accumulator Assy., Renew
Includes: Evacuate and charge system.
All models (1.0) 1.5
Recover refrigerant, add 2

(G) Actuator and/or Motor, Electric, Renew
All models
temperature door (.3) 5

(G) Actuator, Vacuum, Renew
All models
air inlet (.4) 7
upper or lower mode (.4) 7
slave valve (.4) 9
rear HVAC (.9) 1.5

(G) Belt, Compressor Drive, Renew
All models (.2) 4

(G) Blower Motor, Renew
All models
AC
3.1L code D (.5) 8
3.8L code L (.7) 1.1
auxiliary (1.0) 1.3
rear (1.1) 1.4

(G) Coil and/or Pulley Rim, Compressor Clutch, Renew
Includes: R&R hub and drive plate assy.
All models
HR6 compressor (1.8) 2.5
V5 compressor (1.5) 2.2
Recover refrigerant add 2

(G) Coil, Evaporator, Renew
Includes: Evacuate and charge system.
1993-94
front (2.5) 4.0
rear (2.2) 3.5
Recover refrigerant, add 2

(G) Compressor Assy., Renew
Includes: Transfer parts as required. Evacuate and charge system.
All models
V5 compressor (1.6) 2.3
HR6 compressor (1.4) 2.0
w/heavy duty cooling, add 2
Install liq. line filter, add (.9) 1.2
Recover refrigerant, add 2

(G) Condenser Assy., Renew
Includes: Evacuate and charge system.
All models (1.6) 2.3
Recover refrigerant, add 2

(G) Control Assy., Temperature, Renew
All models (.5) 9

(G) Expansion Tube (Orifice), Clean & Inspect or Renew
Includes: Evacuate and charge system.
All models (.7) 1.3
Recover refrigerant, add 2
Install liq. line filter, add (.9) 1.2

(G) Hoses, AC, Renew
Includes: Evacuate and charge system.
All models
suction or discharge (1.0) 1.8
liquid line (1.0) 1.8
evap. to accumulator (.8) 1.6
front to rear unit
one (1.7) 2.5
both (1.8) 2.7
Recover refrigerant, add 2

(G) Relay, Blower Motor, Renew
All models
blower motor (.2) 4
rear aux. blower (.3) 5

(G) Resistor, Blower Motor, Renew
All models
auxiliary or rear (.8) 1.1
AC (.2) 5

(G) Seal, Seat and O-Ring, Compressor Front, Renew
Includes: R&R clutch hub and drive plate assy. Evacuate and charge system.
All models
V5 compressor (1.8) 2.7
HR6 compressor (2.0) 2.8

(G) Sensor, AC Pressure, Renew
All models (.2) 4

(G) Sensor, Outside Temperature, Renew
All models (.2) 4

(G) Switch, Blower Motor, Renew
All models
AC (.5) 8
auxiliary (.2) 4
AC rear (.6) 9

(G) Switch, High Pressure Cut-Off, Renew
All models (.4) 6
Add time to recharge AC system if required.

(G) Tube, Rear Expansion Valve, Renew
All models (2.0) 2.9
Recover refrigerant, add 2

(G) Valve, Expansion, Renew
Includes: Evacuate and charge system.
All models (2.2) 3.2
Recover refrigerant, add 2

GENERAL MOTORS CORPORATION-TRUCKS
S SERIES • BRAVADA

LABOR — COOLING SYSTEM — LABOR

(Factory Time) Chilton Time

TESTING

(M) Pressure Test Cooling System
All models 3

SERVICE

(G) Belt, Drive, Renew
1993-95 serpentine 3
Renew tensioner, add 1

(G) Blades, Fan or Clutch Assy., Renew
All models (.5) 7
w/4.3L V6 add 1

(G) Bypass and/or Tube, Hose, Renew
All models (.3) 5

COOLING SYSTEM

(Factory Time) Chilton Time

(G) Control Assy., Heater, Renew
All models (.3) 6
w/power mirror switch, add 1

(G) Cooler, Engine Oil, Renew
1993 S Series (.5) 8

(G) Core, Heater, R&R or Renew
All models
wo/AC (.9) 1.7
w/AC (1.4) 2.5
Recover or recharge AC system, add 1.0
Boil & Repair, add 1.2
Repair Core, add 9
Recore, add 1.2

(G) Expansion (Freeze) Plugs, Water Jacket, Renew
Add appropriate time to access plug.
All models, each 5

(G) Gauge, Temperature (Dash Unit), Renew
1993 (.8) 1.4

(G) Hoses, Heater, Renew
All models
one (.4) 5
both (.5) 6

(G) Hoses, Radiator, Renew
Includes: Drain and refill cooling system as required.
All models
upper (.4) 5
lower (.5) 6
both (.6) 9
by-pass (.3) 5

(G) Motor, Heater Blower, Renew
All models (.6) 8

(G) Pump and/or Gasket, Water, Renew
Includes: Drain and refill cooling system.
1993-95
Four (.9) 1.3
V6 (.9) 2.0
w/AC or PS add (.2) 2
w/Turbo, add (.2) 3

(G) Radiator Assy., R&R or Renew
All models (.6) 9
w/AT add 1
w/eng. oil cooler, add 1
w/Turbo, add 6
Renew side tank and/or gasket add
one side 3
both sides 6
Boil & Repair, add 1.5
Rod Clean, add 1.9
Repair Core, add 1.3
Renew Tank, add 1.6
Renew Trans. Oil Cooler, add 1.9
Recore Radiator, add 1.7

(G) Relay, Heater Blower Motor, Renew
All models (.3) 4

(G) Resistor, Heater Blower Motor, Renew
1993 (.2) 3
1994-95 (.3) 4

(G) Sending Unit, Engine Coolant Temp., Renew
All models (.4) 5

(G) Switch, Heater Blower Motor, Renew
1993 (.3) 7
1994-95 (.4) 8
w/power mirror switch, add 1

(G) Thermostat, Coolant, Renew
All models
Four (.3) 5
V6 (.4) 6

(G) Winterize Cooling System
Includes: Run engine to check for leaks, tighten all hose connections. Test radiator and pressure cap, drain radiator and engine block. Add antifreeze and refill system.
All models 5

AIR CONDITIONING

(Factory Time) Chilton Time

Note: If more than one item requires replacement where evacuation and discharging the system is already included in the operation, deduct 1.0 hour for each additional item from the time listed.

SERVICE AND TESTING

(G) Drain, Evacuate and Recharge System
All models 1.0
Recover refrigerant, add 2

(G) Flush Refrigerant System, Complete
To be used in conjunction with component replacement which could contaminate system. Includes evacuate and recharge.
All models 1.3

(G) Leak Check
Includes: Check all lines and connections.
All models 6

(G) Recover and/or Recycle AC Refrigerant
Add to evacuate and charge the AC system, as required.
All models 2

(G) Refrigerant, Add (Partial Charge)
All models 6

COMPONENTS

(G) Accumulator Assy., Renew
Includes: Evacuate and charge system.
All models (.8) 1.5
Recover refrigerant, add 2

(G) Belt, Compressor Drive, Renew
All models (.2) 3

(G) Blower Motor, Renew
All models (.4) 6

(G) Clutch and/or Pulley, Compressor, Renew
Includes: R&R compressor.
All models (.5) 1.0
Add time to evacuate & charge system

(G) Clutch Plate & Hub Assy., Compressor, Renew
Includes: R&R hub and drive plate assy. Check air gap.
1993-95
R4 (.5) 8
V5 (.3) 6

(G) Coil and/or Pulley Rim, Compressor Clutch, Renew
Includes: R&R hub and drive plate assy.
1993-95 (.5) 8

(G) Coil, Evaporator, Renew
Includes: Evacuate and charge system.
All models (1.3) 2.8
w/Turbo, add 3
Recover refrigerant, add 2

(G) Compressor Assy., Renew
Includes: Transfer parts as required. Evacuate and charge system.
All models
R4 (.9) 2.0
V5 (1.0) 2.2
Recover refrigerant, add 2

(G) Condenser Assy., Renew
Includes: Evacuate and charge system.
All models
Four (1.3) 2.3
V6 (1.7) 3.0
w/aux. oil cooler, add 1
w/Turbo, add 3
Recover refrigerant, add 2

(G) Control Assy., Temperature, Renew
All models (.3) 6
w/pwr. mirror switch, add 1

(G) Cylinder & Shaft Assy., Compressor, Renew
Includes: R&R compressor. Transfer parts as required. Evacuate and charge system.
All models w/R4 (1.5) 3.0
w/Turbo, add 3
Recover refrigerant, add 2

(Factory Time) Chilton Time

(G) Cylinder Head and/or Valve Plate, Compressor, Renew

Includes: Evacuate and charge system.

All models w/R4 (1.4) **2.9**
w/Turbo, add .... **.3**
Renew two or more valves, add ...... **.2**
Recover refrigerant, add .... **.2**

(G) Expansion Tube (Orifice), Clean & Inspect or Renew

Includes: Evacuate and charge system.

All models (.9) **1.5**
Recover refrigerant, add .... **.2**

(G) Head and/or Seal, Compressor Front, Renew

Includes: R&R compressor. R&R clutch pulley assy., R&R shaft seal assy. Clean and inspect parts. Evacuate and charge system.

All models w/R4 (1.3) **2.8**
w/Turbo, add .... **.3**
Recover refrigerant, add .... **.2**

(G) Hoses, AC, Renew

Includes: Evacuate and charge system.

All models
liquid line (.9) **1.7**
w/Turbo, add .... **.4**
suction, discharge (.8) **1.5**
w/Turbo, add .... **.6**
Recover refrigerant, add .... **.2**

(G) Relay, Blower Motor, Renew

All models (.3) .... **.4**

(G) Resistor, Blower Motor, Renew

1993 (.2) .... **.3**
1994-95 (.3) .... **.4**

(G) Rotor and/or Bearing, Compressor Clutch, Renew

Includes: R&R hub and drive plate assy.

All models
R4 (.6) **1.0**
V5 (.4) .... **.7**

Add time to evacuate & charge system if required.

(G) Seal, Compressor Shaft, Renew

Includes: R&R compressor. Evacuate and charge system.

All models
R4 (1.1) **2.2**
V5 (1.2) **2.4**
Recover refrigerant, add .... **.2**

(G) Switch, Clutch Cycling Pressure, Renew

All models (.2) .... **.3**

(G) Switch, Master Electrical, Renew

All models (.3) .... **.6**
w/pwr. mirror switch, add .... **.1**

ENGLISH TO METRIC CONVERSION: TORQUE

Torque is now expressed as either foot-pounds (ft./lbs.) or inch-pounds (in./lbs.). The metric measurement unit for torque is the Newton-meter (Nm). This unit—the Nm—will be used for all SI metric torque references, both the present ft./lbs. and in./lbs.

ft lbs	N-m	ft lbs	N-m	ft lbs	N-m	ft lbs	N-m
0.1	0.1	33	44.7	74	100.3	115	155.9
0.2	0.3	34	46.1	75	101.7	116	157.3
0.3	0.4	35	47.4	76	103.0	117	158.6
0.4	0.5	36	48.8	77	104.4	118	160.0
0.5	0.7	37	50.7	78	105.8	119	161.3
0.6	0.8	38	51.5	79	107.1	120	162.7
0.7	1.0	39	52.9	80	108.5	121	164.0
0.8	1.1	40	54.2	81	109.8	122	165.4
0.9	1.2	41	55.6	82	111.2	123	166.8
1	1.3	42	56.9	83	112.5	124	168.1
2	2.7	43	58.3	84	113.9	125	169.5
3	4.1	44	59.7	85	115.2	126	170.8
4	5.4	45	61.0	86	116.6	127	172.2
5	6.8	46	62.4	87	118.0	128	173.5
6	8.1	47	63.7	88	119.3	129	174.9
7	9.5	48	65.1	89	120.7	130	176.2
8	10.8	49	66.4	90	122.0	131	177.6
9	12.2	50	67.8	91	123.4	132	179.0
10	13.6	51	69.2	92	124.7	133	180.3
11	14.9	52	70.5	93	126.1	134	181.7
12	16.3	53	71.9	94	127.4	135	183.0
13	17.6	54	73.2	95	128.8	136	184.4
14	18.9	55	74.6	96	130.2	137	185.7
15	20.3	56	75.9	97	131.5	138	187.1
16	21.7	57	77.3	98	132.9	139	188.5
17	23.0	58	78.6	99	134.2	140	189.8
18	24.4	59	80.0	100	135.6	141	191.2
19	25.8	60	81.4	101	136.9	142	192.5
20	27.1	61	82.7	102	138.3	143	193.9
21	28.5	62	84.1	103	139.6	144	195.2
22	29.8	63	85.4	104	141.0	145	196.6
23	31.2	64	86.8	105	142.4	146	198.0
24	32.5	65	88.1	106	143.7	147	199.3
25	33.9	66	89.5	107	145.1	148	200.7
26	35.2	67	90.8	108	146.4	149	202.0
27	36.6	68	92.2	109	147.8	150	203.4
28	38.0	69	93.6	110	149.1	151	204.7
29	39.3	70	94.9	111	150.5	152	206.1
30	40.7	71	96.3	112	151.8	153	207.4
31	42.0	72	97.6	113	153.2	154	208.8
32	43.4	73	99.0	114	154.6	155	210.2

MECHANIC'S DATA

ENGLISH TO METRIC CONVERSION: LENGTH

To convert inches (ins.) to millimeters (mm): multiply number of inches by 25.4

To convert millimeters (mm) to inches (ins.): multiply number of millimeters by .04

Inches	Decimals	Milli-meters	Inches to millimeters inches	mm	Inches	Decimals	Milli-meters	Inches to millimeters inches	mm
1/64	0.051625	0.3969	0.0001	0.00254	33/64	0.515625	13.0969	0.6	15.24
1/32	0.03125	0.7937	0.0002	0.00508	17/32	0.53125	13.4937	0.7	17.78
3/64	0.046875	1.1906	0.0003	0.00762	35/64	0.546875	13.8906	0.8	20.32
1/16	0.0625	1.5875	0.0004	0.01016	9/16	0.5625	14.2875	0.9	22.86
5/64	0.078125	1.9844	0.0005	0.01270	37/64	0.578125	14.6844	1	25.4
3/32	0.09375	2.3812	0.0006	0.01524	19/32	0.59375	15.0812	2	50.8
7/64	0.109375	2.7781	0.0007	0.01778	39/64	0.609375	15.4781	3	76.2
1/8	0.125	3.1750	0.0008	0.02032	5/8	0.625	15.8750	4	101.6
9/64	0.140625	3.5719	0.0009	0.02286	41/64	0.640625	16.2719	5	127.0
5/32	0.15625	3.9687	0.001	0.0254	21/32	0.65625	16.6687	6	152.4
11/64	0.171875	4.3656	0.002	0.0508	43/64	0.671875	17.0656	7	177.8
3/16	0.1875	4.7625	0.003	0.0762	11/16	0.6875	17.4625	8	203.2
13/64	0.203125	5.1594	0.004	0.1016	45/64	0.703125	17.8594	9	228.6
7/32	0.21875	5.5562	0.005	0.1270	23/32	0.71875	18.2562	10	254.0
15/64	0.234375	5.9531	0.006	0.1524	47/64	0.734375	18.6531	11	279.4
1/4	0.25	6.3500	0.007	0.1778	3/4	0.75	19.0500	12	304.8
17/64	0.265625	6.7469	0.008	0.2032	49/64	0.765625	19.4469	13	330.2
9/32	0.28125	7.1437	0.009	0.2286	25/32	0.78125	19.8437	14	355.6
19/64	0.296875	7.5406	0.01	0.254	51/64	0.796875	20.2406	15	381.0
5/16	0.3125	7.9375	0.02	0.508	13/16	0.8125	20.6375	16	406.4
21/64	0.328125	8.3344	0.03	0.762	53/64	0.828125	21.0344	17	431.8
11/32	0.34375	8.7312	0.04	1.016	27/32	0.84375	21.4312	18	457.2
23/64	0.359375	9.1281	0.05	1.270	55/64	0.859375	21.8281	19	482.6
3/8	0.375	9.5250	0.06	1.524	7/8	0.875	22.2250	20	508.0
25/64	0.390625	9.9219	0.07	1.778	57/64	0.890625	22.6219	21	533.4
13/32	0.40625	10.3187	0.08	2.032	29/32	0.90625	23.0187	22	558.8
27/64	0.421875	10.7156	0.09	2.286	59/64	0.921875	23.4156	23	584.2
7/16	0.4375	11.1125	0.1	2.54	15/16	0.9375	23.8125	24	609.6
29/64	0.453125	11.5094	0.2	5.08	61/64	0.953125	24.2094	25	635.0
15/32	0.46875	11.9062	0.3	7.62	31/32	0.96875	24.6062	26	660.4
31/64	0.484375	12.3031	0.4	10.16	63/64	0.984375	25.0031	27	690.6
1/2	0.5	12.7000	0.5	12.70					

ENGLISH TO METRIC CONVERSION: TORQUE

To convert foot-pounds (ft. lbs.) to Newton-meters: multiply the number of ft. lbs. by 1.3

To convert inch-pounds (in. lbs.) to Newton-meters: multiply the number of in. lbs. by .11

in lbs	N·m	in lbs	N·m	in lbs	N·m	in lbs	N·m	in lbs	N·m
0.1	0.01	1	0.11	10	1.13	19	2.15	28	3.16
0.2	0.02	2	0.23	11	1.24	20	2.26	29	3.28
0.3	0.03	3	0.34	12	1.36	21	2.37	30	3.39
0.4	0.04	4	0.45	13	1.47	22	2.49	31	3.50
0.5	0.06	5	0.56	14	1.58	23	2.60	32	3.62
0.6	0.07	6	0.68	15	1.70	24	2.71	33	3.73
0.7	0.08	7	0.78	16	1.81	25	2.82	34	3.84
0.8	0.09	8	0.90	17	1.92	26	2.94	35	3.95
0.9	0.10	9	1.02	18	2.03	27	3.05	36	4.07

ENGLISH TO METRIC CONVERSION: MASS (WEIGHT)

Current mass measurement is expressed in pounds and ounces (lbs. & ozs.). The metric unit of mass (or weight) is the kilogram (kg). Even although this table does not show conversion of masses (weights) larger than 15 lbs, it is easy to calculate larger units by following the data immediately below.

To convert ounces (oz.) to grams (g): multiply th number of ozs. by 28
To convert grams (g) to ounces (oz.): multiply the number of grams by .035

To convert pounds (lbs.) to kilograms (kg): multiply the number of lbs. by .45
To convert kilograms (kg) to pounds (lbs.): multiply the number of kilograms by 2.2

lbs	kg	lbs	kg	oz	kg	oz	kg
0.1	0.04	0.9	0.41	0.1	0.003	0.9	0.024
0.2	0.09	1	0.4	0.2	0.005	1	0.03
0.3	0.14	2	0.9	0.3	0.008	2	0.06
0.4	0.18	3	1.4	0.4	0.011	3	0.08
0.5	0.23	4	1.8	0.5	0.014	4	0.11
0.6	0.27	5	2.3	0.6	0.017	5	0.14
0.7	0.32	10	4.5	0.7	0.020	10	0.28
0.8	0.36	15	6.8	0.8	0.023	15	0.42

ENGLISH TO METRIC CONVERSION: TEMPERATURE

To convert Fahrenheit (°F) to Celsius (°C): take number of °F and subtract 32; multiply result by 5; divide result by 9

To convert Celsius (°C) to Fahrenheit (°F): take number of °C and multiply by 9; divide result by 5; add 32 to total

Fahrenheit (F)		Celsius (C)		Fahrenheit (F)		Celsius (C)		Fahrenheit (F)		Celsius (C)	
°F	°C	°C	°F	°F	°C	°C	°F	°F	°C	°C	°F
−40	−40	−38	−36.4	80	26.7	18	64.4	215	101.7	80	176
−35	−37.2	−36	−32.8	85	29.4	20	68	220	104.4	85	185
−30	−34.4	−34	−29.2	90	32.2	22	71.6	225	107.2	90	194
−25	−31.7	−32	−25.6	95	35.0	24	75.2	230	110.0	95	202
−20	−28.9	−30	−22	100	37.8	26	78.8	235	112.8	100	212
−15	−26.1	−28	−18.4	105	40.6	28	82.4	240	115.6	105	221
−10	−23.3	−26	−14.8	110	43.3	30	86	245	118.3	110	230
−5	−20.6	−24	−11.2	115	46.1	32	89.6	250	121.1	115	239
0	−17.8	−22	−7.6	120	48.9	34	93.2	255	123.9	120	248
1	−17.2	−20	−4	125	51.7	36	96.8	260	126.6	125	257
2	−16.7	−18	−0.4	130	54.4	38	100.4	265	129.4	130	266
3	−16.1	−16	3.2	135	57.2	40	104	270	132.2	135	275
4	−15.6	−14	6.8	140	60.0	42	107.6	275	135.0	140	284
5	−15.0	−12	10.4	145	62.8	44	112.2	280	137.8	145	293
10	−12.2	−10	14	150	65.6	46	114.8	285	140.6	150	302
15	−9.4	−8	17.6	155	68.3	48	118.4	290	143.3	155	311
20	−6.7	−6	21.2	160	71.1	50	122	295	146.1	160	320
25	−3.9	−4	24.8	165	73.9	52	125.6	300	148.9	165	329
30	−1.1	−2	28.4	170	76.7	54	129.2	305	151.7	170	338
35	1.7	0	32	175	79.4	56	132.8	310	154.4	175	347
40	4.4	2	35.6	180	82.2	58	136.4	315	157.2	180	356
45	7.2	4	39.2	185	85.0	60	140	320	160.0	185	365
50	10.0	6	42.8	190	87.8	62	143.6	325	162.8	190	374
55	12.8	8	46.4	195	90.6	64	147.2	330	165.6	195	383
60	15.6	10	50	200	93.3	66	150.8	335	168.3	200	392
65	18.3	12	53.6	205	96.1	68	154.4	340	171.1	205	401
70	21.1	14	57.2	210	98.9	70	158	345	173.9	210	410
75	23.9	16	60.8	212	100.0	75	167	350	176.7	215	414